Katie Meyers
(714) 693-1694

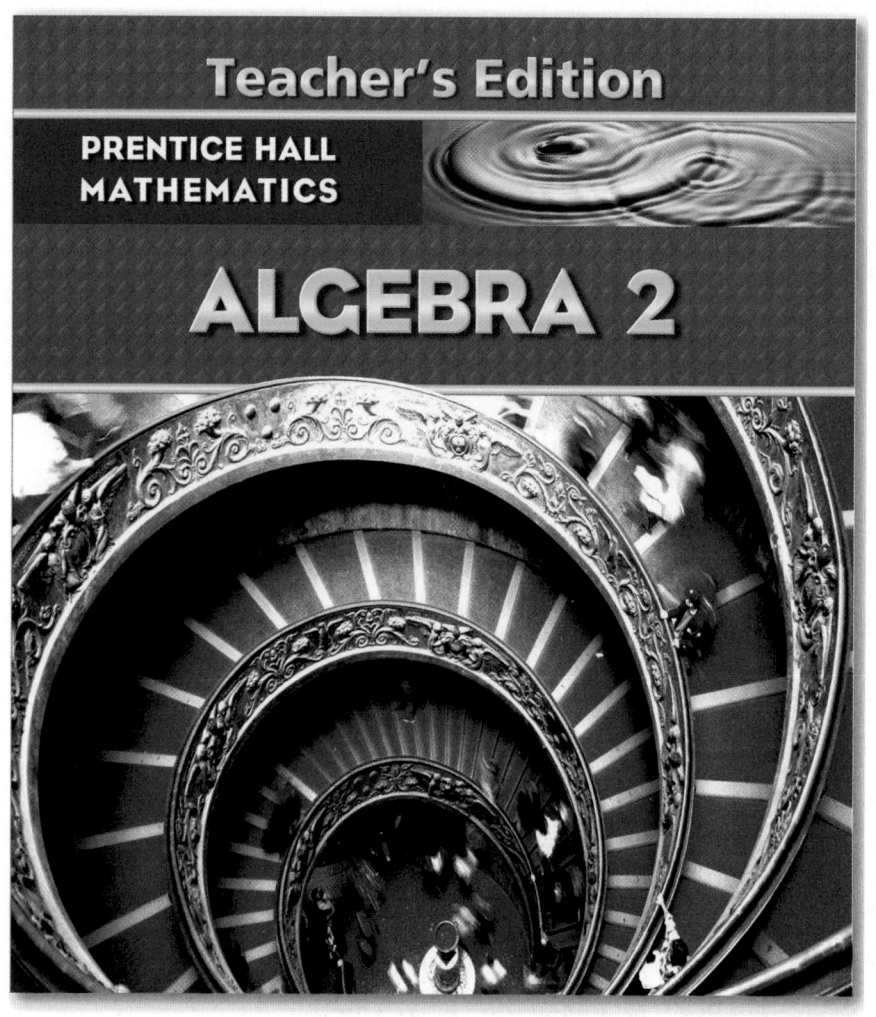

Teacher's Edition

PRENTICE HALL
MATHEMATICS

ALGEBRA 2

Allan E. Bellman

Sadie Chavis Bragg

Randall I. Charles

Basia Hall

William G. Handlin, Sr.

Dan Kennedy

PEARSON

Prentice
Hall

Boston, Massachusetts
Upper Saddle River, New Jersey

Acknowledgments appear on p. T1011, which constitutes an extension of this copyright page.

PEARSON
Prentice
Hall

ISBN 0-13-134006-9
2 3 4 5 6 7 8 9 10   10 09 08 07 06

Algebra 2
Teacher's Edition Contents

Teacher Handbook

Student Edition With Teacher Notes

Authors

Series Authors

Dan Kennedy, Ph.D., is a classroom teacher and the Lupton Distinguished Professor of Mathematics at the Baylor School in Chattanooga, Tennessee. A frequent speaker at professional meetings on the subject of mathematics education reform, Dr. Kennedy has conducted more than 50 workshops and institutes for high school teachers. He is coauthor of textbooks in calculus and precalculus, and from 1990 to 1994 he chaired the College Board's AP Calculus Development Committee. He is a 1992 Tandy Technology Scholar and a 1995 Presidential Award winner.

Randall I. Charles, Ph.D., is Professor Emeritus in the Department of Mathematics and Computer Science at San Jose State University, San Jose, California. He began his career as a high school mathematics teacher, and he was a mathematics supervisor for five years. Dr. Charles has been a member of several NCTM committees and is the former Vice President of the National Council of Supervisors of Mathematics. Much of his writing and research has been in the area of problem solving. He has authored more than 75 mathematics textbooks for kindergarten through college.

Basia Hall currently serves as Manager of Instructional Programs for the Houston Independent School District. With 30 years teaching experience, Ms. Hall has served as a department chair, instructional specialist, instructional supervisor, a school improvement facilitator, and a professional development (TEXTEAMS) trainer. Ms. Hall has developed curriculum for Algebra 1, Geometry, and Algebra 2 and contributed to the development of the Texas Essential Knowledge and Skills. A recipient of the 1992 Presidential Award for Excellence in Mathematics Teaching, Ms. Hall is also a past president of the Texas Association of Supervisors of Mathematics, and she is a state representative for the National Council of Supervisors of Mathematics (NCSM).

Acknowledgments appear on pages 1023–1025, which constitute an extension of this copyright page.

PEARSON
Prentice Hall

Algebra 1 and Algebra 2 Authors

Allan E. Bellman is a Lecturer/Supervisor in the School of Education at the University of California, Davis. Before coming to Davis, he was a mathematics teacher for 31 years in Montgomery County, Maryland. He has been an instructor for both the Woodrow Wilson National Fellowship Foundation and the T^3 program. Mr. Bellman has a particular expertise in the use of technology in education and speaks frequently on this topic. He was a 1992 Tandy Technology Scholar.

Sadie Chavis Bragg, Ed.D., is Senior Vice President of Academic Affairs at the Borough of Manhattan Community College of the City University of New York. A former professor of mathematics, she is a past president of the American Mathematical Association of Two-Year Colleges (AMATYC), co-director of the AMATYC project to revise the standards for introductory college mathematics before calculus, and an active member of the Benjamin Banneker Association. Dr. Bragg has coauthored more than 50 mathematics textbooks for kindergarten through college.

William G. Handlin, Sr., is a classroom teacher and Department Chairman of Technology Applications at Spring Woods High School in Houston, Texas. Awarded Life Membership in the Texas Congress of Parents and Teachers for his contributions to the well-being of children, Mr. Handlin is also a frequent workshop and seminar leader in professional meetings throughout the world.

Geometry Authors

Laurie E. Bass is a classroom teacher at the 9–12 division of the Ethical Culture Fieldston School in Riverdale, New York. Ms. Bass has a wide base of teaching experience, ranging from grade 6 through Advanced Placement Calculus. She was the recipient of a 2000 Honorable Mention for the RadioShack National Teacher Awards. She has been a contributing writer of a number of publications, including software-based activities for the Algebra 1 classroom. Among her areas of special interest are cooperative learning for high school students and geometry exploration on the computer. Ms. Bass has been a presenter at a number of local, regional, and national conferences.

Art Johnson, Ed.D., is a professor of mathematics education at Boston University. He is a mathematics educator with 32 years of public school teaching experience, a frequent speaker and workshop leader, and the recipient of a number of awards. Dr. Johnson received the Tandy Prize for Teaching Excellence in 1995, a Presidential Award for Excellence in Mathematics Teaching in 1992, and New Hampshire Teacher of the Year, also in 1992. He was profiled by the Disney Corporation in the American Teacher of the Year Program.

Reviewers

Algebra 1 Reviewers

Mary Lou Beasley
Southside Fundamental
  Middle School
St. Petersburg, Florida

Blanche Smith Brownley
Washington, D.C., Public
  Schools
Washington, D.C.

Joseph Caruso
Somerville High School
Somerville, Massachusetts

Belinda Craig
Highland West Junior High
  School
Moore, Oklahoma

Jane E. Damaske
Lakeshore Public Schools
Stevensville, Michigan

Stacey A. Ego
Warren Central High School
Indianapolis, Indiana

Earl R. Jones
Formerly, Kansas City
  Public Schools
Kansas City, Missouri

Jeanne Lorenson
James H. Blake High School
Silver Spring, Maryland

John T. Mace
Hibbett Middle School
Florence, Alabama

**Ann Marie Palmieri-
  Monahan**
Director of Mathematics
Bayonne Board of Education
Bayonne, New Jersey

Marie Schalke
Woodlawn Middle School
Long Grove, Illinois

Julie Welling
LaPorte High School
LaPorte, Indiana

Sharon Zguzenski
Naugatuck High School
Naugatuck, Connecticut

Geometry Reviewers

Marian Avery
Great Valley High School
Malvern, Pennsylvania

Mary Emma Bunch
Farragut High School
Knoxville, Tennessee

Karen A. Cannon
K–12 Mathematics
  Coordinator
Rockwood School District
Eureka, Missouri

Johnnie Ebbert
Department Chairman
DeLand High School
DeLand, Florida

Russ Forrer
Math Department Chairman
East Aurora High School
Aurora, Illinois

Andrea Kopco
Midpark High School
Middleburg Heights, Ohio

Gordon E. Maroney III
Camden Fairview High
  School
Camden, Arkansas

Charlotte Phillips
Math Coordinator
Wichita USD 259
Wichita, Kansas

Richard P. Strausz
Farmington Public Schools
Farmington, Michigan

Jane Tanner
Jefferson County
  International
  Baccalaureate School
Birmingham, Alabama

Karen D. Vaughan
Pitt County Schools
Greenville, North Carolina

Robin Washam
Math Specialist
Puget Sound Educational
  Service District
Burien, Washington

Algebra 2 Reviewers

Josiane Fouarge
Landry High School
New Orleans, Louisiana

Susan Hvizdos
Math Department Chair
Wheeling Park High School
Wheeling, West Virginia

Kathleen Kohler
Kearny High School
Kearny, New Jersey

Julia Kolb
Leesville Road High School
Raleigh, North Carolina

Deborah R. Kula
Sacred Hearts Academy
Honolulu, Hawaii

Betty Mayberry
Gallatin High School
Gallatin, Tennessee

John L. Pitt
Formerly, Prince William
   County Schools
Manassas, Virginia

Margaret Plouvier
Billings West High School
Billings, Montana

Sandra Sikorski
Berea High School
Berea, Ohio

Tim Visser
Grandview High School
Cherry Creek School District
Aurora, Colorado

Content Consultants

Ann Bell
Mathematics
Prentice Hall Consultant
Franklin, Tennessee

Blanche Brownley
Mathematics
Prentice Hall Consultant
Olney, Maryland

Joe Brumfield
Mathematics
Prentice Hall Consultant
Altadena, California

Linda Buckhalt
Mathematics
Prentice Hall Consultant
Derwood, Maryland

Andrea Gordon
Mathematics
Prentice Hall Consultant
Atlanta, Georgia

Eleanor Lopes
Mathematics
Prentice Hall Consultant
New Castle, Delaware

Sally Marsh
Mathematics
Prentice Hall Consultant
Baltimore, Maryland

Bob Pacyga
Mathematics
Prentice Hall Consultant
Darien, Illinois

Judy Porter
Mathematics
Prentice Hall Consultant
Leland, North Carolina

Rose Primiani
Mathematics
Prentice Hall Consultant
Harbor City, New Jersey

Jayne Radu
Mathematics
Prentice Hall Consultant
Scottsdale, Arizona

Pam Revels
Mathematics
Prentice Hall Consultant
Sarasota, Florida

Barbara Rogers
Mathematics
Prentice Hall Consultant
Raleigh, North Carolina

Michael Seals
Mathematics
Prentice Hall Consultant
Edmond, Oklahoma

Margaret Thomas
Mathematics
Prentice Hall Consultant
Indianapolis, Indiana

Chapter 1

Tools of Algebra

Assessment and Test Prep

Functions, Equations, and Graphs

Assessment and Test Prep

Chapter 3

Linear Systems

Chapter 4

Matrices

Assessment and Test Prep
  • **Test-Taking Strategies:** Interpreting Data, 228
  • Chapter Review, 229
  • Chapter Test, 232
  • **Standardized Test Prep:** Cumulative Review, 233

Chapter 5

Quadratic Equations and Functions

Chapter 6

Polynomials and Polynomial Functions

Table of Contents

Chapter 7

Radical Functions and Rational Exponents

Chapter 8

Exponential and Logarithmic Functions

Table of Contents

Contents **XV**

T15

Chapter 9

Rational Functions

Chapter 10

Quadratic Relations and Conic Sections

Table of Contents

Sequences and Series

Assessment and Test Prep

Chapter 12

Probability and Statistics

Table of Contents

Contents   **xix**

Chapter 13

Periodic Functions and Trigonometry

Trigonometric
Identities and Equations

Assessment and Test Prep
  • **Test-Taking Strategies:** Answering Open-Ended Questions, 826
  • Chapter Review, 827
  • Chapter Test, 830
  • **Standardized Test Prep:** Cumulative Review, 831

Contents **xxi**

T21

Connect Your Learning
through problem solving, activities, and the Web

Applications: Real-World Applications

Applications: **Algebra at Work**

Applications: **A Point in Time**

Applications: **Interdisciplinary Connections**

Activities

Activities: Activity Labs

Activities: Guided Problem Solving

Go Online

Throughout this book you will find links to the Prentice Hall Web site. Use the Web Codes provided with each link to gain direct access to online material. Here's how to *Go Online*:

1. Go to PHSchool.com
2. Enter the Web Code
3. Click Go!

Lesson Web Codes

Lesson Quiz Web Codes: There is an online quiz for every lesson. Access these quizzes with Web Codes aga-1407 through aga-1407 for Lesson 1-1 through Lesson 14-7. See page 91.

Homework Video Tutor Web Codes: For every lesson, there is additional support online to help students complete their homework. Access this homework help online with Web Codes age-0101 through age-1407 for Lesson 1-1 through Lesson 14-7. See page 9.

Lesson Quizzes
Web Code format: aga-0204 02 = Chapter 2   04 = Lesson 4

Homework Video Tutor
Web Code format: age-0605 06 = Chapter 6   05 = Lesson 5

Chapter Web Codes

Chapter	Vocabulary Quizzes	Chapter Tests	Activity Labs
1	agj-0151	aga-0152	
2	agj-0251	aga-0252	age-0253
3	agj-0351	aga-0352	
4	agj-0451	aga-0452	age-0453
5	agj-0551	aga-0552	
6	agj-0651	aga-0652	age-0653
7	agj-0751	aga-0752	
8	agj-0851	aga-0852	age-0853
9	agj-0951	aga-0952	
10	agj-1051	aga-1052	age-1053
11	agj-1151	aga-1152	
12	agj-1251	aga-1252	age-1253
13	agj-1351	aga-1352	
14	agj-1451	aga-1452	age-1453
End-of-Course		aga-1254	

Additional Web Codes

Video Tutor Help:
Use web code age-0775 to access engaging online instructional videos to help bring math concepts to life. See page 18.

Data Updates:
Use web code agg-9041 to get up-to-date government data for use in examples and exercises. See page 83.

Algebra at Work:
For information about each Algebra at Work feature, use web code agb-2031. See page 24.

Differentiate Instruction with Ease

Students develop and learn in different ways at different paces. Accessible content, presented in a variety of formats, acknowledges these unique differences while providing options for learning. The goal of *Prentice Hall Mathematics* is for all students to be successful and for you to have the tools you need to accomplish this. *Prentice Hall Mathematics* Grade 6 through Algebra 2 provides better solutions for meeting the needs of every student in the classroom by achieving two goals:

• Providing superior teacher support materials for planning how to effectively differentiate instruction
• Providing unique resources for the various populations of students.

Differentiated Instruction
Solutions for All Learners

Adapted Resources for Differentiating Instruction

In addition to the support provided in the Teacher's Editions, Prentice Hall has created resources developed uniquely for Below Level and Special Needs students.

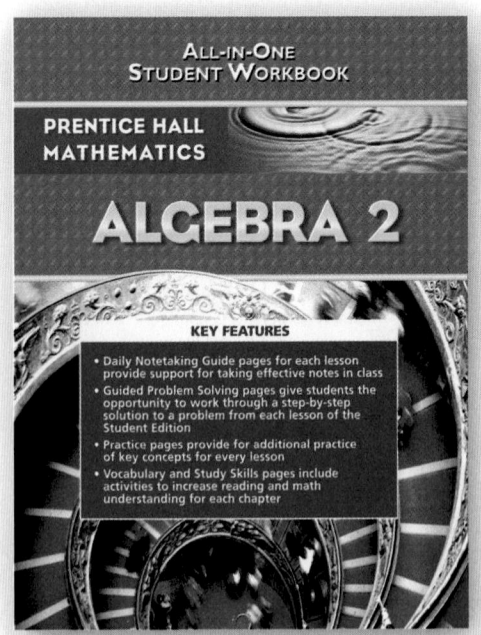

ALL-IN-ONE STUDENT WORKBOOK

PRENTICE HALL MATHEMATICS

ALGEBRA 2

KEY FEATURES

• Daily Notetaking Guide pages for each lesson provide support for taking effective notes in class
• Guided Problem Solving pages give students the opportunity to work through a step-by-step solution to a problem from each lesson of the Student Edition
• Practice pages provide for additional practice of key concepts for every lesson
• Vocabulary and Study Skills pages include activities to increase reading and math understanding for each chapter

All-in-One Student Workbook

This resource includes daily notetaking, practice, guided problem solving, vocabulary, and study skills to support all students. By providing these resources ready for you to use, you can cover the mathematical content and provide students opportunities to practice the lesson's mathematics.

Differentiated Assessments

Prentice Hall Mathematics also recognizes the importance of not only differentiating instruction, but also differentiating the assessments used to monitor student progress and inform future instruction. To achieve this, three versions of each chapter test are provided: L2 for Below Level, L3 for All Students and L4 for Advanced Learners.

ExamView Test Generator

To provide the ultimate flexibility in creating assessments and practice worksheets for all students, the *Prentice Hall Mathematics ExamView* Test Banks contain adapted items written exclusively for your Special Needs and Below Level students.

Prentice Hall Mathematics Teacher's Editions offer comprehensive support in differentiating instruction.

L1 Special Needs
L2 Below Level
L3 All Students
L4 Advanced Learners
ELL English Language Learners

Prentice Hall Mathematics uses a consistent method for labeling and identifying resources for differentiating instruction. This consistency helps you to easily identify and choose the appropriate resources for your students.

Planning and Using Differentiated Resources

These chapter level support pages provide you an easy-to-read overview of the resources available and suggested ways in the instructional lesson to use the resources.

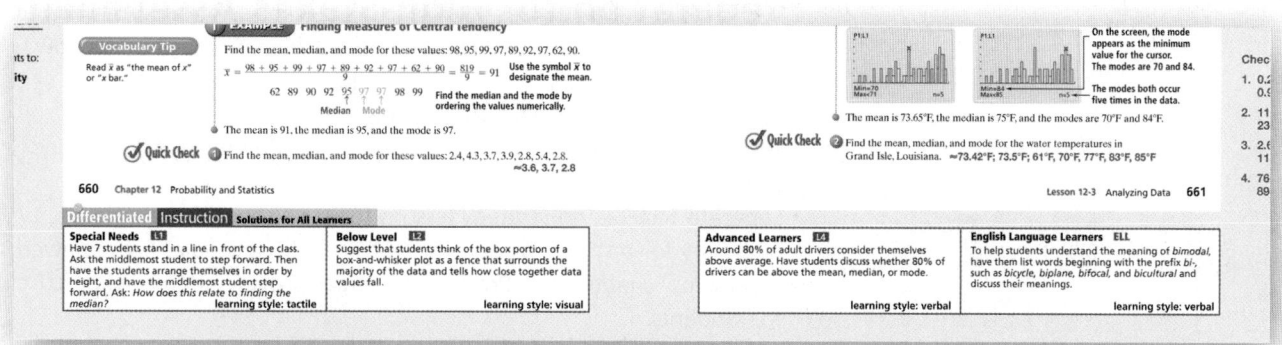

Differentiated Instruction teaching notes

These useful notes help you differentiate the lesson for all learners, including Special Needs, Below Level, Advanced, and English Language Learners.

Assessment to Inform Instruction

Assessment is integral to mathematics instruction. Student assessment should occur often and with a variety of different measures. *Prentice Hall Mathematics* provides an ongoing assessment strand that addresses assessment *for* learning and assessment *of* learning. The formative assessment features – before and during instruction – offer a variety of methods for teachers to assess student understanding and inform future instruction. The summative assessment features – after instruction – document student mastery of mathematical concepts and skills, and further prepare students for success in today's tests.

Instant Check System™ for Ongoing Assessment

This unique feature of *Prentice Hall Mathematics* ensures that students make progress every day, in every lesson. It helps teachers assess necessary prerequisite skills and monitor student understanding. The Instant Check System™ assessments include:

- Check Your Readiness – Assesses prerequisite skills for each chapter
- Check Skills You'll Need – Assesses prerequisite skills for each lesson
- Quick Check – Assesses student understanding after every example in the book
- Check Point – Assesses understanding after completing lessons

All-in-One Progress Monitoring Assessments

This comprehensive teacher support resource contains all the program assessments needed to evaluate student understanding, monitor student progress, and inform future instruction. The following assessments are included:

- Pre-Course Screening Test
- Benchmark Tests to document progress at 6-week intervals
- Quarter, Mid-course, and Final Tests – regular and below level
- Test-Taking Strategy Practice
- Standardized Practice Tests
- Comprehensive Report Forms

Preparation for High-Stakes Assessment

In this era of accountability, *Prentice Hall Mathematics* recognizes how critical it is for teachers to prepare every student for test success. The following features help achieve this:

- Test Prep exercises, focusing on all major question types, are included after every lesson.
- Separate Test-Taking Strategy lessons focus on specific strategies necessary for test success. Specific ACT and SAT strategies are reviewed.
- After every chapter, Test Prep review pages provide additional practice for students.

Help All Students Become

Problem Solvers

One of the major goals of a mathematics program is to develop students' ability to solve problems in class, on assessments, in the context of real-world situations, and outside the classroom. *Prentice Hall Mathematics* helps support this goal by embedding problem-solving instruction in every lesson, providing targeted support for problem-solving strategies throughout the Student Edition, and including sufficient problems to help students practice and reinforce problem solving skills.

Guided Problem Solving Features

These features throughout the Student Edition provide scaffolded support in solving problems. The student walks through how to solve one representative problem, focusing on both the reasoning and the computation that must be done.

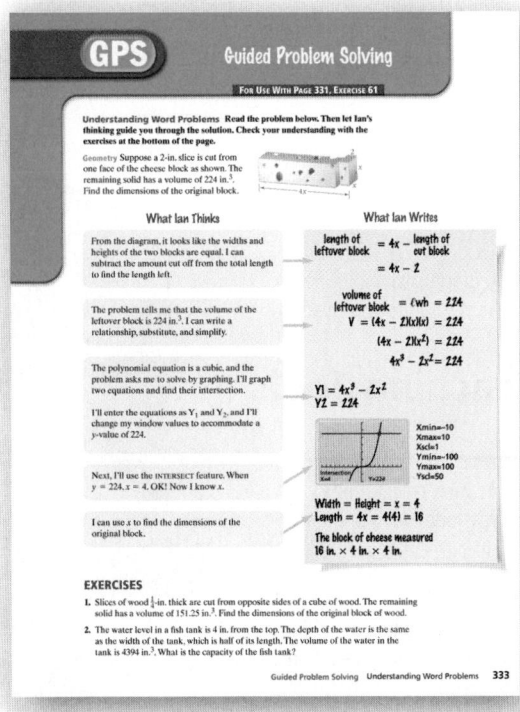

Activities and Activity Labs

Throughout the Student Edition are in-lesson activities and full feature Activity Labs. These provide students an opportunity to complete more in-depth problems and applications of the mathematical content they're learning.

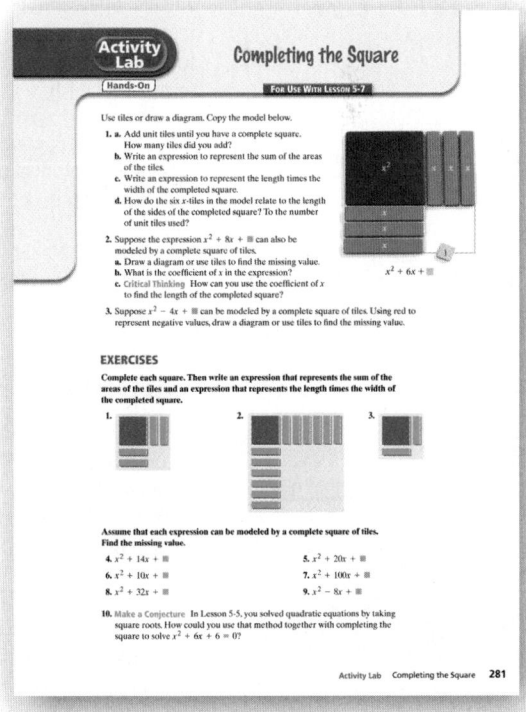

Problem Solving Practice

Every lesson in the Student Edition includes a comprehensive, leveled exercise set. This provides students the opportunity to solve a variety of problems and apply problem solving strategies on a daily basis. Furthermore, additional problems have been added to the end of each book in the Extra Skill and Word Problem Practice section.

Technology – not simply added, but added value

Take Learning to a New Level

Student Express CD-ROM
A suite of learning tools to help students study, learn, and succeed in class. An interactive textbook with instructional videos, built-in activities, vocabulary support, and instant feedback assessments make this the most powerful student study tool available. Interactive Text also available online.

Homework Video Tutor and Online Active Math
Homework Video Tutor provide built-in homework help for every lesson. Narrated by real teachers, these engaging interactive tutorials cover the key concepts of each day's lesson. Additionally, Online Active Math interactive provide an opportunity to explore math concepts.

Use Assessment Technology to Inform Instruction

ExamView 5.0
The most powerful test generator available—with the most comprehensive test banks. Create and modify custom-made tests with ease. Access the Math Art folder to instantly add math images to your questions. Also-instantly translate any test into Spanish.

MindPoint Quiz Show
This creative product allows teachers to involve the entire class in a fun, end-of-chapter review game.

Success Tracker™ Online
Personalized for each student with individual assessment, diagnosis, and remediation. Color-coded reports make it easy for teachers to monitor progress.

Superior Planning and Teaching Tools

TeacherEXPRESS™ CD-ROM—powered by LessonView planning software
An Interactive Teacher's Edition, LessonView planning software, correlations to state and local standards, instructional tools, plus professional development to help teachers plan, teach, and assess.

PresentationEXPRESS CD-ROM with QuickTake
This innovative component includes all the transparencies in interactive, PowerPoint format, making it easier for you to teach and to customize based on your teaching preferences. QuickTake assessments are embedded in every lesson, allowing teachers to quickly and easily monitor student progress.

Worksheets Online
All program worksheets are also conveniently posted online so you and your students can access them anywhere - one more way to make your planning and assignment management easier.

Professional Development
that meets your needs

In-Service On Demand

Now, you have the freedom to access your Prentice Hall in-service training online, anytime, anywhere, at PHSchool.com. This online tutorial library offers in-service training specifically for the Prentice Hall textbook and technology you're teaching with right now.

In-service designed around you!

In-Service On Demand is Prentice Hall's new Web site of in-service training tutorials for your Prentice Hall products. Now you can access the same training for using your Prentice Hall textbook and technology that you would learn in a traditional in-service—from the convenience of your computer!

In-Service for your Prentice Hall program!

The In-Service On Demand library features video-based tutorials to help you maximize the effectiveness of the Prentice Hall program you use. This extensive library is continually being updated with tutorials for Prentice Hall's newest products! Visit the site as often as you like!

In-Service is just a click away!

1. Go to PHSchool.com and click on In-Service On Demand.
2. Select mathematics and then select your *Prentice Hall Mathematics* book.
3. Watch the video-based tutorials and get the in-service training you need when and where it's convenient for you.
4. Download and print PDF tutorial guides on what you've just seen.

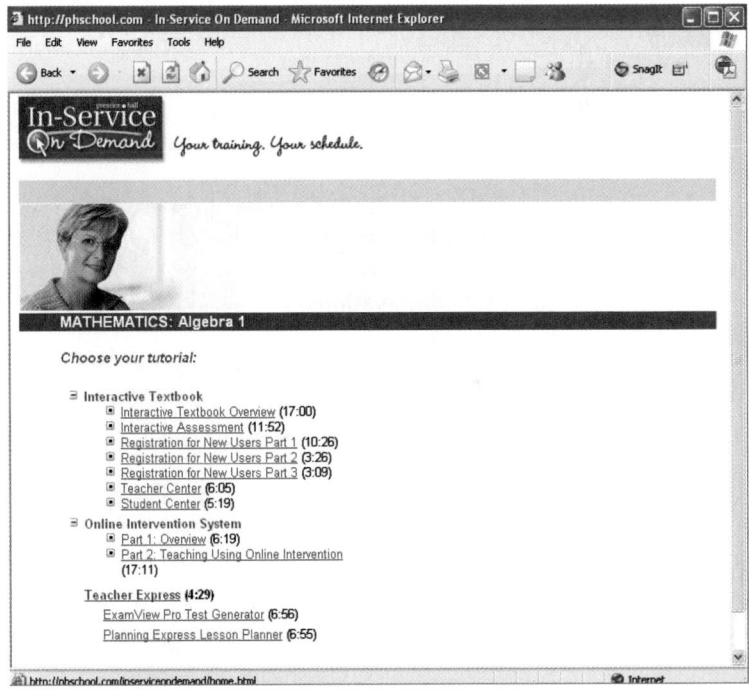

Day-to-Day Professional Development

Math Background in Teacher's Edition

Support instruction at the chapter and lesson level as every Chapter of Prentice Hall Mathematics begins with Math Background related to the content of the chapter in both middle school and high school.

Sustained Development of Mathematics Content

Math Across the Grades

Deepen teacher content knowledge as it relates to the PreK–Algebra curriculum, particularly how mathematics concepts and skills are developed across the grades in the Scott Foresman and Prentice Hall Mathematics programs.

Research-Based and Proven Effective

The stakes for mathematics educators are high. You are expected to raise student achievement. Prentice Hall Mathematics programs are backed by efficacy research to give you the confidence to meet this challenge.

In developing Prentice Hall programs, the use of research is a guiding, central construct. This research was conducted in three phases:

1 Exploratory Needs Assessment
(Quantitative and Qualitative)

Key research events include —
- Teacher interviews
- Classroom observations
- Mail surveys
- Reviews of educational research

2 Formative, Prototype Development and Field Testing
(Quantitative and Qualitative)

Key research events include —
- Field testing of prototypes
- Classroom observations
- Teacher reviews
- Supervisor reviews
- Educator advisory panels

3 Summative, Validation Research
(Experimental and Quasi-Experimental Study Designs & Qualitative Research)

Key research events include —
- Pre-publication learner verification research
- Post-publication efficacy studies
- Classroom observations
- Evaluation of in-market results on standardized tests
- Effect size studies

The facing page contains an example of the latest research carried out for Prentice Hall High School Mathematics.

2005 Research Results:
Prentice Hall
High School Mathematics

Results of independent research show Prentice Hall *Algebra 1* is helping students to succeed in mathematics. The randomized control trial, conducted by PRES Associates, Inc., a national educational evaluation firm with central offices in Jackson, WY, showed that student performance increased significantly from pre- to post-tests as measured by three different standardized assessments. Significant improvements were also observed in several key diagnostic areas.

The study is part of a multi-year research effort commissioned by the publisher and is one of many slated to evaluate the effectiveness of Prentice Hall's educational materials across disciplines and grade levels. Participants represented a mix of urban and suburban districts with diverse socio-economic and ethnic backgrounds.

Among the key findings, PRES Associates reported:
- Student performance significantly improved from the beginning to the end of the school year as measured by a battery of three different standardized assessment measures, chosen because they are aligned to national NCTM standards and have proven reliability and validity.
- Subgroup analyses suggests that the Prentice Hall *Algebra 1* program works equally well with students of Limited English Proficiency (LEP), special education students, and females as compared to non-LEP students, non-special education students, and males, respectively.
- 53% of students performing at below average at the beginning of the year improved to average or advanced by the end of the year.
- 43% of students performing at average at the beginning of the year improved to advanced by the end of the year.
- One hundred percent of teachers participating in the study reported that use of Prentice Hall *Algebra 1* was attributed to an increase in students' skills and knowledge, preparation for state testing, and a decrease in teacher planning time.
- Students using Prentice Hall *Algebra 1* were more satisfied with their textbook, ancillary resources, and technology support and had higher mathematics aspirations than those using other programs.

The study was designed to fully meet the evidence criteria put forth by the What Works Clearinghouse, the Federal agency established in 2002 to provide the educational community and the public with a trusted source of scientific evidence of what works in education. This study was designed so that accurate and appropriate inferences could be made regarding the effectiveness of the Prentice Hall *Algebra 1* program.

Visit PHSchool.com/MathResearch for the full report and additional research in support of Prentice Hall Mathematics programs.

Mathematics Strands

The following 10 strands are from the standards outlined in the NCTM Principles and Standards. The Background and Progressions indicates content students usually have mastered when they enter high school and the progression expected using Prentice Hall Algebra 1, Geometry and Algebra 2.

Number and Operations

- Understand numbers, ways of representing numbers, relationships among numbers, and number systems
- Understand meanings of operations and how they relate to one another
- Compute fluently and make reasonable estimates

Background and Progression Students usually enter an Algebra 1 course having some facility with integers, fractions, and decimals, and with finding square roots.

In *Algebra 1*, students extend their knowledge of rational numbers by using symbolic, graphic, and numeric representations as they solve equations and inequalities. Work with rational and radical expressions, equations, and functions builds a wide base of experience for real numbers

In *Geometry*, students' understanding of the properties of real numbers becomes a base for building reasoned geo-metric arguments. In this year, students first study vectors.

In *Algebra 2*, students study matrices and complex numbers—number systems that do not share all the properties of real numbers.

Data Analysis and Probability

- Formulate questions that can be addressed with data and collect, organize, and display relevant data to answer them
- Select and use appropriate statistical methods to analyze data
- Understand and apply basic concepts of probability

Background and Progression In the middle grades, students gather, display, and interpret many types of data, and can determine the appropriate graph for data among bar, line, and circle graphs. Students can find simple probabilities.

In *Algebra 1*, students work with scatter plots and functions to model two-variable, or bivariate, data. They compute probabilities for simple and compound events.

In *Geometry*, students maintain skills with probability exercises found throughout the text and are introduced to geometric probability.

In *Algebra 2*, students begin a study of theoretical distributions, including binomial and normal.

Algebra

- Understand patterns, relations, and functions
- Represent and analyze mathematical situations and structures using algebraic symbols
- Use mathematical models to represent and understand quantitative relationships
- Analyze change in various contexts

Background and Progression Most middle school students are comfortable using tables, graphs, verbal rules, and variables to represent simple relationships.

In *Algebra 1*, students use tables, graphs, and verbal and symbolic rules to describe linear, quadratic, and exponential functions. They choose a best model for data from among these functions. Rate of change is studied in the context of direct variation, linear equations, and arithmetic sequences.

In *Geometry*, Algebra 1 skills are reinforced with applications involving both linear and quadratic relationships.

In *Algebra 2*, students use multiple representations in studying polynomial, rational, radical, logarithmic, and periodic functions. Using technology, students study residuals as an indicator of the most appropriate model for data.

Geometry

- Analyze characteristics and properties of two- and three-dimensional geometric shapes and develop mathematical arguments about geometric relationships
- Specify locations and describe spatial relationships using coordinate geometry and other representational systems
- Apply transformations and use symmetry to analyze mathematical situations
- Use visualization, spatial reasoning, and geometric modeling to solve problems

Background and Progression In the middle grades, students have explored various plane and space figures to identify and compare properties. This includes working with similarity, congruence, transformations, and graphs of simple figures in the coordinate plane.

In *Algebra 1*, students use geometric models with proportions, percent, and probability. They also explore ways to describe translations of familiar functions in both words and symbols.

In *Geometry*, all key strand content is covered. The first two chapters establish the tools of geometry—methods of reasoning, construction, the coordinate plane, and types of measurement. Subsequent chapters focus on properties and application of lines, triangles, quadrilaterals, similarity, right angle trigonometry, transformations, and circles.

In *Algebra 2*, students apply principles of translating in the coordinate plane to functions and conic sections. They also use geometric models for trigonometric relationships.

Measurement

- Understand measurable attributes of objects and the units, systems, and processes of measurement
- Apply appropriate techniques, tools, and formulas to determine measurements

Background and Progression Middle school students have usually experienced direct and indirect measurement. They have developed and used formulas for the perimeters, areas, and volumes of simple figures.

In *Algebra 1*, students make decisions about appropriate scales with graphical representations of data. They use perimeter and area formulas, and use unit analysis to help set up proportions and other equations.

In *Geometry*, students apply formulas for perimeter and area to composite and irregular plane shapes. They use cross sections to develop formulas for the volume of prisms, cylinders, pyramids, and cones. Through work with circles, students become comfortable with exact measures (which are irrational and expressed in terms of p) and rational approximations of these measures.

In *Algebra 2*, students use polynomials to express the areas and volumes of figures and polynomial equations to find missing measures. With geometric sequences they explore successive approximations and the concept of a limit. In their study of trigonometry, students learn how to use the parallel measuring scales of degrees and radians.

Problem Solving

- Build new mathematical knowledge through problem solving
- Solve problems that arise in mathematics and in other contexts
- Apply and adapt a variety of appropriate strategies to solve problems
- Monitor and reflect on the process of mathematical problem solving

Background and Progression The Prentice Hall Mathematics Program for the middle grades contains a rich problem solving strand, including lessons each year covering ten problem solving strategies.

In *Algebra 1*, *Geometry*, and *Algebra 2* the strategies are reviewed in the Skills Handbook. Each text contains numerous real-world examples, many of which use the "Relate-Define-Write" format to guide the student in choosing and writing symbolic models for real-world problems.

Writing, Critical Thinking, Reasoning, and Error Analysis exercises allow students to analyze and verbalize their own understanding of the problem solving process.

Reasoning and Proof

- Recognize reasoning and proof as fundamental aspects of mathematics
- Make and investigate mathematical conjectures
- Develop and evaluate mathematical arguments and proofs
- Select and use various types of reasoning and methods of proof

Background and Progression In middle grades, students identify the use of Commutative, Associative, Identity, Inverse, and Distributive properties. They use these properties and the Properties of equality to justify steps in solving equations. Students also differentiate deductive and inductive reasoning.

In *Algebra 1*, students solve equations using properties to justify their steps. These justifications are extended to simple algebraic proofs.

In *Geometry*, students develop an understanding of reasoning and proof, building naturally on the step-by-step processes of algebra. They prove theorems using paragraph proofs, flow proofs, and two-column proofs.

In *Algebra 2*, students further their understanding and ability to prove concepts not only by deduction but also by using mathematical induction.

Communication

- Organize and consolidate their mathematical thinking through communication
- Communicate their mathematical thinking coherently and clearly to peers, teachers, and others
- Analyze and evaluate the mathematical thinking and strategies of others
- Use the language of mathematics to express mathematical ideas precisely

Background and Progression The Prentice Hall Mathematics Program for the middle grades gives students numerous opportunities to explain and justify their reasoning.

The *Algebra 1*, *Geometry*, and *Algebra 2* textbooks continue this rich communication strand. In-lesson Activities and Activity Labs have students develop critical concepts, which they first summarize and then apply.

The Guided Problem Solving pages show the thinking process for solving problems. The Vocabulary hints in lessons and the Vocabulary Builder pages help students use the language and notation of mathematics correctly.

Connections

- Recognize and use connections among mathematical ideas
- Understand how mathematical ideas interconnect and build on one another to produce a coherent whole
- Recognize and apply mathematics in contexts outside of mathematics

Background and Progression In middle grades, students make connections between geometric and algebraic concepts through graphing geometric figures in the coordinate plane and using slope to investigate parallelism and perpendicularity.

In *Algebra 1*, students use algebra to develop formulas for geometric measurement and to describe statistical relationships (lines of best fit). Students understand geometric relationships using slope, midpoint, and distance formulas.

In *Geometry*, students use algebra to interpret and apply geometric relationships. Students revisit many geometric facts in the context of the coordinate plane.

In *Algebra 2*, students use matrices to describe transformations in the coordinate plane. They extend algebra-geometry connections to reinforce the structure and processes involving functions and conic sections.

Representation

- Create and use representations to organize, record, and communicate mathematical ideas
- Select, apply, and translate among mathematical representations to solve problems
- Use representations to model and interpret physical, social, and mathematical phenomena

Background and Progression In the middle grades, students have experiences using tables, rules, and graphs to describe functional relationships.

In *Algebra 1*, students gain facility in graphing linear, quadratic, exponential, and rational functions. Using tables and graphs, students determine which function best models a given set of data.

In *Geometry*, students learn to apply and interpret geometric principles in real-world settings and frequently use coordinate methods to take another look at these principles.

In *Algebra 2*, students extend their knowledge of the families of functions to polynomial, logarithmic, and trigonometric functions. They also use three-variable equations to model problem situations.

Algebra 2 Leveled Pacing Chart

This Leveled Pacing Chart will help you customize your course to include topics in discrete math or trigonometry and to provide for differentiated instruction.

The suggested number of days for each chapter is based on a traditional 45-minute class period and on a 90-minute block period. The total of 160 days of instruction leaves time for assessments, projects, assemblies, or other special days that vary from school to school.

Differentiated
Instruction
Solutions for All Learners

T = Traditional B = Block	Regular Course	Course With Discrete Math	Course With Trigonometry	Comprehensive Course
Chapter 1 Tools of Algebra	T = 14 B = 7	T = 11 B = 6	T = 11 B = 5	T = 6 B = 3
1-1 Properties of Real Numbers	✔	✔	✔	
1-2 Algebraic Expressions	✔	✔	✔	
• Activity Lab: Writing Expressions From Tables	✔	✔	✔	
1-3 Solving Equations	✔	✔	✔	
• Activity Lab Technology: Spreadsheets		✔		
1-4 Solving Inequalities	✔	✔	✔	✔
• Guided Problem Solving: Understanding Math Problems	✔	✔	✔	
1-5 Absolute Value Equations and Inequalities	✔	✔	✔	✔
1-6 Probability	✔	✔	✔	✔
Chapter 2 Functions, Equations, and Graphs	T = 18 B = 9	T = 15 B = 7	T = 14 B = 7	T = 12 B = 6
• Algebra 1 Review: The Coordinate Plane	✔	✔	✔	✔
2-1 Relations and Functions	✔	✔	✔	✔
2-2 Linear Equations	✔	✔	✔	✔
• Extension: Piecewise Functions		✔		✔
2-3 Direct Variation	✔	✔	✔	✔
2-4 Using Linear Models	✔	✔	✔	✔
• Activity Lab Technology: Finding a Line of Best Fit	✔	✔	✔	✔
• Vocabulary Builder: High-Use Academic Words	✔	✔	✔	✔
2-5 Absolute Value Functions and Graphs	✔	✔	✔	✔
2-6 Families of Functions	✔	✔	✔	✔
2-7 Two-Variable Inequalities	✔	✔	✔	✔
• Guided Problem Solving: Understanding Math Problems	✔	✔	✔	
• Activity Lab: Applying Functions				✔
Chapter 3 Linear Systems	T = 14 B = 7	T = 12 B = 6	T = 11 B = 6	T = 10 B = 5
3-1 Graphing Systems of Equations	✔	✔	✔	✔
3-2 Solving Systems Algebraically	✔	✔	✔	✔
• Activity Lab Technology: Parametric Equations				✔
• Guided Problem Solving: Understanding Word Problems	✔	✔	✔	
• Activity Lab: Solving Systems Using Tables		✔		✔
3-3 Systems of Inequalities	✔	✔	✔	✔
3-4 Linear Programming	✔	✔	✔	✔
• Activity Lab Technology: Linear Programming		✔		✔
3-5 Graphs in Three Dimensions	✔	✔	✔	✔
3-6 Systems With Three Variables	✔	✔	✔	✔
Chapter 4 Matrices	T = 18 B = 9	T = 16 B = 8	T = 16 B = 8	T = 14 B = 7
4-1 Organizing Data Into Matrices	✔	✔	✔	✔
4-2 Adding and Subtracting Matrices	✔	✔	✔	✔
• Activity Lab Technology: Working With Matrices	✔	✔	✔	✔
4-3 Matrix Multiplication	✔	✔	✔	✔

	Regular Course	Course With Discrete Math	Course With Trigonometry	Comprehensive Course
• Geometry Review: Geometric Transformations	✔	✔	✔	✔
4-4 Geometric Transformations With Matrices	✔	✔	✔	✔
4-5 2 × 2 Matrices, Determinants, and Inverses	✔	✔	✔	✔
4-6 3 × 3 Matrices, Determinants, and Inverses	✔			✔
• Extension: Networks				✔
4-7 Inverse Matrices and Systems	✔	✔	✔	✔
• Guided Problem Solving: Understanding Math Problems	✔	✔	✔	✔
4-8 Augmented Matrices and Systems	✔			✔
• Activity Lab: Applying Inequalities		✔		✔
Chapter 5 Quadratic Equations and Functions	T = 18 B = 9	T = 16 B = 8	T = 16 B = 8	T = 12 B = 6
5-1 Modeling Data With Quadratic Functions	✔	✔	✔	✔
• Activity Lab Technology: Modeling Using Residuals				✔
5-2 Properties of Parabolas	✔	✔	✔	✔
5-3 Transforming Parabolas	✔	✔	✔	✔
5-4 Factoring Quadratic Expressions	✔	✔	✔	✔
• Algebra 1 Review: Square Roots and Radicals	✔	✔	✔	✔
5-5 Quadratic Equations	✔	✔	✔	✔
• Activity Lab: Writing Equations From Roots	✔	✔	✔	✔
5-6 Complex Numbers	✔	✔	✔	✔
5-7 Completing the Square	✔	✔	✔	✔
• Activity Lab Hands-On: Completing the Square	✔	✔	✔	✔
• Guided Problem Solving: Understanding Word Problems	✔	✔	✔	✔
5-8 The Quadratic Formula	✔	✔	✔	✔
• Activity Lab Technology: Quadratic Inequalities				✔
Chapter 6 Polynomials and Polynomial Functions	T = 18 B = 9	T = 13 B = 7	T = 10 B = 5	T = 10 B = 5
6-1 Polynomial Functions	✔	✔	✔	✔
• Extension: End Behavior		✔		✔
6-2 Polynomials and Linear Factors	✔	✔	✔	✔
6-3 Dividing Polynomials	✔	✔	✔	✔
6-4 Solving Polynomial Equations	✔	✔	✔	✔
• Guided Problem Solving: Understanding Word Problems	✔	✔	✔	✔
• Vocabulary Builder: Continuous and Discrete	✔	✔	✔	✔
6-5 Theorems About Roots of Polynomial Equations	✔	✔	✔	✔
6-6 The Fundamental Theorem of Algebra	✔	✔	✔	✔
6-7 Permutations and Combinations		✔		✔
6-8 The Binomial Theorem		✔		✔
• Activity Lab: Pascal's Triangle		✔		✔
• Activity Lab: Applying Quadratic Functions		✔		✔
Chapter 7 Radical Functions and Rational Exponents	T = 18 B = 9	T = 15 B = 7	T = 14 B = 7	T = 12 B = 6
7-1 Roots and Radical Expressions	✔	✔	✔	✔
• Algebra 1 Review: Properties of Exponents	✔	✔	✔	
7-2 Multiplying and Dividing Radical Expressions	✔	✔	✔	✔
7-3 Binomial Radical Expressions	✔	✔	✔	✔
7-4 Rational Exponents	✔	✔	✔	✔
7-5 Solving Square Root and Other Radical Equations	✔	✔	✔	✔
• Geometry Review: Radical Expressions in Formulas	✔	✔	✔	✔
7-6 Function Operations	✔	✔	✔	✔
• Guided Problem Solving: Understanding Word Problems	✔	✔	✔	✔

	Regular Course	Course With Discrete Math	Course With Trigonometry	Comprehensive Course
7-7 Inverse Relations and Functions	✔	✔	✔	✔
• Activity Lab Technology: Graphing Inverses				✔
7-8 Graphing Square Root and Other Radical Functions	✔	✔	✔	✔
• Activity Lab Technology: Radical Inequalities				✔
Chapter 8 Exponential and Logarithmic Functions	T = 16 B = 8	T = 13 B = 7	T = 12 B = 6	T = 12 B = 6
8-1 Exploring Exponential Models	✔	✔	✔	✔
• Activity Lab Technology: Fitting Exponential Curves to Data	✔	✔	✔	✔
8-2 Properties of Exponential Functions	✔	✔	✔	✔
8-3 Logarithmic Functions as Inverses	✔	✔	✔	✔
• Guided Problem Solving: Understanding Word Problems	✔	✔	✔	✔
8-4 Properties of Logarithms	✔	✔	✔	✔
• Vocabulary Builder: Reasonable Context	✔	✔	✔	✔
8-5 Exponential and Logarithmic Equations	✔	✔	✔	✔
• Activity Lab Technology: Linear and Exponential Models	✔	✔	✔	✔
8-6 Natural Logarithms	✔		✔	✔
• Activity Lab Technology: Exponential and Logarithmic Inequalities				✔
• Activity Lab: Applying Exponential Functions		✔		✔
Chapter 9 Rational Functions	T = 12 B = 6	T = 10 B = 5	T = 10 B = 5	T = 10 B = 5
9-1 Inverse Variation	✔	✔	✔	✔
9-2 The Reciprocal Function Family	✔	✔	✔	✔
• Activity Lab Technology: Graphing Rational Functions	✔	✔	✔	✔
9-3 Rational Functions and Their Graphs		✔	✔	✔
9-4 Rational Expressions	✔	✔	✔	✔
9-5 Adding and Subtracting Rational Expressions	✔	✔	✔	✔
9-6 Solving Rational Equations	✔	✔	✔	✔
• Activity Lab: Extraneous Solutions	✔	✔	✔	✔
• Activity Lab Technology: Rational Inequalities				✔
• Guided Problem Solving: Understanding Word Problems	✔	✔	✔	✔
9-7 Probability of Multiple Events		✔		
Chapter 10 Quadratic Relations and Conic Sections	T = 14 B = 7	T = 12 B = 6	T = 12 B = 6	T = 8 B = 4
10-1 Exploring Conic Sections	✔	✔	✔	✔
• Activity Lab Hands-On: Conic Sections	✔	✔	✔	✔
• Activity Lab Technology: Graphing Conic Sections	✔	✔	✔	✔
10-2 Parabolas	✔	✔	✔	✔
10-3 Circles	✔	✔	✔	✔
• Activity Lab Technology: Using Parametric Equations	✔	✔	✔	✔
10-4 Ellipses	✔	✔	✔	✔
10-5 Hyperbolas	✔	✔	✔	✔
• Guided Problem Solving: Understanding Math Problems	✔	✔	✔	
10-6 Translating Conic Sections	✔	✔	✔	✔
• Activity Lab Technology: Solving Quadratic Systems				✔
• Activity Lab: Applying Conic Sections			✔	✔
Chapter 11 Sequences and Series		T = 13 B = 6		T = 12 B = 6
11-1 Mathematical Patterns		✔		✔
11-2 Arithmetic Sequences		✔		✔
• Activity Lab: The Fibonacci Sequence		✔		✔
11-3 Geometric Sequences		✔		✔

	Regular Course	Course With Discrete Math	Course With Trigonometry	Comprehensive Course
• Guided Problem Solving: Understanding Math Problems		✔		
11-4 Arithmetic Series		✔		✔
11-5 Geometric Series		✔		✔
• Activity Lab: Geometry and Infinite Series		✔		✔
• Activity Lab Technology: Evaluating Series		✔		✔
• Extension: Mathematical Induction		✔		✔
11-6 Area Under a Curve				✔
Chapter 12 Probability and Statistics		T = 14 B = 7		T = 12 B = 6
12-1 Probability Distributions		✔		✔
12-2 Conditional Probability		✔		✔
• Extension: Comparing Conditional Probabilities		✔		✔
12-3 Analyzing Data		✔		✔
12-4 Standard Deviation		✔		✔
• Guided Problem Solving: Understanding Math Problems		✔		✔
• Activity Lab: Continuous Probability		✔		✔
12-5 Working With Samples		✔		✔
• Vocabulary Builder: Variable and Parameter		✔		✔
12-6 Binomial Distributions		✔		✔
12-7 Normal Distributions		✔		✔
• Activity Lab Technology: Area Under a Curve				✔
• Activity Lab: Applying Sequences		✔		✔
Chapter 13 Periodic Functions and Trigonometry			T = 18 B = 9	T = 16 B = 8
13-1 Exploring Periodic Data			✔	✔
• Geometry Review: Special Right Triangles			✔	✔
13-2 Angles and the Unit Circle			✔	✔
13-3 Radian Measure			✔	✔
• Activity Lab Hands-On: Measuring Radians			✔	✔
13-4 The Sine Function			✔	✔
• Activity Lab Technology: Graphing Trigonometric Functions			✔	✔
13-5 The Cosine Function			✔	✔
13-6 The Tangent Function			✔	✔
• Guided Problem Solving: Understanding Math Problems			✔	✔
13-7 Translating Sine and Cosine Functions			✔	✔
13-8 Reciprocal Trigonometric Functions			✔	✔
Chapter 14 Trigonometric Identities and Equations			T = 16 B = 8	T = 14 B = 7
14-1 Trigonometric Identities			✔	✔
14-2 Solving Trigonometric Equations Using Inverses			✔	✔
• Activity Lab Technology: Lissajous Figures				✔
14-3 Right Triangles and Trigonometric Ratios			✔	✔
• Guided Problem Solving: Understanding Word Problems			✔	✔
14-4 Area and the Law of Sines			✔	✔
• Extension: The Ambiguous Case			✔	✔
14-5 The Law of Cosines			✔	✔
14-6 Angle Identities			✔	✔
14-7 Double-Angle and Half-Angle Identities			✔	✔
• Activity Lab: Applying Trigonometry			✔	✔

Using Your Book for Success

Welcome to *Prentice Hall Algebra 2*. There are many features built into the daily lessons of this text that will help you learn the important skills and concepts you will need to be successful in this course. Look through the following pages for some study tips that you will find useful as you complete each lesson.

Getting Ready to Learn

Check Your Readiness

Complete the *Check Your Readiness* exercises to see what topics you may need to review before you begin the chapter.

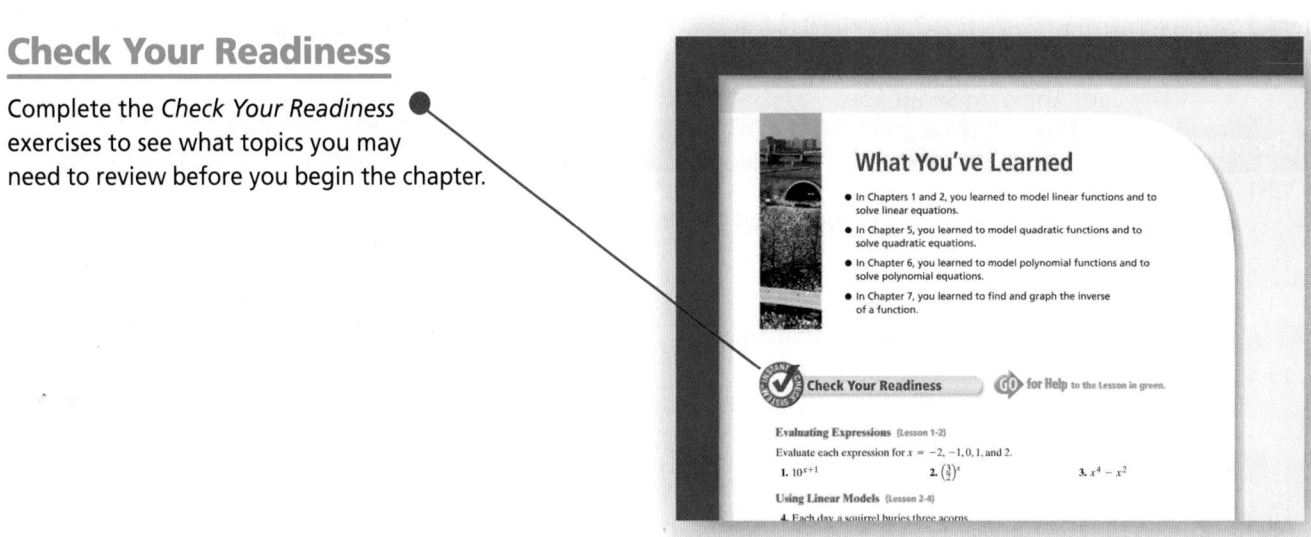

What You've Learned

- In Chapters 1 and 2, you learned to model linear functions and to solve linear equations.
- In Chapter 5, you learned to model quadratic functions and to solve quadratic equations.
- In Chapter 6, you learned to model polynomial functions and to solve polynomial equations.
- In Chapter 7, you learned to find and graph the inverse of a function.

✓ **Check Your Readiness** 〈GO〉 **for Help** to the Lesson in green.

Evaluating Expressions (Lesson 1-2)

Evaluate each expression for $x = -2, -1, 0, 1,$ and 2.

1. 10^{x+1} 2. $\left(\frac{3}{2}\right)^x$ 3. $x^4 - x^2$

Using Linear Models (Lesson 2-4)

4. Each day a squirrel buries three acorns.

Check Skills You'll Need

Complete the *Check Skills You'll Need* exercises to make sure you have the skills needed to successfully learn the concepts in the lesson.

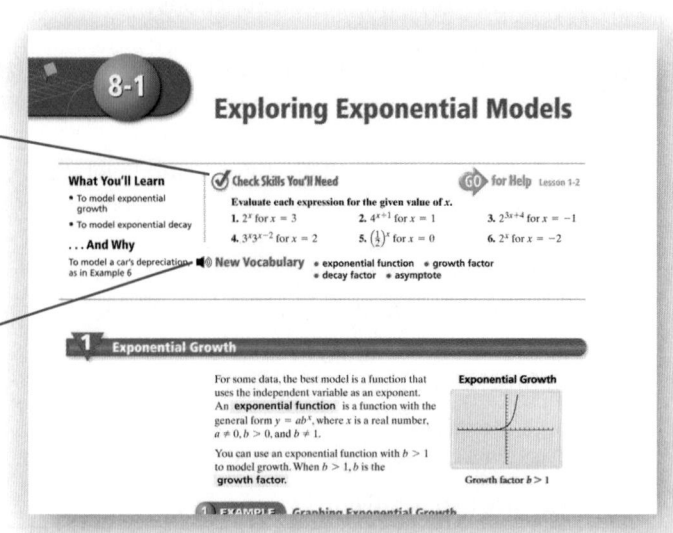

8-1

Exploring Exponential Models

What You'll Learn
- To model exponential growth
- To model exponential decay

. . . And Why

To model a car's depreciation as in Example 6

✓ **Check Skills You'll Need** 〈GO〉 **for Help** Lesson 1-2

Evaluate each expression for the given value of x.

1. 2^x for $x = 3$ 2. 4^{x+1} for $x = 1$ 3. 2^{3x+4} for $x = -1$
4. $3^x 3^{x-2}$ for $x = 2$ 5. $\left(\frac{1}{4}\right)^x$ for $x = 0$ 6. 2^x for $x = -2$

◀)) **New Vocabulary** • exponential function • growth factor
• decay factor • asymptote

New Vocabulary

New Vocabulary is listed for each lesson so you can pre-read the text. As each term is introduced, it is highlighted in yellow.

1 Exponential Growth

For some data, the best model is a function that uses the independent variable as an exponent. An **exponential function** is a function with the general form $y = ab^x$, where x is a real number, $a \neq 0, b > 0,$ and $b \neq 1$.

You can use an exponential function with $b > 1$ to model growth. When $b > 1, b$ is the **growth factor**.

Exponential Growth

Growth factor $b > 1$

1 EXAMPLE Graphing Exponential Growth

Built-In Help

Go for Help

Look for the green labels throughout your book that tell you where to "Go" for help. You'll see this built-in help in the lessons and in the homework exercises.

Video Tutor Help

Go online to see engaging videos to help you better understand important math concepts.

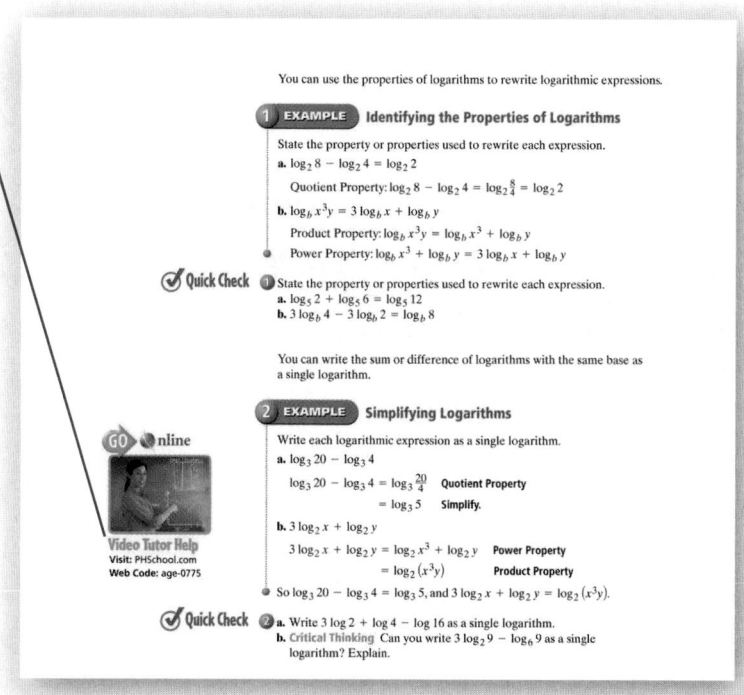

Understanding the Lesson

Quick Check

Every lesson includes numerous Examples, each followed by a *Quick Check* question that you can do on your own to see if you understand the skill being introduced. Check your progress with the answers at the back of the book.

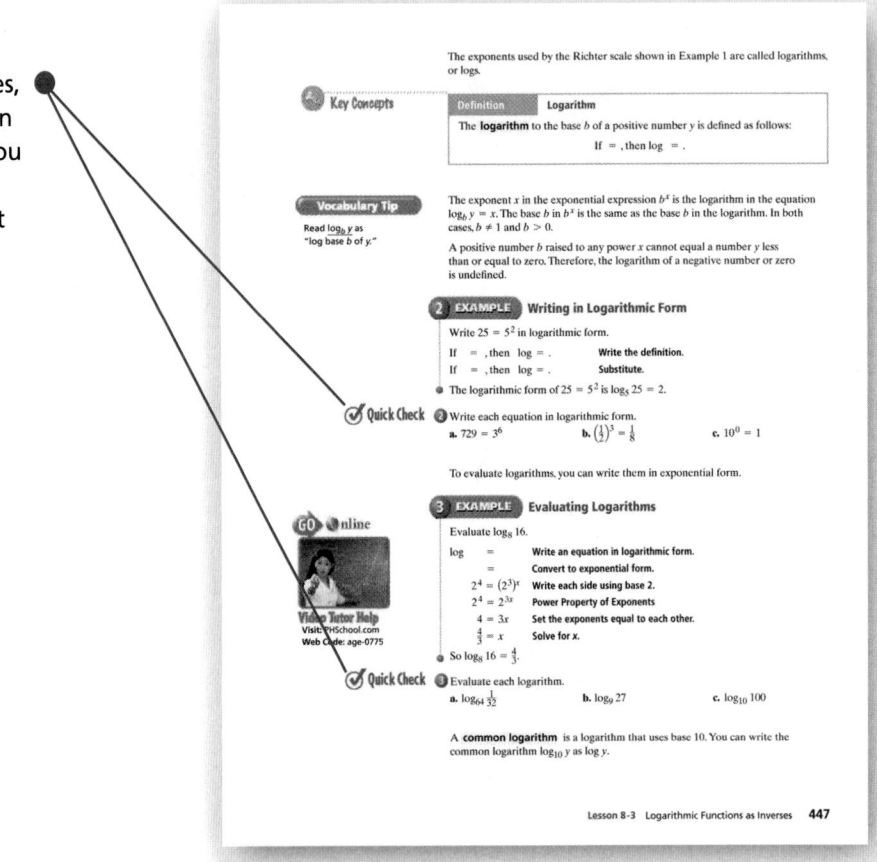

Understanding Key Concepts

Frequent *Key Concept* boxes summarize important definitions, formulas, and properties. Use these to review what you've learned.

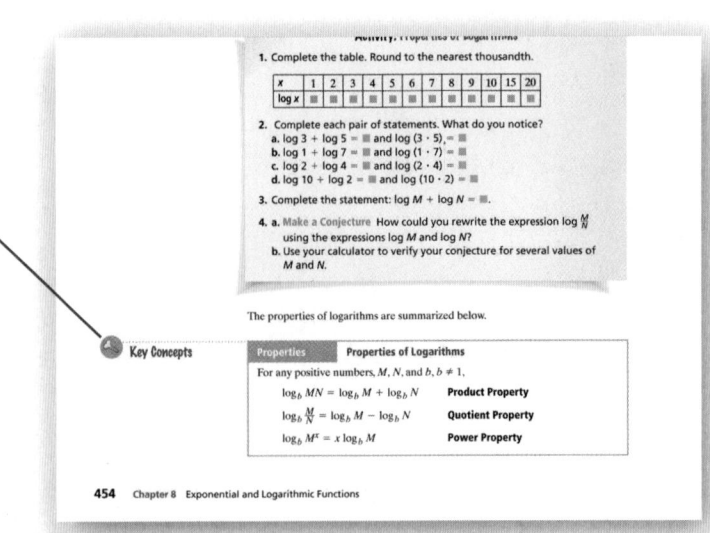

Online Active Math

Make math come alive with these online activities. Review and practice important math concepts with these engaging online tutorials.

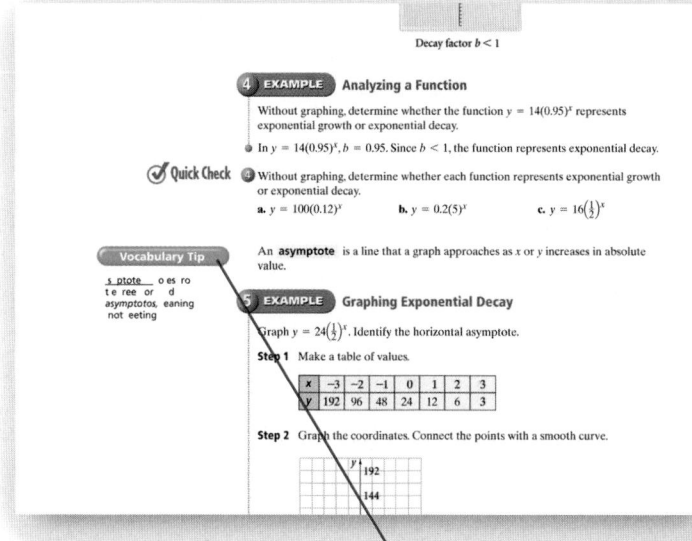

Vocabulary Support

Understanding mathematical vocabulary is an important part of studying mathematics. *Vocabulary Tips* and *Vocabulary Builders* throughout the book help focus on the language of math.

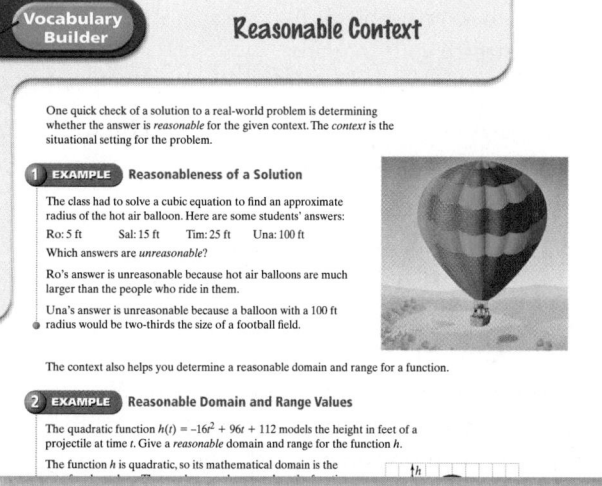

Practice What You've Learned

There are numerous exercises in each lesson that give you the practice you need to master the concepts in the lesson. Each practice set includes the following sections.

A: Practice by Example

Practice by Example exercises refer you back to the Examples in the lesson, in case you need help with completing these exercises.

B: Apply Your Skills

Apply Your Skills exercises combine skills from earlier lessons to offer you richer skill exercises and multi-step application problems.

C: Challenge

Challenge exercises give you an opportunity to solve problems that extend and stretch your thinking.

Test Prep

Test Prep exercises give you daily practice with the types of test question formats that you will encounter on state and national tests.

Preparing for Tests

Test-Taking Strategies

Test-Taking Strategies in every chapter teach you strategies to be successful and give you practice in the skills you need to pass state tests and national tests, including the SAT and ACT.

Standardized Test Prep

Standardized Test Prep pages in every chapter give you more opportunities to prepare for the tests you will have to take.

Test Item Formats

The Standardized Test Prep exercises in your book give you the practice you need to answer all types of test questions.
- Multiple Choice
- Gridded Response, for which you write your answer in a grid
- Short Response, which are scored using a 2-point rubric
- Extended Response, which are scored using a 4-point rubric
- Reading Comprehension

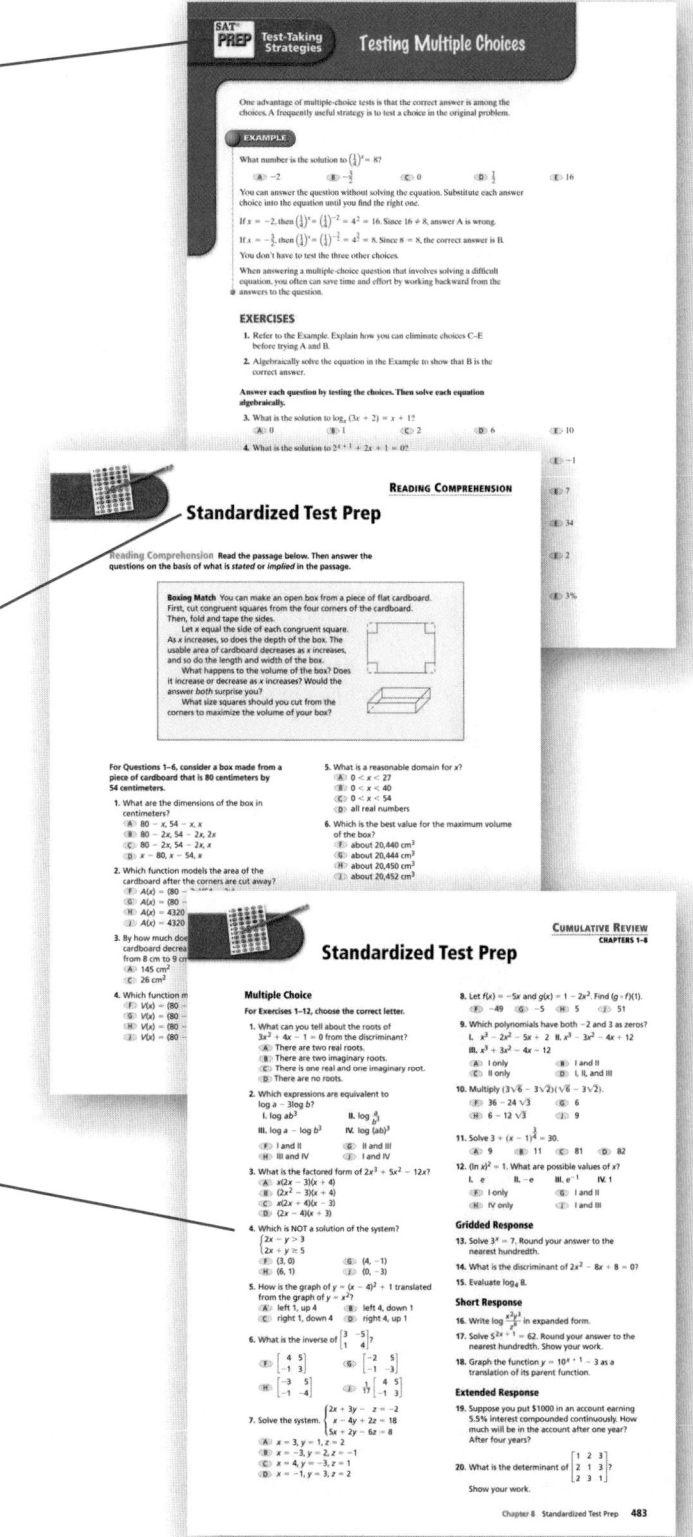

Using Your Book for Success

Intervention This Diagnostic Test covers pre-course skills that students need to succeed in this math program. For intervention, direct students to the following pages from the Skills Handbook and Reviews in their textbooks.

Exercise	Page
1	54
2	871
3	873
4	872
5	875
6	876
7	885
8–9	368
	880
10	883
11	266
12	870
13	871
14	877
15	887
16	865
17	882
18	397
	717
19	878
20	881
21	879
22	884
23	190
24	866
25	874
26	886
27	875

7.

HFCs, PFCs, SF$_6$
N_2O 2.0%
6.4%

CH$_4$
9.2%

CO$_2$
82.4%

Beginning-Of-Course Diagnostic Test

1. Write the coordinates of each point A–E and name the quadrant or axis where each point lies.

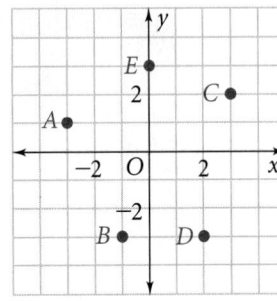

$A(-3, 1)$, II;
$B(-1, -3)$, III;
$C(3, 2)$, I;
$D(2, -3)$, IV;
$E(0, 3)$, y-axis

2. Add $6\frac{3}{5} + 2\frac{1}{8}$. $8\frac{29}{40}$

3. Simplify $6 - (-2)(4) + 3(-2)^2$. **26**

4. Mika hiked 4 mi in 77 min. Use a proportion to find how many miles she will hike in 2 h if she hikes at the same rate. **about 6.2 mi**

5. Find the volume of the figure. **about 94.2 in.^{3}**

10 in.

6 in.

6. Find the midpoint of the segment with the endpoints $(-3, 4)$ and $(2, -6)$. $\left(-\frac{1}{2}, -1\right)$

7. Display the data from the table in a circle graph.

U.S. Greenhouse Gas Emissions From Human Activities, 1999

Gas and Source	Emissions (teragrams of carbon dioxide equivalents)
Carbon dioxide (CO$_2$)	5558.1
Methane (CH$_4$)	619.6
Nitrous Oxide (N$_2$O)	432.6
Hydrofluorocarbons (HFCs), perfluorocarbons (PFCs), sulfer hexafluoride (SF$_6$)	135.7

SOURCE: *The World Almanac and Book of Facts, 2002*

8. Simplify $\dfrac{(3r^{-1}s^2t^3)^2}{27r^3st^{-2}}$. Use only positive exponents. $\dfrac{s^3t^8}{3r^5}$

9. Simplify $\dfrac{x^3y^{-3}z^{-1}}{x^{-2}yz^2}$. Use only positive exponents. $\dfrac{x^5}{y^4z^3}$

10. Simplify $\sqrt{20} + \sqrt{80} - \sqrt{5}$. $5\sqrt{5}$

11. Simplify $-\sqrt{\dfrac{4}{7}}$. $-\dfrac{2\sqrt{7}}{7}$

12. As of the year 2000, the highest wind speed recorded on the top of Mount Washington was 231 mi/h, which is about 298% of the highest wind speed recorded in Chicago. What was the highest wind speed recorded in Chicago as of the year 2000? **77.5 mi/h**
Source: *The World Almanac and Book of Facts, 2002*

13. Divide $4\frac{3}{4} \div 2\frac{1}{3}$. $2\frac{1}{28}$

14. Solve $3y - 2 > 5y$. Graph the solution. $y < -1$

15. Divide $\frac{x^4}{4} \div \frac{x^3}{20}$. $5x$

16. Alisha ran a total of 32 mi during three days of training for a marathon. On the second day of her training session, she ran 6 mi less than on the first day and 2 mi less than on the third day. How many miles did she run on the first day? **14 mi**

17. Write the product $(2.45 \times 10^3)(1.8 \times 10^5)$ in scientific notation. Round to the appropriate number of significant digits. $\mathbf{4.4 \times 10^8}$

18. Let $\triangle ABC$ be an equilateral triangle with side length s. Estimate the percent that the area of the circle circumscribed about $\triangle ABC$ is of the area of the triangle. (It will be greater than 100%.) Recall that the distance from the circumcenter of the triangle to a vertex is equal to the radius of the circumscribed circle. **about 142%**

19. Solve $|4t - 3| = 6$. $-\frac{3}{4}, \frac{9}{4}$

20. Factor $2x^2 - 5x - 12$.
$\mathbf{(2x + 3)(x - 4)}$

21. Graph $2x + 4y < 1$.

22. Find the distance between $(-3, -2)$ and $(1, 7)$. Round to the nearest tenth. **9.8 units**

23. The vertices of $\triangle ABC$ are $A(-1, 2)$, $B(0, 3)$, and $C(3, 1)$. Determine the vertices A', B', and C' of the image of $\triangle ABC$ after a reflection across the x-axis. $\mathbf{A'(-1, -2), B'(0, -3), C'(3, -1)}$

24. How many ways can you roll two standard number cubes and get a sum of 9? **4 ways**

25. The formula $k = \frac{1}{2}mv^2$ relates the kinetic energy of a body to its mass m and speed v. Solve the formula for m. $\mathbf{m = \frac{2k}{v^2}}$

26. Find the mean, median, and mode of the following data set. **3; 3; 7**

$-1 \quad -1 \quad 0 \quad 2 \quad 2 \quad 3 \quad 3 \quad 4 \quad 7 \quad 7 \quad 7$

27. Find the area of a triangle with a base of 14 in. and a height of 6 in. **42 in.²**

Tools of Algebra

Chapter at a Glance

Lesson Titles, Objectives, and Features	Assessment	NCTM Standards	Local Standards
1-1 Properties of Real Numbers • Graphing and ordering real numbers • Identifying and using properties of real numbers	Lesson Quiz	1,2,8	
Activity Lab: Writing Expressions From Tables **1-2 Algebraic Expressions** • Evaluating algebraic expressions • Simplifying algebraic expressions	Lesson Quiz	2,3	
1-3 Solving Equations • Solving equations • Solving problems by writing equations **Activity Lab, Technology:** Spreadsheets	Lesson Quiz Checkpoint Quiz 1	1,3,9	
1-4 Solving Inequalities • Solving and graphing inequalities • Solving and writing compound inequalities **GPS:** Understanding Math Problems	Lesson Quiz	1,2,4,10	
1-5 Absolute Value Equations and Inequalities • Solving absolute value equations • Solving absolute value inequalities	Lesson Quiz Checkpoint Quiz 2	2,7,10	
1-6 Probability • Finding experimental probabilities • Finding theoretical probabilities	Lesson Quiz	3,5,10	

NCTM Standards 2000
1 Number and Operations 2 Algebra 3 Geometry 4 Measurement 5 Data Analysis and Probability
6 Problem Solving 7 Reasoning and Proof 8 Communication 9 Connections 10 Representation

Correlations to Standardized Tests

All content for these tests is contained in *Prentice Hall Algebra 2*. This chart reflects coverage in this chapter only.

	1-1	1-2	1-3	1-4	1-5	1-6
SAT®						
Number and Operations Operations, ratio & proportions, complex numbers, counting, elementary number theory, matrices, sequences	✔	✔	✔	✔	✔	✔
Algebra and Functions Expressions, equations, inequalities, representation and modeling, properties of functions (linear, polynomial, rational, exponential)		✔	✔	✔	✔	
Geometry and Measurement *Plane Euclidean/Measurement Coordinate* Lines, parabolas, circles, symmetry, transformations *Three-dimensional* Solids, surface area & volume (cylinders, cones, pyramids, spheres, prisms) *Trigonometry* Right triangles, identities						✔
Data Analysis, Statistics, and Probability Mean, median, mode, range, interquartile range, graphs and plots, regression, probability						✔
ACT®						
Pre-Algebra Basic operations using whole numbers, decimals, fractions, and integers; place value; square roots and approximations; the concept of exponents; scientific notation; factors, ratio, proportion, and percent; linear equations in one variable; absolute value and ordering numbers by value; elementary counting techniques and simple probability; data collection, representation, and interpretation; and understanding simple descriptive statistics.	✔	✔	✔	✔	✔	✔
Elementary Algebra Properties of exponents and square roots, evaluation of algebraic expressions through substitution, using variables to express functional relationships, understanding algebraic operations, and solving quadratic equations by factoring.	✔	✔	✔	✔	✔	
Intermediate Algebra Understanding of the quadratic formula, rational and radical expressions, absolute value equations and inequalities, sequences and patterns, systems of equations, quadratic inequalities, functions, modeling, matrices, roots of polynomials, and complex numbers.					✔	
Coordinate Geometry Graphing and the relations between equations and graphs, including points, lines, polynomials, circles, and other curves; graphing inequalities; slope; parallel and perpendicular lines; distance; midpoints; and conics.						
Plane Geometry Properties and relations of plane figures, including angles and relations among perpendicular and parallel lines; properties of circles, triangles, rectangles, parallelograms, and trapezoids; transformations; the concept of proof and proof techniques; volume; and applications of geometry to three dimensions.	✔					
Trigonometry Understanding trigonometric relations in right triangles; values and properties of trigonometric functions; graphing trigonometric functions; modeling using trigonometric functions; use of trigonometric identities; and solving trigonometric equations.						
NAEP						
Number Sense, Properties, and Operations	✔	✔	✔	✔		
Measurement			✔			
Geometry and Spatial Sense			✔			
Data Analysis, Statistics, and Probability						✔
Algebra and Functions	✔	✔		✔	✔	

SAT® The College Board, SAT® Reasoning Test   ACT® The ACT Assessment® Test   NAEP National Assessment of Educational Progress, 2005 Mathematics Objectives

Math Background

Skills Trace

BEFORE Chapter 1

In previous courses, students simplified and evaluated expressions, solved equations and inequalities, and applied these skills to solve real-world problems.

DURING Chapter 1

Students review and apply properties of real numbers and properties of equality to simplify expressions and solve equations. Students learn to solve compound inequalities and absolute value equations and inequalities.

AFTER Chapter 1

Students will simplify algebraic expressions and solve equations and inequalities throughout the course.

Chapter Overview

This chapter summarizes and reviews basic concepts and properties of real numbers. The focus is on properties of operations, equality, and inequalities and how these properties are used in solving and graphing one-variable equations and inequalities. Students review absolute value and then solve equations and inequalities that involve absolute value. The chapter concludes with a look at fundamental concepts of experimental, theoretical, and geometric probability.

The ideas and skills discussed in this chapter will be used throughout the course. Appropriate applications of real-world problems are considered at each stage. Many exercises provide good opportunities to relate algebraic concepts to geometric concepts.

Properties of Real Numbers   1-1

Consider reviewing the ordering of positive and negative numbers. In particular, many students confuse the order of numbers between -1 and 1. When ordering irrational numbers, encourage students to estimate their decimal equivalents. For $\sqrt{5}$ students should recognize that $\sqrt{4} = 2$ and $\sqrt{9} = 3$, so $\sqrt{5}$ is between 2 and 3 and much closer to 2. ($\sqrt{5} \approx 2.2$)

Many students also benefit from a discussion of the order relation between a number and its square root, particularly numbers between 0 and 1. For example, $4 > \sqrt{4}$ but $\frac{1}{4} < \sqrt{\frac{1}{4}}$.

Remind students of the difference between opposites and reciprocals. Show how the Additive Inverse Property $a + (-a) = 0$ describes opposites, while the Multiplicative Inverse Property $a \cdot \left(\frac{1}{a}\right) = 1$ describes reciprocals.

This lesson defines the absolute value of a number in terms of its distance from 0 on the number line. A more formal algebraic definition of absolute value is given in Lesson 1-5.

Algebraic Expressions   1-2

Some students may need to review the order of operations. A common student error is to misapply the Distributive Property, especially with negative multipliers. For example, in $3x - (5x - 1)$ some students fail to apply the 'hidden' leading coefficient of -1 to all terms in the parentheses. Show students how $3x - (5x - 1) = 3x - 5x + 1$, or $-2x + 1$.

Remind students that an algebraic expression can have many different values depending on what numbers are substituted into the expression for the variables. This simple fact is a fundamental concept that applies to functions introduced in Chapter 2.

The importance of mathematical modeling cannot be overemphasized to students. The ability to create graphs, tables, and equations that reflect real-world situations is a powerful mathematical tool, important to many business, scientific, and educational endeavors. The model is a shorthand way of approximating a great amount of data. It can be used to interpolate (estimate) data between measured points and to extrapolate (predict) data beyond measured points.

Solving Equations   1-3

Remind students of the difference between an algebraic expression and an algebraic equation--equations are two expressions separated by an equal sign. Another important difference is that expressions are evaluated and equations are solved. When solving an equation, we are trying to find a number, called the solution to the equation, that makes the equation true. Therefore, the goal in solving an equation is to isolate the variable on one side of the equation and a number on the other side. The procedure for isolating the variable involves creating equivalent equations by applying the properties of equality. Students are familiar with the addition, subtraction, multiplication and division properties of equality, but should be reminded that each operation must be applied to both sides of the equation.

Encourage students to check their solutions by substituting the value of the variable back into the original equation. You may also want to call attention to the Substitution Property that provides the necessary justification for this step.

Checking that a solution is reasonable is a important habit for students to develop. It is particularly helpful when students are solving real-world problems. Students may write and solve correct equations but fail to answer the original question asked. Require that students check their homework exercises, and demonstrate checking solutions in class on a regular basis.

Solving Inequalities   1-4

Because the procedures for solving inequalities in one variable are almost identical to solving equations in one variable, the fundamental difference between equations and inequalities may become obscured. It is important to emphasize that equations in one variable have a single solution, while inequalities usually contain an infinite number of solutions. Thus, the solution set for an inequality is generally graphed on the number line.

Inequalities are useful in modeling real-world situations where an exact value is not appropriate. For example, in automotive repair, many engine parts have allowable sizes that fall within a range of values.

A compound inequality is a pair of inequalities joined by *and* or *or*. Inequalities with *and* require that the solutions satisfy *both* inequalities. Inequalities with *or* require that the solutions satisfy at least one inequality. Thus, compound inequalities with *and* can result in no solution while compound inequalities with *or* can result in the solution of all real numbers. Furthermore, compound inequalities with *and* such as $x > -2$ and $x \leq 5$ can be rewritten as $-2 < x \leq 5$.

Absolute Value Equations
and Inequalities   1-5

Remind students that the absolute value of a number is a single positive number (except for 0 which is neither positive nor negative). So, $|-7| = 7$. Then clarify that the absolute value of a

variable $|x|$ can be either x or $-x$ because the variable x can take on positive or negative values. Therefore, absolute value equations such as $|x| = 5$ have two possible answers, 5 or -5. So, the procedure for solving an absolute value equation involves solving two related equations.

Because it is possible to obtain extraneous solutions that do not satisfy the original equation, students must check their solutions when solving absolute value equations.

You might want to show students that solving absolute value inequalities is similar to solving compound inequalities. For |expression| $< k$ where k is a positive real number, students can solve $-k <$ expression $< k$ which represents an *and* statement. Similarly, |expression| $> k$ where k is a positive real number can be solved using expression $< k$ or expression $> k$.

Students who enjoy the logic of compound inequalities will appreciate absolute value inequalities. You might encourage such students to create compound absolute value inequalities such as $|x - 3| > 4$ or $|2x - 3| \leq 3$ [$x < -1$ or $0 \leq x \leq 3$ or $x > 7$]. Then have students replace the *or* with an *and* to solve $|x - 3| > 4$ and $|2x - 3| \leq 3$ [no solution].

Probability   1-6

Remind students that probability measures the likelihood of an event with 0 or 0% as impossible and 1 or 100% as certain. Experimental probabilities are based on actual data, including data obtained from simulations. Simulations often model real-world situations in which it is difficult or costly to obtain actual data.

The theoretical probability of an event is the number of ways the event can occur divided by the total outcomes possible, which is known as the sample space. Although theoretical probabilities can be useful in making predictions, they are simply likelihoods that an event will occur. For a set of actual tosses, the frequency of heads may not be the same as the frequency of tails, as students know from experience.

Additional Professional Development Opportunities

Professional
Development

Math Background notes for Chapter 1: Every lesson has a Math Background in the PLAN section.

Research Overview, Mathematical Strands
Additional support for these topics and more is in the front of this Teacher's Edition.

Lesson Lab
Lesson Lab, a Pearson Education company, offers comprehensive, facilitated professional development designed to help teachers improve student achievement. To learn more, please visit lessonlab.com

Chapter 1 Resources

	1-1	1-2	1-3	1-4	1-5	1-6	For the Chapter
Print Resources							
Lesson Plans	•	•	•	•	•	•	
L3 Practice	•	•	•	•	•	•	
L3 Guided Problem Solving	•	•	•	•	•	•	
L2 Reteaching	•	•	•	•	•	•	
L4 Enrichment	•	•	•	•	•	•	
L3 Daily Notetaking Guide	•	•	•	•	•	•	
L3 Vocabulary and Study Skills Worksheets	•		•	•	•	•	•
L3 Chapter Project							•
L3 Hands On Activities		•			•		
L3 Checkpoint Quiz			•		•		
L2 Below Level Chapter Test							•
L3 Chapter Test							•
L4 Alternative Assessment							•
L3 Cumulative Review							•
L4 Connections to Precalculus Masters	•	•	•	•	•	•	
L2 Technology Activities						•	
Spanish Resources ELL							
L3 Practice	•	•	•	•	•	•	
L3 Vocabulary and Study Skills Worksheets	•		•	•	•	•	•
L3 Checkpoint Quiz				•			
L2 Below Level Chapter Test							•
L3 Chapter Test							•
L4 Alternative Assessment							•
L3 Cumulative Review							•
Transparencies							
Check Skills You'll Need	•	•	•	•	•		
Additional Examples	•	•	•	•	•		
Problem of the Day	•	•	•	•	•		
Classroom Aid							
Student Edition Answers	•	•	•	•	•	•	•
Lesson Quiz	•	•	•	•	•		
Test-Taking Strategies							•
Technology							
TI 83/84 Plus Activities							
Interactive Textbook Online	•	•	•	•	•	•	•
Student Express CD-ROM	•	•	•	•	•	•	•
TI Navigator™, Instant Check System	•	•	•	•	•		
Success Tracker	•	•	•	•	•	•	•
ExamView CD-ROM with Quick Take	•	•	•	•	•	•	•
Teacher Express CD-ROM	•	•	•	•	•	•	•
Presentation Express CD-ROM	•	•	•	•	•	•	•
Mindpoint Quiz Show CD-ROM	•	•	•	•	•	•	•
Prentice Hall Web site: PHSchool.com	•	•	•	•	•	•	•

Also available: Prentice Hall Assessment System (Progress Monitoring Assessments, Skills and Concepts Review, Test Prep Workbook)   Solution Key   Student Workbook
Student Workbook, Adapted Version   Data Analysis and Probability Workbook   Math Notes Study Folder   Spanish Cumulative Assessment

Where You Can Use the Lesson Resources

Here is a suggestion, following the four-step teaching plan, for how you can incorporate Differentiated Instruction Resources into your teaching.

	Instructional Resources L3	**Differentiated** Instruction **Resources**
1. Plan		
Check Skills You'll Need Assign these exercises to review prerequisite skills. **New Vocabulary** Help students pre-read the lesson by pointing out the new terms introduced in the lesson.	**Math Background** **Transparencies & Presentation Express CD** Check Skills You'll Need **Resources** Vocabulary and Study Skills	**Spanish Support** ELL Vocabulary and Study Skills
2. Teach		
L3 **Guided Instruction** Teach each Example. After each Example, assign the Quick Check exercise for that Example.	**Student Edition** Activity Lab **Resources** Daily Notetaking Guide Activity Lab TI-83/84 Activities CD-ROM **Transparencies & Presentation Express CD** Additional Examples Classroom Aids **ExamView CD-ROM with QuickTake** **TI Navigator Instant Check System**	**Teacher's Edition** Every lesson includes suggestions for working with students who need special attention. L1 Special Needs L2 Below Level L4 Advanced Learners ELL English Language Learners
3. Practice		
Assignment Guide **Homework Exercises** Assign the exercises cited in each lesson's Assignment Guide. A Practice by Example B Apply Your Skills C Challenge Test Prep Mixed Review **Homework Quick Check** Discuss in class the exercises cited in each lesson's Assignment Guide.	**Transparencies & Presentation Express CD** Student Answers **Resources** Practice Guided Problem Solving Vocabulary and Study Skills Activity Lab **ExamView CD-ROM with QuickTake**	**Spanish Support** ELL Practice ELL Vocabulary and Study Skills **Resources** L4 Enrichment
4. Assess & Reteach		
Lesson Quiz Assign the Lesson Quiz to assess students' mastery of the lesson content. **Checkpoint Quiz** Use the Checkpoint Quiz to assess student progress over several lessons.	**Transparencies & Presentation Express CD** Lesson Quiz **Resources** Checkpoint Quiz	**Resources** L2 Reteaching ELL Checkpoint Quiz Success Tracker **ExamView CD-ROM with QuickTake**

KEY   L1 Special Needs   L2 Below Level   L3 For All Students   L4 Advanced, Gifted   ELL English Language Learners

Tools of Algebra

Check Your Readiness

Answers are in the back of the textbook.

For intervention, direct students to:

Adding Rational Numbers
Skills Handbook: p. 873, Example 1

Subtracting Rational Numbers
Skills Handbook: p. 873, Example 2

Multiplying and Dividing Rational Numbers
Skills Handbook: p. 873, Example 3

Using the Order of Operations
Skills Handbook: p. 873, Example 4

What You've Learned

- In your first course in algebra, you learned to add, subtract, multiply, and divide rational numbers. Rational numbers are the quotients of integers, and they include integers, positive and negative fractions, and positive and negative decimals.

- You have also learned to use the order of operations, which tells how to simplify expressions with grouping symbols, exponents, and operations.

- You have also learned to use algebraic expressions.

 Check Your Readiness **for Help** to the Skills Handbook.

Adding Rational Numbers (Skills Handbook page 873)

Find each sum.

1. $6 + (-6)$ **0**
2. $-8 + 6$ **-2**
3. $5.31 + (-7.40)$ **-2.09**
4. $-1.95 + 10$ **8.05**

5. $7\frac{3}{4} + \left(-8\frac{1}{2}\right)$ $-\frac{3}{4}$
6. $-2\frac{1}{3} + 3\frac{1}{4}$ $\frac{11}{12}$
7. $6\frac{2}{5} + \left(4\frac{3}{10}\right)$ $10\frac{7}{10}$
8. $-1\frac{5}{6} + 5\frac{1}{3}$ $3\frac{1}{2}$

Subtracting Rational Numbers (Skills Handbook page 873)

Find each difference.

9. $-28 - 14$ **-42**
10. $61 - (-11)$ **72**
11. $-16 - (-25)$ **9**
12. $-6.2 - 3.6$ **-9.8**

13. $-5\frac{2}{3} - \left(-2\frac{1}{3}\right)$ $-3\frac{1}{3}$
14. $-2\frac{1}{4} - 3\frac{1}{4}$ $-5\frac{1}{2}$
15. $2\frac{2}{3} - 7\frac{1}{3}$ $-4\frac{2}{3}$
16. $\frac{5}{2} - \frac{13}{4}$ $-\frac{3}{4}$

Multiplying and Dividing Rational Numbers (Skills Handbook page 873)

Find each product or quotient.

17. $-3 \cdot 7$ **-21**
18. $-2.1 \cdot (-3.5)$ **7.35**
19. $-\frac{2}{3} \div 4$ $-\frac{1}{6}$
20. $-\frac{3}{8} \div \frac{5}{8}$ $-\frac{3}{5}$

Using the Order of Operations (Skills Handbook page 873)

Simplify each expression.

21. $8 \cdot (-3) + 4$ **-20**
22. $3 \cdot 4 - 8 \div 2$ **8**
23. $1 \div 2^2 - 0.54 + 1.26$ **0.97**

24. $9 \div (-3) - 2$ **-5**
25. $5(3 \cdot 5 - 4)$ **55**
26. $1 - (1 - 5)^2 \div (-8)$ **3**

Tools of Algebra

Chapter 1

◀》 **Key Vocabulary**

- absolute value (p. 33)
- absolute value of a real number (p. 8)
- additive inverse (p. 7)
- algebraic expression (p. 12)
- coefficient (p. 13)
- compound inequality (p. 28)
- evaluate (p. 12)
- experimental probability (p. 40)
- extraneous solution (p. 34)
- multiplicative inverse (p. 7)
- opposite (p. 7)
- reciprocal (p. 7)
- sample space (p. 41)
- simulation (p. 40)
- solution of an equation (p. 18)
- term (p. 13)
- theoretical probability (p. 41)
- tolerance (p. 36)
- variable (p. 12)
- variable expression (p. 12)

Chapter 1 Overview

This chapter begins with a review of the properties of real numbers, followed by a review of algebraic expressions. Students are then guided through solving equations, inequalities, and absolute value equations and inequalities. The chapter concludes with a lesson on probability.

Activating Prior Knowledge

Ask:
- *What do you think a "compound inequality" refers to?*

Accept all reasonable answers that indicate a combination of two or more inequalities.

Ask:
- *Can you think of a real-world situation that might be described with a compound inequality?*

Write all reasonable suggestions on the board. Suggestions might include inequalities that limit values to a specific range, such as dietary restrictions (calories or sodium), college SAT® scores for the middle 50%, or acceptable heights for an amusement park ride.

What You'll Learn Next

- In Chapter 1, you will review and extend your knowledge of algebraic expressions and your skill in solving equations and inequalities.

- You will solve absolute value equations and inequalities by changing them to compound equations and inequalities.

- You will apply theoretical and experimental probabilities to real-world situations such as genetic inheritance.

Real-World Connection Applying what you learn, you will use algebraic expressions on page 13 to solve a problem involving elections.

3

Properties of Real Numbers

1. Plan

Objectives
1 To graph and order real numbers
2 To identify and use properties of real numbers

Examples
1 Real-World Connection
2 Graphing Numbers on the Number Line
3 Ordering Real Numbers
4 Finding Inverses
5 Identifying Properties of Real Numbers
6 Finding Absolute Value

Professional Development

Math Background

This lesson reviews key concepts from Algebra 1, such as important subsets of the real numbers, ordering real numbers on the number line, and absolute value. It also summarizes fundamental properties of addition and multiplication. Students will find the material in the Key Concepts boxes on pages 5 and 7 helpful for this lesson and for future reference.

More Math Background: p. 2C

Lesson Planning and Resources

See p. 2E for a list of the resources that support this lesson.

PowerPoint
Bell Ringer Practice

☑ **Check Skills You'll Need**
For intervention, direct students to:
Simplifying Expressions
Skills Handbook: p. 873
Examples 1–3

What You'll Learn
• To graph and order real numbers
• To identify and use properties of real numbers

...And Why
To classify the numbers used in managing an amusement park, as in Example 1

☑ Check Skills You'll Need

Simplify.

1. $-(-7.2)$ **7.2**
2. $1 - (-3)$ **4**
3. $-9 + (-4.5)$ **−13.5**
4. $(-3.4)(-2)$ **6.8**
5. $-15 \div 3$ **−5**
6. $\frac{-2}{5} + \frac{3}{-5}$ **−1**

🔊 **New Vocabulary**
• opposite
• additive inverse
• reciprocal
• multiplicative inverse
• absolute value of a real number

GO **for Help** Skills Handbook page 873

---

1 Graphing and Ordering Real Numbers

Real-World 🌐 Connection

Artists frequently use geometric figures in their work. Juan Gris (1887–1927) used right triangles in this portrait of Picasso.

$\sqrt{2} \approx 1.4$; $\sqrt{3} \approx 1.7$;

$\sqrt{4} = 2$; $\sqrt{5} \approx 2.2$;

$\sqrt{6} \approx 2.4$; $\sqrt{7} \approx 2.6$

Activity: Estimating Square Roots

1. Use the Pythagorean Theorem to calculate *PB, PC, PD,* and so on, in the figure below.

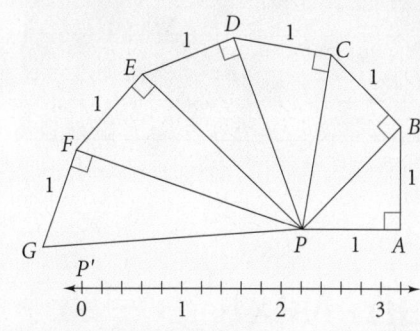

$PB = \sqrt{2}$, $PC = \sqrt{3}$, $PD = 2$, $PE = \sqrt{5}$, $PF = \sqrt{6}$, $PG = \sqrt{7}$

See margin p.5.

2. Copy the number line above. Mark point *B'* so that $P'B' = PB$. Similarly mark points *C', D',* and so on, on your number line.

3. Estimate the decimal coordinates of *B', C', D',* and so on. Copy and complete the table below.

		$\sqrt{3}$	$\sqrt{4}$	$\sqrt{5}$	$\sqrt{6}$
Leg 1	1	$\sqrt{2}$	■	■	■
Leg 2	1	1	1	1	1
Hypotenuse	$\sqrt{2} \approx ?$	■	■	■	■

See left.

4. Evaluate each square root in the table using your calculator. Does the calculator give you exact answers? How do you know? See margin p. 5.

4 Chapter 1 Tools of Algebra

Differentiated Instruction Solutions for All Learners

Special Needs L1
Help students understand that the absolute value of a real number is non-negative since distance cannot be negative.

learning style: verbal

Below Level L2
Complete the table on p. 4 by working through as many examples as necessary. Show students how to transfer the lengths of the hypotenuses to the number line.

learning style: visual

Algebra deals with operations and relations among numbers, including real numbers and imaginary numbers. Listed below are some of the subsets of the real numbers. Imaginary numbers will be introduced in Chapter 5.

 Key Concepts

Summary	Subsets of Real Numbers

Natural numbers $1, 2, 3, 4, \ldots$
- Natural numbers are the numbers used for counting.

Whole numbers $0, 1, 2, 3, 4, \ldots$
- Whole numbers are the natural numbers and 0.

Integers $\ldots -3, -2, -1, 0, 1, 2, 3, 4, \ldots$
- The integers are the natural numbers (also called positive integers), their opposites (also called negative integers), and zero.

Rational numbers   Examples: $\frac{7}{5}, \frac{-3}{2}, -\frac{4}{5}, 0, 0.3, -1.2, 9$
- Rational numbers are all the numbers that can be written as quotients of integers. Each quotient must have a nonzero denominator.
- Some rational numbers can be written as terminating decimals. For example, $\frac{1}{8} = 0.125$.
- All other rational numbers can be written as repeating decimals. For example, $\frac{1}{3} = 0.\overline{3}$.

Irrational numbers   Examples: $\sqrt{2}, \sqrt{7}, \sqrt{\frac{2}{3}}, \pi, 1.0110111011111011111\ldots$
- Irrational numbers are numbers that cannot be written as quotients of integers.
- Their decimal representations neither terminate nor repeat.
- If a positive rational number is not a perfect square such as 25 or $\frac{4}{9}$, then its square root is irrational.

Vocabulary Tip

$\sqrt{2}$ refers to the positive or principal square root of 2. The negative square root of 2 is written as $-\sqrt{2}$.

This diagram shows how the above sets of numbers are related.

Real Numbers   Examples: $-5, -\sqrt{3}, -\frac{1}{2}, 1, \sqrt{5}, \frac{8}{3}$

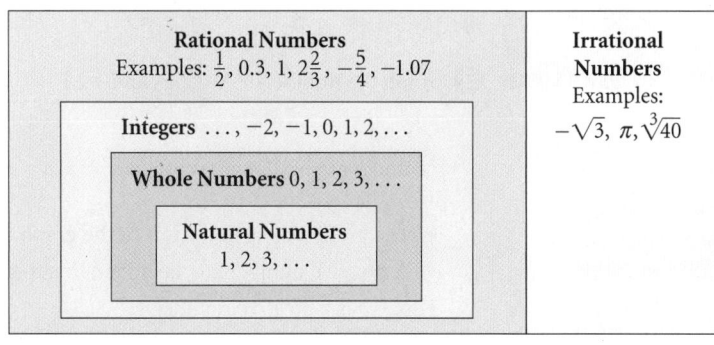

For example, the diagram shows the following:
- The set of whole numbers is a subset of the set of integers, the set of rational numbers, and the set of real numbers.
- The set of rational numbers and the set of irrational numbers do not intersect.
- Integers are not irrational numbers.
- The rational numbers and irrational numbers form the set of real numbers.

Lesson 1-1   Properties of Real Numbers   **5**

Guided Instruction

Activity
The hypotenuse of each right triangle in the diagram is a leg of the next triangle. If necessary, review how the Pythagorean Theorem is used to find the length of the hypotenuse when the lengths of the legs are known.

In Question 3, students will need to use decimal approximations in the last row of the table. In the top row, if the results are not whole numbers, students should write the square roots in radical form to show exact lengths.

page 4   Activity

2.

4. No; squaring the decimals the calculator displays for $\sqrt{2}, \sqrt{3}, \sqrt{5}, \sqrt{6}, \sqrt{7}$ will not give a whole number. Only $\sqrt{4}$ is exact; to show that the decimal displayed for $\sqrt{2}$ is not exact, enter the displayed decimal using the keypad and square it to show that the square is not exactly 2.

Advanced Learners   L4
Have students find Pythagorean "triples," whole numbers such as 3, 4, and 5, that make the Pythagorean Theorem true. **Sample: 8, 15, 17**

learning style: verbal

English Language Learners   ELL
Remind students to consult the Glossary at the back of the textbook. Help students preread and pronounce words such as *integers, rational, irrational, hypotenuse, additive, multiplicative, reciprocal,* and *inverse.*

learning style: verbal

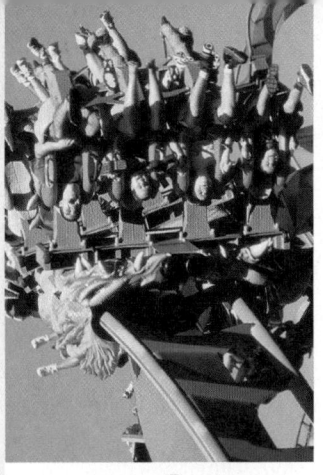

1 EXAMPLE Real-World Connection

Recreation Many mathematical relationships involving variables are related to amusement parks. Which set of numbers best describes the values for each variable?

a. the cost C in dollars of admission for n people

The cost C of admission is a rational number (such as $7.25), and the number n of people is a whole number.

b. the maximum speed s in meters per second on a roller coaster of height h in meters (Use the formula in the caption of the photograph.)

The height h is measured in rational numbers. Since the speed s is calculated using a formula with a square root, s is an irrational number unless h is the square of a rational number.

c. the park's profit (or loss) P in dollars for each week w of the year

The week number w is one of the first 52 natural numbers, and the profit (or loss) P is a rational number.

Quick Check **1** The number r is the ratio of the number of adult tickets sold to the number of children's tickets sold. Which set of numbers best describes the values of r? Which set of numbers best describes the average cost c per family for tickets?
rational numbers; rational numbers

Real numbers are graphed as points on the number line.

2 EXAMPLE Graphing Numbers on the Number Line

Graph the numbers $-\frac{3}{2}$, $1.\overline{7}$, and $\sqrt{5}$.

Since $-\frac{3}{2} = -1\frac{1}{2}$, $-\frac{3}{2}$ is between -1 and -2. Round $1.\overline{7}$ to 1.8. Use a calculator to find that $\sqrt{5} \approx 2.2$.

$$-\frac{3}{2} \qquad 1.\overline{7} \quad \sqrt{5}$$
-2 -1 0 1 2 3

Quick Check **2** Graph the numbers $-\sqrt{2}$, $0.\overline{3}$, and $-2\frac{1}{4}$.

$$-2\frac{1}{4} \quad -\sqrt{2} \qquad 0.\overline{3}$$
-3 -2 -1 0 1 2 3

If a and b are real numbers, then $a = b$, $a < b$, or $a > b$. There are several ways to prove that $a < b$:

- The graph of a is to the left of the graph of b on a number line.
- A positive number can be added to a to get b.
- $b - a$ is a positive number.

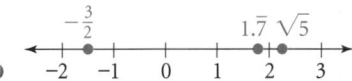
3 EXAMPLE Ordering Real Numbers

Compare $-\sqrt{0.25}$ and $-\sqrt{0.01}$. Use the symbols $<$ and $>$.

$-\sqrt{0.25} = -0.5$, and $-\sqrt{0.01} = -0.1$. Since $-0.1 - (-0.5)$ is positive, $-0.5 < -0.1$. So $-\sqrt{0.25} < -\sqrt{0.01}$ and $-\sqrt{0.01} > -\sqrt{0.25}$.

Quick Check **3** Compare $-\sqrt{0.08}$ and $-\sqrt{0.1}$ using the symbols $<$ and $>$. $-\sqrt{0.08} > -\sqrt{0.1}$, $-\sqrt{0.1} < -\sqrt{0.08}$

6 Chapter 1 Tools of Algebra

The **opposite** or **additive inverse** of any number a is $-a$.
The sum of opposites is 0.

The **reciprocal** or **multiplicative inverse** of any nonzero number a is $\frac{1}{a}$.
The product of reciprocals is 1.

4 EXAMPLE Finding Inverses

Find the opposite and the reciprocal of each number.

a. -3.2 **b.** $\frac{3}{5}$

Opposite $-(-3.2) = 3.2$ **Opposite** $-\left(\frac{3}{5}\right) = -\frac{3}{5}$

Reciprocal $\frac{1}{-3.2} = \frac{10}{-32}$ **Reciprocal** $\frac{1}{\frac{3}{5}} = 1 \cdot \frac{5}{3} = \frac{5}{3}$

$= -\frac{5}{16},$ or -0.3125

Vocabulary Tip

Read $-(-3.2)$ as "the opposite of negative 3.2."

 Quick Check 4 Find the opposite and the reciprocal of each number.

a. 400 $-400, \frac{1}{400}$ **b.** $4\frac{1}{5}$ $-4\frac{1}{5}, \frac{5}{21}$ **c.** -0.002 $0.002, -500$ **d.** $-\frac{4}{9}$ $\frac{4}{9}, -\frac{9}{4}$ $\left(\text{or } -2\frac{1}{4}\right)$

You can summarize the properties of real numbers in terms of addition and multiplication.

Key Concepts

Summary	Properties of Real Numbers

Let $a, b,$ and c represent real numbers.

Property	Addition	Multiplication
Closure	$a + b$ is a real number.	ab is a real number.
Commutative	$a + b = b + a$	$ab = ba$
Associative	$(a + b) + c = a + (b + c)$	$(ab)c = a(bc)$
Identity	$a + 0 = a, 0 + a = a$	$a \cdot 1 = a, 1 \cdot a = a$
Inverse	$a + (-a) = 0$	$a \cdot \frac{1}{a} = 1, a \neq 0$
Distributive	$a(b + c) = ab + ac$	

5 EXAMPLE Identifying Properties of Real Numbers

Which property is illustrated?

a. $6 + (-6) = 0$

Inverse Property of Addition

b. $(-4 \cdot 1) - 2 = -4 - 2$

Identity Property of Multiplication

 Quick Check 5 Which property is illustrated?

a. $(3 + 0) - 5 = 3 - 5$ **b.** $-5 + [2 + (-3)] = (-5 + 2) + (-3)$
Identity Prop. of Add.   **Assoc. Prop. of Add.**

Lesson 1-1 Properties of Real Numbers **7**

Assignment Guide

▼1 A B 1-33, 56-63, 71-78

▼2 A B 34-55, 64-70, 79-84

C Challenge 85-90

Test Prep 91-97
Mixed Review 98-109

Homework Quick Check
To check students' understanding of key skills and concepts, go over Exercises 55, 79-84.

Technology Tip

Exercise 30 To help students see that the square root of a number is not always less than the number, have them use graphing calculators to graph $Y_1 = x$ and $Y_2 = \sqrt{x}$. Tell students to set both Xmin and Ymin at 0, and both Xmax and Ymax at 2. Ask: *For which values of x is $\sqrt{x} < x$?* $x > 1$ *For which values of x is $\sqrt{x} \geq x$?* $0 \leq x \leq 1$

Differentiated Instruction Resources

GPS Guided Problem Solving	L3
Enrichment	L4
Reteaching	L2
Practice	L3

pages 8–10 Exercises

1. natural numbers, whole numbers, integers, rational numbers, real numbers

2. irrational numbers, real numbers

3. irrational numbers, real numbers

4. integers, rational numbers, real numbers

5. whole numbers, integers, rational numbers, real numbers

6. rational numbers, real numbers

7. rational numbers, real numbers

8. irrational numbers, real numbers

The **absolute value of a real number** is its distance from zero on the number line.

6 EXAMPLE Finding Absolute Value

Find $|-4|, |0|,$ and $|-1 \cdot (-2)|$.

$|-1 \cdot (-2)| = |2|$ **Simplify within absolute value symbols first.**

Graph $-4, 0,$ and 2 on a number line.

The distances from the origin are $4, 0,$ and 2. So,

$|-4| = 4 \qquad |0| = 0 \qquad |-1 \cdot (-2)| = |2| = 2$

Vocabulary Tip

Read $|2|$ as "the absolute value of 2."

✓ **Quick Check** 6 a. Simplify $|-10|, |1.5|,$ and $|0 - 3|$. **10, 1.5, 3**
b. **Critical Thinking** For what values of x does $|x| = -x$? **for values of x such that $x \leq 0$**

EXERCISES

For more exercises, see *Extra Skill and Word Problem Practice*.

Practice and Problem Solving

A **Practice by Example**

Example 1 (page 6)

GO for Help

To which sets of numbers does each number belong? **1–8. See margin.**

1. 4
2. $\sqrt{6}$
3. π
4. -6
5. 0
6. $0.\overline{6}$
7. $-\sqrt{0.04}$
8. $\sqrt{0.4}$

Which set of numbers best describes the values of each variable?

9. the number of times n a cricket chirps; the outdoor temperature T in tenths of a degree **whole numbers; rational numbers**

10. the year y; the median selling price p for a house that year **natural numbers; rational numbers**

11. the time t in seconds an object takes to fall d feet, where $t = \frac{\sqrt{d}}{4}$ **real numbers**

Example 2 (page 6)

Graph each number on a number line. **12–16. See margin p. 8–9.**

12. 0
13. $-\sqrt{24}$
14. -2
15. $2\frac{1}{2}$
16. $-4\frac{2}{3}$

Example 3 (page 6)

Replace each ■ with the symbol <, >, or = to make the sentence true.

17. $-7 \overset{>}{■} -9$
18. $3 \overset{=}{■} 3$
19. $14 \overset{>}{■} \sqrt{14}$
20. $\sqrt{6} \overset{<}{■} \sqrt{10}$
21. $0 \overset{<}{■} 0.\overline{3}$
22. $0.8 \overset{=}{■} \frac{4}{5}$
23. $-18 \overset{>}{■} -82$
24. $0.72737475\ldots \overset{}{■} 0.73737373\ldots$

Compare each pair of numbers. Use < and >. **25–33. See margin p. 9.**

25. $-\frac{1}{4}, -\frac{1}{3}$
26. $0.075, 0.39$
27. $-2.\overline{3}, 2.\overline{1}$
28. $-5.2, -4.8$
29. $3.0\overline{4}, 3.4$
30. $0.4, \sqrt{0.4}$
31. $-4, -\sqrt{4}$
32. $\sqrt{5}, \sqrt{7}$
33. $-\sqrt{3}, -\sqrt{5}$

Example 4
(page 7)

Find the opposite and the reciprocal of each number.

34. 200 $-200; \frac{1}{200}$ **35.** $3\frac{3}{5}$ $-3\frac{3}{5}; \frac{5}{18}$ **36.** 0.01 $0.01; -100$ -0.01 **37.** $-\frac{7}{2}$ $\frac{7}{2}; -\frac{2}{7}$

38. $\sqrt{3}$ $-\sqrt{3}; \frac{1}{\sqrt{3}} \left(\text{or } \frac{\sqrt{3}}{3}\right)$ **39.** 2π $-2\pi; \frac{1}{2\pi}$ **40.** -2.34 $2.34; -\frac{50}{117}$ **41.** $\pi - 3$ $3 - \pi; \frac{1}{\pi - 3}$

Example 5
(page 7)

Name the property of real numbers illustrated by each equation.

42. $\pi(a + b) = \pi a + \pi b$ **43.** $-7 + 4 = 4 + (-7)$ **42–45.** See margin.

44. $(2\sqrt{10}) \cdot \sqrt{3} = 2(\sqrt{10} \cdot \sqrt{3})$ **45.** $29\pi = \pi \cdot 29$

46. $-\sqrt{5} + 0 = -\sqrt{5}$ **47.** $\frac{4}{7} \cdot \frac{7}{4} = 1$ **46, 47.** See margin p.10.

Example 6
(page 8)

Simplify each expression.

48. $|10.3|$ **10.3**   **49.** $|-0.06|$ **0.06**   **50.** $-|-25|$ **-25**   **51.** $0.2|-8|$ **1.6**

52. $\left|-\frac{1}{3}\right|$ $\frac{1}{3}$ **53.** $|7 - 10|$ **3**   **54.** $|10 - 7|$ **3**   **55.** $|5| - |-7|$ **-2**

B **Apply Your Skills**

Estimate the numbers graphed at the labeled points.   Exercises 56–63: Answers may vary. Samples are given.

$$A \quad B \quad\quad C \quad D \quad E \quad\quad F\ G\ H$$
$$\leftarrow\!\!+\!\!+\!\!+\!\!+\!\!+\!\!+\!\!+\!\!+\!\!+\!\!+\!\!+\!\!+\!\!\rightarrow$$
$$-5\ -4\ -3\ -2\ -1\ \ 0\ \ 1\ \ 2\ \ 3\ .4\ \ 5$$

56. point A -5 **57.** point B $-3\frac{1}{2}$ **58.** point C $-1\frac{1}{4}$ **59.** point D $\frac{1}{2}$

60. point E $1\frac{2}{3}$ **61.** point F $3\frac{1}{3}$ **62.** point G 4 **63.** point H 4.8

64. Multiple Choice The length of a side of an equilateral triangle is 4. Which type of number best describes the length of the altitude of the triangle? **D**
Ⓐ whole number   Ⓑ integer
Ⓒ rational number   Ⓓ irrational number

Label indicates power in watts **W**.

Tungsten filament creates resistance **R**.

Current **I** enters through base.

🌐 **Electric Circuits** The electric current I in amperes that flows through an appliance is given by the formula $I = \sqrt{\frac{W}{R}}$, where W is the power in watts and R is the resistance in ohms. Which sets of numbers contain the value of I for the given values of W and R? **65–70. See margin p. 10.**

65. $W = 100, R = 25$ **66.** $W = 100, R = 50$ **67.** $W = 500, R = 100$

68. $W = 50, R = 200$ **69.** $W = 250, R = 100$ **70.** $W = 240, R = 100$

Replace each ■ with the symbol $<$, $>$, or $=$ to make the sentence true.

71. $0\ ■\ -4$ $>$ **72.** $-4\ ■\ -9$ $>$ **73.** $-5.2\ ■\ -4.8$ $<$ **74.** $|-8|\ ■\ |3|$ $>$

75. $|2|\ ■\ |-6|$ $<$ **76.** $|7|\ ■\ |-8|$ $<$ **77.** $-|6|\ ■\ |6|$ $<$ **78.** $-|-6|\ ■\ |-6|$ $<$

GPS **Reasoning** Show that each statement is false by finding a counterexample (an example that makes the statement false). **79–83. See back of book.**

79. The reciprocal of each whole number is a whole number.

80. The opposite of each natural number is a natural number.

81. There is no whole number that has an opposite that is a whole number.

82. There is no integer that has a reciprocal that is an integer.

83. The product of two irrational numbers is an irrational number.

84. Open-Ended Write an example of each of the 11 properties of real numbers listed on page 7. **Check students' work.**

GO **Online**
Homework Video Tutor
Visit: PHSchool.com
Web Code: age-0101

15.
$$\leftarrow\!\!+\!\!+\!\!+\!\!+\!\!●\!\!+\!\!●\!\!+\!\!\rightarrow$$
$$-1\ 0\ 1\ 2\ 3\ 4$$

16.
$$\leftarrow\!\!+\!\!●\!\!+\!\!+\!\!+\!\!+\!\!+\!\!+\!\!\rightarrow$$
$$-6\!-\!5\!-\!4\!-\!3\!-\!2\!-\!1\ 0\ 1$$

25. $-\frac{1}{4} > -\frac{1}{3}, -\frac{1}{3} < -\frac{1}{4}$

26. $0.075 < 0.39,$
$\quad 0.39 > 0.075$

27. $-2.\overline{3} < 2.\overline{1}, 2.\overline{1} > -2.\overline{3}$

28. $-5.2 < -4.8,$
$\quad -4.8 > -5.2$

29. $3.0\overline{4} < 3.4, 3.4 > 3.0\overline{4}$

30. $0.4 < \sqrt{0.4}, \sqrt{0.4} > 0.4$

31. $-4 < -\sqrt{4}, -\sqrt{4} > -4$

32. $\sqrt{5} < \sqrt{7}, \sqrt{7} > \sqrt{5}$

PowerPoint
🖱 **Lesson Quiz**

1. Graph $-2.\overline{3}$, $\sqrt{12}$, and $\frac{7}{5}$ on a number line.

$$-2.\overline{3} \qquad \frac{7}{5} \quad \sqrt{12}$$
$$\leftarrow\!\!●\!\!+\!\!+\!\!+\!\!+\!\!+\!\!●\!\!+\!\!+\!\!●\!\!\rightarrow$$
$$-4\!-\!3\!-\!2\!-\!1\ 0\ 1\ 2\ 3\ 4$$

2. Replace each ■ with the symbol $<$, $>$, or $=$ to make the sentence true.
   a. $2.0\overline{8}\ ■\ 2.8$ $<$
   b. $1\frac{2}{9}\ ■\ 1.\overline{2}$ $=$

3. Find the opposite and the reciprocal of $1\frac{5}{8}$. $-1\frac{5}{8}, \frac{8}{13}$

4. Name the property of real numbers illustrated by the equation.
   $(-2)(3 + \pi) = (-2)(\pi + 3)$
   Comm. Prop. of Add.

5. Simplify $|9 - (-5)|$. **14**

Alternative Assessment

Students work in groups of three. Each group creates ten number cards with one number per card. Cards should contain numbers from each subset of the real numbers. A student shuffles the cards and each person draws one card. First, have students tell each other the opposite, reciprocal, and absolute value of their numbers. Then have the three students in each group compare their numbers using $<$, $>$, or $=$.

Error Prevention!

Exercise 55 Point out to students that they cannot begin by changing the two negative signs to a positive sign. They must first find $|-7|$.

33. $-\sqrt{3} > -\sqrt{5},$
$\quad -\sqrt{5} < -\sqrt{3}$

42. Dist. Prop.

43. Comm. Prop. of Add.

44. Assoc. Prop. of Mult.

45. Comm. Prop. of Mult.

Resources

For additional practice with a variety of test item formats:
- Standardized Test Prep, p. 51
- Test-Taking Strategies, p. 46
- Test-Taking Strategies with Transparencies

pages 8–10 Exercises

46. Identity Prop. of Add.

47. Inverse Prop. of Mult.

65. natural numbers, whole numbers, integers, rational numbers, real numbers

66. irrational numbers, real numbers

67. irrational numbers, real numbers

68. rational numbers, real numbers

69. irrational numbers, real numbers

70. irrational numbers, real numbers

85. all except the Identity Prop. of Add. (since 0 is not in the set of natural numbers) and the inverse properties

86. all except the Inverse Prop. of Mult. and the Inverse Prop. of Add.

87. all except the Inverse Prop. of Mult.

96. [2] The opposite of the reciprocal of 5 is the opposite of $\frac{1}{5}$, or $-\frac{1}{5}$, and the reciprocal of the opposite of 5 is the reciprocal of −5, or $-\frac{1}{5}$.

   [1] includes a statement or example that a reciprocal is a multiplicative inverse or that a number times its reciprocal is 1, OR a statement or example that an opposite is an additive inverse or that a number plus its opposite is 0

10

 C Challenge

Critical Thinking Review the eleven properties on page 7. **Which ones still hold true if *real numbers* is replaced by each of the following?** 85–87. See margin.

85. natural numbers   86. whole numbers   87. integers

88. rational numbers   89. irrational numbers
   all the properties   Comm., Asso., and Dist. Prop.

90. **Writing** Are there two integers with a product of −12 and a sum of −3? Explain. No; answers may vary. Sample: The only pairs of integers that have a product of −12 are −1 and 12, −2 and 6, −3 and 4, −4 and 3, −6 and 2, and −12 and 1. None of these pairs has a sum of −3.

Test Prep

Multiple Choice

91. Which of the following is NOT a rational number? **D**
   A. $\frac{\pi}{2\pi}$ B. $-\sqrt{144}$ C. 3.14   D. $\sqrt{8}$

92. If *p* is a multiple of 3 and *q* is a multiple of 5, which of the following is true? **H**
   F. $p + q$ is even.   G. pq is odd.
   H. $5p + 3q$ is a multiple of 15.   J. $3p + 5q$ is a multiple of 15.

93. The number 8.09 belongs to which sets of numbers? **C**
   A. natural numbers, real numbers
   B. irrational numbers, real numbers
   C. rational numbers, real numbers
   D. whole numbers, integers, rational numbers, real numbers

94. Which shows the numbers −3.5, −4.60, and $-3\frac{1}{4}$ in order from greatest to least? **J**
   F. $-4.60, -3\frac{1}{4}, -3.5$ G. $-4.60, -3.5, -3\frac{1}{4}$
   H. $-3\frac{1}{4}, -4.60, -3.5$ J. $-3\frac{1}{4}, -3.5, -4.60$

95. What is the value of $|3 - 7| - |-11 + 3|$? **A**
   A. −4   B. 4   C. 12   D. 24

Short Response

96. Explain why the *opposite of the reciprocal of 5* is the same as the *reciprocal of the opposite of 5.* See margin.

97. Are there any numbers that are their own reciprocals? Explain.
   See margin.

Mixed Review

Skills Handbook

 GO for Help

Simplify each expression.

98. $3.6 + (-1.7)$ 1.9   99. $1.2 - 5$ −3.8   100. $(-3)(-9)$ 27

101. $0(-8)$ 0   102. $-2.8 \div 7$ −0.4   103. $-35 \div (-5)$ 7

Skills Handbook

Use the order of operations to simplify each expression.

104. $3 \div 4 + 6 \div 4$ $\frac{9}{4}$, or $2\frac{1}{4}$ 105. $5[(2 + 5) \div 3]$ $\frac{35}{3}$, or $11\frac{2}{3}$

106. $\frac{8 + 5 \cdot 2}{12}$ $\frac{3}{2}$, or $1\frac{1}{2}$ 107. $(40 + 24) \div 8 - (2^2 - 1)$ 5

108. $40 + 24 \div 8 - 2^2 - 1$ 38   109. $40 + 24 \div (8 - 2^2) - 1$ 45

10   Chapter 1 Tools of Algebra

---

97. [2] Two numbers are their own reciprocals, 1 and −1. For a number *n* to be equal to its reciprocal, $n = \frac{1}{n}$, which means

$n^2 = 1$. So $n = 1$ or −1.

[1] only includes answer 1 and −1 with no explanation

Writing Expressions From Tables

FOR USE WITH LESSON 1-2

You can sometimes describe data in a table by writing an expression.

1 ACTIVITY

Study the polygons below. You can cut each polygon into triangles by connecting one vertex with each of the other nonadjacent vertices.

   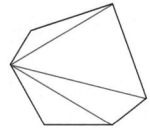

1. a. The sum of the angle measures for each triangle is 180. Fill in the data missing from the table.
  b. Describe the relationship between the number of sides in a polygon and the number of triangles. **There are 2 fewer triangles than sides.**
  c. Describe the relationship between the number of triangles and the sum of the angle measures of the polygon. **See below.**
  d. Complete the sentence: The sum of the angle measures of a polygon is the number of sides of the polygon less __?__, times __?__ . **2; 180**
  e. The number of sides of a polygon is *n*. Write the number of triangles in terms of *n*. **n − 2**
  f. Write the sum of the angle measures of the *n*-sided polygon in terms of *n*. **(n − 2) · 180**

Number of Sides	Number of Triangles	Sum of Angle Measures
3	1	180
4	2	360
5	3	■540
6	4	■720
7	■5	■900
8	■6	1080
9	■7	■1260

1c. The sum of the angle measures is 180 times the number of triangles.

2 ACTIVITY

The diagrams below show arrangements of tables and chairs. Each small table can seat 6 people. When you join tables, you lose space for some chairs. So, an arrangement of two tables has 10 chairs rather than 12 chairs.

Number of tables: 1   2   3   4

2. a. Make a table that lists the number of tables and the number of chairs in each arrangement shown in the diagram.
  b. Find the number of chairs needed for arrangements of 5 tables and 6 tables. **22; 26**
  c. Write an expression for the number of chairs needed for *n* tables. (*Hint:* How many new chairs are needed for each new table?) **4n + 2**

Tables	Chairs
1	6
2	10
3	14
4	18

3. You can arrange the tables and chairs differently. One possible pattern is shown at the right. Write an expression for the number of chairs needed to make one large table out of *k* tables in this way. **2k + 4**

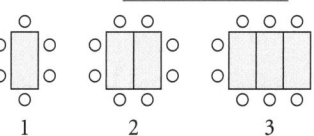
1   2   3

Writing Expressions From Tables

Guided Instruction

Students complete data tables, identify patterns in the data, and write algebraic expressions to represent the *n*th term.

English Language Learners ELL
Review the terms nonadjacent and vertex. For example, adjacent means "next to" and nonadjacent means "not next to". A vertex is a corner of a polygon and vertices is its plural form.

Special Needs   L1
For 1b, students might write incomplete answers. For example, they might state "as the number of sides increase, the number of triangles increase." This fact is accurate but not specific enough to make a prediction. Ask: How is the number of triangles mathematically related to the number of sides? **There are always 2 fewer triangles than sides.**

Error Prevention!

For 1f, watch out for students who leave out the parentheses around the quantity *n* − 2 in (*n* − 2)180.

1-2

Objectives
1 To evaluate algebraic expressions
2 To simplify algebraic expressions

Examples
1 Evaluating an Algebraic Expression
2 Evaluating an Algebraic Expression with Exponents
3 Real-World Connection
4 Combining Like Terms
5 Finding Perimeter

Math Background

Numerical expressions can be simplified by using properties of operations and the order of operations. Algebraic expressions can be evaluated by substituting specific numbers for each variable and simplifying the resulting numerical expression. The properties for simplifying algebraic expressions are based on those for simplifying numerical expressions.

More Math Background: p. 2C

Lesson Planning and Resources

See p. 2E for a list of the resources that support this lesson.

Bell Ringer Practice

✓ **Check Skills You'll Need**
For intervention, direct students to:
Simplifying Expressions with Integers
Skills Handbook: p. 873
Example 4

12

1-2

Algebraic Expressions

What You'll Learn
- To evaluate algebraic expressions
- To simplify algebraic expressions

. . . And Why
To use an expression for the number of voters in U.S. elections, as in Example 3

✓ **Check Skills You'll Need**

 for Help Skills Handbook page 873

Use the order of operations to simplify each expression.

1. $8 \cdot 3 - 2 \cdot 4$ **16**
2. $8 - 4 + 6 \div 3$ **6**
3. $24 \div 12 \cdot 4 \div 3$ **$\frac{8}{3}$**
4. $3 \cdot 8^2 + 12 \div 4$ **195**
5. $27 + 18 \div 9 - 3^2 + 1$ **21**
6. $(40 + 24) \div 8 - (2^3 + 1)$ **−1**

🔊 **New Vocabulary** • variable • algebraic expression • variable expression
• evaluate • term • coefficient

---

1 Evaluating Algebraic Expressions

A **variable** is a symbol, usually a letter, that represents one or more numbers. An expression that contains one or more variables is an **algebraic expression** or a **variable expression**. When you substitute numbers for the variables in an expression and follow the order of operations, you **evaluate** the expression.

 EXAMPLE Evaluating an Algebraic Expression

Evaluate $a - 2b + ab$ for $a = 3$ and $b = -1$.

$a - 2b + ab = 3 - 2(-1) + 3(-1)$	Substitute 3 for a and −1 for b.
$= 3 - (-2) + (-3)$	Multiply first.
$= 3 + 2 + (-3)$	To subtract, add the opposite.
$= 5 + (-3)$	Add from left to right.
$= 2$	Add.

GO for Help

To review the order of operations, go to page 873.

✓ **Quick Check** ❶ Evaluate each expression for $x = 4$ and $y = -2$.
a. $x + y \div x$ **$\frac{7}{2}$**
b. $3x - 4y + x - y$ **26**
c. $x + 2x \div y - 2y$ **4**

❷ **EXAMPLE** Evaluating an Algebraic Expression with Exponents

Evaluate $-x^2 - 2(x + 1)$ for $x = 3$.

$-x^2 - 2(x + 1) = -3^2 - 2(3 + 1)$	Substitute 3 for x.
$= -9 - 2(4)$	Simplify the power 3^2. Add within the parentheses.
$= -9 - 8$	Multiply.
$= -17$	Subtract.

Problem Solving Hint
Note that $-3^2 \neq (-3)^2$.
$-3^2 = -(3 \cdot 3) = -9$
$(-3)^2 = (-3)(-3) = 9$

✓ **Quick Check** ❷ Evaluate each expression for $c = -3$ and $d = 5$.
a. $c^2 - d^2$ **−16**
b. $c(3 - d) - c^2$ **−3**
c. $-d^2 - 4(d - 2c)$ **−69**

12 Chapter 1 Tools of Algebra

In 1971, the U.S. voting age was lowered from 21 to 18.

3 EXAMPLE Real-World Connection

Elections The expression $-0.3y + 61$ models the percent of eligible voters who voted in presidential elections from 1960 to 2000. In the expression, y represents the number of years since 1960. Find the approximate percent of eligible voters who voted in 1988.

Since $1988 - 1960 = 28$, $y = 28$ represents the year 1988.

$-0.3y + 61 = -0.3(28) + 61$ **Substitute 28 for y.**

≈ 53

About 53% of the eligible voters voted in the 1988 presidential election.

 Quick Check **3 a.** Assume that the model in Example 3 holds for future years. What percent of the eligible voters will vote in 2012? In 2020? **about 45%; about 43%**

b. Critical Thinking Give some reasons that the model may not hold in future years. **Answers may vary. Sample: Changing patterns in minority populations might lead to more voter turnout. Less stable international conditions might arouse voter concerns.**

2 Simplifying Algebraic Expressions

In an algebraic expression such as $-4x + 10$, the parts that are added are called terms. A **term** is a number, a variable, or the product of a number and one or more variables. The numerical factor in a term is the **coefficient.** Think of an expression such as $a - 2b$ as the sum $a + (-2b)$ to determine that the coefficient of b is -2.

$$\overbrace{7x^2 + 3y}^{\text{terms}}$$
coefficients

Like terms have the same variables raised to the same powers.

Like terms: $3r^2$ and $-r^2$ $-2xy^3$ and $3xy^3$

You can simplify expressions by combining like terms using the basic properties on page 7 and other properties that can be derived from them. The simplified expressions are equivalent to the original expressions; that is, their values are equal for any replacement of the variables.

Key Concepts

Summary	Properties for Simplifying Algebraic Expressions
Let a, b, and c represent real numbers.	
Definition of Subtraction	$a - b = a + (-b)$
Definition of Division	$a \div b = \frac{a}{b} = a \cdot \frac{1}{b}, b \neq 0$
Distributive Property for Subtraction	$a(b - c) = ab - ac$
Multiplication by 0	$0 \cdot a = 0$
Multiplication by -1	$-1 \cdot a = -a$
Opposite of a Sum	$-(a + b) = -a + (-b)$
Opposite of a Difference	$-(a - b) = b - a$
Opposite of a Product	$-(ab) = -a \cdot b = a \cdot (-b)$
Opposite of an Opposite	$-(-a) = a$

---

4 EXAMPLE Math Tip

Some students may not be sure why $-(m + n)$ can be replaced with $-m + (-n)$. Point out that $-(m + n) = (-1)(m + n) = (-1)m + (-1)n = -m + (-n)$.

5 EXAMPLE Tactile Learners

Have each student trace a finger along the perimeter of the figure. Help students realize that the perimeter of this figure is $2b$ plus the perimeter of the $a \times 2a$ rectangle.

Additional Examples

4 Simplify by combining like terms.
$2h - 3k + 7(2h - 3k)$ **16h − 24k**

5 Find the perimeter of this figure. Simplify the answer. **2c + 4d**

Resources

- Daily Notetaking Guide 1-2 **L3**

Closure

Ask: *How is the Distributive Property useful in simplifying expressions?* **Answers may vary. Sample: It allows you to combine like terms.**

---

4 EXAMPLE Combining Like Terms

Simplify by combining like terms.

a. $3k - k$

$3k - k = 3k - 1k$ **Identity Property of Multiplication**

$ = (3 - 1)k$ **Distributive Property**

$ = 2k$ **Simplify.**

b. $5z^2 - 10z - 8z^2 + z$

$5z^2 - 10z - 8z^2 + z = 5z^2 - 8z^2 + (-10z) + z$ **Commutative Property of Addition**

$ = (5 - 8)z^2 + (-10 + 1)z$ **Distributive Property**

$ = -3z^2 - 9z$

c. $-(m + n) + 2(m - 3n)$

$-(m + n) + 2(m - 3n)$

$= -m + (-n) + 2m + (-6n)$ **Opposite of a Sum, Distributive Property**

$= -m + 2m + (-n) + (-6n)$ **Commutative Property of Addition**

$= -1 \cdot m + 2m + (-1 \cdot n) + (-6n)$ **Multiplication by −1**

$= (-1 + 2)m + [-1 + (-6)]n$ **Distributive Property**

$= m - 7n$

Quick Check **4** Simplify by combining like terms.

a. $2x^2 + 5x - 4x^2 + x - x^2$ **−3x² + 6x** **b.** $-2(r + s) - (2r + 2s)$ **−4r − 4s**

5 EXAMPLE Finding Perimeter

Multiple Choice Which expression represents the perimeter of the figure at the right?

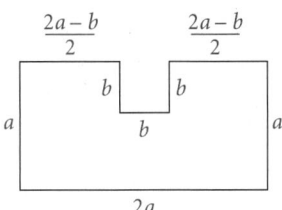

Ⓐ $8a + b$ Ⓑ $6a + b$

Ⓒ $6a + 2b$ Ⓓ $4a + 3b$

$\dfrac{2a - b}{2} + b + b + b + \dfrac{2a - b}{2} + a + 2a + a$

$= \dfrac{2a - b}{2} + \dfrac{2a - b}{2} + 3b + 4a$

$= \dfrac{2(2a - b)}{2} + 3b + 4a$

$= 2a - b + 3b + 4a$

$= 6a + 2b$

The perimeter is $6a + 2b$. The correct choice is C.

Test-Taking Tip

You can check your answer, C, by substituting values. Let $a = 2$ and $b = 1$. The perimeter is 14. Also, $6a + 2b = 6(2) + 2(1) = 14$.

Quick Check **5** Find the perimeter of each figure. Simplify the answer.

a. **10x**

b. **10c + 2d**

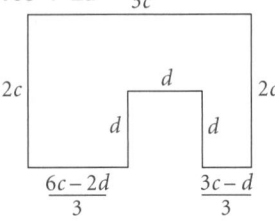

EXERCISES

For more exercises, see *Extra Skill and Word Problem Practice.*

Practice and Problem Solving

A Practice by Example

Examples 1 and 2
(page 12)

GO for Help

Evaluate each expression for the given values of the variables.

1. $4a + 7b + 3a - 2b + 2a; a = -5$ and $b = 3$ **−30**

2. $5y - 3z + 4y - 1z - 3y; y = 3$ and $z = -2$ **26**

3. $12a^2 - 3ab + 2b; a = -5$ and $b = 4$ **368**

4. $-k^2 - (3k - 5n) + 4n; k = -1$ and $n = -2$ **−16**

5. $3y - (4y + 6x); x = 3$ and $y = -2$ **−16**

6. $3(2c + d) - d; c = 5$ and $d = -1$ **28**

7. $-5(x + 2y) + 15(x + 2y); x = 7$ and $y = -7$ **−70**

8. $4(2m - n) - 3(2m - n); m = -15$ and $n = -18$ **−12**

Example 3
(page 13)

Physics The expression $16t^2$ models the distance in feet that an object falls during t seconds after being dropped. Find the distance an object falls during each time.

9. 0.25 second **1 ft**   **10.** 0.5 second **4 ft**

11. 2 seconds **64 ft**   **12.** 10 seconds **1600 ft**

Electrical Engineering The expression $0.01E + 0.003E^2$ gives the thickness in millimeters of the insulation needed for the high voltage cable shown at the left. E is the number of kilovolts carried by the cable. Find the thickness of insulation material needed for each voltage.

Insulation

13. 1 kilovolt
0.013 mm

14. 2 kilovolts
0.032 mm

15. 10 kilovolts
0.4 mm

16. 20 kilovolts
1.4 mm

Investing The expression $1000(1.1)^t$ represents the value of a $1000 investment that earns 10% interest per year, compounded annually for t years. Find the value of a $1000 investment at the end of each period.

17. 2 years **$1210**   **18.** 3 years **$1331**   **19.** 4 years
$1464.10

20. 5 years
$1610.51

Example 4
(page 14)

Simplify by combining like terms.

21. $5a - a$ **4a**

22. $5 + 10s - 8s$ **2s + 5**

23. $-5a - 4a + b$
−9a + b

24. $2a + 3b + 4a$ **6a + 3b**

25. $6r + 3s + 2s + 4r$
10r + 5s

26. $w + 3z + 5w + 2z$
6w + 5z

27. $x^2 + x^2 + x$ **2x² + x**

28. $xy + 2x + x$ **xy + 3x**

29. $0.5x - x$ **−0.5x**

30. $3(2x + 1) - 8$ **6x − 5**

31. $2(5y - 2) + x$
10y + x − 4

32. $3y - (4y + 6x)$
−y − 6x

33. $7b - (3a - 8b)$
−3a + 15b

34. $5 + (4g - 7)$
4g − 2

35. $-(3x - 4y + z)$
−3x + 4y − z

Example 5
(page 14)

Geometry Find the perimeter of each figure. Simplify the answer.

36.

37.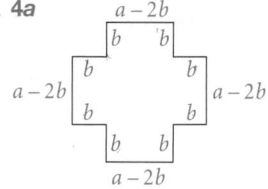

Assignment Guide

1 A B 1-20, 38-46

2 A B 21-37, 47-64

C Challenge   65-67

Test Prep   68-77
Mixed Review   78-87

Homework Quick Check

To check students' understanding of key skills and concepts, go over Exercises 14, 36, 46, 52, 63.

Error Prevention!

Exercises 1–8 Remind students that they need to use parentheses around all negative numbers that they substitute into expressions.

15

Lesson Quiz

1. Evaluate each expression for the given values of the variables.

   a. $4p - 3q + 8$;
   $p = -6$, $q = -10$ **14**

   b. $-3m^2 - (m + n)^2$;
   $m = 2$, $n = -4$ **-16**

2. Simplify by combining like terms.

   a. $7 - 4(x + y) + 2(x - 3y)$
   $7 - 2x - 10y$

   b. $3y^2 + 8 - (2y^2 + 12)$
   $y^2 - 4$

   c. $-12(x^2 + y) + 3(y + x^2)$
   $-9x^2 - 9y$

3. Find the perimeter. Simplify the answer. **$8c + 4d$**

Alternative Assessment

Have students work in pairs. One student writes a simplified expression that contains two variables. The other student creates an expression that can be simplified, using the Distributive Property and combining like terms, to yield the first student's expression. Together, the group checks that its work is reasonable. Then have students substitute several different values for each of the variables into both expressions and verify that both yield the same result. Then, have students switch roles and repeat.

pages 15–17 Exercises

63. Assoc. Prop. of Add.
    Comm. Prop. of Add.
    Assoc. Prop. of Add.
    Identity Prop. of Mult.
    Dist. Prop. of Add.
    Simplify.

64. Dist. Prop.
    Simplify.
    Dist. Prop.

B Apply Your Skills

Evaluate each expression for the given value of the variable.

38. $|x| + |2x| - |x - 1|$; $x = 2$ **5**

39. $|2z + 3| + |5 - 3z|$; $z = -3$ **17**

40. $3|2a + 5| + 2|3 - a|$; $a = 4$ **41**

41. $6|4b - 5| + 3|2 - 2b|$; $b = -1$ **66**

42. $\dfrac{3(2x + 1) - 2(x - 3)}{x + 6}$; $x = -3$ **-1**

43. $\dfrac{5(2k - 3) - 3(k + 4)}{3k + 2}$; $k = -2$ **$\frac{41}{4}$**

46b. about 242 million voters; about 263 million voters

44. $y^2 + 3$; $y = \sqrt{7}$ **10**

45. $5c^3 - 6c^2 - 2c$; $c = -5$ **-765**

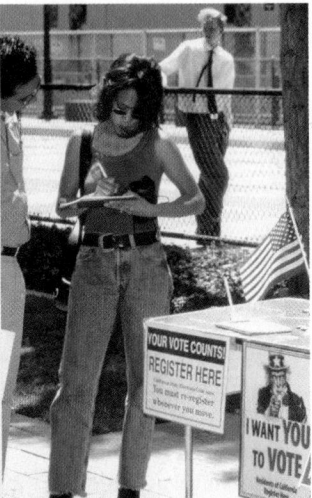

46. **Elections** The expression $2.6y + 107$ models the number of eligible voters in millions in the United States from 1960 to 2000. In the expression, y represents the number of years since 1960.   **about 180 million voters**

    a. Find the approximate number of eligible voters in 1988.

    b. Assume that the model continues to hold for future years. How many eligible voters will there be in 2012? In 2020?   **See left.**

    c. The expression $-0.3y + 61$ models the *percent* of eligible voters who voted in presidential elections from 1960 to 2000. (See Example 3.) Write an expression that models the *number* of voters in presidential elections from 1960 to 2000.   **$-0.0078y^2 + 1.265y + 65.27$**

    d. Use your model from (c) to find the approximate number of voters who voted for president in 1980.   **about 87 million**

Simplify by combining like terms.

47. $-a^2 + 2b^2 + \frac{1}{4}a^2$ **$-\frac{3}{4}a^2 + 2b^2$**

48. $x + \frac{x^2}{2} + 2x^2 - x$ **$\frac{5x^2}{2}$**

49. $\frac{y^2}{4} + \frac{y}{3} + \frac{y^2}{3} - \frac{y}{5}$ **$\frac{7y^2}{12} + \frac{2y}{15}$**

50. $-(2x + y) - 2(-x - y)$ **y**

51. $x(3 - y) + y(x + 6)$ **$3x + 6y$**

52. $4(2x + y) - 2(2x + y)$ **$4x + 2y$**

53. $\frac{1}{2}(x^2 - y^2) - \frac{5}{2}(x^2 - y^2)$ **$-2x^2 + 2y^2$**

Real-World Connection

Each year, millions of U.S. citizens turn 18 and become eligible to vote. Unfortunately, fewer than half of them register.

Match the property name with the appropriate equation.

54. Definition of Subtraction **F**

55. Definition of Division **C**

56. Distributive Property **A**

57. Multiplication by 0 **G**

58. Multiplication by -1 **B**

59. Opposite of a Sum **H**

60. Opposite of a Difference **E**

61. Opposite of a Product **I**

62. Opposite of an Opposite **D**

A. $2(s - t) = 2s - 2t$

B. $-(a - b) = (-1)(a - b)$

C. $(7 - y) \div (2y) = \dfrac{7 - y}{2y}$

D. $-[-(x - 10)] = x - 10$

E. $-(2t - 11) = 11 - 2t$

F. $2t - 11 = 2t + (-11)$

G. $(4a^2 - 9a)(0) + 5a = 0 + 5a$

H. $-[3 + (-y)] = -3 + [-(-y)]$

I. $-(4z^2) = 4(-z^2)$

63–64. See margin.

65. **Answers may vary. Sample:**
    $3x^2 + x - 4x^2 + 2x^2 - 2x$,
    $x^3 + x^2 + x - x^3 - 2x$,
    $-x^2 + 2x^2 + 3x - 3x - x$,
    $x^2 - 5x + 4x - x^5 + x^5$,
    $3x^2 - x^2 - x^2 + 7x - 8x$

GO Online

Homework Video Tutor

Visit: PHSchool.com
Web Code: age-0102

Justifying Steps **Name the property used in each step of simplification.**

63. $(3x + y) + x = 3x + (y + x)$
    $= 3x + (x + y)$
    $= (3x + x) + y$
    $= (3x + 1x) + y$
    $= (3 + 1)x + y$
    $= 4x + y$

64. $2(5 + x) + 4(5 + x) = (2 + 4)(5 + x)$
    $= 6(5 + x)$
    $= 30 + 6x$

C Challenge

65. **Open-Ended** Write four different expressions that simplify to $x^2 - x$. Each expression must have five terms. **See above left.**

66. Simplify $2(b - a) + 5(b - a)$ and explain each step in your simplification. **See margin.**

67. a. Evaluate the expression $2(2x^2 - x) - 3(x^2 - x) + x^2 - x$ for $x = 3$. Do *not* simplify the expression before evaluating it. **18**

   b. Simplify the expression in (a) and then evaluate your answer for $x = 3$. **$2x^2$; 18**

   c. **Writing** Explain why the values in (a) and (b) should be the same. **c–d. See**

   d. **Error Analysis** A student simplified $2x(x - 6)$ to $2x^2 - 6x$. Should the **margin.** student check his work by evaluating both expressions for $x = 0$? Explain.

Test Prep

Test Prep

📁 **Resources**
For additional practice with a variety of test item formats:
- Standardized Test Prep, p. 51
- Test-Taking Strategies, p. 46
- Test-Taking Strategies with Transparencies

Multiple Choice

75. [2] $x = 0$ or $x = 3$ since for $6x(x - 3)$ $= 0$ either $6x$ or $x - 3$ equals 0.

[1] $x = 0$ and $x = 3$ with no explanation

76. [2] an answer of -5, with work shown

[1] one computational error

77. [2] an answer of 8, with work shown

[1] one computational error

Short Response

68. Which of the following expressions is NOT equivalent to the others? **B**
  A. $3x - y - x - y$ **B.** $-2(x - y)$
  C. $2(x - y)$ **D.** $2x - 2y$

69. If xy is negative, which one of the following is possible? **G**
  F. $x < y < 0$ **G.** $x < 0 < y$
  H. $x = y$ **J.** $0 \leq x \leq y$

70. Which factor in the term $-9x^2y$ is the coefficient? **A**
  A. -9 **B.** 2   **C.** x^2 **D.** x^2y

71. Simplify $5a^2 + a^2 + 7a$. **G**
  F. $5a^2 + 7a$ **G.** $6a^2 + 7a$ **H.** $12a^2$ **J.** $13a^3$

72. Which expression is equivalent to $-(p - q)$? **A**
  A. $q - p$ **B.** $p + q$ **C.** $-p - q$ **D.** $p - q$

73. Which expression is equivalent to $4(2n - 1)$? **J**
  F. $7n$ **G.** $8n$ **H.** $8n - 1$ **J.** $8n - 4$

74. Which expression has the greatest value for $x = -4$ and $y = 5$? **D**
  A. $-3xy$ **B.** $3xy$ **C.** xy^2 **D.** x^2y

75. For which values of x does $6x(x - 3) = 0$? Explain your answer. **75–77. See left.**

76. Evaluate the expression $|x + 3| - |x - 6| + |x|$ for $x = -2$. Show your work.

77. Evaluate the expression $3(x^2 - 1) - x(x^2 - 1) - (2 - x)(x^2 - 1)$ for $x = 3$. Show your work.

66. Answers may vary. Sample:
$2(b - a) + 5(b - a)$
$= (2 + 5)(b - a)$
        Dist. Prop.
$= 7(b - a)$ Addition
$= 7b - 7a$ Dist. Prop.

67c. Properties of operations were used to simplify the original expression. Those properties convert one expression into an equivalent expression, and equivalent expressions have equal values for all replacements of their variables.

d. Answers may vary. Sample: Students should check each step in the simplification; they also should substitute more than one value for x in the original and simplified expressions.

Mixed Review

Lesson 1-1

 for Help

Order the numbers from least to greatest.

$-4.3, -|3.4|, |-3.4|, |-4.3|$

78. $-1.5, -0.5, -\sqrt{2}, -1.4$

79. $|-4.3|, -4.3, -|3.4|, |-3.4|$

80. $-\frac{3}{8}, \frac{1}{2}, -\frac{3}{4}, -\frac{5}{6}$ $-\frac{5}{6}, -\frac{3}{4}, -\frac{3}{8}, \frac{1}{2}$

81. $\sqrt{\frac{1}{4}}, \sqrt{\frac{1}{16}}, -\sqrt{\frac{1}{8}}, -\sqrt{\frac{1}{10}}$

Lesson 1-1

Replace each ■ with the symbol <, >, or = to make the sentence true.

78. $-1.5, -\sqrt{2}, -1.4, -0.5$

81. $-\sqrt{\frac{1}{8}}, -\sqrt{\frac{1}{10}}, \sqrt{\frac{1}{16}}, \sqrt{\frac{1}{4}}$

82. $|-11|$ ■ $|9|$ $>$

83. $|11|$ ■ $|9|$ $>$

84. $|-11|$ ■ $|-9|$ $>$

85. $-|-7|$ ■ $|7|$ $<$

86. $-|7|$ ■ $|-7|$ $<$

87. $-|-7|$ ■ $-|7|$ $=$

Objectives
1 To solve equations
2 To solve problems by writing equations

Examples
1 Solving an Equation with a Variable on Both Sides
2 Using the Distributive Property
3 Solving a Formula for One of Its Variables
4 Solving an Equation for One of Its Variables
5 Real-World Connection
6 Using Ratios
7 Real-World Connection

Math Background

Many equations in one variable are solved by using basic operations and the properties of equality. As a result, many application problems are solvable once they have been accurately modeled by an equation.

More Math Background: p. 2C

Lesson Planning and Resources

See p. 2E for a list of the resources that support this lesson.

Bell Ringer Practice

✓ **Check Skills You'll Need**
For intervention, direct students to:

Algebraic Expressions
Lessons 1-2: Example 4
Extra Skills and Word Problems Practice, Ch. 1

Solving Equations

What You'll Learn
• To solve equations
• To solve problems by writing equations

. . . And Why
To solve a problem about aeronautics, as in Example 7

✓ **Check Skills You'll Need**

Simplify each expression.

1. $5x - 9x + 3$ $-4x + 3$
2. $2y + 7x + y - 1$ $7x + 3y - 1$
3. $10h + 12g - 8h - 4g$ $8g + 2h$
4. $\frac{x}{3} + \frac{y}{3} + \frac{2y}{3} - y$ $\frac{x}{3}$
5. $(x + y) - (x - y)$ $2y$
6. $-(3 - c) - 4(c - 1)$ $-3c + 1$

🔊 **New Vocabulary**   • solution of an equation

---

1 Solving Equations

An equation that contains a variable may be true for some replacements of the variable and false for others. A number that makes the equation true is a **solution of the equation.** You can use the properties of equality to solve equations.

 Key Concepts

Summary	Properties of Equality

Let a, b, and c represent real numbers.

Reflexive Property	$a = a$
Symmetric Property	If $a = b$, then $b = a$.
Transitive Property	If $a = b$ and $b = c$, then $a = c$.
Addition Property	If $a = b$, then $a + c = b + c$.
Subtraction Property	If $a = b$, then $a - c = b - c$.
Multiplication Property	If $a = b$, then $ac = bc$.
Division Property	If $a = b$ and $c \neq 0$, then $\frac{a}{c} = \frac{b}{c}$.
Substitution Property	If $a = b$, then b may be substituted for a in any expression to obtain an equivalent expression.

GO Online

Video Tutor Help

Visit: PhSchool.com
Web Code: age-0775

1 EXAMPLE Solving an Equation with a Variable on Both Sides

Solve $13y + 48 = 8y - 47$.

$13y + 48 = 8y - 47$

$5y + 48 = -47$ **Subtract 8y from each side.**

$5y = -95$ **Subtract 48 from each side.**

$y = -19$ **Divide each side by 5.**

Check $13y + 48 = 8y - 47$

$13(-19) + 48 \stackrel{?}{=} 8(-19) - 47$

$-199 = -199$ ✓

Differentiated Instruction Solutions for All Learners

Special Needs L1
For Example 1, remind students to check their solutions in the original equation since they may have made a mistake at an intermediate step.

learning style: verbal

Below Level L2
Students may have difficulty simplifying expressions containing variables. For these students, work through similar expressions that contain only constants.

learning style: visual

Quick Check ❶ Solve each equation. Check your answers.

    a. $8z + 12 = 5z - 21$ −11   **b.** $2t - 3 = 9 - 4t$ 2

❷ **EXAMPLE** **Using the Distributive Property**

Solve $3x - 7(2x - 13) = 3(-2x + 9)$.

$3x - 7(2x - 13) = 3(-2x + 9)$

$3x - 14x + 91 = -6x + 27$ **Distributive Property**

$-11x + 91 = -6x + 27$ **Combine like terms.**

$-5x + 91 = 27$ **Add 6x to each side.**

$-5x = -64$ **Subtract 91 from each side.**

$x = \frac{64}{5}$, or 12.8   **Divide each side by −5.**

> **Vocabulary Tip**
>
> Literally, <u>to</u> <u>solve</u> means "to set apart." Think of solving an equation as setting apart the variable.

 Quick Check ❷ Solve each equation. Check your answers.

    a. $2(y - 3) + 6 = 70$ **35**   **b.** $6(t - 2) = 2(9 - 2t)$ **3**

When you have a formula or equation that has more than one variable, you can solve for any one of the variables.

❸ **EXAMPLE** **Solving a Formula for One of Its Variables**

Geometry The formula for the area of a trapezoid is $A = \frac{1}{2}h(b_1 + b_2)$. Solve the formula for h.

$A = \frac{1}{2}h(b_1 + b_2)$

$2A = h(b_1 + b_2)$ **Multiply each side by 2.**

$\frac{2A}{b_1 + b_2} = h$ **Divide each side by $b_1 + b_2$.**

 Quick Check ❸ Solve the formula for the area of a trapezoid for b_1. $b_1 = \frac{2A}{h} - b_2$

❹ **EXAMPLE** **Solving an Equation for One of Its Variables**

Solve $\frac{x}{a} + 1 = \frac{x}{b}$ for x. Find any restrictions on a and b.

$\frac{x}{a} + 1 = \frac{x}{b}$

$ab\left(\frac{x}{a}\right) + ab(1) = ab\left(\frac{x}{b}\right)$ **Multiply each side by the least common denominator (LCD).**

$bx + ab = ax$ **Simplify.**

$ab = ax - bx$ **Collect terms with x on one side.**

$ab = (a - b)x$ **Distributive Property**

$x = \frac{ab}{a - b}$ **Divide each side by $a - b$.**

The denominators cannot be 0, so $a \neq 0$ and $b \neq 0$. Also $a - b \neq 0$, so $a \neq b$.

 Quick Check ❹ Solve each equation for x. Find any restrictions.

    a. $ax + bx - 15 = 0$

        $x = \frac{15}{a + b}, a \neq -b$

    b. $d = \frac{2x}{a} + b$

        $x = \frac{a(d - b)}{2}, a \neq 0$

Lesson 1-3 Solving Equations   **19**

---

❸ **EXAMPLE** **Teaching Tip**

You may wish to point out that b_1 and b_2 are two different variables, as indicated by their different subscripts. It is not necessary to say that $b_1 \neq -b_2$ since b_1 and b_2 are lengths of segments. This ensures that their sum is not zero.

PowerPoint

Additional Examples

❶ Solve $7x + 3 = 2x - 12$. −3

❷ Solve $4(m + 9) = -3(m - 4)$.

    $-\frac{24}{7}$

❸ The formula for the surface area of a rectangular prism is $A = 2(\ell w + \ell h + wh)$. Solve the formula for w.

    $w = \frac{A - 2\ell h}{2\ell + 2h}$

❹ Solve $\frac{x}{a} + 8 = b$ for x. Find any restrictions on a and b.

    $x = ab - 8a; a \neq 0$

Advanced Learners **L4**

Discuss with students whether an equation such as $y = \sqrt{x}$ requires that $x \geq 0$. If y is to be a real number, $x \geq 0$ must be true.

                    learning style: verbal

English Language Learners **ELL**

Have students look up the words *reflexive*, *symmetric*, and *transitive* in a dictionary. Have them compare the English meanings to the mathematical properties.

                    learning style: verbal

EXAMPLE 5 · Teaching Tip

You may want to encourage students to check their solutions algebraically. However, caution students that they may have found correct solutions to incorrect equations, so it is important they they check that their solutions are reasonable.

EXAMPLE 6 · Teaching Tip

Point out to students that multiplying each number in a ratio of three numbers by x is an extension of the concept of the ratio of two numbers. (If $x \neq 0$, then $a : b = ax : bx$.)

PowerPoint
Additional Examples

5 Adrian will use part of a garage wall as one of the long sides of a rectangular rabbit pen. He wants the pen to be 3 times as long as it is wide. He plans to use 68 ft of fencing. Find the dimensions of the pen. **width = $13\frac{3}{5}$ ft, length = $40\frac{4}{5}$ ft**

6 The sides of a quadrilateral are in the ratio 2 : 3 : 4 : 6. The perimeter is 132 cm. Find the lengths of the sides. **17.6 cm, 26.4 cm, 35.2 cm, 52.8 cm**

7 A plane takes off from an airport and flies east at a speed of 350 mi/h. Ten minutes later, a second plane takes off from the same airport and flies east at a higher altitude at a speed of 400 mi/h. How long does it take the second plane to overtake the first plane? **$1\frac{1}{6}$ h**

Resources
• Daily Notetaking Guide 1-3 **L3**

Closure

Have students describe the procedure used to solve an equation for a variable. **Use properties of operations and equality to isolate the variable on one side of the equation. Then, combine like terms and divide both sides by the coefficient of the variable.**

You can write an equation to model and solve a real-world problem.

EXAMPLE 5 · Real-World Connection

Construction A dog kennel owner has 100 ft of fencing to enclose a rectangular dog run. She wants it to be 5 times as long as it is wide. Find the dimensions of the dog run.

Relate 2 · width + 2 · length = perimeter

Define Let x = the width.
Then $5x$ = the length.

Write $2x + 2(5x) = 100$
$2x + 10x = 100$ **Multiply.**
$12x = 100$ **Combine like terms.**
$x = 8\frac{1}{3}$ **Divide each side by 12.**
$5x = 41\frac{2}{3}$ **Find the length.**

The width is $8\frac{1}{3}$ ft and the length is $41\frac{2}{3}$ ft.

Check Is the answer reasonable? Since the dimensions are about 8 ft and 42 ft, and $2 \cdot 8 + 2 \cdot 42 = 100$, the answer is reasonable.

Real-World Connection

Some states regulate the minimum amount of floor space for animals in kennels.

✓ Quick Check **5** A rectangle is twice as long as it is wide. Its perimeter is 48 cm. Find its dimensions.   **8 cm wide; 16 cm long**

Many geometry problems require writing and solving equations.

EXAMPLE 6 · Using Ratios

Geometry The lengths of the sides of a triangle are in the ratio 3 : 4 : 5. The perimeter of the triangle is 18 in. Find the lengths of the sides.

Relate Perimeter equals the sum of the lengths of the three sides.

Define Let $3x$ = the length of the shortest side.
Then $4x$ = the length of the second side.
Then $5x$ = the length of the third side.

Write $18 = 3x + 4x + 5x$
$18 = 12x$ **Combine like terms.**
$1.5 = x$
$3x = 3(1.5)$ $4x = 4(1.5)$ $5x = 5(1.5)$ **Find the length of each side.**
$= 4.5$ $= 6$ $= 7.5$

The lengths of the sides are 4.5 in., 6 in., and 7.5 in.

Check Is the answer reasonable? Since $5 + 6 + 8 = 19$, the answer is reasonable.

✓ Quick Check **6** The sides of a triangle are in the ratio 12 : 13 : 15. The perimeter is 120 cm. Find the lengths of the sides of the triangle.   **36 cm; 39 cm; 45 cm**

20

7 **EXAMPLE**   Real-World Connection

Aeronautics Radar detected an unidentified plane 5000 mi away, approaching at 700 mi/h. Fifteen minutes later an interceptor plane was dispatched, traveling at 800 mi/h. How long did the interceptor take to reach the approaching plane?

Relate   distance for interceptor + distance for approaching plane = 5000 mi

Define   Let t = the time in hours for the interceptor.
Then $t + 0.25$ = the time in hours for the approaching plane.

Write $800t + 700(t + 0.25) = 5000$

$\qquad 800t + 700t + 175 = 5000$ **Distributive Property**

$\qquad\qquad\qquad 1500t = 4825$ **Solve for t.**

$\qquad\qquad\qquad\quad t \approx 3.217$ or 3 h 13 min

Check   Is the answer reasonable? In $3\frac{1}{4}$ h, the interceptor flies 2600 mi. In $3\frac{1}{2}$ h, the approaching plane flies 2450 mi. $2600 + 2450 \approx 5000$, so the answer is reasonable.

  ⑦ A space probe leaves Earth at the rate of 3 km/s. After 100 days, a radio signal is sent to the probe. Radio signals travel at the speed of light, about 3×10^5 km/s. About how long does the signal take to reach the probe? **about 86.4 seconds, or 1 minute 26.4 seconds**

Real-World Connection
The F-117 is nearly invisible to radar. The faceted construction deflects most radar energy away from the radar receiver.

EXERCISES

For more exercises, see *Extra Skill and Word Problem Practice*.

Practice and Problem Solving

A **Practice by Example**

Example 1
(page 18)

Solve each equation. Check your answers.

1. $7w + 2 = 3w + 94$ **23**

2. $15 - g = 23 - 2g$ **8**

3. $43 - 3d = d + 9$ **$\frac{17}{2}$**

4. $5y + 1.8 = 4y - 3.2$ **−5**

5. $6a - 5 = 4a + 2$ **$\frac{7}{2}$**

6. $7y + 4 = 3 - 2y$ **$-\frac{1}{9}$**

7. $5c - 9 = 8 - 2c$ **$\frac{17}{7}$**

8. $4y - 8 - 2y + 5 = 0$ **$\frac{3}{2}$**

Example 2
(page 19)

9. $6(n - 4) = 3n$ **8**

10. $2 - 3(x + 4) = 8$ **−6**

11. $5(2 - g) = 0$ **2**

12. $2(x + 4) = 8$ **0**

13. $6(t - 2) = 2(9t - 2)$ **$-\frac{2}{3}$**

14. $4w - 2(1 - w) = -38$ **−6**

15. $4(k + 5) = 2(9k - 4)$ **2**

16. $10(1 - 2y) = -5(2y - 1)$ **$\frac{1}{2}$**

Example 3
(page 19)

Solve each formula for the indicated variable.

17. $A = \frac{1}{2}bh$, for h $h = \frac{2A}{b}$ **18.** $s = \frac{1}{2}gt^2$, for g $g = \frac{2s}{t^2}$ **19.** $V = \ell wh$, for w $w = \frac{V}{\ell h}$

20. $I = prt$, for r $r = \frac{I}{pt}$ **21.** $S = 2\pi rh$, for r $r = \frac{S}{2\pi h}$ **22.** $V = \pi r^2 h$, for h $h = \frac{V}{\pi r^2}$

Example 4
(page 19)

Solve each equation for x. Find any restrictions.   **23–28. See margin.**

23. $ax + bx = c$

24. $bx - cx = -c$

25. $\frac{x}{a} + b = c$

26. $\frac{x}{a} - 5 = b$

27. $\frac{x - 2}{2} = m + n$

28. $\frac{2}{5}(x + 1) = g$

Lesson 1-3 Solving Equations   **21**

---

pages 21–24 Exercises

23. $x = \frac{c}{a + b}, a \neq -b$

24. $x = \frac{c}{c - b}, b \neq c$

25. $x = a(c - b)$ or $ac - ab, a \neq 0$

26. $x = a(b + 5)$ or $ab + 5a, a \neq 0$

27. $x = 2(m + n) + 2$ or $2m + 2n + 2$

28. $x = \frac{5g}{2} - 1$

---

3. Practice

Assignment Guide

▽ ① A B 1-28, 36-47, 55-64

▽ ② A B 29-35, 48-54

C Challenge   65-68

Test Prep   69-72
Mixed Review   73-82

Homework Quick Check
To check students' understanding of key skills and concepts, go over Exercises 28, 37, 50, 52, 64.

Exercises 19–22 Students may find it helpful to first rewrite the expression with the indicated variable as the rightmost factor. For example, in Exercise 20, rewrite $I = prt$ as $I = (pt)r$. This makes it easier to see what to multiply or divide each side by to isolate r.

Differentiated Instruction **Resources**

GPS Guided Problem Solving   L3
Enrichment   L4
Reteaching   L2
Practice   L3

21

pages 21–24   Exercises

42. $R = \dfrac{r_1 r_2}{r_1 + r_2}$

43. $r_2 = \dfrac{Rr_1}{r_1 - R}$

44. $h = \dfrac{S - 2\pi r^2}{2\pi r}$

45. $v = \dfrac{h + 5t^2}{t}$

46. $h = \dfrac{2(v - s^2)}{s}$

47. $b_2 = \dfrac{2A}{h} - b_1$

55. $x = ab - b^2 - a, b \neq 0$

56. $x = \dfrac{c - a}{b - d}, b \neq d$

57. $x = \dfrac{b + d}{c - a}, a \neq c$

58. $x = \dfrac{3a - b - 8}{a - b}, a \neq b$

59. $x = \dfrac{3b + 2c - 5}{b - c}, b \neq c$

60. $x = \dfrac{2ab - 2c}{3at - cd}, 3at \neq cd$

61. $x = \dfrac{4a - 3bc}{aq - 5bp}, 5bp \neq aq$

62. $x = \dfrac{cb}{2da} + 6, a, b, d \neq 0$

63. $x = \dfrac{10c}{a}, a \neq 0$

64. $x = \dfrac{a - c}{m} + a, m \neq 0,$
    $x \neq a$

22

Examples 5–7
(pages 20, 21)

35a. $x + (x + 1) +$
    $(x + 2) = 90; 29,$
    $30, 31$

b. $(x - 1) + x +$
    $(x + 1) = 90; 29,$
    $30, 31$

B Apply Your Skills

38. $\frac{27}{5}$, or $5\frac{2}{5}$

Online
Homework Video Tutor
Visit: PHSchool.com
Web Code: age-0103

22   Chapter 1   Tools of Algebra

Write an equation to solve each problem.

29. Two buses leave Houston at the same time and travel in opposite directions. One bus averages 55 mi/h and the other bus averages 45 mi/h. When will they be 400 mi apart? **4 h**

30. Two planes left an airport at noon. One flew east at a certain speed and the other flew west at twice the speed. The planes were 2700 mi apart in 3 h. How fast was each plane flying? **300 mi/h; 600 mi/h**

31. **Geometry** The length of a rectangle is 3 cm greater than its width. The perimeter is 24 cm. Find the dimensions of the rectangle. **width = 4.5 cm; length = 7.5 cm**

32. **Geometry** One side of a triangle is 1 in. longer than the shortest side and is 1 in. shorter than the longest side. The perimeter is 17 in. Find the dimensions of the triangle. $4\frac{2}{3}$ in.; $5\frac{2}{3}$ in.; $6\frac{2}{3}$ in.

33. **Geometry** The sides of a rectangle are in the ratio 3 : 2. What is the length of each side if the perimeter of the rectangle is 55 cm? **11 cm; 11 cm; 16.5 cm; 16.5 cm**

34. **Geometry** The sides of a triangle are in the ratio 3 : 4 : 5. What is the length of each side if the perimeter of the triangle is 30 cm? **7.5 cm; 10 cm; 12.5 cm**

35. The sum of three consecutive integers is 90. **a–b. See left.**
    a. Find the three numbers by letting x represent the first integer.
    b. Find the three numbers by letting x represent the second integer.

Solve each equation. 36. $\frac{46}{39}$, or $1\frac{7}{39}$

36. $0.2(x + 3) - 4(2x - 3) = 3.4$

37. $12 - 3(2w + 1) = 7w - 3(7 + w)$ 3

38. $3(m - 2) - 5 = 8 - 2(m - 4)$

39. $7(a + 1) - 3a = 5 + 4(2a - 1)$ $\frac{3}{2}$

40. $\dfrac{x}{2} + \dfrac{x}{5} + \dfrac{x}{3} = 31$ **30**

41. $0.5\left(2x + \frac{3}{4}\right) - \frac{1}{3}(0.1 + x) = 1$
    $\frac{79}{80}$, or 0.9875

Solve each formula for the indicated variable. **42–47. See margin.**

42. $R(r_1 + r_2) = r_1 r_2$, for R

43. $R(r_1 + r_2) = r_1 r_2$, for r_2

44. $S = 2\pi r^2 + 2\pi rh$, for h

45. $h = vt - 5t^2$, for v

46. $v = s^2 + \frac{1}{2}sh$, for h

47. $A = \frac{1}{2}h(b_1 + b_2)$, for b_2

48. **Geometry** The measure of the supplement of an angle is 20° more than three times the measure of the original angle. Find the measures of the angles. **40°, 140°**

49. **Geometry** The measures of an angle and its complement differ by 22°. Find the measures of the angles. **34°, 56°**

50. Michael drove to a friend's house at a rate of 40 mi/h. He returned by the same route at a rate of 45 mi/h. The driving time for the round trip was 4 h. What is the distance Michael traveled? **about 169.4 mi**

51. **Sports** In the 2004 Olympics, a runner from Belarus won the gold medal in the 100-meter race. Her time was 10.93 seconds. In 1988, Florence Griffith Joyner of the United States set a world record of 10.49 seconds for the 100-meter race. If these two athletes had run in the same race with their respective times above, by how many meters would Griffith Joyner have won? ≈**4.03 m**

52. **Investments** Suppose you have $5000 to invest. A certificate of deposit (CD) earns 6% annual interest, while bonds, which are riskier, earn 8% annual interest. You decide to invest $2000 in a CD and the rest in bonds. How much interest will you have earned at the end of one year? Of two years, compounded annually? **$360; $746.40**

66a. 10 cows; 30 chickens. Sample equation: $4c + 2(40 - c) = 100$, where c is the number of cows

c. Answers may vary. Sample: In all, a repair shop has 11 bicycles and tricycles to repair. These have a total of 26 wheels. How many bicycles and how many tricycles are there? 7 bicycles, 4 tricycles

53. Find 4 consecutive odd integers with a sum of 184. **43, 45, 47, 49**

54. Find 4 consecutive even integers such that the sum of the second and fourth is 76.
34, 36, 38, 40

Solve for x. State any restrictions on the variables. 55–64. See margin p. 22.

55. $\frac{x+a}{b} + b = a$

56. $bx + a = dx + c$

57. $cx - b = ax + d$

58. $a(x - 3) + 8 = b(x - 1)$

59. $c(x + 2) - 5 = b(x - 3)$

60. $a(3tx - 2b) = c(dx - 2)$

61. $b(5px - 3c) = a(qx - 4)$

62. $\frac{a}{b}(2x - 12) = \frac{c}{d}$

63. $\frac{3ax}{5} - 4c = \frac{ax}{5}$

64. $\frac{a-c}{x-a} = m$

 Challenge

65. a. $t = \frac{s - 1055}{1.1}$
b. about 40.9°F
c. $C = \frac{5}{9}(F - 32)$
d. about 4.9°C

65. a. The speed of sound in air s, in ft/s, is given by the formula $s = 1055 + 1.1t$, where t is the temperature in degrees Fahrenheit. Solve the formula for t.
b. Find the Fahrenheit temperature at which the speed of sound is 1100 ft/s.
c. The relationship between the temperature in degrees Fahrenheit F and degrees Celsius C is given by the formula $F = \frac{9}{5}C + 32$. Solve the formula for C.
d. Find the Celsius temperature at which the speed of sound is 1100 ft/s.

66. There are 40 cows and chickens in the farmyard. One quiet afternoon, Jack counted and found that there were 100 legs in all. How many cows and how many chickens are there?
a. Solve this problem by writing and solving an equation. **See margin p. 22.**
b. Critical Thinking This problem can also be solved by reasoning. Suppose all 40 animals are chickens. How many legs would there be? How many too few legs is that? If one chicken is replaced by one cow, by how many would the number of legs be increased? How many cows would have to replace chickens to get the required 100 legs? **80 legs; 20 legs; 2 legs; 10 cows**
c. Open-Ended Write a problem about the number of wheels in a group of bicycles and tricycles. Solve your problem. **See margin p. 22.**

67. Assume that a, b, and c are integers and $a \neq 0$.
a. Proof Prove that the solution of the linear equation $ax - b = c$ must be a rational number. **See margin.**
b. Writing Describe the values of a, b, and c for which the solutions of $ax^2 + b = c$ are rational. **See back of book.**

68. A tortoise crawling at the rate of 0.1 mi/h passes a resting hare. The hare wants to rest another 30 min before chasing the tortoise at the rate of 5 mi/h. How many feet must the hare run to catch the tortoise? **about 269.4 ft**

 Test Prep

Gridded Response

69. What is the only value z for which $6z - 24 = 2z + 50$? Enter your answer as a decimal. **18.5**

70. If 16 less than four times a number is 64, what is the number? **20**

71. The measure of the supplement of an angle is 25° more than 7 times the measure of the angle. To the nearest tenth of a degree, what is the measure of the angle? **19.4**

72. The sides of a rectangle are in the ratio 5 : 7, and its perimeter is 96 cm. What is the area of the rectangle in square centimeters? **560**

67a. If you solve $ax - b = c$ for x, you get $x = \frac{b+c}{a}$. Since b and c are integers, $b + c$ is an integer. But a is a nonzero integer. So $\frac{b+c}{a}$ is the quotient of two integers and hence, by the definition of a rational number, $\frac{b+c}{a}$ is a rational number.

Lesson Quiz

1. Solve $16x - 15 = -5x + 48$. **3**

2. Solve $5(1 - 3m) = 30 - 2(4m + 7)$. $-\frac{11}{7}$

3. Solve $s = \frac{a + b + c}{2}$ for b. $b = 2s - a - c$

4. Mrs. Chern drove at a rate of 45 mi/h from her home to her sister's house. She spent 1.5 hours having lunch with her sister. She then drove back home at a rate of 55 mi/h. The entire trip, including lunch, took 4 hours. How far does Mrs. Chern live from her sister? $61\frac{7}{8}$ mi

5. Find three consecutive odd integers whose sum is 111. **35, 37, 39**

Alternative Assessment

Have students work in groups. Each group creates a quiz containing five questions covering the content of the lesson. At least one question should be an application. Groups trade quizzes and solve each problem. Then, both groups discuss the results together and resolve any difficulties.

Test Prep

A sheet of blank grids is available with the Test-Taking Strategies with Transparencies booklet. Give this sheet to students for practice with filling in the grids.

Resources

For additional practice with a variety of test item formats:
• Standardized Test Prep, p. 51
• Test-Taking Strategies, p. 46
• Test-Taking Strategies with Transparencies

Mixed Review

 GO for Help

Lesson 1-2

Evaluate each expression for $x = -4$ and $y = 3$.

73. $x - 2y + 3$ -7 **74.** $x + x \div y$
$-\frac{16}{3}$, or $-5\frac{1}{3}$

75. $3x - 4y - x$
-20

76. $x + 2y \div x$
$-\frac{11}{2}$, or $-5\frac{1}{2}$

Lesson 1-2

Simplify each expression.

77. $2x^2 + x + 5x^2 - 3x$
$7x^2 - 2x$

78. $ab - a - 5a$
$ab - 6a$

79. $-(3x - y + 4x - y)$
$2y - 7x$

80. $2(5x - 3) + x$
$11x - 6$

81. $5 - 2(3x + 5)$
$-6x - 5$

82. $4r + 2s - (6r + 7s)$
$-2r - 5s$

✓ Checkpoint Quiz 1 Lessons 1-1 through 1-3

1–2. See left.

1. Simplify the expressions and arrange them in order from least to greatest.

$|4 - 11|$ $\quad$ $0.1|-3|$ $\quad$ $|1 - \frac{1}{3}|$ $\quad$ $|3| - |4|$

2. What three properties of real numbers are needed to simplify $3x + (2 + 5x)$?

1. $-1, 0.3, \frac{2}{3}, 7$

2. Comm. Prop. of Add., Assoc. Prop. of Add., Dist. Prop.

Simplify each expression.

3. $-(a + 2b) + 4(a + 2b) - 2(a + 2b)$
$a + 2b$

4. $-3(a^2 + a + 1) - 4(-a^2 - a + 1)$
$a^2 + a - 7$

Solve each equation.

5. $2(4x + 1) = 3(4 + 2x)$ 5

6. $12 - 2(3x + 1) = 4x - 5$ $\frac{3}{2}$, or $1\frac{1}{2}$

7. $\frac{1}{2}(4b + 1) = 7 - \frac{1}{4}(6b - 2)$ 2

Solve for the indicated variable. Find any restrictions. $\quad x = \frac{4b}{7a}, a \neq 0$

8. $A = p(1 + rt)$, for r
$r = \frac{A - p}{pt}, p \neq 0, t \neq 0$

9. $8ax - b = 3b + ax$, for x

10. The perimeter of Sportsland Park is 624 yd. The length of the rectangular park is 8 yd more than 3 times the width. Find the dimensions of the park.
width = 76 yd, length = 236 yd

Algebra at Work

································· **Wildlife Biologist**

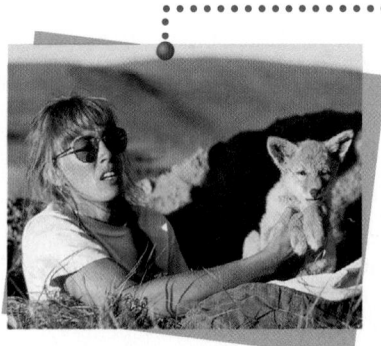

Wildlife biologists can model changes in an animal population. An animal population increases rapidly when conditions are good. However, as the number of animals increases, the food supplies decrease. Hunger and disease then lower the population.

Wildlife biologists take a special interest in extremes of animal populations. If the population of one species becomes too large, it may reduce the population of another species. A continuing decrease may cause the species to become endangered or extinct.

Go Online
PHSchool.com
For: Information about wildlife biology
Web Code: agb-2031

Spreadsheets

FOR USE WITH LESSON 1-3

Suppose that you buy an electronic keyboard and sound system for $500 using a credit card. When you get your first monthly statement, the minimum payment is $25. The minimum payment is either $15 or 5% of your balance, whichever is greater. Interest is calculated at 1.8% per month. You pay the minimum each month.

ACTIVITY

You can examine the situation described above with a spreadsheet. Write cell formulas for row 3 of the spreadsheet.

	A	B	C	D	E	F	G
1	Month	Balance	Interest	Payment	New Balance	Total Interest	Total Paid
2	1	$500.00	$9.00	$25.00	$484.00	$9.00	$25.00
3	2	$484.00	$8.71	$24.20	$468.51	$17.71	$49.20
4	3	$468.51	$8.43	$23.43	$453.52	$26.15	$72.63

Month	$A3 = A2 + 1$	**Increase the month by 1.**
Balance	$B3 = E2$	**balance from the previous month**
Interest	$C3 = B3 \cdot 0.018$	**1.8% of the month's balance**
Payment	$D3 = B3 \cdot 0.05$	**5% of the month's balance**
New Balance	$E3 = B3 + C3 - D3$	**Add the interest and subtract the payment.**
Total Interest	$F3 = F2 + C3$	**Add the month's interest to the previous total interest.**
Total Paid	$G3 = G2 + D3$	**Add the month's payment to the previous total.**

EXERCISES

1. Create a spreadsheet for the situation in the Example.
   a. In which month will the minimum payment first be $15? **month 17**
   b. After how many months will the balance reach zero? **41 months**
   c. What is the total interest paid? **$187.74**
   d. What is the total amount you will pay? **$687.74**
   e. How many payments are required to reduce the balance to $400? **7 payments**
   f. Rewrite the right side of $E3 = B3 + C3 - D3$ in terms of B3.
      $E3 = B3 + (B3 \cdot 0.018) - (B3 \cdot 0.05)$, or $B3 \cdot 0.968$
2. Create a new spreadsheet for an account that charges 14.9% annual interest. Use a minimum payment of 10% or $20, whichever is greater. What is the total interest paid for the keyboard and sound system? **$57.43**

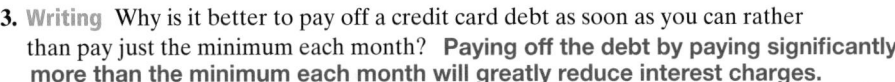

3. **Writing** Why is it better to pay off a credit card debt as soon as you can rather than pay just the minimum each month? **Paying off the debt by paying significantly more than the minimum each month will greatly reduce interest charges.**

Activity Lab

Spreadsheets

Students write cell formulas in a spreadsheet to find the minimum monthly payment, balance, interest, and total amount paid on a credit card.

Guided Instruction

Rounding affects the values in the cells. If formulas and entries are entered correctly, the numbers in the spreadsheet are correct, even if the result of simple arithmetic operations may appear to be slightly different.

If the numbers were truncated and exact, the entries for E4 and F4 would be 453.51 and 26.14, respectively. However, the spreadsheet is "smart enough" to keep track of exact quantities and rounding errors.

Technology Tip

After students have highlighted the cell in which they want to type a formula, they must then type = before they can enter the formula.

Tell students that they may not have to type the cell labels when entering formulas. For example, if they want to enter the formula B5 + C2, they can type = then click on the cell B5, type +, then click on the cell C2.

Advanced Learners L4

Students may want to use the "Fill" or "Fill down" command to enter similar formulas in the same column.

Resources

The instructions in this feature are general enough to work with a variety of different spreadsheet programs.

1. Plan

Objectives
1 To solve and graph inequalities
2 To solve and write compound inequalities

Examples
1 Solving and Graphing Inequalities
2 No Solutions or All Real Numbers as Solutions
3 Real-World Connection
4 Compound Inequality Containing *And*
5 Compound Inequality Containing *Or*
6 Real-World Connection

Math Background

Solving inequalities is much like solving equations. An important difference is that multiplying or dividing both sides by a negative number reverses the direction of the inequality symbol.

The work with compound inequalities in this lesson prepares students for solving absolute value inequalities in the next lesson.

More Math Background: p. 2D

Lesson Planning and Resources

See p. 2E for a list of the resources that support this lesson.

Bell Ringer Practice

☑ **Check Skills You'll Need**
For intervention, direct students to:
Properties of Real Numbers
Lesson 1-1: Example 3
Extra Skills and Word Problems Practice, Ch. 1

Solving Equations
Lesson 1-3: Examples 1, 2
Extra Skills and Word Problems Practice, Ch. 1

Solving Inequalities

What You'll Learn
- To solve and graph inequalities
- To solve and write compound inequalities

... And Why
To analyze quality control, as in Example 6

☑ **Check Skills You'll Need**

GO for Help Lessons 1-1 and 1-3

State whether each inequality is true or false.
1. $5 < 12$ **true**   2. $5 < -12$ **false**   3. $5 \geq 12$ **false**
4. $5 \leq -12$ **false**   5. $5 \leq 5$ **true**   6. $5 \geq 5$ **true**

Solve each equation.
7. $3x + 3 = 2x - 3$ **−6**   8. $5x = 9(x - 8) + 12$ **15**

🔊 **New Vocabulary** • compound inequality

---

1 Solving and Graphing Inequalities

As with an equation, the solutions of an inequality are the numbers that make it true.

An equation such as $-2x = 10$ has only one solution, -5. On the other hand, the inequality $-2x < 10$ is true for many values of x, such as -4.99, -1, and 100. The solutions of $-2x < 10$ are all the numbers x such that $x > -5$, as shown in the graph at the right.

$x > -5$

GO for Help

To review the properties of equality, go to p. 18.

The properties for solving inequalities are similar to the properties for solving equations. The exception occurs when you multiply or divide each side by a negative quantity. Notice that you can obtain $x > -5$ from $-2x < 10$ by dividing each side by -2 and *reversing* the inequality symbol.

The following properties are for $\leq$. There are similar properties for $<, >,$ and $\geq$.

 Key Concepts

Property	Properties of Inequalities
	Let $a, b,$ and c represent real numbers.
Transitive Property	If $a \leq b$ and $b \leq c$, then $a \leq c$.
Addition Property	If $a \leq b$, then $a + c \leq b + c$.
Subtraction Property	If $a \leq b$, then $a - c \leq b - c$.
Multiplication Property	If $a \leq b$ and $c > 0$, then $ac \leq bc$. If $a \leq b$ and $c < 0$, then $ac \geq bc$.
Division Property	If $a \leq b$ and $c > 0$, then $\frac{a}{c} \leq \frac{b}{c}$. If $a \leq b$ and $c < 0$, then $\frac{a}{c} \geq \frac{b}{c}$.

← You must reverse the inequality symbol when *c* is negative.

26   Chapter 1   Tools of Algebra

Differentiated Instruction Solutions for All Learners

Special Needs L1
For Example 6, have students sketch a diagram to illustrate how to trim a 5-in. paper strip so that it is 3 in. long with a tolerance of $\frac{1}{4}$ in.

learning style: tactile

Below Level L2
If students are having difficulty understanding the concept of a solution to an inequality, use substitution to show that many different numbers satisfy the inequality.

learning style: visual

1 EXAMPLE Solving and Graphing Inequalities

Solve each inequality. Graph the solution.

a. $3x - 12 < 3$

$3x - 12 < 3$

$\quad 3x < 15$ **Add 12 to each side.**

$\quad\quad x < 5$ **Divide each side by 3.**

                                     Graph the solution.

     $-1\ \ 0\ \ 1\ \ 2\ \ 3\ \ 4\ \ 5\ \ 6$

Check First check the boundary point: $3(5) - 12 = 3$. ✓

         Then check another point on the graph, such as 4: $3(4) - 12 < 3$. ✓

b. $6 + 5(2 - x) \le 41$

$6 + 10 - 5x \le 41$ **Distributive Property**

$\quad\quad 16 - 5x \le 41$ **Simplify.**

$\quad\quad\quad\quad -5x \le 25$ **Subtract 16 from each side.**

$\quad\quad\quad\quad\quad x \ge -5$ **Divide each side by -5 and reverse the inequality.**

                                   Graph the solution.

     $-6\ {-5}\ {-4}\ {-3}\ {-2}\ {-1}\ \ 0\ \ 1$

Check First check the boundary point: $6 + 5[2 - (-5)] = 41$. ✓

         Then check another point, such as -4: $6 + 5[2 - (-4)] \le 41$. ✓

✓**Quick Check** ➊ Solve each inequality. Graph the solution.

a. $3x - 6 < 27$ $x < 11$

     $5\ \ 6\ \ 7\ \ 8\ \ 9\ \ 10\ 11\ 12\ 13$

b. $12 \ge 2(3n + 1) + 22$ $n \le -2$

     $-6\ {-5}\ {-4}\ {-3}\ {-2}\ {-1}\ 0\ \ 1\ \ 2$

Some inequalities have no solution, and some are true for all real numbers.

2 EXAMPLE No Solutions or All Real Numbers as Solutions

Solve each inequality. Graph the solution.

a. $2x - 3 > 2(x - 5)$

$2x - 3 > 2x - 10$ **Distributive Property**

$\quad\quad 2x > 2x - 7$ **Add 3 to each side.**

$\quad\quad\quad 0 > -7$ **Subtract 2x from each side.**

The last inequality is always true, so $2x - 3 > 2(x - 5)$ is always true. All real numbers are solutions.

     $-3\ {-2}\ {-1}\ \ 0\ \ 1\ \ 2\ \ 3$

b. $7x + 6 < 7(x - 4)$

$7x + 6 < 7x - 28$ **Distributive Property**

$\quad\quad\quad 6 < -28$ **Subtract 7x from each side.**

The last inequality is always false, so $7x + 6 < 7(x - 4)$ is always false. It has no solution.

✓**Quick Check** ➋ **a.** Solve $2x < 2(x + 1) + 3$. Graph the solution.   **All real numbers are solutions.**

     $-4\ {-3}\ {-2}\ {-1}\ 0\ \ 1\ \ 2\ \ 3\ \ 4$

b. Solve $4(x - 3) + 7 \ge 4x + 1$. Graph the solution. **no solutions**

c. **Critical Thinking** If possible, find values of a such that $2x + a > 2x$ has no solution. Then find values of a such that all real numbers are solutions.
values of a less than or equal to 0; values of a greater than 0

Lesson 1-4   Solving Inequalities   **27**

Video Tutor Help
Visit: PHSchool.com
Web Code: age-0775

---

2. Teach

Guided Instruction

1 EXAMPLE Teaching Tip

Remind students that when they graph an inequality, they should use an open circle at the boundary point if the boundary point is not a solution.

2 EXAMPLE Visual Learners

When an inequality has no solution, students may want to represent this situation graphically by drawing a number line without any shading.

3 EXAMPLE Math Tip

The inequality may also be written as $500 \le 200 + 0.25x$. It is customary (but not necessary) to write the final inequality in the solution so that the variable is on the left side of the inequality symbol.

PowerPoint

Additional Examples

➊ Solve $-2x < 3(x - 5)$. Graph the solution. $x > 3$;

    $-2\ {-1}\ 0\ \ 1\ \ 2\ \ 3\ \ 4\ \ 5\ \ 6$

➋ Solve $7x \ge 7(2 + x)$. Graph the solution. **no solution**

    $-4\ {-3}\ {-2}\ {-1}\ 0\ \ 1\ \ 2\ \ 3\ \ 4$

➌ A real estate agent earns a salary of $2000 per month plus 4% of the sales. Find the sales if the salesperson is to have a monthly income of at least $5000. **greater than or equal to $75,000**

Advanced Learners **L4**
Have students try to create inequalities that have a single real-number solution, no solution, or the set of all real numbers as the solution.

                             learning style: verbal

English Language Learners **ELL**
Have volunteers take turns reading aloud the exposition for this lesson. Have students give real-life examples using *and* or *or*, e.g., "Which would you rather have: a $10 AND a $5 bill or a $10 OR a $5 bill?"

                         learning style: verbal

Guided Instruction

 EXAMPLE Teaching Tip

You may wish to use a transparency and erasable color markers to show the graph of $x > -9$ in yellow and the graph of $x < 6$ in blue. The part of the number line that is green is the solution of the compound inequality.

EXAMPLE Teaching Tip

Adapt the Teaching Tip for Example 4. This time the solution of the compound inequality is any part of the number line that has color.

PowerPoint

Additional Examples

④ Graph the solution of
$2x - 1 \le 3x$ and $x > 4x - 9$.

⑤ Graph the solution of
$3x + 9 < -3$ or $-2x + 1 < 5$.

⑥ A strip of wood is to be 17 cm long with a tolerance of ± 0.15 cm. How much should be trimmed from a strip 18 cm long to allow it to meet specifications? **at least 0.85 cm and no more than 1.15 cm**

Resources
• Daily Notetaking Guide 1-4 **L3**

Closure

Ask: *What is one important difference between solving equations and solving inequalities?* Answers may vary. Sample: If you multiply or divide both sides of an inequality by a negative number, you change the direction of the inequality symbol.

pages 29–31 **Exercises**

1.

---

③ **EXAMPLE** Real-World Connection

Revenue The band shown at the left agrees to play for $200 plus 25% of the ticket sales. Find the ticket sales needed for the band to receive at least $500.

Relate $200 + 25%$ of ticket sales $\ge$ $500

Define Let x = ticket sales (in dollars).

Write $200 + 0.25x \ge 500$
$0.25x \ge 300$ **Subtract 200 from each side.**
$x \ge 1200$ **Divide each side by 0.25.**

• The ticket sales must be greater than or equal to $1200.

Quick Check ③ A salesperson earns a salary of $700 per month plus 2% of the sales. What must the sales be if the salesperson is to have a monthly income of at least $1800?
at least $55,000

---

2 Compound Inequalities

A **compound inequality** is a pair of inequalities joined by *and* or *or*.

Examples:
• $-1 < x$ and $x \le 3$, which you can also write as $-1 < x \le 3$
• $x < -1$ or $x \ge 3$

active math

For: Inequalities Activity
Use: Interactive Textbook, 1-4

To solve a compound inequality containing *and*, find all values of the variable that make both inequalities true.

④ **EXAMPLE** Compound Inequality Containing *And*

Graph the solution of $3x - 1 > -28$ and $2x + 7 < 19$.
$3x - 1 > -28$ and $2x + 7 < 19$
$3x > -27$ | $2x < 12$
$x > -9$ and $x < 6$
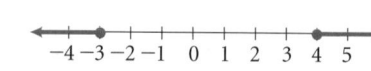

• This compound inequality can be rewritten as $-9 < x < 6$.

Quick Check ④ Graph the solution of $2x > x + 6$ and $x - 7 < 2$.

To solve a compound inequality containing *or*, find all values of the variable that make at least one of the inequalities true.

⑤ **EXAMPLE** Compound Inequality Containing *Or*

Graph the solution of $4y - 2 \ge 14$ or $3y - 4 \le -13$.
$4y - 2 \ge 14$ or $3y - 4 \le -13$
$4y \ge 16$ | $3y \le -9$
$y \ge 4$ or $y \le -3$

Quick Check ⑤ Solve the compound inequality $x - 1 < 3$ or $x + 3 > 8$. Graph the solution.
$x < 4$ or $x > 5$

28 Chapter 1 Tools of Algebra

2.
3.
4.
5.
6.
7.
8.
9.
10.

28

6 EXAMPLE Real-World Connection

Multiple Choice The ideal length of a bolt is 13.48 cm. The length can vary from the ideal by at most 0.03 cm. A machinist finds one bolt that is 13.67 cm long. By how much should the machinist decrease the length so the bolt can be used?

- Ⓐ between 13.45 cm and 13.51 cm
- Ⓑ between 13.64 cm and 13.70 cm
- Ⓒ between 0.16 cm and 0.22 cm
- Ⓓ between 0.13 cm and 0.19 cm

Relate minimum length ≤ final length ≤ maximum length

Define Let x = number of centimeters to remove.

Write

$$13.48 - 0.03 \leq 13.67 - x \leq 13.48 + 0.03$$
$$13.45 \leq 13.67 - x \leq 13.51 \quad \textbf{Simplify.}$$
$$-0.22 \leq -x \leq -0.16 \quad \textbf{Subtract 13.67.}$$
$$0.22 \geq x \geq 0.16 \quad \textbf{Multiply by } -1.$$

The machinist must remove at least 0.16 cm and no more than 0.22 cm.
● The answer is C.

Test-Taking Tip

When you multiply by a negative number across a compound inequality, remember to reverse both inequality symbols.

✓ Quick Check ⑥ The plans for a circular plastic part in a medical instrument require the diameter to be within 0.2 in. of 1.5 in. A machinist finds that the diameter is now 1.73 in. By how much should the machinist decrease the diameter?
by at least 0.03 in., but by no more than 0.43 in.

EXERCISES

For more exercises, see *Extra Skill and Word Problem Practice.*

Practice and Problem Solving

Ⓐ **Practice by Example**

Examples 1 and 2
(page 27)

GO for Help

Solve each inequality. Graph the solution.
1–10. See margin p. 28 for graphs.
11-12. See back of book for graphs.

1. $-12 \geq 24x$ $x \leq -\frac{1}{2}$
2. $-7k < 63$ $k > -9$
3. $8a - 15 > 73$ $a > 11$
4. $57 - 4t \geq 13$ $t \leq 11$
5. $-18 - 5y \geq 52$ $y \leq -14$
6. $14 - 4y \geq 38$ $y \leq -6$
7. $4(x + 3) \leq 44$ $x \leq 8$
8. $2(m - 3) + 7 < 21$ $m < 10$
9. $4(n - 2) - 6 > 18$ $n > 8$
10. $9(x + 2) > 9(x - 3)$
All real numbers are solutions.
11. $6x - 13 < 6(x - 2)$
All real numbers are solutions.
12. $-6(2x - 10) + 12x \leq 180$
All real numbers are solutions.
13. $-7(3x - 7) + 21x \geq 50$
no solutions

Example 3
(page 28)

Solve each problem by writing an inequality.

14. The length of a picture frame is 3 in. greater than the width. The perimeter is less than 52 in. Describe the dimensions of the frame. **The width is less than 11.5 in., and the length is 3 in. greater than the width.**
15. The lengths of the sides of a triangle are in the ratio 5 : 6 : 7. Describe the length of the longest side if the perimeter is less than 54 cm.
The longest side is less than 21 cm.
16. Find the lesser of two consecutive integers with a sum greater than 16.
The smaller number is an integer greater than or equal to 8.
17. The cost of a field trip is $220 plus $7 per student. If the school can spend at most $500, how many students can go on the field trip? **40 students**

Example 4
(page 28)

Solve each compound inequality. Graph the solution.
18–21. See margin for graphs.

18. $2x > -10$ and $9x < 18$ $-5 < x < 2$
19. $3x \geq -12$ and $8x \leq 16$ $-4 \leq x \leq 2$
20. $6x \geq -24$ and $9x < 54$ $-4 \leq x < 6$
21. $7x > -35$ and $5x \leq 30$ $-5 < x \leq 6$

Lesson 1-4 Solving Inequalities   **29**

3. Practice

Assignment Guide

1 A B 1-17, 29-35, 38-40

2 A B 18-28, 36-37, 41-50
C Challenge   51-55

Test Prep   56-61
Mixed Review   62-69

Homework Quick Check
To check students' understanding of key skills and concepts, go over Exercises 17, 27, 35, 37, 38.

Differentiated Instruction Resources

18.
19.

20.
21.

4. Assess & Reteach

PowerPoint

Lesson Quiz

1. Solve $-2(x - 3) \geq 4$. Graph the solution. $x \leq 1$

2. Solve $-5(4 - x) < 5x$. Graph the solution. **all real numbers**

3. Graph the solution of $3x + 4 \geq 1$ and $-2x + 7 \geq 5$.

4. A copper wire is to have a length of 16 cm with a tolerance of ± 0.02 cm. How much must be trimmed from a wire that is 18 cm long for it to meet specifications? **at least 1.98 cm and no more than 2.02 cm**

Alternative Assessment

Students work in pairs. They use masking tape to create a number line from -10 to 10 on a desk. Each student places his or her pencil above the number line, using the tip of the pencil as an arrowhead, indicating a single inequality such as $x \geq 3$. Pencils can point in the same or opposite direction and may or may not have an overlapping region. Each group switches stations and writes down two compound inequalities, one inequality assuming that the pencils represent a conjunction and the other assuming a disjunction. Students graph both inequalities and create problems that result in the solution sets represented by the graphs. Students discuss the results.

Example 5
(page 28)

Solve each compound inequality. Graph the solution. See margin for graphs.

22. $4x < 16$ or $12x > 144$ $x < 4$ or $x > 12$ 23. $3x \geq 3$ or $9x < 54$
All real numbers are solutions.

24. $8x > -32$ or $-6x \leq 48$ $x \geq -8$ 25. $9x \leq -27$ or $4x \geq 36$
$x \leq -3$ or $x \geq 9$

Example 6
(page 29)

Solve each problem by writing a compound inequality.

26. A baker needs between 40 lb and 50 lb of a flour-sugar mixture that contains ten times as much flour as sugar. What are the possible weights of flour the baker can use? **between about 36.4 lb and 45.5 lb flour**

27. Between 15,000 yd³ and 16,000 yd³ of earth must be trucked away from a construction site. The trucks can remove 1000 yd³ per day, and 10,500 yd³ has already been removed. How many days are needed? **between $4\frac{1}{2}$ and $5\frac{1}{2}$ days**

28. By how much should a machinist decrease the length of a rod that is 4.78 cm long if the length must be within 0.02 cm of 4.5 cm?
between 0.26 cm and 0.30 cm

B Apply Your Skills

Solve each inequality. Graph the solution. See margin for graphs.

29. $2 - 3z \geq 7(8 - 2z) + 12$ $z \geq 6$ 30. $17 - 2y \leq 5(7 - 3y) - 15$ $y \leq \frac{3}{13}$

31. $\frac{2}{3}(x - 12) \leq x + 8$ $x \geq -48$ 32. $\frac{3}{5}(x - 12) > x - 24$ $x < 42$

33. $3[4x - (2x - 7)] < 2(3x - 5)$
no solutions 34. $6[5y - (3y - 1)] \geq 4(3y - 7)$
All real numbers are solutions.

35. **Writing** Write a problem that can be solved using the inequality $x + 0.5x \leq 60$.
See margin p. 31.

GO for Help

For a guide to solving Exercise 36, see page 32.

36. **Geometry** The sum of the lengths of any two sides of a triangle is greater than the length of the third side. In $\triangle ABC$, $BC = 4$ and $AC = 8 - AB$. What can you conclude about AB? $2 < AB < 6$

37. **a. Error Analysis** Suppose a classmate writes $y \leq 20$ as the solution of $\frac{1}{2}(y - 16) \geq y + 2$. Prove that your classmate's answer is wrong by checking a number that is less than 20. Choose a number that makes the computation easy.
b. Solve $\frac{1}{2}(y - 16) \geq y + 2$. **a. See margin p. 31.**
b. $y \leq -20$

38. **Construction** A contractor estimated that her expenses for a construction project would be between \$700,000 and \$750,000. She has already spent \$496,000. How much more can she spend and remain within her estimate?
between \$204,000 and \$254,000

Real-World Connection

Careers To bid on a job, a construction contractor must consider all the costs of running a business as well as the costs of materials and labor.

Justifying Steps **Justify each step by identifying the property used.**

39. $3x \leq 4(x - 1) - 8$
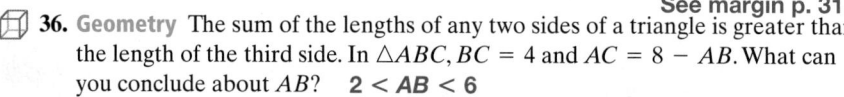

40. $\frac{1}{2}(y + 3) > \frac{1}{3}(4 - y)$ **Mult. Prop.**

Solve each compound inequality. Graph the solutions.
41–49. See margin p. 31 for graphs.

41. $-6 < 2x - 4 < 12$ $-1 < x < 8$ 42. $11 < 3y + 2 < 20$ $3 < y < 6$

43. $-18 > 4x - 3 > -15$ **no solutions** 44. $36 \geq 1 - 5z > -21$ $-7 \leq z < 4\frac{2}{5}$

45. $5a - 4 > 16$ or $3a + 2 < 17$
All real numbers are solutions. 46. $6b + 3 < 15$ or $4b - 2 > 18$
$b < 2$ or $b > 5$

47. $6c \leq 18$ or $-5c \leq 15$
All real numbers are solutions. 48. $8d < -64$ and $5d > 25$
no solutions

49. $4x \leq 12$ or $-7x \leq 21$
All real numbers are solutions. 50. $15x > 30$ and $18x < -36$
no solutions

pages 29–31 Exercises

22.

23.

24.

25.

29.

30.

31.

32.

C Challenge

Visit: PHSchool.com
Web Code: age-0104

51. Answers may vary.
Sample: $2x - 7 \geq -11$

53. Answers may vary.
Sample: $-9 < 5x + 1 < 6$

54. Answers may vary.
Sample: $2x + 4 \leq 0$ or $-3x - 3 \leq 0$

Open-Ended **Write an inequality with a solution that matches the graph. At least two steps should be needed to solve your inequality. Answers may vary.**

Sample: $-3x + 1 > 4$

51. [number line: $-3\ -2\ -1\ 0\ 1\ 2\ 3$]

52. [number line: $-3\ -2\ -1\ 0\ 1\ 2\ 3$]

53. [number line: $-3\ -2\ -1\ 0\ 1\ 2\ 3$]

54. [number line: $-3\ -2\ -1\ 0\ 1\ 2\ 3$]

55. Critical Thinking Consider the compound inequality $x < 8$ and $x > a$.
 a. Are there any values of a such that all real numbers are solutions of the compound inequality? If so, what are they? **no**
 b. Are there any values of a such that no real numbers are solutions of the compound inequality? If so, what are they? **yes; values of a that are 8 or greater**
 c. Repeat parts (a) and (b) for the compound inequality $x < 8$ or $x > a$.
  a. yes; values of a that are less than 8
  b. no

Test Prep

Multiple Choice

56. Which of the following statements are true? **C**
 I. $-(-6) = 6$ and $-(-4) > -4$
 II. $-(-4) < 4$ or $-10 > 10 - 10$
 III. $5 + 6 = 11$ or $9 - 2 = 11$
 IV. $17 > 2$ or $6 < 9$

 A. I and II only
 B. I, II, and III only
 C. I, III, and IV only
 D. III and IV only

57. What is the solution of the inequality $8 - 3x < -3(1 + x) + 1$? **G**
 F. all real numbers **G.** no real numbers **H.** $x > \frac{2}{3}$ **J.** $x < -\frac{11}{6}$

58. What is the solution of the compound inequality $2 < 2(x + 4) < 18$? **C**
 A. all real numbers
 B. no real numbers
 C. $-3 < x < 5$
 D. $-4 < x < 5$

59. What is the solution of the compound inequality $\frac{x}{2} - 4 > 0$ or $\frac{x}{2} + 1 < 0$? **J**
 F. all real numbers
 G. no real numbers
 H. $x > 6$ or $x < 0$
 J. $x > 8$ or $x_y < -2$

Short Response

60. What is the maximum number of 3- to 5-min songs that fill a 90-min CD? What is the minimum number? Explain your reasoning. **See margin.**

Extended Response

61. Fill each box with the word *and* or *or*, so that the solution of one compound inequality is *all real numbers* and the solution of the other is *no real numbers*. Justify each step of your solution. **See back of book.**

$x + 5 > 0$ ▢ $x - 3 < 0$ $x + 5 < 0$ ▢ $x + 5 > 0$

Mixed Review

Lesson 1-3

Solve each equation. Check your answers.

62. $7x - 6(11 - 2x) = 10$ **4**
63. $10x - 7 = 2(13 + 5x)$ **no solution**
64. $4y - \frac{1}{10} = 3y + \frac{4}{5}$ **$\frac{9}{10}$**
65. $0.4x + 1.18 = -3.1(2 - 0.01x)$ **−20**

Lesson 1-2

Simplify each expression.

66. $(2a - 4) + (5a + 9)$ **$7a + 5$**
67. $3(x + 3y) - 5(x - y)$ **$-2x + 14y$**
68. $\frac{1}{3}(b + 12) - \frac{1}{4}(b + 12)$ **$\frac{1}{12}b + 1$**
69. $0.4(k - 0.1) + 0.5(3.3 - k)$
  $1.61 - 0.1k$

---

34. [number line: $-4\ -3\ -2\ -1\ 0\ 1\ 2\ 3\ 4$]

35. $x + 0.5x \leq 60$; answers may vary.
Sample: Mario has a coin collection that consists of dimes and nickels. There are half as many dimes as nickels. There are no more than 60 coins in the collection. Describe the collection.

37a. 0 makes $y \leq 20$ true, but it does not make $\frac{1}{2}(y - 16) \geq y + 2$ true.

41. [number line: $-3\ -2\ -1\ 0\ 1\ 2\ 3\ 4\ 5\ 6\ 7\ 8\ 9$]

42. [number line: $-1\ 0\ 1\ 2\ 3\ 4\ 5\ 6\ 7\ 8$]

Resources
For additional practice with a variety of test item formats:
• Standardized Test Prep, p. 51
• Test-Taking Strategies, p. 46
• Test-Taking Strategies with Transparencies

44.
[number line: $-8\ -6\ -4\ -2\ 0\ 2\ 4\ 6$]

45.
[number line: $-5\ -4\ -3\ -2\ -1\ 0\ 1\ 2\ 3\ 4\ 5$]

46.
[number line: $-1\ 0\ 1\ 2\ 3\ 4\ 5\ 6\ 7\ 8\ 9$]

47.
[number line: $-4\ -3\ -2\ -1\ 0\ 1\ 2\ 3\ 4$]

49.
[number line: $-4\ -3\ -2\ -1\ 0\ 1\ 2\ 3\ 4$]

60. [2] The maximum number of songs can be recorded when the songs are short, so the maximum number of songs is
$$\frac{90 \text{ min}}{3 \text{ min per song}} = 30$$
songs; the minimum number of songs can be recorded when the songs are long, so the minimum number of songs is
$$\frac{90 \text{ min}}{5 \text{ min per song}} = 18$$
songs.

[1] provides 30 and 18 but not the explanation

31

Understanding Math Problems

Guided Problem Solving

Guided Instruction

This feature models the thinking and algebraic manipulations involved in solving a word problem that has multiple solution steps.

Teaching Tip

Remind students to read the problem at least two times to understand what is given and what is being asked. Careful reading is the first step in solving a word problem and students should expect to read a problem a few times.

Visual Learners

Have students draw and label $\triangle ABC$ with the given information. Emphasize that $\triangle ABC$ may not be drawn accurately because only one side, $BC = 4$, is given. Nevertheless, students can use their drawing to visualize the first statement: the sum of the lengths of any two sides of a triangle is greater than the length of the third side. You may want to restate this fact as the shortest distance between two points is a straight line; so the sum of the lengths of any two sides of a triangle is greater than the third side, or straight line path.

Exercise

Encourage students to draw and label a triangle for each exercise. Students should use their drawings to verify that each solution makes sense.

Understanding Math Problems Read the problem below. Then let Malik's thinking guide you through the solution. Check your understanding with the exercises at the bottom of the page.

Geometry The sum of the lengths of any two sides of a triangle is greater than the length of the third side. In $\triangle ABC$, $BC = 4$ and $AC = 8 - AB$. What can you conclude about AB?

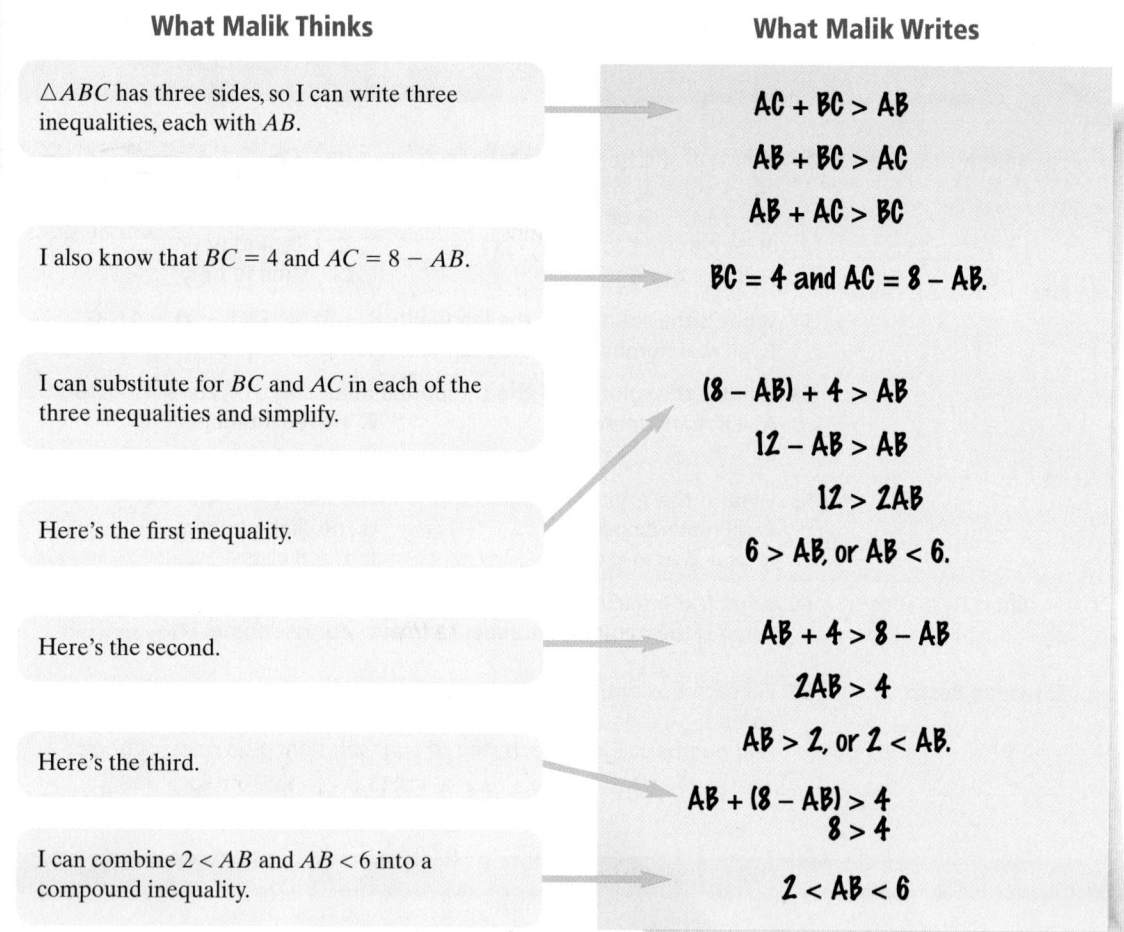

What Malik Thinks	What Malik Writes
$\triangle ABC$ has three sides, so I can write three inequalities, each with AB.	$AC + BC > AB$ $AB + BC > AC$ $AB + AC > BC$
I also know that $BC = 4$ and $AC = 8 - AB$.	$BC = 4$ and $AC = 8 - AB$.
I can substitute for BC and AC in each of the three inequalities and simplify.	$(8 - AB) + 4 > AB$ $12 - AB > AB$ $12 > 2AB$ $6 > AB$, or $AB < 6$.
Here's the first inequality.	
Here's the second.	$AB + 4 > 8 - AB$ $2AB > 4$ $AB > 2$, or $2 < AB$.
Here's the third.	$AB + (8 - AB) > 4$ $8 > 4$
I can combine $2 < AB$ and $AB < 6$ into a compound inequality.	$2 < AB < 6$

EXERCISES

The sum of the lengths of any two sides of a triangle is greater than the length of the third side. What can you conclude about AC in $\triangle ABC$?

1. $AB = 6$; $BC + 2AC = 18$ $4 < AC < 8$

2. $BC = 7$; $AC = 2 + AB$ $AC > 4.5$

3. $AB + AC = 5$; $AC + BC = 4$ $1 < AC < 3$

4. $BC + AC = 22$; $AB + BC = 12$ $10\frac{2}{3} < AC < 12$

Absolute Value Equations and Inequalities

1-5

What You'll Learn

- To solve absolute value equations
- To solve absolute value inequalities

. . . And Why

To write specifications for a basketball, as in Example 6

 Check Skills You'll Need

 GO for Help   Lessons 1-3 and 1-4

Solve each equation.

1. $5(x - 6) = 40$ **14**   **2.** $5b = 2(3b - 8)$ **16**   **3.** $2y + 6y = 15 - 2y + 8$
  2.3

Solve each inequality.

4. $4x + 8 > 20$ $x > 3$ **5.** $3a - 2 \geq a + 6$ $a \geq 4$ **6.** $4(t - 1) < 3t + 5$ $t < 9$

 New Vocabulary   • absolute value   • extraneous solution   • tolerance

1. Plan

Objectives

1 To solve absolute value equations
2 To solve absolute value inequalities

Examples

1 Solving Absolute Value Equations
2 Solving Multi-Step Absolute Value Equations
3 Checking for Extraneous Solutions
4 Solving Absolute Value Inequalities, $|A| \geq b$
5 Solving Absolute Value Inequalities, $|A| < b$
6 Real-World Connection

---

1 Absolute Value Equations

The **absolute value** of a number is its distance from zero on the number line and distance is nonnegative. So the absolute value of a negative number such as -5 is its opposite, $-(-5)$. For $x < 0$, $|x| = -x$.

Key Concepts

Definition	Algebraic Definition of Absolute Value
• If $x \geq 0$, then $|x| = x$.	• If $x < 0$, then $|x| = -x$.

An absolute value equation such as $|2y - 4| = 12$ has two solutions, since the expression $2y - 4$ can equal 12 or -12.

1 EXAMPLE   Solving Absolute Value Equations

Solve $|2y - 4| = 12$.

$|2y - 4| = 12$

$2y - 4 = 12$ or $2y - 4 = -12$ The value of $2y - 4$ can be 12 or -12 since $|12|$ and $|-12|$ both equal 12.

$2y = 16$ $2y = -8$ Add 4 to each side of both equations.

$y = 8$ or $y = -4$ Divide each side of both equations by 2.

Check $|2y - 4| = 12$

$|2(8) - 4| \stackrel{?}{=} 12$ $|2(-4) - 4| \stackrel{?}{=} 12$

$|12| = 12 \checkmark$ $|-12| = 12 \checkmark$

 Quick Check   **1** Solve $|3x + 2| = 7$. Check your answer. $\frac{5}{3}, -3$

You will find it easier to solve a multi-step absolute value equation if you first isolate the absolute value expression on one side of the equation.

Lesson 1-5   Absolute Value Equations and Inequalities   **33**

Math Background

To solve an equation that involves absolute value, it is possible to rewrite the given equation as two equations by first applying the algebraic definition of absolute value. However, first isolating the absolute value expression on one side of the equal sign and understanding that there may be two solutions leads to an approach that involves less algebraic manipulation.

More Math Background: p. 2D

Lesson Planning and Resources

See p. 2E for a list of the resources that support this lesson.

Check Skills You'll Need
For intervention, direct students to:
Solving Equations
Lesson 1-3: Examples 1, 2
  Extra Skills and Word Problems Practice, Ch. 1
Solving Inequalities
Lesson 1-4: Examples 1, 2
  Extra Skills and Word Problems Practice, Ch. 1

Differentiated Instruction   Solutions for All Learners

Special Needs **L1**
Apply the idea from the Error Prevention in Example 4 to $|2x + 6| < 8$ in Example 5 to help students understand the compound inequality.

learning style: verbal

Below Level **L2**
Draw a number line on the board, using inches or centimeters to mark the numbers. Measure the distance of positive and negative numbers from zero.

learning style: visual

Guided Instruction

1 EXAMPLE Auditory Learners

Help students understand that $|a - b|$ represents the distance between a and b, where a and b are real numbers. Then, tell students that $|2y - 4| = 12$ can be read as "the distance between twice a number and 4 is 12." Help students use this statement to draw a number line and determine the solutions of the equation.

2 EXAMPLE Math Tip

It will be helpful to students to stress that $4w - 1$ can be 5 or -5.

3 EXAMPLE Teaching Tip

Point out that this example makes clear why it is always a good idea to check possible solutions to see whether they really *are* solutions.

PowerPoint

Additional Examples

1 Solve $|15 - 3x| = 6$. **3, 7**

2 Solve $4 - 2|x + 9| = -5$.
$-13.5, -4.5$

3 Solve $|3x - 4| = -4x - 1$. **-5**

---

2 EXAMPLE Solving Multi-Step Absolute Value Equations

Solve $3|4w - 1| - 5 = 10$.

$$3|4w - 1| - 5 = 10$$
$$3|4w - 1| = 15 \qquad \text{Add 5 to each side.}$$
$$|4w - 1| = 5 \qquad \text{Divide each side by 3.}$$

$4w - 1 = 5 \quad$ or $\quad 4w - 1 = -5 \qquad$ Rewrite as two equations.

$4w = 6 \qquad\qquad 4w = -4 \qquad$ Add 1 to each side of both equations.

$w = \dfrac{3}{2} \quad$ or $\quad w = -1 \qquad$ Divide each side of both equations by 4.

Check $\quad 3|4w - 1| - 5 = 10 \qquad\qquad 3|4w - 1| - 5 = 10$

$3|4(\tfrac{3}{2}) - 1| - 5 \stackrel{?}{=} 10 \qquad 3|4(-1) - 1| - 5 \stackrel{?}{=} 10$

$3|5| - 5 \stackrel{?}{=} 10 \qquad\qquad 3|-5| - 5 \stackrel{?}{=} 10$

$10 = 10 ✓ \qquad\qquad 10 = 10 ✓$

✓ Quick Check **2** Solve $2|3x - 1| + 5 = 33$. Check your answer. $-\dfrac{13}{3}, 5$

The equation $|2x + 7| = -2$ has no solution because $|2x + 7|$ cannot be negative. It is important to check possible solutions in the original equation. One or more may be extraneous solutions.

Key Concepts

Definition	Extraneous Solution

An **extraneous solution** is a solution of an equation derived from an original equation that is not a solution of the original equation.

Vocabulary Tip

Extraneous is pronounced ek-STRAY-nee-us.

3 EXAMPLE Checking for Extraneous Solutions

Solve $|2x + 5| = 3x + 4$.

$$|2x + 5| = 3x + 4$$

$2x + 5 = 3x + 4 \quad$ or $\quad 2x + 5 = -(3x + 4) \qquad$ Rewrite as two equations.

$-x = -1 \qquad\qquad 2x + 5 = -3x - 4 \qquad$ Solve each equation.

$x = 1 \qquad\qquad\qquad 5x = -9$

$x = 1 \qquad$ or $\qquad x = -\dfrac{9}{5}$

Check $\quad |2x + 5| = 3x + 4 \qquad\qquad |2x + 5| = 3x + 4$

$|2(1) + 5| \stackrel{?}{=} 3(1) + 4 \qquad |2(-\tfrac{9}{5}) + 5| \stackrel{?}{=} 3(-\tfrac{9}{5}) + 4$

$|7| \stackrel{?}{=} 7 \qquad\qquad\qquad |\tfrac{7}{5}| \stackrel{?}{=} -\tfrac{7}{5}$

$7 = 7 ✓ \qquad\qquad\qquad \tfrac{7}{5} \neq -\tfrac{7}{5}$

The only solution is 1. $-\dfrac{9}{5}$ is an extraneous solution.

✓ Quick Check **3** **a.** Solve $|2x + 3| = 3x + 2$. Check for extraneous solutions. **1**
b. Solve $|x| = x - 1$. Check for extraneous solutions. **no solutions**
c. Critical Thinking Find a value for a such that $|x| = x + a$ has exactly one solution. **Answers may vary: any positive real number**

Differentiated Instruction Solutions for All Learners

Advanced Learners L4
All sports use specifications such as diameter of carburetor restrictor plates or width of playing field. Find and write such data as an absolute value inequality.

learning style: verbal

English Language Learners ELL
Help students with the pronunciation and the meaning of *extraneous*. As an example of its common meaning, discuss scenes that are extraneous to the main action of a play or a television show.

learning style: verbal

If $|x| > 3$, then x is more than 3 units from 0 on the number line.

$$\overset{\longleftrightarrow}{\underset{-4\ -3\ -2\ -1\ \ 0\ \ 1\ \ 2\ \ 3\ \ 4}{}}$$

This is also the graph of $x < -3$ or $x > 3$. So the absolute value inequality $|x| > 3$ can be rewritten as the compound inequality $x < -3$ or $x > 3$.

4 **EXAMPLE**   **Solving Absolute Value Inequalities, $|A| \geq b$**

Solve $|3x + 6| \geq 12$. Graph the solution.

$|3x + 6| \geq 12$

$3x + 6 \leq -12$ or $3x + 6 \geq 12$ **Rewrite as a compound inequality.**

$\qquad 3x \leq -18$ $\quad\bigg|\quad$ $3x \geq 6$

$\qquad\quad x \leq -6$ or $\qquad x \geq 2$

$$\overset{\longleftrightarrow}{\underset{-7\ -6\ -5\ -4\ -3\ -2\ -1\ \ 0\ \ 1\ \ 2\ \ 3}{\bullet\!\!-\!\!-\!\!-\!\!-\!\!-\!\!-\!\!-\!\!-\!\!-\!\!-\!\!\bullet}}$$ **Graph the solution.**

 Quick Check   **4** Solve $|2x - 3| > 7$. Graph the solution. $x < -2$ or $x > 5$

$$\overset{\longleftrightarrow}{\underset{-3\ -2\ -1\ \ 0\ \ 1\ \ 2\ \ 3\ \ 4\ \ 5\ \ 6\ \ 7}{\oplus\qquad\qquad\qquad\oplus}}$$

If $|x| < 2$, then x is less than 2 units from 0 on the number line.

$$\overset{\longleftrightarrow}{\underset{-3\ -2\ -1\ \ 0\ \ 1\ \ 2\ \ 3}{\oplus\qquad\qquad\oplus}}$$

This is also the graph of $-2 < x < 2$. So the absolute value inequality $|x| < 2$ can be written as the compound inequality $-2 < x < 2$.

Key Concepts

Properties	Absolute Value Inequalities
Let k represent a positive real number.	
$|x| \geq k$ is equivalent to	$x \leq -k$ or $x \geq k$.
$|x| \leq k$ is equivalent to	$-k \leq x \leq k$.

When an absolute value is combined with other operations, first isolate the absolute value expression on one side of the inequality.

5 **EXAMPLE**   **Solving Absolute Value Inequalities, $|A| < b$**

Solve $3|2x + 6| - 9 < 15$. Graph the solution.

$3|2x + 6| - 9 < 15$

$\qquad 3|2x + 6| < 24$ **Isolate the absolute value expression. Add 9 to each side.**

$\qquad\quad |2x + 6| < 8$ **Divide each side by 3.**

$\quad -8 < 2x + 6 < 8$ **Rewrite as a compound inequality.**

$\quad -14 < \quad 2x \quad < 2$ **Solve for x.**

$\quad\ -7 < \quad x \quad < 1$

$$\overset{\longleftrightarrow}{\underset{-8\ -7\ -6\ -5\ -4\ -3\ -2\ -1\ \ 0\ \ 1\ \ 2}{\oplus\qquad\qquad\qquad\qquad\oplus}}$$

GO for Help

To review the properties of inequalities, go to p. 26.

Quick Check   **5** Solve $|5z + 3| - 7 < 34$. Graph the solution. $-8\frac{4}{5} < z < 7\frac{3}{5}$
   See margin for graph.

5. $$\overset{\longleftrightarrow}{\underset{-12\ -10\ -8\ -6\ -4\ -2\ \ 0\ \ 2\ \ 4\ \ 6\ \ 8\ \ 10}{\circ\qquad\qquad\qquad\qquad\qquad\circ}}$$

Guided Instruction

4 **EXAMPLE**   **Error Prevention**

Encourage students to check that the solutions indicated by their graphs are reasonable. Have students pick a few points in the solution sets and substitute them into the original equation to make certain that the resulting statements are true.

6 **EXAMPLE**   **Teaching Tip**

You may find it helpful to review Example 6 from Lesson 1-4.

PowerPoint

Additional Examples

4 Solve $|2x - 5| > 3$. Graph the solution. $x < 1$ or $x > 4$

$$\overset{\longleftrightarrow}{\underset{-2\ -1\ \ 0\ \ 1\ \ 2\ \ 3\ \ 4\ \ 5\ \ 6}{\oplus\qquad\qquad\oplus}}$$

5 Solve $-2|x + 1| + 5 \geq -3$. Graph the solution. $-5 \leq x \leq 3$

$$\overset{\longleftrightarrow}{\underset{-6\ -5\ -4\ -3\ -2\ -1\ \ 0\ \ 1\ \ 2\ \ 3\ \ 4}{\bullet\qquad\qquad\qquad\bullet}}$$

6 The area A in square inches of a square photo is required to satisfy $8.5 \leq A \leq 8.9$. Write this requirement as an absolute value inequality. $|A - 8.7| \leq 0.2$

Resources
• Daily Notetaking Guide 1-5 **L3**

Closure

Have students describe the procedure used to solve an absolute value equation or inequality. Isolate the absolute value expression on one side of the equation or inequality. Next, rewrite the result as two equations or as a compound inequality. Then, solve.

Assignment Guide

1 A B 1-15, 34-43

2 A B 16-33, 44-60

C Challenge   61-66

Test Prep   67-72
Mixed Review   73-83

Connection to Meteorology

Exercise 54 Meteorologists use experimental probability based on previous weather patterns to make forecasts. Students will learn about experimental probability in Lesson 1-6.

Diversity

Exercise 55 Students who are not familiar with sports, may not realize that there are regulations that govern the size of basketballs for men and women. Discuss the regulations and the reasons behind them.

You can use absolute value inequalities and compound inequalities to specify allowable ranges in measurements. The difference between a desired measurement and its maximum and minimum allowable values is the tolerance. The **tolerance** equals one half of the difference between the maximum and the minimum values.

For example, if a manufacturing specification calls for a dimension d of 10 cm with a tolerance of 0.1 cm, then the allowable difference between d and 10 is less than or equal to 0.1. This specification can be expressed in the following ways.

$$|d - 10| \le 0.1 \qquad \text{absolute value inequality}$$

$$d - 10 \le 0.1 \text{ and } d - 10 \ge -0.1 \quad \text{equivalent compound inequality}$$

$$-0.1 \le d - 10 \le 0.1 \qquad \text{equivalent compound inequality}$$

$$9.9 \le d \le 10.1 \qquad \text{simplified compound inequality}$$

6 **EXAMPLE** Real-World Connection

Basketball The specification for the circumference C in inches of a basketball for men is $29.5 \le C \le 30$. Write the specification as an absolute value inequality.

$$\frac{30 - 29.5}{2} = \frac{0.5}{2} = 0.25 \qquad \text{Find the tolerance.}$$

$$\frac{29.5 + 30}{2} = 29.75 \qquad \text{Find the average of the maximum and minimum values.}$$

$$-0.25 \le C - 29.75 \le 0.25 \qquad \text{Write an inequality.}$$

$$|C - 29.75| \le 0.25 \qquad \text{Rewrite as an absolute value inequality.}$$

Quick Check **6** The specification for the circumference C in inches of a basketball for junior high school is $27.75 \le C \le 28.5$. Write the specification as an absolute value inequality. **$|C - 28.125| \le 0.375$**

EXERCISES

For more exercises, see *Extra Skill and Word Problem Practice*.

Practice and Problem Solving

A Practice by Example

Examples 1 and 2
(pages 33, 34)

 GO for Help

Solve each equation. Check your answers.

1. $|3x| = 18$ **−6, 6**   **2.** $|-4x| = 32$ **−8, 8**   **3.** $|x - 3| = 9$ **−6, 12**

4. $2|3x - 2| = 14$ **3, $-\frac{5}{3}$**   **5.** $|3x + 4| = -3$ **no solution**   **6.** $|2x - 3| = -1$ **no solution**

7. $|x + 4| + 3 = 17$ **−18, 10**   **8.** $|y - 5| - 2 = 10$ **−7, 17**   **9.** $|4 - z| - 10 = 1$ **−7, 15**

Example 3
(page 34)

Solve each equation. Check for extraneous solutions.

10. $|x - 1| = 5x + 10$ **$-\frac{3}{2}$**   **11.** $|2z - 3| = 4z - 1$ **$\frac{2}{3}$**   **12.** $|3x + 5| = 5x + 2$ **$\frac{3}{2}$**

13. $|2y - 4| = 12$ **−4, 8**   **14.** $3|4w - 1| - 5 = 10$ **$-1, \frac{3}{2}$**   **15.** $|2x + 5| = 3x + 4$ **1**

Example 4
(page 35)

Solve each inequality. Graph the solution. 16–23. See margin pp. 36–37.

16. $|x + 3| > 9$ **17.** $|x - 5| \ge 8$ **18.** $|y - 3| \ge 12$

19. $|2x + 1| \ge -9$ **20.** $3|2x - 1| \ge 21$ **21.** $|3z| - 4 > 8$
                                                        24–27. See back of book.

Example 5
(page 35)

22. $3|y - 9| < 27$ **23.** $|6y - 2| + 4 < 22$ **24.** $|3x - 6| + 3 < 15$

25. $\frac{1}{4}|x - 3| + 2 < 1$ **26.** $4|2w + 3| - 7 \le 9$ **27.** $3|5t - 1| + 9 \le 23$

pages 36–38   Exercises

16. $x < -12$ or $x > 6$

−16 −14 −12 −10 −8 −6 −4 −2 0 2 4 6 8

17. $x \le -3$ or $x \ge 13$

−6 −4 −2 0 2 4 6 8 10 12 14 16 18

18. $y \le -9$ or $y \ge 15$

−15 −12 −9 −6 −3 0 3 6 9 12 15 18 21

19. All real numbers are solutions.

Example 6
(page 36)

Write each specification as an absolute value inequality.

28. $1.3 \leq h \leq 1.5$
$|h - 1.4| \leq 0.1$

29. $50 \leq k \leq 51$
$|k - 50.5| \leq 0.5$

30. $27.25 \leq C \leq 27.75$
$|C - 27.5| \leq 0.25$

31. $50 \leq b \leq 55$
$|b - 52.5| \leq 2.5$

32. $1200 \leq m \leq 1300$
$|m - 1250| \leq 50$

33. $0.1187 \leq d \leq 0.1190$
$|d - 0.11885| \leq 0.00015$

B Apply Your Skills

Solve each equation.

GPS **34.** $-|4 - 8b| = 12$ **no solutions**

35. $4|3x + 4| = 4x + 8$ $-\frac{3}{2}, -1$

36. $|3x - 1| + 10 = 25$ $-\frac{14}{3}, \frac{16}{3}$

37. $\frac{1}{2}|3c + 5| = 6c + 4$ $-\frac{1}{3}$

38. $5|6 - 5x| = 15x - 35$ **no solutions**

39. $7|8 - 3h| = 21h - 49$ $\frac{5}{2}$

40. $2|3x - 7| = 10x - 8$ $\frac{11}{8}$

41. $6|2x + 5| = 6x + 24$ $-1, -3$

42. $\frac{1}{4}|4x + 7| = 8x + 16$ $-\frac{71}{36}$

43. $\frac{2}{3}|3x - 6| = 4(x - 2)$ **2**

Homework Video Tutor
Visit: PHSchool.com
Web Code: age-0105

Solve each inequality. Graph the solutions. **44–50. See back of book.**

44. $|3x - 4| + 5 \leq 27$

45. $|2x + 3| - 6 \geq 7$

46. $-2|x + 4| < 22$

47. $2|4t - 1| + 6 > 20$

48. $|3z + 15| \geq 0$

49. $|-2x + 1| > 2$

50. $\frac{1}{9}|5x - 3| - 3 \geq 2$

51. $\frac{1}{11}|2x - 4| + 10 \leq 11$

52. $\left|\frac{x - 3}{2}\right| + 2 < 6$

53. $\left|\frac{x + 5}{3}\right| - 3 > 6$

51–54. See margin p. 38.

 54. Meteorology Write a compound inequality and an absolute value inequality for the snowfall in regions 1, 2, 3, and 4 in the figure at the left.

55. Multiple Choice The circumference of a basketball for college women must be from 28.5 in. to 29.0 in. Which absolute value inequality best represents the circumference of the ball? **C**

Ⓐ $|C - 0.25| \geq 28.5$

Ⓑ $|C - 0.25| \leq 29.0$

Ⓒ $|C - 28.75| \leq 0.25$

Ⓓ $|C - 28.75| \geq 0.25$

56. Writing Describe the differences in the graphs of $|x| < a$ and $|x| > a$, where a is a positive real number.
See back of book.

57. Open-Ended Write an absolute value inequality for which every real number is a solution. Write an absolute value inequality that has no solution.
Answers may vary. Sample: $|x - 1| \geq 0$; $|x| < -5$

Write an absolute value inequality and a compound inequality for each length x with the given tolerance.

58. a length of 36.80 mm with a tolerance of 0.05 mm
$|x - 36.8| \leq 0.05$; $36.75 \leq x \leq 36.85$

59. a length of 9.55 mm with a tolerance of 0.02 mm
$|x - 9.55| \leq 0.02$; $9.53 \leq x \leq 9.57$

60. a length of 100 yd with a tolerance of 4 in.
x is in inches: $|x - 3600| \leq 4$; $3596 \leq x \leq 3604$.

C Challenge

Solve each equation for x. **61–63. See margin.**

61. $|ax| - b = c$

62. $|cx - d| = ab$

63. $a|bx - c| = d$

Graph each solution. **64–66. See back of book.**

64. $|x| \geq 5$ and $|x| \leq 6$

65. $|x| \geq 6$ or $|x| < 5$

66. $|x - 5| \leq x$

A March Snowfall (inches)

Region 1 ☐ 0 – 0.1
Region 2 ☐ 0.1 – 1
Region 3 ☐ 1 – 3
Region 4 ☐ 3 – 6
Region 5 ☐ 6 – 12
Region 6 ☐ 12 – 18
Region 7 ☐ 18 – 24

Source: Northeast River Forecast Center/NOAA

---

4. Assess & Reteach

PowerPoint
Lesson Quiz

1. Solve $|3x + 1| = 4$. $-\frac{5}{3}, 1$

2. Solve $|-2x + 3| + 7 > 9$.
Graph the solution. $x < \frac{1}{2}$ or $x > \frac{5}{2}$

$\leftarrow\!\!+\!\!+\!\!\ominus\!\!+\!\!+\!\!\ominus\!\!+\!\!+\!\!\rightarrow$
$-3\,{-}2\,{-}1\ 0\ 1\ 2\ 3\ 4\ 5$

3. Solve $|4x - 12| \leq 8$.
$1 \leq x \leq 5$

$\leftarrow\!\!+\!\!+\!\!\bullet\!\!+\!\!+\!\!+\!\!+\!\!\bullet\!\!+\!\!+\!\!\rightarrow$
$-2\,{-}1\ 0\ 1\ 2\ 3\ 4\ 5\ 6$

4. A machinist is to drill a hole with diameter D inches, that satisfies $0.16 \leq D \leq 0.19$. Express the specification using an absolute value inequality. $|D - 0.175| \leq 0.015$

Alternative Assessment

Have students work in pairs. Each student writes two absolute value equations and two absolute value inequalities. Each student then solves his or her partner's equations and inequalities. Then, they check one another's work.

Test Prep

Resources
For additional practice with a variety of test item formats:
• Standardized Test Prep, p. 51
• Test-Taking Strategies, p. 46
• Test-Taking Strategies with Transparencies

61. $-\frac{b + c}{a}, \frac{b + c}{a}, a \neq 0$; no solution, $b + c < 0$

62. $\frac{ab + d}{c}, \frac{-ab + d}{c}, c \neq 0$; no solution, $1 \cdot ab < 0$

63. $\frac{ac + d}{ab}, \frac{ac - d}{ab}, ab \neq 0$; no solution, $\frac{d}{a} < 0$

---

20. $x \leq -3$ or $x \geq 4$

$\leftarrow\!\!+\!\!\bullet\!\!+\!\!+\!\!+\!\!\bullet\!\!+\!\!+\!\!\rightarrow$
$-4\,{-}2\ 0\ 2\ 4\ 6$

21. $z < -4$ or $z > 4$

$\leftarrow\!\!+\!\!\ominus\!\!+\!\!+\!\!+\!\!+\!\!+\!\!\ominus\!\!+\!\!\rightarrow$
$-4 \qquad 4$

22. $0 < y < 18$

$\leftarrow\!\!+\!\!\ominus\!\!+\!\!+\!\!+\!\!+\!\!+\!\!+\!\!+\!\!+\!\!\ominus\!\!+\!\!\rightarrow$
$-2\ 0\ 2\ 4\ 6\ 8\ 10\ 12\ 14\ 16\ 18\ 20$

23. $-2\frac{2}{3} < y < 3\frac{1}{3}$

$\leftarrow\!\!+\!\!\ominus\!\!+\!\!+\!\!+\!\!+\!\!+\!\!\ominus\!\!+\!\!\rightarrow$
$-5\,{-}4\,{-}3\,{-}2\,{-}1\ 0\ 1\ 2\ 3\ 4\ 5\ 6$

pages 36–38 Exercises

51. $-3.5 \le x \le 7.5$

-4 0 4 8

52. $-5 < x < 11$

-8 -4 0 4 8 12

53. $x < -32$ or $x > 22$

-40 -20 0 20

54. Region 1
$0 \le s \le 01$,
$|s - 0.05| \le 0.05$
Region 2
$0.1 \le s \le 1$,
$|s - 0.55| \le 0.45$
Region 3
$1 \le s \le 3, |s - 2| \le 1$
Region 4
$3 \le s \le 6$,
$|s - 4.5| \le 1.5$

71. [2] Integers x such that
$-2 \le x \le 8$
$|x - 3| \le 5$
$-5 \le x - 3 \le 5$
$-2 \le x \le 8$

[1] only includes
$-2 \le x \le 8$ and
does not show work

72. [4] $3|2x - 4| + 5 < 41$
$3|2x - 4| < 36$
Subtr. Prop. of Ineq.
$|2x - 4| < 12$
Div. Prop. of Ineq.
$-12 < 2x - 4 < 12$
Def. of absolute value
$-8 < 2x < 16$
Add. Prop. of Ineq.
$-4 < x < 8$
Div. Prop. of Ineq.

[3] appropriate methods,
but with one
computational error

[2] does not include steps

[1] only includes final
answer of $-4 < x < 8$,
with no steps or
justification of steps

38

Multiple Choice

67. Which number is a solution of $|x - 3| = x - 3$? **D**
  A. -3 B. 0 C. 1 D. 3

68. What is the solution of the inequality $\left|\frac{3-x}{2}\right| < 4$? **F**
  F. $-5 < x < 11$ G. $-11 > x > -5$ H. $5 < x < 11$ J. $11 > x > -1$

69. Which of the following inequalities have the same solutions? **C**
  I. $|5x - 7| \le 8$ II. $-8 \le 5x - 7$ or $5x - 7 \le 8$
  III. $8 \le 5x - 7$ and $5x - 7 \ge -8$ IV. $-8 \le 5x - 7$ and $5x - 7 \le 8$
  A. I and II   B. I and III   C. I and IV   D. I, III, and IV

70. Which number is a solution of $|9 - x| = 9 + x$? **G**
  F. -3 G. 0 H. 3 J. 6

Short Response

71. Find all the integers that are solutions of $|x - 3| \le 5$. Show your work. **See margin.**

Extended Response

72. Solve $3|2x - 4| + 5 < 41$. Justify each step of your solution. **See margin.**

Mixed Review

GO for Help

Lesson 1-4

Solve each inequality. Graph the solution. See margin for graphs.

73. $5y - 10 < 20$ **74.** $-5(4s + 1) < 23$ **75.** $4a + 6 \ge 2a + 14$
  $y < 6$ $s > -\frac{7}{5}$ $a \ge 4$
76. $0.5x + 5 \ge x - 1$ **77.** $3(4x - 1) \ge 2(4 - x)$ **78.** $4(3t + 2) \le 43 + 7t$
  $x \le 12$ $x \ge \frac{11}{14}$ $t \le 7$

Lesson 1-2

Evaluate each expression for the given value.

79. $3|4x - 6| - 2x^2$, for $x = -3$ **36**   **80.** $\frac{5r - r^2}{1 - 4r}$, for $r = 4$ $-\frac{4}{15}$

Lesson 1-1

Name the property of real numbers illustrated by each of the following.

81. $16x + (-16x) = 0$ **82.** 5π is a real number.   **83.** $4(x - 9) = (x - 9)4$
  Inverse Prop. of Add.   **Closure Prop. of Mult.**   **Comm. Prop. of Mult.**

Checkpoint Quiz 2   Lessons 1-4 through 1-5

Solve each inequality. Graph the solution.   1–6. See back of book for graphs.

1. $3x + 10 \le 25$ $x \le 5$ **2.** $8x + 15 > 15x - 24$ $x < 5\frac{4}{7}$

3. $z > -1$ **3.** $5z > 2z - 18$ and $3 - 9z < 12$ **4.** $4w > 1 + 3w$ or $12w + 18 < 11w + 15$

4. $w > 1$ or $w < -3$ **5.** $2|x + 4| \le 22$ $-15 \le x \le 7$ **6.** $|2x| + 8 > 12$ $x < -2$ or $x > 2$

Solve each equation.

7. $7|3 - 2y| = 56$ $-\frac{5}{2}, \frac{11}{2}$ **8.** $\frac{1}{4}|4x + 2| = 1 - 2x$ $\frac{1}{6}$

9. Write and solve an inequality to find three consecutive whole numbers with a sum between 13 and 16. $13 < 3n + 3 < 16, n = 4$

10. Geometry The length of any side of a triangle is less than the sum of the lengths of the other two sides. In $\triangle PQR$, $PR = RQ + 4$ and $RQ < 11$. Write and solve an inequality for PQ. $PR - RQ < PQ < PR + RQ; 4 < PQ < 26$

73.
-2 0 2 4 6 8

74.
-2 -1 0 1

75.
-2 0 2 4 6 8

76.
4 6 8 10 12

77.
-1 0 1 2

78.
-4 0 4 8 12

Probability

What You'll Learn

• To find experimental probabilities

• To find theoretical probabilities

. . . And Why

To find the probabilities of inherited traits, as in Example 4

 Check Skills You'll Need

GO for Help Skills Handbook page 870

Write each number as a percent.

1. $\frac{3}{8}$ **37.5%**   2. $1\frac{5}{6}$ **$183\frac{1}{3}$%**   3. 0.0043 **0.43%**

4. $\frac{1}{400}$ **0.25%**   5. 1.04 **104%**   6. 3 **300%**

◀)) **New Vocabulary** • experimental probability
• simulation • sample space
• theoretical probability

---

1 Experimental Probability

 Hands-On Activity: Experimental Probability

Fold an index card slightly off center, as shown at the left. When you drop the card from a height of several feet, how will it land?
1–5. Check students' work.

1. Drop the card 50 times. Record the number of times the card lands in each position.

2. What percent of the time does the card land on its short side? Find the percents for the other positions.

3. In what position is the card most likely to land? Least likely to land?

4. Suppose that you drop the card another 20 times. Predict how many times it will land in each position.

5. a. Drop the card another 20 times. Record your results.

   b. Compare the results with your prediction from Question 4. Are they close? How could you improve your prediction?

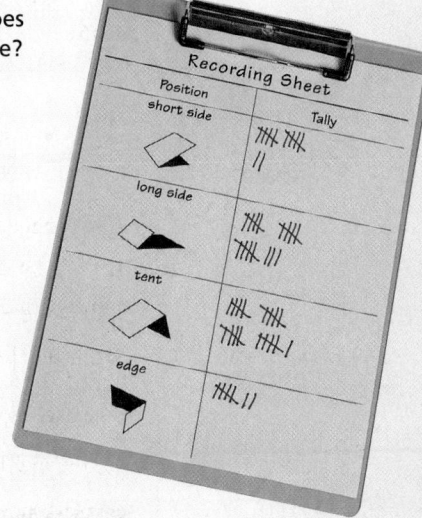

Objectives

1 To find experimental probabilities

2 To find theoretical probabilities

Examples

1 Finding Experimental Probability

2 Using a Simulation

3 Finding Theoretical Probability

4 Real-World Connection

5 Finding Geometric Probability

 Professional Development

Math Background

Experimental probabilities are calculated on the basis of data from experiments, actual or simulated. Given equally likely outcomes, the basis for calculating theoretical probability is being able to determine the number of ways that an event can occur within these outcomes. Comparisons of measures such as length and area are the basis of geometric probability.

More Math Background: p. 2D

Lesson Planning and Resources

See p. 2E for a list of the resources that support this lesson.

 PowerPoint
Bell Ringer Practice

✔ **Check Skills You'll Need**
Percent and Percent Applications
Skills Handbook: p. 870
Example 6

Differentiated Instruction Solutions for All Learners

Special Needs L1	**Below Level** L2
Ask questions such as: *What is the probability you will guess the answer to a true-false question?* **50%** *If there are four answers to a multiple-choice question, what is the probability that you can guess the correct answer?* **25%**	Discuss with students why a 50% chance of rain today and a 50% chance of rain tomorrow does not mean it is certain to rain.
learning style: verbal	learning style: verbal

2. Teach

Guided Instruction

Hands-On Activity
You may want students to work on this Activity with a partner. The results that students obtain may be influenced by a variety of factors, such as how far from the end the card was folded.

① EXAMPLE Diversity

Invite students who are more familiar with other sports, such as cricket, to suggest examples of experimental probabilities related to those sports.

② EXAMPLE Alternative Method

Invite students to suggest other simulations such as spinning a two-section spinner.

Additional Examples

① A player hit the bull's eye on a circular dartboard 8 times out of 50. Find the experimental probability that the player hits the bull's eye. **0.16, or 16%**

② Describe a simulation you could use that involves flipping a coin to find the experimental probability of guessing exactly 2 answers out of 6 correctly on a true-false quiz. **Answers may vary. Sample: Let heads represent a correct answer. Flip the coin 6 times. Record the number of heads. Repeat 100 times. Divide the number of times you got 2 heads by 100.**

Probability measures how likely it is for an event to occur. You can express probabilities as percents (0% through 100%) or as real numbers (0 through 1).

The probability of an impossible event is 0 or 0%. The probability of a certain event, which must happen, is 1 or 100%.

When you gather data from observations, you can calculate an experimental probability. Each observation is called an experiment or a trial.

Key Concepts

Definition	Experimental Probability

experimental probability of event $= P(\text{event})$
$$= \frac{\text{number of times the event occurs}}{\text{number of trials}}$$

① EXAMPLE Finding Experimental Probability

When the University of Texas won college football's national championship in the 2006 Rose Bowl game, its quarterback completed 30 of 40 passes. Find the experimental probability of the quarterback completing a pass.

● $P(\text{completion}) = \frac{30}{40} = 0.75$, or 75%

✓ Quick Check **①** In the same game, the University of Southern California quarterback completed 29 of 40 passes. Find the experimental probability of this player completing a pass.
$\frac{29}{40} = 0.725$, or 72.5%

When actual trials are difficult to conduct, you can find experimental probabilities by using a **simulation,** which is a model of one or more events.

② EXAMPLE Using a Simulation

Suppose you take a true-or-false quiz and guess four answers at random. What is an experimental probability that you will get at least three correct answers?

Step 1 Define how you will do the simulation.
- Generate random numbers on a calculator.
- Since you answer true or false at random, you have a 50% chance of guessing correctly on each question. So let half of the digits represent correct answers. For example, let even digits represent correct answers.
- Since there are four questions, group the random digits in groups of four. List 50 groups to represent taking the test 50 times.

Step 2 Conduct the simulation. Underline groups with at least three even digits.

8767	0447	4672	0872	8315	6495	8778	8634	6243	5756
8958	2295	6246	1520	8491	1214	8495	7450	7068	5798
5584	4142	8990	7101	9949	1991	0625	3347	6158	1612
4792	3973	4563	8888	9895	5466	5612	9428	4065	9518
2096	1117	7578	2776	9142	7787	9594	5969	5858	4068

Step 3 Interpret the simulation. Since 15 of the 50 groups represent at least three correct answers, $P(\text{at least 3 correct}) = \frac{15}{50} = 0.3$.

● This experimental probability of getting at least three correct answers is 30%.

✓ Quick Check **②** What is the experimental probability of getting all four answers correct? $\frac{3}{50}$, or 6%

Vocabulary Tip

Read $P(\text{hit})$ as "probability of a hit."

rand	
	.8767044746
	.7208728315
	.6495877886
	.3462435756
	.8958229562
	.4615208491
■	

	.1214849574
	.5070685798
	.5584414289
	.9071019949
	.1991062533
	.4761581612
	.4792397345
■	

	.6388889895
	.5466561294
	.2840659518
	.2096111775
	.7827769142
	.7787959459
	.6958584068
■	

Differentiated Instruction Solutions for All Learners

Advanced Learners **L4**
To estimate π, drop a toothpick onto parallel lines spaced a toothpick-length apart. Divide twice the number of drops by the number of lines hit. Discuss.

learning style: tactile

English Language Learners **ELL**
In Example 2, be sure that the students understand the meaning of *at random* as having no set pattern or design. If a student guessed "T, F, T, F, T, F, T, F" that would be a pattern. To guess at random could be, for example, "T, T, T, F, T, F, F, T".

learning style: verbal

2 **Theoretical Probability**

When you roll a number cube, the possible outcomes are 1, 2, 3, 4, 5, and 6. The set of all possible outcomes is called the **sample space.** You can calculate theoretical probability as a ratio of outcomes.

 Key Concepts

Definition	Theoretical Probability

If a sample space has n equally likely outcomes and an event A occurs in m of these outcomes, then the **theoretical probability** of event A is $P(A) = \frac{m}{n}$.

Sample space: n outcomes

Event A: m outcomes

3 **EXAMPLE** Finding Theoretical Probability

Find the theoretical probability of getting an even number when you roll a number cube.

The even outcomes are 2, 4, and 6.

3 **outcomes result in an even number.** → $\frac{3}{6}$ ← **6 equally likely outcomes are in the sample space.**

$$= \frac{1}{2}$$

✓ **Quick Check** ❸ Find the theoretical probability of getting a prime number when you roll a number cube. $\frac{1}{2}$, **or 50%**

4 **EXAMPLE** Real-World 🌐 Connection

Biology Fold your hands so your fingers interlace. Do you naturally place your left or right thumb on top? Placing your left thumb on top is a dominant genetic trait.

When a parent has both a dominant and a recessive gene, then the two genes are equally likely to be passed to a child. If you have one or two dominant genes, you normally place your left thumb on top.

Suppose a child has parents who both have just one dominant gene. What is the theoretical probability that the child will naturally place the left thumb on top?

gg
Right thumb on top

GG or *Gg*
Left thumb on top

Make a table. Let G represent the dominant gene (left thumb on top). Let g represent the recessive gene (right thumb on top).

The sample space {GG, Gg, Gg, gg} contains four equally likely outcomes. Three outcomes have at least one G. So P(left thumb on top) = $\frac{3}{4}$.

		Gene from Mother	
		G	**g**
Gene from Father	**G**	GG	Gg
	g	Gg	gg

The theoretical probability that the child will naturally place the left thumb on top is $\frac{3}{4}$, or 75%.

✓ **Quick Check** ❹ What is the theoretical probability that a child of the parents in Example 4 places the right thumb on top? $\frac{1}{4}$, **or 25%**

Lesson 1-6 Probability **41**
Guided Instruction

3 **EXAMPLE** Math Tip

Students need to understand that the theoretical probability of $\frac{1}{2}$ does not mean that, in a particular group of rolls, exactly half the rolls will result in an even number. Probability tells what is *likely* to happen, not what *must* happen.

4 **EXAMPLE** Career Note

Inherited traits are important in understanding many types of health problems. There are exciting career opportunities in health care and the pharmaceutical industry that are related to genetic research.

5 **EXAMPLE** Connection to Math

Students may be interested to know that simulations and ideas about geometric probability can be used to find approximate values of areas and important constants such as π.

PowerPoint
📽 **Additional Examples**

❸ Find the theoretical probability of rolling a multiple of 3 with a number cube. $\frac{1}{3}$

❹ Brown is a dominant eye color for human beings. If a father and mother each carry a gene for brown eyes and a gene for blue eyes, what is the probability of their having a child with blue eyes? $\frac{1}{4}$

❺ For the dartboard in Example 5, find the probability that a dart that lands at random on the dartboard hits the outer ring. $\frac{7}{16}$

Resources
• Daily Notetaking Guide 1-6 **L3**

Closure

Tell students to name two pieces of information that can be used to find the theoretical probability of an event. **number of possible outcomes, number of outcomes representing the event in question**

41

Assignment Guide

1 A B   1-5, 21-23, 40

2 A B   6-20, 24-39, 41-42

C Challenge   43-45

Test Prep   46-51
Mixed Review   52-63

Homework Quick Check
To check students' understanding of key skills and concepts, go over Exercises 4, 14, 38, 40, 41.

Technology Tip
Exercises 3, 4 Students can enter the expression randInt(0,1,5) on the home screen of their graphing calculators using the catalog feature. Then they can press ENTER to generate a random sequence of five integers where each integer is either a 0 or 1. Repeatedly pressing ENTER will generate a new sequence each time. Students may wish to use this idea for their simulation.

Error Prevention!
Exercises 24–26 Students should not overlook the 31 students who take neither math nor science.

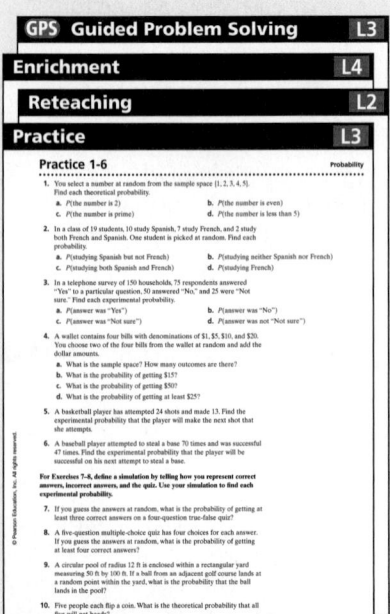

Differentiated Instruction **Resources**

GPS Guided Problem Solving	L3
Enrichment	L4
Reteaching	L2
Practice	L3

42

Online
active math

For: Probability Activity
Use: Interactive Textbook, 1-6

Sometimes you can use areas to find theoretical probability.

5 EXAMPLE   Finding Geometric Probability

Geometry Suppose that all the points on the circular dartboard shown at the right are equally likely to be hit by a dart you have thrown. Find the probability of scoring at least ten points.

P(at least 10 points)

$$= \frac{\text{area of circle with radius } 2r}{\text{area of circle with radius } 4r}$$

$$= \frac{\pi(2r)^2}{\pi(4r)^2}$$

$$= \frac{4\pi r^2}{16\pi r^2} = \frac{1}{4}$$

Width of each ring = r.

● The theoretical probability of scoring at least ten points is $\frac{1}{4}$, or 25%.

✓ Quick Check 5 Use the dartboard from Example 5. Find each probability.
  a. P(scoring 20 points)   **b.** P(scoring 5 points)
  $\frac{1}{16}$, **or 6.25%** $\frac{5}{16}$, **or 31.25%**

EXERCISES
For more exercises, see *Extra Skill and Word Problem Practice.*

Practice and Problem Solving

A Practice by Example

Example 1
(page 40)

GO for Help

1. A class tossed coins and recorded 161 heads and 179 tails. What is the experimental probability of heads? Of tails? $\frac{161}{340} \approx$ 47%; $\frac{179}{340} \approx$ 53%

2. Another class rolled number cubes. Their results are shown in the table. What is the experimental probability of rolling each number? **See margin.**

Number	1	2	3	4	5	6
Occurrences	42	44	45	44	47	46

Example 2
(page 40)

For Exercises 3–5, define a simulation by telling how you represent correct answers, incorrect answers, and the quiz. Use your simulation to find each experimental probability. 3–4. See margin pp. 42–43.

Graphing Calculator Hint

To generate random numbers, press
MATH ◄ 1 ENTER.

3. If you guess the answers at random, what is the probability of getting at least two correct answers on a five-question true-or-false quiz?

4. If you guess the answers at random, what is the probability of getting at least three correct answers on a five-question true-or-false quiz ?

5. A five-question multiple-choice quiz has five choices for each answer. What is the probability of correctly guessing at random exactly one correct answer? Exactly two correct answers? Exactly three correct answers? (*Hint:* You could let any two digits represent correct answers, and the other digits represent wrong answers.) **See back of book.**

Example 3
(page 41)

A jar contains 30 red marbles, 50 blue marbles, and 20 white marbles. You pick one marble from the jar at random. Find each theoretical probability.

6. P(red)   **7.** P(blue)   **8.** P(not white)   **9.** P(red or blue)
   $\frac{3}{10}$, **or 30%** $\frac{1}{2}$, **or 50%** $\frac{4}{5}$, **or 80%** $\frac{4}{5}$, **or 80%**

---

pages 42–45 Exercises

2. the number 1: $\frac{21}{134}$, or about 15.7%; the number 2: $\frac{11}{67}$ or about 16.4%; the number 3: $\frac{45}{268}$ or about 16.8%; the number 4:

$\frac{11}{67}$ or about 16.4%; the number 5: $\frac{47}{268}$ or about 17.5%; the number 6: $\frac{23}{134}$ or about 17.2%

3. Answers may vary. Sample: Generate random numbers

between 0 and 1 using a graphing calculator. In each random number, examine the first five digits. Let even digits represent correct answers and odd digits incorrect answers. If there

10. $\frac{48}{125}$, or 38.4%

11. $\frac{19}{125}$, or 15.2%

12. $\frac{103}{125}$, or 82.4%

13. $\frac{14}{25}$, or 56%

A bag contains 36 red, 48 green, 22 yellow, and 19 purple blocks. You pick one block from the bag at random. Find each theoretical probability.   10–13. See left.

10. P(green)   11. P(purple)   12. P(not yellow)

13. P(green or yellow)   14. P(yellow or not green) $\frac{77}{125}$, or 61.6%

Example 4
(page 41)

For each situation, find the sample space and the theoretical probability that a child will naturally place the left thumb on top. {Gg, Gg, gg, gg}; $\frac{1}{2}$, or 50%

15. The father has gene pair gg and the mother has Gg.

16. The father has gene pair gg and the mother has GG.
{Gg, Gg, Gg, Gg}; 1, or 100%

Example 5
(page 42)

17. $\frac{1}{16}$, or 6.25%

18. $\frac{3}{8}$, or 37.5%

19. $\frac{1}{4}$, or 25%

20. $\frac{3}{4}$, or 75%

Geometry Suppose that a dart lands at random on the dartboard shown at the right. Find each theoretical probability.   17–20.
See left.

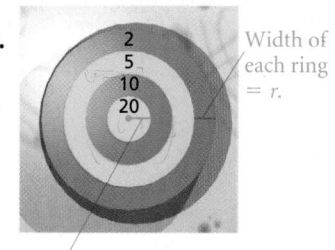

Width of each ring = r.

17. The dart lands in the bull's-eye.

18. The dart lands in a green region.

19. The dart scores at least 10 points.

20. The dart scores less than 10 points.

B Apply Your Skills

21. The common interpretation of Murphy's Law is, If something can go wrong, it will. Assume that Murphy's Law applies to the following situations, and estimate each probability as either 0 or 1.
   a. P(your dog chews up your homework after you've finished it)   1
   b. P(your teacher accepts your excuse for not having your homework)   0

22. Multiple Choice A caterer knows that, on average, there will be one broken egg in every 3 cartons. A carton contains 12 eggs. The caterer plans to serve 1200 eggs at a breakfast. What is the best estimate for the number of cartons the caterer should buy?   C

   (A) 97 cartons   (B) 100 cartons   (C) 103 cartons   (D) 112 cartons

Random Number Table		
31504	51648	40613
79321	80927	42404
15594	84675	68591
34178	00460	31754
49676	58733	00884
85400	72294	22551
22547	86066	93114
85211	07790	20890
21339	09414	51549
13843	18407	87043
34990	16214	46849
11390	01322	82656
45950	37521	77417

23. Use the random number table at the left to simulate tossing a coin 50 times. Find the experimental probability that the outcome of a coin toss is heads.
See margin.

In a class of 147 students, 95 are taking math (M), 73 are taking science (S), and 52 are taking both math and science. One student is picked at random. Find each probability.
24–27. See left.

24. P(taking math or science or both)

25. P(not taking math)

26. P(taking math but not science)

27. P(taking neither math nor science)

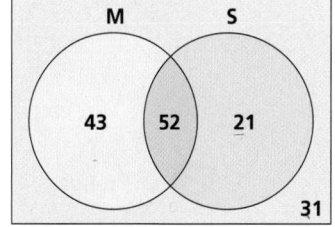

24. $\frac{116}{147}$, or 78.9%

25. $\frac{52}{147}$, or 35.4%

26. $\frac{43}{147}$, or 29.3%

27. $\frac{31}{147}$, or 21.1%

Suppose you roll a number cube. Find each theoretical probability.

28. P(5) $\frac{1}{6}$ 29. P(an even number) $\frac{1}{2}$

30. P(a number less than 5) $\frac{2}{3}$ 31. P(8) 0

32. P(a number greater than 5) $\frac{1}{6}$ 33. P(a number less than 8) 1

Exercise 36 If necessary, remind students that a prime number is a whole number greater than 1 whose only factors are 1 and itself.

Error Prevention!

Exercise 38 It is assumed that the number cubes are distinguishable (for example, of different colors). This means there are *two* ways, not just one, for a pair of numbers such as 2 and 5 to be rolled. It would be beneficial for students to list all the possibilities if they find it difficult to describe the sample space accurately in words.

English Language Learners ELL
Exercise 44 Be sure students understand that exchanges are distinct from area codes.

are two or more even digits, make a tally mark for that number. Do this 100 times. Find the total number of tally marks. This, as a percent, gives the experimental probability.

The simulated probability should be about 80%.

4. Answers may vary. Sample: Toss 5 coins. Keep a tally of the times 3 or more heads are tossed. (A head represents a

correct answer.) Do this 100 times. The total number of tally marks, as a percent, gives the experimental probability. The simulated probability should be about 50%.

23. Answers may vary. Sample: Let odd digits represent heads and even digits represent tails. Use the first four rows of the table. The experimental probability of heads is $\frac{1}{2}$.

1. A bowler rolled the ball 35 times and got 5 strikes. What is the experimental probability that the bowler gets a strike? $\frac{1}{7}$

2. Describe a simulation you could use that involves flipping a coin to find the experimental probability of guessing at least four correct answers on a five-question true or false quiz. **Answers may vary. Sample: Let heads represent a correct answer and tails represent an incorrect answer. Flip the coin five times. Record the number of heads. Repeat 100 times. Divide the number of times you got 4 or 5 heads by 100.**

3. What is the theoretical probability of rolling a sum less than 5 using two number cubes? $\frac{1}{6}$

4. Segments parallel to the sides are used to divide a square board 3 ft on each side into 9 equal-size smaller squares. If the board is in a level position and a grain of rice lands on the board at a random point, what is the probability that it lands on a corner section? $\frac{4}{9}$

Alternative Assessment

Have students work in groups of three. Suppose that each group is planning a vacation. From the possible flights available, the probability of at least one flight being delayed is $\frac{1}{5}$. Have students plan, describe in words, and conduct a simulation to find the experimental probability that two flights selected at random will not be delayed.

38a. (1, 1), (1, 2), (1, 3),
(1, 4), (1, 5), (1, 6),
(2, 1), (2, 2), (2, 3),
(2, 4), (2, 5), (2, 6),
(3, 1), (3, 2), (3, 3),
(3, 4), (3, 5), (3, 6),
(4, 1), (4, 2), (4, 3),
(4, 4), (4, 5), (4, 6),
(5, 1), (5, 2), (5, 3),
(5, 4), (5, 5), (5, 6),
(6, 1), (6, 2), (6, 3),
(6, 4), (6, 5), (6, 6)

GO Online
Homework Video Tutor

Visit: PHSchool.com
Web Code: age-0106

C Challenge

43a. $\frac{a}{a+b}$

b. a to $b - a$ or $\frac{a}{b-a}$

c. A game where the probability of winning is $\frac{1}{2}$; when the odds of winning are $\frac{1}{2}$, the probability of winning is only $\frac{1}{3}$.

Suppose you select a number at random from the sample space {1, 2, 3, 4, 5, 6, 7, 8, 9}. Find each theoretical probability.

34. P(the number is a multiple of 3) $\frac{1}{3}$

35. P(the number is less than 5) $\frac{4}{9}$

36. P(the number is prime) $\frac{4}{9}$

37. P(the number is even) $\frac{4}{9}$

38. Suppose you roll two number cubes.
GPS a. What is the sample space?
    b. How many outcomes are there? **36 outcomes**
    c. What is the theoretical probability of getting a sum of 12? $\frac{1}{36}$
    d. What is the theoretical probability of getting a sum of 7? $\frac{1}{6}$

39. **Sports** The batter's strike zone depends on the height and stance of the batter. Find the geometric probability that a baseball thrown at random within the batter's strike zone as shown in the figure below will be a high-inside strike. This is one of the hardest pitches to hit! $\approx$**6.4%**

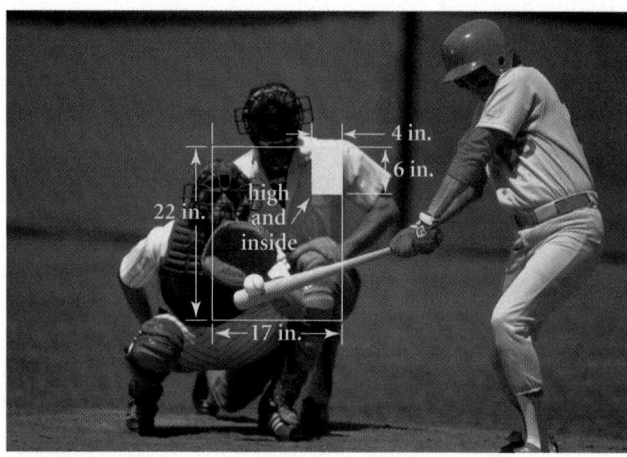

40. a. **Sports** Team A has won one game and team B has won three games in a World Series. What is the experimental probability that team A wins the next game? That team B wins the next game? $\frac{1}{4}; \frac{3}{4}$
    b. **Critical Thinking** Do you think that experimental probability is a good predictor of the winner of the next game? Explain. **Answers may vary. Sample: Variables such as injuries make probability a poor predictor.**

41. **Writing** Explain what you would need to know to determine the theoretical probability that a five-digit postal ZIP code ends in 1. **if there are any restrictions on the last digit of a ZIP code**

42. Suppose you choose a two-digit number at random. What is the theoretical probability that its square root is an integer? $\frac{1}{15}$**, or 6.7%**

43. Assume that an event is neither certain nor impossible. Then the odds in favor of the event are the ratio of the number of favorable outcomes to the number of unfavorable outcomes. **See left.**
    a. If the odds in favor of the event are a to b or $\frac{a}{b}$, what is the probability of the event?
    b. If the probability of the event is $\frac{a}{b}$, what are the odds in favor of the event?
    c. Would you rather play a game where your odds of winning are $\frac{1}{2}$, or a game where your probability of winning is $\frac{1}{2}$? Explain.

44. **Open-Ended** Use a telephone book. Select 50 telephone numbers at random and record the first three digits (the "exchange") of each number. Summarize your results using probability statements. **Check students' work.**

45. On a TV game show, you want to win a prize that is hidden behind one of three doors. You choose one door, but before it is opened the host opens another door and shows that the prize is not there. Now you can switch to the other unopened door or stick with your original choice.
  a. Find the experimental probability of winning the prize if you stick with your original choice. (*Hint:* Simulate the doors with index cards and the prize with a mark on one side of one card. One person can act as the host and another as the contestant.) about $\frac{1}{3}$
  b. Find the experimental probability of winning if you switch to the other door. about $\frac{2}{3}$

Test Prep

Multiple Choice

46. What is the theoretical probability of getting a 2 or a 3 when rolling a number cube? **B**
  A. $\frac{1}{2}$ **B.** $\frac{1}{3}$ **C.** $\frac{1}{4}$ **D.** $\frac{1}{6}$

47. How many outcomes are in the sample space for rolling a number cube and tossing a coin?   **H**
  F. 2   **G.** 6   **H.** 12   **J.** 24

48. The random number table simulates an experiment where you toss a coin 90 times. Even digits represent heads and odd digits represent tails. What is the experimental probability, to the nearest percent, of the coin coming up heads? **C**
  A. 45%   **B.** 50%
  C. 54%   **D.** 56%

Random Number Table		
31504	51648	40613
79321	80927	42404
15594	84675	68591
34178	00460	31754
49676	58733	00884
85400	72294	22551

Short Response

49–51. See margin.

49. What is the sample space for spinning the spinner at the right twice? Are all the outcomes equally likely?

50. For the spinner at the right, what is the probability of spinning a 1 on both spins? Explain.

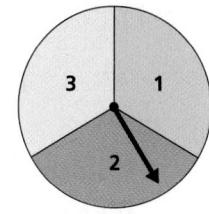

Extended Response

51. For the spinner at the right, which is more likely on two spins, an even sum or a sum that is not prime? Include all the steps of your solution.

Mixed Review

GO for Help

Lesson 1-5

Solve each absolute value equation. Check your answers.

52. $|x + 3| = 9$ $-12, 6$ **53.** $|3x - 5| = 10$ $-\frac{5}{3}, 5$ **54.** $|2x + 7| + 3 = 22$ $-13, 6$

55. $|3x - 6| - 7 = 14$ $-5, 9$ **56.** $|2x + 3| - 9 = 14$ $-13, 10$ **57.** $|6 - 5x| = 18$ $-\frac{12}{5}, \frac{24}{5}$

Lesson 1-5

Solve each absolute value inequality.

58. $2|x| - 3 \geq 5$ $x \leq -4 \text{ or } x \geq 4$ **59.** $|2x - 4| + 16 \leq 24$ $-2 \leq x \leq 6$ **60.** $|3x - 5| - 2 > 0$ $x < 1 \text{ or } x > 2\frac{1}{3}$

61. $|2x + 4| - 6 < 0$ $-5 < x < 1$ **62.** $2|x + 3| \geq 10$ $x \leq -8 \text{ or } x \geq 2$ **63.** $6|x + 9| \leq 36$ $-15 \leq x \leq -3$

Test Prep

📁 **Resources**
For additional practice with a variety of test item formats:
● Standardized Test Prep, p. 51
● Test-Taking Strategies, p. 46
● Test-Taking Strategies with Transparencies

51. [4] a. The favorable outcomes for an even sum are 11, 13, 22, 31, and 33.

  b. The probability of an even sum is
  $\frac{\text{no. of favorable outcomes}}{\text{total no. of outcomes}}$
  $= \frac{5}{9}$.

  c. The favorable outcomes for a composite sum are 13, 22, 31, and 33.

  d. The probability of a composite sum is $\frac{4}{9}$.

  e. $\frac{5}{9} > \frac{4}{9}$, so an even sum is more likely than a composite sum.

[3] omits one of the five parts of the answer

[2] omits two OR three of the five parts of the answer

[1] omits four of the five parts of the answer

---

pages 42–45 **Exercises**

49. [2] (11, 12, 13, 21, 22, 23, 31, 32, 33); all the pairs are equally likely because the three regions have the same area (or are congruent),

and the outcome of the first spin does not affect the outcome of the second spin.

[1] answers one of the two parts

50. [2] $\frac{1}{9}$; the probability of spinning a 1 on each spin is $\frac{1}{3}$. The probability of spinning a 1 on both spins is $\frac{1}{3} \cdot \frac{1}{3}$ or $\frac{1}{9}$.

[1] no explanation included

45

Writing Gridded Responses

This feature helps devise strategies for answering gridded-response questions. The focus of the feature is on recording fractions and decimals in gridded-response blanks after solving equations.

Resources

SAT® and ACT® correlations are on page 2B.

Test-Taking Strategies with Transparencies
- Transparency 1
- Practice sheet p. 25
- Blank Sheet of Grids, p. viii

Guided Instruction

Students are probably accustomed to changing improper fractions into mixed numbers before recording their answer. Point out that it is best to record improper fractions as a correct response for gridded-response questions.

Some tests require that you enter numerical answers in a grid. After finding an answer, write it in the top row of the grid. Then fill in the corresponding bubbles below.

EXAMPLE

A rabbit weighs one pound less than eight times the weight of a guinea pig. The rabbit weighs nine pounds. What is the weight in pounds of the guinea pig?

First find the answer by writing and solving an equation.

$$8x - 1 = 9$$
$$8x = 10$$
$$x = \frac{10}{8} \text{ or } \frac{5}{4} \text{ or } 1.25$$

Enter the answer in the grid. You could write it as $\frac{10}{8}$, as $\frac{5}{4}$, or as 1.25. Do not enter the answer as a mixed number. If you enter 1 1/4, it would be interpreted as $\frac{11}{4}$.

Note how to enter fraction bars and decimal points.

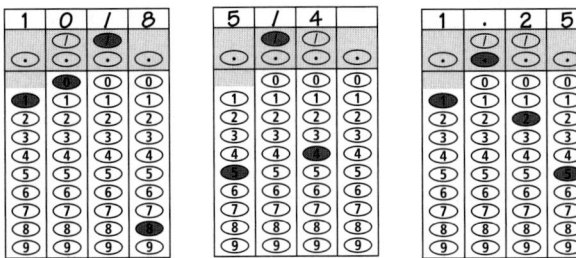

EXERCISES

Use a response grid to answer each question.

1. What is the value of $\frac{x^2 + 1}{2.5}$ when $x = 1.5$? **1.3**

2. A music tape costs a dollar more than half the price of a CD. The music tape costs $5.99. What is the cost in dollars of the CD? **9.98**

3. What is the solution of the equation $3(x - 1) - (x + 2) = 9$? **7**

4. A number is selected at random from the sample space {10, 11, 12, 13, 14, 15}. What is the probability that the number is a multiple of 3? **1/3**

5. Write a 4-digit number that is a multiple of both 5 and 6. **Sample: 4500**

6. Write a rational number between $\sqrt{5}$ and $\sqrt{6}$. **Sample: 12/5**

7. 44.8 is what percent of 128? **35**

8. The length of a picture frame must be at least 4.25 cm greater than the frame's width. The width is 19.5 cm. What is the minimum perimeter, in centimeters, of the picture frame? **86.5**

Chapter Review

Vocabulary Review

absolute value (p. 33)
absolute value of a real
    number (p. 8)
additive inverse (p. 7)
algebraic expression (p. 12)
coefficient (p. 13)
compound inequality (p. 28)

evaluate (p. 12)
experimental probability (p. 40)
extraneous solution (p. 34)
multiplicative inverse (p. 7)
opposite (p. 7)
reciprocal (p. 7)
sample space (p. 41)

simulation (p. 40)
solution of an equation (p. 18)
term (p. 13)
theoretical probability (p. 41)
tolerance (p. 36)
variable (p. 12)
variable expression (p. 12)

Resources

Student Edition
Extra Skills and Word Problem
    Practice, Ch. 1, p. 836
English/Spanish Glossary, p. 899
Properties and Formulas, p. 893
Table of Symbols, p. 889

Differentiated Instruction Resources

Vocabulary and Study Skills
    worksheet 1F
Spanish Vocabulary and Study
    Skills worksheet 1F
Interactive Textbook Audio
    Glossary
Online Vocabulary Quiz

Success Tracker™
Online at PHSchool.com

Choose the correct vocabulary term to complete each sentence.

1. The opposite of a number is also called its ? . **additive inverse**

2. The ? is the set of all possible outcomes of an experiment. **sample space**

3. The ? makes an equation true. **solution of an equation**

4. A pair of inequalities joined by *and* or *or* is called a(n) ? . **compound inequality**

5. ? is another name for a multiplicative inverse of a number. **reciprocal**

6. The ? of an event is the ratio of occurrences to trials. **experimental probability**

7. The ? of an event is the ratio of possible event outcomes to total possible outcomes. **theoretical probability**

8. A possible solution that does not satisfy the original equation is a(n) ? .

9. You can use a(n) ? to find experimental probabilities. **simulation**

10. A number's distance from zero on the number line is its ? . **absolute value**

Go Online
PHSchool.com
For: Vocabulary quiz
Web Code: agj-0151

8. extraneous solution

Skills and Concepts

1-1 Objectives

▼ To graph and order real
    numbers (p. 4)

▼ To identify and use
    properties of real
    numbers (p. 7)

The natural numbers, whole numbers, integers, rational numbers, and irrational numbers are all subsets of the real numbers. Each real number corresponds to a point on the number line. A real number's distance from zero on the number line is its absolute value.

For both addition and multiplication, real numbers satisfy the properties of closure, associativity, and commutativity. Real numbers have **additive inverses (opposites)**. Nonzero real numbers have **multiplicative inverses (reciprocals)**. They also have additive and multiplicative identities. Real numbers satisfy the Distributive Property.

To which sets of numbers does each number belong? **11–15. See margin.**

11. 8.1π **12.** -79 **13.** $\sqrt{121}$ **14.** $\sqrt{200}$ **15.** $12\frac{7}{8}$

Compare each pair of numbers. Use < or >.

16. $-\frac{2}{3}, -\frac{3}{2}$ >   **17.** $\sqrt{6}, 2.\overline{3}$ >   **18.** $0.45, 0.405$ >   **19.** $-7, |-7|$ <

pages 47–49   Chapter Review

11. real numbers, irrational
    numbers

12. real numbers, rational
    numbers, integers

13. real numbers, rational
    numbers, integers,
    whole numbers, natural
    numbers

14. real numbers, irrational
    numbers

15. real numbers, rational
    numbers

20. $3.4; -\frac{1}{3.4}$

21. $-4 - \pi; \frac{1}{4 + \pi}$

22. $-1\frac{7}{8}; \frac{8}{15}$

23. $-\sqrt{12}; \frac{1}{\sqrt{12}}$

Find the opposite and reciprocal of each number. Then graph all three numbers on a number line. 20–23. See margin.

20. -3.4 **21.** $4 + \pi$ **22.** $1\frac{7}{8}$ **23.** $\sqrt{12}$

24–28. Answers may vary.
Open-Ended Write an equation that illustrates each property of real numbers.

24. The Identity Property of Multiplication $(x + 3)(1) = x + 3$

25. The Associative Property of Addition $(2x + 7) + 3y = 2x + (7 + 3y)$

26. The Distributive Property $3(2x - 4) = 6x - 12$

27. The Commutative Property of Multiplication $(5x)(3y) = (3y)(5x)$

28. The Identity Property of Addition $10z + 0 = 10z$

1-2 and 1-3 Objectives

▼ To evaluate algebraic expressions (p. 12)

▼ To simplify algebraic expressions (p. 13)

▼ To solve equations (p. 18)

▼ To solve problems by writing equations (p. 20)

You **evaluate** an **algebraic expression** by substituting numbers for the **variables**. You simplify an algebraic expression by combining like **terms**, using the appropriate properties. To find the **solutions of an equation**, use the properties of equality. To check for **extraneous solutions**, substitute in the original equation. Some equations may have no solutions. Some equations are true for all real numbers.

29. Evaluate $-x^2 + |x - 10|$ for $x = 2$. **4**

30. Evaluate $3t(t + 2) - (3t^2 + 5t)$ for $t = 19$. **19**

31. Simplify $-(3a - 2b) - 3(-a - b)$. **5b**

Solve each equation for x. State any restrictions.

32. $2x - 5 = 17$ **11**   **33.** $8 - \frac{1}{2}x = 3$ **10**

34. $3x = 4x - 5$ **5**   **35.** $0.1x + 1.4 = 1.2x - 3$ **4**

36. $\frac{7 - x}{3} = 5$ **−8**   **37.** $\frac{x + a}{b} = \frac{1}{a}$ $\frac{b - a^2}{a}, a \neq 0, b \neq 0$

Write an equation to solve each problem.

38. Geometry The lengths of the sides of a rectangle are in the ratio $5 : 3$. The perimeter of the rectangle is 32 cm. Find the length of each side. **10 cm, 6 cm**

39. Two planes left St. Louis for Los Angeles at the same time. After 4 h they were 700 mi apart. The slower plane traveled at 350 mi/h. What was the speed of the faster plane? **525 mi/h**

40. Geometry The measures of an angle and its supplement differ by 40°. Find the measures of the angles. **70°, 110°**

1-4 Objectives

▼ To solve and graph inequalities (p. 26)

▼ To solve and write compound inequalities (p. 28)

You can solve inequalities using properties that are similar to the properties for equations. An important difference is that multiplying or dividing each side of an inequality by a negative number reverses the inequality symbol. Just as with equations, some inequalities are true for all real numbers, and some have no solutions. If a **compound inequality** uses *and*, the solutions must satisfy both inequalities. If a compound inequality uses *or*, the solutions satisfy either one or both of the inequalities.

Solve each inequality. Graph the solution. 41–46. See margin for graphs.

41. $4 - 5z \geq 2$ **42.** $2(5 - 3x) < x - 4(3 - x)$ **43.** $0.3(y - 2) > \frac{1}{2}(6 - y)$
$z \leq \frac{2}{5}$ $x > 2$ $y > 4.5$

Solve each compound inequality. Graph the solution.

44. $5 \leq 9 - 4x \leq 13$ **45.** $3 \geq 2x$ or $x - 4 > 2$ **46.** $6y > 2$ and $y - 5 \geq -2y$
$-1 \leq x \leq 1$ $x \leq \frac{3}{2}$ or $x > 6$ $y \geq \frac{5}{3}$

47. A publisher estimates that the cost of publishing a book is from \$980,000 to \$1,240,000. So far, \$824,150 has been spent. Use a compound inequality to describe the amount A that the publisher can still spend while remaining within the estimate. $\$155,850 \leq A \leq \$415,850$

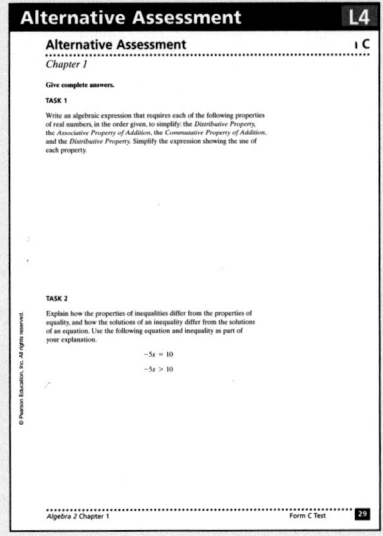

1-5 Objectives

▼ To solve absolute value equations (p. 33)

▼ To solve absolute value inequalities (p. 35)

You can rewrite an equation or inequality that involves the absolute value of an **algebraic expression** as a compound sentence. You must consider both cases of the definition of absolute value. Check for **extraneous solutions.**

Solve each equation. Check for extraneous solutions.

48. $|2x + 8| = 3x + 7$ 1 **49.** $|3x - 5| = 4 + 2x$ $\frac{1}{5}, 9$ **50.** $|x - 4| + 3 = 1$
no solution

Solve each inequality. Graph the solution. 51–53. See margin for graphs.

51. $|3x - 2| + 4 \leq 7$ **52.** $4|y - 9| > 36$ **53.** $\frac{2}{5}|3x - 3| - 4 > 2$
$-\frac{1}{3} \leq x \leq \frac{5}{3}$ $y < 0$ or $y > 18$ $x < -4$ or $x > 6$

54. The specification for a length x is 43.6 cm with a tolerance of 0.1 cm. Write the specification as an absolute value inequality. $|x - 43.6| \leq 0.1$

1-6 Objectives

▼ To find experimental probabilities (p. 39)

▼ To find theoretical probabilities (p. 41)

The probability of an event can be expressed as a number from 0% (impossible) to 100% (certain).

Experimental probability is the ratio of two numbers. The first is the observed number of times an experiment results in a particular event. The second is the number of trials. **Simulation** uses random numbers or other models to determine an experimental probability.

Theoretical probability in a sample space of equally likely outcomes is also the ratio of two numbers. The first is the number of outcomes corresponding to the particular event. The second is the number of elements in the sample space, which is the set of all possible outcomes. Geometric probability is computed as a ratio of areas.

Suppose you select a number at random from the sample space $\{-3, -2, -1, 0, 1, 2, 3, 4\}$. Find each probability.

55. P(a positive number) $\frac{1}{2}$ **56.** P(a number less than 2) $\frac{5}{8}$

57. P(an even number) $\frac{1}{2}$ **58.** P(a multiple of 3) $\frac{3}{8}$

🌐 **59. Games** You have won five games of checkers and your opponent has won three. What is the experimental probability of your winning? $\frac{5}{8}$

🌐 **60. Tests** A five-question multiple-choice quiz has four choices for each answer. Find the experimental probability of getting exactly three correct answers if you guess the answers at random. Define a simulation using the random number table on page 43. Use your simulation to find the experimental probability. **about 9%**

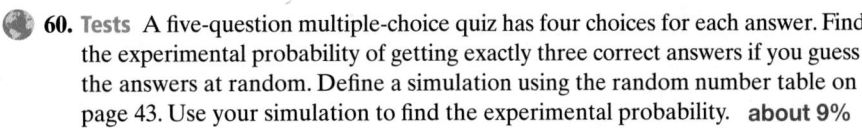

41. 0 1 2 3

42. −2 −1 0 1 2 3

43. 0 1 2 3 4 5 6

44. −3 −2 −1 0 1 2 3

45. 0 1 2 3 4 5 6 7

46. −2 −1 0 1 2 3

51. −2 −1 0 1 2 3

52. −4 0 4 8 12 16 20

53. −6 −4 −2 0 2 4 6 8

Chapter 1

Chapter Test

Go Online
PHSchool.com
For: Chapter Test
Web Code: aga-0152

1. **Writing** Describe the relationships among these sets of numbers: natural numbers, whole numbers, integers, rational numbers, irrational numbers, and real numbers. **Check students' answers.**

2. **Justifying Steps** Justify each step by identifying the property used.

$t + 5(t + 1) = t + (5t + 5)$ **Dist. Prop.**
$\qquad\qquad = (t + 5t) + 5$ **Assoc. Prop. of Add.**
$\qquad\qquad = (1t + 5t) + 5$ **Identity Prop. of Mult.**
$\qquad\qquad = (1 + 5)t + 5$ **Dist. Prop.**
$\qquad\qquad = 6t + 5$ **arithmetic**

Evaluate each expression for $x = 5$.

3. $\frac{5}{3}(3x - 6) - (6 - 4x)$ **29**

4. $3(x^2 - 4) + 7(x - 2)$ **84**

5. $x - 2x + 3x - 4x + 5x$ **15**

Simplify each expression.

6. $a^2 + a + a^2$ **$2a^2 + a$**

7. $2x + 3y - 5x + 2y$ **$-3x + 5y$**

8. $5(a - 2b) - 3(a - 2b)$ **$2a - 4b$**

9. $3[2(x - 3) + 2] + 5(x - 3)$ **$11x - 27$**

Solve each equation.

10. $4y - 6 = 2y + 8$ **7**

11. $3(2z + 1) = 35$ **$\frac{16}{3}$**

12. $5(3w - 2) - 7 = 23$ **$\frac{8}{3}$**

13. $t - 2(3 - 2t) = 2t + 9$ **5**

14. $5(s - 12) - 24 = 3(s + 2)$ **45**

15. $7(3 - 0.5k) = 3k - 5$ **4**

Solve each equation for x. State any restrictions.

                               16–19. See
16. $ax - bx = 2a$ 17. $\frac{x}{c} + c = 4c$ **margin.**

18. $\frac{x - 5}{a} + 1 = b$ 19. $ax + 2 = bx + c$

20. The lateral surface area of a cylinder is given by the formula $S = 2\pi rh$. Solve this equation for r.
$r = \frac{S}{2\pi h}$

Write an equation to solve each problem.

21. **Savings** Briana and her sister Molly both want to buy the same model bicycle. Briana needs $73 more before she can afford the bike. Molly needs $65 more. If they combine their money, they will have just enough to buy one bicycle that they could share. What is the cost of the bicycle? **$138**

22. **Musical** There is only one freshman in the cast of the high school musical. There are 6 sophomores and 11 juniors. One third of the cast are seniors. How many seniors are in the musical? **9**

23–31. See margin pp. 50–51 for graphs.
Solve each inequality or equation. Graph the solution.

23. $3x + 17 \geq 5$ **$x \geq -4$**

24. $25 - 2x < 11$ **$x > 7$**

25. $7t > 4t + 3(1 - t)$ **$t > \frac{1}{2}$**

26. $\frac{3}{8}x < -6$ or $5x > 2$ **$x < -16$ or $x > \frac{2}{5}$**

27. $2 < 10 - 4d < 6$ **$1 < d < 2$**

28. $4 - x = |2 - 3x|$ **$-1, \frac{3}{2}$**

29. $|4x + 4| = 8x + 16$ **$-\frac{5}{3}$**

30. $|5 - p| \leq 2$ **$3 \leq p \leq 7$**

31. $5|3w + 2| - 3 > 7$ **$w < -\frac{4}{3}$ or $w > 0$**

Suppose you select a number at random from the sample space {5, 6, 7, 8, 9, 10, 11, 12, 13, 14}. Find each probability.

32. $P(\text{greater than } 10)$ **$\frac{2}{5}$**

33. $P(\text{multiple of } 30)$ **0**

34. $P(\text{less than 7 or greater than } 10)$ **$\frac{3}{5}$**

35. $P(\text{integer})$ **1**

36. **Open-Ended** Your teacher selects at random two days out of every five days to give a "pop" quiz. Define a simulation to find the experimental probability that you will get a pop quiz on two consecutive days. Then use your simulation to find the probability. **about 40%**

page 50   Chapter Test

16. $x = \frac{2a}{a - b}, a \neq b$

17. $x = 3c^2, c \neq 0$

18. $x = a(b - 1) + 5, a \neq 0$

19. $x = \frac{c - 2}{a - b}, a \neq b$

50

23.
$-6\ -5\ -4\ -3\ -2\ -1\ 0\ 1\ 2$

24.
$-1\ 0\ 1\ 2\ 3\ 4\ 5\ 6\ 7\ 8\ 9$

25.
$-1\ 0\ 1\ 2$

26.
$-16\ -12\ -8\ -4\ 0\ 4$

27.
$0\ 1\ 2$

28.
$-1\ 0\ 1\ 2$

Standardized Test Prep

Reading Comprehension Read the passage below. Then answer the
questions on the basis of what is *stated* or *implied* in the passage.

A-Frame Bookshelf Do-it-yourselfers can build large-capacity, self-supporting bookshelves that are easy to set up and break down. They are called A-frame bookshelves, because the frame and shelves form an A.

Hinge — 2-by-4

Dowel

Not drawn to scale

4 ft

8 ft

7 ft 4 in.

The frame uses four 2-by-4's, each 8 feet long. They are joined in pairs by a hinge. Holes are drilled through the 2-by-4's at 1-foot intervals. Round dowels, $\frac{3}{4}$ of an inch in diameter, connect the two parts of the frame.

The shelves are fastened to the dowels. Each shelf is shorter than the one below it by the same amount. In the six-shelf unit shown above, the top shelf is 4 feet long and the bottom shelf is 7 feet 4 inches long.

1. What is the difference in length between each
C shelf and the one directly below it?
   Ⓐ 4 in.   Ⓑ 6 in.   Ⓒ 8 in.   Ⓓ $14\frac{2}{3}$in.

2. How far beyond each edge of the top shelf does
H each edge of the bottom shelf extend?
   Ⓕ 4 in.   Ⓖ 8 in.
   Ⓗ 1 ft 8 in.   Ⓙ 3 ft 6 in.

3. What is the total length of the shelves?
D Ⓐ 29 ft 8 in.   Ⓑ 32 ft
   Ⓒ 33 ft 4 in.   Ⓓ 34 ft

4. Suppose you can buy 2-by-4's in any length for
G $.29 per foot. About how much will you pay for
the 2-by-4's for the bookcase?
   Ⓕ $5   Ⓖ $10   Ⓗ $15   Ⓙ $20

5. Suppose the 2-by-4's are 2 in. thick, the shelves
B are 8 in. deep, and the dowels are cut flush
with the front and back faces of the bookshelf.
If the dowels are sold in 4-ft lengths, how
many lengths would you have to buy for
the bookcase?
   Ⓐ 2   Ⓑ 3   Ⓒ 4   Ⓓ 12

For Questions 6–10, use the information below. Show your work.

A shorter bookshelf uses 2-by-4's that are 6 ft long, and has five shelves. The top shelf is 3 ft long and the bottom shelf is 6 ft 8 in. long.

6. What is the difference in length from each shelf to the one below it? **11 in.**

7. How much does the bottom shelf extend to the right beyond the right-most edge of the top shelf? **1 ft 10 in.**

8. What is the total length of shelving in the bookshelf? **24 ft 2 in.**

9. In a four-shelf bookshelf, the bottom shelf is 8 ft long. The top shelf is 5 ft $1\frac{1}{2}$ in. long. How long are the other two shelves? **7 ft $\frac{1}{2}$ in., 6 ft 1 in.**

10. Which is greater, the average length of the shelves in Questions 6–8 or the average length of the shelves in Question 9? How much greater is it? **The average length of the shelves in Question 9 is greater by 1 ft $8\frac{3}{4}$ in.**

Students must be able to extract information from reading passages, answer multiple choice questions, and construct responses in order to be successful on current state and national assessments.

To answer the questions, students apply skills and concepts from this chapter and previous chapters.
Multiple Choice: Items 1–5
Free Response: Items 6–10

Resources

Test Prep Workbook

Grab & Go
• **L3** Cumulative Review

ExamView CD-ROM
• Standardized Test Practice

Differentiated Instruction Resources

Spanish Assessment Resources
• **L3** Spanish Cumulative Review

29.
    −4 −3 −2 −1 0 1 2

30.
    1 2 3 4 5 6 7 8 9

31.
    −2 −1 0 1

Functions, Equations, and Graphs

Chapter at a Glance

Lesson Titles, Objectives, and Features	Assessment	NCTM Standards	Local Standards
Algebra 1 Review: The Coordinate Plane **2-1** **Relations and Functions** • Graphing relations • Identifying functions	Lesson Quiz	2, 8, 10	
2-2 **Linear Equations** • Graphing linear equations • Writing equations of lines **Extension:** Piecewise Functions	Lesson Quiz	2, 7, 10	
2-3 **Direct Variation** • Writing and interpreting direct variation equations	Lesson Quiz Checkpoint Quiz 1	2, 8, 9	
2-4 **Using Linear Models** • Writing linear equations that model real-world data • Making predictions from linear models **Vocabulary Builder:** High-Use Academic Words **Activity Lab:** Technology: Finding a Line of Best Fit	Lesson Quiz	2, 5, 6, 9	
2-5 **Absolute Value Functions and Graphs** • Graphing absolute value functions	Lesson Quiz	2, 10	
2-6 **Families of Functions** • Analyzing translations • Analyzing stretches, shrinks, and reflections	Lesson Quiz Checkpoint Quiz 2	2, 3, 10	
2-7 **Two-Variable Inequalities** • Graphing linear inequalities • Graphing absolute value inequalities **GPS:** Understanding Math Problems	Lesson Quiz	2, 10	
Activity Lab: Applying Functions			

NCTM Standards 2000

1 Number and Operations	**2** Algebra	**3** Geometry	**4** Measurement	**5** Data Analysis and Probability
6 Problem Solving	**7** Reasoning and Proof	**8** Communication	**9** Connections	**10** Representation

Correlations to Standardized Tests

All content for these tests is contained in *Prentice Hall Algebra 2*. This chart reflects coverage in this chapter only.

	2-1	2-2	2-3	2-4	2-5	2-6	2-7
SAT®							
Number and Operations Operations, ratio & proportions, complex numbers, counting, elementary number theory, matrices, sequences	✔	✔	✔	✔	✔	✔	✔
Algebra and Functions Expressions, equations, inequalities, representation and modeling, properties of functions (linear, polynomial, rational, exponential)	✔	✔	✔	✔	✔	✔	
Geometry and Measurement *Plane Euclidean/Measurement Coordinate* Lines, parabolas, circles, symmetry, transformations *Three-dimensional* Solids, surface area & volume (cylinders, cones, pyramids, spheres, prisms) *Trigonometry* Right triangles, identities					✔	✔	
Data Analysis, Statistics, and Probability Mean, median, mode, range, interquartile range, graphs and plots, regression, probability				✔			
ACT®							
Pre-Algebra Basic operations using whole numbers, decimals, fractions, and integers; place value; square roots and approximations; the concept of exponents; scientific notation; factors, ratio, proportion, and percent; linear equations in one variable; absolute value and ordering numbers by value; elementary counting techniques and simple probability; data collection, representation, and interpretation; and understanding simple descriptive statistics.	✔	✔	✔	✔	✔	✔	✔
Elementary Algebra Properties of exponents and square roots, evaluation of algebraic expressions through substitution, using variables to express functional relationships, understanding algebraic operations, and solving quadratic equations by factoring.	✔	✔	✔	✔	✔	✔	✔
Intermediate Algebra Understanding of the quadratic formula, rational and radical expressions, absolute value equations and inequalities, sequences and patterns, systems of equations, quadratic inequalities, functions, modeling, matrices, roots of polynomials, and complex numbers.	✔		✔	✔	✔	✔	✔
Coordinate Geometry Graphing and the relations between equations and graphs, including points, lines, polynomials, circles, and other curves; graphing inequalities; slope; parallel and perpendicular lines; distance; midpoints; and conics.	✔	✔	✔	✔	✔	✔	✔
Plane Geometry Properties and relations of plane figures, including angles and relations among perpendicular and parallel lines; properties of circles, triangles, rectangles, parallelograms, and trapezoids; transformations; the concept of proof and proof techniques; volume; and applications of geometry to three dimensions.		✔				✔	
Trigonometry Understanding trigonometric relations in right triangles; values and properties of trigonometric functions; graphing trigonometric functions; modeling using trigonometric functions; use of trigonometric identities; and solving trigonometric equations.							
NAEP							
Number Sense, Properties, and Operations			✔		✔	✔	
Measurement	✔	✔					
Geometry and Spatial Sense							
Data Analysis, Statistics, and Probability				✔			
Algebra and Functions	✔	✔	✔	✔	✔	✔	✔

SAT® The College Board, SAT® Reasoning Test   **ACT®** The ACT Assessment® Test   **NAEP** National Assessment of Educational Progress, 2005 Mathematics Objectives

Math Background

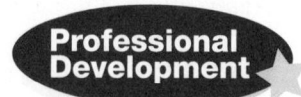

Skills Trace

> ### BEFORE Chapter 2
> In Chapter 1, students reviewed properties of real numbers, solved equations and inequalities in one variable, and examined absolute value equations and inequalities
>
> ▼
>
> ### DURING Chapter 2
> Students distinguish between relations and functions, model data using linear functions, and perform transformations of parent functions.
>
> ▼
>
> ### AFTER Chapter 2
> Students will graph transformations of functions and solve equations and inequalities throughout the course.

Chapter Overview

Relations are defined as sets of ordered pairs and functions are defined as relations that assign exactly one value of the range to each value of the domain. Linear functions are functions whose graphs are lines in the coordinate plane. Students use the concept of slope to write equations for linear functions. They also see how slopes can be used to decide whether two lines in the coordinate plane are parallel or perpendicular.

Direct variations are discussed as a special type of linear function. Students examine mathematical and real-world applications of direct variations.

In the feature following Lesson 2-2, students study piecewise functions. In their study of absolute value functions, students combine what they have learned about linear functions and piecewise functions.

Finally, students examine how the graphs of absolute value functions can be translated in the coordinate plane. Translations will be used in later chapters with more complicated graphs.

Relations and Functions   2-1

Relations and functions can be specified by word descriptions, lists, tables, graphs, mapping diagrams, and equations. It is important that students can represent the same relation or function using multiple formats. Thus, students should feel comfortable making a table and graph from an equation. Nevertheless, a given relation cannot necessarily be expressed in each of the representation formats. Furthermore, each representation format has its merits as well as limitations, depending on how the representation is to be applied. For example, a graph can be used to quickly determine whether a relation is a function by using the vertical-line test. However, a graph may not be helpful for identifying a specific ordered pair.

Of particular interest are relations and functions that are orderly enough to be described by equations. Equations such as $y = 3x - 5$ can be represented using function notation as $f(x) = 3x - 5$. Function notation clearly shows the relationship between the input or domain x and output or range $f(x)$ because "f of x" gives the function value for the given input x. It is essential that students grasp how a function and relation differ—a function is a relation in which each element of the domain is paired with exactly one element in the range. This is well illustrated in mapping diagrams and in graphs that satisfy the vertical-line test.

Linear Equations   2-2

A linear function can be represented by a linear equation in two variables. The input variable x is called the independent variable and the output variable y is the called dependent variable. Thus y, the dependent variable, *depends* on independent variable x.

Because two points determine a line, one only needs to find two points to sketch the graph of a linear function. Two points that can be identified directly are the x- and y-intercepts. When graphing equations in slope-intercept form $y = mx + b$ and point-slope form $y - y_1 = m(x - x_1)$, generally one point is graphed and a second point is found by using the slope as rise over run.

Slope is a fundamental concept, and it is important for students to recognize slope as a rate of change of one variable in terms of another. Thus, a greater rate of change corresponds to a larger slope and vice versa. A horizontal line has a zero slope while a vertical line has an undefined slope. Parallel lines have the same slope and perpendicular lines have slopes that are negative reciprocals.

Direct Variation   2-3

Direct variations give very clear examples of rates of change. Students who have difficulty using different variables to mean the same thing may not recognize the constant of variation k in $y = kx$ as the slope of the line.

Students who have difficulty with the concept of proportions may find these applications helpful in clarifying their thinking. They should also be aware that the phrases *is directly proportional to, varies directly as,* and *varies directly* with are equivalent.

Using Linear Models 2-4

Even though many real-world situations can be modeled by linear equations, the likelihood that real-world data will fall exactly on the graph of a linear equation is quite low. When real data are recorded as a scatter plot, the approximate line of best fit can be drawn by hand.

In the Activity Lab following Lesson 2-4, graphing calculators are used to find an equation for the line of best fit. Students should recognize that positive correlations have positive slopes and negative correlations have negative slopes. Students reluctant to use calculators may be converted if they research the computations needed to actually determine the line of best fit.

To graph data, one or both axes may be drawn with a break to allow us to see the relevant part of the grid in a reasonably compact space. It is often convenient to use non-unit scales on the axes to accommodate the data of a problem. Different scales may be used for the two axes, but then the apparent slope of a line will be distorted, and the slope cannot be calculated by counting grid lines.

Absolute Value Functions and Graphs 2-5

You may wish to show students that the ordered pair $\left(\frac{-b}{m}, c\right)$ for the vertex of the graph of an absolute value function need not be memorized, since it is easily derived. For functions of the form $y = |mx + b| + c$, where $m \neq 0$, solving the equation $mx + b = 0$ gives the first coordinate, and c represents a vertical translation up or down of the parent function $y = |x|$.

For students who have performed the Extension on piecewise functions following Lesson 2-2, the absolute value function $y = |x|$ can be defined as follows.

$$y = \begin{cases} x, \text{ if } x > 0 \\ 0, \text{ if } x = 0 \\ -x, \text{ if } x < 0 \end{cases}$$

Families of Functions 2-6

Students who have difficulty identifying the direction of horizontal translations may be helped by thinking of "speeding up" or "delaying" what happens with values of the function. For example, for $y = |x|$ the value of the function is 0 when $x = 0$. For $y = |x - 3|$, $h = 3$ and moving from left to right, you have to "wait 3 units" until you arrive at 3, the number that will make $y = 0$.

Students should develop an appreciation of the power that understanding translations gives them to take a complicated function and quickly identify various attributes of the function as transformations of the parent function.

Two-Variable Inequalities 2-7

In Lesson 1-4 students reviewed one-variable inequalities whose solutions were graphed on a number line. Two-variable inequalities have solution regions that are graphed in the two-dimensional coordinate plane. A dashed boundary indicates $>$ or $<$ and a solid boundary indicates $\geq$ or $\leq$. For linear two-variable inequalities, the boundary is a line that divides the plane into two regions or half-planes, one above the line and one below the line.

Many real-world situations can be modeled by linear inequalities. However, the domain and range are often restricted so that both variables are positive. A further restriction can be to only whole number solutions.

The tolerances involved in many manufacturing and packaging situations can be represented with absolute value inequalities. Skill in applying the logic involved in solving these will also be needed in later courses.

Additional Professional Development Opportunities

Math Background notes for Chapter 2: Every lesson has a Math Background in the PLAN section.

Research Overview, Mathematical Strands
Additional support for these topics and more is in the front of this Teacher's Edition.

Lesson Lab
Lesson Lab, a Pearson Education company, offers comprehensive, facilitated professional development designed to help teachers improve student achievement. To learn more, please visit lessonlab.com

Chapter 2 Resources

Print Resources

		2-1	2-2	2-3	2-4	2-5	2-6	2-7	For the Chapter
L3	Practice	•	•	•	•	•	•	•	
L3	Guided Problem Solving	•	•	•	•	•	•	•	
L2	Reteaching	•	•	•	•	•	•	•	
L4	Enrichment	•	•	•	•	•	•	•	
L3	Daily Notetaking Guide	•	•	•	•	•	•	•	
L3	Vocabulary and Study Skills Worksheets	•		•	•	•	•		•
L3	Chapter Project								•
L3	Hands On Activities	•	•		•				
L3	Checkpoint Quiz			•			•		
L2	Below Level Chapter Test								•
L3	Chapter Test								•
L4	Alternative Assessment								•
L3	Cumulative Review								•
L4	Connections to Precalculus Masters	•	•	•	•	•	•	•	
L3	Technology Activites		•		•				

Spanish Resources ELL

		2-1	2-2	2-3	2-4	2-5	2-6	2-7	For the Chapter
L3	Practice	•	•	•	•	•	•	•	
L3	Vocabulary and Study Skills Worksheets	•		•	•	•	•		•
L3	Checkpoint Quiz			•			•		
L2	Below Level Chapter Test								•
L3	Chapter Test								•
L4	Alternative Assessment								•
L3	Cumulative Review								•

Transparencies

	2-1	2-2	2-3	2-4	2-5	2-6	2-7	For the Chapter
Check Skills You'll Need	•	•	•	•	•	•	•	
Additional Examples	•	•	•	•	•	•	•	
Problem of the Day	•	•	•	•	•	•	•	
Classroom Aid	•	•		•				
Student Edition Answers	•	•	•	•	•	•	•	•
Lesson Quiz	•	•	•	•	•	•	•	
Test-Taking Strategies								•

Technology

	2-1	2-2	2-3	2-4	2-5	2-6	2-7	For the Chapter
TI 83/84 Plus Activities		•		•	•	•		
Interactive Textbook Online	•	•	•	•	•	•	•	•
Student Express CD-ROM	•	•	•	•	•	•	•	
TI Navigator, Instant Check System	•	•	•	•	•	•	•	
Success Tracker	•	•	•	•	•	•	•	•
ExamView CD-ROM with Quick Take	•	•	•	•	•	•	•	•
Teacher Express CD-ROM	•	•	•	•	•	•	•	•
Presentation Express CD-ROM	•	•	•	•	•	•	•	•
Mindpoint Quiz Show CD-ROM	•	•	•	•	•	•	•	•
Prentice Hall Web site: PHSchool.com	•	•	•	•	•	•	•	•

Also available: Prentice Hall Assessment System (Progress Monitoring Assessments, Skills and Concepts Review, Test Prep Workbook)   Solution Key   Student Workbook
Student Workbook, Adapted Version   Data Analysis and Probability Workbook   Math Notes Study Folder   Spanish Cumulative Assessment

Where You Can Use the Lesson Resources

Here is a suggestion, following the four-step teaching plan, for how you can incorporate Differentiated Instruction Resources into your teaching.

	Instructional Resources L3	**Differentiated** Instruction Resources
1. Plan		
Check Skills You'll Need Assign these exercises to review prerequisite skills. **New Vocabulary** Help students pre-read the lesson by pointing out the new terms introduced in the lesson.	**Math Background** **Transparencies & Presentation Express CD** Check Skills You'll Need **Resources** Vocabulary and Study Skills	**Spanish Support** ELL Vocabulary and Study Skills
2. Teach		
L3 Guided Instruction Teach each Example. After each Example, assign the Quick Check exercise for that Example.	**Student Edition** Activity Lab **Resources** Daily Notetaking Guide Activity Lab TI-83/84 Activities CD-ROM **Transparencies & Presentation Express CD** Additional Examples Classroom Aids **ExamView CD-ROM with QuickTake** **TI Navigator Instant Check System**	**Teacher's Edition** Every lesson includes suggestions for working with students who need special attention. L1 Special Needs L2 Below Level L4 Advanced Learners ELL English Language Learners
3. Practice		
Assignment Guide **Homework Exercises** Assign the exercises cited in each lesson's Assignment Guide. A Practice by Example B Apply Your Skills C Challenge Test Prep Mixed Review **Homework Quick Check** Discuss in class the exercises cited in each lesson's Assignment Guide.	**Transparencies & Presentation Express CD** Student Answers **Resources** Practice Guided Problem Solving Vocabulary and Study Skills Activity Lab **ExamView CD-ROM with QuickTake**	**Spanish Support** ELL Practice ELL Vocabulary and Study Skills **Resources** L4 Enrichment
4. Assess & Reteach		
Lesson Quiz Assign the Lesson Quiz to assess students' mastery of the lesson content. **Checkpoint Quiz** Use the Checkpoint Quiz to assess student progress over several lessons.	**Transparencies & Presentation Express CD** Lesson Quiz **Resources** Checkpoint Quiz	**Resources** L2 Reteaching ELL Checkpoint Quiz Success Tracker **ExamView CD-ROM with QuickTake**

KEY L1 Special Needs L2 Below Level L3 For All Students L4 Advanced, Gifted ELL English Language Learners

Chapter 2

Functions, Equations, and Graphs

 Check Your Readiness

Answers are in the back of the textbook.

For intervention, direct students to:

Graphing Numbers on the Number Line
Lesson 1-1: Example 2
Extra Skills and Word Problems Practice, Ch. 1

Simplifying Expressions
Lesson 1-2: Example 4
Extra Skills and Word Problems Practice, Ch. 1

Solving Absolute Value Inequalities
Lesson 1-5: Examples 4–5
Extra Skills and Word Problems Practice, Ch. 1

Probability
Lesson 1-6: Example 3
Extra Skills and Word Problems Practice, Ch. 1

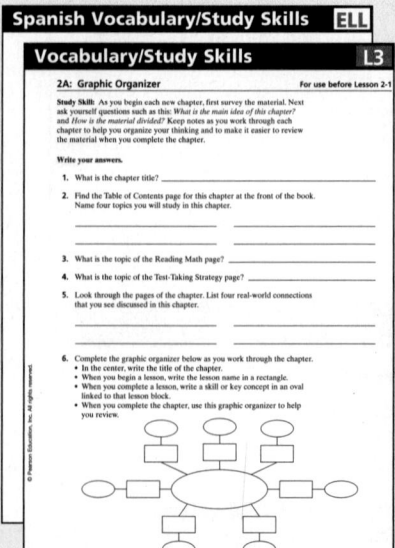

Spanish Vocabulary/Study Skills ELL

Vocabulary/Study Skills L3

2A: Graphic Organizer — For use before Lesson 2-1

What You've Learned

- In first-year algebra, you learned to interpret and solve problems algebraically.

- In geometry, you learned to analyze and manipulate two- and three-dimensional figures.

- In Chapter 1, you learned to represent relationships using variables. You learned to evaluate and simplify variable expressions involving integers and fractions.

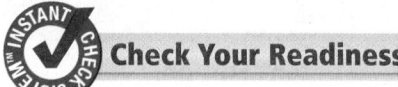 **Check Your Readiness**   **GO for Help** to the Lesson in green.

Graphing Numbers on the Number Line (Lesson 1-1)

Graph each group of numbers on a number line. **1–3. See margin.**

1. $2, -\frac{7}{4}, -1, \frac{15}{2}$ **2.** $0, \frac{2}{3}, -\sqrt{2}, -3$ **3.** $-\frac{5}{4}, \sqrt{7}, 2.\overline{6}, 4$

Simplifying Expressions (Lesson 1-2)

Simplify by combining like terms.

4. $7s - s$ **6s**   **5.** $3a + b + a$ **4a + b**   **6.** $xy - y + x$ **xy − y + x**

7. $0.5g + g$ **1.5g**   **8.** $4t - (t + 3t)$ **0**   **9.** $b - 2(1 + c - b)$ **3b − 2c − 2**

10. $5f - (5d - f)$ **6f − 5d**   **11.** $2(h + 2g) - (g - h)$ **3h + 3g**   **12.** $-(3z - 5) + z$ **−2z + 5**

13. $(2 - d)g - 3d(4 + g)$ **2g − 4dg − 12d**   **14.** $5v - 3(2 - v)$ **8v − 6**   **15.** $7t - 3s(2 + t) + s$ **7t − 3st − 5s**

Solving Absolute-Value Inequalities (Lesson 1-5)

Solve each absolute-value inequality. Graph the solution. **16–21. See margin.**

16. $|x - 3| < 5$ **17.** $|2a - 1| \geq 2a + 1$ **18.** $|3x + 4| > -4x - 3$

19. $|3x + 1| + 1 > 12$ **20.** $3|d - 4| \leq 13 - d$ **21.** $-\frac{1}{3}|f + 3| + 2 \geq -5$

Probability (Lesson 1-6)

A bag contains 12 red, 15 green, 10 yellow, 25 purple, and 2 black blocks. Find each theoretical probability for one block selected at random.

22. $P(\text{green})$ $\frac{15}{64}$ **23.** $P(\text{black})$ $\frac{1}{32}$ **24.** $P(\text{red or yellow})$ $\frac{11}{32}$

25. $P(\text{not red})$ $\frac{13}{16}$ **26.** $P(\text{not yellow})$ $\frac{27}{32}$ **27.** $P(\text{black or not red})$ $\frac{13}{16}$

52 Chapter 2

---

page 52 Check Your Readiness

1.

2.

3.

16. $-2 < x < 8$

17. $a \leq 0$

Functions, Equations, and Graphs

Chapter 2

🔊**Key Vocabulary**

- absolute value function (p. 88)
- constant of variation (p. 72)
- dependent variable (p. 62)
- direct variation (p. 72)
- domain (p. 56)
- function (p. 57)
- independent variable (p. 62)
- linear equation (p. 62)
- linear function (p. 62)
- linear inequality (p. 101)
- parent function (p. 93)
- point-slope form (p. 65)
- range (p. 56)
- relation (p. 55)
- slope (p. 64)
- slope-intercept form (p. 65)
- standard form (p. 63)
- translation (p. 93)
- vertical-line test (p. 57)
- x-intercept (p. 63)
- y-intercept (p. 63)

Chapter 2 Overview

This chapter begins by introducing students to relations and functions. In the next lesson, students learn about linear equations and slope. Students then study direct variation, and using linear models. Absolute value functions and graphs, and families of functions are presented. Students conclude the chapter with a lesson on two-variable inequalities.

Activating Prior Knowledge

Ask:
- *Give a real-world example of a linear relationship between two variables.*

Accept all reasonable answers that involve a constant of proportionality such as cost per pound or miles per gallon.

Ask:
- *Can you give an example of a linear equation?*

Write all reasonable suggestions on the board. Suggestions should include equations with two variables such as $y = 5x$, $y = \frac{1}{2}x + 2$, $y = 5$, and $2x - 3y = 5$.

Inform students that in Chapter 2 they will study relationships between two variables using equations, graphs, tables, and word descriptions.

What You'll Learn Next

- In Chapter 2, you will move from simplifying variable expressions and solving one-variable equations and inequalities to working with two-variable equations and inequalities.

- You will learn how to represent function relationships by writing and graphing linear equations and inequalities.

- By graphing data and trend lines, you will understand how the slope of a line can be interpreted in real-world situations.

Activity Lab Applying what you learn, on pages 114–115 you will do activities involving bridges.

18. $x > -1$

19. $x < -4$ or $x > \frac{10}{3}$

20. $-\frac{1}{2} \leq d \leq \frac{25}{4}$

21. $-24 \leq f \leq 18$

The Coordinate Plane

In this feature, students review the concept of the coordinate plane by graphing points on the coordinate plane, and writing coordinates for specific points on the coordinate plane in order to identify relations and functions in Lesson 2-1.

Resources

The Coordinate Plane
Skills Handbook: p. 876, Example 1

Guided Instruction

You may wish to give students graph paper on which they can draw their own coordinate planes to practice graphing points.

Auditory Learners

Have students graph points on the coordinate plane as you call out the coordinates. Alternatively, have students call out coordinates and you graph them on a coordinate plane on the chalkboard or overhead projector.

page 54   Algebra 1 Review

1.

2.

3.

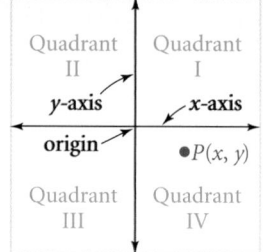

There is a one-to-one correspondence between the points in the coordinate plane and the set of ordered pairs (x, y), where x and y are real numbers. The first number is the x-coordinate, or abscissa. The abscissa gives the horizontal position of a point. The second number is the y-coordinate, or ordinate. The ordinate gives the vertical position of a point.

1 EXAMPLE   Graphing Points

Graph $(4, 3)$ and $(-4, -3)$.

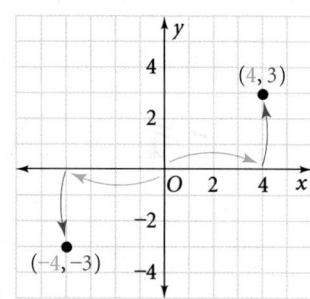

Graph and label each ordered pair.

You can write the coordinates of a point if you are given its graph.

2 EXAMPLE   Writing Coordinates

Write the coordinates of each point in the graph.

The points are $A(2, 4)$, $B(3, 0)$, $C(-4, 0)$, $D(0, -3)$, $E(-5, 4)$, $F\left(4, \frac{1}{2}\right)$, $G(0, 0)$, and $H\left(-3, -3\frac{1}{2}\right)$.

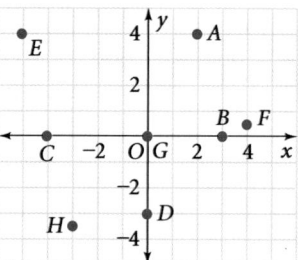

EXERCISES

1–6. See margin for graph.

Graph and label each ordered pair. Name the quadrant or axis where each point lies.

1. $(5, -2)$ **IV**   **2.** $(-3, 4)$ **II**   **3.** $\left(-4, -2\frac{1}{2}\right)$ **III**

4. $\left(5\frac{1}{2}, 0\right)$ **x-axis 5.** $(5, 2)$ **I**   **6.** $(0, -3)$ **y-axis**

Write the coordinates of each point in the graph at the right.

7. C $(4, -4)$ **8.** $G\left(-3, -1\frac{1}{2}\right)$ **9.** J $(3, 2)$ **10.** $A\left(-\frac{1}{2}, 4\frac{1}{2}\right)$

4.

5.

6.

Relations and Functions

What You'll Learn

• To graph relations
• To identify functions

...And Why

To write a function for the area of a square, as in Example 6

 Check Skills You'll Need

 for Help Skills Handbook page 876 and Lesson 1-2

Graph each ordered pair on the coordinate plane. 1–5. See back of book.

1. $(-4, -8)$ **2.** $(3, 6)$ **3.** $(0, 0)$ **4.** $(-1, 3)$ **5.** $(-6, 5)$

Evaluate each expression for $x = -1, 0, 2,$ and 5.

6. $x + 2$
   1, 2, 4, 7
7. $-2x + 3$
   5, 3, -1, -7
8. $2x^2 + 1$
   3, 1, 9, 51
9. $|x - 3|$
   4, 3, 1, 2

🔊 **New Vocabulary** • relation • domain • range • mapping diagram • function • vertical-line test • function notation

---

1 Graphing Relations

A camera recorded the egg's height at various times during its fall.

Suppose you use a motion detector to track an egg as it drops from 10 ft above the ground. The motion detector stores input values (times) and output values (heights). A **relation** is a set of pairs of input and output values. You can write a relation as a set of ordered pairs.

input (time in seconds) → {0   0.1   0.2   0.3   0.4}
                            ↓   ↓   ↓   ↓   ↓
             relation → {(0, 10), (0.1, 9.8), (0.2, 9.4), (0.3, 8.6), (0.4, 7.4)}
                            ↑   ↑   ↑   ↑   ↑
output (height in feet) → {10   9.8   9.4   8.6   7.4}

You can graph a relation on a coordinate plane.

1 EXAMPLE Graphing a Relation

Graph the relation $\{(-2, 4), (3, -2), (-1, 0), (1, 5)\}$.

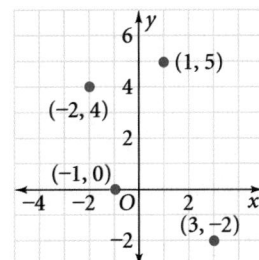

Graph and label each ordered pair.

✓ **Quick Check** ❶ Graph each relation. **a–b. See back of book.**
   a. $\{(0, 4), (-2, 3), (-1, 3), (-2, 2), (1, -3)\}$
   b. $\{(-2, 1), (-1, 0), (0, 1), (1, 2)\}$

Lesson 2-1 Relations and Functions   **55**

Objectives

1 To graph relations
2 To identify functions

Examples

1 Graphing a Relation
2 Finding Domain and Range
3 Making a Mapping Diagram
4 Identifying Functions
5 Using the Vertical-Line Test
6 Real-World Connection

 Professional Development

Math Background

A relation between two sets of numbers can be represented by a set of ordered pairs. The first coordinate of the ordered pair is called the input value, or x-coordinate. The second coordinate of the ordered pair is called the output value, or y-coordinate. It is common to assume that the ordered pairs of a relation are distinct. With this understanding, a function is a relation for which no x-coordinate is paired with more than one y-coordinate.

More Math Background: p. 52C

Lesson Planning and Resources

See p. 52E for a list of the resources that support this lesson.

 PowerPoint

Bell Ringer Practice

✓ **Check Skills You'll Need**
For intervention, direct students to:

The Coordinate Plane
Skills Handbook: p. 876
Example 1

Algebraic Expressions
Lesson 1-2: Examples 1, 2
Extra Skills and Word
   Problems Practice, Ch. 1

Differentiated Instruction Solutions for All Learners

Special Needs L1
Help students distinguish between a relation and a function. A function is a special kind of relation in which each x-value can have only one corresponding y-value. In a graph, the vertical-line test identifies repeated y-values in relations that are not functions.
learning style: visual

Below Level L2
Explain that all functions are relations, but not all relations are functions. The relation $x = y^2$ is not a function because there are two values of y for every positive value of x.

learning style: verbal

2. Teach

Guided Instruction

1 EXAMPLE Math Tip

Many students expect an easily discernable pattern in the coordinates of points for a mathematical relation. Explain that mathematics often uses very broad, inclusive definitions.

2 EXAMPLE Teaching Tip

To help students remember which coordinates to use for the domain and range, use alphabetical order. The letter *d,* for *x*-coordinates, precedes the letter *r,* for *y*-coordinates as *x* precedes *y.*

Additional Examples

1 Graph the relation {(−3, 3), (2, 2), (−2, −2), (0, 4), (1, −2)}.

2 Write the ordered pairs for the relation. Find the domain and range.

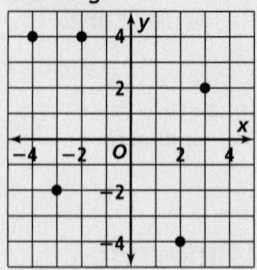

{(−4, 4), (−3, −2), (−2, 4), (2, −4), (3, 2)}; *D* = {−4, −3, −2, 2, 3}, *R* = {−4, −2, 2, 4}

3 Make a mapping diagram for the relation {(−1, 7), (1, 3), (1, 7), (−1, 3)}.

56

The **domain** of a relation is the set of all inputs, or *x*-coordinates of the ordered pairs. The **range** of a relation is the set of all outputs, or *y*-coordinates of the ordered pairs.

You can sometimes find the domain and range of a relation from its graph.

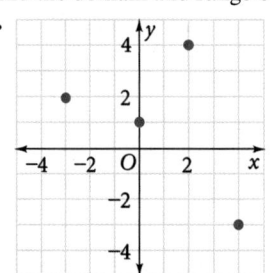

Backpacks or bookbags are used by 93% of students.

2 EXAMPLE Finding Domain and Range

Write the ordered pairs for the relation shown in the graph. Find the domain and range.

{(2, 4), (3, 4.5), (4, 7.5), (5, 7), (6, 5), (6, 7.5)}

The domain is {2, 3, 4, 5, 6}.

The range is {4, 4.5, 5, 7, 7.5}.

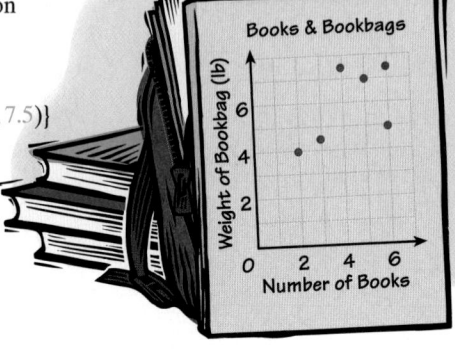

✓ Quick Check **2** Find the domain and range of each relation.

a.

b.

domain {−3, 0, 2, 4}, range {2, 1, 4, −3}

domain {−3, −1, 1}, range {−4, −2, 1, 3}

Another way to show a relation is to use a **mapping diagram,** which links elements of the domain with corresponding elements of the range. Write the elements of the domain in one region and the elements of the range in another. Draw arrows to show how each element from the domain is paired with elements from the range.

3a. domain range

b. domain range

3 EXAMPLE Making a Mapping Diagram

Make a mapping diagram for the relation {(−1, −2), (3, 6), (−5, −10), (3, 2)}.

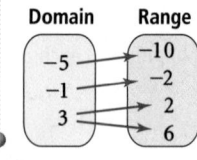

Pair the domain elements with the range elements.

✓ Quick Check **3** Make a mapping diagram for each relation. **See left.**
  a. {(0, 2), (1, 3), (2, 4)}
  b. {(2, 8), (−1, 5), (0, 8), (−1, 3), (−2, 3)}

Advanced Learners **L4**
Have students determine whether the computer spreadsheet function SQRT is a mathematical function. **Yes**

learning style: tactile

English Language Learners **ELL**
Use function notation to reinforce the mathematical meanings of *domain* and *range.* Write a function such as $f(x) = 2x − 3$ on the board. Identify the function name as *f,* the *domain* or input as *x,* and the *range* or output as *f(x)* using colors.

learning style: visual

A **function** is a relation in which each element of the domain is paired with exactly one element in the range.

4 **EXAMPLE** **Identifying Functions**

Determine whether each relation is a function.

a. Domain   Range

The element −2 of the domain is paired with both −1 and 3 of the range. The relation is *not* a function.

b. Domain   Range
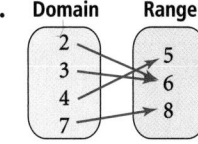

Each element of the domain is paired with exactly one element of the range. The relation is a function.

✓ **Quick Check** **4** Determine whether each relation is a function.

a. Domain   Range   function   **b.** Domain   Range   not a function

You can identify a function by its domain, its range, and the rule that relates the domain to the range. You can represent a function with a mapping diagram as in Example 4, part (b), or with a graph in the coordinate plane. Sometimes the graph of a function may be *discrete*, a collection of isolated points. Other times the graph may be *continuous*, an uninterrupted line or curve.

You can use the **vertical-line test** on the graph of a relation to tell whether the relation is a function. If a vertical line passes through at least two points on the graph, then one element of the domain is paired with more than one element of the range. The relation is *not* a function.

5 **EXAMPLE** **Using the Vertical-Line Test**

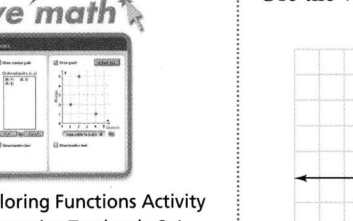

For: Exploring Functions Activity
Use: Interactive Textbook, 2-1

Use the vertical-line test to determine whether each graph represents a function.

Vertical line passes through
← 3 points   1 point →

← Not a function
A function →

Guided Instruction

4 **EXAMPLE**   **Auditory Learners**

Have students verbalize how the arrows in a mapping diagram can be used to decide whether a relation is a function.

Additional Examples

4 Determine whether the relation is a function. **not a function**

Domain   Range

5 Use the vertical-line test to determine whether the graph represents a function. **function**

✓ **Quick Check** **5** Use the vertical-line test to determine whether each graph represents a function.

a.
not a function

b.
function

c.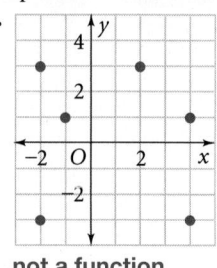
not a function

A function rule expresses an output value in terms of an input value.

Examples of Function Rules

Input	Input	Input
↓	↓	↓
$y = 2x$	$f(x) = x + 5$	$C = \pi d$
↑	↑	↑
Output	Output	Output

GO Online

Video Tutor Help
Visit: PhSchool.com
Web Code: age-0775

You read the **function notation** $f(x)$ as "f of x" or "a function f of x." Note that $f(x)$ does *not* mean "f times x." When the value of x is 3, $f(3)$, read "f of 3," represents the value of the function at $x = 3$.

Input	Function	Output	Ordered Pair
5 ⟶	Subtract 1 ⟶	4	(5, 4)
a ⟶	Add 2 ⟶	$a + 2$	$(a, a + 2)$
3 ⟶	g ⟶	$g(3)$	$(3, g(3))$
x ⟶	f ⟶	$f(x)$	$(x, f(x))$

6 EXAMPLE **Real-World Connection**

Art The area of a square tile is a function of the length of a side of the square. Write a function rule for the area of a square. Evaluate the function for a square tile with side length 3.5 in.

Relate area of a square is (side length)^2

Define Let s = the length of one side of the square tile.
Then $A(s)$ = the area of the square tile.

Write $A(s)$ = s^2

$A(3.5) = (3.5)^2$ **Substitute 3.5 for s.**
$= 12.25$ **Simplify.**

● The area of a square tile with side length 3.5 in. is 12.25 in.^{2}.

Real-World Connection

Square tiles are used as decorative wall and floor coverings.

✓ **Quick Check** **6** Find $f(-3), f(0)$, and $f(5)$ for each function. b. $\frac{-13}{4}, -1, \frac{11}{4}$ c. $\frac{6}{5}, \frac{3}{5}, \frac{-2}{5}$

a. $f(x) = 3x - 5$ b. $f(a) = \frac{3}{4}a - 1$ c. $f(y) = -\frac{1}{5}y + \frac{3}{5}$
 $-14, -5, 10$

pages 59–61   **Exercises**

1.

2.

3.

4.

For more exercises, see *Extra Skill and Word Problem Practice.*

Practice and Problem Solving

Ⓐ Practice by Example

Example 1
(page 55)

 for Help

Graph each relation. 1–7. See margin pp. 58–59.

1. $\{(-1, 3), (-2, 1), (-3, -3), (-4, -5)\}$

2. $\{(0, -2), (2, 0), (3, 1), (5, 3)\}$

3. $\left\{(-1, 0), \left(\frac{1}{2}, -1\right), \left(0, \frac{1}{2}\right), \left(-1, -\frac{1}{2}\right)\right\}$

4. $\left\{\left(2\frac{1}{2}, 0\right), \left(-\frac{1}{2}, 0\right), (2, 0), (0, 0)\right\}$

Example 2
(page 56)

Write the ordered pairs for each relation. Find the domain and range.

5. 　**6.** 　**7.**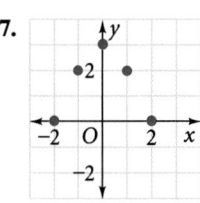

Example 3
(page 56)

Make a mapping diagram for each relation. 8–11. See back of book.

8. $\{(0, 0), (-1, -1), (-2, -8), (-3, -27)\}$

9. $\{(-2, 8), (-1, 1), (0, 0), (1, 1), (2, 8)\}$

10. $\{(-\frac{1}{2}, 11), (0, 10), (\frac{1}{2}, 5), (1, 12)\}$

11. $\{(5, 10), (10, 5), (15, 20), (20, 15)\}$

Example 4
(page 57)

Determine whether each relation is a function.

not a function
12. $\{(1, -2), (-2, 0), (-1, 2), (1, 3)\}$

function
13. $\{(1, 1), (2, 2), (3, 5), (4, 10), (5, 15)\}$

14. $\left\{\left(17, \frac{15}{4}\right), \left(\frac{15}{4}, 17\right), \left(15, \frac{17}{4}\right), \left(\frac{17}{4}, 15\right)\right\}$
function

15. $\left\{\left(-3, \frac{2}{5}\right), \left(-2, \frac{3}{5}\right), \left(\frac{3}{2}, -5\right), \left(5, \frac{2}{5}\right)\right\}$
function

Example 5
(page 57)

Use the vertical-line test to determine whether each graph represents a function.

16. 　**17.** 　**18.**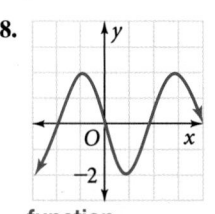

function　　　　not a function　　　　function

19. 　**20.** 　**21.**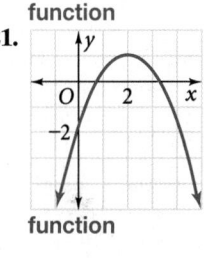

function　　　　not a function　　　　function

Example 6
(page 58)

For each function, find $f(-5)$, $f(-3)$, $f\left(\frac{1}{2}\right)$, **and** $f(4)$.

22. $f(a) = 2a + 3$

23. $f(y) = -3y - 2$

24. $f(z) = z + 9.5$

25. $f(x) = -x - 7$

26. $f(d) = 1 - 4d$

27. $f(x) = 2x - 3$

28. $f(h) = -6h - \frac{2}{3}$

29. $f(x) = \frac{5}{6}x + \frac{1}{3}$

30. $f(t) = \frac{1}{2}t - 2$

22–30. See back of book.

31. Measurement One meter equals about 39.37 in. Write a function rule for converting inches to meters. Evaluate the function for 59 in. $y = \frac{x}{39.37}$, where y is the number of meters and x the number of inches; about 1.50 meters

Lesson 2-1 Relations and Functions **59**

Assignment Guide

1 A B 1-11, 32-35, 40-42

2 A B 12-31, 36-39, 43-54
C Challenge 55-61

Test Prep 62-65
Mixed Review 66-78

Homework Quick Check
To check students' understanding of key skills and concepts, go over Exercises 5, 29, 39, 47, 48.

Exercises 5, 7 If a number is the first element of more than one ordered pair in a relation, it only needs to be listed once in the domain. A similar condition applies for the range.

Error Prevention!

Exercise 3 Point out to students that a function cannot have two different *y*-coordinates for the same *x*-coordinate. Visual learners will benefit from graphing the relation and using the vertical-line test to determine if it is a function.

Differentiated Instruction Resources

GPS Guided Problem Solving	L3
Enrichment	L4
Reteaching	L2
Practice	L3

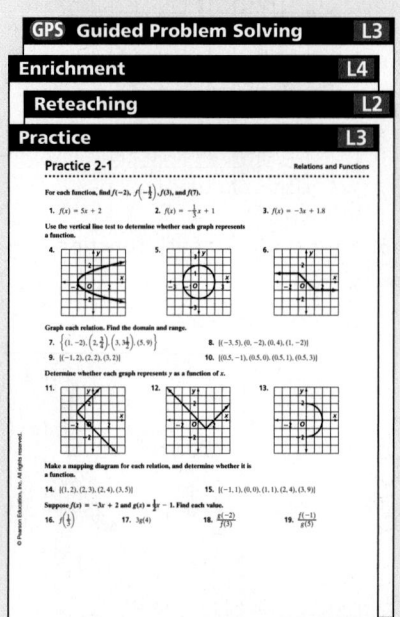

5. $(-2, -2), (-1, 1), (1, 1),$ $(1, 0), (3, 3), (3, -2);$ domain $\{-2, -1, 1, 3\}$, range $\{-2, 0, 1, 3\}$

6. $(-2, 3), (0, 1), (2, -1),$ $(3, -2);$ domain $\{-2, 0, 2, 3\}$, range $\{-2, -1, 1, 3\}$

7. $(-2, 0), (-1, 2), (0, 3),$ $(1, 2), (2, 0);$ domain $\{-2, -1, 0, 1, 2\}$, range $\{0, 2, 3\}$

PowerPoint

Lesson Quiz

1. Write the ordered pairs for the relation. Find the domain and range.

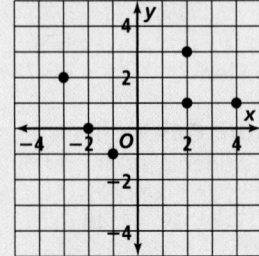

{(−3, 2), (−2, 0), (−1, −1), (2, 1), (2, 3), (4, 1)};
D = {−3, −2, −1, 2, 4},
R = {−1, 0, 1, 2, 3}

2. Determine whether the relation {(−2, 3), (−5, 6), (3, 0), (1, 1)} is a function. **function**

3. Delete one ordered pair so that the relation {(−4, 2), (1, 6), (0, 0), (−4, 6)} is a function. **(−4, 2) or (−4, 6)**

4. Determine whether the graph represents a function. **not a function**

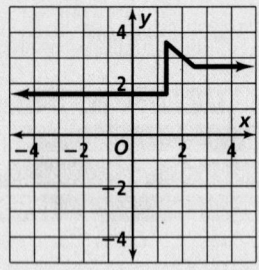

5. Find $f(−5)$ for each function.
   a. $f(x) = 5x + 35$ **10**
   b. $f(x) = x^2 − x$ **30**

pages 59–61 Exercises

32.

domain {2, 3, 4, 5},
range {4, 5, 6, 7}

60

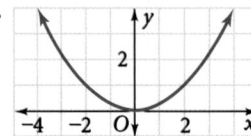
Apply Your Skills

Graph each relation. Find the domain and range. 32–35. See margin pp. 60-61.

32. {(2, 4), (3, 5), (4, 6), (5, 7)}

33. {(−1, 1), (−2, 2), (−3, 3), (−4, 4)}

34. $\left\{\left(-\frac{1}{2}, 2\right), \left(2, \frac{1}{2}\right), \left(0, -\frac{1}{2}\right), \left(-\frac{1}{2}, -2\right)\right\}$

35. $\left\{\left(\frac{3}{2}, -\frac{1}{2}\right), \left(\frac{5}{2}, \frac{1}{2}\right), \left(\frac{1}{2}, \frac{1}{2}\right), \left(-\frac{3}{2}, \frac{1}{2}\right)\right\}$

Find the domain and range of each relation and determine whether it is a function.
36–39. See margin p. 61.

36. {(2, 4), (4, 8), (8, 16)}

37. {(−1, 2), (−2, 5), (−2, 7), (0, 2), (9, 2)}

38.

39.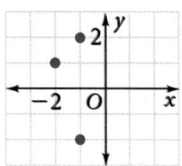

GO **Online**
Homework Video Tutor
Visit: PHSchool.com
Web Code: age-0201

Match each relation with a model.

40. {(1, 2), (−1, −2), (2, −1)} **A**

41. {(2, 1), (1, 2), (1, −2)} **B**

42. {(−1, 2), (−2, 1), (−1, −2)} **C**

A.

B.

C.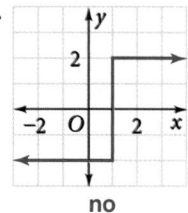

Determine whether each graph represents y as a function of x.

43. 44. 45.

yes no no

46. **Geometry** The volume of a cube is a function of the length of a side of the cube. Write a function for the volume of a cube. Find the volume of a cube with a side 13.5 cm long. $v(s) = s^3$; **2460.375 cm^3**

47. **Sports** The volume of a sphere is a function of the radius of the sphere.
GPS Write a function for the volume of a ball. Evaluate the function for a volleyball of radius 10.5 cm. $v(r) = \frac{4}{3}\pi r^3$; **about 4849 cm^3**

48. No; since 2 in the domain maps to 1 and 4, it is not a function.

48. **Writing** Does the mapping diagram at the left represent a function? Explain.
See left.

49. **Data Collection** Draw a graph to show the relationship between the weight of a letter and the cost of postage. Is it a graph of a function? Explain.
Check students' work.

Suppose $f(x) = 2x + 5$ and $g(x) = -\frac{1}{3}x + 2$. Find each value. (Hint: For 2g(x), find g(x) first, and then multiply the result by 2.)

50. $f(−4)$ **−3**

51. $2g(7)$ **$-\frac{2}{3}$**

52. $-2f(x + 1)$
$-4x − 14$

53. $\frac{f(1)}{g(3)}$ **7**

54. $\frac{f(-2)}{g(f(-2) + 1)}$ **$\frac{3}{4}$**

C **Challenge**

57. Yes; each x is paired with a unique y.

For each relation, determine whether y is a function of x. Explain why or why not.
No; each positive x is paired with two y values.

55. $y = 2x − 3$
Yes; each x is paired with a unique y.

56. $y^2 = x$

57. $x^2 = y − 3$
See left.

60 Chapter 2 Functions, Equations, and Graphs

33.

domain {−4, −3, −2, −1},
range {1, 2, 3, 4}

34.

domain $\left\{-\frac{1}{2}, 0, 2\right\}$,

range $\left\{-2, -\frac{1}{2}, \frac{1}{2}, 2\right\}$

Real-World 🌐 **Connection**

Careers Chemists use math to predict chemical reactions.

🌐 **58. Chemistry** The time required for a certain chemical reaction is related to the amount of catalyst present during the reaction. The domain of the relation is the number of grams of catalyst, and the range is the number of seconds required for a fixed amount of the chemical to react. The following relation is the data from several reactions: {(2, 180), (2.5, 6), (2.7, 0.05), (2.9, 0.001), (3.0, 6), (3.1, 15), (3.2, 37), (3.3, 176)}. Is the relation a function? If the domain and range were interchanged, would the relation be a function? Explain.
See margin.

Suppose a and b are variables representing integers. Find the domain and range of each relation and determine whether it is a function. Justify your reasoning.

59. Domain   Range

60. Domain   Range

61. Domain   Range
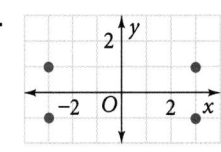

59–61. See back of book.

Test Prep

Multiple Choice

62. Which graph models the relation {(−3, −1), (3, 1), (−3, 1), (3, −1)}? **C**

A.

B.

C.
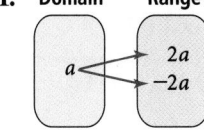

63. Which relation is *not* a function? **G**
  F. {(0, 9), (2, 3), (3, 2), (4, 1)}   **G.** {(3, 2), (4, 1), (0, 9), (3, 3)}
  H. {(0, 3), (2, 3), (3, 3), (4, 3)}   **J.** {(0, 3), (3, 2), (2, 4), (4, 6)}

Short Response

64. If $f(x) = -2x + 3$ and $g(x) = 4x - 3$, which is greater, $f(5)$ or $g(-2)$? Show your work. **See margin.**

Extended Response

65. Is the total surface area S of a cube a function of the edge c of the cube? If it is not a function, explain why not. If it is a function, write the function rule and then evaluate the function for a cube with edge 2.5 cm.
See back of book.

Mixed Review

 for Help

Lesson 1-6

Find each probability for choosing a letter at random from the word *mathematics*.

66. $P(e)$ $\frac{1}{11}$ **67.** $P(m)$ $\frac{2}{11}$ **68.** $P(\text{vowel})$ $\frac{4}{11}$ **69.** $P(n)$ 0

$\frac{6}{11}$ **70.** $P(\text{a letter that occurs more than once})$ **71.** $P(\text{consonant})$ $\frac{7}{11}$ **72.** $P(\text{s or t})$ $\frac{3}{11}$

Lesson 1-5

Solve each equation or inequality. Graph the solution on a number line.
73-75. See back of book.

73. $|x - 4| = 10$ **74.** $3 + |b| \le 5$ **75.** $|6 - y| > 0$

Skills Handbook

Find each percent of increase or decrease.

76. from 9 m to 10 m
  11.1% increase

77. from 1 gal to 1.5 gal
  50% increase

78. from 2 km to 1.5 km
  25% decrease

35.

domain $\left\{-\frac{3}{2}, \frac{1}{2}, \frac{3}{2}, \frac{5}{2}\right\}$,

range $\left\{-\frac{1}{2}, \frac{1}{2}\right\}$

36. domain {2, 4, 8},
  range {4, 8, 16}; function

37. domain {−2, −1, 0, 9},
  range {2, 5, 7};
  not a function

Alternative Assessment

Have students work in groups of three. Each group creates fifteen distinct ordered pairs. Some ordered pairs should have the same *x*-values and some should have the same *y*-values. Each ordered pair is written on its own piece of paper and placed in a box. Each group picks at least five ordered pairs from the box to form a relation. One group member expresses the relation as a set of ordered pairs. Another group member expresses the relation as a mapping diagram and another expresses the relation as a graph. They share results, determine if the relation is a function, and find the domain and range.

Test Prep

📁 **Resources**

For additional practice with a variety of test item formats:
• Standardized Test Prep, p. 113
• Test-Taking Strategies, p. 108
• Test-Taking Strategies with Transparencies

38. domain {all real numbers}, range {$y \ge 0$}; function

39. domain {$-3.2 \le x \le 3.2$}, range {$-1 \le y \le 1$}; not a function

58. Function; if the domain and range are interchanged, it is not a function because 6 would be paired with both 2.5 and 3.0.

64. [2] $f(5)$; $f(5) = -2(5) + 3 = -7$ and $g(-2) = 4(-2) - 3 = -11$, and $-7 > -11$.

  [1] only includes answer $f(5)$ or $g(-2)$

61

Objectives
1 To graph linear equations
2 To write equations of lines

Examples
1 Graphing a Linear Equation
2 Real-World Connection
3 Finding Slope
4 Writing an Equation Given the Slope and a Point
5 Writing an Equation Given Two Points
6 Finding Slope Using Slope-Intercept Form
7 Writing an Equation of a Perpendicular Line

Math Background

A linear function is a function whose graph is a line. When given an equation for a linear function, you can get important information about the graph (slope, intercepts, and so on). Likewise, appropriate information about a line allows you to write an equation for the line.

More Math Background: p. 52C

Lesson Planning and Resources

See p. 52E for a list of the resources that support this lesson.

Bell Ringer Practice

☑ **Check Skills You'll Need**
For intervention, direct students to:

Algebraic Expressions
Lesson 1-2: Examples 1, 2
Extra Skills and Word Problems
Practice, Ch. 1

What You'll Learn
• To graph linear equations
• To write equations of lines

. . . And Why
To solve a transportation problem, as in Example 2

☑ **Check Skills You'll Need**

GO for Help Lesson 1-2

Evaluate each expression for $x = -2, 0, 1,$ and 4.   1–4. See back of book.

1. $\frac{2}{3}x + 7$ 2. $\frac{3}{5}x - 2$ 3. $3x + 1$ 4. $\frac{1}{2}x - 8$

🔊 **New Vocabulary**
• linear function   • linear equation
• dependent variable   • independent variable
• x-intercept   • y-intercept
• standard form of a linear equation   • slope
• point-slope form   • slope-intercept form

---

1   Graphing Linear Equations

A function whose graph is a line is a **linear function**. You can represent a linear function with a **linear equation**, such as $y = 3x + 2$. A solution of a linear equation is any ordered pair (x, y) that makes the equation true.

You can write the solutions of the equation using set notation as $\{(x, y) \mid y = 3x + 2\}$. Read the notation as "the set of ordered pairs x, y such that $y = 3x + 2$." Because the value of y depends on the value of x, y is called the **dependent variable** and x is called the **independent variable.**

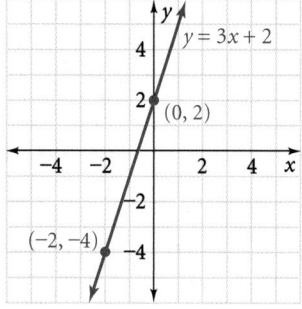

1 EXAMPLE   Graphing a Linear Equation

Graph the equation $y = \frac{2}{3}x + 3$.

Choose two values for x and find the corresponding values of y. Plot the point for each ordered pair and complete the graph by drawing a line through the points.

x	$\frac{2}{3}x + 3$	y	(x, y)
-3	$\frac{2}{3}(-3) + 3$	1	$(-3, 1)$
3	$\frac{2}{3}(3) + 3$	5	$(3, 5)$

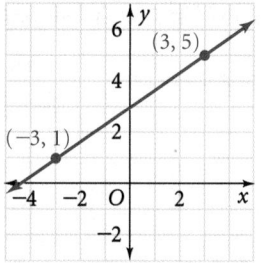

Check Choose a third point on the line and check that its ordered pair satisfies the equation. Since $(0, 3)$ is a point on the line, and $\frac{2}{3}(0) + 3 = 3$, the graph is correct.

....

Problem Solving Hint

Geometry Since two points determine a line, you can use two points to graph a line. Check your line by finding a third point.

Differentiated Instruction Solutions for All Learners

Special Needs L1
Help students identify the multiple ways in which a function can be represented: an equation, a table, a graph, and a word description. You can also include mapping diagrams, sets of ordered pairs, and function notation presented in Lesson 2-1.
learning style: visual

Below Level L2
Students may try to identify a single ordered pair as *the* solution of a linear equation. Emphasize that many ordered pairs satisfy the equation and that all are solutions.
learning style: verbal

Quick Check ① Graph each equation. Check your work.

a. $y = \frac{3}{4}x$ **b.** $x + y = -2$ **c.** $y = -\frac{1}{2}x + \frac{1}{2}$

1a.

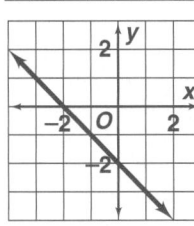

The **y-intercept** of a line is the point at which the line crosses the y-axis. You can use the same term to identify the y-coordinate of this point.

The **x-intercept** of a line is the point at which the line crosses the x-axis. You can use the same term to identify the x-coordinate of this point.

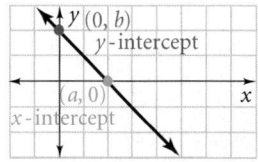

b.

c.

The **standard form of a linear equation** is $Ax + By = C$, where A, B, and C are real numbers, and A and B are not both zero. You can graph a linear equation in standard form by finding the x- and y-intercepts.

② **EXAMPLE**   **Real-World Connection**

Transportation The equation $3x + 2y = 120$ models the number of passengers who can sit in a train car, where x is the number of adults and y is the number of children. Graph the equation. Explain what the x- and y-intercepts represent. Describe the domain and the range.

Set x or y equal to zero to find each intercept.

$3x + 2y = 120$	$3x + 2y = 120$
$3x + 2(0) = 120$	$3(0) + 2y = 120$
$3x = 120$	$2y = 120$
$x = 40$	$y = 60$

Use the intercepts to graph the equation. The x-intercept is $(40, 0)$. When 40 adults are seated, no children can sit. The y-intercept is $(0, 60)$. When no adults are seated, 60 children can sit.

The number of passengers is a whole number. The situation is discrete. The domain is limited to the whole numbers 0 to 40; the range to the whole numbers 0 to 60.

 Quick Check ② **a.** Suppose the train system buys new train cars with molded plastic seats. The model changes to $x + y = 40$. Graph the equation and interpret the x- and y-intercepts. **See back of book.**

b. Explain how using molded seats changes the number of seated passengers. **See left.**

2b. Answers may vary. Sample: Each seat holds one person, whether adult or child.

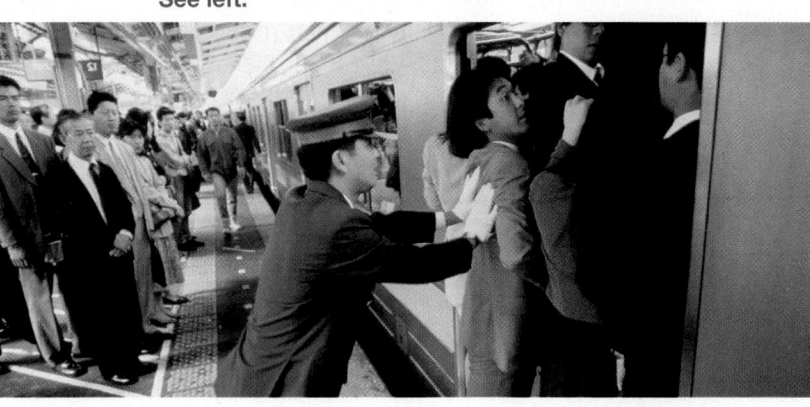

Real-World Connection

In Japan, so many people ride public transportation that they need help getting into the trains.

Advanced Learners L4

$Ax + By = C$ and $Dx + Ey = F$ are perpendicular. Find an expression for A.

$A = -\frac{BE}{D}$

learning style: verbal

English Language Learners ELL

Have students make a chart to connect independent and dependent variables with the domain and range of a function.
    Domain: input, x-values, independent variable
    Range: output, y-values, dependent variable

learning style: visual

---

2. Teach

Guided Instruction

① **EXAMPLE**   **Math Tip**

Accurate graphs are easy to obtain if the two points used for the line have integer coordinates. To get such points in this example, substitute x-values that are multiples of 3.

② **EXAMPLE**   **Auditory Learners**

Have students verbalize why the graph for this situation is a finite set of discrete points rather than a continuous line.

PowerPoint

Additional Examples

① Graph the equation $y = -\frac{4}{3}x + 2$.

② The equation $10x + 5y = 40$ models how you can give $.40 change if you have only dimes and nickels. The variable x is the number of dimes, and y is the number of nickels. Graph the equation. Describe the domain and the range. Explain what the x- and y-intercepts represent.

$D = \{0, 1, 2, 3, 4\}$, $R = \{0, 2, 4, 6, 8\}$; The x-intercept $(4, 0)$ means you use 4 dimes if you give all the change in dimes. The y-intercept $(0, 8)$ means you use 8 nickels if you give all the change in nickels.

Vocabulary Tip

The slope of a line is also the rate of change between two points on the line.

The **slope** of a nonvertical line is the ratio of the vertical change to a corresponding horizontal change. You can calculate slope by subtracting the corresponding coordinates of two points on the line.

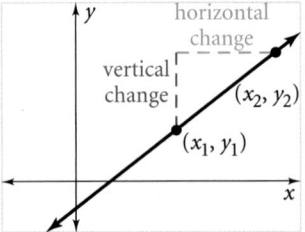

Key Concepts

Definition	Slope Formula

$$\text{slope} = \frac{\text{vertical change (rise)}}{\text{horizontal change (run)}} = \frac{y_2 - y_1}{x_2 - x_1}, \text{where } x_2 - x_1 \neq 0$$

3 EXAMPLE Finding Slope

Find the slope of the line through the points $(3, 2)$ and $(-9, 6)$.

$\text{slope} = \frac{y_2 - y_1}{x_2 - x_1}$ **Use the slope formula.**

$= \frac{6 - 2}{-9 - 3}$ **Substitute (3, 2) for (x_1, y_1) and $(-9, 6)$ for (x_2, y_2).**

$= \frac{4}{-12}$ **Subtract.**

$= -\frac{1}{3}$ **Simplify.**

The slope of the line is $-\frac{1}{3}$.

Quick Check **3** Find the slope of the line through each pair of points.
  a. $(-2, -2)$ and $(4, 2)$ $\frac{2}{3}$
  b. $(0, -3)$ and $(7, -9)$ $-\frac{6}{7}$

2 Writing Equations of Lines

Activity: Point-Slope Form

1. Make a table of values to graph each line. 1–4. See margin pp. 64–65.

   a. $y - 1 = -2(x - 2)$ **b.** $y - 2 = \frac{1}{3}(x - 1)$ **c.** $y - 5 = 3(x - 4)$

2. Find the slope of each line. Compare the slope of the line to the red number in the equation of the line. What do you notice?

3. Find the point on the graph of each line with an x-coordinate that is equal to the green number in the equation line. Then compare the y-coordinate of the point to the blue number in the equation of the line. What do you notice?

4. **Make a Conjecture** All three equations in Question 1 are in the form $y - y_1 = m(x - x_1)$. Make a conjecture about how you can use that form to help you graph an equation.

page 64
Activity

1a.

x	y
−5	15
−2	9
0	5
2	1
5	−5

b.

x	y
−5	0
−2	1
1	2
2	$2\frac{1}{3}$
5	$3\frac{1}{3}$

c.

x	y
−4	−19
−2	−13
0	−7
2	−1
4	5

2. $-2, \frac{1}{3}, 3$; the slopes are the same as the red number in the equation.

When you know the slope and a point on a line, you can use the **point-slope form** to write the equation of the line.

 Key Concepts

| **Definition** | **Point-Slope Form** |

The line through point (x_1, y_1) with slope m has the equation below.

$$y - y_1 = m(x - x_1)$$

4 EXAMPLE Writing an Equation Given the Slope and a Point

Write in standard form an equation of the line with slope $-\frac{1}{2}$ through the point $(8, -1)$.

$y - y_1 = m(x - x_1)$ **Use the point-slope equation.**

$y - (-1) = -\frac{1}{2}(x - 8)$ **Substitute $-\frac{1}{2}$ for m, -1 for y_1, and 8 for x_1.**

$y - (-1) = -\frac{1}{2}x - \left(-\frac{1}{2}\right)(8)$ **Distributive Property**

$y + 1 = -\frac{1}{2}x + 4$ **Simplify.**

$\frac{1}{2}x + y = 3$ **Write in standard form.**

✓ **Quick Check** **4** Write in standard form the equation of each line.

a. slope 2, through $(4, -2)$ **b.** slope $\frac{5}{6}$, through $(5, 6)$

$2x - y = 10$ $\frac{5}{6}x - y = -\frac{11}{6}$ $5x - 6y = -11$

When you know two points on a line, you can write an equation by using the point-slope equation combined with the slope formula.

5 EXAMPLE Writing an Equation Given Two Points

Write in point-slope form the equation of the line through $(1, 5)$ and $(4, -1)$.

$y - y_1 = m(x - x_1)$ **Write the point-slope equation.**

$y - y_1 = \frac{y_2 - y_1}{x_2 - x_1}(x - x_1)$ **Substitute the slope formula for m.**

$y - 5 = \frac{-1 - 5}{4 - 1}(x - 1)$ **Substitute: $x_1 = 1, y_1 = 5, x_2 = 4, y_2 = -1$.**

$y - 5 = \frac{-6}{3}(x - 1)$ **Simplify.**

$y - 5 = -2(x - 1)$ **Write in point-slope form.**

✓ **Quick Check** **5** Write in point-slope form the equation of the line through each pair of points.
a. $(5, 0)$ and $(-3, 2)$ **b.** $(-2, -1)$ and $(-10, 17)$ **c.** $(5, 1)$ and $(-4, -3)$
   $y - 0 = -\frac{1}{4}(x - 5)$ $y + 1 = -\frac{9}{4}(x + 2)$ $y - 1 = \frac{4}{9}(x - 5)$

Another form of the equation of a line is **slope-intercept form,** which you can use to find slope by examining the equation.

 Key Concepts

| **Definition** | **Slope-Intercept Form** |

slope ⌐   ⌐y-intercept

$y = mx + b$

5 EXAMPLE Alternative Method

You may want to have a volunteer show what equation is obtained if $(4, -1)$ is used for (x_1, y_1) and $(1, 5)$ is used for (x_2, y_2). Demonstrate or have a volunteer demonstrate that this new equation and $y - 5 = -2(x - 1)$ can both be rewritten as $2x + y = 7$.

Teaching Tip

You may wish to point out that the slope-intercept form is a special case of the point-slope form. Simply use $(0, b)$ for (x_1, y_1) in the point-slope form.

Additional Examples

4 Write in standard form an equation of the line with slope 3 through the point $(-1, 5)$.
$3x - y = -8$

5 Write in point-slope form an equation of the line through $(4, -3)$ and $(5, -1)$. $y + 3 = 2(x - 4)$ or $y + 1 = 2(x - 5)$

---

3. Where the x-coordinate is the green number, the y-coordinate equals the blue number.

4. Answers may vary. Sample: Using the form $y - y_1 = m(x - x_1)$, you would start at the point

(x_1, y_1) and then use m to graph another point. To graph the eq., draw a straight line through the pts.

Teaching Tip - Have students graph y=3 and x=2...

Example 7 Math Tip...

PowerPoint Additional Examples...

6 Find slope of -7x+2y=8. 7/2

7 Write equation...

Graph with y=4x+1 and y=-1/4x-7/4

Resources, Closure.

Middle/right: Example 6...

Quick Check...

Key Concepts Summary table...

Slopes properties with 4 graphs.

Real-World Connection Eiffel tower...

Bottom: page 67 Quick Check 7a...

6 EXAMPLE Finding Slope Using Slope-Intercept Form

Find the slope of $4x + 3y = 7$.

$$4x + 3y = 7$$
$$3y = -4x + 7 \qquad \text{Subtract } 4x \text{ from each side.}$$
$$y = -\frac{4}{3}x + \frac{7}{3} \qquad \text{Write in slope-intercept form.}$$

● The slope of the line is $-\frac{4}{3}$.

✓ Quick Check **6** Find the slope of each line.

a. $3x + 2y = 1$ $-\frac{3}{2}$ b. $\frac{2}{3}x + \frac{1}{2}y = 1$ $-\frac{4}{3}$ c. $Ax + By = C$ $-\frac{A}{B}, B \neq 0$ undefined, $B = 0$

🔑 Key Concepts

Summary	Equations of a Line	
Point-Slope Form	Standard Form	Slope-Intercept Form
$y - 2 = -3(x + 4)$	$3x + y = -10$	$y = -3x - 10$

The slopes of horizontal, vertical, perpendicular, and parallel lines have special properties.

Horizontal Line

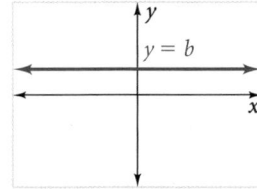

$m = 0$
y is constant.

Vertical Line

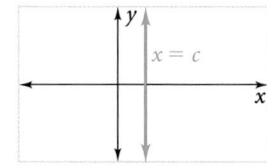

m is undefined.
x is constant.

Perpendicular Lines

$m_1 \cdot m_2 = -1$
(In other words, m_2 is the negative reciprocal of m_1.)

Parallel Lines

$m = m$
$b_1 \neq b_2$

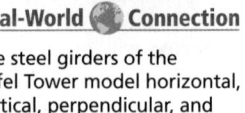

Real-World 🌐 Connection

The steel girders of the Eiffel Tower model horizontal, vertical, perpendicular, and parallel lines.

page 67 Quick Check

7a. $y = -\frac{1}{5}x + \frac{14}{5}$

b. $y = \frac{2}{3}x - \frac{1}{3}$

c. $x = 5$

Video Tutor Help
Visit: PHSchool.com
Web Code: age-0775
Also available on DVD

7 **EXAMPLE** Writing an Equation of a Perpendicular Line

Write an equation of the line through each point and perpendicular to $y = \frac{3}{4}x + 2$.
Graph all three lines.

a. $(0, 4)$

$m = -\left(\frac{1}{\frac{3}{4}}\right) = -\frac{4}{3}$ Find the negative reciprocal of $\frac{3}{4}$.

$y = mx + b$ Use slope-intercept form.

$y = -\frac{4}{3}x + 4$ Substitute: $m = -\frac{4}{3}$ and $b = 4$.

b. $(6, 1)$

$y = -\frac{4}{3}x + b$ Slope is $-\frac{4}{3}$.

$1 = -\frac{4}{3}(6) + b$ Substitute $(6, 1)$ for (x, y).

$1 = -8 + b$ Simplify.

$9 = b$ Solve for b.

$y = -\frac{4}{3}x + 9$ Write the equation.

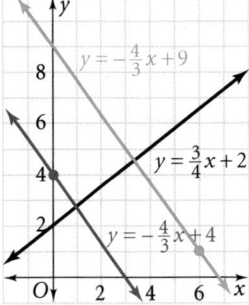

Quick Check **7** Write an equation for each line. Then graph the line. **a–c. See margin p. 66.**
a. through $(-1, 3)$ and perpendicular to the line $y = 5x - 3$
b. through $(2, 1)$ and parallel to the line $y = \frac{2}{3}x + \frac{5}{8}$
c. vertical and through $(5, -3)$

EXERCISES

For more exercises, see *Extra Skill and Word Problem Practice*.

Practice and Problem Solving

 Practice by Example

Example 1
(page 62)

Graph each equation. Check your work. **1–8. See back of book.**

1. $y = 2x$ **2.** $y = -3x - 1$ **3.** $y = 3x - 2$ **4.** $y = -4x + 5$

5. $5x - 2y = -4$ **6.** $-2x + 5y = -10$ **7.** $y - 3 = -2x$ **8.** $y + 4 = -3x$

Example 2
(page 63)

9. Cost Analysis The equation $y - 0.23x = 0$ relates the cost of operating a car to the number of miles driven, where x is the number of miles driven and y is the cost. **a–b. See margin.**
  a. Graph the equation and determine the domain and range.
  b. Explain what the x- and y-intercepts represent.
  c. Explain what 0.23 represents.
  0.23 represents a cost of \$.23 per mile driven.

10. Fund-Raising The school glee club needs a total of \$4500 for a trip to Omaha, Nebraska. To make money, members are selling baseball caps for \$4.50 and sweatshirts for \$12.50. **a–b. See back of book.**
  a. Graph the equation $4.5x + 12.5y = 4500$, where x is the number of baseball caps and y is the number of sweatshirts sold.
  b. Explain the meaning of the x- and y-intercepts in terms of the fund-raising.

Example 3
(page 64)

Find the slope of the line through each pair of points.

11. $(1, 6)$ and $(8, -1)$ **−1**   **12.** $(-3, 9)$ and $(0, 3)$ **−2**   **13.** $(0, 0)$ and $(2, 6)$ **3**

14. $(-4, -3)$ and $(7, 1)$ $\frac{4}{11}$ **15.** $(-2, -1)$ and $(8, -3)$ $-\frac{1}{5}$ **16.** $(1, 2)$ and $(2, 3)$ **1**

undefined **17.** $\left(\frac{2}{3}, \frac{4}{7}\right)$ and $\left(\frac{2}{3}, \frac{11}{7}\right)$ **18.** $(-3, 5)$ and $(4, 5)$ **0**   **19.** $(-5, -7)$ and $(0, 10)$ $\frac{17}{5}$

---

pages 67–70   Exercises

9a.

$y = 0.23x$
domain $\{x \mid x \geq 0\}$
range $\{y \mid y \geq 0\}$

b. x-intercept $(0, 0)$,
y-intercept $(0, 0)$; when
no miles have been
driven, there is no cost.

---

3. Practice

Assignment Guide

1 A B 1-19, 42-50, 63-65, 69, 70

2 A B 20-41, 51-62, 66-68, 71-78

C Challenge   79-84

Test Prep   85-90
Mixed Review   91-98

Homework Quick Check

To check students' understanding of key skills and concepts, go over Exercises 10, 29, 60, 63, 78.

Error Prevention!

Exercises 11–19 Remind students to subtract the x-coordinates in the same order as they subtract the y-coordinates and to be careful when subtracting negative numbers.

Differentiated Instruction Resources

GPS Guided Problem Solving   L3
Enrichment   L4
Reteaching   L2
Practice   L3

Exercises 35, 36 In their answers, students should note any restrictions on *A*, *B*, and *C*.

Exercises 48–50 Remind students that it is a good idea to first multiply each side of the equation by the LCD of all fractions in the equation to clear the equation of fractions.

Math Tip
Exercises 75–77 Even though a standard form of a linear equation uniquely determines a line, be careful to realize that a line does not have a unique standard form.

Example 4
(page 65)

Write in standard form the equation of each line. 20–22. See margin.

20. slope $= 3; (1, 5)$ **21.** slope $= \frac{5}{6}; (22, 12)$ **22.** slope $= -\frac{3}{5}; (-4, 0)$

23. slope $= 0; (4, -2)$ **24.** slope $= -1; (-3, 5)$ **25.** slope $= 5; (0, 2)$
$y = -2$ $x + y = 2$ $5x - y = -2$

Example 5
(page 65)

Write in point-slope form the equation of the line through each pair of points.
26–28. See margin.

26. $(-10, 3)$ and $(-2, -5)$ **27.** $(1, 0)$ and $(5, 5)$ **28.** $(-4, 10)$ and $(-6, 15)$

29. $(0, -1)$ and $(3, -5)$ **30.** $(7, 11)$ and $(13, 17)$ **31.** $(1, 9)$ and $(6, 2)$
$y + 1 = -\frac{4}{3}(x - 0)$ $y - 11 = 1(x - 7)$ $y - 9 = -\frac{7}{5}(x - 1)$

Example 6
(page 66)

Find the slope of each line.

32. $5x + y = 4$ -5 **33.** $-3x + 2y = 7$ $\frac{3}{2}$ **34.** $-\frac{1}{2}x - y = \frac{3}{4}$ $-\frac{1}{2}$

35. $Ax + By = C$ $-\frac{A}{B}$ **36.** $Ax - By = C$ $\frac{A}{B}$ **37.** $y = 7$ 0

Example 7
(page 67)

Write an equation for each line. Then graph the line. 38–39. See margin.

38. through $(-2, 1)$ and parallel to $y = -3x + 1$

39. through $(-3, -1)$ and perpendicular to $y = -\frac{2}{5}x - 4$

40. through $(-7, 10)$ and horizontal **40–41. See back of book.**

41. through $\left(1, -\frac{2}{7}\right)$ and vertical

B Apply Your Skills

Graph each equation. 42–50. See back of book.

42. $y = -\frac{3}{5}x - \frac{12}{5}$ **43.** $y = -2x + 3$ **44.** $y = -x + 7$

45. $3y - 2x = -12$ **46.** $4x + 5y = 20$ **47.** $4x - 3y = -6$

48. $\frac{2}{3}x + \frac{y}{3} = -\frac{1}{3}$ **49.** $\frac{3}{5}y - \frac{x}{5} = -\frac{6}{5}$ **50.** $\frac{4}{5} = -\frac{1}{3}x - \frac{3}{4}y$

Find the slope of each line.

51.   **52.**   **53.**
$\frac{1}{3}$ $\frac{2}{3}$ $-\frac{1}{4}$

    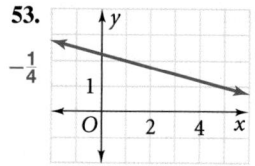

Find the slope and the intercepts of each line. 54–62. See margin.

54. $f(x) = \frac{2}{3}x + 4$ **55.** $y = -x + 1000$ **56.** $y = 0.4 - 0.8x$

57. $g(x) = 54x - 1$ **58.** $x = -3$ **59.** $y = 0$

60. $-\frac{1}{3}x - \frac{2}{3}y = \frac{5}{3}$ **61.** $-Rx + Sy = -T$ **62.** $\frac{A}{D}x + \frac{B}{D}y = \frac{C}{D}$

Find the slope of the line through each pair of points.

GPS **63.** $\left(\frac{3}{2}, -\frac{1}{2}\right)$ and $\left(-\frac{2}{3}, \frac{1}{3}\right) -\frac{5}{13}$ **64.** $\left(-\frac{1}{2}, -\frac{1}{2}\right)$ and $\left(-3, \frac{7}{4}\right)$ **65.** $\left(0, \frac{1}{2}\right)$ and $\left(\frac{5}{7}, 0\right)$ $-\frac{7}{10}$

$-\frac{7}{5}$

Write an equation for each line. Each interval is 1 unit.
$y = 3x + 2$

66.   **67.**   **68.**
$y = \frac{3}{4}x + 3$ $y = -\frac{3}{2}x - \frac{1}{2}$

GO Online
Homework Video Tutor
Visit: PHSchool.com
Web Code: age-0202

68   Chapter 2   Functions, Equations, and Graphs

pages 67–70   Exercises

20. $3x - y = -2$

21. $\frac{5}{6}x - y = \frac{19}{3}$

22. $\frac{3}{5}x + y = -\frac{12}{5}$

26. $y - 3 = -1(x + 10)$

27. $y - 0 = \frac{5}{4}(x - 1)$

28. $y - 10 = -\frac{5}{2}(x + 4)$

38. $y = -3x - 5$

39. $y = \frac{5}{2}x + \frac{13}{2}$

54. $\frac{2}{3}$; $(0, 4)$, $(-6, 0)$

55. -1; $(0, 1000)$, $(1000, 0)$

56. -0.8; $(0, 0.4)$, $(0.5, 0)$

57. 54; $(0, -1)$, $\left(\frac{1}{54}, 0\right)$

58. undefined slope;
no y-intercept, $(-3, 0)$

59. 0; $(0, 0)$, all pts. on x-axis

60. $-\frac{1}{2}$; $\left(0, -\frac{5}{2}\right)$, $(-5, 0)$

61. $\frac{R}{S}$; $\left(0, -\frac{T}{S}\right)$, $\left(\frac{T}{R}, 0\right)$

62. $-\frac{A}{B}$; $\left(0, \frac{C}{B}\right)$, $\left(\frac{C}{A}, 0\right)$

Real-World **Connection**

You can download data from a motion detector to a computer to produce graphs of distance versus time.

Test-Taking Tip

On a graph that plots distance against time, be sure you understand exactly what distance is being modeled. In Exercise 69, it's the distance of the student *from* the detector.

69. Multiple Choice Three students moved away from or toward a motion detector, one at a time. Each graph shows distance from the detector as a function of time. **B**

  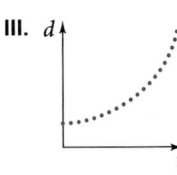

Which of the following statements is true?
- Ⓐ Student I was the only student who moved away from the detector.
- Ⓑ Student II was the only student who moved toward the detector.
- Ⓒ Student I was speeding up.
- Ⓓ Student II was slowing down.

70. Critical Thinking Most graphing calculators are designed to graph equations that are solved for *y*. What lines could not be graphed with this method? **Vertical lines cannot be graphed by this method.**

Write an equation for each line. Then graph the line. 71–74. See margin.

71. $m = 0$, through $(5, -1)$

72. $m = 2$, through $(1, 3)$

73. $m = \frac{5}{6}$, through $(-4, 0)$

74. $m = -\frac{3}{2}$, through $(0, -1)$

Write each equation in standard form.

75. $y = \frac{3}{2}x - 1$
$3x - 2y = 2$

76. $x + \frac{1}{3}y = \frac{2}{9}$
$9x + 3y = 2$

77. $-\left(\frac{1}{2}x + 2y\right) = \frac{2}{3}$
$3x + 12y = -4$

78. a. Open-Ended Write an equation of a line.
  b. Write an equation of the line parallel to the line you wrote in part (a) passing through the point $(0.5, 0.6)$. **a–e. Check students' work.**
  c. Write an equation of the line perpendicular to the line you wrote in part (a) passing through the point $\left(\frac{5}{3}, 2\right)$.
  d. Write an equation of the line parallel to the line you wrote in part (c) passing through the point $(-3, 1)$.
  e. Geometry Graph the lines from parts (a), (b), (c), and (d). If they form a polygon, describe it. **The polygon is a rectangle.**

 Challenge

81. $y = 3x + 6$;
$y = -\frac{1}{3}x + \frac{8}{3}$; $\left(\frac{1}{2}, 2\frac{1}{2}\right)$

Problem Solving Hint

The slopes of parallel lines are equal. The slopes of perpendicular lines are negative reciprocals.

Points that are on the same line are *collinear*. Use the definition of slope to determine whether the given points are collinear.

79. $(-2, 6), (0, 2), (1, 0)$ **yes**

80. $(3, -5), (-3, 3), (0, 2)$ **no**

81. Write an equation of a line *a* through $(-1, 3)$ that is parallel to the line $y = 3x + 1$. Write an equation of a line *b* through $(-1, 3)$ that is perpendicular to line *a*. What is the intersection of line *b* and line $y = 3x + 1$? **See left.**

82. Geometry Prove that the triangle with vertices $(3, 5), (-2, 6)$, and $(1, 3)$ is a right triangle. **See back of book.**

83. Geometry Prove that the quadrilateral with vertices $(2, 5), (4, 8), (7, 6)$, and $(5, 3)$ is a rectangle. **See back of book.**

84. Critical Thinking Lines *p, q*, and *r* all pass through point $(-3, 4)$. Line *p* has slope 4 and is perpendicular to line *q*. Line *r* passes through Quadrants I and II only. Write an equation for each line. Then graph the three lines on the same coordinate plane. **See back of book.**

PowerPoint

Lesson Quiz

1. Find the slope of the line through the points $(-5, -1)$ and $(2, 3)$. $\frac{4}{7}$

2. Write an equation in standard form for the line with slope 3 through $(9, -4)$. $3x - y = 31$

3. Write in point-slope form an equation of the line through the points $(-3, 8)$ and $(7, 6)$. Use $(-3, 8)$ as the point for the equation.
   $y - 8 = -\frac{1}{5}(x + 3)$

4. Write the equation $3x - 12y = 6$ in slope-intercept form.
   $y = \frac{1}{4}x - \frac{1}{2}$

5. What is the slope of a line perpendicular to $y = \frac{2}{3}x - 7$? What is the slope of a line parallel to $y = \frac{2}{3}x - 7$? $-\frac{3}{2}; \frac{2}{3}$

Alternative Assessment

Have students work in pairs. Students use a Geoboard to create a coordinate system by using two red rubberbands, one for the x-axis and one for the y-axis. Each pin along each axis represents one unit. Rubberbands are thought of as representing lines not line segments. One student makes a non-vertical line using a yellow rubberband. The other student names two points on the line, the slope, and the y-intercept, writes an equation of the line, graphs this line, writes an equation of the line perpendicular to the given line at its y-intercept, and graphs this new line using a blue rubberband. Students switch roles and repeat.

71. $y = -1$

72. $y = 2x + 1$

73. $y = \frac{5}{6}x + \frac{10}{3}$

74. $y = -\frac{3}{2}x - 1$

69

Test Prep

Resources
For additional practice with a variety of test item formats:
- Standardized Test Prep, p. 113
- Test-Taking Strategies, p. 108
- Test-Taking Strategies with Transparencies

Test Prep

Multiple Choice

85. Which equation represents a line through (3, 5) that is perpendicular to $y = 2x - 5$? **A**

A. $2y = -x + 13$ B. $2y = x + 13$

C. $2y - x = 13$ D. $2y + x = -13$

86. For the equation $3x - 2y = 12$, which has value -6? **G**

F. the x-intercept   G. the y-intercept

H. the slope   J. the origin

87. Which pair of equations represents perpendicular lines? **D**

A. $y = -\frac{3}{8}x + 12$
     B. $y = -\frac{3}{8}x + 12$

     $(y - 1) = -\frac{3}{8}(x + 4)$ $3x + 8y = 20$

C. $y = -\frac{3}{8}x + 12$
     D. $y = -\frac{3}{8}x + 12$

     $(y - 1) = -\frac{8}{3}(x + 4)$ $(y - 1) = \frac{8}{3}(x + 4)$

Short Response

88. The line $(y - 1) = \frac{2}{3}(x + 1)$ contains point $H(a, -3)$. Find a. Show your work. **88–90. See margin.**

89. The point $(-8, k)$ is on the line with slope $-\frac{5}{8}$ and y-intercept 9. Explain how to find k.

Extended Response

90. A line passes through points $K(4, 4)$ and $W(-2, 10)$.
 a. Write an equation for the line in the form $Ax + By = C$. Show your work.
 b. Find the x- and y-intercepts. **See back of book.**

Mixed Review

Lesson 2-1

Find the domain and range of each relation. Then decide whether it is a function.

91.

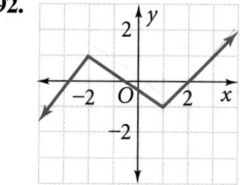

domain $\{-2, 1, 2, 3, 4\}$, range $\{-2, -1, 2, 3\}$; not a function

92.

domain {all reals}, range {all reals}; function

93. Domain   Range

domain $\{-3, 0, 1, 7\}$, range $\{-10, -5, -1, 3\}$; not a function

Lesson 1-1

Identify each demonstrated property (or properties) of real numbers.

94. $7.4 - 3.4 + 2.6 = 7.4 + 2.6 - 3.4$
 Commutative Prop. of Add.

95. $\frac{2}{5} + \frac{27}{5} \cdot \frac{5}{27} = \frac{2}{5} + 1$ multiplicative inverses

96. $97(7) = 100(7) - 3(7)$
 Distributive Prop.

97. $21 + 19.7 - 19.7 = 21$
 additive inverses, additive identity

Skills Handbook   **98. Commission** A fabric designer earns a 60% commission for works sold in a textile studio. The studio receives the other 40%. How much does the studio receive for selling a length of fabric that costs $15.65? How much does the designer receive?
 studio: $6.26; designer: $9.39

Piecewise Functions

A piecewise function has different rules for different parts of its domain.

1 EXAMPLE Writing a Piecewise Function

Write a piecewise function to represent the graph at the right.

The graph has three distinct sections. The function needs a distinct rule for each of the three corresponding sections of the domain. Since $(-2, 3)$ and $(2, -5)$ both lie on two sections of the graph, arbitrarily assign each point to just one section.

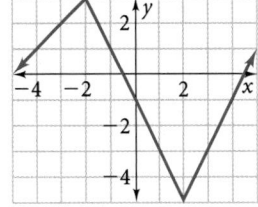

When $x \leq -2$, the rule is $f(x) = x + 5$. When $-2 < x \leq 2$, the rule is $f(x) = -2x - 1$. When $x > 2$, the rule is $f(x) = 2x - 9$.

The piecewise function has three parts. $f(x) = \begin{cases} x + 5, \text{ if } x \leq -2 \\ -2x - 1, \text{ if } -2 < x \leq 2 \\ 2x - 9, \text{ if } x > 2 \end{cases}$

Some piecewise functions are step functions. Their graphs look like the steps of a staircase. One step function is the greatest integer function $f(x) = [x]$, where $[x]$ means the greatest integer less than or equal to x.

2 EXAMPLE Graphing a Piecewise Function

Graph the function $f(x) = [x]$.

Step 1 Choose an interval bounded by two consecutive integers. Make a table of values for the interval $0 \leq x \leq 1$.

x	0	0.25	0.5	0.75	1
f(x)	0	0	0	0	1

Step 2 Graph the function.

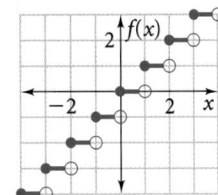

Use closed circles for included endpoints; use open circles for excluded endpoints.

Each section of the graph ends at the y-value at which it starts. The left endpoint of each "step" is a closed circle. The right endpoint is an open circle.

EXERCISES

Graph each piecewise function. 1–6. See margin.

1. $y = [x] + 2$

2. $f(x) = 3[x]$

3. $y = \begin{cases} x + 4, \text{ if } x \leq -2 \\ -x, \text{ if } x > -2 \end{cases}$

4. $f(x) = \begin{cases} -2x + 1, \text{ if } x < 3 \\ x - 8, \text{ if } x \geq 3 \end{cases}$

5. Write a piecewise function to represent the graph at the right.

6. Writing Explain how to graph a piecewise function.

page 71 Extension

1.

Piecewise Functions

In this extension, students study functions whose graphs are formed by piecing together graphs of two or more linear functions. Such functions are important in many situations where no single linear function can adequately model the situation.

Guided Instruction

Error Prevention!

Exercise 3 Some students may think that $(-2, 2)$ should be marked with an open circle. This point is, however, part of the final graph, because the value of $x + 4$ is 2 when $x = -2$.

Resources

Technology
ExamView CD-ROM, Chapter 00, Extension Topics

2.

3.

4.

5.

$f(x) = \begin{cases} -3x - 10, \text{ if } x \leq -2 \\ \frac{1}{2}x - 3, \text{ if } -2 < x < 2 \\ 2x - 6, \text{ if } x \geq 2 \end{cases}$

6. Answers may vary. Sample: Set up a table for each piece of the function. Choose starting and ending values corresponding to its domain. Substitute to find function values.

71

Direct Variation

Objectives
1 To write and interpret direct variation equations

Examples
1 Identifying Direct Variation From a Table
2 Identifying Direct Variation From an Equation
3 Real-World Connection
4 Using a Proportion

Math Background

If y varies directly as x, then as x increases y increases proportionately and as x decreases y decreases proportionately. Furthermore, the rate of increase or decrease remains constant. Geometrically, this means that a direct variation is a linear function of the form $y = kx$ for $k \neq 0$.

More Math Background: p. 52C

Lesson Planning and Resources

See p. 52E for a list of the resources that support this lesson.

Bell Ringer Practice

✓ Check Skills You'll Need
For intervention, direct students to:

Solving Equations
Lesson 1-3: Example 1
Extra Skills and Word Problems Practice, Ch. 1

Proportion
Skills Handbook p. 872
Example 3

What You'll Learn
• To write and interpret direct variation equations

. . . And Why
To model a dripping faucet, as in Example 3

✓ Check Skills You'll Need

 for Help Lesson 1-3 and Skills Handbook page 872

Solve each equation for y.   1. $y = \frac{x}{4}$ 2. $y = \frac{5}{12}x$

1. $12y = 3x$ 2. $12y = 5x$ 3. $\frac{3}{4}y = 15$ 4. $0.9y = 27x$ 5. $5y = 35$
                                   $y = 20$ $y = 30x$ $y = 7$

Tell whether each equation is true.

6. $\frac{1}{4} \overset{?}{=} \frac{2}{8}$ true   7. $\frac{2}{5} \overset{?}{=} \frac{6}{15}$ true   8. $\frac{9}{24} \overset{?}{=} \frac{12}{36}$ false   9. $\frac{20}{24} \overset{?}{=} \frac{30}{36}$ true

◀)) New Vocabulary   • direct variation   • constant of variation

---

1 Writing and Interpreting a Direct Variation

A linear function defined by an equation of the form $y = kx$, where $k \neq 0$, represents **direct variation.** As with any line, the slope k is constant.

When x and y are variables, you can write $k = \frac{y}{x}$, so the ratio $y : x$ equals the constant k, the **constant of variation.**

$y = kx$
Passes through origin

1 EXAMPLE   Identifying Direct Variation From a Table

Vocabulary Tip

You can describe direct variation as "y varies directly as x" or "y varies directly with x."

For each function, determine whether y varies directly with x. If so, find the constant of variation and write the equation.

a.

x	y
2	8
3	12
5	20

$\frac{y}{x} = \frac{8}{2} = \frac{12}{3} = \frac{20}{5} = 4$,

so y varies directly with x.

The constant of variation is 4.

The equation is $y = 4x$.

b.

x	y
1	4
2	7
5	16

Since $\frac{4}{1}, \frac{7}{2}$, and $\frac{16}{5}$ are not equal, $\frac{y}{x}$ is not constant.

y does *not* vary directly with x.

✓ Quick Check ❶ For each function, determine whether y varies directly with x. If so, find the constant of variation and write the equation.

a.   yes; $k = \frac{1}{3}$, $y = \frac{1}{3}x$

x	y
−6	−2
3	1
12	4

b.   no

x	y
−1	−2
3	4
6	7

c.   no

x	y
−9	5
3	$-1\frac{2}{3}$
6	$3\frac{5}{8}$

---

72   Chapter 2   Functions, Equations, and Graphs

Differentiated Instruction   Solutions for All Learners

Special Needs   **L1**
Clear a large area in the room and make a coordinate grid on the floor using masking tape. Direct students to arrange themselves in a line on the grid to model graphs such as $y = -x$, $y = 2x$, and $y = \frac{1}{2}x$.

learning style: tactile

Below Level   **L2**
If students have trouble recognizing direct variation from a table of values, have them graph the number pairs and compare the slopes of the line segments through the pairs.

learning style: visual

You can analyze an equation to determine whether it represents direct variation.

2 EXAMPLE Identifying Direct Variation From an Equation

For each function, determine whether y varies directly with x. If so, find the constant of variation.

a. $3y = 2x$

$3y = 2x$ is equivalent to $y = \frac{2}{3}x$, so y varies directly with x.
The constant of variation is $\frac{2}{3}$.

b. $y = 2x + 3$

Since you cannot write the equation in the form $y = kx$, y does *not* vary directly with x.

✓ **Quick Check** ❷ For each function, determine whether y varies directly with x. If so, find the constant of variation.

a. $y = \frac{x}{2}$ **b.** $2y - 1 = x$ **no**   **c.** $\frac{5}{6}x = \frac{1}{3}y$ **d.** $7x + 4y = 10$ **no**
yes; $k = 0.5$ **yes;** $k = \frac{5}{2}$

You can write an equation to solve a direct variation problem.

3 EXAMPLE Real-World 🌐 Connection

Water Conservation A dripping faucet wastes a cup of water if it drips for three minutes. The amount of water wasted varies directly with the amount of time the faucet drips.

a. Find the constant of variation k and write an equation to model the direct variation.

Relate	water wasted	varies directly	with time

Define Let w = number of cups of water wasted.

Let t = time in minutes the faucet drips.

Write	w	$=$	k	$\cdot$	t

$1 = k(3)$ **Substitute 1 for w and 3 for t.**

$\frac{1}{3} = k$ **Solve for k.**

The constant of variation k is $\frac{1}{3}$. The equation $w = \frac{1}{3}t$ models the direct variation.

b. Find how long the faucet must drip to waste $4\frac{1}{2}$ c of water.

$w = \frac{1}{3}t$ **Use the direct variation.**

$4\frac{1}{2} = \frac{1}{3}t$ **Substitute $4\frac{1}{2}$ for w.**

$\frac{9}{2}(3) = t$ **Solve for t.**

$13\frac{1}{2} = t$ **Simplify.**

The faucet must drip for $13\frac{1}{2}$ min to waste $4\frac{1}{2}$ c of water.

✓ **Quick Check** ❸ **Geometry** The circumference of a circle varies directly with the diameter of the circle. The formula $C = \pi d$ relates the circumference to the diameter.
a. What is the constant of variation? π
b. Find the diameter of a circle with circumference 105 cm to the nearest tenth.
33.4 cm

Lesson 2-3   Direct Variation   **73**

GO Online

Video Tutor Help
Visit: PhSchool.com
Web Code: age-0775

Advanced Learners **L4**
The pressure of a gas in a closed container varies directly with the absolute temperature. Have students find other real-world examples of direct variation.

learning style: verbal

English Language Learners **ELL**
Review the prerequisite terms *ratio* and *proportion*. A ratio is a comparison of two numbers (by division), and a proportion is an equation formed when two ratios are set equal to one another.

learning style: verbal

Additional Examples

4 Suppose y varies directly with x, and $y = 15$ when $x = 27$. Find y when $x = 18$. **10**

Resources

• Daily Notetaking Guide 2-3 **L3**

Closure

If a and b are real numbers and if $y = ax + b$ is a direct variation equation, what do you know about a and b? **$a \neq 0$ and $b = 0$**

You can use proportions to solve some direct variation problems. This can save time when the problem does not ask for the constant of variation.

4 EXAMPLE Using a Proportion

Suppose y varies directly with x, and $x = 27$ when $y = -51$. Find x when $y = -17$.

Let $(x_1, y_1) = (27, -51)$ and let $(x_2, y_2) = (x_2, -17)$.

$\dfrac{y_1}{x_1} = \dfrac{y_2}{x_2}$ Write a proportion.

$\dfrac{-51}{27} = \dfrac{-17}{x_2}$ Substitute.

$-51(x_2) = 27(-17)$ Write the cross products.

$x_2 = \dfrac{27(-17)}{-51}$ Solve for x_2.

$x_2 = 9$ Simplify.

Quick Check **4** Find the missing value for each direct variation.
a. If $y = 4$ when $x = 3$, find y when $x = 6$. **8**
b. If $y = 7$ when $x = 2$, find y when $x = 8$. **28**
c. If $y = 10$ when $x = -3$, find x when $y = 2$. **−0.6**
d. If $y = 1$ when $x = 10$, find y when $x = 2$. **0.2**

EXERCISES

For more exercises, see *Extra Skill and Word Problem Practice*.

Practice and Problem Solving

Ⓐ Practice by Example

Example 1
(page 72)

GO for Help

For each function, determine whether y varies directly with x. If so, find the constant of variation and write the equation. **1–11. See margin.**

1.

x	y
2	4
4	8
16	32

2.

x	y
2	−6
4	−12
5	−15

3.

x	y
11	22
16	32
7	42

4.

x	y
27	9
30	10
60	20

5.

x	y
2	14
3	21
5	35

6.

x	y
3	9
4	13
7	23

7.

x	y
−2	4
−3	6
−5	10

8.

x	y
1	−2
3	−8
5	14

Example 2
(page 73)

Determine whether y varies directly with x. If so, find the constant of variation.

9. $y = 12x$ **10.** $y = 6x$ **11.** $y = -2x$ **12.** $y = 4x + 1$ **no**

13. $y = 4x - 3$ **no** **14.** $y = -5x$ **yes; $k = -5$** **15.** $y - 6x = 0$ **yes; $k = 6$** **16.** $y + 3 = -3x$ **no**

Example 3
(page 73)

For each direct variation, find the constant of variation. Then find the value of y when $x = -5$.

17. $y = 2$ when $x = 7$ $k = \frac{2}{7}; -\frac{10}{7}$ **18.** $y = -5$ when $x = 3$ $k = -\frac{5}{3}; \frac{25}{3}$

19. $y = -2$ when $x = 2$ $k = -1; 5$ **20.** $y = -\frac{2}{3}$ when $x = -\frac{1}{3}$ $k = 2; -10$

21. $y = 17$ when $x = -4$ $k = -\frac{17}{4}; 21\frac{1}{4}$ **22.** $y = \frac{1}{2}$ when $x = -2$ $k = -\frac{1}{4}; 1\frac{1}{4}$

74 Chapter 2 Functions, Equations, and Graphs

---

pages 74–77 Exercises

1. yes; $k = 2$, $y = 2x$

2. yes; $k = -3$, $y = -3x$

3. no

4. yes; $k = \frac{1}{3}$, $y = \frac{1}{3}x$

5. yes; $k = 7$, $y = 7x$

6. no

7. yes; $k = -2$, $y = -2x$

8. no

9. yes; $k = 12$

10. yes; $k = 6$

11. yes; $k = -2$

46. No; $y = 1.7x$ does not contain the point $(9, -9)$.

47. Yes; $y = -\frac{5}{6}x$ contains the point $(15, -12\frac{1}{2})$.

48. Yes; $y = \frac{7}{2}x$ contains the point $(6\frac{1}{2}, 22\frac{3}{4})$.

23. Environment Suppose you work on a tree farm and you need to find the height of each tree. You know that the length of an object's shadow varies directly with its height. Refer to the diagram.
   a. Find the constant of variation. $k = \frac{13}{36}$
   b. Write an equation to calculate the height of the tree. $s = \frac{13}{36}h$
   c. Find the height of a tree with a shadow 8 ft 4 in. long. ≈23 ft 1 in.

?
6 ft
8 ft 4 in.
2 ft 2 in.

Example 4
(page 74)

For Exercises 24–27, y varies directly with x.

24. If $y = 4$ when $x = -2$, find x when $y = 6$. **−3**

25. If $y = 6$ when $x = 2$, find x when $y = 12$. **4**

26. If $y = 7$ when $x = 2$, find y when $x = 3$. **10.5**

27. If $y = 5$ when $x = -3$, find y when $x = -1$. $\frac{5}{3}$

 Apply Your Skills

For each function, determine whether y varies directly with x. If so, find the constant of variation and write the equation.

yes; $k = 1.3$, $y = 1.3x$

28. yes;
$k = \frac{2}{3}$,
$y = \frac{2}{3}x$

28.

x	y
9	6
12	8
15	10

29.
no

x	y
4	1
6	2
8	3

30.
no

x	y
23	24
55	56
66	67

31.

x	y
2	2.6
3	3.9
4	5.2

 for Help

For Gridded Responses, see Test-Taking Strategies, page 46.

32. Gridded Response A speed of 60 mi/h is equal to a speed of 88 ft/s. Find the speed to the nearest mile per hour of an aircraft travelling 1000 ft/s. **682**

Write an equation for a direct variation with a graph that passes through each point.

$y = -500x$

33. $(1, 2)$ $y = 2x$ **34.** $(-3, -7)$ $y = \frac{7}{3}x$ **35.** $(2, -9)$ $y = -\frac{9}{2}x$ **36.** $(-0.1, 50)$

37. $(-5, -3)$ $y = \frac{3}{5}x$ **38.** $(9, -1)$ $y = -\frac{1}{9}x$ **39.** $(7, 2)$ $y = \frac{2}{7}x$ **40.** $(-3, 14)$
$y = -\frac{14}{3}x$

In Exercises 41–45, y varies directly with x.

41. If $y = 7$ when $x = 3$, find x when $y = 21$. **9**

42. If $y = 25$ when $x = 15$, find x when $y = 10$. **6**

43. If $y = 30$ when $x = -3$, find y when $x = -9$. **90**

44. If $y = -20$ when $x = 2$, find x when $x = 14$. **−140**

45. If $y = 0.9$ when $x = 4.8$, find y when $x = 6.4$. **1.2**

Determine whether a line with the given slope through the given point represents a direct variation. Explain. 46–51. See margin pp. 74–75.

46. $m = -1.7, (9, -9)$ **47.** $m = -\frac{5}{6}, \left(15, -12\frac{1}{2}\right)$ **48.** $m = \frac{7}{2}, \left(6\frac{1}{2}, 22\frac{3}{4}\right)$

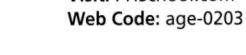 **Online**
Homework Video Tutor
Visit: PHSchool.com
Web Code: age-0203

Open-Ended In Exercises 49–51, choose a value of k within the given range. Then write and graph a direct variation using your value for k. See margin.

49. $0 < k < 1$ **50.** $3 < k < 4.5$ **51.** $-1 < k < -\frac{1}{2}$

Assignment Guide

1 A B 1-54
C Challenge   55-59

Test Prep   60-64
Mixed Review   65-73

Homework Quick Check
To check students' understanding of key skills and concepts, go over Exercises 23, 26, 46, 52, 53.

Error Prevention!

Exercises 1–8 Caution students to check the ratio $\frac{y}{x}$ for each pair of numbers.

Exercises 33–40 One approach is to find the value of k by dividing the y-coordinate of the given point by the x-coordinate. Substitute the resulting value of k in $y = kx$ to get the equation. Another approach is to use the methods of Lesson 2-2 to write an equation for the line through $(0, 0)$ and the given point.

Differentiated Instruction Resources

GPS Guided Problem Solving	L3
Enrichment	L4
Reteaching	L2
Practice	L3

49. Answers may vary.
Sample: $y = 0.5x$

50. Answers may vary.
Sample: $y = 3.2x$

51. Answers may vary.
Sample: $y = -\frac{3}{4}x$

75

4. Assess & Reteach

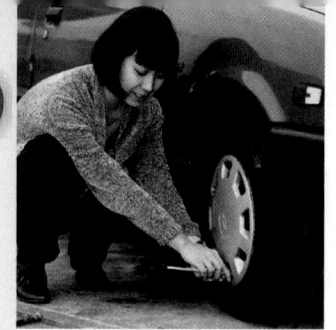

It takes more effort for an engine to propel a car with underinflated tires. Cars with properly inflated tires get better gas mileage.

Lesson Quiz

1. For each function, tell whether y varies directly as x. If so, find the constant of variation and write the equation.

a.

x	y
−4	16
−2	8
8	−32

yes; −4;
$y = -4x$

b.

x	y
2	10
3	15
6	25

no

2. Determine whether y varies directly as x. If so, find the constant of variation.

a. $y = 7x + 4$ no

b. $y = \frac{5}{3}x$ yes; $\frac{5}{3}$

c. $2y = -12x$ yes; −6

3. Assume y varies directly as x. If $y = 8$ when $x = 42$, find y when $x = 126$. 24

4. How can you tell from the graph of a linear function whether the function is a direct variation? **If the graph is a nonhorizontal line through the origin, then the linear function is a direct variation.**

Alternative Assessment

Have students work in pairs. Each student writes six linear equations, three of which describe direct variations and three of which do not. The other student identifies each direct variation that his or her partner wrote and names the constant of variation.

pages 74–77 Exercises

53. Answers may vary. Sample: No, the line $y = 0$ passes through the origin, but is not a direct variation.

52. Gas Mileage Suppose you drive a car 392 mi on one tank of gas. The tank **GPS** holds 14 gallons. The number of miles traveled varies directly with the number of gallons of gas you use.
  a. Write an equation that relates miles traveled to gallons of gas used. $y = 28x$
  b. You only have enough money to buy 3.7 gallons of gas. How far can you drive before refueling? 103.6 mi
  c. Last year you drove 11,700 mi. About how many gallons of gas did you use? c. 417.9 gal
  d. Suppose the price of gas averaged $1.57 per gallon last year. Find the cost per mile. $0.056/mi

53. Writing Suppose you use the origin to test whether a linear equation is a direct variation. Does this method work? Support your answer with an example. **See margin.**

54. Error Analysis Find the error in the following computation: If y varies directly with x^2, and $y = 2$ when $x = 4$, then $y = 3$ when $x = 9$. **See margin.**

Challenge

In Exercises 55–58, y varies directly with x.

55. If x is doubled, what happens to y? **y is doubled.**

56. If x is halved, what happens to y? **y is halved.**

57. If x is divided by 7, what happens to y? **y is divided by 7.**

58. If x is multiplied by 10, what happens to y? **y is multiplied by 10.**

59. If z varies directly with the product of x and y ($z = kxy$), then z is said to vary jointly with x and y.
  a. Geometry The area of a triangle varies jointly with its base and height. What is the constant of variation? $\frac{1}{2}$
  b. Suppose q varies jointly with v and s, and $q = 24$ when $v = 2$ and $s = 3$. Find q when $v = 4$ and $s = 2$. **32**
  c. Critical Thinking Suppose z varies jointly with x and y, and x varies directly with w. Show that z varies jointly with w and y. **$z = kxy$, and $x = k_1w$, so $z = kk_1wy$, and z varies jointly with w and y.**

Test Prep

Multiple Choice

60. Which equation does NOT represent a direct variation? **B**
  A. $y - 3x = 0$ **B.** $y + 2 = \frac{1}{2}x$ **C.** $\frac{y}{x} = \frac{2}{3}$ **D.** $y = \frac{x}{17}$

61. Suppose y varies directly with x. If x is 30 when y is 10, what is x when y is 9? **G**
  F. 3   **G.** 27   **H.** 29   **J.** $\frac{300}{9}$

62. Suppose y varies directly with x. If x is −7 when y is 3, what is x when y is −5?
  A. $-11\frac{2}{3}$ **B.** $-4\frac{1}{5}$ **C.** $4\frac{1}{5}$ **D.** $11\frac{2}{3}$ **D**

63. Which equation represents the direct variation in the table at the right? **J**

x	3	4	9
y	8.1	10.8	24.3

  F. $4y - 10x = 0$ **G.** $8x = 3y$
  H. $y + 8.1x = 0$ **J.** $10y = 27x$

Short Response

64. Do the values in the table below represent a direct variation? Explain. **See margin.**

x	4	5	7
y	13.1	16.3	22.6

54. Answers may vary. Sample: If y varies directly with x^2, and $y = 2$ when $x = 4$, then $y = 10\frac{1}{8}$ when $x = 9$.

64. [2] No; the ratio $\frac{y}{x}$ is not constant.
  [1] only has answer no, with no explanation

Lesson 2-2

Go for Help

Use the given information to graph each line. **65–68. See back of book.**

65. slope $= -\frac{3}{5}$, through $(-2, 5)$ **66.** slope $= -\frac{3}{2}$, through $(1, -4)$

67. slope $= -4$, through $(0, -1)$ **68.** slope $= -2$, $(-1, 6)$

Lesson 2-1

Graph each relation. Find the domain and range. 69–72. See margin.

69. $\{(0, 1), (1, -3), (-2, -3), (3, -3)\}$ **70.** $\{(4, 0), (7, 0), (4, -1), (7, -1)\}$

71. $\{(1, -2), (2, -1), (4, 1), (5, 2)\}$ **72.** $\{(1, 7), (2, 8), (3, 9), (4, 10)\}$

Skills Handbook **73. Aviation** On June 21, 2004, Simon Oliphant-Hope completed a record-setting helicopter trip around the world in 17 d 14 h 2 min 27 s. He spent 196.4 h in flight. What percent of the time was he not in the air? **about 53.5%**

✓ Checkpoint Quiz 1   Lessons 2-1 through 2-3

Find the x- and y-intercepts of each line. 2. $\left(-\frac{5}{7}, 0\right)$; $(0, 5)$

1. $x - 3y = 9$ **2.** $y = 7x + 5$ **3.** $y = 6x$ **4.** $-4x + y = 10$
   (9, 0); (0, −3)   **(0, 0); (0, 0)** $\left(-\frac{5}{2}, 0\right)$; **(0, 10)**

Write the equation of each line in slope-intercept form.

5. $2x - y = 9$ **6.** $4x = 2 + y$ **7.** $5y = -3x - 10$ **8.** $4x + 6y = 12$
   $y = 2x - 9$ $y = 4x - 2$ $y = -\frac{3}{5}x - 2$ $y = -\frac{2}{3}x + 2$

9. a. A group of friends is going to the movies. Each ticket costs $7.00. Write an equation to model the total cost of the group's tickets. **a–c. See margin.**

   b. Graph the equation. Explain what the x- and y-intercepts represent.

   c. Writing Could the domain include fractions? Explain.

10. Which line is perpendicular to $3x + 2y = 6$? **A**

   A. $4x - 6y = 3$ **B.** $y = -\frac{3}{2}x + 4$ **C.** $2x + 3y = 12$ **D.** $y = \frac{3}{2}x + 1$

Algebra at Work

·······················Miniaturist

People who make a career out of designing and creating miniature models of actual objects are called miniaturists. They apply direct variations to reproduce realistic models of items such as houses, stores, or scenes. Common scales used to create miniatures are the following.
- the one-inch scale (1 in. : 1 ft or 1 : 12)
- the half-inch scale (0.5 in. : 1 ft or 1 : 24)
- the quarter-inch scale (0.25 in. : 1 ft or 1 : 48)

 Go Online **For:** Information about careers in model design
PHSchool.com **Web Code:** agb-2031

Lesson 2-3 Direct Variation   **77**

69.

domain $\{0, 1, -2, 3\}$,
range $\{1, -3\}$

70.

domain $\{4, 7\}$,
range $\{0, -1\}$

71.

domain $\{1, 2, 4, 5\}$,
range $\{-2, -1, 1, 2\}$

72.

domain $\{1, 2, 3, 4\}$,
range $\{7, 8, 9, 10\}$

page 77   Checkpoint Quiz 1

9a. $y = 7x$

b.

Both intercepts are 0 when no one has bought any tickets.

c. No; the number of people must be a whole number.

Using Linear Models

1. Plan

Objectives
1. To write linear equations that model real-world data
2. To make predictions from linear models

Examples
1. Real-World Connection
2. Real-World Connection
3. Using a Linear Model
4. Real-World Connection

Math Background

Linear equations are useful in modeling many real-world problems. A scatter plot provides a visual representation of two-variable data sets and is useful in determining whether there is a linear relationship between the variables. A trend line that comes close to the points in a scatter plot can be helpful in studying the related data and in making predictions.

More Math Background: p. 52D

Lesson Planning and Resources

See p. 52E for a list of the resources that support this lesson.

Bell Ringer Practice

✓ Check Skills You'll Need
For intervention, direct students to:

Relations and Functions
Lesson 2-1: Example 6
Extra Skills and Word Problems Practice, Ch. 2

Linear Equations
Lesson 2-2: Example 3
Extra Skills and Word Problem Practice, Ch. 2

What You'll Learn
- To write linear equations that model real-world data
- To make predictions from linear models

. . . And Why
To model a burning candle, as in Example 2

✓ Check Skills You'll Need

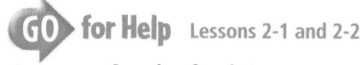
Find the change in x and the change in y between each pair of points.

1. $(-0.2, 9)$ and $(3.4, 7.3)$ **2.** $(10, 17)$ and $(11.5, 13.5)$ **3.** $\left(0, \frac{3}{10}\right)$ and $\left(-1, \frac{2}{5}\right)$
     $3.6, -1.7$ $1.5, -3.5$ $-1, \frac{1}{10}$

Evaluate each function for the given values.

4. $f(x) = \frac{4}{3}x - 2$ for $x = -3, 0, \frac{1}{2}$ **5.** $g(x) = 3(2 - x)$ for $x = 0, \frac{1}{6}, 1$
     $-6, -2, -\frac{4}{3}$ $6, \frac{11}{2}, 3$

🔊 **New Vocabulary** • scatter plot • trend line

---

1   Modeling Real-World Data

You can write linear equations to model real-world problems.

1 EXAMPLE   Real-World Connection

Transportation Jacksonville, Florida has an elevation of 12 ft above sea level. A hot-air balloon taking off from Jacksonville rises 50 ft/min. Write an equation to model the balloon's elevation as a function of time. Graph the equation. Interpret the intercept at which the graph intersects the vertical axis.

Relate   balloon's elevation   =   rate   ·   time   +   starting elevation

Define   Let h = the balloon's elevation.

           Let t = time (in minutes) since the hot-air balloon lifted off.

Write h = 50 · t + 12

An equation that models the balloon's elevation is $h = 50t + 12$.

The h-intercept is $(0, 12)$.

The t-coordinate, 0, represents the time at the start of the trip.

The h-coordinate, 12, represents the elevation of the balloon at the start of the trip.

Real-World Connection

Careers Hot-air balloonists use mathematics to plot courses, calculate wind speed, and determine their air speed.

✓ Quick Check

❶ Suppose a balloon begins descending at a rate of 20 ft/min from an elevation of 1350 ft.
    a. Write an equation to model the balloon's elevation as a function of time. What is true about the slope of this line? $h = -20t + 1350$; the slope is negative.
    b. Graph the equation. Interpret the h-intercept.   See back of book.

78   Chapter 2   Functions, Equations, and Graphs

Differentiated Instruction   Solutions for All Learners

Special Needs   **L1**
Help students connect the different correlation descriptions with their respective graphs: weak or strong, positive or negative, or no correlation.

learning style: visual

Below Level   **L2**
Because they want to "connect the dots," students may have difficulty drawing trend lines. Emphasize that a trend line is not exact but is an estimate.

learning style: tactile

You can use two data points from a linear relationship to write a model.

Science A candle is 6 in. tall after burning for 1 h. After 3 h, it is $5\frac{1}{2}$ in. tall. Write a linear equation to model the height y of the candle after burning x hours.

Step 1 Identify the data points $(1, 6)$ and $\left(3, \frac{11}{2}\right)$ as (x_1, y_1) and (x_2, y_2).

Step 2 Find the slope of the line.

$m = \dfrac{y_2 - y_1}{x_2 - x_1}$ **Use the slope formula.**

$m = \dfrac{\frac{11}{2} - 6}{3 - 1}$ **Substitute.**

$m = \dfrac{-\frac{1}{2}}{2}$ **Simplify the numerator and denominator.**

$m = -\dfrac{1}{4}$ **Simplify.**

Step 3 Use one of the points and the point-slope form to write an equation for the line.

$y - y_1 = m(x - x_1)$ **Use point-slope form.**

$y - 6 = -\dfrac{1}{4}(x - 1)$ **Substitute.**

$y = -\dfrac{1}{4}x + 6\dfrac{1}{4}$ **Solve for y.**

● An equation of the line that models the height of the candle is $y = -\frac{1}{4}x + 6\frac{1}{4}$.

6 in. $5\frac{1}{2}$ in.

after 1 h   after 3 h

✓ **Quick Check** ② **a. Reasoning** What does the slope $-\frac{1}{4}$ represent? **The candle is burning down at the rate of $\frac{1}{4}$ inch per hour.**

b. What does the y-intercept $6\frac{1}{4}$ represent? **the original height of the candle**

c. Another candle is 7 in. tall after burning for 1 h and 5 in. tall after burning for 2 h. Write a linear equation to model the height of the candle. $y = -2x + 9$

---

2 Predicting With Linear Models

You can use a linear model to make predictions.

3 EXAMPLE   Using a Linear Model

Gridded Response Use the equation from Example 2. In how many hours will the candle be 4 in. tall?

$y = -\dfrac{1}{4}x + 6\dfrac{1}{4}$ **Write the equation.**

$4 = -\dfrac{1}{4}x + 6\dfrac{1}{4}$ **Substitute 4 for y.**

$-4\left(4 - 6\dfrac{1}{4}\right) = x$ **Solve for x.**

$9 = x$ **Simplify.**

The candle will be 4 in. tall after burning for 9 h.

● The answer is 9.

Test-Taking Tip

You can enter the 9 in any column of the grid.

✓ **Quick Check** ③ **a.** How tall will the candle be after burning for 11 h? $3\frac{1}{2}$ in.

b. What was the original height of the candle? $6\frac{1}{4}$ in.

c. When will the candle burn out? **after 25 hours**

Guided Instruction

2 EXAMPLE   Auditory Learners

Have students explain aloud why it is reasonable for the slope to be a negative number.

PowerPoint

Additional Examples

❶ Suppose an airplane descends at a rate of 300 ft/min from an elevation of 8000 ft. Write and graph an equation to model the plane's elevation as a function of the time it has been descending. Interpret the intercept at which the graph intersects the vertical axis. $d = -300t + 8000$

The intercept $(0, 8000)$ shows that the elevation was 8000 ft when the descent began.

❷ A spring has a length of 8 cm when a 20-g mass hangs at the bottom end. Each additional gram stretches the spring another 0.15 cm. Write an equation to model the length y of the spring as a function of the mass x of the attached weight. $y = 0.15x + 5$

Advanced Learners L4

Ask students to find the original height of the candle in Quick Check 2c.

9 in.

learning style: verbal

English Language Learners ELL

Help students relate the concept of a mathematical model to other real-world models such as a model airplane. Lead students to understand that a model is a simplified representation of a real-world situation.

learning style: verbal

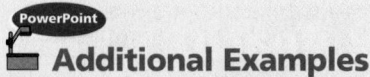
3 Use the equation from Additional Example 2. What mass would be needed to stretch the spring to a length of 9.5 cm? **30 g**

4 An art expert visited a gallery and jotted down her guesses for the selling price of five different paintings. Then, she checked the actual prices. The data points (guess, actual) show the results, where each number is in thousands of dollars {(12, 11), (7, 8.5), (10, 12), (5, 3.8), (9, 10)}.
a. Draw a scatter plot. Decide whether a linear model is reasonable.
b. Draw a trend line. Write the equation of the line.

A linear model seems reasonable; Answers may vary. Sample: $y = \frac{10}{9}x - \frac{2}{3}$

Resources
• Daily Notetaking Guide 2-4 **L3**

Closure

Suppose a linear model seems appropriate for the data represented in a scatter plot. How can you find an equation for a trend line? **Draw a line that comes close to the data points. Use the coordinates of two points on the line to write an equation of the line in point-slope form.**

A **scatter plot** is a graph that relates two different sets of data by plotting the data as ordered pairs. You can use a scatter plot to determine a relationship between the data sets.

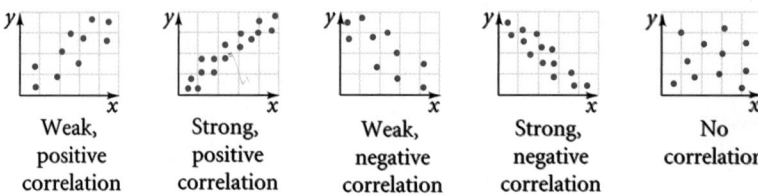

| Weak, positive correlation | Strong, positive correlation | Weak, negative correlation | Strong, negative correlation | No correlation |

A **trend line** is a line that approximates the relationship between the data sets of a scatter plot. You can use a trend line to make predictions.

4 EXAMPLE Real-World Connection

Automobiles A woman is considering buying the 1999 car shown in the photo. She researches prices for various years of the same model and records the data in a table.

Model Year	2000	2001	2002	2003	2004
Prices	$5784	$6810	$8237	$9660	$10,948
	$5435	$6207	$7751	$9127	$10,455

a. Let x represent the model year. (Use 1 for 2000, 2 for 2001, and so forth.) Let y be the price of the car. Draw a scatter plot. Decide whether a linear model is reasonable.

A linear model seems reasonable, since the points fall close to a line.

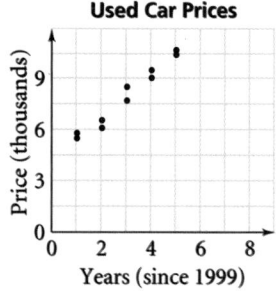

b. Draw a trend line. Write the equation of the line. Determine whether the asking price is reasonable.

Draw a line that has about the same number of data points above and below it. Use the slope and the y-intercept to find the equation of the line. Plot the data point for the asking price.

The equation of the trend line in the graph is $y = 1.3x + 4.1$. A fair price would be the value of y for $x = 0$, or about $4100.

The asking price of $4200 is reasonable.

 Quick Check ④ Graph each set of data. Decide whether a linear model is reasonable. If so, draw a trend line and write its equation. **a–b. See back of book.**
a. {(−7.5, 19.75), (−2, 9), (0, 6.5), (1.5, 3), (4, −1.5)}
b. {(0, −3), (0.5, −2.5), (1, −1), (3.5, 21.5), (6, 69), (7, 35)}

80   Chapter 2   Functions, Equations, and Graphs

EXERCISES

For more exercises, see *Extra Skill and Word Problem Practice.*

Practice and Problem Solving

A Practice by Example

Example 1
(page 78)

GO for Help

1. A car enters an interstate highway 15 mi north of a city. The car travels due north at an average speed of 62.5 mi/h. Write an equation to model the car's distance *d* from the city after traveling for *h* hours. Graph the equation. **1–2. See back of book.**

2. A pump removes 1000 gal of water from a pool at a constant rate of 50 gal/min.
  a. Write an equation to find the amount of water *y* in the pool after *t* minutes.
  b. Graph the equation and interpret the *t*- and *y*-intercepts.

3. A tree 5 ft tall grows an average of 8 in. each year. Write and graph an equation to model the tree's height *h* after *x* years. **See margin.**

Examples 2 and 3
(page 79)

For each situation, find a linear model and use it to make a prediction.

4. There are 2 leaves along 3 in. of an ivy vine. There are 14 leaves along 15 in. of the same vine. How many leaves are there along 6 in. of the vine? $y = x - 1$; **5 leaves**

5. An empty 5-gal water jug weighs 0.75 lb. With 3 c of water inside, the jug weighs 2.25 lb. Predict the weight of the jug with 5 c of water inside. $y = 0.5x + 0.75$; **3.25 lb**

6. There are 55 blades of grass in 1 in.^{2} of lawn. There are 230 blades of grass in 4 in.^{2} of the same lawn. How many blades of grass are in 3 in.^{2} of lawn? $y = 58.3x - 3.3$;**172 blades of grass**

7. A 2-mi cab ride costs \$5.25. A 5-mi cab ride costs \$10.50. How much does a 3.8-mi cab ride cost? $y = 1.75x + 1.75$; **\$8.40**

Example 4
(page 80)

Graph each set of data. Decide whether a linear model is reasonable. If so, draw a trend line and write its equation. **8–11. See back of book.**

8. $\{(0, 11), (2, 8), (3, 7), (7, 2), (8, 0)\}$

9. $\{(1.2, 1), (2.5, 6), (2.5, 7.5), (4.1, 11), (7.9, 19)\}$

10. $\left\{\left(-10, 3\frac{1}{2}\right), \left(-5\frac{1}{2}, 1\frac{1}{2}\right), \left(-\frac{1}{10}, -4\right), \left(3\frac{1}{2}, -7\frac{1}{2}\right), (12, -12)\right\}$

11. $\{(-15, 8), (-8, -7), (-3, 0), (0, 5), (7, -3)\}$

B Apply Your Skills

Daily Energy Requirements for Males

Age (years)	Energy Needed (Calories)
1	1100
2	1300
5	1800
8	2200
11	2500
14	2800
17	3000

SOURCE: *Go Figure: The Numbers You Need for Everyday Life*

12. **Measurement** The numbering system used in Europe for shoe sizes is different from the system used in the United States. Use the data in the table at the right to create a model for converting between systems. **a. See back of book.**
  a. Graph the data. Is a linear model reasonable?
  b. Find the European equivalent of U.S. size 8. **40**
  c. **Writing** Explain how to use a model to convert European sizes to U.S. sizes. **See margin.**

Women's Shoe Sizes

U.S. Size	European Size
1	31
3	34
5	36
7	39
9	41
11	44

SOURCE: *Sizes*

13. **Nutrition** The table at the left shows the average daily energy requirements for male children and adolescents.
  a. Graph the data. Model the data with a linear equation. **See back of book.**
  b. Estimate the daily energy requirements for a male 16 years old. **2930 Cal**
  c. **Reasoning** Do you think your model also applies to adult males? Explain. **Answers may vary. Sample: No; adults need fewer Calories, not more.**

Assignment Guide

1 A B 1-3, 15-19

2 A B 4-14, 20-25

C Challenge 26-28

Test Prep 29-34
Mixed Review 35-45

Homework Quick Check
To check students' understanding of key skills and concepts, go over Exercises 3, 5, 12, 14, 20.

Differentiated Instruction Resources

GPS Guided Problem Solving	L3
Enrichment	L4
Reteaching	L2
Practice	L3

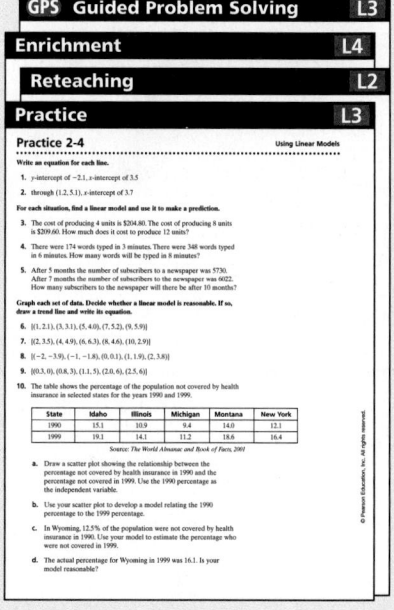

---

pages 81–84 Exercises

3. $h = 8x + 60$

12c. Answers may vary. Sample: After drawing a trend line, locate the European size on the *y*-axis. Then find the corresponding U.S. size on the *x*-axis.

14a. See back of book.

14b. Answers may vary.
Sample: $c = 0.04A$

14c–d. See margin.

14. **Sales** Suppose you manufacture and sell tarps. The table displays your current sizes and prices.

Tarps

Size	Price	Size	Price
5 × 7 ft	$1.39	18 × 20 ft	$14.39
6 × 8 ft	$1.99	15 × 30 ft	$17.99
8 × 10 ft	$3.19	20 × 30 ft	$23.99
10 × 12 ft	$4.79	20 × 40 ft	$31.99
12 × 16 ft	$7.69	25 × 45 ft	$44.99
10 × 20 ft	$7.99	30 × 50 ft	$59.99
16 × 20 ft	$12.79	30 × 60 ft	$71.99

a. Draw a scatter plot showing the relationship between a tarp's area and its cost. Use area as the independent variable.

b. Use your scatter plot to develop a model relating the area of a tarp to its cost.

c. How good a model do you feel you have? Explain.

d. Is $7.00 a reasonable price for a tarp that measures 10 ft by 15 ft? Explain.

e. Using your model and the prices in the table, determine which tarp size varies the most from your predicted price. How great is the discrepancy between your model and the actual price? **6 × 8 ft; $0.07**

Write an equation for each line.
$y = -4x + 10$
15. through $(2, 2)$, y-intercept 10
$y = -7.5x - 2.5$
17. y-intercept $-\frac{5}{2}$, x-intercept $-\frac{1}{3}$

16. x-intercept -2, y-intercept -6 $y = -3x - 6$
$y = 1.4375x - 7.33125$
18. through $(3.5, -2.3)$, x-intercept 5.1

19. **Entertainment** Refer to the diagram below. Suppose you are trying to decide whether to subscribe to cable service or just rent videos.

19a–b. See margin.

19c. See back of book.

a. Write an equation to model the cost y of the cable service for 1 month.

b. Write a second equation to model the cost y of renting x movies from the video store. What is the slope? What is the y-intercept?

c. **Open-Ended** Suppose you currently rent 8 to 12 movies each month. Graph the two equations from parts (a) and (b). Interpret the graph. Use your interpretation to choose between the alternatives. Explain your reasoning.

20. **a.** Answers may vary. Sample: $y = 0.0714x - 9.3$

b. 14.3 g

c. 200 Cal; a 200-Cal hamburger has about 5 g of fat.

20. **Nutrition** The table below shows the relationship between Calories and fat in various fast-food hamburgers.

Hamburger	A	B	C	D	E	F	G	H	I
Calories	720	530	510	500	305	410	440	320	598
Fat (g)	46	30	27	26	13	20	25	13	26

SOURCE: *The Fat Counter*

a. Develop a model for the relationship between Calories and fat.

b. How much fat would you expect a 330–Calorie hamburger to have?

c. **Error Analysis** A student reports these estimates: 10 g of fat for a 200-Calorie hamburger and 36 g of fat for a 660-Calorie hamburger. Which estimate is *not* reasonable? Explain.

82 Chapter 2 Functions, Equations, and Graphs

pages 81–84 **Exercises**

14c. Answers may vary. Sample: The model fits the data very closely.

d. Answers may vary. Sample: No; the area of the tarp is 150 ft^2 so the price should be $6.00.

19a. $y = 29.95$

b. $y = 2.95x$; slope = 2.95; y-intercept = 0

21. Data Analysis Is the population of a state related to the number of licensed drivers in that state? The table shows population and licensed-driver statistics from a recent year.

a. Which variable should be the independent variable? **population**
b. Draw a scatter plot. **b–c. See back**
c. Draw a trend line. **of book.**
d. The population of Michigan was approximately 10 million that year. About how many licensed drivers lived in Michigan that year? **7 million**

 e. Writing Is the correlation between population and number of licensed drivers strong or weak? Explain.

State	Population (millions)	Licensed Drivers (millions)
Arkansas	2.7	2.0
Illinois	12.6	8.0
Kansas	2.7	1.9
Massachusetts	6.4	4.7
Pennsylvania	12.3	8.3
Texas	21.7	13.2

Source: U.S. Census Bureau, National Highway Administration. Go to www.PHSchool.com for a data update. Web Code: agg-9041

21e. Answers may vary. Sample: Strong; the points fall close to a straight line.

22. Multiple Choice At a restaurant, Elena wants to leave a tip that is 15% of the bill B plus $1. Which linear model best describes the total T? **D**

Ⓐ $T = 15B + 1$ Ⓑ $T = B + 15$
Ⓒ $T = 1.15B$ Ⓓ $T = 1.15B + 1$

A linear model for each situation passes through the origin. Find each missing value. Round your answer to the nearest tenth.

23. 47.5 min to jog 5 mi, ■ min to jog 11 mi **104.5**

24. 8.5 gal of gas to drive 243.1 mi, 3 gal of gas to drive ■ mi **85.8**

25. $9.45 to buy 7 lb of apples, $17.55 to buy ■ lb **13**

Ⓒ Challenge **26. Social Studies** The table at the right shows per capita revenues and expenditures for selected states from a recent year.

a. Show the data on a scatter plot. Draw a trend line.
b. If a state collected revenue of $2000 per capita, how much would you expect it to spend per capita? **about $2100**
c. Ohio spent $3427 per capita during that year. According to your model, how much did it collect in taxes per capita? **about $3400**
d. In that same year, New Jersey collected $3581 per capita in taxes and spent $4039 per capita. Does this information follow the trend? Explain.

26a. See back of book.
d. See margin.

Vocabulary Tip

Per capita means "for each person." Capita is a form of the Latin word for "head."

State	Per Capita Revenue ($)	Per Capita Expenditure ($)
Arizona	2858	2926
Georgia	3023	3053
Maryland	3535	3573
Mississippi	3608	3710
New Mexico	4780	4587
Nevada	2753	2798
New York	4810	4676
Texas	2835	2723
Utah	3585	3725

Source: U.S. Census Bureau. Go to www.PHSchool.com for a data update. Web Code: agg-9041

27. a. Use the first and last data points to find a linear model for the data in the table at the right.
b. Use the middle two data points to find a linear model for the data.
c. Which model better represents the data? Can you find a third model that you think best represents the data? Explain.
Answers may vary. Sample: neither; $y = -1.5x + 12$

x	−5	−2	−1	1	3	6
y	22	15	12	8	7	5

27a. $y = -\frac{17}{11}x + 14.27$
b. $y = -2x + 10$

28. Geometry Write the equation of the perpendicular bisector of the segment with endpoints $(-3, 5)$ and $(7, 1)$. $y = \frac{5}{2}x - 2$

26. d. Answers may vary. Sample: No, expenditure would be predicted to be about $3600.

PowerPoint
Lesson Quiz

1. A family built a house in a beach resort area. In 1990, the house was 430 ft from the water. With erosion, the house was 400 ft from the water in 2000.

a. Assuming a linear relationship between the number of years x since 1990 and the distance y of the house from the water, write an equation for y as a function of x.
$y = -3x + 430$

b. In what year will the house be only 250 ft from the water?
2050

2. Graph the set of data. Decide whether a linear model is reasonable. If so, draw a trend line and write its equation.
{(1, 2), (3, 3), (3, 3.75), (4, 4), (5, 3.25), (6, 4.5)}

A linear model seems reasonable; Answers may vary. Sample: $y = 0.4x + 2$

Alternative Assessment

Have students work in pairs. Each student draws a scatter plot of data for which a linear model is reasonable. They trade scatter plots. Each student draws a trend line and finds an equation for the trend line for the scatter plot that the partner drew. Each student checks the other student's work.

A sheet of blank grids is available in the Test-Taking Strategies with Transparencies booklet. Give this sheet to students for practice with filling in the grids.

Resources

For additional practice with a variety of test item formats:
- Standardized Test Prep, p. 113
- Test-Taking Strategies, p. 108
- Test-Taking Strategies with Transparencies
- Blank Sheet of Grids, p. viii

pages 81–84 Exercises

39. {−7, −3, −1, 2, 7}

40. {1, 3.5, 5, 6, 8}

41. {3, 4, 5.25, 12, 19}

42. $\left\{-\frac{7}{2}, -\frac{5}{2}, -2, -\frac{5}{4}, 0\right\}$

43. {−299, −99, 1, 151, 401}

44. {1, 6, 9, 11, 15}

Test Prep

Gridded Response   Each set of three points is collinear. Find each missing x- or y-value to the nearest hundredth.

29. (2, 3.37), (10, 23.37), (4, y) **8.37**

30. (6, 10.2), (1.5, 3.45), (x, 2.85) **1.10**

31. (0.5, 1), (2.2, y), (1.6, 4.3) **6.10**

32. (x, 0.8), (15, −0.4), (−4, 2.9) **8.09**

Short Response   Use the newspaper article below for Exercises 34 and 35.

What's Harming Japan's Oysters?

A 1994 red tide killed off thousands of *akoya* oysters in Japan's Ago Bay. For years following the red tide, oysters continued to die, confounding pearl farmers and scientists alike. Scientists have suggested many possible causes, from a virus to pollutants.

Whatever the reason, in 1996, Japanese pearl farmers harvested only 56.6 tons of pearls from *akoya* oysters, down from 72.6 tons in 1993.

Source: *NOVA*, "The Perfect Pearl"

33. Use a linear model. Estimate the number of tons of pearls harvested in 2000. **35.3 tons**

34. In 2002, pearl farmers harvested 24 tons of pearls from akoya oysters. Use the harvests from 1996 and 2002 to estimate the 2000 harvest. **34.9 tons**

Mixed Review

Lesson 2-3

Find each constant of variation. Then find the value of y when x = −5.

35. y = 27 when x = −10 **−2.7; 13.5**   **36.** y = −36 when x = 12 **−3; 15**

37. $y = -\frac{2}{5}$ when $x = \frac{1}{3}$ **$-\frac{6}{5}$; 6**   **38.** $y = -\frac{21}{4}$ when $x = -\frac{5}{8}$ **$\frac{42}{5}$; −42**

Lesson 2-1

Find the range of each function when the domain is {−3, −1, 0, 1.5, 4}.
39–44. See margin.

39. f(x) = 2x − 1   **40.** y = −(x − 5)   **41.** y = x² + 3

42. $g(x) = \frac{x-4}{2}$ **43.** y = 100x + 1   **44.** y = 9 − 2x

Skills Handbook   **45. Track** Svetlana Masterkova of Russia set a record for running the mile, in 4 minutes 12.56 seconds.   **20.91 ft/s; 2091 ft**

a. Find Svetlana's rate in feet per second. How far did she run in 100 seconds?

b. Write an equation that relates the distance she ran to time. Use feet per second as the unit. **d = 20.91t**

c. Calculate Svetlana's speed in miles per hour. **14.25 mi/h**

84   Chapter 2   Functions, Equations, and Graphs

page 85 Vocabulary Builder

3a–b. Answers may vary. Samples are given.

3a. No; you might have answered correctly by accident.

High-Use Academic Words

High-use academic words are words that you often see in textbooks and on tests. These words are not math vocabulary terms, but they are important for you to know to be successful in mathematics.

Words to Learn: Direction Words

Some words tell you what to do in a problem. You need to understand what these words are asking so that you give the correct answer.

Word(s)	Meaning
Explain (after a ye s-no" question)	"Yes" or "no" is only part of the correct answer. You must also write your reasons for your answer.
Determine whether	This is another form of a "yes-no" question. For a correct answer, you must show your process or support your "yes" or "no" response with evidence or reasons.

EXERCISES   1–2. Check student's work.

1. If the fire alarm sounds, do you know what to do? Explain.

2. Determine whether physical education classes could be held outdoors today.

3. Suppose that a "yes-no" question asks you to "explain." **a–b. See margin.**
   a. Does a correct answer with poor reasons have any value? Explain.
   b. Does an incorrect answer with good reasons have any value? Explain.

The library keeps information on overdue-book returns. A five-day record is shown in the table.

4. Determine whether the overdue fines vary directly with the total number of days overdue. **yes**

5. Does the total number of days overdue vary directly with the number of overdue books returned? Explain. **no; $\frac{20}{12} \neq \frac{44}{30}$**

6. In general, if x varies directly with y and y varies directly with z, does x vary directly with z? Explain. **See margin.**

7. Explain why the equation $y = 0.15x$ models the amount of fines from overdue books. **See margin.**

8. Word Knowledge Think about the word *model*.
   a. Choose the letter for how well you know the word. **a–c. Check students' work.**
      A. I know its meaning.
      B. I've seen it, but I don't know its meaning.
      C. I don't know it.
   b. Research Look up *model* in a dictionary or online. Write any definition that might apply to its use in mathematics.
   c. Write a sentence involving mathematics that uses the word *model*.

Overdue-Book Returns

Number of Books	Total Days Overdue	Overdue Fines ($)
21	32	4.80
12	20	3.00
30	44	6.60
9	16	2.40
18	28	4.20

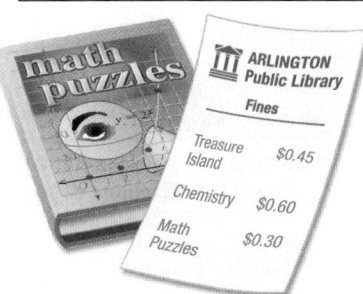

The direct variation $y = 0.15x$ models the total fines y in dollars for x days of overdue books.

b. Yes; if you follow the reasoning closely, you can find out where you made a mistake.

6. Yes; if x varies directly with y, you can write $y = kx$ for some constant k. If y varies directly with z, you can write $z = ny$ for some constant n. If you substitute y from the first equation into the second, you get $z = (nk)x$. Since nk is constant, x varies directly with z.

Vocabulary Builder

High-Use Academic Words

This feature presents key words that students can use on tests to identify when a written response is required.

Guided Instruction

English Language Learners ELL
Make sure students know that *directions* refer to statements that tell you what to do. You may want to point out how in the text, directions that apply to more than one exercise are printed with boldface type.

Special Needs [L1]
For Exercise 3, ask: *Why is partial credit sometimes given on a test?* Sample: The teacher wants to reward students for their thinking process as well as getting the correct answer.

Teaching Tip
Help students grasp the subtlety of *determine whether*. In some contexts, *determine whether* means the reasoning of your response is more important than your "yes" or "no" answer. For example, Exercise 2 can have more than one correct answer, depending on your explanation. However, in other contexts *determine whether* may be asking for only a positive (yes) or negative (no) response, as in Exercise 4.

Resources

Vocabulary and Study Skills worksheet

7. Answers may vary. Sample:
each ratio
$\frac{\text{overdue fine}}{\text{days overdue}}$ is 0.15.
So you can write
$\frac{y}{x} = 0.15$, or
$y = 0.15x$

Finding a Line of Best Fit

Finding a Line of Best Fit

Students use a graphing calculator to enter data and display a scatter plot. Next, they use the LinReg feature to find an equation of the line of best fit. Then, they display the graph of the line of best fit along with the scatter plot. Finally, students use the line of best fit to estimate values between the plotted data.

Guided Instruction

English Language Learners ELL

Have students look up *waggle* in a dictionary. Then select a student to demonstrate a waggle or the description of a bee's dance.

Math Tip

In each exercise, rounding the coefficients of the regression equation gives a slightly different line of fit. Students may want to enter the equation with rounded coefficients on the Y= list and display the graph. The graphs of the two equations will be essentially indistinguishable.

Error Prevention!

If a student decides, for whatever reason, not to use ZOOM 9 to display the scatter plot and line of best fit, it is important to use window settings that include all the x-values and y-values in the data set. Otherwise some of the points of the scatter plot will not be displayed.

Resources

Students may use any graphing calculator that is able to display scatter plots and generate linear regression equations.

Activity Lab

Technology

Finding a Line of Best Fit

FOR USE WITH LESSON 2-4

You can use your graphing calculator to display data sets, draw scatter plots, and draw a line to fit the data. The line is the linear regression line—a line of best fit. The LinReg feature on your calculator fits the model $y = ax + b$ to the data.

Go Online
PHSchool.com
For: Graphing calculator procedures
Web Code: age-2122

① ACTIVITY Finding the LinReg Line of Best Fit

When a honeybee finds a source of food, it returns to the beehive and communicates to other bees the direction and distance of the source. The bee makes a loop, waggles its belly along a line, makes another loop, and then another waggle. The bee repeats its dance several times. The time for each cycle (one loop and waggle) reveals the approximate distance to the food source.

Distance to Food (km)	1.35	1.5	1.5	2	2.15	2.65	2.75	3.5	4	5	6
Cycle Time (seconds)	3.5	3.8	3.9	4.4	4.3	5	5.1	5.6	6	7	7.6

Enter the given data on your calculator. Show a scatter plot of the data. Find the LinReg line of best fit. Then show a graph of the line.

Step 1 Clear any existing lists, and clear any equations from Y= .

Step 2 Enter the data. Press STAT ENTER . Enter the x-values in L1 and the y-values in L2.

Step 3 Find the LinReg line of best fit. Press STAT ▶ 4 ENTER to find LinReg(ax+b) values. Press Y= VARS 5 ▶ ▶ 1 to enter the regression equation as Y1.

Step 4 Draw the graph. Use the STAT PLOT feature and press 1 ENTER to turn on Plot 1.

Use the ▼ key to move down the rows to select a scatter plot using L1 and L2. Press ZOOM 9 to show the scatter plot and the line of best fit.

② ACTIVITY Using the Line of Best Fit to Predict

A bee finds food 3 km from the hive. Use the Activity 1 line of best fit and the CALC feature to predict the time of a waggle dance cycle.

With the graph shown, select the CALC feature. Press 1, then 3 ENTER to see the y-value for x = 3. A waggle dance cycle should take about 5.2 s.

3 ACTIVITY — Using the Line of Best Fit to Estimate

A waggle dance cycle is 7.4 s. Use the line of best fit from Activity 1 and the TRACE feature to estimate the distance to the food source.

With the graph shown on the screen, press [TRACE] [▲]. Then press [▶] or [◀] to get the y-value (shown on the screen) as close to 7.4 as possible. You may have to adjust the window dimension Xmax to allow for a large enough trace. The food source is approximately 5.6 km from the beehive.

Y1=.87X+2.55

X=5.57   Y=7.4

Careers

Students may be interested to learn some facts about beekeepers and honeybees. Migrant beekeepers move live beehives on flatbed trucks from one place to another for pollinating crops. About one-third of our food is dependent on pollinators such as honeybees. Finally, honeybees fly on average 24,000 miles and visit 3 to 9 million flowers to make one pound of honey.

EXERCISES

In [MODE] , (second line), fix the number of decimal places to be 2. Then the slope and y-intercept values of the LinReg line will round to the nearest hundredth.

1. Find the LinReg line of best fit for this data set. $y = 1.24x + 0.66$
   $\{(-5, 6.3), (-4, 5.6), (-3, 4.8), (-2, 3.1), (-1, 2.5), (0, 1.0), (1, -1.4)\}$

2. **Health** Find the LinReg line of best fit for the National Health Expenditures data. Then predict national health expenditures for 2010. (*Hint:* You may have to expand the calculator window to include the year 2010 on the screen.) **Answers may vary. Sample: Use 0 for 1990.** $y = 91.4x + 423.2$; $2250 billion

Year	1997	1998	1999	2000	2001	2002
National Health Expenditures (billions of dollars)	1093	1150	1223	1309	1421	1553

3. **Congress** Find the LinReg line of best fit for the data below. Then estimate the number of U. S. Representatives for Texas. Texas's population for 2000 was 20.0 million. $y = 1.54x - 0.22$; **31 U.S. Representatives**

State	AZ	CO	CT	GA	IL	MO	OH	RI	UT	WA	WI
Population (millions)	5.6	4.6	3.5	8.7	13	5.7	11	1.1	2.4	6.1	5.5
Representatives	8	7	5	13	19	9	18	2	3	9	8

4. There are different ways to find a line of best fit. The line of best fit found by the *least squares* method passes through the point $(\bar{x}, \bar{y})$, where $\bar{x}$ is the mean of the x-values of the data points (x, y), and $\bar{y}$ is the mean of the y-values.

   a. In [MODE] , change the number of fixed decimal places to 3. Use the data in the table below. Enter the numbers of teachers in L1. Enter the average salaries in L2. Find the LinReg line of best fit. $y = 24.193x - 27.704$

   Numbers and Average Salaries of Classroom Teachers

Year	1999	2000	2001	2002
Teachers (millions)	2.81	2.89	2.94	2.98
Average Salary (thousands of dollars)	40.5	41.8	43.4	44.6

   b. Calculate $\bar{x}$ and $\bar{y}$, the means for each data set. (To find $\bar{x}$, for example, press [2nd] [STAT] [▶] [▶] 3 L1 [ENTER].) **2.905; 42.575**

   c. Graph the LinReg line of best fit. Select the CALC feature. Press 1, enter the value of $\bar{x}$, and then press [ENTER]. Compare the y-value shown to $\bar{y}$. **The y-value is the same as $\bar{y}$ to two decimal places.**

   d. **Critical Thinking** Does $(\bar{x}, \bar{y})$ lie on the LinReg line of best fit? From this result can you conclude that the LinReg line of best fit and the least squares line of best fit are the same? are different? Explain.
   Yes; the lines are likely the same; both lines pass through the same point and are close to data points.

Activity Lab   Finding a Line of Best Fit   **87**

Absolute Value Functions and Graphs

1. Plan

Objectives

1 To graph absolute value functions

Examples

1 Graphing an Absolute Value Function
2 Using a Graphing Calculator
3 Writing Two Linear Equations
4 Real-World Connection

Math Background

An absolute value function is a special kind of piecewise function. The pieces can be determined by applying the definition of absolute value.

More Math Background: p. 52D

Lesson Planning and Resources

See p. 52E for a list of the resources that support this lesson.

PowerPoint

Bell Ringer Practice

✓ **Check Skills You'll Need**

For intervention, direct students to:

Linear Equations
Lesson 2-2: Example 1
Extra Skills and Word Problems Practice, Ch. 2

Graphing
Skills Handbook: p. 879

What You'll Learn

• To graph absolute value functions

. . . And Why

To model distance, as in Example 4

✓ **Check Skills You'll Need**

for Help Lesson 2-2 and Skills Handbook page 879

Graph each equation for the given domain and range. 1–2. See below left.

1. $y = x$ for real numbers x and $y \geq 0$

2. $y = 2x - 4$ for real numbers x and $y \geq 0$

3. $y = -x + 6$ for real numbers x and $y \leq 3$ **See back of book.**

🔊 **New Vocabulary** • absolute value function • vertex

1 **Graphing Absolute Value Functions**

1.

2.

A function of the form $f(x) = |mx + b| + c$, where $m \neq 0$, is an **absolute value function.** The related equation $y = |mx + b| + c$ is an absolute value equation in two variables. Graphs of absolute value equations in two variables look like angles.

$y = |x|$

$y = |2x - 4|$

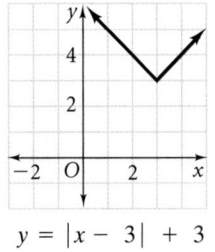
$y = |x - 3| + 3$

Vocabulary Tip

Vertex means "turning point."

The **vertex** of a function is a point where the function reaches a maximum or minimum. In general, the vertex of $y = |mx + b| + c$ is located at $\left(-\frac{b}{m}, c\right)$. In the middle graph above, the x-coordinate of the vertex is $-\left(\frac{-4}{2}\right) = 2$.

1 **EXAMPLE** **Graphing an Absolute Value Function**

Graph $y = |3x + 12|$.

Evaluate the equation for several values of x, beginning with $x = -\frac{b}{m} = -\frac{12}{3} = -4$.

Make a table of values.

x	−6	−4	−3	−2
y	6	0	3	6

Graph the function.

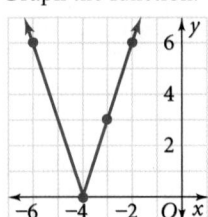

---

88 Chapter 2 Functions, Equations, and Graphs

Differentiated **Instruction** **Solutions for All Learners**

Special Needs **L1**
Write "absolute Value functions" on the board and ask students to describe the shape of their graphs.
V shape Emphasize that the graph can open upward or downward, with the vertex as either a minimum or maximum, respectively.

learning style: verbal

Below Level **L2**
Help students understand that, to create a table for the graph, they must choose x-values both less than and greater than the vertex x-coordinate $\frac{-b}{m}$.

learning style: visual

✓ **Quick Check** ❶ Graph each equation.   a–b. See margin.

a. $y = |2x - 5|$ 　　　　　　　　**b.** $y = -|x + 1| - 2$

You can use a graphing calculator to graph an absolute value equation.

Graphing Calculator Hint

For a calculator screen that shows x- and y-intervals of equal width, press ZOOM, and then select ZSquare.

❷ EXAMPLE 　**Using a Graphing Calculator**

Graph $y = -|3x + 4| + 6$ on a graphing calculator.

Use the absolute value function.
Graph the equation
$Y1 = -abs(3X + 4) + 6$.

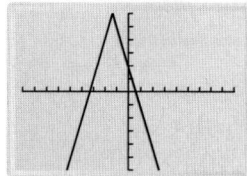

✓ **Quick Check** ❷ Graph each equation on a graphing calculator. Then sketch the graph.

a. $y = -|-x| + 5$ 　　　　　　**b.** $y = 3 - \left|\frac{x}{2}\right|$
　　See margin. 　　　　　　　　　　See back of book.

You can also graph an absolute value equation by first writing it as two linear equations with restricted domains.

❸ EXAMPLE 　**Writing Two Linear Equations**

Graph $y = |x - 3| + 5$.

Step 1 Isolate the absolute value.

$$y = |x - 3| + 5$$
$$y - 5 = |x - 3|$$

Step 2 Use the definition of absolute value. Write one equation for $x - 3 \geq 0$ and a second equation for $x - 3 < 0$.

when $x - 3 \geq 0$	when $x - 3 < 0$
$y - 5 = x - 3$	$y - 5 = -(x - 3)$
$y = x + 2$	$y = -x + 8$

Step 3 Graph each equation for the appropriate domain.

When $x - 3 \geq 0$, or $x \geq 3$, $y = x + 2$.

When $x - 3 < 0$, or $x < 3$, $y = -x + 8$.

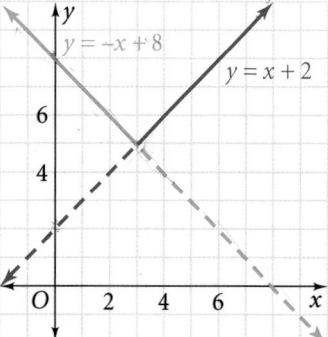

Online active math

For: Absolute Value Activity
Use: Interactive Textbook, 2-5

✓ **Quick Check** ❸ Graph each equation by writing two equations.

a. $y = \left|\frac{3}{2}x + 4\right| - 3$ 　　　　　**b.** $y = 2 - |x + 1|$
　　a–b. See back of book.

---

2. Teach

Guided Instruction

❶ EXAMPLE　**Math Tip**

Students should be able to see that the minimum value of y occurs when $3x + 12 = 0$.

❷ EXAMPLE　**Technology Tip**

The absolute value function is accessed when you press MATH ▶ 1.

PowerPoint

Additional Examples

❶ Graph $y = |2x - 1|$ by using a table of values.

❷ Graph $y = |x - 1| - 1$ on a graphing calculator.

page 89　Quick Check

1a.

b.

2a.

89

Additional Examples

④ EXAMPLE Math Tip

Point out that the rate of motion determines the coefficient of t.

③ Use the definition of absolute value to graph $y = |3x + 6| - 2$.

④ A train traveling on a straight track at 50 mi/h passes a certain crossing halfway through its journey each day. Sketch a graph of its trip based on its distance and time from the crossing.

Resources

• Daily Notetaking Guide 2-5 **L3**

Closure

Have students describe the shape of the graph of a function of the form $y = |mx + b|$, where $m \neq 0$.
The graph looks like an angle.

Real-World Connection

According to legend, Betsy Ross made the first flag of the United States in her house in Philadelphia, Pennsylvania.

✓ **Quick Check**

You can use absolute value functions to model time and distance problems. You can consider the time before you arrive at a destination to be negative.

④ EXAMPLE Real-World Connection

Travel Suppose you pass the Betsy Ross House halfway along your trip to school each morning. You walk at a rate of one city block per minute. Sketch a graph of your trip to school based on your distance and time from the Betsy Ross House.

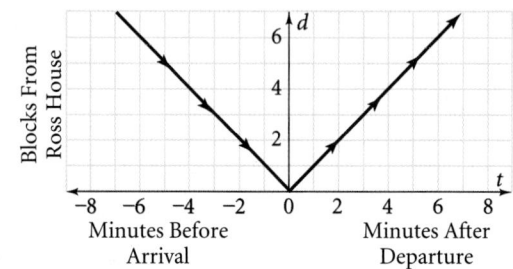

The equation $d = |t|$ models your distance from the Betsy Ross House.

④ a. Critical Thinking Suppose you ride your bicycle to school at a rate of three city blocks per minute. How would the graph of your trip to school change?
b. Sketch a new graph.   **The graph would stretch upward.**

EXERCISES

For more exercises, see *Extra Skill and Word Problem Practice.*

Practice and Problem Solving

Ⓐ **Practice by Example**

Example 1
(page 88)

GO for Help

Make a table of values for each equation. Then graph the equation.

1. $y = |4x|$ **2.** $y = |4x| - 1$ **3.** $y = |4x - 1|$

4. $y = |-3x|$ **5.** $y = |-3x| + 2$ **6.** $y = |-3x + 2|$

7. $y = -|2x|$ **8.** $y = -|2x| + 5$ **9.** $y = -|2x + 5|$

1–18. See back of book.

Example 2
(page 89)

Graph each equation on a graphing calculator. Then sketch the graph.

10. $y = |x + 2| - 4$ **11.** $y = 4 - |x + 2|$ **12.** $y = 4|x + 2|$

13. $y = \frac{1}{3}|3 - 3x|$ **14.** $y = 3\left|\frac{1}{3} - \frac{1}{3}x\right|$ **15.** $y = \frac{3}{2}|x| - \frac{5}{2}$

16. $y = |x| + \frac{1}{2}|x|$ **17.** $y = \frac{1}{2}|x| - |x|$ **18.** $y = \frac{1}{2}\left|x - \frac{1}{2}\right|$

Example 3
(page 89)

Graph each equation by writing two linear equations.   **19–28. See back of book.**

19. $y = |x + 6|$ **20.** $y = |3x + 6|$ **21.** $y = |3x - 6|$

22. $y = -|x - 5|$ **23.** $y = |2x + 1|$ **24.** $y = \frac{3}{2}|3x - 1|$

25. $y = |x - 2| - 6$ **26.** $y = \left|\frac{1}{2}x - 4\right| + 4$ **27.** $y = \frac{1}{2}\left|\frac{1}{2}x + 2\right| - 2$

Example 4
(page 90)

28. Manufacturing The conveyor belt at a factory operates continuously 24 hours a day, carrying vitamin bottles and moving two feet each minute. Sketch a graph showing the distance in feet from the filling arm of one bottle on the conveyor belt before and after it is filled. Use the x-axis for time before and after the bottle is filled and the y-axis for distance from the filling arm.

B **Apply Your Skills**

Match each equation with its graph. Each interval is 1 unit.

29. $y = |3x| - 4$ **B** **30.** $y = |3x - 4|$ **C** **31.** $y = 3|x - 4|$ **A** **32.** $y = |3x + 12|$ **D**

A.

B.

C.

D.

Graph each absolute value equation. 33–50. See back of book.

33. $y = |4x + 2|$

34. $y = |-3x + 5|$

35. $y = |4 - 2x|$

36. $y = \left|-\frac{1}{4}x - 1\right|$

37. $y = \left|\frac{5}{2}x - 2\right|$

38. $y = \left|\frac{3}{2}x + 2\right|$

39. $y = |3x - 6| + 1$

40. $y = -|x - 3|$

41. $y = |2x + 6|$

42. $y = 2|x + 2| - 3$

43. $y = 6 - |3x|$

44. $y = 6 - |3x + 1|$

45. $y = -|-2x - 1| + 1$

46. $y = 2|x - 3|$

47. $y = -\frac{3}{2}\left|\frac{1}{2}x\right|$

48. $2y = \frac{1}{2}|x + 2|$

49. $\frac{1}{3}y - 3 = -|x + 2|$

50. $-3y = |3x - 6|$

Problem Solving Hint
Before graphing, rewrite each absolute value equation as two linear equations with restricted domains.

51. Multiple Choice The graph at the right models a car traveling at a constant speed. Which equation best represents the relation shown in the graph?
A
  Ⓐ $y = |60x|$
  Ⓑ $y = |x + 60|$
  Ⓒ $y = |60 - x|$
  Ⓓ $y = |x| + 60$

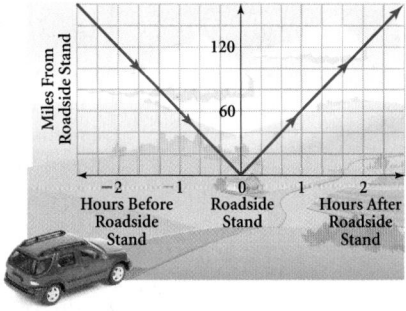

GO Online
Homework Video Tutor
Visit: PHSchool.com
Web Code: age-0205

52. a. Graph the equations $y = \left|\frac{1}{2}x - 6\right| + 3$ and $y = -\left|\frac{1}{2}x + 6\right| - 3$ on the same set of axes. **a–b. See back of book.**
GPS
  b. Writing Describe the similarities and differences in the graphs.

C **Challenge** 📟 **Graph each absolute value equation. 53–58. See back of book.**

53. $y = |3x| - x\left|\frac{1}{3}\right|$

54. $y = x - |2x|$

55. $y = |2x| - x$

56. $y = \frac{1}{2}|x - 3| + 5$

57. $y = \frac{1}{2}|x| + 4|x - 1|$

58. $y = |x + 1| + |x|$

59. Answers may vary. Samples:

59. a. Open-Ended Find two absolute value equations with graphs that share a vertex. $y = |x|, y = -|x|$
  b. Find two absolute value equations with graphs that share part of a ray. $y = |x|, y = |x - 1| + 1$

Assignment Guide

1 A B   1-52
C   Challenge   53-59

Test Prep   60-66
Mixed Review   67-82

Homework Quick Check
To check students' understanding of key skills and concepts, go over Exercises 18, 26, 45, 51, 52.

Error Prevention!

Exercises 10–18, 29–32 Students should be careful to use parentheses in the appropriate places when they enter the function on the Y= list.

Exercises 53–58 Suggest that students check their graphs by graphing the functions on a graphing calculator.

Lesson Quiz

1. Graph $y = -|x + 3|$.

2. Graph $y = |2x - 6| - 2$.

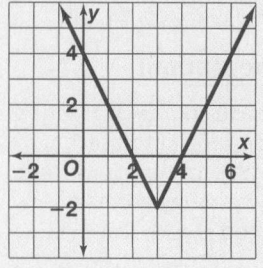

Alternative Assessment

Have students work in pairs. Each student writes a function of the form $y = |mx + b|$ and a function of the form $y = |mx + b| + c$. Students trade functions, and each graphs the functions provided by the partner. Have the partners verify that the graphs are correctly drawn.

Test Prep

Resources

For additional practice with a variety of test item formats:
- Standardized Test Prep, p. 113
- Test-Taking Strategies, p. 108
- Test-Taking Strategies with Transparencies

Test Prep

Multiple Choice

60. The graph at the right models which equation? B
    A. $y = |3x - 1| + 2$ B. $y = |x - 1| - 2$
    C. $y = |x - 1| + 2$ D. $y = |3x - 3| - 2$

61. What is the vertex of $y = |x| - 5$? J
    F. (5, 0)   G. (−5, 0)
    H. (0, 5)   J. (0, −5)

62. What is the vertex of $y = -|x| - 2$? A
    A. (0, −2)   B. (0, 2)
    C. (2, 0)   D. (2, −2)

63. What is the vertex of $y = |x - 3| + 5$? J
    F. (−3, 5)   G. (−3, 11)   H. (0, 5)   J. (3, 5)

64. Which pair of linear equations represents the equation $y = |x + 3| - 4$? C
    A. $y = x + 1$ for $x \geq 3$ B. $y = x - 1$ for $x \geq 3$
       $y = x - 1$ for $x < 3$ $y = -x - 1$ for $x < 3$
    C. $y = x - 1$ for $x \geq -3$ D. $y = -x - 1$ for $x \geq -3$
       $y = -x - 7$ for $x < -3$ $y = -x + 7$ for $x < -3$

Short Response

65. Explain how to find the x-coordinate of the vertex of $y = |3x - 6|$. See margin.

Extended Response

66. How can you graph the equation $y = -|5x + 1|$ by writing two linear equations? Show both equations, and label the coordinates of the vertex in your graph. See back of book.

Mixed Review

Lesson 2-4

Graph each set of data. Decide whether a linear model is reasonable. If so, draw a trend line and write its equation. 67–70. See back of book.

67. {(0, −5), (5, 25), (7, 44), (9, 70), (11, 90)}

68. {(−10, 0), (−4, 4), (−1, 6), (2, 8), (5, 10)}

69. {(−5, 6), (−1, 4), (0, 5), (3, 8), (4, 7)}

70. {(0, 7), (2, 6), (5, 4.5), (6, 4), (9, 2.5)}

Lesson 2-4

Find the slope of each line.

71. $3x + y = 1$ –3   72. $5y - 20x = 6$ 4   73. $y = \frac{-x}{9}$ $-\frac{1}{9}$

74. $12x = 3y - 2$ 4   75. $\frac{x}{2} + \frac{y}{3} = 1$ $-\frac{3}{2}$ 76. $0.1y = 0.5x + 0.1$ 5

77. A tutor earns $18 per hour. Write a function to model the tutor's earnings after h hours. What kind of function is this? $y = 18h$; linear

Lesson 1-3

Solve each equation.

78. $17x = 187$ 11   79. $13c - 26 = 91$ 9   80. $2(a - 6) + 11 = 25$ 13

81. $7(b + 3) - 18(1 - b) = 103$ 4   82. $6(m + 3) = 3(5 - m) + 66$ 7

---

pages 88–90 **Exercises**

65. [2] The vertex of $y = |3x - 6|$ would be where $3x - 6 = -(3x - 6)$ because that would be where the graphs of both lines meet. In this case it is at $x = 2$.

[1] only includes solution $x = 2$

Families of Functions

What You'll Learn

- To analyze translations
- To analyze stretches, shrinks, and reflections

. . . And Why

To analyze a fabric design, as in Example 3

✓ Check Skills You'll Need

GO for Help Lessons 2-2 and 2-5

Graph each pair of functions on the same coordinate plane. 1–6. See margin

1. $y = x, y = x + 4$
2. $y = -2x, y = -2x - 3$ p. 95.
3. $y = |x|, y = |x| - 2$
4. $y = -|2x|, y = -|2x| + 1$
5. $y = |x|, y = |x - 1|$
6. $y = -\left|\frac{1}{2}x\right|, y = -\left|\frac{1}{2}x + 2\right|$

🔊 **New Vocabulary** • parent function • translation • stretch • shrink • reflection • transformation • parameter

---

1 Translations

Vocabulary Tip

Translate is a synonym for transfer.

Technology Activity: A Family of Functions

The four functions in each group are related. Graph each set of functions in the same viewing window. Explain how they are related. **1–8. See back of book.**

1. $y_1(x) = |x|$ $y_2(x) = |x| + 2$ $y_3(x) = |x| + 4$ $y_4(x) = |x| - 2$
2. $y_1(x) = |x|$ $y_2(x) = |x + 2|$ $y_3(x) = |x + 4|$ $y_4(x) = |x - 2|$
3. $y_1(x) = |x|$ $y_2(x) = 2|x|$ $y_3(x) = 4|x|$ $y_4(x) = \frac{1}{2}|x|$
4. $y_1(x) = |x|$ $y_2(x) = -|x|$ $y_3(x) = 2|x|$ $y_4(x) = -2|x|$

Use the graphs from parts 1–4 to predict the graph of each function below. On graph paper and without plotting points, sketch what you think the graph of f should be. Then check your sketch on a graphing calculator.

5. $f(x) = |x + 4| - 2$
6. $f(x) = -2|x| + 4$

7. Sketch what you think the graph of $f(x) = -3|x + 2| - 1$ should be. Then check your sketch on a graphing calculator.

8. Considering all the functions in Exercises 1–7, which function would you call the simplest? Explain.

A family of functions is made up of functions with certain common characteristics.

A **parent function** is the simplest function with these characteristics. The equations of the functions in a family resemble each other. So do the graphs. Offspring of parent functions include translations, stretches, and shrinks.

A **translation** shifts a graph horizontally, vertically, or both. It results in a graph of the same shape and size but possibly in a different position.

---

1. Plan

Objectives

1 To analyze translations
2 To analyze stretches, shrinks, and reflections

Examples

1 Vertical Translation
2 Horizontal Translations
3 Real-World Connection
4 Graphing $y = a|x|$
5 Graphing $y = -a|x|$

Math Background

If $f(x)$ is any function and h is a real number, then the graph of $f(x - h)$ corresponds to a horizontal translation, of h units, of the graph of $f(x)$. If k is a real number, then the graph of $f(x) + k$ corresponds to a vertical translation, of k units, of the graph of $f(x)$. If a is a real number, then the graph of $af(x)$ is a reflection in the x-axis for $a < 0$, and a stretch by a factor of a for $|a| > 1$ or a shrink by a factor of a for $0 < |a| < 1$.

More Math Background: p. 52D

Lesson Planning and Resources

See p. 52E for a list of the resources that support this lesson.

✓ Check Skills You'll Need

For intervention, direct students to:

Linear Equations
Lesson 2-2: Example 1
Extra Skills and Word Problems Practice, Ch. 2

Absolute Value Functions and Graphs
Lesson 2-5: Examples 1–3
Extra Skills and Word Problem Practice, Ch. 2

Special Needs L1
Have students each create a textile design that is made using only horizontal and vertical translations and then write a description of it. Have students exchange descriptions and try to draw each design.

learning style: visual

Below Level L2
As a memory device to help students recognize whether a function is translated horizontally or vertically, the h in $f(x - h)$ could signify a <u>h</u>orizontal translation.

learning style: verbal

Guided Instruction

Students can trace the graph of $y = |x|$ on tracing paper and slide the traced graph straight down 3 units to check that they get the graph of $y = |x| - 3$.

② EXAMPLE Teaching Tip

Students may find it difficult to understand that the negative sign in part (a) means to move to the right and the plus sign in part (b) means to move to the left. Encourage students to make a table of values for each given function along with its parent function. Have students find an ordered pair for the given function and an ordered pair for the parent function that have the same *y*-value. Then, have students examine their *x*-values and discuss how this helps them determine which direction to shift the given function.

③ EXAMPLE Diversity

Invite students to look for patterned textile designs that they can describe with translations. Focus on those that might relate to diverse cultural backgrounds.

1a. $y = |x| + 1$ is $y = |x|$ shifted 1 unit up.

Real-World Connection

Translations of two lines result in the diamond shapes in this window.

The parent absolute value function is $y = |x|$. For a positive number k, $y = |x| \pm k$ is a vertical translation. To graph the function $y = |x| + k$, translate the graph of the parent function up k units. To graph the function $y = |x| - k$, translate the graph of the parent down k units.

① EXAMPLE Vertical Translation

a. Describe the translation $y = |x| - 3$ and draw its graph.

$y = |x| - 3$ is a translation of $y = |x|$ by 3 units downward. Each *y*-value for $y = |x| - 3$ is 3 less than the corresponding *y*-value for $y = |x|$.

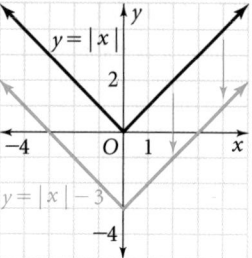

b. Write an equation to translate $y = |x|$ up $\frac{1}{2}$ unit.

An equation that translates $y = |x|$ up $\frac{1}{2}$ unit is $y = |x| + \frac{1}{2}$.

✓ **Quick Check** ① **a.** Describe the translation $y = |x| + 1$. Then draw the graphs of $y = |x|$ and $y = |x| + 1$ in the same coordinate plane. **See margin.**

b. Write an equation for the translation of $y = |x|$ down $\frac{1}{2}$ unit; Up 3.5 units.

$$y = |x| - \tfrac{1}{2}; \, y = |x| + 3.5$$

Horizontal translations of the parent function $y = |x|$ share some of the characteristics of vertical translations.

For a positive number h, $y = |x \pm h|$ is a horizontal translation. To graph the function $y = |x - h|$, translate the graph of the parent function right h units. To graph the function $y = |x + h|$, translate the graph left h units.

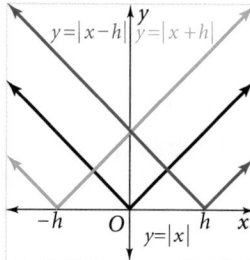

② EXAMPLE Horizontal Translations

a. The blue graph at the right is a translation of $y = |x|$. Write an equation for the graph.

The graph of $y = |x|$ is translated 5 units to the right. An equation for the graph is $y = |x - 5|$.

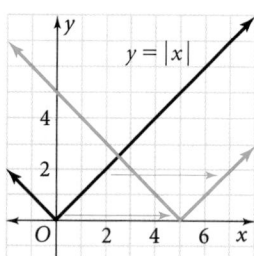

b. Describe the translation $y = |x + 3|$ and draw its graph.

$y = |x + 3|$ is a translation of $y = |x|$ by 3 units to the left.

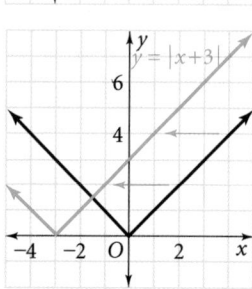

Quick Check **2** **a.** The graph is a translation of $y = |x|$.
Write an equation for the graph.
$y = \left| x + \frac{3}{2} \right|$

b. Describe the translation $y = |x - 1|$. Then draw the graphs of $y = |x|$ and $y = |x - 1|$ in the same coordinate plane. **See back of book.**

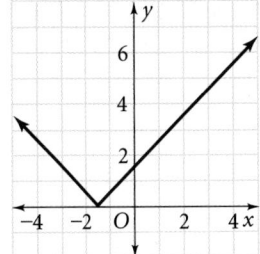

The parent absolute value function is $y = |x|$. For values h and k, $y = |x - h| + k$ is a combined translation of h units horizontally and k units vertically.

 Key Concepts

Summary	The Family of Absolute Value Functions

Vertical Translation

Parent function:	$y = |x|$	$y = f(x)$
Translation up k units, $k > 0$:	$y = |x| + k$	$y = f(x) + k$
Translation down k units, $k > 0$:	$y = |x| - k$	$y = f(x) - k$

Horizontal Translation

Parent function:	$y = |x|$	$y = f(x)$
Translation right h units, $h > 0$:	$y = |x - h|$	$y = f(x - h)$
Translation left h units, $h > 0$:	$y = |x + h|$	$y = f(x + h)$

Combined Translation $\qquad y = |x - h| + k \qquad y = f(x - h) + k$
(right h units, up k units)

3 EXAMPLE **Real-World** **Connection**

Fabric Design Describe possible translations of Figures A and B in the Nigerian textile design below.

Online active math

For: Translating Activity
Use: Interactive Textbook, 2-6

A translation of Figure A
5 units up or 5 units down

A translation of Figure B
about 5 units left and about 3 units up

Quick Check **3** Describe a possible translation of Figure C in the textile design.
Answers may vary. Sample: 4.5 units right and 3 units up

Lesson 2-6 Families of Functions **95**

PowerPoint

Additional Examples

1 a. Describe the translation $y = |x| - 2$ and draw its graph by translating the parent function.
translation of $y = |x|$ down 2 units

b. Write an equation for the translation of $y = |x|$ up 8 units.
$y = |x| + 8$

2 a. Describe the translation $y = |x + 4|$ and draw its graph by translating the parent function.
translation of $y = |x|$ left 4 units

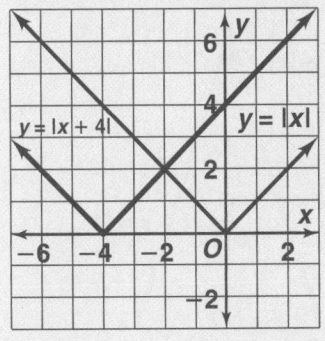

b. Write an equation for the translation of $y = |x|$ right 2 units.
$y = |x - 2|$

3 Describe a possible translation of Figures M and N in the design shown below.

Figure M: 2 units down; Figure N: 4 units down, or else 1 unit right and 2 units down

---

page 93 **Check Skills You'll Need**

1.

2.

3.

4.

5.

6.

95

⑤ EXAMPLE Teaching Tip

Students can confirm that the equation is correct by graphing it on a graphing calculator.

PowerPoint

🖥 Additional Examples

4 a. Describe and draw the graph of $y = \frac{1}{4}|x|$.
vertical shrink of $y = |x|$ by a factor of $\frac{1}{4}$

b. Write an equation for a vertical stretch of $y = |x|$ by a factor of 6.
$y = 6|x|$

5. Write the equation for the graph.

$y = -3|x|$

Resources
• Daily Notetaking Guide 2-6 **L3**

Closure

Ask students to describe the ways the graph of the parent function $y = |x|$ can be transformed. Transformations of $y = |x|$ include up, down, right, left, or combined; a reflection in the x-axis; a vertical stretch by a factor of $a > 1$, or a vertical shrink by a factor of $0 < a < 1$.

---

② Stretches, Shrinks, and Reflections

A vertical **stretch** multiplies all y-values by the same factor greater than 1, thereby stretching a graph vertically. A vertical **shrink** reduces y-values by a factor between 0 and 1, thereby compressing the graph vertically.

More formally, for the parent function $y = |x|$ and a number a, $a > 1$, $y = a|x|$ is a vertical stretch. For $0 < a < 1$, $y = a|x|$ is a vertical shrink.

④ EXAMPLE Graphing $y = a|x|$

a. Describe and then draw the graph of $y = 2|x|$.

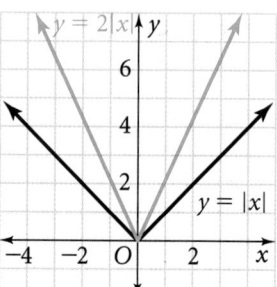

$y = 2|x|$ is a vertical stretch of $y = |x|$ by a factor of 2. Each y-value for $y = 2|x|$ is twice the corresponding y-value for $y = |x|$.

Note that $(2, 2)$ lies on $y = |x|$, whereas $(2, 4)$ lies on $y = 2|x|$.

b. Write an equation for a vertical shrink of $y = |x|$ by a factor of $\frac{1}{2}$.

A vertical shrink of $y = |x|$ by a factor of $\frac{1}{2}$ is $y = \frac{1}{2}|x|$.

✓ Quick Check **④ a.** Describe the stretch or shrink $y = \frac{1}{3}|x|$. Then draw the graphs of $y = |x|$ and $y = \frac{1}{3}|x|$ in the same coordinate plane. **See back of book.**
b. Write an equation for the vertical stretch of $y = |x|$ by a factor of 3. $y = 3|x|$

A **reflection** in the x-axis changes y-values to their opposites. When you change the y-values of a graph to their opposites, the graph reflects across the x-axis.

For the parent function $y = |x|$, indeed for any function of the form $y = a|x|$, multiplying by –1 gives the reflection $y = -a|x|$, whose graph is a reflection of $y = a|x|$ across the x-axis.

⑤ EXAMPLE Graphing $y = -a|x|$

Multiple Choice Which equation describes the graph?

A $y = \frac{1}{2}|x|$

B $y = \frac{1}{2}x$

C $y = -\frac{1}{2}|x|$

D $y = -\frac{1}{2}x$

The parent function is $y = |x|$. This is a reflection across the x-axis of $y = \frac{1}{2}|x|$. The answer is C.

✓ Quick Check **⑤** A function is a vertical stretch of $y = |x|$ by a factor of 5. Write an equation for the reflection of the function across the x-axis. $y = -5|x|$

Test-Taking Tip

Learn to recognize the parent function from the shape of the graph.

pages 97–100 **Exercises**

1.

2.

3.

4.

What you have learned about the absolute value function extends to functions in general.

Each member of a family of functions is a **transformation**, or change, of a parent function. Algebraically, the transformations take the same form using **parameters**, like h, k, and a. Graphically, the results are similar—shifts, stretches, shrinks, and reflections of the parent function.

 Key Concepts

Summary	Families of Functions: Absolute Value Functions

Vertical Stretch or Shrink, and Reflection in x-axis

Parent function:	$y = |x|$	$y = f(x)$
Reflection in x-axis:	$y = -|x|$	$y = -f(x)$
Stretch $(a > 1)$ Shrink $(0 < a < 1)$ } by factor a:	$y = a|x|$	$y = af(x)$
Reflection in x-axis:	$y = -a|x|$	$y = -af(x)$
Combined Transformation	$y = a|x - h| + k$	$y = af(x - h) + k$

EXERCISES

For more exercises, see *Extra Skill and Word Problem Practice.*

Practice and Problem Solving

 Practice by Example

Example 1
(page 94)

 for Help

For each function, graph the function by translating the parent function.

1–4. See margin p. 96.

1. $y = |x| - 3$ **2.** $y = |x| + 4\frac{1}{2}$ **3.** $y = |x| + 2$ **4.** $y = |x| - 6$

Write an equation for each vertical translation of $y = |x|$.

5. $\frac{2}{3}$ unit down
$y = |x| - \frac{2}{3}$

6. 4 units up
$y = |x| + 4$

7. 2 units up
$y = |x| + 2$

Example 2
(page 94)

For each function, identify the translation of the parent function. Then graph the function. 8–11. See margin.

8. $y = |x - 4|$ **9.** $y = |x + 5|$ **10.** $y = |x - 1|$ **11.** $y = |x + 2|$

Write an equation for each horizontal translation of $y = |x|$.

12.

13.

14.

$y = |x + 2|$ $y = |x - 3|$ $y = |x - 4|$

Example 3
(page 95)

Describe a possible translation for each figure.

15. Answers may vary. Sample: 4.5 units to the left.

16. Answers may vary. Sample: $\frac{17}{4}$ units to the right.

15.

16.

8. right 4 units

9. left 5 units

10. right 1 unit

11. left 2 units

Assignment Guide

1 A B 1-16, 29-36, 38, 39, 41, 42, 46, 48-51

2 A B 17-28, 37, 40, 43–45, 47

C Challenge   52-53

Test Prep   54-57
Mixed Review   58-64

Homework Quick Check

To check students' understanding of key skills and concepts, go over Exercises 12, 27, 38, 39, 40.

Error Prevention!

Exercises 8–11 Students often forget that when $h > 0$, replacing x with $x - h$ in the parent function translates the graph to the *right*. Replacing x with $x + h$ when $h > 0$ translates the graph to the *left*.

Differentiated Instruction Resources

29. vertical

30. combined

31. horizontal

32. combined

39. Answers may vary.
Sample: Since a vert.
translation affects
only y-values and a
horiz. translation
affects only x-values,
order is irrelevant.

40a.

GO **Online**
Homework Video Tutor

Visit: PHSchool.com
Web Code: age-0206

Example 4
(page 96)

Graph each function. 17–22. See back of book.

17. $y = 4|x|$ **18.** $y = \frac{1}{2}|x|$ **19.** $y = 2|x - 1|$

20. $y = \frac{1}{2}|x| + 2$ **21.** $y = 1.5|x| - 1$ **22.** $y = 0.5|x + 3|$

Write the equation for each graph. Each interval is 1 unit.

$y = \frac{2}{3}|x|$

23. $y = 2|x|$ **24.**   **25.**

24. $y = \frac{1}{4}|x|$

24. See left.

Example 5
(page 96)

26.   **27.**   **28.**

$y = -2|x|$ $y = -\frac{1}{3}|x|$ $y = -\frac{2}{5}|x|$

B **Apply Your Skills**

Describe each translation of $f(x) = |x|$ as *vertical*, *horizontal*, or *combined*. Then graph each translation. 29–32. See margin.

29. $f(x) = |x| - 5$ **30.** $f(x) = |x - 5| + 3$ **31.** $f(x) = |x + 1|$

32. $f(x) = \left| x + \frac{1}{2} \right| - 4\frac{1}{2}$ **33.** $f(x) = |x| - 3$ **34.** $f(x) = |x - 3| - 6$

33–34. See back of book.

Write the equation for each graph. Each interval is 1 unit.

35.   **36.**   **37.**

$y = |x - 2| - 2$ $y = -|x - 1|$ $y = -\frac{1}{2}|x + 2| + 4$

38. Data Analysis Suppose you plot data with years as the independent variable.
GPS What type of translation are you making when you start with $x = 0$ rather than a year such as 1998? Explain. **Horizontal; the graph is shifted left.**

39. Writing Explain why applying a vertical translation and then a horizontal translation produces the same result as applying a horizontal translation and then a vertical translation. **See left.**

40. a. Graph the parent function $f(x) = x$ and the function $g(x) = 3x$ on a coordinate plane.
  $y = 3x + 5$
  b. Translate the second graph 5 units up. Write an equation for the new line.
  c. Translate the graph from part (b) 2 units right. Write an equation for the new line. $y = 3x - 1$
  d. Which equation describes the line you graphed in part (c)? **E**
    A. $y = 3x + 5$ **B.** $y = 3x + 2$ **C.** $y = 3x - 2$
    D. $y = 3(x - 5) + 2$ **E.** $y = 3(x - 2) + 5$
  e. Critical Thinking Write the equation of the translation of $y = mx$ that has a graph passing through point (h, k). $y = m(x - h) + k$

41. Open-Ended Draw a figure in Quadrant I. Use a translation to move your figure into Quadrant III. Describe your translation. **Check students' work.**

Each graph shows an absolute value function after a translation 4 units up and 3 units left. Write the equation of the original function.

42.
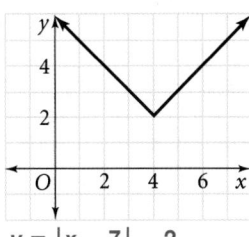
$y = |x - 7| - 2$

43.
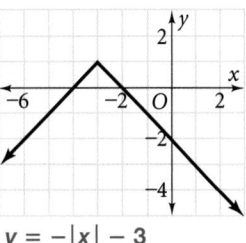
$y = -|x| - 3$

Write an equation for the translation so the graph has the given vertex.

44. $y = -|x|$; vertex $(-5, 0)$
$y = -|x + 5|$

45. $y = 2|x|$; vertex $(-4, 3)$
$y = 2|x + 4| + 3$

46. $y = |x|$; vertex (a, b)
$y = |x - a| + b$

47. $y = -|x|$; vertex (p, q)
$y = -|x - p| + q$

Graph each pair of functions on the same coordinate plane. Describe the translation that takes the first function to the second function.

48. $y = |x + 1|$, $y = |x - 5|$

49. $y = |x| + 3$, $y = |x - 4|$

50. $y = |x - 3|$, $y = |x| + 1$

51. $y = |x + 1| - 1$, $y = |x - 2| + 2$

48–51. See back of book.

C Challenge

52. Suppose you are playing with a yo-yo, as shown at the right.

3 ft

52a.

  a. Sketch a graph of $h(t)$ to show the height h of the yo-yo above the floor over time t. At $t = 0$, the yo-yo leaves your hand.

  b. Critical Thinking Should your graph be that of a function? Explain.

  c. Suppose you demonstrate your yo-yo ability on an auditorium stage that is 5 ft above the floor. Describe the translation of the graph of $h(t)$ that represents the height of the yo-yo above the auditorium floor. **vertical translation 5 ft up**

  d. Choose a function $g(t)$ that represents the height of the yo-yo above the auditorium floor when you are on stage. **C**

  A. $g(t) = h(t + 5)$ **B.** $g(t) = h(t - 5)$
  C. $g(t) = h(t) + 5$ **D.** $g(t) = h(t) - 5$

b. Yes; sample explanation: Each t is paired with a unique height.

53. Use the graph of the function $y = f(x)$ at the right. Sketch the graph of each function.   a–d. See margin.
  a. $f(x + 1)$
  b. $f(x) - 2$
  c. $f(x + 2) + 1$
  d. $-2f(x)$

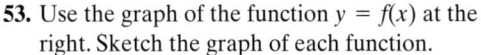

Test Prep

Multiple Choice

54. Which translation takes $y = |x + 2| - 1$ to $y = |x| + 2$?   **C**
  A. 2 units right, 3 units down   **B.** 2 units left, 3 units up
  C. 2 units right, 3 units up   **D.** 2 units left, 3 units down

55. The graph of which equation will NOT have a y-intercept of 5?   **H**
  F. $y = |x| + 5$ **G.** $y = |x - 5|$ **H.** $y = |x - 5| + 5$ **J.** $y = |x + 5|$

53a.

b.

c.

d.

99

Test Prep

Resources
For additional practice with a variety of test item formats:
• Standardized Test Prep, p. 113
• Test-Taking Strategies, p. 108
• Test-Taking Strategies with Transparencies

Checkpoint Quiz

Use this Checkpoint Quiz to check students' understanding of the skills and concepts of Lessons 2-4 through 2-6

Resources
Grab & Go
• Checkpoint Quiz 2

pages 97–100 Exercises

57. [4] The graph of
$y = |x + 3| - 2$ is
$y = |x|$ first translated
3 units to the left for
$y = |x + 3|$ and then
2 units down for
$y = |x + 3| - 2$.

[3] includes equations
and graph with no
explanation

[2] includes either the
translation equations
OR graph

100

56. The graph of $y = |x - 1|$ is translated 3 units left and 2 units down. What is the equation of the new graph? **A**
 A. $y = |x + 2| - 2$ **B.** $y = |x - 4| - 2$
 C. $y = |x + 4| + 2$ **D.** $y = |x - 4| + 2$

Extended Response
57. Start with the parent function of $y = |x + 3| - 2$. Explain how to describe the graph of $y = |x + 3| - 2$ as two consecutive translations of the parent function. Include graphs of the parent function and each translation.
See margin.

Mixed Review

GO for Help

Lesson 2-5 Evaluate each function for five values of x. Then graph each function.
58. $f(x) = |x - 3| + 2$ **59.** $f(x) = |2x + 1| - 3$ **60.** $f(x) = \frac{1}{3}\left|\frac{1}{3}x - 3\right|$
58. See margin. 59–63. See back of book.

Lesson 1-4 Solve each inequality. Graph each solution on a number line.
61. $x + 7 \le -3$ **62.** $2a + 6 > 15$ **63.** $7.5 - 3b < 12$

Lesson 1-3 **64. Geometry** Keiko, an orca whale who starred in a number of movies, moved into an outdoor pool with a volume of 281,250 cubic feet. The pool's surface is a 150 ft-by-75 ft rectangle. Write and solve an equation to find the depth of the pool.
$150 \cdot 75 \cdot x = 281{,}250$; 25 ft

Checkpoint Quiz 2   Lessons 2-4 through 2-6

Graph each function. 1–6. See back of book.

1. $y = x - 5$ **2.** $y = |x + 1| + 4$ **3.** $f(x) = \frac{2}{3}x - 2$
4. $f(x) = |x| - 4$ **5.** $y = |2x - 1| - 2$ **6.** $y = 3x + 3$

Write an equation for each graph.

7.

$y = x - 4$

8.
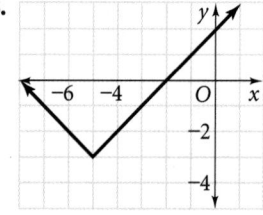
$y = |x + 5| - 3$

9a.

9. a. Use the table below. Model the relation with a scatter plot and a trend line.
b. Predict the value of y when $x = 10$. **about 7**

x	1.0	2.0	3.0	4.0	5.0	6.0	7.0
y	-1.5	0.0	1.5	2.0	2.5	3.5	4.0

10. The graph of $y = |x|$ is translated down 5 units and right 4 units. What is the equation of the new graph? **D**
 A. $y = |x + 4| + 5$ **B.** $y = |x + 4| - 5$
 C. $y = |x - 4| + 5$ **D.** $y = |x - 4| - 5$

100 Chapter 2 Functions, Equations, and Graphs

[1] attempts to interpret the translation for $y = |x + 3| - 2$ and graphs it but makes an error and does not translate it 3 units left and 2 units down

58. Answers may vary.
Sample: $f(0) = 5$;
$f(1) = 4$; $f(2) = 3$;
$f(3) = 2$; $f(-1) = 6$

Two-Variable Inequalities

What You'll Learn

• To graph linear inequalities

• To graph absolute value inequalities

. . . And Why

To solve problems involving combinations, as in Example 2

 Check Skills You'll Need

GO for Help Lessons 1-4 and 1-5

Solve each inequality. Graph the solution on a number line.

1. $12p \le 15$ **2.** $4 + t > 17$ **3.** $5 - 2t \ge 11$

1-6. See back of book.
Solve and graph each absolute value equation or inequality.

4. $|4c| = 18$ **5.** $|5 - b| = 3$ **6.** $|2h| \ge 7$

New Vocabulary • linear inequality

---

1 Graphing Linear Inequalities

Activity: Linear Inequalities

1. Graph the line $y = 2x + 3$ on graph paper.   1-2. See back of book.

2. a. Plot each point listed below.
  $(-2, -3), (-2, -1), (-1, -1), (-1, 5), (0, 4), (0, 5), (1, 6), (2, 3), (2, 7)$
  b. Classify each point as *on the line*, *above the line*, or *below the line*.

3. Are all the points that satisfy the inequality $y > 2x + 3$ *above*, *below*, or *on* the line? **above the line**

Vocabulary Tip

$<$ less than

$\le$ less than or equal to

$>$ greater than

$\ge$ greater than or equal to

$\ne$ not equal to

A **linear inequality** is an inequality in two variables whose graph is a region of the coordinate plane that is bounded by a line. To graph a linear inequality, first graph the boundary line. Then decide which side of the line contains solutions to the inequality and whether the boundary line is included.

$y > \frac{1}{2}x - 1$

For an inequality with $y <$ or $y \le$, shade below the line.
For an inequality with $y >$ or $y \ge$, shade above the line.

A *dashed* boundary line indicates that the line is not part of the solution.

A *solid* boundary line indicates that the line is part of the solution.

Choose a test point above or below the boundary line. The test point (0, 0) makes the inequality true. Shade the region containing this point.

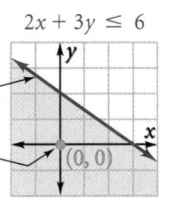

$2x + 3y \le 6$

(0, 0)

Lesson 2-7 Two-Variable Inequalities **101**

Objectives

1 To graph linear inequalities
2 To graph absolute value inequalities

Examples

1 Graphing a Linear Inequality
2 Real-World Connection
3 Graphing Absolute Value Inequalities
4 Writing Inequalities

 Professional Development

Math Background

Graphing a two-variable inequality is the first step in learning how to graph a system of two-variable inequalities. Such systems play an important role in many applications, including maximizing and minimizing linear functions given a set of linear constants. This topic will be studied in Lesson 3-4.

More Math Background: p. 52D

Lesson Planning and Resources

See p. 52E for a list of the resources that support this lesson.

 PowerPoint

Bell Ringer Practice

✓ **Check Skills You'll Need**
For intervention, direct students to:
Solving Inequalities
Lesson 1-4: Example 1
Extra Skills and Word
  Problems Practice, Ch. 1
Absolute Value Equations and Inequalities
Lesson 1-5: Example 4
Extra Skills and Word
  Problems Practice, Ch. 1

---

2. Teach

Guided Instruction

Activity

A vertical line in the coordinate plane will always intersect the graph of $y = 2x + 3$. Points on the vertical line that lie above the point of intersection have coordinates that satisfy $y > 2x + 3$. Points on the vertical line that lie below the point of intersection have coordinates that satisfy $y < 2x + 3$.

① EXAMPLE Alternative Method

You can also test points to decide which region to shade. Pick a point above the line and a point below the line. The coordinates of the point below the line will satisfy the inequality, but those of the point above the line will not. This tells you that the region below the line is the region to shade.

② EXAMPLE Teaching Tip

Quickcheck 2b provides a good opportunity to discuss how mathematical results must be interpreted in the light of restrictions imposed by a specific situation.

Additional Examples

① Graph $y > \frac{3}{2}x + 1$.

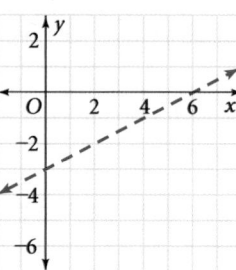

Online active math

For: Linear Inequalities Activity
Use: Interactive Textbook, 2-7

① EXAMPLE Graphing a Linear Inequality

Graph the inequality $y < \frac{1}{2}x - 3$.

Step 1 Graph the boundary line $y = \frac{1}{2}x - 3$. Since the inequality is *less than*, not *less than or equal to*, use a dashed boundary line.

Step 2 Since the inequality is *less than*, y-values must be less than those on the boundary line. Shade the region *below* the boundary line.

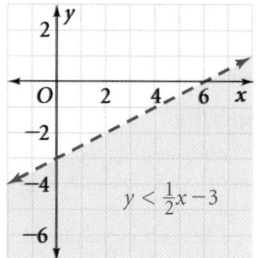

$y < \frac{1}{2}x - 3$

✓ Quick Check ①

Graph each inequality. **See back of book.**

a. $4x + 2y \le 4$ b. $y \ge 3x$ c. $\frac{x}{3} < -y + 2$

You can use linear inequalities to solve problems.

② EXAMPLE Real-World Connection

Entertainment At least 35 performers of the Big Tent Circus are in the grand finale. Some pile into cars, while others balance on bicycles. Seven performers are in each car, and five performers are on each bicycle. Draw a graph showing all the combinations of cars and bicycles possible for the finale.

Relate	the number of performers in cars	plus the number of performers on bicycles	is greater than or equal to	35

Define   Let x = the number of cars.

         Let y = the number of bicycles.

Write $7x \quad + \quad 5y \quad \ge \quad 35$

Step 1 Find the intercepts of the boundary line. Use the intercepts to graph the boundary line.

When $y = 0$, $7x + 5(0) = 35$.
$$7x = 35$$
$$x = 5$$

When $x = 0$, $7(0) + 5y = 35$.
$$5y = 35$$
$$y = 7$$

Graph the intercepts $(5, 0)$ and $(0, 7)$. Since the inequality is *greater than or equal to*, use a solid boundary line.

102   Chapter 2   Functions, Equations, and Graphs

GO Online
Video Tutor Help
Visit: PhSchool.com
Web Code: age-0775

Step 2 Choose a test point not on the boundary line. The test point (6, 4) makes the inequality true. Shade the region containing (6, 4).

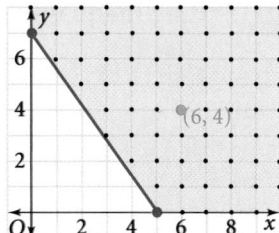

The numbers of cars x and bicycles y are whole numbers. The situation is discrete. In the shaded region, all points with whole number coordinates (shown by dots) represent possible combinations of cars and bicycles for the grand finale.

✓ Quick Check **2** **a.** Find the minimum number of bicycles that will be needed if three cars are available. Then determine three other possible combinations of bicycles and cars. **3; Answers may vary. Sample: (2, 5), (1, 6), (0, 7).**

b. **Critical Thinking** What inequalities describe the shaded region bounded by the x- and y-axes and the line in the graph above? **$7x + 5y \geq 35$, $x > 0$, $y > 0$**

2 **Graphing Two-Variable Absolute Value Inequalities**

You can graph two-variable absolute value inequalities the same way you graph linear inequalities.

3 **EXAMPLE** **Graphing Absolute Value Inequalities**

Graph each absolute value inequality.

a. $y \leq |x - 4| + 5$

Graph $y = |x - 4| + 5$.
Since the inequality is *less than or equal to,* the boundary is solid and the shaded region is below the boundary.

b. $-y + 3 > |x + 1|$

$-y > |x + 1| - 3$
$y < -|x + 1| + 3$

Graph $y = -|x + 1| + 3$.
Since the inequality is *less than,* the boundary is dashed and the shaded region is below the boundary.

GO for Help

To review graphing absolute value functions, go to Lessons 2-5 and 2-6.

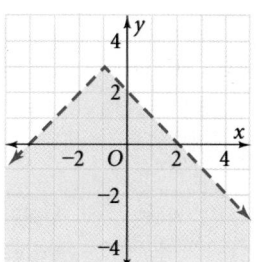

✓ Quick Check **3** Graph each absolute value inequality. **See margin.**
a. $y > -|x + 2| - 3$ **b.** $2y + 3 \leq -|x - 5|$

---

page 103 Quick Check

3a.

b.

PowerPoint

Additional Examples

2 A restaurant has only 15 eggs to last until the next delivery. An order of scrambled eggs requires 2 eggs. An omelet requires 3 eggs. Write an inequality to model all possible combinations of orders of scrambled eggs and omelets the restaurant can fill till more eggs arrive. Graph the inequality. If x = orders of scrambled eggs and y = omelet orders, then $2x + 3y \leq 15$. All ordered pairs with whole-number coordinates in the shaded area and on the line represent a combination of x orders of scrambled eggs and y orders of omelets that the restaurant can fill.

Guided Instruction

3 **EXAMPLE** **Math Tip**

Verify that the correct region is shaded by picking a point in the shaded region and making sure that it satisfies the inequality.

PowerPoint

Additional Examples

3 Graph $y \geq |2x| - 3$.

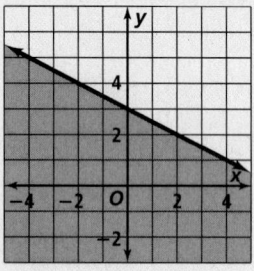
You can write an inequality by examining a graph.

4 EXAMPLE Writing Inequalities

Multiple Choice The graph is the solution of which inequality?

Ⓐ $y > |x - 3| + 2$
Ⓑ $y < |x - 3| + 2$
Ⓒ $y \geq |x - 3| + 2$
Ⓓ $y \leq |x - 3| + 2$

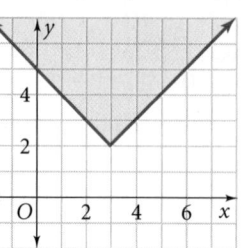

The boundary is $y = |x - 3| + 2$. The boundary is solid. The shaded region is above the boundary. This is the graph of $y \geq |x - 3| + 2$.

● The correct choice is C.

☑ **Quick Check** 4 Write an inequality for each graph.

a.

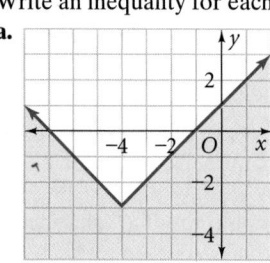

$y \leq |x + 4| - 3$

b.

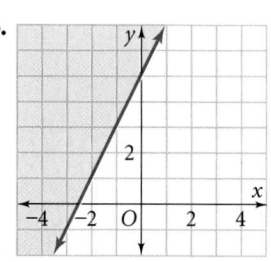

$y \geq 2x + 5$

EXERCISES

For more exercises, see *Extra Skill and Word Problem Practice*.

Practice and Problem Solving

Ⓐ Practice by Example

Graph each inequality. 1–9. See margin pp. 104–105.

Example 1
(page 102)

1. $y > 2x + 1$ **2.** $y < 3$ **3.** $x \leq 0$
4. $y \leq x - 5$ **5.** $2x + 3y \geq 12$ **6.** $2y \geq 4x - 6$
7. $y > \frac{2}{3}x + \frac{1}{3}$ **8.** $3x - 2y \leq 9$ **9.** $5x > -y + 3$

Example 2
(pages 102–103)

10. Cooking The time needed to roast a chicken depends on its weight. Allow at least 20 min/lb for a chicken weighing as much as 6 lb. Allow at least 15 min/lb for a chicken weighing more than 6 lb. **a–b. See back of book.**
   a. Write two inequalities to represent the time needed to roast a chicken.
   b. Graph the inequalities.

Example 3
(page 103)

Graph each absolute value inequality. 11–19. See back of book.

11. $y \geq |2x - 1|$ **12.** $y \leq |3x| + 1$ **13.** $y \leq |4 - x|$
14. $y > |-x + 4| + 1$ **15.** $y - 7 > |x + 2|$ **16.** $y + 2 \leq \left|\frac{1}{2}x\right|$
17. $3 - y \geq -|x - 4|$ **18.** $1 - y < |2x - 1|$ **19.** $y + 3 \leq |3x| - 1$

1.

2.

3.

4.

5.

Example 4
(page 104)

Write an inequality for each graph. The equation for the boundary is given.

20. $y = -x - 2$

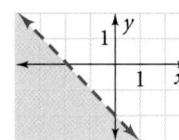

$y < -x - 2$

21. $5x + 3y = 9$

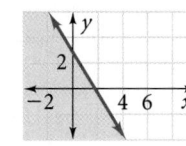

$5x + 3y \leq 9$

22. $2y = |2x + 6|$

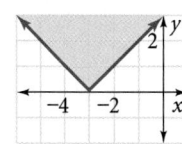

$2y \geq |2x + 6|$

B Apply Your Skills

Graph each inequality on a coordinate plane. 23–34. See back of book.

23. $5x - 2y \geq -10$

24. $2x - 5y < -10$

25. $\frac{3}{4}x + \frac{2}{3}y > \frac{5}{2}$

26. $3(x - 2) + 2y \leq 6$

27. $0.5x + 1.2y < 6$

28. $-3x + 4y > -6$

29. $\frac{1}{2}x + \frac{2}{3}y \geq 1$

30. $|x - 1| > y + 7$

31. $y - |2x| \leq 21$

32. $\frac{2}{3}x + 2 \leq \frac{2}{9}y$

33. $0.25y - 1.5x \geq -4$

34. $8x - 4y \geq -3$

35. Open-Ended Write an inequality that has $(10, 15)$, $(-10, 20)$, $(-20, -25)$, and $(25, -10)$ as solutions. **Answers may vary. Sample: $y \leq -\frac{5}{3}x + \frac{95}{3}$**

GO for Help

For a guide to solving Exercise 35, see p. 107.

Write an inequality for each graph.

36.

37.

38.
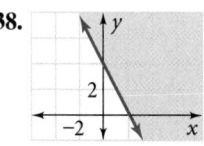

36. $x > -3$

37. $y \leq \frac{3}{2}x + 2$

38. $y \geq -2x + 4$

39. $y \leq |x + 2|$

40. $y < -|x - 4|$

41. $y > |x + 1| - 1$

39.

40.

41.
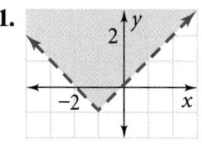

GO Online
Homework Video Tutor
Visit: PHSchool.com
Web Code: age-0207

42. Multiple Choice Which graph best represents the solution of the inequality $y \geq 2|x - 1| - 2$? **C**

Ⓐ   Ⓑ   Ⓒ   Ⓓ

C Challenge

43. Writing When you graph an inequality, you can often use the point $(0, 0)$ to test which side of the boundary line to shade. Describe a situation in which you could *not* use $(0, 0)$ as a test point. **Answers may vary. Sample: when it lies on the boundary line**

Graph each inequality on a graphing calculator. Then sketch the graph.

44. $y \leq |x + 1| - |x - 1|$

45. $y > |x| + |x + 3|$

46. $y < |x - 3| - |x + 3|$

47. $y < 7 - |x - 4| + |x|$

44–47. See back of book.

Assignment Guide

1 A B 1-10, 23-29, 32-38

2 A B 11-22, 30, 31, 39-42

C Challenge   43-47

Test Prep   48-53
Mixed Review   54-71

Homework Quick Check

To check students' understanding of key skills and concepts, go over Exercises 10, 21, 35, 41, 42.

Error Prevention!

Exercises 13, 14 Students may find it easier to graph the boundaries if they write the inequalities as $y \leq |x - 4|$ and $y > |x - 4| + 1$. Be sure they understand why this is permissible.

Differentiated Instruction Resources

GPS Guided Problem Solving	L3
Enrichment	L4
Reteaching	L2
Practice	L3

6.

7.

8.

9.

Lesson Quiz

Graph each inequality.

1. $y \geq -\frac{1}{4}x + 3$

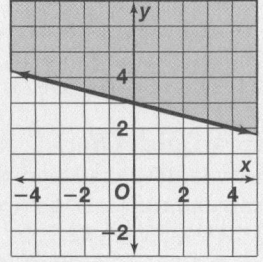

2. $-y + 1 > -|x + 3|$

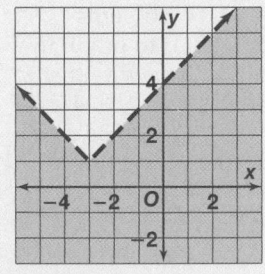

Alternative Assessment

Have students work in pairs. Each student gives the coordinates of two points not on the same vertical line. The partner writes and graphs a linear inequality whose boundary contains the given points. Each partner checks the other's work.

Test Prep

Resources
For additional practice with a variety of test item formats:
- Standardized Test Prep, p. 113
- Test-Taking Strategies, p. 108
- Test-Taking Strategies with Transparencies

Test Prep

Multiple Choice

48. The graph at the right shows which inequality? **A**
  A. $y > |x + 4| - 4$
  B. $y > |x - 4| + 4$
  C. $y < |x + 4| - 4$
  D. $y < |x - 4| + 4$

49. The graph of which inequality has its vertex at $\left(2\frac{1}{2}, -5\right)$? **J**
  F. $y < |2x - 5| + 5$ **G.** $y < |2x + 5| - 5$
  H. $y > |2x + 5| - 5$ **J.** $y > |2x - 5| - 5$

50. Which inequality is NOT equivalent to the others? **D**
  A. $y \leq \frac{2}{3}x - 3$ **B.** $3y \leq 2x - 9$
  C. $2x - 3y \geq 9$ **D.** $2x - 3y \leq 9$

51. The graph at the right shows which inequality? **F**
  F. $y \leq -2.5x + 5$
  G. $2.5x + y \geq 5$
  H. $-2.5x + y < 5$
  J. $5x + 2y \leq 5$

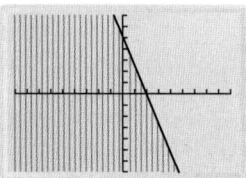

52. Which point(s) are solutions of the inequality $5x + 3y \geq 2$? **C**
  I. $(0, 0)$ **II.** $(-1, 0)$ and $\left(0, -\frac{2}{3}\right)$ **III.** $\left(0, \frac{2}{3}\right)$ and $\left(1, -\frac{2}{3}\right)$
  A. I only   **B.** I and II   **C.** III only   **D.** II and III

Short Response

53. At least 300 tornadoes occur in the United States each year. Write an inequality to model the number of tornadoes that could occur during the next x years. Describe the domain and range of the inequality. **See margin.**

Mixed Review

Lesson 2-6

Graph each function by translating its parent function.

54. $y = 2x + 5$ **55.** $y = |x| - 3$ **56.** $f(x) = |x + 6|$

57. $f(x) = x - 2$ **58.** $y = |x + 2|$ **59.** $y = |x - 1| + 5$
54–59. See margin p. 107.

Lesson 2-3

Determine whether y varies directly with x. If so, find the constant of variation.

60. $y = x + 1$ no   **61.** $y = 100x$ yes; 100   **62.** $5x + y = 0$ yes; −5   **63.** $y - 2 = 2x$ no

64. $x = \frac{y}{3}$ yes; 3   **65.** $-4 = y - x$ no   **66.** $y = -10x$ yes; −10   **67.** $xy = 1$ no

68. Commissions The amount of a commission is directly proportional to the amount of a sale. A realtor received a commission of \$13,500 on the sale of a \$225,000 house. How much would the commission be on a \$130,000 house? \$7800

Lesson 2-2

Graph each pair of equations on the same coordinate plane.

69. $y = x, y = -x + 5$ **70.** $y = -2x + 1, y = 2x$ **71.** $y = 4x - 1, y = x$
69–71. See margin p. 107.

pages 102–104 Exercises

53. [2] $y \geq 300x$, where y is the number of tornadoes that could occur in the next x years. The domain is all whole numbers greater than 0, since years are whole numbers and can't be negative. The range is whole numbers ≥ 300, since you cannot have a fraction of a tornado and in the first year you will have at least 300.

[1] includes only inequality with no explanation of domain and range

Understanding Math Problems Read the problem below. Then let Carmen's thinking guide you through the solution. Check your understanding with the exercises at the bottom of the page.

Open-Ended Write an inequality that has $(10, 15)$, $(-10, 20)$, $(-20, -25)$, and $(25, -10)$ as solutions.

What Carmen Thinks

These points are not necessarily on the same line. I'll plot the points and see where they lie on the coordinate plane.

The problem asks me to write an inequality with these points as solutions. But the graph of a linear inequality has a boundary line with shading on one side. So, I'll have to choose a boundary line.

There are so many possibilities! I need only two points to draw a line, so I'll use $(-20, -25)$ and $(25, -10)$.

The boundary line is solid since the points lie on it. I can include the other two points in the solution set by shading above the boundary line.

Since I have two points, I can use point-slope form to write the equation of the boundary line.

I can substitute the values of $m, x,$ and y into my equation and simplify.

I need to write an inequality. I shaded above the line toward greater y-values, so the inequality includes "greater than." Since I used a solid boundary line, the inequality is "greater than or equal to."

What Carmen Writes

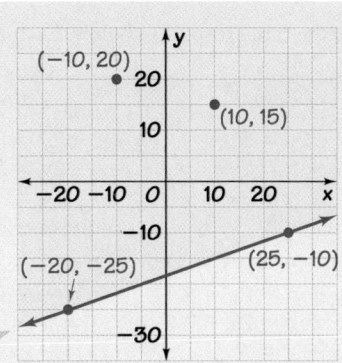

Boundary line through $(-20, -25)$ and $(25, -10)$ has slope $m = \dfrac{-10 - (-25)}{25 - (-20)}$.

$y - y_1 = m(x - x_1)$

$y - (-25) = \dfrac{-10 - (-25)}{25 - (-20)}(x - (-20))$

$y + 25 = \dfrac{15}{45}(x + 20)$

$y = \dfrac{1}{3}(x + 20) - 25$

$y = \dfrac{1}{3}x - \dfrac{55}{3}$ equation of boundary line

$y \geq \dfrac{1}{3}x - \dfrac{55}{3}$ inequality

1. Answers may vary. Sample: $y < \dfrac{2}{3}x + 40$

2. Answers may vary. Sample: $y \leq \dfrac{1}{2}x + 7$

EXERCISES

Write a different inequality that has the following ordered pairs as solutions.

1. $(10, 15), (-10, 20), (-20, -25), (25, -10)$

2. $(5, 2), (-2, 3), (-4, 5), (4, 9)$

Understanding Math Problems

Students read an annotated example problem to determine how to write an inequality that has a set of given points as solutions.

Guided Instruction

Point out to students that it does not matter whether the boundary line is above or below the points. However, if the boundary line is above the points, then the area below the line must be shaded. If the line is below the points, then the area above the line must be shaded.

Exercises

Remind students that there are many different possible solutions to each problem. Caution them that if the boundary line passes through any of the points, then the line must be solid.

58.

59.

69.

70.

71.

54.

55.

56.

57.

Writing Short Responses

This feature explains that in order to receive full credit for short-response questions, students must show their work or justify their reasoning.

Resources

SAT® and ACT® correlations are on page 52B.

Test-Taking Strategies with Transparencies
• Transparency 2
• Practice sheet, p. 26

Guided Instruction

Share your grading policy with regard to giving partial credit for short-response questions. Explain what work or reasoning you expect to see in these types of questions in order to give partial or full credit. Have students record your policy along with examples in their notebooks.

Test-Taking Strategies with Transparencies

Test-Taking Strategy: Writing Short Responses

Della went to the carnival at the county fair. The admission to the carnival was $5.00 and the rides were $1.25 each. Della spent $20 at the carnival. Write and solve an equation to find out how many rides Della rode at the carnival.

Scoring Guide
2 The equation and solution are correct, AND all work is shown.
1 An incorrect equation is used, but the procedure for solving the equation is incorrect.
1 The correct equation or solution is given, but no work is shown.
0 No response, OR completely incorrect response with no work shown.

Answer earning 2 points	In the 2-point response, the student used the correct equation, found the correct answer, AND showed all the work.
$5 + 1.25x = 20$ $1.25x = 15$ $x = 12$ Della rode 12 rides.	

Answer earning 1 point	In this 1-point response, an incorrect equation is used, but the procedure is correct for the used equation.
$1.25x = 20$ $x = 16$ Della rode 16 rides	

Answer earning 1 point	In this 1-point response, the correct solution is given, but no work is shown.
Della rode 12 rides.	

Answer earning 0 points	In the 0-point response, the solution is incorrect, AND no work is shown.
15 rides	

Transparency 2

Short-response questions are usually worth two points. To get full credit you must not only give the correct answer, but also show your work or justify your reasoning.

EXAMPLE

A line parallel to $4x - 2y = 5$ passes through the point $(2, -3)$. Write the equation of the line in standard form, $Ax + By = C$.

Study the three responses below. Each received a different score.

2 points	1 point	0 points
$4x - 2y = 5$ $4x - 5 = 2y$ $y = 2x - \frac{5}{2}$ Slope is 2. $y + 3 = 2(x - 2)$ $y + 3 = 2x - 4$ $y = 2x - 7$ $2x - y = 7$	$4x - 2y = 5$ $-2y = 5 + 4x$ $y = -2x - \frac{5}{2}$ Slope is -2. $y = -2x + b$ $-3 = -4 + b$ $1 = b$ $y = -2x + 1$ $2x + y = 1$	$4x - 2y = -3$

In the 2-point response, the student found the correct answer and showed all the work.

In the 1-point response, the student made a computational error in the second line. The final answer is wrong, but still the student received a point because the rest of the work is correct.

In the 0-point response, the student gave an incorrect answer without showing any work. The answer is not far off, so the student probably would have received a point if some work had been shown.

EXERCISES   1–3. See right.

1. At the right is another response to the Example above. How many points does the response deserve? Explain your reasoning.

Answer each question. Show your work.

2. As an orange grows over a five-week period, there is a linear relationship between the volume of the orange and time. At the beginning of the period, the volume is about 34 cm³. Four weeks later, the volume is about 50 cm³. What is the volume at the end of the five-week period?

3. A line perpendicular to $x + 3y = 5$ passes through $(1, -1)$. What is the equation of the line in standard form?

---

1. 2 points; answer is correct and student showed work.

2. [2] slope $= \frac{50 - 34}{4 - 0} = 4$
   y-intercept $= 34$
   The equation is
   $V = 4t + 34$,
   so $V = 4(5) + 34 = 54$
   (volume is 54 cm³).
   [1] incorrect volume OR no work shown

3. [2] $y = -\frac{1}{3}x + \frac{5}{3}$, so a line perpendicular to it would have a slope of 3. Using the point-slope form $y - (-1) = 3(x - 1)$ you get $3x - y = 4$.
   [1] incorrect equation OR no work shown

The equation is
$4x - 2y = k$
$4(2) - 2(-3) = k$
$14 = k$
$4x - 2y = 14$

Chapter Review

Vocabulary Review

🔊 absolute value function (p. 88)
constant of variation (p. 72)
dependent variable (p. 62)
direct variation (p. 72)
domain (p. 56)
function (p. 57)
function notation (p. 58)
independent variable (p. 62)
linear equation (p. 62)
linear function (p. 62)
linear inequality (p. 101)

mapping diagram (p. 56)
parameter (p. 97)
parent function (p. 93)
point-slope form (p. 65)
range (p. 56)
reflection (p. 96)
relation (p. 55)
scatter plot (p. 80)
shrink (p. 96)
slope (p. 64)

slope-intercept form (p. 65)
standard form (p. 63)
stretch (p. 96)
transformation (p. 97)
translation (p. 93)
trend line (p. 80)
vertex (p. 88)
vertical-line test (p. 57)
x-intercept (p. 63)
y-intercept (p. 63)

Go Online
PHSchool.com

For: Vocabulary quiz
Web Code: agj-0251

Choose the correct term to complete each sentence.

1. In the function $y = f(x)$, y is the (*dependent, independent*) variable. **dependent**

2. All functions are (*relations, domains*). **relations**

3. The graph of a function is (*always, sometimes*) a line. **sometimes**

4. An equation of the form $y - y_1 = m(x - x_1)$ is in (*point-slope, slope-intercept*) form. **point-slope**

5. The vertex of the graph of an absolute value function is (*always, sometimes*) the lowest point on the graph. **sometimes**

Skills and Concepts

2-1 Objectives

▼ To graph relations (p. 55)

▼ To identify functions (p. 57)

A **relation** is a set of ordered pairs that can be represented by points in the coordinate plane or by a **mapping diagram.** The **domain** of a relation is the set of x-coordinates. The **range** is the set of y-coordinates.

When each element of the domain of a relation is paired with exactly one element of the range, the relation is a **function.** You can write a function using the notation $f(x)$, called **function notation.**

6–10. See margin.

Determine whether each relation is a function. Find the domain and range.

6. $\{(5, 0), (8, 1), (1, 3), (5, 2), (3, 8)\}$

7. $\{(10, 2), (-10, 2), (6, 4), (5, 3), (-6, 7)\}$

8.

9. **Domain   Range**

10. **Domain   Range**
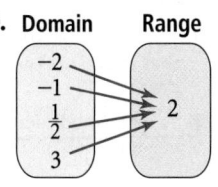

For each function, find $f(-2)$, $f(-0.5)$, and $f(3)$.

11. $f(x) = -x + 4$

6, 4.5, 1

12. $f(x) = \frac{3}{8}x - 3$

$-3\frac{3}{4}, -3\frac{3}{16}, -1\frac{7}{8}$

13. $f(x) = -\frac{5}{12}x + 2$

$2\frac{5}{6}, 2\frac{5}{24}, \frac{3}{4}$

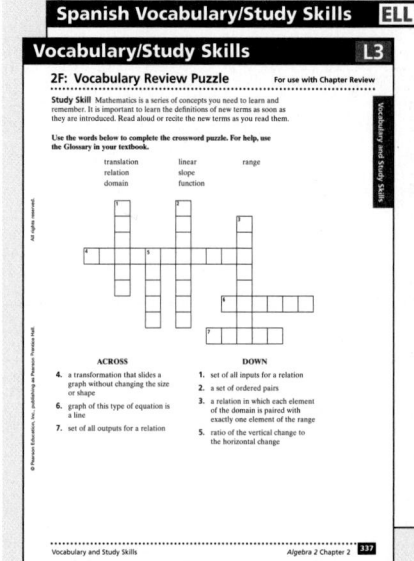
pages 109–111   Chapter Review

6. not a function;
domain {1, 3, 5, 8},
range {0, 1, 2, 3, 8}

7. function;
domain {−10, −6, 5, 6, 10},
range {2, 3, 4, 7}

8. not a function; domain
$\{-2, -\frac{3}{2}, -1, \frac{1}{2}, 1, 2, 3\}$,
range
$\{-\frac{7}{2}, -\frac{1}{2}, 0, \frac{1}{2}, \frac{3}{2}, 2, \frac{5}{2}\}$

9. function;
domain {−4, −2, −1, 1, 3},
range {−1, 2, 4}

10. function;
domain $\{-2, -1, \frac{1}{2}, 3\}$,
range {2}

pages 109–111   Chapter
                Review

26a, b.

Answers may vary.
Sample:
$y = 2.5x + 21.5$

27.

Answers may vary.
Sample: reasonable;
$y = x + 3$; 18

28.

Answers may vary.
Sample: reasonable;
$y = -0.8x + 19.9$; 7.9

2-2 Objectives

▼ To graph linear
  equations (p. 62)

▼ To write equations of
  lines (p. 64)

19c.

The graph of a **linear function** is a line. You can represent a linear function with a **linear equation.** In a function, the value of y depends on the value of x, so y is the **dependent variable** and x is the **independent variable.**

Given two points on a line, the **slope** of the line is the ratio of the difference of the y-coordinates to the corresponding difference of the x-coordinates. The slope equals the coefficient of x when you write a linear equation in **slope-intercept form.** You can also write a linear equation in **point-slope form** or **standard form.** You can use the slopes of lines to determine whether or not they are parallel, perpendicular, or horizontal. A vertical line has no slope.

Write in standard form an equation for each line.

14. slope $= -3$, through $(4, 0)$ **15.** through $(2, 3)$ and $(3, 5)$
    $3x + y = 12$ $2x - y = 1$

Find the slope, x-intercept, and y-intercept of each line.

16. $4x - 2y = 3$ **17.** $Mx = Ny + P$ **18.** $5 - x = y$
    $2; \left(\frac{3}{4}, 0\right), \left(0, -\frac{3}{2}\right)$ $\frac{M}{N}; \left(\frac{P}{M}, 0\right), \left(0, -\frac{P}{N}\right)$ $-1; (5, 0), (0, 5)$

19. a. Write an equation of the line parallel to $x + 2y = 6$ through $(8, 3)$.
    b. Write an equation of the line perpendicular to $x + 2y = 6$ through $(8, 3)$.
    c. Graph the three lines on the same coordinate plane.
    a. $y = -\frac{1}{2}x + 7$ **b.** $y = 2x - 13$

2-3 Objectives

▼ To write and interpret
  direct variation
  equations (p. 72)

A linear equation of the form $y = kx$ represents a **direct variation.** The **constant of variation** is k. You can use proportions to solve some direct variation problems.

For each function, determine whether y varies directly with x. If so, find the constant of variation and write the equation.

20.

x	y
-2	3
0	4
2	7

no

21.

x	y
4	5
6	9
10	17

no

22.

x	y
0	0
1	1
5	5

yes; 1,
$y = x$

Find each constant of variation. Then find the value of y when $x = -0.3$.

23. $y = 2$ when $x = -\frac{1}{2}$ **24.** $y = \frac{2}{3}$ when $x = 0.2$ **25.** $y = 7$ when $x = 2$
    $-4; 1.2$ $\frac{10}{3}; -1$ $\frac{7}{2}; -1\frac{1}{20}$

2-4 Objectives

▼ To write linear equations
  that model real-world
  data (p. 78)

▼ To make predictions from
  linear models (p. 79)

You can use mathematical models such as **scatter plots** to show relationships between data sets. You can use the models to make predictions. Sometimes you can draw a **trend line** to model the relation and make predictions.

 26. a. Data Analysis Draw a scatter plot of the data below. **a–b. See margin.**
    b. Draw a trend line. Write its equation.
    c. Estimate the number of cable TV subscribers in 2010. **Answers may vary. Sample: about 96.5 million**

Cable TV Subscribers

Year	1980	1985	1990	1995	2000
Millions of Subscribers	17.5	35.4	50.5	60.6	66.3

SOURCE: Television Bureau of Advertising

29.

30.

31.

Draw a scatter plot of each set of data. Decide whether a linear model is reasonable. If so, draw a trend line and write its equation. Then predict the value of y when x is 15. 27–28. See margin p. 110.

27.

x	3	4	5	7	8	9	10
y	5	7	9	10	10	11	13

28.

x	6	7	8	9	10	11	12
y	15.5	14.0	13.0	12.5	12.0	11.5	10.0

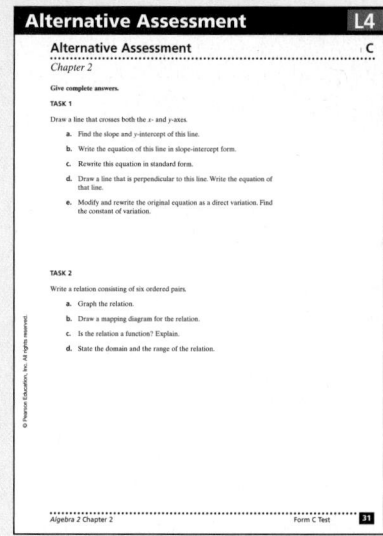
2-5 and 2-6 Objectives

▼ To graph absolute value functions (p. 88)

▼ To analyze translations (p. 93)

▼ To analyze stretches, shrinks, and reflections (p. 96)

The **absolute value function** $y = |x|$ has a graph in the shape of a V. It is the **parent function** for the family of functions of the form $y = a|x - h| + k$. The maximum or minimum point of the V is the **vertex** of the graph.

The value of h represents a horizontal translation of the parent graph by h units left (h is positive) or right (h is negative). The k represents a vertical translation of the graph by k units up (k is positive) or down (k is negative). The a represents a vertical stretch for $a > 1$; a vertical shrink for $0 < a < 1$. $y = -a|x|$ is a reflection of $y = a|x|$ in the x-axis.

Graph each equation by writing two linear equations. 29–31. See margin p. 110.

29. $y = |x - 7|$ **30.** $y = -|x + 10|$ **31.** $y = \frac{1}{3}|2x + 6| + 2$

Write an equation for each translation of the graph of $y = |x|$.

$y = |x - 2| + 4$ **32.** 4 units up, 2 units right   **33.** vertex $(-3, 0)$ $y = |x + 3|$

34. vertex $(5, 2)$ $y = |x - 5| + 2$ **35.** vertex $(4, 1)$ $y = |x - 4| + 1$

Graph each function. 36–38. See margin. 39–41. See back of book.

36. $f(x) = |x| - 8$ **37.** $f(x) = 2|x - 5|$ **38.** $f(x) = \frac{1}{2}|x - 3| + 3$

39. $y = 3|x + 4|$ **40.** $y = -\frac{1}{4}|x - 2| + \frac{1}{2}$ **41.** $y = -2|x + 1| - 1$

2-7 Objectives

▼ To graph linear inequalities (p. 101)

▼ To graph absolute value inequalities (p. 103)

A **linear inequality** describes a region of the coordinate plane that has a boundary. To graph an inequality involving two variables, first graph the boundary. Then decide which side of the boundary contains solutions. Points on a dashed boundary are not solutions. Points on a solid boundary are solutions.

Graph each inequality. 42–46. See margin.

42. $y \geq -2$ **43.** $y < 3x + 1$ **44.** $y \leq -|x - 5|$ **45.** $y > |2x + 1|$

🌐 **46. Transportation** An air cargo plane can transport as many as 15 regular shipping containers. One super-size container takes up the space of 3 regular containers.
  a. Write an inequality to model the situation.
  b. Describe the domain and range.
  c. Graph the inequality you wrote in part (a).

47. Open-Ended Write an absolute value inequality with a solid boundary that has solutions below the x-axis only. **Answers may vary. Sample:** $y \leq -|x| - 1$

42.

43.

44.

45.

**46a. Answers may vary.
Sample:** $x + 3y \leq 15$

**b. Answers may vary.
Sample: domain**
$\{0, 1, 2, 3, 4, 5, 6, 7, 8, 9, 10, 11, 12, 13, 14, 15\}$,
range $\{0, 1, 2, 3, 4, 5\}$

c.

36.   37.   38.

Go Online
PHSchool.com
For: Chapter test
Web Code: aga-0252

Differentiated Instruction Resources

- **L3** Ch. 2 Test
- **L2** Below Level Ch. 2 Test
- **L4** Ch. 2 Alternative Assessment
- **L3** Spanish Ch. 2 Test
- **L4** Spanish Ch. 2 Alternative Assessment
- ExamView CD-ROM
  - Ch. 2 Pre-Made Test
  - Make your own Ch. 2 test
- Online Chapter 2 Test at www.PHSchool.com

Find the domain and range. Graph each relation.

1. $\{(0,0),(1,-1),(2,-4),(3,-9),(4,-16)\}$ 1–2. See back of book.

2. $\{(3,2),(4,3),(5,4),(6,5),(7,6)\}$

Determine whether each relation is a function.

3. Domain Range

4. Domain Range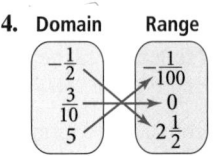

3–4. See margin.

Suppose $f(x) = 2x - 5$ and $g(x) = |-3x - 1|$. Find each value.

5. $f(3)$ 1 **6.** $f(1) + g(2)$ 4 **7.** $g(0)$ 1

8. $g(2) - f(0)$ 12 **9.** $f(-1) - g(3)$ −17 **10.** $2g(-4)$ 22

11. Open-Ended Graph a relation that is *not* a function. Find its domain and range. **Check students' work.**

Find the slope of each line.

12. through $(3,5)$ and $(1,1)$ 2 **13.** $4x + 3y = 2$ $-\frac{4}{3}$

14. through $(-0.5, 0.5)$, perpendicular to $y = -2x - 4\frac{1}{2}$

Write in standard form an equation of the line with the given slope through the given point.

15. slope $= -3, (0,0)$ $3x + y = 0$ **16.** slope $= \frac{2}{5}, (6,7)$ $2x - 5y = -23$

17. slope $= 4, (-2,-5)$ $4x - y = -3$ **18.** slope $= -0.5, (0,6)$ $x + 2y = 12$

Write in point-slope form an equation of the line through each pair of points. Answers may vary. Samples:

19. $(0,0)$ and $(-4,7)$ $y = -\frac{7}{4}x$ **20.** $(-1,-6)$ and $(-2,10)$ $y + 6 = -16(x + 1)$

21. $(3,0)$ and $(-1,-2)$ $y = \frac{1}{2}(x-3)$ **22.** $(9,5)$ and $(8,2)$ $y - 2 = 3(x - 8)$

23. a. Open-Ended Write an equation of a line with negative slope. **a–e. See back of book.**

  b. Write an equation of the line perpendicular to the line from part (a) passing through $(-6,9)$.

  c. Write an equation of the line parallel to the line from part (b) passing through $(12,12)$.

  d. Write an equation of the line perpendicular to the line from part (c) passing through $(-1,-4)$.

  e. Graph the lines from parts (a), (b), (c), and (d). If they form a polygon, describe it.

For each direct variation, find the constant of variation. Then find the value of y when $x = -0.5$.

24. $y = 4$ when $x = 0.5$ 8; −4 **25.** $y = 2$ when $x = 3$ $\frac{2}{3}, -\frac{1}{3}$

26. Transportation The number of minutes a freight train takes to pass an intersection varies directly with the number of cars in the train. A 150-car train passes in 3 min. How long will a 210-car train take to pass? **4.2 min**

Graph each function. 27–30. See back of book.

27. $y = 3x + 4$ **28.** $y = |5x - 3| + 1$

29. $y = -|x - 3| + 1$ **30.** $y = 3 - \frac{2}{5}x$

31. Recreation The table displays the amounts the Jackson family spent on vacations during the years 1996–2006.

Jackson Family Vacation Costs

Year	Cost	Year	Cost
1996	$1000	2002	$2750
1997	$1750	2003	$3200
1998	$1750	2004	$2900
1999	$2000	2005	$3100
2000	$2200	2006	$3300
2001	$2700		

a–c. See back of book.
  a. Make a scatter plot of the data.
  b. Draw a trend line. Write its equation.
  c. Estimate the cost to the Jackson family of vacations in 2008.
  d. Writing Explain how to use a trend line with a scatter plot. **Check students' work.**

32–37. See back of book.
Describe each transformation of the parent function $y = |x|$. Then, graph each function.

32. $y = |x| - 4$ **33.** $y = |x - 1| - 5$

34. $y = -|x + 4| + 3$ **35.** $y = 2|x + 1|$

36. $y = |x| + 5$ **37.** $y = -\frac{1}{2}|x + 2| - 3$

Graph each inequality. 38–41. See back of book.

38. $y \geq x + 7$ **39.** $y > |2x + 3| - 3$

40. $4x + 3y < 2$ **41.** $y \leq -|x + 1| - 2$

page 112 Chapter Test

3. domain: $\left\{-2, 1, 3, 4\frac{1}{2}\right\}$, range: {1, 2, 3, 4, 5}

4. domain: $\left\{-\frac{1}{2}, 0.3, 5\right\}$, range: {−0.01, 0, 2.5}

112

Standardized Test Prep

Multiple Choice

For Exercises 1–13, choose the correct letter.

1. Which phrase could NOT describe $\sqrt{625}$?
B
- Ⓐ whole number
- Ⓑ irrational number
- Ⓒ integer
- Ⓓ rational number

2. Which value is in the solution set of
F $4 < -4x - 2 < 8$ and $3 > 4x + 2 > -10$?
- Ⓕ −2
- Ⓖ 0
- Ⓗ 3
- Ⓙ 4

3. Which point could NOT be on the graph of a
B function that includes (5, 4), (8, −1), (7, 3), (0, 5), and (10, −2)?
- Ⓐ (6, 4)
- Ⓑ (10, 1)
- Ⓒ (11, −1)
- Ⓓ (9, 3)

4. Which relations are functions?
F

I.   II.

III.   IV.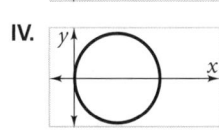

- Ⓕ I and II
- Ⓖ I and III
- Ⓗ II and III
- Ⓙ II and IV

5. Which lines are parallel?
C
I. $y = -2x + 1$ II. $y = x - 4$
III. $y = -x + 5$ IV. $y = 3 - 2x$
- Ⓐ I and II
- Ⓑ I and III
- Ⓒ I and IV
- Ⓓ II and III

6. Which values are solutions of $y < 2x + 3$?
H
I. (0, 2)   II. (−1, 1)   III. (2, 0)
- Ⓕ I only
- Ⓖ II only
- Ⓗ I and III
- Ⓙ II and III

7. Which line is perpendicular to $y = 2x - 4$?
D
- Ⓐ $y = -2x + 4$
- Ⓑ $y = -4 - 2x$
- Ⓒ $y = -x - 2$
- Ⓓ $y = -\frac{1}{2}x + 4$

8. Which equation is in standard form?
F
- Ⓕ $x - y = 7$
- Ⓖ $y = 3x - 1$
- Ⓗ $x = 4y + 2$
- Ⓙ $10 - 5x = 2y$

9. Which equation represents the graph of
B $y = -|4x|$ translated down 1 unit and right 5 units?
- Ⓐ $y = -|4(x + 5)| - 1$
- Ⓑ $y = -|4(x - 5)| - 1$
- Ⓒ $y = -|4(x - 1)| + 5$
- Ⓓ $y = -4|(x - 1)| - 5$

10. Solve $2|7 - x| < 2$ for x.
F
- Ⓕ $6 < x < 8$
- Ⓖ $x < 6$ or $x > 8$
- Ⓗ $-8 < x < -6$
- Ⓙ $x < 8$ or $x > 6$

11. Use the Addition Property of Equality to
C complete the statement: If $p = q$, then $x + p = $ ■.
- Ⓐ $p + x$
- Ⓑ $x + 0$
- Ⓒ $x + q$
- Ⓓ $p + q$

12. A bag contains 18 red chips, 24 blue chips,
H 30 yellow chips, and 48 green chips. You pick a chip from the bag at random. Find the probability that the chip is red or green.
- Ⓕ 37.5%
- Ⓖ 45%
- Ⓗ 55%
- Ⓙ 66%

13. Which inequality has the same graph as
D $8 - y < |x + 3|$?
- Ⓐ $y < -|x + 3| - 8$
- Ⓑ $y < -|x + 3| + 8$
- Ⓒ $y > -|x + 3| - 8$
- Ⓓ $y > -|x + 3| + 8$

Gridded Response

14. What is the y-coordinate of the point through **0** which the graph of every direct variation passes?

15. In one roll of two number cubes, what is the probability that the product of the faces is 12?
1/9 or .111

Short Response   16–17. See back of book.

16. Graph $y < |x + 3|$. Identify the parent function of the boundary and describe the translation.

17. Suppose y varies directly as x, and $y = 2$ when $x = -2$. Find the constant of variation. Then find the value of x when $y = 3$.

Extended Response

18. a. Write an equation of the line through (−2, 6) with slope 2. **a–c. See back of book.**
b. Write an equation of the line through (1, 1) perpendicular to the line in part (a).
c. Graph the two lines on the same set of axes.

Chapter 2   Standardized Test Prep   **113**

Students must be able to extract information from reading passages, answer multiple choice questions, and construct responses in order to be successful on current state and national assessments.

To answer the questions, students apply skills and concepts from this chapter and previous chapters.
Multiple Choice: Items 1–13
Gridded Response: Items 14–15
Short Response: 16–17
Extended Response: Items 18

Resources

Test Prep Workbook

Grab & Go
- **L3** Cumulative Review

ExamView CD-ROM
- Standardized Test Practice

Differentiated Instruction Resources

Progress Monitoring Assessments
- Benchmark Test 1

Spanish Assessment Resources
- **L3** Spanish Cumulative Review

Item	1	2	3	4	5	6	7	8	9	10	11	12	13	14	15	16	17	18
Lesson	1-1	1-4	2-1	2-1	2-2	1-4	2-2	2-2	2-6	1-5	1-3	1-6	2-7	2-3	1-6	2-6	2-3	2-2

Bridges, Beams, and Tension

In this activity students apply their knowledge of functions, equations, and graphs.

Activating Prior Knowledge

Have students share their experiences in bending something until it breaks, for example, a pencil or a plastic spoon. Elicit the fact that the bending is the result of force that the person is applying to the material.

Guided Instruction

Have a volunteer read the introductory paragraph. Ask: *What large bridges have you seen? Where are there long or high bridges in our area?*

Teaching Tip

Try this activity yourself before you assign it to students in order to make sure you have thin enough dowels and heavy enough washers to produce a measurable deflection. Make sure that one end of the paper clip fits over the dowel and that the washers can be hung by their center hole on a hook made by bending the other end of the paper clip.

Tactile Learners

In order to give everyone a chance to work with the materials, have students working in pairs or small groups rotate tasks, such as setting up the experiment, making changes, and recording results.

Connection to Science

Have students research famous bridges and share their findings with the class.

 Activity Lab

Bridges, Beams, and Tension

Applying Functions Even steel bends when heavy loads are applied to it. In designing bridges and other structures, civil engineers use functions to predict how much a beam will deflect, or bend, under a given load. They design bridges so that the stress from the combined weights of the bridge materials and the vehicles that cross the bridge, along with stress from winds, does not exceed allowable limits.

Communication Bridges Countries

Each note of the euro currency, which debuted in 12 countries in January 2002, has a bridge on the reverse side, symbolizing communication among the people of Europe and between Europe and the rest of the world.

Main cable
Length: 2332 m
Diameter: 92 cm

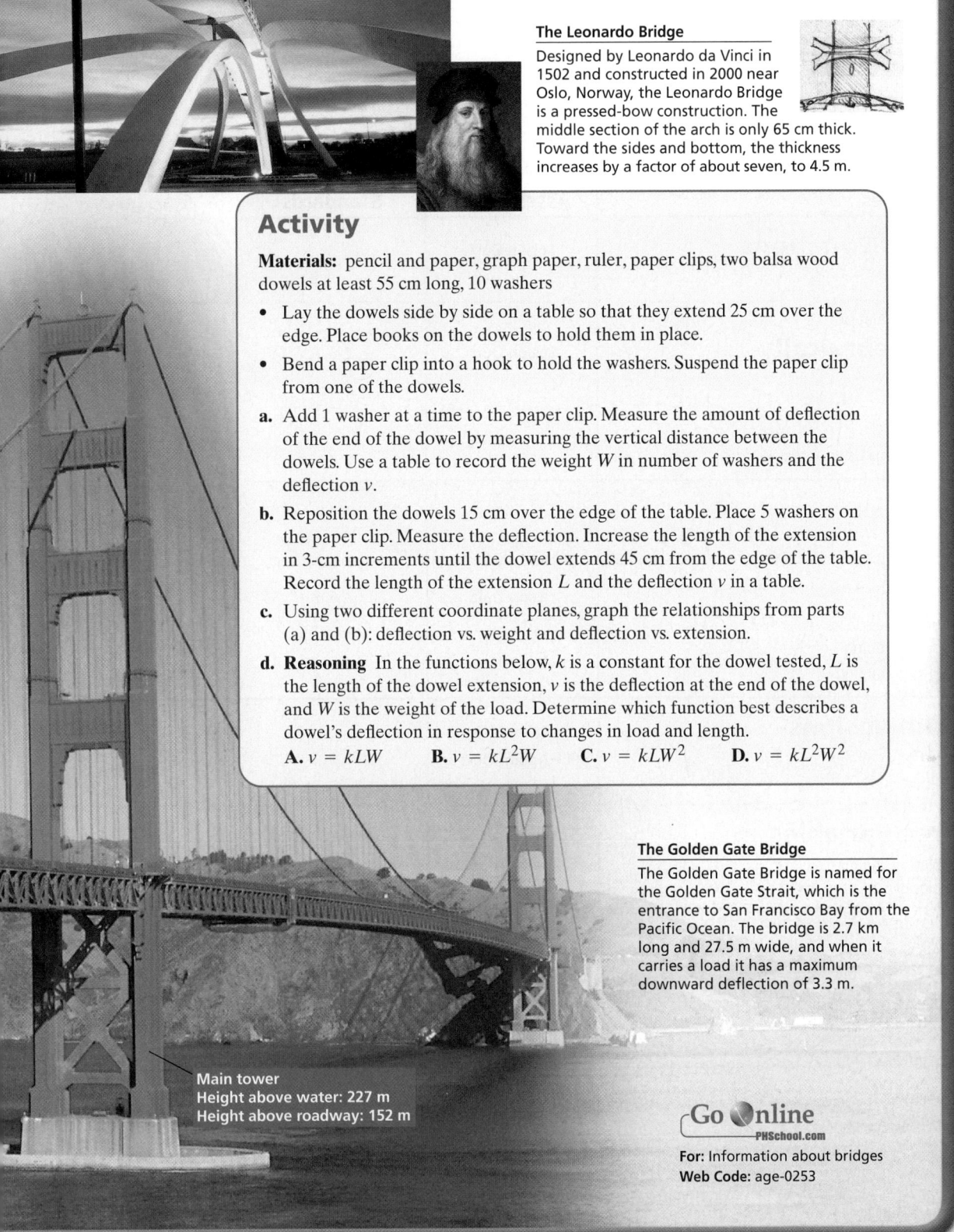

The Leonardo Bridge

Designed by Leonardo da Vinci in 1502 and constructed in 2000 near Oslo, Norway, the Leonardo Bridge is a pressed-bow construction. The middle section of the arch is only 65 cm thick. Toward the sides and bottom, the thickness increases by a factor of about seven, to 4.5 m.

Activity

Materials: pencil and paper, graph paper, ruler, paper clips, two balsa wood dowels at least 55 cm long, 10 washers

- Lay the dowels side by side on a table so that they extend 25 cm over the edge. Place books on the dowels to hold them in place.
- Bend a paper clip into a hook to hold the washers. Suspend the paper clip from one of the dowels.

a. Add 1 washer at a time to the paper clip. Measure the amount of deflection of the end of the dowel by measuring the vertical distance between the dowels. Use a table to record the weight W in number of washers and the deflection v.

b. Reposition the dowels 15 cm over the edge of the table. Place 5 washers on the paper clip. Measure the deflection. Increase the length of the extension in 3-cm increments until the dowel extends 45 cm from the edge of the table. Record the length of the extension L and the deflection v in a table.

c. Using two different coordinate planes, graph the relationships from parts (a) and (b): deflection vs. weight and deflection vs. extension.

d. Reasoning In the functions below, k is a constant for the dowel tested, L is the length of the dowel extension, v is the deflection at the end of the dowel, and W is the weight of the load. Determine which function best describes a dowel's deflection in response to changes in load and length.

A. $v = kLW$ **B.** $v = kL^2W$ **C.** $v = kLW^2$ **D.** $v = kL^2W^2$

The Golden Gate Bridge

The Golden Gate Bridge is named for the Golden Gate Strait, which is the entrance to San Francisco Bay from the Pacific Ocean. The bridge is 2.7 km long and 27.5 m wide, and when it carries a load it has a maximum downward deflection of 3.3 m.

Main tower
Height above water: 227 m
Height above roadway: 152 m

Go Online
PHSchool.com

For: Information about bridges
Web Code: age-0253

115

Teaching Tip

Before students begin the activity, discuss the illustrations and their captions. Have students work in pairs or in small groups to complete the activities. Have each team read through the activity before beginning to work.

Activity

Materials: paper and pencil, ruler, paper clips, 2 balsa wood dowels, 10 washers

Special Needs   L1

Help students organize their work by making a table for recording the results. Work with students to identify appropriate labels for the rows and columns.

Scoring Rubric

This scoring rubric can be used for evaluating student work on the activity. Share this scoring rubric with students before they begin work.

4 Equations, calculations, and graphs are correct. Steps are neat, accurate, and clearly show the mathematics. Responses are clearly indicated and give the appropriate units.

3 Equations, calculations, and graphs are mostly correct, with some minor errors. Steps are neat and mostly accurate. Units are not completely accurate.

2 Equations, calculations, and graphs contain both major and minor errors.

1 Correct answer, but no work is shown.

page 115   Activity Lab

Activity

a–d. Check students' work.

Linear Systems

Chapter at a Glance

Lesson Titles, Objectives, and Features	Assessment	NCTM Standards	Local Standards
3-1 Graphing Systems of Equations • Solving a system by graphing	Lesson Quiz	2, 5, 9, 10	
Activity Lab: Technology: Parametric Equations **3-2 Solving Systems Algebraically** • Solving a system by substitution • Solving a system by elimination **GPS:** Understanding Word Problems **Activity Lab:** Technology: Solving Systems Using Tables	Lesson Quiz	2, 6, 9	
3-3 Systems of Inequalities • Solving systems of linear inequalities	Lesson Quiz Checkpoint Quiz 1	2, 9	
3-4 Linear Programming • Finding maximum and minimum values • Solving problems with linear programming **Activity Lab:** Technology: Linear Programming	Lesson Quiz	2, 6, 8	
3-5 Graphs in Three Dimensions • Graphing points in three dimensions • Graphing equations in three dimensions	Lesson Quiz Checkpoint Quiz 2	2, 3, 10	
3-6 Systems With Three Variables • Solving systems in three variables by elimination • Solving systems in three variables by substitution	Lesson Quiz	2, 3, 6, 10	

NCTM Standards 2000

1 Number and Operations	**2** Algebra	**3** Geometry
6 Problem Solving	**7** Reasoning and Proof	**8** Communication

4 Measurement	**5** Data Analysis and Probability
9 Connections	**10** Representation

Correlations to Standardized Tests

All content for these tests is contained in *Prentice Hall Algebra 2*. This chart reflects coverage in this chapter only.

	3-1	3-2	3-3	3-4	3-5	3-6
SAT®						
Number and Operations Operations, ratio & proportions, complex numbers, counting, elementary number theory, matrices, sequences	✔	✔	✔	✔	✔	✔
Algebra and Functions Expressions, equations, inequalities, representation and modeling, properties of functions (linear, polynomial, rational, exponential)	✔	✔	✔	✔	✔	✔
Geometry and Measurement *Plane Euclidean/Measurement Coordinate* Lines, parabolas, circles, symmetry, transformations *Three-dimensional* Solids, surface area & volume (cylinders, cones, pyramids, spheres, prisms) *Trigonometry* Right triangles, identities						
Data Analysis, Statistics, and Probability Mean, median, mode, range, interquartile range, graphs and plots, regression, probability						
ACT®						
Pre-Algebra Basic operations using whole numbers, decimals, fractions, and integers; place value; square roots and approximations; the concept of exponents; scientific notation; factors, ratio, proportion, and percent; linear equations in one variable; absolute value and ordering numbers by value; elementary counting techniques and simple probability; data collection, representation, and interpretation; and understanding simple descriptive statistics.						
Elementary Algebra Properties of exponents and square roots, evaluation of algebraic expressions through substitution, using variables to express functional relationships, understanding algebraic operations, and solving quadratic equations by factoring.	✔	✔	✔	✔	✔	✔
Intermediate Algebra Understanding of the quadratic formula, rational and radical expressions, absolute value equations and inequalities, sequences and patterns, systems of equations, quadratic inequalities, functions, modeling, matrices, roots of polynomials, and complex numbers.	✔	✔	✔	✔	✔	✔
Coordinate Geometry Graphing and the relations between equations and graphs, including points, lines, polynomials, circles, and other curves; graphing inequalities; slope; parallel and perpendicular lines; distance; midpoints; and conics.	✔		✔	✔		
Plane Geometry Properties and relations of plane figures, including angles and relations among perpendicular and parallel lines; properties of circles, triangles, rectangles, parallelograms, and trapezoids; transformations; the concept of proof and proof techniques; volume; and applications of geometry to three dimensions.					✔	✔
Trigonometry Understanding trigonometric relations in right triangles; values and properties of trigonometric functions; graphing trigonometric functions; modeling using trigonometric functions; use of trigonometric identities; and solving trigonometric equations.						
NAEP						
Number Sense, Properties, and Operations						
Measurement						
Geometry and Spatial Sense					✔	✔
Data Analysis, Statistics, and Probability						
Algebra and Functions	✔	✔	✔	✔		✔

SAT® The College Board, SAT® Reasoning Test   **ACT®** The ACT Assessment® Test   **NAEP** National Assessment of Educational Progress, 2005 Mathematics Objectives

Math Background

Skills Trace

BEFORE Chapter 3

In previous chapters, students solved and graphed one- and two-variable equations and inequalities.

DURING Chapter 3

Students algebraically solve two- and three-variable systems of equations, graphically solve two-variable systems of inequalities, and solve linear programming problems.

AFTER Chapter 3

Students will solve two- and three-variable systems of equations using matrices, and solve non-linear systems of equations.

Chapter Overview

Solutions to many real-world problems and mathematical problems hinge on finding solutions of systems of linear equations or inequalities. Solutions that are adequate for a given situation can often be found graphically. When graphs are not adequate, algebraic methods can be used.

In this chapter, students learn to solve systems of linear equations and inequalities. They learn some of the basics of linear programming. They consider graphs of linear equations in three dimensions. Finally, they extend the algebraic methods they have learned for solving systems of linear equations with two variables to solve systems of linear equations with three variables.

Graphing Systems of Equations   3-1

Students are by now aware that not all systems of linear equations have easily determined solutions.

The system $\begin{cases} 3x + 7y = 5 \\ 6x - 7y = 1 \end{cases}$ has $\left(\frac{2}{3}, \frac{3}{7}\right)$ as its exact solution. If students

graph this system using a scale of 1 grid unit $= \frac{1}{21}$ unit (an unlikely choice, seeing only the equations), their solution will be exact. If

they graph it using any other scale that is not a multiple of $\frac{1}{21}$, their solution will probably be approximate. If their estimate of the solution, to the nearest hundredth, is (0.67, 0.43), checking these estimates in the equations will yield $5.02 \approx 5$ from the first equation, and $1.01 \approx 1$ from the second equation. Actually, the student is more likely to estimate the solution to the nearest tenth—perhaps (0.7, 0.4)—yielding $4.9 \approx 5$ and $1.4 \approx 1$.

These check results are certainly close *enough* to assure the student that the estimated solution is close to the actual solution. Whether the estimated solution is close enough depends on the accuracy appropriate to the actual situation—for example, whether the concern is to build a bridge or a microscope and whether the units are miles or millimeters.

The discussion of independent, dependent, and inconsistent systems will provide convincing evidence of the importance of slope-intercept form in the study of systems of linear equations. Throughout, stress the importance of checking solutions in both original equations of the system.

Solving Systems Algebraically   3-2

The examples and exercises in this lesson are generally also suitable for solving by graphing. The system

$$\begin{cases} y = -0.143x + 294.015 \\ y = -0.247x + 321.009 \end{cases}$$

is more easily recognized as unsuitable for solving by graphing. Its solution is $\left(\frac{13,497}{52}, \frac{1,027,593}{4000}\right)$. No matter how carefully students graph this system by hand, their solution is most likely to be approximate and difficult to determine. Checking by substituting their approximations for the coordinates into each equation will most likely lead them to conclude that their work is fairly accurate, but not exact. Students should recognize this system as suitable for the substitution method, because each equation is already solved for y.

In both substitution and elimination, the solution strategy is to obtain an equation in one variable that can be solved using the Properties of Equality. The resulting value of the variable is then substituted back into one of the original equations to find the value of the other variable.

Systems in which both variables are eliminated and have no unique solution often confuse students. When the resulting equation is true, the system is dependent and has an infinite number of solutions that are graphically represented by coinciding lines. When the resulting equation is false, the system is inconsistent and has no solutions since the system is represented by parallel lines.

Systems of Inequalities

3-3

Systems of relationships can be extended from equations to inequalities. The solution to a system of linear inequalities is the intersection of each of the corresponding half-plane solutions. Thus, two linear inequalities generally divide the plane into four distinct regions, one of which represents the solution region for the system. The exceptions to this include systems with parallel or coincident lines, as well as systems that include absolute value inequalities. Students may be interested to find examples of systems of linear inequalities with solution regions of: no solution, all ordered pairs in the coordinate plane, and a line. Encourage students to use a graphing calculator to represent linear inequalities.

Linear Programming

3-4

Linear programming is a branch of mathematics that was developed during World War II to cope with the complex task of transporting men and supplies. Linear programming applications are widespread in business and industry. Such applications are often referred to as optimization problems because a maximum or minimum value is sought. Analyzing real-world situations and writing correct inequalities for the constraints is an important application of mathematical modeling. Students sometimes overlook the constraints on variables to non-negative values and/or integer values.

Graphs in Three Dimensions

3-5

The graph of a one-variable equation on the number line is a point. The graph of a two-variable linear equation on the coordinate plane is a line. The graph of a three-variable linear equation in coordinate space is a plane. Thus, the solution is a number for a one-variable equation, an ordered pair for a two-variable equation, and an ordered triple for a three-variable equation.

Students who have difficulty visualizing figures in three dimensions may find it helpful to use rectangular boxes or other models to understand points in coordinate space. When the graph of a plane intersects one of the coordinate planes, a line is formed that is called a trace. This is analogous to the x- and y-intercepts for a line as it intersects the x- and y-axes, respectively. So, similar to graphing a line using intercepts, students can graph the intercepts of traces, draw the traces, and shade the plane to graph a three-variable equation in coordinate space.

Systems With Three Variables

3-6

Two planes can be parallel, they can intersect in a line, or they can coincide. The graphs of three simultaneous equations in three variables are three planes and they can intersect in one point, a line, a plane, or can have no point of intersection. There is no point of intersection if any two of the planes are parallel, or if each pair of planes intersect in lines that are parallel to each other.

The solution methods for systems of linear equations in three variables presented are the algebraic methods of elimination and substitution. Thus, solving systems of three equations in three variables is a straightforward extension of the procedure used for systems with two equations and two variables.

As with two-variable systems, students should be encouraged to check their ordered triple solutions in all three of the original equations of the system. Also, there are three-variable systems that have no unique solution and all three variables would be eliminated in the solution process. However, the complications involved with such systems are not presented in the lesson.

Additional Professional Development Opportunities

Math Background notes for Chapter 3: Every lesson has a Math Background in the PLAN section.

Research Overview, Mathematical Strands
Additional support for these topics and more is in the front of this Teacher's Edition.

Lesson Lab
Lesson Lab, a Pearson Education company, offers comprehensive, facilitated professional development designed to help teachers improve student achievement. To learn more, please visit lessonlab.com

Chapter 3 Resources

Print Resources

	3-1	3-2	3-3	3-4	3-5	3-6	For the Chapter
L3 Practice	•	•	•	•	•	•	
L3 Guided Problem Solving	•	•	•	•	•	•	
L2 Reteaching	•	•	•	•	•	•	
L4 Enrichment	•	•	•	•	•	•	
L3 Daily Notetaking Guide	•	•	•	•	•	•	
L3 Vocabulary and Study Skills Worksheets	•		•	•	•	•	•
L3 Chapter Project							•
L3 Hands-On Activities	•		•				
L3 Checkpoint Quiz			•		•		
L2 Below Level Chapter Test							•
L3 Chapter Test							•
L4 Alternative Assessment							•
L3 Cumulative Review							•
L4 Connections to Precalculus Masters	•	•	•	•	•	•	
L3 Technology Activities	•						

Spanish Resources ELL

	3-1	3-2	3-3	3-4	3-5	3-6	For the Chapter
L3 Practice	•	•	•	•	•	•	
L3 Vocabulary and Study Skills Worksheets	•		•	•	•	•	•
L3 Checkpoint Quiz			•		•		
L2 Below Level Chapter Test							•
L3 Chapter Test							•
L4 Alternative Assessment							
L3 Cumulative Review							•

Transparencies

	3-1	3-2	3-3	3-4	3-5	3-6	For the Chapter
Check Skills You'll Need	•	•	•	•	•	•	
Additional Examples	•	•	•	•	•	•	
Problem of the Day	•	•	•	•	•	•	
Classroom Aid	•						
Student Edition Answers	•	•	•	•	•	•	•
Lesson Quiz	•	•	•	•	•	•	
Test-Taking Strategies							•

Technology

	3-1	3-2	3-3	3-4	3-5	3-6	For the Chapter
TI 83/84 Plus Activities			•	•			
Interactive Textbook Online	•	•	•	•	•	•	•
Student Express CD-ROM	•	•	•	•	•	•	
TI Navigator, Instant Check System	•	•	•	•	•	•	
Success Tracker	•	•	•	•	•	•	•
ExamView CD-ROM with Quick Take	•	•	•	•	•	•	•
Teacher Express CD-ROM	•	•	•	•	•	•	•
Presentation Express CD-ROM	•	•	•	•	•	•	
Mindpoint Quiz Show CD-ROM	•	•	•	•	•	•	•
Prentice Hall Web site: PHSchool.com	•	•	•	•	•	•	•

Also available: Prentice Hall Assessment System (Progress Monitoring Assessments, Skills and Concepts Review, Test Prep Workbook)   Solution Key   Student Workbook
Student Workbook, Adapted Version   Data Analysis and Probability Workbook   Math Notes Study Folder   Spanish Cumulative Assessment

Where You Can Use the Lesson Resources

Here is a suggestion, following the four-step teaching plan, for how you can incorporate Differentiated Instruction Resources into your teaching.

	Instructional Resources L3	Differentiated Instruction Resources
1. Plan		
Check Skills You'll Need Assign these exercises to review prerequisite skills. **New Vocabulary** Help students pre-read the lesson by pointing out the new terms introduced in the lesson.	**Math Background** **Transparencies & Presentation Express CD** Check Skills You'll Need **Resources** Vocabulary and Study Skills	**Spanish Support** ELL Vocabulary and Study Skills
2. Teach		
L3 Guided Instruction Teach each Example. After each Example, assign the Quick Check exercise for that Example.	**Student Edition** Activity Lab **Resources** Daily Notetaking Guide Activity Lab TI-83/84 Activities CD-ROM **Transparencies & Presentation Express CD** Additional Examples Classroom Aids **ExamView CD-ROM with QuickTake** **TI Navigator Instant Check System**	**Teacher's Edition** Every lesson includes suggestions for working with students who need special attention. L1 Special Needs L2 Below Level L4 Advanced Learners ELL English Language Learners
3. Practice		
Assignment Guide **Homework Exercises** Assign the exercises cited in each lesson's Assignment Guide. A Practice by Example B Apply Your Skills C Challenge Test Prep Mixed Review **Homework Quick Check** Discuss in class the exercises cited in each lesson's Assignment Guide.	**Transparencies & Presentation Express CD** Student Answers **Resources** Practice Guided Problem Solving Vocabulary and Study Skills Activity Lab **ExamView CD-ROM with QuickTake**	**Spanish Support** ELL Practice ELL Vocabulary and Study Skills **Resources** L4 Enrichment
4. Assess & Reteach		
Lesson Quiz Assign the Lesson Quiz to assess students' mastery of the lesson content. **Checkpoint Quiz** Use the Checkpoint Quiz to assess student progress over several lessons.	**Transparencies & Presentation Express CD** Lesson Quiz **Resources** Checkpoint Quiz	**Resources** L2 Reteaching ELL Checkpoint Quiz Success Tracker **ExamView CD-ROM with QuickTake**

KEY   L1 Special Needs   L2 Below Level   L3 For All Students   L4 Advanced, Gifted   ELL English Language Learners

Chapter 3

Linear Systems

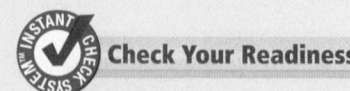
Check Your Readiness

Answers are in the back of the textbook.

For intervention, direct students to:

Combining Like Terms
Lesson 1-2: Example 4
Extra Skills and Word
  Problems Practice, Ch. 1

Solving and Graphing Inequalities
Lesson 1-4: Example 1
Extra Skills and Word
  Problems Practice, Ch. 1

Graphing Relations
Lesson 2-1: Example 1
Extra Skills and Word
  Problems Practice, Ch. 2

Graphing Equations
Lesson 2-2: Example 1
Extra Skills and Word
  Problems Practice, Ch. 2

Writing a Linear Model
Lesson 2-4: Example 2
Extra Skills and Word
  Problems Practice, Ch. 2

Graphing Inequalities
Lesson 2-7: Example 1
Extra Skills and Word
  Problems Practice, Ch. 2

What You've Learned

- In Chapter 1, you learned to write and solve equations and inequalities in one variable.

- In Chapter 2, you learned to write and solve equations and inequalities in two variables.

- In Chapter 2, you learned to graph points and equations in two dimensions.

Check Your Readiness   **GO for Help** to the Lesson in green.

Combining Like Terms (Lesson 1-2)

Simplify by combining like terms.

1. $3x + (4x - 1)$ **2.** $12 - (p + 7)$ **3.** $(2z + 10) - 8z$ **4.** $(r - 1) - 3$
   $7x - 1$ $5 - p$ $-6z + 10$ $r - 4$

Solving and Graphing Inequalities (Lesson 1-4)

Solve each inequality. Graph the solutions on a number line. **5–8. See margin for graphs.**

5. $6a \le 9$ $a \le \frac{3}{2}$ **6.** $8b + 11 > 27$ **7.** $3(24 + 2c) < 0$ **8.** $5(0.2 + d) \le -4$
                         $b > 2$ $c < -12$ $d \le -1$

Graphing Relations (Lesson 2-1)

Graph each relation on a coordinate plane. **9–10. See margin.**

9. $\{(0, 4), (-2, 1), (2, 7), (-4, 4), (4, 4)\}$ **10.** $\left\{\left(0, \frac{1}{2}\right), \left(1, \frac{5}{2}\right), \left(2, \frac{9}{2}\right), \left(3, \frac{13}{2}\right), \left(4, \frac{17}{2}\right)\right\}$

Graphing Equations (Lesson 2-2)

Graph each equation on a coordinate plane. **11–12, 14. See margin.**

11. $y = 4x + 1$ **12.** $-6y + x = 3$ **13.** $15x - 3y = 5$ **14.** $x = 2y - 7$
                                             See back
                                             of book.

Writing a Linear Model (Lesson 2-4)

15. Each minute, a toll collector serves an average of six motorists. Write an equation to model the average number of motorists this toll collector assists as a function of time. Graph the equation. **See back of book.**

Graphing Inequalities (Lesson 2-7)

Graph each inequality on a coordinate plane. **16–18. See back of book.**

16. $y > 8x + 3$ **17.** $2y + x \le -10$ **18.** $18x - 9y < 2$ **19.** $x \ge 4y - 5$
                                                   See margin
                                                   p. 117.

---

page 116   **Check Your Readiness**

5.

6.

7.

8.

9.

Linear Systems

What You'll Learn Next

- In Chapter 3, you will learn to solve systems of equations and inequalities in two variables algebraically and by graphing.

- You will learn to graph points and equations in three dimensions.

- You will learn to solve systems of equations in three variables.

 Real-World Connection Applying what you learn, on page 143 you will solve a problem about planting trees.

◄)) **Key Vocabulary**

- constraints (p. 139)
- coordinate space (p. 146)
- dependent system (p. 120)
- equivalent systems (p. 127)
- feasible region (p. 140)
- inconsistent system (p. 120)
- independent system (p. 120)
- linear programming (p. 139)
- linear system (p. 118)
- objective function (p. 139)
- ordered triples (p. 146)
- system of equations (p. 118)
- trace (p. 148)

Chapter 3 Overview

This chapter begins by introducing students to the methods of solving systems of equations graphically and algebraically. Students then apply what they learned about systems of equations to solving systems of inequalities. They then learn to model real-world situations with linear programming. Finally, students are introduced to graphs in three dimensions and systems in three variables.

Activating Prior Knowledge

Ask:
- *What do you think a "system of equations" refers to?*

Accept all reasonable answers that indicate a combination of two or more equations.

Ask:
- *Based on your understanding of a system of equations, what might a "linear system" refer to?*

Student suggestions should identify a system of equations in which all the equations are linear equations.

117

10.
11.
12.
14.
19.

3-1

Graphing Systems of Equations

Objectives

1 To solve a system by graphing

Examples

1 Solving by Graphing
2 Real-World Connection
3 Classifying Systems Without Graphing

Math Background

When you solve a system of equations by graphing, the *x*- and *y*-coordinates give an estimated point of intersection which can help verify solutions found using the methods in the following lessons.

More Math Background: p. 116C

Lesson Planning and Resources

See p. 116E for a list of the resources that support this lesson.

PowerPoint

Bell Ringer Practice

☑ **Check Skills You'll Need**

For intervention, direct students to:

Linear Equations
Lesson 2-2: Example 1
Extra Skills and Word
    Problems Practice, Ch. 2

What You'll Learn

• To solve a system by graphing

. . . And Why

To make predictions from data, as in Example 2

 New Vocabulary

• system of equations • linear system
• independent system • dependent system
• inconsistent system

☑ **Check Skills You'll Need**

 for Help Lesson 2-2

Graph each equation. 1–6. See back of book.

1. $y = 3x - 2$ **2.** $y = -x$ **3.** $y = -\frac{1}{2}x + 4$

Graph each equation. Use one coordinate plane for all three graphs.

4. $2x - y = 1$ **5.** $2x - y = -1$ **6.** $x + 2y = 2$

Technology Activity: Analyzing Graphs

1. Use a graphing calculator to graph each pair of equations. 1a–c. See back of book.

a. $y = x + 5$
$y = -2x + 5$

b. $y = 3x + 2$
$y = 3x - 1$

c. $y = -4x - 2$
$y = \frac{8x + 4}{-2}$

2. For each pair, answer the following questions. a–b. See back of book.
a. Do the graphs have any points in common; if so, how many?
b. Compare the slopes of the graphs. What is the relationship between the slopes and the number of points in common?

3. Copy and complete the table for the graphs of two linear equations.

Description of Lines	How Many Points of Intersection?	Equal Slopes? (yes/no)	Same *y*-intercepts? (yes/no)
intersecting	▧ 1	▧ no	either
parallel	▧ 0	▧ yes	▧ no
coinciding	▧ infinite	▧ yes	▧ yes

For: Linear Systems Activity
Use: Interactive Textbook, 3-1

A **system of equations** is a set of two or more equations that use the same variables. If the graph of each equation in a system of two variables is a line, then the system is a **linear system.**

A brace is used to keep the equations of a system together.

$$\begin{cases} y = x + 3 \\ y = -2x + 3 \end{cases}$$

 Differentiated Instruction Solutions for All Learners

Special Needs **L1**
Have students identify and touch three different pairs of lines suggested by objects in the classroom: intersecting lines, parallel lines, and lines that coincide.

learning style: tactile

Below Level **L2**
Review the concept of slope. Have students hold their pencils in the air and slowly rotate them to visualize slope as a measure of steepness. Review positive and negative slope and how to graph a line in slope-intercept form, such as $y = \frac{1}{2}x + 1$ and $y = 3x - 2$.

learning style: visual

A solution of a system of equations is a set of values for the variables that makes all the equations true. You can solve some linear systems by graphing the equations. The points where both (or all) the graphs intersect represent solutions.

1 EXAMPLE Solving by Graphing

Multiple Choice Which ordered pair of numbers is the solution of the system?

$$\begin{cases} x + 2y = -7 \\ 2x - 3y = 0 \end{cases}$$

Ⓐ $(1, -4)$ Ⓑ $(-1, -3)$ Ⓒ $(-6, -4)$ Ⓓ $(-3, -2)$

Graph the equations and find the intersection. The solution appears to be $(-3, -2)$.

Check Show that $(-3, -2)$ makes both equations true.

$x + 2y = -7$	$2x - 3y = 0$
$-3 + 2(-2) \overset{?}{=} -7$	$2(-3) - 3(-2) \overset{?}{=} 0$
$-3 - 4 \overset{?}{=} -7$	$-6 + 6 \overset{?}{=} 0$
$-7 = -7$ ✔	$0 = 0$ ✔

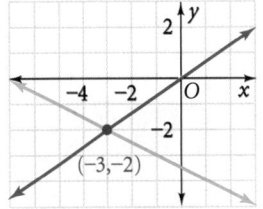

- The answer is D.

✓ **Quick Check** ① Solve $\begin{cases} 2x + y = 5 \\ -x + y = 2 \end{cases}$ by graphing. Check your solution. **(1, 3)**

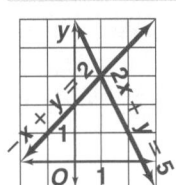

2 EXAMPLE Real-World 🌐 Connection

Sports Winning times for the Olympic 400-m run have been decreasing more rapidly for women than for men. Use the data in the table to find linear models for women's and men's times. Assuming that these trends continue, predict the year in which the women's winning time could equal that of the men.

Winning Times for the Olympic 400-Meter Dash (seconds)

Year	1968	1972	1976	1980	1984	1988	1992	1996	2000
Men's Time	43.86	44.66	44.26	44.60	44.27	43.87	43.50	43.49	43.84
Women's Time	52.03	51.08	49.29	48.88	48.83	48.65	48.83	48.25	49.11

SOURCE: *The World Almanac*

Step 1 Let x = number of years since 1968.
Let y = winning times in seconds.

Use the **LinReg** feature of a graphing calculator to find linear models.
Men's time: $y \approx -0.02433x + 44.43$
Women's time: $y \approx -0.08883x + 50.86$

Step 2 Graph each model. Use the Intersect feature on the graphing calculator. The two lines meet at about (99.7, 42.0).

If the trends continue, the times for men and women will be equal about 100 years from 1968, in 2068.

✓ **Quick Check** ②
a. Use the models in Example 2 to predict the winning times for the 400-m run at the Olympics in 2008 and in 2024.
b. *Critical Thinking* Example 2 assumes that current trends will continue. Explain why that assumption may not be valid. **It would mean that eventually the 400-m run would be run in zero seconds, and this could not happen.**

2a. 2008 men: 43.46 s, women: 47.31 s 2024 men: 43.07 s, women: 45.89 s

Test-Taking Tip
You can also substitute values from each answer choice into the equations in a system. But be careful. Some choices will make one equation true but not the other.

Real-World 🌐 Connection
Cathy Freeman won the 400-m run in the 2000 Olympics.

Lesson 3-1 Graphing Systems of Equations **119**

2. Teach

Guided Instruction

Technology Activity
Some students may think that all lines with equal slopes are parallel. Remind them that the lines might coincide.

1 EXAMPLE Teaching Tip

Point out that when the point of intersection does not have integer coordinates, a graphing calculator may be helpful.

2 EXAMPLE Connection to Physical Education

Every year, more and more girls are joining sports teams. Many are breaking into sports such as football that have generally been thought of as "for boys only."

PowerPoint
📊 **Additional Examples**

① Solve the system by graphing.
$$\begin{cases} x + 3y = 2 \\ 3x + 3y = -6 \end{cases} \quad (-4, 2)$$

② The table shows the number of pairs of shoes sold by two new employees at a shoe store. Find linear models for each employee's sales. Use the graph of the models to predict the week in which they could sell the same number of pairs of shoes.

Week	1	2	3	4
Ed	50	55	63	67
Jo	40	47	56	62

Ed: $y = 5.9x + 44$;
Jo: $y = 7.5x + 32.5$;
during week 7

Advanced Learners L4
Have students explain why linear systems must be either independent, dependent, or inconsistent. **The graphs intersect, coincide, or are parallel.**

learning style: verbal

English Language Learners ELL
Some students may have difficulty distinguishing between the terms *independent, dependent,* and *inconsistent.* Have students sketch and label graphs for each corresponding system and its number of solutions. Have students use their diagrams as a reference.

learning style: visual

3 Classify the system without graphing.
$$\begin{cases} y = 3x + 2 \\ -6x + 2y = 4 \end{cases}$$
dependent system

Resources
• Daily Notetaking Guide 3-1 **L3**

Closure

Ask students to describe the graph of an independent system of linear equations in two variables. The graph consists of two lines that intersect in one point.

pages 120–123   Exercises

1. (3, 1)

2. (2, 1)

3. (−2, 4)

4. (−3, 5)

120

Vocabulary Tip

<u>Unique</u> means "exactly one."

Key Concepts

Video Tutor Help
Visit: PhSchool.com
Web Code: age-0775

You can classify a system of two linear equations by the number of solutions. A system that has a unique solution, as in Examples 1 and 2, is an **independent system.** However, not every system has a unique solution.

A **dependent system** does not have a unique solution. An **inconsistent system** is a system that has no solution.

Summary	**Graphical Solutions of Linear Systems in Two Variables**	
Intersecting Lines	Coinciding Lines	Parallel Lines
		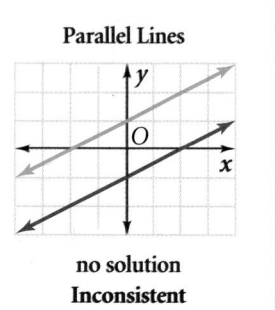
one solution **Independent**	no unique solution **Dependent**	no solution **Inconsistent**

You can also classify a system of equations without graphing. By comparing the slopes and y-intercepts of the equations, you can find the number of solutions.

3 EXAMPLE   Classifying Systems Without Graphing

Classify the system without graphing. $\begin{cases} y = 2x + 3 \\ -2x + y = 1 \end{cases}$

$y = 2x + 3$ **Rewrite in slope-intercept form.** → $y = 2x + 1$

$m = 2, b = 3$ ← **Find the slope and y-intercept.** → $m = 2, b = 1$

Since the slopes are the same, the lines could coincide. Compare the y-intercepts. Since the y-intercepts are different, the lines are parallel. There is no solution. The system is an inconsistent system.

Quick Check ③ Without graphing, classify each system as *independent*, *dependent*, or *inconsistent*.

a. $\begin{cases} 3x + y = 5 \\ 15x + 5y = 2 \end{cases}$ b. $\begin{cases} y = 2x + 3 \\ -4x + 2y = 6 \end{cases}$ c. $\begin{cases} x - y = 5 \\ y + 3 = 2x \end{cases}$

inconsistent   dependent   independent

EXERCISES
For more exercises, see Extra Skill and Word Problem Practice.

Practice and Problem Solving

A   Practice by Example

Example 1
(page 119)

for Help

Solve each system by graphing. Check your answers.   1–5. See margin.

1. $\begin{cases} y = x - 2 \\ y = -2x + 7 \end{cases}$ 2. $\begin{cases} y = -x + 3 \\ y = \frac{3}{2}x - 2 \end{cases}$ 3. $\begin{cases} 2x + 4y = 12 \\ x + y = 2 \end{cases}$

4. $\begin{cases} x = -3 \\ y = 5 \end{cases}$ 5. $\begin{cases} 2x - 2y = 4 \\ y - x = 6 \end{cases}$ 6. $\begin{cases} 3x + y = 5 \\ x - y = 7 \end{cases}$

7. $\begin{cases} -5x + y = -9 \\ x + 3y = 21 \end{cases}$ 8. $\begin{cases} y = x \\ y - 5x = 0 \end{cases}$ 9. $\begin{cases} x = 10 \\ x = y - 10 \end{cases}$

6–9. See back of book.

---

5. no solution

12a. Anwers may vary.
$\begin{cases} y = 3000x + 5200 \\ y = -900x + 35,700 \end{cases}$

b. If Feb = 1, the revenue will equal expenses in the 7.82 month or August.

Example 2
(page 119)

For Exercises 10–11, use your graphing calculator. Find linear models for each set of data. Use each model to predict the year in which the quantities will be equal.

10–11. Models may vary. Samples are given

10. Use 0 for 1980.
$$\begin{cases} y = 0.232x + 1.328 \\ y = 0.145x + 3.673 \end{cases}$$
about 2007

11. Use 0 for 1970.
$$\begin{cases} y = 0.22x + 67.5 \\ y = 0.15x + 75.507 \end{cases}$$
about 2085

10.

Year	Broccoli (lb/person)	Cucumbers (lb/person)
1980	1.5	3.9
1985	2.6	4.4
1990	3.4	4.7
1995	4.3	5.6
1998	5.1	6.5
1999	6.5	6.8
2000	6.1	6.4

Annual U.S. Consumption of Vegetables

SOURCE: *Statistical Abstract of the United States.*
Go to **www.PHSchool.com** for a data update.
Web Code: agg-9041

11.

Year	Men (years)	Women (years)
1970	67.1	74.7
1975	68.8	76.6
1980	70.0	77.4
1985	71.1	78.2
1990	71.8	78.8
1995	72.5	78.9
2000	74.3	79.7

U.S. Life Expectancy at Birth

SOURCE: U.S. Census Bureau.
Go to **www.PHSchool.com** for a data update.
Web Code: agg-9041

12. a. **Business** The spreadsheet shows the monthly revenue and monthly expenses for a new business. Find a linear model for monthly revenue and a linear model for monthly expenses. **a–b. See margin p. 120.**
   b. Use the models to predict the month in which revenue will equal expenses.

	A	B	C
1	Month	Revenue	Expenses
2	Feb	8000	35000
3	Mar	12000	33000
4	Apr	13000	34000
5	May	18000	32000
6	Jun	20000	31000

Example 3
(page 120)

Without graphing, classify each system as *independent*, *dependent*, or *inconsistent*.

13. $\begin{cases} 7x - y = 6 \\ -7x + y = -6 \end{cases}$ dependent
14. $\begin{cases} -3x + y = 4 \\ x - \frac{1}{3}y = 1 \end{cases}$ inconsistent
15. $\begin{cases} 4x + 8y = 12 \\ x + 2y = -3 \end{cases}$ inconsistent

16. $\begin{cases} y = 2x - 1 \\ y = -2x + 5 \end{cases}$ independent
17. $\begin{cases} x = 6 \\ x = -2 \end{cases}$ inconsistent
18. $\begin{cases} 2y = 5x + 6 \\ -10x + 4y = 8 \end{cases}$ inconsistent

19. $\begin{cases} x - 3y = 2 \\ 4x - 12y = 8 \end{cases}$ dependent
20. $\begin{cases} x + 4y = 12 \\ 2x - 8y = 4 \end{cases}$ independent
21. $\begin{cases} 4x + 8y = -6 \\ 6x + 12y = -9 \end{cases}$ dependent

22. $\begin{cases} 4y - 2x = 6 \\ 8y = 4x - 12 \end{cases}$ inconsistent
23. $\begin{cases} y - x = 0 \\ y = -x \end{cases}$ independent
24. $\begin{cases} 2y - x = 4 \\ \frac{1}{2}x - y = 2 \end{cases}$ inconsistent

B Apply Your Skills

25–36. See back of book.

Graph and solve each system. Where necessary, estimate the solution.

25. $\begin{cases} 3 = 4y + x \\ 4y = -x + 3 \end{cases}$
26. $\begin{cases} x - 2y + 1 = 0 \\ x + 4y - 6 = 0 \end{cases}$
27. $\begin{cases} 3x + 6y - 12 = 0 \\ x + 2y = 8 \end{cases}$

28. $\begin{cases} -x + 3y = 6 \\ 2x - y = 8 \end{cases}$
29. $\begin{cases} 3x + y = 3 \\ 2x - y = 7 \end{cases}$
30. $\begin{cases} 2x + 3y = 6 \\ 4x = 6y + 3 \end{cases}$

31. $\begin{cases} 10 - 3x = -3y \\ 2 = 2x + y \end{cases}$
32. $\begin{cases} 3x = -5y + 4 \\ 250 + 150x = 300 \end{cases}$
33. $\begin{cases} x + 3y = 6 \\ 6y + 2x = 12 \end{cases}$

34. $\begin{cases} 2y + x = 8 \\ y - 2x = -6 \end{cases}$
35. $\begin{cases} y = -2x + 6 \\ x - 3y = -6 \end{cases}$
36. $\begin{cases} -x - 2 = -2y \\ 2x - 4y - 4 = 0 \end{cases}$

Lesson 3-1 Graphing Systems of Equations **121**

Assignment Guide

① A B 1-50
C Challenge 51-55

Test Prep 56-61
Mixed Review 62-74

Homework Quick Check
To check students' understanding of key skills and concepts, go over Exercises 6, 12, 39, 45, 50.

Exercise 5 If students draw the graphs correctly, the lines should look parallel. Be sure students understand how slope can be used to confirm that the lines really are parallel.

Differentiated Instruction **Resources**

GPS Guided Problem Solving	L3
Enrichment	L4
Reteaching	L2
Practice	L3

Lesson Quiz

1. Graph and solve the system.
$$\begin{cases} 4x + y = -1 \\ -x + 3y = 10 \end{cases} \quad (-1, 3)$$

Classify each system without graphing. Tell how many solutions there are.

2. $\begin{cases} 5x + 3y = 10 \\ -x - 0.6y = -2 \end{cases}$
   dependent; infinitely many

3. $\begin{cases} 12x - 18y = 9 \\ -6x + 9y = 13 \end{cases}$
   inconsistent; no solutions

4. $\begin{cases} 4x + 5y = -10 \\ 3x - 8y = 15 \end{cases}$
   independent; one solution

Alternative Assessment

Have students work in groups of three. Students 1 and 2 each write an equation of the form $Ax + By = C$, where A, B, and C are non-zero integers from -9 to 9. Student 3 classifies and graphs the system. If there is a unique solution with integer x- and y-values, student 3 identifies the solution and checks that it is correct. Otherwise, student 3 estimates the solution. Students 1 and 2 then confirm the correctness of the work. Students change roles until each student has graphed two systems.

Exercise 53 Check that students understand what the solution set notation means geometrically.

Real-World 🌐 **Connection**

Groomers must be able to handle dogs of every breed and temperament.

GO 🌐 **nline**
Homework Video Tutor
Visit: PHSchool.com
Web Code: age-0301

C Challenge

53. Answers may vary.
    Sample:
    $\begin{cases} -10x + 2y = 4 \\ 5x - y = -2 \end{cases}$

37. **Banking** To pay your monthly bills, you can either open a checking account or use an online banking service. A local bank charges $3 per month and $.40 per check, while an online services charges a flat fee of $9 per month.
    a. Write and graph a system of linear equations to model the cost c of each service for b bills that you need to pay monthly. **See back of book.**
    b. Find the point of intersection of the two linear models. What does this answer represent? **b–c. See margin.**
    c. If you pay about 12 bills per month, which service should you choose? Explain.

Classify each system without graphing.

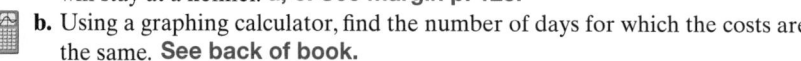
inconsistent   dependent   independent

38. $\begin{cases} 3x - 2y = 8 \\ 4y = 6x - 5 \end{cases}$

39. $\begin{cases} 2x + 8y = 6 \\ x = -4y + 3 \end{cases}$

40. $\begin{cases} 3a + 6b = 14 \\ -a + 2b = 3 \end{cases}$

41. $\begin{cases} 3m = -5n + 4 \\ n - \frac{6}{5} = -\frac{3}{5}m \end{cases}$
   inconsistent

42. $\begin{cases} -12x + 4y = 8 \\ y - 4 = 3x \end{cases}$
   inconsistent

43. $\begin{cases} -6y + 18 = 12x \\ 3y + 6x = 9 \end{cases}$
   dependent

44. **Fees** Suppose you are going on vacation and leaving your dog in a kennel. The Bowowery charges $25 per day, which includes a one-time grooming treatment. The Poochpad charges $20 per day and a one-time fee of $30 for grooming.
    a. Write a system of equations to represent the cost c for d days that your dog will stay at a kennel. **a, c. See margin p. 123.**
    b. Using a graphing calculator, find the number of days for which the costs are the same. **See back of book.**
    c. If your vacation is a week long, which kennel should you choose? Explain.

45. **Advertising** You and your business partner are mailing advertising flyers to **GPS** your customers. You address 6 flyers each minute and have already done 80. Your partner addresses 4 flyers each minute and has already done 100. Graph and solve a system of equations to find when the two of you will have addressed equal numbers of flyers. **See back of book.**

Open-Ended Write a second equation for each system so that the system will have the indicated number of solutions. 46–48. **Answers may vary. Samples:**

46. one
$\begin{cases} y = -3x + 2 \\ \underline{\quad\quad?\quad\quad} \end{cases}$
$y = x + 3$

47. none
$\begin{cases} y = -4x - 6 \\ \underline{\quad\quad?\quad\quad} \end{cases}$
$y = -4x + 8$

48. an infinite number
$\begin{cases} 3y = 6x + 7 \\ \underline{\quad\quad?\quad\quad} \end{cases}$
$y = 2x + \frac{7}{3}$

49. **Reasoning** Is it possible for an inconsistent linear system to consist of two lines with the same y-intercept? Explain. **No; they would be the same line, and the system would be dependent and consistent.**

50. **Writing** Summarize the possible relationships for the y-intercepts, slopes, and number of solutions in a system of two linear equations of two variables. **See margin p. 123.**

Open-Ended Write a second equation for each system so that the system will have the indicated number of solutions. 51–52. **Answers may vary. Samples:**

51. infinite number of solutions
$\begin{cases} \frac{x}{4} + \frac{y}{3} = 1 \\ \underline{\quad?\quad} \end{cases}$
$3x + 4y = 12$

52. no solutions
$\begin{cases} 5x + 2y = 10 \\ \underline{\quad?\quad} \end{cases}$
$y = -\frac{5x}{2} + 7$

53. Write a system of linear equations with the solution set $\{(x, y) \mid y = 5x + 2\}$.

54. **Critical Thinking** Look back through the exercises on the previous two pages to find several dependent systems. What relationship exists between the equations in each system? **They are the same equation written in different forms.**

pages 120–123 Exercises

37b. **(15, 9); the point represents where the cost of using the bank or online service would be the same.**

c. **The local bank would be cheaper if you only have 12 bills to pay per month.**

Vocabulary Tip

A widget is a small, unspecified gadget.

55. Economics Research shows that in a certain market only 2000 widgets can be sold at $8 each, but if the price is reduced to $3, then 10,000 can be sold.
  a. Let p represent price and n represent the number of widgets. Identify the independent variable and the dependent variable.
  b. Use the information above to write a linear *demand* equation.
  c. A shop can make 2000 widgets for $5 each and 20,000 widgets for $2 each. Use this information to write a linear *supply* equation.
  d. Find the equilibrium point where supply is equal to demand and profit is a maximum. Explain the meaning of the coordinates of this point within the context of the exercise.

a. p: independent, n: dependent
b. $n = -1600p + 14,800$
c. $n = -6000p + 32,000$
d. About (3.91, 8545); profits are maximized if about 8545 widgets are sold for about $3.91 each.

Test Prep

Multiple Choice

56. Which is an equation for Line 2? **C**
  A. $3x - 5y = 15$ **B.** $3x + 5y = 3$
  C. $3x + 5y = 15$ **D.** $5x + 3y = 15$

57. Which is NOT an equation for Line 1? **G**
  F. $y = x$ **G.** $x + y = 0$
  H. $x - y = 0$ **J.** $y - x = 0$

58. Which point lies on both Line 1 and Line 2? **B**
  A. (0, 0)   **B.** (1.875, 1.875)
  C. (1.95, 1.95)   **D.** (2, 2)

Exercises 56–58.

59. What is the solution of the system? $\begin{cases} 5x + 6y = -24 \\ -2x + 3y = 15 \end{cases}$ **H**

  F. (6, −1)   **G.** (6, 1)   **H.** (−6, 1)   **J.** (−6, −1)

Short Response

60. Explain how you can use slopes to show that the system $\begin{cases} 2x - 5y = 23 \\ 3y - 7x = -8 \end{cases}$ is NOT inconsistent.

60–61. See margin.

Extended Response

61. One equation of a system of equations is $2x - 3y = 5$.
  a. Find a second equation such that the system is dependent.
  b. Find a second equation such that the system is inconsistent.

Mixed Review

GO for Help

Lesson 2–7 Graph each inequality on a coordinate plane.   62–64. See back of book.

  62. $3x - 4y \geq 16$ **63.** $-5x > 8y + 4$ **64.** $x < -4$

Lesson 2–2 Write an equation for each line.

  65. $m = -\frac{2}{3}$; contains $(-9, 4)$ $y = \frac{-2x}{3} - 2$ **66.** $m = 0$; contains $(3, 4)$ $y = 4$

  67. $m = 2$; contains $(-2, -3)$ $y = 2x + 1$ **68.** $m = -\frac{1}{2}$; contains $(2, -6)$ $y = -\frac{1}{2}x - 5$

Lesson 1–3 Solve each equation and check the solution.

  69. $3n = -4(2 + n)$ $-\frac{8}{7}$ **70.** $-4a + a = 7a - 6$ $\frac{3}{5}$ **71.** $\frac{x}{3} + 5 = \frac{1}{6}$ -14.5

  72. $4x - 2 = \frac{1}{2}x$ $\frac{4}{7}$ **73.** $\frac{r}{5} + 5 = r - 3$ 10   **74.** $2(m - 3) = -4$ 1

Resources

For additional practice with a variety of test item formats:
- Standardized Test Prep, p. 165
- Test-Taking Strategies, p. 160
- Test-Taking Strategies with Transparencies

60. [2] The slope of $2x - 5y = 23$ is $\frac{2}{5}$ and the slope of $3y - 7x = -8$ is $\frac{7}{3}$. Since the slopes are not equal, the lines are not parallel and they do not coincide. So the lines intersect; the system has exactly one solution and is consistent.
[1] does not include explanation

61. [4] (a) A second equation is $4x - 6y = 10$, or any equation of the form $2ax - 3ay = 5a$, where $a \neq 0$.
  (b) A second equation is $2x - 3y = 6$ or any equation of the form $2ax - 3ay = 5b$, where $a \neq b$, where $a = 0$.
  [3] minor error in either part (a) or (b)
  [2] minor error in both parts (a) and (b)
  [1] only completes part (a) or (b)

44a. $\begin{cases} c = 20d + 30 \\ c = 25d \end{cases}$

  c. The Pooch Pad would be cheaper for a 7-day stay.

50. An independent system has one solution. The slopes are different, but the y-intercepts could be the same. An inconsistent system has no solution. The slopes are the same, and the y-intercepts are different. A dependent system has an infinite number of solutions. The slopes and y-intercepts are the same.

123

Parametric Equations

Activity Lab

Technology

Parametric Equations

FOR USE WITH LESSON 3-2

Students use a graphing calculator to explore graphs of parametric equations.

Guided Instruction

You may want to discuss how the flight path looks in three dimensions. The shape of the path in three dimensions is not necessarily a straight line.

English Language Learners ELL

Discuss with students the meaning of *parameter* and how it relates to the phrase *parametric equation*.

Error Prevention!

Be sure students use window settings that allow them to solve the problem they write in Exercise 4.

Resources

Students may use any graphing calculator that has parametric graphing capabilities.

Parametric equations are equations that express the coordinates x and y as separate functions of a common third variable, called the parameter. You can use parametric equations to determine the position of an object over time.

ACTIVITY

Starting from a birdbath 3 ft above the ground, a bird takes flight. Let t equal time in seconds, x equal horizontal distance in feet, and y equal vertical distance in feet. The equations $x(t) = 5t$ and $y(t) = 8t + 3$ model the bird's distance from the base of the birdbath. Graph the equations. Describe the position of the bird at time $t = 3$.

Step 1 Press MODE. Change the function mode to Parametric.

Step 2 Enter the equations. (When you press Y= you will see a list of pairs of equations.)

Step 3 Set the window values as shown.

```
WINDOW
Tmin = 0
Tmax = 6
Tstep = .1
Xmin = 0
Xmax = 50
Xscl = 2
↓Ymin = 0
```

```
WINDOW
↑Tstep = .1
Xmin = 0
Xmax = 50
Xscl = 2
Ymin = 0
Ymax = 50
Yscl = 2
```

Step 4 Graph the equations. Press TRACE to find $t = 3$.

Three seconds after taking flight, the bird is 15 ft horizontally and 27 ft vertically from the base of the birdbath.

EXERCISES 1–4. See margin.

Graph each pair of parametric equations. Set the window with the t-values at the right. Find the values of x and y at time $t = 3$.

1. $x(t) = t$
$y(t) = -t + 6$

2. $x(t) = -3t$
$y(t) = t - 6$

3. $x(t) = |t - 2|$
$y(t) = t + 2$

```
WINDOW
Tmin = -10
Tmax = 10
Tstep = .1
Xmin = -10
Xmax = 10
Xscl = 1
↓Ymin = -10
```

 4. Writing Write a word problem involving the graph of $x(t) = 3t$ and $y(t) = 10t$. Interpret the x- and y-values at times $t = 0$, $t = 5$, and $t = -2$.

124 Activity Lab Parametric Equations

page 124 Technology

1. $x_3 = 3; y_3 = 3$

2. $x_3 = -9; y_3 = -3$

3. $x_3 = 1; y_3 = 5$

4. Check students' work.
$x_0 = 0; y_0 = 0$
$x_5 = 15; y_5 = 50$
$x_{-2} = -6; y_{-2} = -20$

Solving Systems Algebraically

What You'll Learn

- To solve a system by substitution
- To solve a system by elimination

. . . And Why

To find the cost of joining a health club, as in Example 2

 Check Skills You'll Need

GO for Help Lessons 1-1 and 1-3

Find the additive inverse of each term.

1. 4 -4 **2.** $-x$ x **3.** $5x$ $-5x$ **4.** $8y$ $-8y$

Substitute $2y - 1$ for x in each equation. Solve for y.

5. $x + 2y = 3$ 1 **6.** $y - 2x = 8$ -2 **7.** $2y + 3x = -5$ $-\frac{1}{4}$

New Vocabulary • equivalent systems

1. Plan

Objectives

1. To solve a system by substitution
2. To solve a system by elimination

Examples

1. Solving by Substitution
2. Real-World Connection
3. Solving by Elimination
4. Solving an Equivalent System
5. Solving a System Without a Unique Solution

Math Background

Solving systems algebraically is more exact than solving by graphing. The methods of substitution and elimination both result in the solution of an equation in one variable. That solution is then used to find the value of another variable, and so on. The substitution method is most helpful when one equation is presented as solved for one of the variables. The method of elimination is a good way to begin when the coefficients of a variable are opposites.

More Math Background: p. 116C

Lesson Planning and Resources

See p. 116E for a list of the resources that support this lesson.

Bell Ringer Practice

Check Skills You'll Need
For intervention, direct students to:
Properties of Real Numbers
Lesson 1-1: Example 4
Extra Skills and Word Problems Practice, Ch. 1

Solving Equations
Lesson 1-3: Example 2
Extra Skills and Word Problems Practice, Ch. 1

1. Solving Systems by Substitution

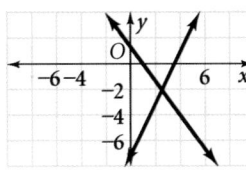

$$\begin{cases} 4x + 3y = 4 \\ 2x - y = 7 \end{cases}$$

Not every system can be solved easily by graphing. Consider the system at the left. Although you can graph each line easily, the exact point of intersection is not obvious. Substitution allows you to find exact solutions without using a graphing calculator.

1 EXAMPLE Solving by Substitution

Solve the system by substitution. $\begin{cases} 4x + 3y = 4 \\ 2x - y = 7 \end{cases}$

Step 1 Solve for one of the variables. Solving the second equation for y is easiest.

$$2x - y = 7$$
$$y = 2x - 7$$

Step 2 Substitute the expression for y into the other equation. Solve for x.

$$4x + 3y = 4$$
$$4x + 3(2x - 7) = 4 \quad \textbf{Substitute for } y.$$
$$4x + 6x - 21 = 4 \quad \textbf{Distributive Property}$$
$$4x + 6x = 25$$
$$x = 2.5$$

Step 3 Substitute the value of x into either equation. Solve for y.

$$y = 2x - 7$$
$$y = 2(2.5) - 7 \quad \textbf{Substitute for } x.$$
$$y = -2$$

The solution is $(2.5, -2)$.

Quick Check **1** Solve each system by substitution. Check your answers.

a. $\begin{cases} 2x - 3y = 6 \\ x + y = -12 \end{cases}$ $(-6, -6)$ **b.** $\begin{cases} 3x - y = 0 \\ 4x + 3y = 26 \end{cases}$ $(2, 6)$

Differentiated Instruction Solutions for All Learners

Special Needs L1
Many students find the value of one variable and stop, thinking they are done. Draw a pair of intersecting lines and illustrate that the solution is given by the point of intersection, which is an ordered pair (x, y).

learning style: visual

Below Level L2
Have students explain the substitution method orally in their own words. Then have students explain the elimination method orally in their own words.

learning style: verbal

2. Teach

Guided Instruction

1 EXAMPLE Auditory Learners

Have students explain the substitution method orally in their own words.

Teaching Tip

In Quick Check 1a, students can solve just as easily for *x* or for *y*. You might want to show on the board how both methods result in the same answer, $(-6, -6)$.

Error Prevention!

When using substitution, some students correctly solve one equation for a variable, but incorrectly substitute the variable expression into the *same* original equation. Tell students they solve *one* equation (for one variable), and substitute the resulting variable expression into the *other* equation.

PowerPoint

Additional Examples

1 Solve the system by substitution. $(2.1, 3.3)$

$$\begin{cases} x + 3y = 12 \\ -2x + 4y = 9 \end{cases}$$

2 At Renaldi's Pizza, a soda and two slices of the pizza-of-the-day cost $10.25. A soda and four slices of the pizza-of-the-day cost $18.75. Find the cost of each item. soda: $1.75; pizza: $4.25

---

2 EXAMPLE Real-World Connection

Fees Refer to the advertisement at the left. The cost of membership in a health club includes a monthly charge and a one-time initiation fee. Find the monthly charge and the initiation fee.

Relate 2 · monthly charge + initiation fee = $100

6 · monthly charge + initiation fee = $200

Define Let m = the monthly charge. Let f = the initiation fee.

Write $$\begin{cases} 2m + f = 100 \\ 6m + f = 200 \end{cases}$$

$2m + f = 100$	Solve for one of the variables.
$f = -2m + 100$	
$6m + (-2m + 100) = 200$	Substitute the expression for *f* into the other equation. Solve for *m*.
$m = 25$	
$2(25) + f = 100$	Substitute the value of *m* into one of the equations. Solve for *f*.
$f = 50$	

● The monthly charge is $25, and the initiation fee is $50.

Health Club Membership Fees

2 months: $100
6 months: $200

✓ Quick Check **2** **Shopping** You can buy CDs at a local store for $15.49 each. You can buy them at an online store for $13.99 each plus $6 for shipping. Solve a system of equations to find the number of CDs that you can buy for the same amount at the two stores.

$$\begin{cases} c = 15.49x \\ c = 6 + 13.99x \end{cases}$$ The number of CDs is 4.

---

2 Solving Systems by Elimination

You can solve a system of equations using the Addition Property of Equality. If the quantities you add contain a pair of additive inverses, you can eliminate a variable. You can also eliminate a variable by subtracting like terms.

3 EXAMPLE Solving by Elimination

Gridded Response Find the *y*-value in the solution of $\begin{cases} 4x - 2y = 7 \\ x + 2y = 3. \end{cases}$

 Test-Taking Tip

You can grid the answer in columns 1–3 or columns 2–4.

$4x - 2y = 7$	
$\underline{x + 2y = 3}$	Two terms are additive inverses, so add.
$5x = 10$	
$x = 2$	Solve for *x*.
$x + 2y = 3$	Choose one of the original equations.
$2 + 2y = 3$	Substitute for *x*.
$y = \frac{1}{2}$	Solve for *y*.

● The solution is $\left(2, \frac{1}{2}\right)$. The *y*-value is $\frac{1}{2}$.

✓ Quick Check **3** Solve each system by elimination.

a. $\begin{cases} 3x - 2y = 14 \\ 2x + 2y = 6 \end{cases}$ $(4, -1)$

b. $\begin{cases} 4x + 9y = 1 \\ 4x + 6y = -2 \end{cases}$ $(-2, 1)$

Advanced Learners **L4**

You have $13.50 to buy one pound of coffee. Blend A costs $16 a pound. Blend H costs $8 per pound. How many ounces of each can you buy? **11 oz, 5 oz**

learning style: verbal

English Language Learners **ELL**

For Example 2, some students may be unfamiliar with health clubs. Make sure students understand what an *initiation fee* is. You may want to ask how the term is related to the word *initial*.

learning style: verbal

To make two terms additive inverses, you may need to multiply one or both equations in a system by a nonzero number. In doing so, you create a system equivalent to the original one. **Equivalent systems** are systems that have the same solution(s).

GO **Online**

Video Tutor Help
Visit: PhSchool.com
Web Code: age-0775

4. Answers may vary. Sample: Multiply (1) by −5. Multiply (2) by 3. Add equations together, solving for *y*. Substitute the value of *y* into either original equation and solve for *x*.

4 EXAMPLE Solving an Equivalent System

Solve the system below by elimination.
$$\begin{cases} 3x + 7y = 15 \\ 5x + 2y = -4 \end{cases}$$

To eliminate the *y* terms, make them additive inverses by multiplying.

① $3x + 7y = 15$	$6x + 14y = 30$	**Multiply ① by 2.**
② $5x + 2y = -4$	$\underline{-35x - 14y = 28}$	**Multiply ② by −7.**
	$-29x \qquad = 58$	**Add.**
	$x = -2$	**Solve for *x*.**
	$3x + 7y = 15$	**Choose an original equation.**
	$3(-2) + 7y = 15$	**Substitute the value of *x*.**
	$-6 + 7y = 15$	**Simplify.**
	$7y = 21$	
	$y = 3$	**Solve for *y*.**

● The solution is $(-2, 3)$.

 Quick Check ④ Explain how to solve the system in Example 4 by eliminating *x*.

Solving a system algebraically does not always result in a unique solution, as in Examples 3 and 4. You may get an equation that is always true, or one that is never true.

5 EXAMPLE Solving a System Without a Unique Solution

Solve each system by elimination.

a. $\begin{cases} 2x - y = 3 \\ -2x + y = -3 \end{cases}$
$\overline{\qquad 0 = 0 \qquad}$

b. $\begin{cases} 2x - 3y = 18 \\ -2x + 3y = -6 \end{cases}$
$\overline{\qquad 0 = 12 \qquad}$

Online
active math

For: Special Solutions Activity
Use: Interactive Textbook, 3-2

Elimination gives an equation that is always true. The two equations in the system represent the same line. The system has an infinite number of solutions:
$\{(x, y) \mid y = 2x - 3\}$.

Elimination gives an equation that is always false. The two equations in the system represent parallel lines. The system has no solution.

 Quick Check ⑤ Solve each system by substitution or elimination.

a. $\begin{cases} -3x + 5y = 7 \\ 6x - 10y = -14 \end{cases}$
infinite number of solutions
$\{(x, y) \mid -3x + 5y = 7\}$

b. $\begin{cases} -2x + 4y = 6 \\ -3x + 6y = 8 \end{cases}$ no solution

Guided Instruction

3 EXAMPLE Math Tip

Make sure students notice that it helps to write both equations in standard form when using the elimination method.

4 EXAMPLE Teaching Tip

Ask students how they would solve the system by eliminating the *y* terms. Answers may vary. Sample: Multiply the first equation by 2, and multiply the second equation by −7.

5 EXAMPLE Alternative Method

If a student suspects the two lines are the same or parallel, have them find the slopes first by solving each equation in a system for *y*.

PowerPoint
Additional Examples

③ Use the elimination method to solve the system. $(-2, -3)$
$\begin{cases} 3x + y = -9 \\ -3x - 2y = 12 \end{cases}$

④ Solve the system by elimination. $(4, -3)$
$\begin{cases} 2m + 4n = -4 \\ 3m + 5n = -3 \end{cases}$

⑤ Solve each system by elimination.

a. $\begin{cases} -3x + 5y = 6 \\ 6x - 10y = 0 \end{cases}$ no solution

b. $\begin{cases} -3x + 5y = 6 \\ 6x - 10y = -12 \end{cases}$
$\{(x,y) \mid y = \frac{3}{5}x + \frac{6}{5}\}$

Resources
• Daily Notetaking Guide 3-2 **L3**

Closure

Have students tell how you know whether a system is ready to be solved by elimination. The terms involving one of the variables, when written on the same side of the equal sign, are additive inverses.

EXERCISES

For more exercises, see *Extra Skill and Word Problem Practice*.

Practice and Problem Solving

Assignment Guide

1 A B 1–17

2 A B 18–62

C Challenge 63–66

Test Prep 67–72
Mixed Review 73–81

Homework Quick Check
To check students' understanding of key skills and concepts, go over Exercises 13, 33, 43, 56, 62.

Teaching Tip
Alert students that for systems with variables other than x and y, the convention is to list the solution in alphabetical order. So, for Exercise 2 the solution is of the form (c, d).

A Practice by Example

GO for Help

Example 1
(page 125)

Solve each system by substitution. Check your answers.

1. $\begin{cases} 4x + 2y = 7 \\ y = 5x \end{cases}$ **(0.5, 2.5)**

2. $\begin{cases} 3c + 2d = 2 \\ d = 4 \end{cases}$ **(c, d) = (−2, 4)**

3. $\begin{cases} x + 12y = 68 \\ x = 8y − 12 \end{cases}$ **(20, 4)**

4. $\begin{cases} 4p + 2q = 8 \\ q = 2p + 1 \end{cases}$ **(p, q) = (0.75, 2.5)**

5. $\begin{cases} x + 3y = 7 \\ 2x − 4y = 24 \end{cases}$ **(10, −1)**

6. $\begin{cases} x + 6y = 2 \\ 5x + 4y = 36 \end{cases}$ **(8, −1)**

7. $\begin{cases} 3a + b = 3 \\ 2a − 5b = −15 \end{cases}$ **(a, b) = (0, 3)**

8. $\begin{cases} t = 2r + 3 \\ 5r − 4t = 6 \end{cases}$ **(r, t) = (−6, −9)**

9. $\begin{cases} y = 2x − 1 \\ 3x − y = −1 \end{cases}$ **(−2, −5)**

10. $\begin{cases} 2m + 4n = 10 \\ 3m + 5n = 11 \end{cases}$ **(m, n) = (−3, 4)**

11. $\begin{cases} −6 = 3x − 6y \\ 4x = 4 + 5y \end{cases}$ **(6, 4)**

12. $\begin{cases} r + s = −12 \\ 2r − 3s = 6 \end{cases}$ **(r, s) = (−6, −6)**

Example 2
(page 126)

13a. $\begin{cases} d = 0.50m \\ d = 15 \end{cases}$

13. **Fund-Raising** Suppose you have signed up for a bike-a-thon to raise money for charity. One person is sponsoring you at a rate of $.50 per mile. Each of the other sponsors plans to donate $15 no matter how far you bike.
   a. Write a system of equations to model the donation d for m miles biked.
   b. For how many miles will all sponsors donate the same amount? **30 miles**

14. **Transportation** A youth group with 26 members is going skiing. Each of the five chaperones will drive a van or a sedan. The vans can seat seven people, and the sedans can seat five people. How many of each type of vehicle could transport all 31 people to the ski area in one trip? **3 vans and 2 sedans, or 4 vans and 1 sedan, or 5 vans and 0 sedans**

15. Suppose you have a part-time job delivering packages. Your employer pays you at a flat rate of $7 per hour. You discover that a competitor pays employees $2 per hour plus $.35 per delivery.
   a. Write a system of equations to model the pay p for d deliveries. Assume a four-hour shift.
   b. How many deliveries would the competitor's employees have to make in four hours to earn the same pay you earn in a four-hour shift? **58**

15a. $\begin{cases} p = 28 \\ p = 8 + 0.35d \end{cases}$

16. A boat can travel 24 mi in 3 h when traveling with a current. Against the same current, it can travel only 16 mi in 4 h. Find the rate of the current and the rate of the boat in still water. **2 mi/h, 6 mi/h**

17. **Geometry** The measure of one acute angle of a right triangle is 30° more than twice the measure of the other acute angle. Find the measures of the angles. **20°, 70°, 90°**

Example 3
(page 126)

Solve each system by elimination.

18. $\begin{cases} x + y = 12 \\ x − y = 2 \end{cases}$ **(7, 5)**

19. $\begin{cases} x + 2y = 10 \\ x + y = 6 \end{cases}$ **(2, 4)**

20. $\begin{cases} 3a + 4b = 9 \\ −3a − 2b = −3 \end{cases}$ **(a, b) = (−1, 3)**

21. $\begin{cases} 4x + 2y = 4 \\ 6x + 2y = 8 \end{cases}$ **(2, −2)**

22. $\begin{cases} 2w + 5y = −24 \\ 3w − 5y = 14 \end{cases}$ **(w, y) = (−2, −4)**

23. $\begin{cases} 3u + 3v = 15 \\ −2u + 3v = −5 \end{cases}$ **(u, v) = (4, 1)**

24. $\begin{cases} x + 3y = 11 \\ x + 4y = 14 \end{cases}$ **(2, 3)**

25. $\begin{cases} 5x + 3y = 30 \\ 3x + 3y = 18 \end{cases}$ **(6, 0)**

26. $\begin{cases} x − 14 = −y \\ x − y = 2 \end{cases}$ **(8, 6)**

27. $\begin{cases} 3x + 2y = 6 \\ 3x + 3 = y \end{cases}$ **(0, 3)**

28. $\begin{cases} 5x − y = 4 \\ 2x − y = 1 \end{cases}$ **(1, 1)**

29. $\begin{cases} 2r + s = 3 \\ 4r − s = 9 \end{cases}$ **(r, s) = (2, −1)**

pages 128–130 Exercises

30. $\{(x, y): −2x + 3y = 13\}$

31. $\{(a, d) \mid −3a + d = −1\}$

32. $(a, b) = (3, 2)$

33. **no solution**

34. **(5, 4)**

35. **no solution**

36. $\left(\frac{20}{17}, \frac{19}{17}\right)$

37. **(−3, 2)**

38. $(r, s) = (4, 1)$

39. **(1, 3)**

40. **no solution**

41. $(m, n) = (1, −4)$

Examples 4, 5
(page 127)

Solve each system by elimination. 30–41. See margin p. 128.

30. $\begin{cases} 4x - 6y = -26 \\ -2x + 3y = 13 \end{cases}$

31. $\begin{cases} 9a - 3d = 3 \\ -3a + d = -1 \end{cases}$

32. $\begin{cases} 2a + 3b = 12 \\ 5a - b = 13 \end{cases}$

33. $\begin{cases} 2x - 3y = 6 \\ 6x - 9y = 9 \end{cases}$

34. $\begin{cases} 20x + 5y = 120 \\ 10x + 7.5y = 80 \end{cases}$

35. $\begin{cases} 6x - 2y = 11 \\ -9x + 3y = 16 \end{cases}$

36. $\begin{cases} 2x - 3y = -1 \\ 3x + 4y = 8 \end{cases}$

37. $\begin{cases} 5x - 2y = -19 \\ 2x + 3y = 0 \end{cases}$

38. $\begin{cases} r + 3s = 7 \\ 2r - s = 7 \end{cases}$

39. $\begin{cases} y = 4 - x \\ 3x + y = 6 \end{cases}$

40. $\begin{cases} 3x + 2y = 10 \\ 6x + 4y = 15 \end{cases}$

41. $\begin{cases} 3m + 4n = -13 \\ 5m + 6n = -19 \end{cases}$

GO for Help

For a guide to solving
Exercise 42, see p. 131.

42. **Elections** In a mayoral election, the number of votes for the incumbent was 25% more than the number for the opponent. Altogether, the two candidates received 5175 votes. How many votes did the incumbent mayor receive?
2875 votes

43. **Writing** Explain how you decide whether to use substitution or elimination to solve a system. **See margin.**

B Apply Your Skills

45. $(m, n) = (4, -3)$

46. $\left(-1, -\frac{1}{2}\right)$

47. $(t, v) = (50, 750)$

48. $(0.5, 0.75)$

49. $\left(\frac{3}{11}, -\frac{2}{11}\right)$

Solve each system.

44. $\begin{cases} 5x + y = 0 \\ 5x + 2y = 30 \end{cases}$ (−6, 30)

45. $\begin{cases} 2m = -4n - 4 \\ 3m + 5n = -3 \end{cases}$

46. $\begin{cases} 7x + 2y = -8 \\ 8y = 4x \end{cases}$

47. $\begin{cases} v = 9t + 300 \\ v = 7t + 400 \end{cases}$

48. $\begin{cases} 80x + 60y = 85 \\ 100x - 40y = 20 \end{cases}$

49. $\begin{cases} 2x + 3y = 0 \\ 7x = 3(2y) + 3 \end{cases}$

50. $\begin{cases} \frac{x}{3} + \frac{4y}{3} = 300 \\ 3x - 4y = 300 \end{cases}$
(300, 150)

51. $\begin{cases} 0.02a - 1.5b = 4 \\ 0.5b - 0.02a = 1.8 \end{cases}$
$(a, b) = (-235, -5.8)$

52. $\begin{cases} 4y = 2x \\ 2x + y = \frac{x}{2} + 1 \end{cases}$
(0.5, 0.25)

53. **Multiple Choice** The equation $3x - 4y = 2$ and which equation below form a system with no solutions? **A**

  Ⓐ $2y = 1.5x - 2$ Ⓑ $2y = 1.5x - 1$
  Ⓒ $3x + 4y = 2$ Ⓓ $4y - 3x = -2$

**For each system, choose the method of solving that seems easier to use.
Explain why you made each choice.** 54–59. See margin.

54. $\begin{cases} 3x - 5y = 26 \\ -2x - 3y = -11 \end{cases}$

55. $\begin{cases} y = \frac{2}{3}x - 3 \\ -x + 3y = 18 \end{cases}$

56. $\begin{cases} 2m + 3n = 12 \\ -5m + n = -13 \end{cases}$

57. $\begin{cases} 3x - y = 5 \\ y = 4x + 2 \end{cases}$

58. $\begin{cases} 2x - 3y = 4 \\ 2x - 5y = -6 \end{cases}$

59. $\begin{cases} 6x - 3y = 3 \\ 5x - 5y = 10 \end{cases}$

GO Online
Homework Video Tutor

Visit: PHSchool.com
Web Code: age-0302

60. **Open-Ended** Write a system of equations in which both equations must be multiplied by a nonzero number before using elimination. Solve your system.
See margin p. 130.

61. **Internet Access** The ads at the left show the costs of Internet access for two companies. **a–d. See margin p. 130.**

  a. Write a system of equations to represent the cost c for t hours of access in one month for each company.
  b. Graph the system from part (a). Label each line.
  c. For how many hours of use will the costs for the companies be the same? How is this information represented on the graph?
  d. If you use the Internet about 20 hours each month, which company should you choose? Explain how you reached an answer.

internet ACTION
$2.25 per hour
$9.95 base fee
(per month)

Webster's WEB
$2.95 per hour
no base fee

43. In determining whether to use substitution or elimination to solve an equation, look at the equations to determine if one is solved or can be easily solved for a particular variable. If that is the case, substitution can easily be used. Otherwise, elimination might be easier.

54. Elimination; substitution would be difficult since no coefficient is 1.

55. Substitution; the first equation is solved for y.

4. Assess & Reteach

PowerPoint
Lesson Quiz

1. Solve by substitution.
$\begin{cases} -2x + 5y = -2 \\ x - 3y = 3 \end{cases}$ (−9, −4)

2. A bookstore took in $167 on the sale of 5 copies of a new cookbook and 3 copies of a new novel. The next day it took in $89 on the sale of 3 copies of the cookbook and 1 copy of the novel. What was the price of each book?
cookbook: $25; novel: $14

Solve each system.

3. $\begin{cases} 10x + 6y = 0 \\ -7x + 2y = 31 \end{cases}$
(−3, 5)

4. $\begin{cases} 7x + 5y = 18 \\ -7x - 9y = 4 \end{cases}$
(6.5, −5.5)

5. $\begin{cases} -3x + y = 6 \\ 6x - 2y = 25 \end{cases}$
no solutions

Alternative Assessment

Ask three students each to state a different equation in standard form. Write the equations where all students can see them. Instruct half of the students to solve the system by finding x first. Instruct the other half to find y first. Have students compare solutions.

56. Substitution; the second equation is easily solved for n.

57. Substitution; the second equation is solved for y.

58. Elimination; $2x$ would be eliminated from the system if the equations were subtracted.

59. Elimination; substitution would be difficult since no coefficient is 1.

129

A sheet of blank grids is available in the Test-Taking Strategies with Transparencies booklet. Give this sheet to students for practice with filling in the grids.

📁 **Resources**

For additional practice with a variety of test item formats:
- Standardized Test Prep, p. 165
- Test-Taking Strategies, p. 160
- Test-Taking Strategies with Transparencies

pages 128–130   Exercises

60. Answers may vary.
Sample:
$$\begin{cases} -3x + 4y = 12 \\ 5x - 3y = 13 \end{cases}$$
(8, 9)

61a. $c = 9.95 + 2.25t$,
$c = 2.95t$

b.

c. about 14.2 h; It is where the graphs intersect.

d. Answers may vary. Sample: Internet Action, because it would cost $4.05 less per month

76. $y = (x + 3) - 4$ or $y = x - 1$

77. $y = |x - 2| + \frac{1}{2}$

78. $y = 2(x - 1) - 4$ or $y = 2x - 6$

79. $y = |x + 2| + 6$

🌐 **62. Break-Even Point** A theater production costs $40,000 plus $2800 per
GPS performance. A sold-out performance brings in $3675. How many sold-out performances will the production need to break even? **46 performances**

C Challenge 🌐 **63. Weather** The equation $F = \frac{9}{5}C + 32$ relates temperatures on the Celsius and Fahrenheit scales. Does any temperature have the same number reading on both scales? If so, what is the number? **yes; for −40 degrees**

Find the value of *a* that makes each system a dependent system.

64. $\begin{cases} y = 3x + a \\ 3x - y = 2 \end{cases}$ **−2**   65. $\begin{cases} 3y = 2x \\ 6y - a - 4x = 0 \end{cases}$ **0**   66. $\begin{cases} y = \frac{x}{2} + 4 \\ 2y - x = a \end{cases}$ **8**

Test Prep

Gridded Response   Use the following system of equations for Exercises 67–70.
$$\begin{cases} 5x - 3y = 11 \\ -x + 12y = 3.5 \end{cases}$$

67. If you want to solve the system by eliminating *x* (with addition), by what would you multiply the second equation? **5**

68. If you want to solve the system by eliminating *y* (with addition), by what would you multiply the first equation? **4**

69. What is the value of *x* in the solution? Enter your answer as a decimal. **2.5**

70. What is the value of *y* in the solution? Enter your answer as a decimal. **0.5**

Use the following system of equations for Exercises 71–72.
$$\begin{cases} 4x - 10y = -3 \\ 12x + 5y = 12 \end{cases}$$

71. What is the value of *x* in the solution? Enter your answer as a fraction in simplest form. $\frac{3}{4}$

72. What is the value of *y* in the solution? Enter your answer as a decimal. **0.6**

Mixed Review

GO for Help

Lesson 3-1   **Solve each system of equations by graphing.**

73. $\begin{cases} y = 3x + 4 \\ 2y = 6x - 2 \end{cases}$ 74. $\begin{cases} -3y = 9x + 1 \\ 6y = -18x - 2 \end{cases}$ 75. $\begin{cases} 4x - y = -5 \\ -8x + 2y = 15 \end{cases}$
no solution   {(x, y) | −9x − 3y = 1}   no solution

Lesson 2-6   **Write an equation for each diagonal translation. 76–79. See margin.**

76. $y = x$, 4 units down, 3 units left   77. $y = |x|$, $\frac{1}{2}$ unit up, 2 units right

78. $y = 2x - 3$, 1 unit down, 1 unit right   79. $y = |x| + 2$, 4 units up, 2 units left

Lesson 1-1   80. What subset(s) of real numbers contain(s) 6? **natural, whole, integer, rational**

81. The sum of the first and last of four consecutive odd integers is 48. What are the four integers? **21, 23, 25, 27**

Understanding Word Problems Read the problem below. Then let David's thinking guide you through the solution. Check your understanding with the exercises at the bottom of the page.

Elections In a mayoral election, the number of votes for the incumbent was 25% more than the number for the opponent. Altogether, the two candidates received 5175 votes. How many votes did the incumbent mayor receive?

What David Thinks

I'll restate the important information. In the first sentence, 25% more means the greater number is 1.25 times the lesser number.

The second sentence gives me the total number of votes.

What quantities are being used in the problem? I'll assign variables to the number of votes each received.

Now I can write a system of equations.

Great! The first equation defines the value of n. I'll solve the system by substituting $1.25p$ from the first equation into the second equation.

The problem asks me to find the number of incumbent votes. That's n. I'll use one of the original equations and substitute.

Now I'll write my answer as a sentence.

What David Writes

Incumbent received 25% more votes than opponent.

$$\frac{\text{incumbent's}}{\text{votes}} = 1.25\left(\frac{\text{opponent's}}{\text{votes}}\right)$$

5175 votes total for both candidates.

$$\frac{\text{incumbent's}}{\text{votes}} + \frac{\text{opponent's}}{\text{votes}} = 5175$$

n = number of incumbent's votes
p = number of opponent's votes

$$\begin{cases} n = 1.25p \\ n + p = 5175 \end{cases}$$

$$n + p = 5175$$
$$1.25p + p = 5175$$
$$2.25p = 5175$$
$$p = 2300$$

$$n = 1.25p$$
$$n = 1.25(2300)$$
$$n = 2875$$

The incumbent mayor received 2875 votes.

EXERCISES

1. Two baseball cards together are worth $30. One card is worth 40% more than the other card. How much is the more expensive card worth? **$17.50**

2. A washer and dryer have the same retail price. The store discounts the washer by 10% and the dryer by 20%. The combined sale price for both appliances is $1020. What was the original price of each appliance? **$600**

Guided Problem Solving   Understanding Word Problems   **131**

Understanding Word Problems

Students read a problem then investigate a sample solution of the problem. They see examples both of what the person who is solving the problem thinks, and of what he writes. Students learn how to restate important information and how to identify the significant quantities given. Finally, they learn how to assign variables to the unknown quantities and then use the given information to solve a system of equations for the unknown quantities.

Guided Instruction

Before students look at how David thinks about or solves the problem, ask them to discuss the problem itself. Ask: *How would you solve the problem? What information in the problem is important?* Then have students compare their thoughts about the problem to the way David handled it.

Math Tip

A more literal way to represent the number of incumbent's votes would be $n = p + 0.25p$, which can then simplify to $n = 1.25p$.

Auditory Learners

Read the problem aloud to the class while they write down any important information that they hear. Repeat sections of the problem as needed.

Exercises

Have students make a two-column table on a sheet of paper. In the left column, ask students to record their thoughts about what they need to do to solve the problem. In the right column, have them record the steps that they follow to solve the problem.

131

Solving Systems Using Tables

Guided Instruction

Students write a system of linear equations for a real-world problem. They make two tables in which each row represents ordered pairs that satisfy each corresponding equation. From the table, students identify the solution for both equations.

Special Needs   L1

Review the geometry terms *polygon, pentagon,* and *hexagon.*

Teaching Tip

For Exercise 6, encourage students to first define each variable and represent it with a descriptive variable, such as *v* for number of vans and *b* for number of minibuses.

Math Tip

For Exercises 6-10, you may wish to explore that the solution set is restricted to discrete values. Ask:
- *What restrictions apply to the variables in your system?* The variables must be whole numbers, or non-negative integers. (Some students might answer positive integers, but positive integers do not include zero which is possible for either variable).
- *What would an answer of 3.5 vans represent? Is this an acceptable answer?* 3 and a half vans; Because only full vehicles are allowed, this answer is not possible.

Solving Systems Using Tables

FOR USE WITH LESSON 3-2

To solve systems with tables, you compare numbers in the table lists.

ACTIVITY

A magnetic construction set has 38 bars. For a project, Carlos and Colleen need to make 7 regular polygons using the bars. Each polygon must be either a pentagon or a hexagon. Carlos wants to use all the bars. He can write two equations that represent the situation. Then he can solve the system using tables.

1. One equation relates the number of pentagons p and the number of hexagons h. What is that equation? $p + h = 7$

2. Another equation shows that the total number of bars used by p pentagons and h hexagons is 38. Write that equation. $5p + 6h = 38$

3. Carlos made two tables side by side. One table lists the numbers of pentagons and hexagons that solve the first equation. The second table lists the numbers that solve the second equation. Build and complete the two tables. **See back of book.**

Number of Pentagons	Number of Hexagons
0	7
1	6
2	

Number of Pentagons	Number of Hexagons
0	Not possible
1	

row 5

4. Find the rows in the two tables that list the same pairs of numbers.

5. How many polygons of each type do Carlos and Colleen need to make? **4 pentagons, 3 hexagons**

EXERCISES

A school track team is going to a track meet. The school has minivans that seat 8 passengers and minibuses that seat 12 passengers, in addition to the drivers in each case. The school wants to fill each vehicle used. There are 4 drivers who can drive any of the vehicles. There are 40 members on the team.

6. Write a system of equations that represents the situation. $v + b = 4;\ 8v + 12b = 40$

7. Use tables to solve the system. $v = 2, b = 2$

8. Explain what the solution of the system represents. **2 minivans and 2 minibuses**

You can enter two equations as Y1 and Y2 in a graphing calculator. Then you can display a table showing X, Y1, and Y2. Decide how you can use such a table to solve each system of equations below. Then do so. (*Hint:* The screen at the right shows the table for Exercise 9.)

X	Y1	Y2
20.00	14.00	16.00
21.00	15.00	16.50
22.00	16.00	17.00
23.00	17.00	17.50
24.00	18.00	18.00
25.00	19.00	18.50
26.00	20.00	19.00
X=20		

9. $\begin{cases} y = x - 6 \\ y = \frac{1}{2}x + 6 \end{cases}$

(24, 18)

10. $\begin{cases} y = 2x - 3 \\ y = -3x + 19.5 \end{cases}$

(4.5, 6)

11. $\begin{cases} y = 1.5x \\ y = -0.75x + 9.75 \end{cases}$

$\left(\frac{13}{3}, \frac{13}{2}\right)$

Systems of Inequalities

1. Plan

What You'll Learn

• To solve systems of linear inequalities

. . . And Why

To model college entrance requirements, as in Example 3

✓ Check Skills You'll Need

 GO for Help Lessons 1-4, 2-5, and 2-7

Solve each inequality.

1. $5x - 6 > 27$ $x > \frac{33}{5}$

2. $-18 - 5y \geq 52$ $y \leq -14$

3. $-5(4x + 1) < 23$ $x > -\frac{7}{5}$

Graph each inequality.   4–9. See back of book.

4. $y \leq 4x - 1$

5. $3y \geq 6x + 3$

6. $-5y + 2x > -5$

7. $y \leq |x|$

8. $y \geq |x + 3|$

9. $y < |x - 2| + 4$

Objectives

1 To solve systems of linear inequalities

Examples

1 Solving a System by Using a Table
2 Solving a System by Graphing
3 Real-World Connection
4 Solving a Linear Absolute Value System

---

1 Solving Systems of Inequalities

You can model a situation by writing a system of linear inequalities or a system that combines equations and inequalities.

1 EXAMPLE   Solving a System by Using a Table

Classroom Management A science class has 6 computers for 20 students. Students have the option of using a computer program to investigate frog biology or using a computer and their graphing calculators to investigate the properties of heat transfer. Each frog lab must have 3 students in a group. Each heat lab must have 4 students in a group. In how many ways can you set up the lab groups?

Relate   number of frog lab groups + number of heat lab groups ≤ 6

3 · number of frog lab groups + 4 · number of heat lab groups = 20

Define   Let f = the number of frog lab groups.

Let h = the number of heat lab groups.

Write $f + h \leq 6$

$3f + 4h = 20$

The situation is discrete. The replacement values for f and h must be whole numbers.

To solve the system $\begin{cases} f + h \leq 6 \\ 3f + 4h = 20 \end{cases}$

first make a table of values of f and h that solve the inequality.

f	h
0	6, 5, 4, 3, 2, 1, 0
1	5, 4, 3, 2, 1, 0
2	4, 3, 2, 1, 0
3	3, 2, 1, 0
4	2, 1, 0
5	1, 0
6	0

Math Background

The graph of a system of inequalities may or may not include parts of the boundaries as part of the solution.

More Math Background: p. 116C

Lesson Planning and Resources

See p. 116E for a list of the resources that support this lesson.

PowerPoint

Bell Ringer Practice

✓ Check Skills You'll Need

For intervention, direct students to:

Solving Inequalities
Lesson 1-4: Example 1
Extra Skills and Word
   Problems Practice, Ch. 1

Absolute Value Functions and Graphs
Lesson 2-5: Example 1
Extra Skills and Word
   Problems Practice, Ch. 2

Two-Variable Inequalities
Lesson 2-7: Example 1
Extra Skills and Word
   Problems Practice, Ch. 2

Lesson 3-3 Systems of Inequalities   **133**

Differentiated Instruction   Solutions for All Learners

Special Needs L1
For Example 2, use masking tape to make a coordinate grid on the floor. Let four students use string to model the two boundary lines. Have other students fill in the overlapping area and stand on the "solid" line to model the solution region.
learning style: tactile

Below Level L2
Have students use colored pencils to lightly shade the graph of each linear inequality. Have them describe how this helps show the region containing the solution of the system.
learning style: visual

Guided Instruction

1 EXAMPLE Teaching Tip

Some students may not understand why an inequality is required because no key phrases such as *at most*, or *no more than* are used. Help these students identify the limitation on the number of computers available.

2 EXAMPLE

Error Prevention!

Call attention to the graph of $x - 2y < 6$. Point out that students often shade below the boundary line when they see $<$. Note that this only applies when the inequality has the form $y <$, and when solved for y the resulting inequality is $y > -\frac{1}{2}x - 6$.

Teaching Tip

Contrast the types of solutions in Example 1 and Example 2. Ask:
• *How many solutions does Example 1 have?* two
• *How many solutions does Example 2 have?* an infinite number

3 EXAMPLE Technology Tip

Urge students to be careful with boundary points when interpreting graphs that use the shading feature of the calculator.

4 EXAMPLE

Error Prevention!

Some students may confuse the graphs of linear equations of the form $y < c$ with graphs of $x < c$. Help students recognize that $y < 4$ intersects the y-axis at 4, thus having a horizontal boundary line. Similarly, $x < c$ intersects the x-axis at c and has a vertical boundary line.

Math Tip

Ask: *What is the solution to a system of two inequalities whose shaded regions do not overlap?* no solution

134

In that table look for values of f and h that solve the equation. Circle any that you find.

The only two whole number solutions of the system are $(0, 5)$ and $(4, 2)$.

There are two possible ways to set up the lab groups. You can assign all students to 5 heat lab groups, or you can assign them to 4 frog lab groups and 2 heat lab groups.

f	h
⓪	6, ⑤, 4, 3, 2, 1, 0
1	5, 4, 3, 2, 1, 0
2	4, 3, 2, 1, 0
3	3, 2, 1, 0
④	② 1, 0
5	1, 0
6	0

✓ Quick Check 1 Use tables to solve each system. Assume that replacement values for the variables are whole numbers. **See left.**

1a. (0, 1), (1, 2), (2, 3), (3, 4), (4, 5), (5, 6), (6, 7)

1b. (1, 0), (2, 1), (2, 0), (3, 2), (3, 1), (3, 0), (4, 3), (4, 2), (4, 1), (4, 0), (5, 3), (5, 2), (5, 1), (5, 0), (6, 3), (6, 2), (6, 1), (6, 0), (7, 2), (7, 1), (7, 0), (8, 1), (8, 0), (9, 1), (9, 0), (10, 0)

a. $\begin{cases} -x + y = 1 \\ x + 2y \le 20 \end{cases}$

b. $\begin{cases} x - y \ge 1 \\ 2x + 3y \le 21 \end{cases}$

You can solve a system of linear inequalities by graphing. Recall from Lesson 2-7 that when the variables represent real numbers, the solutions of an inequality include all the points on one side of a boundary line. Thus, for two inequalities, every point in the region of overlap of the two solutions is a solution of the system.

Problem Solving Hint

After graphing a boundary line, test whether (0, 0) satisfies the inequality. If it does, shade the side of the line containing (0, 0).

2 EXAMPLE Solving a System by Graphing

Solve the system of inequalities. $\begin{cases} x - 2y < 6 \\ y \le -\frac{3}{2}x + 5 \end{cases}$

Graph each inequality. First graph the boundary lines. Then decide which side of each boundary line contains solutions and whether the boundary line is included.

$x - 2y < 6$

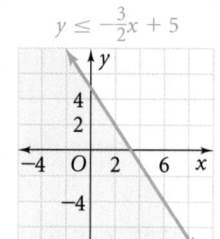
$y \le -\frac{3}{2}x + 5$

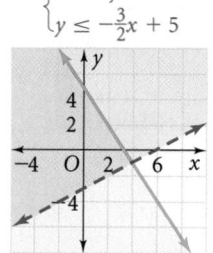
$\begin{cases} x - 2y < 6 \\ y \le -\frac{3}{2}x + 5 \end{cases}$

Every point in the red region above the dashed line is a solution of $x - 2y < 6$.

Every point in the blue region or on the solid line is a solution of $y \le -\frac{3}{2}x + 5$.

Every point in the purple region where the red and blue regions intersect is a solution of the system. For example, $(1, 1)$ is a solution.

Check Check $(1, 1)$ in both inequalities of the system.

$x - 2y < 6$

$1 - 2(1) < 6$

$-1 < 6$ ✓

$y \le -\frac{3}{2}x + 5$

$1 \le -\frac{3}{2}(1) + 5$

$1 \le \frac{7}{2}$ ✓

✓ Quick Check 2 Solve each system of inequalities. **a–b. See back of book.**

a. $\begin{cases} y \le -2x + 4 \\ x > -3 \end{cases}$

b. $\begin{cases} y \le 3x - 6 \\ y > -4x + 2 \end{cases}$

134 Chapter 3 Linear Systems

Differentiated Instruction Solutions for All Learners

Advanced Learners L4

Have students create a real–world example to be solved with a linear system. Let them exchange exercises and solve.

learning style: verbal

English Language Learners ELL

Many students have difficulty translating a word problem into a system of equations and/or inequalities. Have students work in pairs or small groups and sketch illustrations to represent the situation described in each real-world problem.

learning style: verbal

③ EXAMPLE **Real-World** **Connection**

College Admissions An entrance exam has two parts, a verbal part and a mathematics part. You can score a maximum total of 1600 points. For admission, the school of your choice requires a math score of at least 600. Write a system of inequalities to model scores that meet the school's requirements. Then solve the system.

Real-World **Connection**

Most college admission requirements include standardized test scores.

Relate verbal score + math score ≤ 1600

math score ≥ 600

Define Let x = the verbal score.

Let y = the mathematics score.

Write $x + y ≤ 1600$, or $y ≤ 1600 - x$

$y ≥ 600$

The system of inequalities is $\begin{cases} y ≤ 1600 - x \\ y ≥ 600. \end{cases}$

Xmin = 0   Ymin = 10
Xmax = 1600   Ymax = 1600

Use a graphing calculator to graph the corresponding equations $y = 1600 - x$ and $y = 600$. Since the first inequality is ≤, shade below the first line. Since the second inequality is ≥, shade above the second line. The region of overlap is a graph of the solution.

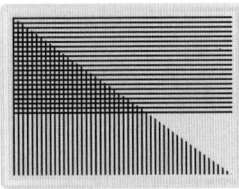

✓ **Quick Check** ③ Another school requires a math score of at least 550 points and a total score of at least 1100 points. You can score up to 800 points on each part. Write and solve a system of inequalities to model scores that meet the school's requirements. **See back of book.**

Some systems consist of linear and absolute value inequalities.

Online *active math*

For: Inequality Systems Activity
Use: Interactive Textbook, 3-3

④ EXAMPLE **Solving a Linear Absolute Value System**

Solve the system of inequalities. $\begin{cases} y < 4 \\ y ≥ |x - 3| \end{cases}$

$y < 4$

$y ≥ |x - 3|$
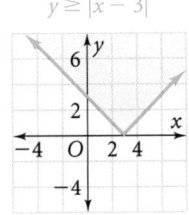

$\begin{cases} y ≥ |x - 3| \\ y < 4 \end{cases}$
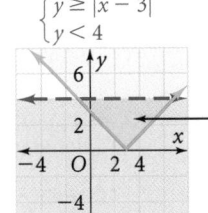

The region of overlap represents the solution.

✓ **Quick Check** ④ Solve each system of inequalities. **a–b. See back of book.**

a. $\begin{cases} y ≥ x \\ y ≤ |x + 5| - 2 \end{cases}$

b. $\begin{cases} y ≥ -2x + 4 \\ y ≤ |x - 4| \end{cases}$

c. Critical Thinking Write a system that includes an absolute value inequality but has no solutions. **Check students' work.**

---

2. Teach

PowerPoint
Additional Examples

① Find whole number solutions of the system using tables.
$\begin{cases} x + y = 2 \\ 2x + y ≤ 5 \end{cases}$ (0, 2), (1, 1), (2, 0)

② Solve the system of inequalities.
$\begin{cases} -x + y > -1 \\ x + y > 3 \end{cases}$

③ Jenna spends at most 150 min a night on math and science homework. She spends at least 60 min on math. Write and solve a system of inequalities to model how she allots her time for these two subjects. **See back of book.**

④ Solve the system.
$\begin{cases} y ≥ 3 \\ y > -|x + 2| + 5 \end{cases}$
See back of book.

Resources
• Daily Notetaking Guide 3-3 **L3**

Closure

Ask: *How do you solve a system of inequalities by graphing?* Graph the individual inequalities. Shade the region where the graphs overlap.

Lesson 3-3 Systems of Inequalities   **135**

Homework Quick Check
To check students' understanding of key skills and concepts, go over Exercises 10, 35–40, 45.

Error Prevention!

Exercises 12, 13, 15 Students should be careful to have y, not $-y$, on the left side of each inequality when determining whether to shade above or below a boundary line.

Exercises 43–45 Students' diagrams should make it clear that the solutions of the systems are the points whose coordinates satisfy *all three* inequalities.

EXERCISES

For more exercises, see *Extra Skill and Word Problem Practice.*

Practice and Problem Solving

Ⓐ Practice by Example

Example 1
(page 133)

Example 2
(page 134)

1. (0, 4), (0, 5), (0, 6), (0, 7), (0, 8)

2. (3, 0), (4, 1), (5, 2), (6, 3), (7, 4)

Find the whole number solutions of each system using tables.

1. $\begin{cases} y + 3x \leq 8 \\ y - 3 > 2x \end{cases}$ 2. $\begin{cases} x = y + 3 \\ x + y \leq 12 \end{cases}$ 3. $\begin{cases} x + y < 8 \\ 3x \leq y + 6 \end{cases}$
   1–2. See left.   **See back of book.**

Tell whether $(-3, 3)$ is a solution of each system.

4. $\begin{cases} y \geq x + 2 \\ 3y < -6x + 6 \end{cases}$ **yes**   5. $\begin{cases} y - 2x \leq 1 \\ y < -2x - 2 \end{cases}$ **no**   6. $\begin{cases} -2y + x \leq 4 \\ 3y < -9x + 3 \end{cases}$ **yes**

Solve each system of inequalities by graphing.   **7–9. See margin.**

7. $\begin{cases} y \leq 2x + 2 \\ y < -x + 1 \end{cases}$ 8. $\begin{cases} y > -2 \\ x < 1 \end{cases}$ 9. $\begin{cases} y \leq 3 \\ y \leq \frac{1}{2}x + 1 \end{cases}$

10. $\begin{cases} y \leq 3x + 1 \\ -6x + 2y > 5 \end{cases}$ 11. $\begin{cases} x + 2y \leq 10 \\ x + y \leq 3 \end{cases}$ 12. $\begin{cases} -x - y \leq 2 \\ y - 2x > 1 \end{cases}$

13. $\begin{cases} y > -2x \\ 2x - y \geq 2 \end{cases}$ 14. $\begin{cases} c \geq d - 3 \\ c < \frac{1}{2}d + 3 \end{cases}$ 15. $\begin{cases} 2x + y < 1 \\ -y + 3x < 1 \end{cases}$

10–17. See back of book.

Example 3
(page 135)

16. **Fund-Raising** You want to bake at least 6 and at most 11 loaves of bread for a bake sale. You want at least twice as many loaves of banana bread as nut bread. Write and graph a system of inequalities to model the situation.

17. **Psychology** A psychologist needs at least 40 subjects for her experiment. She cannot use more than 30 children. Write and graph a system of inequalities.

Example 4
(page 135)

Solve each system of inequalities by graphing.   **18–29. See back of book.**

18. $\begin{cases} y > 4 \\ y < |x - 1| \end{cases}$ 19. $\begin{cases} y < -\frac{1}{3}x + 1 \\ y > |2x - 1| \end{cases}$ 20. $\begin{cases} y > x - 2 \\ y \geq |x + 2| \end{cases}$

21. $\begin{cases} y \leq -\frac{4}{3}x \\ y \geq -|x| \end{cases}$ 22. $\begin{cases} 3y < -x - 1 \\ y \leq |x + 1| \end{cases}$ 23. $\begin{cases} y > -2 \\ y \leq -|x - 3| \end{cases}$

24. $\begin{cases} -2x + y > 3 \\ y \leq -|x + 4| \end{cases}$ 25. $\begin{cases} 5y \geq 2x - 5 \\ y < |x + 3| \end{cases}$ 26. $\begin{cases} y \geq -3x + 3 \\ y > |x + 2| \end{cases}$

27. $\begin{cases} -2y < 4x + 2 \\ y > |2x + 1| \end{cases}$ 28. $\begin{cases} -x \geq 4 - y \\ y \geq |3x - 6| \end{cases}$ 29. $\begin{cases} y \leq x - 4 \\ y > |x - 6| \end{cases}$

Ⓑ Apply Your Skills

In Exercises 30–39, identify the inequalities A, B, and C for which the given ordered pair is a solution.

A. $x + y \leq 2$ **B.** $y \leq \frac{3}{2}x - 1$ **C.** $y > -\frac{1}{3}x - 2$

       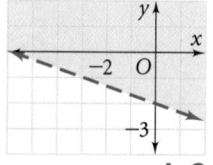

30. $(0, 0)$ **A, C**   31. $(-2, -5)$ 32. $(-2, 0)$ **A, C**   33. $(0, -2)$ **A, B**   34. $(-15, 15)$
35. $(3, 2)$ **B, C**   36. $(2, 0)$ **A, B, C**   37. $(-6, 0)$ **A**   38. $(4, -1)$ **B, C**   39. $(-8, -11)$

GO ●nline
Homework Video Tutor
Visit: PHSchool.com
Web Code: age-0303

pages 136–138   **Exercises**

7. $y \leq 2x + 2$ $y < -x + 1$

8. $x < 1$ $y > -2$

9. $y \leq 3$ $y \leq \frac{1}{2}x + 1$

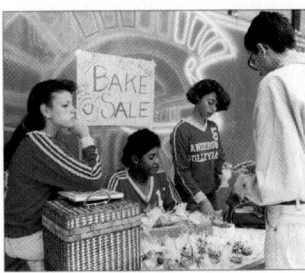

Real-World 🌐 **Connection**

Bake sales are a popular way to raise money.

40. Fund-Raising Suppose the Student Council has asked you to form a committee **GPS** to run a bake sale. The committee needs from 7 to 10 members. The number of seniors should be greater than the number of juniors.
   a. Write a system of inequalities to model the problem.
   b. Graph the system and list the combinations of juniors and seniors that may participate in the committee. **a–c. See back of book.**
   c. Critical Thinking Explain why your list in part (b) is finite.

41. Open-Ended Write and graph a system of inequalities for which the solution is bounded by a dashed vertical line and a solid horizontal line.

✏️ **42. Writing** Explain how you determine where to shade when solving a system of inequalities.
41–51. See back of book.

Solve each system of inequalities by graphing.

43. $\begin{cases} x + y < 8 \\ x \geq 0 \\ y \geq 0 \end{cases}$ **44.** $\begin{cases} 2y - 4x \leq 0 \\ x \geq 0 \\ y \geq 0 \end{cases}$ **45.** $\begin{cases} y \geq -2x + 4 \\ x > -3 \\ y \geq 1 \end{cases}$

46. $\begin{cases} y \leq \frac{2}{3}x + 2 \\ y \geq |x| + 2 \end{cases}$ **47.** $\begin{cases} y < x - 1 \\ y > -|x - 2| + 1 \end{cases}$ **48.** $\begin{cases} 2x + y \leq 3 \\ y > |x + 3| - 2 \end{cases}$

C **Challenge** 📦 **Geometry** **Write a system of inequalities to describe each shaded figure.**

49.   **50.**   **51.**

52a.

52. a. Graph the "bowtie" inequality, $|y| \leq |x|$.
   b. Write a system of inequalities to describe the graph shown at the right.
   Answers may vary.
   Sample: $|y| \leq \frac{1}{2}|x|$
   $|x| \leq 2$

Test Prep

Multiple Choice

53. When you graph Inequality ① at the right, the boundary line should be __?__ and the shading should be __?__ the line. **B**   ① $\begin{cases} y < -2x + 3 \\ y \geq x - 4 \end{cases}$ ②
   A. dashed, above   **B.** dashed, below   **C.** solid, above   **D.** solid, below

54. When you graph Inequality ②, the boundary line should be __?__ and the shading should be __?__ the line. **H**
   F. dashed, above   **G.** dashed, below   **H.** solid, above   **J.** solid, below

55. What is the x-value of the intersection of the boundary lines? **D**
   A. $\frac{-7}{3}$ **B.** $\frac{-3}{7}$ **C.** $\frac{3}{7}$ **D.** $\frac{7}{3}$

Short Response

56. How would you test whether $(2, -2)$ is a solution of the system?
   See back of book.

📊 **Lesson Quiz**

1. Solve the system of inequalities by graphing.
$\begin{cases} x + y \leq 6 \\ -x - 4y < 8 \end{cases}$

2. A 24-hour radio station plays only classical music, jazz, talk programs, and news. It plays at most 12 h of music per day, of which at least 4 h is classical. Jazz gets at least 25% as much time as classical. Write and graph a system of inequalities. Let c = hours for classical and j = hours for jazz.
$c + j \leq 12, c \geq 4, j \geq 0.25c$

3. Solve the system of inequalities by graphing.
$\begin{cases} y \leq x + 3 \\ y \geq |x - 2| + 1 \end{cases}$

Alternative Assessment

Have students work in pairs. Each student writes one inequality for a system. They combine the two inequalities to make a system, and each graphs the system. They check one another's work.

137

Test Prep

Resources

For additional practice with a variety of test item formats:
- Standardized Test Prep, p. 165
- Test-Taking Strategies, p. 160
- Test-Taking Strategies with Transparencies

Use this Checkpoint Quiz to check students' understanding of the skills and concepts of Lessons 3-1 through 3-3.

Resources
Grab & Go
- Checkpoint Quiz 1

Mixed Review

Lesson 3-2

Solve each system by elimination or substitution.

57. $\begin{cases} y = 3x + 1 \\ 2x - y = 8 \end{cases}$ (−9, −26)

58. $\begin{cases} 3x + y = 4 \\ 2x - 4y = 7 \end{cases}$ $\left(\frac{23}{14}, -\frac{13}{14}\right)$

59. $\begin{cases} -x + 5y = 3 \\ 2x - 10y = 4 \end{cases}$ **no solution**

60. $\begin{cases} 2x + 4y = -8 \\ -5x + 4y = 6 \end{cases}$ (−2, −1)

61. $\begin{cases} y - 3 = x \\ 4x + y = -2 \end{cases}$ (−1, 2)

62. $\begin{cases} 2 = 4y - 3x \\ 5x = 2y - 3 \end{cases}$ $\left(-\frac{4}{7}, \frac{1}{14}\right)$

Lesson 2-3

For each function, y varies directly as x.

63. If $y = -6$ when $x = -2$, find y when $x = 3$. **9**

64. If $y = -8$ when $x = 2$, find x when $y = 2$. **$-\frac{1}{2}$**

65. If $y = 4$ when $x = 7$, find y when $x = -14$. **−8**

66. If $y = 9$ when $x = 15$, find x when $y = 6$. **10**

Lesson 1-5

Solve each equation. Check your answers.

67. $|2x + 5| = 6$ $\frac{1}{2}, -\frac{11}{2}$

68. $|x + 7| = -2$ **no solution**

69. $3|x - 4| + 1 = 13$ **8, 0**

70. $-2|x + 1| - 5 = -7$ **−2, 0**

71. $\frac{1}{2}|3x + 2| - 3 = 4$ $-\frac{16}{3}, 4$

72. $-|2x + 5| = -3$ **−4, −1**

Checkpoint Quiz 1   **Lessons 3-1 through 3-3**

Solve each system of equations.

1. $\begin{cases} 3x + 2y = 6 \\ x - 2y = 10 \end{cases}$ (4, −3)

2. $\begin{cases} 4x + 7y = 28 \\ y = 2x - 14 \end{cases}$ (7, 0)

3. $\begin{cases} 4x + 5y = -12 \\ 3x - 4y = 22 \end{cases}$ (2, −4)

4. $\begin{cases} 3y - 2x = 7 \\ 2y - 2 = 4x \end{cases}$ (1, 3)

5. $\begin{cases} 2n + 3m = 158 \\ 2n + 5m = 181 \end{cases}$
**$61.75 cost per night
$11.50 cost per meal**

5. The Village Inn offers two special packages. For two nights and three meals the cost is $158. For two nights and five meals the cost is $181. Write and solve a system of linear equations to find the costs per night and per meal.

 6. **Smart Shopping** An ordinary refrigerator costs $489 and has an estimated annual operating cost of $84. An energy-saving model costs $599, with an estimated annual cost of $61. After how many years will the costs to buy and to operate the two models be equal? **approximately 4.8 years**

7. Each week you must do a minimum of 18 hours of homework. Participation in sports requires at least 12 hours per week. You have no more than 35 hours per week in total to devote to these activities. **a–b. See margin.**
   a. Write a system of inequalities to model the situation.
   b. Graph and solve the system.

Solve each system of inequalities by graphing. 8–10. See margin.

8. $\begin{cases} y \le -2 \\ y > |x + 1| \end{cases}$

9. $\begin{cases} 8x + 2y > 5 \\ x + 2y \le -3 \end{cases}$

10. $\begin{cases} 4y < 3x - 1 \\ y > 2|x| - 3 \end{cases}$

---

page 138 Checkpoint Quiz 1

7a. $\begin{cases} h \ge 18 \\ s \ge 12 \\ s + h \le 35 \end{cases}$

b.

8.

9.

10.

Linear Programming

What You'll Learn

- To find maximum and minimum values
- To solve problems with linear programming

. . . And Why

To maximize profit, as in Example 2

Objectives

1 To find maximum and minimum values
2 To solve problems with linear programming

Examples

1 Testing Vertices
2 Real-World Connection

 Check Skills You'll Need   **GO for Help** Lessons 3-2 and 3-3

Solve each system of equations.   (1, 1)

1. $\begin{cases} y = -3x + 3 \\ y = 2x - 7 \end{cases}$ (2, −3) 2. $\begin{cases} x + 2y = 5 \\ x - y = -1 \end{cases}$ (1, 2) 3. $\begin{cases} 4x + 3y = 7 \\ 2x - 5y = -3 \end{cases}$

Solve each system of inequalities by graphing.   4–6. See back of book.

4. $\begin{cases} x \geq 5 \\ y > -3x + 6 \end{cases}$ 5. $\begin{cases} 3y > 5x + 2 \\ y \leq -x + 7 \end{cases}$ 6. $\begin{cases} x + 3y < -6 \\ 2x - 3y \leq 4 \end{cases}$

🔊 **New Vocabulary** • linear programming • objective function • constraints
  • feasible region

Math Background

Linear programming is an extension of solving linear inequalities. You are given constraints represented by linear inequalities that are graphed. All of the points in the overlapping region are solutions, but linear programming problems are usually looking for maximum or minimum values. You substitute the coordinates of the vertices into an objective function to determine which yield the maximum or minimum value.

More Math Background: p. 116D

Lesson Planning and Resources

See p. 116E for a list of the resources that support this lesson.

---

1 Finding Maximum and Minimum Values

2.

Activity: Finding a Minimum Value

Music Suppose you want to buy some tapes and CDs. You can afford as many as 10 tapes or 7 CDs. You want at least 4 CDs and at least 10 hours of recorded music. Each tape holds about 45 minutes of music, and each CD holds about an hour.

1. Write a system of inequalities to model the problem. Let x represent the number of tapes purchased. Let y represent the number of CDs purchased.

$\begin{cases} x \leq 10 \\ 4 \leq y \leq 7 \\ \frac{3x}{4} + y \geq 10 \end{cases}$

2. Graph your system of inequalities.   See left.

3. Does each ordered pair satisfy the system you have graphed?
   a. (4, 7)   b. (12, 7)   c. (7, 6)   d. (9, 4)   e. (10, 4)
      yes   no   yes   yes   yes

Vocabulary Tip

Constraints are sometimes referred to as restrictions.

Linear programming is a technique that identifies the minimum or maximum value of some quantity. This quantity is modeled with an **objective function.** Limits on the variables in the objective function are **constraints,** written as linear inequalities.

The first paragraph of the Activity describes the constraints on buying tapes and CDs. Suppose you buy x tapes and y CDs. The constraints on x and y can be modeled with inequalities as follows.

as many as 10 tapes $x \leq 10$ at least 4 CDs $y \geq 4$

as many as 7 CDs $y \leq 7$ at least 10 hours $\frac{3}{4}x + y \geq 10$

Lesson 3-4 Linear Programming   **139**

 Bell Ringer Practice

✓ **Check Skills You'll Need**
For intervention, direct students to:
Graphing Systems of Equations
Lesson 3-1: Example 1
Extra Skills and Word Problems Practice, Ch. 3
Solving Systems Algebraically
Lesson 3-2: Examples 1, 3
Extra Skills and Word Problems Practice, Ch. 3
Systems of Inequalities
Lesson 3-3: Example 1
Extra Skills and Word Problems Practice, Ch. 3

Differentiated Instruction Solutions for All Learners

Special Needs L1
After students have graphed the restrictions, ask them to label their graph with each of the following: *left boundary, right boundary, upper boundary,* and *lower boundary.* Then discuss why the maximum and minimum values occur at the vertices.

learning style: visual

Below Level L2
Linear programming can be quite abstract for some students. Carefully review all the vocabulary terms and new concepts.

learning style: verbal

Guided Instruction

Activity
The graph of the system of inequalities encloses a region in the coordinate plane. The only points of this region that make sense for this situation are the points that have whole number coordinates.

1 EXAMPLE Visual Learners

After students have graphed the restrictions, have them graph the lines $3x + 2y = 18$, $3x + 2y = 6$, and $3x + 2y = 0$. Discuss with the students why the maximum and minimum values occur at the vertices.

Additional Examples

1 Find the values of x and y that maximize and minimize P if $P = -5x + 4y$.
$$\begin{cases} y \geq -\frac{2}{3}x + \frac{11}{3} \\ y \leq \frac{1}{4}x + \frac{11}{4} \\ y \geq 3x - 11 \end{cases}$$

maximum of 7 when $x = 1$ and $y = 3$, minimum of -16 when $x = 4$ and $y = 1$

Vocabulary Tip

Feasible means "doable" or "suitable."

The constraints form the system of inequalities at the right. The red region in the graph, the **feasible region,** contains all the points that satisfy all the constraints.

$$\begin{cases} x \leq 10 \\ y \leq 7 \\ y \geq 4 \\ \frac{3}{4}x + y \geq 10 \end{cases}$$

If you buy tapes at $8 each and CDs at $12 each, then the objective function for the total cost C is $C = 8x + 12y$. The blue line is the graph for the total cost $140. The green line is for the total cost $112.

Graphs of the objective function for various values of C are parallel lines. Lines closer to the origin represent lower costs. The graph closest to the origin that intersects the feasible region intersects it at the vertex $(8, 4)$. The graph of the objective function farthest from the origin that intersects the feasible region intersects it at the vertex $(10, 7)$. Graphs of an objective function that represent a maximum or minimum value intersect a feasible region at a vertex.

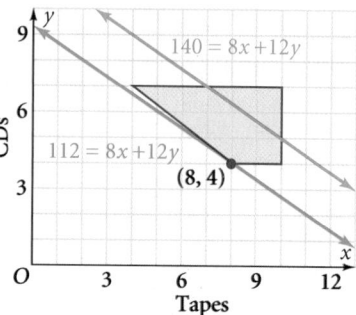

Key Concepts

Property	Vertex Principle of Linear Programming

If there is a maximum or a minimum value of the linear objective function, it occurs at one or more vertices of the feasible region.

Test-Taking Tip

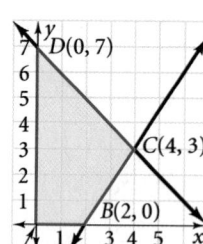

Remember to check the value of the objective function at *each* vertex when solving linear programming problems.

1. $P = 2(0) + 3(0) = 0$
$P = 2(2) + 3(0) = 4$
$P = 2(4) + 3(3) = 17$
$P = 2(0) + 3(7) = 21$
When $x = 0$ and $y = 7$, P is maximized at 21.
When $x = 0$ and $y = 0$, P is minimized at 0.

1 EXAMPLE Testing Vertices

Multiple Choice What values of x and y maximize P for the objective function $P = 3x + 2y$?

Constraints $\begin{cases} y \geq \frac{3}{2}x - 3 \\ y \leq -x + 7 \\ x \geq 0, y \geq 0 \end{cases}$

Ⓐ $(2, 0)$　　　Ⓑ $(2, 6)$
Ⓒ $(4, 3)$　　　Ⓓ $(4, 4)$

Step 1
Graph the constraints.

Step 2
Find coordinates for each vertex.

Step 3
Evaluate P at each vertex.

Vertex	$P = 3x + 2y$
$A(0, 0)$	$P = 3(0) + 2(0) = 0$
$B(2, 0)$	$P = 3(2) + 2(0) = 6$
$C(4, 3)$	$P = 3(4) + 2(3) = 18$
$D(0, 7)$	$P = 3(0) + 2(7) = 14$

When $x = 4$ and $y = 3$, P has its maximum value of 18. The answer is C.

Quick Check **1** Use the constraints in Example 1 with the objective function $P = 2x + 3y$. Find the values of x and y that maximize and minimize P. Find the value of P at each point. **See left.**

Differentiated Instruction Solutions for All Learners

Advanced Learners L4
Have students use catalogs or the Internet to find products and prices to write a linear programming problem. Have them share the problem and its solution.

learning style: verbal

English Language Learners ELL
Students can easily confuse the new vocabulary terms. Have students write the terms *objective function, constraints,* and *feasible region* next to the corresponding function, system of inequalities, and bounded region on the graph.

learning style: visual

You can use linear programming to solve many real-world problems.

2 **EXAMPLE** **Real-World** **Connection**

Profit Suppose you are selling cases of mixed nuts and roasted peanuts. You can order no more than a total of 500 cans and packages and spend no more than $600. How can you maximize your profit? How much is the maximum profit?

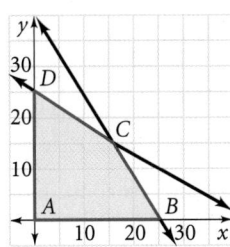

Mixed Nuts
12 cans per case

You pay ......$24 per case
Sell at ....$3.50 per can

$18 profit per case!

Roasted Peanuts
20 packages per case

You pay ......$15 per case
Sell at...$1.50 per package

$15 profit per case!

Define Let x = number of cases of mixed nuts ordered.
Let y = number of cases of roasted peanuts ordered.
Let P = total profit.

Relate Organize the information in a table.

	Mixed Nuts	Roasted Peanuts	Total	
Number of Cases	x	y	$x+y$	
Number of Units	$12x$	$20y$	500	constraint
Cost	$24x$	$15y$	600	constraint
Profit	$18x$	$15y$	$18x + 15y$	objective

Write Write and simplify the constraints. Write the objective function.

$$\begin{cases} 12x + 20y \le 500 \\ 24x + 15y \le 600 \\ x \ge 0, y \ge 0 \end{cases} \Rightarrow \begin{cases} 3x + 5y \le 125 \\ 8x + 5y \le 200 \\ x \ge 0, y \ge 0 \end{cases} \qquad P = 18x + 15y$$

Step 1
Graph the constraints.

Step 2
Find the coordinates of each vertex.

Step 3
Evaluate P at each vertex.

Vertex	$P = 18x + 15y$
$A(0,0)$	$P = 18(0) + 15(0) = 0$
$B(25,0)$	$P = 18(25) + 15(0) = 450$
$C(15,16)$	$P = 18(15) + 15(16) = 510$
$D(0,25)$	$P = 18(0) + 15(25) = 375$

You can maximize your profit by selling 15 cases of mixed nuts and 16 cases of roasted peanuts. The maximum profit is $510.

Quick Check **2** If you sell mixed nuts for $4.25 per can, what should you order to maximize profit?
Order 25 cases of mixed nuts and no cases of roasted peanuts.

Online active math*

For: Linear Program Activity
Use: Interactive Textbook, 3-4

Vocabulary Tip

Linear programming got its name because it provides a plan, or a program, that uses linear equations and inequalities.

---

2 **EXAMPLE** **Math Tip**

You may wish to point out that the vertices of the feasible region have whole number coordinates and make sense in terms of this situation. If the vertices were not whole numbers, a more detailed analysis would be necessary.

Additional Examples

2 A furniture manufacturer can make from 30 to 60 tables a day and from 40 to 100 chairs a day. It can make at most 120 units in one day. The profit on a table is $150, and the profit on a chair is $65. How many tables and chairs should they make per day to maximize profit? How much is the maximum profit? **60 tables, 60 chairs; $12,900**

Resources
• Daily Notetaking Guide 3-4 **L3**

Closure

In a linear programming problem, what values do you test to find the values that maximize or minimize the objective function? **the coordinates of each vertex of the feasible region**

Assignment Guide

▼**1** A B   1-9, 12, 14-19

▼**2** A B   10-11, 13, 20

C Challenge   21-23

Test Prep   24-27
Mixed Review   28-42

Homework Quick Check

To check students' understanding of key skills and concepts, go over Exercises 7, 10, 12, 17, 20.

Error Prevention!

Exercises 1–9 Students may think that the "highest" point on a graph is the maximum. Remind students that the only way to determine a maximum or a minimum is through substitution of the vertices' coordinates into the objective function to find the greatest and least values of the objective function.

Ⓐ Practice by Example

Example 1
(page 140)

GO for Help

1. When $x = 4$ and $y = 2$, P is maximized at 16.

2. When $x = 600$ and $y = 0$, P is maximized at 4200.

3. When $x = 6$ and $y = 8$, C is minimized at 36.

4–9. See back of book.

Example 2
(page 141)

10a. $\begin{cases} 2x + y \le 30 \\ 2y \le 16 \\ x \ge 0, y \ge 0 \end{cases}$
$P = 500x + 200y$

Find the values of x and y that maximize or minimize the objective function for each graph.   1–3. See left.

1.
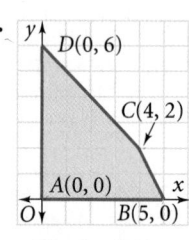
Maximum for
$P = 3x + 2y$

2.
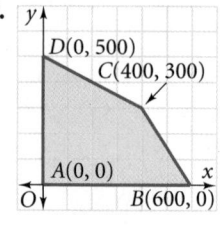
Maximum for
$P = 7x + 4y$

3.
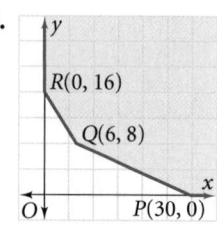
Minimum for
$C = 2x + 3y$

Graph each system of constraints. Name all vertices. Then find the values of x and y that maximize or minimize the objective function.

4. $\begin{cases} x \le 5 \\ y \le 4 \\ x \ge 0, y \ge 0 \end{cases}$
Maximum for
$P = 3x + 2y$

5. $\begin{cases} x + y \ge 8 \\ y \ge 5 \\ x \ge 0 \end{cases}$
Minimum for
$P = 3x + 2y$

6. $\begin{cases} x + y \le 8 \\ 2x + y \le 10 \\ x \ge 0, y \ge 0 \end{cases}$
Maximum for
$N = 100x + 40y$

7. $\begin{cases} x + y \ge 6 \\ x \le 8 \\ y \le 5 \end{cases}$
Minimum for
$C = x + 3y$

8. $\begin{cases} x + 2y \ge 8 \\ x \ge 2 \\ y \ge 0 \end{cases}$
Minimum for
$C = x + 3y$

9. $\begin{cases} 2 \le x \le 6 \\ 1 \le y \le 5 \\ x + y \le 8 \end{cases}$
Maximum for
$P = 3x + 2y$

10. **Ecology** Teams chosen from 30 forest rangers and 16 trainees are planting trees. An experienced team consisting of two rangers can plant 500 trees per week. A training team consisting of one ranger and two trainees can plant 200 trees per week.

	Experienced Teams	Training Teams	Total
Number of Teams	x	y	$x + y$
Number of Rangers	$2x$	y	30
Number of Trainees	0	$2y$	16
Number of Trees Planted	$500x$	$200y$	$500x + 200y$

a. Write an objective function and constraints for a linear program that models the problem.

b. How many of each type of team should be formed to maximize the number of trees planted? How many trainees are used in this solution? How many trees are planted? **15 experienced teams, 0 training teams; none; 7500**

c. Find a solution that uses all the trainees. How many trees will be planted in this case? **11 experienced teams; 8 training teams; 7100 trees**

11. Air Quality Trees in urban areas help keep air fresh by absorbing carbon dioxide. A city has $2100 to spend on planting spruce and maple trees. The land available for planting is 45,000 ft². How many of each tree should the city plant to maximize carbon dioxide absorption? **70 spruce; 0 maple**

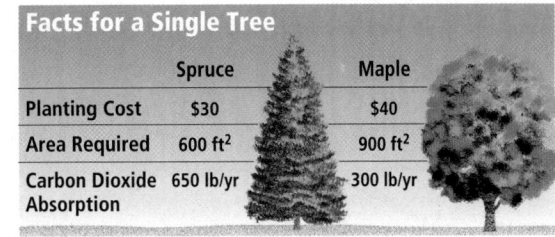

Facts for a Single Tree		
	Spruce	Maple
Planting Cost	$30	$40
Area Required	600 ft²	900 ft²
Carbon Dioxide Absorption	650 lb/yr	300 lb/yr

SOURCES: Auburn University and Anderson & Associates

 Apply Your Skills

12. Writing Explain why solving a system of linear equations is a necessary skill for linear programming. **Solving a system of linear equations is a necessary skill used to locate the vertex points.**

13. Multiple Choice A biologist is developing two new strains of bacteria. Each sample of Type I bacteria produces four new viable bacteria, and each sample of Type II produces three new viable bacteria. Altogether, at least 240 new viable bacteria must be produced. At least 30, but not more than 60, of the original samples must be Type I. Not more than 70 of the samples can be Type II. A sample of Type I costs $5 and a sample of Type II costs $7. How many samples of Type II bacteria should be used to minimize cost? **A**

(A) 0   (B) 30   (C) 60   (D) 70

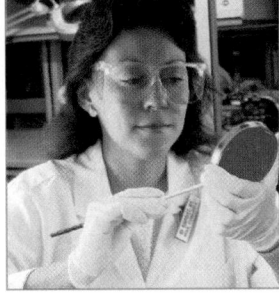

Real-World Connection

Careers A microbiologist studies microorganisms, such as bacteria and viruses, to determine their structure and function.

Graph each system of constraints. Name all vertices. Then find the values of x and y that maximize or minimize the objective function. Find the maximum or minimum value. 14–19. See back of book.

14. $\begin{cases} 3x + y \le 7 \\ x + 2y \le 9 \\ x \ge 0, y \ge 0 \end{cases}$

Maximum for
$P = 2x + y$

15. $\begin{cases} 25 \le x \le 75 \\ y \le 110 \\ 8x + 6y \ge 720 \end{cases}$

Minimum for
$C = 8x + 5y$

16. $\begin{cases} x + y \le 11 \\ 2y \ge x \\ x \ge 0, y \ge 0 \end{cases}$

Maximum for
$P = 3x + 2y$

17. $\begin{cases} 2x + y \le 300 \\ x + y \le 200 \\ x \ge 0, y \ge 0 \end{cases}$

Maximum for
$P = x + 2y$

18. $\begin{cases} 5x + y \ge 10 \\ x + y \ge 6 \\ x + 4y \ge 12 \\ x \ge 0, y \ge 0 \end{cases}$

Minimum for
$C = 10{,}000x + 20{,}000y$

19. $\begin{cases} 6 \le x + y \le 13 \\ x \ge 3 \\ y \ge 1 \end{cases}$

Maximum for
$P = 4x + 3y$

Homework Video Tutor

Visit: PHSchool.com
Web Code: age-0304

20. Cooking Baking a tray of corn muffins takes 4 c milk and 3 c wheat flour. A tray of bran muffins takes 2 c milk and 3 c wheat flour. A baker has 16 c milk and 15 c wheat flour. He makes $3 profit per tray of corn muffins and $2 profit per tray of bran muffins. How many trays of each type of muffin should the baker make to maximize his profit? **3 trays of corn muffins and 2 trays of bran muffins**

 Challenge

21. A vertex of a feasible region does not always have whole-number coordinates. Sometimes you may need to round coordinates to find the solution. Using the objective function and the constraints at the right, find the whole-number values of x and y that minimize C. Then find C for those values of x and y. **See back of book.**

$C = 6x + 9y$
$\begin{cases} x + 2y \ge 50 \\ 2x + y \ge 60 \\ x \ge 0, y \ge 0 \end{cases}$

22. Open-Ended Write a system of constraints whose graphs determine a trapezoid. Write an objective function and evaluate it at each vertex. **Check students' work.**

PowerPoint
Lesson Quiz

1. Graph the system of constraints. Name all vertices of the feasible region. Then find the values of x and y that maximize and minimize the objective function $P = 2x + 7y + 4$.
$\begin{cases} -2 \le x \le 4 \\ -1 \le y \le 3 \\ y \ge -\frac{2}{3}x + \frac{5}{3} \end{cases}$

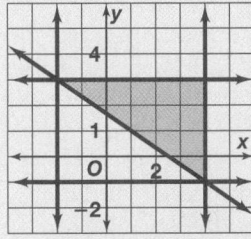

$(-2, 3), (4, 3), (4, -1)$;
maximum of 33 when $x = 4$ and $y = 3$, minimum of 5 when $x = 4$ and $y = -1$

2. If the constraint on y in the system for Question 1 is changed to $1 \le y \le 3$, how does the minimum value for the objective function change? **There is a new minimum value of 13 when $x = 1$ and $y = 1$.**

Alternative Assessment

Have students work in small groups. Each group should write and solve a real-world linear programming problem. Groups then exchange problems and solve. Groups should compare answers and resolve any differences.

143

pages 142–144   Exercises

26. **[2]** The boundary line through $R(0, 40)$ and $Q(10, 20)$ is $y = -2x + 40$, so the constraint is $y \geq -2x + 40$. The boundary line through $Q(10, 20)$ and $P(50, 0)$ is $y = -\frac{1}{2}x + 25$, so the constraint is $y \geq -\frac{1}{2}x + 25$.

[1] includes only one of the two parts of the answer above OR makes a minor error in calculation

27. **[4]**

The vertices are $(0, 0)$, $(2, 0)$, $(0, 3)$, and $(1, 2)$.

[3] incorrectly graphs equations, but interprets inequalities correctly

[2] answer of vertices only

[1] only 2 correct vertices with no work shown

28.
 $y < -2x + 8$

---

23. **Critical Thinking** Sometimes two corners of a graph both yield the maximum profit. In this case, many other points may also yield the maximum profit. Evaluate the profit formula $P = x + 2y$ for the graph shown. Find four points that yield the maximum profit. **Answers may vary. Sample: (4, 6), (6, 5), (9, 3.5), (10, 3)**

 Test Prep

Multiple Choice

24. Which point maximizes $N = 4x + 3y$ and lies within the feasible region of the constraints at the right? **C**
   A. $(0, 0)$ B. $(9, 0)$ C. $(3, 6)$ D. $(0, 9)$
$$\begin{cases} y \leq 9 \\ 2x + 2y \leq 18 \\ x \leq 3 \end{cases}$$

25. The vertices of a feasible region are $(0, 0)$, $(0, 2)$, $(5, 2)$, and $(4, 0)$. For which objective function is the maximum cost C found at the vertex $(4, 0)$? **H**
   F. $C = -2x + 3y$ G. $C = 2x + 7y$
   H. $C = 4x - 3y$ J. $C = 5x + 3y$

Short Response

26. The figure at the right shows the feasible region for a system of constraints. This system includes $x \geq 0$ and $y \geq 0$. Find the remaining constraint(s). **See margin.**

Extended Response

27. What are the vertices of the feasible region bounded by the constraints at the right? **See margin.**
$$\begin{cases} x + y \leq 3 \\ 2x + y \leq 4 \\ x \geq 0, y \geq 0 \end{cases}$$

 Mixed Review

Lesson 3-3

GO for Help

Solve each system of inequalities by graphing.

28. $\begin{cases} y < -2x + 8 \\ 3y \geq 4x - 6 \end{cases}$ **29.** $\begin{cases} x - 2y \geq 11 \\ 5x + 4y < 27 \end{cases}$ **30.** $\begin{cases} 2x + 6y > 12 \\ 3x + 9y \leq 27 \end{cases}$

31. $\begin{cases} 2y + x < 4 \\ y - 2x \geq 4 \end{cases}$ **32.** $\begin{cases} y + 5 \geq -2x \\ y - x \geq -2 \end{cases}$ **33.** $\begin{cases} 2y - 4x < 6 \\ 6x < 3y + 12 \end{cases}$

28–33. See margin pp. 144–145.

Lesson 2-4

34. Data Analysis Use the data below.

A Survey of Paperback Books: How Long and How Much?

Pages	326	450	246	427	208	339	367	445	404	465	378	265
Price ($)	7.50	7.99	6.99	7.99	6.99	7.95	7.50	7.95	7.95	7.99	7.99	6.99

a. Make a scatter plot of the data. **See back of book.**
b. What kind of correlation do you see? **positive**
c. Find a linear model. **c–d. See margin p. 145.**
d. What price would you predict for a paperback containing 100 pages?

Lesson 1-2

Evaluate each expression for $a = 3$ and $b = -5$.

35. $2a + b$ **1**   **36.** $a - b$ **8**   **37.** $-4 + 2ab$ **−34**   **38.** $a + \frac{3b}{a}$ **−2**

39. $3(a - b)$ **24**   **40.** $4a - 2 + 3b$ **−5**   **41.** $\frac{a - b}{2a}$ **$\frac{4}{3}$**   **42.** $b(2b - a)$ **65**

29.

30.

31.

Linear Programming

You can solve linear programming problems with your graphing calculator.

Go Online
PHSchool.com
For: Graphing calculator procedures
Web Code: age-2109

ACTIVITY

Find the values of x and y that will maximize the objective function $P = 13x + 2y$ for the constraints at the right. What is the value of P at this maximum point?

$$\begin{cases} -3x + 2y \le 8 \\ -8x + y \ge -48 \\ x \ge 0, \ y \ge 0 \end{cases}$$

Step 1 Rewrite the first two inequalities to isolate y. Enter the inequalities.

Step 2 Graph, using the window $0 \le x \le 12$, $0 \le y \le 20$.

Step 3 Use the value option of **CALC** to find the upper left vertex. Press 0 ENTER.

Step 4 Enter the expression for the objective function on the home screen. Press ENTER for the value of P at the vertex.

Step 5 Use the intersect option of **CALC** to find the upper right vertex. Go to the home screen and press ENTER for the value of P.

Step 6 Use the zero option of **CALC** to find the lower right vertex. Go to the home screen and press ENTER for the value of P.

Compare the values of P for the coordinates of the three vertices you found. The objective function has a value of 0 for the vertex located at the origin. The maximum value 136 occurs when $x = 8$ and $y = 16$.

EXERCISES

Find the values of x and y that maximize or minimize the objective function.

1. $\begin{cases} 4x + 3y \ge 30 \\ x + 3y \ge 21 \\ x \ge 0, y \ge 0 \end{cases}$
3, 6; $C = 63$
Minimum for
$C = 5x + 8y$

2. $\begin{cases} 3x + 5y \le 35 \\ 2x + y \le 14 \\ x \ge 0, y \ge 0 \end{cases}$
5, 4; $P = 23$
Maximum for
$P = 3x + 2y$

3. $\begin{cases} x + y \ge 8 \\ x + 5y \ge 20 \\ x \ge 0, y \ge 2 \end{cases}$
5, 3; $C = 27$
Minimum for
$C = 3x + 4y$

4. $\begin{cases} x + 2y \le 24 \\ 3x + 2y \le 34 \\ 3x + y \le 29 \\ x \ge 0 \end{cases}$
5, 9.5; $P = 38.5$
Maximum for
$P = 2x + 3y$

32.

33.

Linear Programming

Students use various **CALC** functions to find the minimum or maximum values of objective functions in linear programming problems.

Guided Instruction

Technology Tip

It is important that students include the parentheses around (3/2)X when entering the first inequality. Also, remind students that they must select whether the graph is shaded above or below the line by changing the symbol in front of each equation in the Y= list. For inequalities that are > or ≥, the shading is above the line. For inequalities that are < or ≤, the shading is below the line.

Auditory Learners

Place students in pairs to complete the activity. Have one student read the steps aloud while the other enters the information into the calculator.

Resources

Students may use any graphing calculator to explore solving linear programming problems.

34c. $y = 0.0046x + 5.98$, where x = number of pages, y = price in dollars

d. **Answers may vary. Sample: using the equation from part (d), $6.44**

Graphs in Three Dimensions

3-5

1. Plan

Objectives
1 To graph points in three dimensions
2 To graph equations in three dimensions

Examples
1 Graphing in Coordinate Space
2 Real-World Connection
3 Sketching a Plane

Math Background

Since space is three-dimensional, a three-dimensional coordinate system describes positions in space. The points in this system have three coordinates, usually *x, y,* and *z*. To locate a point in a three-dimensional coordinate system, you start at the origin and first move forward or backward, then right or left, and finally up or down.

More Math Background: p. 116D

Lesson Planning and Resources

See p. 116E for a list of the resources that support this lesson.

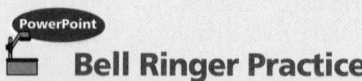

Bell Ringer Practice

✓ Check Skills You'll Need
For intervention, direct students to:
Linear Equations
Lesson 2-2: Examples 1, 2
Extra Skills and Word Problems Practice, Ch. 2

What You'll Learn
• To graph points in three dimensions
• To graph equations in three dimensions

. . . And Why
To locate points on a virtual bicycle helmet, as in Example 2

✓ Check Skills You'll Need

for Help Lesson 2-2

Find the *x*- and *y*-intercepts of the graph of each linear equation.

1. $y = 2x + 6$ *x:* −3, *y:* 6   **2.** $2x + 9y = 36$ *x:* 18, *y:* 4

3. $3x − 8y = −24$ *x:* −8, *y:* 3   **4.** $4x − 5y = 40$ *x:* 10, *y:* −8

Graph each linear equation.   5–8. See back of book.

5. $y = 3x$ **6.** $y = −2x + 4$

7. $4y = 3x − 8$ **8.** $−3x − 2y = 7$

 New Vocabulary   • coordinate space   • ordered triples   • trace

---

1 Graphing Points in Three Dimensions

Suppose you want to describe how to get from point *A* to point *B* along the grid shown at the right. You could say "Move down one unit, forward two units, and left three units," or "Move left three units, forward two units, and down one unit."

To describe positions in space, you need a three-dimensional coordinate system.

You have learned to graph on an *xy*-coordinate plane using ordered pairs. Adding a third axis, the *z*-axis, to the *xy*-coordinate plane creates **coordinate space.** In coordinate space you graph points using **ordered triples** of the form (x, y, z).

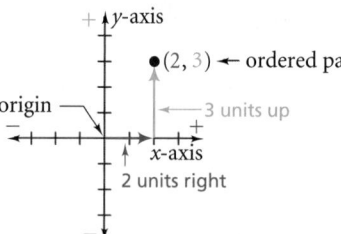

Points in a Plane

Points in Space

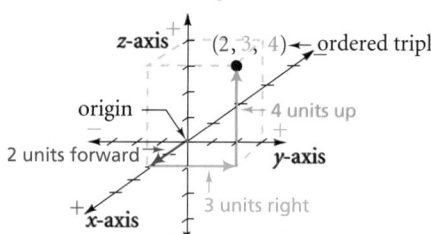

A two-dimensional coordinate system allows you to graph points in a plane.

A three-dimensional coordinate system allows you to graph points in space.

In the coordinate plane, point $(2, 3)$ is two units right and three units up from the origin. In coordinate space, point $(2, 3, 4)$ is two units forward, three units right, and four units up.

Real-World 🌐 Connection

The global positioning system locates persons or objects in three dimensions.

Differentiated Instruction   **Solutions for All Learners**

Special Needs L1
Make rectangular prisms from small boxes by dividing each face into a square grid as shown in the text. Have students label points *A* and *B* on different faces and illustrate with colors how to move along the grid to get from one point to the other.
learning style: tactile

Below Level L2
To assist students in visualizing graphs in three dimensions, set up a coordinate system in your classroom. Use tape and string to represent graphs.
learning style: visual

1 EXAMPLE Graphing in Coordinate Space

Graph each point in coordinate space.

a. $(0, 3, -2)$
Sketch the axes. From the origin, move right 3 units and down 2 units.

b. $(-2, -1, 3)$
Sketch the axes. From the origin, move back 2 units, left 1 unit, and up 3 units.

✓ **Quick Check** Graph each point in coordinate space. **a–d. See back of book.**
a. $(0, -4, -2)$ **b.** $(-1, 1, 3)$ **c.** $(3, -5, 2)$ **d.** $(3, 3, -3)$

2 EXAMPLE Real-World 🌐 Connection

Product Design Computers are used to design three-dimensional objects. Programs allow the designer to view the object from different perspectives. Find coordinates for points A, B, and C in the diagram below.

$A(0, 0, 0)$, $B(4, 0, 0)$, $C(3, -2, 1)$

✓ **Quick Check** ② **a.** Find coordinates for point D in the diagram. **(0, 5, 0)**
b. Does the point $(-3, 2, 4)$ lie inside or outside the helmet? Explain.
outside the helmet, since the helmet is curved

Lesson 3-5 Graphs in Three Dimensions   **147**

2. Teach

Guided Instruction

1 EXAMPLE Connection to Geometry

Ask students to name three dimensions used to describe a prism. **length, width, and height**

2 EXAMPLE Careers

Product designers' diagrams have the viewer situated in the part of space where all three coordinates are positive. Ask students why it is important for a designer to be able to view an object from several different perspectives.

PowerPoint

Additional Examples

① Graph each point in coordinate space.
a. $(-3, 3, -4)$ **b.** $(-3, -4, 2)$
See back of book.

② In the diagram, the origin is at the center of a cube that has edges 6 units long. The x-, y-, and z-axes are perpendicular to the faces of the cube. Give the coordinates of the corners of the cube.

$A(-3, -3, 3)$, $B(-3, 3, 3)$, $C(3, 3, 3)$, $D(3, -3, 3)$, $E(3, -3, -3)$, $F(3, 3, -3)$, $G(-3, 3, -3)$, $H(-3, -3, -3)$

Advanced Learners L4
Have students research how computer graphics imaging works and share their findings with the class.

learning style: verbal

English Language Learners ELL
Have students look up the word *trace* in a dictionary. Have them compare the English meanings to the mathematical definition, a line formed by the intersection of a plane with the xy-plane, the yz-plane, or the zx-plane.

learning style: verbal

147

3 EXAMPLE Math Tip

Stress similarities with the corresponding concepts for two dimensions. In two dimensions, the intercepts of a line are the points where the line intersects the *x*- and *y*-axes. In three dimensions, the intercepts of a plane are the points where the plane intersects the *x*-, *y*-, and *z*-axes. The traces associated with a linear equation $Ax + By + Cz = D$ are the lines that are the intersections of the graph of the equation with the *xy*-, *xz*-, and *yz*-planes.

Additional Examples

3 Sketch the graph of $-3x - 2y + z = 6$.

Resources
• Daily Notetaking Guide 3-5 **L3**

Closure

Describe how you would locate the point $(-2, 4, -3)$ in a three-dimensional coordinate system. Start at the origin. Move 2 units in the negative direction along the *x*-axis. Then move parallel to the *y*-axis 4 units in the positive direction. Then move parallel to the *z*-axis 3 units in the negative direction.

page 148   Quick Check

3a.

148

The graph of an equation is a picture of all the solutions to the equation. In two dimensions, the graph of $3x - 2y = 6$ is a line. In three dimensions, the graph of $3x - 2y + z = 6$ is a plane, as shown at the right.

Vocabulary Tip

The *x-intercept* of a line or plane is the point of intersection with the *x*-axis.

If the graph of a plane intersects one of the coordinate planes in a line, then the line is called a **trace**. For example, the *xy*-trace is the line in the *xy*-plane that contains the *x*- and the *y*-intercepts. The *xz*-trace and the *yz*-trace are defined similarly.

To sketch a plane, find the *x*-, *y*-, and *z*- intercepts. Then draw the traces and show the plane with shading.

3 EXAMPLE Sketching a Plane

Sketch the graph of $2x + 3y + 4z = 12$.

Step 1 Find the intercepts.

$$2x + 3y + 4z = 12$$
$$2x + 3(0) + 4(0) = 12 \quad \text{To find the } x\text{-intercept, substitute 0 for } y \text{ and } z.$$
$$2x = 12$$
$$x = 6 \quad \text{The } x\text{-intercept is 6.}$$
$$2(0) + 3y + 4(0) = 12 \quad \text{To find the } y\text{-intercept, substitute 0 for } x \text{ and } z.$$
$$3y = 12$$
$$y = 4 \quad \text{The } y\text{-intercept is 4.}$$
$$2(0) + 3(0) + 4z = 12 \quad \text{To find the } z\text{-intercept, substitute 0 for } x \text{ and } y.$$
$$4z = 12$$
$$z = 3 \quad \text{The } z\text{-intercept is 3.}$$

Step 2 Graph the intercepts.   **Step 3** Draw the traces. Shade the plane.

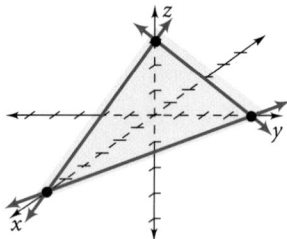

Each point on the plane represents a solution to $2x + 3y + 4z = 12$.

✓ **Quick Check** **3** Sketch the graph of each equation.
   a. $x + y + z = 5$ **b.** $2x - y + 3z = 6$ **c.** $x + 2y - z = -4$
   a–c. See margin.

b.

c.

pages 149–151   Exercises

1. 1 unit back, 5 units right

2. 3 units forward, 3 units left, four units up

EXERCISES

For more exercises, see *Extra Skill and Word Problem Practice.*

Practice and Problem Solving

A Practice by Example

Example 1
(page 147)

Describe the location of each point in coordinate space. 1–7. See margin.

1. $(-1, 5, 0)$ **2.** $(3, -3, 4)$

3. $(2, 0, 5)$ **4.** $(-4, -7, -1)$

Graph each point in coordinate space.

5. $(5, 0, -2)$ **6.** $(0, 0, 4)$

7. $(10, -2, -5)$ **8.** $(-1, -1, -1)$

9. $(-4, -5, 3)$ **10.** $(25, 40, -30)$

11. $(1, 1, 0)$ **12.** $(0, -2, 2)$

8–12. See back of book.

Example 2
(page 147)

Find the coordinates of each point in the diagram.

13. A **(0, 0, 0)**

14. B **(0, 0, 50)**

15. C **(0, 40, 0)**

16. D **(60, 0, 50)**

17. E **(0, 80, 100)**

18. F **(60, 30, 100)**

Example 3
(page 148)

Sketch the graph of each equation. 19–24. See back of book.

19. $x + y + 2z = 4$ **20.** $x + y + z = 2$ **21.** $2x + 6y + z = 6$

22. $x - y - 4z = 8$ **23.** $-x + 3y + z = 6$ **24.** $2x - y - 5z = 10$

B Apply Your Skills

25. Writing While visiting friends in New York, you go to a concert. Explain how the seat information on your ticket at the right represents a point in three-dimensional coordinate space. **See back of book.**

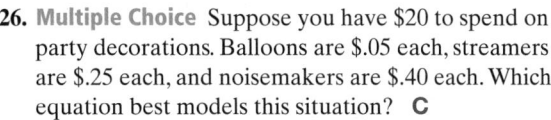

26. Multiple Choice Suppose you have $20 to spend on party decorations. Balloons are $.05 each, streamers are $.25 each, and noisemakers are $.40 each. Which equation best models this situation? **C**

Ⓐ $5b + 25s + 40n = 20$

Ⓑ $20(b + s + n) = 0.05 + 0.25 + 0.4$

Ⓒ $0.05b + 0.25s + 0.4n = 20$

Ⓓ $0.05b + 0.25s + 0.4n + 20 = 0$

Sketch the graph of each equation. 27–36. See back of book.

27. $7x + 14y - z = 7$ **28.** $-3x + 5y + 10z = 15$

29. $32x + 16y - 8z = 32$ **30.** $-25x + 30y + 50z = 75$

31. $50x + 25y + 100z = 200$ **32.** $14x - 8y + 28z = 28$

Homework Video Tutor
Visit: PHSchool.com
Web Code: age-0305

Sketch the graph of each equation and find the equation of each trace.

GPS **33.** $6x + 6y - 12z = 36$ **34.** $-20x + 10y + 50z = 100$

35. $-12x - 32y - 48z = 96$ **36.** $25x + 125y - 25z = 125$

Online lesson quiz, PHSchool.com, Web Code: aga-0305

Lesson 3-5 Graphs in Three Dimensions   **149**

Assignment Guide

⚊① **A B** 1-18, 25, 37-46

⚊② **A B** 19-24, 26-36, 47

C Challenge   48-52

Test Prep   53-57
Mixed Review   58-62

Homework Quick Check

To check students' understanding of key skills and concepts, go over Exercises 19, 25, 28, 31, 45.

Error Prevention!

Exercises 5–12 Urge students to be careful to refer to the appropriate axis for each coordinate. Diagrams for three-dimensional coordinate systems do not show the *x*- and *y*-axes in the positions to which students have grown accustomed from their work in two dimensions.

Differentiated Instruction Resources

GPS Guided Problem Solving	**L3**
Enrichment	**L4**
Reteaching	**L2**
Practice	**L3**

3. 2 units forward, 5 units up

4. 4 units back, 7 units left, 1 unit down

5.

6.

7.

149

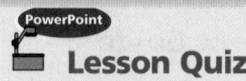

4. Assess & Reteach

PowerPoint

Lesson Quiz

Graph each point in coordinate space.

1. $(2, -3, 5)$ **2.** $(0, 4, -2)$

3. Graph $2x + 4y - 4z = 12$.

Alternative Assessment

Place a transparency with a three-dimensional coordinate grid on the overhead. Draw a point on the grid and have students describe the location using ordered triples. Repeat a few times. Draw traces representing a plane. Instruct students to find an equation that the plane can represent.

Test Prep

📁 **Resources**
For additional practice with a variety of test item formats:
- Standardized Test Prep, p. 165
- Test-Taking Strategies, p. 160
- Test-Taking Strategies with Transparencies

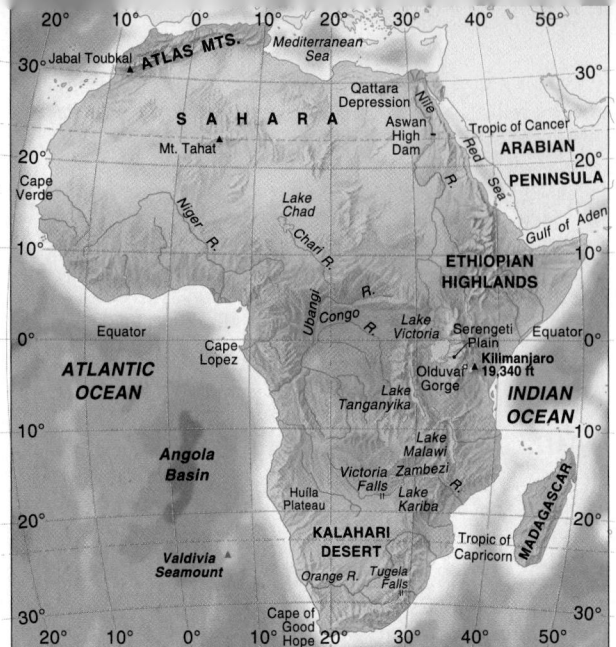

🌐 **Geography** Use the map to identify the geographic feature found at each location.

37. latitude 3° S
longitude 37° E
elevation 19,340 ft
Mt. Kilimanjaro

38. latitude 23° N
longitude 5° E
elevation 9,573 ft
Mt. Tahat

39. latitude 25° S
longitude 6° E
elevation −3,072 ft
Valdivia Seamount

40. latitude 15° N
longitude 18° W
elevation 0 ft
Cape Verde

41. latitude 30° N
longitude 27° E
elevation −440 ft
Qattara Depression

42. latitude 13° N
longitude 14° E
elevation 919 ft
Lake Chad

43. latitude 31° N
longitude 8° W
elevation 49,212 ft
Jabal Toubkal

44. latitude 18° S
longitude 25° E
elevation 2,927 ft
Victoria Falls

45. latitude 22° N
longitude 31° E
elevation 600 ft
Aswan High Dam

46. latitude 1° S
longitude 33° E
elevation 3,720 ft
Lake Victoria

47. Error Analysis A student claims to find the x-intercept of a plane by substituting 0 for x in the equation of the plane. Explain the student's error. **See margin.**

Ⓒ **Challenge** 🎲 **48. a. Geometry** Use the Pythagorean Theorem to find the distance between $(1, 2, 4)$ and $(3, -2, 7)$. (*Hint:* Recall the Distance Formula.) $\sqrt{29}$
b. Make a Conjecture Make a conjecture about how to find the coordinates of the midpoint of a segment in coordinate space. **See margin.**

49. a. Critical Thinking Does every plane have three traces? Explain.
b. Must any two traces of a plane intersect? Explain. **a–b. See margin p. 151.**

Graph each equation in three-dimensional coordinate space.

50. $x = 3$ **51.** $2x + 3y = 6$ **52.** $y = 0$
50–52. See back of book.

Test Prep

Multiple Choice

53. Which point is NOT on the graph of $2x + 3y - z - 12 = 0$? **D**
A. $(6, 0, 0)$ **B.** $(3, 3, 3)$ **C.** $(0, 4, 0)$ **D.** $(1, 1, 7)$

54. Which point is NOT on the plane with equation $-2x - 3y + 5z = 7$? **G**
F. $(1, 2, 3)$ **G.** $(-2, -3, 5)$ **H.** $(-2, 4, 3)$ **J.** $(-4, 2, 1)$

55. What are the intercepts of $-3x + 5y - 2z = 60$? **B**
A. $x = -180, y = 300, z = -120$ **B.** $x = -20, y = 12, z = -30$
C. $x = -3, y = 5, z = -2$ **D.** $x = -60, y = 60, z = -60$

56. What is the xy-trace of $2x - 4y + z = 8$? **G**
F. $-4y + z = 8$ **G.** $x - 2y = 4$ **H.** $2x + z = 8$ **J.** $z = 8$

Short Response

57. What is the intersection of the xz-traces for the two planes $2x - 3y - 4z = -4$ and $x + 3y + z = 7$?
Explain each step of your answer. **See margin p. 151.**

150 Chapter 3 Linear Systems

---

pages 149–150 Exercises

47. The student is actually finding the equation of the y–z–trace. If the student wants the x-intercept, the student should substitute 0 for both y and z in the equation of the plane.

48b. $\left(\dfrac{x_1 + x_2}{2}, \dfrac{y_1 + y_2}{2}, \dfrac{z_1 + z_2}{2} \right)$

150

Lesson 3-4

58. Maximize the objective function $P = x + 3y$ under the given constraints. At what vertex does this maximum value occur?
P = 12 for (0, 4)

$$\begin{cases} x + y \le 5 \\ x + 2y \le 8 \\ x \ge 0, y \ge 0 \end{cases}$$

Lesson 2-7

Graph each inequality. 59–61. See back of book.

59. $y \le x - 3$ **60.** $3y - x > -4$ **61.** $2x - y \ge 0$

Lesson 1-6

62. Probability Your town has a drawing for 50 summer jobs. Including you, 150 students apply.
a. What is the probability that you will get one of the jobs? $\frac{1}{3}$
b. You and a friend apply. What is the probability that you both get jobs?
       about 0.11

Checkpoint Quiz 2   Lessons 3-4 through 3-5

1. Find the values of x and y that minimize the objective function $C = 2x + 3y$ for the constraints at the right.
C = 25 for (5, 5)

$$\begin{cases} y \ge x \\ x + y \le 32 \\ x \ge 5, y \ge 3 \end{cases}$$

2. Agriculture A farmer has at most 400 acres and $45,000 available to grow corn and soybeans. Use the cost and profit information at the right to decide how many acres of each crop will maximize profit.
300 acres corn and 100 acres soybeans

Cost and Profit for Corn and Soybeans

	Corn	Soybeans
Number of Acres	x	y
Cost	$100x$	$150y$
Profit	$60x$	$75y$

Graph each equation. Use traces and intercepts. 3–5. See margin.

3. $3x + 2y + z = 6$ **4.** $x - y + z = 4$ **5.** $4x + y + z = 8$

Algebra at Work

·············· Radiologist

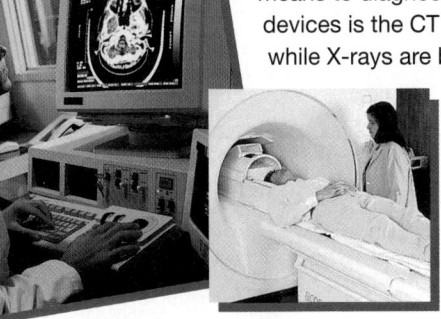

Radiologists are medical doctors who use X-rays, sound waves, and other means to diagnose diseases. Among the radiologist's most powerful diagnostic devices is the CT (computerized tomography) scan. The patient lies on a table while X-rays are beamed through the patient's body from different angles. Images are recorded and fed into a computer. The computer uses a three-dimensional coordinate system to record information and then to produce images of a cross section of the patient's body.

Go Online
PHSchool.com   **For:** Information about radiology   **Web Code:** agb-2031

49a. No, a plane that is parallel to two of the axes (and is therefore perpendicular to the third axis) has only two traces, which are perpendicular.

b. No, a plane that intersects two of the axes and is parallel to the third axis has three traces, two of which are parallel.

Use this Checkpoint Quiz to check students' understanding of the skills and concepts of Lessons 3-4 through 3-5.

Resources
Grab & Go
• Checkpoint Quiz 2

57. [2] For the two *xz*–traces, let $y = 0$ in each of the equations, which become
$2x - 4z = -4$
$x + z = 7$
One way to solve the system is by elimination:
$2x - 4z = -4$
$4x + 4z = 28$
$6x = 24$
$x = 4$
$z = 3$
Since $y = 0$, the point is (4, 0, 3).
[1] answer only, with no explanation

page 151   Checkpoint Quiz 2

3.

4.

5.

Systems With Three Variables

1. Plan

Objectives
1 To solve systems in three variables by elimination
2 To solve systems in three variables by substitution

Examples
1 Solving by Elimination
2 Solving an Equivalent System
3 Solving by Substitution
4 Real-World Connection

Math Background

Both the elimination method and the substitution method are used to solve systems of three equations in three variables. There is either no solution, one solution, or infinitely many solutions. Numbering the equations helps to avoid confusion.

More Math Background: p. 116D

Lesson Planning and Resources

See p. 116E for a list of the resources that support this lesson.

Bell Ringer Practice

✓ **Check Skills You'll Need**
For intervention, direct students to:

Solving Equations
Lesson 1-3: Example 2
Extra Skills and Word
  Problems Practice, Ch. 1

Graphing Systems of Equations
Lesson 3-1: Example 1
Extra Skills and Word
  Problems Practice, Ch. 3

Solving Systems Algebraically
Lesson 3-2: Examples 1, 3–5
Extra Skills and Word
  Problems Practice, Ch. 3

What You'll Learn

• To solve systems in three variables by elimination
• To solve systems in three variables by substitution

. . . And Why

To choose an investment strategy, as in Example 4

✓ **Check Skills You'll Need**

GO for **Help** Lessons 3-1 and 3-2

Solve each system.

1. $\begin{cases} 2x - y = 11 \\ x + 2y = -7 \end{cases}$ (3, −5)   2. $\begin{cases} -x + 6y = 8 \\ 2x - 12y = -14 \end{cases}$ no solution   3. $\begin{cases} 3x + 2y = -5 \\ 4x + 3y = -8 \end{cases}$ (1, −4)

Let $y = 4x - 2$. Solve each equation for x.

4. $3x + y = 5$ **1**   5. $x - 2y = -3$ **1**   6. $4x + 3y = 2$ **$\frac{1}{2}$**

Determine whether the given ordered pair is a solution of each equation in the system.

7. $(1, 3)$ $\begin{cases} 2x + 5y = 17 \\ -4x + 3y = 5 \end{cases}$ **yes**   8. $(-4, 2)$ $\begin{cases} x + 2y = 0 \\ 3x - 2y = -16 \end{cases}$ **yes**

---

1 Solving Three-Variable Systems by Elimination

You can represent systems of equations in three variables as graphs in three dimensions. As you learned in Lesson 3-5, the graph of any equation of the form $Ax + By + Cz = D$, where A, B, and C are not all zero, is a plane. The solutions of a three-variable system can be shown graphically as the intersections of planes.

GO for **Help**

To review solving systems in two variables by graphing, go to Lesson 3-1.

No solution
No point lies in all three planes.

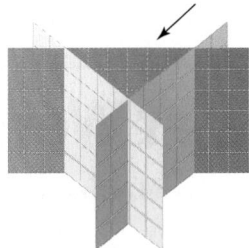

One solution
The planes intersect at one common point.

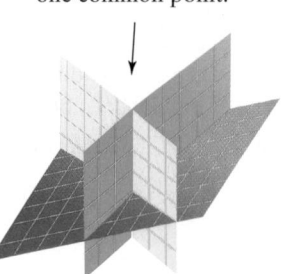

An infinite number of solutions
The planes intersect at all the points along a common line.

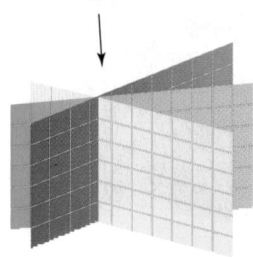

152   Chapter 3   Linear Systems

Differentiated Instruction Solutions for All Learners

Special Needs L1
Have students highlight each equation with a different color. Alternatively, students can circle the terms of one variable that are additive inverses, and put a square around the terms of another variable that are additive inverses.

learning style: visual

Below Level L2
When subtracting equations that contain negative coefficients, suggest that students multiply one equation by −1, and then add the equations.

learning style: verbal

When the solution of a system of equations in three variables is represented by one point, you can write it as an ordered triple (x, y, z).

You can solve a system of three equations in three variables by working with the equations in pairs. You will use one of the equations *twice*.

1 EXAMPLE Solving by Elimination

Solve the system by elimination. The equations are numbered to make the procedure easy to follow.

$$① \begin{cases} x - 3y + 3z = -4 \\ ② 2x + 3y - z = 15 \\ ③ 4x - 3y - z = 19 \end{cases}$$

Step 1 Pair the equations to eliminate y because the y terms are already additive inverses.

$$① \begin{cases} x - 3y + 3z = -4 \\ ② 2x + 3y - z = 15 \end{cases} \text{Add.}$$
$$④ 3x + 2z = 11$$

$$② \begin{cases} 2x + 3y - z = 15 \\ ③ 4x - 3y - z = 19 \end{cases}$$
$$⑤ 6x - 2z = 34$$

Step 2 Write the two new equations as a system. Solve for x and z.

$$④ \begin{cases} 3x + 2z = 11 \\ ⑤ 6x - 2z = 34 \end{cases}$$
$$9x = 45$$
$$x = 5$$

$$④ 3x + 2z = 11$$
$$3(5) + 2z = 11 \quad \text{Substitute the value of } x.$$
$$2z = -4$$
$$z = -2$$

Step 3 Substitute the values for x and z into one of the original equations ($①, ②,$ or $③$) and solve for y.

$$① x - 3y + 3z = -4$$
$$5 - 3y + 3(-2) = -4$$
$$5 - 3y - 6 = -4$$
$$-3y = -3$$
$$y = 1$$

The solution of the system is $(5, 1, -2)$.

Check Show that $(5, 1, -2)$ makes each equation true.

$$x - 3y + 3z = -4 \qquad 2x + 3y - z = 15 \qquad 4x - 3y - z = 19$$
$$5 - 3(1) + 3(-2) \overset{?}{=} -4 \quad 2(5) + 3(1) - (-2) \overset{?}{=} 15 \quad 4(5) - 3(1) - (-2) \overset{?}{=} 19$$
$$5 - 3 - 6 \overset{?}{=} -4 \qquad 10 + 3 + 2 \overset{?}{=} 15 \qquad 20 - 3 + 2 \overset{?}{=} 19$$
$$-4 = -4 ✓ \qquad\qquad 15 = 15 ✓ \qquad\qquad 19 = 19 ✓$$

✓ **Quick Check** 1 Solve each system by elimination. Check your answers.

a. $\begin{cases} 2x + y - z = 5 \\ 3x - y + 2z = -1 \\ x - y - z = 0 \end{cases}$ **(1, 2, −1)**

b. $\begin{cases} 2x - y + z = 4 \\ x + 3y - z = 11 \\ 4x + y - z = 14 \end{cases}$ **(3, 3, 1)**

c. **Critical Thinking** Suppose, in a three-variable system, the coefficient of one of the variables in one of the equations is zero. When pairing the equations to solve the system, would you use that equation twice? Explain.
No; you wouldn't need to use any of the original equations twice.

You can apply the method in Example 1 to any system of three equations in three variables. You may need to multiply one or more of the equations by a nonzero number to form an equivalent system.

Real-World 🌐 Connection

You can use a system in three variables to model the amounts of vitamin C, potassium, and beta carotene in this three-fruit salad.

Guided Instruction

1 EXAMPLE Teaching Tip

For Quick Check 1a and 1b, remind students to check their ordered triples by substituting them into *each* equation in the system.

PowerPoint
Additional Examples

1 Solve the system by elimination.
$$\begin{cases} -5x + 3y + 2z = 11 \\ 8x - 5y + 2z = -55 \\ 4x - 7y - 2z = -29 \end{cases}$$
$(-2, 5, -7)$

Lesson 3-6 Systems With Three Variables **153**

Advanced Learners L4
Challenge students to create and solve a system of four equations in four variables. Assure students that they will learn a simpler method in Chapter 4.

learning style: verbal

English Language Learners ELL
Review the geometric terms *point, line,* and *plane* and guide students in recognizing how they are related to the solutions of three-variable systems.

learning style: verbal

If some students are already familiar with using matrices on graphing calculators to solve equations, they may prefer this method. First students write a matrix that contains the coefficients of the system of equations. To enter the matrix, press **MATRX** ▷ ▷ ENTER 3 ENTER 3 ENTER . Then enter the coefficients. Each row of the matrix represents one equation.

$$A = \begin{bmatrix} 2 & 1 & -1 \\ 1 & 4 & 2 \\ 15 & 6 & -2 \end{bmatrix}$$

Press **QUIT**. Now, write a matrix that contains the constants and enter this as matrix **[B]**. Be sure to press 2 for matrix **[B]** before entering the dimensions.

$$B = \begin{bmatrix} 5 \\ 16 \\ 12 \end{bmatrix}$$

Press **QUIT** again. Tell students that they are going to use the inverse of the coefficient matrix. This is explained in detail in Chapter 4. Now press **MATRX 1** ⁻¹ **MATRX 2** ENTER . The solution is $(-2, 6, -3)$.

Additional Examples

2 Solve the system by elimination.
$$\begin{cases} x + 2y + 5z = 1 \\ -3x + 3y + 7z = 4 \\ -8x + 5y + 12z = 11 \end{cases}$$
$(-1, -9, 4)$

---

2 EXAMPLE   Solving an Equivalent System

Solve the system by elimination.
$$\begin{array}{l} ① \\ ② \\ ③ \end{array} \begin{cases} 2x + y - z = 5 \\ x + 4y + 2z = 16 \\ 15x + 6y - 2z = 12 \end{cases}$$

Step 1 Pair the equations to eliminate z.

$$\begin{array}{l} ① \\ ② \end{array} \begin{cases} 2x + y - z = 5 \\ x + 4y + 2z = 16 \end{cases} \qquad \begin{array}{rl} 4x + 2y - 2z = 10 & \textbf{Multiply by 2.} \\ \underline{x + 4y + 2z = 16} & \\ ④\ 5x + 6y \qquad\quad = 26 & \end{array}$$

$$\begin{array}{l} ② \\ ③ \\ ⑤ \end{array} \begin{array}{l} x + 4y + 2z = 16 \\ \underline{15x + 6y - 2z = 12} \\ 16x + 10y \qquad = 28 \end{array}$$

Step 2 Write the two new equations as a system. Solve for x and y.

$$\begin{array}{l} ④ \\ ⑤ \end{array} \begin{cases} 5x + 6y = 26 \\ 16x + 10y = 28 \end{cases} \qquad \begin{array}{rl} 25x + 30y = 130 & \textbf{Multiply by 5.} \\ \underline{-48x - 30y = -84} & \textbf{Multiply by -3.} \\ -23x \qquad = 46 & \\ x = -2 & \end{array}$$

$$\begin{array}{l} ④ \qquad 5x + 6y = 26 \\ \qquad\quad 5(-2) + 6y = 26 \quad \textbf{Substitute the value of } x. \\ \qquad\qquad\qquad\quad y = 6 \end{array}$$

Step 3 Substitute the values for x and y into one of the original equations (①, ②, or ③). Solve for z.

$$\begin{array}{l} ① \qquad 2x + y - z = 5 \\ \qquad 2(-2) + 6 - z = 5 \\ \qquad\qquad\qquad z = -3 \end{array}$$

● The solution of the system is $(-2, 6, -3)$.

✓ **Quick Check** **2** Solve the system by elimination. Check your answers.
$$\begin{cases} x + 4y - 5z = -7 \\ 3x + 2y + 3z = 7 \\ 2x + y + 5z = 8 \end{cases}$$

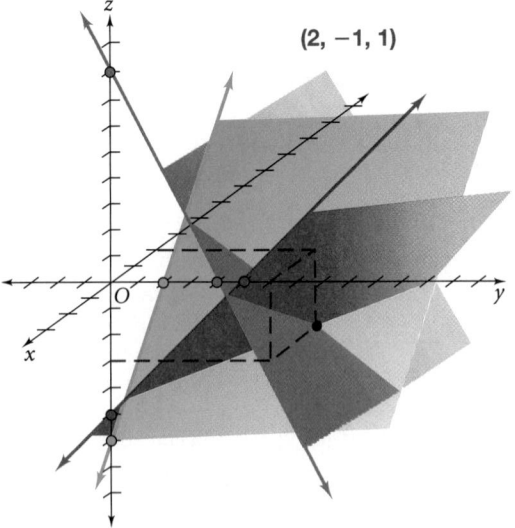
$(2, -1, 1)$

The graph illustrates the solution to Example 2. Each equation in the system represents a tilted plane. The graph of ① is red, the graph of ② is blue, and the graph of ③ is green. The three planes intersect at $(-2, 6, -3)$.

You can also use the substitution method to solve a system of three equations. Substitution is the best method to use when one of the equations can be solved easily for one variable.

3 EXAMPLE Solving by Substitution

GO for Help

To review the substitution method, go to Lesson 3-2.

Solve the system by substitution.

$$\begin{cases} ① & x - 2y + z = -4 \\ ② & -4x + y - 2z = 1 \\ ③ & 2x + 2y - z = 10 \end{cases}$$

Step 1 Choose one equation to solve for one of its variables.

① $x - 2y + z = -4$ **Solve the first equation for x.**

$x - 2y = -z - 4$

$x = 2y - z - 4$

Step 2 Substitute the expression for x into each of the other two equations.

② $-4x + y - 2z = 1$	③ $2x + 2y - z = 10$
$-4(2y - z - 4) + y - 2z = 1$ **Simplify.**	$2(2y - z - 4) + 2y - z = 10$
$-8y + 4z + 16 + y - 2z = 1$	$4y - 2z - 8 + 2y - z = 10$
$-7y + 2z + 16 = 1$	$6y - 3z - 8 = 10$
④ $-7y + 2z = -15$	⑤ $6y - 3z = 18$

Step 3 Write the two new equations as a system. Solve for y and z.

$$\begin{cases} ④ & -7y + 2z = -15 \\ ⑤ & 6y - 3z = 18 \end{cases}$$

$\begin{aligned} -21y + 6z &= -45 \quad \textbf{Multiply by 3.} \\ \underline{12y - 6z} &= \underline{36} \quad \textbf{Multiply by 2.} \\ -9y &= -9 \\ y &= 1 \end{aligned}$

④ $-7y + 2z = -15$

$-7(1) + 2z = -15$ **Substitute the value of y.**

$-7 + 2z = -15$

$2z = -8$

$z = -4$

Step 4 Substitute the values for y and z into one of the original equations (①, ②, or ③). Solve for x.

① $x - 2y + z = -4$

$x - 2(1) + (-4) = -4$

$x - 2 - 4 = -4$

$x - 6 = -4$

$x = 2$

The solution of the system is $(2, 1, -4)$.

✓ Quick Check ③ Solve each system by substitution. Check your answers.

a. $\begin{cases} x - 3y + z = 6 \\ 2x - 5y - z = -2 \\ -x + y + 2z = 7 \end{cases}$ **(4, 1, 5)**

b. $\begin{cases} 3x + 2y - z = 12 \\ -4x + y - 2z = 4 \\ x - 3y + z = -4 \end{cases}$ **(2, 0, -6)**

3 EXAMPLE Teaching Tip

Have students observe that in Step 1, it would also be easy to solve for y (using equation 2) or for z (using equation 3). The amount of work required for solving the system is about the same no matter which variable is used as the basis for the substitution. Use this example to reinforce the idea that there may be a variety of approaches for solving a system. Ask students if they see another approach for this system. If necessary, point out that an efficient approach would be to add equations 1 and 3. Ask students how they would proceed from that point on.

Additional Examples

3 Solve the system by substitution.

$$\begin{cases} 12x + 7y + 5z = 16 \\ -2x + y - 14z = -9 \\ -3x - 2y + 9z = -12 \end{cases}$$

$(7, -9, -1)$

Investment Options

Growth 10%

Income 7%

Money Market 5%

Fund | Percent Return Rate

0 2 4 6 8 10 12

④ EXAMPLE Real-World ⊕ Connection

Money Management Suppose you have saved $3200 from a part-time job and you want to invest your savings in a growth fund, an income fund, and a money market fund. Refer to the graph. To maximize your return, you decide to put twice as much money in the growth fund as in the money market fund. How should you invest the $3200 to get a return of $250 in one year?

Relate   growth fund + income fund + money market fund = 3200

growth fund = 2 times money market fund

10% of growth + 7% of income + 5% of money market = 250

Define   Let g = amount invested in a growth fund.

Let i = amount invested in an income fund.

Let m = amount invested in a money market fund.

Write   ① $\begin{cases} g + i + m = 3200 \\ g = 2m \\ 0.10g + 0.07i + 0.05m = 250 \end{cases}$
②
③

Step 1 Substitute $2m$ for g in equations ① and ③. Simplify.

① $g + i + m = 3200$ ③ $0.10g + 0.07i + 0.05m = 250$

$2m + i + m = 3200$ $0.10(2m) + 0.07i + 0.05m = 250$

④ $3m + i = 3200$ ⑤ $0.25m + 0.07i = 250$

Step 2 Write the two new equations as a system. Solve for m and i.

④ $\begin{cases} 3m + \quad i = 3200 \\ 0.25m + 0.07i = 250 \end{cases}$ $3m + \quad i = 3200$
⑤ $3m + 0.84i = 3000$ **Multiply by 12.**

$0.16i = 200$

$i = 1250$

④ $3m + i = 3200$

$3m + 1250 = 3200$ **Substitute the value of i.**

$3m = 1950$

$m = 650$

Step 3 Substitute the value of m into equation 2 and solve for g.

② $g = 2m$

$g = 2(650)$

$g = 1300$

You should invest $1300 in the growth fund, $1250 in the income fund, and $650 in the money market fund to get a return of $250 in one year.

✓ **Quick Check** ④ Suppose you discover that your growth fund, income fund, and money market fund return rates are better estimated at 12%, 6%, and 3% per year respectively. How should you invest the $3200 to get a return of $255 in one year? **$1400 growth, $1100 income, and $700 money market**

You have learned how to solve systems of equations using the methods of graphing, elimination, and substitution. In Chapter 4, you will learn how to use matrices to solve systems of equations.

156   Chapter 3 Linear Systems

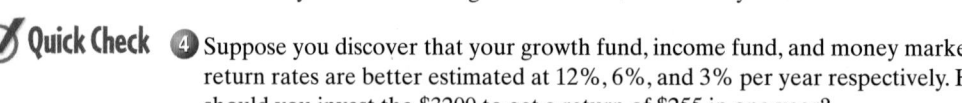

pages 157–159   Exercises

10. $(8, -4, 2)$

11. $(a, b, c) = (2, 3, -2)$

12. $(r, s, t) = (-2, -1, -3)$

13. $(5, 2, 2)$

14. $(0, 1, 7)$

15. $(4, 1, 6)$

EXERCISES

For more exercises, see *Extra Skill and Word Problem Practice*.

Practice and Problem Solving

A Practice by Example

Examples 1 and 2
(pages 153 and 154)

for
Help

Solve each system by elimination. Check your answers.

1. $\begin{cases} x - y + z = -1 \\ x + y + 3z = -3 \\ 2x - y + 2z = 0 \end{cases}$
$(4, 2, -3)$

2. $\begin{cases} x - y - 2z = 4 \\ -x + 2y + z = 1 \\ -x + y - 3z = 11 \end{cases}$
$(0, 2, -3)$

3. $\begin{cases} 2x - y + z = -2 \\ x + 3y - z = 10 \\ x + 2z = -8 \end{cases}$
$(2, 1, -5)$

4. $\begin{cases} a + b + c = -3 \\ 3b - c = 4 \\ 2a - b - 2c = -5 \end{cases}$
$(a, b, c) = (-3, 1, -1)$

5. $\begin{cases} 6q - r + 2s = 8 \\ 2q + 3r - s = -9 \\ 4q + 2r + 5s = 1 \end{cases}$
$(q, r, s) = \left(\frac{1}{2}, -3, 1\right)$

6. $\begin{cases} x - y + 2z = -7 \\ y + z = 1 \\ x = 2y + 3z \end{cases}$
$(0, 3, -2)$

7. $\begin{cases} x + y + 2z = 3 \\ 2x + y + 3z = 7 \\ -x - 2y + z = 10 \end{cases}$
$(1, -4, 3)$

8. $\begin{cases} 3x - y + z = 3 \\ x + y + 2z = 4 \\ x + 2y + z = 4 \end{cases}$
$(1, 1, 1)$

9. $\begin{cases} x - 2y + 3z = 12 \\ 2x - y - 2z = 5 \\ 2x + 2y - z = 4 \end{cases}$
$(4, -1, 2)$

Examples 3 and 4
(pages 155 and 156)

Solve each system by substitution. Check your answers. 10–18. See margin.

10. $\begin{cases} x + 2y + 3z = 6 \\ y + 2z = 0 \\ z = 2 \end{cases}$

11. $\begin{cases} 3a + b + c = 7 \\ a + 3b - c = 13 \\ b = 2a - 1 \end{cases}$

12. $\begin{cases} 5r - 4s - 3t = 3 \\ t = s + r \\ r = 3s + 1 \end{cases}$

Real-World Connection

Careers Stadium designers must take into account the profitability of different types of seating.

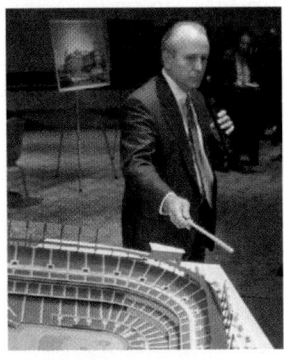

13. $\begin{cases} 13 = 3x - y \\ 4y - 3x + 2z = -3 \\ z = 2x - 4y \end{cases}$

14. $\begin{cases} x + 3y - z = -4 \\ 2x - y + 2z = 13 \\ 3x - 2y - z = -9 \end{cases}$

15. $\begin{cases} x - 4y + z = 6 \\ 2x + 5y - z = 7 \\ 2x - y - z = 1 \end{cases}$

16. $\begin{cases} x - y + 2z = 7 \\ 2x + y + z = 8 \\ x - z = 5 \end{cases}$

17. $\begin{cases} x + y + z = 2 \\ x + 2z = 5 \\ 2x + y - z = -1 \end{cases}$

18. $\begin{cases} 5x - y + z = 4 \\ x + 2y - z = 5 \\ 2x + 3y - 3z = 5 \end{cases}$

19. **Finance** A company placed $1,000,000 in three different accounts. It placed part in short-term notes paying 4.5% per year, twice as much in government bonds paying 5%, and the rest in utility bonds paying 4%. The income after one year was $45,500. How much did the company place in each account?
See margin.

20. **Sports** A stadium has 49,000 seats. Seats sell for $25 in Section A, $20 in Section B, and $15 in Section C. The number of seats in Section A equals the total number of seats in Sections B and C. Suppose the stadium takes in $1,052,000 from each sold-out event. How many seats does each section hold?
See margin.

21. A change machine contains nickels, dimes, and quarters. There are 75 coins in the machine, and the value of the coins is $7.25. There are 5 times as many nickels as dimes. Find the number of coins of each type in the machine.
50 nickels, 10 dimes, and 15 quarters

B Apply Your Skills

Find the number of solutions of each system.

22.

infinitely
many solutions

23.

one solution

24.

no solution

Lesson 3-6 Systems With Three Variables **157**

---

16. $(5, -2, 0)$

17. $(1, -1, 2)$

18. $(1, 3, 2)$

19. $220,000 was placed in short-term notes. $440,000 was placed in government bonds. $340,000 was placed in utility bonds.

20. Section A has 24,500 seats. Section B has 14,400 seats. Section C has 10,100 seats.

Assignment Guide

▼1 **A B** 1-9, 22-24, 39-40

▼2 **A B** 10-21, 25-38, 41
C Challenge   42-45

Test Prep   46-49
Mixed Review   50-67

Homework Quick Check
To check students' understanding of key skills and concepts, go over Exercises 6, 12, 31, 40, 41.

Error Prevention!

Exercises 5–9 When students need to multiply to eliminate a variable, they may not multiply all terms by the number they choose for the multiplication. Urge students to be careful and thorough in using properties of equality and operations.

Differentiated Instruction Resources

GPS Guided Problem Solving	L3
Enrichment	L4
Reteaching	L2
Practice	L3

PowerPoint

🖳 Lesson Quiz

Solve each system by elimination.

1. $\begin{cases} -3x + 2y - 5z = -3 \\ 3x - y + 3z = 4 \\ 3x + 5y - 8z = 6 \end{cases}$
$(3, -7, -4)$

2. $\begin{cases} 7x - y - z = 2 \\ 13x - 4y + 5z = -7 \\ -4x + 3y - 4z = -5 \end{cases}$
$(-2, -11, -5)$

3. Solve by substitution.
$\begin{cases} 2x - 3y + 6z = -21 \\ -5x + 4y + z = 3 \\ 7x - 7y - 4z = -6 \end{cases}$
$(3, 5, -2)$

Alternative Assessment

Ask a student to state a three-variable equation. Ask another student to state a three variable equation that contains an additive inverse of one of the terms in the first equation. Ask another student to state an equation that has a multiple of the additive inverse. Write all of the equations where they can be seen as the students give them to you. Instruct all members of the class to solve the system. Students may want to work in pairs.

pages 157–158   Exercises

41. Answers may vary. Sample: When one of the equations can easily be solved for one variable, it is easier to use substitution.

42. The student is thinking that 0 means that there is no solution. The point (0, 0, 0) is the solution.

44. Answers may vary. Sample: Solution is (1, 2, 3)
$x + y + z = 6$
$2x - y + 2z = 6$
$3x + 3y + z = 12$

45. Let E, F, and V represent the numbers of edges,

158

Solve each system.

25. $\begin{cases} x - 3y + 2z = 11 \\ -x + 4y + 3z = 5 \\ 2x - 2y - 4z = 2 \end{cases}$ $(8, 1, 3)$

26. $\begin{cases} x + 2y + z = 4 \\ 2x - y + 4z = -8 \\ -3x + y - 2z = -1 \end{cases}$ $(3, 2, -3)$

27. $\begin{cases} 4x - y + 2z = -6 \\ -2x + 3y - z = 8 \\ 2y + 3z = -5 \end{cases}$ $\left(\frac{1}{2}, 2, -3\right)$

28. $\begin{cases} 4A + 2U + I = 2 \\ 5A - 3U + 2I = 17 \\ A - 5U = 3 \end{cases}$ $(-2, -1, 12)$

29. $\begin{cases} 4x - 2y + 5z = 6 \\ 3x + 3y + 8z = 4 \\ x - 5y - 3z = 5 \end{cases}$ no solution

30. $\begin{cases} 2\ell + 2w + h = 72 \\ \ell = 3w \\ h = 2w \end{cases}$ $(21.6, 7.2, 14.4)$

31. $\begin{cases} 3x + 2y - z = 17.8 \\ x - 3y + 2z = 7.9 \\ 2x + y - 3z = 3.9 \end{cases}$ $(6, 1.5, 3.2)$

32. $\begin{cases} x + 2y = 2 \\ 2x + 3y - z = -9 \\ 4x + 2y + 5z = 1 \end{cases}$ $\left(-\frac{122}{11}, \frac{72}{11}, \frac{71}{11}\right)$

33. $\begin{cases} 3x + 2y + 2z = -2 \\ 2x + y - z = -2 \\ x - 3y + z = 0 \end{cases}$ $\left(-\frac{10}{13}, -\frac{2}{13}, \frac{4}{13}\right)$

34. $\begin{cases} 6x + y - 4z = -8 \\ \frac{y}{4} - \frac{z}{6} = 0 \\ 2x - z = -2 \end{cases}$ $(2, 4, 6)$

35. $\begin{cases} 4y + 2x = 6 - 3z \\ x + z - 2y = -5 \\ x - 2z = 3y - 7 \end{cases}$ $(-1, 2, 0)$

36. $\begin{cases} 5z + 4y = 4 \\ 3x - 2y = 0 \\ x + 3z = -8 \end{cases}$ $(4, 6, -4)$

37. $\begin{cases} x + 6z = 12 \\ -2x + 3y = 6 \\ y - \frac{z}{2} = \frac{5}{2} \end{cases}$ $\left(2, \frac{10}{3}, \frac{5}{3}\right)$

38. $\begin{cases} 4x - y + z = -5 \\ -x + y - z = 5 \\ 2x - z - 1 = y \end{cases}$ $(0, 2, -3)$

🌐 **History Exercises 39 and 40 appeared in the book *Algebraical Problems*, published in 1824. Write and solve a system for each problem.**

39. Ten apples cost a penny, and 25 pears cost two pennies. Suppose I buy 100 apples and pears for $9\frac{1}{2}$ pennies. How many of each shall I have?
75 apples; 25 pears

🔵 Online
Homework Video Tutor

Visit: PHSchool.com
Web Code: age-0306

40. A fish was caught whose tail weighed 9 lb. Its head weighed as much as its tail plus half its body. Its body weighed as much as its head and tail. What did the fish weigh? **72 pounds**

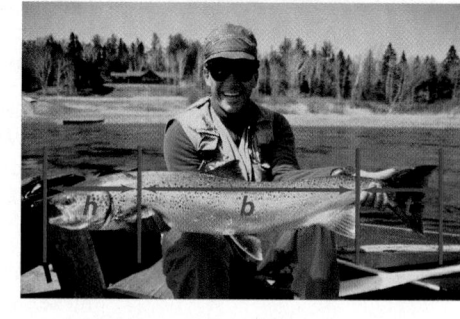

43. $x + 2y = 180$
$y + z = 180$
$5z = 540$
$x = 36, y = 72, z = 108$

41. **Writing** How do you decide whether substitution is the best method to solve a system in three variables?
See margin.

🔴 Challenge

42. **Error Analysis** A student says that the system consisting of $x = 0$, $y = 0$, and $z = 0$ has no solutions. Explain the student's error. **See margin.**

Problem Solving Hint

Sum of angles in a pentagon: 540°

43. **Geometry** Refer to the regular five-pointed star at the right. Write and solve a system of three equations to find the measure of each labeled angle. **See above left.**

44. **Open-Ended** Write your own system having three variables. Begin by choosing the solution. Then write three equations that are true for your solution. Use elimination to solve the system. **See margin.**

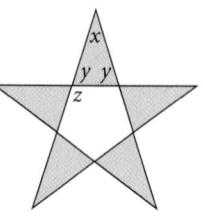

158   Chapter 3 Linear Systems

---

faces, and vertices, respectively. From the statement Every face has five edges, and the number of edges is 5 times the number of faces: $E = 5F$. But since

each edge is part of two faces, this counts each edge twice. So $E = \frac{5}{2}F$. Since every face has five vertices and every vertex is shared by three faces, $3V = 5F$ or $V = \frac{5}{3}F$.

Euler's formula: $V + F = E + 2$. Solving this system of three equations yields $E = 30, F = 12,$ and $V = 20$.

45. Geometry In the regular polyhedron described below, all faces are congruent polygons. Use a system of three linear equations to find the numbers of vertices, edges, and faces. **See margin p. 158.**

Every face has five edges and every edge is shared by two faces. Every face has five vertices and every vertex is shared by three faces. The sum of the number of vertices and faces is two more than the number of edges.

Test Prep

Resources
For additional practice with a variety of test item formats:
- Standardized Test Prep, p. 165
- Test-Taking Strategies, p. 160
- Test-Taking Strategies with Transparencies

Multiple Choice

46. What is the solution of the system?
$$\begin{cases} -3x + 2y - z = 6 \\ 3x + y + 2z = 5 \\ 2x - 2y - z = -5 \end{cases} \text{ B}$$

A. $(6, 5, -3)$ **B.** $(1, 4, -1)$

C. $\left(0, \frac{17}{5}, \frac{4}{5}\right)$ **D.** no solution

47. What is the solution of the system?
$$\begin{cases} x + 3y - 2z = -8 \\ 3x - y + z = 11 \\ 2x + 4y + 2z = 14 \end{cases} \text{ F}$$

F. $(2, 0, 5)$ **G.** $(-8, 11, 14)$

H. $\left(-2, \frac{4}{3}, 5\right)$ **J.** no solution

48. What is the solution of the system?
$$\begin{cases} y = -2x + 10 \\ -x + y - 2z = -2 \\ 3x - 2y + 4z = 7 \end{cases} \text{ D}$$

A. $\left(3, -4, \frac{3}{2}\right)$ **B.** $\left(3, 16, \frac{15}{2}\right)$

C. $\left(-3, 16, \frac{15}{2}\right)$ **D.** $\left(3, 4, \frac{3}{2}\right)$

Short Response

49. Why is there no solution to the system? Explain your answer in terms of intersecting planes. **See back of book.**

① $\begin{cases} 2x - 3y + z = 5 \\ ② \quad 2x - 3y + z = -2 \\ ③ \quad -4x + 6y - 2z = 10 \end{cases}$

Mixed Review

Lesson 3-5

Graph each equation. 50–52. See margin. 53–55. See back of book.

50. $x + y + 4z = 8$ **51.** $2x + 3y - z = 12$ **52.** $-3x + y + 5z = 15$

53. $-2x + 3y - z = 6$ **54.** $6x + 4y - 3z = -12$ **55.** $3x - 6y - 2z = 18$

Graph each equation. 56–61. See margin.

Lesson 2-5

56. $y = |x + 4|$ **57.** $y = |3x - 2|$ **58.** $y = \left|\frac{1}{2}x + 3\right| - 2$

59. $y = |x - 2| + 1$ **60.** $y = |2x + 1|$ **61.** $y = |x + 3| - 2$

Lesson 1-4

Solve each inequality. Graph the solution on a number line. **62–67. See back of book.**

62. $-4x + 3 \leq 9$ **63.** $-(x + 4) - 3 \geq 11$ **64.** $2(3x - 1) < x - 7$

65. $6 - 2x > 2$ **66.** $3x + 2 < -x + 10$ **67.** $-2(x + 3) \geq x$

56.

57.

58.

59.

60.

61.

50.

51.

52.

Writing Extended Responses

This feature helps devise strategies for answering extended-response questions. The focus of the feature is on identifying partial and full credit responses to extended response questions.

Resources

SAT® and ACT® correlations are on page 116B.

Test-Taking Strategies with Transparencies
- Transparency 1
- Practice sheet p. 25

Guided Instruction

Point out to students that it is very important to show their work when answering extended-response questions. Even if their eventual answer is wrong, showing their work may allow them to receive partial credit for their response. Partial credit is always preferable to no credit.

Test-Taking Strategies with Transparencies

Extended-response questions usually are worth 4 points and have multiple parts. If you can't answer one part, you may be able to get partial credit for the other parts.

EXAMPLE

You plan to put a fence around a rectangular lot. The length of the lot must be at least 52 feet. The cost of the fence along the length of the lot is $2 per foot, and the cost of the fence along the width is $3 per foot. The total cost cannot exceed $360.

a. Use two variables to write a system of inequalities that models the problem.

b. Graph the system, and shade the feasible region.

c. What is the maximum width of the lot if the length is 60 feet?

4 points	3 points	2 points
Let x = length y = width $2(2x) + 3(2y) \leq 360$ $\begin{cases} y \leq -\frac{2}{3}x + 60 \\ x \geq 52 \quad y \geq 0 \end{cases}$	$\begin{cases} x \geq 52 \\ y \geq 0 \\ 4x + 6y \leq 360 \end{cases}$	x = length y = width $\begin{cases} 2(2x) + 3(2y) \leq 360 \\ x \geq 52 \\ y \geq 0 \end{cases}$ $4x + 6y \leq 360$ $4(60) + 6y \leq 360$ $6y \leq 120$ $y \leq 20$ The width must be at most 20 ft.
For $x = 60$, $y \leq 20$. Maximum width = 20 ft	When $x = 60$, $y = 20$.	

The 4-point response gives a complete and correct answer to each part. The 3-point response lost credit for not showing all the work. The 2-point response does not include an answer for part (b), but answers the other parts correctly.

EXERCISES

1. What did the 3-point response to the Example leave out?

1. Answers may vary. Sample: The 3-point response did not define the variables or answer the question.

2. Open-Ended Describe a response to the Example that would deserve only 1 point. **Answers may vary. Sample: The student answers only 1 part of a, b, and c.**

3. Suppose the minimum length of the lot in the Example is changed to 60 feet, the cost of the fence along the width is changed to $2 per foot, and the cost of the fence along the length is changed to $1.50 per foot. Find the new answers to parts (a), (b), and (c). Show your work. **a, c. See margin. b. See back of book.**

4. In Exercise 3, what is the maximum length of the lot if the width can be at most 36 ft? **72 ft**

---

page 160   Test-Taking Strategies

3a. Let x = length, y = width.

$\begin{cases} x \geq 60 \quad y \geq 0 \\ 1.50(2x) + 2(2y) \leq 360 \end{cases}$

$3x + 4y \leq 360$
$x = 0, y = 90$
$y = 0, x = 120$

c. for length 60:
$3(60) + 4y \leq 360$
$4y \leq 180$
$y \leq 45$

Chapter Review

Vocabulary Review

🔊 constraints (p. 139)
coordinate space (p. 146)
dependent system (p. 120)
equivalent systems (p. 127)
feasible region (p. 140)

inconsistent system (p. 120)
independent system (p. 120)
linear programming (p. 139)
linear system (p. 118)
objective function (p. 139)

ordered triples (p. 146)
system of equations (p. 118)
trace (p. 148)

Match the vocabulary term in column 1 with the most appropriate phrase in column 2.

Go ●**nline**
PHSchool.com

For: Vocabulary quiz
Web Code: agj-0351

Column 1

1. dependent linear systems   **A**

2. equivalent systems   **D**

3. inconsistent linear systems   **B**

4. independent linear systems   **E**

5. three-variable systems   **C**

Column 2

A. have many solutions

B. have no solutions

C. have solutions that can be shown as the intersection of planes

D. have the same solutions

E. have unique solutions

Resources

Student Edition
Extra Skills and Word Problems Practice, Ch. 3, p. 840
English/Spanish Glossary, p. 899
Properties and Formulas, p. 893
Table of Symbols, p. 889

Differentiated Instruction Resources

Vocabulary and Study Skills worksheet 3F
Spanish Vocabulary and Study Skills worksheet 3F
Interactive Textbook Audio Glossary
Online Vocabulary Quiz

Success 🎯 **Tracker™**
Online at PHSchool.com

Skills and Concepts

3-1 Objectives

▼ To solve a system by graphing (p. 118)

A **system of equations** is a set of two or more equations that use the same variables. The points where all the graphs intersect represent solutions. You must check the coordinates of the points of intersection in the original equations to be sure you have a solution. A **linear system** consists of linear equations.

An **independent system** has a unique solution while a **dependent system** does not have a unique solution. An **inconsistent system** has no solutions.

Solve each system by graphing.

6. $\begin{cases} y = 2x + 1 \\ y = 4x + 5 \end{cases}$ $(-2, -3)$ **7.** $\begin{cases} y = 3x - 2 \\ y = -2x + 8 \end{cases}$ $(2, 4)$ **8.** $\begin{cases} y = 3x - 5 \\ 2y = 6x + 4 \end{cases}$ no solution

9. $\begin{cases} 3x + 2y = -6 \\ x - y = -2 \end{cases}$ $(-2, 0)$ **10.** $\begin{cases} 4x - y = 6 \\ -2x + 3y = 12 \end{cases}$ $(3, 6)$ **11.** $\begin{cases} 12x + 3y = -9 \\ 4x + y = 7 \end{cases}$ no solution

Without graphing, classify each system as *independent,* *dependent,* **or** *inconsistent.*

12. consistent and dependent

13. consistent and independent

14. inconsistent

12. $\begin{cases} 6x + 3y = 12 \\ y = -2x + 4 \end{cases}$ **13.** $\begin{cases} y = -x + 5 \\ x - y = -3 \end{cases}$ **14.** $\begin{cases} x + 2y = 2 \\ y = -0.5x - 2 \end{cases}$

🌐 **15.** Banking Suppose a bank charges a monthly rate of $10 for your checking account. You can switch to a different account that charges $6 plus $.20 per check. For what number of checks is the cost of the two accounts the same? **20 checks**

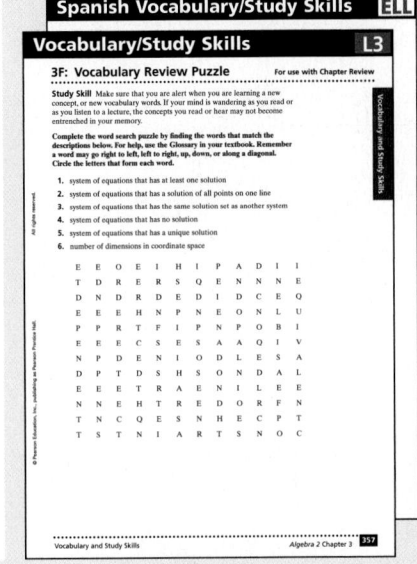

Spanish Vocabulary/Study Skills ELL
Vocabulary/Study Skills L3
3F: Vocabulary Review Puzzle   For use with Chapter Review

23.

24.

25.

26. Let r = number of gallons of regular coffee, and d = number of gallons of decaffeinated coffee.

$$r + d \geq 10$$
$$\tfrac{1}{3}r \geq d$$

27.

vertices: (0, 0), (8, 0), (8, 5), (0, 5)
$C = 0$ at (0, 0)

28.

vertices: (4, 0) (2, 3)
$C = 11$ at (2, 3)

3-2 Objectives

▼ To solve a system by substitution (p. 125)

▼ To solve a system by elimination (p. 126)

If you can easily solve one equation in a system of two equations for one of the variables, you can substitute that expression in the other equation. Then you can find the value of the other variable.

Otherwise, you can multiply one or both equations by a nonzero quantity to create two terms that are additive inverses. This creates an **equivalent system** of equations. Adding the two equations then eliminates one variable. Again, you can solve for the other variable.

In either case, you substitute the value of this second variable into either of the original equations to find the value of the first variable. Recall that some systems have an infinite number of solutions and some have no solutions.

Solve using substitution.

16. $\begin{cases} 3x + 5y = 10 \\ y = -4 \end{cases}$
(10, −4)

17. $\begin{cases} 4x + 3y = 12 \\ x = 5y - 20 \end{cases}$
(0, 4)

18. $\begin{cases} 8x + y = 17 \\ x + 4y = 37 \end{cases}$
(1, 9)

Solve using elimination.

19. $\begin{cases} 2x + y = 13 \\ x - y = -4 \end{cases}$
(3, 7)

20. $\begin{cases} 2x + 3y = 4 \\ 4x + 6y = 9 \end{cases}$
no solution

21. $\begin{cases} a + b = \tfrac{1}{3} \\ a - b = \tfrac{1}{4} \end{cases}$ $\left(\tfrac{7}{24}, \tfrac{1}{24}\right)$

 22. Nutrition Roast beef has 25 g of protein and 11 g of calcium per serving. A serving of mashed potatoes has 2 g of protein and 25 g of calcium. How many servings of each are needed to supply exactly 29 g of protein and 61 g of calcium?
1 serving of roast beef and 2 servings of mashed potatoes

3-3 Objectives

▼ To solve systems of linear inequalities (p. 133)

The solution of a system of inequalities is represented on a graph by the region of overlap of the inequalities. To solve a system by graphing, first graph the boundaries for each inequality. Then shade the regions of the plane containing the solutions for both inequalities.

Solve each system by graphing. 23–25. See margin.

23. $\begin{cases} y < -x + 1 \\ y \geq \tfrac{3}{4}x - 6 \end{cases}$

24. $\begin{cases} x + y \leq 4 \\ y < 6 \end{cases}$

25. $\begin{cases} y > |x - 4| \\ y < \tfrac{1}{3}x \end{cases}$

26. For a community breakfast there should be at least three times as much regular coffee as decaffeinated coffee. A total of ten gallons is sufficient for the breakfast. Model this situation with a system of inequalities. Graph to solve the system. **See margin.**

3-4 Objectives

▼ To find maximum and minimum values (p. 139)

▼ To solve problems with linear programming (p. 141)

Linear programming is a technique used to find the maximum or minimum value of an **objective function**. Linear inequalities are **constraints** on the variables of the objective function. The solutions to the system of constraints are contained in the **feasible region**. The maximum or minimum value of the objective function occurs at a vertex of the feasible region.

Graph each system of constraints. Find all vertices. Then find the variable values that maximize or minimize the objective function. 27–29. See margin pp. 162–163.

27. $\begin{cases} x \le 8 \\ y \le 5 \\ x \ge 0, y \ge 0 \end{cases}$

Minimum for
$C = x + 5y$

28. $\begin{cases} x \ge 2 \\ y \ge 0 \\ 3x + 2y \ge 12 \end{cases}$

Minimum for
$C = 4x + y$

29. $\begin{cases} 3x + 2y \le 12 \\ x + y \le 5 \\ x \ge 0, y \ge 0 \end{cases}$

Maximum for
$P = 3x + 5y$

 30. Profit A lunch stand makes $.75 profit on each chef's salad and $1.20 profit on each Caesar salad. On a typical weekday, it sells between 40 and 60 chef's salads and between 35 and 50 Caesar salads. The total number sold has never exceeded 100 salads. How many of each type should be prepared in order to maximize profit? **50 of each type**

3-5 Objectives

▼ To graph points in three dimensions (p. 146)

▼ To graph equations in three dimensions (p. 148)

You can plot **ordered triples** in **coordinate space.** To sketch a plane that is the graph of an equation in three variables, find the intercepts. To find the x-intercept, substitute 0 for y and z. Then find the other two intercepts. If the plane does not pass through the origin, connect the resulting intercepts on the three axes. These lines are called the **traces** of the plane. **31–35. See margin.**

Graph each point in coordinate space.

31. $(0, 2, 0)$ **32.** $(1, 0, 0)$ **33.** $(0, 0, 3)$ **34.** $(2, 3, 0)$ **35.** $(1, 0, 4)$

Find the coordinates of each point in the diagram at the right.

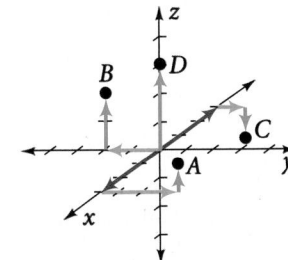

36. A **(3, 3, 1)**

37. B **(0, −2, 2)**

38. C **(−3, 1, −1)**

39. D **(0, 0, 3)**

Sketch the graph of each equation. 40–42. See back of book.

40. $x - 2y + z = 4$ **41.** $10x - 4y - 5z = 20$ **42.** $2x + 6y + 3z = 18$

3-6 Objectives

▼ To solve systems in three variables by elimination (p. 152)

▼ To solve systems in three variables by substitution (p. 155)

You can solve systems of three equations in three variables using the technique of substitution you learned in Lesson 3-2.

Elimination with three equations in three variables involves pairing the equations. Use one equation twice. Then eliminate the same variable in both pairs. The result is a system of two equations in two variables. Proceed using the methods you learned in Lesson 3-2.

Solve each system.

43. $\begin{cases} x + y + z = 10 \\ 2x - y + z = 2 \\ -x + 2y - z = 5 \end{cases}$
(2, 5, 3)

44. $\begin{cases} x + 2y + z = 14 \\ y = z + 1 \\ x = -3z + 6 \end{cases}$
no solution

45. $\begin{cases} 3x + y - 2z = 22 \\ x + 5y + z = 4 \\ x = -3z \end{cases}$
(6, 0, −2)

Chapter 3   Chapter Review   **163**

29.

vertices: (0, 0), (4, 0),
(2, 3), (0, 5)
$P = 25$ at (0, 5)

31.

(0, 2, 0)

32.

(1, 0, 0)

33.

(0, 0, 3)

34.

(2, 3, 0)

35.

(1, 0, 4)

Chapter 3

Chapter Test

Go Online
PHSchool.com
For: Chapter test
Web Code: aga-0352

Classify each system without graphing. Then graph each system. 1–2. See back of book.

1. $\begin{cases} y = 5x - 2 \\ y = x + 4 \end{cases}$
2. $\begin{cases} 3x + 2y = 9 \\ 3x + 2y = 4 \end{cases}$

Solve using substitution.

3. $\begin{cases} 3x + 2y = 9 \\ x + y = 4 \end{cases}$ **(1, 3)**
4. $\begin{cases} 0.3x - y = 0 \\ y = 2 + 0.25x \end{cases}$ **(40, 12)**

Solve using elimination.

5. $\begin{cases} 3x - y = 1 \\ 2x + y = 14 \end{cases}$ **(3, 8)**
6. $\begin{cases} 4x - 2y = 3 \\ 2y - 4x = \frac{3}{2} \end{cases}$ **no solution**

7. **Writing** Describe how to identify situations in which substitution may be the best method for solving a system of equations. **See margin.**

Graph each system. 8–11. See back of book.

8. $\begin{cases} 2x + y < 3 \\ x < y + 3 \end{cases}$
9. $\begin{cases} 3y + 9x < 3 \\ y \geq 2 \end{cases}$

10. $\begin{cases} |x + 3| > y \\ y > 2x - 1 \end{cases}$
11. $\begin{cases} y > -2x + 6 \\ y \leq \frac{1}{4}x - 3 \end{cases}$

Graph each system of constraints. Find all vertices. Evaluate the objective function at each vertex to find the maximum or minimum value.

12. $\begin{cases} x \leq 5 \\ y \leq 4 \\ x \geq 0, y \geq 0 \end{cases}$
13. $\begin{cases} x + y \leq 8 \\ x + 2y \geq 6 \\ x \geq 0, y \geq 0 \end{cases}$

Maximum for $P = 2x + y$ Minimum for $C = x + 3y$

12–13. See back of book.

14. **Sales** A pizza shop makes $1.50 on each small pizza and $2.15 on each large pizza. On a typical Friday, it sells between 70 and 90 small pizzas and between 100 and 140 large pizzas. The shop can make no more than 210 pizzas in a day. How many of each size of pizza must be sold in order to maximize profit? **70 small, 140 large**

15. **Open-Ended** Write a system of constraints whose graph is a parallelogram. **Check students' work.**

Graph each point in coordinate space.

16. $(0, 5, 0)$ 17. $(-1, 0, 0)$ 18. $(1, 0, 4)$

19. $(3, 0, -1)$ 20. $(1, 4, -1)$ 21. $(2, -2, 3)$

16–21. See margin pp. 164–165.

Graph each equation. Use intercepts and traces.

22. $x + y + z = 6$ 23. $2x - 3y + z = 6$

24. $-2x + y - 5z = 10$ 25. $x - y + 2z = 8$

22–26. See back of book.

26. You are planning a party. You have $24 to spend on decorations. Balloons cost $.06 each, party favors cost $.48 each, and streamers cost $.08 each. Write and graph an equation for the number of each you can buy if you spend all the money.

Solve each system of equations.

27. $\begin{cases} x - y + z = 0 \\ 3x - 2y + 6z = 9 \\ -x + y - 2z = -2 \end{cases}$ **(1, 3, 2)**

28. $\begin{cases} 2x + y + z = 8 \\ x + 2y - z = -5 \\ z = 2x - y \end{cases}$ **(2, -1, 5)**

Write a system of equations to solve each problem.

29. **Investing** A company invested $50,000 in three funds. After a year it had $54,500. The growth fund had a return rate of 12%, the income fund had a return rate of 8%, and the money market fund had a return rate of 5%. The company invested twice as much in the income fund as in the money market fund. How much did the company invest in each fund? **29–31. See back of book.**

30. **Earnings** A student can make a weekly salary of $200 plus 15% commission on sales at the Radio Barn or a weekly salary of $300 plus 10% commission on sales at Woofer, Etc. For what amount of sales do these two jobs pay the same?

31. **Purchasing** To help passengers stranded by bad weather one winter, an airport made the purchases detailed below. Find the cost of a cot, a table, and a chair.

	Number of Cots	Number of Tables	Number of Chairs	Total Costs ($)
Nov	10	10	40	1950
Dec	20	0	20	1800
Jan	10	5	20	1350

164 Chapter 3 Chapter Test

page 164 Chapter Test

7. Substitution is used when an equation is easily solved for one of the variables.

164

16.

17.

18.

Standardized Test Prep

Reading Comprehension Read the passage below. Then answer the questions on the basis of what is *stated* or *implied* in the passage.

Hot and Cold Do you ever think about the math involved in filling a bathtub? Depending on the location and the season, the temperature of the cold water that enters a home may be 55°F. Some of the water goes to a water heater, where its temperature may be raised to 122°F.

Suppose you want a tub of 22 gallons of water at 78°F. You can write two equations, using x and y to represent the numbers of gallons of cold and hot water.

$$x + y = 22 \qquad \text{The full tub contains 22 gal.}$$

$$55x + 122y = 22 \cdot 78 \qquad \begin{array}{l}\text{x gal at 55° plus y gal at 122° is equivalent to}\\ \text{22 gal at 78°.}\end{array}$$

If you solve the system of equations, you find that you need about 14.4 gallons of cold water.

---

1. In the given system of equations, what
B does x represent?

   Ⓐ the number of gallons of hot water

   Ⓑ the number of gallons of cold water

   Ⓒ the capacity of the tub

   Ⓓ the temperature of the hot water

2. In the given system of equations, what is the
J value of y?

   Ⓕ about 1716   Ⓖ about 22

   Ⓗ about 14.4   Ⓙ about 7.6

3. Which equation results from solving for x in the
B first equation of the system and then substituting that result into the second equation of the system?

   Ⓐ $55x + 122(22 - x) = 1716$

   Ⓑ $55(22 - y) + 122y = 1716$

   Ⓒ $x = \dfrac{1716 - 122y}{55}$

   Ⓓ $y = \dfrac{1716 - 55x}{122}$

4. Suppose a tub with 22 gallons of water contains
H a mixture of a gallons of cold water at 60°F and b gallons of hot water at 120°F. The desired bath temperature is 80°F. Which of the following systems models the problem?

   Ⓕ $a + b = 80$
      $60a + 120b = 22(80)$

   Ⓖ $a + b = 120$
      $120a + 60b = 12(80)$

   Ⓗ $a + b = 22$
      $60a + 120b = 22(80)$

   Ⓙ $a + b = 22$
      $120a + 60b = 22(80)$

5. How many gallons of hot water are needed for
A the bath described in Question 4?

   Ⓐ $7\frac{1}{3}$

   Ⓑ 11

   Ⓒ $14\frac{2}{3}$

   Ⓓ $16\frac{1}{2}$

6. Suppose a tub with 21 gallons of water contains a mixture of cold water at 65°F and hot water at 128°F. The desired bath temperature is 82°F. Write a system of equations to model the volume h of hot water and the volume c of cold water needed for the bath.
$c + h = 21, 65c + 128h = 21(82)$

7. Consider the bath described in Question 6.
  a. How many gallons of hot water are needed?
  b. How many gallons of cold water are needed?
  a. $5\frac{2}{3}$ gallons   b. $15\frac{1}{3}$ gallons

Students must be able to extract information from reading passages, answer multiple choice questions, and construct responses in order to be successful on current state and national assessments.

To answer the questions, students apply skills and concepts from this chapter and previous chapters.
Multiple Choice: Items 1–5
Free Response: Items 6, 7

Resources

Test Prep Workbook

Grab & Go
• 🄻🄴 Cumulative Review

ExamView CD-ROM
• Standardized Test Practice

Differentiated Instruction Resources
Progress Monitoring Assessments
• Quarter 1 Test
  • 🄻🄴 Forms A & B
  • 🄻🄴 Forms D & E

Spanish Assessment Resources
• 🄻🄴 Spanish Cumulative Review
• Spanish Quarter 1 Test
  • 🄻🄴 Forms A & B

19.

20.

21. $(2, -2, 3)$

Chapter 4

Matrices

Chapter at a Glance

Lesson Titles, Objectives, and Features	Assessment	NCTM Standards	Local Standards
4-1 Organizing Data Into Matrices • Identifying matrices and their elements • Organizing data into matrices	Lesson Quiz	1, 2, 9, 10	
4-2 Adding and Subtracting Matrices • Adding and subtracting matrices • Solving certain matrix equations **Activity Lab:** Technology: Working With Matrices	Lesson Quiz	1, 2, 9, 10	
4-3 Matrix Multiplication • Multiplying a matrix by a scalar • Multiplying two matrices	Lesson Quiz Checkpoint Quiz 1	1, 2, 9, 10	
Geometry Review: Geometric Transformations **4-4 Geometric Transformations With Matrices** • Representing translations and dilations with matrices • Representing reflections and rotations with matrices	Lesson Quiz	1, 2, 3, 7, 9	
4-5 2 x 2 Matrices, Determinants, and Inverses • Evaluating determinants of 2 × 2 matrices and finding inverse matrices • Using inverse matrices in solving matrix equations	Lesson Quiz	1, 2, 3, 7, 9	
4-6 3 x 3 Matrices, Determinants, and Inverses • Evaluating determinants of 3 × 3 matrices • Using inverse matrices in solving matrix equations **Extension:** Networks	Lesson Quiz Checkpoint Quiz 2	1, 2, 6, 7, 9	
4-7 Inverse Matrices and Systems • Solving systems of equations using inverse matrices **GPS:** Understanding Math Problems	Lesson Quiz	1, 2, 3, 10	
4-8 Augmented Matrices and Systems • Solving a system of equations using Cramer's Rule • Solving a system of equations using augmented matrices	Lesson Quiz	1, 2, 8, 9, 10	
Activity Lab: Applying Inequalities			

NCTM Standards 2000

1 Number and Operations	**2** Algebra	**3** Geometry	**4** Measurement	**5** Data Analysis and Probability
6 Problem Solving	**7** Reasoning and Proof	**8** Communication	**9** Connections	**10** Representation

Correlations to Standardized Tests

All content for these tests is contained in *Prentice Hall Algebra 2*. This chart reflects coverage in this chapter only.

	4-1	4-2	4-3	4-4	4-5	4-6	4-7	4-8
SAT®								
Number and Operations Operations, ratio & proportions, complex numbers, counting, elementary number theory, matrices, sequences	✔	✔	✔	✔	✔	✔	✔	✔
Algebra and Functions Expressions, equations, inequalities, representation and modeling, properties of functions (linear, polynomial, rational, exponential)					✔	✔	✔	✔
Geometry and Measurement *Plane Euclidean/Measurement Coordinate* Lines, parabolas, circles, symmetry, transformations *Three-dimensional* Solids, surface area & volume (cylinders, cones, pyramids, spheres, prisms) *Trigonometry* Right triangles, identities								
Data Analysis, Statistics, and Probability Mean, median, mode, range, interquartile range, graphs and plots, regression, probability								
ACT®								
Pre-Algebra Basic operations using whole numbers, decimals, fractions, and integers; place value; square roots and approximations; the concept of exponents; scientific notation; factors, ratio, proportion, and percent; linear equations in one variable; absolute value and ordering numbers by value; elementary counting techniques and simple probability; data collection, representation, and interpretation; and understanding simple descriptive statistics.		✔	✔					
Elementary Algebra Properties of exponents and square roots, evaluation of algebraic expressions through substitution, using variables to express functional relationships, understanding algebraic operations, and solving quadratic equations by factoring.		✔	✔		✔	✔	✔	✔
Intermediate Algebra Understanding of the quadratic formula, rational and radical expressions, absolute value equations and inequalities, sequences and patterns, systems of equations, quadratic inequalities, functions, modeling, matrices, roots of polynomials, and complex numbers.	✔	✔	✔	✔	✔	✔	✔	✔
Coordinate Geometry Graphing and the relations between equations and graphs, including points, lines, polynomials, circles, and other curves; graphing inequalities; slope; parallel and perpendicular lines; distance; midpoints; and conics.					✔			
Plane Geometry Properties and relations of plane figures, including angles and relations among perpendicular and parallel lines; properties of circles, triangles, rectangles, parallelograms, and trapezoids; transformations; the concept of proof and proof techniques; volume; and applications of geometry to three dimensions.							✔	
Trigonometry Understanding trigonometric relations in right triangles; values and properties of trigonometric functions; graphing trigonometric functions; modeling using trigonometric functions; use of trigonometric identities; and solving trigonometric equations.								
NAEP								
Number Sense, Properties, and Operations		✔	✔					
Measurement								
Geometry and Spatial Sense				✔				
Data Analysis, Statistics, and Probability								
Algebra and Functions					✔	✔	✔	✔

SAT® The College Board, SAT® Reasoning Test   **ACT®** The ACT Assessment® Test   **NAEP** National Assessment of Educational Progress, 2005 Mathematics Objectives

Math Background

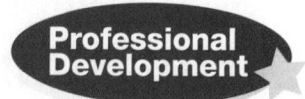

Skills Trace

BEFORE Chapter 4
In previous chapters, students solved equations and systems of equations in two- and three-variables.

DURING Chapter 4
Students represent data with matrices, operate on matrices, transform geometric figures, and solve matrix equations that represent systems of equations in two- and three-variables.

AFTER Chapter 4
Students will perform operations on functions, find inverse functions, and transform various parent functions.

Chapter Overview

Matrices are rectangular arrays of numbers that are used to organize and manipulate data. Students are familiar with operating with numbers and will be interested to operate on matrices including representing them with variables.

Matrices and determinants are in large measure the result of efforts to describe, classify, and solve systems of linear equations. The definitions of matrix operations are closely related to those efforts. Matrix operations provide a powerful tool for the investigation of transformations of geometric figures.

Organizing Data Into Matrices   4-1

Matrices were first developed to facilitate the work of linear transformations. Later, a formal linear algebra was developed. Linear algebra has widespread applications in other areas of mathematics, including multivariable calculus, differential equations, and probability theory. Diverse applications of linear algebra include linear programming, lines and planes, quadratic forms, graph theory, game theory, least squares, linear economic models, Markov processes, and the Fibonacci sequence.

A standard form for a matrix is $[a_{ij}]$. Make sure students understand that the subscript numbers in the notation a_{23} do not mean "twenty-three," but instead refer to the second row (the 2) and the third column (the 3).

Adding and Subtracting Matrices   4-2

The addition and subtraction operations for matrices will seem natural for most students. The operations are performed on pairs of corresponding elements, and the dimensions of the sum and difference match those of the dimensions of the matrices that are added or subtracted. Students who master this easily may enjoy exploring the properties of the transpose of a matrix, in which rows and columns are interchanged (the first row becomes the first column, and so on). Here are some properties of transposes that some students may enjoy exploring.

$$1.\ (A^T)^T = A \qquad 2.\ (A + B)^T = A^T + B^T$$

$$3.\ (AB)^T = B^T A^T \qquad 4.\ (rA)^T = rA^T$$

1. and 4. can be convincingly proved discursively.

1. To prove that the transpose of a transpose of a matrix A is the original matrix, consider that row i in A becomes column i in A^T and returns to being row i in $(A^T)^T$.

4. If r is a scalar (a real number, or a variable representing a real number; see Lesson 4-3), then the transpose of the matrix in which every element of A has been multiplied by r is equal to the transpose of A with the r "factored out."

Formal proofs of 2. and 3. are tedious, but demonstrations with 2 by 2 matrices are illustrative, and students can easily produce them.

Matrix Multiplication   4-3

Scalar, as used in this lesson, is related to the ideas of map scales and scaled drawings. For example, if the matrix representation of a parallelogram is multiplied by any number k, clearly the vertices of the figure change, and the area of the parallelogram is multiplied by k^2.

One might wonder why matrix addition is defined in such a natural way while multiplication of two matrices appears to be much more complicated. A thorough understanding of the composition of functions and the relationship between matrices and linear transformations is required to show that the definition of matrix multiplication is the natural one. Most students will probably never *learn* that a linear transformation is a type of function that maps one vector space into another vector space. However, students can *use* linear transformations in many areas of mathematics, as well as in numerous applied problems in the physical sciences, the social sciences, and economics.

Geometric Transformations With Matrices   4-4

The use of matrix operations to perform transformations on geometric figures may help make the definitions of matrix operations more reasonable to students. Encourage the use of diagrams to confirm results obtained by matrix addition and multiplication.

Rigid transformations do not change the size or shape of a figure. Therefore, a dilation is the only non-rigid transformation, assuming the scale factor is not ± 1. Rotations are different from translations, dilations, and reflections in that they require two quantities be specified, the center of rotation and the angle (with direction) through which the figure is rotated.

2×2 Matrices, Determinants, and Inverses   4-5

The concept of an $n \times n$ identity matrix I for multiplication will probably seem natural to students, as will the concept of a multiplicative inverse for $n \times n$ matrices $AA^{-1} = A^{-1}A = I$. However, the concept and notation of a determinant will be new for most students. First, students should understand that the determinant of a matrix is a number. Next, a matrix with a determinant of zero has no inverse. Finally, if the determinant is nonzero, the inverse matrix can be obtained by use of the determinant. Given the matrix equation $AX = B$, students can use the inverse matrix A^{-1} to solve for the solution matrix X using $X = A^{-1}B$ and matrix multiplication.

3×3 Matrices, Determinants, and Inverses   4-6

Although students are shown how to find the determinant for 3×3 matrices, most students will prefer using graphing calculators to find determinants and inverse matrices. Finding solutions for 3×3 matrix equations is greatly facilitated by technology and access to graphing calculators is assumed in the lesson exercises.

Inverse Matrices and Systems   4-7

Once students have the knack of matrix multiplication, they will probably have little difficulty moving back and forth between systems of linear equations and the related matrix equations. Then the solution procedures from Lesson 4-6 can be applied whereby the equation $AX = B$ is solved using $X = A^{-1}B$ and matrix multiplication.

Students should recognize that they are solving systems of equations when they apply matrix equations. Furthermore, systems with no unique solution will give an error when students use calculators, because the inverse matrix A^{-1} does not exist.

Augmented Matrices and Systems   4-8

Students learn another method to solve systems of linear equations, Cramer's Rule, which uses determinants to directly compute the solution of a system. Although the lesson only applies Cramer's Rule to systems of two-variable equations, Cramer's Rule can be extended to three-variable systems as shown in the Challenge Exercises.

Augmented matrices present an additional method for solving systems of linear equations. Solving a system using augmented matrices is analogous to solving a system using the elimination method. An augmented matrix is altered using row operations that produce a new but equivalent matrix. When the augmented matrix has been simplified to the "reduced row echelon form," the solution matrix forms the last column of the matrix. The calculator command that performs these steps is the rref feature. Students should understand that when a system of n equations in n unknowns has a unique solution, the part of the reduced row echelon matrix to the left of the last column will look like an $n \times n$ identity matrix.

Additional Professional Development Opportunities

Math Background notes for Chapter 4: Every lesson has a Math Background in the PLAN section.

Research Overview, Mathematical Strands
Additional support for these topics and more is in the front of this Teacher's Edition.

Lesson Lab
Lesson Lab, a Pearson Education company, offers comprehensive, facilitated professional development designed to help teachers improve student achievement. To learn more, please visit lessonlab.com

Chapter 4 Resources

Print Resources

		4-1	4-2	4-3	4-4	4-5	4-6	4-7	4-8	For the Chapter
L3	Practice	●	●	●	●	●	●	●	●	
L3	Guided Problem Solving	●	●	●	●	●	●	●	●	
L2	Reteaching	●	●	●	●	●	●	●	●	
L4	Enrichment	●	●	●	●	●	●	●	●	
L3	Daily Notetaking Guide	●	●	●	●	●	●	●	●	
L3	Vocabulary and Study Skills Worksheets	●		●		●	●	●		●
L3	Chapter Project									●
L3	Hands-On Activities		●	●						
L3	Checkpoint Quiz			●			●			
L2	Below Level Chapter Test									●
L3	Chapter Test									●
L4	Alternative Assessment									●
L3	Cumulative Review									●
L4	Connections to Precalculus Masters	●	●	●	●	●	●	●	●	
L3	Technology Activities								●	

Spanish Resources ELL

		4-1	4-2	4-3	4-4	4-5	4-6	4-7	4-8	For the Chapter
L3	Practice	●	●	●	●	●	●	●	●	
L3	Vocabulary and Study Skills Worksheets	●		●		●	●	●		●
L3	Checkpoint Quiz			●			●			
L2	Below Level Chapter Test									●
L3	Chapter Test									●
L4	Alternative Assessment									
L3	Cumulative Review									●

Transparencies

	4-1	4-2	4-3	4-4	4-5	4-6	4-7	4-8	For the Chapter
Check Skills You'll Need	●	●	●	●	●	●	●	●	
Additional Examples	●	●	●	●	●	●	●	●	
Problem of the Day	●	●	●	●	●	●	●	●	
Classroom Aid									
Student Edition Answers	●	●	●	●	●	●	●	●	●
Lesson Quiz	●	●	●	●	●	●	●	●	
Test-Taking Strategies									●

Technology

	4-1	4-2	4-3	4-4	4-5	4-6	4-7	4-8	For the Chapter
TI 83/84 Plus Activities									
Interactive Textbook Online	●	●	●	●	●	●	●	●	●
Student Express CD-ROM	●	●	●	●	●	●	●	●	●
TI Navigator, Instant Check System	●	●	●	●	●	●	●	●	●
Success Tracker	●	●	●	●	●	●	●	●	●
ExamView CD-ROM with Quick Take	●	●	●	●	●	●	●	●	●
Teacher Express CD-ROM	●	●	●	●	●	●	●	●	●
Presentation Express CD-ROM	●	●	●	●	●	●	●	●	●
Mindpoint Quiz Show CD-ROM	●	●	●	●	●	●	●	●	●
Prentice Hall Web site: PHSchool.com	●	●	●	●	●	●	●	●	●

Also available: Prentice Hall Assessment System (Progress Monitoring Assessments, Skills and Concepts Review, Test Prep Workbook)   Solution Key   Student Workbook
Student Workbook, Adapted Version   Data Analysis and Probability Workbook   Math Notes Study Folder   Spanish Cumulative Assessment

Where You Can Use the Lesson Resources

Here is a suggestion, following the four-step teaching plan, for how you can incorporate Differentiated Instruction Resources into your teaching.

	Instructional Resources L3	**Differentiated** Instruction **Resources**
1. Plan		
Check Skills You'll Need Assign these exercises to review prerequisite skills. **New Vocabulary** Help students pre-read the lesson by pointing out the new terms introduced in the lesson.	**Math Background** **Transparencies & Presentation Express CD** Check Skills You'll Need **Resources** Vocabulary and Study Skills	**Spanish Support** **ELL** Vocabulary and Study Skills
2. Teach		
L3 Guided Instruction Teach each Example. After each Example, assign the Quick Check exercise for that Example.	**Student Edition** Activity Lab **Resources** Daily Notetaking Guide Activity Lab TI-83/84 Activities CD-ROM **Transparencies & Presentation Express CD** Additional Examples Classroom Aids **ExamView CD-ROM with QuickTake** **TI Navigator Instant Check System**	**Teacher's Edition** Every lesson includes suggestions for working with students who need special attention. **L1** Special Needs **L2** Below Level **L4** Advanced Learners **ELL** English Language Learners
3. Practice		

Assignment Guide
 	
Homework Exercises
Assign the exercises cited in each lesson's Assignment Guide.
  A Practice by Example
  B Apply Your Skills
  C Challenge
  Test Prep
  Mixed Review
 	
Homework Quick Check
Discuss in class the exercises cited in each lesson's Assignment Guide.
	Transparencies & Presentation Express CD
	Student Answers
	Resources
	Practice
	Guided Problem Solving
	Vocabulary and Study Skills
	Activity Lab
	ExamView CD-ROM with QuickTake
		Spanish Support
		ELL Practice
		ELL Vocabulary and Study Skills
		Resources
		L4 Enrichment

4. Assess & Reteach		
Lesson Quiz Assign the Lesson Quiz to assess students' mastery of the lesson content. **Checkpoint Quiz** Use the Checkpoint Quiz to assess student progress over several lessons.	**Transparencies & Presentation Express CD** Lesson Quiz **Resources** Checkpoint Quiz	**Resources** **L2** Reteaching **ELL** Checkpoint Quiz Success Tracker **ExamView CD-ROM with QuickTake**

KEY **L1** Special Needs **L2** Below Level **L3** For All Students **L4** Advanced, Gifted **ELL** English Language Learners

Chapter 4

Matrices

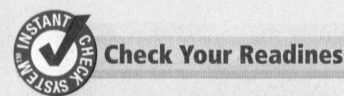

Check Your Readiness

Answers are in the back of the textbook.

For intervention, direct students to:

Evaluating Expressions
Lesson 1-2: Examples 1, 2
Extra Skills and Word
   Problems Practice, Ch. 1

Solving Equations and Inequalities
Lesson 1-3: Examples 1, 2
Extra Skills and Word
   Problems Practice, Ch. 1
Lesson 1-4: Example 1
Extra Skills and Word
   Problems Practice, Ch. 1

Graphing Equations
Lesson 2-2: Example 1
Extra Skills and Word
   Problems Practice, Ch. 2

Solving Systems of Equations
Lesson 3-2: Example 1
Extra Skills and Word
   Problems Practice, Ch. 3
Lesson 3-6: Example 2
Extra Skills and Word
   Problems Practice, Ch. 3

What You've Learned

- In Chapter 1, you learned to represent relationships using variables. You learned to evaluate and simplify variable expressions involving integers and fractions.

- In Chapter 2, you learned to represent two-variable equations in a variety of ways. You learned to graph linear equations and inequalities.

- In Chapter 3, you learned to graph systems of equations and inequalities, including systems of three equations in three variables.

Check Your Readiness

GO for Help to the Lesson in green.

Evaluating Expressions (Lesson 1-2)

Evaluate $ad - bc$ for the given values of the variables.

1. $a = -1, b = -2, c = 5, d = 4$ **6**

2. $a = \frac{1}{2}, b = -1, c = -\frac{2}{3}, d = 2$ **$\frac{1}{3}$**

3. $a = 2, b = \frac{1}{2}, c = \frac{1}{4}, d = -\frac{1}{8}$ **$-\frac{3}{8}$**

4. $a = -\frac{1}{3}, b = \frac{1}{2}, c = \frac{1}{4}, d = -\frac{2}{3}$ **$\frac{7}{72}$**

Solving Equations and Inequalities (Lessons 1-3 and 1-4)

Solve each equation or inequality. Check your answers.

5. $23 - x = 13 + 2x$ **$\frac{10}{3}$**

6. $\frac{x - 1}{5} = -2$ **−9**

7. $a + 17 = -3a$ **$-\frac{17}{4}$**

8. $2y - 3 \leq 2y + 5$ **all real numbers**

9. $11 + 3t > -t$ **$t > -\frac{11}{4}$**

10. $\frac{3s - 2}{2} < s$ **$s < 2$**

Graphing Equations (Lesson 2-2)

Graph each equation on a coordinate plane. **11–18. See back of book.**

11. $3x - 2y = 4$

12. $-3x = y$

13. $-7x - 3y = 14$

14. $y = \frac{2}{3}x - 3$

15. $y = 2x - 1$

16. $2x - 3y = -6$

17. $-2x = 3y + 12$

18. $-2y - 4x = 15$

Solving Systems of Equations (Lessons 3-2 and 3-6)

Solve each system.

19. $\begin{cases} -2x + y = -5 \\ 4x + y = -2 \end{cases}$ $\left(\frac{1}{2}, -4\right)$

20. $\begin{cases} 4x - y = -2 \\ -\frac{1}{2}x - y = 1 \end{cases}$ $\left(-\frac{2}{3}, -\frac{2}{3}\right)$

21. $\begin{cases} 3x + y = 5 \\ -x + y = 2 \end{cases}$ $\left(\frac{3}{4}, \frac{11}{4}\right)$

22. $\begin{cases} x + y + z = 10 \\ 2x - y = 5 \\ y - z = 15 \end{cases}$ **(7, 9, −6)**

23. $\begin{cases} -x + y + 2z = 16 \\ 2x - 2y - 2z = -16 \\ x + y = 0 \end{cases}$ **(0, 0, 8)**

24. $\begin{cases} -2x + 3y + z = 1 \\ x - 3z = 7 \\ -y + z = -5 \end{cases}$ **(7, 5, 0)**

Matrices

◀)) Key Vocabulary

- augmented matrix (p. 222)
- determinant (p. 200)
- dilation (p. 192)
- equal matrices (p. 177)
- image (p. 192)
- matrix (p. 168)
- matrix addition (p. 174)
- matrix element (p. 169)
- matrix equation (p. 176)
- matrix multiplication (p. 184)
- preimage (p. 192)
- row operations (p. 223)
- scalar multiplication (p. 182)
- variable matrix (p. 214)
- zero matrix (p. 175)

Chapter 4 Overview

This chapter introduces students to organizing data into matrices. Students then learn addition and subtraction of matrices, and matrix multiplication. Next, students investigate geometric transformations with matrices. Students also learn about 2 × 2 and 3 × 3 matrices, determinants, and inverses. Finally, students learn about inverse matrices, matrices of systems, and augmented matrices and systems.

Activating Prior Knowledge

Ask:
- *What do you think the term "matrix" refers to?*

Accept all reasonable answers that suggest a material that encloses or embeds something else, or a substance in which something else develops.

Discuss the mathematical definition of a matrix as a rectangular arrangement of numbers into rows and columns.

Ask:
- *How can the term "matrix" be made plural? Or, complete the sentence 'I want to add two _____.'*

Student should arrive at similar terms to "matrices."

Inform students that they will learn to add, subtract, multiply, and perform other operations using matrices.

What You'll Learn Next

- In Chapter 4, you will move from using matrices in organizing data to manipulating matrices through algebra.

- You will learn to represent real-world relationships by writing matrices and using operations such as addition and multiplication to develop new matrices.

- You will learn, by working with geometric figures, how matrices relate to graphic art.

Activity Lab Applying what you learn, on pages 234–235 you will do activities involving the profits and losses of a chocolate-making business.

1. Plan

Objectives
1 To identify matrices and their elements
2 To organize data into matrices

Examples
1 Writing the Dimensions of a Matrix
2 Identifying a Matrix Element
3 Real-World Connection
4 Real-World Connection

Math Background

Matrices are rectangular arrays of numbers frequently used in organizing and manipulating data. In subsequent lessons students will learn how to interpret the sum, difference, and product of matrices that represent various data. They will also learn how to model geometric transformations with matrices.

More Math Background: p. 166C

Lesson Planning and Resources

See p. 166E for a list of the resources that support this lesson.

Bell Ringer Practice

✓ **Check Skills You'll Need**
For intervention, direct students to:

Percents and Percent Applications
Skills Handbook: p. 870
Example 3

Organizing Data Into Matrices

What You'll Learn
- To identify matrices and their elements
- To organize data into matrices

... And Why
To organize gymnastics data, as in Example 4

✓ **Check Skills You'll Need**

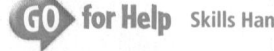 **Skills Handbook page 870.**

Use the table at the right. 1–4. See margin p. 170.

1. How many units were imported to the United States in 1996? In 2000?

2. How many more units were imported in 1998 than in 1996?

3. How many more units were imported than exported in 2000?

4. Compare the percent increase of imports from 1996 to 2000 with the percent increase of exports from 1996 to 2000.

U.S. Passenger Vehicles and Light Trucks Imports and Exports (millions)

	1996	1998	2000
Imports	4.678	5.185	6.964
Exports	1.295	1.331	1.402

SOURCE: U.S. Department of Commerce.
Go to **www.PHSchool.com** for a data update.
Web code: agg-9041

🔊 **New Vocabulary** • matrix • matrix element

---

1 Identifying Matrices

A **matrix** (plural: matrices) is a rectangular array of numbers written within brackets. You represent a matrix with a capital letter and classify it by its dimensions. The number of horizontal rows and the number of vertical columns determine the dimensions of a matrix.

Vocabulary Tip

When describing matrices, read × as "by." For example, read 2 × 3 as "two by three."

$$A = \begin{bmatrix} 2 & 3 & 4 \\ 6 & 7 & 0 \end{bmatrix} \begin{matrix} \leftarrow \\ \leftarrow \end{matrix} 2 \text{ rows}$$

3 columns

Matrix A is a 2 × 3 matrix.

1 EXAMPLE Writing the Dimensions of a Matrix

Write the dimensions of each matrix.

a. $\begin{bmatrix} 4 & 6 & 5 \\ 2 & -3 & -7 \\ 1 & 0 & 9 \end{bmatrix}$

b. $\begin{bmatrix} -4 & \frac{1}{3} & -3 \end{bmatrix}$

c. $\begin{bmatrix} 1 \\ 2 \\ 0 \\ 0.5 \end{bmatrix}$

3 rows × 3 columns

1 row × 3 columns

4 rows × 1 column

This is a 3 × 3 matrix.

This is a 1 × 3 matrix.

This is a 4 × 1 matrix.

✓ **Quick Check** 1 Write the dimensions of each matrix.

a. $\begin{bmatrix} 4 & 5 & 0 \\ -2 & 0.5 & 17 \end{bmatrix}$ **2 × 3**

b. $\begin{bmatrix} 8 & -3 & 15 \end{bmatrix}$ **1 × 3**

c. $\begin{bmatrix} 10 & 0 \\ 1 & -5 \\ -6.2 & 9 \end{bmatrix}$ **3 × 2**

---

168 Chapter 4 Matrices

Differentiated Instruction Solutions for All Learners

Special Needs L1
Have students arrange their desks into rows and columns. Tape row and column number labels on the walls in line with the desks. Call random matrix entries and have the corresponding student stand.

learning style: tactile

Below Level L2
Emphasize that matrices are more than just tables, since they can be added, subtracted, multiplied and divided.

learning style: verbal

Each number in a matrix is a **matrix element.** You can identify a matrix element by its position within the matrix. Use a lowercase letter with subscripts. The subscripts represent the element's row number and column number.

2 EXAMPLE   Identifying a Matrix Element

Identify element a_{13} in matrix A below.

$$A = \begin{bmatrix} 17 & 24 & 3 \\ 10.4 & 12 & 15 \\ 9 & 30 & 15 \end{bmatrix}$$ a_{13} **is the element in the first row and the third column.**

Element a_{13} is 3.

✓ **Quick Check** ② Use the matrix from Example 2. Identify each matrix element.
a. a_{33} **15** **b.** a_{11} **17** **c.** a_{21} **10.4** **d.** a_{12} **24**

2   Organizing Statistical Data

Successful businesses must track great amounts of data in order to plan the best use of their resources. They use matrices to organize and compare statistical data.

3 EXAMPLE   Real-World Connection

Real-World Connection

New appliances have labels that tell how much energy the appliance uses each year.

Energy Energy is often measured in British thermal units (Btus). Write a matrix to represent the data below. Estimate the values from the graph.

Annual Energy Production and Consumption

SOURCE: Energy Information Administration, International Energy Database.
Go to www.PHSchool.com for a data update.
Web Code: agg-9041

Let each row represent a country and each column represent production or consumption levels.

$$\begin{array}{c} \\ \text{China} \\ \text{Russia} \\ \text{United States} \end{array} \begin{array}{cc} \text{Production} & \text{Consumption} \\ \begin{bmatrix} 42 & 43 \\ 46 & 28 \\ 71 & 98 \end{bmatrix} \end{array}$$

✓ **Quick Check** ③ **a.** Rewrite the matrix as a 2×3 matrix. Label the rows and columns.
   b. How could you modify your matrix to include data from other countries?
   c. **Critical Thinking** Explain the difference between a $c \times d$ matrix and a $d \times c$ matrix.
   a–c. See back of book.

Lesson 4-1 Organizing Data Into Matrices **169**

---

2. Teach

Guided Instruction

2 EXAMPLE **Visual learners**

To help students remember that a_{ij} names the element in row i and column j, ask them to think about how they would help someone locate a word on a printed page. Normally, you would tell the person in which line to look and then how far from the beginning of the line.

PowerPoint
Additional Examples

① Write the dimensions of each matrix.

a. $\begin{bmatrix} 7 & -4 \\ 12 & 9 \end{bmatrix}$ **b.** $[0 \ 6 \ 15]$
   2×2 1×3

② Identify each matrix element.

$$K = \begin{bmatrix} 3 & -1 & -8 & 5 \\ 1 & 8 & 4 & 9 \\ 8 & -4 & 7 & -5 \end{bmatrix}$$

a. k_{12} -1 **b.** k_{32} -4
c. k_{23} 4 **d.** k_{34} -5

Guided Instruction

3 EXAMPLE **Alternative Method**

Point out that the columns of the matrix may be interchanged provided the labels that go with them are also interchanged. Similarly, rows may be interchanged.

PowerPoint
Additional Examples

③ Three students kept track of the games they won and lost in a chess competition. They showed their results in a chart. Write a 2×3 matrix to show the data.

	✓ = win			× = loss			
Ed	✓	×	✓	✓	×	✓	✓
Jo	✓	✓	✓	✓	×	✓	✓
Lew	×	✓	×	×	✓	✓	×

$$\begin{array}{c} \\ \text{Wins} \\ \text{Losses} \end{array} \begin{array}{ccc} \text{Ed} & \text{Jo} & \text{Lew} \\ \begin{bmatrix} 5 & 6 & 3 \\ 2 & 1 & 4 \end{bmatrix} \end{array}$$

169

4 EXAMPLE — Diversity

Some students may not be familiar with the sport of gymnastics. Ask students who are to describe to the class the different types of gymnastic events.

Additional Examples

4 Refer to the table at the top of page 168.
a. Write a matrix *N* to represent the information.

	1996	1998	2000
Imports	4.678	5.185	6.964
Exports	1.295	1.331	1.402

b. Which element represents exports for 1995? n_{23}

Resources
• Daily Notetaking Guide 4-1 **L3**

Closure

Ask students what is meant by the *dimensions* of a matrix? **the number of rows and columns in the matrix**

You can use matrices to show data from a table.

4 EXAMPLE — Real-World Connection

Gymnastics The table below shows scores from the 2004 Olympics in Athens, Greece.

U.S. Women's Olympic Gymnastics Team Qualifying Scores

Gymnast	Floor Exercise	Vault	Balance Beam	Uneven Bars
Mohini Bhardwaj	9.525	9.337	9.350	9.487
Courtney Kupets	9.400	9.350	9.550	9.637
Courtney McCool	9.250	9.350	9.112	9.575
Carly Patterson	9.500	9.512	9.725	9.600

SOURCE: Athens 2004 Olympic Games

a. Write a matrix *W* to represent the information. Use a 4 × 4 matrix.

Each column represents a different event.

$$W = \begin{array}{c} \text{M. Bhardwaj} \\ \text{C. Kupets} \\ \text{C. McCool} \\ \text{C. Patterson} \end{array} \begin{bmatrix} 9.525 & 9.337 & 9.350 & 9.487 \\ 9.400 & 9.350 & 9.550 & 9.637 \\ 9.250 & 9.350 & 9.112 & 9.575 \\ 9.500 & 9.512 & 9.725 & 9.600 \end{bmatrix}$$

Each row represents a different gymnast.

b. Which element represents Courtney McCool's score on the vault?

Courtney McCool's scores are in the third row. The vault scores are in the second column. Element w_{32} represents Courtney's score on the vault.

 Quick Check
4 a. Write a matrix *M* to represent the information from the table below. **a–b. See margin.**
b. Identify element m_{15}. What does this element represent?

Men's Olympic Gymnastics Individual Medal Winners, 2004

Gymnast	Floor Exercise	Pommel Horse	Still Rings	Vault	Parallel Bars	Horizontal Bars
Paul Hamm	9.725	9.700	9.587	9.137	9.837	9.837
Dae Eun Kim	9.650	9.537	9.712	9.412	9.775	9.725
Tae-Young Yang	9.512	9.650	9.725	9.700	9.712	9.475

SOURCE: Athens 2004 Olympic Games

Real-World Connection

In the vault, as in each of the other gymnastics events, a perfect individual score is 10.

EXERCISES

For more exercises, see *Extra Skill and Word Problem Practice*.

Practice and Problem Solving

A Practice by Example

GO for Help

Example 1 (page 168)

State the dimensions of each matrix.

1. $\begin{bmatrix} 4 & -2 & 2 \\ 1 & 4 & 1 \\ 0 & 5 & -7 \end{bmatrix}$
3 × 3

2. $\begin{bmatrix} 1 \\ -9 \\ 5 \end{bmatrix}$
3 × 1

3. $[2 \quad \sqrt{5}]$
1 × 2

4. $\begin{bmatrix} 3 & 2 & 1 \\ 2 & 0 & -3 \end{bmatrix}$
2 × 3

5. $\begin{bmatrix} 2.5 \\ -3 \\ -1.6 \\ 10.0 \end{bmatrix}$
4 × 1

page 168   Check Skills You'll Need

1. 4.678 million units; 6.964 million units

2. 0.507 million units

3. 5.562 million units

4. The export percent increase of 8.3% was smaller than the 48.9% increase for the imports.

page 170   Quick Check

4a. $\begin{bmatrix} 9.725 & 9.700 & 9.587 & 9.137 & 9.837 & 9.837 \\ 9.650 & 8.537 & 9.712 & 9.412 & 9.775 & 9.725 \\ 9.512 & 9.650 & 9.725 & 9.700 & 9.712 & 9.475 \end{bmatrix}$

b. 9.837; Paul Hamm's score on the parallel bars

Example 2
(page 169)

Refer to matrices A and B at the right.
Identify each matrix element.

$$A = \begin{bmatrix} 0 & -1 \\ 1.5 & 3 \\ 7 & -2 \end{bmatrix} \quad B = \begin{bmatrix} 6 & -3 & \frac{1}{2} \end{bmatrix}$$

6. a_{21} **1.5**   **7.** b_{12} **−3**   **8.** a_{31} **7**

9. b_{13} $\frac{1}{2}$ **10.** a_{32} **−2**   **11.** a_{12} **−1**

Example 3
(page 169)

Use the graph below for Exercises 12 and 13.

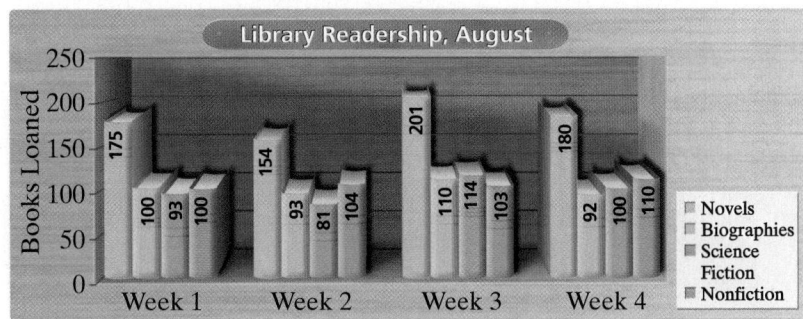

Library Readership, August

12. Write a matrix to represent the data. Label the rows and columns.
See back of book.
13. Write a different matrix to represent the data. Label the rows and columns.
See back of book.

Example 4
(page 170)

14. a. Write a matrix H to represent the data in the table below. **a–b. See**
b. Find element h_{23}. What does this element represent?   **back of book.**

Percent of Public Libraries Offering Programs

Location	Computer Instruction	Book Discussion	Parenting Skills	Employment Guidance
Urban	68	56	28	31
Suburban	59	50	24	18
Rural	49	34	15	12

SOURCE: U.S. National Center for Educational Statistics.
Go to **www.PHSchool.com** for a data update. Web Code: agg-9041

B **Apply Your Skills**

Use the table below for Exercises 15–17.   **15–16. See back of book.**

15. Display the data in a matrix A with columns representing years. Identify a_{23} and tell what it represents.

Manufacturer's Shipments of Recordings (millions)

Type	1998	1999	2000	2001	2002	2003
CDs	847.0	938.9	942.5	881.9	803.3	745.9
DVDs	0.5	2.5	3.3	7.9	10.7	17.5

SOURCE: Recording Industry Association of America.
Go to **www.PHSchool.com** for a data update. Web Code: agg-9041

16. Display the data in a matrix A with rows representing years. Identify a_{41} and tell what it represents.

17. State the dimensions of the matrices in Exercises 15 and 16.   **2 × 6, 6 × 2**

18. **Error Analysis** A student identified element g_{32} from matrix G at the right as −3. What was the student's error?

$$G = \begin{bmatrix} 3 & 2.5 & 4.5 \\ 1.5 & 0 & -3 \\ -3 & 4.5 & 1.5 \end{bmatrix}$$

18. The student identified the data in column 3, row 2 when he or she should have looked at row 3, column 2.

✏️ **19.** **Writing** Describe the information necessary to make a matrix containing numerical data meaningful.   **You must include what the columns and rows represent.**

Assignment Guide

▼**1** **A B**   1-11, 17–18, 20-25

▼**2** **A B**   12-16, 19, 26
C Challenge   27-29

Test Prep   30-32
Mixed Review   33-44

Homework Quick Check

To check students' understanding of key skills and concepts, go over Exercises 12, 13, 18, 19, 26.

Error Prevention!

Exercises 15–17 Students may include the years in the matrices. Remind them that row and column headings do not appear in the matrix. The years are headings, not data.

Differentiated Instruction Resources

GPS Guided Problem Solving	L3
Enrichment	L4
Reteaching	L2
Practice	L3

1. Write the dimensions of the matrix.

$$M = \begin{bmatrix} 8 & 4 & 0 & 1 \\ 9 & 3 & -5 & 0 \\ -1 & 2 & 6 & 1 \end{bmatrix} \; 3 \times 4$$

2. Identify the elements m_{24}, m_{32}, and m_{13} of the matrix M in question 1. **0, 2, 0**

3. The table shows the amounts of the deposits and withdrawals for the checking accounts of four bank customers. Show the data in a 2×4 matrix. Label the rows and columns.

	Deposits	Withdrawals
A	$450	$370
B	$475	$289
C	$364	$118
D	$420	$400

$$\begin{array}{c} \\ \text{Deposits} \\ \text{Withdrawals} \end{array} \begin{array}{cccc} A & B & C & D \\ \end{array}$$

$$\begin{array}{l} \text{Deposits} \\ \text{Withdrawals} \end{array} \begin{bmatrix} 450 & 475 & 364 & 420 \\ 370 & 289 & 118 & 400 \end{bmatrix}$$

Alternative Assessment

Have students work in small groups. They should use almanacs, encyclopedias, or other references to find data that can be presented in a matrix A. They should write the matrix, specify its dimensions, and identify at least four elements of A by using subscript notation.

page 172   Exercises

26a. **Estimates may vary. Sample:**

Types of CDs	Wk 1	Wk 2	Wk 3	Wk 4
Rock	165	150	200	180
R & B	100	94	110	98
Rap	96	90	110	100
Classical	98	97	97	102

State the dimensions of each matrix. Identify the indicated element.

20. 3×3; -7
21. 2×3; 1
22. 3×3; 0

20. $\begin{bmatrix} 4 & 6 & 5 \\ 2 & -3 & -7 \\ 1 & 0 & 9 \end{bmatrix}, a_{23}$ 21. $\begin{bmatrix} -4 & 1 & -3 \\ 2 & 1 & 0 \end{bmatrix}, a_{12}$ 22. $\begin{bmatrix} 1 & 1 & 1 \\ 1 & 0 & 0 \\ 1 & 0 & 0 \end{bmatrix}, a_{32}$

23. $\begin{bmatrix} -4 & 8 & 12 \end{bmatrix}, a_{13}$ 24. $\begin{bmatrix} -5 \\ 4 \\ 3 \end{bmatrix}, a_{31}$ 3×1; 3   25. $\begin{bmatrix} -16 & 24 \\ 8 & -2 \end{bmatrix}, a_{21}$
   1×3; 12 2×2; 8

26. **Retail Sales** The graph shows August sales figures at a music store.

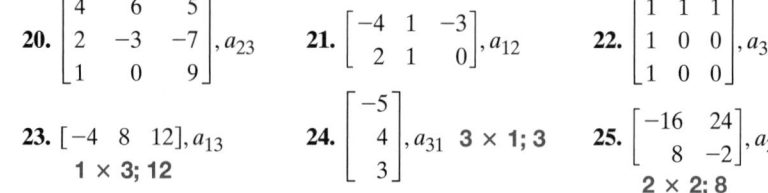

Music Store Sales, August

a. **Estimation** Record the data in a table. **a–b. See margin.**
b. Show the data in a matrix. What do the columns represent? What do the rows represent?

C Challenge

27. **Jobs** The four tables display data from a study conducted by a school principal.
   a. Use the information to create four 2×2 matrices. **See margin p. 173.**
   b. How many boys in the school have part-time jobs? **175**
   c. How many girls in the school have part-time jobs? **185**
   d. What percent of the students with part-time jobs are girls? **about 51.4%**

Numbers of Students Who Work Part-time

9th Grade	Has Part-time Job	No Part-time Job
Boys	5	95
Girls	15	90

10th Grade	Has Part-time Job	No Part-time Job
Boys	35	65
Girls	30	55

11th Grade	Has Part-time Job	No Part-time Job
Boys	65	35
Girls	75	30

12th Grade	Has Part-time Job	No Part-time Job
Boys	70	25
Girls	65	45

28. **Transportation Costs** A computer accessory company makes computer carrying cases at four plants located in Atlanta, Boston, Chicago, and Denver. Represent the company's shipping costs in a matrix. Label the rows and columns. **See margin p. 173.**

Shipping Costs

b.

$$\begin{array}{l} \text{Rock} \\ \text{R\&B} \\ \text{Rap} \\ \text{Classical} \end{array} \begin{array}{cccc} \text{Wk 1} & \text{Wk 2} & \text{Wk 3} & \text{Wk 4} \\ \end{array}$$

$$\begin{bmatrix} 165 & 150 & 200 & 180 \\ 100 & 94 & 110 & 98 \\ 96 & 90 & 110 & 100 \\ 98 & 97 & 97 & 102 \end{bmatrix};$$

Columns represent the weeks in August and rows are the type of CDs sold.

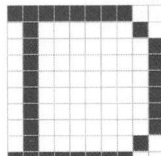

29. a. Open-Ended Using a 10×10 grid, create at least three different letters of the alphabet with a style similar to the one at the left.
  b. Technology The tiny lights that make up a computer screen are called pixels. To make a letter, the computer tells the screen which pixels to light up. Represent each letter from part (a) by writing a matrix. Use 1 for a lit pixel and 0 for an unlit pixel.   **a–b. See back of book.**

Test Prep

Multiple Choice

30. Which element in matrix $A = \begin{bmatrix} 5 & -2 & -\frac{1}{2} & 0 \end{bmatrix}$ is the number 0? **C**

  A. a_{40} **B.** a_4 **C.** a_{14} **D.** a_{41}

31. In which matrix is the value of a_{32} less than the value of a_{21}? **F**

  F. $\begin{bmatrix} -1 & 0 & 5 \\ 4 & 3 & -1 \\ -3 & 2 & 6 \end{bmatrix}$ **G.** $\begin{bmatrix} -1 & 5 & 0 \\ 3 & 4 & -1 \\ -3 & 6 & 2 \end{bmatrix}$ **H.** $\begin{bmatrix} 0 & 5 & -1 \\ -1 & 4 & 3 \\ 6 & 2 & -3 \end{bmatrix}$ **J.** $\begin{bmatrix} 0 & -1 & 5 \\ 0 & 3 & 4 \\ -3 & 1 & 6 \end{bmatrix}$

Extended Response

32. Anna made a table to show how much money she and two of her friends earned for summer chores.
  a. Display the data in Anna's table in a matrix A with each row representing someone's earnings.
  b. Rob made his own matrix, R, to show the earnings.

$$R = \begin{bmatrix} 12 & 20 & 15 \\ 35 & 40 & 55 \\ 40 & 0 & 70 \end{bmatrix}$$

What do values in the first column of matrix R represent?

Summer Earnings for Odd Jobs

	Weeding Gardens	Mowing Lawns	Pruning Bushes
Anna	$20	$40	$0
Rob	$12	$35	$40
Carla	$15	$55	$70

a–b. See back of book.

Mixed Review

Lesson 3-6 Solve each system.

33. $\begin{cases} 3x + 2y - 2z = -9 \\ 5x - 3z = -7 \\ x + 4y + 3z = 5 \end{cases}$ **(1, −2, 4)**

34. $\begin{cases} 2x + 3y + 4z = -1 \\ x - 2y + z = 9 \\ x + 4y - 2z = -12 \end{cases}$ **(2, −3, 1)**

Lesson 3-1 Solve each system by graphing.   **35–37. See margin.**

35. $\begin{cases} 2x + y = 8 \\ x - 3y = -3 \end{cases}$ **36.** $\begin{cases} 2x + y = 7 \\ x + y = -5 \end{cases}$ **37.** $\begin{cases} x + 6y = 7 \\ 2x + 4y = -2 \end{cases}$

Lesson 2-3 Find the constant of variation for a direct variation that includes the given values.

38. $(2, 4)$ **2**   **39.** $(-1, 7)$ **−7**   **40.** $(-4, -10)$ **$\frac{5}{2}$**   **41.** $(3, 5)$ **$\frac{5}{3}$**   **42.** $\left(\frac{1}{2}, 9\right)$ **18**

In each relation, y varies directly as x. Find y when $x = 9$.

43. $y = 6$ when $x = 4$ **$\frac{27}{2}$**   **44.** $y = 8$ when $x = 4$ **18**

27a.

	Job	No Job
9th gr. boys	5	95
9th gr. girls	15	90

	Job	No Job
10th gr. boys	35	65
10th gr. girls	30	55

	Job	No Job
11th gr. boys	65	35
11th gr. girls	75	30

	Job	No Job
12th gr. boys	70	25
12th gr. girls	65	45

Resources
For additional practice with a variety of test item formats:
• Standardized Test Prep, p. 233
• Test-Taking Strategies, p. 228
• Test-Taking Strategies with Transparencies

28.

	Atl.	Bos.	Chi.	Denv.
Atl.	0	19	12	23
Bos.	19	0	10	21
Chi.	12	10	0	15
Denv.	23	21	15	0

35.

36.

37.

173

Adding and Subtracting Matrices

1. Plan

Objectives
1 To add and subtract matrices
2 To solve certain matrix equations

Examples
1 Real-World Connection
2 Using Identity and Inverse Matrices
3 Subtracting Matrices
4 Soving a Matrix Equation
5 Determining Equal Matrices
6 Finding Unknown Matrix Elements

Math Background

One consequence of the definitions of matrix addition and matrix subtraction is that these matrix operations possess many of the properties associated with addition and subtraction of real numbers. This is of great importance in the field of Linear Algebra.

More Math Background: p. 166C

Lesson Planning and Resources

See p. 166E for a list of the resources that support this lesson.

Bell Ringer Practice

✓ **Check Skills You'll Need**
For intervention, direct students to:

Simplifying Expressions
Skills Handbook: p. 873
Examples 1, 2

What You'll Learn

- To add and subtract matrices
- To solve certain matrix equations

... And Why

To find SAT score totals, as in Example 1

✓ **Check Skills You'll Need**   **for Help** Skills Handbook page 873.

Simplify the elements of each matrix. 1–6. See margin p. 177.

1. $\begin{bmatrix} 10+4 & 0+4 \\ -2+4 & -5+4 \end{bmatrix}$
2. $\begin{bmatrix} 5-2 & 3-2 \\ -1-2 & 0-2 \end{bmatrix}$
3. $\begin{bmatrix} -2+3 & 0-3 \\ 1-3 & -5+3 \end{bmatrix}$
4. $\begin{bmatrix} 3+1 & 4+9 \\ -2+0 & 5+7 \end{bmatrix}$
5. $\begin{bmatrix} 8-4 & -5-1 \\ 9-1 & 6-9 \end{bmatrix}$
6. $\begin{bmatrix} 2+4 & 6-8 \\ 4-3 & 5+2 \end{bmatrix}$

🔊 **New Vocabulary** • matrix addition • zero matrix • matrix equation
• equal matrices

---

1 Adding and Subtracting Matrices

Video Tutor Help
Visit: PhSchool.com
Web Code: age-0775

Real-World Connection

Many schools have programs for students to help one another prepare for standardized tests.

Sometimes you want to add or subtract matrices to get new information. You perform **matrix addition** on matrices with equal dimensions by adding the corresponding elements, which are elements in the same position in each matrix.

1 EXAMPLE **Real-World 🌐 Connection**

Statistics Use the data in the table.

a. Write two 2×4 matrices to represent the mean verbal and math SAT scores.

Mean SAT Scores				
	Verbal		Math	
Year	Male	Female	Male	Female
2000	507	504	533	498
2001	509	502	533	498
2002	507	502	534	500
2003	512	503	537	503
SOURCE: College Entrance Examination Board				

Verbal
$$\begin{array}{c} \\ \text{Male} \\ \text{Female} \end{array} \begin{array}{cccc} 2000 & 2001 & 2002 & 2003 \end{array} \\ \begin{bmatrix} 507 & 509 & 507 & 512 \\ 504 & 502 & 502 & 503 \end{bmatrix}$$

Math
$$\begin{array}{c} \\ \text{Male} \\ \text{Female} \end{array} \begin{array}{cccc} 2000 & 2001 & 2002 & 2003 \end{array} \\ \begin{bmatrix} 533 & 533 & 534 & 537 \\ 498 & 498 & 500 & 503 \end{bmatrix}$$

b. Find the combined mean SAT scores for each year in the table.

$$\begin{bmatrix} 507 & 509 & 507 & 512 \\ 504 & 502 & 502 & 503 \end{bmatrix} + \begin{bmatrix} 533 & 533 & 534 & 537 \\ 498 & 498 & 500 & 503 \end{bmatrix}$$

$$= \begin{bmatrix} 507+533 & 509+533 & 507+534 & 512+537 \\ 504+498 & 502+498 & 502+500 & 503+503 \end{bmatrix}$$

$$= \begin{array}{c} \\ \text{Male} \\ \text{Female} \end{array} \begin{array}{cccc} 2000 & 2001 & 2002 & 2003 \end{array} \\ \begin{bmatrix} 1040 & 1042 & 1041 & 1049 \\ 1002 & 1000 & 1002 & 1006 \end{bmatrix}$$

Differentiated Instruction Solutions for All Learners

Special Needs L1
For matrix addition, have students use colors such as blue and yellow to highlight each respective matrix. Then have students use green, which is formed by combining blue and yellow, to highlight the matrix sum.

learning style: visual

Below Level L2
Emphasize that the zero matrix is not the same as the number zero. There is only one number zero, but there are many different zero matrices of different dimensions.

learning style: verbal

Quick Check ① Find each sum. See below left.

a. $\begin{bmatrix} 1 & -2 & 0 \\ 3 & -5 & 7 \end{bmatrix} + \begin{bmatrix} 3 & 9 & -3 \\ -9 & 6 & 12 \end{bmatrix}$

b. $\begin{bmatrix} -12 & 24 \\ -3 & 5 \\ -1 & 10 \end{bmatrix} + \begin{bmatrix} -3 & 1 \\ 2 & -4 \\ -1 & 5 \end{bmatrix}$

🔑 **Key Concepts**

Definition	Matrix Addition

To add matrices A and B with the same dimensions, add corresponding elements.

$$A = \begin{bmatrix} a & b & c \\ d & e & f \end{bmatrix} \qquad B = \begin{bmatrix} r & s & t \\ u & v & w \end{bmatrix}$$

$$A + B = \begin{bmatrix} a & b & c \\ d & e & f \end{bmatrix} + \begin{bmatrix} r & s & t \\ u & v & w \end{bmatrix} = \begin{bmatrix} a+r & b+s & c+t \\ d+u & e+v & f+w \end{bmatrix}$$

Online active math

For: Matrix Addition Activity
Use: Interactive Textbook, 4-2

The additive identity matrix for the set of all $m \times n$ matrices is the **zero matrix** O, or $O_{m \times n}$, whose elements are all zeros. The opposite, or additive inverse, of an $m \times n$ matrix A is $-A$. $-A$ is the $m \times n$ matrix with elements that are the opposites of the corresponding elements of A.

② **EXAMPLE** Using Identity and Inverse Matrices

1a. $\begin{bmatrix} 4 & 7 & -3 \\ -6 & 1 & 19 \end{bmatrix}$

b. $\begin{bmatrix} -15 & 25 \\ -1 & 1 \\ -2 & 15 \end{bmatrix}$

Find each sum.

a. $\begin{bmatrix} 1 & 2 \\ 5 & -7 \end{bmatrix} + \begin{bmatrix} 0 & 0 \\ 0 & 0 \end{bmatrix}$

$= \begin{bmatrix} 1+0 & 2+0 \\ 5+0 & -7+0 \end{bmatrix}$

$= \begin{bmatrix} 1 & 2 \\ 5 & -7 \end{bmatrix}$

b. $\begin{bmatrix} 2 & 8 \\ -3 & 0 \end{bmatrix} + \begin{bmatrix} -2 & -8 \\ 3 & 0 \end{bmatrix}$

$= \begin{bmatrix} 2+(-2) & 8+(-8) \\ -3+3 & 0+0 \end{bmatrix}$

$= \begin{bmatrix} 0 & 0 \\ 0 & 0 \end{bmatrix}$

 Quick Check ② Find each sum.

2b. $\begin{bmatrix} -1 & 10 & -5 \\ 0 & 2 & -3 \end{bmatrix}$

a. $\begin{bmatrix} 14 & 5 \\ 0 & -2 \end{bmatrix} + \begin{bmatrix} -14 & -5 \\ 0 & 2 \end{bmatrix} \begin{bmatrix} 0 & 0 \\ 0 & 0 \end{bmatrix}$

b. $\begin{bmatrix} 0 & 0 & 0 \\ 0 & 0 & 0 \end{bmatrix} + \begin{bmatrix} -1 & 10 & -5 \\ 0 & 2 & -3 \end{bmatrix} \begin{bmatrix} 0 & 0 \\ 0 & 0 \end{bmatrix}$

Some of the properties of real number addition also apply to matrix addition.

🔑 **Key Concepts**

Properties	Matrix Addition

If A, B, and C are $m \times n$ matrices, then

$A + B$ is an $m \times n$ matrix.	Closure Property
$A + B = B + A$	Commutative Property of Addition
$(A + B) + C = A + (B + C)$	Associative Property of Addition
There exists a unique $m \times n$ matrix O such that $O + A = A + O = A$.	Additive Identity Property
For each A, there exists a unique opposite, $-A$. $A + (-A) = O$	Additive Inverse Property

Lesson 4-2 Adding and Subtracting Matrices **175**

Guided Instruction

PowerPoint
⬛ **Additional Examples**

① The table shows information on ticket sales for a new movie that is showing at two theaters. Sales are for children (C) and adults (A).

Theater	Matinee		Evening	
	C	A	C	A
1	198	350	54	439
2	201	375	58	386

a. Write two 2×2 matrices to represent matinee and evening sales.

Matinee
C   A
$\begin{matrix} 1 \\ 2 \end{matrix} \begin{bmatrix} 198 & 350 \\ 201 & 375 \end{bmatrix}$

Evening
C   A
$\begin{matrix} 1 \\ 2 \end{matrix} \begin{bmatrix} 54 & 439 \\ 58 & 386 \end{bmatrix}$

b. Find the combined sales for the two showings.

C   A
$\begin{matrix} 1 \\ 2 \end{matrix} \begin{bmatrix} 252 & 789 \\ 259 & 761 \end{bmatrix}$

② Find each sum.

a. $\begin{bmatrix} 9 & 0 \\ -4 & 6 \end{bmatrix} + \begin{bmatrix} 0 & 0 \\ 0 & 0 \end{bmatrix} \begin{bmatrix} 9 & 0 \\ -4 & 6 \end{bmatrix}$

b. $\begin{bmatrix} 3 & -8 \\ -5 & 1 \end{bmatrix} + \begin{bmatrix} -3 & 8 \\ 5 & -1 \end{bmatrix} \begin{bmatrix} 0 & 0 \\ 0 & 0 \end{bmatrix}$

Advanced Learners L4
Have students discuss whether there are any properties of matrix addition that differ from those of integer addition.

learning style: verbal

English Language Learners ELL
Help students understand that *equal matrices* have the same dimensions, and that the elements in corresponding positions are equal. Similarly, the opposite of a matrix has the same dimensions but corresponding elements are opposites.

learning style: verbal

You can define matrix subtraction by using the Additive Inverse Property.

 Key Concepts

Property	**Matrix Subtraction**

If two matrices, A and B, have the same dimensions, then $A - B = A + (-B)$.

3 EXAMPLE | **Subtracting Matrices**

$A = \begin{bmatrix} 3 & 2 & 4 \\ -1 & 4 & 0 \end{bmatrix}$ and $B = \begin{bmatrix} 1 & 4 & 3 \\ -2 & 2 & 4 \end{bmatrix}$. Find $A - B$.

Vocabulary Tip

You can extend the meaning of <u>matrix</u> to describe a rectangular arrangement (rows and columns) of any objects.

Method 1 Use additive inverses.

$A - B = A + (-B) = \begin{bmatrix} 3 & 2 & 4 \\ -1 & 4 & 0 \end{bmatrix} + \begin{bmatrix} -1 & -4 & -3 \\ 2 & -2 & -4 \end{bmatrix}$ **Write the elements of $-B$.**

$= \begin{bmatrix} 3 + (-1) & 2 + (-4) & 4 + (-3) \\ -1 + 2 & 4 + (-2) & 0 + (-4) \end{bmatrix}$ **Add corresponding elements.**

$= \begin{bmatrix} 2 & -2 & 1 \\ 1 & 2 & -4 \end{bmatrix}$ **Simplify.**

Method 2 Use subtraction.

$A - B = \begin{bmatrix} 3 & 2 & 4 \\ -1 & 4 & 0 \end{bmatrix} - \begin{bmatrix} 1 & 4 & 3 \\ -2 & 2 & 4 \end{bmatrix}$

$= \begin{bmatrix} 3 - 1 & 2 - 4 & 4 - 3 \\ -1 - (-2) & 4 - 2 & 0 - 4 \end{bmatrix}$ **Subtract corresponding elements.**

$= \begin{bmatrix} 2 & -2 & 1 \\ 1 & 2 & -4 \end{bmatrix}$ **Simplify.**

Quick Check **3** Find each difference.

a. $\begin{bmatrix} 6 & -9 & 7 \\ -2 & 1 & 8 \end{bmatrix} - \begin{bmatrix} -4 & 3 & 0 \\ 6 & 5 & 10 \end{bmatrix}$

$\begin{bmatrix} 10 & -12 & 7 \\ -8 & -4 & -2 \end{bmatrix}$

b. $\begin{bmatrix} -3 & 5 \\ -1 & 10 \end{bmatrix} - \begin{bmatrix} -3 & 1 \\ 2 & -4 \end{bmatrix}$

$\begin{bmatrix} 0 & 4 \\ -3 & 14 \end{bmatrix}$

2 Solving Matrix Equations

A **matrix equation** is an equation in which the variable is a matrix. You can use the addition and subtraction properties of equality to solve matrix equations.

4 EXAMPLE | **Solving a Matrix Equation**

Solve $X - \begin{bmatrix} 1 & 1 \\ 3 & 2 \end{bmatrix} = \begin{bmatrix} 0 & 1 \\ 8 & 9 \end{bmatrix}$ for the matrix X.

$X - \begin{bmatrix} 1 & 1 \\ 3 & 2 \end{bmatrix} = \begin{bmatrix} 0 & 1 \\ 8 & 9 \end{bmatrix}$

$X - \begin{bmatrix} 1 & 1 \\ 3 & 2 \end{bmatrix} + \begin{bmatrix} 1 & 1 \\ 3 & 2 \end{bmatrix} = \begin{bmatrix} 0 & 1 \\ 8 & 9 \end{bmatrix} + \begin{bmatrix} 1 & 1 \\ 3 & 2 \end{bmatrix}$ **Add $\begin{bmatrix} 1 & 1 \\ 3 & 2 \end{bmatrix}$ to each side of the equation.**

$X = \begin{bmatrix} 1 & 2 \\ 11 & 11 \end{bmatrix}$ **Simplify.**

Quick Check ④ Solve $X + \begin{bmatrix} -1 & 0 \\ 2 & 5 \end{bmatrix} = \begin{bmatrix} 10 & 7 \\ -4 & 4 \end{bmatrix}$. $\begin{bmatrix} 11 & 7 \\ -6 & -1 \end{bmatrix}$

Equal matrices are matrices with the same dimensions and equal corresponding elements.

5 EXAMPLE Determining Equal Matrices

Multiple Choice Which matrix is equal to matrix M?

$M = \begin{bmatrix} -0.75 & \frac{1}{5} & 0 \\ \frac{1}{2} & -2 & 1.25 \end{bmatrix}$

Ⓐ $\begin{bmatrix} \frac{1}{2} & -2 & 1.25 \\ -0.75 & \frac{1}{5} & 0 \end{bmatrix}$

Ⓑ $\begin{bmatrix} -\frac{3}{4} & 0.2 \\ 0.5 & -2 \end{bmatrix}$

Ⓒ $\begin{bmatrix} -\frac{3}{4} & 0.2 & 0 \\ 0.5 & \frac{-4}{2} & \frac{5}{4} \end{bmatrix}$

Ⓓ $\begin{bmatrix} -0.75 & \frac{1}{2} \\ \frac{1}{5} & -2 \\ 0 & 1.25 \end{bmatrix}$

Test-Taking Tip

If you think you can eliminate all but one choice, it is good practice to check that the remaining choice is correct.

Matrix M is 2×3. Any matrix equal to it must have the same dimensions. Choice B is 2×2. Choice D is 3×2. You can eliminate choices B and D.

Choice A has first-row elements equal to second-row elements in M, but different from first-row elements in M. You can eliminate choice A.

Corresponding elements of M and choice C are equal.

$$-0.75 = -\frac{3}{4}, \quad \frac{1}{5} = 0.2, \quad 0 = 0; \quad \frac{1}{2} = 0.5, \quad -2 = \frac{-4}{2}, \quad 1.25 = \frac{5}{4}$$

The answer is choice C.

Quick Check ⑤ Determine whether the two matrices in each pair are equal.

a. $\begin{bmatrix} 4 & 9 \\ 8 & 5 \end{bmatrix}, \begin{bmatrix} \frac{8}{2} & \frac{10}{2} \\ \frac{16}{2} & \frac{18}{2} \end{bmatrix}$ no

b. $\begin{bmatrix} -2 & 3 \\ 5 & 0 \end{bmatrix}, \begin{bmatrix} -\frac{8}{4} & 6-3 \\ \frac{15}{3} & 4-4 \end{bmatrix}$ yes

6 EXAMPLE Finding Unknown Matrix Elements

Solve the equation $\begin{bmatrix} 2x - 5 & 4 \\ 3 & 3y + 12 \end{bmatrix} = \begin{bmatrix} 25 & 4 \\ 3 & y + 18 \end{bmatrix}$ for x and y.

$\begin{bmatrix} 2x - 5 & 4 \\ 3 & 3y + 12 \end{bmatrix} = \begin{bmatrix} 25 & 4 \\ 3 & y + 18 \end{bmatrix}$

$2x - 5 = 25$	$3y + 12 = y + 18$	Since the two matrices are equal, their
$2x = 30$	$2y = 6$	corresponding elements are equal.
$x = 15$	$y = 3$	

The solutions are $x = 15$ and $y = 3$.

6a. $x = 30, y = 2$

b. $x = -3, y = 7$

Quick Check ⑥ Solve each equation for x and y. **See left.**

a. $\begin{bmatrix} x + 8 & -5 \\ 3 & -y \end{bmatrix} = \begin{bmatrix} 38 & -5 \\ 3 & 4y - 10 \end{bmatrix}$

b. $[3x \quad 4] = [-9 \quad x + y]$

---

⑤ Determine whether the matrices in each pair are equal.

a. $M = \begin{bmatrix} 8 + 9 & 5 \\ -6 & -1 \\ 0 & 0.\overline{7} \end{bmatrix}$;

$N = \begin{bmatrix} 17 & 5 \\ 4 - 10 & -2 + 1 \\ 0 & -\frac{7}{9} \end{bmatrix}$ no

b. $P = \begin{bmatrix} 3 & -4 \\ 40 & -3 \end{bmatrix}$;

$Q = \begin{bmatrix} \frac{27}{9} & \frac{-16}{4} \\ \frac{8}{0.2} & \frac{12}{-4} \end{bmatrix}$ yes

⑥ Solve the equation

$\begin{bmatrix} 2m - n & -3 \\ 8 & -4m + 2n \end{bmatrix} = \begin{bmatrix} 15 & m + n \\ 8 & -30 \end{bmatrix}$ for m and n.

$m = 4, n = -7$

Resources
• Daily Notetaking Guide 4-2 **L3**

Closure

Ask students: *How might you solve a matrix equation such as*

$X - \begin{bmatrix} 1 & 4 \\ -3 & 9 \end{bmatrix} + \begin{bmatrix} -4 & 7 \\ 10 & -2 \end{bmatrix} = \begin{bmatrix} 5 & -1 \\ 6 & 3 \end{bmatrix}$?

On the left side of the equal sign, add the additive inverse of the first matrix (because of the negative sign) to the second matrix. Then use the subtraction property of equality to solve the resulting matrix equation.

---

page 174 Check Skills You'll Need

1. $\begin{bmatrix} 14 & 4 \\ 2 & -1 \end{bmatrix}$

2. $\begin{bmatrix} 3 & 1 \\ -3 & -2 \end{bmatrix}$

3. $\begin{bmatrix} 1 & -3 \\ -2 & -2 \end{bmatrix}$

4. $\begin{bmatrix} 4 & 13 \\ -2 & 12 \end{bmatrix}$

5. $\begin{bmatrix} 4 & -6 \\ 8 & -3 \end{bmatrix}$

6. $\begin{bmatrix} 6 & -2 \\ 1 & 7 \end{bmatrix}$

For more exercises, see *Extra Skill and Word Problem Practice*.

Assignment Guide

1 A B 1-9, 18-23, 26-28

2 A B 10-17, 24-25, 29-31
C Challenge   32-34

Test Prep   35-38
Mixed Review   39-44

Homework Quick Check
To check students' understanding
of key skills and concepts, go over
Exercises 7, 13, 26, 27, 28.

Error Prevention!

Exercises 18–22 Suggest students
first make sure the matrices have
the same dimension.

Differentiated Instruction Resources

GPS Guided Problem Solving	L3
Enrichment	L4
Reteaching	L2
Practice	L3

pages 178–179 Exercises

2. $\begin{bmatrix} 2 & -3 & 4 \\ 5 & 6 & -7 \end{bmatrix}$

3. $\begin{bmatrix} 1 & 3 \\ 4 & 0 \end{bmatrix}$

4. $\begin{bmatrix} 3.9 & -2.3 \\ -0.6 & 9.1 \end{bmatrix}$

5. $\begin{bmatrix} 0 & 0 \\ 0 & 0 \end{bmatrix}$

178

EXERCISES

Practice and Problem Solving

Ⓐ Practice by Example

Example 1
(page 174)

GO for Help

1. Sports The modern pentathlon is a grueling all-day competition. Each member of a team competes in five events: target shooting, fencing, swimming, horseback riding, and cross-country running. Here are scores for the U.S. women at the 2004 Olympic Games.

U.S. Women's Pentathlon Scores, 2004 Olympics

Event	Anita Allen	Mary Beth Iagorashvili
Shooting	952	760
Fencing	720	832
Swimming	1108	1252
Riding	1172	1144
Running	1044	1064

SOURCE: Athens 2004 Olympic Games

See back of book.
a. Write two 5×1 matrices to represent the individual scores for each event.
b. Find the total score for each woman. **4996; 5052**

Examples 2 and 3
(pages 175 and 176)

Find each sum or difference. 2–9. See margin.

2. $\begin{bmatrix} 2 & -3 & 4 \\ 5 & 6 & -7 \end{bmatrix} + \begin{bmatrix} 0 & 0 & 0 \\ 0 & 0 & 0 \end{bmatrix}$

3. $\begin{bmatrix} 1 & 3 \\ 4 & 0 \end{bmatrix} + \begin{bmatrix} 0 & 5 \\ -1 & 2 \end{bmatrix} + \begin{bmatrix} 0 & -5 \\ 1 & -2 \end{bmatrix}$

4. $\begin{bmatrix} 6.4 & -1.9 \\ -6.4 & 0.8 \end{bmatrix} + \begin{bmatrix} -2.5 & -0.4 \\ 5.8 & 8.3 \end{bmatrix}$

5. $\begin{bmatrix} 6 & -3 \\ -7 & 2 \end{bmatrix} + \begin{bmatrix} -6 & 3 \\ 7 & -2 \end{bmatrix}$

6. $\begin{bmatrix} 5 & 4 & 3 \\ 1 & -2 & 6 \end{bmatrix} - \begin{bmatrix} 1 & 1 & 1 \\ 1 & 1 & 1 \end{bmatrix}$

7. $\begin{bmatrix} 2 & 1 & 2 \\ 1 & 2 & 1 \end{bmatrix} - \begin{bmatrix} 2 & 3 & 2 \\ 3 & 2 & 3 \end{bmatrix}$

8. $\begin{bmatrix} 0.5 & 9.5 \\ -3.5 & 5.5 \end{bmatrix} - \begin{bmatrix} 0.5 & 9.5 \\ -3.5 & 5.5 \end{bmatrix}$

9. $\begin{bmatrix} 1.5 & -1.9 \\ 0 & 4.6 \end{bmatrix} - \begin{bmatrix} 8.3 & -3.2 \\ 2.1 & 5.6 \end{bmatrix}$

Example 4
(page 176)

Solve each matrix equation. 10–13. See margin.

10. $\begin{bmatrix} 1 & 2 \\ 2 & 1 \\ -3 & 4 \end{bmatrix} + X = \begin{bmatrix} 5 & -6 \\ 1 & 0 \\ 8 & 5 \end{bmatrix}$

11. $\begin{bmatrix} 2 & 1 & -1 \\ 0 & 2 & 1 \end{bmatrix} - X = \begin{bmatrix} 11 & 3 & -13 \\ 15 & -9 & 8 \end{bmatrix}$

12. $X - \begin{bmatrix} 1 & 4 \\ -2 & 3 \end{bmatrix} = \begin{bmatrix} 5 & -2 \\ 1 & 0 \end{bmatrix}$

13. $X + \begin{bmatrix} 6 & 1 \\ -2 & 3 \end{bmatrix} = \begin{bmatrix} 2 & 0 \\ -3 & 1 \end{bmatrix}$

Example 5
(page 177)

Determine whether the two matrices in each pair are equal. Justify your reasoning.
14–15. See margin
pp. 178–179.

14. $\begin{bmatrix} -2 & 3 \\ 5 & 0 \end{bmatrix}, \begin{bmatrix} 2(-1) & 2(1.5) \\ 2(2.5) & 2(0) \end{bmatrix}$

15. $\begin{bmatrix} 4 \\ -6 \\ -8 \end{bmatrix}, \begin{bmatrix} \sqrt{16} & -6 & \sqrt{64} \end{bmatrix}$

Example 6
(page 177)

Find the value of each variable.

16. $\begin{bmatrix} 2 & 2 \\ -1 & 6 \end{bmatrix} - \begin{bmatrix} 4 & -1 \\ 0 & 5 \end{bmatrix} = \begin{bmatrix} x & y \\ -1 & z \end{bmatrix}$

$x = -2, y = 3, z = 1$

17. $\begin{bmatrix} 2 & 4 \\ 8 & 12 \end{bmatrix} = \begin{bmatrix} 4x - 6 & -10t + 5x \\ 4x & 15t + 1.5x \end{bmatrix}$

$x = 2, t = \frac{3}{5}$

6. $\begin{bmatrix} 4 & 3 & 2 \\ 0 & -3 & 5 \end{bmatrix}$

7. $\begin{bmatrix} 0 & -2 & 0 \\ -2 & 0 & -2 \end{bmatrix}$

8. $\begin{bmatrix} 0 & 0 \\ 0 & 0 \end{bmatrix}$

9. $\begin{bmatrix} -6.8 & 1.3 \\ -2.1 & -1 \end{bmatrix}$

10. $\begin{bmatrix} 4 & -8 \\ -1 & -1 \\ 11 & 1 \end{bmatrix}$

11. $\begin{bmatrix} -9 & -2 & 12 \\ -15 & 11 & -7 \end{bmatrix}$

12. $\begin{bmatrix} 6 & 2 \\ -1 & 3 \end{bmatrix}$

13. $\begin{bmatrix} -4 & -1 \\ -1 & -2 \end{bmatrix}$

14. Yes; $-2 = 2(-1)$,
$3 = 2(1.5)$, $5 = 2(2.5)$,
and $0 = 2(0)$ are
all correct.

B **Apply Your Skills**

Find each matrix sum or difference if possible. If not possible, explain.

18–22. See back of book.

$$A = \begin{bmatrix} 3 & 4 \\ 6 & -2 \\ 1 & 0 \end{bmatrix} \qquad B = \begin{bmatrix} -3 & 1 \\ 2 & -4 \\ -1 & 5 \end{bmatrix} \qquad C = \begin{bmatrix} 1 & 2 \\ -3 & 1 \end{bmatrix} \qquad D = \begin{bmatrix} 5 & 1 \\ 0 & 2 \end{bmatrix}$$

18. $A + B$ **19.** $B + D$ **20.** $C + D$ **21.** $B - A$ **22.** $C - D$

23. Multiple Choice You can put the pentathlon scores below into three matrices, one for each athlete. If you add the matrices, what does the sum matrix show?

B

U.S. Men's Pentathlon Scores, 2000 World Championship

Event	James Gregory	Velizar Iliev	Chad Senior
Shooting	1132	1072	1072
Fencing	760	910	610
Swimming	1173	1177	1285
Riding	1100	1100	1070
Running	1114	1118	1174

SOURCE: U.S. Modern Pentathlon Association

A the total team score   B the team score for each event

C each athlete's total score   D each athlete's score for each event

Solve each matrix equation for X.

24. $\begin{bmatrix} 1 & 2 & -3 \\ 2 & 1 & 3 \end{bmatrix} + X = \begin{bmatrix} 5 & 1 & 8 \\ -6 & 0 & 5 \end{bmatrix}$

25. $X - \begin{bmatrix} 4 & 12 \\ 75 & -1 \end{bmatrix} = \begin{bmatrix} 5 & 50 \\ 50 & -10 \end{bmatrix}$

24. $\begin{bmatrix} 4 & -1 & 11 \\ -8 & -1 & 2 \end{bmatrix}$

25. $\begin{bmatrix} 9 & 62 \\ 125 & -11 \end{bmatrix}$

26. Data Analysis Refer to the table.
a. Find the total number of people participating in each activity.
b. Find the difference between the numbers of males and females in each activity.
c. Reasoning In part (b), does the order of the matrices matter? Explain. **a–c. See margin.**

U.S. Participation in Selected Leisure Activities (millions)

Activity	Male	Female
Movies	59.2	65.4
Exercise Programs	54.3	59.0
Sports Events	40.5	31.1
Home Improvement	45.4	41.8

SOURCE: U.S. National Endowment for the Arts.
Go to **www.PHSchool.com** for a data update.
Web-Code: agg-9041

27. Manufacturing The table below
GPS shows the number of beach balls produced during one shift at two manufacturing plants. Plant 1 has two shifts per day and Plant 2 has three shifts per day.

Beach Ball Production Per Shift

	1-color		3-color	
	Plastic	Rubber	Plastic	Rubber
Plant 1	500	700	1300	1900
Plant 2	400	1200	600	1600

a–b. See back of book.

a. Write matrices to represent one day's total output at the two plants.
b. Use your results from part (a). Find the difference between production totals at the plants. Which plant produces more three-color plastic balls? Which plant produces more one-color rubber balls?

Real-World Connection

In the riding portion of the modern pentathlon, the athletes are given 20 min to get to know their horses before riding a 400-m course with 15 obstacles.

GO Online
Homework Video Tutor
Visit: PHSchool.com
Web Code: age-0402

15. No; the matrices have different dimensions.

26a. $\begin{bmatrix} 124.6 \\ 113.3 \\ 71.6 \\ 87.2 \end{bmatrix}$

b. $\begin{bmatrix} -6.2 \\ -4.7 \\ 9.4 \\ 3.6 \end{bmatrix}$

c. Yes, order matters because subtraction is not commutative.

4. Assess & Reteach

PowerPoint
Lesson Quiz

Find each sum or difference.

1. $\begin{bmatrix} 2 & 8 \\ 0 & -12 \end{bmatrix} + \begin{bmatrix} -9 & 6 \\ 6 & -5 \end{bmatrix}$

$\begin{bmatrix} -7 & 14 \\ 6 & -17 \end{bmatrix}$

2. $\begin{bmatrix} -3 & 1 \\ 4 & 8 \\ -5 & 4 \end{bmatrix} - \begin{bmatrix} -3 & -2 \\ 9 & 5 \\ 4 & -6 \end{bmatrix}$

$\begin{bmatrix} 0 & 3 \\ -5 & 3 \\ -9 & 10 \end{bmatrix}$

3. What is the additive identity for 2 × 4 matrices?

$\begin{bmatrix} 0 & 0 & 0 & 0 \\ 0 & 0 & 0 & 0 \end{bmatrix}$

4. Solve the equation for x and y.

$\begin{bmatrix} -2x & -1 \\ 5 & x+y \end{bmatrix} = \begin{bmatrix} 18 & -3x+4y \\ x-2y & -16 \end{bmatrix}$

$x = -9, y = -7$

5. Are the following matrices equal?

$\begin{bmatrix} 3 & 0.5 \\ \frac{2}{5} & -\frac{2}{3} \end{bmatrix}; \begin{bmatrix} \frac{6}{2} & 0.50 \\ 0.4 & -0.6 \end{bmatrix}$ **no**

6. Solve $X - \begin{bmatrix} 4 & 3 \\ 1 & 5 \end{bmatrix} = \begin{bmatrix} 2 & 7 \\ 0 & 6 \end{bmatrix}$ for the matrix X.

$\begin{bmatrix} 6 & 10 \\ 1 & 11 \end{bmatrix}$

Alternative Assessment

Have students work in pairs. Each student writes a 3 × 2 matrix. Next, each student subtracts the matrix that he or she wrote from the matrix that the partner wrote. They add their results. The sum should be the 3 × 2 additive identity matrix. If it is not, each student needs to check the other's work to discover where the errors occurred.

Test Prep

 Resources
For additional practice with a variety of test item formats:
• Standardized Test Prep, p. 233
• Test-Taking Strategies, p. 228
• Test-Taking Strategies with Transparencies

pages 178–180   Exercises

28a. To find $A + B$ you would add the corresponding elements. To find $A - B$ you would subtract the elements in B from the corresponding elements in A.

b. Matrix C would be the same dimension as A. Its elements would be the opposites of the corresponding elements in A.

29. $a = 2, b = \frac{9}{4}, c = -1,$
$d = 0, f = \frac{1}{2}, g = -4$

30. $x = \pm 3, y = 0$ or 5

31. $c = \frac{5}{2}, d = \frac{2}{5}, f = 7,$
$g = 5, h = -1$

33. Consider any two 2×2 matrices, $A = \begin{bmatrix} a & b \\ c & d \end{bmatrix}$ and $B = \begin{bmatrix} w & x \\ y & z \end{bmatrix}$. By the def. of matrix addition and the Comm. Prop. of Add.,

$A + B = \begin{bmatrix} a & b \\ c & d \end{bmatrix} + \begin{bmatrix} w & x \\ y & z \end{bmatrix} =$

$\begin{bmatrix} a + w & b + x \\ c + y & d + z \end{bmatrix} =$

$\begin{bmatrix} w + a & x + b \\ y + c & z + d \end{bmatrix} = B + A$

34. Consider any three 2×2 matrices

$A = \begin{bmatrix} a & b \\ c & d \end{bmatrix}, B = \begin{bmatrix} e & f \\ g & h \end{bmatrix},$

and $C = \begin{bmatrix} w & x \\ y & z \end{bmatrix}$.

By the definition of matrix addition and the Assoc. Prop. of Add.,

$A + (B + C) =$

180

---

 28. **Writing** Suppose A and B are two matrices with the same dimensions.
 a. Explain how to find $A + B$ and $A - B$.   a–b. See margin.
 b. Explain how to find a matrix C such that $A + C = O$.

Solve each equation for each variable.   29–31. See margin.

29. $\begin{bmatrix} 4b + 2 & -3 & 4d \\ -4a & 2 & 3 \\ 2f - 1 & -14 & 1 \end{bmatrix} = \begin{bmatrix} 11 & 2c - 1 & 0 \\ -8 & 2 & 3 \\ 0 & 3g - 2 & 1 \end{bmatrix}$

30. $\begin{bmatrix} x^2 & 4 \\ -2 & y^2 \end{bmatrix} = \begin{bmatrix} 9 & 4 \\ -2 & 5y \end{bmatrix}$

31. $\begin{bmatrix} 4c & 2 - d & 5 \\ -3 & -1 & 2 \\ 0 & -10 & 15 \end{bmatrix} = \begin{bmatrix} 2c + 5 & 4d & g \\ -3 & h & f - g \\ 0 & -4c & 15 \end{bmatrix}$

Ⓒ Challenge

32. Find the sum of $E = \begin{bmatrix} 3 \\ 4 \\ 7 \end{bmatrix}$ and the additive inverse of $G = \begin{bmatrix} -2 \\ 0 \\ 5 \end{bmatrix}$. $\begin{bmatrix} 5 \\ 4 \\ 2 \end{bmatrix}$

33. Prove that matrix addition is commutative for 2×2 matrices. **See margin.**

34. Prove that matrix addition is associative for 2×2 matrices. **See margin.**

 Test Prep

Multiple Choice

Use matrices $A = \begin{bmatrix} 5 & 7 & 3 \\ -1 & 0 & -4 \end{bmatrix}$ and $C = \begin{bmatrix} -7 & 4 & 2 \\ 1 & -2 & -3 \end{bmatrix}$ for Exercises 35 and 36.

35. What is the sum $A + C$? **B**
 A. The matrices cannot be added.
 B. $\begin{bmatrix} -2 & 11 & 5 \\ 0 & -2 & -7 \end{bmatrix}$ **C.** $\begin{bmatrix} 12 & 3 & 1 \\ -2 & 2 & -1 \end{bmatrix}$ **D.** $\begin{bmatrix} -35 & 28 & 6 \\ -1 & 0 & 12 \end{bmatrix}$

36. What is matrix Y if $Y - A = \begin{bmatrix} 1 & 0 & 1 \\ 0 & 1 & 0 \end{bmatrix}$? **G**
 F. $\begin{bmatrix} 4 & 7 & 2 \\ -1 & -1 & -5 \end{bmatrix}$ **G.** $\begin{bmatrix} 6 & 7 & 4 \\ -1 & 1 & -4 \end{bmatrix}$ **H.** $\begin{bmatrix} -6 & 4 & 3 \\ 1 & -1 & -3 \end{bmatrix}$ **J.** $\begin{bmatrix} -4 & -7 & -2 \\ 1 & 1 & 5 \end{bmatrix}$

Short Response

Find the value of each variable. **37–38. See margin.**

37. $\begin{bmatrix} x & y - 2 \\ z & w + 4 \end{bmatrix} + \begin{bmatrix} 2 & 5 \\ -2 & 4 \end{bmatrix} = \begin{bmatrix} 6 & 1 \\ 4 & 8 \end{bmatrix}$

38. $\begin{bmatrix} x & 3 \\ x & -2 \end{bmatrix} + \begin{bmatrix} y & 6 \\ -y & 3 \end{bmatrix} = \begin{bmatrix} 6 & 9 \\ 4 & 1 \end{bmatrix}$

Mixed Review

GO for Help

Lesson 4-1

39. **Open-Ended** Write a real-world problem that you can represent with a matrix. Write a matrix for the problem. Label the rows and columns.
 Check students' work.

Lesson 3-2 🌐 **40.** **Business** Your friend's mother plans to open a restaurant. The initial investment is \$90,000. Weekly expenses will be about \$8200. If the weekly income is about \$8900, in how many weeks will she get back her investment?
 about 129 weeks

Lesson 2-2

Find the slope and y-intercept of the graph of each function.

41. $y = 2x - 6$ **42.** $3y = 6 + 2x$ **43.** $-x - 2y = 12$ **44.** $y = 5x$
  $2, -6$ $\frac{2}{3}, 2$ $-\frac{1}{2}, -6$ $5, 0$

$\begin{bmatrix} a & b \\ c & d \end{bmatrix} + \left(\begin{bmatrix} e & f \\ g & h \end{bmatrix} + \begin{bmatrix} w & x \\ y & z \end{bmatrix} \right)$

$= \begin{bmatrix} a & b \\ c & d \end{bmatrix} + \begin{bmatrix} e + w & f + x \\ g + y & h + z \end{bmatrix}$

$= \begin{bmatrix} a + (e + w) & b + (f + x) \\ c + (g + y) & d + (h + z) \end{bmatrix}$

$= \begin{bmatrix} (a + e) + w & (b + f) + x \\ (c + g) + y & (d + h) + z \end{bmatrix}$

$= \begin{bmatrix} a + e & b + f \\ c + g & d + h \end{bmatrix} + \begin{bmatrix} w & x \\ y & z \end{bmatrix}$

$= (A + B) + C$

37. [2] $x = 4, y = -2,$
    $w = 0, z = 6$
   [1] contains a minor error

38. [2] $x = 5, y = 1$
   [1] contains a minor error

Working With Matrices

FOR USE WITH LESSON 4-2

Go Online
PHSchool.com
For: Graphing calculator procedures
Web Code: age-2113

You can use a graphing calculator to work with matrices. First you need to enter the matrix into the calculator.

1 EXAMPLE

Enter matrix $A = \begin{bmatrix} -3 & 4 \\ 7 & -5 \\ 0 & -2 \end{bmatrix}$ into your graphing calculator. Select the **EDIT** option of

the **MATRIX** feature to edit matrix [A]. Specify a 3×2 matrix by pressing 3 ENTER 2 ENTER.

Enter the matrix elements one row at a time, pressing ENTER after each element. Then use the **QUIT** feature to return to the main screen.

You can use a graphing calculator to perform matrix operations.

2 EXAMPLE

Perform each operation for matrix $A = \begin{bmatrix} -3 & 4 \\ 7 & -5 \\ 0 & -2 \end{bmatrix}$ and matrix $B = \begin{bmatrix} 10 & -7 \\ 4 & -3 \\ -12 & 11 \end{bmatrix}$.

a. $A + B$

Use the **EDIT** option to select the matrices you want to add. Press ENTER to see the sum.

```
[A] + [B]
   [[ 7     -3   ]
    [ 11    -8   ]
    [ -12    9   ]]
```

b. $A - B$

Use the **EDIT** option to select the matrices you want to subtract. Press ENTER to see the difference.

```
[A] − [B]
   [[ -13   11   ]
    [ 3     -2   ]
    [ 12    -13  ]]
```

EXERCISES

Find each sum or difference. 1–6. See margin.

1. $\begin{bmatrix} 0 & -3 \\ 5 & -7 \end{bmatrix} - \begin{bmatrix} -5 & 3 \\ 4 & 10 \end{bmatrix}$

2. $\begin{bmatrix} 3 & 5 & -7 \\ 0 & -2 & 0 \end{bmatrix} + \begin{bmatrix} -1 & 6 & 2 \\ -9 & 4 & 0 \end{bmatrix}$

3. $\begin{bmatrix} 3 \\ 5 \end{bmatrix} - \begin{bmatrix} -6 \\ 7 \end{bmatrix}$

4. $[3 \quad 5 \quad -8] + [-6 \quad 4 \quad 1]$

5. $\begin{bmatrix} 17 & 8 & 0 \\ 3 & -5 & 2 \end{bmatrix} - \begin{bmatrix} 4 & 6 & 5 \\ 2 & -2 & 9 \end{bmatrix}$

6. $[-9 \quad 6 \quad 4] + [-3 \quad 8 \quad 4]$

---

1. $\begin{bmatrix} 5 & -6 \\ 1 & -17 \end{bmatrix}$

2. $\begin{bmatrix} 2 & 11 & -5 \\ -9 & 2 & 0 \end{bmatrix}$

3. $\begin{bmatrix} 9 \\ -2 \end{bmatrix}$

4. $[-3 \quad 9 \quad -7]$

5. $\begin{bmatrix} 13 & 2 & -5 \\ 1 & -3 & -7 \end{bmatrix}$

6. $[-12 \quad 14 \quad 8]$

Working With Matrices

Students enter matrices on a graphing calculator and use the calculator to calculate sums and differences of matrices. Calculators can be especially useful in later lessons where students consider matrix multiplication, determinants, and inverse matrices.

Guided Instruction

Technology Tip

Point out that the NAMES menu on the 2nd [MATRX] screen shows the dimensions of the matrices currently stored in the calculator. This listing can be helpful when you want to check quickly whether there has been an error entering the dimensions of a matrix.

Error Prevention!

Students will find it a good idea to check that they have entered all elements correctly in the matrices before they perform calculations on the matrices. They can do this by returning to the appropriate matrix edit screen or by pressing 2nd [MATRX], the key for the name of the matrix they wish to check, and the ENTER key. The calculator will display the matrix on the home screen.

Resources

Students may use any graphing calculator with matrix calculation capabilities.

4-3

Matrix Multiplication

Objectives
1 To multiply a matrix by a scalar
2 To multiply two matrices

Examples
1 Real-World Connection
2 Using Scalar Products
3 Solving Matrix Equations with Scalars
4 Multiplying Matrices
5 Real-World Connection
6 Determining Whether a Product Matrix Exists

Math Background

Matrices are typically students' first exposure to a set with addition and multiplication operations that do not satisfy all the usual properties of real numbers. For instance, matrix multiplication is not commutative. Also, multiplicative inverses only exist for $n \times n$ matrices with nonzero determinants.

More Math Background: p. 166C

Lesson Planning and Resources

See p. 166E for a list of the resources that support this lesson.

Bell Ringer Practice

✓ **Check Skills You'll Need**
For intervention, direct students to:

Adding and Subtracting Matrices
Lesson 4-2: Example 2
Extra Skills and Word Problems Practice, Ch. 4

What You'll Learn

• To multiply a matrix by a scalar

• To multiply two matrices

. . . And Why

To calculate the gross income, as in Example 5

✓ **Check Skills You'll Need**

GO for Help Lesson 4-2

Find each sum.

1. $\begin{bmatrix} 3 & 5 \\ 2 & 8 \end{bmatrix} + \begin{bmatrix} 3 & 5 \\ 2 & 8 \end{bmatrix} + \begin{bmatrix} 3 & 5 \\ 2 & 8 \end{bmatrix}$ $\begin{bmatrix} 9 & 15 \\ 6 & 24 \end{bmatrix}$

2. $\begin{bmatrix} -4 \\ 7 \end{bmatrix} + \begin{bmatrix} -4 \\ 7 \end{bmatrix} + \begin{bmatrix} -4 \\ 7 \end{bmatrix} + \begin{bmatrix} -4 \\ 7 \end{bmatrix} + \begin{bmatrix} -4 \\ 7 \end{bmatrix}$ $\begin{bmatrix} -20 \\ 35 \end{bmatrix}$

3. $\begin{bmatrix} -1 & 3 & 4 \\ 0 & -2 & -5 \end{bmatrix} + \begin{bmatrix} -1 & 3 & 4 \\ 0 & -2 & -5 \end{bmatrix} + \begin{bmatrix} -1 & 3 & 4 \\ 0 & -2 & -5 \end{bmatrix} + \begin{bmatrix} -1 & 3 & 4 \\ 0 & -2 & -5 \end{bmatrix}$

🔊 **New Vocabulary** • scalar • scalar multiplication • matrix multiplication

3. $\begin{bmatrix} -4 & 12 & 16 \\ 0 & -8 & -20 \end{bmatrix}$

1 Multiplying a Matrix by a Scalar

You can multiply a matrix by a real number.

$$3\begin{bmatrix} 3 & 5 \\ 2 & 8 \end{bmatrix} = \begin{bmatrix} 9 & 15 \\ 6 & 24 \end{bmatrix}$$

The real number factor (such as 3) is called a **scalar.**

Key Concepts

Definition	**Scalar Multiplication**

Scalar multiplication multiplies a matrix A by a scalar c. To find the resulting matrix cA, multiply each element of A by c.

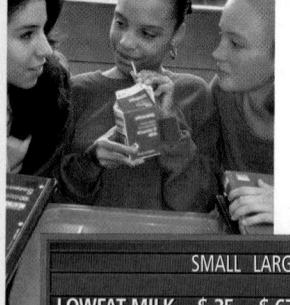

1 EXAMPLE Real-World Connection

Prices Use the price list. The cafeteria plans to raise the cost of each beverage to one and a half times the current cost. How much will each beverage cost?

$$1.5\begin{bmatrix} 0.35 & 0.67 \\ 0.65 & 0.89 \\ 0.58 & 0.75 \end{bmatrix} = \begin{bmatrix} 1.5(0.35) & 1.5(0.67) \\ 1.5(0.65) & 1.5(0.89) \\ 1.5(0.58) & 1.5(0.75) \end{bmatrix}$$ Multiply each element by 1.5.

$$\approx \begin{bmatrix} 0.53 & 1.01 \\ 0.98 & 1.34 \\ 0.87 & 1.13 \end{bmatrix}$$ Simplify.

	SMALL	LARGE
LOWFAT MILK	$.35	$.67
ORANGE JUICE	$.65	$.89
TOMATO JUICE	$.58	$.75

Milk will cost $.53 and $1.01. Orange juice will cost $.98 and $1.34. Tomato juice will cost $.87 and $1.13.

✓ **Quick Check** ❶ Find $-3\begin{bmatrix} 15 & -12 & 10 & 0 \\ 20 & -10 & 7 & 0 \end{bmatrix}$. $\begin{bmatrix} -45 & 36 & -30 & 0 \\ -60 & 30 & -21 & 0 \end{bmatrix}$

182 Chapter 4 Matrices

Differentiated Instruction **Solutions for All Learners**

Special Needs L1
To help students with Example 6, have students write the dimensions of the matrices side by side and circle the two middle numbers. If these numbers are equal, then the product exists. If they are not equal, then the product does not exist.

learning style: verbal

Below Level L2
Carefully demonstrate how, in a matrix product, the number of columns of the first matrix must equal the number of rows of the second.

learning style: visual

You can find sums and differences of matrices multiplied by scalars.

2 **EXAMPLE** Using Scalar Products

Find the difference $5A - 3B$ for $A = \begin{bmatrix} 2 & 3 & -7 \\ 1 & 4 & 5 \end{bmatrix}$ and $B = \begin{bmatrix} 3 & 0 & 6 \\ -1 & 8 & 2 \end{bmatrix}$.

$5A - 3B = 5\begin{bmatrix} 2 & 3 & -7 \\ 1 & 4 & 5 \end{bmatrix} - 3\begin{bmatrix} 3 & 0 & 6 \\ -1 & 8 & 2 \end{bmatrix}$

$= \begin{bmatrix} 10 & 15 & -35 \\ 5 & 20 & 25 \end{bmatrix} - \begin{bmatrix} 9 & 0 & 18 \\ -3 & 24 & 6 \end{bmatrix} = \begin{bmatrix} 1 & 15 & -53 \\ 8 & -4 & 19 \end{bmatrix}$

2a. $\begin{bmatrix} 7 & -12 & 58 \\ -9 & 24 & -10 \end{bmatrix}$

b. $\begin{bmatrix} 20 & 3 & 29 \\ -5 & 52 & 17 \end{bmatrix}$

✓ **Quick Check** 2 Use matrices A and B from Example 2. Find each sum or difference.

    a. $5B - 4A$ **b.** $A + 6B$

🔑 **Key Concepts**

Properties	**Scalar Multiplication**
If $A, B,$ and O are $m \times n$ matrices and c and d are scalars, then	
cA is an $m \times n$ matrix.	Closure Property
$(cd)A = c(dA)$	Associative Property of Multiplication
$c(A + B) = cA + cB$ $(c + d)A = cA + dA$	Distributive Property
$1 \cdot A = A$	Multiplicative Identity Property
$0 \cdot A = O$ and $cO = O$	Multiplicative Property of Zero

Vocabulary Tip

O is the <u>zero</u> <u>matrix</u>—the $m \times n$ matrix with every element zero.

You can use the properties of scalar multiplication to solve matrix equations.

3 **EXAMPLE** Solving Matrix Equations with Scalars

Solve $4X + 2\begin{bmatrix} 3 & 4 \\ -2 & 1 \end{bmatrix} = \begin{bmatrix} 10 & 0 \\ 4 & 2 \end{bmatrix}$.

$4X + 2\begin{bmatrix} 3 & 4 \\ -2 & 1 \end{bmatrix} = \begin{bmatrix} 10 & 0 \\ 4 & 2 \end{bmatrix}$

$4X + \begin{bmatrix} 6 & 8 \\ -4 & 2 \end{bmatrix} = \begin{bmatrix} 10 & 0 \\ 4 & 2 \end{bmatrix}$ Scalar multiplication

$4X = \begin{bmatrix} 10 & 0 \\ 4 & 2 \end{bmatrix} - \begin{bmatrix} 6 & 8 \\ -4 & 2 \end{bmatrix}$ Subtract $\begin{bmatrix} 6 & 8 \\ -4 & 2 \end{bmatrix}$ from each side.

$4X = \begin{bmatrix} 4 & -8 \\ 8 & 0 \end{bmatrix}$ Simplify.

$X = \frac{1}{4}\begin{bmatrix} 4 & -8 \\ 8 & 0 \end{bmatrix} = \begin{bmatrix} 1 & -2 \\ 2 & 0 \end{bmatrix}$ Multiply each side by $\frac{1}{4}$ and simplify.

Check $4X + 2\begin{bmatrix} 3 & 4 \\ -2 & 1 \end{bmatrix} = \begin{bmatrix} 10 & 0 \\ 4 & 2 \end{bmatrix}$

$4\begin{bmatrix} 1 & -2 \\ 2 & 0 \end{bmatrix} + 2\begin{bmatrix} 3 & 4 \\ -2 & 1 \end{bmatrix} \overset{?}{=} \begin{bmatrix} 10 & 0 \\ 4 & 2 \end{bmatrix}$ Substitute.

$\begin{bmatrix} 4 & -8 \\ 8 & 0 \end{bmatrix} + \begin{bmatrix} 6 & 8 \\ -4 & 2 \end{bmatrix} \overset{?}{=} \begin{bmatrix} 10 & 0 \\ 4 & 2 \end{bmatrix}$ Multiply.

$\begin{bmatrix} 10 & 0 \\ 4 & 2 \end{bmatrix} = \begin{bmatrix} 10 & 0 \\ 4 & 2 \end{bmatrix}$ ✓ Simplify.

---

2. Teach

Guided Instruction

1 **EXAMPLE**   **Connection to Algebra**

Relate scalar multiplication to the Distributive Property. You multiply the scalar by each element inside the matrix brackets.

💻 **PowerPoint**

📽 **Additional Examples**

① The table shows the salaries of the three managers (M1, M2, M3) in each of two branches (A and B) of a retail clothing company. The president of the company has decided to give each manager an 8% raise. Show the new salaries in a matrix.

Store	M1	M2	M3
A	$38,500	$40,000	$44,600
B	$39,000	$37,800	$43,700

       M1   M2   M3

$\begin{matrix} A \\ B \end{matrix}\begin{bmatrix} 41{,}580 & 43{,}200 & 48{,}168 \\ 42{,}120 & 40{,}824 & 47{,}196 \end{bmatrix}$

② Find the sum $-3M + 7N$ for $M = \begin{bmatrix} 2 & -3 \\ 0 & 6 \end{bmatrix}$ and $N = \begin{bmatrix} -5 & -1 \\ 2 & 9 \end{bmatrix}$.

$\begin{bmatrix} -41 & 2 \\ 14 & 45 \end{bmatrix}$

③ Solve the equation for Y.

$-3Y + 2\begin{bmatrix} 6 & 9 \\ -12 & 15 \end{bmatrix} = \begin{bmatrix} 27 & -18 \\ 30 & 6 \end{bmatrix}$

$\begin{bmatrix} -5 & 12 \\ -18 & 8 \end{bmatrix}$

Advanced Learners   **L4**

Have students find examples of matrices A and B where $AB = BA$, and where AB and BA exist, but $AB \neq BA$

learning style: verbal

English Language Learners   **ELL**

Emphasize that a *scalar* is a value that can be described using a single number, such as the number 3. The point (0, 3) is not a scalar because it cannot be described using one number. A matrix is not a scalar.

learning style: verbal

Activity

Students may have difficulty understanding why one matrix is written as a single row and the other as a single column. It may help to point out that this format emphasizes that the matrices represent different categories of data—the costs of lunches and the number of lunches sold.

4 EXAMPLE **Visual Learners**

Suggest students imagine that they are physically lifting a column of elements out of the second factor and turning it to fit on a row of the first factor. Help students relate this procedure to the definition of matrix multiplication that follows the example.

5 EXAMPLE **Auditory Learners**

Students may find it helpful to explain orally what each term represents in the matrix after the first equal sign.

6 EXAMPLE **Math Tip**

Call attention to the fact that $GH \neq HG$. Unlike multiplication of scalars, such as numbers, a matrix product is not likely to be commutative under multiplication. So, one product can exist while the other does not exist.

PowerPoint

Additional Examples

4 Find the product of $\begin{bmatrix} -2 & 5 \\ 3 & -1 \end{bmatrix}$ and $\begin{bmatrix} 4 & -4 \\ 2 & 6 \end{bmatrix}$.

$\begin{bmatrix} 2 & 38 \\ 10 & -18 \end{bmatrix}$

 Quick Check **3** Solve each matrix equation. Check your answer.

a. $2X = \begin{bmatrix} 4 & 12 \\ 1 & -4 \end{bmatrix} + \begin{bmatrix} -2 & 0 \\ 3 & 4 \end{bmatrix}$ **b.** $-3X + \begin{bmatrix} 7 & 0 & -1 \\ 2 & -3 & 4 \end{bmatrix} = \begin{bmatrix} 10 & 0 & 8 \\ -19 & -18 & 10 \end{bmatrix}$

3a. $\begin{bmatrix} 1 & 6 \\ 2 & 0 \end{bmatrix}$ **3b.** $\begin{bmatrix} -1 & 0 & -3 \\ 7 & 5 & -2 \end{bmatrix}$

2 Multiplying Matrices

 Test-Taking Tip

Read questions about tables carefully. Make sure you choose the correct rows, columns, and cells.

Activity: Using Matrices

Use the data in the table.

	Lunch 1	Lunch 2	Lunch 3
Cost per Lunch	$2.50	$1.75	$2.00
Number Sold	50	100	75

1. How much money did the cafeteria collect selling lunch 1? Selling lunch 2? Selling lunch 3? **$125; $175; $150**

2. a. How much did the cafeteria collect selling all three lunches? **$450**
   b. Explain how you used the data in the table to find your answer.
                                                    See margin.

3. a. Write a 1 × 3 matrix to represent the cost of the lunches.
   b. Write a 3 × 1 matrix to represent the number of lunches sold.
   c. Writing Describe a procedure for using your matrices to find how much money the cafeteria collected from selling all three lunches. Use the words *row*, *column*, and *element*.
   a–c. See margin.

 Graphing Calculator Hint

You can use the MATRIX feature of a graphing calculator to multiply matrices.

To perform **matrix multiplication,** multiply the elements of each *row* of the first matrix by the elements of each *column* of the second matrix. Add the products.

4 EXAMPLE **Multiplying Matrices**

Find the product of $\begin{bmatrix} -1 & 0 \\ 3 & -4 \end{bmatrix}$ and $\begin{bmatrix} -3 & 3 \\ 5 & 0 \end{bmatrix}$.

Multiply a_{11} and b_{11}. Then multiply a_{12} and b_{21}. Add the products.

$\begin{bmatrix} -1 & 0 \\ 3 & -4 \end{bmatrix}\begin{bmatrix} -3 & 3 \\ 5 & 0 \end{bmatrix} = \begin{bmatrix} ? & \blacksquare \\ \blacksquare & \blacksquare \end{bmatrix}$ $(-1)(-3) + (0)(5) = 3$

The result is the element in the first row and first column. Repeat with the rest of the rows and columns.

$\begin{bmatrix} -1 & 0 \\ 3 & -4 \end{bmatrix}\begin{bmatrix} -3 & 3 \\ 5 & 0 \end{bmatrix} = \begin{bmatrix} 3 & ? \\ \blacksquare & \blacksquare \end{bmatrix}$ $(-1)(3) + (0)(0) = -3$

$\begin{bmatrix} -1 & 0 \\ 3 & -4 \end{bmatrix}\begin{bmatrix} -3 & 3 \\ 5 & 0 \end{bmatrix} = \begin{bmatrix} 3 & -3 \\ ? & \blacksquare \end{bmatrix}$ $(3)(-3) + (-4)(5) = -29$

$\begin{bmatrix} -1 & 0 \\ 3 & -4 \end{bmatrix}\begin{bmatrix} -3 & 3 \\ 5 & 0 \end{bmatrix} = \begin{bmatrix} 3 & -3 \\ -29 & ? \end{bmatrix}$ $(3)(3) + (-4)(0) = 9$

The product of $\begin{bmatrix} -1 & 0 \\ 3 & -4 \end{bmatrix}$ and $\begin{bmatrix} -3 & 3 \\ 5 & 0 \end{bmatrix}$ is $\begin{bmatrix} 3 & -3 \\ -29 & 9 \end{bmatrix}$.

---

page 184 Activity

2b. For each lunch, multiply the number of lunches sold by the cost per lunch. Then add the three products.

3a. A = Cost per lunch

	Lunch 1	Lunch 2	Lunch 3
	[2.50	1.75	2.00]

b. Number Sold

B = $\begin{matrix} \text{Lunch 1} \\ \text{Lunch 2} \\ \text{Lunch 3} \end{matrix} \begin{bmatrix} 50 \\ 100 \\ 75 \end{bmatrix}$

c. Multiply each element in the row of matrix A by the corresponding element in the column for matrix B. Then add the 3 products to find the amount collected from all 3 lunches.

Quick Check ④ **a.** Find the product of $\begin{bmatrix} -3 & 3 \\ 5 & 0 \end{bmatrix}$ and $\begin{bmatrix} -1 & 0 \\ 3 & -4 \end{bmatrix}$. **a–b. See margin.**

b. Critical Thinking Is matrix multiplication commutative? Explain.

Key Concepts

Definition	Matrix Multiplication

To find element c_{ij} of the product matrix AB, multiply each element in the ith row of A by the corresponding element in the jth column of B, and then add.

Real-World Connection

The music on an LP record (a) plays continuously as the stylus travels along the groove. The music on a CD (b) plays in discrete intervals read by a laser.

a   b

5 EXAMPLE Real-World Connection

Gridded Response A used-record store sells tapes, LP records, and compact discs. The matrices show today's information. Find the store's gross income for the day, in dollars.

Prices

Tapes LPs CDs
$[\$8 \quad \$6 \quad \$13]$

Number of Items Sold

$\begin{array}{c} \text{Tapes} \\ \text{LPs} \\ \text{CDs} \end{array} \begin{bmatrix} 9 \\ 30 \\ 20 \end{bmatrix}$

Multiply each price by the number of items sold and add the products.

$[8 \quad 6 \quad 13]\begin{bmatrix} 9 \\ 30 \\ 20 \end{bmatrix} = [8(9) + 6(30) + 13(20)] = [512]$

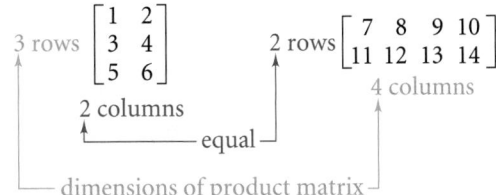

● The store's gross income for the day was $512.

 Quick Check ⑤ Find each product if it exists.

a. $[12 \quad 3]\begin{bmatrix} 10 \\ -5 \end{bmatrix}$ **[105]**

b. $\begin{bmatrix} 10 \\ -5 \end{bmatrix}\begin{bmatrix} 12 & 3 \\ 0 & 0 \end{bmatrix}$ **Product does not exist**

The product of two matrices A and B exists only if the number of *columns* of A is equal to the number of *rows* of B.

Key Concepts

Property	Dimensions of a Product Matrix

If matrix A is an $m \times n$ matrix and matrix B is an $n \times p$ matrix, then the product matrix AB is an $m \times p$ matrix.

Example   matrix A •   matrix B

3 rows $\begin{bmatrix} 1 & 2 \\ 3 & 4 \\ 5 & 6 \end{bmatrix}$ 2 rows $\begin{bmatrix} 7 & 8 & 9 & 10 \\ 11 & 12 & 13 & 14 \end{bmatrix}$

2 columns   4 columns

equal

dimensions of product matrix

The dimensions of product matrix AB are 3×4.

---

5 Matrix A gives the prices of shirts and jeans on sale at a discount store. Matrix B gives the number of these items sold on one day. Find the income for the day from the sale of the shirts and jeans.

$\quad\quad\quad$ Shirts $\quad$ Jeans
$A = [\quad \$18 \quad \$22 \quad]$

$B = \begin{array}{c} \text{Shirts} \\ \text{Jeans} \end{array}\begin{bmatrix} 109 \\ 76 \end{bmatrix}$ \$3634

6 Use the matrices

$P = \begin{bmatrix} 3 & -1 & 2 \\ 5 & 9 & 0 \\ 0 & 1 & 8 \end{bmatrix}$ and

$Q = \begin{bmatrix} 6 & 5 & 7 & 0 \\ 2 & 0 & 3 & 1 \\ 1 & -1 & 5 & 2 \end{bmatrix}$.

Determine whether PQ and QP are defined or undefined. Determine the dimensions of each product.
PQ is defined and is a 3×4 matrix. QP is undefined.

Resources
• Daily Notetaking Guide 4-3 L3

Closure

Ask students how to determine whether a matrix product AB is defined. **The number of columns in A must be the same as the number of rows in B.**

page 185 **Quick Check**

4a. $\begin{bmatrix} 12 & -12 \\ -5 & 0 \end{bmatrix}$

b. No; explanations may vary. Sample: For the matrices in part (a),

$AB = \begin{bmatrix} 12 & -12 \\ -5 & 0 \end{bmatrix}$.

However,

$BA = \begin{bmatrix} 3 & -3 \\ -29 & 9 \end{bmatrix}$,

so $AB \neq BA$.

3. Practice

Assignment Guide

1 A B 1-10, 30-32, 39, 42

2 A B 11-29, 33-38, 40, 41,
43-50

C Challenge   51-56

Test Prep   57-60
Mixed Review   61-68

Homework Quick Check

To check students' understanding
of key skills and concepts, go over
Exercises 9, 19, 37, 49, 50.

Error Prevention!

Exercise 9 Remind students to
perform the scalar multiplication
before using the Subtraction
Property.

Differentiated Instruction Resources

GPS Guided Problem Solving	**L3**
Enrichment	**L4**
Reteaching	**L2**
Practice	**L3**

pages 186–187 Exercises

1. $\begin{bmatrix} 9 & 12 \\ 18 & -6 \\ 3 & 0 \end{bmatrix}$

2. $\begin{bmatrix} -12 & 4 \\ 8 & -16 \\ -4 & 20 \end{bmatrix}$

3. $\begin{bmatrix} -3 & -6 \\ 9 & -3 \end{bmatrix}$

4. $\begin{bmatrix} -5 & -1 \\ 0 & -2 \end{bmatrix}$

186

---

6 **EXAMPLE** **Determining Whether a Product Matrix Exists**

Use matrices $G = \begin{bmatrix} 2 & 3 \\ -1 & 8 \\ 4 & 0 \end{bmatrix}$ and $H = \begin{bmatrix} 8 & 0 \\ 2 & -5 \end{bmatrix}$. Determine whether products GH
and HG are *defined* (exist) or *undefined* (do not exist).

Find the dimensions of each product matrix.

GH	HG
$(3 \times 2)(2 \times 2) \rightarrow 3 \times 2$	$(2 \times 2)(3 \times 2)$
↑ ↑ product	↑ ↑
equal matrix	*not* equal

Product GH is defined and is a 3×2 matrix. Product HG is undefined, because the
number of columns of H is not equal to the number of rows of G.

✓ Quick Check **6** Let $R = \begin{bmatrix} 4 & -2 \\ 5 & -4 \end{bmatrix}$ and $S = \begin{bmatrix} 8 & 0 & -1 & 0 \\ 2 & -5 & 1 & 8 \end{bmatrix}$.

6a. *RS* is defined, but *SR*
is undefined.

b. $RS = \begin{bmatrix} 28 & 10 & -6 & -16 \\ 32 & 20 & -9 & -32 \end{bmatrix}$

a. Determine whether products RS and SR are *defined* or *undefined*.
b. Find each defined product.

Matrix multiplication has some of the properties of real number multiplication.

🔧 Key Concepts

Properties	**Matrix Multiplication**
If A, B, and C are $n \times n$ matrices, then	
AB is an $n \times n$ matrix.	Closure Property
$(AB)C = A(BC)$	Associative Property of Multiplication
$A(B + C) = AB + AC$ $(B + C)A = BA + CA$	Distributive Property
$OA = AO = O$, where O has the same dimensions as A.	Multiplicative Property of Zero

EXERCISES

For more exercises, see *Extra Skill and Word Problem Practice*.

Practice and Problem Solving

A **Practice by Example**

Examples 1 and 2
(pages 182 and 183)

GO for Help

1–8. See margin.

Use matrices A, B, C, and D. Find each product, sum, or difference.

$A = \begin{bmatrix} 3 & 4 \\ 6 & -2 \\ 1 & 0 \end{bmatrix}$ $B = \begin{bmatrix} -3 & 1 \\ 2 & -4 \\ -1 & 5 \end{bmatrix}$ $C = \begin{bmatrix} 1 & 2 \\ -3 & 1 \end{bmatrix}$ $D = \begin{bmatrix} 5 & 1 \\ 0 & 2 \end{bmatrix}$

1. $3A$ **2.** $4B$ **3.** $-3C$ **4.** $-D$

5. $A - 2B$ **6.** $3A + 2B$ **7.** $4C + 3D$ **8.** $2A - 5B$

Example 3
(page 183)

Solve each matrix equation. Check your answers.   9–10. See margin.

9. $3\begin{bmatrix} 2 & 0 \\ -1 & 5 \end{bmatrix} - 2X = \begin{bmatrix} -10 & 5 \\ 0 & 17 \end{bmatrix}$

10. $5X - \begin{bmatrix} 1.5 & -3.6 \\ -0.3 & 2.8 \end{bmatrix} = \begin{bmatrix} 0.2 & 1.3 \\ -5.6 & 1.7 \end{bmatrix}$

5. $\begin{bmatrix} 9 & 2 \\ 2 & 6 \\ 3 & -10 \end{bmatrix}$

6. $\begin{bmatrix} 3 & 14 \\ 22 & -14 \\ 1 & 10 \end{bmatrix}$

7. $\begin{bmatrix} 19 & 11 \\ -12 & 10 \end{bmatrix}$

8. $\begin{bmatrix} 21 & 3 \\ 2 & 16 \\ 7 & -25 \end{bmatrix}$

9. $\begin{bmatrix} 8 & -2.5 \\ -1.5 & -1 \end{bmatrix}$

10. $\begin{bmatrix} 0.34 & -0.46 \\ -1.18 & 0.9 \end{bmatrix}$

Example 4
(page 184)

Find each product. 11–18. See margin.

11. $\begin{bmatrix} -3 & 4 \\ 5 & 2 \end{bmatrix}\begin{bmatrix} 1 & 0 \\ 2 & -3 \end{bmatrix}$ **12.** $\begin{bmatrix} 1 & 0 \\ 2 & -3 \end{bmatrix}\begin{bmatrix} -3 & 4 \\ 5 & 2 \end{bmatrix}$ **13.** $\begin{bmatrix} 0 & 2 \\ -4 & 0 \end{bmatrix}\begin{bmatrix} 0 & 2 \\ -4 & 0 \end{bmatrix}$

14. $\begin{bmatrix} -3 & 5 \end{bmatrix}\begin{bmatrix} -3 \\ 5 \end{bmatrix}$ **15.** $\begin{bmatrix} -3 & 5 \end{bmatrix}\begin{bmatrix} -3 & 0 \\ 5 & 0 \end{bmatrix}$ **16.** $\begin{bmatrix} -3 & 5 \end{bmatrix}\begin{bmatrix} 0 & -3 \\ 0 & 5 \end{bmatrix}$

17. $\begin{bmatrix} 0 & -3 \\ 0 & 5 \end{bmatrix}\begin{bmatrix} -3 & 0 \\ 5 & 0 \end{bmatrix}$ **18.** $\begin{bmatrix} 1 & 0 \\ -1 & -5 \\ 0 & 3 \end{bmatrix}\begin{bmatrix} -1 & 0 \\ 0 & -1 \end{bmatrix}$

Example 5
(page 185)

19. Business A florist makes three special floral arrangements. One uses three lilies. The second uses three lilies and four carnations. The third uses four daisies and three carnations. Lilies cost $2.15 each, carnations cost $.90 each, and daisies cost $1.30 each.
  a. Write a matrix to show the number of each type of flower in each arrangement.
  b. Write a matrix to show the cost of each type of flower.
  c. Find the matrix showing the cost of each floral arrangement. a–c. See back of book.

Example 6
(page 186)

Determine whether each product is defined or undefined.

$F = \begin{bmatrix} 2 & 3 \\ 6 & 9 \end{bmatrix}$ $G = \begin{bmatrix} -3 & 6 \\ 2 & -4 \end{bmatrix}$ $H = \begin{bmatrix} -5 \\ 6 \end{bmatrix}$ $J = \begin{bmatrix} 0 & 7 \end{bmatrix}$

20. FG defined **21.** GF defined **22.** FH defined **23.** HF undefined **24.** GH defined
25. HG undefined **26.** FJ undefined **27.** JF defined **28.** HJ defined **29.** JH defined

B Apply Your Skills

Mental Math Find each product. 30–34. See margin.

30. $2\begin{bmatrix} -1 & 4 \\ 2 & 5 \end{bmatrix}$ **31.** $-1\begin{bmatrix} 9 & -7 & -4 \\ -8 & -2 & 3 \end{bmatrix}$ **32.** $0.5\begin{bmatrix} 3 & 14 \\ 7 & -4 \end{bmatrix}$

33. $\begin{bmatrix} -1 & 0 \\ 0 & -1 \end{bmatrix}\begin{bmatrix} -1 & 0 & 1 \\ 0 & -1 & 1 \end{bmatrix}$ **34.** $\begin{bmatrix} 1 & 0 \\ 0 & -1 \end{bmatrix}\begin{bmatrix} -1 & 0 \\ 0 & -1 \end{bmatrix}$

35. Multiple Choice Columns in matrix $A = \begin{bmatrix} 3 & 8 \\ 0 & 12 \end{bmatrix}$ show, respectively, the numbers of erasers and pencils sold. The rows show, respectively, the numbers sold on Monday and Tuesday. Matrix $B = \begin{bmatrix} 0.50 \\ 0.25 \end{bmatrix}$ shows the 50¢ cost of one eraser and the quarter cost of one pencil. What does the product AB show? **B**
  Ⓐ the total paid for erasers on Monday and Tuesday and the total paid for pencils on Monday and Tuesday
  Ⓑ the total paid for erasers and pencils on Monday and the total paid for erasers and pencils on Tuesday.
  Ⓒ the total paid for pencils and erasers
  Ⓓ the cost of 1 pencil and 1 eraser

GO Online
Homework Video Tutor
Visit: PHSchool.com
Web Code: age-0403

Find the dimensions of each product matrix. Then find each product. 36–37. See margin.

36. $\begin{bmatrix} 5 & 7 & 0 \\ -\frac{4}{5} & 3 & 6 \\ 0 & -\frac{2}{3} & 4 \end{bmatrix}\begin{bmatrix} 2 & -1 \\ 1 & 1 \\ 0 & -1 \end{bmatrix}$ **37.** $\begin{bmatrix} 1 & 0 & 0 \\ 1 & 0 & -2 \\ 0 & 0 & 2 \\ -1 & 0 & 1 \end{bmatrix}\begin{bmatrix} a & 0 & b & 0 \\ 0 & c & 0 & d \\ e & 0 & 0 & f \end{bmatrix}$

30. $\begin{bmatrix} -2 & 8 \\ 4 & 10 \end{bmatrix}$

31. $\begin{bmatrix} -9 & 7 & 4 \\ 8 & 2 & -3 \end{bmatrix}$

32. $\begin{bmatrix} 1.5 & 7 \\ 3.5 & -2 \end{bmatrix}$

33. $\begin{bmatrix} 1 & 0 & -1 \\ 0 & 1 & -1 \end{bmatrix}$

34. $\begin{bmatrix} -1 & 0 \\ 0 & 1 \end{bmatrix}$

36. 3×2; $\begin{bmatrix} 17 & 2 \\ \frac{7}{5} & -\frac{11}{5} \\ -\frac{2}{3} & -\frac{14}{3} \end{bmatrix}$

37. 4×4; $\begin{bmatrix} a & 0 & b & 0 \\ a-2e & 0 & b & -2f \\ 2e & 0 & 0 & 2f \\ -a+e & 0 & -b & f \end{bmatrix}$

---

11. $\begin{bmatrix} 5 & -12 \\ 9 & -6 \end{bmatrix}$

12. $\begin{bmatrix} -3 & 4 \\ -21 & 2 \end{bmatrix}$

13. $\begin{bmatrix} -8 & 0 \\ 0 & -8 \end{bmatrix}$

14. $\begin{bmatrix} 34 \end{bmatrix}$

15. $\begin{bmatrix} 34 & 0 \end{bmatrix}$

16. $\begin{bmatrix} 0 & 34 \end{bmatrix}$

17. $\begin{bmatrix} -15 & 0 \\ 25 & 0 \end{bmatrix}$

18. $\begin{bmatrix} -1 & 0 \\ 1 & 5 \\ 0 & -3 \end{bmatrix}$

PowerPoint

Lesson Quiz

Use matrices *A*, *B*, *C*, and *D*.

$A = \begin{bmatrix} 2 & 3 & -1 \\ 0 & -5 & 4 \end{bmatrix}$

$B = \begin{bmatrix} -7 & 1 & 0 \\ 2 & 6 & -6 \end{bmatrix}$

$C = \begin{bmatrix} 2 \\ 9 \\ 4 \end{bmatrix}$

$D = \begin{bmatrix} -3 & 2 & -1 \end{bmatrix}$

1. Find 8*A*. $\begin{bmatrix} 16 & 24 & -8 \\ 0 & -40 & 32 \end{bmatrix}$

2. Find *AC*. $\begin{bmatrix} 27 \\ -29 \end{bmatrix}$

3. Find *CD*. $\begin{bmatrix} -6 & 4 & -2 \\ -27 & 18 & -9 \\ -12 & 8 & -4 \end{bmatrix}$

4. Is *BD* defined or undefined? **undefined**

5. What are the dimensions of (*BC*)*D*? **2 × 3**

Alternative Assessment

Have students work in groups of three. Each student writes a 3 × 3 matrix. Students name the matrices *A*, *B*, and *C*. Each student then finds 5*A*, 2*B* − 3*C*, *AB*, and *CA*. Students check one another's work.

pages 186–189 Exercises

38. $\begin{bmatrix} 1 & -6 & -5 \\ 6 & 1 & -5 \\ -3 & -12 & 0 \end{bmatrix}$

39. $\begin{bmatrix} 9 & -6 \\ 15 & -3 \\ -6 & -12 \end{bmatrix}$

40. $\begin{bmatrix} 17 & -24 \\ -33 & -7 \\ 69 & -18 \end{bmatrix}$

41. $\begin{bmatrix} 17 & -24 \\ -33 & -7 \\ 69 & -18 \end{bmatrix}$

42. $\begin{bmatrix} -3 & 12 & -1 \\ -2 & 3 & 5 \\ -4 & -3 & -4 \end{bmatrix}$

188

For Exercises 38–45, use matrices *D*, *E*, and *F* shown below. Perform the indicated operations if they are defined. If an operation is not defined, label it undefined.

$$D = \begin{bmatrix} 1 & 2 & -1 \\ 0 & 3 & 1 \\ 2 & -1 & -2 \end{bmatrix} \quad E = \begin{bmatrix} 2 & -5 & 0 \\ 1 & 0 & -2 \\ 3 & 1 & 1 \end{bmatrix} \quad F = \begin{bmatrix} -3 & 2 \\ -5 & 1 \\ 2 & 4 \end{bmatrix}$$

38. *DE*   **39.** −3*F*   **40.** (*DE*)*F*   **41.** *D*(*EF*)

42. *D* − 2*E*   **43.** (*E* − *D*)*F*   **44.** (*DD*)*E*   **45.** (2*D*)(3*F*)

38–45. See margin.

 46. Business A hardware store chain displays prices in a 1 × 3 matrix and daily purchases at its three stores in a 3 × 3 matrix.

	Prices			**Number of Items Sold**		
					Store A	Store B	Store C
Hammers	Flashlights	Lanterns		Hammers	10	9	8
[$3	$5	$7]		Flashlights	3	14	6
				Lanterns	2	5	7

a. Find the product of the two matrices. Explain what the product represents.
b. How would you find the total gross revenue from all three stores?
c. Find the total gross revenue from the flashlights sold at all three stores.
a–c. See margin p. 189.

OFF THE MARK

47. Math in the Media Refer to the cartoon. An algorithm is a step-by-step description of a calculation rule. What is the algorithm for matrix multiplication?

48. Open-Ended Find two 2 × 2 matrices *X* and *Y*, with not all elements equal, such that *XY* = *YX*.

49. Writing Suppose *A* is a 2 × 3 matrix and *B* is a 3 × 2 matrix. Are *AB* and *BA* equal? Explain your reasoning. Include examples. **See back of book.**

47. Answers may vary. Sample: Multiply the elements in each row of the first matrix by the elements in each column of the second matrix. Then add to get the corresponding entry in the resultant matrix.

48. Answers may vary. Sample:
$\begin{bmatrix} 1 & 0 \\ 0 & 1 \end{bmatrix}$ and $\begin{bmatrix} 0 & 1 \\ 1 & 0 \end{bmatrix}$

 50. Revenue Write a matrix that represents the daily revenue from the play.
GPS **See back of book.**

Ticket Prices		
Orchestra	Mezzanine	Balcony
$7.00	$6.00	$5.00

Number of Tickets Sold			
Location	Thursday	Friday	Saturday
Orchestra	150	130	160
Mezzanine	125	130	175
Balcony	60	52	80

Challenge

Solve for *x* and *y*.

51. $\begin{bmatrix} 2x & 1 \\ 2 & 0 \end{bmatrix}\begin{bmatrix} 1 & 3 \\ 2 & -y \end{bmatrix} = \begin{bmatrix} -4 & -9 \\ 2 & 6 \end{bmatrix}$
x = −3, *y* = −9

52. $\begin{bmatrix} 2x & 1 \\ 2 & 0 \end{bmatrix}\begin{bmatrix} 0 & 3 \\ 2x & -y \end{bmatrix} = \begin{bmatrix} -4 & -9 \\ 0 & 6 \end{bmatrix}$
x = −2, *y* = −3

For Exercises 53–56, use matrices *P*, *Q*, *R*, *S*, and *I*. Determine whether the two expressions in each pair are equal.

$$P = \begin{bmatrix} 3 & 4 \\ 1 & 2 \end{bmatrix} \quad Q = \begin{bmatrix} -1 & 0 \\ 3 & -2 \end{bmatrix} \quad R = \begin{bmatrix} 1 & 4 \\ -2 & 1 \end{bmatrix} \quad S = \begin{bmatrix} 0 & 1 \\ 2 & 0 \end{bmatrix} \quad I = \begin{bmatrix} 1 & 0 \\ 0 & 1 \end{bmatrix}$$

53. (*P* + *Q*)*R* and *PR* + *QR* **yes**   **54.** (*P* + *Q*)*I* and *PI* + *QI* **yes**

55. (*P* + *Q*)(*R* + *S*) and (*P* + *Q*)*R* + (*P* + *Q*)*S* **yes**

56. (*P* + *Q*)(*R* + *S*) and *PR* + *PS* + *QR* + *QS* **yes**

188 Chapter 4 Matrices

43. $\begin{bmatrix} 34 & -1 \\ 6 & -13 \\ -7 & 16 \end{bmatrix}$

44. $\begin{bmatrix} 16 & 8 & -15 \\ 15 & -9 & -15 \\ 2 & 11 & -5 \end{bmatrix}$

45. $\begin{bmatrix} -90 & 0 \\ -78 & 42 \\ -30 & -30 \end{bmatrix}$

Multiple Choice

57. Which product is NOT defined? **B**

A. $\begin{bmatrix} -1 \\ 2 \end{bmatrix}\begin{bmatrix} -1 & 2 \end{bmatrix}$ B. $\begin{bmatrix} -1 & 2 \\ -1 & 2 \end{bmatrix}\begin{bmatrix} -1 & 2 \end{bmatrix}$ C. $\begin{bmatrix} -1 & 2 \\ -1 & 2 \end{bmatrix}\begin{bmatrix} 2 & -1 \\ 2 & -1 \end{bmatrix}$ D. $\begin{bmatrix} -1 & 2 \end{bmatrix}\begin{bmatrix} -1 \\ 2 \end{bmatrix}$

58. Given $P = \begin{bmatrix} 4 & 3 & -2 \\ -1 & 0 & 5 \end{bmatrix}$ and $Q = \begin{bmatrix} 3 & -2 & -5 \\ -1 & -2 & -1 \end{bmatrix}$, what is $2P - 3Q$? **H**

F. $\begin{bmatrix} 1 & -5 & 3 \\ 0 & -2 & 6 \end{bmatrix}$ G. $\begin{bmatrix} 17 & 0 & 19 \\ -5 & 6 & 7 \end{bmatrix}$ H. $\begin{bmatrix} -1 & 12 & 11 \\ 1 & 6 & 13 \end{bmatrix}$ J. $\begin{bmatrix} 1 & 5 & 3 \\ 0 & 2 & 6 \end{bmatrix}$

Short Response

59. Solve $3Y + 2\begin{bmatrix} -1 & -3 \\ 2 & 5 \end{bmatrix} = \begin{bmatrix} 13 & -9 \\ 4 & 16 \end{bmatrix}$. Show the steps of your solution.
See back of book.

Extended Response

60. Given $M = \begin{bmatrix} -3 & 4 \\ 1 & -2 \end{bmatrix}$ and $N = \begin{bmatrix} 0 & 1 \\ -2 & 5 \end{bmatrix}$, does $M \times N = N \times M$? Explain.
See back of book.

Mixed Review

for Help

Lesson 4-2

Add or subtract. **61–62. See margin.**

61. $\begin{bmatrix} -1 & 2 \\ 0 & 17 \end{bmatrix} - \begin{bmatrix} 32 & 14 \\ 6 & -10 \end{bmatrix}$ **62.** $\begin{bmatrix} 0 & -1 & 5 \\ 6 & 10 & 12 \end{bmatrix} + \begin{bmatrix} 9 & -5 & 7 \\ -4 & 10 & 0 \end{bmatrix}$

Lesson 3-4

Graph each system of constraints. Find all vertices. Then find the values of x and y that maximize or minimize the objective function. **63–65. See back of book.**

63. $\begin{cases} x + y \le 3 \\ x \ge 0 \\ y \le 2 \end{cases}$ **64.** $\begin{cases} x + 2y \le 8 \\ x \ge 2 \\ y \ge 0 \end{cases}$ **65.** $\begin{cases} x + y \le 6 \\ 2x + y \le 10 \\ x \ge 0, y \ge 0 \end{cases}$

Maximize for   Minimize for   Maximize for
$P = 3x + 4y$. $C = x + 3y$. $P = 4x + y$.

Lesson 2-7

Graph each inequality. **66–68. See back of book.**

66. $y < 4x - 1$ **67.** $y \le -3x + 8$ **68.** $y \ge |2x + 5| - 3$

Checkpoint Quiz 1   Lessons 4-1 through 4-3

State the dimensions of each matrix. Identify the indicated element.

1. $\begin{bmatrix} 5 & 2 \\ -8 & 3 \\ 10 & 1 \end{bmatrix}; a_{32}$ **2.** $\begin{bmatrix} 9 & 1 & 7 \\ 6 & -2 & 4 \end{bmatrix}; a_{22}$ **3.** $\begin{bmatrix} 8 & 1 & 5 \\ 9 & 4 & 2 \\ 7 & 0 & 3 \end{bmatrix}; a_{13}$
$3 \times 2; 1$ $2 \times 3; -2$ $3 \times 3; 5$

Use matrices $A, B, C,$ and D. Perform each operation.

$A = \begin{bmatrix} 3 & 1 \\ 5 & 7 \end{bmatrix}$ $B = \begin{bmatrix} 4 & 6 \\ 1 & 0 \end{bmatrix}$ $C = \begin{bmatrix} -5 & 3 \\ 1 & 9 \end{bmatrix}$ $D = \begin{bmatrix} 1.5 & 2 \\ 9 & -6 \end{bmatrix}$

4. $A + C$ **5.** $B - A$ **6.** $3D$ **7.** BA **8.** $C(DB)$
4–10. See margin.

9. Writing How can you decide whether you can multiply two matrices?

10. Open-Ended Write a matrix equation with solution $\begin{bmatrix} 12 & 7 & -3 & 8 \\ 9 & 0 & -11 & 1 \end{bmatrix}$.

46. a. [59 132 103]; the elements are the total sales for the three items at each store.
b. Add the elements of the product matrix in part (a).
c. $115

61. $\begin{bmatrix} -33 & -12 \\ -6 & 27 \end{bmatrix}$

62. $\begin{bmatrix} 9 & -6 & 12 \\ 2 & 20 & 12 \end{bmatrix}$

 Resources

For additional practice with a variety of test item formats:
• Standardized Test Prep, p. 233
• Test-Taking Strategies, p. 228
• Test-Taking Strategies with Transparencies

 Checkpoint Quiz

Use this Checkpoint Quiz to check students' understanding of the skills and concepts of Lessons 4-1 through 4-3.

Resources
Grab & Go
• Checkpoint Quiz 1

page 189   Checkpoint Quiz 1

4. $\begin{bmatrix} -2 & 4 \\ 6 & 16 \end{bmatrix}$

5. $\begin{bmatrix} 1 & 5 \\ -4 & -7 \end{bmatrix}$

6. $\begin{bmatrix} 4.5 & 6 \\ 27 & -18 \end{bmatrix}$

7. $\begin{bmatrix} 42 & 46 \\ 3 & 1 \end{bmatrix}$

8. $\begin{bmatrix} 50 & 117 \\ 278 & 495 \end{bmatrix}$

9. Make sure that the number of columns in the first matrix is the same as the number of rows in the second matrix.

10. Answers may vary. Sample:

$2X + \begin{bmatrix} 1 & 2 & 2 & 4 \\ 0 & 3 & 0 & 5 \end{bmatrix} = \begin{bmatrix} 25 & 16 & -4 & 20 \\ 18 & 3 & -22 & 7 \end{bmatrix}$

189

Geometric Transformations

Students will find it helpful to review basic terminology about geometric transformations before they begin Lesson 4-4.

Guided Instruction

Teaching Tip

You may wish to discuss some of the key features of the four kinds of transformations. For example, translations, reflections and rotations do not change the size or shape of a figure. Dilations do not change the shape of a figure, though they usually change its size. Reflections change orientation, whereas the other transformations do not.

Error Prevention!

Exercise 5a You may wish to tell students that vertices of the preimage can be assumed to be at points with integer coordinates or midway between two points with integer coordinates.

Tactile Learners

Allow students to perform transformations with cut-outs, blocks, or algebra tiles. The actual manipulation of the objects will reinforce the concepts for students.

page 190   Geometry Review

5a. $(-1, 0)$, $(1, 0)$; $(1, 1)$; $(-3, 0)$, $(3, 0)$, $(3, 3)$.

b. **Answers may vary. Sample: You multiply the preimage x- and y-coordinates by the same number to find the x- and y-coordinates of the image. In this transformation, the factor is 3. For example, this is also true for the y-intercept of the slanted side: the preimage is $(0, 0.5)$ and the image is $(3 \cdot 0, 3 \cdot 0.5) = (0, 1.5)$.**

190

Geometric patterns, such as those formed by geese flying south for the winter or tiles on a plane surface, can be described using geometric transformations. A transformation is a change made to a figure. There are four types.

A translation slides a figure a given distance and direction without changing its size or shape.

preimage

image

A rotation turns a figure through a given angle about a point called the center.

preimage

image

A reflection flips a figure over a given line called its axis of reflection.

preimage

image

A dilation enlarges or reduces a figure by a given scale factor.

image
preimage

EXERCISES

Describe each transformation from the black figure (preimage) to the blue figure (image) as a *translation*, *rotation*, *reflection*, or *dilation*.

1.

dilation

2.

translation

3.

reflection

4.
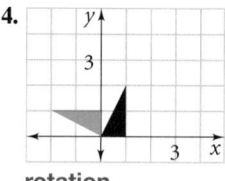
rotation

5. **a.** For Exercise 1, list the coordinates of the preimage vertices. Then list the coordinates of the image vertices. **a–b. See margin.**

   b. **Make a Conjecture** For the type of transformation you found, describe how the coordinates of the image relate to the coordinates of its preimage. Use other examples of that transformation to verify your conjecture.

   c. **Make More Conjectures** Repeat parts (a) and (b) for Exercises 2–4. **See back of book.**

6. **Open-Ended** In a coordinate plane, draw a rectangle with center not at the origin. Then construct a dilation with center at the origin and scale factor 2.   **Check students' work.**

4-4 Geometric Transformations with Matrices

What You'll Learn

- To represent translations and dilations with matrices
- To represent reflections and rotations with matrices

...And Why

To transform a photo, as in Example 2

✓ **Check Skills You'll Need** ⟶ **for Help** Lesson 2-6

Without using graphing technology, graph each function and its translation. Write the new function. 1–6. See back of book.

1. $y = x + 2$; left 4 units
2. $f(x) = \frac{1}{2}x + 2$; up 5 units
3. $g(x) = |x|$; right 3 units
4. $y = x$; down 2 units
5. $y = \frac{1}{3}|x - 3|$; down 2 units
6. $f(x) = -2|x|$; right 2 units

🔊 **New Vocabulary** • image • preimage • dilation • rotation • center of rotation

---

1 Translations and Dilations with Matrices

Activity: Translating a Geometric Figure

Geometry In Chapter 2 you used vertical and horizontal translations to graph functions. A translation shifts a graph without changing its size or shape. 2–7. See back of book.

1. Draw the figure on a coordinate grid as shown. **Check students' work.**

2. Translate the figure 4 units right and 6 units down. Label the new figure.

3. Identify the coordinates of the vertices of the original figure and the new figure.

4. How does the translation *4 units right and 6 units down* relate the coordinates of the new figure to the coordinates of the original figure?

5. Without graphing, identify the coordinates that result from a translation of the original figure 10 units right and 3 units up.

6. Suppose the original figure is translated so that two vertices have coordinates (0, 0) and (2, 0). Find two possible translations. Write the coordinates for the vertices of each translated figure.

7. **Critical Thinking** What translations of the original figure will result in a tessellation?

8. **Open-Ended** Design another simple figure that will tessellate the plane. Describe the translations needed to fill the plane. **Check students' work.**

Vocabulary Tip

A <u>tessellation</u> is a repeating pattern of figures that covers a plane, without gaps or overlaps.

Objectives

1 To represent translations and dilations with matrices
2 To represent reflections and rotations with matrices

Examples

1 Translating a Figure
2 Real-World Connection
3 Reflecting a Figure
4 Rotating a Figure

Math Background

Matrices are a powerful tool to represent translations, dilations, reflections, and rotations. Understanding these fundamental concepts can help students to grasp the idea of how compressing music files into a mp3 format will allow a 700 MB CD to hold 200 songs.

More Math Background: p. 166C

Lesson Planning and Resources

See p. 166E for a list of the resources that support this lesson.

Bell Ringer Practice

✓ **Check Skills You'll Need**
For intervention, direct students to:

Vertical and Horizontal Translations
Lesson 2-6: Examples 1–5
Extra Skills and Word Problems Practice, Ch. 2

Differentiated Instruction Solutions for All Learners

Special Needs L1
Have students put one finger on a vertex of the figure and another finger on the corresponding matrix column. Have students compare each vertex and matrix column to see how they relate.

learning style: tactile

Below Level L2
The mathematical meanings of the terms *transformation*, *translation*, and *rotation* may be unfamiliar to students. For each term, have a student act out the movement.

learning style: tactile

Activity

When you discuss Question 4, be sure students understand that *4 units right* signifies a change in each *x*-coordinate and that *6 units down* signifies a change in each *y*-coordinate.

2 EXAMPLE Tactile Learners

Draw a polygon very closely centered on a piece of plain paper. Make several photocopies on graph paper. Now make more photocopies of the polygon on plain paper at various enlargement and reduction sizes. On each photocopy, note the enlargement or reduction setting you used. Organize the class into small groups. Give each group one copy at the original size and one that you have enlarged or reduced. Instruct students to copy or trace the copy onto graph paper. Ask students to use approximate coordinates and determine if the photocopier did the enlargement or reduction correctly. Have students exchange photocopies so that each group does one enlargement and one reduction.

You can write the vertices of a figure as a matrix. For example, the matrix below represents the vertices of figure *ABCD*.

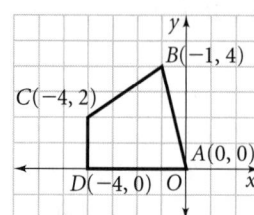

$$\begin{matrix} & A & B & C & D \\ x\text{-coordinate} & \begin{bmatrix} 0 & -1 & -4 & -4 \\ y\text{-coordinate} & 0 & 4 & 2 & 0 \end{bmatrix} \end{matrix}$$

A change made to a figure is a transformation of the figure. The transformed figure is the **image.** The original figure is the **preimage.** A translation (Lesson 2–6) is a transformation that slides a figure without changing the size or shape of the figure. You can use matrix addition to translate all the vertices of a figure in one step.

Vocabulary Tip

Read the notation *A′* as "*A* prime," *A″* as "*A* double prime," and so on. The prime symbol tells you that *A′* is related to *A* in some special way.

1 EXAMPLE Translating a Figure

Geometry Quadrilateral *ABCD* above has vertices $A(0,0), B(-1,4), C(-4,2)$, and $D(-4,0)$. Use a matrix to find the coordinates of the vertices of the image translated 6 units right and 2 units down. Then graph *ABCD* and its image $A'B'C'D'$.

Vertices of the Quadrilateral	Translation Matrix	Vertices of the Image

Add 6 to each *x*-coordinate.

$$\begin{matrix} A & B & C & D \\ \begin{bmatrix} 0 & -1 & -4 & -4 \\ 0 & 4 & 2 & 0 \end{bmatrix} \end{matrix} + \begin{bmatrix} 6 & 6 & 6 & 6 \\ -2 & -2 & -2 & -2 \end{bmatrix} = \begin{matrix} A' & B' & C' & D' \\ \begin{bmatrix} 6 & 5 & 2 & 2 \\ -2 & 2 & 0 & -2 \end{bmatrix} \end{matrix}$$

Subtract 2 from each *y*-coordinate.

The vertices of the image are $A'(6,-2), B'(5,2), C'(2,0),$ and $D'(2,-2)$.

Graph both quadrilaterals.

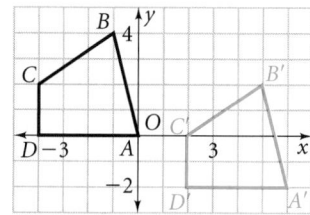

Graphing Calculator Hint

Enter the preimage and translation matrices as [A] and [B]. Use matrix addition to find the coordinates of the image.

✓ **Quick Check** ❶ **a. Critical Thinking** Explain how to translate quadrilateral $A'B'C'D'$ from Example 1 so that its image is quadrilateral *ABCD*. **a–c. See margin.**

b. What matrix would you use to translate the vertices of a pentagon 3 units left and 2 units up?

c. Use your answer to part (b) to translate the pentagon with vertices $(0,-5), (-1,-1), (-5,0), (1,3),$ and $(4,0)$. Find the coordinates of the vertices of the image. Graph the preimage and the image.

A **dilation** is a transformation that changes the size of a figure. When the center of the dilation is the origin, you can use scalar multiplication to find the coordinates of the vertices of an image. All dilations in this book are centered at the origin.

192 Chapter 4 Matrices

2 EXAMPLE Real-World 🌐 Connection

Graphic Arts An artist sends you a photo electronically. You increase the photo dimensions by a factor of 1.2. Find the coordinates of the enlargement's vertices.

Write a matrix to represent the coordinates of the vertices, which are at $(0, 0)$, $(0, 5.875)$, $(9.75, 5.875)$, and $(9.75, 0)$. Then multiply by the factor 1.2.

$$1.2 \begin{bmatrix} 0 & 0 & 9.75 & 9.75 \\ 0 & 5.875 & 5.875 & 0 \end{bmatrix} = \begin{bmatrix} 0 & 0 & 11.7 & 11.7 \\ 0 & 7.05 & 7.05 & 0 \end{bmatrix}$$

● The new coordinates are $(0, 0)$, $(0, 7.05)$, $(11.7, 7.05)$, and $(11.7, 0)$.

☑ **Quick Check** **2** The coordinates of the vertices of figure ABC are $A(-5, 0)$, $B(8, -1)$, and $C(4, 5)$. Find the coordinates of each image under the following dilations. Then graph each image and its preimage on the same coordinate plane. **a–c. See margin.**

  a. 4   **b.** $\frac{1}{5}$ **c.** -1.5

2 Reflections and Rotations with Matrices

A reflection, or flip, is a transformation that results in symmetry on the coordinate plane. A reflection maps a point in the plane to its mirror image, using a specific line as the mirror. The lines used in this book are the x-axis (see Lesson 2-6), the y-axis, and the lines $y = x$ and $y = -x$.

You can use matrix multiplication to graph reflections in the coordinate plane.

🔑 **Key Concepts**

Properties	Matrices for Reflections in the Coordinate Plane		
Reflection in the y-axis	Reflection in the x-axis	Reflection in the line $y = x$	Reflection in the line $y = -x$
$\begin{bmatrix} -1 & 0 \\ 0 & 1 \end{bmatrix}$	$\begin{bmatrix} 1 & 0 \\ 0 & -1 \end{bmatrix}$	$\begin{bmatrix} 0 & 1 \\ 1 & 0 \end{bmatrix}$	$\begin{bmatrix} 0 & -1 \\ -1 & 0 \end{bmatrix}$

Lesson 4-4   Geometric Transformations with Matrices   **193**

PowerPoint
📽 **Additional Examples**

1 Triangle ABC has vertices $A(1, -2)$, $B(3, 1)$, and $C(2, 3)$. Use a matrix to find the coordinates of the vertices of the image translated 3 units left and 1 unit up. Graph ABC and its image $A'B'C'$.

Vertices: $A'(-2, -1)$, $B'(0, 2)$, $C'(-1, 4)$

2 The figure in the diagram is to be reduced by a factor of $\frac{2}{3}$. Find the coordinates of the vertices of the reduced figure.

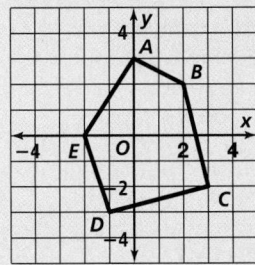

$A'(0, 2)$, $B'\left(\frac{4}{3}, \frac{4}{3}\right)$, $C'\left(2, -\frac{4}{3}\right)$, $D'\left(-\frac{2}{3}, -2\right)$, $E'\left(-\frac{4}{3}, 0\right)$

---

pages 192–193   Quick Check

1a. Subtract 6 from each x-coordinate and add 2 to each y-coordinate.

b. $\begin{bmatrix} -3 & -3 & -3 & -3 & -3 \\ 2 & 2 & 2 & 2 & 2 \end{bmatrix}$

c. $(-3, -3)$, $(-4, 1)$, $(-8, 2)$, $(-2, 5)$, $(1, 2)$
See back of book for graph.

2a–c. *See back of book for graphs.*

2a. $(-20, 0)$, $(32, -4)$, $(16, 20)$

b. $(-1, 0)$, $(1.6, -0.2)$, $(0.8, 1)$

c. $(7.5, 0)$, $(-12, 1.5)$, $(-6, -7.5)$

Additional Examples

3 Reflect the triangle with coordinates $A(2, -1)$, $B(3, 0)$, and $C(4, -2)$ in each line. Graph triangle ABC and each image on the same coordinate plane.

a. x-axis
$$\begin{bmatrix} 2 & 3 & 4 \\ 1 & 0 & 2 \end{bmatrix}$$

b. y-axis
$$\begin{bmatrix} -2 & -3 & -4 \\ -1 & 0 & -2 \end{bmatrix}$$

c. $y = x$
$$\begin{bmatrix} -1 & 0 & -2 \\ 2 & 3 & 4 \end{bmatrix}$$

d. $y = -x$
$$\begin{bmatrix} 1 & 0 & 2 \\ -2 & -3 & -4 \end{bmatrix}$$

4 Rotate the triangle from Additional Example 3 as indicated. Graph triangle ABC and each image on a coordinate plane.

a. 90°
$$\begin{bmatrix} 1 & 0 & 2 \\ 2 & 3 & 4 \end{bmatrix}$$

b. 180°
$$\begin{bmatrix} -2 & -3 & -4 \\ 1 & 0 & 2 \end{bmatrix}$$

c. 270°
$$\begin{bmatrix} -1 & 0 & -2 \\ -2 & -3 & -4 \end{bmatrix}$$

d. 360°
$$\begin{bmatrix} 2 & 3 & 4 \\ -1 & 0 & -2 \end{bmatrix}$$

Resources
• Daily Notetaking Guide 4-4 **L3**

Closure

Ask students what matrix operations you can use to translate, dilate, reflect, and rotate figures in the coordinate plane. addition, scalar multiplication, matrix multiplication

---

3 EXAMPLE Reflecting a Figure

Reflect the triangle with coordinates $A(0,0)$, $B(2,5)$, and $C(-2,3)$ in each line. Then graph each pair of triangles on the same coordinate plane.

a. y-axis
$$\begin{bmatrix} -1 & 0 \\ 0 & 1 \end{bmatrix}\begin{bmatrix} 0 & 2 & -2 \\ 0 & 5 & 3 \end{bmatrix} = \begin{bmatrix} 0 & -2 & 2 \\ 0 & 5 & 3 \end{bmatrix}$$

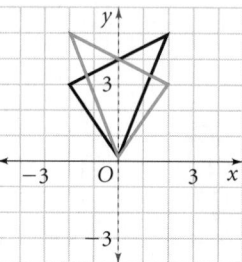

b. x-axis
$$\begin{bmatrix} 1 & 0 \\ 0 & -1 \end{bmatrix}\begin{bmatrix} 0 & 2 & -2 \\ 0 & 5 & 3 \end{bmatrix} = \begin{bmatrix} 0 & 2 & -2 \\ 0 & -5 & -3 \end{bmatrix}$$

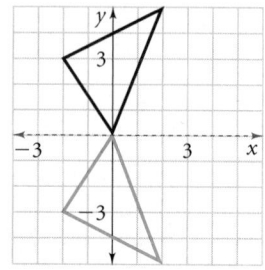

c. $y = x$
$$\begin{bmatrix} 0 & 1 \\ 1 & 0 \end{bmatrix}\begin{bmatrix} 0 & 2 & -2 \\ 0 & 5 & 3 \end{bmatrix} = \begin{bmatrix} 0 & 5 & 3 \\ 0 & 2 & -2 \end{bmatrix}$$

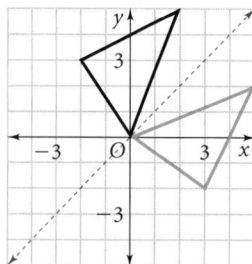

d. $y = -x$
$$\begin{bmatrix} 0 & -1 \\ -1 & 0 \end{bmatrix}\begin{bmatrix} 0 & 2 & -2 \\ 0 & 5 & 3 \end{bmatrix} = \begin{bmatrix} 0 & -5 & -3 \\ 0 & -2 & 2 \end{bmatrix}$$

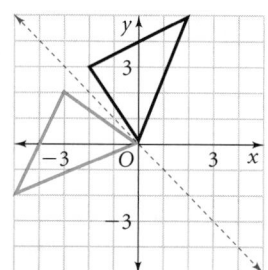

Quick Check **3** Reflect the triangle with coordinates $D(-3,0)$, $E(-4,4)$, and $F(1,1)$ in each line. Then graph each pair of triangles on the same coordinate plane.

a. y-axis　　　**b.** x-axis　　　**c.** $y = x$　　　**d.** $y = -x$

a–d. See margin.

A **rotation** is a transformation that turns a figure about a fixed point called the **center of rotation.** You can rotate a figure as much as 360 degrees. In this book, all rotations are counterclockwise about the origin.

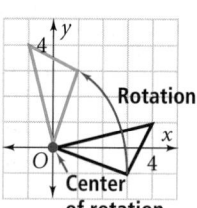

Key Concepts

Properties	Matrices for Rotations in the Coordinate Plane		
Rotation of 90°	Rotation of 180°	Rotation of 270°	Rotation of 360°
$\begin{bmatrix} 0 & -1 \\ 1 & 0 \end{bmatrix}$	$\begin{bmatrix} -1 & 0 \\ 0 & -1 \end{bmatrix}$	$\begin{bmatrix} 0 & 1 \\ -1 & 0 \end{bmatrix}$	$\begin{bmatrix} 1 & 0 \\ 0 & 1 \end{bmatrix}$

pages 194–195 Quick Check

3, 4. See back of book for graphs.

3a. $\begin{bmatrix} 3 & 4 & -1 \\ 0 & 4 & 1 \end{bmatrix}$

b. $\begin{bmatrix} -3 & -4 & 1 \\ 0 & -4 & -1 \end{bmatrix}$

c. $\begin{bmatrix} 0 & 4 & 1 \\ -3 & -4 & 1 \end{bmatrix}$

d. $\begin{bmatrix} 0 & -4 & -1 \\ 3 & 4 & -1 \end{bmatrix}$

4 EXAMPLE Rotating a Figure

Rotate the triangle with coordinates $A(0,0)$, $B(2,5)$, and $C(-2,3)$. Then graph each pair of triangles on the same coordinate plane.

a. 90°

$$\begin{bmatrix} 0 & -1 \\ 1 & 0 \end{bmatrix}\begin{bmatrix} 0 & 2 & -2 \\ 0 & 5 & 3 \end{bmatrix} = \begin{bmatrix} 0 & -5 & -3 \\ 0 & 2 & -2 \end{bmatrix}$$

b. 180°

$$\begin{bmatrix} -1 & 0 \\ 0 & -1 \end{bmatrix}\begin{bmatrix} 0 & 2 & -2 \\ 0 & 5 & 3 \end{bmatrix} = \begin{bmatrix} 0 & -2 & 2 \\ 0 & -5 & -3 \end{bmatrix}$$

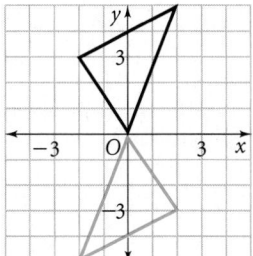

c. 270°

$$\begin{bmatrix} 0 & 1 \\ -1 & 0 \end{bmatrix}\begin{bmatrix} 0 & 2 & -2 \\ 0 & 5 & 3 \end{bmatrix} = \begin{bmatrix} 0 & 5 & 3 \\ 0 & -2 & 2 \end{bmatrix}$$

d. 360°

$$\begin{bmatrix} 1 & 0 \\ 0 & 1 \end{bmatrix}\begin{bmatrix} 0 & 2 & -2 \\ 0 & 5 & 3 \end{bmatrix} = \begin{bmatrix} 0 & 2 & -2 \\ 0 & 5 & 3 \end{bmatrix}$$

 4 Rotate the quadrilateral with coordinates $A(1,1)$, $B(3,1)$, $C(6,4)$, and $D(1,3)$. Then graph each pair of quadrilaterals on the same coordinate plane.
a. 90° **b.** 180° **c.** 270° **d.** 360°
a–d. See margin.

EXERCISES

For more exercises, see *Extra Skill and Word Problem Practice*.

Practice and Problem Solving

 A Practice by Example

Example 1
(page 192)

Use matrix addition to find the coordinates of each image after a translation of 3 units left and 5 units up. If possible, graph each pair of figures on the same coordinate plane. 1–4. See margin.

1. $A(1, -3)$, $B(1, 1)$, $C(5, 1)$, $D(5, -3)$

2. $G(0, 0)$, $H(4, 4)$, $I(4, -4)$, $J(8, 0)$

3. $J(-10, 2)$, $K(-16, a)$, $L(12, -5)$

4. $R(9, 3)$, $S(3, 6)$, $T(3, 3)$, $U(6, -3)$

5–9. See back of book.

Example 2
(page 193)

Graph each figure and its image after the given dilation.

5. $\begin{bmatrix} 0 & 2 & 5 & 8 \\ 0 & 4 & 5 & 1 \end{bmatrix}, 2$

6. $\begin{bmatrix} -7 & -3 & 4 \\ -5 & 4 & 0 \end{bmatrix}, 0.5$

7. $\begin{bmatrix} 0 & -2 & -5 \\ 0 & 0 & 5 \end{bmatrix}, \frac{9}{10}$

8. $\begin{bmatrix} -10 & -5 & 0 & 5 & 10 \\ 8 & 16 & 20 & 16 & 8 \end{bmatrix}, \frac{1}{4}$

9. $\begin{bmatrix} -8 & 2 & 3 & 1 & -2 \\ 6 & 4 & 0 & -4 & 0 \end{bmatrix}, 1.5$

Lesson 4-4 Geometric Transformations with Matrices **195**

4a. $\begin{bmatrix} -1 & -1 & -4 & -3 \\ 1 & 3 & 6 & 1 \end{bmatrix}$

b. $\begin{bmatrix} -1 & -3 & -6 & -1 \\ -1 & -1 & -4 & -3 \end{bmatrix}$

c. $\begin{bmatrix} 1 & 1 & 4 & 3 \\ -1 & -3 & -6 & -1 \end{bmatrix}$

d. $\begin{bmatrix} 1 & 3 & 6 & 1 \\ 1 & 1 & 4 & 3 \end{bmatrix}$

pages 195–198 Exercises
1, 2, 4. *See back of book for graphs.*

3. Practice

Assignment Guide

1 A B 1-9, 24-30, 36, 37, 39–41, 43, 44

2 A B 10-23, 31-35, 38, 42

C Challenge   45-50

Test Prep   51-54
Mixed Review   55-63

Homework Quick Check

To check students' understanding of key skills and concepts, go over Exercises 6, 20, 24, 38, 40.

Error Prevention!

Exercises 1–4 Suggest that students write "− 3" below each x-coordinate and "+ 5" below each y-coordinate.

Differentiated Instruction Resources

GPS Guided Problem Solving L3
Enrichment L4
Reteaching L2
Practice L3

1. $\begin{bmatrix} -2 & -2 & 2 & 2 \\ 2 & 6 & 6 & 2 \end{bmatrix}$

2. $\begin{bmatrix} -3 & 1 & 1 & 5 \\ 5 & 9 & 1 & 5 \end{bmatrix}$

3. $\begin{bmatrix} -13 & -19 & 9 \\ 7 & a+5 & 0 \end{bmatrix}$;
graph not possible

4. $\begin{bmatrix} 6 & 0 & 0 & 3 \\ 8 & 11 & 8 & 2 \end{bmatrix}$

195

pages 195–198   Exercises

10.

11.

12.

13. $\begin{bmatrix} 3 & -3 & -3 & 3 \\ -3 & -6 & -3 & -6 \end{bmatrix}$

14. $\begin{bmatrix} 0 & 4 & 8 & 6 \\ 0 & -4 & -4 & -2 \end{bmatrix}$

15. $\begin{bmatrix} 3 & 2 & 2 & 3 & 5 \\ 1 & 2 & 3 & 4 & 2.5 \end{bmatrix}$

16. $\begin{bmatrix} -1 & -2 & -4 & -6 & -2 \\ 4 & 0 & 0 & 3 & 4 \end{bmatrix}$

20. $\begin{bmatrix} -3 & 3 & 3 & -3 \\ -3 & -6 & -3 & -6 \end{bmatrix}$

21. $\begin{bmatrix} 0 & 4 & 8 & 6 \\ 0 & 4 & 4 & 2 \end{bmatrix}$

22. $\begin{bmatrix} -1 & -2 & -3 & -4 & -2.5 \\ -3 & -2 & -2 & -3 & -5 \end{bmatrix}$

Example 3
(page 194)

Graph each figure and its image after reflection in the given line.   10–12. See margin.

10. $\begin{bmatrix} 0 & -3 & 5 \\ 0 & 1 & 2 \end{bmatrix}$; $y = x$ **11.** $\begin{bmatrix} -1 & 0 & 5 \\ -1 & 5 & 0 \end{bmatrix}$; y-axis   **12.** $\begin{bmatrix} -3 & -5 & -10 \\ 4 & 7 & 1 \end{bmatrix}$; x-axis

Find the coordinates of each image after reflection in the given line.   13–16. See margin.

13. $\begin{bmatrix} 3 & 6 & 3 & 6 \\ -3 & 3 & 3 & -3 \end{bmatrix}$; $y = -x$ **14.** $\begin{bmatrix} 0 & 4 & 8 & 6 \\ 0 & 4 & 4 & 2 \end{bmatrix}$; x-axis

15. $\begin{bmatrix} 1 & 2 & 3 & 4 & 2.5 \\ 3 & 2 & 2 & 3 & 5 \end{bmatrix}$; $y = x$ **16.** $\begin{bmatrix} -1 & -2 & -4 & -6 & -2 \\ -4 & 0 & 0 & -3 & -4 \end{bmatrix}$; x-axis

Example 4
(page 195)

Graph each figure and its image after the given rotation.

17. $\begin{bmatrix} 0 & -3 & 5 \\ 0 & 1 & 2 \end{bmatrix}$; $90°$ **18.** $\begin{bmatrix} -1 & 0 & 5 \\ -1 & 5 & 0 \end{bmatrix}$; $180°$ **19.** $\begin{bmatrix} -5 & 6 & 0 \\ -1 & 2 & 4 \end{bmatrix}$; $90°$

17–19. See back of book.

Find the coordinates of each image after the given rotation.   20–23. See margin.

20. $\begin{bmatrix} 3 & 6 & 3 & 6 \\ -3 & 3 & 3 & -3 \end{bmatrix}$; $270°$ **21.** $\begin{bmatrix} 0 & 4 & 8 & 6 \\ 0 & 4 & 4 & 2 \end{bmatrix}$; $360°$

22. $\begin{bmatrix} 1 & 2 & 3 & 4 & 2.5 \\ 3 & 2 & 2 & 3 & 5 \end{bmatrix}$; $180°$ **23.** $\begin{bmatrix} -1 & -2 & -4 & -6 & -2 \\ -4 & 0 & 0 & -3 & -4 \end{bmatrix}$; $270°$

B   Apply Your Skills   Geometry Each matrix represents the vertices of a polygon. Translate each figure 5 units left and 1 unit up. Express your answer as a matrix.   24–26. See margin.

GPS 24. $\begin{bmatrix} -3 & -3 & 2 & 2 \\ -2 & -4 & -2 & -4 \end{bmatrix}$ **25.** $\begin{bmatrix} -3 & 0 & 3 & 0 \\ -9 & -6 & -9 & -12 \end{bmatrix}$ **26.** $\begin{bmatrix} 0 & 1 & -4 \\ 0 & 3 & 5 \end{bmatrix}$

For Exercises 27–34, use $\triangle ABC$. Write the coordinates of each image in matrix form.   27–28. See margin.

27. a dilation four times the original size

28. a translation 2 units left and 3 units down

29. a dilation half the original size

30. a translation 1 unit right and 7 units up

31. a rotation of $90°$

32. a reflection in $y = x$ **29–34. See margin p. 197.**

33. a rotation of $180°$

34. a reflection in the x-axis

35. Multiple Choice What is true about $\begin{bmatrix} -3 & 0 \\ 0 & -3 \end{bmatrix}\begin{bmatrix} 1 & -2 & 4 \\ 1 & -1 & 2 \end{bmatrix}$ and $-3\begin{bmatrix} 1 & -2 & 4 \\ 1 & -1 & 2 \end{bmatrix}$

  Ⓐ They are equal matrices.   Ⓑ They are opposite matrices.   A
  Ⓒ Both are matrices for reflection. Ⓓ Neither product exists.

36. Writing Graph $\begin{bmatrix} 9 & 10 & 6 \\ 1 & -3 & -2 \end{bmatrix}$ and $2\begin{bmatrix} 9 & 10 & 6 \\ 1 & -3 & -2 \end{bmatrix}$. Compare the graphs.
   Generalize how a dilation changes a graph. **See back of book.**

37. Geometry Create a tessellation based on the quadrilateral $\begin{bmatrix} 0 & -3 & -5 & 0 \\ 1 & 3 & -1 & -1 \end{bmatrix}$.

   Translate the quadrilateral using $\begin{bmatrix} 5 & 5 & 5 & 5 \\ 2 & 2 & 2 & 2 \end{bmatrix}$ and $\begin{bmatrix} 3 & 3 & 3 & 3 \\ -4 & -4 & -4 & -4 \end{bmatrix}$.
   See back of book.

38. Writing Explain why you might want to represent a transformation as a matrix.
   Check students' work.

196   Chapter 4   Matrices

---

23. $\begin{bmatrix} -4 & 0 & 0 & -3 & -4 \\ 1 & 2 & 4 & 6 & 2 \end{bmatrix}$

24. $\begin{bmatrix} -8 & -8 & -3 & -3 \\ -1 & -3 & -1 & -3 \end{bmatrix}$

25. $\begin{bmatrix} -8 & -5 & -2 & -5 \\ -8 & -5 & -8 & -11 \end{bmatrix}$

26. $\begin{bmatrix} -5 & -4 & -9 \\ 1 & 4 & 6 \end{bmatrix}$

27. $\begin{bmatrix} -12 & 4 & -4 \\ 4 & 8 & 16 \end{bmatrix}$

28. $\begin{bmatrix} -5 & -1 & -3 \\ -2 & -1 & 1 \end{bmatrix}$

Use matrices to represent the vertices of graph f and graph g. Name each transformation. 39–44. See back of book.

39.

40.

41.

42.

GO **Online**
Homework Video Tutor
Visit: PHSchool.com
Web Code: age-0404

Graph each triangle and its translation on the same coordinate plane.

43. $\begin{bmatrix} 0 & 2 & 3 \\ 0 & 0 & 5 \end{bmatrix}$; 3 units right, 4 units down **44.** $\begin{bmatrix} -5 & 3 & 4 \\ 5 & 1 & -4 \end{bmatrix}$; 2 units left, 5 units up

C Challenge **45. Architecture** Use the pattern of brown tiles shown.

a. Copy the graph. Mark scales on the axes so that the dimensions of the square tiles are 1 unit by 1 unit.

b. Write a matrix for the translation of tile $ABCD$ to tile $A'B'C'D'$. What are the coordinates of the vertices of the preimage and the image?

c. A brown tile is 6 units right and 6 units down from tile $ABCD$. Write a matrix to represent the coordinates of its vertices. **a–c. See back of book.**

d. A tile has vertices at $(-6, 9)$, $(-6, 8)$, $(-7, 9)$, and $(-7, 8)$. What translation of tile $ABCD$ results in these coordinates? **Translate the vertices of $ABCD$ left 12 units.**

Geometry Each matrix represents the vertices of a polygon. Write a matrix to represent the vertices of the image after each transformation. 46–49. See back of book.

46. $\begin{bmatrix} -3 & 0.5 & -5 \\ 0 & 3 & 3 \end{bmatrix}$; dilation of 2 **47.** $\begin{bmatrix} 4 & 7 & 10 \\ 0 & 2 & 0 \end{bmatrix}$; rotation of 270°

48. $\begin{bmatrix} 17 & 6 & 6 & 2 \\ 5 & 10 & 2 & 6 \end{bmatrix}$; reflection in $y = x$ **49.** $\begin{bmatrix} 3 & 4.5 & 5 & 3.5 \\ 3 & 1.5 & 2 & 4 \end{bmatrix}$; rotation of 90°

29. $\begin{bmatrix} -1.5 & 0.5 & -0.5 \\ 0.5 & 1 & 2 \end{bmatrix}$ **31.** $\begin{bmatrix} -1 & -2 & -4 \\ -3 & 1 & -1 \end{bmatrix}$ **33.** $\begin{bmatrix} 3 & -1 & 1 \\ -1 & -2 & -4 \end{bmatrix}$

30. $\begin{bmatrix} -2 & 2 & 0 \\ 8 & 9 & 11 \end{bmatrix}$ **32.** $\begin{bmatrix} 1 & 2 & 4 \\ -3 & 1 & -1 \end{bmatrix}$ **34.** $\begin{bmatrix} -3 & 1 & -1 \\ -1 & -2 & -4 \end{bmatrix}$

---

4. Assess & Reteach

Lesson Quiz

For these questions, use triangle ABC with vertices $A(-1, 1)$, $B(2, 2)$, and $C(1, -2)$.

1. Write a matrix equation that represents a translation of triangle ABC 7 units left and 3 units up.
$$\begin{bmatrix} -1 & 2 & 1 \\ 1 & 2 & -2 \end{bmatrix} +$$
$$\begin{bmatrix} -7 & -7 & -7 \\ 3 & 3 & 3 \end{bmatrix} =$$
$$\begin{bmatrix} -8 & -5 & -6 \\ 4 & 5 & 1 \end{bmatrix}$$

2. Write a matrix equation that represents a dilation of triangle ABC with a scale factor of 5.
$$5\begin{bmatrix} -1 & 2 & 1 \\ 1 & 2 & -2 \end{bmatrix} =$$
$$\begin{bmatrix} -5 & 10 & 5 \\ 5 & 10 & -10 \end{bmatrix}$$

3. Use matrix multiplication to reflect triangle ABC in the line $y = -x$. Then draw the preimage and image on the same coordinate plane.
$$\begin{bmatrix} 0 & -1 \\ -1 & 0 \end{bmatrix}\begin{bmatrix} -1 & 2 & 1 \\ 1 & 2 & -2 \end{bmatrix} =$$
$$\begin{bmatrix} -1 & -2 & 2 \\ 1 & -2 & -1 \end{bmatrix}$$

Alternative Assessment

Have each student draw their first initial on graph paper using only line segments. The letter must be at least eight units tall, and the endpoints and vertices must have coordinates that are integers. Express each vertex and endpoint in the letter as an ordered pair. Write the ordered pairs in matrix form. State five different transformations, such as the ones in Exercises 27–34. Have the student graph the transformations.

Resources

For additional practice with a variety of test item formats:
- Standardized Test Prep, p. 233
- Test-Taking Strategies, p. 228
- Test-Taking Strategies with Transparencies

pages 195–198   Exercises

50a.

53. [2]
$\begin{bmatrix} -2 & -2 & -2 \\ 6 & 6 & 6 \end{bmatrix};$

(–6, 2), (–4, 8), (2, 3)

[1] does not represent the combined transformation in matrix form OR does not state new vertices

54a. [4]

b. $\begin{bmatrix} -5 & -4 & 4 & 3 \\ 3 & 4 & -3 & -4 \end{bmatrix}$

c.

d. 90° rotation

---

50. Let the matrix $\begin{bmatrix} x \\ y \end{bmatrix}$ represent points on the graph $y = |x|$.

  a. Complete the table. Sketch the graph. **See margin.**

x	–3	–2	–1	0	1	2	3
y	■	■	■	■	■	■	■

3 2 1 0 1 2 3

  b. Critical Thinking What does the matrix addition $\begin{bmatrix} x \\ y \end{bmatrix} + \begin{bmatrix} -1 \\ 2 \end{bmatrix}$ represent?
  Show your answer on your graph from part (a).
  Answers may vary. Sample: The addition represents a translation of the pt. (x, y) 1 unit to the left and 2 units up.

Test Prep

Multiple Choice

51. What are the coordinates of X(5, 1), Y(−5, −3), and Z(−1, 3) reflected in the line $y = x$? **B**
  A. X′(−5, −1), Y′(5, 3), Z′(1, −3)   **B.** X′(1, 5), Y′(−3, −5), Z′(3, −1)
  C. X′(−1, −5), Y′(3, 5), Z′(−3, 1)   **D.** X′(5, 1), Y′(−5, −3), Z′(−1, 3)

52. Reflection in which line takes the figure with vertices A(0, 0), B(−2, 4), C(−4, 2), and D(−3, 0) to A′(0, 0), B′(−2, −4), C′(−4, −2), and D′(−3, 0)? **F**
  F. x-axis   **G.** y-axis   **H.** $y = x$ **J.** $y = -x$

Short Response

53. Each vertex of the triangle at the right is transformed by *right 3, up 2* and then by *left 5, up 4*. What is a matrix for the combined transformation? What are the coordinates of the vertices of the final triangle? **See margin.**

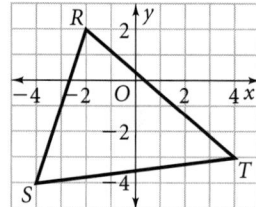

Extended Response

54. A quadrilateral has coordinates $\begin{bmatrix} 3 & 4 & -3 & -4 \\ 5 & 4 & -4 & -3 \end{bmatrix}$.
  a. Graph the quadrilateral.
  b. Find the product $\begin{bmatrix} 0 & -1 \\ 1 & 0 \end{bmatrix}\begin{bmatrix} 3 & 4 & -3 & -4 \\ 5 & 4 & -4 & -3 \end{bmatrix}$.
  c. Graph the result as a new quadrilateral.
  d. What is the relationship between the quadrilaterals in parts (a) and (c)?
  a–d. See margin.

Mixed Review

GO for Help

Lesson 4-3

If possible, find the dimensions of each product matrix; then find each product. If the product is not defined, explain why not.   **55–56. See back of book.**

55. $\begin{bmatrix} 1 & 0 & -5 \\ 2 & -1 & 6 \end{bmatrix}\begin{bmatrix} 2 & 4 & -2 \\ 0 & 10 & 4 \\ 0 & 1 & -7 \end{bmatrix}$ **56.** $\begin{bmatrix} 0 & 7 & k & 5 \\ 0 & 6 & 0 & 5 \end{bmatrix}\begin{bmatrix} 9 & -1 & 3 & 0 \\ 7 & 0 & 7 & 0 \end{bmatrix}$

Lesson 3-5

Graph each equation. **57–59. See back of book.**

57. $x + y - z = 5$ **58.** $2x - y + 3z = 12$ **59.** $-x + 4y - z = -6$

Lesson 2-1

Make a mapping diagram for each relation. Determine whether it is a function.

60. {(−2, 4), (−1, 1), (0, 0), (1, 1), (2, 4)} **yes**   **61.** {(27, −2), (3, −1), (0, 0), (3, 1), (27, 2)} **no**

62. {(−2, 15), (−1, 1), (0, −3), (1, 3), (2, 15)} **yes**   **63.** {(−3, 8), (−2, 1), (1, −2), (0, −1), (1, 4)} **no**

60–63. See back of book for diagram.

[3] appropriate methods, but with one computational error in determining the product

[2] unable to graph matrix or unable to recognize transformation

[1] correct graph in part (a), but with the rest completed incorrectly

2 × 2 Matrices, Determinants, and Inverses

What You'll Learn

- To evaluate determinants of 2 × 2 matrices and find inverse matrices
- To use inverse matrices in solving matrix equations

...And Why

To predict cell phone ownership, as in Example 5

 Check Skills You'll Need　　**GO for Help**　Skills Handbook page 873

Simplify each group of expressions.

1. a. 3(4) **12**　　　　**b.** 2(6) **12**　　　　**c.** 3(4) − 2(6) **0**

2. a. 3(−4) **−12**　　　**b.** 2(−6) **−12**　　　**c.** 3(−4) − 2(−6) **0**

3. a. −3(−4) **12**　　　**b.** 2(−6) **−12**　　　**c.** −3(−4) − 2(−6) **24**

4. a. −3(4) **−12**　　　**b.** −2(−6) **12**　　　**c.** −3(4) − (−2)(−6) **−24**

 New Vocabulary　• square matrix　• multiplicative identity matrix
　　　　　　　　　　　　• multiplicative inverse of a matrix　• determinant

---

1　Evaluating Determinants of 2 × 2 Matrices

A **square matrix** is a matrix with the same number of columns as rows.

For any real number a, the number 1 is the multiplicative identity of a, since $a \cdot 1 = 1 \cdot a = a$. Square matrices also have a multiplicative identity.

 Key Concepts

Definition	**Multiplicative Identity Matrix**

For an $n \times n$ square matrix, the **multiplicative identity matrix** is an $n \times n$ square matrix I, or I_n, with 1's along the main diagonal and 0's elsewhere.

$$I_2 = \begin{bmatrix} 1 & 0 \\ 0 & 1 \end{bmatrix}, \qquad I_3 = \begin{bmatrix} 1 & 0 & 0 \\ 0 & 1 & 0 \\ 0 & 0 & 1 \end{bmatrix}, \qquad \text{and so forth}$$

If the product of the real numbers a and b is 1, then a and b are multiplicative inverses. Some, but not all, square matrices have multiplicative inverses.

Key Concepts

Definition	**Multiplicative Inverse of a Matrix**

If A and X are $n \times n$ matrices, and $AX = XA = I$, then X is the multiplicative inverse of A, written A^{-1}.

$$AA^{-1} = A^{-1}A = I$$

If B is the multiplicative inverse of A, then A is the multiplicative inverse of B. To show that A and B are multiplicative inverses, show that $AB = I$ or that $BA = I$.

---

1. Plan

Objectives
1　To evaluate determinants of 2 × 2 matrices and find inverse matrices
2　To use inverse matrices in solving matrix equations

Examples
1　Verifying Inverses
2　Evaluating the Determinant of a 2 × 2 Matrix
3　Finding an Inverse Matrix
4　Finding Inverses
5　Solving a Matrix Equation
6　Real-World Connection

Math Background

Many $n \times n$ matrices have multiplicative inverses. Inverse matrices play a central role in answering questions about the existence of solutions for systems of linear equations. For square matrices, verifying either that $AB = I$ or that $BA = I$ is sufficient to show that A and B are inverses of each other.

More Math Background: p. 166D

Lesson Planning and Resources

See p. 166E for a list of the resources that support this lesson.

Bell Ringer Practice

 Check Skills You'll Need
For intervention, direct students to:
Simplifying Expressions with Integers
Skills Handbook: p. 873
Example 3

Differentiated Instruction　Solutions for All Learners

Special Needs　L1
When calculating a determinant, students may forget to subtract bc from ad or add it. Emphasize that students are finding a difference when evaluating a determinant. Point out that both difference and determinant start with d to help students remember.
learning style: verbal

Below Level　L2
Students may confuse a matrix with its determinant because they look similar. Remind students that the determinant of a matrix is a real number, not a matrix.
learning style: verbal

Guided Instruction

2 EXAMPLE Error Prevention

Students may want to set the products *ad* and *bc* equal to each other as is done when solving proportions. Emphasize to students that they should find the *difference* of the products when evaluating a *determinant*. Stress the initial *d* in each word.

3 EXAMPLE Alternative Method

Point out that the quickest way to determine if a 2 × 2 matrix has an inverse is to determine whether $ad - bc = 0$, or equivalently $ad = bc$. If $ad = bc$ there is no inverse.

GO Online

Video Tutor Help
Visit: PhSchool.com
Web Code: age-0775

---

1 EXAMPLE Verifying Inverses

Show that *B* is the multiplicative inverse of *A*.

$$A = \begin{bmatrix} 2 & 3 \\ 1 & 2 \end{bmatrix} \qquad B = \begin{bmatrix} 2 & -3 \\ -1 & 2 \end{bmatrix}$$

$$AB = \begin{bmatrix} 2 & 3 \\ 1 & 2 \end{bmatrix}\begin{bmatrix} 2 & -3 \\ -1 & 2 \end{bmatrix} = \begin{bmatrix} 2(2) + 3(-1) & 2(-3) + 3(2) \\ 1(2) + 2(-1) & 1(-3) + 2(2) \end{bmatrix} = \begin{bmatrix} 1 & 0 \\ 0 & 1 \end{bmatrix}$$

$AB = I$, so *B* is the multiplicative inverse of *A*. *A* is also the multiplicative inverse of *B*.

Check $BA = \begin{bmatrix} 2 & -3 \\ -1 & 2 \end{bmatrix}\begin{bmatrix} 2 & 3 \\ 1 & 2 \end{bmatrix} = \begin{bmatrix} 2(2) + (-3)(1) & 2(3) + (-3)(2) \\ -1(2) + 2(1) & -1(3) + 2(2) \end{bmatrix} = \begin{bmatrix} 1 & 0 \\ 0 & 1 \end{bmatrix}$ ✓

✓ Quick Check ➊ Show that the matrices are multiplicative inverses.

a. $\begin{bmatrix} 2 & 1 \\ 2.5 & 1 \end{bmatrix}$ and $\begin{bmatrix} -2 & 2 \\ 5 & -4 \end{bmatrix}$

b. $\begin{bmatrix} -2 & -5 \\ -3 & -8 \end{bmatrix}$ and $\begin{bmatrix} -8 & 5 \\ 3 & -2 \end{bmatrix}$

a–b. See margin p. 201.

Every square matrix with real-number elements has a real-number determinant. Determinants can help you find inverses.

Write	Read	Evaluate
↓	↓	↓

$$A = \begin{bmatrix} a & b \\ c & d \end{bmatrix} \qquad \det A = \begin{vmatrix} a & b \\ c & d \end{vmatrix} \qquad \text{the determinant of } A \qquad \begin{vmatrix} a & b \\ c & d \end{vmatrix} = ad - bc$$

 Key Concepts

Definition	**Determinant of a 2 × 2 Matrix**

The **determinant** of a 2 × 2 matrix $\begin{bmatrix} a & b \\ c & d \end{bmatrix}$ is $ad - bc$.

Symbols for the determinant of a matrix
↓ ↓

$$\det A \qquad \begin{vmatrix} a & b \\ c & d \end{vmatrix}$$

2 EXAMPLE Evaluating the Determinant of a 2 × 2 Matrix

Evaluate each determinant.

a. $\det \begin{bmatrix} -3 & 4 \\ 2 & -5 \end{bmatrix} = \begin{vmatrix} -3 & 4 \\ 2 & -5 \end{vmatrix} = (-3)(-5) - (4)(2) = 15 - 8 = 7$

b. $\det \begin{bmatrix} 2 & -3 \\ 3 & -2 \end{bmatrix} = \begin{vmatrix} 2 & -3 \\ 3 & -2 \end{vmatrix} = (2)(-2) - (-3)(3) = -4 - (-9) = 5$

c. $\det \begin{bmatrix} a & 0 \\ 0 & a \end{bmatrix} = \begin{vmatrix} a & 0 \\ 0 & a \end{vmatrix} = a^2 - 0 = a^2$

✓ Quick Check ➋ Evaluate the determinant of each matrix.

a. $\begin{bmatrix} 4 & 2 \\ 4 & 2 \end{bmatrix}$ 0

b. $\begin{bmatrix} 8 & 7 \\ 2 & 3 \end{bmatrix}$ 10

c. $\begin{bmatrix} k & 3 \\ 3 - k & -3 \end{bmatrix}$ −9

---

200 Chapter 4 Matrices

Differentiated Instruction Solutions for All Learners

Advanced Learners L4
Have students use the definition of A^{-1} to prove that, if A^{-1} exists, $AA^{-1} = A^{-1}A = I$.

learning style: verbal

English Language Learners ELL
Discuss the geometric term *square* and how the dimensions of a *square matrix* are the same. Relate the *identity matrix* to the identity property of multiplication, $a \cdot 1 = a$, and the *inverse of a matrix* to the inverse property of multiplication, $a \cdot \frac{1}{a} = 1$.

learning style: verbal

The following test will help you determine whether a 2 × 2 matrix has an inverse. The test will also help you find the inverse, if it exists.

Key Concepts

| **Property** | **Inverse of a 2 × 2 Matrix** |

Let $A = \begin{bmatrix} a & b \\ c & d \end{bmatrix}$. If det $A = 0$, then A has no inverse.

If det $A \neq 0$, then $A^{-1} = \dfrac{1}{\det A} \begin{bmatrix} d & -b \\ -c & a \end{bmatrix} = \dfrac{1}{ad - bc} \begin{bmatrix} d & -b \\ -c & a \end{bmatrix}$.

1 Show that the matrices are multiplicative inverses.

$A = \begin{bmatrix} 3 & -1 \\ 7 & 1 \end{bmatrix}$

$B = \begin{bmatrix} 0.1 & 0.1 \\ -0.7 & 0.3 \end{bmatrix}$

Both *AB* and *BA* are equal to $\begin{bmatrix} 1 & 0 \\ 0 & 1 \end{bmatrix}$.

3 EXAMPLE Finding an Inverse Matrix

Determine whether each matrix has an inverse. If an inverse matrix exists, find it.

a. $M = \begin{bmatrix} -2 & 2 \\ 5 & -4 \end{bmatrix}$ $ad - bc = (-2)(-4) - (2)(5)$ **Find det M.**

$= -2$ **Simplify.**

Since det $M \neq 0$, the inverse of M exists.

Change signs.

$M^{-1} = \begin{bmatrix} -2 & 2 \\ 5 & -4 \end{bmatrix}^{-1}$

Switch positions.

$= \dfrac{1}{\det M} \begin{bmatrix} -4 & -2 \\ -5 & -2 \end{bmatrix}$ **Use the determinant to write the inverse.**

$= \dfrac{1}{-2} \begin{bmatrix} -4 & -2 \\ -5 & -2 \end{bmatrix}$ **Substitute −2 for det M.**

$= \begin{bmatrix} 2 & 1 \\ 2.5 & 1 \end{bmatrix}$ **Multiply.**

b. $N = \begin{bmatrix} 3 & 9 \\ 2 & 6 \end{bmatrix}$ $ad - bc = (3)(6) - (9)(2)$ **Find det N.**

$= 0$ **Simplify.**

Since det $N = 0$, the inverse of N does *not* exist.

2 Evaluate each determinant.

a. det $\begin{bmatrix} 7 & 8 \\ -5 & -9 \end{bmatrix}$ −23

b. det $\begin{bmatrix} 4 & -3 \\ 5 & 6 \end{bmatrix}$ 39

c. det $\begin{bmatrix} a & -b \\ b & a \end{bmatrix}$ $a^2 + b^2$

3 Determine whether each matrix has an inverse. If it does, find it.

a. $\begin{bmatrix} 12 & 4 \\ 9 & 3 \end{bmatrix}$ no

b. $\begin{bmatrix} 6 & 5 \\ 25 & 20 \end{bmatrix}$ yes; $\begin{bmatrix} -4 & 1 \\ 5 & -1.2 \end{bmatrix}$

Quick Check **3** Determine whether each matrix has an inverse. If an inverse matrix exists, find it.

a. $\begin{bmatrix} 2 & 4 \\ 1 & 3 \end{bmatrix}$ yes; $\begin{bmatrix} 1.5 & -2 \\ -0.5 & 1 \end{bmatrix}$ **b.** $\begin{bmatrix} 0.5 & 2.3 \\ 3 & 7.2 \end{bmatrix}$ yes; $\begin{bmatrix} -\frac{24}{11} & \frac{23}{33} \\ \frac{10}{11} & -\frac{5}{33} \end{bmatrix}$

2 Using Inverse Matrices to Solve Equations

If the inverse of matrix A exists, you can use it to solve matrix equations of the form $AX = B$. Multiply each side of the equation by A^{-1} to find X.

$AX = B$

$A^{-1}(AX) = A^{-1}B$ **Multiply each side by A^{-1}.**

$(A^{-1}A)X = A^{-1}B$ **Associative Property of Multiplication**

$IX = A^{-1}B$ **definition of multiplicative inverse**

$X = A^{-1}B$ **definition of multiplicative identity**

page 200 Quick Check

1a. $\begin{bmatrix} 2 & 1 \\ 2.5 & 1 \end{bmatrix} \begin{bmatrix} -2 & 2 \\ 5 & -4 \end{bmatrix} =$

$\begin{bmatrix} 2(-2) + 1(5) & 2(2) + 1(-4) \\ 2.5(-2) + 1(5) & 2.5(2) + 1(-4) \end{bmatrix} = \begin{bmatrix} 1 & 0 \\ 0 & 1 \end{bmatrix}$

b. $\begin{bmatrix} -2 & -5 \\ -3 & -8 \end{bmatrix} \begin{bmatrix} -8 & 5 \\ 3 & -2 \end{bmatrix} =$

$\begin{bmatrix} -2(-8) + (-5)(3) & -2(5) + (-5)(-2) \\ -3(-8) + (-8)(3) & -3(5) + (-8)(-2) \end{bmatrix} = \begin{bmatrix} 1 & 0 \\ 0 & 1 \end{bmatrix}$

Additional Examples

4 Solve $\begin{bmatrix} 9 & 25 \\ 4 & 11 \end{bmatrix} X = \begin{bmatrix} 3 \\ -7 \end{bmatrix}$ for

the matrix X. $\begin{bmatrix} -208 \\ 75 \end{bmatrix}$

5 In a city with a stable group of 45,000 households, 25,000 households use long distance carrier A, and 20,000 use long distance carrier B. Over a 1-year period, 84% of the households remain with carrier A, while 16% switch to B. 93% of the households using B stay with B, while 7% switch to A.

a. Write a matrix to represent the changes in long distance carriers.

$$\text{To } \begin{matrix} & \text{From} \\ & \text{A} \quad \text{B} \\ \text{A} & \begin{bmatrix} 0.84 & 0.07 \\ \text{B} & 0.16 & 0.93 \end{bmatrix} \end{matrix}$$

b. Predict the number of households that will be using long distance carrier B next year.
22,600 households
c. Use the inverse of the matrix from part a to find, to the nearest hundred households, how many households used carrier A last year.
about 28,400 households

Resources
• Daily Notetaking Guide 4-5 **L3**

Closure

How can you find out whether a 2 × 2 matrix has an inverse? If it does, how can you find the inverse? *Calculate the determinant of the matrix. If the determinant is not 0, then the matrix has an inverse. If a 2 × 2 matrix $\begin{bmatrix} a & b \\ c & d \end{bmatrix}$ does have an inverse, you can find it by multiplying the matrix $\begin{bmatrix} d & -b \\ -c & a \end{bmatrix}$ by the reciprocal of the determinant of $\begin{bmatrix} a & b \\ c & d \end{bmatrix}$.*

Real-World Connection

Martin Cooper invented the portable cellular radio telephone in 1973.

---

4 EXAMPLE Solving a Matrix Equation

Solve $\begin{bmatrix} -2 & -5 \\ 1 & 3 \end{bmatrix} X = \begin{bmatrix} -2 \\ 2 \end{bmatrix}$ for the matrix X.

The matrix equation has the form $AX = B$. First find A^{-1}.

$A^{-1} = \dfrac{1}{ad - bc} \begin{bmatrix} d & -b \\ -c & a \end{bmatrix} = \dfrac{1}{-2(3) - (-5)1} \begin{bmatrix} 3 & 5 \\ -1 & -2 \end{bmatrix}$ **Use the definition of inverse.**

$= \begin{bmatrix} -3 & -5 \\ 1 & 2 \end{bmatrix}$ **Simplify.**

Use the equation $X = A^{-1}B$. $\quad X = \begin{bmatrix} -3 & -5 \\ 1 & 2 \end{bmatrix} \begin{bmatrix} -2 \\ 2 \end{bmatrix}$ **Substitute.**

$= \begin{bmatrix} -3(-2) + -5(2) \\ 1(-2) + 2(2) \end{bmatrix} = \begin{bmatrix} -4 \\ 2 \end{bmatrix}$ **Multiply and simplify.**

Check $\begin{bmatrix} -2 & -5 \\ 1 & 3 \end{bmatrix} X = \begin{bmatrix} -2 \\ 2 \end{bmatrix}$ **Use the original equation.**

$\begin{bmatrix} -2 & -5 \\ 1 & 3 \end{bmatrix} \begin{bmatrix} -4 \\ 2 \end{bmatrix} \overset{?}{=} \begin{bmatrix} -2 \\ 2 \end{bmatrix}$ **Substitute.**

$\begin{bmatrix} -2(-4) + (-5)(2) \\ 1(-4) + 3(2) \end{bmatrix} \overset{?}{=} \begin{bmatrix} -2 \\ 2 \end{bmatrix}$ **Multiply.**

$\begin{bmatrix} -2 \\ 2 \end{bmatrix} = \begin{bmatrix} -2 \\ 2 \end{bmatrix}$ ✓ **Simplify.**

Quick Check **4** Solve each matrix equation in the form $AX = B$. Use the equation $X = A^{-1}B$.

a. $\begin{bmatrix} 3 & -4 \\ 4 & -5 \end{bmatrix} X = \begin{bmatrix} 0 & -22 \\ 0 & -28 \end{bmatrix} \begin{bmatrix} 0 & -2 \\ 0 & 4 \end{bmatrix}$ **b.** $\begin{bmatrix} 7 & 5 \\ 3 & 2 \end{bmatrix} X = \begin{bmatrix} -9 \\ -4 \end{bmatrix} \begin{bmatrix} -2 \\ 1 \end{bmatrix}$

You can use matrices to make predictions about trends.

5 EXAMPLE Real-World Connection

Communications The diagram shows the trends in cell phone ownership over four consecutive years.

a. Write a matrix to represent the changes (or transitions) in cell phone use.

$$\text{To } \begin{matrix} & \text{From} \\ & \text{No cell} \quad \text{Cell} \\ \text{No cell} & \begin{bmatrix} 0.57 & 0.13 \\ \text{Cell} & 0.43 & 0.87 \end{bmatrix} \end{matrix}$$ **Write the percents as decimals.**

b. In a stable population of 16,000 people, 9927 own cell phones, while 6073 do not. Assume the trends continue. Predict the number of people who will own cell phones next year.

$\begin{matrix} \text{No cell} & \begin{bmatrix} 6073 \\ \text{Cell} & 9927 \end{bmatrix} \end{matrix}$ **Write the information in a matrix.**

$\begin{bmatrix} 0.57 & 0.13 \\ 0.43 & 0.87 \end{bmatrix} \begin{bmatrix} 6073 \\ 9927 \end{bmatrix} \approx \begin{bmatrix} 4752 \\ 11,248 \end{bmatrix}$ **Use the transition matrix from part (a). Multiply.**

Next year, about 11,248 people in the population will own cell phones.

Cell Phone

87%

No Cell Phone

43%

13%

57%

---

202 Chapter 4 Matrices

pages 203–204 Exercises

14. yes; $\begin{bmatrix} 0 & 1 \\ -1 & 2 \end{bmatrix}$

15. yes; $\begin{bmatrix} -1 & 3 \\ 1 & -2 \end{bmatrix}$

16. yes; $\begin{bmatrix} 2 & -1.5 \\ -1 & 1 \end{bmatrix}$

17. yes; $\begin{bmatrix} 0 & \frac{1}{2} \\ \frac{1}{3} & -\frac{1}{6} \end{bmatrix}$

18. no

c. Use the inverse of the matrix from part (a) to find the number of people who owned cell phones last year.

$$\begin{bmatrix} 0.57 & 0.13 \\ 0.43 & 0.87 \end{bmatrix}^{-1} \begin{bmatrix} 6073 \\ 9927 \end{bmatrix} = \begin{bmatrix} 9075 \\ 6925 \end{bmatrix}$$

● Last year, 6925 people owned cell phones.

 Quick Check ⑤ **a. Critical Thinking** Find the percent of the population owning cell phones last year, this year, and next year. Estimate the percent two years from now.
b. Use the answer to Example 5, part (b), and the transition matrix to predict the number of people who will own cell phones two years from now.
c. Use the answer to Example 5, part (c), and the inverse of the transition matrix to estimate the number of people who owned cell phones two years ago.

  5. a. 43.3%, 62.0%, 70.3%; 73.9%

      b. about 11,829 people

      c. about 102 people

EXERCISES

For more exercises, see *Extra Skill and Word Problem Practice*.

Practice and Problem Solving

 A Practice by Example

Example 1
(page 200)

 for Help

Show that the matrices are multiplicative inverses. 1–3. See back of book.

1. $\begin{bmatrix} 3 & 2 \\ 4 & 3 \end{bmatrix}, \begin{bmatrix} 3 & -2 \\ -4 & 3 \end{bmatrix}$ **2.** $\begin{bmatrix} -3 & 7 \\ -2 & 5 \end{bmatrix}, \begin{bmatrix} -5 & 7 \\ -2 & 3 \end{bmatrix}$ **3.** $\begin{bmatrix} \frac{1}{5} & -\frac{1}{10} \\ 0 & \frac{1}{4} \end{bmatrix}, \begin{bmatrix} 5 & 2 \\ 0 & 4 \end{bmatrix}$

Example 2
(page 200)

Evaluate the determinant of each matrix.

4. $\begin{bmatrix} 7 & 2 \\ 0 & -3 \end{bmatrix}$ −21 **5.** $\begin{bmatrix} 6 & 2 \\ -6 & -2 \end{bmatrix}$ 0 **6.** $\begin{bmatrix} 0 & 0.5 \\ 1.5 & 2 \end{bmatrix}$ −0.75 **7.** $\begin{bmatrix} \frac{1}{2} & \frac{2}{3} \\ \frac{3}{5} & \frac{1}{4} \end{bmatrix}$ −$\frac{11}{40}$ **8.** $\begin{bmatrix} -1 & 3 \\ 5 & 2 \end{bmatrix}$ −17

9. $\begin{bmatrix} -2 & 0 \\ 2 & -1 \end{bmatrix}$ 2 **10.** $\begin{bmatrix} 5 & 3 \\ -2 & 1 \end{bmatrix}$ 11 **11.** $\begin{bmatrix} 5 & 2 \\ 1 & 3 \end{bmatrix}$ 13 **12.** $\begin{bmatrix} 2 & -1 \\ 5 & -4 \end{bmatrix}$ −3 **13.** $\begin{bmatrix} -4 & 3 \\ 2 & 0 \end{bmatrix}$ −6

Example 3
(page 201)

Determine whether each matrix has an inverse. If an inverse matrix exists, find it.
14–21. See margin pp. 202–203.

14. $\begin{bmatrix} 2 & -1 \\ 1 & 0 \end{bmatrix}$ **15.** $\begin{bmatrix} 2 & 3 \\ 1 & 1 \end{bmatrix}$ **16.** $\begin{bmatrix} 2 & 3 \\ 2 & 4 \end{bmatrix}$ **17.** $\begin{bmatrix} 1 & 3 \\ 2 & 0 \end{bmatrix}$

18. $\begin{bmatrix} 6 & -8 \\ -3 & 4 \end{bmatrix}$ **19.** $\begin{bmatrix} 4 & 8 \\ -3 & -2 \end{bmatrix}$ **20.** $\begin{bmatrix} -1.5 & 3 \\ 2.5 & -0.5 \end{bmatrix}$ **21.** $\begin{bmatrix} 1 & -2 \\ 3 & 0 \end{bmatrix}$

Example 4
(page 202)

Solve each matrix equation. If an equation cannot be solved, explain why.
22–24. See margin.

22. $\begin{bmatrix} 12 & 7 \\ 5 & 3 \end{bmatrix} X = \begin{bmatrix} 2 & -1 \\ 3 & 2 \end{bmatrix}$ **23.** $\begin{bmatrix} 0 & -4 \\ 0 & -1 \end{bmatrix} X = \begin{bmatrix} 0 \\ 4 \end{bmatrix}$ **24.** $\begin{bmatrix} 5 & -3 \\ 4 & -2 \end{bmatrix} X = \begin{bmatrix} 5 \\ 10 \end{bmatrix}$

Example 5
(pages 202–203)

25. Data Analysis Use the information in the diagram.
a. Write a transition matrix to represent the changes in cable television subscribers. a–c. See back of book.
b. In a stable population of 30,000 people, 20,000 people subscribe to cable television, while 10,000 do not. Predict the number of people who will subscribe to cable television next year.
c. Use the inverse of the matrix from part (a) to find the number of people who subscribed to cable television last year.

Cable
99.5% TV

No
Cable
TV
2%

0.5%

98%

Lesson 4-5 2 × 2 Matrices, Determinants, and Inverses **203**

3. Practice

Assignment Guide

① **A** **B** 1-21, 26-41, 44

② **A** **B** 22-25, 42-43, 45
C Challenge   46-51

Test Prep   52-55
Mixed Review   56-63

Homework Quick Check
To check students' understanding of key skills and concepts, go over Exercises 17, 25, 42, 44, 45.

Error Prevention!

Exercises 14–21 Students need to be cautious when calculating inverses of matrices. Urge them to be especially careful when writing the matrix that is to be multiplied by the reciprocal of the determinant. They may forget to switch the elements on the main diagonal of the original. Also, they may forget to use the opposites of the elements on the other diagonal.

19. yes; $\begin{bmatrix} -\frac{1}{8} & -\frac{1}{2} \\ \frac{3}{16} & \frac{1}{4} \end{bmatrix}$

20. yes; $\begin{bmatrix} \frac{2}{27} & \frac{4}{9} \\ \frac{10}{27} & \frac{2}{9} \end{bmatrix}$

21. yes; $\begin{bmatrix} 0 & \frac{1}{3} \\ -\frac{1}{2} & \frac{1}{6} \end{bmatrix}$

22. $\begin{bmatrix} -15 & -17 \\ 26 & 29 \end{bmatrix}$

23. No solutions; the determinant of $\begin{bmatrix} 0 & -4 \\ 0 & -1 \end{bmatrix}$ is 0.

24. $\begin{bmatrix} 10 \\ 15 \end{bmatrix}$

Lesson Quiz

1. Is $\begin{bmatrix} 5 & 2 \\ -2 & 1 \end{bmatrix}$ the inverse of

$\begin{bmatrix} 1 & 2 \\ 2 & 5 \end{bmatrix}$? How do you know?

no; Answers may vary.

Sample: $\begin{bmatrix} 1 & 2 \\ 2 & 5 \end{bmatrix}\begin{bmatrix} 5 & 2 \\ -2 & -1 \end{bmatrix}$ is

$\begin{bmatrix} 1 & 0 \\ 0 & -1 \end{bmatrix}$, which is not the

2×2 identity matrix.

2. Find the determinant of

$\begin{bmatrix} -12 & 5 \\ -16 & 4 \end{bmatrix}$. 32

3. Find the inverse of $\begin{bmatrix} -2 & 4 \\ 3 & -7 \end{bmatrix}$.

$\begin{bmatrix} -3.5 & -2 \\ -1.5 & -1 \end{bmatrix}$

4. Solve the equation

$\begin{bmatrix} 20 & 35 \\ 1 & 2 \end{bmatrix} X = \begin{bmatrix} -3 \\ 7 \end{bmatrix}. \begin{bmatrix} -50.2 \\ 28.6 \end{bmatrix}$

Alternative Assessment

Have students work in pairs. One student writes three nonzero elements in a 2×2 matrix. The other student supplies the fourth element. The first student tells whether or not the completed matrix has an inverse, and if it does, names the inverse. The other student checks the results. Students switch roles. They continue in this fashion for two more rounds.

pages 203–205 Exercises

32. No; answers may vary.
    Sample: the product is
    $\begin{bmatrix} 23 & 8 \\ -46 & -16 \end{bmatrix}$.

33. No; answers may vary.
    Sample: the product is
    $\begin{bmatrix} 0 & 1 \\ 1 & 0 \end{bmatrix}$.

34. yes; $\begin{bmatrix} -3 & 4 \\ 1 & -1 \end{bmatrix}$

35. yes; $\begin{bmatrix} -5 & 7 \\ 3 & -4 \end{bmatrix}$

36. yes; $\begin{bmatrix} 7 & 11 \\ 2 & 3 \end{bmatrix}$

37. yes; $\begin{bmatrix} 0.5 & 0 \\ 0 & 0.5 \end{bmatrix}$

38. yes; $\begin{bmatrix} 0 & \frac{1}{3} \\ \frac{1}{3} & 0 \end{bmatrix}$

39. yes; $\begin{bmatrix} 0 & \frac{1}{2} \\ \frac{1}{3} & \frac{1}{6} \end{bmatrix}$

40. yes; $\begin{bmatrix} -\frac{1}{3} & \frac{2}{3} \\ \frac{2}{3} & -\frac{1}{3} \end{bmatrix}$

41. No; the determinant is 0.

B Apply Your Skills

GO Online
Homework Video Tutor
Visit: PHSchool.com
Web Code: age-0405

42. $\begin{bmatrix} 1 & -3 \\ 0 & 1 \end{bmatrix}$

43. $\begin{bmatrix} 8 & -2 \\ -6 & 1 \end{bmatrix}$

DVD Player

100%

No DVD Player
17%

0%

83%

C Challenge

Evaluate each determinant.

26. $\begin{vmatrix} 4 & 5 \\ -4 & 4 \end{vmatrix}$ 　 27. $\begin{vmatrix} -3 & 10 \\ 6 & 20 \end{vmatrix}$ 　 28. $\begin{vmatrix} -\frac{1}{2} & 2 \\ -2 & 8 \end{vmatrix}$ 　 29. $\begin{vmatrix} 2 & 0 \\ 0 & 1 \end{vmatrix}$ 　 30. $\begin{vmatrix} 6 & 9 \\ 3 & 6 \end{vmatrix}$

36 　　　　 −120 　　　　 0 　　　　 2 　　　　 9

Determine whether the matrices are multiplicative inverses. If they are not, explain why not. 32–33. See margin.

31. $\begin{bmatrix} 2 & 0.5 \\ 5 & 1 \end{bmatrix}, \begin{bmatrix} -2 & 1 \\ 10 & -4 \end{bmatrix}$ 　 32. $\begin{bmatrix} -3 & 4 \\ 6 & -8 \end{bmatrix}, \begin{bmatrix} -1 & 0 \\ 5 & 2 \end{bmatrix}$ 　 33. $\begin{bmatrix} -2 & -5 \\ -2 & -4 \end{bmatrix}, \begin{bmatrix} -2.5 & 2 \\ 1 & -1 \end{bmatrix}$

yes

Determine whether each matrix has an inverse. If an inverse matrix exists, find it. If it does not exist, explain why not. 34–41. See margin.

34. $\begin{bmatrix} 1 & 4 \\ 1 & 3 \end{bmatrix}$ 　 35. $\begin{bmatrix} 4 & 7 \\ 3 & 5 \end{bmatrix}$ 　 36. $\begin{bmatrix} -3 & 11 \\ 2 & -7 \end{bmatrix}$ 　 37. $\begin{bmatrix} 2 & 0 \\ 0 & 2 \end{bmatrix}$

38. $\begin{bmatrix} 0 & 3 \\ 3 & 0 \end{bmatrix}$ 　 39. $\begin{bmatrix} -1 & 3 \\ 2 & 0 \end{bmatrix}$ 　 40. $\begin{bmatrix} 1 & 2 \\ 2 & 1 \end{bmatrix}$ 　 41. $\begin{bmatrix} 3 & 0 \\ 6 & 0 \end{bmatrix}$

Solve each matrix equation.

GPS 42. $\begin{bmatrix} 4 & 7 \\ 1 & 2 \end{bmatrix} X + \begin{bmatrix} 2 & 7 \\ -3 & 4 \end{bmatrix} = \begin{bmatrix} 6 & 2 \\ -2 & 3 \end{bmatrix}$ 　 43. $\begin{bmatrix} 1 & 9 \\ 6 & -6 \end{bmatrix} = \begin{bmatrix} -7 & -9 \\ 4 & 5 \end{bmatrix} X + \begin{bmatrix} 3 & 4 \\ 4 & -3 \end{bmatrix}$

44. **Writing** Suppose $A = \begin{bmatrix} a & b \\ c & d \end{bmatrix}$ has an inverse. In your own words, describe how to switch or change the elements of A to write A^{-1}. **See margin p. 205.**

45. **Entertainment** Use the information in the diagram at the left.
    a. Write a transition matrix to represent the changes in DVD-player ownership.
    b. In a stable population of 30,000 people, 7000 people own DVD players, while 23,000 do not. Predict the number of people in the population who will own DVD players next year. **about 10,910 people**
    c. Use the inverse of the matrix from part (a) to estimate the number of people in the population who owned DVD players last year.
    d. **Error Analysis** A student estimated that the number of people in the population who owned DVD players last year was 8434. What was the student's error? **a, c–d. See margin p. 205.**

46. **Critical Thinking** Suppose $A = \begin{bmatrix} a & b \\ c & d \end{bmatrix}$. For what values of $a, b, c,$ and d will A be its own inverse? (*Hint:* There is more than one correct answer.)
    Answers may vary. Sample: $a = \pm1, d = \pm1, b = c = 0$

Solve each matrix equation.

47. $-2\begin{bmatrix} -2 & 0 \\ 0 & -1 \end{bmatrix} + \begin{bmatrix} 0 & -3 \\ 5 & -4 \end{bmatrix} X + \begin{bmatrix} 0 & -3 \\ 5 & -4 \end{bmatrix} = \begin{bmatrix} 19 & -27 \\ 10 & -24 \end{bmatrix} \begin{bmatrix} -3 & 2 \\ -5 & 8 \end{bmatrix}$

48. $\begin{bmatrix} 0 & -6 \\ 1 & 2 \end{bmatrix} - \begin{bmatrix} 5 & 2 \\ 4 & 3 \end{bmatrix} X - \begin{bmatrix} 2 & -26 \\ 3 & -18 \end{bmatrix} = \begin{bmatrix} 3 & 25 \\ 2 & 24 \end{bmatrix} \begin{bmatrix} -1 & -1 \\ 0 & 0 \end{bmatrix}$

49. **Critical Thinking** Explain why a 2×3 matrix does not have a multiplicative inverse. **See margin p. 205.**

50. Let $M = \begin{bmatrix} a & b \\ c & d \end{bmatrix}$ and $N = \begin{bmatrix} e & f \\ g & h \end{bmatrix}$. Prove that the product of the determinants of M and N equals the determinant of the matrix product MN. **See back of book.**

(1, 3)   (3, 3)

(−2, −4)

51. a. Coordinate Geometry Find the area of the parallelogram at the left. **6 units²**

    b. Evaluate the determinant $\begin{vmatrix} 2 & 0 \\ 1 & 3 \end{vmatrix}$. Compare the value of the determinant to the area from part (a). **6; it is the same.**

    c. Make a Conjecture Consider the triangle at the left to be half a parallelogram. Make a conjecture about its area and the value of

    $\dfrac{1}{2}\begin{vmatrix} -4 & 0 \\ -2 & -4 \end{vmatrix}$. **They are the same.**

    d. Open-Ended Graph a different triangle with one vertex at the origin. Find the area of the triangle by writing and evaluating a determinant. **Check students' work.**

Test Prep

Gridded Response

52. What is the determinant of $\begin{bmatrix} -2 & -3 \\ 5 & 0 \end{bmatrix}$? **15**

53. What is the determinant of $\begin{bmatrix} \frac{3}{10} & \frac{1}{5} \\ \frac{1}{8} & \frac{1}{3} \end{bmatrix}$? Enter your answer as a fraction. **3/40**

54. If $A = \begin{bmatrix} 4 & 2 \\ -3 & -1 \end{bmatrix}$, and the inverse of A is $x\begin{bmatrix} -1 & -2 \\ 3 & 4 \end{bmatrix}$, what is the value of x? Enter your answer as a fraction. **1/2**

55. If $B = \begin{bmatrix} 4 & -1 \\ 2 & 0 \end{bmatrix}$, what is det B^{-1}? **1/2**

Mixed Review

for Help

Lesson 4-4

Each matrix represents the vertices of a polygon. Write a matrix to represent the vertices of the image after each transformation. **56–59. See margin.**

56. $\begin{bmatrix} 0 & 0 & 5 \\ 0 & -4 & 0 \end{bmatrix}$; rotation of 90°   **57.** $\begin{bmatrix} -2 & -5 & 0 \\ 0 & 3 & 5 \end{bmatrix}$; reflection in $y = x$

58. $\begin{bmatrix} 5 & 3 & 2 \\ 7 & 1 & 3 \end{bmatrix}$; 2 units left, 1 unit down   **59.** $\begin{bmatrix} -3 & -2 & -1 \\ 4 & 1 & 5 \end{bmatrix}$; dilation of 2

Lesson 3-6

Solve each system by substitution. $\left(\frac{70}{11}, -\frac{10}{11}, \frac{50}{11}\right)$ $\left(\frac{36}{13}, \frac{9}{13}, \frac{18}{13}\right)$

60. $\begin{cases} x = 5 \\ x - y + z = 5 \\ x + y - z = -5 \end{cases}$ **61.** $\begin{cases} x - 3y = 2z \\ x + 2y - z = 0 \\ x + y + z = 10 \end{cases}$ **62.** $\begin{cases} 3x + 3y - z = 9 \\ 2y = x - z \\ x - y + 5z = 9 \end{cases}$

    no solution

Lesson 2-4 🌐 **63. a. Exercise** Suppose you begin a training program by walking 2 miles every day. During the first week, the walk takes you 40 minutes per day. Each week after that, you reduce your time by one minute. Write a linear model for the number of minutes you take to walk 2 miles in week w. **a–b. See margin.**

    b. Critical Thinking Can you continue to improve at the same rate? Explain.

---

44. Answers may vary. Sample: Form a new matrix by switching the element in row 1, column 1 with the element in row 2, column 2. Then replace the other two elements with their opposites. Finally divide each element by the determinant of the original matrix.

A sheet of blank grids is available in the Test-Taking Strategies with Transparencies booklet. Give this sheet to students for practice with filling in the grids.

📁 **Resources**

For additional practice with a variety of test item formats:
- Standardized Test Prep, p. 233
- Test-Taking Strategies, p. 228
- Test-Taking Strategies with Transparencies

45a.

		From	
		No DVD	DVD
To	No DVD	0.83	0
	DVD	0.17	1

  c. about 2289 people

  d. The student used

$\begin{bmatrix} 0.17 & 1 \\ 0.83 & 0 \end{bmatrix}$

for the transition matrix.

49. Multiplicative inverses are only defined for square matrices because square matrices have an equal number of rows and columns.

56. $\begin{bmatrix} 0 & 4 & 0 \\ 0 & 0 & 5 \end{bmatrix}$

57. $\begin{bmatrix} 0 & 3 & 5 \\ -2 & -5 & 0 \end{bmatrix}$

58. $\begin{bmatrix} 3 & 1 & 0 \\ 6 & 0 & 2 \end{bmatrix}$

59. $\begin{bmatrix} -6 & -4 & -2 \\ 8 & 2 & 10 \end{bmatrix}$

63a. $t = 40 - (w - 1)$, where t = number of minutes you walk and w = week number.

  b. No; if you continue to reduce your time by 1 minute every week, eventually you would reach 0.

4-6

3 × 3 Matrices, Determinants, and Inverses

1. Plan

Objectives
1 To evaluate determinants of 3 × 3 matrices
2 To use inverse matrices in solving matrix equations

Examples
1 Evaluating the Determinant of a 3 × 3 Matrix
2 Using a Graphing Calculator
3 Ordering Real Numbers
4 Verifying Inverses
5 Solving a Matrix Equation
6 Real-World Connection

Math Background

This lesson extends the work in Lesson 4-5 to 3 × 3 matrices. Calculating the inverse of a 3 × 3 matrix is rather complicated. Students are therefore encouraged to use graphing calculators for many of the calculations in this lesson. Calculators are essential in finding the inverse of an $n \times n$ matrix for large values of n.

More Math Background: p. 166D

Lesson Planning and Resources

See p. 166E for a list of the resources that support this lesson.

Bell Ringer Practice

✓ **Check Skills You'll Need**
For intervention, direct students to:

Simplifying Expressions with Integers
Skills Handbook: p. 873
Example 3

What You'll Learn
- To evaluate determinants of 3 × 3 matrices
- To use inverse matrices in solving matrix equations

. . . And Why

To decode messages, as in Example 5

✓ Check Skills You'll Need

GO for Help Skills Handbook page 873

Find the product of the red elements in each matrix.

1. $\begin{bmatrix} 2 & 3 & 0 \\ -1 & 3 & -2 \\ 4 & -3 & -4 \end{bmatrix}$ −24

2. $\begin{bmatrix} 2 & 3 & 0 \\ -1 & 3 & -2 \\ 4 & -3 & -4 \end{bmatrix}$ 0

3. $\begin{bmatrix} 2 & 3 & 0 \\ -1 & 3 & -2 \\ 4 & -3 & -4 \end{bmatrix}$ −24

4. $\begin{bmatrix} 2 & 3 & 0 \\ -1 & 3 & -2 \\ 4 & -3 & -4 \end{bmatrix}$ 12

5. $\begin{bmatrix} 2 & 3 & 0 \\ -1 & 3 & -2 \\ 4 & -3 & -4 \end{bmatrix}$ 12

6. $\begin{bmatrix} 2 & 3 & 0 \\ -1 & 3 & -2 \\ 4 & -3 & -4 \end{bmatrix}$ 0

1 Evaluating Determinants of 3 × 3 Matrices

As you learned in Lesson 4-5, the determinant of a matrix helps you to find an inverse matrix and solve a matrix equation.

Key Concepts

Definition   **The Determinant of a 3 × 3 Matrix**

The determinant of a 3 × 3 matrix $\begin{bmatrix} a_1 & b_1 & c_1 \\ a_2 & b_2 & c_2 \\ a_3 & b_3 & c_3 \end{bmatrix}$ is

$$\begin{vmatrix} a_1 & b_1 & c_1 \\ a_2 & b_2 & c_2 \\ a_3 & b_3 & c_3 \end{vmatrix} = (a_1 b_2 c_3 + a_2 b_3 c_1 + a_3 b_1 c_2) - (a_1 b_3 c_2 + a_2 b_1 c_3 + a_3 b_2 c_1)$$

Visualize the pattern this way:
$$\begin{array}{ccc} a_1 & b_1 & c_1 \\ a_2 & b_2 & c_2 \\ a_3 & b_3 & c_3 \end{array} - \begin{array}{ccc} a_1 & b_1 & c_1 \\ a_2 & b_2 & c_2 \\ a_3 & b_3 & c_3 \end{array}$$

1 EXAMPLE   Evaluating the Determinant of a 3 × 3 Matrix

Evaluate the determinant of $F = \begin{bmatrix} -1 & 3 & 5 \\ 2 & -4 & 6 \\ 0 & 1 & -1 \end{bmatrix}$.

$$\begin{vmatrix} -1 & 3 & 5 \\ 2 & -4 & 6 \\ 0 & 1 & -1 \end{vmatrix} = [-1(-4)(-1) + 2(1)(5) + 0(3)(6)] - [-1(1)(6) + 2(3)(-1) + 0(-4)(5)]$$ Use the definition.

$$= [-4 + 10 + 0] - [-6 + (-6) + 0]$$ Multiply.

$$= 6 - (-12) = 18$$ Simplify.

● The determinant of F is 18.

Differentiated Instruction   Solutions for All Learners

Special Needs   L1
Show similarities between regular and matrix equations.

$$ax = b \qquad AX = B$$
$$\left(\tfrac{1}{a}\right)ax = \left(\tfrac{1}{a}\right)b \qquad (A^{-1}A)X = A^{-1}B$$
$$1x = \tfrac{1}{a}b \qquad (I)X = A^{-1}B$$
$$x = \tfrac{1}{a}b \qquad X = A^{-1}B$$

learning style: visual

Below Level   L2
A 3 × 3 determinant can be determined using the diagonals of the array

learning style: visual

Quick Check ❶ Evaluate each determinant.

a. $\begin{vmatrix} -3 & 4 & 0 \\ 2 & -5 & 1 \\ 0 & 2 & 3 \end{vmatrix}$ 27   **b.** $\begin{vmatrix} 1 & -1 & 2 \\ 0 & 4 & 2 \\ 3 & -6 & 10 \end{vmatrix}$ 22   **c.** $\begin{vmatrix} 2 & 0 & -1 \\ 0 & 0 & 0 \\ 1 & -5 & 3 \end{vmatrix}$ 0

You can use a graphing calculator to evaluate the determinant of a 3 × 3 matrix.

❷ EXAMPLE Using a Graphing Calculator

Enter matrix A into your graphing calculator. Use the matrix submenus to evaluate the determinant of A.

$$A = \begin{bmatrix} 1 & 7 & 2 \\ -1 & 1 & -2 \\ 1 & 1 & 1 \end{bmatrix}$$

Quick Check ❷ Use a graphing calculator to evaluate the determinant of $\begin{bmatrix} 13 & 21 & 11 \\ -2 & 4 & -1 \\ 17 & -2 & 0 \end{bmatrix}$.
−1087

❷ Using Inverse 3 × 3 Matrices

You can test whether two 3 × 3 matrices are inverses by finding their product.

❸ EXAMPLE Verifying Inverses

Vocabulary Tip

If A and B are <u>inverse</u> <u>matrices</u>, then $AB = BA = I$. If A has no inverse, then A is <u>singular</u> and det $A = 0$.

Determine whether the matrices are multiplicative inverses of each other.

a. $A = \begin{bmatrix} 1 & 5 & -1 \\ 1 & 0 & -1 \\ 1 & 0 & 0 \end{bmatrix}$, $B = \begin{bmatrix} 0 & 0 & 1 \\ 0.2 & -0.2 & 0 \\ 0 & -1 & 1 \end{bmatrix}$

$$\begin{bmatrix} 1 & 5 & -1 \\ 1 & 0 & -1 \\ 1 & 0 & 0 \end{bmatrix}\begin{bmatrix} 0 & 0 & 1 \\ 0.2 & -0.2 & 0 \\ 0 & -1 & 1 \end{bmatrix} = \begin{bmatrix} 1 & 0 & 0 \\ 0 & 1 & 0 \\ 0 & 0 & 1 \end{bmatrix}$$

Since $AB = I$, A and B are multiplicative inverses.

b. $C = \begin{bmatrix} 3 & 4 & 1 \\ -2 & 0 & 2 \\ 1 & 5 & 3 \end{bmatrix}$, $D = \begin{bmatrix} 0 & 1 & 0 \\ 1 & 0 & 1 \\ 0 & 1 & 0 \end{bmatrix}$

$$\begin{bmatrix} 3 & 4 & 1 \\ -2 & 0 & 2 \\ 1 & 5 & 3 \end{bmatrix}\begin{bmatrix} 0 & 1 & 0 \\ 1 & 0 & 1 \\ 0 & 1 & 0 \end{bmatrix} = \begin{bmatrix} 4 & 4 & 4 \\ 0 & 0 & 0 \\ 5 & 4 & 5 \end{bmatrix}$$

Since $CD \ne I$, C and D are not multiplicative inverses.

Quick Check ❸ **a.** Verify that A and B are inverses by showing that $BA = I$.
b. Verify that C and D are not inverses by showing that $DC \ne I$.
a–b. See back of book.

Lesson 4-6   3 × 3 Matrices, Determinants, and Inverses   **207**

---

2. Teach

Guided Instruction

❷ EXAMPLE Technology Tip

After entering matrix A, be sure to press **2nd** [QUIT] before using the matrix submenus.

PowerPoint

Additional Examples

❶ Evaluate the determinant of $\begin{bmatrix} 8 & -4 & 3 \\ -2 & 9 & 5 \\ 1 & 6 & 0 \end{bmatrix}$. −323

❷ Use a graphing calculator to evaluate the determinant of $\begin{bmatrix} 4 & 2 & 3 \\ -2 & -1 & 5 \\ 1 & 3 & 6 \end{bmatrix}$. −65

Guided Instruction

❸ EXAMPLE Math Tip

Point out that matrix multiplication is usually not commutative. However, if two matrices are inverses of each other, it does not matter in which order you multiply them. Thus, $AB = BA = I$.

PowerPoint

Additional Examples

❸ Determine whether the matrices are multiplicative inverses.

a. $\begin{bmatrix} 0.5 & 0 & 0 \\ 0 & 0 & 0.5 \\ 0 & 1 & 1 \end{bmatrix}$; $\begin{bmatrix} 2 & 0 & 0 \\ 0 & 2 & 1 \\ 0 & 2 & 0 \end{bmatrix}$ no

b. $\begin{bmatrix} 0 & 0 & 1 \\ 0 & 1 & 0 \\ 1 & 0 & -1 \end{bmatrix}$; $\begin{bmatrix} 1 & 0 & 1 \\ 0 & 1 & 0 \\ 1 & 0 & 0 \end{bmatrix}$ yes

---

Advanced Learners L4
Ask students to research expanding a 3 × 3 determinant by its 'minors' and compare the result to the definition.

learning style: verbal

English Language Learners ELL
Write *encode* and *decode* on the board. Ask students to volunteer short definitions of these words. Point out that encoding and decoding are opposite processes.

learning style: verbal

5 EXAMPLE Teaching Tip

It is crucial that the message first be written in a matrix that has 3 rows. Use 0 for a space between words and for spaces at the end of the message if the message does not fill the last row of the matrix. Multiply E by the matrix just constructed to obtain the coded message.

Additional Examples

4 Solve the equation.

$$\begin{bmatrix} 2 & 0 & 1 \\ 0 & 1 & 4 \\ 1 & 0 & 0 \end{bmatrix} X = \begin{bmatrix} -1 \\ 8 \\ -2 \end{bmatrix} \begin{bmatrix} -2 \\ -4 \\ 3 \end{bmatrix}$$

5 Use the alphabet table on page 208 and the encoding matrix

$$K = \begin{bmatrix} 0.5 & 0.25 & 0.25 \\ 0.25 & -0.5 & 0.5 \\ 0.5 & 1 & -1 \end{bmatrix}.$$

a. Find the decoding matrix K^{-1}.

$$\begin{bmatrix} 0 & 2 & 1 \\ 2 & -2.5 & -0.75 \\ 2 & -1.5 & -1.25 \end{bmatrix}$$

b. Decode the following text.

$$\begin{bmatrix} 11.25 & 16.75 & 24.5 \\ 5.75 & 17 & 5.5 \\ 1.5 & -12 & 15 \end{bmatrix}$$

NEAT CODE

Resources

• Daily Notetaking Guide 4-6 **L3**

Closure

Ask: *How do you determine whether two 3 × 3 matrices are inverses of each other?* Multiply them to see if the product is

$$\begin{bmatrix} 1 & 0 & 0 \\ 0 & 1 & 0 \\ 0 & 0 & 1 \end{bmatrix}.$$

Graphing Calculator Hint

If a square matrix has no inverse, you will see ERR: SINGULAR MAT on the screen.

You can use 3 × 3 matrices to solve matrix equations.

4 EXAMPLE Solving a Matrix Equation

Solve the matrix equation $\begin{bmatrix} 0 & 0 & 2 \\ 1 & 3 & -2 \\ 1 & -2 & 1 \end{bmatrix} X = \begin{bmatrix} 6 \\ -11 \\ 8 \end{bmatrix}.$

Let $A = \begin{bmatrix} 0 & 0 & 2 \\ 1 & 3 & -2 \\ 1 & -2 & 1 \end{bmatrix}$. Find A^{-1}.

```
[A]⁻¹
[[ .1   .4   .6  ]
 [ .3   .2  -.2  ]
 [ .5   0    0  ]]
```

$$X = \begin{bmatrix} 0.1 & 0.4 & 0.6 \\ 0.3 & 0.2 & -0.2 \\ 0.5 & 0 & 0 \end{bmatrix} \begin{bmatrix} 6 \\ -11 \\ 8 \end{bmatrix}$$

← Use the equation $X = A^{-1}C.$

Multiply. →

```
[A]⁻¹[C]
[[1 ]
 [-2]
 [3 ]]
```

$$X = \begin{bmatrix} 1 \\ -2 \\ 3 \end{bmatrix}$$

✓ Quick Check **4** **a.** Verify that A and A^{-1} are inverses. **See back of book.**

b. Solve the matrix equation $\begin{bmatrix} 0 & 0 & 2 \\ 1 & 3 & -2 \\ 1 & -2 & 1 \end{bmatrix} X = \begin{bmatrix} 0 \\ -6 \\ 19 \end{bmatrix}.$ $\begin{bmatrix} 9 \\ -5 \\ 0 \end{bmatrix}$

You can use 3 × 3 matrices to encode and decode messages.

5 EXAMPLE Real-World Connection

Cryptography Use the alphabet table and the encoding matrix E at the left.

a. Find the decoding matrix E^{-1}.

```
[E]⁻¹
[[  1  -2   2  ]
 [  0   4  -2  ]
 [  1  -2   0  ]]
```

Use a graphing calculator.

b. Use the decoding matrix to decode $\begin{bmatrix} 22.5 & 26 & 15.5 \\ 0.25 & 9 & 7.75 \\ -4 & 9 & 3.5 \end{bmatrix}.$

$$\begin{bmatrix} 1 & -2 & 2 \\ 0 & 4 & -2 \\ 1 & -2 & 0 \end{bmatrix} \begin{bmatrix} 22.5 & 26 & 15.5 \\ 0.25 & 9 & 7.75 \\ -4 & 9 & 3.5 \end{bmatrix} = \begin{bmatrix} 14 & 26 & 7 \\ 9 & 18 & 24 \\ 22 & 8 & 0 \end{bmatrix}$$

Use the decoding matrix from part (a). Multiply.

In the result, 0 is a space-holder.
The numbers 14 26 7 9 18 24 22 8 correspond to the letters MATRICES.

✓ Quick Check **5** **Literature** Use the information from Example 5. Decode the matrix at the right, which gives the title of a Pablo Neruda poem. **POETRY**

$$\begin{bmatrix} 21 & 10.5 \\ 6 & 4.25 \\ 1 & 5 \end{bmatrix}$$

Alphabet table:

A	26	N	13
B	25	O	12
C	24	P	11
D	23	Q	10
E	22	R	9
F	21	S	8
G	20	T	7
H	19	U	6
I	18	V	5
J	17	W	4
K	16	X	3
L	15	Y	2
M	14	Z	1

$$E = \begin{bmatrix} 0.5 & 0.5 & 0.5 \\ 0.25 & 0.25 & -0.25 \\ 0.5 & 0 & -0.5 \end{bmatrix}$$

208 Chapter 4 Matrices

EXERCISES

For more exercises, see *Extra Skill and Word Problem Practice*.

Practice and Problem Solving

 Practice by Example

Example 1
(page 206)

 for Help

Evaluate the determinant of each matrix.

1. $\begin{bmatrix} 1 & 2 & 5 \\ 3 & 1 & 0 \\ 1 & 2 & 1 \end{bmatrix}$ 20
2. $\begin{bmatrix} 1 & 4 & 0 \\ 2 & 3 & 5 \\ 0 & 1 & 0 \end{bmatrix}$ −5
3. $\begin{bmatrix} -2 & 4 & 1 \\ 3 & 0 & -1 \\ 1 & 2 & 1 \end{bmatrix}$ −14
4. $\begin{bmatrix} 2 & 3 & 0 \\ 1 & 2 & 5 \\ 7 & 0 & 1 \end{bmatrix}$ 106

Example 2
(page 207)

Use a graphing calculator to evaluate the determinant of each 3 × 3 matrix.

5. $\begin{bmatrix} 1 & 0 & 0 \\ 0 & 1 & 0 \\ 0 & 0 & 1 \end{bmatrix}$ 1
6. $\begin{bmatrix} 0 & -2 & -3 \\ 1 & 2 & 4 \\ -2 & 0 & 1 \end{bmatrix}$ 6
7. $\begin{bmatrix} 12.2 & 13.3 & 9 \\ 1 & -4 & -17 \\ 21.4 & -15 & 0 \end{bmatrix}$

−7314.14

Example 3
(page 207)

Determine whether the matrices are multiplicative inverses.

8. $\begin{bmatrix} 1 & 2 & -1 \\ -1.5 & -3 & 1.75 \\ 0 & -1 & 0.5 \end{bmatrix}, \begin{bmatrix} 1 & 0 & 2 \\ 3 & 2 & -1 \\ 6 & 4 & 0 \end{bmatrix}$
yes

9. $\begin{bmatrix} 2 & 2 & 2 \\ -2 & 2 & -2 \\ -2 & -2 & -2 \end{bmatrix}, \begin{bmatrix} 2 & 2 & 2 \\ -2 & 2 & -2 \\ -2 & -2 & -2 \end{bmatrix}$
no

Example 4
(page 208)

Solve each matrix equation.

10. $\begin{bmatrix} 5 & 1 & -4 \\ 2 & -3 & -5 \\ 7 & 2 & -6 \end{bmatrix} X = \begin{bmatrix} 5 \\ 2 \\ 5 \end{bmatrix}$ $\begin{bmatrix} 3 \\ -2 \\ 2 \end{bmatrix}$

11. $\begin{bmatrix} 6 & 10 & -13 \\ 4 & -2 & 7 \\ 0 & 9 & -8 \end{bmatrix} X = \begin{bmatrix} 84 \\ 18 \\ 56 \end{bmatrix}$ $\begin{bmatrix} 5 \\ 8 \\ 2 \end{bmatrix}$

Example 5
(page 208)

Literature Use the information from Example 5. Decode each title.

12. Emily Dickinson, **AUTUMN** $\begin{bmatrix} 23.5 & 12.5 \\ 4.75 & -0.25 \\ 6 & -3.5 \end{bmatrix}$

13. E. E. Cummings, **PORTRAIT** $\begin{bmatrix} 18 & 14 & 17.5 \\ 0 & 3.5 & 8.75 \\ -3.5 & 2.5 & 4.5 \end{bmatrix}$

 Apply Your Skills

14. Multiple Choice If matrix A has an inverse, what must be true? **D**

I. $AA^{-1} = I$ **II.** $A^{-1}A = I$ **III.** $A^{-1}I = A^{-1}$

Ⓐ I only   Ⓑ II only   Ⓒ I and II only   Ⓓ I, II, and III

15. Cryptography Two members of the Hopewell High School math club share messages in code. They use the alphabet table from Example 5.

a. One of the students has lost her encoding matrix. Luckily, she remembers that the decoding matrix is **a–b. See margin.**

$E^{-1} = \begin{bmatrix} 1 & -1 & 0 \\ 0 & 1 & -1 \\ 0 & 0 & 1 \end{bmatrix}$. Compute E to find the encoding matrix.

b. Use your answer to part (a) to encode the message MATH IS COOL.

c. Open-Ended Use the encoding matrix from part (a) to encode a short sentence. Use the decoding matrix to check your work.
Check students' work.

Evaluate the determinant of each matrix.

16. $\begin{bmatrix} 0 & 2 & -3 \\ 1 & 2 & 4 \\ -2 & 0 & 1 \end{bmatrix}$ −30
17. $\begin{bmatrix} 5 & 1 & 0 \\ 0 & 2 & -1 \\ -2 & -3 & 1 \end{bmatrix}$ −3
18. $\begin{bmatrix} 4 & 6 & -1 \\ 2 & 3 & 2 \\ 1 & -1 & 1 \end{bmatrix}$ 25
19. $\begin{bmatrix} -3 & 2 & -1 \\ 2 & 5 & 2 \\ 1 & -2 & 0 \end{bmatrix}$ 1

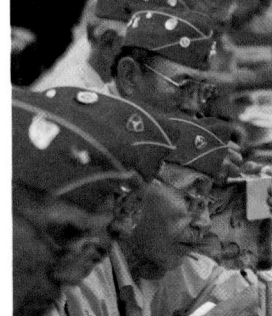

Real-World Connection

During World War II, these Navajo code talkers transmitted messages in an unbreakable code.

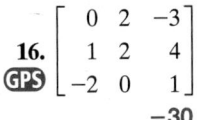

Assignment Guide

1 A B 1-7, 16-19, 24

2 A B 8-15, 20-23

C Challenge   25-28

Test Prep   29-33
Mixed Review   34-39

Homework Quick Check

To check students' understanding of key skills and concepts, go over Exercises 8, 10, 15, 16, 26.

Error Prevention!

Exercises 1–4 Urge students to show all their work when they apply the definition of the determinant of a 3 × 3 matrix. The visual pattern that accompanies the definition may be helpful. Students may choose to use a graphing calculator to check their final answers.

Differentiated Instruction Resources

GPS Guided Problem Solving		L3
Enrichment		L4
Reteaching		L2
Practice		L3

---

pages 209–211 Exercises

15a. $\begin{bmatrix} 1 & 1 & 1 \\ 0 & 1 & 1 \\ 0 & 0 & 1 \end{bmatrix}$

b. $\begin{bmatrix} 38 & 56 & 27 & 34 \\ 24 & 30 & 20 & 15 \\ 24 & 12 & 12 & 15 \end{bmatrix}$

Lesson Quiz

1. Use pencil and paper to evaluate the determinant of
$$\begin{bmatrix} -2 & -4 & 2 \\ 3 & 1 & 0 \\ 5 & -6 & -2 \end{bmatrix}. \; -66$$

2. Determine whether the matrices are multiplicative inverses.
$$\begin{bmatrix} 1 & 1 & -1 \\ -1 & 0 & 1 \\ 0 & -1 & 1 \end{bmatrix}; \begin{bmatrix} 1 & 0 & 1 \\ 1 & 1 & 0 \\ 1 & 1 & 1 \end{bmatrix}$$
yes

3. Solve the equation.
$$\begin{bmatrix} -1 & -1 & 1 \\ 1 & 2 & -1 \\ 0 & -1 & 1 \end{bmatrix} M = \begin{bmatrix} -1 \\ -4 \\ 3 \end{bmatrix}$$
$$\begin{bmatrix} 4 \\ -5 \\ -2 \end{bmatrix}$$

Alternative Assessment

Have each student create and encode a message using the alphabet table and encoding matrix in Example 5. Direct students to exchange coded messages and decode them.

Test Prep

Resources
For additional practice with a variety of test item formats:
• Standardized Test Prep, p. 233
• Test-Taking Strategies, p. 228
• Test-Taking Strategies with Transparencies

C **Challenge**

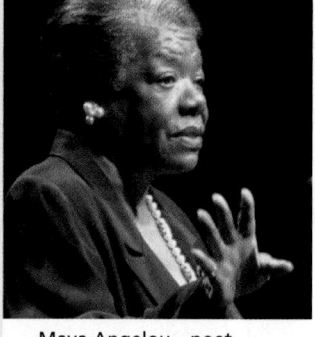

Maya Angelou—poet, educator, historian, novelist, actress, and playwright

Multiple Choice

Short Response

32. The identity matrix *I*. The product of any matrix and its inverse is *I*.

Find the inverse of each matrix, if it exists. 20–22. See margin.

20. $\begin{bmatrix} -2 & 1 & -1 \\ 2 & 0 & 4 \\ 0 & 2 & 5 \end{bmatrix}$ 21. $\begin{bmatrix} 2 & 0 & -1 \\ -1 & -1 & 1 \\ 3 & 2 & 0 \end{bmatrix}$ 22. $\begin{bmatrix} 0 & 0 & 2 \\ 1 & 4 & -2 \\ 3 & -2 & 1 \end{bmatrix}$ 23. $\begin{bmatrix} 1 & 2 & 6 \\ 1 & -1 & 0 \\ 1 & 0 & 2 \end{bmatrix}$
no inverse

24. **Writing** Evaluate the determinant of each matrix. Describe any patterns.

a. $\begin{bmatrix} 1 & 2 & 3 \\ 1 & 2 & 3 \\ 1 & 2 & 3 \end{bmatrix} 0$ b. $\begin{bmatrix} -1 & -2 & -3 \\ -3 & -2 & -1 \\ -1 & -2 & -3 \end{bmatrix} 0$ c. $\begin{bmatrix} 1 & 2 & 3 \\ 2 & 3 & 1 \\ 1 & 2 & 3 \end{bmatrix} 0$ d. $\begin{bmatrix} -1 & 2 & -3 \\ 2 & -3 & -1 \\ -1 & 2 & -3 \end{bmatrix} 0$

See margin for pattern.

Literature Use the table and decoding matrix from Example 5. Decode each title.

25. Maya Angelou, $\begin{bmatrix} 26.5 & 28 & 15.5 & 16.5 & 13.5 \\ 0.25 & 2 & -3.25 & 8.25 & 6.75 \\ -6 & -6 & -6.5 & 6.5 & 9 \end{bmatrix}$ **MORNING GRACE**

26. Oliver Wendell Holmes, $\begin{bmatrix} 19 & 24 & 24.5 & 18.5 & 26.5 & 13.5 & 19.5 & 20 \\ 6.5 & 8.5 & 3.25 & 1.75 & 10.25 & 2.75 & 9.75 & 10 \\ 0.5 & 6 & 2 & -7.5 & 9 & 5.5 & 13 & 7 \end{bmatrix}$
THE CHAMBERED NAUTILUS

Solve each matrix equation.

27. $\begin{bmatrix} 7 & -5 & 3 \\ 0 & 1 & 3 \\ 8 & 4 & -2 \end{bmatrix} X + \begin{bmatrix} 5 \\ -9 \\ 0 \end{bmatrix} = \begin{bmatrix} 54 \\ -12 \\ 96 \end{bmatrix}$ $\begin{bmatrix} 10 \\ 3 \\ -2 \end{bmatrix}$

28. $\left(\begin{bmatrix} -1 & 0 & 2 \\ -6 & -5 & 0 \\ 1 & 4 & 1 \end{bmatrix} - \begin{bmatrix} -4 & 0 & 2 \\ 0 & 3 & 6 \\ 0 & 5 & 0 \end{bmatrix} \right) X = \begin{bmatrix} -21 & 10 & 26 \\ -54 & 1 & -15 \\ 1 & 4 & -24 \end{bmatrix}$ $\begin{bmatrix} -1 & 2 & 6 \\ 0 & 0 & 5 \\ 8 & -1 & 0 \end{bmatrix}$

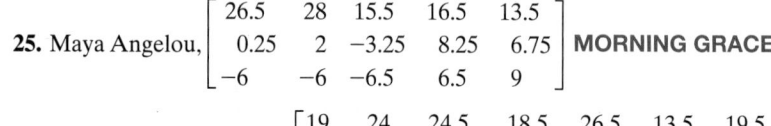

Test Prep

29. What is the determinant of $\begin{bmatrix} 5 & 0 & 0 \\ 0 & 5 & 0 \\ 0 & 0 & 5 \end{bmatrix}$? **C**

A. 5   B. 25   C. 125   D. 555

30. Which matrix has no inverse? **F**

F. $\begin{bmatrix} 1 & 0 & 0 \\ 0 & 0 & 0 \\ 0 & 0 & 1 \end{bmatrix}$ G. $\begin{bmatrix} 1 & 0 & 1 \\ 0 & 1 & 0 \\ 0 & 0 & 1 \end{bmatrix}$ H. $\begin{bmatrix} 0 & 0 & 1 \\ 0 & -1 & 0 \\ 1 & 1 & 0 \end{bmatrix}$ J. $\begin{bmatrix} 1 & -1 & 0 \\ 0 & 0 & 1 \\ -1 & 0 & 1 \end{bmatrix}$

31. What is the determinant of the identity matrix *I*? 1

32. The matrix *A* at the right has an inverse A^{-1}. What is the product AA^{-1}? Explain. $A = \begin{bmatrix} 1 & 1 & 2 \\ 2 & -1 & 1 \\ 1 & 4 & -1 \end{bmatrix}$

33. Matrices *B* and *C* are inverses of each other.

$B = \begin{bmatrix} 1 & 1 & 0 \\ 0 & 2 & 1 \\ -2 & 0 & 2 \end{bmatrix}$ $C = \begin{bmatrix} 2 & -1 & 0.5 \\ -1 & 1 & -0.5 \\ 2 & -1 & 1 \end{bmatrix}$ $D = \begin{bmatrix} 2 \\ 0 \\ -1 \end{bmatrix}$ $\begin{bmatrix} 3.5 \\ -1.5 \\ 3 \end{bmatrix}$

Solve the matrix equation $BX = D$.

---

20. $\begin{bmatrix} -4 & -3.5 & 2 \\ -5 & -5 & 3 \\ 2 & 2 & -1 \end{bmatrix}$

21. $\begin{bmatrix} 0.4 & 0.4 & 0.2 \\ -0.6 & -0.6 & 0.2 \\ -0.2 & 0.8 & 0.4 \end{bmatrix}$

22. $\begin{bmatrix} 0 & \frac{1}{7} & \frac{2}{7} \\ \frac{1}{4} & \frac{3}{14} & -\frac{1}{14} \\ \frac{1}{2} & 0 & 0 \end{bmatrix}$

24. **Answers may vary. Sample:** When the top row and bottom row are identical and the middle row has the same numbers as both rows, then the determinant is zero.

Checkpoint Quiz

Use this Checkpoint Quiz to check students' understanding of the skills and concepts of Lessons 4-4 through 4-6.

Resources
Grab & Go
• Checkpoint Quiz 2

GO for Help

Lesson 4-5 | **Determine whether each matrix has an inverse. If an inverse matrix exists, find it.**

34. $\begin{bmatrix} -9 & 3 \\ 4 & 2.5 \end{bmatrix}$ **35.** $\begin{bmatrix} 2 & 3 \\ 8 & 12 \end{bmatrix}$ **36.** $\begin{bmatrix} -3 & 4 \\ 9 & 10 \end{bmatrix}$ **37.** $\begin{bmatrix} 0 & -1 \\ -1 & 0 \end{bmatrix}$

34–37. See margin.

Lesson 3-1 | **Solve each system of equations.**

38. $\begin{cases} 2x + 2y = 10 \\ 3x - y = 4 \end{cases}$ $\left(\frac{9}{4}, \frac{11}{4}\right)$

39. $\begin{cases} -x + y + z = 5 \\ 2x + y - z = 2 \\ 3x + 2y + 4z = 0 \end{cases}$

$\left(-\frac{13}{8}, \frac{69}{16}, -\frac{15}{16}\right)$

Checkpoint Quiz 2   Lessons 4-4 through 4-6

Use △ABC at the right. Find the coordinates of the image under each transformation. 1–4. See margin.

1. a dilation of 2

2. a translation 3 units left and 3 units up

3. a rotation of 270°

4. a reflection in $y = -x$

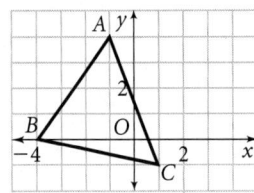

Solve each matrix equation. 5–7. See margin.

5. $\begin{bmatrix} 0 & 3 \\ 5 & 0 \end{bmatrix} X = \begin{bmatrix} -12 & -15 \\ 10 & 15 \end{bmatrix}$ **6.** $\begin{bmatrix} -1 & 2 & 3 \\ 0 & 3 & 2 \\ 3 & -2 & 0 \end{bmatrix} X = \begin{bmatrix} 17 \\ 18 \\ 11 \end{bmatrix}$ **7.** $\begin{bmatrix} 4 & 5 \\ -1 & 5 \end{bmatrix} X = \begin{bmatrix} 32 \\ 42 \end{bmatrix}$

Evaluate the determinant of each matrix.

8. $\begin{bmatrix} -2 & 3 \\ 0 & 5 \end{bmatrix}$ −10 **9.** $\begin{bmatrix} 0 & 5 & 4 \\ -1 & -1 & 3 \\ 2 & 5 & 0 \end{bmatrix}$ 18 **10.** $\begin{bmatrix} -3 & 2 & 0 \\ 4 & 17 & 10 \\ 1 & -5 & -1 \end{bmatrix}$ −71

A Point in Time

1500   1600   1700   1800   1900   2000

An artist who paints murals creates a sketch and then uses a dilation of the sketch for the actual mural. Judith Francisca Baca is a muralist who serves as the artistic director of the Great Wall of Los Angeles. The 13-ft-by-2400-ft mural, which depicts California's multicultural history, has involved over 400 youths, 100 scholars, and 50 assisting artists.

Go Online
PHSchool.com
For: Information about murals
Web Code: age-2032

page 211   Checkpoint Quiz 2

1. $A'(-2, 8)$, $B'(-8, 0)$, $C'(2, -2)$

2. $A'(-4, 7)$, $B'(-7, 3)$, $C'(-2, 2)$

3. $A'(4, 1)$, $B'(0, 4)$, $C'(-1, -1)$

4. $A'(-4, 1)$, $B'(0, 4)$, $C'(1, -1)$

5. $\begin{bmatrix} 2 & 3 \\ -4 & -5 \end{bmatrix}$

6. $\begin{bmatrix} 5 \\ 2 \\ 6 \end{bmatrix}$

7. $\begin{bmatrix} -2 \\ 8 \end{bmatrix}$

34. yes; $\begin{bmatrix} -\frac{5}{69} & \frac{2}{23} \\ \frac{8}{69} & \frac{6}{23} \end{bmatrix}$ **36.** yes; $\begin{bmatrix} -\frac{5}{33} & \frac{2}{33} \\ \frac{3}{22} & \frac{1}{22} \end{bmatrix}$

35. no

37. yes; $\begin{bmatrix} 0 & -1 \\ -1 & 0 \end{bmatrix}$

21

Overview

The smooth operation of many of the systems we depend on in everyday life often require detailed analyses of how various locations are linked by channels of transportation or communication. Matrices are helpful in developing mathematical models for such studies.

Guided Instruction

1 EXAMPLE **Teaching Tip**

Expand on the comment at the end of the example. Point out that N_1 and N_4 are not directly linked by a single path. You can get from N_1 to N_4 only by way of other points.

2 EXAMPLE **Teaching Tip**

Ask students what type of situation might yield a graph of this kind. There are various possibilities. The arrows could indicate traffic flow along streets in a city. They could indicate who provides information to whom within an organization.

3 EXAMPLE **Teaching Tip**

You may again wish to ask for real-world examples. One possibility is that arrows indicate payees for checks written by three people.

Resources

Technology
ExamView CD-ROM, Chapter 00,
Extension Topics

pages 212–213   Extension

A finite graph is a set of points, called vertices, connected by curves, or paths.

You can use a matrix to describe a finite graph. A 1 indicates a path between two vertices or one vertex and itself. A 0 indicates that no path exists between two vertices or from one vertex to itself.

1 EXAMPLE

Write a matrix A to represent the finite graph. Explain the significance of element a_{41}.

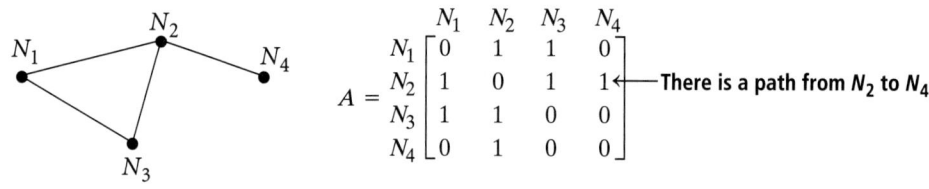

$$A = \begin{array}{c} \\ N_1 \\ N_2 \\ N_3 \\ N_4 \end{array} \begin{array}{cccc} N_1 & N_2 & N_3 & N_4 \\ \begin{bmatrix} 0 & 1 & 1 & 0 \\ 1 & 0 & 1 & 1 \\ 1 & 1 & 0 & 0 \\ 0 & 1 & 0 & 0 \end{bmatrix} \end{array}$$

← There is a path from N_2 to N_4.

● Element a_{41} is 0. It indicates that there is no path between N_4 and N_1.

Directed graphs are finite graphs that indicate the direction of a path. The directed graph at the right below represents the information in the map.

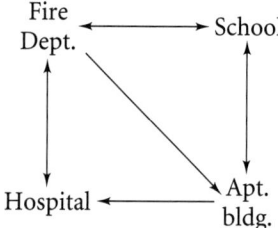

You can use a matrix to represent the information in a directed graph.

2 EXAMPLE

Write a matrix B to represent the information from the directed graph. Compare elements b_{12} and b_{21}.

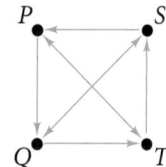

$$B = \begin{array}{c} \text{From} \rightarrow \\ \\ \end{array} \begin{array}{c} \\ P \\ Q \\ S \\ T \end{array} \begin{array}{cccc} \text{To} \rightarrow P & Q & S & T \\ \begin{bmatrix} 0 & 1 & 0 & 1 \\ 0 & 0 & 1 & 1 \\ 1 & 1 & 0 & 0 \\ 1 & 0 & 1 & 0 \end{bmatrix} \end{array}$$

● Element b_{12} is 1, and element b_{21} is 0. The path between P and Q is one way from P to Q.

1.

$$\begin{array}{c} N_1 \\ N_2 \\ N_3 \\ N_4 \end{array} \begin{array}{cccc} N_1 & N_2 & N_3 & N_4 \\ \begin{bmatrix} 0 & 1 & 0 & 1 \\ 1 & 0 & 1 & 1 \\ 0 & 1 & 0 & 1 \\ 1 & 1 & 1 & 0 \end{bmatrix} \end{array}$$

2.

$$\begin{array}{c} S \\ T \\ U \\ V \end{array} \begin{array}{cccc} S & T & U & V \\ \begin{bmatrix} 0 & 0 & 1 & 0 \\ 0 & 0 & 1 & 0 \\ 1 & 1 & 0 & 1 \\ 0 & 0 & 1 & 0 \end{bmatrix} \end{array}$$

3.

$$\begin{array}{c} V_1 \\ V_2 \\ V_3 \\ V_4 \\ V_5 \end{array} \begin{array}{ccccc} V_1 & V_2 & V_3 & V_4 & V_5 \\ \begin{bmatrix} 0 & 1 & 0 & 0 & 0 \\ 1 & 0 & 1 & 0 & 0 \\ 0 & 1 & 0 & 1 & 1 \\ 0 & 0 & 1 & 0 & 1 \\ 0 & 0 & 1 & 1 & 0 \end{bmatrix} \end{array}$$

4.

$$\begin{array}{c} A \\ B \\ C \\ D \\ E \end{array} \begin{array}{ccccc} A & B & C & D & E \\ \begin{bmatrix} 0 & 1 & 0 & 0 & 1 \\ 1 & 0 & 1 & 0 & 0 \\ 0 & 1 & 0 & 1 & 0 \\ 0 & 0 & 0 & 0 & 1 \\ 0 & 0 & 0 & 1 & 0 \end{bmatrix} \end{array}$$

You can use information in a matrix to draw a directed graph.

③ EXAMPLE

Draw a directed graph to represent the information in the matrix.

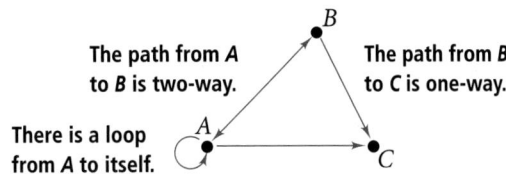

$$\begin{array}{c} \text{To} \to \\ \text{From} \to \end{array} \begin{array}{c} A \\ B \\ C \end{array} \begin{bmatrix} 1 & 1 & 1 \\ 1 & 0 & 1 \\ 0 & 0 & 0 \end{bmatrix}$$

The path from *A* to *B* is two-way.

There is a loop from *A* to itself.

The path from *B* to *C* is one-way.

EXERCISES

Write a matrix to represent each finite or directed graph. 1–6. See margin pp. 212–213.

1.

2.

3.

4.

5.

6.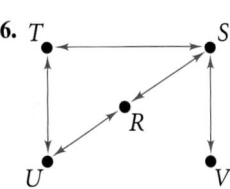

Draw a directed graph to represent the information in each matrix. 7–10. See back of book.

7.
$$\begin{array}{c} J \\ K \\ L \\ M \end{array} \begin{array}{cccc} J & K & L & M \\ \begin{bmatrix} 0 & 0 & 0 & 1 \\ 0 & 0 & 1 & 1 \\ 0 & 1 & 0 & 1 \\ 1 & 1 & 1 & 0 \end{bmatrix} \end{array}$$

8.
$$\begin{array}{c} A \\ B \\ C \\ D \end{array} \begin{array}{cccc} A & B & C & D \\ \begin{bmatrix} 0 & 0 & 1 & 1 \\ 1 & 1 & 0 & 0 \\ 0 & 1 & 0 & 1 \\ 1 & 0 & 1 & 0 \end{bmatrix} \end{array}$$

9.
$$\begin{array}{c} N_1 \\ N_2 \\ N_3 \\ N_4 \end{array} \begin{array}{cccc} N_1 & N_2 & N_3 & N_4 \\ \begin{bmatrix} 1 & 1 & 1 & 1 \\ 0 & 0 & 1 & 1 \\ 1 & 0 & 0 & 0 \\ 0 & 0 & 1 & 0 \end{bmatrix} \end{array}$$

🌐 10. **Travel** Alice and Becky live on Parkway East, at the intersections of Owens Bridge and Bay Bridge, respectively. Carl and David live on Parkway West, at the intersections of Bay Bridge and Owens Bridge, respectively. Parkway East is a one-way street running east. Parkway West is one way running west. Both bridges are two way.
   a. Draw a directed graph indicating road travel between the houses.
   ✏️ **b.** Write a matrix T to represent the information in the directed graph.
   c. **Writing** Calculate T^2. What does the new matrix model? Explain.

Extension Networks **213**

Extension

🔨 **Additional Examples**

① Write a matrix to represent the finite graph.

$$\begin{array}{c} A_1 \\ A_2 \\ A_3 \\ A_4 \\ A_5 \end{array} \begin{array}{ccccc} A_1 & A_2 & A_3 & A_4 & A_5 \\ \begin{bmatrix} 0 & 1 & 1 & 0 & 1 \\ 1 & 0 & 0 & 0 & 0 \\ 1 & 0 & 0 & 1 & 0 \\ 0 & 0 & 1 & 0 & 0 \\ 1 & 0 & 0 & 0 & 0 \end{bmatrix} \end{array}$$

② Write a matrix to represent the information in the directed graph.

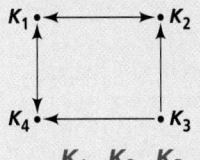

$$\begin{array}{c} K_1 \\ K_2 \\ K_3 \\ K_4 \end{array} \begin{array}{cccc} K_1 & K_2 & K_3 & K_4 \\ \begin{bmatrix} 0 & 1 & 0 & 1 \\ 1 & 0 & 0 & 0 \\ 0 & 1 & 0 & 1 \\ 1 & 0 & 0 & 0 \end{bmatrix} \end{array}$$

③ Draw a directed graph to represent the information in the matrix.

$$\begin{array}{c} A_1 \\ A_2 \\ A_3 \\ A_4 \end{array} \begin{array}{cccc} A_1 & A_2 & A_3 & A_4 \\ \begin{bmatrix} 0 & 1 & 1 & 0 \\ 1 & 1 & 1 & 0 \\ 0 & 0 & 0 & 1 \\ 0 & 1 & 0 & 1 \end{bmatrix} \end{array}$$

5.
$$\begin{array}{c} A \\ B \\ C \\ D \end{array} \begin{array}{cccc} A & B & C & D \\ \begin{bmatrix} 0 & 1 & 0 & 0 \\ 0 & 0 & 0 & 0 \\ 0 & 1 & 1 & 1 \\ 1 & 1 & 0 & 1 \end{bmatrix} \end{array}$$

6.
$$\begin{array}{c} S \\ T \\ U \\ V \\ R \end{array} \begin{array}{ccccc} S & T & U & V & R \\ \begin{bmatrix} 0 & 1 & 0 & 1 & 1 \\ 1 & 0 & 1 & 0 & 0 \\ 0 & 1 & 0 & 0 & 1 \\ 1 & 0 & 0 & 0 & 0 \\ 1 & 0 & 1 & 0 & 0 \end{bmatrix} \end{array}$$

213

Inverse Matrices and Systems

Objectives
1 To solve systems of equations using inverse matrices

Examples
1 Writing a System as a Matrix Equation
2 Solving a System of Two Equations
3 Solving a System of Three Equations
4 Real-World Connection
5 Unique Solutions

Math Background

A system of n linear equations in n variables can be represented by a matrix equation of the form $AX = B$, where A is an $n \times n$ matrix and B is an $n \times 1$ matrix. If A has an inverse, then the solution of the system can be found by solving $A^{-1}B = X$ for X.

More Math Background: p. 166D

Lesson Planning and Resources

See p. 166E for a list of the resources that support this lesson.

✓ Check Skills You'll Need
For intervention, direct students to:

Systems With Three Variables
Lesson 3-6: Examples 1–3
Extra Skills and Word Problems Practice, Ch. 3

What You'll Learn

- To solve systems of equations using inverse matrices

... And Why

To calculate business costs, as in Example 4

✓ Check Skills You'll Need

GO for Help Lesson 3-6

Solve each system.

1. $\begin{cases} 5x + y = 14 \\ 4x + 3y = 20 \end{cases}$
   (2, 4)

2. $\begin{cases} x - y - z = -9 \\ 3x + y + 2z = 12 \\ x = y - 2z \end{cases}$
   (0, 6, 3)

3. $\begin{cases} -x + 2y + z = 0 \\ y = -2x + 3 \\ z = 3x \end{cases}$
   (3, −3, 9)

🔊 **New Vocabulary** • coefficient matrix • variable matrix • constant matrix

---

1 Solving Systems of Equations Using Inverse Matrices

You can represent a system of equations with a matrix equation.

System of equations	Matrix equation
$\begin{cases} x + 2y = 5 \\ 3x + 5y = 14 \end{cases}$	$\begin{bmatrix} 1 & 2 \\ 3 & 5 \end{bmatrix}\begin{bmatrix} x \\ y \end{bmatrix} = \begin{bmatrix} 5 \\ 14 \end{bmatrix}$

Each matrix in an equation of the form $AX = B$ has a name.

GO for Help

To review the definitions of *coefficient* and *variable,* go to Lesson 1-2.

Coefficient matrix A	Variable matrix X	Constant matrix B
$\begin{bmatrix} 1 & 2 \\ 3 & 5 \end{bmatrix}$	$\begin{bmatrix} x \\ y \end{bmatrix}$	$\begin{bmatrix} 5 \\ 14 \end{bmatrix}$

1 EXAMPLE Writing a System as a Matrix Equation

Write the system $\begin{cases} -b + 2c = 4 \\ a + b - c = 0 \\ 2a + 3c = 11 \end{cases}$ as a matrix equation. Then identify the coefficient matrix, the variable matrix, and the constant matrix.

Matrix equation: $\begin{bmatrix} 0 & -1 & 2 \\ 1 & 1 & -1 \\ 2 & 0 & 3 \end{bmatrix}\begin{bmatrix} a \\ b \\ c \end{bmatrix} = \begin{bmatrix} 4 \\ 0 \\ 11 \end{bmatrix}$

Coefficient matrix	Variable matrix	Constant matrix
$\begin{bmatrix} 0 & -1 & 2 \\ 1 & 1 & -1 \\ 2 & 0 & 3 \end{bmatrix}$	$\begin{bmatrix} a \\ b \\ c \end{bmatrix}$	$\begin{bmatrix} 4 \\ 0 \\ 11 \end{bmatrix}$

✓ Quick Check
1 Write each system as a matrix equation. Identify the coefficient matrix, the variable matrix, and the constant matrix. **a–b. See back of book.**

a. $\begin{cases} 3x + 2y = 16 \\ y = 5 \end{cases}$

b. $\begin{cases} x - y + z = 0 \\ x - 2y - z = 5 \\ 2x - y + 2z = 8 \end{cases}$

Differentiated Instruction Solutions for All Learners

Special Needs L1
When multiplying matrices, have students show their work to identify and correct any errors with signed numbers. A sample is shown for Example 2.

$\begin{bmatrix} 2 & -3 \\ -1 & 2 \end{bmatrix}\begin{bmatrix} 11 \\ 6 \end{bmatrix} = \begin{bmatrix} 2(11) + (-3)(6) \\ -1(11) + 2(6) \end{bmatrix} = \begin{bmatrix} 22 - 18 \\ -11 + 12 \end{bmatrix} = \begin{bmatrix} 4 \\ 1 \end{bmatrix}$

learning style: visual

Below Level L2
Remind students that each equation must be written with the variables in the same order and zeroes must be written as coefficients of missing variables.

learning style: verbal

Sometimes you can find the inverse of the coefficient matrix. Then you can use it to solve systems of equations quickly.

2 EXAMPLE Solving a System of Two Equations

To review how to find the inverse of a 2 × 2 matrix, see page 201.

Solve the system $\begin{cases} 2x + 3y = 11 \\ x + 2y = 6 \end{cases}$.

$\begin{bmatrix} 2 & 3 \\ 1 & 2 \end{bmatrix} \begin{bmatrix} x \\ y \end{bmatrix} = \begin{bmatrix} 11 \\ 6 \end{bmatrix}$ **Write the system as a matrix equation.**

$A^{-1} = \begin{bmatrix} 2 & -3 \\ -1 & 2 \end{bmatrix}$ **Find A^{-1}.**

$\begin{bmatrix} x \\ y \end{bmatrix} = A^{-1}B = \begin{bmatrix} 2 & -3 \\ -1 & 2 \end{bmatrix} \begin{bmatrix} 11 \\ 6 \end{bmatrix} = \begin{bmatrix} 4 \\ 1 \end{bmatrix}$ **Solve for the variable matrix.**

The solution of the system is $(4, 1)$.

Check	$2x + 3y = 11$	$x + 2y = 6$	**Use the original equations.**
	$2(4) + 3(1) \stackrel{?}{=} 11$	$4 + 2(1) \stackrel{?}{=} 6$	**Substitute.**
	$8 + 3 = 11 ✓$	$4 + 2 = 6 ✓$	**Simplify.**

✓ Quick Check **2** Solve each system. Check your answers.

a. $\begin{cases} 5a + 3b = 7 \\ 3a + 2b = 5 \end{cases}$ $(-1, 4)$

b. $\begin{cases} x + 3y = 22 \\ 3x + 2y = 10 \end{cases}$ $(-2, 8)$

You can use a graphing calculator to solve a system of three equations.

3 EXAMPLE Solving a System of Three Equations

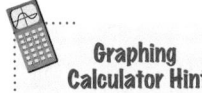

Graphing Calculator Hint

To select A^{-1}, use the MATRIX feature and the x^{-1} key.

Solve the system $\begin{cases} 2x + y + 3z = 1 \\ 5x + y - 2z = 8 \\ x - y - 9z = 5 \end{cases}$.

Step 1 Write the system as a matrix equation.

$\begin{bmatrix} 2 & 1 & 3 \\ 5 & 1 & -2 \\ 1 & -1 & -9 \end{bmatrix} \begin{bmatrix} x \\ y \\ z \end{bmatrix} = \begin{bmatrix} 1 \\ 8 \\ 5 \end{bmatrix}$

Step 2 Enter the coefficient matrix as matrix A and the constant matrix as matrix B.

Step 3

```
[A]⁻¹[B]
    [[4  ]
     [-10]
     [1  ]]
```

The solution is $(4, -10, 1)$.

✓ Quick Check **3** **a.** Check the solution from Example 3 in each of the original equations.
See back of book.

b. Solve the system $\begin{cases} x + y + z = 2 \\ 2x + y = 5 \\ x + 3y - 3z = 14 \end{cases}$. Check your solution. $(1.25, 2.5, -1.75)$

Advanced Learners **L4**
Challenge students to research and explain how to find the inverses of larger square matrices. Have the students share their results with the class.

learning style: verbal

English Language Learners **ELL**
Have students read the matrix equation $AX = B$ as "the *coefficient matrix* times the *variable matrix* equals the *constant matrix.*" Similarly, students can read $X = A^{-1}B$ as "the *variable matrix* equals the *inverse coefficient matrix* times the *constant matrix.*"

learning style: verbal

---

2. Teach

Guided Instruction

3 EXAMPLE Teaching Tip

After discussing the example, ask students whether the matrix method, the substitution method, or the elimination method requires less work.

PowerPoint

Additional Examples

1 Write the system
$\begin{cases} 3x - 4y + 5z = 11 \\ -2x + 7y = -6 \\ -5x + y - z = 20 \end{cases}$
as a matrix equation. Then identify the coefficient matrix, the variable matrix, and the constant matrix.
$\begin{bmatrix} 3 & -4 & 5 \\ -2 & 7 & 0 \\ -5 & 1 & -1 \end{bmatrix} \begin{bmatrix} x \\ y \\ z \end{bmatrix} = \begin{bmatrix} 11 \\ -6 \\ 20 \end{bmatrix}$
The first matrix is the coefficient matrix, the second is the variable matrix, and the third is the constant matrix.

2 Solve the system.
$\begin{cases} 2x + 3y = -1 \\ x - y = 12 \end{cases}$ $(7, -5)$

3 Solve the system.
$\begin{cases} 7x + 3y + 2z = 13 \\ -2x + y - 8z = 26 \\ x - 4y + 10z = -13 \end{cases}$
$(9, -12, -7)$

215

Caution students that if the determinant is zero, the only thing you can be sure of is that there is not a *unique* solution. There could be no solutions or there could be infinitely many solutions.

Additional Examples

4 A linen shop has several tables of sheets and towels on special sale. The sheets are all priced the same, and so are the towels. Mario bought 3 sheets and 5 towels at a cost of $137.50. Marco bought 4 sheets and 2 towels at a cost of $118.00. Find the price of each item. **sheets: $22.50; towels: $14.00**

5 Write the coefficient matrix for each system. Use it to determine whether the system has a unique solution.

a. $\begin{cases} 4x - 2y = 7 \\ -6x + 3y = 5 \end{cases}$

$\begin{bmatrix} 4 & -2 \\ -6 & 3 \end{bmatrix}$; no

b. $\begin{cases} 12x + 8y = -3 \\ 3x - 7y = 50 \end{cases}$

$\begin{bmatrix} 12 & 8 \\ 3 & -7 \end{bmatrix}$; yes

Resources
• Daily Notetaking Guide 4-7 **L3**

Closure

Ask students to describe how to find the solution of a system of three linear equations in three variables. (Assume there is exactly one solution.) **Answers may vary. Sample: Write each equation so that all the variables are on the left side of the equal sign, and all constants on the right. Represent the system by a matrix equation of the form $AX = B$, where A is the coefficient matrix and B is the constant matrix. Then calculate $A^{-1}B$.**

$3.25

$4.75

Quick Check

Problem Solving Hint

$\det \begin{bmatrix} a & b \\ c & d \end{bmatrix} = ad - bc$

There are many business applications for matrices of systems of equations.

4 **EXAMPLE** Real-World Connection

Business A bead store has a sale on certain beads. Find the price of each size of bead.

Relate 2 large beads and 3 small beads cost $3.25.
3 large beads and 4 small beads cost $4.75.

Define Let x = the price of one large bead.
Let y = the price of one small bead.

Write $\begin{bmatrix} 2 & 3 \\ 3 & 4 \end{bmatrix}\begin{bmatrix} x \\ y \end{bmatrix} = \begin{bmatrix} 3.25 \\ 4.75 \end{bmatrix}$ Write the system as a matrix equation.

$[A]^{-1}[B]$
$[[1.25]$
$[.25]]$

Use a graphing calculator. Store the coefficient matrix as matrix A and the constant matrix as matrix B.

● The price of a large bead is $1.25. The price of a small bead is $.25.

4 Suppose the sale is over, and the price of each package increases. The price of a package of two large beads and three small beads increases to $5.55. The price of a package of three large beads and four small beads increases to $8.05. Find the new price of each type of bead. **one large bead = $1.95, one small bead = $.55**

When the coefficient matrix of a system has an inverse, the system has a unique solution. Similarly, when the coefficient matrix does *not* have an inverse, the system does *not* have a unique solution. In that case, the system either has no solution or has an infinite number of solutions.

5 **EXAMPLE** Unique Solutions

Write the coefficient matrix for each system. Use it to determine whether the system has a unique solution.

a. $\begin{cases} x + y = 3 \\ x - y = 7 \end{cases}$

$A = \begin{bmatrix} 1 & 1 \\ 1 & -1 \end{bmatrix}$; $\det A = \begin{vmatrix} 1 & 1 \\ 1 & -1 \end{vmatrix} = 1(-1) - 1(1) = -2$

Since $\det A \neq 0$, the matrix has an inverse, so the system has a unique solution.

b. $\begin{cases} x + 2y = 5 \\ 2x + 4y = 8 \end{cases}$

$A = \begin{bmatrix} 1 & 2 \\ 2 & 4 \end{bmatrix}$; $\det A = \begin{vmatrix} 1 & 2 \\ 2 & 4 \end{vmatrix} = 1(4) - 2(2) = 0$

Since $\det A = 0$, the matrix does not have an inverse and the system does *not* have a unique solution.

Quick Check **a.** Determine whether the system $\begin{cases} 3x + 5y = 1 \\ 2x - y = -8 \end{cases}$ has a unique solution. **yes**

b. You can use an inverse matrix to solve a system of equations. What happens when you try to do this with a graphing calculator and the system does not have a unique solution? **The graphing calculator indicates that there is a "singular matrix" error.**

EXERCISES

For more exercises, see *Extra Skill and Word Problem Practice.*

Practice and Problem Solving

A **Practice by Example**

Example 1
(page 214)

GO for Help

Write each system as a matrix equation. Identify the coefficient matrix, the variable matrix, and the constant matrix. **1–6. See back of book.**

1. $\begin{cases} x + y = 5 \\ x - 2y = -4 \end{cases}$
2. $\begin{cases} y = 3x - 7 \\ x = 2 \end{cases}$
3. $\begin{cases} 3a + 5b = 0 \\ a + b = 2 \end{cases}$

4. $\begin{cases} x + 3y - z = 2 \\ x + 2z = 8 \\ 2y - z = 1 \end{cases}$
5. $\begin{cases} r - s + t = 150 \\ 2r + t = 425 \\ s + 3t = 0 \end{cases}$
6. $\begin{cases} x + 2y = 11 \\ 2x + 3y = 18 \end{cases}$

Examples 2 and 3
(page 215)

Solve each system of equations. Check your answers.

7. $\begin{cases} x + 3y = 5 \\ x + 4y = 6 \end{cases}$ **(2, 1)**
8. $\begin{cases} p - 3q = -1 \\ -5p + 16q = 5 \end{cases}$ **(-1, 0)**
9. $\begin{cases} 300x - y = 130 \\ 200x + y = 120 \end{cases}$ **$\left(\frac{1}{2}, 20\right)$**

10. $\begin{cases} x + 5y = -4 \\ x + 6y = -5 \end{cases}$ **(1, -1)**
11. $\begin{cases} 2x + 3y = 12 \\ x + 2y = 7 \end{cases}$ **(3, 2)**
12. $\begin{cases} 2x + 3y = 5 \\ x + 2y = 6 \end{cases}$ **(-8, 7)**

13. $\begin{cases} x + y + z = 4 \\ 4x + 5y = 3 \\ y - 3z = -10 \end{cases}$
(2, -1, 3)
14. $\begin{cases} 9y + 2z = 18 \\ 3x + 2y + z = 5 \\ x - y = -1 \end{cases}$
(-3, -2, 18)
15. $\begin{cases} 9y + 2z = 14 \\ 3x + 2y + z = 5 \\ x - y = -1 \end{cases}$
(1, 2, -2)

Example 4
(page 216)

16. Shopping Suppose you want to fill nine 1-lb tins with a holiday snack mix. You plan to buy almonds for $2.45/lb, peanuts for $1.85/lb, and raisins for $.80/lb. You have $15 and want the mix to contain twice as much of the nuts as of the raisins by weight. How much of each ingredient should you buy?

a. Writing Explain how each equation in the system at the right relates to the problem. What does each variable represent? **See margin.**

b. Solve the system. **(2.5, 3.5, 3)**

$\begin{cases} x + y + z = 9 \\ 2.45x + 1.85y + 0.8z = 15 \\ x + y = 2z \end{cases}$

Example 5
(page 216)

Determine whether each system has a unique solution.

17. $\begin{cases} 20x + 5y = 240 \\ y = 20x \end{cases}$ **yes**
18. $\begin{cases} 20x + 5y = 145 \\ 30x - 5y = 125 \end{cases}$ **yes**
19. $\begin{cases} y = 2000 - 65x \\ y = 500 + 55x \end{cases}$ **yes**

20. $\begin{cases} y = \frac{2}{3}x - 3 \\ y = -x + 7 \end{cases}$ **yes**
21. $\begin{cases} 3x + 2y = 10 \\ 6x + 4y = 16 \end{cases}$ **no**
22. $\begin{cases} x + 2y + z = 4 \\ y = x - 3 \\ z = 2x \end{cases}$ **yes**

B **Apply Your Skills**

Solve each matrix equation. If the coefficient matrix has no inverse, write *no unique solution.*

25. **(16, -22)**

23. $\begin{bmatrix} 1 & 1 \\ 1 & 2 \end{bmatrix}\begin{bmatrix} x \\ y \end{bmatrix} = \begin{bmatrix} 8 \\ 10 \end{bmatrix}$ **(6, 2)**
24. $\begin{bmatrix} 2 & -3 \\ -4 & 6 \end{bmatrix}\begin{bmatrix} a \\ b \end{bmatrix} = \begin{bmatrix} 1 \\ -2 \end{bmatrix}$ **no unique solution**
25. $\begin{bmatrix} 2 & 1 \\ 4 & 3 \end{bmatrix}\begin{bmatrix} x \\ y \end{bmatrix} = \begin{bmatrix} 10 \\ -2 \end{bmatrix}$ **See left.**

Assignment Guide

1 A B 1-37
C Challenge — 38-42

Test Prep — 43-48
Mixed Review — 49-56

Homework Quick Check
To check students' understanding of key skills and concepts, go over Exercises 8, 11, 26, 32, 37.

Error Prevention!

Exercises 17–22 Suggest that students first write each equation of the system in the form $Ax + By = C$. This will help ensure that they use the correct coefficient matrix.

Differentiated Instruction Resources

GPS Guided Problem Solving	L3
Enrichment	L4
Reteaching	L2
Practice	L3

pages 217–219 Exercises

16a. *x* is the number of pounds of almonds, *y* is the number of pounds of peanuts, and *z* is the number of pounds of raisins that must be bought. The first equation states that the total weight will be 9 pounds. The second equation states that the total cost will be $15. The third equation states that the combined weights of almonds and peanuts should be double the weight of the raisins.

217

4. Assess & Reteach

Lesson Quiz

Write each system as a matrix equation. Then solve the system.

1. $\begin{cases} 3x + 2y = -6 \\ 2x - 3y = 61 \end{cases}$

$\begin{bmatrix} 3 & 2 \\ 2 & -3 \end{bmatrix} \begin{bmatrix} x \\ y \end{bmatrix} = \begin{bmatrix} -6 \\ 61 \end{bmatrix}$; (8, −15)

2. $\begin{cases} 2x + 4y + 5z = -3 \\ 7x + 9y + 4z = 19 \\ -3x + 2y + 8z = 0 \end{cases}$

$\begin{bmatrix} 2 & 4 & 5 \\ 7 & 9 & 4 \\ -3 & 2 & 8 \end{bmatrix} \begin{bmatrix} x \\ y \\ z \end{bmatrix} = \begin{bmatrix} -3 \\ 19 \\ 0 \end{bmatrix}$;
(−10, 13, −7)

Determine whether each system has a unique solution.

3. $\begin{cases} 7x - 2y = 15 \\ -28x + 8y = 7 \end{cases}$ no

4. $\begin{cases} 20x + 5y = 33 \\ -32x + 8y = 47 \end{cases}$ yes

Alternative Assessment

Have each student write a system of two linear equations in two variables and a system of three linear equations in three variables. Each student then solves the systems using matrices. If a system does not have exactly one solution, the student should explain how he or she knows that this is the case.

pages 217–219   Exercises

41. The tea temperature was 126°F and the milk temperature was 36°F.

42a. Let c = lb of chicken, r = lb of rice, and s = lb of shellfish.
$\begin{cases} c + r + s = 18 \\ 1.50c + 0.40r + 6.00s \\ \quad = 29.50 \\ 100c + 20r + 50s \\ \quad = 850 \end{cases}$

b. (5, 10, 3); 5 lb of chicken, 10 lb of rice, 3 lb of shellfish

218

Online
Homework Video Tutor
Visit: PHSchool.com
Web Code: age-0407

GO for Help

For a guide to solving Exercise 36, see p. 220.

C Challenge

26. (−2, −1)

27. (2, 4)

28. (−1, 0)

29. (4, 1, 3)

30. (5, 0, 1)

31. (−19, 22, 13)

Solve each system.   26–31. See below left.

26. $\begin{cases} -3x + 4y = 2 \\ x - y = -1 \end{cases}$

27. $\begin{cases} x + 2y = 10 \\ 3x + 5y = 26 \end{cases}$

28. $\begin{cases} x - 3y = -1 \\ -6x + 19y = 6 \end{cases}$

29. $\begin{cases} x = 5 - y \\ 3y = z \\ x + z = 7 \end{cases}$

30. $\begin{cases} -x = -4 - z \\ 2y = z - 1 \\ x = 6 - y - z \end{cases}$

31. $\begin{cases} -b + 2c = 4 \\ a + b - c = -10 \\ 2a + 3c = 1 \end{cases}$

32. $\begin{cases} x + y + z = 4 \\ 4x + 5y = 4 \\ y - 3z = -9 \end{cases}$ (1, 0, 3)

33. $\begin{cases} x + y + z = 4 \\ 4x + 5y = 3 \\ y - 3z = -10 \end{cases}$ (2, −1, 3)

34. $\begin{cases} -2w + x + y = 0 \\ -w + 2x - y + z = 1 \\ -2w + 3x + 3y + 2z = 6 \\ w + x + 2y + z = 5 \end{cases}$
(1, 1, 1, 1)

35. $\begin{cases} -2w + x + y = -2 \\ -w + 2x - y + z = -4 \\ -2w + 3x + 3y + 2z = 2 \\ w + x + 2y + z = 6 \end{cases}$
(2, 0, 2, 0)

36. **Coordinate Geometry** The coordinates (x, y) of a point in a plane are the solution of the system $\begin{cases} 2x + 3y = 13 \\ 5x + 7y = 31 \end{cases}$. Find the coordinates of the point.
(2, 3)

37. **Geometry** A rectangle is twice as long as it is wide. The perimeter is 840 ft.
GPS Find the dimensions of the rectangle.   length = 280 ft, width = 140 ft

Open-Ended Complete each system for the given number of solutions.
39–40. Answers may vary.

38. infinitely many   39. one solution   40. no solution

38. $\begin{cases} x + y = 7 \\ 2x + 2y = \blacksquare \ 14 \end{cases}$

39. $\begin{cases} x + y + z = 7 \\ y + z = \blacksquare \ 0 \\ z = \blacksquare \ 0 \end{cases}$

40. $\begin{cases} x + y + z = 7 \\ y + z = \blacksquare \ 0 \\ y + z = \blacksquare \ 1 \end{cases}$

41. **Physics** When you mix hot and cold liquids, you can find the temperature of the mixture by using the formula $T = \frac{ah + bc}{a + b}$, where T is the temperature of the mixture, h is the temperature of the hot liquid, c is the temperature of the cold liquid, and a and b represent the amounts of hot and cold liquids. Suppose you mix hot tea and cold milk in a ratio $a : b$ of $9 : 1$, and find that the temperature of the mixture is 117°F. You then change the tea : milk ratio to $2 : 1$, and the temperature drops to 96°F. Find the initial temperatures of the tea and the milk.
See margin.

42. **Nutrition** A caterer combines ingredients to make a paella, a Spanish fiesta dish. The paella weighs 18 lb, costs $29.50, and supplies 850 g of protein.
a. Write a system of three equations to find the weight of each ingredient.
b. Solve the system. How many pounds of each ingredient did she use?
a–b. See margin.

Paella Nutrition Chart

Food	Cost/lb	Protein/lb
Chicken	$1.50	100 g
Rice	$.40	20 g
Shellfish	$6.00	50 g

---

48. **[2]** First write each equation in standard form. Then place the coefficients in a matrix, with the coefficients of x in the first column, the coefficients of y in the second column, and the coefficients of z in the third:

$\begin{bmatrix} 2 & -3 & 1 \\ 1 & 4 & -2 \\ -3 & -2 & 3 \end{bmatrix}$

Multiple Choice

43. Which matrix equation represents the system $\begin{cases} 2x - 3y = -3 \\ -5x + y = 14 \end{cases}$? **B**

A. $\begin{bmatrix} x \\ y \end{bmatrix}\begin{bmatrix} 2 & -3 \\ -5 & 1 \end{bmatrix} = \begin{bmatrix} -3 \\ 14 \end{bmatrix}$

B. $\begin{bmatrix} 2 & -3 \\ -5 & 1 \end{bmatrix}\begin{bmatrix} x \\ y \end{bmatrix} = \begin{bmatrix} -3 \\ 14 \end{bmatrix}$

C. $\begin{bmatrix} 2 & -3 \\ -5 & 1 \end{bmatrix}\begin{bmatrix} -3 \\ 14 \end{bmatrix} = \begin{bmatrix} x \\ y \end{bmatrix}$

D. $\begin{bmatrix} -3 \\ 14 \end{bmatrix}[x \;\; y] = \begin{bmatrix} 2 & -3 \\ -5 & 1 \end{bmatrix}$

44. What is the solution to the matrix equation $\begin{bmatrix} 3 & -1 \\ -1 & 2 \end{bmatrix}\begin{bmatrix} a \\ b \end{bmatrix} = \begin{bmatrix} 7 \\ -9 \end{bmatrix}$? **J**

F. $a = 7, b = -9$ **G.** $a = 2, b = 1$ **H.** $a = \frac{7}{3}, b = -\frac{9}{2}$ **J.** $a = 1, b = -4$

Use the system $\begin{cases} 2x - 3y + z = 6 \\ x + 2y - 4z = 5 \\ -3x - 2y + 3z = -5 \end{cases}$ for Exercises 45–47.

45. Which matrix is the coefficient matrix for the system? **C**

A. $\begin{bmatrix} 2 & 3 & 1 \\ 1 & 2 & 4 \\ 3 & 2 & 3 \end{bmatrix}$ **B.** $\begin{bmatrix} 2 & -3 & 1 & 6 \\ 1 & 2 & -4 & 5 \\ -3 & -2 & 3 & -5 \end{bmatrix}$ **C.** $\begin{bmatrix} 2 & -3 & 1 \\ 1 & 2 & -4 \\ -3 & -2 & 3 \end{bmatrix}$ **D.** $\begin{bmatrix} 6 \\ 5 \\ -5 \end{bmatrix}$

46. Which matrix is the constant matrix for the system? **J**

F. $\begin{bmatrix} 2 & 3 & 1 \\ 1 & 2 & 4 \\ 3 & 2 & 3 \end{bmatrix}$ **G.** $\begin{bmatrix} 2 & -3 & 1 & 6 \\ 1 & 2 & -4 & 5 \\ -3 & -2 & 3 & -5 \end{bmatrix}$ **H.** $\begin{bmatrix} 2 & -3 & 1 \\ 1 & 2 & -4 \\ -3 & -2 & 3 \end{bmatrix}$ **J.** $\begin{bmatrix} 6 \\ 5 \\ -5 \end{bmatrix}$

47. What is the determinant of the coefficient matrix? **B**
   A. -150 **B.** -27 **C.** 6   **D.** 29

Short Response

48. How can you write the three equations at the right as a matrix equation for a system? Explain your steps.
See margin.

$2x - 3y + z + 10 = 0$
$x + 4y = 2z + 11$
$-2y + 3z + 7 = 3x$

Mixed Review

GO for Help

Lesson 4-6

Evaluate the determinant of each matrix.

49. $\begin{bmatrix} -1 & 3 & 7 \\ 5 & -4 & -2 \\ 0 & 2 & 10 \end{bmatrix}$ -44 **50.** $\begin{bmatrix} 17 & 0 & 0 \\ 0 & 17 & 0 \\ 0 & 0 & 17 \end{bmatrix}$ 4913   **51.** $\begin{bmatrix} -3 & 0 & 5 \\ 5 & -3 & 2 \\ -3 & -5 & -2 \end{bmatrix}$ -218

Lesson 4-2

Add or subtract.

52. $\begin{bmatrix} 5 & -3 \\ 4 & 11 \end{bmatrix} + \begin{bmatrix} 4 & 0 \\ -9 & 1 \end{bmatrix}$ $\begin{bmatrix} 9 & -3 \\ -5 & 12 \end{bmatrix}$ **53.** $\begin{bmatrix} -1 & 2 & 0 \\ 10 & -5 & 15 \\ 17 & 3 & -4 \end{bmatrix} - \begin{bmatrix} 0 & 6 & -3 \\ 4 & -7 & 11 \\ -9 & 10 & -1 \end{bmatrix}$

See margin.

Lesson 2-6

Describe each translation of $f(x) = |x|$ **as** *vertical, horizontal,* **or** *combined.* **Then graph the translation.** **54–56. See margin.**

54. $f(x) = |x + 4|$ **55.** $f(x) = |x| - 3$ **56.** $f(x) = |x - 5| + 3$

53. $\begin{bmatrix} -1 & -4 & 3 \\ 6 & 2 & 4 \\ 26 & -7 & -3 \end{bmatrix}$

54. horizontal

55. vertical

56. combined

Finally, put this in an equation with the variable matrix $\begin{bmatrix} x \\ y \\ z \end{bmatrix}$ and the constant matrix $\begin{bmatrix} -10 \\ 11 \\ -7 \end{bmatrix}$, to get $\begin{bmatrix} 2 & -3 & 1 \\ 1 & 4 & -2 \\ -3 & -2 & 3 \end{bmatrix}\begin{bmatrix} x \\ y \\ z \end{bmatrix} = \begin{bmatrix} -10 \\ 11 \\ -7 \end{bmatrix}$.

[1] answer only, without explanation of steps

219

Understanding Math Problems

In this problem solving example, students not only see how a sample problem is worked out, but they also see the thought processes of the person who is working out the problem. The notes in the left-hand column explain the actions taken in the right-hand column.

Guided Instruction

Tell students to read through the example, looking carefully at both how the problem is worked out, and what Jaime thinks as he works out the problem. Tell students to look back at the examples in this lesson if they do not recall how to find the reciprocal of a matrix, or how to multiply matrices by their reciprocals.

Exercises

Place students in pairs. Have one student record the steps used in solving Exercise 1, while the other records the thought processes that they used for each step.

2. **Answers may vary. For a system with no solutions or infinitely many solutions, the determinant would be 0. So Jaime would not be able to find the inverse matrix.**

Guided Problem Solving

Understanding Math Problems Read the problem below. Then let Jaime's thinking guide you through the solution. Check your understanding with the exercises at the bottom of the page.

Coordinate Geometry The coordinates (x, y) of a point in a plane are the solution of the system $\begin{cases} 2x + 3y = 13 \\ 5x + 7y = 31 \end{cases}$. Find the coordinates of the point.

What Jaime Thinks

The problem tells me that the solution of this system is (x, y). I could graph the lines to see where they intersect, but that's not necessary when I can solve the system with matrices. I'll rewrite the system as a matrix equation.

To solve for the variable matrix that includes x and y, I should multiply each side of the equation by the inverse of the coefficient matrix. I'll use the formula on page 201.

Now that I have the inverse, I can multiply.

Something is wrong. I can't multiply the matrices on the right side of this equation because the dimensions don't match.

Oh!!! I have to multiply the inverse matrix on the left, because matrix multiplication is not commutative!

I'll rewrite the equation correctly. The result will be a 2×1 matrix.

This means the x-coordinate is 2 and the y-coordinate is 3. I'll write my answer in a sentence.

What Jaime Writes

$$\begin{cases} 2x + 3y = 13 \\ 5x + 7y = 31 \end{cases} \quad \begin{bmatrix} 2 & 3 \\ 5 & 7 \end{bmatrix}\begin{bmatrix} x \\ y \end{bmatrix} = \begin{bmatrix} 13 \\ 31 \end{bmatrix}$$

Inverse of
$$\begin{bmatrix} 2 & 3 \\ 5 & 7 \end{bmatrix} = \frac{1}{(2)(7) - (5)(3)}\begin{bmatrix} 7 & -3 \\ -5 & 2 \end{bmatrix}$$
$$= -1\begin{bmatrix} 7 & -3 \\ -5 & 2 \end{bmatrix} = \begin{bmatrix} -7 & 3 \\ 5 & -2 \end{bmatrix}$$

$$\begin{bmatrix} -7 & 3 \\ 5 & -2 \end{bmatrix}\begin{bmatrix} 2 & 3 \\ 5 & 7 \end{bmatrix}\begin{bmatrix} x \\ y \end{bmatrix} = \begin{bmatrix} 13 \\ 31 \end{bmatrix}\begin{bmatrix} -7 & 3 \\ 5 & -2 \end{bmatrix}$$
$$\qquad\qquad\qquad\qquad\qquad 2 \times 1 \quad 2 \times 2$$
doesn't work!

$$\begin{bmatrix} -7 & 3 \\ 5 & -2 \end{bmatrix}\begin{bmatrix} 2 & 3 \\ 5 & 7 \end{bmatrix}\begin{bmatrix} x \\ y \end{bmatrix} = \begin{bmatrix} -7 & 3 \\ 5 & -2 \end{bmatrix}\begin{bmatrix} 13 \\ 31 \end{bmatrix}$$

$$\begin{bmatrix} x \\ y \end{bmatrix} = \begin{bmatrix} (-7)(13) + (3)(31) \\ (5)(13) + (-2)(31) \end{bmatrix} = \begin{bmatrix} 2 \\ 3 \end{bmatrix}$$

The coordinates of the point are (2, 3).

EXERCISES

1. The coordinates (x, y) of a point in a plane are the solution of the system $\begin{cases} 12x + 13y = 14 \\ 5x + 7y = 9 \end{cases}$. Find the coordinates of the point. $\qquad$ (−1, 2)

2. What difficulty would Jaime have with his solution process for a system that has no solutions? Infinitely many solutions? **See margin.**

Augmented Matrices and Systems

1. Plan

What You'll Learn

- To solve a system of equations using Cramer's Rule
- To solve a system of equations using augmented matrices

. . . And Why

To solve systems of three equations, as in Example 2

 Check Skills You'll Need

GO for Help Lessons 4-5 and 4-6

Evaluate the determinant of each matrix.

1. $\begin{bmatrix} -1 & 2 \\ 0 & 3 \end{bmatrix}$ -3
2. $\begin{bmatrix} 0 & 1 \\ -1 & 3 \end{bmatrix}$ 1
3. $\begin{bmatrix} 2 & 1 \\ -1 & 5 \end{bmatrix}$ 11

4. $\begin{bmatrix} 0 & 1 & -3 \\ 4 & 5 & -1 \\ -1 & 0 & 1 \end{bmatrix}$ -18
5. $\begin{bmatrix} 3 & 4 & 5 \\ -1 & 2 & 0 \\ 0 & -1 & 1 \end{bmatrix}$ 15
6. $\begin{bmatrix} 0 & 2 & -1 \\ 3 & 4 & 0 \\ -2 & -1 & 5 \end{bmatrix}$ -35

New Vocabulary • Cramer's Rule • augmented matrix • row operations

Objectives

1 To solve a system of equations using Cramer's Rule
2 To solve a system of equations using augmented matrices

Examples

1 Using Cramer's Rule
2 Using Cramer's Rule with Three Equations
3 Writing an Augmented Matrix
4 Writing a System From an Augmented Matrix
5 Using an Augmented Matrix
6 Using a Graphing Calculator

Math Background

Cramer's Rule and using row operations on augmented matrices are tools for solving linear systems. Augmented matrices can identify systems that have no solution or infinitely many solutions. For instance, 2×2 matrices having final augmented matrices of the form $\begin{bmatrix} 1 & 0 & | & a \\ 0 & 1 & | & b \end{bmatrix}$, $\begin{bmatrix} 1 & c & | & a \\ 0 & 0 & | & 1 \end{bmatrix}$, and $\begin{bmatrix} 1 & d & | & a \\ 0 & 0 & | & 0 \end{bmatrix}$, represent systems with one solution, no solutions, and infinitely many solutions, respectively.

More Math Background: p. 166D

---

1 · Solving Systems Using Cramer's Rule

You can solve a system of linear equations that has a unique solution by using determinants and a pattern called Cramer's Rule.

 Key Concepts

Definition	Cramer's Rule

	Use the x- and y-coefficients. ↓	Replace the x-coefficients with the constants. ↓	Replace the y-coefficients with the constants. ↓
System $\begin{cases} ax + by = m \\ cx + dy = n \end{cases}$	$D = \begin{vmatrix} a & b \\ c & d \end{vmatrix}$	$D_x = \begin{vmatrix} m & b \\ n & d \end{vmatrix}$	$D_y = \begin{vmatrix} a & m \\ c & n \end{vmatrix}$

The solution of the system is $x = \dfrac{D_x}{D}$ and $y = \dfrac{D_y}{D}$, or $\left(\dfrac{D_x}{D}, \dfrac{D_y}{D} \right)$.

1 EXAMPLE Using Cramer's Rule

Use Cramer's Rule to solve the system $\begin{cases} 3x + 2y = 0 \\ x - y = -5 \end{cases}$.

Evaluate three determinants. Then find x and y.

$$D = \begin{vmatrix} 3 & 2 \\ 1 & -1 \end{vmatrix} = -5 \qquad D_x = \begin{vmatrix} 0 & 2 \\ -5 & -1 \end{vmatrix} = 10 \qquad D_y = \begin{vmatrix} 3 & 0 \\ 1 & -5 \end{vmatrix} = -15$$

$$x = \frac{D_x}{D} = \frac{10}{-5} = -2 \qquad y = \frac{D_y}{D} = \frac{-15}{-5} = 3$$

● The solution of the system is $(-2, 3)$.

 Quick Check ❶ Use Cramer's Rule to solve the system $\begin{cases} 3x + y = 5 \\ 2x + 3y = 8 \end{cases}$. **(1, 2)**

Lesson Planning and Resources

See p. 166E for a list of the resources that support this lesson.

 Check Skills You'll Need

For intervention, direct students to:

2 × 2 and 3 × 3 Matrices, Determinants, and Inverses
Lesson 4-5: Example 2
Lesson 4-6: Example 1
Extra Skills and Word Problems Practice, Ch. 4

 Instruction Solutions for All Learners

Special Needs L1
For Example 1, direct students to the use of color in the text showing how D_x and D_y are formed. For D_x, the x-column values are replaced with the rightmost members of the equation. For D_y, the y-column values are replaced.

learning style: visual

Below Level L2
It may help students to write the identity matrix so they can check that they are computing 1s and 0s in the proper places.

learning style: visual

Guided Instruction

 2 EXAMPLE Error Prevention

When writing matrices for three-variable systems, students may place coefficients in the wrong columns. Encourage students to write the variable letters over the appropriate columns when writing the coefficient matrix.

PowerPoint

Additional Examples

1 Use Cramer's Rule to solve the system.
$$\begin{cases} 7x - 4y = 15 \\ 3x + 6y = 8 \end{cases} \left(\frac{61}{27}, \frac{11}{54}\right)$$

2 Find the y-coordinate of the solution of the system.
$$\begin{cases} -2x + 8y + 2z = -3 \\ -6x \quad\quad + 2z = 1 \\ -7x - 5y + z = 2 \end{cases} -\frac{5}{6}$$

You can also use Cramer's Rule to solve a system of three equations.

2 EXAMPLE Using Cramer's Rule With Three Equations

Multiple Choice What is the value of x in the solution of the system at the right?

$$\begin{cases} y + 4z = 5 \\ x + y + z = 8 \\ 2x - 5y = 7 \end{cases}$$

Ⓐ −156 Ⓑ −26 Ⓒ 1 Ⓓ 6

Test-Taking Tip

When solving a system, make sure to match each value you find with the correct variable.

$$D = \begin{vmatrix} 0 & 1 & 4 \\ 1 & 1 & 1 \\ 2 & -5 & 0 \end{vmatrix} = -26 \quad \text{Evaluate the determinant.}$$

$$D_x = \begin{vmatrix} 5 & 1 & 4 \\ 8 & 1 & 1 \\ 7 & -5 & 0 \end{vmatrix} = -156 \quad \text{Replace the } x\text{-coefficients with the constants and evaluate again.}$$

$$x = \frac{D_x}{D} = \frac{-156}{-26} = 6 \quad \text{Find } x.$$

● The x-coordinate of the solution is 6. The answer is D.

✓ Quick Check **2 a. Critical Thinking** How would you modify the determinant D to find D_z?
b. Solve the system for y and z.
b. $y = 1, z = 1$

a. In D, replace the z-coefficients with the constants.

---

2 Solving Systems Using Augmented Matrices

Vocabulary Tip

Augmented means "increased in size" or "added to."

You can solve some linear systems by using an augmented matrix. An **augmented matrix** contains the coefficients and the constants from a system of equations. Each row of the matrix represents an equation.

3 EXAMPLE Writing an Augmented Matrix

Write an augmented matrix to represent the system.
$$\begin{cases} -6x + 2y = 10 \\ 4x = -20 \end{cases}$$

System of equations
$$\begin{cases} -6x + 2y = 10 \\ 4x \quad\quad = -20 \end{cases}$$
x-coefficients ↕   ↕ y-coefficients ↕ constants

Augmented matrix
$$\begin{bmatrix} -6 & 2 & | & 10 \\ 4 & 0 & | & -20 \end{bmatrix}$$

└─ Draw a vertical bar to separate the coefficients from the constants.

An augmented matrix that represents the system is $\begin{bmatrix} -6 & 2 & | & 10 \\ 4 & 0 & | & -20 \end{bmatrix}$.

✓ Quick Check **3** Write an augmented matrix to represent each system.

3b. $\begin{bmatrix} 1 & 2 & 3 & | & -4 \\ 0 & 1 & -2 & | & 8 \\ 0 & 0 & 1 & | & -3 \end{bmatrix}$

a. $\begin{cases} x - 5y = 15 \\ 3x + 3y = 3 \end{cases}$ $\begin{bmatrix} 1 & -5 & | & 15 \\ 3 & 3 & | & 3 \end{bmatrix}$

b. $\begin{cases} x + 2y + 3z = -4 \\ y - 2z = 8 \\ z = -3 \end{cases}$ **See left.**

An augmented matrix contains an entry of zero for any term missing from the system. You can write a system of equations from an augmented matrix.

Differentiated Instruction Solutions for All Learners

Advanced Learners L4
Discuss the advantage of using an augmented matrix instead of the technique of elimination to solve a system of equations.

learning style: verbal

English Language Learners ELL
The term *augmented* means enlarged and has a similar meaning in music. Have students look up its meaning in a dictionary or music book. Sample: A perfect or major interval that has been enlarged by a semitone.

learning style: verbal

4 EXAMPLE Writing a System From an Augmented Matrix

Write a system of equations for the augmented matrix $\begin{bmatrix} 6 & 0 & | & 3 \\ 1 & 1 & | & -5 \end{bmatrix}$.

Augmented matrix

$$\begin{bmatrix} 6 & 0 & | & 3 \\ 1 & 1 & | & -5 \end{bmatrix}$$

x-coefficients ↕   ↕ y-coefficients ↕ constants

System of equations $\begin{cases} 6x & + & & = & 3 \\ x & & y & = & -5 \end{cases}$

✓ **Quick Check** 4 Write a system of equations for each augmented matrix.

4b. $\begin{cases} -x + 3z = -4 \\ 7x + 2y - z = 0 \\ y + 2z = -3 \end{cases}$

a. $\begin{bmatrix} 5 & 7 & | & -3 \\ 0 & -8 & | & 6 \end{bmatrix}$ $\begin{cases} 5x + 7y = -3 \\ -8y = 6 \end{cases}$

b. $\begin{bmatrix} -1 & 0 & 3 & | & -4 \\ 7 & 2 & -1 & | & 0 \\ 0 & 1 & 2 & | & -3 \end{bmatrix}$

See left.

In Chapter 3 you learned how to solve systems of equations by using multiples of one or more of the equations to eliminate variables. You can do the same thing to an augmented matrix by using row operations.

🔧 Key Concepts

Definition	Row Operations

To solve a system of equations using an augmented matrix, you can use one or more of the following **row operations.**

- Switch any two rows.
- Multiply a row by a constant.
- Add one row to another.
- Combine one or more of these steps.

5 EXAMPLE Using an Augmented Matrix

Use an augmented matrix to solve the system $\begin{cases} x + 2y = -1 \\ 2x + 5y = -4 \end{cases}$.

$\begin{bmatrix} 1 & 2 & | & -1 \\ 2 & 5 & | & -4 \end{bmatrix}$ **Write an augmented matrix.**

$\begin{matrix} -2(1 & 2 & -1) \\ \underline{2 & 5 & -4} \\ 0 & 1 & -2 \end{matrix}$

$\begin{bmatrix} 1 & 2 & | & -1 \\ 0 & 1 & | & -2 \end{bmatrix}$ **Multiply Row 1 by –2 and add it to Row 2.**
Write the new augmented matrix.

$\begin{matrix} 1 & 2 & -1 \\ -2(0 & 1 & -2) \\ \underline{1 & 0 & 3} \end{matrix}$ **Multiply new Row 2 by –2 and add it to Row 1. Write the final augmented matrix.**

$\begin{bmatrix} 1 & 0 & | & 3 \\ 0 & 1 & | & -2 \end{bmatrix}$

The solution to the system is $(3, -2)$.

Check $x + 2y = -1$ $2x + 5y = -4$ **Use the original equations.**

$3 + 2(-2) \stackrel{?}{=} -1$ $2(3) + 5(-2) \stackrel{?}{=} -4$ **Substitute.**

$3 + (-4) \stackrel{?}{=} -1$ $6 + (-10) \stackrel{?}{=} -4$ **Multiply.**

$-1 = -1 ✓$ $-4 = -4 ✓$ **Simplify.**

✓ **Quick Check** 5 Solve $\begin{cases} x + y = -10 \\ -x + y = 20 \end{cases}$. Check your solution. (−15, 5)

Guided Instruction

6 EXAMPLE Technology Tip

Tell students that if the calculator displays a matrix with elements that are lengthy decimals, they can press MATH 1 ENTER to see if the calculator can change the decimals to fractions. Otherwise, they can adjust the decimal display.

📄 PowerPoint
Additional Examples

3 Write an augmented matrix to represent the system.
$\begin{cases} -7x + 4y = -3 \\ x + 8y = 9 \end{cases}$
$\begin{bmatrix} -7 & 4 & | & -3 \\ 1 & 8 & | & 9 \end{bmatrix}$

4 Write a system of equations for the augmented matrix.
$\begin{bmatrix} 9 & -7 & | & -1 \\ 2 & 5 & | & -6 \end{bmatrix}$
$\begin{cases} 9x - 7y = -1 \\ 2x + 5y = -6 \end{cases}$

5 Use an augmented matrix to solve the system.
$\begin{cases} x - 3y = -17 \\ 4x + 2y = 2 \end{cases}$ (−2, 5)

6 Use the rref feature on a graphing calculator to solve the system.
$\begin{cases} 4x + 3y + z = -1 \\ -2x - 2y + 7z = -10 \\ 3x + y + 5z = 2 \end{cases}$
(7, −9, −2)

Resources
- Daily Notetaking Guide 4-8 **L3**

Closure

Ask: *In an initial augmented matrix, where do you find the coefficients of the variables for the related system of equations?* to the left of the vertical bar

223

3. Practice

Assignment Guide

1 A B 1-5, 24-28, 32-34

2 A B 6-23, 29-31, 35-39
C Challenge   40-45

Test Prep   46-49
Mixed Review   50-57

Homework Quick Check
To check students' understanding of key skills and concepts, go over Exercises 4, 19, 29, 32, 38.

Error Prevention!

Exercises 12–17 Students will find it helpful to follow the lead of Example 5 and write notes indicating what row operations they used at each stage.

Differentiated Instruction **Resources**

GPS Guided Problem Solving	L3
Enrichment	L4
Reteaching	L2
Practice	L3

Graphing Calculator Hint

In Step 2, rref stands for "reduced row-echelon form." To find rref, use the MATRIX feature, MATH menu. Scroll to item B, then press ENTER.

You can use augmented matrices and row operations to solve systems of three equations. Graphing calculators have a feature that uses row operations to simplify matrices.

6 EXAMPLE Using a Graphing Calculator

Use a graphing calculator to solve the system $\begin{cases} 2x + 3y - z = 11 \\ 3x - 2y + 4z = 10. \\ x + 4y - 2z = 8 \end{cases}$

Step 1 Enter the augmented matrix as matrix A.

Step 2 Use the rref feature of your graphing calculator.

```
[A]
[[  2   3   -1   11  ]
 [  3  -2    4   10  ]
 [  1   4   -2    8  ]]
```

```
rref([A])
[[  1   0   0   4  ]
 [  0   1   0   1  ]
 [  0   0   1   0  ]]
```

The simplified augmented matrix is equivalent to $\begin{cases} x = 4 \\ y = 1. \\ z = 0 \end{cases}$ The solution is $(4, 1, 0)$.

Partial Check

$2x + 3y - z = 11$ Use the first equation.

$2(4) + 3(1) - (0) \stackrel{?}{=} 11$ Substitute.

$8 + 3 - 0 \stackrel{?}{=} 11$ Multiply.

$11 = 11$ ✓   Simplify.

✓ **Quick Check** **6 a.** Check the solution to Example 6 in the remaining two equations. **See margin.**

b. Use a graphing calculator to solve the system $\begin{cases} x + 4y - z = 4 \\ x - 2y + z = -2. \\ 5x - 3y + 8z = 13 \end{cases}$ Check your answer. **(−1, 2, 3)**

EXERCISES

For more exercises, see *Extra Skill and Word Problem Practice*.

Practice and Problem Solving

A Practice by Example

Examples 1 and 2
(pages 221 and 222)

for
Help

Use Cramer's Rule to solve each system.

                                                                                   (3, 1)

1. $\begin{cases} 2x + y = 4 \\ 3x - y = 6 \end{cases}$ **(2, 0)**   **2.** $\begin{cases} 2x + y = 7 \\ -2x + 5y = -1 \end{cases}$ **(3, 1)**   **3.** $\begin{cases} 2x + 4y = 10 \\ 3x + 5y = 14 \end{cases}$

4. $\begin{cases} y + 4z = 5 \\ x + y + z = 8 \\ 2x - 5y = 7 \end{cases}$ **(6, 1, 1)**   **5.** $\begin{cases} 2x + 3y + z = 5 \\ x + y - 2z = -2 \\ -3x + z = -7 \end{cases}$ **(3, −1, 2)**

Example 3
(page 222)

Write an augmented matrix for each system.   **6–8. See margin.**

6. $\begin{cases} 3x - 4y = 17 \\ 8x + y = -3 \end{cases}$ **7.** $\begin{cases} 3x - 7y + 3z = -3 \\ x + y + 2z = -3 \\ 2x - 3y + 5z = -8 \end{cases}$ **8.** $\begin{cases} -x + 5y = -1 \\ x - 2y = 1 \end{cases}$

---

page 224 Quick Check

6a. $3(4) - 2(1) + 4(0) \stackrel{?}{=} 10$
$12 - 2 + 0 \stackrel{?}{=} 10$
$10 = 10$ ✓
$4 + 4(1) - 2(0) \stackrel{?}{=} 8$
$4 + 4 - 0 \stackrel{?}{=} 8$
$8 = 8$ ✓

pages 224–227 Exercises

6. $\begin{bmatrix} 3 & -4 & | & 17 \\ 8 & 1 & | & -3 \end{bmatrix}$ **7.** $\begin{bmatrix} 3 & -7 & 3 & | & -3 \\ 1 & 1 & 2 & | & -3 \\ 2 & -3 & 5 & | & -8 \end{bmatrix}$ **8.** $\begin{bmatrix} -1 & 5 & | & -1 \\ 1 & -2 & | & 1 \end{bmatrix}$

Careers

Exercise 33 Financial planners can use matrices to help find the best way to invest money. Many have computer programs that have been programmed to perform the functions of these matrices.

Example 4
(page 223)

Write a system of equations for each augmented matrix. 9–11. See margin.

9. $\begin{bmatrix} 5 & 1 & | & -3 \\ -2 & 2 & | & 4 \end{bmatrix}$

10. $\begin{bmatrix} -1 & 2 & | & -6 \\ 1 & 1 & | & 7 \end{bmatrix}$

11. $\begin{bmatrix} 2 & 1 & 1 & | & 1 \\ 1 & 1 & 1 & | & 2 \\ 1 & -1 & 1 & | & -2 \end{bmatrix}$

Example 5
(page 223)

Use an augmented matrix to solve each system.

(5, −2.5)
12. $\begin{cases} 2x - 2y = 15 \\ 4x + 4y = 10 \end{cases}$

(−2, −6)
13. $\begin{cases} 2x - 4y = 20 \\ 4x + 2y = -20 \end{cases}$

(−3, 3)
14. $\begin{cases} x + 2y = 3 \\ 4x + 2y = -6 \end{cases}$

15. $\begin{cases} x + 5y = -25 \\ 5x + y = 25 \end{cases}$

16. $\begin{cases} -x + 5y = 15 \\ 2x + 3y = 9 \end{cases}$

17. $\begin{cases} 3x + 6y = 2 \\ 2x - y = 3 \end{cases}$

(6.25, −6.25) (0, 3) $\left(\frac{4}{3}, -\frac{1}{3}\right)$

Example 6
(page 224)

Solve each system.

18. (1, 1, 0)

19. (3, 1, 1)

20. no unique solution

18. $\begin{cases} x + y + z = 2 \\ 2y - 2z = 2 \\ x - 3z = 1 \end{cases}$

19. $\begin{cases} x - y + z = 3 \\ x + 3z = 6 \\ y - 2z = -1 \end{cases}$

20. $\begin{cases} x + y - z = -1 \\ 3x + 4y - z = 8 \\ 6x + 8y - 2z = 16 \end{cases}$

21. $\begin{cases} x + y - z = 1 \\ 3x + 3y + z = 3 \\ 2x + 2y - 2z = 2 \end{cases}$

22. $\begin{cases} x + y = 1 \\ y + z = 2 \\ x - z = -1 \end{cases}$

23. $\begin{cases} x + z = -4 \\ y - z = 1 \\ x + y = -3 \end{cases}$

no unique solution no unique solution no unique solution

B Apply Your Skills

Use Cramer's Rule to solve each system.

24. $\begin{cases} 0.5x + 1.5y = 7 \\ 2.5x - 3.5y = -9 \end{cases}$

25. $\begin{cases} -1.2x - 0.3y = 2.1 \\ -0.2x + 0.8y = 4.6 \end{cases}$

26. $\begin{cases} \dfrac{x}{5} - \dfrac{2y}{5} = 4 \\ \dfrac{2x}{5} - \dfrac{3y}{5} = 5 \end{cases}$

(2, 4) (−3, 5) (−10, −15)

27. $\begin{cases} \dfrac{x}{2} + \dfrac{y}{4} = 4 \\ \dfrac{x}{4} - \dfrac{3y}{8} = -2 \end{cases}$ (4, 8)

28. $\begin{cases} 2x + 3y + 5z = 12 \\ 4x + 2y + 4z = -2 \\ 5x + 4y + 7z = 7 \end{cases}$ (−4, 5, 1)

Use an augmented matrix to solve each system.

29. $\begin{cases} x + y + z = 1 \\ y - 3z = 4 \\ x - z = 2 \end{cases}$

30. $\begin{cases} x + y + z = 0 \\ y + 4z = -6 \\ 2x - 2z = 4 \end{cases}$

31. $\begin{cases} 2x + y = 8 \\ x + z = 5 \\ y - z = -1 \end{cases}$

(1, 1, −1) (0, 2, −2) (4, 0, 1)

32. Business A manufacturer sells pencils and erasers in packages. The price of a package of five erasers and two pencils is $.23. The price of a package of seven erasers and five pencils is $.41. Find the price of one eraser and one pencil.
one eraser = $.03, one pencil = $.04

33. Multiple Choice Suppose you invested $5000 in three different funds for one year. The funds paid simple interest of 8%, 10%, and 7%, respectively. The total interest at the end of one year was $405. You invested $500 more at 10% than at 8%. How much did you invest in the 10% fund? **C**

Ⓐ $150 Ⓑ $1000 Ⓒ $1500 Ⓓ $2500

34. Open-Ended Write and solve a system of three equations in three unknowns using Cramer's Rule. **Check students' work.**

Solve each system.

35. $\begin{cases} 2x - 3y + 2z = 10 \\ x + 3y + 4z = 14 \\ 3x - y + z = 9 \end{cases}$

36. $\begin{cases} 4x - y + z = 3 \\ x + 2y + z = 0 \\ 3x + 7y - 3z = 6 \end{cases}$

37. $\begin{cases} x + 2y + z = 4 \\ 3x + 6y + 3z = 2 \\ x - y + z = 3 \end{cases}$

(2, 0, 3) (1, 0, −1) no unique solution

GO Online
Homework Video Tutor
Visit: PHSchool.com
Web Code: age-0408

9. $\begin{cases} 5x + y = -3 \\ -2x + 2y = 4 \end{cases}$

11. $\begin{cases} 2x + y + z = 1 \\ x + y + z = 2 \\ x - y + z = -2 \end{cases}$

10. $\begin{cases} -x + 2y = -6 \\ x + y = 7 \end{cases}$

PowerPoint

Lesson Quiz

1. Use Cramer's Rule to solve the system.

$$\begin{cases} 3x + 2y = -2 \\ 5x + 4y = 8 \end{cases} \quad (-12, 17)$$

2. Suppose you want to use Cramer's Rule to find the value of z in the following system. Write the determinants you would need to evaluate.

$$\begin{cases} -7x + 3y + 9z = 12 \\ 5x + 3z = 8 \\ 4x - 6y + z = -2 \end{cases}$$

$$D = \begin{vmatrix} -7 & 3 & 9 \\ 5 & 0 & 3 \\ 4 & -6 & 1 \end{vmatrix},$$

$$D_z = \begin{vmatrix} -7 & 3 & 12 \\ 5 & 0 & 8 \\ 4 & -6 & -2 \end{vmatrix}$$

3. Solve the system by using an augmented matrix.

$$\begin{cases} 5x + y = 1 \\ 3x - 2y = 24 \end{cases} \quad (2, -9)$$

4. Solve the system by using an augmented matrix.

$$\begin{cases} 4x + y - z = 7 \\ -2x + 2y + 5z = 3 \\ 7x - 3y - 9z = -4 \end{cases}$$

$(-1, 8, -3)$

Alternative Assessment

Have each student write a system of two equations in two variables and a system of three equations in three variables. Then solve the systems. They should use Cramer's Rule for one system and an augmented matrix for the other system.

pages 224–227 Exercises

38a. Let r = price of 1 pt of red and let y = price of 1 pt of yellow.

$$\begin{cases} 2r + 6y = 25 \\ 5r + 3y = 28 \end{cases}$$

c. A quart of red paint = $7.75 and a quart of yellow paint = $5.75.

Problem Solving Hint

1 gal = 4 qt = 8 pt

🌐 **38. Colors** A hardware store mixes paints in a ratio of two parts red to six parts yellow to make pumpkin orange. A ratio of five parts red to three parts yellow makes red-pepper red. A gallon of pumpkin orange sells for $25, and a gallon of red-pepper red sells for $28. **a, c. See margin.**
   a. Write a system of equations to model the situation.
   b. Solve the system. **(3.875, 2.875)**
   c. Find the cost of 1 qt of red paint and the cost of 1 qt of yellow paint.

🌐 **39. Sales** Refer to the signs below. Find the price per pound of each type of nut.
   almonds: $2/lb, pecans: $4/lb, pistachios: $6/lb

2 lb almonds
3 lb pecans
only $16

1 lb almonds
1 lb pecans
1 lb pistachios
only $12

3 lb pecans
2 lb pistachios
only $24

C **Challenge** **Solve using Cramer's Rule.** (*Hint:* Start by substituting $m = \frac{1}{x}$ and $n = \frac{1}{y}$.)

40. $\begin{cases} \dfrac{4}{x} + \dfrac{1}{y} = 1 \\ \dfrac{8}{x} + \dfrac{4}{y} = 3 \end{cases}$

41. $\begin{cases} \dfrac{4}{x} - \dfrac{2}{y} = 1 \\ \dfrac{10}{x} + \dfrac{20}{y} = 0 \end{cases}$ **(5, −10)**

🖩 **Solve each system.**

42. $\begin{cases} w + x + y + z = 3 \\ -w + x - 2y + z = -2 \\ 2x - y + z = 1 \\ w + y - z = 2 \end{cases}$
   (1, 1, 1, 0)

43. $\begin{cases} 2x + 2y + z = 4 \\ w + y - z = -2 \\ w + x + y + z = 3 \\ -4w + z = 2 \end{cases}$
   (0, 1, 0, 2)

🌐 **44. Nutrition** While stranded on an island, the crew of a sailboat has access to only three sources of food, as shown in the table below. One of the crew members designs a daily diet to supply each person with 120 g of fat, 220 g of carbohydrates, and 80 g of protein.

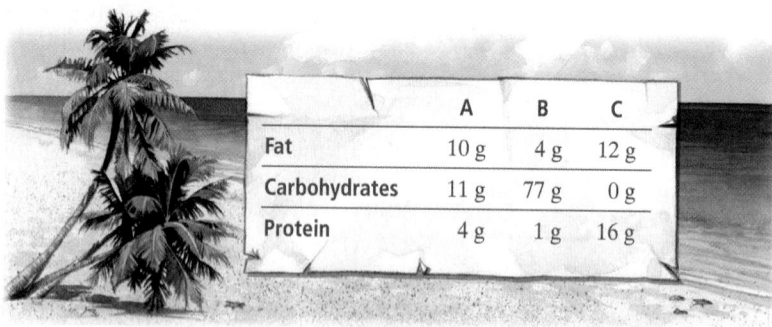

	A	B	C
Fat	10 g	4 g	12 g
Carbohydrates	11 g	77 g	0 g
Protein	4 g	1 g	16 g

a. Write a system of three equations in three variables to find the number of portions of each food each person must have to meet the daily diet.
b. Use an augmented matrix to solve the system of equations from part (a). Round each answer to the nearest tenth. **about (7.8, 1.7, 3.0)**
🖊 **c. Writing** Suppose food C runs out. How would this change the number of portions of food required each day?

44a. Let a, b, and c be the number of portions per day of food sources A, B, and C.
   $10a + 4b + 12c = 120$
   $11a + 77b = 220$
   $4a + b + 16c = 80$

c. Answers may vary. Sample: Adding 12 more portions of food A would compensate for C running out.

226 Chapter 4 Matrices

45. Geometry The perimeter of the rectangle at the right is 28 cm. The perimeter of each of the triangles is 24 cm. The diagonal of the rectangle is 2 cm longer than the longer side of the rectangle.
   a. Write a system of three equations in three unknowns. **a–c. See margin.**
   b. Simplify the system to a system of two equations in two unknowns.
   c. Write an augmented matrix for the system in part (b).
   d. Find the dimensions of the rectangle. **6 cm × 8 cm**
   e. Find the length of the diagonal. **10 cm**

Test Prep

Multiple Choice Use the system $\begin{cases} 5x - 4y = -13 \\ -3x + 6y = 6 \end{cases}$ for Exercises 46 and 47.

46. Which is the determinant D_x? **B**

   A. $\begin{vmatrix} 5 & -4 \\ -3 & 6 \end{vmatrix}$ **B.** $\begin{vmatrix} -13 & -4 \\ 6 & 6 \end{vmatrix}$ **C.** $\begin{vmatrix} 5 & -13 \\ -3 & 6 \end{vmatrix}$ **D.** $\begin{vmatrix} 5 & 4 & -13 \\ -3 & 6 & 6 \end{vmatrix}$

47. What is the solution of the system? **H**

   F. $(-13, 6)$ **G.** $\left(-\frac{13}{5}, 1\right)$ **H.** $\left(-3, -\frac{1}{2}\right)$ **J.** $2x + 2y = -7$

Use the system $\begin{cases} 2x + y - 3z = -2 \\ 4x - 3y + 6z = 9 \\ -2x - 2y + 9z = 7 \end{cases}$ for Exercises 48 and 49.

48. What is the value of the determinant D_y? **D**
   A. -36 **B.** -24 **C.** -18 **D.** 36

49. What is the value of the determinant D_z? **G**
   F. -36 **G.** -24 **H.** -18 **J.** 36

45a margin

45a. Let x = the width of the rectangle, let y = the length of the rectangle, and let z = the diagonal.

$$\begin{cases} 2x + 2y & = 28 \\ x + y + z & = 24 \\ x - z & = -2 \end{cases}$$

b. $\begin{cases} 2x + 2y = 28 \\ 2x + y = 22 \end{cases}$

c. $\begin{bmatrix} 2 & 2 & 28 \\ 2 & 1 & 22 \end{bmatrix}$

52.

53.

54.

Mixed Review

Lesson 4-7

Solve each system of equations by using the inverse of the coefficient matrix.

50. $\begin{cases} x + 4y + 3z = 3 \\ 2x - 5y - z = 5 \\ 3x + 2y - 2z = -3 \end{cases}$ **(1, −1, 2)**

51. $\begin{cases} x + y + z = -1 \\ y + 3z = -5 \\ x + z = -2 \end{cases}$ **(0, 1, −2)**

Lesson 3-3

Solve each system of inequalities by graphing. **52–54. See margin.**

52. $\begin{cases} 2x + y < 3 \\ -x - y \ge 1 \end{cases}$ **53.** $\begin{cases} 2x \le 0 \\ -x + y > -1 \end{cases}$ **54.** $\begin{cases} x < 3 \\ y \ge -4 \\ -x + y < 5 \end{cases}$

55–57. Answers may vary. Samples are given.

Lesson 2-2 **Write in point-slope form the equation of the line through each pair of points.**

55. $(0, 1)$ and $(2, -5)$
   $y - 1 = -3x$

56. $(-9, 3)$ and $(-4, -4)$
   $y - 3 = \frac{-7}{5}(x + 9)$

57. $(1, 8)$ and $(7, 2)$
   $y - 8 = -1(x - 1)$

Interpreting Data

This feature helps students connect the graphs of real-world situations to their word descriptions.

Resources

SAT® and ACT® correlations are on page 166B.

Test-Taking Strategies with Transparencies
• Transparency 4
• Practice sheet p. 28

Guided Instruction

Point out that there are only three possibilities for how a variable or graph can change: increase, decrease, or stay the same.

English Language Learners ELL

Discuss the terms *rodent* and *predator*. A predator is an animal that lives by killing and eating other animals, and a rodent is a small mammal like a mouse, squirrel, or rabbit.

A test item may give you a graph and ask you to choose a situation that best interprets the graph. Or it may give you a situation and ask you to choose a graph that best models the situation.

To make the choice, you must break down each situation to find the features that must be present in the graph.

EXAMPLE

In a research study, a rodent population remained stable for some time. It increased rapidly when a predator was removed. Then it declined rapidly as overpopulation caused a food shortage. Which graph best models this situation?

 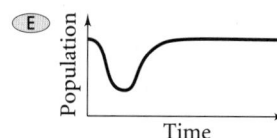

As time increases (from left to right), the correct graph must

• begin with a horizontal part to show a stable population.
• rise rapidly to show the predator's absence.
• fall rapidly to show the food shortage.

Only one graph has all three parts in the correct order. The answer is C.

EXERCISES

1. **Multiple Choice** A test item gives you the graph from choice E above. Which situation below best interprets this graph? **A**
   A An infection reduced the population of rodents. Then the population recovered and stabilized as the health of the remaining animals improved.
   B The rodent population grew because food was abundant.
   C The rodent population declined suddenly because of a mutant gene.
   D The rodent birthrate steadily declined because of contaminated food.
   E A flood displaced half the rodents. The remaining rodents moved to a different location during the year.

2. Repeat Exercise 1 for Graph A from the Example. **choice D**

3. Describe a situation that fits Graph D from the Example.
   Answers may vary. Check students' work.

Chapter Review

Vocabulary Review

Resources

Student Edition
Extra Skills and Word Problems
    Practice, Ch. 4, p. 842
English/Spanish Glossary, p. 899
Properties and Formulas, p. 893
Table of Symbols, p. 889

augmented matrix (p. 222)
center of rotation (p. 194)
coefficient matrix (p. 214)
constant matrix (p. 214)
Cramer's Rule (p. 221)
determinant (p. 200)
dilation (p. 192)
equal matrices (p. 177)

image (p. 192)
matrix (p. 168)
matrix addition (p. 174)
matrix element (p. 169)
matrix equation (p. 176)
matrix multiplication (p. 184)
multiplicative identity matrix (p. 199)
multiplicative inverse matrix (p. 199)

preimage (p. 192)
rotation (p. 194)
row operations (p. 223)
scalar (p. 182)
scalar multiplication (p. 182)
square matrix (p. 199)
variable matrix (p. 214)
zero matrix (p. 175)

Choose the correct vocabulary term to complete each sentence.

1. A __?__ is a rectangular array of numbers. **matrix**

2. Translations, dilations, reflections, and rotations are all __?__. **transformations**

3. Cramer's Rule uses __?__ to solve a system of equations. **determinants**

4. If corresponding elements of matrices are equal, the matrices are __?__.
    equal matrices

5. The additive identity of a matrix is the __?__. **zero matrix**

6. A __?__ consists of a coefficient matrix, a variable matrix, and a
    constant matrix. **matrix equation**

7. An $n \times n$ matrix is called a __?__. **square matrix**

8. The image of a figure is a transformation of the __?__. **preimage**

9. The product of a real number and a matrix is called a __?__. **scalar product**

10. A matrix is the inverse of another matrix if their product is the __?__.
    multiplicative identity matrix

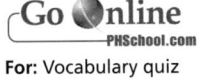
Go Online
PHSchool.com
For: Vocabulary quiz
Web Code: agj-0451

Skills and Concepts

4-1 Objectives

▼ To identify matrices and
    their elements (p. 168)

▼ To organize data into
    matrices (p. 169)

It is often useful to organize data into matrices. A **matrix** is a rectangular array of
numbers classified by its dimensions. An $m \times n$ matrix has m rows and n columns.
A **matrix element** a_{ij} is in the ith row and jth column of matrix A.

State the dimensions of each matrix A. Identify the indicated element.

11. $\begin{bmatrix} 5 & 8 & -7 \\ 1 & 11 & 3 \end{bmatrix}; a_{13}$
   $2 \times 3; -7$

12. $\begin{bmatrix} 3 & 1 \\ -5 & 0 \\ 7 & 6 \end{bmatrix}; a_{21}$
   $3 \times 2; -5$

13. $\begin{bmatrix} 5 & 1 & -2 \\ 4 & -7 & 12 \\ 0 & 78 & 3 \end{bmatrix}; a_{32}$
   $3 \times 3; 78$

Use the matrix at the right for Exercises 14–16.

14. How many points has Tamika scored? **226**

15. How many three-point shots has Tran made? **50**

16. What percent of Johanna's points were from
    one-point shots? **about 9%**

	1-pt Shots	2-pt Shots	3-pt Shots
Tamika	22	30	48
Johanna	21	31	48
Tran	21	29	50

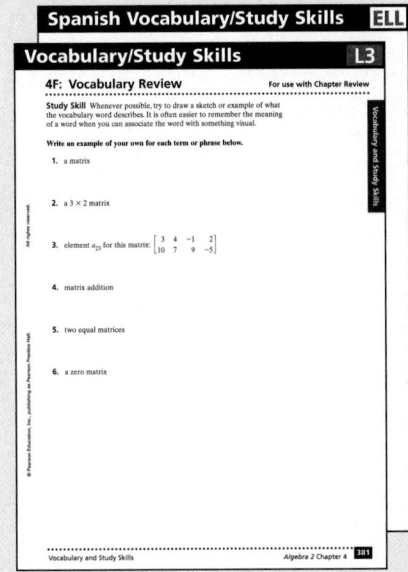

23. $\begin{bmatrix} 18 & 3 & 0 & 24 \\ -12 & 9 & 21 & 33 \end{bmatrix}$

24. $\begin{bmatrix} -9 & 7 \\ -8 & -8 \end{bmatrix}$

25. undefined

26. $\begin{bmatrix} -6 & 10 & 21 & 41 \\ -28 & 10 & 28 & 28 \end{bmatrix}$

27. $\begin{bmatrix} -14 & -2 \\ 43 & -7 \end{bmatrix}$

28. $\begin{bmatrix} 4 & -1 & 2 \\ -1 & -2 & 3 \end{bmatrix}$

29. $\begin{bmatrix} 0 & -5 & -2 \\ 5 & 4 & 9 \end{bmatrix}$

30. $\begin{bmatrix} -3 & 2 & -1 \\ 1 & 0 & 5 \end{bmatrix}$

31. $\begin{bmatrix} 1 & 0 & 5 \\ 3 & -2 & 1 \end{bmatrix}$

32. $\begin{bmatrix} 1 & 0 & 5 \\ -3 & 2 & -1 \end{bmatrix}$

33. $\begin{bmatrix} 1.5 & -1 & 0.5 \\ 0.5 & 0 & 2.5 \end{bmatrix}$

34. $\begin{bmatrix} 6 & -4 & 2 \\ 2 & 0 & 10 \end{bmatrix}$

35. $\begin{bmatrix} -1 & 0 & -5 \\ 3 & -2 & 1 \end{bmatrix}$

4-2 and 4-3 Objectives

▼ To add and subtract matrices (p. 174)

▼ To solve certain matrix equations (p. 176)

▼ To multiply a matrix by a scalar (p. 182)

▼ To multiply two matrices (p. 184)

To perform **matrix addition** or subtraction, add or subtract the corresponding elements in the matrices. To obtain the product of a matrix and a **scalar,** multiply each matrix element by the scalar. **Matrix multiplication** uses both multiplication and addition. The element in the ith row and jth column of the product of two matrices is the sum of the products of each element of the ith row of the first matrix and the corresponding element of the jth column of the second matrix. The first matrix must have the same number of columns as the second has rows.

Two matrices are **equal matrices** when they have the same dimensions and corresponding elements are equal. This principle is used to solve a **matrix equation.**

Solve each matrix equation for matrix X.

17. $\begin{bmatrix} 2 & -6 & 8 \end{bmatrix} + \begin{bmatrix} -1 & -2 & 4 \end{bmatrix} = X$
$\begin{bmatrix} 1 & -8 & 12 \end{bmatrix}$

18. $\begin{bmatrix} t \\ 6 \end{bmatrix} - \begin{bmatrix} 1 \\ 3 \end{bmatrix} = X \quad \begin{bmatrix} t-1 \\ 3 \end{bmatrix}$

19. $\begin{bmatrix} 7 & -1 \\ 0 & 8 \end{bmatrix} + X = \begin{bmatrix} 4 & 9 \\ -3 & 11 \end{bmatrix} \begin{bmatrix} -3 & 10 \\ -3 & 3 \end{bmatrix}$

20. $X - \begin{bmatrix} -7 & 13 & 5 \\ 31 & 0 & -4 \end{bmatrix} = \begin{bmatrix} 9 & -5 & 8 \\ 2 & 0 & -3 \end{bmatrix}$
$\begin{bmatrix} 2 & 8 & 13 \\ 33 & 0 & -7 \end{bmatrix}$

Solve for each variable.

21. $\begin{bmatrix} x-5 & 9 \\ 4 & t+2 \end{bmatrix} = \begin{bmatrix} -7 & w+1 \\ 8-r & 1 \end{bmatrix}$
$x = -2, w = 8, r = 4, t = -1$

22. $\begin{bmatrix} -4+t & 2y \\ r & w+4 \end{bmatrix} = \begin{bmatrix} 2t & 11 \\ -2r+12 & 9 \end{bmatrix}$
$t = -4, y = \frac{11}{2}, r = 4, w = 5$

Use matrices $A, B, C,$ and D. Find each scalar product, sum, or difference, if possible. If an operation is not defined, label it undefined. 23–27. See margin.

$A = \begin{bmatrix} 6 & 1 & 0 & 8 \\ -4 & 3 & 7 & 11 \end{bmatrix}$
$B = \begin{bmatrix} 1 & 3 \\ -2 & 4 \end{bmatrix}$
$C = \begin{bmatrix} -2 & 1 \\ 4 & 0 \\ 2 & 2 \\ 1 & 1 \end{bmatrix}$
$D = \begin{bmatrix} 5 & -2 \\ 3 & 6 \end{bmatrix}$

23. $3A$ **24.** $B - 2D$ **25.** AB **26.** BA **27.** $AC - BD$

4-4 Objectives

▼ To represent translations and dilations with matrices (p. 191)

▼ To represent reflections and rotations with matrices (p. 193)

A change made to a figure is a transformation. The original figure is the **preimage,** and the transformed figure is the **image.** A translation slides a figure without changing its size or shape. A **dilation** changes the size of a figure. You can use matrix addition to translate a figure and scalar multiplication to dilate a figure.

You can use multiplication by the appropriate matrix to perform transformations that are specific reflections or **rotations.** For example, to reflect a figure in the y-axis, multiply by $\begin{bmatrix} -1 & 0 \\ 0 & 1 \end{bmatrix}$. To rotate a figure 180°, multiply by $\begin{bmatrix} -1 & 0 \\ 0 & -1 \end{bmatrix}$.

For Exercises 28–35, use $\triangle ABC$ with vertices $A(3, 1), B(-2, 0),$ and $C(1, 5)$. Write the coordinates of each image in matrix form. 28–35. See margin.

28. a translation 1 unit right and 2 units down

29. a translation 3 units left and 4 units up

30. a reflection in the y-axis **31.** a reflection in the line $y = x$

32. a rotation of 270° **33.** a dilation half the original size

34. a dilation twice the original size **35.** a rotation of 90°

4-5, 4-6 and 4-7 Objectives

▼ To evaluate determinants of 2 × 2 matrices and find inverse matrices (p. 199)

▼ To use inverse matrices in solving matrix equations (pp. 201 and 207)

▼ To evaluate determinants of 3 × 3 matrices (p. 206)

▼ To solve systems of equations using inverse matrices (p. 214)

A **square matrix** with 1's along its main diagonal and 0's elsewhere is the **multiplicative identity matrix,** I. If A and X are square matrices such that $AX = I$, then X is the **multiplicative inverse matrix** of A, A^{-1}.

You can use formulas to evaluate the determinants of 2 × 2 and 3 × 3 matrices.

$$\begin{vmatrix} a & b \\ c & d \end{vmatrix} = ad - bc \qquad \begin{vmatrix} a_1 & b_1 & c_1 \\ a_2 & b_2 & c_2 \\ a_3 & b_3 & c_3 \end{vmatrix} = a_1b_2c_3 + a_2b_3c_1 + a_3b_1c_2 \\ - a_1b_3c_2 - a_2b_1c_3 - a_3b_2c_1$$

You can use a calculator to find the inverse of a matrix. The inverse of a 2 × 2 matrix can be found by using its determinant.

$$\begin{bmatrix} a & b \\ c & d \end{bmatrix}^{-1} = \frac{1}{ad - bc} \begin{bmatrix} d & -b \\ -c & a \end{bmatrix}$$

You can use inverse matrices to solve some matrix equations.

You can also use inverse matrices to solve some systems of equations. When equations in a system are in standard form, the product of the **coefficient matrix** and the **variable matrix** equals the **constant matrix.** You solve the equation by multiplying both sides of the equation by the inverse of the coefficient matrix. If that inverse does not exist, the system does not have a unique solution.

Evaluate the determinant of each matrix, and find the inverse, if possible.
36–39. See margin.

36. $\begin{bmatrix} 6 & 1 \\ 0 & 4 \end{bmatrix}$ 37. $\begin{bmatrix} 5 & -2 \\ 10 & -4 \end{bmatrix}$ 38. $\begin{bmatrix} 10 & 1 \\ 8 & 5 \end{bmatrix}$ 🖩 39. $\begin{bmatrix} 1 & 0 & 2 \\ -1 & 0 & 1 \\ -1 & -2 & 0 \end{bmatrix}$

Use an inverse matrix to solve each equation or system. 40–43. See margin.

40. $\begin{bmatrix} 3 & 5 \\ 6 & 2 \end{bmatrix} X = \begin{bmatrix} -2 & 6 \\ 4 & 12 \end{bmatrix}$ 41. $\begin{cases} x - y = 3 \\ 2x - y = -1 \end{cases}$ 42. $\begin{bmatrix} 4 & 1 \\ 2 & 1 \end{bmatrix} \begin{bmatrix} x \\ y \end{bmatrix} = \begin{bmatrix} 10 \\ 6 \end{bmatrix}$

43. $\begin{bmatrix} -6 & 0 \\ 7 & 1 \end{bmatrix} X = \begin{bmatrix} -12 & -6 \\ 17 & 9 \end{bmatrix}$ 44. $\begin{cases} x + 2y = 15 \\ 2x + 4y = 30 \end{cases}$ 🖩 45. $\begin{cases} a + 2b + c = 14 \\ b = c + 1 \\ a = -3c + 6 \end{cases}$

                     no unique solution   **no unique solution**

🌐 46. **Physical Fitness** A club of 17 students is going on a canoe trip. The group of people on the trip includes 5 chaperones, one for each canoe. Some canoes hold 5 people, while some hold 4 people. How many of each kind of canoe should the group rent? **3 small canoes, 2 large canoes**

4-8 Objectives

▼ To solve a system of equations using Cramer's Rule (p. 221)

▼ To solve a system of equations using augmented matrices (p. 222)

Cramer's Rule for solving systems of equations uses determinants to solve for each variable. D is the determinant of the coefficient matrix. D_y is the determinant formed by replacing the coefficients of y in D with the constant terms.

You can also use **row operations** on an augmented matrix to solve a system.

Solve each system using Cramer's Rule. Check your answers by solving each system using an augmented matrix.

47. $\begin{cases} 2x - y = 15 \\ x + 3y = -17 \end{cases}$ 48. $\begin{cases} 3r + s - 2t = 22 \\ r + 5s + t = 4 \\ r = -3t \end{cases}$
       $(4, -7)$ $(6, 0, -2)$

36. $24;$ $\begin{bmatrix} \frac{1}{6} & -\frac{1}{24} \\ 0 & \frac{1}{4} \end{bmatrix}$

37. $0;$ **does not exist**

38. $42;$ $\begin{bmatrix} \frac{5}{42} & -\frac{1}{42} \\ -\frac{4}{21} & \frac{5}{21} \end{bmatrix}$

39. $6;$ $\begin{bmatrix} \frac{1}{3} & -\frac{2}{3} & 0 \\ -\frac{1}{6} & \frac{1}{3} & -\frac{1}{2} \\ \frac{1}{3} & \frac{1}{3} & 0 \end{bmatrix}$

40. $\begin{bmatrix} 1 & 2 \\ -1 & 0 \end{bmatrix}$

41. $(-4, -7)$

42. $\begin{bmatrix} 2 \\ 2 \end{bmatrix}$

43. $\begin{bmatrix} 2 & 1 \\ 3 & 2 \end{bmatrix}$

Chapter Test

Go Online
PHSchool.com
For: Chapter Test
Web Code: aga-0452

Differentiated Instruction Resources

- **L3** Ch. 4 Test
- **L2** Below Level Ch. 4 Test
- **L4** Ch. 4 Alternative Assessment
- **L3** Spanish Ch. 4 Test
- **L4** Spanish Ch. 4 Alternative Assessment
- ExamView CD-ROM
  - Ch. 4 Pre-Made Test
  - Make your own Ch. 4 test
- Online Chapter 4 Test at www.PHSchool.com

History Use the table below for Exercises 1–3.

President	Years	Vetoes	Overrides
Kennedy	3	21	9
Johnson	5	30	0
Nixon	5.5	43	7
Ford	2.5	66	12
Carter	4	31	2
Reagan	8	78	9
G.H.W. Bush	4	46	1
Clinton	8	38	2

SOURCE: Congressional Research Service.
Go to **www.PHSchool.com** for a data update.
Web Code: agg-2041

1. Display the data in a matrix in which each row represents a president. **See back of book.**

2. State the dimensions of the matrix. **8 × 3**

3. Find and identify a_{32}. **43, the number of Nixon's vetoes**

Find each sum or difference.

4. $\begin{bmatrix} 4 & 7 \\ -2 & 1 \end{bmatrix} - \begin{bmatrix} -9 & 3 \\ 6 & 0 \end{bmatrix}$ $\begin{bmatrix} 13 & 4 \\ -8 & 1 \end{bmatrix}$

5. $\begin{bmatrix} 4 & -5 & 1 \\ 10 & 7 & 4 \\ 21 & -9 & -6 \end{bmatrix} + \begin{bmatrix} -7 & -10 & 4 \\ 17 & 0 & 3 \\ -2 & -6 & 1 \end{bmatrix}$ **See margin.**

Find each product. 6–8. See margin.

6. $\begin{bmatrix} 2 & 6 \\ 1 & 0 \end{bmatrix} \begin{bmatrix} -1 & 5 \\ 3 & 1 \end{bmatrix}$

7. $2 \begin{bmatrix} -8 & 5 & -1 \\ 0 & 9 & 7 \end{bmatrix}$

8. $\begin{bmatrix} 0 & 3 \\ -4 & 9 \end{bmatrix} \begin{bmatrix} -4 & 6 & 1 & 3 \\ 9 & -8 & 10 & 7 \end{bmatrix}$

Parallelogram $ABCD$ has coordinates $A(2, -1)$, $B(4, 3)$, $C(1, 5)$, and $D(-1, 1)$. Write a matrix for the vertices of its image after each transformation.

9. a dilation of size $\frac{2}{3}$ **See margin.**

10. a translation right 2 units and down 4 units

11. a reflection in $y = x$ **12.** a rotation of $270°$

13. Graph parallelogram $ABCD$ and its image from Question 11 on the same coordinate plane.
10–13. See back of book.

14. Open-Ended Write a matrix that has no inverse.

15. Writing Explain how to determine whether two matrices can be multiplied and what the dimensions of the product matrix will be.
14–15. See back of book.

16. Find the value of each variable.
$\begin{bmatrix} x & 1 & y \\ 2 & 0 & 1 \end{bmatrix} = \begin{bmatrix} 1-x & z & 2 \\ 2+w & 4-t & 1 \end{bmatrix}$
$x = \frac{1}{2}, z = 1, y = 2, w = 0, t = 4$

Find the determinant of each matrix.

17. $\begin{bmatrix} 1 & 0 & 0 \\ 0 & 1 & 0 \\ 0 & 0 & 1 \end{bmatrix}$ **1** **18.** $\begin{bmatrix} 2 & 3 & 0 \\ -1 & 1 & 0 \\ 4 & 2 & 1 \end{bmatrix}$ **5** **19.** $\begin{bmatrix} 8 & -3 \\ 2 & 9 \end{bmatrix}$ **78**

20. $\begin{bmatrix} 0 & 3 \\ x & t \end{bmatrix}$ **$-3x$** **21.** $\begin{bmatrix} \frac{1}{2} & -1 \\ 3 & 0 \end{bmatrix}$ **3**

22–26. See back of book.

Find the inverse of each matrix, if it exists.

22. $\begin{bmatrix} 3 & 8 \\ -7 & 10 \end{bmatrix}$ **23.** $\begin{bmatrix} 0 & -5 \\ 9 & 6 \end{bmatrix}$ **24.** $\begin{bmatrix} \frac{1}{2} & -1 \\ 0 & 4 \end{bmatrix}$

25. $\begin{bmatrix} -8 & 4 & -11 \\ 5 & 2 & 9 \\ -5 & 6 & 2 \end{bmatrix}$ **26.** $\begin{bmatrix} 1 & 1 & 2 \\ 2 & 1 & 3 \\ 2 & 1 & 1 \end{bmatrix}$

Solve each matrix equation.

27. $\begin{bmatrix} 3 & -8 \\ 10 & 5 \end{bmatrix} - X = \begin{bmatrix} 2 & 8 \\ -1 & 12 \end{bmatrix}$ $\begin{bmatrix} 1 & -16 \\ 11 & -7 \end{bmatrix}$

28. $\begin{bmatrix} 3 & 2 \\ -1 & 5 \end{bmatrix} X = \begin{bmatrix} -10 & -11 \\ 26 & -36 \end{bmatrix}$ $\begin{bmatrix} -6 & 1 \\ 4 & -7 \end{bmatrix}$

29. $2X - \begin{bmatrix} -2 & 0 \\ 1 & 4 \end{bmatrix} = \begin{bmatrix} 5 & 10 \\ -15 & 9 \end{bmatrix}$ $\begin{bmatrix} \frac{3}{2} & 5 \\ -7 & \frac{13}{2} \end{bmatrix}$

Solve each system using inverse matrices.

30. $\begin{cases} 2x - y = 5 \\ x + 4y = 7 \end{cases}$ **(3, 1)**

31. $\begin{cases} x + 2y + z = -1 \\ 4x - y - z = -1 \\ 2z = -3y \end{cases}$ **(0, −2, 3)**

32. Solve $\begin{cases} -2x + 7y = 19 \\ x + 3y = 10 \end{cases}$ using Cramer's Rule. **(1, 3)**

33. Solve the system using an augmented matrix. **(7, −8, 10)**
$\begin{cases} x + y + z = 9 \\ 4x + 3y - z = -6 \\ -x - y + 2z = 21 \end{cases}$

Below Level Chapter Test **L2**

Chapter Test **L3**

Chapter Test
Chapter 4

1. The table shows record high and low temperatures in degrees Fahrenheit in each of six cities.

City	Record High	Record Low
Anchorage	85	−34
Chicago	104	−27
Houston	107	7
Miami	98	30
Pittsburgh	103	−18
San Diego	111	29

Source: World Almanac and Book of Facts 1995

a. Display the data in a matrix whose rows indicate the data for each city. State the dimensions of the matrix.
b. Identify a_{42}.

Find each sum or difference.
2. ... 3. ...
Find each product if possible. If not possible, write product undefined.
4. ... 5. ...
6. ... 7. ...
11. $\triangle ABC$ has coordinates (1, 1), (3, 4), and (0, −5). Write the vertices in matrix form.
a. Find the coordinates of the image of the triangle after a dilation of size $\frac{1}{2}$.
b. Find the coordinates of the image of the triangle after a translation right 3 units and up 2 units.
c. Find the coordinates of the image of the triangle after a rotation of 180°.
d. Find the coordinates of the image of the triangle after a reflection in the line $y = x$.
Find the determinant of each matrix.
9. ... 10. ... 11. ...

Algebra 2 Chapter 4 21

page 232 Chapter Test

5. $\begin{bmatrix} -3 & -15 & 5 \\ 27 & 7 & 7 \\ 19 & -15 & -5 \end{bmatrix}$

6. $\begin{bmatrix} 16 & 16 \\ -1 & 5 \end{bmatrix}$

7. $\begin{bmatrix} -16 & 10 & -2 \\ 0 & 18 & 14 \end{bmatrix}$

8. $\begin{bmatrix} 27 & -24 & 30 & 21 \\ 97 & -96 & 86 & 51 \end{bmatrix}$

9. $\begin{bmatrix} \frac{4}{3} & \frac{8}{3} & \frac{2}{3} & -\frac{2}{3} \\ -\frac{2}{3} & 2 & \frac{10}{3} & \frac{2}{3} \end{bmatrix}$

Standardized Test Prep

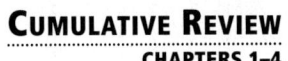

Standardized Test Prep

Multiple Choice

For Exercises 1–12, choose the correct letter.

1 Which number is irrational?
D
Ⓐ $8.\overline{12}$ Ⓑ $\sqrt{121}$ Ⓒ -5 Ⓓ $\sqrt{35}$

2. Which numbers are solutions of $\frac{5}{4}|2x - 9| = 5$?
G
Ⓕ $\frac{11}{8}, \frac{61}{8}$ Ⓖ $\frac{5}{2}, \frac{13}{2}$ Ⓗ $\frac{8}{5}, \frac{28}{5}$ Ⓙ 2, 7

3. Which equation represents the *xy*-trace of
A $20x - 70y - 50z = 100$?

Ⓐ $2x - 7y = 10$ Ⓑ $-7y - 5z = 10$
Ⓒ $2x - 5z = 10$ Ⓓ $5z = -10$

4. Which ordered pair is *not* a solution of
H the system $\begin{cases} x + y \le 4 \\ 2x - y \ge -3 \end{cases}$?

Ⓕ (1, 1)   Ⓖ (0, 3)   Ⓗ (−5, −1)   Ⓙ (3, 0)

5. What is the solution of $\begin{cases} 2x - y = 4 \\ y = 2 - x \end{cases}$?
B

Ⓐ (0, 2)   Ⓑ (2, 0)
Ⓒ (2, 4)   Ⓓ (0, −4)

6. Suppose *y* varies directly with *x*. When *x* is 16,
D *y* is 10. What is *x* when *y* is −16?

Ⓐ −0.625   Ⓑ −1.6   Ⓒ −10   Ⓓ −25.6

7. What is the sum $\begin{bmatrix} 3 & 7 & -2 \\ 0 & 10 & 5 \end{bmatrix} + \begin{bmatrix} 6 & -8 & 1 \\ 9 & -4 & 11 \end{bmatrix}$?
A

Ⓐ $\begin{bmatrix} 9 & -1 & -1 \\ 9 & 6 & 16 \end{bmatrix}$ Ⓑ $\begin{bmatrix} 9 & 15 & -1 \\ 9 & 6 & 16 \end{bmatrix}$

Ⓒ $\begin{bmatrix} 9 & 15 & -3 \\ 9 & 6 & 16 \end{bmatrix}$ Ⓓ $\begin{bmatrix} -3 & 1 & -3 \\ -9 & 14 & -6 \end{bmatrix}$

8. Which equation has the solution $\begin{bmatrix} 1 & -2 & 0 \\ -5 & 4 & 7 \end{bmatrix}$?
H

Ⓕ $\begin{bmatrix} 7 & -2 & -3 \\ 0 & 1 & 8 \end{bmatrix} - X = \begin{bmatrix} 8 & -4 & -3 \\ -5 & 5 & 15 \end{bmatrix}$

Ⓖ $\begin{bmatrix} 10 & -8 & 12 \\ 4 & 0 & 5 \end{bmatrix} - \begin{bmatrix} -9 & -6 & 12 \\ -1 & -4 & -2 \end{bmatrix} = X$

Ⓗ $\begin{bmatrix} 0 & 6 & 5 \\ 2 & -1 & -9 \end{bmatrix} + X = \begin{bmatrix} 1 & 4 & 5 \\ -3 & 3 & -2 \end{bmatrix}$

Ⓙ $X - \begin{bmatrix} 3 & 7 & 4 \\ 8 & -6 & 1 \end{bmatrix} = \begin{bmatrix} 2 & -5 & 4 \\ -3 & 2 & 6 \end{bmatrix}$

9. Which equation represents a translation of the
B graph of $y = |x|$?

Ⓐ $y = -|x + 4|$ Ⓑ $y = |-x + 4|$
Ⓒ $y = |2x| + 4$ Ⓓ $y = 2|x - 2| + 4$

10. Which lines are perpendicular to $y = 3x - 8$?
J
I. $y = \frac{1}{3}x - 1$ II. $y = -\frac{1}{3}x + 1$
III. $y = 3x + 2$ IV. $y = 6x + 4$

Ⓕ I only   Ⓖ III and IV
Ⓗ I and II   Ⓙ II only

11. Which graph shows the solution of $8 < 4 - 2y < 15$?
A

Ⓐ ![number line −6 −4 −2 0]   Ⓑ ![number line 0 2 4 6]
Ⓒ ![number line −6 −4 −2 0]   Ⓓ ![number line 0 2 4 6]

12. Find the domain of the relation
H {(3, −9), (2, 5), (−1, 6), (0, 0)}.

Ⓕ {−9, −1, 0, 2, 3, 5, 6}   Ⓖ {2, 3, 5, 6}
Ⓗ {−1, 0, 2, 3}   Ⓙ {−9, 0, 5, 6}

Gridded Response

13. What is the slope of the graph of $8x - 2y = 3$?

14. What is the value of $\begin{vmatrix} 7 & -1 \\ 3 & 2 \end{vmatrix}$? 17

Short Response

15. Write a matrix to translate $\begin{bmatrix} -1 & 4 & 5 \\ 0 & 7 & 2 \end{bmatrix}$ 7 units left and 2 units up. Use the matrix to find the coordinates of the image. **See back of book.**

Extended Response

16. A dietitian wants to prepare a meal with 24 g of protein, 27 g of fat, and 20 g of carbohydrates using the three foods shown in the table.

Food	Protein	Fat	Carbohydrates
A	2 g/oz	3 g/oz	4 g/oz
B	3 g/oz	3 g/oz	1 g/oz
C	3 g/oz	3 g/oz	2 g/oz

a. Set up a matrix equation for the data.
b. Solve the matrix equation.
c. How many ounces of each food are needed?
a–c. **See back of book.**

Students must be able to extract information from reading passages, answer multiple choice questions, and construct responses in order to be successful on current state and national assessments.

To answer the questions, students apply skills and concepts from this chapter and previous chapters.
Multiple Choice: Items 1–12
Gridded Response: Items 13–14
Short Response: Item 15
Extended Response: Items 16

Resources

Test Prep Workbook

Grab & Go
• **L3** Cumulative Review

ExamView CD-ROM
• Standardized Test Practice

Differentiated Instruction Resources

Progress Monitoring Assessments
• Benchmark Test 2

Spanish Assessment Resources
• **L3** Spanish Cumulative Review

Item	1	2	3	4	5	6	7	8	9	10	11	12	13	14	15	16
Lesson	1-1	1-5	3-5	3-3	3-2	2-2	4-2	4-2	2-6	2-2	1-4	2-1	2-2	4-5	4-4	4-3

Building a Business

In these activities students apply their knowledge of inequalities, systems of inequalities, and linear programming.

Activating Prior Knowledge

Have students research the different kinds of chocolate (milk, dark, white) and forms (cocoa, bars, syrup), what products contain chocolate, what countries grow the cacao tree, and how the beans are processed.

Guided Instruction

Have a volunteer read the introductory paragraph. Ask: *Has anyone ever visited a factory or a bakery that produces a large quantity of a product each day?* Have students describe the various processes they observed.

Teaching Tip

Discuss how students might conduct a test to compare the tastes of two or more chocolate bars, including hiding the brand names for a blind test, and recording the various responses in such a way that they can be analyzed numerically.

Connection to Science

Have students research recent findings about the chemical contents of chocolate and its effects, including whether eating chocolate may be a cause of complexion or skin problems.

English Language Learners ELL

Have volunteers describe what is meant by *the efficiency of a factory* and *maximizing profits.*

234

Activity Lab

Building a Business

Applying Inequalities The efficiency of a factory depends on how you divide limited resources among the products produced. The bad news is that in any factory you have a limited number of machines and raw materials available. The good news is that these limitations lead to inequalities that you can use to decide how to maximize your profits.

◀1 The cacao tree grows in tropical jungles. It produces melonlike fruits, each containing 20–40 cocoa beans.

3 The inside of the cocoa bean is ground into a concentrated chocolate liquid.

2 After roasting, cocoa beans pass through a machine that separates the shell from the inside of the bean.

Activity

You are in charge of a small private chocolate factory that makes two popular and profitable chocolate bars, Cocoa Bar and Choco-Lot. Your goal is to figure out how many of each type of chocolate bar you should produce each day to maximize your company's profits.

Here are a few key pieces of information:

- The success of your chocolate recipes lies in your use of two secret ingredients, referred to as Flavor A and Flavor B to protect the company's interests. The table shows the production rate and requirements of the flavors.

	Flavor A	Flavor B
Production rate	126 kg/day	136 kg/day
Cocoa Bar requirements	1.8 g/bar	4.0 g/bar
Choco-Lot requirements	2.8 g/bar	1.7 g/bar

- One machine wraps both candy bars. It can wrap 50,000 chocolate bars per day.
- Your profit on each Cocoa Bar bar is 14¢, and your profit on each Choco-Lot bar is 12¢.

a. Write inequalities to describe each objective and constraint.

b. Graph the inequalities you wrote in part (a).

c. Find the quantity of each chocolate bar you should manufacture to maximize your daily profit. Calculate the profit you will earn.

---

pages 234–235 Activity Lab

Activity

a. Let B = number of Cocoa Bar bars, L = number of Choco-Lot bars. Constraints:

$B \geq 0$; $L \geq 0$
$B + L \leq 50,000$
$1.8B + 2.8L \leq 126,000$
$4.0B + 1.7L \leq 136,000$
Objective:
maximize $0.14B + 0.12L$

b.

234

Chocolate Fondue

To make chocolate fondue, melt chocolate gently over low heat. Dip pieces of fruit in the melted chocolate.

4 Milk and sugar are mixed together before being added to the cocoa bean liquid.

6 Any gritty particles are removed by machine.

7 The chocolate paste is ready to be cooled and molded.

5 The cocoa, milk, and sugar mixture is dried to a powder and mixed with cocoa butter to make a chocolate paste.

White Chocolate

White chocolate is not a real chocolate, since it does not contain cocoa solids. A good white chocolate is made with cocoa butter as well as milk solids and sugar.

8 The molded chocolate takes a bumpy ride along a conveyor belt to eliminate air bubbles as it cools. It's ready for wrapping!

Go Online
PHSchool.com

For: Information about manufacturing
Web Code: age-0453

235

Teaching Tip

Before students begin the activity, discuss the illustrations and their captions. Have students work in pairs or in small groups to complete the activities. Have each team read through the activity before beginning to work. If time permits, have students do one or the other, or both, of the additional activities.

Activity 1

Materials: paper and pencil, ruler, graph paper

Special Needs   L1

Help students understand the task by having them predict how many inequalities they are going to write, and which variables each inequality will describe.

Scoring Rubric

This scoring rubric can be used for evaluating student work on the activity. Share this scoring rubric with students before they begin work.

4 Equations, calculations, and graphs are correct.
Steps are neat, accurate, and clearly show the mathematics. Responses are clearly indicated and give the appropriate units.

3 Equations, calculations, and graphs are mostly correct, with some minor errors. Steps are neat and mostly accurate. Units are not completely accurate.

2 Equations, calculations, and graphs contain both major and minor errors.

1 Correct answer, but no work is shown.

c. $L = 28,000$; $B = 22,000$; $6440

Quadratic Equations and Functions

Chapter at a Glance

Lesson Titles, Objectives, and Features	Assessment	NCTM Standards	Local Standards
5-1 Modeling Data With Quadratic Functions • Identifying quadratic functions and graphs • Modeling data with quadratic functions **Activity Lab:** Technology: Modeling Using Residuals	Lesson Quiz	2, 5, 10	
5-2 Properties of Parabolas • Graphing quadratic functions • Finding maximum and minimum values of quadratic functions	Lesson Quiz	2, 3, 6	
5-3 Transforming Parabolas • Using the vertex form of a quadratic function	Lesson Quiz Checkpoint Quiz 1	2, 3, 10	
5-4 Factoring Quadratic Expressions • Finding common and binomial factors of quadratic expressions • Factoring special quadratic expressions	Lesson Quiz	1, 2	
Algebra 1 Review: Square Roots and Radicals **5-5 Quadratic Equations** • Solving quadratic equations by factoring and by finding square roots • Solving quadratic equations by graphing **Activity Lab:** Writing Equations From Roots	Lesson Quiz	1, 2, 6, 9	
5-6 Complex Numbers • Identifying and graphing complex numbers • Adding, subtracting, and multiplying complex numbers	Lesson Quiz Checkpoint Quiz 2	1, 2, 10	
Activity Lab: Hands-On: Completing the Square **5-7 Completing the Square** • Solving equations by completing the square • Rewriting functions by completing the square **GPS:** Understanding Word Problems	Lesson Quiz	2, 6, 7	
5-8 The Quadratic Formula • Solving quadratic equations by using the Quadratic Formula • Determining types of solutions by using the discriminant **Activity Lab:** Technology: Quadratic Inequalities	Lesson Quiz	2, 6, 7	

NCTM Standards 2000

1 Number and Operations	**2** Algebra	**3** Geometry	**4** Measurement	**5** Data Analysis and Probability
6 Problem Solving	**7** Reasoning and Proof	**8** Communication	**9** Connections	**10** Representation

Correlations to Standardized Tests

All content for these tests is contained in *Prentice Hall Algebra 2*. This chart reflects coverage in this chapter only.

	5-1	5-2	5-3	5-4	5-5	5-6	5-7	5-8
SAT®								
Number and Operations Operations, ratio & proportions, complex numbers, counting, elementary number theory, matrices, sequences					✔	✔		
Algebra and Functions Expressions, equations, inequalities, representation and modeling, properties of functions (linear, polynomial, rational, exponential)	✔	✔	✔	✔	✔		✔	✔
Geometry and Measurement *Plane Euclidean/Measurement Coordinate* Lines, parabolas, circles, symmetry, transformations *Three-dimensional* Solids, surface area & volume (cylinders, cones, pyramids, spheres, prisms) *Trigonometry* Right triangles, identities								
Data Analysis, Statistics, and Probability Mean, median, mode, range, interquartile range, graphs and plots, regression, probability	✔	✔						
ACT®								
Pre-Algebra Basic operations using whole numbers, decimals, fractions, and integers; place value; square roots and approximations; the concept of exponents; scientific notation; factors, ratio, proportion, and percent; linear equations in one variable; absolute value and ordering numbers by value; elementary counting techniques and simple probability; data collection, representation, and interpretation; and understanding simple descriptive statistics.								
Elementary Algebra Properties of exponents and square roots, evaluation of algebraic expressions through substitution, using variables to express functional relationships, understanding algebraic operations, and solving quadratic equations by factoring.	✔	✔	✔	✔	✔	✔	✔	✔
Intermediate Algebra Understanding of the quadratic formula, rational and radical expressions, absolute value equations and inequalities, sequences and patterns, systems of equations, quadratic inequalities, functions, modeling, matrices, roots of polynomials, and complex numbers.	✔	✔		✔	✔	✔	✔	✔
Coordinate Geometry Graphing and the relations between equations and graphs, including points, lines, polynomials, circles, and other curves; graphing inequalities; slope; parallel and perpendicular lines; distance; midpoints; and conics.		✔	✔		✔	✔		
Plane Geometry Properties and relations of plane figures, including angles and relations among perpendicular and parallel lines; properties of circles, triangles, rectangles, parallelograms, and trapezoids; transformations; the concept of proof and proof techniques; volume; and applications of geometry to three dimensions.								
Trigonometry Understanding trigonometric relations in right triangles; values and properties of trigonometric functions; graphing trigonometric functions; modeling using trigonometric functions; use of trigonometric identities; and solving trigonometric equations.								
NAEP								
Number Sense, Properties, and Operations				✔	✔			
Measurement								
Geometry and Spatial Sense				✔				
Data Analysis, Statistics, and Probability	✔							
Algebra and Functions	✔	✔	✔	✔	✔	✔	✔	✔

SAT® The College Board, SAT® Reasoning Test   **ACT®** The ACT Assessment® Test   **NAEP** National Assessment of Educational Progress, 2005 Mathematics Objectives

Math Background

Skills Trace

> ### BEFORE Chapter 5
> In previous chapters, students modeled data using linear functions and transformed graphs of absolute value functions.
>
> ▼
>
> ### DURING Chapter 5
> Students model data using quadratic functions, factor quadratic expressions, transform graphs of quadratic functions, and solve quadratic equations using algebraic, graphical, and tabular methods.
>
> ▼
>
> ### AFTER Chapter 5
> Students will model data with higher degree polynomial functions and solve higher degree polynomial equations.

Chapter Overview

Students study the symmetry of parabolas and learn to locate their maximum or minimum points. They graph quadratic functions and learn to use the vertex form of a quadratic function $y = a(x - h)^2 + k$ to graph transformations of $y = ax^2$.

There is a detailed examination of factoring quadratic expressions including perfect square trinomials and the difference of two squares. Students then solve quadratic equations by factoring. After learning about complex numbers, students go on to solve quadratic equations by completing the square and by using the Quadratic Formula.

Modeling Data With Quadratic Functions   5-1

The definition of a quadratic function as being of the form $f(x) = ax^2 + bx + c$ requires that $a \neq 0$. Thus, the x-squared term cannot be eliminated because a quadratic function is defined by having this term (and no higher degree terms).

Students learn how a system of linear equations can be used to find a quadratic function whose graph passes through three noncollinear points. They should enjoy this blending of their new

skill and finding quadratic models for data in real-world situations. When three or more noncollinear points or data pairs are available, a statistical regression model can also be found with a graphing calculator. The resulting quadratic function rule represents the best fitting quadratic curve. Students are often interested to learn that just as two points determine a unique line, three noncollinear points define a unique quadratic curve. Thus, three data pairs is the minimum number needed to use the quadratic regression feature on a graphing calculator.

Properties of Parabolas   5-2

Students must recognize that, just as the graph of a linear function is always a line, the graph of a quadratic function is always a parabola. Emphasize that a parabola is a curve and has no section that is linear, even when several plotted points appear to be collinear. This can be shown on a graphing calculator by carefully selecting a small viewing window, and zooming out until a maximum or minimum value is observed.

Students should also recognize that both a and b in $f(x) = ax^2 + bx + c$ affect the location of the axis of symmetry $x = -\frac{b}{2a}$. The vertex $\left(-\frac{b}{2a}, f\left(-\frac{b}{2a}\right)\right)$ depends on a, b, and c, with c changing the y-value of the vertex by moving it up or down.

Transforming Parabolas   5-3

Students should be able to establish the relationship between the two forms used to write quadratic functions, and relate h, k, a, b, and c. By rewriting $ax^2 + bx + c = a(x - h)^2 + k$, students find that the a in each equation is the same, $b = -2ah$, and $c = ah^2 + k$. This analysis helps students understand and appreciate the vertex form for graphing quadratic functions.

The transformations of the parent function $y = x^2$ are similar to the transformations presented in Lesson 2-6 for absolute value functions and include: reflections in the x-axis, stretches or shrinks, and translations right or left and translations up or down.

Factoring Quadratic Expressions   5-4

Usually, when we ask for the factors of a number such as 28, we expect the answer 1, 2, 4, 7, 14, and 28 because these are the whole-number factors. However, when factoring a trinomial such as $x^2 - 3x + 2$ we factor 2 with respect to the integers as $-1 \times (-2)$ to get $(x - 1)(x - 2)$. When we factor $x^2 - 0.25$ we factor 0.25 with respect to the rational numbers as -0.5×0.5 to get $(x - 0.5)(x + 0.5)$. Finally, we can also factor $x^2 - 3$ by factoring 3 with respect to the real numbers, yielding $(x - \sqrt{3})(x + \sqrt{3})$. In each quadratic, students can check their results by multiplication, which is a good habit because student often make sign errors.

You may wish to introduce students to the method of substituting values for the variables as another way to check factoring. This type of check will generally reveal an error, but does not guarantee correctness. For example, to check $pg - 2g + 6 - 3p = (p - 2)(g - 3)$ choose values for p and g that make the computations easy. If 2 is substituted for p and 1 is substituted for g, the right side of the equation is easily seen to equal 0. The left side yields $2 \cdot 1 - 2 \cdot 1 + 6 - 3 \cdot 2 = 0$. The values of the two sides of the equation are equal, suggesting that the factoring is probably correct.

Quadratic Equations   5-5

Students solve equations using factoring and taking square roots. In each case, the solution set has either one or two solutions. Multiple solutions can confuse students because the word *or* has different meanings based on the context it is used in. For instance, in the principle of zero products (if $ab = 0$, then $a = 0$ or $b = 0$) the *or* is used inclusively to mean that $a = 0$ or $b = 0$ or that both a and b equal 0. However, when we solve the equation $(x - 1)(x - 2) = 0$ and say that $x = 1$ or $x = 2$, the *or* is not inclusive. We mean that both 1 and 2 are solutions of the equation, but x is not equal to both 1 and 2 at the same time. This second use of *or* indicates one of two possibilities but not both of them. Hence, many students prefer writing the solution set using set notation, or $\{1,2\}$.

Solving quadratic equations graphically results in approximate or estimated answers. Nevertheless, graphical solutions are often the fastest way to arrive at useful information for real-world problems.

Complex Numbers   5-6

Students may be surprised to learn that numbers are actually invented or defined. Negative numbers were invented to solve equations like $x + 8 = 1$. Irrational numbers were invented to solve equations like $x^2 = 2$. And imaginary numbers were invented to

solve equations like $x^2 = -3$, using the definition $i^2 = -1$ or $i = \sqrt{-1}$. Although i looks like a variable, and we can manipulate it as we do a variable, it is a number. Also, it does not make sense to order the complex numbers; there is no way to graph them on the real number line.

Completing the Square   5-7

Students should recognize that the technique of completing the square yields the vertex form of a parabola. This technique also leads directly to the derivation of the Quadratic Formula presented in Lesson 5-8.

Students are often interested to learn that in some countries the standard form of a quadratic equation is defined as $x^2 + 2bx + c = 0$. Completing the square gives a slightly simpler formula for the roots: $x = -b \pm \sqrt{b^2 - c}$. Students should not have much difficulty showing that, for this form, the sum of the roots written in this way is $-2b$, the product of the roots is c, and the axis of symmetry and x-coordinate of the vertex are $x = -b$.

The Quadratic Formula   5-8

The Quadratic Formula completes the techniques students learn to solve quadratic equations: factoring, taking square roots, tables, graphs, completing the square, and the Quadratic Formula. Students may be interested to know that similar formulas exist for cubic and quartic equations (that will be studied in Chapter 6). However these formulas are not as straightforward as the Quadratic Formula.

Additional Professional Development Opportunities

Math Background notes for Chapter 5: Every lesson has a Math Background in the PLAN section.

Research Overview, Mathematical Strands
Additional support for these topics and more is in the front of this Teacher's Edition.

Lesson Lab
Lesson Lab, a Pearson Education company, offers comprehensive, facilitated professional development designed to help teachers improve student achievement. To learn more, please visit lessonlab.com

Chapter 5 Resources

Print Resources	5-1	5-2	5-3	5-4	5-5	5-6	5-7	5-8	For the Chapter
L3 Practice	•	•	•	•	•	•	•	•	
L3 Guided Problem Solving	•	•	•	•	•	•	•	•	
L2 Reteaching	•	•	•	•	•	•	•	•	
L4 Enrichment	•	•	•	•	•	•	•	•	
L3 Daily Notetaking Guide	•	•	•	•	•	•	•	•	
L3 Vocabulary and Study Skills Worksheets	•		•		•	•			•
L3 Chapter Project									•
L3 Hands On Activities		•			•	•			
L3 Checkpoint Quiz			•			•			
L2 Below Level Chapter Test									•
L3 Chapter Test									•
L4 Alternative Assessment									•
L3 Cumulative Review									•
L4 Connections to Precalculus Masters	•	•	•	•	•	•	•	•	
L3 Technology Activities	•		•		•				

Spanish Resources ELL	5-1	5-2	5-3	5-4	5-5	5-6	5-7	5-8	For the Chapter
L3 Practice	•	•	•	•	•	•	•	•	
L3 Vocabulary and Study Skills Worksheets	•		•		•		•	•	•
L3 Checkpoint Quiz			•			•			
L2 Below Level Chapter Test									•
L3 Chapter Test									•
L4 Alternative Assessment									
L3 Cumulative Review									•

Transparencies	5-1	5-2	5-3	5-4	5-5	5-6	5-7	5-8	For the Chapter
Check Skills You'll Need	•	•	•	•	•	•	•	•	
Additional Examples	•	•	•	•	•	•	•	•	
Problem of the Day	•	•	•	•	•	•	•	•	
Classroom Aid		•	•						
Student Edition Answers	•	•	•	•	•	•	•	•	•
Lesson Quiz	•	•	•	•	•	•	•	•	
Test-Taking Strategies									•

Technology	5-1	5-2	5-3	5-4	5-5	5-6	5-7	5-8	For the Chapter
TI 83/84 Plus Activities		•	•						
Interactive Textbook Online	•	•	•	•	•	•	•	•	
Student Express CD-ROM	•	•	•	•	•	•	•	•	•
TI Navigator, Instant Check System	•	•	•	•	•	•	•	•	
Success Tracker	•	•	•	•	•	•	•	•	•
ExamView CD-ROM with Quick Take	•	•	•	•	•	•	•	•	•
Teacher Express CD-ROM	•	•	•	•	•	•	•	•	•
Presentation Express CD-ROM	•	•	•	•	•	•	•	•	•
Mindpoint Quiz Show CD-ROM	•	•	•	•	•	•	•	•	•
Prentice Hall Web site: PHSchool.com	•	•	•	•	•	•	•	•	•

Also available: Prentice Hall Assessment System (Progress Monitoring Assessments, Skills and Concepts Review, Test Prep Workbook)   Solution Key   Student Workbook
Student Workbook, Adapted Version   Data Analysis and Probability Workbook   Math Notes Study Folder   Spanish Cumulative Assessment

Where You Can Use the Lesson Resources

Here is a suggestion, following the four-step teaching plan, for how you can incorporate Differentiated Instruction Resources into your teaching.

	Instructional Resources L3	**Differentiated** Instruction **Resources**
1. Plan		
Check Skills You'll Need Assign these exercises to review prerequisite skills. **New Vocabulary** Help students pre-read the lesson by pointing out the new terms introduced in the lesson.	**Math Background** **Transparencies & Presentation Express CD** Check Skills You'll Need **Resources** Vocabulary and Study Skills	**Spanish Support** **ELL** Vocabulary and Study Skills
2. Teach		
L3 Guided Instruction Teach each Example. After each Example, assign the Quick Check exercise for that Example.	**Student Edition** Activity Lab **Resources** Daily Notetaking Guide Activity Lab TI-83/84 Activities CD-ROM **Transparencies & Presentation Express CD** Additional Examples Classroom Aids **ExamView CD-ROM with QuickTake** **TI Navigator Instant Check System**	**Teacher's Edition** Every lesson includes suggestions for working with students who need special attention. **L1** Special Needs **L2** Below Level **L4** Advanced Learners **ELL** English Language Learners
3. Practice		
Assignment Guide **Homework Exercises** Assign the exercises cited in each lesson's Assignment Guide. A Practice by Example B Apply Your Skills C Challenge Test Prep Mixed Review **Homework Quick Check** Discuss in class the exercises cited in each lesson's Assignment Guide.	**Transparencies & Presentation Express CD** Student Answers **Resources** Practice Guided Problem Solving Vocabulary and Study Skills Activity Lab **ExamView CD-ROM with QuickTake**	**Spanish Support** **ELL** Practice **ELL** Vocabulary and Study Skills **Resources** **L4** Enrichment
4. Assess & Reteach		
Lesson Quiz Assign the Lesson Quiz to assess students' mastery of the lesson content. **Checkpoint Quiz** Use the Checkpoint Quiz to assess student progress over several lessons.	**Transparencies & Presentation Express CD** Lesson Quiz **Resources** Checkpoint Quiz	**Resources** **L2** Reteaching **ELL** Checkpoint Quiz Success Tracker **ExamView CD-ROM with QuickTake**

KEY **L1** Special Needs   **L2** Below Level   **L3** For All Students   **L4** Advanced, Gifted   **ELL** English Language Learners

Chapter 5

Quadratic Equations and Functions

Check Your Readiness

Answers are in the back of the textbook.

For intervention, direct students to:

Simplifying Expressions
Lesson 1-2: Example 4
Extra Skills and Word
  Problems Practice, Ch. 1

Solving Linear Equations
Lesson 1-3: Examples 1, 2
Extra Skills and Word
  Problems Practice, Ch. 1

Using and Graphing Linear Equations
Lesson 2-2: Example 1
Lesson 2-4: Example 4
Extra Skills and Word
  Problems Practice, Ch. 2

Graphing Translations
Lesson 2-6: Example 4
Extra Skills and Word
  Problems Practice, Ch. 2

What You've Learned

● In Chapter 1, you learned to write and solve linear equations.

● In Chapter 2, you learned to graph linear functions.

● In Chapter 2, you learned to use linear functions to model real-world data.

Check Your Readiness   **GO for Help** to the Lesson in green.

Simplifying Expressions (Lesson 1-2)

Simplify each expression.

1. $x^2 + 3x^2 - 5x$ $4x^2 - 5x$ **2.** $\frac{x^2}{2} - \frac{x^2}{3} + \frac{x^2}{5}$ $\frac{11x^2}{30}$ **3.** $-6x(x + 2) - x(x + 1)$ $-7x^2 - 13x$

Solving Linear Equations (Lesson 1-3)

Solve each equation. Check your answers.

4. $4 - 2x = x + 2$ $\frac{2}{3}$ **5.** $6x + 2.5 = 4x - 1.1$ -1.8 **6.** $3(x - 1) = 8(2x - 2)$ **1**

Graphing Linear Functions (Lesson 2-2)

Graph each function. **7–12. See back of book.**

7. $y = -5x - 1$ **8.** $y = 3x + 12$ **9.** $y = -6x + 6$

10. $2x - 3y = -4$ **11.** $-3x + 9y = -12$ **12.** $y - 1 = -4x$

Using Linear Models (Lesson 2-4)

Graph each set of ordered pairs. Decide whether a linear model is reasonable. If so, draw a trend line and write its equation. **13–15. See back of book.**

13. $\{(0, 12), (2, 17), (4, 25), (6, 29), (8, 36)\}$

14. $\{(5.5, 16), (6.8, 18.4), (7.5, 19.3), (8, 20), (8.5, 20.8)\}$

15. Each second, a car that begins with a speed of 40 ft/s increases its speed by 6 ft/s. Write and graph an equation to model the car's speed at s seconds.

Graphing Translations (Lesson 2-6)

16. Identify the parent function of $y = |x - 5|$. Graph $y = |x - 5|$ by translating its parent function. **See back of book.**

Quadratic Equations and Functions

◄))Key Vocabulary

- axis of symmetry (p. 239)
- completing the square (p. 282)
- complex number (p. 275)
- complex number plane (p. 275)
- difference of two squares (p. 263)
- discriminant (p. 291)
- factoring (p. 259)
- i (p. 274)
- imaginary number (p. 274)
- parabola (p. 239)
- perfect square trinomial (p. 262)
- Quadratic Formula (p. 289)
- quadratic function (p. 238)
- standard form of a quadratic function (p. 238)
- vertex form of a quadratic function (p. 252)
- zero of a function (p. 268)
- Zero Product Property (p. 267)

What You'll Learn Next

- In Chapter 5, you will learn to use quadratic functions to model real-world data.

- You will learn to graph and to solve quadratic equations.

- You will learn to graph complex numbers and to use them in solving quadratic equations.

 Real-World Connection Applying what you learn, on page 269 you will solve a problem involving art.

Chapter 5 Overview

This chapter begins by introducing the concept of modeling data with quadratic functions. Students then learn about the properties of parabolas, and how to translate parabolas. Next, students are introduced to factoring quadratic expressions, followed by a lesson on solving quadratic equations by factoring or finding square roots. The chapter continues by introducing students to complex numbers. Students complete the chapter with lessons on solving quadratic equations by completing the square and by using the Quadratic Formula.

Activating Prior Knowledge

Ask:

- *What do you think a "parabola" is?*

Accept all reasonable answers that suggest a U-shaped curve. Discuss that a ball tossed up in the air follows a parabolic path.

Ask:

- *What do you think an "imaginary" number is?'*

Acknowledge student suggestions, and inform them that that they will not only define imaginary numbers but add, subtract, and multiply them in this chapter.

237

Modeling Data With Quadratic Functions

Objectives
1 To identify quadratic functions and graphs
2 To model data with quadratic functions

Examples
1 Classifying Functions
2 Points on a Parabola
3 Fitting a Quadratic Function to 3 Points
4 Real-World Connection

Math Background

The study of quadratic equations and their graphs plays an important role in many applications. For instance, physicists can model the height of an object over time *t* with quadratic equations. Economists can model revenue and profit functions with quadratic equations.

More Math Background: p. 236C

Lesson Planning and Resources

See p. 236E for a list of the resources that support this lesson.

Bell Ringer Practice

✓ Check Skills You'll Need
For intervention, direct students to:

Algebraic Expressions
Lesson 1-2: Examples 1 and 2
Extra Skills and Word Problems Practice, Ch. 1

Linear Equations
Lesson 2-2: Example 6
Extra Skills and Word Problems Practice, Ch. 2

238

What You'll Learn
- To identify quadratic functions and graphs
- To model data with quadratic functions

. . . And Why
To model the flow of water from a container, as in Example 4

✓ Check Skills You'll Need   for Help   Lessons 1-2 and 2-2

Evaluate each function for $x = -3, -1, 0, 1,$ and 3.

1. $f(x) = x$ $-3, -1, 0, 1, 3$ **2.** $f(x) = x^2$ 9, 1, 0, 1, 9

3. $f(x) = -x$ 3, 1, 0, -1, -3   **4.** $f(x) = -x^2$ $-9, -1, 0, -1, -9$

5. $f(x) = \frac{1}{3}x^2$ $3, \frac{1}{3}, 0, \frac{1}{3}, 3$ **6.** $f(x) = -\frac{1}{3}x^2$ $-3, -\frac{1}{3}, 0, -\frac{1}{3}, -3$

Write each equation in slope-intercept form.

7. $3x + 4y = 8$ **8.** $2x - y = -7$ **9.** $\frac{1}{2}x + 3y = 9$
    $y = -\frac{3}{4}x + 2$ $y = 2x + 7$ $y = -\frac{1}{6}x + 3$

🔊 **New Vocabulary**   • quadratic function • standard form of a quadratic function • parabola • axis of symmetry • vertex of a parabola

---

1 Quadratic Functions and Their Graphs

A **quadratic function** is a function that can be written in the standard form $f(x) = ax^2 + bx + c$, where $a \neq 0$. The domain of a quadratic function is all real numbers.

 Key Concepts

Definition	Standard Form of a Quadratic Function
$f(x) = \quad ax^2 \quad + \quad bx \quad + \quad c$ quadratic term $\quad$ linear term $\quad$ constant term	

The condition $a \neq 0$ gives every quadratic function a quadratic term, but not necessarily a linear term or a constant term. If $a = 0$, then the function has no quadratic term, and it is not a quadratic function.

Vocabulary Tip

You can use the FOIL acronym to remember how to multiply.

First   Last
$y = (2x + 3)(x - 4)$
       Inner
       Outer

1 EXAMPLE   Classifying Functions

Determine whether each function is linear or quadratic. Identify the quadratic, linear, and constant terms.

a. $y = (2x + 3)(x - 4)$

$= 2x^2 - 8x + 3x - 12$ **Multiply.**

$= 2x^2 - 5x - 12$ **Write in standard form.**

This is a quadratic function.
Quadratic term: $2x^2$
Linear term: $-5x$
Constant term: -12

b. $f(x) = 3(x^2 - 2x) - 3(x^2 - 2)$

$= 3x^2 - 6x - 3x^2 + 6$

$= -6x + 6$

This is a linear function.
Quadratic term: none
Linear term: $-6x$
Constant term: 6

238   Chapter 5   Quadratic Equations and Functions

Differentiated Instruction   Solutions for All Learners

Special Needs L1
In Example 1, suggest that students put their fingers under the two terms that they are multiplying at each step. After multiplying, they should combine like terms.

learning style: tactile

Below Level L2
Discuss the domain in Example 4. This is an extension of the fact that, while quadratic equations often have two solutions, one solution may not make sense.

learning style: verbal

Real-World Connection

Objects tossed into the air follow parabolic paths.

1a. linear; none, 5x, none

b. quadratic; $3x^2$, $-16x$, 5

c. quadratic; x^2, $3x$, none

✓ Quick Check ❶ Determine whether each function is linear or quadratic. Identify the quadratic, linear, and constant terms. **See below left.**
a. $f(x) = (x^2 + 5x) - x^2$ b. $f(x) = (x - 5)(3x - 1)$ c. $f(x) = x(x + 3)$

The graph of a quadratic function is a **parabola.** The **axis of symmetry** is the line that divides a parabola into two parts that are mirror images. The **vertex of a parabola** is the point at which the parabola intersects the axis of symmetry. The y-value of the vertex of a parabola represents the maximum or minimum value of the function.

Maximum Value   Minimum Value

The axis of symmetry of the graph of a quadratic function is always a vertical line defined by the x-coordinate of the vertex. In each graph above, the axis of symmetry is the y-axis, $x = 0$.

Each point of the parabola has a corresponding point on its mirror image. Two corresponding points are the same distance from the axis of symmetry. In general the domain of a quadratic function is all real numbers.

❷ **EXAMPLE**   **Points on a Parabola**

Below is the graph of $f(x) = 2x^2 - 8x + 8$. Identify the vertex, axis of symmetry, points P' and Q' corresponding to P and Q, and the range of $f(x)$.

The vertex is $(2, 0)$.

The axis of symmetry is $x = 2$, the vertical line passing through the vertex.

$P(1, 2)$ is one unit to the left of the axis of symmetry. Corresponding point $P'(3, 2)$ is one unit to the right of the axis of symmetry.

$Q(0, 8)$ is two units to the left of the axis of symmetry. Corresponding point $Q'(4, 8)$ is two units to the right of the axis of symmetry.

● The range of this function is all nonnegative real numbers.

✓ Quick Check ❷ Identify the vertex and the axis of symmetry of each parabola. Identify points corresponding to P and Q.

a.
$(1, -1)$, $x = 1$;
$P'(3, 3)$, $Q'(0, 0)$

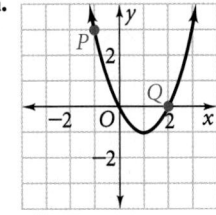

b.
$(-1, 2)$, $x = -1$;
$P'(0, 1)$,
$Q'(-3, -2)$

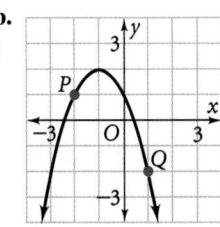

Lesson 5-1 Modeling Data with Quadratic Functions   **239**

2. Teach

Guided Instruction

❶ **EXAMPLE** **Math Tip**

The key point to remember is that $f(x) = ax^2 + bx + c$ is a quadratic function if and only if $a \neq 0$. Though the function in part b is initially defined as an expression with x^2 terms, there are no x^2 terms when the expression is simplified. The expression is thus linear.

PowerPoint

Additional Examples

❶ Determine whether each function is linear or quadratic. Identify the quadratic, linear, and constant terms.
a. $f(x) = (2x - 1)^2$
quadratic; $4x^2$, $-4x$, 1
b. $f(x) = x^2 - (x + 1)(x - 1)$
linear; none, none, 1

❷ Below is the graph of $y = x^2 - 6x + 11$. Identify the vertex and the axis of symmetry. Identify points corresponding to P and Q.

$(3, 2)$, $x = 3$; $P'(5, 6)$, $Q'(2, 3)$

Advanced Learners L4	**English Language Learners** ELL
Have students use the first three table entries in Example 4 to generate a regression model, and compare the results with the model in the example.	Have students make a poster showing a *parabola* with its *axis of symmetry* and *vertex* labeled using colors.
learning style: verbal	**learning style: visual**

Remind students that they can press the key and use ZoomStat to automatically select an appropriate window setting.

PowerPoint

Additional Examples

3 Find a quadratic function that includes the values in the table.

x	−2	1	5
y	−17	10	−10

$y = -2x^2 + 7x + 5$

4 The table shows data about the wavelength x (in meters) and the wave speed y (in meters per second) of deep water ocean waves. Model the data with a quadratic function. Graph the data and the function. Use the model to estimate the wave speed of a deep water wave that has a wavelength of 6 meters.

Wavelength x (m)	Wave speed y (m/s)
3	6
5	16
7	31
8	40

$y = 0.59x^2 + 0.34x - 0.33$

about 23 m/s

Resources
• Daily Notetaking Guide 5-1 **L3**

Closure

Have students describe the shape of the graph of a quadratic function and basic properties of the graph. **Answers may vary. Sample: The graph is a parabola with a high or low point. The vertical line through this point is the axis of symmetry.**

240

---

2 Using Quadratic Models

Given three noncollinear points, you can find a quadratic function whose graph passes through those points.

3 EXAMPLE Fitting a Quadratic Function to 3 Points

Find a quadratic function that includes the values in the table.

x	y
2	3
3	13
4	29

Substitute the values of x and y into $y = ax^2 + bx + c$. The result is a system of three linear equations.

$y = ax^2 + bx + c$

$3 = a(2)^2 + b(2) + c = 4a + 2b + c$ **Use (2, 3).**

$13 = a(3)^2 + b(3) + c = 9a + 3b + c$ **Use (3, 13).**

$29 = a(4)^2 + b(4) + c = 16a + 4b + c$ **Use (4, 29).**

Using one of the methods of Chapter 3, solve the system. $\begin{cases} 4a + 2b + c = 3 \\ 9a + 3b + c = 13 \\ 16a + 4b + c = 29 \end{cases}$

The solution is $a = 3, b = -5, c = 1$. Substitute these values into standard form.

$y = (3)x^2 + (-5)x + (1)$

● The quadratic function is $y = 3x^2 - 5x + 1$.

✓ Quick Check **3** Find a quadratic function with a graph that includes $(1, 0)$, $(2, -3)$, and $(3, -10)$.
$$y = -2x^2 + 3x - 1$$

You can use the quadratic regression feature of a graphing calculator to model data with a quadratic function.

4 EXAMPLE Real-World ● Connection

Hydraulics The table at the left shows the height of a column of water as it drains from its container. Model the data with a quadratic function. Graph the data and the function. Use the model to estimate the water level at 35 seconds.

Elapsed Time	Water Level
0 s	120 mm
10 s	100 mm
20 s	83 mm
30 s	66 mm
40 s	50 mm
50 s	37 mm
60 s	28 mm

Step 1 Enter the data. Use **QuadReg**.

Step 2 Graph the data and the function.

Step 3 Use the table feature to find $f(35)$.

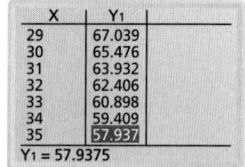

An approximate model of the quadratic function is $y = 0.009167x^2 - 2.10x + 120$.
● At 35 seconds the water level is approximately 58 mm.

4c. No; the tank is empty at 109 seconds.

✓ Quick Check **4 a.** Use the quadratic model to estimate the water level at 25 seconds. **73 mm**
b. Use the quadratic model to predict the water level at 3 minutes. **39 mm**
c. Critical Thinking Is your prediction in part (b) reasonable? Explain. **See left.**

1. linear; none, x, 4

2. quadratic; $2x^2$, $-3x$, 5

3. quadratic; $3x^2$, $-6x$, none

4. quadratic; x^2, none, -7

EXERCISES

For more exercises, see *Extra Skill and Word Problem Practice*.

Practice and Problem Solving

 Practice by Example

Example 1
(page 238)

Determine whether each function is linear or quadratic. Identify the quadratic, linear, and constant terms. 1–9. See margin pp. 240–241.

1. $y = x + 4$

2. $y = 2x^2 - (3x - 5)$

3. $y = 3x(x - 2)$

4. $f(x) = x^2 - 7$

5. $y = (x - 2)(x + 5)$

6. $g(x) = -7(x - 4)$

7. $h(x) = (3x)(2x) + 6$

8. $y = x(1 - x) - (1 - x^2)$

9. $f(x) = -x(2x + 8)$

Example 2
(page 239)

Identify the vertex and the axis of symmetry of each parabola.

10.

11.

12.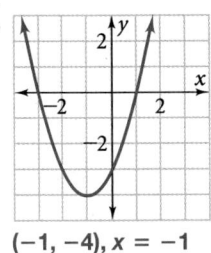

$(0, -4), x = 0$

$(-1, 0), x = -1$

$(-1, -4), x = -1$

For each parabola, identify points corresponding to P and Q.

13.

14.

15.

$P'(6, 9), Q'(2, 1)$

$P'(1, 5), Q'(-2, 8)$

$P'(-1, -1), Q'(-4, -4)$

Example 3
(page 240)

Find a quadratic function that includes each set of values. 16–18. See margin.

16. $(1, -2), (2, -2), (3, -4)$ **17.** $(1, -2), (2, -4), (3, -4)$ **18.** $(-1, 6), (1, 4), (2, 9)$

19.

x	−1	1	2
f(x)	−1	3	8

$y = x^2 + 2x$

20.

x	−1	1	2
f(x)	17	17	8

$y = -3x^2 + 20$

Example 4
(page 240)

21. Physics A man throws a ball off the top of a building. The table shows the height of the ball at different times.
a. Find a quadratic model for the data. **See margin.**
b. Use the model to estimate the height of the ball at 2.5 seconds. **28.5 ft**

Height of a Ball

Time	Height
0 s	46 ft
1 s	63 ft
2 s	48 ft
3 s	1 ft

22. Communications The table shows the percent of U.S. houses with cable TV.
a. Find a quadratic model using 1960 as year 0, 1970 as year 10, and so on.
b. Use the model to estimate the percent of households with cable TV in 1995.

Television Cable Access

Year	1960	1970	1980	1990	2000
% of Households	0	7	20	56	68

SOURCE: *Time Almanac*

22a. $y = 0.0236x^2 + 0.907x - 2.09$

b. 58.5%

Assignment Guide

1 A B 1-15, 27-29

2 A B 16-26, 30-39

C Challenge 40-43

Test Prep 44-48
Mixed Review 49-58

Homework Quick Check
To check students' understanding of key skills and concepts, go over Exercises 12, 21, 31, 34, 38.

Error Prevention!

Exercises 1–9 Tell students to simplify the expression on the right side of each equation before they attempt to classify the function.

Teaching Tip

Exercises 23–26 Help students recall that $f(x) = ax^2 + bx + c$ is a quadratic function if and only if $a \neq 0$.

Differentiated Instruction Resources

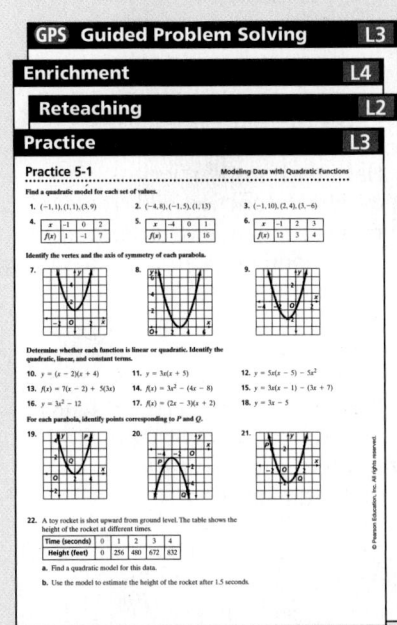

5. quadratic; x^2, 3x, −10

6. linear; none, −7x, 28

7. quadratic; $6x^2$, none, 6

8. linear; none, x, −1

9. quadratic; $-2x^2$, −8x, none

16. $y = -x^2 + 3x - 4$

17. $y = x^2 - 5x + 2$

18. $y = 2x^2 - x + 3$

21a. $y = -16x^2 + 33x + 46$, where x is the number of seconds after release and y is the height in ft.

241

1. Below is the graph of $y = x^2 + 2x - 2$. Identify the vertex and axis of symmetry. Identify points corresponding to P and Q.

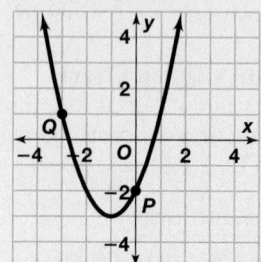

$(-1, -3), x = -1;$
$P'(-2, -2), Q'(1, 1)$

Find a quadratic function to model the values in each table.

2.

x	y
-2	-18
0	-4
2	-14

$y = -3x^2 + x - 4$

3.

x	y
-2	24
-1	13
3	9

$y = 2x^2 - 5x + 6$

Alternative Assessment

Have each student write a quadratic function and create a table listing at least three pairs of corresponding x- and y-values for the function. Instruct students to exchange tables only. Direct students to find a quadratic model for the set of values in the table. They can check their quadratic model with the student who wrote the quadratic function.

31d. Never; the quadratic model is useful over a limited number of years, but because it increases and then decreases, it

B Apply Your Skills

27. $\left(-\frac{1}{2}, -\frac{1}{2}\right), x = -\frac{1}{2}$
28. $(-1, 4), x = -1$
29. $\left(\frac{1}{2}, 0\right), x = \frac{1}{2}$

Real-World Connection

Aremy McCann won a stamp-design competition sponsored by the U.S. government.

31b. Answers may vary. Sample: domain, whole numbers from 0 to 50; range, positive whole numbers to 200.

GO Online
Homework Video Tutor
Visit: PHSchool.com
Web Code: age-0501

Determine whether a quadratic model exists for each set of values. If so, write the model.

$y = 4x^2$
23. $f(-2) = 16, f(0) = 0, f(1) = 4$
24. $f(0) = 5, f(2) = 3, f(-1) = 0$ $y = -2x^2 + 3x + 5$
25. $f(-1) = -4, f(1) = -2, f(2) = -1$ **no**
26. $f(-2) = 7, f(0) = 1, f(2) = 0$ $y = \frac{5}{8}x^2 - \frac{7}{4}x + 1$

Identify the vertex and the axis of symmetry for each function.

27.   28.   29.

30. **a. Geometry** Copy and complete the table. It shows the total number of segments that can be drawn among x points, no three of which are collinear.
    x: 4, 5; *y*: 6, 10

Number of points, x	2	3	■	■
Number of segments, y	1	3	■	■

   b. Write a quadratic model for the data. $y = \frac{1}{2}x^2 - \frac{1}{2}x$
   c. Predict the number of segments that can be drawn among ten points.
     45 segments

31. **a. Postal Rates** Find a quadratic model for the data. Use 1974 as year 0.
    GPS $y = -0.0112x^2 + 1.24x + 9.97$
Price of First-Class Stamp

Year	1974	1978	1981	1983	1988	1995	2001	2002
Price (cents)	10	15	18	20	25	32	34	37

   b. Describe a reasonable domain and range for your model. (*Hint:* This is a discrete, real situation.) **See left.**
   c. Estimation Estimate when first-class postage was 29¢. **1992**
   d. Use your model to predict when first-class postage will be 50¢. Explain why your prediction may not be valid. **See margin.**

The graph of each function contains the given point. Find the value of c.

32. $y = x^2 + c; (0, 3)$ **3**   33. $y = x^2 - c; (4, 8)$ **8**
34. $y = -5x^2 + c; (2, -14)$ **6**   35. $y = 2x^2 + c; \left(-\frac{3}{4}, -\frac{1}{4}\right)$ $-\frac{11}{8}$
36. $y = -\frac{3}{4}x^2 + c; \left(3, -\frac{1}{2}\right)$ $\frac{25}{4}$ 37. $y = (x + c)^2; (10, 0)$ -10

38. **Road Safety** The table below gives the stopping distance for an automobile under certain road conditions.

Speed (mi/h)	20	30	40	50	55
Stopping Distance (ft)	17	38	67	105	127

   a. Find a linear model for the data. $y = 3.157x - 52.34$
   b. Find a quadratic model for the data. $y = 0.04243x^2 - 0.04080x + 0.8890$
   c. Writing Compare the models. Which is better? Explain. **See margin.**

39. **Open-Ended** Write three different quadratic functions, each with a graph that includes $(0, 0)$ and $(5, -1)$. **See margin.**

does not model the data over extended periods of time.

38c. Answers may vary. Sample: Quadratic; the quadratic model comes closer to most data points than the linear model because the data follow a curve.

39. Answers may vary. Sample: $y = -\frac{1}{25}x^2$, $y = \frac{1}{25}x^2 - \frac{2}{5}x$, $y = \frac{1}{5}x^2 - \frac{6}{5}x$

C Challenge

40. Critical Thinking What is the minimum number of data points you need to find a quadratic model for a data set? Explain. **See margin.**

41. How are the graphs of $y = x^2$ and $y = |x|$ similar? How are they different? **See margin.**

42. A parabola contains the points $(0, -4)$, $(2, 4)$, and $(4, 4)$. Find the vertex. **(3, 5)**

43. A model for the height of an arrow shot into the air is $h(t) = -16t^2 + 72t + 5$, where t is time and h is height. Without graphing, consider the function's graph.
a. What can you learn by finding the graph's intercept with the h-axis?
b. What can you learn by finding the graph's intercept(s) with the t-axis?
a–b. See margin.

Test Prep
 Resources

For additional practice with a variety of test item formats:
- Standardized Test Prep, p. 303
- Test-Taking Strategies, p. 298
- Test-Taking Strategies with Transparencies

Test Prep

Multiple Choice

44. For which quadratic function is -3 the constant term? **A**
A. $y = (3x + 1)(-x - 3)$ **B.** $y = x^2 - 3x + 3$
C. $f(x) = (x - 3)(x - 3)$ **D.** $g(x) = -3x^2 + 3x + 9$

45. The vertex of a parabola is $(3, 2)$. A second point on the parabola is $(1, 7)$. Which point is also on the parabola? **H**
F. $(-1, 7)$ **G.** $(3, 7)$ **H.** $(5, 7)$ **J.** $(3, -2)$

46. The graph of a quadratic function has vertex $(-3, -2)$. What is the axis of symmetry? **A**
A. $x = -3$ **B.** $x = 3$ **C.** $y = -2$ **D.** $y = 2$

47. Which function is NOT a quadratic function? **J**
F. $y = (x - 1)(x - 2)$ **G.** $y = x^2 + 2x - 3$
H. $y = 3x - x^2$ **J.** $y = -x^2 + x(x - 3)$

Extended Response

48. What is the quadratic function with a graph that includes $(1, 6)$, $(2, 11)$, and $(3, 20)$? Find the function by writing and solving a system of equations. Write the function in standard form. Show all your work. **See margin.**

43a. You can find how high the arrow was when it was released.

b. The negative intercept tells you how much earlier you would have to shoot the arrow from height zero for its height to be described by the same function. The positive intercept tells you how many seconds after the release the arrow will take to hit the ground.

48. [4] System:
$a(1)^2 + b(1) + c = 6$,
$a(2)^2 + b(2) + c = 11$,
$a(3)^2 + b(3) + c = 20$;
$a = 2, b = -1, c = 5$;
$y = 2x^2 - x + 5$

[3] appropriate methods, but with one computational error

[2] incorrect system solved correctly OR correct system solved incorrectly

[1] correct function, without work shown

Mixed Review

 for Help

Lesson 4-8 Write the augmented matrix for each system. Then solve the system.
49–50. See margin.

49. $\begin{cases} 3x - y = 7 \\ 2x + 2y = 10 \end{cases}$

50. $\begin{cases} 3x + y - 2z = -3 \\ x - 3y - z = -2 \\ 2x + 2y + 3z = 11 \end{cases}$

Lesson 4-3 Find each product.

51. $\begin{bmatrix} 2 & -3 \end{bmatrix} \begin{bmatrix} 3 & -2 & 4 & 1 \\ 2 & 0 & -3 & 2 \end{bmatrix}$
$\begin{bmatrix} 0 & -4 & 17 & -4 \end{bmatrix}$

52. $\begin{bmatrix} 3 & 10 \\ 1 & 5 \end{bmatrix} \begin{bmatrix} -7 & 2 \\ 8 & 4 \end{bmatrix}$ $\begin{bmatrix} 59 & 46 \\ 33 & 22 \end{bmatrix}$

Lesson 3-2 Solve each system by elimination.

53. $\begin{cases} x + y = 7 \\ 5x - y = 5 \end{cases}$ **(2, 5)**   **54.** $\begin{cases} 2x - 3y = -14 \\ 3x - y = 7 \end{cases}$ **(5, 8)**   **55.** $\begin{cases} x - 3y = 2 \\ x - 2y = 1 \end{cases}$ **(−1, −1)**

Lesson 2-3 For each direct variation, find the value of y when $x = 2$.

56. $y = 2$ when $x = 5$ $\frac{4}{5}$ **57.** $y = 1$ when $x = 4$ $\frac{1}{2}$ **58.** $y = -2$ when $x = 4$ $\frac{-1}{4}$

49. $\begin{bmatrix} 3 & -1 & | & 7 \\ 2 & 2 & | & 10 \end{bmatrix}$; (3, 2)

50. $\begin{bmatrix} 3 & 1 & -2 & | & -3 \\ 1 & -3 & -1 & | & -2 \\ 2 & 2 & 3 & | & 11 \end{bmatrix}$;
(1, 0, 3)

40. Answers may vary. Sample: You need at least 3 points; you are going to substitute x- and y-values into $y = ax^2 + bx + c$ to set up and solve a linear system for finding values of a, b, and c.

41. Answers may vary. Sample: They are similar in that both are symmetric with respect to the y-axis, have only non-negative y-values, lie in Quadrants I and II, and have minimums at $(0, 0)$; they are different in that the graph of $y = x^2$ rises more steeply, while $y = |x|$ rises at a steady rate as $|x|$ increases.

243

Modeling Using Residuals

Students use a graphing calculator to compare the residuals for a linear and a quadratic model for a set of data.

Guided Instruction

Students who want to duplicate the work in the example on their calculators can have the calculator enter the linear model into Y1 by having the cursor next to Y1 in the Y = window and then pressing [VARS] 5 [▶] [▶] 1 immediately after finding the linear model. They can then find the quadratic model and follow the same procedure to enter the quadratic model for Y2.

Error Prevention!

Students should follow the procedure in the teaching note to get the best results. The values of the residuals can be affected greatly if the student rounds the coefficients in the models. Students can appreciate this fact by comparing the residuals for the quadratic model in the example to those for a model such as $y = -0.05x^2 + 9.57x - 416.96$, which uses rounded coefficients.

Resources

Students may use any graphing calculator with regression capabilities.

3. Range and explanation may vary. Samples are given. For Exercise 1: discrete; whole numbers; positive rational numbers to one decimal place up to 150; the year can be 0 or a positive integer and the money spent is rounded to the nearest tenth of a billion dollars.

Activity Lab — Modeling Using Residuals

Technology

FOR USE WITH LESSON 5-1

You can use more than one model for a set of data. You can determine which is a better model by analyzing the differences between the y-values of the data and the y-values of each model. These differences are called residuals. The better model will have residuals that are closer to zero.

ACTIVITY

The calculator screen shows the graphs of a linear model and a quadratic model for the data below. Which model better fits the data?

Participation in Backpacking or Wilderness Camp Activities

Year (1990 = 0)	1995	1997	1999	2001	2003
Millions of Participants	10.2	12.0	15.3	14.5	13.7

SOURCE: National Sporting Goods Association

Step 1 Press [STAT] [ENTER] to enter the data in L_1 and L_2. Then use the LinReg and QuadReg features to find linear and quadratic models.

Step 2 Enter the linear model as Y_1 and the quadratic model as Y_2.

Step 3 To find the residuals of the linear model and store the differences in L_3, enter L_2 − [VARS] [▶] 1 1 [(] L_1 [)] [STO▶] L_3 [ENTER].

Step 4 Find the residuals of the quadratic model. Store the differences in L_4.

Step 5 Compare the residuals in L_3 and L_4. The values in L_4 are closer to zero, so the quadratic model is the better fit.

L2	L3	L4	2
10.2	−1.04	.28857	
12	−.19	−.8543	
15.3	2.16	.83143	
14.5	.41	−.2543	
13.7	−1.34	−.0114	
------	------	------	

L2(6) =

EXERCISES

For each set of data, find a linear model and a quadratic model. Which model is the better fit? Justify your reasoning.

1. **Money Spent in the U.S. on Personal Technology**

Year (0 = 1970)	0	10	20	22	24	26
Billions of Dollars	8.8	17.6	53.8	61.2	78.5	89.7

2. **Fishing Licenses Sold**

Year (0 = 1970)	0	5	10	15	20	25	30
Millions Sold	31.1	34.7	35.2	35.7	36.9	37.9	37.6

3. For each of Exercises 1 and 2, state whether the situation is discrete and describe a reasonable domain and range. Explain your responses.

1. linear: $y = 3.090x - 0.9375$; quadratic: $y = 0.1457x^2 - 0.6930x + 9.0852$; the quadratic model is better. The residuals are closer to zero for the quadratic model.

2. linear: $y = 0.1971x + 32.63$; quadratic: $y = -0.0074x^2 + 0.4200x + 31.70$; the quadratic model seems slightly better. The residuals are closer to zero for the quadratic model.

3. See margin.

For Exercise 2: discrete; whole numbers; rational numbers to one decimal place between 30 and 40; the year can be 0 or a positive integer and the number of licenses is rounded to the nearest tenth of a million.

5-2

Properties of Parabolas

1. Plan

Objectives
1. To graph quadratic functions
2. To find maximum and minimum values of quadratic functions

What You'll Learn

- To graph quadratic functions
- To find maximum and minimum values of quadratic functions

. . . And Why

To maximize a company's revenue

✓ Check Skills You'll Need

GO for Help   Lessons 2-2 and 2-5

Find the y-intercept of the graph of each function.

1. $y = 3x + 3$ **3**
2. $y = -2x - 1$ **−1**
3. $4x - 3y = 12$ **−4**

Find the vertex of the graph of each function.

4. $y = |-2x|$ **(0, 0)**
5. $y = \left|-\frac{2}{3}x - 1\right|$ $\left(-\frac{3}{2}, 0\right)$
6. $y = |3x + 7|$ $\left(-\frac{7}{3}, 0\right)$

Graph each equation. **7–9. See back of book.**

7. $y = -4x - 3$
8. $\frac{1}{2}x + y = -2$
9. $y = |5x - 5|$

Examples
1. Graphing a Function of the Form $y = ax^2 + c$
2. Graphing a Function of the Form $y = ax^2 + bx + c$
3. Finding a Minimum Value
4. Real-World Connection

1 Graphing Parabolas

The standard form of a quadratic function is $y = ax^2 + bx + c$ with $a \neq 0$. When $b = 0$, the function simplifies to $y = ax^2 + c$.

The graph of $y = ax^2 + c$ is a parabola with an axis of symmetry $x = 0$, the y-axis. The vertex of the graph is the y-intercept $(0, c)$.

Vocabulary Tip

The word <u>symmetry</u> comes from a prefix meaning "same" and a root meaning "measure."

1 EXAMPLE   Graphing a Function of the Form $y = ax^2 + c$

Graph $y = -\frac{1}{2}x^2 + 2$.

Step 1 Graph the vertex, which is the y-intercept $(0, 2)$.

Step 2 Make a table of values to find some points on one side of the axis of symmetry $x = 0$. Graph the points.

x	1	2	3	4
y	$1\frac{1}{2}$	0	$-2\frac{1}{2}$	−6

Step 4 Graph corresponding points on the other side of the axis of symmetry.

Step 5 Sketch the curve.

✓ Quick Check

1. a. Graph $y = 2x^2 - 4$.
   b. Graph $y = -5 + 3x^2$. **a–b. See back of book.**
   c. **Reasoning** What are the coordinates of the vertex of the graph of a function in the form $y = ax^2$? **(0, 0)**

Lesson 5-2 Properties of Parabolas   **245**

Math Background

An intuitive approach to locating the vertex of a parabola can be seen by examining the graph of a function such as $f(x) = x^2 - 2x$. It is evident that the x-coordinate of the vertex is the average of the x-intercepts, assuming they are given. An alternative method, using $x = -\frac{b}{2a}$ to find the x-coordinate of the vertex, depends only on the ability to identify a and b in the standard form of a quadratic equation.

More Math Background: p. 236C

Lesson Planning and Resources

See p. 236E for a list of the resources that support this lesson.

✓ Check Skills You'll Need

For intervention, direct students to:

Linear Equations and Slope
Lesson 2-2: Examples 1 and 2
Extra Skills and Word Problems Practice, Ch. 2

Absolute Value Functions and Graphs
Lesson 2-5: Example 1
Extra Skills and Word Problems Practice, Ch. 2

Differentiated Instruction Solutions for All Learners

Special Needs **L1**
Have students draw a variety of parabolas on the board, with some opening up and some opening down. Point out how parabolas that open up form a smile ($a > 0$), while parabolas that open down frown ($a < 0$).

learning style: tactile

Below Level **L2**
Sketch parabolas illustrating why a quadratic equation might have two real roots, one real root, or no real roots, or use a graphing calculator to display graphs.

learning style: visual

Guided Instruction

Point out that the graph of $y = ax^2 + c$ is the graph of $y = ax^2$ translated up if $c > 0$ or down if $c < 0$.

Additional Examples

1 Graph $y = \frac{1}{3}x^2 + 1$.

2 Graph $y = \frac{1}{2}x^2 + x + 3$. Label the vertex and axis of symmetry.

When $b \neq 0$ in the standard form of a quadratic function, $y = ax^2 + bx + c$, the values of both a and b affect the position of the axis of symmetry.

You can use the values of a, b, and c to find characteristics of the graph of a quadratic function.

Key Concepts

Vocabulary Tip

The y-intercept is the point at which a line crosses the y-axis or the y-coordinate of that point.

Properties	Graph of a Quadratic Function in Standard Form

The graph of $f(x) = ax^2 + bx + c$ is a parabola when $a \neq 0$.

- When $a > 0$, the parabola opens up. When $a < 0$, the parabola opens down.
- The axis of symmetry is the line $x = -\frac{b}{2a}$.
- The x-coordinate of the vertex is $-\frac{b}{2a}$. The y-coordinate of the vertex is the y value of the function when $x = -\frac{b}{2a}$, or $y = f\left(-\frac{b}{2a}\right)$.
- The y-intercept is $(0, c)$.

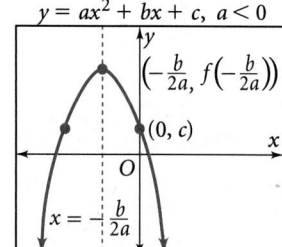

2 **EXAMPLE** Graphing a Function of the Form $y = ax^2 + bx + c$

Graph $y = x^2 - 2x - 3$. Label the vertex and the axis of symmetry.

Step 1 Find and graph the axis of symmetry.
$$x = -\frac{b}{2a} = -\frac{(-2)}{2(1)} = 1$$

Step 2 Find and graph the vertex. The x-coordinate of the vertex is $-\frac{b}{2a}$, or 1.

The y-coordinate is $y = (1)^2 - 2(1) - 3 = -4$. So the vertex is $(1, -4)$.

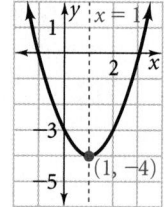

Since $a > 0$, the graph opens up.

Step 3 Find and graph the y-intercept and its reflection. Since $c = -3$, the y-intercept is $(0, -3)$ and its reflection is $(2, -3)$.

Step 4 Evaluate the function for another value of x, such as $y = (3)^2 - 2(3) - 3 = 0$. Graph $(3, 0)$ and its reflection $(-1, 0)$.

Step 5 Sketch the curve.

Quick Check 2 Graph each function. Label the vertex and the axis of symmetry.
a. $y = -x^2 + 4x + 2$ a–b. See margin page 247.
b. $y = -\frac{1}{3}x^2 - 2x - 3$

Differentiated Instruction   Solutions for All Learners

Advanced Learners   L4
Have students determine what happens to the graph of the equation $y = x^2 - 2x - 3$ when the signs of any of the coefficients are changed.

learning style: verbal

English Language Learners   ELL
Clarify that the *maximum* or *minimum* value of a quadratic function is the y-value or y-coordinate of the vertex of the parabola, and not an ordered pair that represents the vertex.

learning style: verbal

2 Finding Maximum and Minimum Values

The y-coordinate of the vertex of a parabola represents the maximum or minimum value of a quadratic function.

Online active math

For: Quadratic Activity
Use: Interactive Textbook, 5-2

3 EXAMPLE Finding a Minimum Value

Graph $y = 3x^2 + 12x + 8$. What is the minimum value of the function?

Since $a > 0$, the graph of the function opens up, and the vertex represents the minimum value. Find the coordinates of the vertex.

$x = -\frac{b}{2a} = -\frac{12}{2(3)} = -2$ **Find the x-coordinate of the vertex.**

$y = 3(-2)^2 + 12(-2) + 8 = -4$ **Find the y-coordinate of the vertex.**

Graph the vertex and the axis of symmetry $x = -2$.
Graph two points on one side of the axis of symmetry,
such as $(0, 8)$ and $(-1, -1)$. Then graph corresponding
points $(-4, 8)$ and $(-3, -1)$.

● The minimum value of the function is -4.

✓ **Quick Check** ③ **a.** Graph $y = 2x^2 + 8x - 1$. Find the minimum value of the function. **See margin.**
b. Critical Thinking What is the maximum value of the function? **none**

You can find a maximum or minimum value without graphing the function.

4 EXAMPLE Real-World Connection

Economics A company knows that $-2.5p + 500$ models the number it sells per month of a certain make of unicycle, where the price p can be set as low as \$70 or as high as \$120. Revenue from sales is the product of the price and the number sold. What price will maximize the revenue? What is the maximum revenue?

Relate   revenue equals price times number of unicycles sold

Define   Let R = revenue. Let p = price of a unicycle.

Let $-2.5p + 500$ = number of unicycles sold.

Write $R = p \ (-2.5p + 500)$

$= -2.5p^2 + 500p$ **Write in standard form.**

Find the maximum value of the function. Since $a < 0$, the graph of the function opens down, and the vertex represents a maximum value.

$p = -\frac{b}{2a} = -\frac{500}{2(-2.5)} = 100$ **Find p at the vertex.**

$R = -2.5(100)^2 + 500(100)$ **Evaluate R for $p = 100$.**

$= 25,000$ **Simplify.**

● A price of \$100 will maximize revenue. The maximum revenue is \$25,000.

Real-World Connection

It generally takes 2–6 weeks of regular practice to learn to ride a unicycle.

✓ **Quick Check** ④ The number of widgets the Woodget Company sells can be modeled by $-5p + 100$, where p is the price of a widget. What price will maximize revenue? What is the maximum revenue? **\$10; \$500**

Lesson 5-2   Properties of Parabolas   **247**

page 247   **Quick Check**

2a.

2b.

3a.

minimum: -9

---

③ EXAMPLE Alternative Method

Discuss that the y-coordinate of the vertex of a quadratic function is always the maximum or minimum, depending on which way the parabola opens. Thus, students can substitute $-\frac{b}{2a}$ for x in the equation to find the minimum or maximum without graphing.

④ EXAMPLE Visual Learners

Suggest that students graph the function on a graphing calculator and press 2nd [CALC] 4, then 90 ENTER 110 ENTER ENTER so they can see that the maximum of the graph actually lies at \$25,000.

Additional Examples

③ Graph $y = -\frac{1}{4}x^2 + 2x - 3$.
What is the maximum value of the function? **1**

④ The number of weekend get-away packages a hotel can sell can be modeled by $-0.12p + 60$, where p is the price of a get-away package. The revenue is the product of the price and the number of packages sold. What price will maximize the revenue? What is the maximum revenue? **\$250; \$7500**

Resources
• Daily Notetaking Guide 5-2 **L3**

Closure

Ask students how to determine whether a quadratic function has a maximum or minimum and how to find it. If $a > 0$, the value is a minimum. If $a < 0$, the value is a maximum. Substitute $x = -\frac{b}{2a}$ into the function to find the maximum or minimum value.

3. Practice

Assignment Guide

▼ **1** A B 1-21, 31-34, 37-40, 44-53, 57-66

▼ **2** A B 22-30, 35-36, 41-43, 54-56

C Challenge 67-73

Test Prep 74-79
Mixed Review 80-83

Homework Quick Check
To check students' understanding of key skills and concepts, go over Exercises 24, 29, 42, 44, 66.

Connection to Physics
Exercise 29 Students should note that the function given in the exercise does not describe the shape of the trajectory of the ball. The trajectory will be a straight vertical path. If the ball is not fired straight up, the trajectory will be a parabola.

Differentiated Instruction Resources

GPS Guided Problem Solving	**L3**
Enrichment	**L4**
Reteaching	**L2**
Practice	**L3**

EXERCISES

For more exercises, see *Extra Skill and Word Problem Practice*.

Practice and Problem Solving

A Practice by Example

GO for Help

Example 1
(page 245)

Graph each function. 1–9. See margin pp. 248–249.

1. $y = -x^2 + 1$ **2.** $y = -x^2 - 1$ **3.** $y = 2x^2 + 4$

4. $y = 3x^2 - 6$ **5.** $y = -\frac{1}{3}x^2 - 1$ **6.** $y = -5x^2 + 12$

7. $y = \frac{1}{2}x^2 + 3$ **8.** $y = \frac{1}{4}x^2 - 3$ **9.** $y = -2x^2 + \frac{3}{4}$

Example 2
(page 246)

Graph each function. Label the vertex and the axis of symmetry.
10–21. See back of book.

10. $y = x^2 + 2x + 1$ **11.** $y = -x^2 + 2x + 1$

12. $y = x^2 + 4x + 1$ **13.** $y = x^2 + 6x + 9$

14. $y = -x^2 - 3x + 6$ **15.** $y = 2x^2 + 4x$

16. $y = 4x^2 - 12x + 9$ **17.** $y = -6x^2 - 12x - 1$

18. $y = -\frac{3}{4}x^2 + 6x + 6$ **19.** $y = 3x^2 - 12x + 10$

20. $y = \frac{1}{2}x^2 + 2x - 8$ **21.** $y = -4x^2 - 24x - 36$

Example 3
(page 247)

Graph each function. If $a > 0$ find the minimum value. If $a < 0$ find the maximum value. 22–27. See back of book.

22. $y = -x^2 + 2x + 5$ **23.** $y = 3x^2 - 4x - 2$

24. $y = -2x^2 - 3x + 4$ **25.** $y = \frac{1}{3}x^2 + 2x + 5$

26. $y = -x^2 - x + 6$ **27.** $y = 2x^2 + 5$

Example 4
(page 247)

28. Revenue A model for a company's revenue is $R = -15p^2 + 300p + 12{,}000$, where p is the price in dollars of the company's product. What price will maximize revenue? Find the maximum revenue. **$10; $13,500**

29. Physics The equation for the motion of a projectile fired straight up at an initial velocity of 64 ft/s is $h = 64t - 16t^2$, where h is the height in feet and t is the time in seconds. Find the time the projectile needs to reach its highest point. How high it will go? **2 s; 64 ft**

30. Manufacturing The equation for the cost in dollars of producing automobile tires is $C = 0.000015x^2 - 0.03x + 35$, where x is the number of tires produced. Find the number of tires that minimizes the cost. What is the cost for that number of tires? **1000 tires; $20**

B Apply Your Skills

Sketch each parabola using the given information. 31–34. See margin p. 249.

31. vertex $(3, 6)$, y-intercept 2   **32.** vertex $(-1, -4)$, y-intercept 3

33. vertex $(0, 5)$, point $(1, -2)$ **34.** vertex $(2, 3)$, point $(6, 9)$

35. Find a pair of numbers with a sum of 26 and a product that is a maximum. Find the maximum product. **13, 13; 169**

36. Find two numbers with a difference of 10 and a product that is a minimum. Find the minimum product. **−5, 5; −25**

1.

2.

3.

4.

5.

Match each function with its graph.

37. $y = x^2 + 4x + 1$ **B**   **38.** $y = -x^2 - 4x + 1$ **C**   **39.** $y = -\frac{1}{2}x^2 - 2x + 1$ **A**

A.   **B.**   **C.**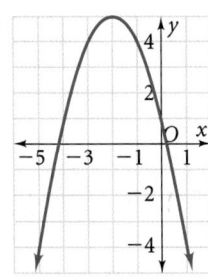

**40. Answers may vary.
Sample:**
$y = x^2 + 20x + 96$

Real-World Connection

Careers Picture framers choose the dimensions of frames that best suit works of art.

40. Open-Ended Write the equation of a parabola symmetric about $x = -10$.

41. Woodworking Suppose you want to frame a collage of pictures. You have a 9-ft strip of wood for the frame. What dimensions of the frame give you the maximum area for the collage? What is the maximum area?
2.25 ft by 2.25 ft; 5.0625 ft²

42. Physics Suppose you throw a ball over a 10-ft fence. Barely clearing the fence, the ball reaches its highest point directly above the fence and lands 10 ft from the fence. Using the fence as the axis of symmetry, write a quadratic function that models the ball's height. $y = -\frac{1}{10}x^2 + 10$

43. Packaging The bottom of a box is to be a rectangle with a perimeter of 36 cm. The box must be 4 cm high. What dimensions give the maximum volume?
length = 9 cm, width = 9 cm

For each function, the vertex of the function's graph is given. Find c.

44. $y = x^2 - 6x + c; (3, -4)$ **5**   **45.** $y = -3x^2 + 6x + c; (1, 0)$ **−3**

46. $y = x^2 + 10x + c; (-5, -27)$ **−2**   **47.** $y = c - x^2 - 2x; (-1, 3)$ **2**

Find the quadratic function $y = ax^2 + c$ with a graph that has the given points.
48–53. See margin.

48. $(0, 2), (3, 5)$ **49.** $(0, -3), (1, -7)$ **50.** $\left(2, \frac{5}{2}\right), \left(0, -\frac{1}{2}\right)$

51. $(-3, 89), (2, 39)$ **52.** $(-2, -10), (4, -40)$ **53.** $(-1, 14), (4, 104)$

**54. a. $20
   b. $6050**

54. A rock club's profit from booking local bands depends on the ticket price. Using past receipts, the owners find that the profit p can be modeled by the function $p = -15t^2 + 600t + 50$, where t represents the ticket price in dollars.
   a. What price yields the maximum profit?
   b. What is the maximum profit?
   c. Open-Ended What price would you pay to see your favorite local band? How much profit would the club owner make using that ticket price?
   Check students' work.

Homework Video Tutor
Visit: PHSchool.com
Web Code: age-0502

55. Multiple Choice A town is planning a playground. It wants to fence in a rectangular space using an existing wall. What is the greatest area it can fence in using 100 ft of donated fencing? **B**

Ⓐ 1000 ft².   Ⓑ 1250 ft²
Ⓒ 2500 ft²   Ⓓ 10,000 ft²

6.   **7.**   **8.**   **9.**

Teaching Tip
Exercise 42 Students can assume that the fence is straight and that the plane of the fence is perpendicular to the plane of the parabola.

Error Prevention!

Exercises 48–53 Be sure students understand that each function is to have the form $y = ax^2 + c$.

Error Prevention!

Exercise 55 Be sure students do not think that all four sides of the playground are bounded by fencing. Stress the importance of reading the problem carefully.

31.

32.

33.

34.

48. $y = \frac{1}{3}x^2 + 2$

49. $y = -4x^2 - 3$

50. $y = \frac{3}{4}x^2 - \frac{1}{2}$

51. $y = 10x^2 - 1$

52. $y = -\frac{5}{2}x^2$

53. $y = 6x^2 + 8$

1. Graph $y = -2x^2 - 4x + 2$. Label the vertex and axis of symmetry.

2. What is the minimum value of the function $y = 3x^2 + 2x - 8$? $-\frac{25}{3}$

3. The equation $h = 40t - 16t^2$ describes the height h, in feet, of a ball that is thrown straight up as a function of the time t, in seconds, that the ball has been in the air. At what time does the ball reach its maximum height? What is the maximum height? **1.25 s; 25 ft**

Alternative Assessment

Let a volunteer write a quadratic function on the board or overhead transparency. Call on students one at a time to name the axis of symmetry, the vertex, and the maximum or minimum. Repeat until all students have answered the same number of times.

57. $y = x^2 + 1$; up

58. $y = 5x^2 + 1$; up

59. $y = -\frac{1}{2}x^2 + 1$; down

60. $y = -\frac{1}{2}x^2 + 1$; down

61. $y = \frac{1}{3}x^2 + 1$; up

250

 Real-World **Connection**

The archaeological remains of the Harappan city Mohenjo Daro show the thick walls that were built to keep out the hot sun.

56. **History** Around 2500 B.C. in the Indus Valley of South Asia, the Harappan people built one of the first cities. The Harappans built rectangular houses that had open central courtyards surrounded by solid brick walls.
   a. Suppose you build a model of a Harappan house. For the outer walls you plan to use 2400 bricks. The walls of the model are 10 bricks high and 1 brick thick. Draw several possible floor plans. **Check students' work.**
   b. Find the dimensions of the floor plan that give the model of maximum area. **60 bricks by 60 bricks**

Each point lies on a parabola that has its vertex at (0, 1). Write the equation of the parabola. Indicate whether the graph opens up or down. 57–64. See margin.

57. $(-3, 10)$ 58. $(-1, 6)$ 59. $(2, -1)$ 60. $(4, -7)$

61. $(3, 4)$ 62. $(5, -4)$ 63. $(8, -15)$ 64. $(-6, -2)$

65. **Construction** A construction worker places his toolbox on a board that rests on two cement posts 10 ft apart. The toolbox is halfway between the posts. Under the weight of the toolbox, the board sags by one quarter inch. Model the shape of the board in three different ways by writing a function whose graph satisfies each condition below. **a–c. See margin.**

|← 10 ft →|

   a. The origin of the graph corresponds to the position of the toolbox.
   b. The origin of the graph corresponds to the position of the post on the left.
   c. The origin of the graph corresponds to the position of the post on the right.

66. A student says that the graph of $y = ax^2 + bx + c$ gets wider as a increases.
   a. **Error Analysis** Use examples to show that the student is wrong.
   b. **Writing** Summarize the relationship between $|a|$ and the width of the graph of $y = ax^2 + bx + c$. **a–b. See margin.**

C **Challenge**

For each function, the vertex of the function's graph is given. Find a and b.

67. $y = ax^2 + bx - 27$; $(2, -3)$ **−6, 24**   68. $y = ax^2 + bx + 5$; $(-1, 4)$ **1, 2**

69. $y = ax^2 + bx + 8$; $(2, -4)$ **3, −12**   70. $y = ax^2 + bx$; $(-3, 2)$ **$-\frac{2}{9}$, $-\frac{4}{3}$**

The formula for the area enclosed by a parabola and the x-axis from x-intercepts x_1 to x_2 is $A = \frac{2}{3}h(x_2 - x_1)$, where h is the height. Find the enclosed area for each parabola.

71.

$10\frac{2}{3}$ square units

72.

$10\frac{2}{3}$ square units

73.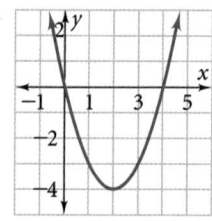

$10\frac{2}{3}$ square units

62. $y = -\frac{1}{5}x^2 + 1$; down

63. $y = -\frac{1}{4}x^2 + 1$; down

64. $y = -\frac{1}{12}x^2 + 1$; down

65a. $y = \frac{1}{14,400}x^2$

b. $y = \frac{1}{14,400}x^2 - \frac{1}{120}x$

c. $y = \frac{1}{14,400}x^2 + \frac{1}{120}x$

66a. Check students' work.

b. Answers may vary. Sample: The widths of

$y = ax^2 + bx + c$ and $y = -ax^2 + bx + c$ are the same. As $|a|$ increases, the widths of $y = ax^2 + bx + c$ and $y = -ax^2 + bx + c$ decrease.

Multiple Choice

74. What is the vertex of $y = -2x^2 - 4x - 5$? **D**
  A. $(-2, -3)$ **B.** $(1, -3)$ **C.** $(1, -11)$ **D.** $(-1, -3)$

75. What is the y-intercept of $y = (x + 1)^2 - 2$? **F**
  F. $(0, -1)$ **G.** $(0, -3)$ **H.** $(0, 1)$ **J.** $(0, -2)$

76. What is the maximum area in square units of a rectangle with a perimeter of 128 units? **B**
  A. 4096   **B.** 1024   **C.** 256   **D.** 32

77. The vertex of the graph of $y = -x^2 - 16x - 62$ lies in which quadrant? **H**
  F. IV   **G.** III   **H.** II   **J.** I

78. What percent of nonzero integers have squares that are odd numbers? **B**
  A. 25   **B.** 50   **C.** 75   **D.** 100

Short Response

79. Sketch the graph of $y = x^2 - 6x + 2$. Explain how to identify the vertex and two other points on the parabola. **See margin.**

Mixed Review

Lesson 5-1

Answers may vary. Sample: $y = -0.14857x^2 + 5.1714x + 16.9714$
80. Find a quadratic model for the values in the table.

x	0	5	10	15	20
y	17	39	54	61	61

Lesson 4-2

Solve each matrix equation.

81. $X + \begin{bmatrix} 0 & 4 \\ -2 & 1 \end{bmatrix} = \begin{bmatrix} 3 & 0 \\ 1 & 1 \end{bmatrix} \begin{bmatrix} 3 & -4 \\ 3 & 0 \end{bmatrix}$ **82.** $X - \begin{bmatrix} 3 & 3 \\ -2 & -1 \end{bmatrix} = \begin{bmatrix} 1 & 0 \\ 0 & 1 \end{bmatrix} \begin{bmatrix} 4 & 3 \\ -2 & 0 \end{bmatrix}$

Lesson 3-3 **83.** **Manufacturing** A new factory will require at least 40,000 ft² of storage space. No more than 25,000 ft² of the space will be covered with a roof. Write a system of inequalities to represent the constraints. Solve the system by graphing.
  See margin.

Algebra at Work

·······················Landscape Architect

Landscape architects create outdoor environments for parks, office buildings, and homes. They plan walls, staircases, pools, walkways, and plantings. Landscape architects blend ideas from art, science, nature, and math in their work. They need training in all three areas before they begin their careers. For example, when planning a decorative fountain, an architect needs to predict the parabolic path of the spray. The height and distance of the spray depend on the speed of the water and the angle at which it exits a pipe. Basic principles of physics often help architects. By making adjustments to a model, they can plan the effect they want.

 For: Information about landscape architecture
PHSchool.com **Web Code:** agb-2031

Lesson 5-2 Properties of Parabolas **251**

Resources
For additional practice with a variety of test item formats:
• Standardized Test Prep, p. 303
• Test-Taking Strategies, p. 298
• Test-Taking Strategies with Transparencies

79. [2]

The axis of symmetry is $x = -\frac{b}{2a}$ or $x = 3$. The y-coordinate of the vertex is $3^2 - 6 \cdot 3 + 2 = -7$. So the vertex is $(3, -7)$. The y-intercept is where $x = 0$ or $0^2 - 6 \cdot 0 + 2 = 2$. So $(0, 2)$ is on the parabola. The point corresponding to $(0, 2)$ with respect to $x = 3$ is $(6, 2)$ so $(6, 2)$ is also on the parabola.

[1] incorrect graph OR no explanation

83. Let x = amount of storage space and y = amount of space to be covered by the roof.
$x \geq 40{,}000$
$y \leq 25{,}000$

1. Plan

Objective

1 To use the vertex form of a quadratic function

Examples

1 Using the Vertex Form to Graph a Parabola
2 Writing the Equation of a Parabola
3 Real-World Connection
4 Converting to Vertex Form

Math Background

The vertex form of a quadratic equation can be used when analyzing data that form a quadratic pattern. That is, given a set of points in the plane that form an approximately parabolic pattern, a quadratic function that approximately models the data can be found if the vertex of the model is known and one other point on the graph. This is an alternative to having to solve a system of three equations in three unknowns.

More Math Background: p. 236C

Lesson Planning and Resources

See p. 236E for a list of the resources that support this lesson.

PowerPoint

Bell Ringer Practice

✓ **Check Skills You'll Need**
For intervention, direct students to:

Vertical and Horizontal Translations
Lesson 2-6: Examples 2, 4, 7
Extra Skills and Word Problems Practice, Ch. 2

5-3

Transforming Parabolas

What You'll Learn

• To use the vertex form of a quadratic function

. . . And Why

To model a suspension bridge, as in Example 3

🔊 **New Vocabulary** • vertex form of a quadratic function

✓ **Check Skills You'll Need**

for Help Lesson 2-6

Identify the parent function of each function. Then graph the function by transforming the graph of the parent function. 1–3. See back of book.

1. $y = x + 2$ 2. $y = 3|x| + 2$ 3. $y = -|x + 1| - 1$

Write an equation for each translation.

4. $y = x$, 2 units down $y = x - 2$ 5. $y = |x|$, 4 units up, 1 unit right $y = |x - 1| + 4$

---

1 **Using Vertex Form**

Activity: Vertex Form

1. Each function in the first column is written in standard form. In the second column, each function has been rewritten in vertex form. Use multiplication to verify that the functions in each row are equivalent. 1–2. See back of book.

Standard Form $y = ax^2 + bx + c$	$-\dfrac{b}{2a}$	Vertex Form $y = a(x - h)^2 + k$	h
$y = x^2 - 4x + 4$	▨	$y = (x - 2)^2$	▨
$y = x^2 + 6x + 8$	▨	$y = (x + 3)^2 - 1$	▨
$y = -3x^2 - 12x - 8$	▨	$y = -3(x + 2)^2 + 4$	▨
$y = 2x^2 + 12x + 19$	▨	$y = 2(x + 3)^2 + 1$	▨

2. a. **Patterns** Copy and complete the table.
   b. Compare the values of $-\frac{b}{2a}$ and h in each row. Write a formula to show the relationship between $-\frac{b}{2a}$ and h.

In Chapter 2, you learned to graph absolute value functions as transformations of their parent function $y = |x|$. Similarly, you can graph a quadratic function as a transformation of the parent function $y = x^2$.

To transform the graph of a quadratic function, you can use the **vertex form of a quadratic function,** $y = a(x - h)^2 + k$.

252   Chapter 5   Quadratic Equations and Functions

Differentiated Instruction **Solutions for All Learners**

Special Needs L1
Write a quadratic function on the board of the form $y = a(x - h)^2 + k$. Have students stand up and move left, right, forward, and backward to demonstrate the translation left, right, up, and down, respectively.

learning style: tactile

Below Level L2
On a coordinate grid on the overhead projector place the graph of a parabola. Have students identify the vertex and axis of symmetry for different positions of the parabola.

learning style: visual

Key Concepts

| Summary | The Family of Quadratic Functions |

Vertical Stretch or Shrink, and/or Reflection in x-axis

Parent function:	$y = x^2$
Reflection in x-axis:	$y = -x^2$
Stretch ($a > 1$) or shrink ($0 < a < 1$) by factor a:	$y = ax^2$
Reflection in x-axis:	$y = -ax^2$

Vertex Form $y = a(x - h)^2 + k$

The graph (and vertex) of $y = ax^2$ shifts
h units horizontally and k units vertically.

For $h > 0$, the graph shifts right.
For $h < 0$, the graph shifts left.
For $k > 0$, the graph shifts up.
For $k < 0$, the graph shifts down.

The vertex is (h, k), and the axis of symmetry is the line $x = h$.

Vocabulary Tip

Vertex means "turning point."

---

2. Teach

Guided Instruction

Activity
Ask students if they can make a conjecture to explain why $y = a(x - h)^2 + k$ is called *vertex form*. The coordinates of the vertex are shown.

1 EXAMPLE Alternative Method

You can also graph the function by translating $y = -\frac{1}{2}x^2$ right 2 units and up 3 units. The vertex of the parent function is at (0, 0), and two other points on its graph are $(-2, -2)$ and $(2, -2)$. If you translate these three points 2 units right and 3 units up, you get the points (2, 3), (0, 1), and (4, 1). Plot the points and sketch the curve.

PowerPoint

Additional Examples

1 Graph $y = \frac{2}{3}(x + 1)^2 - 2$.

2 Write the equation of the parabola shown below.

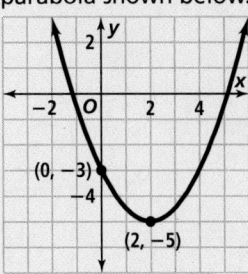

$y = \frac{1}{2}(x - 2)^2 - 5$

---

1 EXAMPLE Using Vertex Form to Graph a Parabola

Graph $y = -\frac{1}{2}(x - 2)^2 + 3$.

The vertex of $y = -\frac{1}{2}(x - 2)^2 + 3$ is 2 units right and 3 units up from the origin. The axis of symmetry is $x = 2$.

1a.

Step 1 Graph the vertex (2, 3). Draw the axis of symmetry $x = 2$.

Step 2 Find another point. When $x = 0$, $y = -\frac{1}{2}(0 - 2)^2 + 3 = 1$. Graph (0, 1).

Step 3 Graph the point (4, 1). It is 2 units to the right of the axis of symmetry at (4, 1).

Step 4 Sketch the curve.

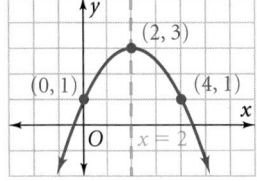

✓ Quick Check **1** **a.** Graph $y = 2(x + 1)^2 - 4$. **See left.**
  b. In graphing the function in part (a), which method did you choose—stretching the parent function to graph $y = 2x^2$ and then translating the graph of $y = 2x^2$, or graphing the vertex and axis of symmetry? Explain your choice. **Check Students' work.**

You can use the vertex form to write the equation of a parabola.

2 EXAMPLE Writing the Equation of a Parabola

Write the equation of the parabola at the right.

$y = a(x - h)^2 + k$	**Use the vertex form.**
$y = a(x - 3)^2 + 4$	**Substitute $h = 3$ and $k = 4$.**
$-4 = a(5 - 3)^2 + 4$	**Substitute $(5, -4)$.**
$-8 = 4a$	**Simplify.**
$-2 = a$	**Solve for a.**

The equation of the parabola is $y = -2(x - 3)^2 + 4$.

Online
active math

For: Vertex Form Activity
Use: Interactive Textbook, 5-3

Advanced Learners **L4**
After Example 3, have students research other suspension bridges, and attempt to model the suspension cables with quadratic functions.

learning style: verbal

English Language Learners **ELL**
Make sure students understand the terms *stretch*, *shrink, reflection,* and *shift* as they apply to graphs of quadratic functions. Have students draw examples on the board for each transformation along with its corresponding function rule in vertex form.

learning style: visual

254

EXAMPLE Math Tip

Students should note that the value of *a* is always the same whether the equation is in vertex form or in standard form.

PowerPoint

Additional Examples

3 A long strip of colored paper is attached as a party decoration at the top corners of a wall of a rectangular room. The strip approximates a parabola with equation $y = 0.008(x - 25)^2 + 10$. The bottom left corner of the wall is the origin, and *x* and *y* are measured in feet. How far apart are the corners? How high are they? **50 ft; 15 ft**

4 Write $y = -7x^2 - 70x - 169$ in vertex form. $y = -7(x + 5)^2 + 6$

Resources
• Daily Notetaking Guide 5-3 **L3**

Closure

Ask: *How can you use the values of a, b, and c to write a quadratic function in vertex form?* Find *h* by evaluating $-\frac{b}{2a}$. Substitute this for *x* in the standard form equation and use the result as the value of *k*. Substitute the values of *a*, *h*, and *k* into the vertex form $y = a(x - h)^2 + k$.

✓ Quick Check **2** Use vertex form to write the equation of the parabola below. $y = 2(x + 1)^2$

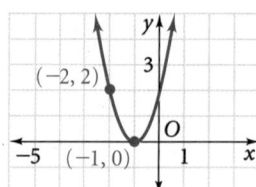

You can use vertex form to model real-world problems.

3 EXAMPLE Real-World Connection

Civil Engineering The photo shows the Verrazano–Narrows Bridge in New York, which has the longest span of any suspension bridge in the United States. A suspension cable of the bridge forms a curve that resembles a parabola. The curve can be modeled with the function $y = 0.0001432(x - 2130)^2$, where *x* and *y* are measured in feet. The origin of the function's graph is at the base of one of the two towers that support the cable. How far apart are the towers? How high are they?

Start by drawing a diagram.

The function is in vertex form. Since $h = 2130$ and $k = 0$, the vertex is at $(2130, 0)$. The vertex is halfway between the towers, so the distance between the towers is $2(2130 \text{ ft}) = 4260 \text{ ft}$.

To find the tower's height, find *y* for $x = 0$.

$$y = 0.0001432(0 - 2130)^2$$
$$y = 0.0001432(-2130)^2$$
$$\approx 650$$

• The towers are 4260 ft apart and about 650 ft high.

✓ Quick Check **3** Suppose the towers in Example 3 are 4000 ft apart and 600 ft high. Write a function that could model the curve of the suspension cable. $y = 0.00015(x - 2000)^2$

Both the vertex form and the standard form give useful information about a parabola. The standard form makes it easy to identify the *y*-intercept. The vertex form makes it easy to identify the vertex and the axis of symmetry, and to graph the parabola as a transformation of the parent function. The graph shows the relationship between the two forms.

1.

$x = 1$

2.

$x = -3$

3.

$x = 2$

4.

$x = -1$

5.

$x = -7$

6.
$x = 2$

You can convert a function from standard form to vertex form.

4 EXAMPLE Converting to Vertex Form

Write $y = 2x^2 + 10x + 7$ in vertex form.

$x = -\dfrac{b}{2a}$ Find the *x*-coordinate of the vertex.

$= -\dfrac{10}{2(2)}$ Substitute for *a* and *b*.

$= -2.5$

$y = 2(-2.5)^2 + 10(-2.5) + 7$ Find the *y*-coordinate of the vertex.

$= -5.5$

The vertex is at $(-2.5, -5.5)$.

$y = a(x - h)^2 + k$ Write the vertex form.

$= 2(x - (-2.5))^2 - 5.5$ Substitute for *a*, *h*, and *k*.

$= 2(x + 2.5)^2 - 5.5$ Simplify.

The vertex form of the function is $y = 2(x + 2.5)^2 - 5.5$.

✓ **Quick Check** ④ Write $y = -3x^2 + 12x + 5$ in vertex form. $y = -3(x - 2)^2 + 17$

3. Practice

Assignment Guide

▼ A B 1-77
C Challenge   78-84

Test Prep   85-90
Mixed Review   91-96

Homework Quick Check
To check students' understanding of key skills and concepts, go over Exercises 15, 39, 42, 48, 57, 58.

Error Prevention!

Exercises 1–12 Remind students that the sign of *h* is the opposite of the sign in the parentheses, while the sign of *k* is the same as the sign before it.

EXERCISES

For more exercises, see *Extra Skill and Word Problem Practice*.

Practice and Problem Solving

 A Practice by Example

Example 1
(page 253)

 GO for Help

Graph each function. Identify the axis of symmetry. 1–12. See margin pp. 254–255.

1. $y = (x - 1)^2 + 2$ **2.** $y = (x + 3)^2 - 4$

3. $y = 2(x - 2)^2 + 5$ **4.** $y = 2(x + 1)^2$

5. $y = -3(x + 7)^2 - 8$ **6.** $y = -\frac{1}{2}(x - 2)^2 + 1$

7. $y = (x - 5)^2 - 3$ **8.** $y = (x + 2)^2 - 3$

9. $y = -(x - 1)^2 + 4$ **10.** $y = 3(x + 5)^2 - 8$

11. $y = -(x - 7)^2 + 10$ **12.** $y = -4(x + 8)^2 - 6$

Example 2
(page 253)

Write the equation of each parabola in vertex form.

13.

$y = \frac{1}{4}x^2$

14.

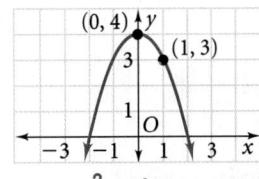

$y = -x^2 + 4$

15.

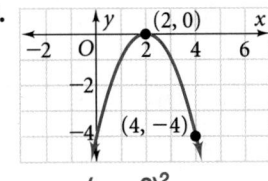

$y = -(x - 2)^2$

16.

$y = -(x + 2)^2$

Lesson 5-3   Transforming Parabolas   **255**

Differentiated Instruction Resources

GPS Guided Problem Solving	L3
Enrichment	L4
Reteaching	L2
Practice	L3

11.

    $x = 7$

7.

$x = 5$

8.

$x = -2$

9.

$x = 1$

10.

$x = -5$

12.

    $x = -8$

255

Visual Learners

Exercise 57 It may help students to sketch graphs if they do not immediately see how to use the spreadsheets alone to find the axes of symmetry.

27. $y = (x - 2)^2 + 2$

28. $y = (x + 1)^2 + 4$

29. $y = 6x^2 - 10$

30. $y = -5x^2 + 12$

31. $y = 4\left(x + \frac{7}{8}\right)^2 - \frac{49}{16}$

32. $y = 2\left(x + \frac{1}{4}\right)^2 - \frac{1}{8}$

33. $y = 2\left(x - \frac{5}{4}\right)^2 + \frac{71}{8}$

34. $y = -2(x - 2)^2 + 11$

35. $y = \frac{9}{4}\left(x + \frac{2}{3}\right)^2 - 2$

42a. **All nonnegative numbers; a price cannot be negative; it would imply that the bakery pays people to take bread.**

43. $y = -7(x - 1)^2 + 2$

44. $y = -\frac{4}{9}(x - 3)^2 + 6$

45. $y = -\frac{1}{2}(x + 3)^2 + 6$

46. $y = \frac{3}{2}(x + 2)^2 + 6$

47. $y = 7(x + 1)^2 - 4$

48. $y = -7x^2 + 5$

49. $y = -10\left(x - \frac{1}{10}\right)^2 - \frac{9}{10}$

50. $y = 8\left(x - \frac{1}{4}\right)^2 - \frac{3}{2}$

57a. **first: $x = 4$, second: $x = 2.5$**

b. **For the first spreadsheet the x_1-values 3 and 5 are equidistant from 4 and their y_1-values are both -3. In the second spreadsheet, the x_2-values 2 and 3 are equidistant from 2.5 and their y_2-values are both 2.**

c. $y = -4(x - 4)^2 + 1$;
$y = 4\left(x - \frac{5}{2}\right)^2 + 1$

256

Write the equation of each parabola in vertex form.

17.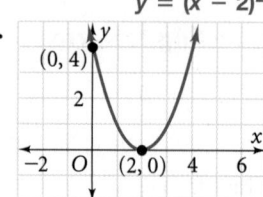
$y = (x - 2)^2$

18.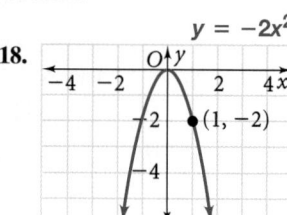
$y = -2x^2$

19.

20.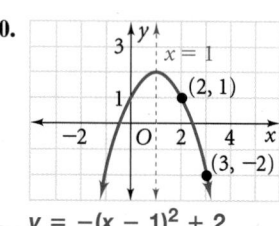

$y = 6(x + 3)^2 - 2$ $y = -(x - 1)^2 + 2$

Example 3
(page 254)

Identify the vertex and the y-intercept of the graph of each function.

21. $y = -1.5(x + 20)^2$ $(-20, 0)$, -600

22. $y = 0.1(x - 3.2)^2$ $(3.2, 0)$, 1.024

23. $y = 24(x + 5.5)^2$ $(-5.5, 0)$, 726

24. $y = 0.0035(x + 1)^2 - 1$
$(-1, -1)$, -0.9965

25. $y = -(x - 4)^2 - 25$ $(4, -25)$, -41

26. $y = (x - 125)^2 + 125$
$(125, 125)$, $15,750$

Example 4
(page 255)

Write each function in vertex form. 27–35. See margin.

27. $y = x^2 - 4x + 6$

28. $y = x^2 + 2x + 5$

29. $y = 6x^2 - 10$

30. $y = -5x^2 + 12$

31. $y = 4x^2 + 7x$

32. $y = 2x^2 + x$

33. $y = 2x^2 - 5x + 12$

34. $y = -2x^2 + 8x + 3$

35. $y = \frac{9}{4}x^2 + 3x - 1$

B **Apply Your Skills**

Sketch each parabola. Identify the axis of symmetry. 36–41. See back of book.

36. $y = 2(x + 2)^2 - 3$

37. $y = -3(x - 2)^2$

38. $y = 5(x + 0.3)^2 - 10$

39. $y = -0.5(x - 2)^2 - 5$

Begin with the parent $y = x^2$ graph. Show how to transform it to graph each function below. Draw the final graph in a different color.

40. $y = -2(x + 1)^2 + 1$

41. $y = 0.2(x - 12)^2 - 3$

42. **Business** The Big Brick Bakery sells more bagels when it reduces its prices, but then its profit changes. The function $y = -1000(x - 0.55)^2 + 300$ models the bakery's daily profit in dollars, from selling bagels, where x is the price of a bagel in dollars. The bakery wants to maximize the profit. **See margin.**
   a. What is the domain of the function? Can x be negative? Explain. **$277.50;**
   b. Find the daily profit for selling bagels for \$.40 each; for \$.85 each. **\$210.00**
   c. What price should the bakery charge to maximize its profit from bagels?
   d. What is the maximum profit? **\$300.00**   **\$0.55**

Real-World 🌐 **Connection**

Bagel sales in the United States total nearly \$3 billion each year.

Write the equation of each parabola in vertex form. 43–50. See margin.

43. vertex $(1, 2)$, point $(2, -5)$

44. vertex $(3, 6)$, y-intercept 2

45. vertex $(-3, 6)$, point $(1, -2)$

46. vertex $(-2, 6)$, y-intercept 12

47. vertex $(-1, -4)$, y-intercept 3

48. vertex $(0, 5)$, point $(1, -2)$

49. vertex $\left(\frac{1}{10}, -\frac{9}{10}\right)$, y-intercept -1

50. vertex $\left(\frac{1}{4}, -\frac{3}{2}\right)$, point $(1, 3)$

Write each function in standard form.

51. $y = 25x^2 + 60x + 27$

52. $y = -9x^2 + 24x - 10$

53. $y = 2x^2 + 22x$

54. $y = \frac{1}{2}x^2 - 5x + \frac{35}{2}$

55. $y = -10x^2 - 40x - 40$

56. $y = 16x^2 - 8x + 2$

51. $y = (5x + 6)^2 - 9$ 52. $y = -(3x - 4)^2 + 6$ 53. $y = 2x(x + 7) + 8x$

54. $y = \frac{1}{2}(x - 5)^2 + 5$ 55. $y = -0.1(10x + 20)^2$ 56. $y = (1 - 4x)^2 + 1$

 57. **a. Technology** Determine the axis of symmetry for each parabola defined by the spreadsheet values at the right.

   b. How could you use the spreadsheet columns to verify that the axes of symmetry are correct?

   c. Write functions in vertex form that model the data. Check that the axes of symmetry are correct.
   a–c. See margin p. 256.

	A	B			A	B
1	X1	Y1		1	X2	Y2
2	1	−35		2	1	10
3	2	−15		3	2	2
4	3	−3		4	3	2
5	4	1		5	4	10
6	5	−3		6	5	26

58. **Writing** Describe the family of quadratic functions whose members each have $(3, 4)$ as its vertex. **See margin.**

Determine whether each function is written in vertex form. If a function is not in vertex form, rewrite the function.

61. no; $y = -3\left(x + \frac{1}{3}\right)^2 + \frac{4}{3}$

63. no; $y = (x + 1)^2 + 7$

67. no; $y = 100\left(x - \frac{1}{5}\right)^2 + 6$

59. $y = -2x^2 + 35$ **yes**   60. $y = -8x^2$ **yes**   61. $y = -3x^2 - 2x + 1$

62. $y = -2(x + 1)^2 - 1$ **yes**   63. $y = x^2 + 2x + 8$ 64. $y = \frac{3}{10}x^2 - 1$ **yes**

65. $y = -4x^2 + 6x + 3$ no; $y = -4\left(x - \frac{3}{4}\right)^2 + \frac{21}{4}$ 66. $y = 0.5x^2 + 10$ **yes**   67. $y = 100x^2 - 40x + 10$

Determine a and k so both points are on the graph of the function.
68–73. See margin.

68. $(0, 1), (2, 1); y = a(x - 1)^2 + k$ 69. $(-3, 2), (0, 11); y = a(x + 2)^2 + k$

70. $(1, 11), (2, -19); y = a(x + 1)^2 + k$ 71. $(-2, 6), (3, 1); y = a(x - 3)^2 + k$

72. $(-2, 10), (1, -34); y = 2a(x + 1)^2 + k$ 73. $(4, 26), (5, -25); y = a(x - 30)^2 + k$

Homework Video Tutor
Visit: PHSchool.com
Web Code: age-0503

74. **Multiple Choice** One parabola shown has equation **A** $y = (x - 4)^2 + 2$. What is an equation for the other?
   Ⓐ $y = -(x - 4)^2 + 2$ Ⓑ $y = (x + 4)^2 - 2$
   Ⓒ $y = (-x - 4)^2 + 2$ Ⓓ $y = -(x + 4)^2 - 2$

75. **Open-Ended** Write a quadratic function in vertex form for which the graph has a vertex at $(-2, 5)$. Rewrite the function in standard form.
   Check students' work.

76. Determine whether the function $f(x) = 0.25(2x - 15)^2 + 150$ has a maximum or a minimum value. Then find the value.
   minimum; 150

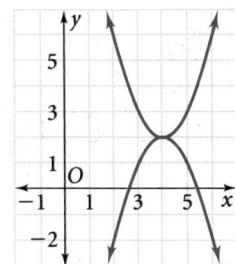

77. **Critical Thinking** Describe the differences between the graphs of $y = (x + 6)^2$ and $y = (x - 6)^2 + 7$. **See margin.**

Ⓒ **Challenge**

78. **a.** In the function $y = ax^2 + bx + c$, c represents the y-intercept. Find the value of the y-intercept in the function $y = a(x - h)^2 + k$. $ah^2 + k$
   b. Under what conditions does k represent the y-intercept? $h = 0$ or $a = 0$
   (Note, however, that if $a = 0$, the function will not be quadratic.)

Find a quadratic function $y = a(x - h)^2$ for which the graph includes the given points. **79–84. See margin.**

79. $(-2, 1), (2, 1)$ 80. $(-5, 2), (-1, 2)$ 81. $(-1, -4), (7, -4)$

82. $(2, -1), (4, 0)$ 83. $(-2, 18), (1, 0)$ 84. $(1, -64), (-3, 0)$

58. **Each function of the family has (3, 4) as the vertex and $x = 3$ as the line of symmetry. Functions in the family have different stretch** factors. So the equation for the family is $f(x) = a(x - 3)^2 + 4$, where a is any real number.

68. Any real numbers a and k such that $a + k = 1$ will work. However, if $a = 0$ and $k = 1$, the function will be linear rather than quadratic.

4. Assess & Reteach

PowerPoint
Lesson Quiz

1. Graph the function $y = 4(x - 3)^2$.

2. Identify the vertex and the y-intercept of the graph of $y = -2(x + 5)^2 + 8$.
   $(-5, 8), -42$

3. Write the equation $y = 3x^2 + 12x - 1$ in vertex form.
   $y = 3(x + 2)^2 - 13$

Alternative Assessment

Give students the coordinates of a point (a, b) in the coordinate plane. Then give them the coordinates of another point (c, d), for which $c \neq a$ and $d \neq b$. Have students write an equation for a parabola having vertex (a, b) and passing through (c, d), and an equation for a parabola having vertex (c, d) and passing through (a, b).

69. $a = 3, k = -1$

70. $a = -6, k = 35$

71. $a = \frac{1}{5}, k = 1$

72. $a = -\frac{22}{3}, k = \frac{74}{3}$

73. $a = 1, k = -650$

77. Answers may vary. Sample: The graph of $y = (x - 6)^2 + 7$ is the graph of $y = (x + 6)^2$ translated right 12 units and up 7 units.

79. $y = \frac{1}{4}x^2$

80. $y = \frac{1}{2}(x + 3)^2$

81. $y = -\frac{1}{4}(x - 3)^2$

82. $y = -\frac{1}{4}(x - 4)^2$

83. $y = 2(x - 1)^2$

84. $y = -4(x + 3)^2$

257

A sheet of blank grids is available in the Test-Taking Strategies with Transparencies booklet. Give this sheet to students for practice with filling in grids.

Resources

For additional practice with a variety of test item formats:
- Standardized Test Prep, p. 303
- Test-Taking Strategies, p. 298
- Test-Taking Strategies with Transparencies

Checkpoint Quiz

Use this Checkpoint Quiz to check students' understanding of the skills and concepts of Lessons 5-1 through 5-3.

Resources
Grab & Go
- Checkpoint Quiz 1

Checkpoint Quiz

4.

5.

258

Test Prep

Gridded Response   Use the following information about quadratic functions for Exercises 85–90.

$$\text{vertex form: } y = a(x - h)^2 + k \qquad \text{standard form: } y = ax^2 + bx + c$$

85. When $y = -3x^2 - 18x - 23$ is written in vertex form, what is the value of k? **4**

86. When $y = 2(x - 3)(x + 5)$ is written in standard form, what is the value of b? **4**

87. When $y = -2(x + 3)^2 + 25$ is written in standard form, what is the value of c? **7**

88. For $y = 3x^2 - 7x + 5$, what is the x-value of the vertex? Enter your answer as an improper fraction in simplest form. **7/6**

89. What is the y-coordinate of the vertex of $y = -2(x + 1)^2 + 3$? **3**

90. How many units down must you shift the graph of $y = 3(x + 3)^2$ to get the graph of $y = 3(x + 3)^2 - 2$? **2**

Mixed Review

GO for Help

Lesson 5-2   **Graph each function.**   91–93. See back of book.

91. $y = x^2 - 5$ 92. $y = x^2 - 4x + 8$ 93. $y = 3x^2 + 6x + 5$

Lesson 4-5   **Solve each matrix equation.**

94. $\begin{bmatrix} 0 & 1 \\ -1 & 2 \end{bmatrix} X = \begin{bmatrix} 20 \\ 10 \end{bmatrix} \begin{bmatrix} 30 \\ 20 \end{bmatrix}$ 95. $\begin{bmatrix} -1 & 3 \\ 1 & -2 \end{bmatrix} X = \begin{bmatrix} 4 \\ -4 \end{bmatrix} \begin{bmatrix} -4 \\ 0 \end{bmatrix}$

Lesson 3-4   96. Find the maximum and minimum values of the objective function $P = 2x + y$, under the constraints at the right. **max: 6, min: 0** $\begin{cases} y \geq 2x - 2 & x \geq 0 \\ y \leq -x + 4 & y \geq 0 \end{cases}$

Checkpoint Quiz 1   **Lessons 5-1 through 5-3**

Find a quadratic model in standard form for each set of values.

1. $(0, 3), (1, 10), (2, 19)$ 2. $(-2, -15), (0, 1), (2, 1)$ 3. $(0, 0), (1, -5), (2, 0)$
   $y = x^2 + 6x + 3$ $y = -2x^2 + 4x + 1$ $y = 5x^2 - 10x$

Graph each function.   4–6. See margin.

4. $y = 4x^2 + 16x + 7$ 5. $y = (x + 8)^2 - 3$ 6. $y = -(x + 2)^2 - 7$

Determine whether each function has a maximum or minimum value. Then find the value.

7. $y = -x^2 + 6x + 5$ **max.; 14**   8. $y = \frac{1}{2}(x - 6)^2 + 7$ **min.; 7**

9. Rewrite the equation $y = -3x^2 - 6x - 8$ in vertex form. Identify the vertex and the axis of symmetry. $y = -3(x + 1)^2 - 5; (-1, -5); x = -1$

10. Answers may vary.
    Sample:
    $y = (x - 3)^2 + 2;$
    $x = 3; (0, 11), (6, 11)$

10. **Open-Ended** Write the equation of a parabola with a vertex at $(3, 2)$. Write the axis of symmetry and the coordinates of two other points on the graph.

258   Chapter 5   Quadratic Equations and Functions

6.

Factoring Quadratic Expressions

What You'll Learn

- To find common and binomial factors of quadratic expressions
- To factor special quadratic expressions

... And Why

To model the cross section of a pipe, as in Example 8

 Check Skills You'll Need

GO for Help Lessons 1-2 and 5-1

Simplify each expression.

1. $x^2 + x + 4x - 1$
   $x^2 + 5x - 1$

2. $6x^2 - 4(3)x + 2x - 3$
   $6x^2 - 10x - 3$

3. $4x^2 - 2(5 - x) - 3x$
   $4x^2 - x - 10$

Multiply.

4. $2x(5 - x)$
   $-2x^2 + 10x$

5. $(2x - 7)(2x - 7)$
   $4x^2 - 28x + 49$

6. $(4x + 3)(4x - 3)$
   $16x^2 - 9$

New Vocabulary • factoring • greatest common factor (GCF) of an expression • perfect square trinomial • difference of two squares

---

1. Plan

Objectives
1 To find common and binomial factors of quadratic expressions
2 To factor special quadratic expressions

Examples
1 Finding Common Factors
2 Factoring When $ac > 0$ and $b > 0$
3 Factoring When $ac > 0$ and $b < 0$
4 Factoring When $ac < 0$
5 Factoring When $a \neq 1$ and $ac > 0$
6 Factoring When $a \neq 1$ and $ac < 0$
7 Factoring a Perfect Square Trinomial
8 Real-World Connection

Math Background

A quadratic function of the form $f(x) = ax^2 + bx + c$ factors into two linear factors. When trying to factor a quadratic function, we look for two factors whose sum is b and whose product is ac.

More Math Background: p. 236C

Lesson Planning and Resources

See p. 236E for a list of the resources that support this lesson.

 Bell Ringer Practice

Check Skills You'll Need
For intervention, direct students to:

Algebraic Expressions
Lesson 1-2: Example 4
Extra Skills and Word Problems Practice, Ch. 1

Modeling Data With Quadratic Functions
Lesson 5-1: Example 1
Extra Skills and Word Problems Practice, Ch. 5

---

1 Finding Common and Binomial Factors

1a. −1 and −18, −2 and −9, −3 and −6, 1 and 18, 2 and 9

Activity: Factoring

1. Since $6 \cdot 3 = 18$, 6 and 3 make up a factor pair for 18.
   a. Find the other factor pairs for 18, including negative integers.
   b. Find the sum of the integers in each factor pair for 18.
      −19, −11, −9, 19, 11, 9
2. a. Does 12 have a factor pair with a sum of −8? A sum of −9? **yes; no**
   b. Using all the factor pairs of 12, how many sums are possible? **6**
   c. How many sums are possible for the factor pairs of −12? **6**

Vocabulary Tip

One number is a factor of another if the first divides into the second with no remainder.

Factoring is rewriting an expression as the product of its factors. The **greatest common factor (GCF) of an expression** is a common factor of the terms of the expression. It's the common factor with the greatest coefficient and the greatest exponent. You can factor any expression that has a GCF not equal to 1.

1 EXAMPLE Finding Common Factors

Factor each expression.

a. $4x^2 + 20x - 12$

$4x^2 + 20x - 12 = 4x^2 + 4(5x) - 4(3)$ **Factor out the GCF, 4.**

$= 4(x^2 + 5x - 3)$ **Rewrite using the Distributive Property.**

b. $9n^2 - 24n$

$9n^2 - 24n = 3n(3n) - 3n(8)$ **Factor out the GCF, 3n.**

$= 3n(3n - 8)$ **Rewrite using the Distributive Property.**

Quick Check ① Factor each expression.

a. $9x^2 + 3x - 18$
   $3(3x^2 + x - 6)$

b. $7p^2 + 21$
   $7(p^2 + 3)$

c. $4w^2 + 2w$
   $2w(2w + 1)$

Lesson 5-4 Factoring Quadratic Expressions   **259**

Differentiated Instruction Solutions for All Learners

Special Needs L1
Pair students who have difficulty remembering their multiplication facts with students who know them well. Require students to check their answers by multiplying their factors using FOIL.

learning style: verbal

Below Level L2
Have students make a table summarizing the procedures in the examples for various combinations of signs of ac and b.

learning style: visual

Guided Instruction

Activity

In order to factor quadratic expressions, students must be able to find factor pairs for integers. Have students complete the Activity to practice finding factor pairs. Tell students it is important to include negative factors.

② EXAMPLE Math Tip

In the first part of Step 2, show students that the order in which they write the addends is important. The goal is to have the first two terms and the last two terms have a common factor.

③ EXAMPLE Error Prevention

Some students may look for any numbers whose sum is -17. Remind them that only the factor pair in the table with a sum of -17 can be used to factor the expression.

④ EXAMPLE Math Tip

Placement of the signs is very important. To emphasize this, have students switch the signs in the binomial factors and multiply.

A <u>monomial</u> is an expression with one term. A <u>binomial</u> has two terms, and a <u>trinomial</u> has three terms.

You can use algebra tiles to factor the expression in Example 2.

A quadratic trinomial is an expression in the form $ax^2 + bx + c$. You can factor many quadratic trinomials into two binomial factors. First find two factors with a product ac and a sum b. Then find common factors.

If ac and b are positive, then the factors of ac are both positive.

② EXAMPLE Factoring When $ac > 0$ and $b > 0$

Factor $x^2 + 8x + 7$.

Step 1 Find factors with product ac and sum b.

Since $ac = 7$ and $b = 8$, find positive factors with product 7 and sum 8.

Factors of 7	1, 7
Sum of factors	8

These are the only positive factors of 7.

Step 2 Rewrite the term bx using the factors you found. Group the remaining terms and find the common factors for each group. After removing common factors from each group, you should find two identical binomials.

$x^2 + 8x + 7$

$x^2 + x + 7x + 7$ **Rewrite bx: $8x = x + 7x$.**

$x(x + 1) + 7(x + 1)$ **Find common factors.**

Step 3 Rewrite the expression as the product of two binomials.

$x(x + 1) + 7(x + 1)$

$(x + 1)(x + 7)$ **Rewrite using the Distributive Property.**

Check $(x + 1)(x + 7) = x^2 + 7x + x + 7$

$\qquad\qquad\qquad\quad = x^2 + 8x + 7$ ✓

✓ Quick Check ② Factor each expression. Check your answers.

   a. $x^2 + 6x + 8$ **b.** $x^2 + 12x + 32$ **c.** $x^2 + 14x + 40$

     $(x + 2)(x + 4)$ $(x + 4)(x + 8)$ $(x + 4)(x + 10)$

If ac is positive and b is negative, then the factors of ac are both negative.

③ EXAMPLE Factoring When $ac > 0$ and $b < 0$

Factor $x^2 - 17x + 72$.

Step 1 Find factors with product ac and sum b.

Since $ac = 72$ and $b = -17$, find negative factors with product 72 and sum -17.

Factors of 72	$-1, -72$	$-2, -36$	$-3, -24$	$-4, -18$	$-6, -12$	$-8, -9$
Sum of factors	-73	-38	-27	-22	-18	-17

Step 2 Rewrite the term bx using the factors you found. Then find common factors and rewrite the expression as the product of two binomials.

$x^2 - 17x + 72$

$x^2 - 8x - 9x + 72$ **Rewrite bx.**

$x(x - 8) - 9(x - 8)$ **Find common factors.**

$(x - 9)(x - 8)$ **Rewrite using the Distributive Property.**

---

260   Chapter 5   Quadratic Equations and Functions

✅ **Quick Check** ③ Factor each expression.

a. $x^2 - 6x + 8$

$(x - 2)(x - 4)$

b. $x^2 - 7x + 12$

$(x - 3)(x - 4)$

c. $x^2 - 11x + 24$

$(x - 3)(x - 8)$

Note in Example 3 that the factors of c, -9 and -8, appear in the binomials of the factored form, $(x - 9)(x - 8)$. That is also the case for the factors in Example 2, and it is the case whenever $a = 1$. So when $a = 1$, you can skip a few steps in factoring. See Example 4.

If ac is negative, then the factors of ac have different signs.

4 EXAMPLE **Factoring When** $ac < 0$

Factor $x^2 - x - 12$.

Step 1 Find factors with product ac and sum b.

Since $ac = -12$ and $b = -1$, find factors with product -12 and sum -1.

Factors of −12	1, −12	−1, 12	2, −6	−2, 6	3, −4	−3, 4
Sum of factors	−11	11	−4	4	−1	1

Step 2 Since $a = 1$, you can write binomials using the factors you found.

$x^2 - x - 12$

● $(x - 4)(x + 3)$ **Use the factors you found.**

✅ **Quick Check** ④ Factor each expression.

a. $x^2 - 14x - 32$

$(x + 2)(x - 16)$

b. $x^2 + 3x - 10$

$(x + 5)(x - 2)$

c. $x^2 + 4x - 5$

$(x + 5)(x - 1)$

If ac is positive, as in Examples 2 and 3, then the factors of ac have the same sign. This is true even when $a \neq 1$.

5 EXAMPLE **Factoring When** $a \neq 1$ **and** $ac > 0$

Factor $3x^2 - 16x + 5$.

Step 1 Find factors with product ac and sum b.

Since $ac = 15$ and $b = -16$, find negative factors with product 15 and sum -16.

Factors of 15	−1, −15	−3, −5
Sum of factors	−16	−8

Step 2 Rewrite the term bx using the factors you found. Then find common factors and rewrite the expression as the product of two binomials.

$3x^2 - 16x + 5$

$3x^2 - x - 15x + 5$ **Rewrite** bx.

$x(3x - 1) - 5(3x - 1)$ **Find common factors.**

● $(x - 5)(3x - 1)$ **Rewrite using the Distributive Property.**

✅ **Quick Check** ⑤ Factor each expression. Check your answers.

a. $2x^2 + 11x + 12$

$(x + 4)(2x + 3)$

b. $4x^2 + 7x + 3$

$(x + 1)(4x + 3)$

c. $2x^2 - 7x + 6$

$(x - 2)(2x - 3)$

Lesson 5-4 Factoring Quadratic Expressions **261**

6 EXAMPLE **Alternative Method**

Have students draw a square with four sections, such as the one shown. Then follow these steps:

1. Write the first and the last term as shown.

$4x^2$	
	-15

2. Multiply a and c. Then find factors of the product that have a sum of b.

$4(-15) = -60$

$6(-10) = -60$

and $6 + (-10) = -4$

3. Write the factors with their signs and variables in the other two boxes. Order does not matter. Then find the GCF of each column and each row. A GCF is negative if both terms are negative.

$2x$ $4x^2$ $6x$

-5 $10x$ -15

$2x$ $+ 3$

$(2x - 5)(2x + 3)$

PowerPoint

🖥 **Additional Examples**

① Factor each expression.

a. $15x^2 + 25x + 100$

$5(3x^2 + 5x + 20)$

b. $8m^2 + 4m$ $4m(2m + 1)$

② Factor $x^2 + 10x + 24$.

$(x + 4)(x + 6)$

③ Factor $x^2 - 14x + 33$.

$(x - 3)(x - 11)$

④ Factor $x^2 + 3x - 28$.

$(x - 4)(x + 7)$

⑤ Factor $6x^2 - 31x + 35$.

$(3x - 5)(2x - 7)$

⑥ Factor $6x^2 + 11x - 35$.

$(3x - 5)(2x + 7)$

Teaching Tip

Point out that you can only use this formula for the *difference* of two squares. If it was the *sum* of two squares, the last term would be positive. Therefore the signs in the factors would have to be the same resulting in a middle term when multiplied.

Additional Examples

7 Factor $100x^2 + 180x + 81$.
$(10x + 9)^2$

8 A square photo is enclosed in a square frame, as shown in the diagram. Express the area of the frame (the shaded area) in completely factored form.
$(x + 7)(x - 7)$ in.^{2}

7 in.   x in.

Resources
• Daily Notetaking Guide 5-4 **L3**

Closure

Ask: *What is usually the first step in factoring a quadratic trinomial that is not a perfect square trinomial and whose terms have no common factor greater than 1?* Find two integers that have product *ac* and sum *b*.

Again, if *ac* is negative, then the factors of *ac* have different signs.

6 EXAMPLE Factoring When $a \neq 1$ and $ac < 0$

Factor $4x^2 - 4x - 15$.

Step 1 Find factors with product *ac* and sum *b*.

Since $ac = -60$ and $b = -4$, find factors with product -60 and sum -4.

Factors of −60	1, −60	−1, 60	2, −30	−2, 30	3, −20	−3, 20
Sum of factors	−59	59	−28	28	−17	17
Factors of −60	4, −15	−4, 15	5, −12	−5, 12	6, −10	−6, 10
Sum of factors	−11	11	−7	7	−4	4

Step 2 Rewrite the term *bx* using the factors you found. Then find common factors and rewrite the expression as the product of two binomials.

$4x^2 - 4x - 15$
$4x^2 + 6x - 10x - 15$ **Rewrite bx.**
$2x(2x + 3) - 5(2x + 3)$ **Find common factors.**
$(2x - 5)(2x + 3)$ **Rewrite using the Distributive Property.**

✓**Quick Check** **6** Factor each expression.
a. $2x^2 + 7x - 9$
$(x - 1)(2x + 9)$
b. $3x^2 - 16x - 12$
$(x - 6)(3x + 2)$
c. $4x^2 + 5x - 6$
$(x + 2)(4x - 3)$

2 **Factoring Special Expressions**

A **perfect square trinomial** is the product you obtain when you square a binomial. An example is $x^2 + 10x + 25$, which can be written as $(x + 5)^2$. The first term and the third term of the trinomial are always positive, as they represent the squares of the two terms of the binomial. The middle term of the trinomial is two times the product of the terms of the binomial.

 Key Concepts

Property	Factoring Perfect Square Trinomials
$a^2 + 2ab + b^2 = (a + b)^2$	$a^2 - 2ab + b^2 = (a - b)^2$

7 EXAMPLE Factoring a Perfect Square Trinomial

Factor $9x^2 - 42x + 49$.

$9x^2 - 42x + 49 = (3x)^2 - 42x + 7^2$ **Rewrite the first and third terms as squares.**

$= (3x)^2 - 2(3x)(7) + 7^2$ **Rewrite the middle term to verify the perfect square trinomial pattern.**

$= (3x - 7)^2$ $a^2 - 2ab + b^2 = (a - b)^2$

✓**Quick Check** **7** Factor each expression.
a. $4x^2 + 12x + 9$
$(2x + 3)^2$
b. $64x^2 - 16x + 1$
$(8x - 1)^2$
c. $25x^2 + 90x + 81$
$(5x + 9)^2$

An expression of the form $a^2 - b^2$ is defined as the **difference of two squares**. It also follows a pattern that makes it easy to factor.

 Key Concepts

Property	Factoring a Difference of Two Squares
	$a^2 - b^2 = (a + b)(a - b)$

8 **EXAMPLE** **Real-World** **Connection**

Multiple Choice The photo shows the thin ring that is the cross-section of the pipe. Which expression gives the area of the cross-section in completely factored form?

Ⓐ $\pi(3 + r)(3 - r)$　　Ⓑ $\pi(3 - r)(3 - r)$

Ⓒ $\pi(9 - r^2)$　　Ⓓ $9 - \pi r^2$

Relate pipe's area equals the outer area

minus the inner area

Define Let r = inner radius in feet.

Write area = $\pi(3)^2$ − πr^2

$$\text{area} = \pi(3)^2 - \pi r^2$$
$$= \pi(3^2 - r^2)$$
$$= \pi(3 + r)(3 - r)$$

● The cross-sectional area is $\pi(3 + r)(3 - r)$ ft². The correct choice is A.

Test-Taking Tip

A correct solution to the problem may not be the correct answer to the question asked.

✓ **Quick Check** **8** Factor each expression: **a.** $x^2 - 64$　　**b.** $4a^2 - 49$
$(x - 8)(x + 8)$　　$(2a + 7)(2a - 7)$

EXERCISES

For more exercises, see *Extra Skill and Word Problem Practice*.

Practice and Problem Solving

Ⓐ **Practice by Example**

Example 1
(page 259)

 for Help

Find the GCF of each expression. Then factor the expression.

1. $3a^2 + 9$　3; $3(a^2 + 3)$　**2.** $25b^2 - 35$　5; $5(5b^2 - 7)$　**3.** $x^2 - 2x$　x; $x(x - 2)$

4. $5t^2 + 7t$　t; $t(5t + 7)$　**5.** $14y^2 + 7y$　7y; $7y(2y + 1)$　**6.** $27p^2 - 9p$
　　　　　　　　　　　　　　　　　　　　　　　　9p; $9p(3p - 1)$

Factor each expression. 7–30. See margin.

Example 2
(page 260)

7. $x^2 + 3x + 2$　　**8.** $x^2 + 5x + 6$　　**9.** $x^2 + 7x + 10$

10. $x^2 + 10x + 16$　　**11.** $y^2 + 15y + 36$　　**12.** $x^2 + 22x + 40$

Example 3
(page 260)

13. $x^2 - 3x + 2$　　**14.** $x^2 - 13x + 12$　　**15.** $r^2 - 11r + 18$

16. $x^2 - 10x + 24$　　**17.** $d^2 - 12d + 27$　　**18.** $x^2 - 13x + 36$

Example 4
(page 261)

19. $x^2 - 5x - 14$　　**20.** $x^2 + x - 20$　　**21.** $x^2 - 3x - 40$

22. $c^2 + 2c - 63$　　**23.** $x^2 + 10x - 75$　　**24.** $t^2 - 7t - 44$

Example 5
(page 261)

25. $3x^2 + 31x + 36$　　**26.** $2x^2 - 19x + 24$　　**27.** $5r^2 + 23r + 26$

28. $2m^2 - 11m + 15$　　**29.** $5t^2 + 28t + 32$　　**30.** $2x^2 - 27x + 36$

Lesson 5-4 Factoring Quadratic Expressions **263**

7. $(x + 1)(x + 2)$

8. $(x + 2)(x + 3)$

9. $(x + 2)(x + 5)$

10. $(x + 2)(x + 8)$

11. $(y + 3)(y + 12)$

12. $(x + 2)(x + 20)$

13. $(x - 1)(x - 2)$

14. $(x - 12)(x - 1)$

15. $(r - 2)(r - 9)$

16. $(x - 4)(x - 6)$

17. $(d - 3)(d - 9)$

18. $(x - 4)(x - 9)$

19. $(x - 7)(x + 2)$

20. $(x + 5)(x - 4)$

21. $(x - 8)(x + 5)$

3. Practice

Assignment Guide

1 A B　1-36, 48-50, 67-70

2 A B　37-47, 51-66

C　Challenge　71-78

Test Prep　79-84
Mixed Review　85-91

Homework Quick Check

To check students' understanding of key skills and concepts, go over Exercises 25, 45, 49, 66, 68, 70.

Differentiated **Instruction** **Resources**

GPS Guided Problem Solving	L3
Enrichment	L4
Reteaching	L2
Practice	L3

Practice 5-4 Factoring Quadratic Expressions

22. $(c + 9)(c - 7)$

23. $(x + 15)(x - 5)$

24. $(t - 11)(t + 4)$

25. $(3x + 4)(x + 9)$

26. $(x - 8)(2x - 3)$

27. $(r + 2)(5r + 13)$

28. $(m - 3)(2m - 5)$

29. $(t + 4)(5t + 8)$

30. $(x - 12)(2x - 3)$

PowerPoint

Lesson Quiz

Factor each expression completely.

1. $12x^2 + 6x + 18$
   $6(2x^2 + x + 3)$

2. $m^2 + 11m + 18$
   $(m + 2)(m + 9)$

3. $x^2 - 14x - 15$
   $(x - 15)(x + 1)$

4. $x^2 - 13x + 42$
   $(x - 6)(x - 7)$

5. $64x^2 + 144x + 81$ $(8x + 9)^2$

6. $3x^2 + 5x - 50$
   $(3x - 10)(x + 5)$

7. $5k^2 - 125$ $5(k + 5)(k - 5)$

8. $15n^2 - 8n + 1$
   $(5n - 1)(3n - 1)$

Alternative Assessment

Have students work in pairs. Each student multiplies five pairs of binomials of the form $mx + n$, where m and n are nonzero integers. Tell students to write only the trinomial products (without the factors) on a sheet of paper. Students trade the sheets that have the products written on them. Have each student then factor the products that he or she received. Then ask the partners to make sure that the factorization is complete and correct.

Error Prevention!

Exercises 51–65 Students may forget to factor out the GCF of the terms of the given expression. Remind them that if they do not factor out the GCF, the expression has not been factored completely.

31. $(x + 4)(3x - 5)$
32. $(y + 4)(5y - 8)$
33. $(x - 2)(7x + 6)$
34. $(z + 4)(2z - 7)$
35. $(x + 4)(3x - 4)$
36. $(4k + 3)(7k - 2)$

264

Example 6
(page 262)

Example 7
(page 262)

Example 8
(page 263)

Factor each expression. 31–45. See margin.

31. $3x^2 + 7x - 20$
32. $5y^2 + 12y - 32$
33. $7x^2 - 8x - 12$
34. $2z^2 + z - 28$
35. $3x^2 + 8x - 16$
36. $28k^2 + 13k - 6$
37. $x^2 + 2x + 1$
38. $t^2 - 14t + 49$
39. $x^2 - 18x + 81$
40. $4n^2 - 20n + 25$
41. $9x^2 + 48x + 64$
42. $81z^2 + 36z + 4$
43. $x^2 - 4$
44. $c^2 - 64$
45. $9x^2 - 1$

46. **Manufacturing** Refer to the diagram at the right. A machine will cut a small square of plastic from a larger square. Write an expression for the remaining area. Factor the expression. $x^2 - 16; (x + 4)(x - 4)$

47. The area in square centimeters of a square mat is $25x^2 - 10x + 1$. Find the dimensions of the mat in terms of x. **5x − 1 by 5x − 1**

48. The area of a rectangular cloth is $(6x^2 - 19x - 85)$ cm^2. The length is $(2x + 5)$ cm. Find the width. **(3x − 17) cm**

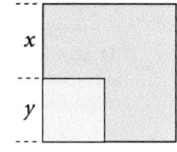

49. Refer to the diagram at the right. Suppose you cut a
GPS small square from a square sheet of cardboard. Write an expression for the remaining area. Factor the expression.
   $(x + y)^2 - y^2; x(x + 2y)$

50. **Interior Design** Refer to the photo at the left. The area of the rug is $(x^2 - 11x + 28)$ ft^2. What is the width?
   (x − 7) ft

Factor each expression completely. 51–65. See margin.

51. $9x^2 - 36$
52. $18z^2 - 8$
53. $12y^2 - 75$
54. $64t^2 - 16$
55. $12x^2 + 36x + 27$
56. $16x^2 - 80x + 100$
57. $2a^2 - 16a + 32$
58. $3x^2 - 24x - 27$
59. $18b^2 + 24b - 10$
60. $4n^2 - 20n + 24$
61. $3y^2 + 24y + 45$
62. $-x^2 + 5x - 4$
63. $4x^2 - 22x + 10$
64. $\frac{1}{2}x^2 - \frac{1}{2}$
65. $-6z^2 - 600$

$(x - 4)$ ft

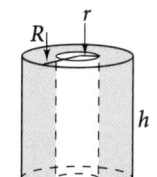

66. **Geometry** Express the volume of the shaded pipe at the right in completely factored form. $\pi h(R + r)(R - r)$

67. **Agriculture** The area in square feet of a rectangular field is $x^2 - 120x + 3500$. The width in feet is $x - 50$. Find the length. **(x − 70) ft**

68. **Writing** Explain how to factor $3x^2 + 6x - 72$ completely.
   See margin p. 265.

69. **Open-Ended** Write a quadratic trinomial that can be factored, where $a \neq 1$, $ac > 0$, and $b < 0$. Factor the expression. **Check students' work.**

70. **Error Analysis** Find the error below. Then factor the expression correctly.
   The third line should be $x(2x - 5) - (2x - 5)$, and the final line should be $(x - 1)(2x - 5)$.

   $2x^2 - 7x + 5$
   $2x^2 - 5x - 2x + 5$
   $x(2x - 5) + (2x - 5)$
   $(x + 1)(2x - 5)$

GO Online

Homework Video Tutor

Visit: PHSchool.com
Web Code: age-0504

(B) **Apply Your Skills**

---

37. $(x + 1)^2$
38. $(t - 7)^2$
39. $(x - 9)^2$
40. $(2n - 5)^2$
41. $(3x + 8)^2$

42. $(9z + 2)^2$
43. $(x + 2)(x - 2)$
44. $(c + 8)(c - 8)$
45. $(3x + 1)(3x - 1)$
51. $9(x + 2)(x - 2)$

52. $2(3z + 2)(3z - 2)$
53. $3(2y + 5)(2y - 5)$
54. $16(2t + 1)(2t - 1)$
55. $3(2x + 3)^2$
56. $4(2x - 5)^2$

C Challenge

71. Critical Thinking Explain how to factor $4x^4 + 24x^3 + 32x^2$. **See margin.**

Factor each expression completely. 72–76. See margin.

72. $0.25t^2 - 0.16$ **73.** $8100x^2 - 10,000$ **74.** $3600z^2 - 4900$

75. $(x + 3)^2 + 3(x + 3) - 54$ **76.** $(x - 2)^2 - 15(x - 2) + 56$

77. $6(x + 5)^2 - 5(x + 5) + 1$ **78.** $3(2a - 3)^2 + 17(2a - 3) + 10$
$(2x + 9)(3x + 14)$ $2(a + 1)(6a - 7)$

Test Prep

Multiple Choice

79. Which term is NOT a common factor of $4a^2c^2 + 2a^2c - 6ac^2$? **A**
  A. $4c$ **B.** $2a$ **C.** $2ac$ **D.** ac

80. How can you write $(m - 5)(m + 4) + 8$ as a product of two binomials? **G**
  F. $(m - 1)(m + 8)$ **G.** $(m - 4)(m + 3)$
  H. $(m + 8)(m + 8)$ **J.** $(m - 5)(8m + 32)$

81. What is the factored form of $4x^2 + 15x - 4$? **D**
  A. $(2x + 2)(2x - 2)$ **B.** $(2x - 4)(2x + 1)$
  C. $(4x + 1)(x - 4)$ **D.** $(4x - 1)(x + 4)$

82. Which is a factored form of $0.81p^2 - 0.09$? **H**
  F. $(0.9p + 0.045)(0.9p - 0.045)$ **G.** $(0.09p + 0.03)(0.09p - 0.03)$
  H. $(0.9p + 0.3)(0.9p - 0.3)$ **J.** $(0.9p + 0.81)(0.9p - 0.81)$

Short Response

83. Explain how to rewrite the expression $a^2 - 2ab + b^2 - 25$ as the product of two trinomial factors. **See margin.**

Extended Response

84. Suppose you hit a baseball and its flight takes a parabolic path. The height of the ball at certain times appears in the table below. **a–b.**

See back of book.

Time (s)	0.5	0.75	1	1.25
Height (ft)	10	10.5	9	5.5

  a. Find a quadratic model for the ball's height as a function of time.
  b. Write the quadratic function in factored form.

Mixed Review

 for Help

Lesson 5-3   **Write each function in vertex form.**

85. $y = x^2 - 2x + 1$ **86.** $y = -2x^2 + 2x + 5$ **87.** $y = 5x^2 - 1$
    $y = (x - 1)^2$ $y = -2\left(x - \frac{1}{2}\right)^2 + \frac{11}{2}$ $y = 5x^2 - 1$

Lesson 4-6   **Evaluate each determinant.**

88. $\begin{vmatrix} 2 & -1 & 0 \\ 1 & 0 & 3 \\ 4 & -2 & 1 \end{vmatrix}$ **1**   **89.** $\begin{vmatrix} 1 & 5 & 0 \\ 3 & 3 & 5 \\ 0 & 1 & 2 \end{vmatrix}$ **−29**   **90.** $\begin{vmatrix} 0 & 4 & 1 \\ 1 & 0 & 1 \\ 1 & 2 & 1 \end{vmatrix}$ **2**

Lesson 3-6   🌐 **91. Coins** The combined mass of a penny and a nickel and a dime is 9.8 g. Ten nickels and three pennies have the same mass as 25 dimes. Fifty dimes have the same mass as 18 nickels and 10 pennies. Write and solve a system of equations to find the mass of each type of coin. **penny: 2.5 g, nickel: 5 g, dime 2.3 g**

57. $2(a - 4)^2$

58. $3(x - 9)(x + 1)$

59. $2(3b - 1)(3b + 5)$

60. $4(n - 2)(n - 3)$

61. $3(y + 3)(y + 5)$

62. $-(x - 1)(x - 4)$

63. $2(x - 5)(2x - 1)$

64. $\frac{1}{2}(x + 1)(x - 1)$

65. $-6(z^2 + 100)$

68. Factor 3 from the terms to get $3(x^2 + 2x - 24)$. Look for numbers whose product is -24 and whose sum is 2. The numbers -4 and 6 work. The complete factorization is $3(x - 4)(x + 6)$.

Test Prep

📁 **Resources**
For additional practice with a variety of test item formats:
• Standardized Test Prep, p. 303
• Test-Taking Strategies, p. 298
• Test-Taking Strategies with Transparencies

71. First factor out $4x^2$ to get $4x^2(x^2 + 6x + 8)$. To factor $x^2 + 6x + 8$, note that the numbers 2 and 4 have a product of 8 and a sum of 6. The complete factorization is $4x^2(x + 2)(x + 4)$.

72. $(0.5t + 0.4)(0.5t - 0.4)$

73. $100(9x - 10)(9x + 10)$

74. $100(6z - 7)(6z + 7)$

75. $(x + 12)(x - 3)$

76. $(x - 10)(x - 9)$

83. **[2]** First separate out -25 so it reads $(a^2 - 2ab + b^2) - 25$, and then factor $a^2 - 2ab + b^2$. This leaves you with $(a - b)^2 - 25$. Factor this as the difference of 2 perfect squares and you get $(a - b + 5)$ $(a - b - 5)$.

    [1] no work shown, only answer, OR work shown with minor error

265

Square Roots and Radicals

Algebra 1 Review

Square Roots and Radicals

Students will find this a helpful review of square roots and simplifying radical expressions. They will be using square roots in the remaining lessons of this chapter.

Guided Instruction

1 EXAMPLE Alternative Method

Another way to find the principal square root of a number is to first list the prime factorization of the number. Find pairs of matching prime factors and take the square root of each pair. For example, the principal square root of (2×2) is 2. Find the product of all the square roots of all the pairs. Write this product in front of a radical sign. Write the product of the non-paired prime factors inside the radical sign.

$48 = (2 \times 2) \times (2 \times 2) \times 3$
$\sqrt{48} = 2 \times 2\sqrt{3} = 4\sqrt{3}$

2 EXAMPLE Math Tip

Remind students that expressions that have a radical as a denominator are not considered to be in simplest form. To simplify, multiply by 1 in the form of the denominator divided by itself.

Resources

ExamView CD-ROM, Chapter 00, Integer, Decimal, and Fraction Operations

---

A radical symbol $\sqrt{\ }$ indicates a square root. The expression $\sqrt{16}$ means the principal, or positive, square root of 16. The expression $-\sqrt{16}$ means the negative square root of 16. In general, $\sqrt{x^2} = |x|$ for all real numbers x.

Properties	Square Roots

Multiplication Property of Square Roots

For any numbers $a \geq 0$ and $b \geq 0$, $\sqrt{ab} = \sqrt{a} \cdot \sqrt{b}$.

Division Property of Square Roots

For any numbers $a \geq 0$ and $b > 0$, $\sqrt{\frac{a}{b}} = \frac{\sqrt{a}}{\sqrt{b}}$.

You can use the properties of square roots to simplify radical expressions.

1 EXAMPLE Radical Expressions Containing Perfect Squares

Simplify $\sqrt{48}$.

$\sqrt{48} = \sqrt{16} \cdot \sqrt{3}$ **Multiplication Property of Square Roots**

$= 4\sqrt{3}$ **Simplify.**

2 EXAMPLE Denominators Containing Radical Expressions

Simplify $-\sqrt{\frac{5}{7}}$.

$-\sqrt{\frac{5}{7}} = -\frac{\sqrt{5}}{\sqrt{7}}$ **Division Property of Square Roots**

$= -\frac{\sqrt{5}}{\sqrt{7}} \cdot \frac{\sqrt{7}}{\sqrt{7}}$ **Multiply both the numerator and the denominator by $\sqrt{7}$.**

$= -\frac{\sqrt{35}}{\sqrt{49}}$ **Multiplication Property of Square Roots**

$= -\frac{\sqrt{35}}{7}$ **Simplify.**

EXERCISES

Simplify each radical expression.

1. $\sqrt{18}$ $3\sqrt{2}$

2. $\sqrt{75}$ $5\sqrt{3}$

3. $-\sqrt{32}$ $-4\sqrt{2}$

4. $\sqrt{\frac{3}{5}}$ $\frac{\sqrt{15}}{5}$

5. $-\sqrt{\frac{7}{12}}$ $-\frac{\sqrt{21}}{6}$

6. $\sqrt{\frac{3}{8}}$ $\frac{\sqrt{6}}{4}$

7. $-\sqrt{200}$ $-10\sqrt{2}$

8. $5\sqrt{320}$ $40\sqrt{5}$

9. $(2\sqrt{27})^2$ 108

10. $-\sqrt{10^4}$ -100

11. $\sqrt{x^2 y^2}$ $|xy|$

12. $\sqrt{\frac{8}{x^2}}$ $\frac{2\sqrt{2}}{|x|}$

Quadratic Equations

What You'll Learn

- To solve quadratic equations by factoring and by finding square roots
- To solve quadratic equations by graphing

... And Why

To solve equations involving art, as in Example 5

 Check Skills You'll Need

GO for Help Lessons 5-2 and 5-4

Factor each expression.

1. $x^2 + 5x - 14$
   $(x + 7)(x - 2)$

2. $4x^2 - 12x$
   $4x(x - 3)$

3. $9x^2 - 16$
   $(3x - 4)(3x + 4)$

Graph each function. 4–6. See margin p. 269.

4. $y = x^2 - 2x - 5$

5. $y = x^2 - 4x + 4$

6. $y = x^2 - 4x$

🔊 **New Vocabulary**
- standard form of a quadratic equation
- Zero-Product Property
- zero of a function

---

1 Solving by Factoring and Finding Square Roots

The **standard form of a quadratic equation** is $ax^2 + bx + c = 0$, where $a \neq 0$. You can solve some quadratic equations in standard form by factoring the quadratic expression and then using the Zero-Product Property.

 Key Concepts

Property	Zero-Product Property
If $ab = 0$, then $a = 0$ or $b = 0$.	
Example	If $(x + 3)(x - 7) = 0$, then $(x + 3) = 0$ or $(x - 7) = 0$.

1 EXAMPLE Solving by Factoring

Solve $2x^2 - 11x = -15$.

$2x^2 - 11x + 15 = 0$ **Write in standard form.**

$(x - 3)(2x - 5) = 0$ **Factor the quadratic expression.**

$x - 3 = 0$ or $2x - 5 = 0$ **Use the Zero-Product Property.**

$x = 3$ or $x = \frac{5}{2}$ **Solve for x.**

The solutions are 3 and $\frac{5}{2}$.

Check

$2x^2 - 11x = -15$

$2(3)^2 - 11(3) \overset{?}{=} -15$

$18 - 33 \overset{?}{=} -15$

$-15 = -15$ ✓

$2x^2 - 11x = -15$

$2\left(\frac{5}{2}\right)^2 - 11\left(\frac{5}{2}\right) \overset{?}{=} -15$

$\frac{25}{2} - \frac{55}{2} \overset{?}{=} -15$

$-15 = -15$ ✓

✓ **Quick Check** ❶ Solve each equation by factoring. Check your answers.

a. $x^2 + 7x = 18$
   $-9, 2$

b. $2x^2 + 4x = 6$
   $-3, 1$

c. $16x^2 = 8x$
   $0, \frac{1}{2}$

Lesson 5-5   Quadratic Equations   **267**

Differentiated Instruction Solutions for All Learners

Special Needs L1
Help students recognize the different methods for solving quadratic equations. Emphasize that tables and graphs give approximate solutions, while algebraic solutions are exact.

learning style: verbal

Below Level L2
Remind students that finding square roots yields two possible solutions to an equation. $x^2 = 4$ has two solutions, $x = \pm 2$.

learning style: verbal

---

1. Plan

Objectives
1 To solve quadratic equations by factoring and by finding square roots
2 To solve quadratic equations by graphing

Examples
1 Solving by Factoring
2 Solving by Finding Square Roots
3 Real-World Connection
4 Solving by Tables
5 Solving by Graphing

 Professional Development

Math Background

The use of the Zero-Product Property allows students to solve quadratic equations that can be factored. Other useful techniques include finding square roots and graphing. However, each of these techniques has limitations. This should begin to convince students of the need for a method without limitations. Such a method is presented in Lesson 5-8.

More Math Background: p. 236D

Lesson Planning and Resources

See p. 236E for a list of the resources that support this lesson.

 PowerPoint

Bell Ringer Practice

✓ **Check Skills You'll Need**
For intervention, direct students to:

Properties of Parabolas
Lesson 5-2: Example 2
Extra Skills and Word Problems Practice, Ch. 5

Factoring Quadratic Expressions
Lesson 5-4: Examples 2, 3
Extra Skills and Word Problems Practice, Ch. 5

Guided Instruction

1 EXAMPLE Connection to Logic

Point out that the word *or* is the appropriate word to use when the Zero-Product Property is being used. This is so, because $x = 3$ and $x = \frac{5}{2}$ cannot simultaneously be true. On the other hand, the word *and* is the appropriate word when you are listing the solutions, because each of the numbers will make the original equation true.

3 EXAMPLE Careers

This example demonstrates just how important Algebra is to smoke jumpers or any other skydivers. Without equations such as these, they would not know when to release their parachutes, possibly endangering their lives.

PowerPoint Additional Examples

① Solve $3x^2 - 20x - 7 = 0$. $-\frac{1}{3}$, 7

② Solve $6x^2 - 486 = 0$. ± 9

③ The function $y = -16x^2 + 270$ models the height y in feet of a heavy object x seconds after it is dropped from the top of a building that is 270 feet tall. How long does it take the object to hit the ground? about 4.1 s

---

You can solve an equation in the form $ax^2 = c$ by finding square roots.

2 EXAMPLE Solving by Finding Square Roots

Solve $5x^2 - 180 = 0$.

$$5x^2 - 180 = 0$$
$$5x^2 = 180 \quad \text{Rewrite in the form } ax^2 = c.$$
$$\frac{5x^2}{5} = \frac{180}{5} \quad \text{Isolate } x^2.$$
$$x^2 = 36 \quad \text{Simplify.}$$
$$x = \pm 6 \quad \text{Find square roots.}$$

✓ **Quick Check** ② Solve each equation by finding square roots.
  a. $4x^2 - 25 = 0$ $-\frac{5}{2}, \frac{5}{2}$ **b.** $3x^2 = 24$ $-2\sqrt{2}, 2\sqrt{2}$ **c.** $x^2 - \frac{1}{4} = 0$ $-\frac{1}{2}, \frac{1}{2}$

3 EXAMPLE Real-World 🌐 Connection

Firefighting Smoke jumpers are in free fall from the time they jump out of a plane until they open their parachutes. The function $y = -16t^2 + 1600$ models a jumper's height y in feet at t seconds for a jump from 1600 ft. How long is a jumper in free fall if the parachute opens at 1000 ft?

$$y = -16t^2 + 1600$$
$$1000 = -16t^2 + 1600 \quad \text{Substitute 1000 for } y.$$
$$-600 = -16t^2 \quad \text{Isolate } t^2.$$
$$37.5 = t^2$$
$$\pm 6.1 \approx t \quad \text{Find square roots.}$$

The jumper is in free fall for about 6.1 seconds.

Check Is the answer reasonable? The negative number -6.1 is also a solution to the equation. However, since a negative value for time has no meaning in this case, only the positive solution is reasonable.

Real-World 🌐 Connection

Careers Smoke jumpers are firefighters who parachute into areas near forest fires.

✓ **Quick Check** ③ **a.** A smoke jumper jumps from 1400 ft. The function describing the height is $y = -16t^2 + 1400$. Using square roots, find the time during which the jumper is in free fall if the parachute opens at 1000 ft. **5 s**
  b. Solve the equation in part (a) by factoring. Which method do you prefer—using square roots or factoring? Explain. $t = 5$ or $t = -5$, and use positive solution because it describes time; check students' work.

2 Solving by Graphing

Not every quadratic equation can be solved by factoring or by finding square roots. You can solve $ax^2 + bx + c = 0$ by graphing $y_1 = ax^2 + bx + c$—its related quadratic function. The value of y_1 is 0 where the graph intersects the x-axis. Each x-intercept is a **zero of the function** and a root of the equation.

You can also solve $ax^2 + bx + c = 0$ by displaying values of $y_1 = ax^2 + bx + c$ in a table. Scroll through the table to find where y_1 changes sign, effectively where the graph crosses the x-axis. Then "zoom-in" on the y_1 values by adjusting TblStart and Δ Tbl.

Differentiated Instruction Solutions for All Learners

Advanced Learners L4	English Language Learners ELL
Have students research the trajectory of a specific projectile, and graph the equation.	Ask students what the term *similar* means in everyday language. Use this definition to help students understand the geometric meaning of *similar figures* as having the same shape (angles) but different size (sides are proportionally related).
learning style: verbal	learning style: verbal

For: Factored-Form Activity
Use: Interactive Textbook, 5-5

4 EXAMPLE Solving by Tables

Solve $x^2 - 5x + 2 = 0$.

Enter $y_1 = x^2 - 5x + 2$ in your graphing calculator. Use the TABLE window to see where y_1 changes sign. Change Δ Tbl to 0.01 and look again for the sign change. Continue this tabular zoom-in and find one solution to be $x \approx 0.44$.

X	Y1		
0	2		
1	-2		
2	-4		
3	-4		
4	-2		
5	2		
6	8		

Y1 =X²−5X+2

X	Y1		
.4	.16		
.41	.1181		
.42	.0764		
.43	.0349		
.44	−.0064		
.45	−.0475		
.46	−.0884		

Y1 =X²−5X+2

✓ **Quick Check** ④ In the first window above, the second sign change occurs between $x = 4$ and $x = 5$. Use tabular zoom-in to find the other solution to two decimal places.

4.56

5 EXAMPLE Solving by Graphing

Art Artists often use a golden rectangle in their work because forms based on it are visually pleasing. You can divide a golden rectangle into a square of side length one and a smaller rectangle that is similar to the original one. The ratio of the longer side to the shorter side of a golden rectangle is the golden ratio. Use the figure at the right to find the golden ratio.

Vocabulary Tip

Two rectangles are <u>similar</u> if their corresponding sides are in proportion.

Rectangle A

Rectangle B

Relate $\dfrac{\text{longer side of } A}{\text{shorter side of } A} = \dfrac{\text{longer side of } B}{\text{shorter side of } B}$

Define Let x = longer side of rectangle A. Then $x - 1$ = shorter side of rectangle B.

Write $\dfrac{x}{1} = \dfrac{1}{x - 1}$

$x^2 - x = 1$ **Find cross-products.**

$x^2 - x - 1 = 0$ **Write in standard form.**

Graph the function $y_1 = x^2 - x - 1$. Use "zero" in the CALC feature to find the positive solution.

Zero
X= 1.618034   Y= 0

The ratio is about $1.62 : 1$.

✓ **Quick Check** ⑤ Solve each equation. When necessary, round to the nearest hundredth.
a. $x^2 - 2x = 4$ **−1.24, 3.24**   **b.** $x^2 + \frac{1}{2}x - \frac{1}{4} = 0$ **−0.81, 0.31**

Real-World 🌐 **Connection**

Francisco José de Goya y Lucientes (1746–1828) was a Spanish painter. In *Portrait of a Man*, Goya placed the most significant elements of the painting within golden rectangles.

Guided Instruction

5 EXAMPLE Connection to Algebra

The golden ratio has an interesting relation to the famous Fibonacci sequence. The Fibonacci sequence is the infinite sequence 1, 1, 2, 3, 5, 8, . . . that has 1 as its first two terms and thereafter has new terms formed by adding the two immediately preceding terms. If the nth term is denoted by F_n, then the ratios $\dfrac{F_n}{F_{n-1}}$ approach the golden ratio as n is increased.

PowerPoint

Additional Examples

④ Solve $2x^2 + 7x - 1 = 0$. Find the solutions to two decimal places. **−3.64, 0.14**

⑤ A carpenter wants to cut a piece of plywood in the shape of a right triangle. The carpenter wants the hypotenuse of the triangle to be 6 feet long and the legs to be as shown in the diagram. About how long should the perpendicular sides be?

6 ft $x + 1$

x

about 3.7 ft and 4.7 ft

Resources
• Daily Notetaking Guide 5-5 **L3**

Closure

Ask students how factoring can be used to solve a quadratic equation? Write the equation in standard form. Factor to express the quadratic expression as the product of two linear factors. Set each factor equal to zero and solve each equation for the variable. Or graph the function and find the zeros.

---

page 267   Check Skills You'll Need

4.

5.

6.

Assignment Guide

❶ A B 1-19, 33-35, 54-61

❷ A B 20-32, 36-53
C Challenge   62-66

Test Prep   67-77
Mixed Review   78-85

Homework Quick Check
To check students' understanding of key skills and concepts, go over Exercises 17, 29, 34, 35, 57, 35.

Technology Tip
Exercises 23–31 If students use the zero feature on the CALC menu, it is crucial to select the left bound first and the right bound second. Remind students to repeat the procedure for each point where the parabola crosses the x-axis.

Exercise 33 Ask students which solution method they would use and why.

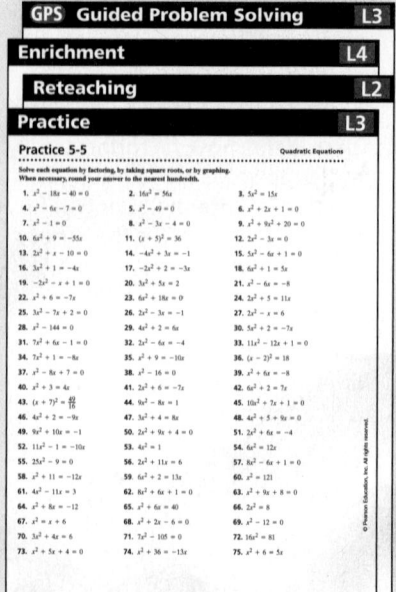

EXERCISES

For more exercises, see *Extra Skill and Word Problem Practice.*

Practice and Problem Solving

Ⓐ **Practice by Example**

GO for Help

Example 1
(page 267)

Solve each equation by factoring. Check your answers.

1. $x^2 + 6x + 8 = 0$ **−4, −2** **2.** $x^2 + 18 = 9x$ **3, 6** **3.** $2x^2 - x = 3$ $-1, \frac{3}{2}$

4. $x^2 - 10x + 25 = 0$ **5** **5.** $2x^2 + 6x = -4$ **−2, −1** **6.** $3x^2 = 16x + 12$ $-\frac{2}{3}, 6$

Example 2
(page 268)

Solve each equation by finding square roots.

7. $5x^2 = 80$ **−4, 4** **8.** $x^2 - 4 = 0$ **−2, 2** **9.** $2x^2 = 32$ **−4, 4**

10. $9x^2 = 25$ $-\frac{5}{3}, \frac{5}{3}$ **11.** $3x^2 - 15 = 0$ $-\sqrt{5}, \sqrt{5}$ **12.** $5x^2 - 40 = 0$ $-2\sqrt{2}, 2\sqrt{2}$

Example 3
(page 268)

Solve each equation by factoring or by taking square roots.

13. $x^2 - 4x = 0$ **0, 4** **14.** $6x^2 + 4x = 0$ $-\frac{2}{3}, 0$ **15.** $12x^2 - 147 = 0$ $-\frac{7}{2}, \frac{7}{2}$

16. $3x^2 = 48$ **−4, 4** **17.** $2x^2 = 8x$ **0, 4** **18.** $4x^2 - 80 = 0$ $-2\sqrt{5}, 2\sqrt{5}$

19. Firefighters A smoke jumper jumps from a plane that is 1700 ft above the ground. The function $y = -16t^2 + 1700$ gives the jumper's height y in feet at t seconds.
a. How long is the jumper in free fall if the parachute opens at 1000 ft? **about 6.61 s**
b. How long is the jumper in free fall if the parachute opens at 940 ft? **about 6.89 s**

Example 4
(page 269)

Solve each equation using tables. Give each answer to at most two decimal places.
20–31. See margin.
20. $x^2 + 5x + 3 = 0$ **21.** $x^2 - 7x = 11$ **22.** $2x^2 - x = 2$

Example 5
(page 269)

Solve each equation by graphing. Give each answer to at most two decimal places.

23. $6x^2 = -19x - 15$ **24.** $3x^2 - 5x - 4 = 0$ **25.** $5x^2 - 7x - 3 = 8$

26. $6x^2 + 31x = 12$ **27.** $1 = 4x^2 + 3x$ **28.** $\frac{1}{2}x^2 - x = 8$

29. $x^2 = 4x + 8$ **30.** $x^2 + 4x = 6$ **31.** $2x^2 - 2x - 5 = 0$

Ⓑ **Apply Your Skills**

32a. Answers may vary.
Sample:
$\frac{\ell}{w} \approx \frac{7.2}{4.4} \approx 1.6$
b. the tree trunk

32. a. Art Verify that the Chinese painting at the right is a golden rectangle. **a–b. See left.**
b. What element in the painting divides it into a square and another golden rectangle?

GO Online

Homework Video Tutor

Visit: PHSchool.com
Web Code: age-0505

33. Multiple Choice The period of a pendulum is the time the pendulum takes to swing back and forth. The function $\ell = 0.81t^2$ relates the length ℓ in feet of a pendulum to the time t in seconds that it takes to swing back and forth. The convention center in Portland, Oregon, has the longest pendulum in the United States. The pendulum's length is 90 ft. Find the period. **B**
Ⓐ 8.5 seconds Ⓑ 10.5 seconds Ⓒ 90 seconds Ⓓ 111 seconds

34. Open-Ended Write an equation in standard form that you can solve by factoring and an equation that you cannot solve by factoring.
Check students' work.

20. −4.30, −0.70
21. −1.32, 8.32
22. −0.78, 1.28
23. −1.67, −1.5
24. −0.59, 2.26

25. −0.94, 2.34
26. −5.53, 0.36
27. −1, 0.25
28. −3.12, 5.12
29. −1.46, 5.46

30. −5.16, 1.16
31. −1.16, 2.16

35. Gardening Suppose you want to expand the garden shown at the right by planting a border of flowers. The border will be of the same width around the entire garden. The flowers you bought will fill an area of 276 ft². How wide should the border be? **3 ft**

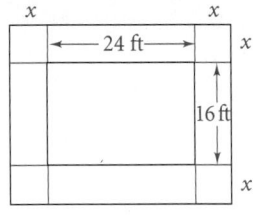

Solve each equation by factoring, by taking square roots, or by graphing. If necessary, round your answer to the nearest hundredth. **36–53. See margin.**

36. $x^2 + 6x + 5 = 45$ **37.** $x^2 - 11x + 24 = 0$ **38.** $3x^2 = 27$

39. $2x^2 - 5x - 3 = 0$ **40.** $x^2 + 2x = 6 - 6x$ **41.** $6x^2 + 13x + 6 = 0$

42. $2x^2 + 8x = 5x + 20$ **43.** $7x^2 - 243 = 0$ **44.** $3x^2 + 7x = 9$

45. $12x^2 - 154 = 0$ **46.** $x^2 + 4x = 0$ **47.** $x^2 = 8x - 7$

48. $x^2 + 2x = 15$ **49.** $x^2 + 11x + 10 = 0$ **50.** $4x^2 + 4x = 3$

51. $(x + 3)^2 = 9$ **52.** $2x^2 - 6x = 8$ **53.** $2x^2 + x - 28 = 0$

Critical Thinking The graphs of each pair of functions intersect. Find their points of intersection without using a calculator. (***Hint:*** Solve as a system using substitution.)

54. $y = x^2$
$y = -\frac{1}{2}x^2 + \frac{3}{2}x + 3$
(−1, 1), (2, 4)

55. $y = x^2 - 2$
$y = 3x^2 - 4x - 2$
(0, −2), (2, 2)

56. $y = -x^2 + x + 4$
$y = 2x^2 - 6$
$\left(-\frac{5}{3}, -\frac{4}{9}\right)$**, (2, 2)**

 57. Writing Explain how you found the intersections in Exercises 54–56. **See left.**

Open-Ended Write a quadratic equation with the given solutions. **58–61. See margin.**

58. 3 and 5   **59.** −3 and 2   **60.** −1 and −6   **61.** $\frac{1}{2}$ and $\frac{2}{3}$

C Challenge

62. Matrices Find the possible values of x and y. (A matrix with exponent 2 means that you multiply the matrix by itself.)

$\begin{bmatrix} x & 2 \\ 3 & y \end{bmatrix}^2 = \begin{bmatrix} 22 & 10 \\ 15 & \blacksquare \end{bmatrix}$ **x = 4, y = 1 or x = −4, y = 9**

63. Using tables, how might you recognize that a quadratic equation likely has exactly one solution? no solutions?

64. The equation $x^2 - 10x + 24 = 0$ can be written in factored form as $(x - 4)(x - 6) = 0$. How can you use this fact to find the vertex of the graph of $y = x^2 - 10x + 24$? **See back of book.**

65. Physics Suppose you throw a ball straight up from the ground with a velocity of 80 ft/s. As the ball moves upward, gravity slows it. Eventually the ball begins to fall back to the ground. The height h of the ball after t seconds in the air is given by the quadratic function $h(t) = -16t^2 + 80t$.
a. How high does the ball go? **100 ft**
b. For how many seconds is the ball in the air before it hits the ground? **5 s**

66. a. Let $a > 0$. Use algebraic or arithmetic ideas to explain why the lowest point on the graph of $y = a(x - h)^2 + k$ must occur when $x = h$.
b. Suppose that the function in part (a) is $y = a(x - h)^3 + k$. Is your reasoning still valid? Explain. **a–b. See back of book.**

57. To find the x-coordinates, set the right side of the first equation equal to the right side of the second equation and solve for x. Then find the corresponding y-values by substituting each solution into the simpler of the two original equations.

63. Answers may vary. Sample: If tables show same-sign values approaching 0, there likely is one solution. If same-sign values never approach 0, there likely are no solutions.

36. −10, 4

37. 3, 8

38. −3, 3

39. $-\frac{1}{2}$, 3

40. −8.69, 0.69

41. $-\frac{3}{2}$, $-\frac{2}{3}$

42. $-4, \frac{5}{2}$

43. −5.89, 5.89

44. −3.25, 0.92

45. −3.58, 3.58

46. −4, 0

47. 1, 7

48. −5, 3

49. −10, −1

50. −1.5, 0.5

PowerPoint
Lesson Quiz

Solve each equation by factoring.
1. $4x^2 - 17x - 15 = 0$ $-\frac{3}{4}, 5$
2. $10x^2 + 19x + 6 = 0$ $-\frac{3}{2}, -\frac{2}{5}$
3. Solve $3x^2 = 4800$ by using square roots. **±40**
4. Use a graphing calculator to solve $2x^2 + 5x - 9 = 0$. Round the solutions to the nearest hundredth. **−3.71, 1.21**

Alternative Assessment

Give students a quadratic equation to solve and ask them to solve it both by factoring and by graphing with a graphing calculator. Ask students to write a short paragraph explaining which method they prefer, and why. Then ask students to explain why the graphing method might be easier for some problems, while factoring might be easier for others.

Error Prevention!

Exercise 62 Be sure students understand that the matrix on the left is to be multiplied by itself. The exponent does *not* indicate that the individual elements of the matrix are to be squared.

51. −6, 0

52. −1, 4

53. −4, 3.5

58–61. Answers may vary. Samples are given.

58. $x^2 - 8x + 15 = 0$

59. $x^2 + x - 6 = 0$

60. $x^2 + 7x + 6 = 0$

61. $6x^2 - 7x + 2 = 0$

271

Test Prep

Resources

For additional practice with a variety of test item formats:
- Standardized Test Prep, p. 303
- Test-Taking Strategies, p. 298
- Test-Taking Strategies with Transparencies

Test Prep

Multiple Choice

67. What are the values of x that satisfy the equation $3 - 27x^2 = 0$? **B**

A. $x = \pm 3$ B. $x = \pm\frac{1}{3}$

C. $x = \frac{1}{9}$ or $x = -\frac{1}{9}$ D. $x = 2\sqrt{6}$ or $x = -2\sqrt{6}$

68. What are the solutions of the equation $6x^2 + 9x - 15 = 0$? **G**

F. $1, -15$ G. $1, -\frac{5}{2}$

H. $-1, -5$ J. $3, \frac{5}{2}$

69. For which equation is -3 NOT a solution? **D**

A. $x^2 - 2x - 15 = 0$ B. $x^2 - 21 = 4x$

C. $2x^2 + 12x = -18$ D. $9 + x^2 = 0$

70. What are the solutions of the equation $(2x - 7)^2 = 25$? **G**

F. $6, -6$ G. $6, 1$ H. $6, -1$ J. $-6, -1$

71. Find the sum of the solutions to the equation $x^2 + 2x - 15 = 0$. **D**

A. 8   B. -8 C. 2   D. -2

72. Find the product of the solutions to the equation $x^2 - 8x = 9$. **J**

F. 6   G. -6 H. 9   J. -9

73. Which equation has $-\frac{2}{5}$ as a solution? **D**

A. $(2x - 5)(x + 1) = 0$ B. $(2x + 5)(x + 1) = 0$

C. $(5x - 2)(x + 1) = 0$ D. $(5x + 2)(x + 1) = 0$

74. How many times does the graph of $y = x^2 - 4x + 5$ cross the x-axis? **F**

F. 0   G. 1   H. 2   J. 33

75. The equation $x^2 - 3x + a = 0$ has two roots. One root of the equation is 2. What is the other root? **C**

A. -2 B. -1 C. 1   D. 3

Short Response

76. A quadratic equation has solutions 3 and -4. Write a possible equation.

76–77. See left.

77. One solution to the equation $x^2 + bx - 20 = 0$ is 5. Find the other solution.

---

76. [2] $(x - 3)(x + 4) = 0$, or $x^2 + x - 12 = 0$, or any constant multiple of this equation
[1] the correct factoring, not written as an equation

77. [2] $(x - a)(x - 5) = x^2 + bx - 20$
$5a = -20$
$a = -4$
The other solution is -4.
[1] -4, with no work shown

Mixed Review

Lesson 5-4

Factor each expression.

78. $3x^2 - 4x + 1$
$(3x - 1)(x - 1)$

79. $25z^2 - 9$
$(5z + 3)(5z - 3)$

80. $6s^2 + 9s$
$3s(2s + 3)$

Lesson 4-1

State the dimensions of each matrix. Identify the indicated element.

81. $\begin{bmatrix} 4 & 6 & 5 \\ 1 & -3 & 0 \\ 1 & 1 & 9 \end{bmatrix}; a_{13}$
$3 \times 3; 5$

82. $\begin{bmatrix} 4 & -1 & 6 \\ 2 & 0 & 0 \end{bmatrix}; a_{21}$
$2 \times 3; 2$

83. $\begin{bmatrix} -9 & 1 & -1 \\ 0 & 6 & 0 \\ 1 & 0 & -2 \end{bmatrix}; a_{32}$
$3 \times 3; 0$

Lesson 1-1

Name the property of real numbers illustrated by each equation.

84. Distributive Property

85. Comm. Prop. of Add.

84. $3(2x + y) = 6x + 3y$

85. $3x^2 + 7y = 7y + 3x^2$

86. $4(3x) = (4 \cdot 3)x$
Assoc. Prop. of Mult.

87. $3 + (-3) = 0$
Additive Inverse Prop.

272 Chapter 5 Quadratic Equations and Functions

Writing Equations From Roots

FOR USE WITH LESSON 5-5

You can use the Zero-Product Property to write a quadratic function from its zeros or a quadratic equation from its roots.

1 ACTIVITY

1–2. Answers may vary. Samples are given.

1. a. Write a nonzero linear function $f(x)$ that has a zero at $x = 3$. $f(x) = x - 3$
b. Write a nonzero linear function $g(x)$ that has a zero at $x = 2$. $g(x) = 2x - 4$

2. a. For f and g from Part 1, write the product function $h(x) = f(x) \cdot g(x)$.
b. What kind of function is $h(x)$? **c.** Solve the equation $h(x) = 0$. **2, 3**
a. $h(x) = (x - 3)(2x - 4)$ **b.** quadratic

Mental Math Write a quadratic function with zeros at each pair of values. **3–12. See margin.**

3. 3 and 4   **4.** 2 and 2.5   **5.** -1 and $\frac{3}{2}$ **6.** 1 and -1 **7.** -6 and -6

Mental Math Write a quadratic equation with each pair of values as roots.

8. 2 and 1   **9.** 1.5 and 3   **10.** -2 and 2   **11.** 6 and 12   **12.** $\frac{1}{2}$ and -4

You can also use zeros or roots to write quadratic expressions in standard form.

2 ACTIVITY

13b. Yes; the sum of the numbers is the opposite of the coefficient of the x term; the product is the constant term.

13. a. Copy and complete the table. Write the product $(x - a)(x - b)$ in standard form for each pair a and b.

b. Is there a pattern in the table? Explain. **See above.**

14. a. If you know the roots, you can write a quadratic function or equation with a quadratic expression in standard form. Explain how.
b. Demonstrate your method for each pair of values in Exercises 3–12. **14. See margin.**

a	b	a + b	ab	(x − a)(x − b)
2	3	5	6	$x^2 - 5x + 6$
−2	3	1	−6	■
2	−3	■	■	■
−2	−3	■	■	■
−5	−6	■	■	■
7	−12	■	■	■

$$\begin{array}{rrl}
& & x^2 - x - 6 \\
-1; & -6; & x^2 + x - 6 \\
-5; & 6; & x^2 + 5x + 6 \\
-11; & 30; & x^2 + 11 + 30 \\
-5; & -84; & x^2 + 5x - 84
\end{array}$$

EXERCISES   **15–16. See margin.**

15. Explain how to write a quadratic equation that has 2 as its only root.

16. Write the equation $q(x) = 0$ suggested by each graph. Each tick mark is 1 unit.

a.   **b.**   **c.**

17. Describe the family of quadratic functions that have zeros at r and s. Sketch several members of the family in the coordinate plane. $y = a(x - r)(x - s)$, $a \neq 0$. Check students' sketches.

18. True or False? The x-value of the vertex of a quadratic function with two zeros is the average of the zeros. Give a convincing argument. **true; check students' work.**

3. $f(x) = (x - 3)(x - 4)$

4. $f(x) = (x - 2)(x - 2.5)$

5. $f(x) = (x - (-1))(x - \frac{3}{2})$

6. $f(x) = (x - 1)(x - (-1))$

7. $f(x) = (x - (-6))(x - (-6))$ or $f(x) = (x + 6)^2$

8. $(x - 2)(x - 1) = 0$

9. $(x - 1.5)(x - 3) = 0$

10. $(x - (-2))(x - 2) = 0$

11. $(x - 6)(x - 12) = 0$

12. $(x - \frac{1}{2})(x - (-4)) = 0$

Writing Equations From Roots

This feature helps students write a quadratic function or quadratic equation given its zeros or roots, respectively.

Guided Instruction

Review the meaning of *zero of a function* and *roots* (or solutions) *of an equation*. Clarify for students that both give the identical *x*-values, and not an ordered pair.

Special Needs   **L1**

Review the Zero-Product Property by solving an easily factorable quadratic as shown below.

$x^2 + 5x - 6 = 0$
$(x - 1)(x + 6) = 0$
$(x - 1) = 0$ or $(x + 6) = 0$
$x = 1$ or $x = -6$

Error Prevention!

In Questions 1-12, watch for students who incorrectly write the linear function by using the same sign as the zero. For example, in 1a students may incorrectly write $f(x) = x + 3$ for a zero of $x = 3$, instead of $f(x) = x - 3$.

14a. For roots a and b, the constant term is ab and the x-coefficient is $-(a + b)$. The x^2-coefficient is 1.

b. $x^2 - 7x + 12$; $x^2 - 4.5x + 5$; $x^2 - \frac{1}{2}x - \frac{3}{2}$; $x^2 - 0x - 1$; $x^2 + 12x + 36$; $x^2 - 3x + 2 = 0$; $x^2 - 4.5x + 4.5 = 0$; $x^2 - 0x - 4 = 0$; $x^2 - 18x + 72 = 0$; $x^2 + 3\frac{1}{2}x - 2 = 0$

15. If a quadratic function has only one root, then the corresponding quadratic expression is a perfect square. The equation is $(x - 2)^2 = 0$.

16a. $x^2 + x - 12 = 0$
b. $x^2 + 6x + 8 = 0$
c. $-x^2 + 9 = 0$

273

Complex Numbers

Objectives

1 To identify and graph complex numbers
2 To add, subtract, and multiply complex numbers

Examples

1 Simplifying Numbers Using i
2 Simplifying Imaginary Numbers
3 Finding Absolute Value
4 Additive Inverse of a Complex Number
5 Adding Complex Numbers
6 Multiplying Complex Numbers
7 Finding Complex Solutions
8 Real-World Connection

Math Background

 Professional Development

Imaginary numbers, by name, are typically believed by students to not exist or to be "made up." However, they arise naturally from trying to find solutions to equations such as $x^2 + 1 = 0$.

More Math Background: p. 236D

Lesson Planning and Resources

See p. 236E for a list of the resources that support this lesson.

 PowerPoint

Bell Ringer Practice

✓ **Check Skills You'll Need**
For intervention, direct students to:

Operations with Radicals
Skills Handbook, p. 883
Example 1

What You'll Learn

• To identify and graph complex numbers
• To add, subtract, and multiply complex numbers

. . . And Why

To explore fractals, as in Example 8

✓ **Check Skills You'll Need** **GO for Help** Skills Handbook page 883

Simplify each expression. Assume variables are nonnegative.

1. $\sqrt{3^2 + 4^2}$ 5
2. $\sqrt{(-2)^2 + 8^2}$ $2\sqrt{17}$
3. $\sqrt{5^2 + (-12)^2}$ 13
4. $\sqrt{6^2 + 10^2}$ $2\sqrt{34}$
5. $\sqrt{x^2 + x^2}$ $x\sqrt{2}$
6. $\sqrt{(3x)^2 + (4x)^2}$ $5x$

🔊 **New Vocabulary** • i • **imaginary number** • **complex numbers**
• **complex number plane**
• **absolute value of a complex number**

---

1 Identifying Complex Numbers

When you learned to count, you used the natural numbers 1, 2, 3, and so on. Your number system has grown to include other types of numbers. You have used real numbers, which include both rational numbers such as $\frac{1}{2}$ and irrational numbers such as $\sqrt{2}$. Now your number system will expand to include numbers such as $\sqrt{-2}$.

The imaginary number i is defined as the number whose square is -1. So $i^2 = -1$ and $i = \sqrt{-1}$. An **imaginary number** is any number of the form $a + bi$, where a and b are real numbers, and $b \neq 0$.

 Key Concepts

Property	Square Root of a Negative Real Number

For any positive real number a, $\sqrt{-a} = i\sqrt{a}$.

Example $\sqrt{-4} = i\sqrt{4} = i \cdot 2 = 2i$
Note that $(\sqrt{-4})^2 = (i\sqrt{4})^2 = i^2\sqrt{4}^2 = -1 \cdot 4 = -4$ (not 4).

 GO Online

Video Tutor Help
Visit: PHSchool.com
Web Code: age-0775

1 EXAMPLE Simplifying Numbers Using i

Simplify $\sqrt{-8}$ by using the imaginary number i.

$\sqrt{-8} = i \cdot \sqrt{8}$ Use the Square Root Property of Negative Numbers.
$= i \cdot 2\sqrt{2}$ Simplify $\sqrt{8}$.
$= 2i\sqrt{2}$ Use the Commutative Property.

 ✓ **Quick Check** ❶ Simplify each number by using the imaginary number i.

a. $\sqrt{-2}$ $i\sqrt{2}$
b. $\sqrt{-12}$ $2i\sqrt{3}$
c. $\sqrt{-36}$ $6i$
d. Now that $\sqrt{a}$ is defined for $a < 0$, explain why $\sqrt{a^2} \neq (\sqrt{a})^2$.
$\sqrt{a^2} = |a|, (\sqrt{a})^2 = a$

Differentiated Instruction Solutions for All Learners

Special Needs L1
Some students may think $i^2 = 1$ because they believe all squares are positive. Write the following on the board: $i = \sqrt{-1}$, $i^2 = \sqrt{-1} \cdot \sqrt{-1}$, so $i^2 = -1$. Also, some students may think $\sqrt{-25} = \sqrt{25}i = 5\sqrt{i}$ instead of $\sqrt{-25} = \sqrt{25} \cdot \sqrt{-1} = 5i$.

learning style: verbal

Below Level L2
Have students graph 3, 4, and 3 + 4 on a real number line, and then graph $3 + 4i$ on the complex plane. Discuss the fact that $3 + 4i$ cannot be simplified.

learning style: visual

Imaginary numbers and real numbers together make up the set of
complex numbers.

![key concept icon] **Key Concepts**

Definition	Complex Numbers

A complex number can be written in the form $a + bi$,
where a and b are real numbers, including 0.

$$a \ + \ bi$$

↑ Real part   ↑ Imaginary part

2 EXAMPLE   **Simplifying Imaginary Numbers**

Write the complex number $\sqrt{-9} + 6$ in the form $a + bi$.

$\sqrt{-9} + 6 = 3i + 6$ **Simplify the radical expression.**

$= 6 + 3i$ **Write in the form $a + bi$.**

✓ **Quick Check** ② Write the complex number $\sqrt{-18} + 7$ in the form $a + bi$. $7 + 3i\sqrt{2}$

The diagram below shows the sets of numbers that are part of the complex number system, and examples of each set.

Complex Numbers

Real Numbers: $-5, -\sqrt{3}, 0, \sqrt{5}, \frac{8}{3}, 9$	Imaginary Numbers:

Rational Numbers: $-5, 0, \frac{8}{3}, 9$ | Irrational Numbers:

Integers: $-5, 0, 9$

Whole Numbers: $0, 9$

Natural Numbers: 9

$-\sqrt{3}$

$\sqrt{5}$

$-4i$

$3 + 2i$

$2i\sqrt{2}$

① EXAMPLE   Teaching Tip

Some students may find the example easier to follow if you insert a third line such as $\sqrt{i^2} \cdot \sqrt{8}$. This will help students see the substitution of i^2 for -1.

② EXAMPLE   Teaching Tip

Students are used to algebraic expressions with the variable terms written before the constant. Explain that i is not a variable. In the standard form of a complex number, the imaginary portion (in this case, $3i$) always comes after the real portion.

③ EXAMPLE   Error Prevention

A common error in finding the absolute value of a complex number is to somehow include i in the formula $\sqrt{a^2 + b^2}$. Emphasize that the distance formula does NOT include i.

Additional Examples

① Simplify $\sqrt{-54}$ by using the imaginary number i. $3i\sqrt{6}$

② Write the complex number $\sqrt{-121} - 7$ in the form $a + bi$. $-7 + 11i$

③ Find each absolute value.
a. $|-7i|$ 7
b. $|10 + 24i|$ 26

You can use the **complex number plane** to represent a complex number geometrically. Locate the real part of the number on the horizontal axis and the imaginary part on the vertical axis. You graph $3 - 4i$ in the same way you would graph $(3, -4)$ on the coordinate plane.

Vocabulary Tip

Pythagorean Theorem:
$c^2 = a^2 + b^2$ and
$c = \sqrt{a^2 + b^2}$

The **absolute value of a complex number** is its distance from the origin on the complex number plane. You can find the absolute value by using the Pythagorean Theorem. In general,
$|a + bi| = \sqrt{a^2 + b^2}$.

3 EXAMPLE   **Finding Absolute Value**

3a. $2\sqrt{13}$

b. $\sqrt{29}$

c. 4

a. Find $|5i|$.

$5i$ is 5 units from the origin on the imaginary axis. So $|5i| = 5$.

b. Find $|3 - 4i|$.

$|3 - 4i| = \sqrt{3^2 + (-4)^2}$
$= \sqrt{9 + 16} = 5$

✓ **Quick Check** ③ Find the absolute value of each complex number.
a. $|6 - 4i|$ **b.** $|-2 + 5i|$ **c.** $|4i|$

Lesson 5-6   Complex Numbers   **275**

Advanced Learners L4
Discuss the difference between $\sqrt{-2} \cdot \sqrt{-3}$ and $\sqrt{(-2)(-3)}$ and have students check their understanding by using a calculator.

learning style: verbal

English Language Learners ELL
Have students write a variety of complex numbers on the board and label each *real part* and *imaginary part*. Then have students graph the numbers on the complex plane and find their absolute values.

learning style: visual

4 EXAMPLE **Math Tip**

Students should observe that the additive inverse of $a + bi$ is $-a + (-bi)$ or $-a - bi$.

5 EXAMPLE **Connection to Algebra**

Point out that you are basically combining like terms. In the case of complex numbers, first add or subtract the real components, then add or subtract the imaginary components.

6 EXAMPLE **Alternative Method**

Instead of using FOIL, you can use FLOI when multiplying $(a + bi)(a - bi)$ to keep the pairs of real and imaginary numbers side-by-side.

PowerPoint

Additional Examples

4 Find the additive inverse of $-7 - 9i$. $7 + 9i$

5 Simplify the expression $(3 + 6i) - (4 - 8i)$. $-1 + 14i$

6 Find each product.
a. $(3i)(8i)$ -24
b. $(3 - 7i)(2 - 4i)$ $-22 - 26i$

You can apply the operations of real numbers to complex numbers.

If the sum of two complex numbers is 0, then each number is the opposite, or additive inverse, of the other.

4 EXAMPLE **Additive Inverse of a Complex Number**

Find the additive inverse of $-2 + 5i$.

$-2 + 5i$

$-(-2 + 5i)$ **Find the opposite.**

$2 - 5i$ **Simplify.**

✓ **Quick Check** **4** Find the additive inverse of each number.

a. $-5i$ $\;$ $5i$ $\qquad$ b. $4 - 3i$ $\;$ $-4 + 3i$ $\qquad$ c. $a + bi$ $\;$ $-a - bi$

To add or subtract complex numbers, combine the real parts and the imaginary parts separately.

5 EXAMPLE **Adding Complex Numbers**

Simplify the expression $(5 + 7i) + (-2 + 6i)$.

$(5 + 7i) + (-2 + 6i) = 5 + (-2) + 7i + 6i$ **Use commutative and associative properties.**

$= 3 + 13i$ **Simplify.**

✓ **Quick Check** **5** Simplify each expression.

a. $(8 + 3i) - (2 + 4i)$ $\qquad$ b. $7 - (3 + 2i)$ $\qquad$ c. $(4 - 6i) + 3i$
$\quad$ $6 - i$ $\qquad\qquad\qquad$ $4 - 2i$ $\qquad\qquad\qquad$ $4 - 3i$

For two imaginary numbers bi and ci, $(bi)(ci) = bc(i)^2 = bc(-1) = -bc$.

You can multiply two complex numbers of the form $a + bi$ by using the procedure for multiplying binomials.

6 EXAMPLE **Multiplying Complex Numbers**

a. Find $(5i)(-4i)$.

$(5i)(-4i) = -20i^2$ **Multiply the real numbers.**

$= -20(-1)$ **Substitute -1 for i^2.**

$= 20$ **Multiply.**

b. Find $(2 + 3i)(-3 + 5i)$.

$(2 + 3i)(-3 + 5i) = -6 + 10i - 9i + 15i^2$ **Multiply the binomials.**

$= -6 + 10i - 9i + 15(-1)$ **Substitute -1 for i^2.**

$= -21 + i$ **Simplify.**

✓ **Quick Check** **6** Simplify each expression.

a. $(12i)(7i)$ $\;$ -84 $\qquad$ b. $(6 - 5i)(4 - 3i)$ $\qquad$ c. $(4 - 9i)(4 + 3i)$
$\qquad\qquad\qquad\qquad$ $9 - 38i$ $\qquad\qquad\qquad$ $43 - 24i$

Some quadratic equations have solutions that are complex numbers.

7 EXAMPLE **Finding Complex Solutions**

Solve $4x^2 + 100 = 0$.

$4x^2 + 100 = 0$

$\qquad 4x^2 = -100 \qquad$ Isolate x^2.

$\qquad x^2 = -25$

$\qquad x = \pm\sqrt{-25} \qquad$ Find square roots.

$\qquad = \pm 5i \qquad$ Simplify.

Check $\qquad 4x^2 + 100 = 0$

$\qquad 4(5i)^2 + 100 \stackrel{?}{=} 0$

$\qquad 4(25i^2) \stackrel{?}{=} -100$

$\qquad 4(-25) \stackrel{?}{=} -100$

$\qquad -100 = -100 \checkmark$

$\qquad 4x^2 + 100 = 0$

$\qquad 4(-5i)^2 + 100 \stackrel{?}{=} 0$

$\qquad 4(25i^2) \stackrel{?}{=} -100$

$\qquad 4(-25) = -100$

$\qquad -100 = -100 \checkmark$

 Quick Check **7** Solve each equation. Check your answers.

a. $3x^2 + 48 = 0$ **b.** $-5x^2 - 150 = 0$ **c.** $8x^2 + 2 = 0$
    $\pm 4i$ $\pm i\sqrt{30}$ $\pm\frac{1}{2}i$

Functions of the form $f(z) = z^2 + c$ where c is a complex number generate fractal graphs on the complex plane like the one at the left. To test if z belongs to the graph, use 0 as the first input value and repeatedly use each output as the next input. If the output values do not become infinitely large, then z is on the graph.

8 EXAMPLE **Real-World 🌐 Connection**

Fractals Find the first three output values for $f(z) = z^2 + i$.

$\qquad f(z) = z^2 + i$

$\qquad f(0) = 0^2 + i \qquad$ Use $z = 0$ as the first input value.

$\qquad\quad = i$

$\qquad f(i) = i^2 + i \qquad$ First output becomes second input. Evaluate for $z = i$.

$\qquad\quad = -1 + i$

$\qquad f(-1 + i) = (-1 + i)^2 + i \qquad$ Second output becomes third input.
$\qquad\qquad\qquad\qquad\qquad\qquad$ Evaluate for $z = -1 + i$.

$\qquad\quad = [(-1)^2 + (-1)(i) + (-1)(i) + (i)^2] + i$

$\qquad\quad = (1 - 2i - 1) + i$

$\qquad\quad = -i \qquad$ Third output would be next input.

The first three output values are i, $-1 + i$, and $-i$.

Quick Check **8** Find the first three output values for $f(z) = z^2 - 1 + i$.
$\qquad\qquad\qquad\qquad\qquad -1 + i, -1 - i, -1 + 3i$

Point out that the equation $x^2 = -25$ has two solutions, $\sqrt{-25}$ and $-\sqrt{-25}$, which are simplified as $5i$ and $-5i$.

PowerPoint

Additional Examples

7 Solve $9x^2 + 54 = 0$. $\pm i\sqrt{6}$

8 Find the first three output values for $f(z) = z^2 - 4i$. Use $z = 0$ as the first input value. $-4i$, $-16 - 4i$, $240 + 124i$

Resources
• Daily Notetaking Guide 5-6 **L3**

Closure

Ask: *What are the two complex numbers that have a square of -1?* i, $-i$

Assignment Guide

1 A B 1-23, 53-55

2 A B 24-52, 56-70

C Challenge   71-75

Test Prep   76-80
Mixed Review   81-89

Homework Quick Check
To check students' understanding of key skills and concepts, go over Exercises 21, 43, 53, 55, 56, 64.

Error Prevention!

Exercises 20–23 Remind students that the absolute value of a complex number is its distance from the origin in the complex plane. Thus, in Exercise 20, $|5 + 12i|$ is not $|5| + |12i| = 17$ but rather $\sqrt{5^2 + 12^2} = 13$.

Exercise 35 Avoid saying that the exercise involves multiplying a negative by a positive imaginary number. The terms *positive* and *negative* connote *greater than 0* and *less than 0*. Order relations $<$, $\leq$, $>$, and $\geq$ are undefined for imaginary numbers.

EXERCISES

For more exercises, see *Extra Skill and Word Problem Practice*.

Practice and Problem Solving

A Practice by Example

 for Help

Example 1 (page 274)

Simplify each number by using the imaginary number i.

1. $\sqrt{-4}$ **2i**   2. $\sqrt{-7}$ $i\sqrt{7}$ 3. $\sqrt{-15}$ $i\sqrt{15}$ 4. $\sqrt{-81}$ **9i**   5. $\sqrt{-50}$ $5i\sqrt{2}$

6. $\sqrt{-16}$ **4i**   7. $\sqrt{-32}$ $4i\sqrt{2}$ 8. $3\sqrt{-9}$ **9i**   9. $-\sqrt{-100}$ $-10i$ 10. $\sqrt{-72}$ $6i\sqrt{2}$

Example 2 (page 275)

Write each number in the form $a + bi$. **11–18. See margin.**

11. $2 + \sqrt{-3}$ 12. $\sqrt{-8} + 8$ 13. $6 - \sqrt{-28}$ 14. $\sqrt{-4} + 3$

15. $7 - \sqrt{-25}$ 16. $\sqrt{-1} + 2$ 17. $-\sqrt{-50} - 2$ 18. $\sqrt{-72} + 4$

Example 3 (page 275)

Find the absolute value of each complex number.

19. $|2i|$ **2**   20. $|5 + 12i|$ **13**   21. $|2 - 2i|$ $2\sqrt{2}$ 22. $|1 - 4i|$ $\sqrt{17}$ 23. $|3 - 6i|$ $3\sqrt{5}$

Example 4 (page 276)

Find the additive inverse of each number.

24. $4i$ $-4i$ 25. $5 - 3i$ $-5 + 3i$ 26. $9 + i$ $-9 - i$ 27. $-3 - 2i$ $3 + 2i$ 28. $-4 + 7i$ $4 - 7i$

Example 5 (page 276)

Simplify each expression. **29–40. See margin p. 278–279.**

29. $(2 + 4i) + (4 - i)$ 30. $(-3 - 5i) + (4 - 2i)$ 31. $(7 + 9i) + (-5i)$

32. $6 - (8 + 3i)$ 33. $(12 + 5i) - (2 - i)$ 34. $(-6 - 7i) - (1 + 3i)$

Example 6 (page 276)

35. $(-2i)(5i)$ 36. $(4 - 3i)(5 + 2i)$ 37. $(8 + i)(2 + 7i)$

38. $(-6 - 5i)(1 + 3i)$ 39. $(-6i)^2$ 40. $(9 + 4i)^2$

Example 7 (page 277)

Solve each equation. Check your answers.

41. $x^2 + 25 = 0$ $\pm 5i$ 42. $2x^2 + 1 = 0$ $\pm\frac{i\sqrt{2}}{2}$ 43. $3s^2 + 2 = -62$ $\pm\frac{8i\sqrt{3}}{3}$

44. $x^2 = -7$ $\pm i\sqrt{7}$ 45. $x^2 + 36 = 0$ $\pm 6i$ 46. $-5x^2 - 3 = 0$ $\pm\frac{i\sqrt{15}}{5}$

Example 8 (page 277)

Find the first three output values of each fractal-generating function. Use $z = 0$ as the first input value.

47. $z^2 - i$ $-i, -1 - i, i$ 48. $f(z) = z^2 - 2i$ $-2i, -4 - 2i, 12 + 14i$ 49. $f(z) = z^2 + 1 - i$ $1 - i, 1 - 3i, -7 - 7i$

B Apply Your Skills

Solve each equation.

50. $x^2 + 16 = -49$ $\pm i\sqrt{65}$ 51. $x^2 - 30 = -79$ $\pm 7i$ 52. $3x^2 + 1 = x^2 - 1$ $\pm i$

53. **Writing** In reality, is it possible for Mr. Milde's average to be an imaginary number? Explain. **See margin p. 279.**

ROBOTMAN by Jim Meddick

11. $2 + i\sqrt{3}$

12. $8 + 2i\sqrt{2}$

13. $6 - 2i\sqrt{7}$

14. $3 + 2i$

15. $7 - 5i$

16. $2 + i$

17. $-2 - 5i\sqrt{2}$

18. $4 + 6i\sqrt{2}$

29. $6 + 3i$

30. $1 - 7i$

31. $7 + 4i$

32. $-2 - 3i$

33. $10 + 6i$

54. a. Name the complex number represented by each point on the graph at the right.
   b. Find the additive inverse of each number. **a–b. See margin.**
55. Multiple Choice In a complex number plane, what geometric figure describes the complex numbers with absolute value 10? **B**

　Ⓐ square　　Ⓑ circle
　Ⓒ line　　　Ⓓ two points

56. Solve $(x + 3i)(x - 3i) = 34$. **−5, 5**

GPS

Simplify each expression.

57. $(8i)(4i)(-9i)$ **288i**

58. $(2 + \sqrt{-1}) + (-3 + \sqrt{-16})$　**−1 + 5i**

59. 10 − 4i

59. $(4 + \sqrt{-9}) + (6 - \sqrt{-49})$

60. 8 − 2i

60. $(10 + \sqrt{-9}) - (2 + \sqrt{-25})$

61. 11 − 5i

61. $(8 - \sqrt{-1}) - (-3 + \sqrt{-16})$

62. $2i(5 - 3i)$　**6 + 10i**

63. $-5(1 + 2i) + 3i(3 - 4i)$　**7 − i**

64. $(3 + \sqrt{-4})(4 + \sqrt{-1})$　**10 + 11i**

65. $(-2 + \sqrt{-9})(6 + \sqrt{-25})$　**−27 + 8i**　**66.** $(1 - \sqrt{-4})(-3 - \sqrt{-25})$　**−13 + i**

67. a. Copy and complete the table.
   b. Number pairs such as p and q in the table are complex conjugates. Describe at least three patterns you see in complex conjugate pairs.

Values of p and q	$p + q$	$p \cdot q$	$|p|$	$|q|$
$p = 1 + 2i,\ q = 1 - 2i$	■	■	■	■
$p = 3 - i,\ q = 3 + i$	■	■	■	■
$p = -6 + 8i,\ q = -6 - 8i$	■	■	■	■

   c. Plot each pair of conjugates. How are the points of each pair related?
   d. True or false: The conjugate of an additive inverse is equal to the additive inverse of the conjugate. Explain your answer. **a–d. See back of book.**

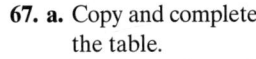

Visit: PHSchool.com
Web Code: age-0506

Two complex numbers $a + bi$ and $c + di$ are equal when $a = c$ and $b = d$. Solve each equation for x and y.

68. $2x + 3yi = -14 + 9i$
   $x = -7, y = 3$

69. $3x + 19i = 16 - 8yi$
   $x = \frac{16}{3}, y = -\frac{19}{8}$

70. $-14 - 3i = 2x + yi$
   $x = -7, y = -3$

Ⓒ **Challenge**

71. Show that the product of a nonzero complex number $a + bi$ and its conjugate (as described in Exercise 67) is a real number. **See margin.**

72. Fractals The fractal at the left can be described by the function $f(z) = z^2 + c$. If $c = 0.383 + 0.11i$, find the first two output values of the function. Use $z = 0$ as the first input value.
0.383 + 0.11i, 0.517589 + 0.19426i

73. For what real values of x and y is $(x + yi)^2$ an imaginary number?
nonzero real numbers x and y

74. Complex numbers can be used to generate interesting patterns. Here is a pattern generated by powers of $1 + 3i$. **See back of book.**

$(1 + 3i)^1 = 1 + 3i$ and $1^2 + 3^2 = 10$
$(1 + 3i)^2 = -8 + 6i$ and $(-8)^2 + 6^2 = 10^2$
$(1 + 3i)^3 = -26 - 18i$ and $(-26)^2 + (-18)^2 = 10^3$
$(1 + 3i)^4 = 28 - 96i$ and $28^2 + (-96)^2 = 10^4$

Find the powers of $3 + 4i$ through $(3 + 4i)^5$. Generate and verify a similar pattern.

Exercise 72

34. −7 − 10i

35. 10

36. 26 − 7i

37. 9 + 58i

38. 9 − 23i

39. −36

40. 65 + 72i

53. No; the test scores were real numbers. He added the scores and divided by the number of scores. The set of real numbers is closed with respect to addition and division so he should have gotten a real number

PowerPoint

Lesson Quiz

1. Simplify $-\sqrt{-169}$. **−13i**

2. Find $|-1 + i|$. $\sqrt{2}$

Simplify each expression.

3. $(-7i)(-3i)$ **−21**

4. $(9 + 10i) + (-7 + 4i)$
   2 + 14i

5. $(-3 + 4i) - (-3 - 8i)$ **12i**

6. $(-5 + 2i)(7 - 4i)$
   −27 + 34i

7. Solve $\frac{1}{2}x^2 + 2 = 0$. **±2i**

Alternative Assessment

Ask each student to write two complex numbers, where a and b are nonzero, on a sheet of paper. Students trade papers. Each student then adds, subtracts, and multiplies the numbers on the paper he or she received. Students also find the absolute value of each complex number. Students check one another's work.

Exercise 55 Have students review the definition of the absolute value of a complex number.

54a. *A*: −5, *B*: 3 + 2i,
   C: 2 − i, *D*: 3i,
   E: −6 − 4i,
   F: −1 + 5i

b. 5, −3 − 2i, −2 + i, −3i,
   6 + 4i, 1 − 5i

71. $(a + bi)(a - bi) = a^2 + b^2$; since a and b are real, so is $a^2 + b^2$.

279

Test Prep

Resources

For additional practice with a variety of test item formats:
- Standardized Test Prep, p. 303
- Test-Taking Strategies, p. 298
- Test-Taking Strategies with Transparencies

Checkpoint Quiz

Use this Checkpoint Quiz to check students' understanding of the skills and concepts of Lessons 5-4 through 5-6.

Resources
Grab & Go
- Checkpoint Quiz 2

75. Critical Thinking Graph $1 + 3i$ and $6 + 2i$. Also graph their sum. Draw the quadrilateral that has these three points and the origin as vertices. Repeat with other complex numbers. What do you notice?   **See margin.**

Test Prep

Multiple Choice

76. What is the number $\sqrt{-225} + 36$ when written in the form $a + bi$? **D**
   A. $-15 + 6i$ B. $6 + 15i$ C. $6 - 15i$ D. $36 + 15i$

77. How can you rewrite the expression $(8 - 5i)^2$ in the form $a + bi$? **G**
   F. $39 + 80i$ G. $39 - 80i$ H. $69 + 80i$ J. $69 - 80i$

78. What are the solutions of $-4x^2 - 72 = 0$? **B**
   A. $\pm 2i\sqrt{3}$ B. $\pm 3i\sqrt{2}$ C. $\pm 2\sqrt{3}$ D. $\pm 3\sqrt{2}$

79. Which description of the graph of $y = ax^2 + bx + c$ is NOT possible? **H**
   F. There are two x-intercepts, the vertex is below the x-axis, and $a > 0$.
   G. There is one x-intercept and the vertex is on the x-axis.
   H. There are two x-intercepts, the vertex is below the x-axis, and $a < 0$.
   J. There are no x-intercepts, the vertex is above the x-axis, and $a > 0$.

Extended Response

80. Use factoring to find all complex solutions to $x^4 - 16 = 0$. Show your work.
   See back of book.

Mixed Review

GO for Help

Lesson 5-5

Solve each equation using a graphing calculator.

81. $2x^2 + 3x - 4 = 0$
   $-2.351, 0.851$

82. $4x^2 + x = 1$
   $-0.640, 0.390$

83. $x^2 = -7x - 8$
   $-5.562, -1.438$

Lesson 5-2

Graph each function. **84–86. See margin.**

84. $y = -2(x + 1)^2 - 3$ **85.** $y = \frac{1}{2}(x - 4)^2 + 1$ **86.** $y = 3(x - 1)^2 - 5$

Lesson 3-5

Graph each point in coordinate space. **87–89. See margin p. 280–281.**

87. $(2, 0, -4)$ **88.** $(0, -3, 5)$ **89.** $(9, -1, 0)$

Checkpoint Quiz 2

Lessons 5-4 through 5-6

Factor each quadratic expression.

1. $2x^2 + x - 6$
   $(2x - 3)(x + 2)$

2. $5x^2 - 45$
   $5(x + 3)(x - 3)$

3. $4x^2 - 36x + 81$
   $(2x - 9)^2$

Solve each equation.

4. $(3x - 3)(2x + 8) = 0$
   $-4, 1$

5. $x^2 - 2x + 1 = 0$ 1

6. $x^2 + 121 = 0$
   $\pm 11i$

Find the absolute value of each number.

7. $5 - 2i$ $\sqrt{29}$

8. $9 - i$ $\sqrt{82}$

9. $7 + 4i$ $\sqrt{65}$

10. Can you solve the equation $x^2 + 7x + 14 = 0$ by graphing the related function $y = x^2 + 7x + 14$? Explain. **No; the graph does not intersect the x-axis.**

280   Chapter 5   Quadratic Equations and Functions

75.

If the points for the origin, $a + bi$, $c + di$, and the sum are not collinear, then they form the vertices of a parallelogram.

84.

85.

86.

87.

$(2, 0, -4)$

Completing the Square

Use tiles or draw a diagram. Copy the model below.

1. a. Add unit tiles until you have a complete square. How many tiles did you add?   **9**
  b. Write an expression to represent the sum of the areas of the tiles. $x^2 + 6x + 9$
  c. Write an expression to represent the length times the width of the completed square. $(x + 3)(x + 3)$
  d. How do the six x-tiles in the model relate to the length of the sides of the completed square? To the number of unit tiles used?   **See margin.**

$x^2 + 6x + \blacksquare$

2. Suppose the expression $x^2 + 8x + \blacksquare$ can also be modeled by a complete square of tiles.   **a. See margin.**
  a. Draw a diagram or use tiles to find the missing value.
  b. What is the coefficient of x in the expression?   **8**
  c. **Critical Thinking** How can you use the coefficient of x to find the length of the completed square?   **Add half the coefficient of x to x.**

3. Suppose $x^2 - 4x + \blacksquare$ can be modeled by a complete square of tiles. Using red to represent negative values, draw a diagram or use tiles to find the missing value.   **See margin.**

EXERCISES

Complete each square. Then write an expression that represents the sum of the areas of the tiles and an expression that represents the length times the width of the completed square.   1–3. See back of book.

1.

2.

3.

Assume that each expression can be modeled by a complete square of tiles. Find the missing value.

4. $x^2 + 14x + \blacksquare$ **49**

5. $x^2 + 20x + \blacksquare$ **100**

6. $x^2 + 10x + \blacksquare$ **25**

7. $x^2 + 100x + \blacksquare$ **2500**

8. $x^2 + 32x + \blacksquare$ **256**

9. $x^2 - 8x + \blacksquare$ **16**

10. Make a Conjecture In Lesson 5-5, you solved quadratic equations by taking square roots. How could you use that method together with completing the square to solve $x^2 + 6x + 6 = 0$?   **See back of book.**

88.

89. (in margin bottom)

Using algebra tiles for demonstrating the process of completing the square is very helpful to both visual and tactile learners. They make and see the square.

Guided Instruction

Special Needs   **L1**
Students who have difficulty drawing diagrams will find it helpful to use algebra tiles for this investigation.

Error Prevention!

Exercise 10 Some students may try to get a perfect-square trinomial on the left side by rewriting the equation as $x^2 + 4x + 4 = -2x - 2$. Help students see why this leads to a dead end.

Resources

Students may use algebra tiles or diagrams for the work in this investigation.

Activity Lab

1d. Half of the six x-tiles complete the length of each side of the square; the square of this number is the number of unit tiles.

2a.

3.

1. Plan

Objectives

1 To solve equations by completing the square
2 To rewrite functions by completing the square

Examples

1 Solving a Perfect Square Trinomial Equation
2 Completing the Square
3 Solving by Completing the Square
4 Finding Complex Solutions
5 Solving When $a \neq 1$
6 Rewriting in Vertex Form
7 Real-World Connection

Math Background

Completing the square provides a useful tool for locating the vertex of a quadratic function. This method explains the formula $x = -\frac{b}{2a}$ that was used in Lesson 5-2. Also, completing the square and the square root technique learned in Lesson 5-5 combine in the proof of the quadratic formula in Lesson 5-8. This is the method that will allow students to solve any quadratic equation.

More Math Background: p. 236D

Lesson Planning and Resources

See p. 236E for a list of the resources that support this lesson.

Bell Ringer Practice

✓ Check Skills You'll Need
For intervention, direct students to:

Modeling Data With Quadratic Functions
Lesson 5-1: Example 1
Extra Skills and Word Problems Practice, Ch. 5

5-7

Completing the Square

What You'll Learn

• To solve equations by completing the square
• To rewrite functions by completing the square

. . . And Why

To find a price to maximize profit, as in Example 7

✓ **Check Skills You'll Need**

 for Help Lesson 5-1 and page 266

Simplify each expression.

1. $(x - 3)(x - 3)$ $x^2 - 6x + 9$ 2. $(2x - 1)(2x - 1)$ $4x^2 - 4x + 1$

3. $(x + 4)(x + 4) - 3$ $x^2 + 8x + 13$ 4. $\pm\sqrt{25}$ ± 5

5. $\pm\sqrt{48}$ $\pm 4\sqrt{3}$ 6. $\pm\sqrt{-4}$ $\pm 2i$ 7. $\pm\sqrt{\frac{9}{16}}$ $\pm\frac{3}{4}$

🔊 **New Vocabulary** • completing the square

---

1 Solving Equations by Completing the Square

You can solve an equation in which one side is a perfect square trinomial by finding square roots.

Vocabulary Tip

<u>Quadratic</u> comes from the Latin word for "square."

1 EXAMPLE Solving a Perfect Square Trinomial Equation

Solve $x^2 + 10x + 25 = 36$.

$x^2 + 10x + 25 = 36$

$(x + 5)^2 = 36$ **Factor the trinomial.**

$x + 5 = \pm 6$ **Find square roots.**

$x + 5 = 6$ or $x + 5 = -6$ **Solve for x.**

$x = 1$ or $x = -11$

✓ **Quick Check** ❶ Solve $x^2 - 14x + 49 = 81$. **−2, 16**

If one side of an equation is not a perfect square trinomial, you can rewrite the constant term to get a perfect square trinomial. The process of finding the last term of a perfect square trinomial is called **completing the square.** Use the following relationship to find the term that will complete the square.

GO nline

Video Tutor Help
Visit: PHSchool.com
Web Code: age-0775

$$x^2 + bx + \left(\frac{b}{2}\right)^2 = \left(x + \frac{b}{2}\right)^2$$

2 EXAMPLE Completing the Square

Find the missing value to complete the square: $x^2 - 8x + \blacksquare$.

$\left(\frac{b}{2}\right)^2 = \left(\frac{-8}{2}\right)^2 = 16$ **Find $\left(\frac{b}{2}\right)^2$. Substitute −8 for b.**

$x^2 - 8x + 16$ **Complete the square.**

✓ **Quick Check** ❷ Find the missing value to complete the square: $x^2 + 7x + \blacksquare$. $\frac{49}{4}$

282   Chapter 5 Quadratic Equations and Functions

Differentiated Instruction Solutions for All Learners

Special Needs L1	**Below Level** L2
In Example 5, point out that you can complete the square only if the x^2-term has a coefficient of 1. In this example, you have to divide both sides by 5 before you can complete the square.	Have students explain why the constant term, c, must be greater than or equal to zero in order for the trinomial to be a perfect square.
learning style: verbal	learning style: verbal

You can solve any quadratic equation by completing the square.

This stamp commemorates the 1200th birthday of al-Khwarizmi (780-850), who showed how to solve equations by completing the square. His book *Al-jabr w'al muqabala* gave algebra its name.

3 EXAMPLE Solving by Completing the Square

Solve $x^2 - 12x + 5 = 0$.

$$\left(\frac{-12}{2}\right)^2 = 36 \qquad \text{Find } \left(\frac{b}{2}\right)^2.$$

$$x^2 - 12x = -5 \qquad \text{Rewrite so all terms containing } x \text{ are on one side.}$$

$$x^2 - 12x + 36 = -5 + 36 \qquad \text{Complete the square by adding 36 to each side.}$$

$$(x - 6)^2 = 31 \qquad \text{Factor the perfect square trinomial.}$$

$$x - 6 = \pm\sqrt{31} \qquad \text{Find square roots.}$$

$$x = 6 \pm\sqrt{31} \qquad \text{Solve for } x.$$

Check

$$x^2 - 12x + 5 \overset{?}{=} 0$$

$$(6 + \sqrt{31})^2 - 12(6 + \sqrt{31}) + 5 \overset{?}{=} 0$$

$$6^2 + 2(6\sqrt{31}) + (\sqrt{31})^2 - 72 - 12\sqrt{31} + 5 \overset{?}{=} 0$$

$$36 + 12\sqrt{31} + 31 - 72 - 12\sqrt{31} + 5 \overset{?}{=} 0$$

$$(36 + 31 - 72 + 5) + (12\sqrt{31} - 12\sqrt{31}) \overset{?}{=} 0$$

$$0 = 0 \checkmark$$

$$x^2 - 12x + 5 \overset{?}{=} 0$$

$$(6 - \sqrt{31})^2 - 12(6 - \sqrt{31}) + 5 \overset{?}{=} 0$$

$$6^2 - 2(6\sqrt{31}) + (\sqrt{31})^2 - 72 + 12\sqrt{31} + 5 \overset{?}{=} 0$$

$$36 - 12\sqrt{31} + 31 - 72 + 12\sqrt{31} + 5 \overset{?}{=} 0$$

$$(36 + 31 - 72 + 5) - (12\sqrt{31} - 12\sqrt{31}) \overset{?}{=} 0$$

$$0 = 0 \checkmark$$

✓ Quick Check ③ Solve each equation. Check your solution.
a. $x^2 + 4x - 4 = 0$ $-2 \pm 2\sqrt{2}$ **b.** $x^2 - 2x - 1 = 0$ $1 \pm \sqrt{2}$

By completing the square, you can solve equations that cannot be solved by factoring, finding square roots, or graphing.

4 EXAMPLE Finding Complex Solutions

Solve $x^2 - 8x + 36 = 0$.

$$\left(\frac{-8}{2}\right)^2 = 16 \qquad \text{Find } \left(\frac{b}{2}\right)^2.$$

$$x^2 - 8x = -36 \qquad \text{Rewrite so all terms containing } x \text{ are on one side.}$$

$$x^2 - 8x + 16 = -36 + 16 \qquad \text{Complete the square by adding 16 to each side.}$$

$$(x - 4)^2 = -20 \qquad \text{Factor the perfect square trinomial.}$$

$$x - 4 = \pm\sqrt{-20} \qquad \text{Find square roots.}$$

$$x = 4 \pm 2i\sqrt{5} \qquad \text{Solve for } x \text{ and simplify.}$$

✓ Quick Check ④ **a.** Check the solution to Example 4. **a–b. See back of book.**
b. Try solving the same equation with a graphing calculator. Explain your results.
c. Solve $x^2 + 6x = -34$. $-3 \pm 5i$

Lesson 5-7 Completing the Square **283**

Point out that the technique used in this example can be combined with the technique used in Example 5 to rewrite, in vertex form, an equation in which $a \neq 1$, such as $y = 4x^2 + 9x + 3$.

⑦ EXAMPLE Teaching Tip

You may want to start with a simpler example with a leading coefficient of -1, such as $P = -x^2 - 6x + 3$. Then move on to the more difficult function in the example.

PowerPoint

📖 Additional Examples

⑥ Write $y = x^2 + 5x + 2$ in vertex form.
$y = \left(x + \frac{5}{2}\right)^2 - \frac{17}{4}$

⑦ The monthly profit P from the sale of rugs woven by a family rug-making business depends on the price r that they charge for a rug. The profit is modeled by $P = -r^2 + 500r - 59,500$. Write the function in vertex form. Use the vertex form to find the price that yields the maximum monthly profit and the amount of the maximum profit.
$P = -(r - 250)^2 + 3000$;
price = \$250, profit = \$3000

Resources
• Daily Notetaking Guide 5-7 **L3**

Closure

Ask: *If a quadratic expression is not a perfect-square trinomial, how can you find the number you would add to each side to get a perfect-square trinomial on the left side of the equation?* Divide each side by the coefficient of x^2. Then find half the coefficient of x and square the result. Add this value to each side.

When the quadratic term has a coefficient that is not 1, you can still solve by completing the square. First divide each side of the equation by the coefficient.

⑤ EXAMPLE Solving When $a \neq 1$

Solve $5x^2 = 6x + 8$.

$$5x^2 = 6x + 8$$
$$x^2 = \frac{6}{5}x + \frac{8}{5} \qquad \text{Divide each side by 5.}$$
$$x^2 - \frac{6}{5}x = \frac{8}{5} \qquad \text{Rewrite so all terms containing } x \text{ are on one side.}$$
$$\left(\frac{-\frac{6}{5}}{2}\right)^2 = \left(-\frac{3}{5}\right)^2 = \frac{9}{25} \qquad \text{Find } \left(\frac{b}{2}\right)^2.$$
$$x^2 - \frac{6}{5}x + \frac{9}{25} = \frac{8}{5} + \frac{9}{25} \qquad \text{Complete the square by adding } \frac{9}{25} \text{ to each side.}$$
$$\left(x - \frac{3}{5}\right)^2 = \frac{49}{25} \qquad \text{Factor the perfect square trinomial.}$$
$$x - \frac{3}{5} = \pm\sqrt{\frac{49}{25}} \qquad \text{Find square roots.}$$
$$x = \frac{3}{5} \pm \frac{7}{5} \qquad \text{Solve for } x.$$
$$x = 2, -\frac{4}{5} \qquad \text{Simplify.}$$

Test-Taking Tip

When you solve $x^2 = a$ by finding square roots, you get $|x| = \sqrt{a}$, which is equivalent to $x = \pm\sqrt{a}$. For speed, you can go from $x^2 = a$ to $x = \pm\sqrt{a}$.

✓ Quick Check **⑤** Solve each quadratic equation by completing the square.
   a. $2x^2 + x = 6$ $-2, \frac{3}{2}$ **b.** $2x^2 = 3x - 4$ $\frac{3}{4} \pm \frac{i\sqrt{23}}{4}$

---

2   Rewriting a Function by Completing the Square

In Lesson 5-3 you converted quadratic functions into vertex form by using $x = -\frac{b}{2a}$ to find the x-coordinate of the parabola's vertex. Then, by substituting for x, you found the y-coordinate of the vertex. Another way of rewriting a function is to complete the square.

Vocabulary Tip

Vertex <u>form</u> of a quadratic function:
$y = a(x - h)^2 + k$

When completing the square, you can work with just one side of the function equation. For example, $y = x^2 + 6x + 2$ is equivalent to $y = x^2 + 6x + 9 + 2 - 9$. When you add 9 to the right side of the equation, you must remember to subtract 9 to keep the equations equivalent.

⑥ EXAMPLE Rewriting in Vertex Form

Write $y = x^2 + 6x + 2$ in vertex form.

$$y = x^2 + 6x + 2$$
$$= x^2 + 6x + 3^2 + 2 - 3^2 \qquad \text{Complete the square. Add and subtract } 3^2 \text{ on the right side.}$$
$$= (x + 3)^2 + 2 - 9 \qquad \text{Factor the perfect square trinomial.}$$
$$= (x + 3)^2 - 7 \qquad \text{Simplify.}$$

● The vertex form is $y = (x + 3)^2 - 7$.

✓ Quick Check **⑥** Write each equation in vertex form.
   a. $y = x^2 - 10x - 2$ $y = (x - 5)^2 - 27$ **b.** $y = x^2 + 5x + 3$ $y = \left(x + \frac{5}{2}\right)^2 - \frac{13}{4}$

13. $-4, 7$

14. $-1, 4$

15. $-3 \pm 4i\sqrt{2}$

When the coefficient of the quadratic term is not 1, factor out the coefficient from the quadratic and linear terms. Remember that the factored coefficient is distributed to all terms within the parentheses.

7 EXAMPLE Real-World Connection

Gridded Response The profit P from handmade sweaters depends on the price s at which each sweater is sold. The function $P = -s^2 + 120s - 2000$ models the monthly profit from sweaters for one custom tailor. What is the maximum monthly profit, in dollars, determined by this model?

$P = -s^2 + 120s - 2000$

$= -(s^2 - 120s) - 2000$ **Factor out −1.**

$= -[s^2 - 120s + (-60)^2] - 2000 + (-60)^2$

                                     Complete the square.

$= -(s - 60)^2 - 2000 + 3600$ **Factor.**

$= -(s - 60)^2 + 1600$ **Simplify.**

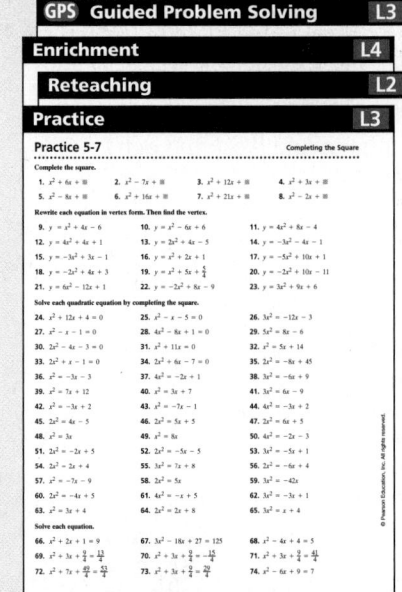

The quadratic function is in vertex form. The vertex is $(60, 1600)$. A price of \$60 per sweater gives a maximum monthly profit of \$1600.

✓ Quick Check **7** **a.** Use vertex form to find the vertex of $P = -\frac{1}{2}s^2 + 280s - 1200$. **(280, 38,000)**
b. How do you know the vertex represents a maximum point?
The coefficient of s^2 is negative, so the parabola opens downward.

Careers Custom tailors use math to design clothing and to calculate profit.

EXERCISES

For more exercises, see *Extra Skill and Word Problem Practice*.

Practice and Problem Solving

 A **Practice by Example**

 GO for Help

Example 1 (page 282)

Solve each equation.
1. $x^2 + 6x + 9 = 1$ −4, −2
2. $x^2 - 4x + 4 = 100$ −8, 12
3. $x^2 - 2x + 1 = 4$ −1, 3
4. $x^2 + 8x + 16 = \frac{16}{9}$ $-\frac{16}{3}, -\frac{8}{3}$
5. $4x^2 + 4x + 1 = 49$ −4, 3
6. $x^2 - 12x + 36 = 25$ 1, 11

Example 2 (page 282)

Complete the square.
7. $x^2 + 18x + \blacksquare$ 81
8. $x^2 - x + \blacksquare$ $\frac{1}{4}$
9. $x^2 - 24x + \blacksquare$ 144
10. $x^2 + 20x + \blacksquare$ 100
11. $m^2 - 3m + \blacksquare$ $\frac{9}{4}$
12. $x^2 + 4x + \blacksquare$ 4

Examples 3 and 4 (page 283)

Solve each quadratic equation by completing the square.
13. $x^2 - 3x = 28$
14. $x^2 - 3x = 4$
15. $x^2 + 6x + 41 = 0$

13–27. See margin.

16. $x^2 - 2x = -2$
17. $w^2 - 8w - 9 = 0$
18. $x^2 + 6x = -22$
19. $x^2 + 4 = 0$
20. $-x^2 - 2x = 5$
21. $6x - 3x^2 = -12$

Example 5 (page 284)

22. $2p^2 = 6p - 20$
23. $3x^2 - 12x + 7 = 0$
24. $4c^2 + 10c = -7$
25. $2x^2 + x - 28 = 0$
26. $9x^2 - 12x + 5 = 0$
27. $4x^2 + 4x = 3$

Example 6 (page 284)

Rewrite each equation in vertex form. 28–33. See margin.
28. $y = x^2 + 4x - 7$
29. $y = -x^2 + 4x - 1$
30. $y = -2x^2 + 6x + 1$
31. $y = x^2 + 4x + 1$
32. $y = 2x^2 - 8x + 1$
33. $y = -x^2 - 2x + 3$

16. $1 \pm i$
17. −1, 9
18. $-3 \pm i\sqrt{13}$
19. $\pm 2i$
20. $-1 \pm 2i$
21. $1 \pm \sqrt{5}$
22. $\frac{3}{2} \pm \frac{i\sqrt{31}}{2}$
23. $2 \pm \frac{\sqrt{15}}{3}$
24. $-\frac{5}{4} \pm \frac{i\sqrt{3}}{4}$
25. $-4, \frac{7}{2}$
26. $\frac{2}{3} \pm \frac{1}{3}i$
27. $-\frac{3}{2}, \frac{1}{2}$

3. Practice

Assignment Guide

1 A B   1-27, 40-48, 51-56
2 A B   28-39, 49-50
C Challenge   57-63

Test Prep   64-68
Mixed Review   69-77

Homework Quick Check
To check students' understanding of key skills and concepts, go over Exercises 17, 35, 38, 47, 50, 54.

Error Prevention!

Exercises 21–27 Students may add the wrong amount to the right side of the equation when they are completing the square. Caution them to remember to use the Distributive Property in deciding what number they should add on the right side.

Differentiated Instruction Resources

GPS Guided Problem Solving	L3
Enrichment	L4
Reteaching	L2
Practice	L3

28. $y = (x + 2)^2 - 11$
29. $y = -(x - 2)^2 + 3$
30. $y = -2\left(x - \frac{3}{2}\right)^2 + \frac{11}{2}$
31. $y = (x + 2)^2 - 3$
32. $y = 2(x - 2)^2 - 7$
33. $y = -(x + 1)^2 + 4$

285

📊 Lesson Quiz

Complete the square.

1. $x^2 + 60x + \blacksquare$ 900

2. $x^2 - 7x + \blacksquare$ $\frac{49}{4}$

Solve each equation by completing the square.

3. $x^2 - 6x - 16 = 0$ $-2, 8$

4. $x^2 - 14x + 74 = 0$ $7 \pm 5i$

5. $3x^2 + 5x - 28 = 0$ $-4, \frac{7}{3}$

6. $4x^2 - 6x + 3 = 0$ $\frac{3}{4} \pm i\frac{\sqrt{3}}{4}$

Alternative Assessment

Give students several quadratic equations to solve by completing the square. When students have solved the problems, ask them to use graphing calculators to check their solutions. If they have any discrepancies, ask them to work through the problem again to find their mistakes.

Diversity

Exercise 39 Some students may not be familiar enough with football to understand the terms used in this exercise. Ask for a volunteer to explain the meaning of *punted football, defensive player,* and *block the punt.*

34. $y = -4\left(x + \frac{5}{8}\right)^2 + \frac{73}{16}$;

$\left(-\frac{5}{8}, \frac{73}{16}\right)$

35. $y = \frac{1}{2}(x - 5)^2 - \frac{1}{2}$;

$\left(5, -\frac{1}{2}\right)$

36. $y = -\frac{1}{5}(x - 2)^2 + 3$;

$(2, 3)$

38. Add -11 to each side of the given equation to obtain $x^2 + 8x = -11$. Then add the square of half the coefficient of x to each side to obtain $x^2 + 8x + 4^2 = -11 + 4^2$, or $x^2 + 8x + 16 = 5$. Rewrite the left side of the last equation as $(x + 4)^2$ to obtain $(x + 4)^2 = 5$.

286

Example 7
(page 285)

37b. positive rational numbers less than 130; whole numbers up to 5000

 for Help

For a guide to solving Exercise 39, see page 288.

Apply Your Skills Ⓑ

GO ●nline
Homework Video Tutor
Visit: PHSchool.com
Web Code: age-0507

39e. Answers may vary. Sample: The path is parabolic. Also, the linear model does not predict that the ball will eventually hit the ground.

Rewrite each equation in vertex form. Then find the vertex of the graph.
34–36. See margin.

34. $y = -4x^2 - 5x + 3$

35. $y = \frac{1}{2}x^2 - 5x + 12$

36. $y = -\frac{1}{5}x^2 + \frac{4}{5}x + \frac{11}{5}$

37. **Manufacturing** An electronics company has a new line of portable radios with CD players. Their research suggests that the daily sales s for the new product can be modeled by $s = -p^2 + 120p + 1400$, where p is the price of each unit.
   a. Find the vertex of the graph of the function by completing the square.
   b. Describe a reasonable domain and range for the sales function. Explain.
   c. What price gives maximum daily sales? What are the maximum daily sales?
   a. $(60, 5000)$ c. $60; \$5000$

38. **Writing** Explain the process of rewriting $x^2 + 8x + 11 = 0$ as $(x + 4)^2 = 5$.
See margin.

39. **Sports** The height of a punted football can be modeled with the quadratic function $h = -0.01x^2 + 1.18x + 2$. The horizontal distance in feet from the point of impact with the kicker's foot is x, and h is the height of the ball in feet.

(59, 36.81)

   a. Find the vertex of the graph of the function by completing the square.
   b. What is the maximum height of the punt? **36.81 ft**
   c. The nearest defensive player is 5 ft horizontally from the point of impact. How high must the player reach to block the punt? **7.65 ft**
   d. Suppose the ball was not blocked but continued on its path. How far down field would the ball go before it hit the ground? **about 120 ft**
   e. **Critical Thinking** The linear equation $h = 1.13x + 2$ could model the path of the football shown in the graph. Why is this not a good model?
See margin.

Find the value of k that would make the left side of each equation a perfect square trinomial.

40. $x^2 + kx + 25 = 0$ $-10, 10$

41. $x^2 - kx + 100 = 0$ $-20, 20$

42. $x^2 - kx + 121 = 0$ $-22, 22$

43. $x^2 + kx + 64 = 0$ $-16, 16$

44. $x^2 - kx + 81 = 0$ $-18, 18$

45. $25x^2 - kx + 1 = 0$ $-10, 10$

46. $x^2 + kx + \frac{1}{4} = 0$ $-1, 1$

47. $9x^2 - kx + 4 = 0$ $-12, 12$

48. $36x^2 - kx + 1 = 0$ $-12, 12$

 49. **Geometry** The table shows some possible dimensions of rectangles with a perimeter of 100 units. Complete the table.   a–e. See back of book.

Width	1	2	3	4	5	6	7	8	9	10
Length	49	48	■	■	■	■	■	■	■	■
Area	49	■	■	■	■	■	■	■	■	■

   a. Plot the points (width, area). Find a model for the data set.
   b. Find another point in the data set and use it to verify your model.
   c. What is a reasonable domain for this function? Explain.
   d. Find the maximum possible area. Find its dimensions.
   e. Find an equation for area in terms of width without using the table. Do you get the same equation as in part (a)? Explain.

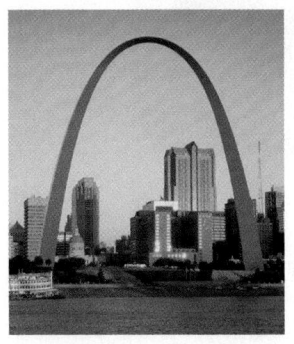

Gateway Arch in St. Louis

50. Architecture The shape of the Gateway Arch in St. Louis, Missouri, is a catenary curve, which closely resembles a parabola. The function $y = -\frac{2}{315}x^2 + 4x$ models the shape of the arch, where y is the height in feet and x is the horizontal distance from the base of the left side of the arch in feet.
   a. Graph the function and find its vertex. **a–b. See margin.**
   b. Describe a reasonable domain and range for the function. Explain.
   c. According to the model, what is the maximum height of the arch? **630 ft**
   d. What is the width of the arch at the base? **630 ft**

Solve each quadratic equation by completing the square. **51–56. See margin.**

51. $\frac{1}{3}x^2 + 8x - 3 = 0$ **52.** $\frac{1}{2}x^2 + 4x = 2$ **53.** $x^2 - \frac{1}{2}x = \frac{1}{3}$

54. $3x^2 + x = \frac{2}{3}$ **55.** $2x^2 - \frac{1}{2}x = \frac{1}{8}$ **56.** $x^2 + \frac{3}{4}x = \frac{1}{2}$

 Challenge   Solve for x in terms of a. **57–62. See margin.**

57. $2x^2 - ax = 6a^2$ **58.** $3x^2 + ax = a^2$ **59.** $2a^2x^2 - 8ax = -6$

60. $4a^2x^2 + 8ax + 3 = 0$ **61.** $3x^2 + ax^2 = 9x + 9a$ **62.** $6a^2x^2 - 11ax = 10$

63. Solve $x^2 = (6\sqrt{2})x + 7$ by completing the square. $-5 + 3\sqrt{2}, 5 + 3\sqrt{2}$

Test Prep

Test Prep

Resources
For additional practice with a variety of test item formats:
• Standardized Test Prep, p. 303
• Test-Taking Strategies, p. 298
• Test-Taking Strategies with Transparencies

Multiple Choice
64. What can you add to $x^2 + 5x$ to get a perfect square trinomial? **A**
   A. $\frac{25}{4}$ **B.** $\frac{25}{2}$ **C.** 25   **D.** 2.5x

65. How can you rewrite the equation $x^2 + 12x + 5 = 3$ so the left side of the equation is in the form $(x + a)^2$? **G**
   F. $(x - 6)^2 = 28$ **G.** $(x + 6)^2 = 34$
   H. $(x + 6)^2 = 39$ **J.** $(x + 12)^2 = -2$

66. What are the solutions of the equation $x^2 + 10x + 40 = 5$? **C**
   A. $10 \pm i\sqrt{5}$ **B.** $5 \pm i\sqrt{10}$ **C.** $-5 \pm i\sqrt{10}$ **D.** $-10 \pm i\sqrt{5}$

Short Response
67. Solve $14x = x^2 + 36$. Show your work. **See back of book.**

Extended Response
68. List the steps for solving the equation $3x^2 - 6 = -7x$ by the method of completing the square. Explain each step. **See back of book.**

Mixed Review

GO for Help

Lesson 5-6   **Simplify each expression.**

69. $(2 - 3i) + (-4 + 5i)$ **70.** $(7 + 3i) - (2 + i)$ **71.** $(4 - 9i)(3 + 8i)$
   $-2 + 2i$ $5 + 2i$ $84 + 5i$

Lesson 5-1   **Find a quadratic model for each set of data.**

72. $(-4, 3), (-3, 3), (-2, 4)$ **73.** $\left(-1, \frac{1}{2}\right), (0, 2), (2, 2)$ **74.** $(0, 2), (1, 0), (2, 4)$
   $y = \frac{1}{2}x^2 + \frac{7}{2}x + 9$ $y = -\frac{1}{2}x^2 + x + 2$ $y = 3x^2 - 5x + 2$

Lesson 4-8   **Use Cramer's Rule to solve each system.**

75. $\begin{cases} 2x + y = 4 \\ 3x - y = 6 \end{cases}$ **(2, 0)**   **76.** $\begin{cases} 2x + y = 7 \\ -2x + 5y = -1 \end{cases}$ **(3, 1)** **77.** $\begin{cases} 2x + 4y = 10 \\ 3x + 5y = 14 \end{cases}$ **(3, 1)**

50a.

(315, 630)

b. The domain is all real numbers from 0 to 630. The range is all real numbers from 0 to 630.

51. $-12 \pm 3\sqrt{17}$

52. $-4 \pm 2\sqrt{5}$

53. $\frac{1}{4} \pm \frac{\sqrt{57}}{12}$

54. $-\frac{2}{3}, \frac{1}{3}$

55. $\frac{1}{8} \pm \frac{\sqrt{5}}{8}$

56. $-\frac{3}{8} \pm \frac{\sqrt{41}}{8}$

57. $-\frac{3}{2}a, 2a$

58. $\frac{-a \pm a\sqrt{13}}{6}$

59. $\frac{3}{a}, \frac{1}{a}, a \neq 0$

60. $-\frac{3}{2a}, -\frac{1}{2a}, a \neq 0$

61. $3, -\frac{3a}{a+3}, a \neq -3$

62. $-\frac{2}{3a}, \frac{5}{2a}, a \neq 0$

Understanding Word Problems

Students learn how to read and interpret formulas that are mathematical relationships among quantities. The example involves a formula for the height of the football in terms of the horizontal distance traveled.

Guided Instruction

Make sure students understand that in this formula, h is equivalent to y in a standard quadratic equation, and the h-axis is the same as the y-axis.

Explain that the ball is two feet above the ground when it is kicked because the punter holds the ball and then drop-kicks it during a punt. During a place kick, the ball is kicked from the ground.

For part c, explain that the defensive player is five feet horizontally, or directly in front of, the punter when the ball is kicked. How high must the defensive player reach in order to touch, or block the ball after it has been kicked, assuming that the player is still five feet from where the ball was kicked?

Tactile Learners

Have students model the kick outdoors with an actual football to get a better understanding of the fact that the point of impact is two feet off the ground, and that the flight of the football after it is kicked actually resembles a parabola.

Exercises

Remind students that the quantities in the formula are in feet, not yards, so the answers should be in feet, or in both feet and yards.

 GPS Guided Problem Solving

Understanding Word Problems Read the problem below. Let the explanation guide you in using the formula. Check your understanding with the Exercises.

Sports The height of a punted football can be modeled with the quadratic function $h = -0.01x^2 + 1.18x + 2$. The horizontal distance in feet from the point of impact with the kicker's foot is x, and h is the height of the ball in feet.

    a. Find the vertex of the graph of the function by completing the square.
    b. What is the maximum height of the punt?
    c. The nearest defensive player is 5 ft horizontally from the point of impact. How high must the player reach to block the punt?

To understand a formula, identify the formula and its parts.

From the problem, the formula is
$h = -0.01x^2 + 1.18x + 2$.
The graph gives you other information.

$$
\underset{\underset{\text{height of the ball}}{\uparrow}}{h} = -0.01 \underset{\underset{\underset{\text{height at}}{\underset{\text{time of kick}}{}}}{\uparrow}}{x^2} + 1.18 \underset{\underset{\underset{\text{horizontal distance from}}{\text{the kicker's foot}}}{\uparrow}}{x} + 2
$$

Part (a) of the problem asks you to find the vertex of the graph. By completing the square, you can get an equation in vertex form.

$h = -0.01\underset{\underset{x\text{-coordinate}}{\uparrow}}{(x - 59)}^2 + \underset{\underset{y\text{-coordinate}}{\uparrow}}{36.81}$ **vertex form**

Since the y-coordinate of the vertex is 36.81, you know that the maximum height of the football is 36.81 ft. That answers part (b).

To block the punt, the defensive player must touch the football along its path. To answer part (c), find the height of the ball (and the height of the defensive player's hand) when it is horizontally 5 ft from the kicker, or when $x = 5$.

$h(5) = -0.01x^2 + 1.18x + 2$ **Use the formula.**
$ = -0.01(5)^2 + 1.18(5) + 2$ **Substitute.**
$ = 7.65$ **Simplify.**

The defensive player must reach 7.65 ft above the ground to block the punt.

EXERCISES

  1. What is the ball's height when it has traveled 20 yd (60 ft) downfield? **36.8 ft**

  2. How far downfield has the ball traveled when it reaches its maximum height? **59 ft**

  3. a. How far downfield has the ball traveled when it reaches a height of 6 ft? **3.49 ft, 114.51 ft**
     b. Reasoning Explain why part (a) has more than one answer. **The ball reaches 6 ft on the way up and on the way down.**

The Quadratic Formula

1. Plan

What You'll Learn

- To solve quadratic equations by using the Quadratic Formula
- To determine types of solutions by using the discriminant

... And Why

To investigate the motion of a field hockey ball, as in Example 5

 Check Skills You'll Need

 for Help Lessons 1-2 and 5-1

Write each quadratic equation in standard form. 1–4. See margin p. 290.

1. $y = 8 - 10x^2$

2. $y = (x + 2)^2 - 1$

3. $y = -2x(x - 1) + (x + 1)^2$

4. $y = (3x)^2 - (x - 1)^2$

Evaluate the expression $b^2 - 4ac$ for the given values of a, b, and c.

5. $a = 1, b = 6, c = 3$ **24**

6. $a = -5, b = 2, c = 4$ **84**

7. $a = 3, b = -6, c = 7$ **−48**

8. $a = 2, b = 3, c = -10$ **89**

🔊 **New Vocabulary** • Quadratic Formula • discriminant

Objectives

1 To solve quadratic equations by using the Quadratic Formula

2 To determine types of solutions by using the discriminant

Examples

1 Using the Quadratic Formula
2 Finding Complex Solutions
3 Real-World Connection
4 Using the Discriminant
5 Real-World Connection

1 Using the Quadratic Formula

You can derive a formula for solving quadratic equations by completing the square. Below is the equation $2x^2 + 6x + 1 = 0$. Next to it is the general form of a quadratic equation, $ax^2 + bx + c = 0$. Each equation is solved for x.

$$2x^2 + 6x + 1 = 0 \qquad\qquad ax^2 + bx + c = 0$$

$$x^2 + 3x + \frac{1}{2} = 0 \qquad\qquad x^2 + \frac{b}{a}x + \frac{c}{a} = 0$$

$$x^2 + 3x = -\frac{1}{2} \qquad\qquad x^2 + \frac{b}{a}x = -\frac{c}{a}$$

$$x^2 + 2\left(\frac{3}{2}\right)x + \left(\frac{3}{2}\right)^2 = \left(\frac{3}{2}\right)^2 - \frac{1}{2} \qquad x^2 + 2\left(\frac{b}{2a}\right)x + \left(\frac{b}{2a}\right)^2 = \left(\frac{b}{2a}\right)^2 - \frac{c}{a}$$

$$\left(x + \frac{3}{2}\right)^2 = \frac{9}{4} - \frac{2}{4} \qquad\qquad \left(x + \frac{b}{2a}\right)^2 = \frac{b^2}{4a^2} - \frac{c}{a}$$

$$\left(x + \frac{3}{2}\right)^2 = \frac{7}{4} \qquad\qquad \left(x + \frac{b}{2a}\right)^2 = \frac{b^2 - 4ac}{4a^2}$$

$$x + \frac{3}{2} = \pm\sqrt{\frac{7}{4}} \qquad\qquad x + \frac{b}{2a} = \pm\sqrt{\frac{b^2 - 4ac}{4a^2}}$$

$$x = -\frac{3}{2} \pm \frac{\sqrt{7}}{2} \qquad\qquad x = -\frac{b}{2a} \pm \frac{\sqrt{b^2 - 4ac}}{2a}$$

$$x = \frac{-3 \pm \sqrt{7}}{2} \qquad\qquad x = \frac{-b \pm \sqrt{b^2 - 4ac}}{2a}$$

 Key Concepts

Theorem	**Quadratic Formula**

A quadratic equation written in standard form $ax^2 + bx + c = 0$ can be solved with the Quadratic Formula.

$$x = \frac{-b \pm \sqrt{b^2 - 4ac}}{2a}$$

Math Background

The development of the quadratic formula, which provides a solution to any quadratic equation in terms of its coefficients, leads one to ask whether or not such formulas exists for cubic and quartic equations. Formulas that depend solely on the coefficients do exist, but are not as straight-forward as the quadratic formula. These methods were first published in Cardano's book *Ars magna* in 1545.

More Math Background: p. 236D

Lesson Planning and Resources

See p. 236E for a list of the resources that support this lesson.

 Bell Ringer Practice

✓ **Check Skills You'll Need**
For intervention, direct students to:

Algebraic Expressions
Lesson 1-2: Example 2
Extra Skills and Word Problems Practice, Ch. 1

Modeling Data With Quadratic Formulas
Lesson 5-1: Example 1
Extra Skills and Word Problems Practice, Ch. 5

Lesson 5-8 The Quadratic Formula **289**

Differentiated Instruction **Solutions for All Learners**

Special Needs L1
Write the quadratic formula on the board using a different color for the discriminant. Point out that the discriminant is the expression under the radical, and thus does not include the radical sign.

learning style: visual

Below Level L2
Students may make fewer errors if they memorize the quadratic formula as $\frac{-b}{2a} \pm \frac{\sqrt{b^2 - 4ac}}{2a}$.

learning style: verbal

Guided Instruction

2 EXAMPLE **Math Tip**

Stress to students the importance of first writing the equation in standard form.

3 EXAMPLE **Teaching Tip**

Have students refer to Example 5 on page 269 to refresh their memories on how to obtain the equation $x^2 - x - 1 = 0$.

GO Online

Video Tutor Help

Visit: PHSchool.com
Web Code: age-0775

page 289   Check Skills
              You'll Need

1. $y = -10x^2 + 8$

2. $y = x^2 + 4x + 3$

3. $y = -x^2 + 4x + 1$

4. $y = 8x^2 + 2x - 1$

Quick Check

2b.

The graph does not intersect the *x*-axis.

290

---

1 EXAMPLE **Using the Quadratic Formula**

Use the Quadratic Formula to solve $3x^2 - 5x = 2$.

$3x^2 - 5x - 2 = 0$	Write in standard form.
$a = 3, b = -5, c = -2$	Find the values of *a*, *b*, and *c*.
$x = \dfrac{-b \pm \sqrt{b^2 - 4ac}}{2a}$	Write the Quadratic Formula.
$= \dfrac{-(-5) \pm \sqrt{(-5)^2 - 4(3)(-2)}}{2(3)}$	Substitute.
$= \dfrac{5 \pm \sqrt{25 - (-24)}}{6}$	Simplify.
$= \dfrac{5 \pm \sqrt{49}}{6}$	
$= \dfrac{5 \pm 7}{6}$	
$= \dfrac{12}{6}$ or $\dfrac{-2}{6}$	
$= 2$ or $-\dfrac{1}{3}$	

Check

$$3x^2 - 5x = 2 \qquad\qquad 3x^2 - 5x = 2$$
$$3(2)^2 - 5(2) \stackrel{?}{=} 2 \qquad 3\left(-\tfrac{1}{3}\right)^2 - 5\left(-\tfrac{1}{3}\right) \stackrel{?}{=} 2$$
$$12 - 10 \stackrel{?}{=} 2 \qquad\qquad \tfrac{1}{3} + \tfrac{5}{3} \stackrel{?}{=} 2$$
$$2 = 2 \checkmark \qquad\qquad 2 = 2 \checkmark$$

✓ Quick Check **①** Use the Quadratic Formula to solve $3x^2 - x = 4$. Check your solutions. $-1, \frac{4}{3}$

The Quadratic Formula will give you complex solutions that you cannot find by graphing or factoring.

2 EXAMPLE **Finding Complex Solutions**

Solve $2x^2 = -6x - 7$.

$2x^2 + 6x + 7 = 0$	Write in standard form.
$a = 2, b = 6, c = 7$	Find the values of *a*, *b*, and *c*.
$x = \dfrac{-(6) \pm \sqrt{(6)^2 - 4(2)(7)}}{2(2)}$	Substitute.
$= \dfrac{-6 \pm \sqrt{36 - 56}}{4}$	Simplify.
$= \dfrac{-6 \pm \sqrt{-20}}{4}$	
$= \dfrac{-6 \pm 2i\sqrt{5}}{4}$	
$= -\dfrac{3}{2} \pm \dfrac{i\sqrt{5}}{2}$	

✓ Quick Check **②** **a.** Use the Quadratic Formula to solve $-2x^2 = 4x + 3$. $-1 \pm \frac{i\sqrt{2}}{2}$
    b. Graph the related quadratic function $y = 2x^2 + 4x + 3$. Explain why you cannot use the graph to find the solution. **See margin.**

290   Chapter 5   Quadratic Equations and Functions

Differentiated Instruction **Solutions for All Learners**

Advanced Learners **L4**
Have students rewrite the quadratic formula for the special cases $b = 0$ or $c = 0$. Ask them to describe how these cases fit into the summary on p. 293.

learning style: verbal

English Language Learners **ELL**
In Example 5, discuss the meaning of the terms *scoop*, *velocity*, and *height* in the context of the problem. Then graph the function to illustrate that the ball does not reach the height of 20 feet

learning style: verbal

In Lesson 5-5, you found an approximate value for the golden ratio by graphing the related function for the equation $x^2 - x - 1 = 0$. Now you can use the Quadratic Formula to find an exact value for the golden ratio.

3 EXAMPLE Real-World 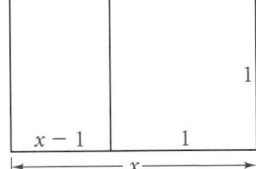 Connection

Art The golden ratio is the ratio of the longer side to the shorter side of a golden rectangle. Solve $x^2 - x - 1 = 0$ for x to find the exact value of the golden ratio.

$x^2 - x - 1 = 0$

$a = 1, b = -1, c = -1$ **Find the values of a, b, and c.**

$x = \dfrac{-b \pm \sqrt{b^2 - 4ac}}{2a}$ **Use the Quadratic Formula.**

$= \dfrac{-(-1) \pm \sqrt{(-1)^2 - 4(1)(-1)}}{2(1)}$ **Substitute for a, b, and c.**

$= \dfrac{1 \pm \sqrt{5}}{2}$ **Simplify.**

The golden ratio is $\dfrac{1 + \sqrt{5}}{2} : 1$, or simply $\dfrac{1 + \sqrt{5}}{2}$.

Check Is the answer reasonable? Since $\dfrac{1 - \sqrt{5}}{2}$ is a negative number, and a ratio of actual lengths cannot be negative, that answer is not reasonable. Since $\dfrac{1 + \sqrt{5}}{2} \approx 1.62$, which is the approximate value for the golden ratio found in Lesson 5-5, that answer is reasonable.

Real-World Connection

The golden ratio occurs in nature as well as in art. In sunflowers, the ratio of the number of clockwise spirals to the number of counterclockwise spirals approximates the golden ratio.

 Quick Check ❸ Use the Quadratic Formula to solve each equation. Find the exact solutions. Then approximate any radical solutions. Round to the nearest hundredth.

    a. $4x^2 = 8x - 3$ $\frac{1}{2}, \frac{3}{2}$ **b.** $x^2 + 4x = 41$ $-2 \pm 3\sqrt{5}$; $-8.71, 4.71$

2   Using the Discriminant

Quadratic equations can have real or complex solutions. You can determine the type and number of solutions by finding the discriminant.

Key Concepts

Definition	Discriminant of a Quadratic Equation

The **discriminant** of a quadratic equation in the form $ax^2 + bx + c = 0$ is the value of the expression $b^2 - 4ac$.

$$x = \dfrac{-b \pm \sqrt{\overset{\downarrow}{b^2 - 4ac}}}{2a} \quad \leftarrow \text{discriminant}$$

The table on the next page shows the relationships among the value of the discriminant, the solutions of a quadratic equation, and the graph of the related function. These relationships are true for real number values of a, b, and c.

291

Additional Examples

❶ Use the Quadratic Formula to solve $3x^2 + 23x + 40 = 0$. $-5, -\frac{8}{3}$

❷ Solve $3x^2 + 2x = -4$.

   $-\frac{1}{3} \pm \dfrac{i\sqrt{11}}{3}$

❸ The longer leg of a right triangle is 1 unit longer than the shorter leg. The hypotenuse is 3 units long. What is the length of the shorter leg?

   $\dfrac{\sqrt{17} - 1}{2}$ units

1. 1, 3
2. −6, −2
3. $-\frac{7}{2}$, 1
4. $-1, \frac{1}{3}$
5. −5
6. $-\frac{5}{2}$, 1
7. $\frac{3 \pm \sqrt{5}}{2}$
8. $-3 \pm \sqrt{14}$
9. $\frac{2 \pm \sqrt{10}}{3}$

292

For: Roots Activity
Use: Interactive Textbook, 5-8

Value of the Discriminant	Type and Number of Solutions for $ax^2 + bx + c = 0$	Examples of Graphs of Related Functions $y = ax^2 + bx + c$
$b^2 - 4ac > 0$	two real solutions	two x-intercepts
$b^2 - 4ac = 0$	one real solution	one x-intercept
$b^2 - 4ac < 0$	no real solution; two imaginary solutions	no x-intercept

4 EXAMPLE Using the Discriminant

Determine the type and number of solutions of $x^2 + 6x + 8 = 0$.

$a = 1, b = 6, c = 8$ **Find the values of a, b, and c.**

$b^2 - 4ac = (6)^2 - 4(1)(8)$ **Evaluate the discriminant.**

$= 4$ **Simplify.**

Since the discriminant is positive, $x^2 + 6x + 8 = 0$ has two real solutions.

Quick Check Determine the type and number of solutions of each equation.
  a. $x^2 + 6x + 9 = 0$ **b.** $x^2 + 6x + 10 = 0$
    one real solution   two imaginary solutions

5 EXAMPLE Real-World Connection

Multiple Choice Suppose a scoop releases a field hockey ball with an upward velocity of 34 ft/s. The function $h = -16t^2 + 34t$ models the height h in feet of the ball at time t in seconds. When will the ball reach a height of 20 ft?
  Ⓐ in 2 seconds   Ⓑ in 6 seconds   Ⓒ in 11 seconds   Ⓓ never

Real-World Connection

A scoop is a field hockey pass that propels the ball from the ground into the air.

$h = -16t^2 + 34t$

$20 = -16t^2 + 34t$ **Substitute 20 for h.**

$0 = -16t^2 + 34t - 20$ **Write the equation in standard form.**

$a = -16, b = 34, c = -20$ **Find the values of a, b, and c.**

$b^2 - 4ac = (34)^2 - 4(-16)(-20)$ **Evaluate the discriminant.**

$= 1156 - 1280$ **Simplify.**

$= -124$

Since the discriminant is negative, the equation $20 = -16t^2 + 34t$ has no real solutions. The ball will not reach a height of 20 ft. The answer is choice D.

Quick Check Will the ball in Example 5 ever reach a height of 15 ft? Explain.
                                Yes; the discriminant is positive.

10. $-\frac{1}{2}, \frac{3}{4}$
11. 1, 4
12. $-\frac{5}{3}, \frac{1}{3}$
13. $3 \pm i\sqrt{2}$
14. $1 \pm 2i$
15. $-\frac{3}{2} \pm \frac{i\sqrt{11}}{2}$
16. $-2 \pm i\sqrt{2}$
17. $1 \pm i\sqrt{2}$
18. $-\frac{2}{3} \pm \frac{i\sqrt{26}}{3}$
19. $\frac{5}{2} \pm \frac{i\sqrt{3}}{2}$
20. $\frac{7}{4} \pm \frac{i\sqrt{15}}{4}$

You are now familiar with six methods of solving quadratic equations: finding square roots, factoring, using tables, graphing, completing the square, and using the Quadratic Formula. For $ax^2 = c$, finding square roots works best. The discriminant can help you decide how to solve equations that have an x-term.

Key Concepts

Test-Taking Tip

Learn to use a tool like the discriminant. It may not answer a test item but it could help you find an answer quickly.

Summary	Methods for Solving Quadratic Equations
Discriminant	**Methods**
positive square number	• factoring, tables, graphing, Quadratic Formula, or completing the square
positive nonsquare number	• for approximate solutions: tables, graphing, Quadratic Formula, or completing the square • for exact solutions: Quadratic Formula or completing the square
zero	• factoring, graphing, Quadratic Formula, or completing the square
negative	• Quadratic Formula or completing the square

EXERCISES

For more exercises, see *Extra Skill and Word Problem Practice*.

Practice and Problem Solving

A Practice by Example

Example 1
(page 290)

 for Help

Solve each equation using the Quadratic Formula. 1–21. See margin pp. 292–293.

1. $x^2 - 4x + 3 = 0$ **2.** $x^2 + 8x + 12 = 0$ **3.** $2x^2 + 5x - 7 = 0$

4. $3x^2 + 2x - 1 = 0$ **5.** $x^2 + 10x = -25$ **6.** $2x^2 + 3x - 5 = 0$

7. $x^2 = 3x - 1$ **8.** $x^2 + 6x - 5 = 0$ **9.** $3x^2 - 4x - 2 = 0$

10. $8x^2 - 2x - 3 = 0$ **11.** $x(x - 5) = -4$ **12.** $9x^2 + 12x - 5 = 0$

Example 2
(page 290)

13. $x^2 - 6x + 11 = 0$ **14.** $x^2 = 2x - 5$ **15.** $x^2 + 3x + 5 = 0$

16. $2x^2 + 8x + 12 = 0$ **17.** $x^2 - 2x + 3 = 0$ **18.** $3x^2 + 4x + 10 = 0$

19. $-x^2 + 5x - 7 = 0$ **20.** $2x^2 = 7x - 8$ **21.** $15x^2 + 2x + 1 = 0$

Example 3
(page 291)

Solve each equation using the Quadratic Formula. Find the exact solutions. Then approximate any radical solutions. Round to the nearest hundredth.

22. $2x^2 - 5x - 3 = 0$ **23.** $3x^2 - 10x + 5 = 0$ **24.** $3x^2 + 4x - 3 = 0$

25. $6x^2 - 5x - 1 = 0$ **26.** $7x^2 - x - 12 = 0$ **27.** $5x^2 + 8x - 11 = 0$

28. $4x^2 + 4x = 22$ **29.** $2x^2 - 1 = 5x$ **30.** $2x^2 + x = \frac{1}{2}$
22–30. See margin.

Examples 4 and 5
(page 292)

Evaluate the discriminant of each equation. Tell how many solutions each equation has and whether the solutions are real or imaginary. 31–39. See margin.

31. $x^2 + 4x + 5 = 0$ **32.** $x^2 - 4x - 5 = 0$ **33.** $4x^2 + 20x + 25 = 0$

34. $2x^2 + x + 28 = 0$ **35.** $2x^2 + 7x - 15 = 0$ **36.** $6x^2 - 2x + 5 = 0$

37. $2x^2 + 7x = -6$ **38.** $x^2 - 12x + 36 = 0$ **39.** $x^2 = 8x - 16$

Lesson 5-8   The Quadratic Formula   **293**

21. $-\frac{1}{15} \pm \frac{i\sqrt{14}}{15}$

22. $-\frac{1}{2}, 3$

23. $\frac{5}{3} \pm \frac{\sqrt{10}}{3}$; 0.61, 2.72

24. $-\frac{2}{3} \pm \frac{\sqrt{13}}{3}$; -1.87, 0.54

25. $-\frac{1}{6}, 1$

26. $\frac{1}{14} \pm \frac{\sqrt{337}}{14}$; -1.24, 1.38

27. $-\frac{4}{5} \pm \frac{\sqrt{71}}{5}$; -2.49, 0.89

28. $-\frac{1}{2} \pm \frac{\sqrt{23}}{2}$; -2.90, 1.90

29. $\frac{5}{4} \pm \frac{\sqrt{33}}{4}$; -0.19, 2.69

30. $-\frac{1}{4} \pm \frac{\sqrt{5}}{4}$; -0.81, 0.31

31. -4; two, imaginary

32. 36; two, real

3. Practice

Assignment Guide

1 A B 1-30, 41-54, 56, 67

2 A B 31-40, 55, 57-66, 68
C Challenge   69-75

Test Prep   76-80
Mixed Review   81-87

Homework Quick Check

To check students' understanding of key skills and concepts, go over Exercises 29, 36, 55, 56, 65, 66.

Error Prevention!

Exercises 31–39 Watch for students who describe the solutions as complex numbers rather than imaginary numbers. At this stage *all* numbers are complex numbers.

Differentiated Instruction Resources

GPS Guided Problem Solving	L3
Enrichment	L4
Reteaching	L2
Practice	L3

33. 0; one, real

34. −223; two, imaginary

35. 169; two, real

36. −116; two, imaginary

37. 1; two, real

38. 0; one, real

39. 0; one, real

293

Use the Quadratic Formula to solve each equation.

1. $6x^2 + 19x + 8 = 0$ $-\frac{8}{3}, -\frac{1}{2}$

2. $x^2 - 2x - 11 = 0$ $1 \pm 2\sqrt{3}$

3. $x^2 - 2x - 15 = 0$ $-3, 5$

4. $3x^2 - 7x + 5 = 0$ $\frac{7 \pm i\sqrt{11}}{6}$

Find the value of the discriminant for each quadratic equation. Tell how many different solutions each equation has and whether the solutions are real or imaginary.

5. $2x^2 - 5x + 7 = 0$ -31; two, imaginary

6. $-3x^2 + 14x - 8 = 0$ 100; two, real

7. $4x^2 - 5x + 10 = 7x + 1$ 0; one, real

Alternative Assessment

Have students work in groups of four. Each student writes three quadratic equations in standard form on separate slips of paper. Students mix the slips. Have groups exchange papers. Each student draws two slips and uses the quadratic formula to solve the quadratic equations written on the slips. Then students each draw one more slip and find the discriminant and determine the number of solutions. Students work in pairs to check each other's work.

43. $-\frac{3}{2}, \frac{1}{2}$

44. $-3.45, 1.45$

45. $1 \pm i$

46. $-1.70, 4.70$

47. $-7, 7$

48. $-8.47, 0.47$

49. $3 \pm i\sqrt{2}$

294

---

40. Business The weekly revenue for a company is $R = -3p^2 + 60p + 1060$, where p is the price of the company's product. Use the discriminant to find whether there is a price for which the weekly revenue would be $1500. **no**

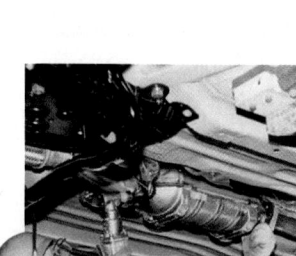

B **Apply Your Skills**

Solve each equation using any method. When necessary, round real solutions to the nearest hundredth. For imaginary solutions, write exact solutions. 43–49. See margin.

41. $x^2 = 11x - 10$ **1, 10**   **42.** $5x^2 = 210x$ **0, 42**   **43.** $4x^2 + 4x = 3$

44. $2x^2 + 4x = 10$ **45.** $x^2 - 2x + 2 = 0$ **46.** $x^2 - 3x - 8 = 0$

47. $-3x^2 + 147 = 0$ **48.** $x^2 + 8x = 4$ **49.** $x^2 = 6x - 11$

50. $4x^2 - 4x - 3 = 0$ $-\frac{1}{2}, \frac{3}{2}$ **51.** $\frac{x-3}{2} = \frac{6}{x-2}$ $-1, 6$ **52.** $\frac{x+2}{5} = \frac{3}{x+1}$ $-5.41, 2.41$

53a. $w(18 - w) = 36$

b. 2.29 in. by 15.71 in.

53. a. The area of a rectangle is 36 in.². The perimeter of the rectangle is 36 in. Write an equation using one variable to find the dimensions of the rectangle.
b. Find the dimensions of the rectangle to the nearest hundredth of an inch.

54. Matrices Find the value of n in the determinant at the right. $\begin{vmatrix} 2 & n & 4 \\ n & 2 & -1 \\ 4 & n & 7 \end{vmatrix} = -37$ 3 or $-\frac{11}{3}$

55. Writing Summarize how to use the discriminant to analyze the types of solutions of a quadratic equation. See margin.

56. Air Pollution The function $y = 0.0721x^2 - 2.8867x + 117.061$ models the emissions of carbon monoxide in the United States since 1985. In the function, y represents the amount of carbon monoxide released in a year in millions of tons, and $x = 0$ represents the year 1985. a–b. See margin pp. 294–295.
a. How can you use a graph to estimate the year in which less than 100 million tons of carbon monoxide were released into the air?
b. How can you use the Quadratic Formula to estimate the year in which less than 100 million tons of carbon monoxide were released into the air?
c. Which method do you prefer? Explain why. **Check students' work**

Real-World **Connection**

Automobiles are the primary source of carbon monoxide in the U.S. This worker is installing a catalytic converter, which decreases carbon monoxide emissions in cars.

Without graphing, tell how many x-intercepts each function has.

57. $y = -2x^2 + 3x - 1$ **two**   **58.** $y = 0.25x^2 + 2x + 4$ **one**   **59.** $y = x^2 + 3x + 5$ **none**

60. $y = -x^2 + 3x + 10$ **two**   **61.** $y = 3x^2 - 10x + 6$ **two**   **62.** $y = 10x^2 + 13x - 3$ **two**

63. Critical Thinking Determine the value(s) of k for which $3x^2 + kx + 12 = 0$ has each type of solution. a–c. See margin p. 295.
a. exactly one real solution   **b.** two imaginary solutions   **c.** two real solutions

64. Open-Ended Find a value of k for which $x^2 + kx + 9 = 0$ has the given type of solution. a–c. See margin p. 295.
a. two imaginary solutions   **b.** two real solutions   **c.** one real solution

65. Error Analysis After analyzing a quadratic equation with real coefficients, a student says that the equation has exactly one imaginary solution. Explain how you know that the student is wrong. **See margin p. 295.**

66. Use the discriminant to match each function with its graph.
a. $f(x) = x^2 - 4x + 2$ **II**   **b.** $f(x) = x^2 - 4x + 4$ **III**   **c.** $f(x) = x^2 - 4x + 6$ **I**

I.   **II.**   **III.**

GO Online

Homework Video Tutor

Visit: PHSchool.com
Web Code: age-0508

---

55. Answers may vary. Sample: Assume the coefficients are real numbers. If the discriminant is negative, then there are 2 imaginary solutions. If the discriminant is 0, then there is 1 real solution. If the discriminant is positive, then there are 2 real solutions.

56a. Answers may vary. Sample: Graph $y = 0.0721x^2 - 2.8867x + 117.061$ and $y = 100$. Where they intersect is the year when 100 million tons were released in the

67. a. Geometry Write an equation to find the dimensions of a square that has the same area as the circle at the left. $x^2 = 100\pi$
   b. Find the length of a side of the square, to the nearest hundredth centimeter.
   17.72 cm

10 cm

 68. Physics The equation $h = 80t - 16t^2$ models the height h feet reached in t seconds by an object propelled straight up from the ground.
   a. Will the object ever reach a height of 90 ft? **yes**
   b. Verify your answer to part (a) with a graph. **See margin.**
   c. For what values of t will the object be in the air? $0 < t < 5$

C Challenge

Write a quadratic equation with the given solutions. **69–71. See margin.**

69. $\dfrac{3 + \sqrt{5}}{2}, \dfrac{3 - \sqrt{5}}{2}$ **70.** $\dfrac{-5 + \sqrt{13}}{2}, \dfrac{-5 - \sqrt{13}}{2}$ **71.** $\dfrac{5 + i\sqrt{3}}{2}, \dfrac{5 - i\sqrt{3}}{2}$

Use the Quadratic Formula to solve each equation for x in terms of a.

72. $\dfrac{3 \pm i}{2a}$

73. $\dfrac{5 \pm \sqrt{85}}{5a}$

72. $2a^2x^2 - 6ax = -5$ **73.** $5a^2x^2 - 10ax = 12$ **74.** $x^2 + 2ax = 25a^2$
   $-a \pm a\sqrt{26}$

75. Use the Quadratic Formula to prove each statement. **a–b. See margin.**
   a. The sum of the solutions of the quadratic equation $ax^2 + bx + c = 0$ is $-\dfrac{b}{a}$.
   b. The product of the solutions of the quadratic equation $ax^2 + bx + c = 0$ is $\dfrac{c}{a}$.

Test Prep

Multiple Choice

76. What is the discriminant of $qx^2 + rx + s = 0$? **C**
   A. $|a + b|$ **B.** $q^2 - 4rs$ **C.** $r^2 - 4qs$ **D.** $s^2 - 4qr$

77. How many different real solutions are there for $2x^2 - 3x + 5 = 0$? **F**
   F. 0   **G.** 1   **H.** 2   **J.** i

78. Which equation has $-3 \pm 5i$ as its solutions? **A**
   A. $x^2 + 6x = -34$ **B.** $x^2 + 6x = -14$ **C.** $x^2 + 3x = 4$ **D.** $x^2 + 3x = 2$

Short Response

79. What is the discriminant of a quadratic equation, and what does its value tell you about the solution(s) of the equation? **See back of book.**

Extended Response

80. Explain how you can use the Quadratic Formula to solve $3x^2 + 5 = x + 9$.
   See back of book.

Mixed Review

GO for Help

Lesson 5-7

Solve by completing the square.

81. $x^2 - 8x - 20 = 0$ **82.** $2y^2 = 4y - 1$ $\dfrac{2 \pm \sqrt{2}}{2}$ **83.** $x^2 - 3x - 8 = 0$ $\dfrac{3 \pm \sqrt{41}}{2}$
   $-2, 10$

Lesson 4-4

Each matrix represents vertices of a polygon. Translate each figure 3 units right and 2 units down. Express your answer as a matrix.

84. $\begin{bmatrix} 2 & 3 & -1 \\ -5 & 1 & 0 \end{bmatrix}$ $\begin{bmatrix} 5 & 6 & 2 \\ -7 & -1 & -2 \end{bmatrix}$ **85.** $\begin{bmatrix} 0 & -3 & 1 & -5 \\ 2 & -1 & 4 & -2 \end{bmatrix}$ $\begin{bmatrix} 3 & 0 & 4 & -2 \\ 0 & -3 & 2 & -4 \end{bmatrix}$

Lesson 4-3

Multiply.

86. $\begin{bmatrix} 0 & -3 \\ -3 & 1 \end{bmatrix}\begin{bmatrix} 4 & 0 \\ -9 & 1 \end{bmatrix}$ $\begin{bmatrix} 27 & -3 \\ -21 & 1 \end{bmatrix}$ **87.** $\begin{bmatrix} 3 & 10 \\ 1 & 5 \end{bmatrix}\begin{bmatrix} -2 & 4 \\ -1 & 4 \end{bmatrix}$ $\begin{bmatrix} -16 & 52 \\ -7 & 24 \end{bmatrix}$

air. Wherever $y = 0.0721x^2 - 2.8867x + 117.061$ is below $y = 100$ is where less than 100 million tons were released.

b. Answers may vary. Sample: Where $y = 0.0721x^2 - 2.8867x + 117.061 < 100$ is the solution. Subtract 100 from both sides and you

get $y = 0.0721x^2 - 2.8867x + 17.061 < 0$. You then use the quadratic formula to solve.

63a. 12 or -12
   b. k such that $|k| < 12$
   c. k such that $|k| > 12$

64a. k such that $|k| < 6$
   b. k such that $|k| > 6$
   c. 6, -6

65. Imaginary solutions always come in pairs because they are the positive and negative solutions of the square root of a negative number.

68b.

69. Answers may vary.
   Sample: $x^2 - 3x + 1 = 0$

70. Answers may vary.
   Sample: $x^2 + 5x + 3 = 0$

71. Answers may vary.
   Sample: $x^2 - 5x + 7 = 0$

75a. $\dfrac{-b + \sqrt{b^2 - 4ac}}{2a} + \dfrac{-b - \sqrt{b^2 - 4ac}}{2a}$
   $= \dfrac{-2b}{2a} = \dfrac{-b}{a}$

   b. $\left(\dfrac{-b}{2a} + \dfrac{\sqrt{b^2 - 4ac}}{2a}\right) \times \left(\dfrac{-b}{2a} - \dfrac{\sqrt{b^2 - 4ac}}{2a}\right) =$
   $\left(\dfrac{-b}{2a}\right)^2 - \left(\dfrac{\sqrt{b^2 - 4ac}}{2a}\right)^2 =$
   $\dfrac{4ac}{4a^2} = \dfrac{c}{a}$

295

Quadratic Inequalities

This feature guides students in solving quadratic inequalities with a graphing calculator using tables and using graphs.

Guided Instruction

Teaching Tip
Consider matching students with partners so that they can carefully read and answer the questions, correctly manipulate the calculator, and check one another when solving the inequalities.

Special Needs L1
Consider rewriting the inequality as $Y_1 > Y_2$ and $Y_1 < Y_2$ to help student identify the corresponding x-values in the table.

English Language Learners ELL
For Question 3, have a student read the question aloud. Make sure students understand *all values of x* means all of the possible x-values.

Advanced Learners L4
For Question 8, ask students what would happen if $x^2 - 12 < 3x + 6$ is changed to $12 - x^2 < 3x + 6$. The solution set changes from $-3 < x < 6$ to $x < -4.37$ and $x > 1.37$.

Resources

Students may use any graphing calculator to make tables and graphs.

Activity Lab
Technology

Quadratic Inequalities

FOR USE WITH LESSON 5-8

You can solve quadratic inequalities using graphs, tables, and algebraic methods. Indeed, the most effective way may be a combination of methods.

1 ACTIVITY

To find which of $x^2 - 12$ or $3x + 6$ is greater, enter the two functions as Y_1 and Y_2 in your graphing calculator, you could use the TABLE option to compare the two functions for various values of x, as shown below.

1. For which values of x in the table is $x^2 - 12 > 3x + 6$? **−10, −5, 10, 15, 20**

2. For which values of x in the table is $x^2 - 12 < 3x + 6$? **0, 5**

3. Does this table tell you all values of x for which $x^2 - 12 < 3x + 6$? Explain. **Sample: No; the table checks values of x in increments of 5.**

4. In the TBLSET (TABLE SETUP) menu, change TblStart to −9 and ΔTbl to 3. Display the table again. Does the table with this setup give you more information? Why? **Sample: Yes; $Y_1 = Y_2$ when $x = -3$ or $x = 6$.**

You can compare functions more efficiently by making one side of the inequality 0.

5. Show that $x^2 - 12 < 3x + 6$ is equivalent to $x^2 - 3x - 18 < 0$. **Check students' work.**

6. Enter $x^2 - 3x - 18$ as Y_3 in your graphing calculator. Place the cursor on the = sign after Y_1 and press ENTER. This operation turns off the display of the equation Y_1. Turn off Y_2 as well, and then display the table. You will see the screen shown at the right. For which values of x in the table is $x^2 - 3x - 18 < 0$? **0, 3**

2 ACTIVITY

For a visual model, look at the same inequalities graphically. Turn off Y_3 and turn on Y_1 and Y_2. Begin by graphing the two functions in the original inequality as shown in the screens below.

7. Which graph represents the function $f(x) = x^2 - 12$? Which graph represents $f(x) = 3x + 6$? How can you tell? **the parabola; the line**

English Language Learners ELL

Question 17 Have a student look up the word *compelling* in a dictionary. Make sure students understand that in this context the use of *compelling* is *demanding attention*. Consider reviewing the terms *intersection*, *points*, and *x-intercepts* to help students describe the relationships they observe.

8. Use your calculator to find the values of x for which $x^2 - 12 < 3x + 6$ in this window. **all x-values between −3 and 6**

9. Do you think there are values of x outside this window for which
$x^2 - 12 < 3x + 6$? Explain. **Sample: No; the parabola has only one turning point, so it will not cross the line again.**

Now turn off Y_1 and Y_2 and turn on Y_3. Graph Y_3 in the same window as above.

10. Use your calculator to find the values of x for which $x^2 - 3x - 18 < 0$. Are these the same values of x you found in Exercise 8? **−3 < x < 6; yes**

11. Compare the strategy in Exercise 8 with the strategy in Exercise 10 for solving the inequality $x^2 - 12 < 3x + 6$ graphically. Is one easier than the other? Explain. **Sample: Yes; Exercise 10 uses only one function.**

3 ACTIVITY

Error Prevention!

Questions 17-21 Remind students that they need to switch the direction of the inequality symbol when multiplying or dividing inequalities by a negative number.

As an added tool, you can incorporate some algebra into the solution.

12. Factor the quadratic to find the two values of x for which $x^2 - 3x - 18 = 0$. **−3, 6**

13. Shown at the left below is the graph of $y_3 = x^2 - 3x - 18$. What happens in this graph at the two x-values you found in Exercise 12? **The graph crosses the x-axis.**

14. Shown at the right above is the graph of the functions $y_1 = x^2 - 12$ and $y_2 = 3x + 6$. What happens with these graphs at the two x-values you found in Exercise 12? **The graphs intersect.**

15. Tell how you can combine the algebra of Exercise 12 with the geometry of one of the graphs in Exercises 13 or 14 to give a complete solution of the inequality $x^2 - 12 < 3x + 6$. **See margin.**

EXERCISES

16. Sample: The points where $Y_1 = Y_2$ are in line vertically with the x-intercepts of Y_3.

16. It is compelling to graph Y_1, Y_2, and Y_3 in the same window. When you do (see right), there is no relationship immediately apparent. However, based on your work above, what can you say is true about the graphs of Y_1, Y_2, and Y_3?

Here are some special quadratic inequalities to solve. You can use what you know about the family of quadratic functions to help solve some of them.

17. a. $x^2 - 2 < -x - 3$ b. $x^2 - 2 > -x - 3$
   no solution   **all real numbers**
18. a. $x^2 < 2x^2$ b. $x^2 < \frac{1}{2}x^2$ **no solution**
   all real numbers except $x = 0$
19. a. $2(x - 2)(x + 3) < (x - 2)(x + 3)$
   −3 < x < 2
   b. $-2(x - 2)(x + 3) < (x - 2)(x + 3)$
   x < −3 or x > 2
20. a. $-3x(x - 2) < (x - 2)(x - 4)$
   x < 1 or x > 2
   b. $-\frac{1}{3}x(x - 2) < (x - 2)(x - 4)$
   x < 2 or x > 3
   c. $-x(x - 2) < (x - 2)(x - 4)$
   all real numbers except $x = 2$

21. Let $y_1 = f(x)$ and $y_2 = g(x)$. **21–22. See margin.**
   a. Describe how you could use graphs to solve the inequality $f(x) < g(x)$.
   b. How are the solutions of $f(x) < g(x)$ and $f(x) > g(x)$ related?

22. Assume that f and g are discrete functions whose domains are whole numbers. Describe how you could use a table to solve the inequality $f(x) < g(x)$.

for the points where graphs intersect.

21b. Between two consecutive intersections, either $f(x) < g(x)$ or $f(x) > g(x)$. All of the values of x for each interval are solutions of one of the inequalities.

22. Write a function of $f - g$. Then make a table of $(f - g)(x)$ for whole number x. The solution of the inequality $f(x) < g(x)$ are the values of x for which the values of the function in the table are negative.

15. $(x^2 - 3x - 18) = (x + 3)(x - 6)$
The graph of $y_3 = x^2 - 3x - 18$ crosses the x-axis for $x = -3$ and $x = 6$. The graph of $y_2 = 3x + 6$

crosses the graph of $y_1 = x^2 - 12$ for the same two values of x. For $-3 < x < 6$, the graph of y_1 is below the graph of y_2, so the solution of the inequality

$x^2 - 12 < 3x + 6$ is $-3 < x < 6$.

21a. Graph $y_1 = f(x)$ and $y_2 = g(x)$ in the same coordinate plane. Look

Using a Variable

Most word problems require you to define one or more variables and to write equations or inequalities to model the situations in the problems. This requires careful reading of the problem and careful thinking about how the quantities in the problem are related to one another.

Resources

SAT® and ACT® correlations are on page 236B.

Test-Taking Strategies with Transparencies
• Transparency 5
• Practice sheet p. 29

Guided Instruction

Remember that when you are given the ratio of two quantities, the ratio tells you by what factor you can multiply one of the quantities to obtain the other.

When you are told that an unknown quantity is a solution of a certain equation, you know that substituting that quantity for the variable will give an equation that you can assume must be true.

Remind students that a diagram can often help to understand the relationship between the quantities in a problem.

Test-Taking Strategies with Transparencies

> *Test-Taking Strategy: Using a Variable*
>
> Sometimes you can use a variable to solve a problem.
>
> *Example* A taxi ride costs a flat fee of $1.75 plus $.80 per mile. What is the fare for traveling 5 miles?
>
> A. $4.00   B. $1.75   C. $5.75   D. $41.75
>
> Choose variables: Let m = miles traveled and c = cost.
>
> Describe the situation in words:
>
>   Cost = flat fee + cost for traveling m miles
>
> Use variables to express the cost: $c = 1.75 + 0.80m$
>
> Substitute $m = 5$: $c = 1.75 + 0.80(5)$
>
> $= 1.75 + 4$
>
> $= \$5.75$
>
> The answer is $5.75, or choice C.
>
> Use a variable to find the answer. Explain your reasoning.
>
> 1. The measures of the angles of a triangle are in the ratio 2 : 4 : 6. Find the measure of the smallest angle.
>
>   A. 15°   B. 20°   C. 30°   D. 60°
>
> 2. One side of a rectangle is 3 times the other side. The perimeter is 16 cm. How long is the long side?
>
>   F. 8 cm   G. 2 cm   H. 3 cm   I. 16 cm
>
> Solutions
>
> 1. C
> 2. I
>
>   Transparency 5

298

You can solve many problems by defining a variable to represent an unknown quantity. Use the variable to write and solve an equation or inequality.

EXAMPLE

The two nonzero roots of the quadratic equation $x^2 - 9x + k = 0$ are in the ratio $2:1$. Find the roots and the value of k.

Since the roots are in the ratio $2:1$, define one root as $2r$ and the other root as r. Substituting each expression into the equation yields a system of two equations in two unknowns.

$$x^2 - 9x + k = 0 \qquad\qquad x^2 - 9x + k = 0$$
$$(2r)^2 - 9(2r) + k = 0 \quad \textbf{Substitute.} \quad (r)^2 - 9(r) + k = 0$$
$$4r^2 - 18r + k = 0 \quad \textbf{Simplify.} \quad r^2 - 9r + k = 0$$

$$4r^2 - 18r + k - (r^2 - 9r + k) = 0 - 0 \quad \textbf{Subtract equations to solve by elimination.}$$
$$3r^2 - 9r = 0 \qquad \textbf{Simplify.}$$
$$\frac{3r^2 - 9r}{r} = \frac{0}{r} \qquad \textbf{Since } r \neq 0 \textbf{, you can divide each side by } r.$$
$$3r - 9 = 0 \qquad \textbf{Simplify.}$$
$$3r = 9 \qquad \textbf{Solve for } r.$$
$$r = 3$$
$$2r = 6 \qquad \textbf{Find } 2r.$$

Now that you know r and $2r$, you can find k.

$$(3)^2 - 9(3) + k = 0 \qquad \textbf{Substitute into the original equation.}$$
$$9 - 27 + k = 0 \qquad \textbf{Simplify.}$$
$$k = 18 \qquad \textbf{Solve for } k.$$

● The nonzero roots of $x^2 - 9x + k = 0$ are 3 and 6, and $k = 18$.

EXERCISES

Write an equation to solve each problem. Clearly define the variables you use.

1. The nonzero roots of the equation $3x^2 - 4x + k = 0$ are in the ratio $3:1$. Find the roots and the value of k. **$1, \frac{1}{3}; k = 1$**

2. The roots of the equation $x^2 - 3x + k = 0$ differ by 2. Find the roots and the value of k. **$\frac{1}{2}, \frac{5}{2}; k = \frac{5}{4}$**

3. The perimeter of a rectangle is 21 cm. Its area is 20 cm². Find the dimensions of the rectangle. **2.5 cm by 8 cm**

4. The point $(0, 0)$ is on the parabola $y = 5x - x^2$. What other point on the parabola has x- and y-coordinates that are equal? **(4, 4)**

5. The length of the diagonal of a rectangle is 5 ft. The rectangle's perimeter is 13 ft. Find the rectangle's dimensions. Round your answers to the nearest tenth.
   4.6 ft by 1.9 ft

Chapter Review

Vocabulary Review

 absolute value of a complex number
    (p. 275)
axis of symmetry (p. 239)
completing the square (p. 282)
complex number (p. 275)
complex number plane (p. 275)
difference of two squares (p. 263)
discriminant (p. 291)
factoring (p. 259)

greatest common factor (GCF)
    of an expression (p. 259)
i (p. 274)
imaginary number (p. 274)
parabola (p. 239)
perfect square trinomial (p. 262)
Quadratic Formula (p. 289)
quadratic function (p. 238)

standard form of a quadratic equation
    (p. 267)
standard form of a quadratic function
    (p. 238)
vertex form of a quadratic function
    (p. 252)
vertex of a parabola (p. 239)
zero of a function (p. 268)
Zero Product Property (p. 267)

Go Online
PHSchool.com
For: Vocabulary quiz
Web Code: agj-0551

Choose the correct vocabulary term to complete each sentence.

1. The square of a binomial is a(n) __?__. **perfect square trinomial**

2. Every quadratic equation can be solved with the __?__. **Quadratic Formula**

3. The __?__ reveals a translation of a parent quadratic function.
vertex form of a quadratic function

4. A(n) __?__ is also an *x*-intercept of the graph of the function.
zero of a function

5. The __?__ completely determines the types of roots of a quadratic function.
discriminant

Skills and Concepts

5-1 Objectives

▼ To identify quadratic
functions and graphs
(p. 238)

▼ To model data with
quadratic functions
(p. 240)

The **standard form of a quadratic function** is $f(x) = ax^2 + bx + c$, where $a \neq 0$.
The quadratic term is ax^2. The graph of a **quadratic function** is a **parabola**.

The **axis of symmetry** is a line that divides a parabola into two mirror images.
The **vertex of a parabola** is the point at the intersection of the parabola and its axis
of symmetry. Corresponding points on the parabola are the same distance from the
axis of symmetry.

You can find a quadratic model for a set of data by solving a system of three
equations for a, b, and c, or by using the quadratic regression feature of a
graphing calculator.

**Determine whether each function is linear or quadratic. Identify the quadratic,
linear, and constant terms.**

6. $y = (3 - x)(2x + 1)$
quadratic; $-2x^2$, 5x, 3

7. $y = x - x^2 + 3$
quadratic; $-x^2$, x, 3

8. $y = 3 - 4x$
linear; none, $-4x$, 3

Identify the vertex, the axis of symmetry, and the points corresponding to *P* and *Q*.

9. $(0, -1), x = 0$,
$(2, 3)$ and $(-1, 0)$

10. $(-2, 1), x = -2$,
$(-2, 1)$ and $(-4, 0)$

11. $(1, -4), x = 1$,
$(3, -1)$ and $\left(2, -3\frac{1}{4}\right)$

9.

10.

11.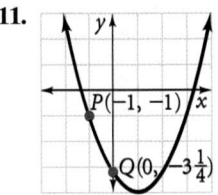

Resources

Student Edition
Extra Skills and Word Problems
    Practice, Ch. 5, p. 844
English/Spanish Glossary, p. 871
Properties and Formulas, p. 893
Table of Symbols, p. 889

Differentiated Instruction Resources

Vocabulary and Study Skills
    worksheet 5F
Spanish Vocabulary and Study
    Skills worksheet 5F
Interactive Textbook Audio
    Glossary
Online Vocabulary Quiz

Success **Tracker**
Online at PHSchool.com

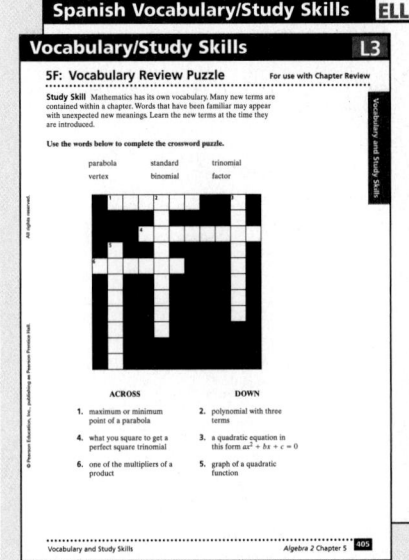

12a. $y = 614x^2 - 342x + 4962$, where $x = 0$ corresponds to 1995 and y is in thousands.

b. around 1999

c. $y = -25.5x^2 + 917.8x + 4776.7$

d. around 2007

e. $\approx 13,000,000$

13.

vertex $(-1, -4)$,
y-intercept: -2; $x = -1$

14.

vertex $(5, 0)$,
y-intercept: 25; $x = 5$

15.

vertex $(2, 1)$,
y-intercept: -3; $x = 2$

16.

vertex $(0, 7)$,
y-intercept: 7; $x = 0$

17. $y = \left(x + \frac{1}{2}\right)^2 - 12\frac{1}{4}$;
minimum: $-12\frac{1}{4}$

18. $y = -(x - 1)^2 + 3$;
maximum: 3

19. $y = 2(x + 2)^2 - 11$;
minimum: -11

20. $y = -0.5(x - 0)^2 + 5$;
maximum: 5

21. $y = -\frac{1}{2}(x - 1)^2 + 2$;
maximum: 2

22. $y = \frac{4}{9}(x - 3)^2 - 1$;
minimum: -1

300

---

12. a. Sports Find a quadratic model for the attendance at women's college basketball games from 1995–1997 by solving three equations in a, b, and c.
b. Predict the year attendance will reach 12,000,000.
c. Use the quadratic regression feature of your calculator to find a model for all the data.
d. What does this regression model predict as the first year attendance will reach 12,000,000?
e. Find the maximum likely attendance.
a–e. See margin.

Year	Attendance (thousands)
1995	4962
1996	5234
1997	6734
1998	7387
1999	8010
2000	8698

Source: National Collegiate Athletic Association

5-2 and 5-3 Objectives

▼ To graph quadratic functions (p. 245)

▼ To find maximum and minimum values of quadratic functions (p. 247)

▼ To use the vertex form of a quadratic function (p. 252)

The parent function for the family of quadratic functions is $f(x) = x^2$. The constants a, b, and c characterize the graph of $y = ax^2 + bx + c$. The axis of symmetry is $x = -\frac{b}{2a}$, the vertex is at $\left(-\frac{b}{2a}, f\left(-\frac{b}{2a}\right)\right)$, and $f\left(-\frac{b}{2a}\right)$ is the maximum or minimum value. The **vertex form of a quadratic function** is $y = a(x - h)^2 + k$. The vertex is (h, k), the maximum or minimum value is k, and the axis of symmetry is the line $x = h$. If $a > 0$, the parabola opens up. If $a < 0$, it opens down.

Graph each function. Identify the vertex, y-intercept, and axis of symmetry.

13. $y = 2(x + 1)^2 - 4$
14. $y = (x - 5)^2$
15. $y = -(x - 2)^2 + 1$
16. $y = -x^2 + 7$

13–23. See margin.

Write each function in vertex form. Find its maximum or minimum value.

17. $y = x^2 + x - 12$
18. $y = -x^2 + 2x + 2$
19. $y = 2x^2 + 8x - 3$
20. $y = -0.5x^2 + 5$

21.
22.
23.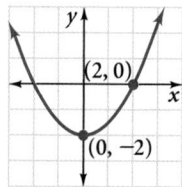

5-4 and 5-5 Objectives

▼ To find common and binomial factors of quadratic expressions (p. 259)

▼ To factor special quadratic expressions (p. 262)

▼ To solve quadratic equations by factoring and by finding square roots (p. 267)

▼ To solve quadratic equations by graphing (p. 268)

You can solve some quadratic equations by finding square roots of both sides or by finding the zeros of the related function. You can solve some quadratic equations in the **standard form of a quadratic equation** $ax^2 + bx + c = 0$ by **factoring** and using the **Zero Product Property**. For a **perfect square trinomial**, $ax^2 \pm 2abx + b^2 = (a \pm b)^2$. For the **difference of two squares**, $a^2 - b^2 = (a + b)(a - b)$. In all cases, first factor out the **greatest common factor (GCF)** of the expression.

24–38. See margin.

Solve by factoring, taking square roots, or, if necessary, by graphing. Give exact radical answers. For answers found by graphing, round to the nearest hundredth.

24. $x^2 - 7x = 0$
25. $x^2 + 2x - 8 = 0$
26. $(x + 3)^2 = 9$
27. $4(x - 2)^2 = 32$
28. $2x^2 - 6x - 8 = 0$
29. $x^2 - 5x - 5 = 0$
30. $3x^2 - 14x + 8 = 0$
31. $x^2 - 3x - 4 = 0$
32. $x^2 + 8x + 16 = 0$
33. $x^2 - 6x + 9 = 0$
34. $4x^2 - 12x + 9 = 0$
35. $x^2 - 9 = 0$
36. $6x^2 - 13x - 5 = 0$
37. $4x^2 + 3 = -8x$
38. $3x^2 + 4x - 10 = 0$

---

23. $y = \frac{1}{2}(x - 0)^2 - 2$;
minimum: -2

24. 0, 7

25. $-4, 2$

26. $-6, 0$

27. $2 - 2\sqrt{2}, 2 + 2\sqrt{2}$

28. $-1, 4$

29. $-0.85, 5.85$ or $\frac{5 \pm 3\sqrt{5}}{2}$

30. $\frac{2}{3}, 4$

31. $-1, 4$

32. -4

33. 3

34. $\frac{3}{2}$

300

5-6 Objectives

▼ To identify and graph complex numbers (p. 274)

▼ To add, subtract, and multiply complex numbers (p. 276)

An **imaginary number** has the form $a + bi$, where $b \neq 0$. The imaginary number i is defined as $i^2 = -1$. A **complex number** has the form $a + bi$, where a and b are any real numbers. The **absolute value of a complex number** is its distance from the origin in the **complex number plane**. You graph $a + bi$ in the complex plane just as you graphed (a, b) in the coordinate plane. Complex numbers follow rules of operation like those of real numbers. Some quadratic equations have imaginary numbers as roots. Functions of complex numbers may be used to generate fractals.

Simplify each expression.

39. $\sqrt{-25}$ $5i$

40. $\sqrt{-2} - 1$ $-1 + i\sqrt{2}$

41. $-4 - \sqrt{-1}$ $-4 - i$

42. $\sqrt{-27}$ $3i\sqrt{3}$

43. $2\sqrt{-32} + 4$ $4 + 8i\sqrt{2}$

44. $|3 - i|$ $\sqrt{10}$

45. $|-2 + 3i|$ $\sqrt{13}$

46. $|4i|$ 4

47. $(3 + 4i) - (7 - 2i)$ $-4 + 6i$

48. $(5 - i)(9 + 6i)$ $51 + 21i$

49. $(3 + 8i) + (5 - 2i)$ $8 + 6i$

50. $(4 + 6i)(2 + i)$ $2 + 16i$

Find the additive inverse of each number. Graph the number and its inverse.

51. $2 - i$

52. $-4 + 3i$

53. $-7 - 4i$

54. $-2i$

51–54. See margin.

Solve each equation.

55. $x^2 + 2 = 0$ $-i\sqrt{2}, i\sqrt{2}$

56. $x^2 = -5$ $-i\sqrt{5}, i\sqrt{5}$

57. $3x^2 + 12 = 0$ $-2i, 2i$

58. $6x^2 + 4 = 0$ $\dfrac{-i\sqrt{6}}{3}, \dfrac{i\sqrt{6}}{3}$

Find the first three outputs of each fractal-generating function. Begin with $z = 0$.

59. $f(z) = z^2 - i$ $-i, -1 - i, i$

60. $f(z) = i - z^2$ $i, 1 + i, -i$

5-7 and 5-8 Objectives

▼ To solve equations by completing the square (p. 282)

▼ To rewrite functions in vertex form by completing the square (p. 284)

▼ To solve quadratic equations by using the Quadratic Formula (p. 289)

▼ To determine types of solutions by using the discriminant (p. 291)

Completing the square is based on the relationship $x^2 + bx + \left(\frac{b}{2}\right)^2 = \left(x + \frac{b}{2}\right)^2$. You can use it to write a quadratic function in vertex form. If the coefficient of the quadratic term is not 1, you must factor out the coefficient from the variable terms.

You can solve any quadratic equation by using the Quadratic Formula.

If $ax^2 + bx + c = 0$, then $x = \dfrac{-b \pm \sqrt{b^2 - 4ac}}{2a}$.

The discriminant $b^2 - 4ac$ determines the number and type of solutions of the equation. If $b^2 - 4ac > 0$, the equation has two real solutions. If $b^2 - 4ac = 0$, the equation has one real solution. If $b^2 - 4ac < 0$, the equation has no real solutions and two imaginary solutions.

Solve each equation by completing the square. 61–72. See margin.

61. $9x^2 + 6x + 1 = 4$

62. $x^2 + 3x = -25$

63. $x^2 - 2x + 4 = 0$

64. $-x^2 + x - 7 = 0$

65. $2x^2 + 3x = 8$

66. $4x^2 - x - 3 = 0$

Rewrite the equation in vertex form by completing the square. Find the vertex.

67. $y = x^2 + 3x - 1$

68. $y = 2x^2 - x - 1$

69. $y = x^2 + x + 2$

Determine the number and type of solutions. Solve using the Quadratic Formula.

70. $x^2 - 6x + 2 = 0$

71. $-2x^2 + 7x = 10$

72. $x^2 + 4 = 6x$

---

35. $-3, 3$

36. $-\frac{1}{3}, \frac{5}{2}$

37. $-\frac{3}{2}, -\frac{1}{2}$

38. $-2.61, 1.28$ or $\dfrac{-2 \pm \sqrt{34}}{3}$

51. $-2 + i$;

52. $4 - 3i$;

---

53. $7 + 4i$;

54. $2i$;

61. $-1, \frac{1}{3}$

62. $-\frac{3}{2} + \frac{i\sqrt{91}}{2}, -\frac{3}{2} - \frac{i\sqrt{91}}{2}$

63. $1 + i\sqrt{3}, 1 - i\sqrt{3}$

64. $\frac{1}{2} + \frac{3i\sqrt{3}}{2}, \frac{1}{2} - \frac{3i\sqrt{3}}{2}$

65. $-\frac{3}{4} + \frac{\sqrt{73}}{4}, -\frac{3}{4} - \frac{\sqrt{73}}{4}$

66. $-\frac{3}{4}, 1$

67. $y = \left(x + \frac{3}{2}\right)^2 - \frac{13}{4}$; $\left(-\frac{3}{2}, -\frac{13}{4}\right)$

68. $y = 2\left(x - \frac{1}{4}\right)^2 - \frac{9}{8}$; $\left(\frac{1}{4}, -\frac{9}{8}\right)$

69. $y = \left(x + \frac{1}{2}\right)^2 + \frac{7}{4}$; $\left(-\frac{1}{2}, \frac{7}{4}\right)$

70. 2 real solutions; $3 + \sqrt{7}$, $3 - \sqrt{7}$

71. 2 imaginary solutions; $\frac{7}{4} + \frac{i\sqrt{31}}{4}, \frac{7}{4} - \frac{i\sqrt{31}}{4}$

72. 2 real solutions; $3 + \sqrt{5}$, $3 - \sqrt{5}$

301

Chapter Test

Go Online
PHSchool.com
For: Chapter Test
Web Code: aga-0552

Differentiated Instruction Resources

- **L3** Ch. 5 Test
- **L2** Below Level Ch. 5 Test
- **L4** Ch. 5 Alternative Assessment
- **L3** Spanish Ch. 5 Test
- **L4** Spanish Ch. 5 Alternative Assessment
- ExamView CD-ROM
  - Ch. 5 Pre-Made Test
  - Make your own Ch. 5 test
- Online Chapter 5 Test at www.PHSchool.com

Below Level Chapter Test — L2

Chapter Test — L3

1. Write the equation of the parabola in standard form. Find the coordinates of the points corresponding to P, Q, and R. **See margin.**

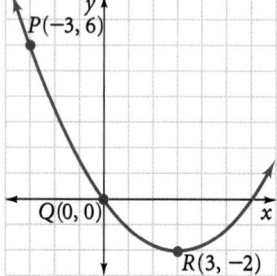

Sketch a graph of the parabola with the given vertex through the given point. **2–3. See back of book.**

2. vertex $(0, 0)$, point $(-3, 3)$

3. vertex $(1, 5)$, point $(2, 11)$

4–7. See back of book for graphs.
Graph each quadratic function. Identify the axis of symmetry and the coordinates of the vertex.

4. $y = x^2 - 7$ $x = 0$, $(0, -7)$

5. $y = x^2 + 2x + 6$ $x = -1$, $(-1, 5)$

6. $y = -x^2 + 5x - 3$ $x = 2.5$, $(2.5, 3.25)$

7. $y = -\frac{1}{2}x^2 - 8$ $x = 0$, $(0, -8)$

Simplify each expression.

8. $\sqrt{-16}$ $4i$

9. $4\sqrt{-9} - 2$ $-2 + 12i$

10. $(4 - i) + (5 - 9i)$ $9 - 10i$

11. $(2 + 3i)(8 - 5i)$ $31 + 14i$

12. $(-3 + 2i) - (6 + i)$ $-9 + i$

13. $(7 - 4i)(10 - 2i)$ $62 - 54i$

 14. **Physics** For a model rocket, the altitude h, in meters, as a function of time t, in seconds, is given by $h = 68t - 4.9t^2$. Find the maximum height of the rocket. How long does it take to reach the maximum height? $h = 235.9$ m; $t = 6.94$ s

Find the additive inverse of each number.

15. $3 - 7i$ $-3 + 7i$

16. $-2 + i$ $2 - i$

Graph each number on the complex plane. Then find its absolute value. **17–22. See back of book.**

17. $7 - 2i$

18. $8i$

19. $4 + 8i$

20. 5

21. $6 - 4i$

22. $-2 + 3i$

23. **Writing** Compare graphing a number on the complex plane to graphing a point on the coordinate plane. How are they similar? How are they different? **See margin.**

Solve each quadratic equation. **24–32. See margin.**

24. $x^2 - 25 = 0$

25. $x^2 + 5x - 24 = 0$

26. $x^2 + 8x - 9 = 0$

27. $3x^2 - 21x + 3 = 0$

28. $6x^2 = 9x$

29. $4x^2 + 4x + 4 = 0$

30. $5x^2 + x + 2 = 0$

31. $-3x^2 - 2x + 7 = 0$

32. $2x^2 + 6x + 12 = 0$

Write each function in vertex form. Sketch the graph of the function and label its vertex. **33–36. See back of book.**

33. $y = x^2 - 6x + 5$

34. $y = -x^2 + 8x - 10$

35. $y = 2x^2 - 3x - 1$

36. $y = -\frac{1}{2}x^2 + 4x - 9$

Evaluate the discriminant of each equation. How many real and imaginary solutions does each have?

37. $x^2 + 6x - 7 = 0$ **64; 2 real solutions**

38. $3x^2 - x + 3 = 0$ **−35; 2 imaginary solutions**

39. $-2x^2 - 4x + 1 = 0$ **24; 2 real solutions**

40. $-x^2 + 6x - 9 = 0$ **0; 1 real solution**

41. **Open-Ended** Sketch the graph of a quadratic function $f(x) = ax^2 + bx + c$ whose related quadratic equation $ax^2 + bx + c = 0$ has no real solutions. **Check students' work.**

23. **Answers may vary. Sample:** In the coordinate plane you graph ordered pairs (a, b); in the complex plane you graph complex numbers $a + bi$. For both, you find a on the horizontal axis and you find b on the vertical axis.

24. $-5, 5$

25. $-8, 3$

26. $-9, 1$

27. $\frac{7 - 3\sqrt{5}}{2}, \frac{7 + 3\sqrt{5}}{2}$

28. $0, \frac{3}{2}$

29. $-\frac{1}{2} - \frac{i\sqrt{3}}{2}, -\frac{1}{2} + \frac{i\sqrt{3}}{2}$

1. $y = \frac{2}{9}x^2 - \frac{4}{3}x$; $(9, 6)$, $(6, 0)$, $(3, -2)$

Standardized Test Prep

Reading Comprehension Read the passage below. Then answer the questions on the basis of what is *stated* or *implied* in the passage.

Dealing with Setbacks The boundary of a lot of land is called the property line. Many communities do not allow you to build up to the property line. Zoning laws may require a "setback" of several feet to ensure some distance between buildings and between a building and the property line.

Suppose the setback for a building is s feet on all four sides of a lot that has width 50 feet and length 60 feet. Then the maximum width of the building is $(50 - 2s)$ feet, and the maximum length of the building is $(60 - 2s)$ feet.

You can write and use functions in terms of s for the maximum area of the base of the building.

Students must be able to extract information from reading passages, answer multiple choice questions, and construct responses in order to be successful on current state and national assessments.

To answer the questions, students apply skills and concepts from this chapter and previous chapters.
Multiple Choice: Items 1–4, 11
Free Response: Items 5–10

Resources

Test Prep Workbook

Grab & Go
• **L3** Cumulative Review

ExamView CD-ROM
• Standardized Test Practice

Differentiated Instruction Resources

Spanish Assessment Resources
• **L3** Spanish Cumulative Review

1. What is the area of the entire lot?
C
   Ⓐ 220 ft
   Ⓑ 2576 ft²
   Ⓒ 3000 ft²
   Ⓓ $(3000 - 4s^2)$ ft²

2. Which function does NOT express the maximum
J area of the base of the building in terms of s?
   Ⓕ $A(s) = (50 - 2s)(60 - 2s)$
   Ⓖ $A(s) = 3000 - 220s + 4s^2$
   Ⓗ $A(s) = 4s^2 - 220s + 3000$
   Ⓙ $A(s) = 2[(50 - 2s) + (60 - 2s)]$

3. What is the maximum area of the base of the
C building when s = 8 ft?
   Ⓐ 64 ft²
   Ⓑ 156 ft
   Ⓒ 1496 ft²
   Ⓓ 2184 ft²

4. What is the minimum area that is NOT occupied
F by the base of the building when s = 6 ft?
   Ⓕ 1176 ft²
   Ⓖ 1824 ft²
   Ⓗ 2376 ft²
   Ⓙ 2856 ft²

5. Suppose the building is set back five feet. Find the maximum area of the base of the building.
   2000 ft²

6. Suppose the maximum area of the base of the building is 2376 ft². What is the value of the setback? 3 ft

7. Suppose the minimum area that is NOT occupied by the building is 1344 ft². What is the value of the setback? 7 ft

8. Write a function for the perimeter of the base of the building in terms of s. $P(s) = 220 - 8s$

9. Suppose a lot is 30 feet by 90 feet. The setback is s feet. Write an expression for the maximum area of the base of the building.
   $A(s) = 2700 - 240s + 4s^2$

10. Suppose a lot has length ℓ, width w, and setback s.
   a. Write an expression for the maximum area of the base of the building. a–b. See margin.
   b. Write an expression for the maximum perimeter of the base of the building.

11. A lot is 22 ft by 58 ft, and the setback on each side is s ft. Which formula expresses the maximum area of the base of the building in terms of s? A
   Ⓐ $f(s) = 4s^2 - 160s + 1276$
   Ⓑ $f(s) = 1276 - 160s - 4s^2$
   Ⓒ $f(s) = (58 - s)(22 - s)$
   Ⓓ $f(s) = 1276 - s^2$

Chapter 5 Standardized Test Prep **303**

30. $-\frac{1}{10} - \frac{i\sqrt{39}}{10}, -\frac{1}{10} + \frac{i\sqrt{39}}{10}$

31. $-\frac{1}{3} - \frac{\sqrt{22}}{3}, -\frac{1}{3} + \frac{\sqrt{22}}{3}$

32. $-\frac{3}{2} + \frac{i\sqrt{15}}{2}, -\frac{3}{2} - \frac{i\sqrt{15}}{2}$

Standardized Test Prep

10a. $A(s) = \ell w - 2\ell s - 2ws + 4s^2$

b. $P(s) = 2\ell + 2w - 8s$

Polynomials and Polynomial Functions

Chapter at a Glance

Lesson Titles, Objectives, and Features	Assessment	NCTM Standards	Local Standards
6-1 Polynomial Functions • Classifying polynomials • Modeling data using polynomial functions **Extension:** End Behavior	Lesson Quiz	2, 5, 10	
6-2 Polynomials and Linear Factors • Analyzing the factored form of a polynomial • Writing a polynomial function from its zeros	Lesson Quiz	1, 2, 6, 9	
6-3 Dividing Polynomials • Dividing polynomials using long division • Dividing polynomials using synthetic division	Lesson Quiz Checkpoint Quiz 1	1, 2, 9	
6-4 Solving Polynomial Equations • Solving polynomial equations by graphing • Solving polynomial equations by factoring **GPS:** Understanding Word Problems **Vocabulary Builder:** Continuous and Discrete	Lesson Quiz	2, 6, 9	
6-5 Theorems About Roots of Polynomial Equations • Solving equations using the Rational Root Theorem • Using the Irrational Root Theorem and the Imaginary Root Theorem	Lesson Quiz	1, 2, 7	
6-6 The Fundamental Theorem of Algebra • Using the Fundamental Theorem of Algebra in solving polynomial equations with complex roots and finding all zeros of a polynomial function	Lesson Quiz	2, 7, 8	
6-7 Permutations and Combinations • Counting permutations • Counting combinations	Lesson Quiz Checkpoint Quiz 2	1, 2, 5, 6, 10	
Activity Lab: Pascal's Triangle **6-8 The Binomial Theorem** • Using Pascal's Triangle • Using the Binomial Theorem	Lesson Quiz	2, 5, 7, 9	
Activity Lab: Applying Quadratic Functions			

NCTM Standards 2000

1 Number and Operations	**2** Algebra	**3** Geometry	**4** Measurement	**5** Data Analysis and Probability
6 Problem Solving	**7** Reasoning and Proof	**8** Communication	**9** Connections	**10** Representation

Correlations to Standardized Tests

All content for these tests is contained in *Prentice Hall Algebra 2*. This chart reflects coverage in this chapter only.

	6-1	6-2	6-3	6-4	6-5	6-6	6-7	6-8
SAT®								
Number and Operations Operations, ratio & proportions, complex numbers, counting, elementary number theory, matrices, sequences							✔	✔
Algebra and Functions Expressions, equations, inequalities, representation and modeling, properties of functions (linear, polynomial, rational, exponential)	✔	✔	✔	✔	✔	✔	✔	✔
Geometry and Measurement *Plane Euclidean/Measurement Coordinate* Lines, parabolas, circles, symmetry, transformations *Three-dimensional* Solids, surface area & volume (cylinders, cones, pyramids, spheres, prisms) *Trigonometry* Right triangles, identities								
Data Analysis, Statistics, and Probability Mean, median, mode, range, interquartile range, graphs and plots, regression, probability	✔						✔	✔
ACT®								
Pre-Algebra Basic operations using whole numbers, decimals, fractions, and integers; place value; square roots and approximations; the concept of exponents; scientific notation; factors, ratio, proportion, and percent; linear equations in one variable; absolute value and ordering numbers by value; elementary counting techniques and simple probability; data collection, representation, and interpretation; and understanding simple descriptive statistics.							✔	✔
Elementary Algebra Properties of exponents and square roots, evaluation of algebraic expressions through substitution, using variables to express functional relationships, understanding algebraic operations, and solving quadratic equations by factoring.	✔	✔	✔	✔	✔	✔	✔	✔
Intermediate Algebra Understanding of the quadratic formula, rational and radical expressions, absolute value equations and inequalities, sequences and patterns, systems of equations, quadratic inequalities, functions, modeling, matrices, roots of polynomials, and complex numbers.	✔	✔	✔	✔	✔	✔	✔	✔
Coordinate Geometry Graphing and the relations between equations and graphs, including points, lines, polynomials, circles, and other curves; graphing inequalities; slope; parallel and perpendicular lines; distance; midpoints; and conics.	✔	✔		✔				
Plane Geometry Properties and relations of plane figures, including angles and relations among perpendicular and parallel lines; properties of circles, triangles, rectangles, parallelograms, and trapezoids; transformations; the concept of proof and proof techniques; volume; and applications of geometry to three dimensions.	✔							
Trigonometry Understanding trigonometric relations in right triangles; values and properties of trigonometric functions; graphing trigonometric functions; modeling using trigonometric functions; use of trigonometric identities; and solving trigonometric equations.								
NAEP								
Number Sense, Properties, and Operations			✔					
Measurement		✔	✔	✔				
Geometry and Spatial Sense		✔	✔	✔				
Data Analysis, Statistics, and Probability	✔						✔	✔
Algebra and Functions		✔	✔	✔	✔	✔	✔	✔

SAT® The College Board, SAT® Reasoning Test   **ACT®** The ACT Assessment® Test   **NAEP** National Assessment of Educational Progress, 2005 Mathematics Objectives

Math Background

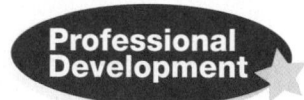
Skills Trace

> ### BEFORE Chapter 6
> In previous chapters, students solved linear and quadratic equations and applied linear and quadratic function models.
>
> ▼
>
> ### DURING Chapter 6
> Students model data using cubic and quartic functions, divide polynomial expressions, solve polynomial equations of degree 3 and higher, and find permutations and combinations.
>
> ▼
>
> ### AFTER Chapter 6
> Students will graph rational, radical, and reciprocal functions as well as solve their related equations.

Chapter Overview

Students have already studied properties of linear and quadratic functions, the two simplest kinds of polynomial functions. Now they examine polynomial functions in general. They consider how to factor polynomials that have integer coefficients. They study the connection between zeros and linear factors. Students see how the Rational Roots Theorem and Factor Theorem can be used to solve higher degree polynomial equations. The Factor Theorem and the Fundamental Theorem of Algebra lead to the conclusion that polynomial equations of degree n have exactly n complex solutions. Permutations and combinations are studied and then used to present the Binomial Theorem.

Polynomial Functions   6-1

Remind students that in a term involving only variables, such as x^5m^2, "1" is understood to be the coefficient as shown below.
$x^6 - x^5m^2 + 2x^5m^2 = x^6 + (-1)x^5m^2 + 2x^5m^2 = x^6 + (-1 + 2)x^5m^2 = x^6 + x^5m^2$.

Students should be encouraged to write out this application of the Distributive Property if they have difficulty remembering it.

Students should recognize that the cubic model usually has a rotated 90° S shape with two turning points. Furthermore the graph of a cubic has a slope that, from left to right, either increases-decreases-increases or decreases-increases-decreases. Graphs help students see that the term with the highest degree determines the "end" behavior of a polynomial function for very large positive values and very small negative values of the variable.

Polynomials and Linear Factors   6-2

Equations have solutions or roots. Graphically these values represent the x-intercepts of the graph of the related function. Because the y-value of the function is zero at the x-intercepts, or $f(x) = 0$, these x-values are called zeros. Thus, we find the roots of an equation but the zeros of a function; and a zero of a polynomial function $P(x)$ is also a root of the corresponding polynomial equation $P(x) = 0$.

The linear factors of a polynomial are closely connected to the zeros of the related polynomial function. By applying the Zero Product Property, each linear factor is set equal to zero and solved to obtain the zeros. The Factor Theorem makes the connection explicit, stating $x - a$ is a linear factor when the value a is a zero of the related polynomial function.

Dividing Polynomials   6-3

Polynomials may be divided by factors of the form $x - a$ by using long division or synthetic division. Either method can be checked by multiplying the resulting divisor by the quotient. The product should be the dividend as shown below.

$$\frac{\text{Dividend}}{\text{Divisor}} = \text{Quotient} \qquad \text{Dividend} = \text{Divisor} \cdot \text{Quotient}$$

Note that these statements apply whether or not a remainder exists as long as the quotient includes the remainder (which is divided by the divisor).

Students who have difficulty choosing r for synthetic division should observe that when $P(x) = (x - r) \cdot Q(x) = 0$, the equation $x - r = 0$ or $x - r$ finds a root of the polynomial P.

Solving Polynomial Equations   6-4

A wisely selected substitution can be made so a given polynomial equation becomes a quadratic equation and can be solved more easily. The difficulty lies in selecting a substitution that works. Here are examples to help students see how to select u.

1. $x^4 + 3x^2 - 4 = 0$ Let $u = x^2$. Then $u^2 = x^4$.
Solve $u^2 + 3u - 4 = 0$.

2. $x - 6\sqrt{x} + 9 = 0$ Let $u = \sqrt{x}$. Then $u^2 = x$.
Solve $u^2 - 6u + 9 = 0$

3. $(x + 4)^2 + (x + 4) - 2 = 0$ Let $u = (x + 4)$.
Solve $u^2 + u - 2 = 0$.

Theorems About Roots of Polynomials   6-5

This is an excellent place for students to review the rules for divisibility of integers that they learned in arithmetic.

A number is divisible by

2 if it ends in an even digit (0, 2, 4, 6, or 8).

3 if the sum of its digits is divisible by 3.

4 if the number formed by its last two digits is divisible by 4.

5 if it ends in 5 or 0.

6 if it is divisible by 2 and 3.

8 if the number formed by its last three digits is divisible by 8.

9 if the sum of its digits is divisible by 9.

10 if it ends in 0.

11 if, when − and + operations are alternated between its digits, the result is divisible by 11. (Try 54, 109 = 5 − 4 + 1 − 0 + 9 = 11; 54,109 = 11 · 4919.)

any composite number if it is divisible by each of the powers of the primes in the factorization of the composite number. (For example, $60 = 2^2 \cdot 3 \cdot 5$, $45 = 3^2 \cdot 5$, and $12 = 2^2 \cdot 3$, so 60 is divisible by 12, since 2^2 and 3 are factors of 60, but 60 is not divisible by $45 = 3^2 \cdot 5$, since 3^2 is not a factor of 60.)

The rules for divisibility by 2, 5, and 10 are probably those with which the students feel most comfortable. There are rules for divisibility by 7 and 13, but they are complex.

The Fundamental Theorem of Algebra   6-6

Some students may have difficulty distinguishing between a conjugate and an opposite. Whether s is irrational or $s = \sqrt{-1}$, the opposite of $a + bs$ is $-a - bs$, while its conjugate is $a - bs$. Relating conjugate pairs to the difference of two squares can often be helpful.

$$(x + 2)(x - 2) = x^2 - 4 \quad (x + i)(x - i) = x^2 - i^2 = x^2 + 1$$

Permutations and Combinations   6-7

Three different notations are used for the number of combinations of n objects taken r at a time: $_nC_r$, $\binom{n}{r}$, and $C(n,r)$. The third form emphasizes that a combination is a function of n and r. Only two of these notations are used for the number of permutations of n objects taken r at time, $_nP_r$ and $P(n,r)$, but $\binom{n}{r}$ is the classic notation for the Binomial Theorem. Students should locate these functions, along with factorial, on their calculators and learn how to use them.

In everyday language, the term *combination* is used even when a mathematical permutation is involved. For instance, the combination for a lock generally has a specific order associated with it and would more precisely be called a permutation.

The Binomial Theorem   6-8

The Binomial Theorem provides an expansion of $(a + b)^n$, where n is a positive integer, that uses combinations. Students can also use Pascal's Triangle to expand a binomial, or students can use the Distributive Property to multiply the binomial terms.

The Binomial Theorem offers an elegant connection between algebra and probability. The same binomial coefficients from the binomial expansion are used in the probability distribution called the Binomial Distribution, which is introduced in Lesson 12-6.

Additional Professional Development Opportunities

Math Background notes for Chapter 6: Every lesson has a Math Background in the PLAN section.

Research Overview, Mathematical Strands
Additional support for these topics and more is in the front of this Teacher's Edition.

Lesson Lab
Lesson Lab, a Pearson Education company, offers comprehensive, facilitated professional development designed to help teachers improve student achievement. To learn more, please visit lessonlab.com

Chapter 6 Resources

	6-1	6-2	6-3	6-4	6-5	6-6	6-7	6-8	For the Chapter
Print Resources									
L3 Practice	●	●	●	●	●	●	●	●	
L3 Guided Problem Solving	●	●	●	●	●	●	●	●	
L2 Reteaching	●	●	●	●	●	●	●	●	
L4 Enrichment	●	●	●	●	●	●	●	●	
L3 Daily Notetaking Guide	●	●	●	●	●	●	●	●	
L3 Vocabulary and Study Skills Worksheets	●	●		●		●	●		●
L3 Chapter Project									●
L3 Hands On Activity				●		●			
L3 Checkpoint Quiz			●				●		
L2 Below Level Chapter Test									●
L3 Chapter Test									●
L4 Alternative Assessment									●
L3 Cumulative Review									●
L4 Connections to Precalculus Masters	●	●	●	●	●	●	●	●	
L3 Technology Activities									
Spanish Resources ELL									
L3 Practice	●	●	●	●	●	●	●		
L3 Vocabulary and Study Skills Worksheets	●	●		●		●	●		●
L3 Checkpoint Quiz			●				●		
L2 Below Level Chapter Test									●
L3 Chapter Test									●
L4 Alternative Assessment									
L3 Cumulative Review									●
Transparencies									
Check Skills You'll Need	●	●	●	●	●	●	●	●	
Additional Examples	●	●	●	●	●	●	●	●	
Problem of the Day	●	●	●	●	●	●	●	●	
Classroom Aid	●	●	●	●	●	●	●	●	
Student Edition Answers	●	●	●	●	●	●	●	●	●
Lesson Quiz	●	●	●	●	●	●	●	●	
Test-Taking Strategies									●
Technology									
TI 83/84 Plus Activities		●							
Interactive Textbook Online	●	●	●	●	●	●	●	●	●
Student Express CD-ROM	●	●	●	●	●	●	●	●	
TI Navigator, Instant Check System	●	●	●	●	●	●	●	●	
Success Tracker	●	●	●	●	●	●	●	●	●
ExamView CD-ROM with Quick Take	●	●	●	●	●	●	●	●	●
Teacher Express CD-ROM	●	●	●	●	●	●	●	●	●
Presentation Express CD-ROM	●	●	●	●	●	●	●	●	●
Mindpoint Quiz Show CD-ROM	●	●	●	●	●	●	●	●	●
Prentice Hall Web site: PHSchool.com	●	●	●	●	●	●	●	●	●

Also available: Prentice Hall Assessment System (Progress Monitoring Assessments, Skills and Concepts Review, Test Prep Workbook)　Solution Key　Student Workbook
Student Workbook, Adapted Version　Data Analysis and Probability Workbook　Math Notes Study Folder　Spanish Cumulative Assessment

Where You Can Use the Lesson Resources

Here is a suggestion, following the four-step teaching plan, for how you can incorporate Differentiated Instruction Resources into your teaching.

	Instructional Resources L3	**Differentiated** Instruction **Resources**
1. Plan		
Check Skills You'll Need Assign these exercises to review prerequisite skills. **New Vocabulary** Help students pre-read the lesson by pointing out the new terms introduced in the lesson.	**Math Background** **Transparencies & Presentation Express CD** Check Skills You'll Need **Resources** Vocabulary and Study Skills	**Spanish Support** ELL Vocabulary and Study Skills
2. Teach		
L3 **Guided Instruction** Teach each Example. After each Example, assign the Quick Check exercise for that Example.	**Student Edition** Activity Lab **Resources** Daily Notetaking Guide Activity Lab TI-83/84 Activities CD-ROM **Transparencies & Presentation Express CD** Additional Examples Classroom Aids **ExamView CD-ROM with QuickTake** **TI Navigator Instant Check System**	**Teacher's Edition** Every lesson includes suggestions for working with students who need special attention. L1 Special Needs L2 Below Level L4 Advanced Learners ELL English Language Learners
3. Practice		

Assignment Guide
 	
Homework Exercises
Assign the exercises cited in each lesson's Assignment Guide.
  A Practice by Example
  B Apply Your Skills
  C Challenge
  Test Prep
  Mixed Review
 	
Homework Quick Check
Discuss in class the exercises cited in each lesson's Assignment Guide.
	Transparencies & Presentation Express CD
	Student Answers
	Resources
	Practice
	Guided Problem Solving
	Vocabulary and Study Skills
	Activity Lab
	ExamView CD-ROM with QuickTake
		Spanish Support
		ELL Practice
		ELL Vocabulary and Study Skills
		Resources
		L4 Enrichment

4. Assess & Reteach		
Lesson Quiz Assign the Lesson Quiz to assess students' mastery of the lesson content. **Checkpoint Quiz** Use the Checkpoint Quiz to assess student progress over several lessons.	**Transparencies & Presentation Express CD** Lesson Quiz **Resources** Checkpoint Quiz	**Resources** L2 Reteaching ELL Checkpoint Quiz Success Tracker **ExamView CD-ROM with QuickTake**

KEY   L1 Special Needs   L2 Below Level   L3 For All Students   L4 Advanced, Gifted   ELL English Language Learners

Chapter 6

Polynomials and Polynomial Functions

 Check Your Readiness

Answers are in the back of the textbook.

For intervention, direct students to:

Finding Models
Lesson 5-1: Example 3
Extra Skills and Word
  Problems Practice, Ch. 5

Graphing Functions
Lesson 2-2: Example 1
Lesson 5-2: Example 1
Extra Skills and Word
  Problems Practice, Ch. 2, 5

Solving Systems by Graphing
Solving Equations Algebraically
Lesson 5-5: Examples 1, 4–5
Lesson 5-8: Examples 1–2
Extra Skills and Word
  Problems Practice, Ch. 5

Finding the Number and Type of Solutions
Lesson 5-8: Examples 4-5

Finding Probability
Lesson 1-6: Example 1
Extra Skills and Word
  Problems Practice, Ch. 1

What You've Learned

- In Chapter 2, you learned to write and graph linear functions and to solve linear equations and inequalities.

- In Chapter 3, you learned to write, graph, and solve systems of linear equations and inequalities.

- In Chapter 5, you learned to write and graph quadratic functions and to solve quadratic equations.

 Check Your Readiness **GO for Help** to the Lesson in green.

Finding models (Lesson 5-1)

Find a quadratic model for each set of values.

1. $(-1, 3), (0, 1), (2, 9)$
$y = 2x^2 + 1$

2. $(0, -1), (2, -2), (4, -5)$
$y = -\frac{1}{4}x^2 - 1$

3. $(-4, 75), (0, 3), (11, 300)$
$y = 3x^2 - 6x + 3$

Graphing functions (Lessons 2-2 and 5-2)

Graph each function. **4–5. See margin.**

4. $6x - 4y = -10$

5. $y = 3x^2 - 10x + 2$

6. $y = \frac{3}{4}(x^2 + 12) + 1$
See back of book.

Solving systems by graphing (Lesson 5-5)

 Solve each equation by graphing. Round to the nearest hundredth.

7. $1 = 4x^2 - 3x$
$x = -0.25, 1$

8. $\frac{1}{2}x^2 + x - 14 = 0$
$x \approx -6.39, 4.39$

9. $5x^2 + 30x = 12$
$x \approx -6.38, 0.38$

Solving equations algebraically (Lessons 5-5 and 5-8)

Solve each equation algebraically.

10. $x^2 - 5x - 36 = 0$
$x = -4, 9$

11. $2x^2 - 13x + 21 = 0$
$x = 3, \frac{7}{2}$

12. $3x^2 - 4x = 3$
$x = \frac{2 \pm \sqrt{13}}{3}$

Finding the number and type of solutions (Lesson 5-8)

Evaluate the discriminant of each equation. Tell how many solutions each equation has and whether the solutions are real or imaginary.

13. $x^2 - 12x + 30 = 0$
24; 2 real solutions

14. $-4x^2 + 20x - 25 = 0$
0; 1 real solution

15. $2x^2 = 8x - 8$
0; 1 real solution

Finding probability (Lesson 1-6)

16. Suppose you select an integer from 100 to 200 at random. What is $P(\text{odd})$? $\frac{50}{101}$

304 Chapter 6

page 304

4.

5.

304

Polynomials and Polynomial Functions

🔊 Key Vocabulary

- Binomial Theorem (p. 354)
- combination (p. 346)
- conjugates (p. 337)
- Factor Theorem (p. 315)
- Fundamental Theorem of Algebra (p. 341)
- Imaginary Root Theorem (p. 338)
- Irrational Root Theorem (p. 337)
- multiplicity (p. 316)
- Pascal's Triangle (p. 353)
- polynomial function (p. 307)
- Rational Root Theorem (p. 335)
- Remainder Theorem (p. 323)
- standard form of a polynomial (p. 307)
- synthetic division (p. 321)

What You'll Learn Next

- In Chapter 6, you will learn to write and graph polynomial functions and to solve polynomial equations.

- You will learn to use important theorems about the number of solutions to polynomial equations.

- You will learn to solve problems involving permutations, combinations, and binomial probability.

 Activity Lab Applying what you learn, on pages 364–365 you will do activities involving soccer.

305

Chapter 6 Overview

This chapter introduces students to polynomials and polynomial functions. Students begin by defining and identifying polynomial functions. They then learn how to find linear factors of polynomials, and how to divide polynomials. Next students learn how to solve polynomial equations. They also learn theorems about roots of polynomial equations, and the Fundamental Theorem of Algebra. Students then apply what they have learned to solve problems involving permutations and combinations, and then learn the Binomial Theorem.

Activating Prior Knowledge

Ask:
- *What are some examples of linear functions? quadratic functions?*

Write their suggestions on the board. Note that the form of the linear and quadratic functions can be written as $y = mx + b$ and $y = ax^2 + bx + c$, respectively.

Ask:
- *How are linear functions related to quadratic functions?*

Accept all reasonable answers.

Guide students to recall the fact that quadratic functions can be expressed as a product of linear factors, such as $y = x^2 - 4 = (x + 2)(x - 2)$.

Tell students that they will be studying polynomial functions, which are functions that can be expressed as a product of linear factors. Linear and quadratic functions are examples of polynomial functions.

Also inform students that polynomial functions are used to model other types of functions (such as trigonometric functions in Chapter 13) in advanced mathematics, which is one reason why they are important to study.

Objectives
1 To classify polynomials
2 To model data using polynomial functions

Examples
1 Classifying Polynomials
2 Comparing Models
3 Real-World Connection

Math Background

The degree of a polynomial $P(x)$ determines the number of zeros of the related polynomial function. The end behavior of a polynomial function of even degree tends toward either infinity, or negative infinity. For a polynomial function of odd degree, the end behavior tends toward infinity on one end and negative infinity on the other end.

More Math Background: p. 304C

Lesson Planning and Resources

See p. 304E for a list of the resources that support this lesson.

Bell Ringer Practice

✓ **Check Skills You'll Need**
For intervention, direct students to:

Algebraic Expressions
Lesson 1-2: Example 4
Extra Skills and Word
   Problems Practice, Ch. 1

Polynomial Functions

What You'll Learn
• To classify polynomials
• To model data using polynomial functions

. . . And Why
To model the world's gold production, as in Example 3

 Check Skills You'll Need

 GO for Help Lesson 1-2

Simplify each expression by combining like terms.

1. $3x + 5x - 7x$ x
2. $-8xy^2 - 2x^2y + 5x^2y$ $3x^2y - 8xy^2$
3. $-4x + 7x^2 + x$ $7x^2 - 3x$

Find the number of terms in each expression.

4. $\frac{1}{2}bh$ 1 term
5. $1 - x$ 2 terms
6. $4x^3 - x^2 - 9$ 3 terms

🔊 **New Vocabulary** • polynomial • polynomial function • degree • standard form of a polynomial • degree of a polynomial

---

1 Exploring Polynomial Functions

1. They are lines with the same slope.

3. Answers may vary. Sample: The ends of each graph extend away from each other in either Quadrants I and III or II and IV. The number of x-intercepts varies for each graph.

4a. for $y = x - 4$, 4; for $y = x^3$, 0; for $y = x^3 - 2x^2 - x + 2$, -1, 1, 2; for $y = x$, 0; for $y = -x^3 + 3x - 2$, -2, 1; for $y = x^2 - 3x + 3$, none; for $y = x^3 - 2x^2 - x - 4$, 2.8; for $y = -x^3 + 4x$, -2, 0, 2; for $y = x^2$, 0; for $y = -x^2 + 4x$, 0, 4

Technology Activity: Graphs of Polynomial Functions

• Use a graphing calculator to graph each equation listed at the right.

• Sketch each graph on a separate index card or sheet of paper. Label the graph with its equation.

• Sort the graphs into groups based on their shapes.

1. How are the graphs of the linear equations alike? **See left.**

2. How are the graphs of the quadratic equations alike? They are all parabolas.

3. How are the graphs of the remaining equations alike? How are they different? **See left.**

4. a. Estimate the x-intercept(s) of each graph. Write them on each card.
   4a. See left.
   b. **Make a Conjecture** Compare the number of x-intercepts of each graph and the greatest exponent found in its equation. What is the relationship? The number of x-intercepts is less than or equal to the greatest exponent.

Differentiated Instruction Solutions for All Learners

Special Needs L1	**Below Level** L2
Help students connect higher degree polynomial functions to the shape of their graphs. A quadratic function is U-shaped, a cubic function has a sideways S shape, and a quartic function has a rounded W shape.	Review with students the meanings of the words cubic, quartic, quintic, etc.
learning style: visual	learning style: verbal

A monomial is an expression that is either a real number, a variable, or a product of real numbers and variables with whole-number exponents. A **polynomial** is a monomial or the sum of monomials. For any polynomial, you can write the corresponding polynomial function, as shown below.

 Key Concepts

Definition	Polynomial Function
$P(x) = a_n x^n + a_{n-1} x^{n-1} + \ldots + a_1 x + a_0$	where n is a nonnegative integer and the coefficients $a_n, \ldots, a_0$ are real numbers.

Vocabulary Tip

The prefix poly means "many."

The exponent of the variable in a term determines the **degree** of that term. The terms in the polynomial shown below are in *descending order* by degree. This order demonstrates the **standard form of a polynomial.** A one-variable polynomial in standard form has no two terms with the same degree, since all like terms have been combined.

$$P(x) = 2x^3 - 5x^2 - 2x + 5 \quad \text{Polynomial}$$

Degree

Leading coefficient — Cubic term — Quadratic term — Linear term — Constant term

You can classify a polynomial by the number of terms it contains. A polynomial of more than three terms does not usually have a special name. You can also classify a polynomial by its degree. The **degree of a polynomial** is the largest degree of any term of the polynomial. The name assigned to each degree is listed below.

Degree	Name Using Degree	Polynomial Example	Number of Terms	Name Using Number of Terms
0	constant	6	1	monomial
1	linear	$x + 3$	2	binomial
2	quadratic	$3x^2$	1	monomial
3	cubic	$2x^3 - 5x^2 - 2x$	3	trinomial
4	quartic	$x^4 + 3x^2$	2	binomial
5	quintic	$-2x^5 + 3x^2 - x + 4$	4	polynomial of 4 terms

1 EXAMPLE Classifying Polynomials

Write each polynomial in standard form. Then classify it by degree and by number of terms.

a. $-7x + 5x^4$

$5x^4 - 7x$

The term with the largest degree is $5x^4$, so the polynomial is degree 4. It has two terms. The polynomial is a quartic binomial.

b. $x^2 - 4x + 3x^3 + 2x$

$3x^3 + x^2 - 2x$

The term with the largest degree is $3x^3$, so the polynomial is degree 3. It has three terms. The polynomial is a cubic trinomial.

1a. $-2x + 5$; linear binomial

b. $5x^3 + x^2 - 4x$; cubic trinomial

c. $-2x^5 + 6$; quintic binomial

 Quick Check **1** Write each polynomial in standard form. Then classify it by degree and by number of terms. a–c. See left.
a. $4x - 6x + 5$ **b.** $3x^3 + x^2 - 4x + 2x^3$ **c.** $6 - 2x^5$

307

---

2. Teach

Guided Instruction

Technology Activity

Math Tip
Without using the terminology of polynomial functions, this activity indicates that the shape of the graph of a polynomial function has a great deal to do with the degree of the related polynomial. It also suggests a connection between the degree of the related polynomial and the number of times the graph can touch or cross the x-axis.

1 EXAMPLE **Connection to Geometry**

Students may wonder why, when the degree of a polynomial is 3, the polynomial is classified as cubic. Remind them that a cube has 3 dimensions: length, width, and height.

PowerPoint

Additional Examples

1 Write each polynomial in standard form. Then classify it by degree and by number of terms.
a. $9 + x^3$ $x^3 + 9$, degree 3, cubic binomial
b. $x^3 - 2x^2 - 3x^4$
$-3x^4 + x^3 - 2x^2$, degree 4, quartic trinomial

Advanced Learners **L4**
Challenge students to explain why *quad,* meaning *four,* is the prefix in the word *quadratic* that describes a second-degree polynomial.

learning style: verbal

English Language Learners **ELL**
Have students associate the name of each polynomial with its degree. For example, a monomial relates to a monologue, or speech by one person; and a quartic relates to a quartet, or singing group with four people.

learning style: verbal

307

2 Using a graphing calculator, determine whether a linear, quadratic, or cubic model best fits the values in the table.

X	Y
0	2.8
2	5
4	6
6	5.5
8	4

cubic

3 The table shows data on the number of employees that a small company had from 1975 to 2000. Find a cubic function to model the data. Use it to estimate the number of employees in 1998. Let 0 represent 1975.

Year	Number of Employees
1975	60
1980	65
1985	70
1990	60
1995	55
2000	64

$f(x) = 0.00963x^3 - 0.3754x^2 + 3.541x + 58.96$; about 59 employees

Resources
- Daily Notetaking Guide 6-1 **L3**

Closure

Ask students how to determine the degree of a polynomial. **Find the largest degree of any term of the polynomial.** Describe a method for estimating values between known data points. **Graph the known data, choose an appropriate model to fit the data, and use the model to estimate the values between the known data points.**

---

2 — Modeling Data With a Polynomial Function

You have already used lines and parabolas to model data. Sometimes you can fit data more closely by using a polynomial model of degree three or greater.

2 EXAMPLE — Comparing Models

Using a graphing calculator, determine whether a linear model, a quadratic model, or a cubic model best fits the values in the table.

x	0	5	10	15	20
y	10.1	2.8	8.1	16.0	17.8

Enter the data. Use the LinReg, QuadReg, and CubicReg options of a graphing calculator to find the best-fitting model for each polynomial classification.

Graph each model and compare.

Linear model   **Quadratic model**   **Cubic model**

● The cubic model appears to best fit the given values.

2. Answers may vary. Sample: No; when $x = 25$ then, based on the cubic model, $y \approx 3.76$, but because of its turning points the cubic model is unreliable.

✓ Quick Check **2** Can you use the model in Example 2 to predict the value of y for $x = 25$? Explain.

Finding a close fit helps you estimate values between known data points.

3 EXAMPLE — Real-World Connection

Gold The table below shows world gold production for several years. Find a quartic function to model the data. Use it to estimate production in 1988.

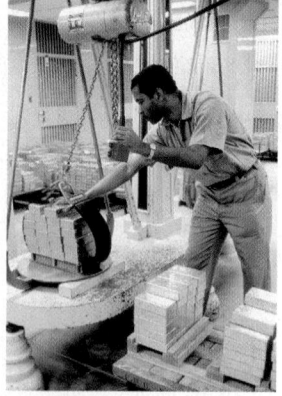

Real-World Connection

The Federal Reserve stores gold in bars that weigh 400 troy ounces each.

World Gold Production

Year	1975	1980	1985	1990	1995	2000
Production (millions of troy ounces)	38.5	39.2	49.3	70.2	71.8	82.6

SOURCES: *The World Almanac* and *World Gold*

Enter the data. Let 0 represent 1975. To find a quartic model, use the QuarticReg option of a graphing calculator. Graph the model.

```
QuarticReg
 y=ax^4+bx^3+...+e
 a=9.0333333E-4
 b=-.0519296296
 c=.9590277778
 d=-3.898862434
↓e=38.85753968
```

X	Y₁
7	42.915
8	46.157
9	49.519
10	52.875
11	56.12
12	59.168
13	61.959

X=13

The function $f(x) = 0.0009033x^4 - 0.05193x^3 + 0.959x^2 - 3.899x + 38.86$ is an approximate model for a quartic function.

To estimate gold production in 1988, you can use the Table option of a graphing calculator to find that $f(13) \approx 61.96$. According to the model, about 62 million troy ounces of gold were produced in 1988.

 Quick Check ❸ Use the quartic model in Example 3 to estimate gold production in 1997.
75.9 million troy oz

EXERCISES

For more exercises, see *Extra Skill and Word Problem Practice*.

Practice and Problem Solving

 Practice by Example

Example 1
(page 307)

 GO for Help

Write each polynomial in standard form. Then classify it by degree and by number of terms. 1–12. See margin.

1. $7x + 3x + 5$

2. $5 - 3x$

3. $2m^2 - 3 + 7m$

4. $-x^3 + x^4 + x$

5. $-4p + 3p + 2p^2$

6. $5a^2 + 3a^3 + 1$

7. $-x^5$

8. $3 + 12x^4$

9. $6x^3 - x^3$

10. $7x^3 - 10x^3 + x^3$

11. $4x + 5x^2 + 8$

12. $x^2 - x^4 + 2x^2$

Example 2
(page 308)

Find a cubic model for each set of values. 13–17. See back of book.

13. $(-2, -7), (-1, 0), (0, 1), (1, 2), (2, 9)$

14. $(0, -12), (1, 10), (2, 4), (3, 42)$

15. $(-1, 2.5), (0, 1), (1, 1.5), (2, 13)$

16. $(-3, 91), (-2, 84), (-1, 93), (0, 100)$

17. Vital Statistics The data at the right indicate that the life expectancy for residents of the United States has been increasing. Recall that in Chapter 3 you found linear models for this data set.
a. Find quadratic models for the data set.
b. Find cubic models for the data set.
c. Graph each model. Compare the quadratic and cubic models to determine whether one is a better fit.

Life Expectancy (years)

Year of Birth	Males	Females
1970	67.1	74.7
1980	70.0	77.4
1990	71.8	78.8
2000	74.3	79.7
2010	74.5	81.3

Source: U.S. Bureau of the Census.
Go to www.PHSchool.com for a data update.
Web Code: agg-9041

Example 3
(pages 308–309)

Find a cubic model for each function. Then use your model to estimate the value of y when $x = 17$. 18–23. See back of book.

18. $(-1, -3), (0, 0), (1, -1), (2, 0)$

19. $(10, 0), (11, 121), (12, 288), (13, 507)$

20. $(10, 500), (14, 588), (16, 512), (20, 0)$

21. $(1, 91), (10, 95), (20, 260), (30, 365)$

22.

x	0	3	5	6	9	11	12	14	16	18	20
y	42	31	26	21	17	15	19	22	28	30	29

23.

x	0	2	3	6	8	10	12	14	16	18	20
y	4.1	6	15.7	21.1	23.6	23.1	24.7	24.9	23.9	25.2	29.5

B **Apply Your Skills**

24. Open-Ended Write a third-degree polynomial function. Make a table of values and a graph. Find the x- and y-intercepts. **Check students' work.**

Lesson 6-1 Polynomial Functions **309**

1. $10x + 5$; linear binomial

2. $-3x + 5$; linear binomial

3. $2m^2 + 7m - 3$; quadratic trinomial

4. $x^4 - x^3 + x$; quartic trinomial

5. $2p^2 - p$; quadratic binomial

6. $3a^3 + 5a^2 + 1$; cubic trinomial

7. $-x^5$; quintic monomial

8. $12x^4 + 3$; quartic binomial

9. $5x^3$; cubic monomial

10. $-2x^3$; cubic monomial

11. $5x^2 + 4x + 8$; quadratic trinomial

12. $-x^4 + 3x^3$; quartic binomial

3. Practice

Assignment Guide

❶ A B 1–12, 24–30, 33–58

❷ A B 13–23, 31–32, 59
C Challenge 60-61

Test Prep 62-68
Mixed Review 69-75

Homework Quick Check
To check students' understanding of key skills and concepts, go over Exercises 10, 17, 31, 32, 55, 59.

Exercise 17 Challenge interested students to research why the life expectancies for males and females differ. Invite students to share their findings with the class.

Careers
Exercise 17 Insurance companies use vital statistics, such as life expectancies of males and females, and current age, to determine the cost of life insurance.

Differentiated Instruction Resources

GPS Guided Problem Solving	L3
Enrichment	L4
Reteaching	L2
Practice	L3

309

4. Assess & Reteach

Lesson Quiz

Write each polynomial in standard form. Then classify it by degree and by number of terms.

1. $-x^2 + 2x + x^2$ $2x$; degree 1, linear monomial

2. $7x^2 + 10 + 4x^3$
   $4x^3 + 7x^2 + 10$; degree 3, cubic trinomial

3. $3x(4x) + x^2(2x^2)$
   $2x^4 + 12x^2$; degree 4, quartic binomial

4.

x	1	2	3	5	8
y	3	2.2	3	7	5

a. Find a cubic and a quadratic model for the table of values.

Xmin=0.3 Ymin=1.384
Xmax=8.7 Ymax=9
Xscl=1   Yscl=1

$y = -0.14401x^3 + 1.7805x^2 - 5.229x + 6.62$,
$y = -0.1319x^2 + 1.682x + 0.37$

b. Which model appears to give the better fit? the cubic model

c. Using the model you selected in part b, estimate the value of y when x = 12. −48.6

Alternative Assessment

Organize students into groups of two. Have students search for data about sports, economics, science, or other topics of interest. Direct them to enter portions of the data on a graphing calculator to see if the data can be modeled in a reasonable way by a linear, quadratic, or cubic polynomial function. Students then record the equations for the models and sketch graphs of the data points and models. Have students classify their models by degree and number of terms.

31a. $V = 10\pi r^2$

b. $V = \frac{2}{3}\pi r^3$

c. $V = \frac{2}{3}\pi r^3 + 10\pi r^2$

Vocabulary Tip

To interpolate means to estimate a value inside the range of known values. To extrapolate means to estimate a value outside the range of known values.

46–58. See margin p. 311.

GO Online
Homework Video Tutor
Visit: PHSchool.com
Web Code: age-0601

Write each polynomial in standard form. Then classify it by degree and by number of terms. 25–30. See margin.

25. $8x - 4x + x^3$
26. $a^2 + a^3 - 4a^4$
27. 7
28. $2x(3x)$
29. $x^3(2 + x)$
30. $\frac{3x^5 + 4x}{6}$

31. **Packaging Design** The diagram at the right shows a cologne bottle that consists of a cylindrical base and a hemispherical top.
   a. Write an expression for the cylinder's volume.
   b. Write an expression for the volume of the hemispherical top.
   c. Write a polynomial to represent the total volume.

$h = 10$ cm

32. **Writing** Explain why cubic functions are useful for interpolating between known data points. Why are they often not reliable for extrapolating data? See margin.

Simplify. Classify each result by number of terms. 33–45. See margin p. 311.

33. $(2c^2 + 9) - (3c^2 - 7)$
34. $(-8d^3 - 7) + (-d^3 - 6)$
35. $(7x^2 + 8x - 5) + (9x^2 - 9x)$
36. $(5x^3 - 6x + 8) - (3x^3 - 9)$
37. $(3a - 2b) + (6b - 2a)$
38. $(4x - 5y) - (4x + 7y)$
39. $(3x^2 - 6y - 1) + (5x^2 + 1)$
40. $(-a^2 - 3) - (3a - a^2 - 5)$
41. $(7x^3 + 9x^2 - 8x + 11) - (5x^3 - 13x - 16)$
42. $(-12x^3 + 5x - 23) - (4x^4 + 31 - 9x^3)$
43. $(30x^3 - 49x^2 + 7x) + (50x^3 - 75 - 60x^2)$
44. $(-3x^3 + 7x^2 - 8) - (-5x^3 + 9x^2 - 8x + 19)$
45. $(3a^2 - ab - 7) + (5a^2 + ab + 8) - (-2a^2 + 3ab - 9)$

Find each product. Classify the result by number of terms.

46. $x(2x)(4x + 1)$
47. $5x^2(6x - 2)$
48. $(2a - 5)(a^2 - 1)$
49. $b(b - 3)^2$
50. $(x - 2)^3$
51. $(x^2 + 1)^2$
52. $(2x + 5)^3 + 1$
53. $(a - b)^2(a + b)$
54. $(a - 1)^4$
55. $(s + 3)(4s - 1)(3s + 7)$
56. $(x + 1)(x - 1)(x + 2)$
57. $(2c - 3)(2c + 4)(2c - 1)$
58. $(s + t)(s - t)(s + t)(s - t)$

59. The table shows U.S. energy production for a number of years.
   a. Find a linear model, a cubic model, and a quartic model for the data set. Let 0 represent 1960. See margin p. 311.
   b. Graph each model. Compare the three models to determine which fits best. b. See back of book.
   c. Use your answer to part (b) to estimate U.S. energy production in 1997. ≈71.7 × 10^15 Btu for part (b) sample answer

U.S. Energy Production

Year	1960	1965	1970	1975	1980	1985	1990	1995	2000
Production (×10^15 Btu)	41.5	49.3	62.1	59.9	64.8	64.9	70.8	71.0	71.2

SOURCE: Energy Information Administration. Go to www.PHSchool.com for a data update. Web Code: agg-9041

25. $x^3 + 4x$; cubic binomial
26. $-4a^4 + a^3 + a^2$; quartic trinomial
27. 7; constant monomial
28. $6x^2$; quadratic monomial
29. $x^4 + 2x^3$; quartic binomial
30. $\frac{1}{2}x^5 + \frac{2}{3}x$; quintic binomial
32. Answers may vary. Sample: Cubic functions represent curvature in the data. Because of their turning points they can be unreliable for extrapolation.

C Challenge 60. **Geometry** Use the formula $V = \frac{\pi h}{3}(r^2 + rs + s^2)$ to find the volume of the truncated cone. Express your answer in scientific notation with the appropriate number of significant digits.

60. 2.5×10^8 cm^3

$s = 3.8 \times 10^2$ cm

$h = 3.5 \times 10^2$ cm

$r = 5.6 \times 10^2$ cm

61. **Critical Thinking** Recall that each family of functions has a simplest function called the parent function.
  a. Compare the graphs of $y = x^3$ and $y = x^3 + 4$. Describe how the graph of $y = x^3 + 4$ relates to the graph of $y = x^3$. **up 4 units**
  b. Compare the graphs of $y = x^3$ and $y = 4x^3$. Describe how the graph of $y = 4x^3$ relates to the graph of $y = x^3$. **$y = 4x^3$ is more narrow.**
  c. Identify the parent function among the functions in parts (a) and (b). **$y = x^3$**

Test Prep

Multiple Choice

62. Which expression is a cubic polynomial? **A**
  A. x^3 **B.** $3x + 3$ **C.** $2x^2 + 3x - 1$ **D.** $3x$

63. Which expression is a binomial? **J**
  F. $2x$ **G.** $\frac{x}{2}$ **H.** $3x^2 + 2x + 4$ **J.** $x - 9$

64. What is the degree of the polynomial $5x + 4x^2 + 3x^3 - 5x$? **C**
  A. 1   **B.** 2   **C.** 3   **D.** 4

65. Which expression is equivalent to $2x^4 - 3x + 6$? **H**
  F. $(x^4 - 2x^2 + 3) - (x^4 - x^2 - 9)$ **G.** $2x^4 - 3(x + 6)$
  H. $(3x^4 - x + 3) + (3 - 2x - x^4)$ **J.** $x(2x^3 - 3x) + 6$

Short Response

66. Simplify $(9x^3 - 4x + 2) - (x^3 + 3x^2 + 1)$. **[2] $8x^3 - 3x^2 - 4x + 1$**
  [1] Minor computational error

67. Simplify $x^2(3x^2 - 2x) - 3x^4$. Then name the polynomial by degree and the number of terms. **[2] $-2x^3$; cubic monomial**
  [1] Minor computational error

68. Why is finding the degree of a polynomial simplified when the polynomial is written in standard form? **See back of book.**

Mixed Review

GO for Help

Lesson 5-8

Use the discriminant to find the number of real solutions.

69. $3x^2 + x - 6 = 0$ **2**   70. $5x^2 - 9 = 0$ **2**   71. $-x^2 + 2x - 8 = 0$ **none**

Lesson 5-3

72. Graph $f(x) = 3x^2 - 1$. Translate the graph right five units and down two units. What is the vertex of the new graph? **See back of book.**

Lesson 4-4

Each matrix represents the vertices of a polygon. Translate each figure 3 units left and 2 units down. Express your answer as a matrix. **73–75. See back of book.**

73. $\begin{bmatrix} 4 & 0 & 4 & 8 \\ -6 & -1 & 2 & -1 \end{bmatrix}$ 74. $\begin{bmatrix} 5 & 0 & -3 \\ 7 & 0 & 2 \end{bmatrix}$ 75. $\begin{bmatrix} 1 & 2 & 1 & 2 \\ -1 & -1 & -2 & -2 \end{bmatrix}$

33. $-c^2 + 16$; binomial

34. $-9d^3 - 13$; binomial

35. $16x^2 - x - 5$; trinomial

36. $2x^3 - 6x + 17$; trinomial

37. $a + 4b$; binomial

38. $-12y$; monomial

39. $8x^2 - 6y$; binomial

40. $-3a + 2$; binomial

41. $2x^3 + 9x^2 + 5x + 27$; polynomial of 4 terms

42. $-4x^4 - 3x^3 + 5x - 54$; polynomial of 4 terms

43. $80x^3 - 109x^2 + 7x - 75$; polynomial of 4 terms

Test Prep

44. $2x^3 - 2x^2 + 8x - 27$; polynomial of 4 terms

45. $10a^2 - 3ab + 10$; trinomial

46. $8x^3 + 2x^2$; binomial

47. $30x^3 - 10x^2$; binomial

48. $2a^3 - 5a^2 - 2a + 5$; polynomial of 4 terms

49. $b^3 - 6b^2 + 9b$; trinomial

50. $x^3 - 6x^2 + 12x - 8$; polynomial of 4 terms

51. $x^4 + 2x^2 + 1$; trinomial

52. $8x^3 + 60x^2 + 150x + 126$; polynomial of 4 terms

53. $a^3 - a^2b - b^2a + b^3$; polynomial of 4 terms

54. $a^4 - 4a^3 + 6a^2 - 4a + 1$; polynomial of 5 terms

55. $12s^3 + 61s^2 + 68s - 21$; polynomial of 4 terms

56. $x^3 + 2x^2 - x - 2$; trinomial

57. $8c^3 - 26c + 12$; trinomial

58. $s^4 - 2t^2s^2 + t^4$; trinomial

59a. $y = 0.6877x + 47.97$
  $y = 0.000712x^3 - 0.06366x^2 + 2.169x + 41.59$
  $y = -0.00005632x^4 + 0.005218x^3 - 0.1757x^2 + 3.046x + 40.73$

311

Students learn to predict the behavior of the graph of a polynomial function by examining the term of highest degree and its coefficient. This will also help students check their graphs.

Guided Instruction

Special Needs L1

The arrow notation may be helpful for students who have difficulty describing the behavior with words.

Error Prevention

Students need to realize that it is the leading coefficient of a polynomial function *written in standard form* that should be inspected.

Auditory Learners

Stress the initial *o* in the words *odd* and *opposite* when describing the left behavior.

Resources

Technology

ExamView CD-ROM, Chapter 00, Extension Topics

The end behavior of a graph describes the far left and the far right portions of the graph. The graphs of polynomial functions show four types of end behavior— *up and up, down and down, down and up,* and *up and down.*

Up and Up	Down and Down	Down and Up	Up and Down
($\nwarrow$, $\nearrow$)	($\swarrow$, $\searrow$)	($\swarrow$, $\nearrow$)	($\nwarrow$, $\searrow$)
Example	Example	Example	Example

$y = x^4 - 3x^3 + 5x$ $y = -x^2 + 6x$ $y = x^3$ $y = -0.3x^3 + 4x + 2$

You can determine *by inspection* the end behavior of the graph of a polynomial function in standard form. Look at the coefficient and degree of the leading term.

Right If the leading coefficient is positive, then the graph rises to the right. If the leading coefficient is negative, then the graph falls to the right.

Left If the degree of the polynomial is even, then the left behavior is the same as the right behavior. If the degree of the polynomial is odd, then the left behavior is the opposite of the right behavior.

EXAMPLE Describing End Behavior

Determine by inspection the end behavior of the graph of each polynomial.

a. $y = 4x^3 - 3x$

The leading coefficient 4 is positive, so the graph rises to the right. The degree of the polynomial is 3, which is odd. The left behavior is opposite the right behavior, so the graph falls to the left. The end behavior is ($\swarrow$, $\nearrow$) .

b. $f(x) = -2x^4 + 8x^3 - 8x^2$

The leading coefficient –2 is negative, so the graph falls to the right. The degree of the polynomial is 4, which is even. The left behavior is the same as the right behavior, so the graph falls to the left. The end behavior is ($\swarrow$, $\searrow$).

EXERCISES

Determine by inspection the end behavior of the graph of each function.

1. $y = 3x + 2$ ($\swarrow$,$\nearrow$)

2. $y = 4x^3$ ($\swarrow$,$\nearrow$)

3. $g(t) = -t^2 + t$ ($\swarrow$,$\searrow$)

4. $f(x) = 2x + x^5$ ($\swarrow$,$\nearrow$)

5. $g(x) = x^6$ ($\nwarrow$,$\nearrow$)

6. $y = 3x^5 - 4x^4$ ($\swarrow$,$\nearrow$)

7. $y = -7x^8$ ($\swarrow$,$\searrow$)

8. $f(x) = \frac{1}{2}x^4 - 2$ ($\nwarrow$,$\nearrow$)

9. $y = -\frac{1}{2}x^3 + 4x^2 + x - 1$ ($\nwarrow$,$\searrow$)

10. $g(x) = x - x^3 + 5$ ($\nwarrow$,$\searrow$)

Polynomials and Linear Factors

What You'll Learn

- To analyze the factored form of a polynomial
- To write a polynomial function from its zeros

. . . And Why

To find the dimensions of carry-on luggage, as in Example 3

 Check Skills You'll Need **for Help** Lessons 5-1 and 5-4

Factor each quadratic expression.

1. $x^2 + 7x + 12$
$(x + 4)(x + 3)$

2. $x^2 + 8x - 20$
$(x + 10)(x - 2)$

3. $x^2 - 14x + 24$
$(x - 12)(x - 2)$

Find each product.

4. $x(x + 4)$
$x^2 + 4x$

5. $(x + 1)^2$
$x^2 + 2x + 1$

6. $(x - 3)^2(x + 2)$
$x^3 - 4x^2 - 3x + 18$

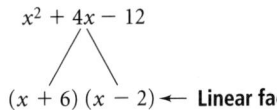 **New Vocabulary** • relative maximum • relative minimum • Factor Theorem • multiple zero • multiplicity

---

1 The Factored Form of a Polynomial

Just as you can rewrite a whole number as a product of its prime factors, you can write a polynomial as a product of its linear factors. Compare the factor trees for the whole number 6 and the quadratic expression $x^2 + 4x - 12$.

$$6 \qquad\qquad x^2 + 4x - 12$$

Prime factors → 2   3 $(x + 6)\ (x - 2)$ ← Linear factors

In the factor tree for the whole number 6, each branch ends with a prime number. Likewise, in the factor tree for the polynomial $x^2 + 4x - 12$, each branch ends with a "prime" linear factor. A linear factor is similar to a prime number in that it cannot be factored any further. Once a polynomial has been factored completely to its linear factors, it is in factored form.

1 EXAMPLE Writing a Polynomial in Standard Form

Write the expression $(x + 1)(x + 2)(x + 3)$ as a polynomial in standard form.

$(x + 1)(x + 2)(x + 3) = (x + 1)(x^2 + 3x + 2x + 6)$ Multiply $(x + 2)$ and $(x + 3)$.

$\qquad\qquad\qquad = (x + 1)(x^2 + 5x + 6)$ Simplify.

$\qquad\qquad\qquad = x(x^2 + 5x + 6) + 1(x^2 + 5x + 6)$ Distributive Property

$\qquad\qquad\qquad = x^3 + 5x^2 + 6x + x^2 + 5x + 6$ Multiply.

$\qquad\qquad\qquad = x^3 + 6x^2 + 11x + 6$ Simplify.

The expression $(x + 1)(x + 2)(x + 3)$ is the factored form of $x^3 + 6x^2 + 11x + 6$.

 Quick Check **1** Write the expression $(x + 1)(x + 1)(x + 2)$ as a polynomial in standard form.
$x^3 + 4x^2 + 5x + 2$

Lesson 6-2 Polynomials and Linear Factors **313**

---

1. Plan

Objectives
1 To analyze the factored form of a polynomial
2 To write a polynomial function from its zeros

Examples
1 Writing a Polynomial in Standard Form
2 Writing a Polynomial in Factored Form
3 Real-World Connection
4 Finding Zeros of a Polynomial Function
5 Writing a Polynomial Function From its Zeros
6 Finding the Multiplicity of a Zero

Math Background

There is a close connection between the problem of factoring a polynomial and the problem of finding its zeros. If $P(x)$ is a polynomial function, then $x - a$ is a linear factor of $P(x)$ if and only if $P(a) = 0$.

More Math Background: p. 304C

Lesson Planning and Resources

See p. 304E for a list of the resources that support this lesson.

 Bell Ringer Practice

Check Skills You'll Need
For intervention, direct students to:

Factoring Quadratic Expressions
Lesson 5-4: Examples 2–4
Extra Skills and Word Problems Practice, Ch. 5

Modeling Data With Quadratic Functions
Lesson 5-1: Example 1
Extra Skills and Word Problems Practice, Ch. 5

Differentiated Instruction Solutions for All Learners

Special Needs L1
Model multiplying two binomials using FOIL. Next multiply three binomials by first applying FOIL to two binomials; then multiply the resulting trinomial by the remaining binomial using the Distributive Property.

learning style: visual

Below Level L2
Help students understand why odd functions have only relative minima and maxima whereas even functions have at least one absolute minimum or maximum.

learning style: verbal

313

Guided Instruction

2 EXAMPLE Error Prevention

Some students may stop factoring after they find the GCF. Remind them to keep factoring as long as a polynomial is factorable.

3 EXAMPLE Diversity

Some students may not have had the opportunity to fly in an airplane and, therefore, may not understand what *carry-on* luggage is. Ask a student to explain the difference between *carry-on* and *checked* luggage.

PowerPoint

Additional Examples

1 Write $(x - 1)(x + 3)(x + 4)$ as a polynomial in standard form. $x^3 + 6x^2 + 5x - 12$

2 Write $3x^3 - 18x^2 + 24x$ in factored form. $3x(x - 2)(x - 4)$

3 Another airline has different carry-on luggage regulations. The sum of the length, width, and depth may not exceed 50 in.
a. Assume that the sum of the length, width, and depth is 50 in. and the length is 10 in. greater than the depth. Graph the function relating the volume V to depth x. Find the x-intercepts. What do they represent? x-intercepts: 0, −10, and 20; These values of x produce a volume of zero.

Xmin=−20 Ymin=−2000
Xmax=50 Ymax=5000
Xscl=5   Yscl=1000

b. Describe a realistic domain for $V(x)$. $0 < x < 20$
c. What is the maximum possible volume of the box? What are the corresponding dimensions of the box? about 4225 in.³; depth: about 12.2 in., length: about 22.2 in., width: about 15.6 in.

314

You can sometimes use the GCF of the terms to help you factor a polynomial.

2 EXAMPLE Writing a Polynomial in Factored Form

Write $2x^3 + 10x^2 + 12x$ in factored form.

$2x^3 + 10x^2 + 12x = 2x(x^2 + 5x + 6)$ **Factor out the GCF, 2x.**

$= 2x(x + 2)(x + 3)$ **Factor $x^2 + 5x + 6$.**

Check $2x(x + 2)(x + 3) = 2x(x^2 + 5x + 6)$ **Multiply $(x + 2)(x + 3)$.**

$= 2x^3 + 10x^2 + 12x$ ✓   **Distributive Property**

Quick Check **2** Write $6x^3 - 15x^2 - 36x$ in factored form. Check by multiplication.
$3x(x - 4)(2x + 3)$

You can use polynomial functions to solve real-world problems. Consider the formula for volume: $V = $ depth $\cdot$ length $\cdot$ width. Each dimension can represent a linear factor of a polynomial function.

3 EXAMPLE Real-World Connection

Travel Several popular models of carry-on luggage have a length 10 in. greater than their depth. To comply with airline regulations, the sum of the length, width, and depth may not exceed 40 in.

a. Assume that the sum of the length, width, and depth is 40 in. Graph the function relating volume V to depth x. Find the x-intercepts. What do they represent?

Relate   Volume = depth $\cdot$ length $\cdot$ width

Define   Let x = depth. Then $x + 10$ = length, and

$40 - ($depth + length$)$ = width.

Write $V(x) = x \ (x + 10) \ (40 - (x + x + 10))$

$= x(x + 10)(30 - 2x)$

Graph the function for volume. The x-intercepts of the function are $x = 0, x = -10,$ and $x = 15$. These values of x produce a volume of zero.

Xmin=−15
Xmax=20
Xscl=5
Ymin=−1500
Ymax=2500
Yscl=500

b. Describe a realistic domain.

The function has values over the set of all real numbers x. Since x represents the depth of the luggage, $x > 0$. Since the volume must be positive, $x < 15$. A realistic domain is $0 < x < 15$.

c. What is the maximum possible volume of a piece of luggage? What are the corresponding dimensions of the luggage?

Look for the greatest value of y that occurs within the domain $0 < x < 15$. Use the Maximum feature of a graphing calculator to find the maximum volume. A volume of approximately 2052 in.³ occurs for a depth of about 8.9 in. Then the length is about 18.9 in. and the width is about 12.2 in.

Real-World Connection

Airlines regulate the size of carry-on luggage because space is limited in a plane's overhead compartments.

Quick Check **3** Suppose an airline raises the allowable sum of the luggage dimensions to 45 in. Find the maximum possible volume and the corresponding dimensions.
$V \approx 3014$ in.³; depth ≈ 10.5 in., length ≈ 20.5 in., width ≈ 14 in.

Differentiated Instruction Solutions for All Learners

Advanced Learners L4
Have students write the polynomial equation of degree three that has roots 2, $3i$, and $-3i$, and check each other's work.

learning style: verbal

English Language Learners ELL
Discuss the everyday meaning of *relative* as someone who is *related* or connected through blood. In the context of a *relative maximum* or *relative minimum*, *relative* indicates close or nearby in distance.

learning style: verbal

The maximum value in Example 3 is the greatest value of the points in a region of the graph. It is called a **relative maximum.** Similarly, a **relative minimum** is the least y-value among nearby points on a graph.

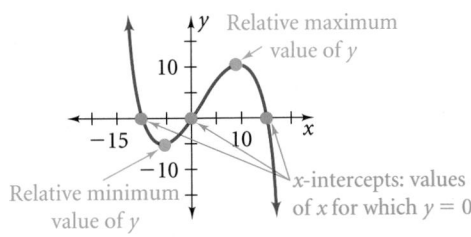

Recall that the x-intercepts of the graph of a function are called zeros because the value of the function is zero at each x-intercept.

2 Factors and Zeros of a Polynomial Function

If a polynomial is in factored form, you can use the Zero Product Property to find values that will make the polynomial equal zero.

4 EXAMPLE Finding Zeros of a Polynomial Function

Find the zeros of $y = (x - 2)(x + 1)(x + 3)$. Then graph the function.

Using the Zero Product Property, find a zero for each linear factor.

$$x - 2 = 0 \quad \text{or} \quad x + 1 = 0 \quad \text{or} \quad x + 3 = 0$$
$$x = 2 \qquad\qquad x = -1 \qquad\qquad x = -3$$

The zeros of the function are 2, -1, and -3. Now graph the function.

4b.

Zeros

✓ **Quick Check** ④ **a.** Find the zeros of the function $y = (x - 7)(x - 5)(x - 3)$. **7, 5, 3**
b. Graph the function and label the zeros.

You can reverse the process and write linear factors when you know the zeros. The relationship between the linear factors of a polynomial and the zeros of a polynomial is described by the Factor Theorem.

Key Concepts

Theorem	Factor Theorem

The expression $x - a$ is a linear factor of a polynomial if and only if the value a is a zero of the related polynomial function.

5 EXAMPLE **Math Tip**

Point out that any constant multiple of $f(x)$ will also have two distinct zeros at -2 and 3. Other functions with these zeros can be obtained by using other powers of the linear factors.

6 EXAMPLE **Teaching Tip**

Have students observe that if a polynomial function is written as a product of linear factors, they can use the factorization to identify multiple roots and their multiplicity. You may want to mention that if they do not see a way to write the polynomial in factored form, the graph may provide clues about multiple roots. Often, however, from mere visual inspection of the graph, there are no definitive answers to questions about multiple roots.

PowerPoint

Additional Examples

5 Write a polynomial function in standard form with zeros at 2, −3, and 0. **Answers may vary. Sample:** $f(x) = x^3 + x^2 - 6x$

6 Find any multiple zeros of $f(x) = x^5 - 6x^4 + 9x^3$ and state the multiplicity. **The number 0 is a zero with multiplicity 3, and 3 is a zero with multiplicity 2.**

Resources
• Daily Notetaking Guide 6-2 **L3**

Closure

Ask: *Suppose you are given a polynomial of degree greater than 1 and want to know whether $x - 2$ is a factor of the polynomial. How can you find out without dividing?* **Find the value of the polynomial for $x = 2$. If the value is 0, then $x - 2$ is a factor.**

316

Online active math

For: Linear Factors Activity
Use: Interactive Textbook, 6-2

✔ Quick Check

5a. $y = x^3 + 5x^2 + 2x - 8$

b. $y = x^3 + 6x^2 + 8x$

Vocabulary Tip

Distinct means "separate and different."

5c. Answers may vary. Sample: The zero at 0 can be from $x = 0$, $x^2 = 0$, $x^3 = 0$, and so on. Each power will lead to a different answer.

✔ Quick Check

---

5 EXAMPLE **Writing a Polynomial Function From its Zeros**

Write a polynomial function in standard form with zeros at $-2, 3,$ and 3.

$$\begin{array}{ccc} -2 & 3 & 3 \\ \downarrow & \downarrow & \downarrow \end{array} \qquad \text{zeros}$$

$f(x) = (x + 2)(x - 3)(x - 3)$ Write a linear factor for each zero.
$\quad = (x + 2)(x^2 - 6x + 9)$ Multiply $(x - 3)$ and $(x - 3)$.
$\quad = x(x^2 - 6x + 9) + 2(x^2 - 6x + 9)$ Distributive Property
$\quad = x^3 - 6x^2 + 9x + 2x^2 - 12x + 18$ Distributive Property
$\quad = x^3 - 4x^2 - 3x + 18$ Simplify.

● The function $f(x) = x^3 - 4x^2 - 3x + 18$ has zeros at $-2, 3,$ and 3.

5 a. Write a polynomial function in standard form with zeros at $-4, -2,$ and 1.
 b. Write a polynomial function in standard form with zeros at $-4, -2,$ and 0.
 c. **Critical Thinking** Explain why the zero at 0 produces more than one possible answer to part (b). **a–c. See left.**

While the polynomial function in Example 5 has three zeros, it has only two distinct zeros: -2 and 3. If a linear factor of a polynomial is repeated, then the zero is repeated. A repeated zero is called a **multiple zero.** A multiple zero has a **multiplicity** equal to the number of times the zero occurs. In Example 5, the zero 3 has multiplicity 2.

6 EXAMPLE **Finding the Multiplicity of a Zero**

Find any multiple zeros of $f(x) = x^4 + 6x^3 + 8x^2$ and state the multiplicity.

$f(x) = x^4 + 6x^3 + 8x^2$
$f(x) = x^2(x^2 + 6x + 8)$ **Factor out the GCF, x^2.**
$f(x) = x^2(x + 4)(x + 2)$ **Factor $x^2 + 6x + 8$.**

Since you can rewrite x^2 as $(x - 0)(x - 0)$, or $(x - 0)^2$, the number 0 is a multiple zero of the function, with multiplicity 2.

6 For each function, find any multiple zeros and state the multiplicity.
 a. $f(x) = (x - 2)(x + 1)(x + 1)^2$ b. $y = x^3 - 4x^2 + 4x$
  −1, multiplicity of 3   **2, multiplicity of 2**

The Factor Theorem helps relate four key facts about a polynomial. These facts are equivalent—that is, if you know one of them, you know them all.

Key Concepts

Summary	Equivalent Statements about Polynomials
① -4 is a solution of $x^2 + 3x - 4 = 0$. ② -4 is an x-intercept of the graph of $y = x^2 + 3x - 4$. ③ -4 is a zero of $y = x^2 + 3x - 4$. ④ $x + 4$ is a factor of $x^2 + 3x - 4$.	

Exercises

1. $x^2 + x - 6$

2. $x^3 + 12x^2 + 47x + 60$

3. $x^3 - 7x^2 + 15x - 9$

7. $x(x - 6)(x + 6)$

8. $3x(3x - 1)(x + 1)$

9. $5x(2x^2 - 2x + 3)$

EXERCISES

For more exercises, see *Extra Skill and Word Problem Practice*.

Practice and Problem Solving

A **Practice by Example**

Example 1
(page 313)

GO for **Help**

Example 2
(page 314)

7–9. See margin p. 316.

Example 3
(page 314)

15a. $h = x, \ell = 16 - 2x$,
$w = 12 - 2x$

b. $V = x(16 - 2x)$
$(12 - 2x)$

Example 4
(page 315)

Example 5
(page 316)

Example 6
(page 316)

29. -3 (mult. 3)

30. 0, 1 (mult. 3)

B **Apply Your Skills**

Write each expression as a polynomial in standard form. 1–3. See margin p. 316.

1. $(x + 3)(x - 2)$ **2.** $(x + 3)(x + 4)(x + 5)$ **3.** $(x - 3)^2(x - 1)$

4. $x(x + 2)^2$ **5.** $x(x + 5)^2$ **6.** $x(x - 1)(x + 1)$
$x^3 + 4x^2 + 4x$ $x^3 + 10x^2 + 25x$ $x^3 - x$

Write each polynomial in factored form. Check by multiplication.

7. $x^3 - 36x$ **8.** $9x^3 + 6x^2 - 3x$ **9.** $10x^3 - 10x^2 + 15x$

10. $x^3 + 7x^2 + 10x$ **11.** $x^3 + 8x^2 + 16x$ **12.** $x^3 - 7x^2 - 18x$
$x(x + 5)(x + 2)$ $x(x + 4)^2$ $x(x - 9)(x + 2)$

Find the relative maximum, relative minimum, and zeros of each function.

13. $f(x) = x^3 + 4x^2 - 5x$ **14.** $f(x) = -x^3 + 16x^2 - 76x + 96$
about 24.2, -1.4; 0, -5, 1   about 5.0, -16.9; 2, 6, 8

15. Metalwork A metalworker wants to make an open box from a sheet of metal, by cutting equal squares from each corner as shown.
  a. Write an expression for the length, width, and height of the open box. **a–b. See margin.**
  b. Use your answer from part (a) to write a function for volume. (*Hint*: Use factored form.)
  c. Graph the function. Find the maximum volume that can be contained by the box and the size of the square cut that produces this volume. **See back of book.**

Find the zeros of each function. Then graph the function.

16. $y = (x - 1)(x + 2)$ **17.** $y = (x - 2)(x + 9)$ **18.** $y = x(x + 5)(x - 8)$

19. $y = (x + 1)(x - 2)(x - 3)$ **20.** $y = (x + 1)(x - 1)(x - 2)$
16–20. See back of book.

Write a polynomial function in standard form with the given zeros.
21–28. See margin.
21. $x = 5, 6, 7$ **22.** $x = -2, 0, 1$ **23.** $x = -5, -5, 1$ **24.** $x = 3, 3, 3$

25. $x = 1, -1, -2$ **26.** $x = -1, -2, -3$ **27.** $x = 0, 0, 2$ **28.** $x = -\frac{1}{2}, 0, 4$

Find the zeros of each function. State the multiplicity of multiple zeros.
$-1, 0, \frac{1}{2}$
29. $y = (x + 3)^3$ **30.** $y = x(x - 1)^3$ **31.** $y = 2x^3 + x^2 - x$

32. $y = 3x^3 - 3x$ $-1, 0, 1$ **33.** $y = (x - 4)^2$ **34.** $y = (x - 2)^2(x - 1)$
                             4 (mult. 2)   1, 2 (mult. 2)
35. $y = (2x + 3)(x - 1)^2$ **36.** $y = (x + 1)^2(x - 1)(x - 2)$
$-\frac{3}{2}$, 1 (mult. 2) -1 (mult. 2), 1, 2

37. Geometry A box has length $2x + 1$ units, width $x + 4$ units, and height $x + 3$ units. To build the box using $x^3, x^2, x,$ and unit (1) blocks, how many of each will you need?   **2** x^3 **blocks, 15** x^2 **blocks, 31** x **blocks, 12 unit blocks**

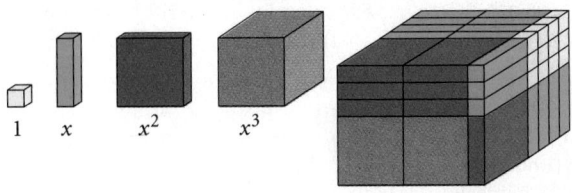

$1 \quad x \quad x^2 \quad x^3$

Lesson 6-2   Polynomials and Linear Factors   **317**

15a. $h = x, \ell = 16 - 2x$,
$w = 12 - 2x$

b. $V = x(16 - 2x)$
$(12 - 2x)$

21. $y = x^3 - 18x^2 + 107x$
$- 210$

22. $y = x^3 + x^2 - 2x$

23. $y = x^3 + 9x^2 + 15x - 25$

24. $y = x^3 - 9x^2 + 27x - 27$

25. $y = x^3 + 2x^2 - x - 2$

26. $y = x^3 + 6x^2 + 11x + 6$

27. $y = x^3 - 2x^2$

28. $y = x^3 - \frac{7}{2}x^2 - 2x$

---

3. Practice

Assignment Guide

▼**1** **A B** 1–15, 37–39, 40–46, 57–58

▼**2** **A B** 16–36, 47–56, 59–61
C Challenge   62–64

Test Prep   65–69
Mixed Review   70–78

Homework Quick Check

To check students' understanding of key skills and concepts, go over Exercises 15, 25, 38, 40, 58, 60.

Error Prevention!

Exercises 16–20 Students often multiply the factors before they graph the function. This usually requires more calculation than substituting in the factored form, and more work results in a greater chance of error. Encourage students to use the factored form to find the points they need to sketch the graph.

Differentiated Instruction Resources

GPS Guided Problem Solving	**L3**
Enrichment	**L4**
Reteaching	**L2**
Practice	**L3**

317

PowerPoint

Lesson Quiz

1. Find the zeros of
$y = (x + 7)(x - 3)(x - 2)$. Then
write the polynomial in
standard form. $-7, 2, 3$;
$x^3 + 2x^2 - 29x + 42$

2. Factor $x^3 - 2x^2 - 15x$.
Find the relative maximum and
relative minimum.
$x(x + 3)(x - 5)$; $\frac{400}{27}$, -36

3. Write a polynomial function in
standard form with zeros at
$-5, -4$, and 3. **Answers may
vary. Sample:**
$f(x) = x^3 + 6x^2 - 7x - 60$

4. Find any multiple zeros of $f(x)$
$= x^4 - 25x^2$ and state the
multiplicity. **The number 0 is a
zero with multiplicity 2.**

Alternative Assessment

Have each student write a linear
binomial on an index card. Direct
them to gather into groups of
three. Each group should write
the standard form of the
polynomial that has the binomials
of the group as its factors.
Students also find the zeros,
graph the function, and find the
relative maximum or minimum
values.

38a. $V = 2x^3 + 15x^2 + 31x$
$+ 12; 2x^3 + 7x^2 + 7x$
$+ 2$

b. $V = 8x^2 + 24x + 10$

40a. $h = x + 3; w = x$

b.

0, −3, 2; where the
volume is zero

Real-World Connection

Careers Carpenters use
math to design and measure
components of buildings,
furniture, and art.

57. **Answers may vary.
Sample: Write the
polynomial in
standard form. The
constant term is the
value of the
y-intercept.**

GO Online

Homework Video Tutor

Visit: PHSchool.com
Web Code: age-0602

38. **Carpentry** A carpenter hollowed out
the interior of a block of wood as shown at
the right.
a. Express the volume of the original block
and the volume of the wood removed as
polynomials in standard form.
b. Write a polynomial for the volume
of the wood remaining. **a–b. See margin.**

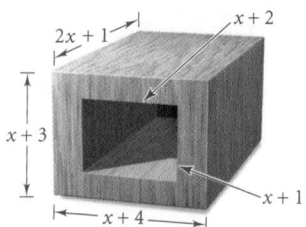

39. **Geometry** A rectangular box is $2x + 3$ units long, $2x - 3$ units wide, and
$3x$ units high. Express its volume as a polynomial. $V = 12x^3 - 27x$

40. **Measurement** The volume in cubic feet of a CD holder can be expressed
as $V(x) = -x^3 - x^2 + 6x$, or, when factored, as the product of its three
dimensions. The depth is expressed as $2 - x$. Assume that the height is greater
than the width. **a–b. See margin.**
a. Factor the polynomial to find linear expressions for the height and the width.
b. Graph the function. Find the x-intercepts. What do they represent?
c. Describe a realistic domain for the function. $0 < x < 2$
d. Find the maximum volume of the CD holder. **about 4.06 ft^3**

Write each function in standard form.

41. $y = (x + 1)(x - 4)(3 - 2x)$ 42. $y = (x + 7)(5x + 2)(x - 6)^2$
$y = -2x^3 + 9x^2 - x - 12$ $y = 5x^4 - 23x^3 - 250x^2 +$
Write each function in factored form. Check by multiplication. $1164x + 504$

43. $y = 3x^3 - 27x^2 + 24x$ 44. $y = -2x^3 - 2x^2 + 40x$
$y = 3x(x - 8)(x - 1)$ $y = -2x(x + 5)(x - 4)$
45. $y = x^4 + 3x^3 - 4x^2$ 46. $y = \frac{1}{2}x^3 - \frac{1}{8}x$
$y = x^2(x + 4)(x - 1)$ $y = \frac{1}{2}x\left(x - \frac{1}{2}\right)\left(x + \frac{1}{2}\right)$

Find the relative maximum, relative minimum, and zeros of each function.

47. $y = 2x^3 - 23x^2 + 78x - 72$ 48. $y = x^4 + 3x^3 - x^2 - 3x$

49. $y = 8x^3 - 10x^2 - x - 3$ 50. $y = (x + 1)^4 - 1$
47–53. See margin pp. 312–313.
Write a polynomial function in standard form with the given zeros.

51. $5, -2, 0$ 52. 7 multiplicity 3   53. $-2, -1, 3, 4$

For each function, determine the zeros. State the multiplicity of any multiple zeros.

54. $y = (x + 4)(x - 5)^3$ 55. $f(x) = x^4 + 2x^3 + x^2$ 56. $f(x) = x^3 - 36x$
$-4, 5$ **(mult. 3)**   0 **(mult. 2),** −1 **(mult. 2)**   0, 6, −6
57. **Critical Thinking** How can you find where the graph of a polynomial function
crosses the y-axis?

58. A storage company needs to design a new storage box that has twice the
GPS volume of its largest box. Its largest box is 5 ft long, 4 ft wide, and 3 ft high.
The new box must be formed by increasing each dimension by the same
amount. Find the increase in each dimension. **1 ft**

59. **Open-Ended** Write a polynomial function with the following features: it has
three distinct zeros; one of the zeros is 1; another zero has a multiplicity of 2.
See margin p. 319.
60. **Writing** Explain how the graph of a polynomial function can help you factor
the polynomial. **Answers may vary. Sample: The linear factors can be
determined by examining the x-intercepts of the graph.**
61. **Critical Thinking** A polynomial function has a zero at $x = -2a$. Find one
of its factors. $x + 2a$

318   Chapter 6   Polynomials and Polynomial Functions

47. about 10.5, −7.1; $\frac{3}{2}$, 4, 6   49. about −2.98, −6.17; 1.5   51. **Answers may vary.
Sample:** $y = x^3 - 3x^2$
48. about 0.9, −6.9, −1.4; 0, −3,   50. none, −1; −2, 0 $- 10x$
−1, 1

52. $y = x^3 - 21x^2 + 147x$
$- 343$

Challenge **62. Coordinate Geometry** The diagram at the right shows a rectangular region with one corner on the graph of $y = -x^2 + 2x + 4$.

62a. $A = -x^3 + 2x^2 + 4x$

    a. Write a polynomial in standard form for the area A of the rectangular region.

    b. Find the area of the rectangular region for $x = 2\frac{1}{2}$. $6\frac{7}{8}$ **square units**

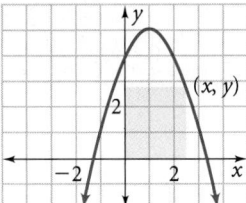

63. Find a fourth-degree polynomial function with zeros $1, -1, i$, and $-i$. Write the function in both factored form and standard form. $y = (x - 1)(x + 1)(x - i)$ $(x + i); y = x^4 - 1$

64a. Answers may vary. Sample: translation to the right 4 units

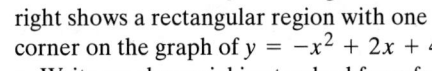 **64. a.** Compare the graphs of $y = (x + 1)(x + 2)(x + 3)$ and $y = (x - 1)(x - 2)(x - 3)$. What transformation could you use to describe the change from one graph to the other?

b. No; the second graph is not the result of a horizontal translation.

    b. Compare the graphs of $y = (x + 1)(x + 3)(x + 7)$ and $y = (x - 1)(x - 3)(x - 7)$. Does the transformation that you chose in part (a) still hold true? Explain.

    c. Make a Conjecture What transformation could you use to describe the effect of changing the signs of the zeros of a polynomial function? Answers may vary. Sample: Rotation of 180° about the origin.

Test Prep

Multiple Choice

65. Which expression is the factored form of $x^3 + 2x^2 - 5x - 6$? **C**
    A. $(x + 1)(x + 1)(x - 6)$ **B.** $(x + 2)(2x - 5)(x - 6)$
    C. $(x + 3)(x + 1)(x - 2)$ **D.** $(x - 3)(x - 1)(x + 2)$

66. What are the zeros of the polynomial function $y = (x - 3)(2x + 1)(x - 1)$? **H**
    F. $\frac{1}{2}, 1, 3$ **G.** $-1, 1, 3$ **H.** $-\frac{1}{2}, 1, 3$ **J.** $-3, \frac{1}{2}, 1$

67. Which polynomial function has zeros at $-4, 3$, and 5? **B**
    A. $f(x) = (x + 4)(x + 3)(x + 5)$ **B.** $g(x) = (x + 4)(x - 3)(x - 5)$
    C. $h(x) = (x - 4)(x - 3)(x - 5)$ **D.** $k(x) = (x - 4)(x + 3)(x + 5)$

Short Response

68. What is the factored form of $f(x) = x^4 + 8x^3 - 9x^2$? **See margin.**

Extended Response

69. What is the polynomial function, in standard form, whose zeros are $-2, 5$, and 6, and whose leading coefficient is -2? Justify your reasoning. **See margin.**

Mixed Review

GO for Help

Lesson 6-1

Write each polynomial in standard form. Then classify it by degree and by number of terms. 70–72. See margin.

70. $x^2 - 1 - 3x^5 + 2x^2$ **71.** $-2x^3 - 7x^4 + x^3$ **72.** $6x + x^3 - 6x - 2$

Lesson 5-4

Factor each expression.

73. $x^2 + 5x + 4$ **74.** $x^2 - 2x - 15$ **75.** $x^2 - 12x + 36$
    $(x + 4)(x + 1)$ $(x - 5)(x + 3)$ $(x - 6)^2$

Lesson 4-5

Evaluate the determinant of each matrix.

76. $A = \begin{bmatrix} 1 & -4 \\ 2 & 0 \end{bmatrix}$ 8   **77.** $B = \begin{bmatrix} 5 & 3 \\ 2 & -1 \end{bmatrix}$ -11   **78.** $C = \begin{bmatrix} 3 & -2 \\ 3 & -2 \end{bmatrix}$ 0

53. $y = x^4 - 4x^3 - 7x^2 + 22x + 24$

59. Answers may vary. Sample: $y = x^4 - x^2$, and zeros are $0, \pm 1$.

68. [2] $f(x) = x^2(x + 9)(x - 1)$

    [1] incomplete factoring of $x^2 + 8x - 9$ or other minor errors

Test Prep

Resources
For additional practice with a variety of test item formats:
- Standardized Test Prep, p. 363
- Test-Taking Strategies, p. 358
- Test-Taking Strategies with Transparencies

69. [4] The student multiplies $(x + 2)$, $(x - 5), (x - 6)$ and -2 to get $y = -2x^3 + 18x^2 - 16x - 120$.

    [3] appropriate methods but with one computational error

    [2] appropriate methods to find basic polynomial with given roots, but no multiplication of polynomial by -2

    [1] correct function, without work shown

70. $-3x^5 + 3x^2 - 1$; quintic trinomial

71. $-7x^4 - x^3$; quartic binomial

72. $x^3 - 2$; cubic binomial

319

Dividing Polynomials

What You'll Learn

- To divide polynomials using long division
- To divide polynomials using synthetic division

. . . And Why

To find the dimensions of a sarcophagus, as in Example 4

☑ **Check Skills You'll Need** **for Help** Lessons 5-1 and 6-1

Simplify each expression.

1. $(x + 3)(x - 4) + 2$ $x^2 - x - 10$
2. $(2x + 1)(x - 3)$ $2x^2 - 5x - 3$
3. $(x + 2)(x + 1) - 11$ $x^2 + 3x - 9$
4. $-3(2 - x)(x + 5)$
   $3x^2 + 9x - 30$

Write each polynomial in standard form. Then list the coefficients. 5–8. See below left.

5. $5x - 2x^2 + 9 + 4x^3$
6. $10 + 5x^3 - 9x^2$
7. $3x + x^2 - x + 7 - 2x^2$
8. $-4x^4 - 7x^2 + x^3 + x^4$

🔊 **New Vocabulary** • synthetic division • Remainder Theorem

---

1 Using Long Division

Vocabulary Tip

$$\begin{array}{r} 4 \leftarrow \text{Quotient} \\ 6\overline{)24} \leftarrow \text{Dividend} \\ \uparrow \\ \text{Divisor} \end{array}$$

5. $4x^3 - 2x^2 + 5x + 9$;
   $4, -2, 5, 9$

6. $5x^3 - 9x^2 + 10$;
   $5, -9, 0, 10$

7. $-x^2 + 2x + 7$;
   $-1, 2, 7$

8. $-3x^4 + x^3 - 7x^2$;
   $-3, 1, -7, 0, 0$

You can use polynomial division to help find all the zeros of a polynomial function. Division of polynomials is similar to numerical division.

Recall that when a numerical division has a remainder of zero, as shown below, the divisor and quotient are both factors of the dividend.

$$\begin{array}{r} 7 \\ 8\overline{)56} \\ \underline{56} \\ 0 \end{array}$$ **7 and 8 are factors of 56.**

If numerical division leaves a nonzero remainder, as shown below, then neither the divisor nor the quotient is a factor of the dividend.

$$\begin{array}{r} 8 \\ 5\overline{)42} \\ \underline{40} \\ 2 \end{array}$$ **Neither 5 nor 8 is a factor of 42.**

Division serves as a test of whether one number is a factor of another.

The same is true for polynomial division. If you divide a polynomial by one of its factors, then you get another factor. When a polynomial division leaves a zero remainder, as shown below with monomials, you have factored the polynomial.

$$\begin{array}{r} 2x \\ x\overline{)2x^2} \\ \underline{2x^2} \\ 0 \end{array}$$ **x and $2x$ are factors of $2x^2$.**

To divide polynomials other than monomials, follow the same procedure you use to divide whole numbers.

320   Chapter 6   Polynomials and Polynomial Functions

Video Tutor Help
Visit: PhSchool.com
Web Code: age-0775

1 EXAMPLE Polynomial Long Division

Divide $x^2 + 3x - 12$ by $x - 3$.

$$\begin{array}{r} x \\ x - 3\overline{)x^2 + 3x - 12} \\ \underline{x^2 - 3x} \\ 6x - 12 \end{array}$$

Divide: $\frac{x^2}{x} = x$.

Multiply: $x(x - 3) = x^2 - 3x$.

Subtract: $x^2 + 3x - (x^2 - 3x) = 6x$. Bring down -12.

Repeat the process of dividing, multiplying, and subtracting.

$$\begin{array}{r} x + 6 \\ x - 3\overline{)x^2 + 3x - 12} \\ \underline{x^2 - 3x} \\ 6x - 12 \\ \underline{6x - 18} \\ 6 \end{array}$$

Divide: $\frac{6x}{x} = 6$.

Multiply: $6(x - 3) = 6x - 18$.

Subtract: $6x - 12 - (6x - 18) = 6$.

The quotient is $x + 6$ with a remainder of 6, or simply $x + 6$, R 6.

Check Show that (divisor)(quotient) + remainder = dividend.

$$(x - 3)(x + 6) + 6 = (x^2 + 6x - 3x - 18) + 6 \quad \textbf{Multiply } (x - 3)(x + 6).$$
$$= x^2 + 3x - 12 \quad \textbf{Simplify.}$$

 Quick Check **1** Divide $x^2 - 3x + 1$ by $x - 4$. Check your answer. $x + 1$, R 5

You can use polynomial long division to find the factors of a polynomial.

2 EXAMPLE Checking Factors

Determine whether $x + 4$ is a factor of each polynomial.

a. $x^2 + 6x + 8$

$$\begin{array}{r} x + 2 \\ x + 4\overline{)x^2 + 6x + 8} \\ \underline{x^2 + 4x} \\ 2x + 8 \\ \underline{2x + 8} \\ 0 \end{array}$$

b. $x^3 + 3x^2 - 6x - 7$

$$\begin{array}{r} x^2 - x - 2 \\ x + 4\overline{)x^3 + 3x^2 - 6x - 7} \\ \underline{x^3 + 4x^2} \\ -x^2 - 6x \\ \underline{-x^2 - 4x} \\ -2x - 7 \\ \underline{-2x - 8} \\ 1 \end{array}$$

Since the remainder is zero, $x + 4$ is a factor of $x^2 + 6x + 8$.

Since the remainder $\neq 0$, $x + 4$ is not a factor of $x^3 + 3x^2 - 6x - 7$.

 Quick Check **2** Determine whether each divisor is a factor of each dividend.
a. $(2x^2 - 19x + 24) \div (x - 8)$ **yes** **b.** $(x^3 - 4x^2 + 3x + 2) \div (x + 2)$ **no**

2 Using Synthetic Division

To divide by a linear factor, you can use a simplified process that is known as **synthetic division.** In synthetic division, you omit all variables and exponents. By reversing the sign in the divisor, you can add throughout the process instead of subtracting.

---

3 EXAMPLE Teaching Tip

Have two volunteers work the example on the board using long division and synthetic division. Have other volunteers point out the similarities between the two methods. They may want to circle or box these similarities. Help students see how synthetic division is a highly condensed form of the long division algorithm. Omitting the variables and exponents does not involve the loss of any essential data, because the position of a coefficient indicates the power associated with the coefficient.

4 EXAMPLE Connection to History

A sarcophagus is a coffin placed above the ground. They were usually made of stone, but sometimes wood or terra-cotta were used. The name means "flesh-eating" in Greek. The limestone used by the ancient Greeks allegedly consumed the whole body, except for teeth, within 40 days.

Math Tip

If $x - a$ is a factor of a polynomial $P(x)$, then $P(x) = Q(x)(x - a)$ for some polynomial $Q(x)$. Thus,
$$P(a) = Q(a)(a - a)$$
$$= Q(a) \cdot 0$$
$$= 0$$
So, a is a zero of $P(x)$.

5 EXAMPLE Alternative Method

To verify the truth of the Remainder Theorem, have students use a calculator to evaluate the polynomial for $x = -4$.

Vocabulary Tip

Synthetic division is sometimes called the method of detached coefficients.

---

3 EXAMPLE Using Synthetic Division

Use synthetic division to divide $3x^3 - 4x^2 + 2x - 1$ by $x + 1$.

Step 1 Reverse the sign of the constant term in the divisor. Write the coefficients of the polynomial in standard form.

Write $x + 1 \overline{)3x^3 - 4x^2 + 2x - 1}$

as $\underline{-1}\ \ 3 \quad -4 \quad 2 \quad -1$

Step 2 Bring down the first coefficient.

$$\underline{-1}\ \ 3 \quad -4 \quad 2 \quad -1$$

Bring down the 3. This begins the quotient.

$$3$$

Step 3 Multiply the first coefficient by the new divisor. Write the result under the next coefficient. Add.

$$\underline{-1}\ \ 3 \quad -4 \quad 2 \quad -1$$
$$\times \quad\quad -3$$
$$3 \quad -7$$

Multiply 3 by –1. Write the result under –4.

Add –4 and –3.

Step 4 Repeat the steps of multiplying and adding until the remainder is found.

$$\underline{-1}\ \ 3 \quad -4 \quad 2 \quad -1$$
$$\quad\quad -3 \quad 7 \quad -9$$
$$3 \quad -7 \quad 9 \quad -10$$
$$3x^2 - 7x + 9 \quad \text{Remainder}$$

The quotient is $3x^2 - 7x + 9, \text{R} -10$.

Quick Check ③ Use synthetic division to divide $x^3 + 4x^2 + x - 6$ by $x + 1$.

$$x^2 + 3x - 2, \text{R} -4$$

4 EXAMPLE Real-World Connection

The volume in cubic feet of a sarcophagus (excluding the cover) can be expressed as the product of its three dimensions: $V(x) = x^3 - 13x + 12$. The length is $x + 4$.

a. Find linear expressions with integer coefficients for the other dimensions. Assume that the width is greater than the height.

$$\underline{-4}\ \ 1 \quad 0 \quad -13 \quad 12$$
$$\quad\quad -4 \quad 16 \quad -12$$
$$1 \quad -4 \quad 3 \quad 0$$
$$x^2 - 4x + 3 \quad \text{Remainder}$$

Divide. Use 0 as a place holder for any missing term.

$x^2 - 4x + 3 = (x - 1)(x - 3)$ **Factor the quotient.**

The width and the height are $x - 1$ and $x - 3$, respectively.

Real-World Connection

For the ancient Greeks, Romans, and Egyptians, a sarcophagus was a work of art created to honor a loved one. They decorated the stone tomb with elaborate inscriptions and ornaments.

b. If the length of the sarcophagus is 10 ft, what are the other two dimensions?

$x + 4 = 10$ **The length, $x + 4$, is 10.**

$x = 6$ **Find x.**

Since the width equals $x - 1$ and the height equals $x - 3$, the width is 5 ft and the height is 3 ft.

 Quick Check ④ **a.** Use synthetic division to divide $x^3 - 2x^2 - 5x + 6$ by $x + 2$. $x^2 - 4x + 3$

b. Use your answer from part (a) to completely factor $x^3 - 2x^2 - 5x + 6$.
$(x + 2)(x - 3)(x - 1)$

For: Synthetic Division Activity
Use: Interactive Textbook, 6-3

In Example 1, you saw that $x - 3$ is not a factor of $x^2 + 3x - 12$ because their quotient has a remainder of 6. If $x - 3$ were a factor of $x^2 + 3x - 12$, then 3 would be a zero of $P(x) = x^2 + 3x - 12$, and $P(3)$ would equal zero. You know that $P(3)$ does not equal zero, but what *does* it equal?

You can find $P(3)$ by substituting 3 for x.

$P(x) = x^2 + 3x - 12$

$P(3) = (3)^2 + 3(3) - 12$

$= 6$

$P(3)$ equals the remainder in Example 1, because

dividend = divisor × quotient + remainder.

$P(x) = (x - 3)(x + 6) + 6$

$P(3) = (3 - 3)(3 + 6) + 6$

$= 0(3 + 6) + 6$

$= 6$

This relationship is defined by the **Remainder Theorem.**

 Key Concepts

Theorem	**Remainder Theorem**

If a polynomial $P(x)$ of degree $n \geq 1$ is divided by $(x - a)$, where a is a constant, then the remainder is $P(a)$.

You can use the Remainder Theorem to find values of $P(x)$.

⑤ EXAMPLE **Evaluating a Polynomial by Synthetic Division**

Gridded Response Find $P(-4)$ for
$P(x) = x^4 - 5x^2 + 4x + 12$.

 Test-Taking Tip

If you know two ways to solve a problem, the second way is an excellent check that your answer is correct (if you have the time).

By the Remainder Theorem, $P(-4)$ equals the remainder when $P(x)$ is divided by $x - (-4)$.

$$\begin{array}{r|rrrrr} -4 & 1 & 0 & -5 & 4 & 12 \\ & & -4 & 16 & -44 & 160 \\ \hline & 1 & -4 & 11 & -40 & 172 \end{array}$$

The remainder is 172, so $P(-4) = 172$.

 Quick Check ⑤ Use synthetic division to find $P(-1)$ for $P(x) = 2x^4 + 6x^3 - 5x^2 - 60$. -69

PowerPoint

Additional Examples

③ Use synthetic division to divide $5x^3 - 6x^2 + 4x - 1$ by $x - 3$.
$5x^2 + 9x + 31$, R 92

④ The volume in cubic feet of a shipping carton is $V(x) = x^3 - 6x^2 + 3x + 10$. The height is $x - 5$ feet.
a. Find linear expressions for the other dimensions. Assume that the length is greater than the width.
length = $x + 1$, width = $x - 2$
b. If the width of the carton is 4 feet, what are the other two dimensions? height = 1 ft, length = 7 ft

⑤ Use synthetic division to find $P(3)$ for $P(x) = x^4 - 2x^3 + x - 9$.
21

Resources
• Daily Notetaking Guide 6-3 **L3**

Closure

Say: *Suppose you use synthetic division to divide a polynomial of degree n (where n ≥ 1) by x − 5. What does the last number in the bottom line of the synthetic division represent?* It is the remainder for the division problem. It is also the value of the polynomial when $x = 5$.

▼ A B 1–12, 34–47

▼ A B 13–33, 48–55

C Challenge 56–60

Test Prep 61–64
Mixed Review 65–74

Homework Quick Check
To check students' understanding
of key skills and concepts, go over
Exercises 7, 25, 35, 39, 48, 54.

Differentiated Instruction **Resources**

GPS Guided Problem Solving	L3
Enrichment	L4
Reteaching	L2
Practice	L3

Practice 6-3 .... Dividing Polynomials

Determine whether each binomial is a factor of $x^3 + 3x^2 - 18x - 24$.
1. $x + 4$ 2. $x - 3$ 3. $x + 6$ 4. $x + 2$

Divide using synthetic division.
5. $(x^3 - 8x^2 + 17x - 10) \div (x - 5)$ 6. $(x^3 + 5x^2 - x - 9) \div (x + 2)$
7. $(-2x^3 + 15x^2 - 22x - 15) \div (x - 3)$ 8. $(x^3 + 7x^2 + 15x + 9) \div (x + 1)$
9. $(x^3 + 2x^2 + 5x + 12) \div (x + 3)$ 10. $(x^3 - 5x^2 - 7x + 25) \div (x - 5)$
11. $(x^4 - x^3 + x^2 - x + 1) \div (x - 1)$ 12. $(x^4 + \frac{3}{2}x^3 - \frac{9}{2}x^2 + 6x - 2) \div (x - \frac{1}{2})$
13. $(x^4 - 5x^3 + 5x^2 + 7x - 12) \div (x - 4)$ 14. $(2x^4 + 23x^3 + 60x^2 - 125x - 500) \div (x + 4)$

Use synthetic division and the Remainder Theorem to find $P(a)$.
15. $P(x) = 3x^3 - 4x^2 - 5x + 1; a = 2$ 16. $P(x) = x^3 + 7x^2 + 12x - 3; a = -5$
17. $P(x) = x^3 + 6x^2 + 10x + 3; a = -3$ 18. $P(x) = 2x^4 - 9x^3 + 7x^2 - 5x + 11; a = 4$

Divide using long division. Check your answers.
19. $(x^2 - 13x - 48) \div (x + 3)$ 20. $(2x^2 + x - 7) \div (x - 5)$
21. $(x^2 + 5x^2 - 3x - 1) \div (x - 1)$ 22. $(3x^3 - x^2 - 7x + 6) \div (x + 2)$

Use synthetic division and the given factor to completely factor each polynomial function.
23. $y = x^3 + 3x^2 - 13x - 15; (x + 5)$ 24. $y = x^3 - 3x^2 - 10x + 24; (x - 2)$

Divide.
25. $(6x^3 + 2x^2 - 11x + 12) \div (3x + 4)$ 26. $(x^4 + 2x^3 + x - 3) \div (x - 1)$
27. $(2x^4 + 3x^3 - 4x^2 + x + 1) \div (2x - 1)$ 28. $(x^3 - 1) \div (x - 1)$
29. $(x^4 - 5x^2 - 10) \div (x - 2)$ 30. $(3x^3 - 2x^2 + 2x + 1) \div (x + \frac{1}{3})$

31. A box is to be mailed. The volume in cubic inches of the box
can be expressed as the product of its three dimensions:
$V(x) = x^3 - 16x^2 + 79x - 120$. The length is $x - 8$. Find linear
expressions for the other dimensions. Assume that the width is
greater than the height.

3. $x^2 + 4x + 3$, R 5

4. $2x^2 + 5x + 2$

5. $3x^2 - 7x + 2$

6. $9x - 12$, R −32

13. $x^2 + 4x + 3$

14. $x^2 - 2x + 2$

15. $x^2 - 11x + 37$, R −128

16. $x^2 + 2x + 5$

17. $x^2 - x - 6$

18. $-2x^2 + 9x - 19$, R 40

19. $x + 1$, R 4

324

EXERCISES

For more exercises, see *Extra Skill and Word Problem Practice.*

Practice and Problem Solving

Ⓐ **Practice by Example**

Example 1
(page 321)

GO for Help

Divide using long division. Check your answers. 3–6. See margin.

1. $(x^2 - 3x - 40) \div (x + 5)$ **$x - 8$**
2. $(3x^2 + 7x - 20) \div (x + 4)$ **$3x - 5$**
3. $(x^3 + 3x^2 - x + 2) \div (x - 1)$
4. $(2x^3 - 3x^2 - 18x - 8) \div (x - 4)$
5. $(9x^3 - 18x^2 - x + 2) \div (3x + 1)$
6. $(9x^2 - 21x - 20) \div (x - 1)$
7. $(x^2 - 7x + 10) \div (x + 3)$
   $x - 10$, R 40
8. $(x^3 - 13x - 12) \div (x - 4)$
   $x^2 + 4x + 3$

Example 2
(page 321)

Determine whether each binomial is a factor of $x^3 + 4x^2 + x - 6$.

9. $x + 1$ **no** 10. $x + 2$ **yes** 11. $x + 3$ **yes** 12. $x - 3$ **no**

Example 3
(page 322)

Divide using synthetic division. 13–20. See margin.

13. $(x^3 + 3x^2 - x - 3) \div (x - 1)$
14. $(x^3 - 4x^2 + 6x - 4) \div (x - 2)$
15. $(x^3 - 7x^2 - 7x + 20) \div (x + 4)$
16. $(x^3 - 3x^2 - 5x - 25) \div (x - 5)$
17. $(x^3 - 2x^2 - 5x + 6) \div (x - 1)$
18. $(-2x^3 + 5x^2 - x + 2) \div (x + 2)$
19. $(x^2 + 3) \div (x - 1)$
20. $(3x^3 + 17x^2 + 21x - 9) \div (x + 3)$
21. $(x^3 + 27) \div (x + 3)$
    $x^2 - 3x + 9$
22. $(6x^2 - 8x - 2) \div (x - 1)$
    $6x - 2$, R −4

Example 4
(pages 322–323)

Use synthetic division and the given factor to completely factor each polynomial function.

$y = (x + 3)(x - 4)(x - 3)$

23. $y = x^3 + 2x^2 - 5x - 6; (x + 1)$
    $y = (x + 1)(x + 3)(x - 2)$
24. $y = x^3 - 4x^2 - 9x + 36; (x + 3)$

25. **Geometry** Refer to the
diagram. The volume in cubic
inches of the decorative box
can be expressed as the
product of the lengths of its
sides as $V(x) = x^3 + x^2 - 6x$.
Write linear expressions with
integer coefficients for the
locker's length and height. $\ell = x + 3$ and $h = x$

width = $x - 2$

Example 5
(page 323)

Use synthetic division and the Remainder Theorem to find $P(a)$.

26. $P(x) = x^3 + 4x^2 - 8x - 6; a = -2$ **18**
27. $P(x) = x^3 + 4x^2 + 4x; a = -2$ **0**
28. $P(x) = x^3 - 7x^2 + 15x - 9; a = 3$ **0**
29. $P(x) = x^3 + 7x^2 + 4x; a = -2$ **12**
30. $P(x) = 6x^3 - x^2 + 4x + 3; a = 3$ **168**
31. $P(x) = 2x^3 - x^2 + 10x + 5; a = \frac{1}{2}$ **10**
32. $P(x) = 2x^3 + 4x^2 - 10x - 9; a = 3$ **51**
33. $P(x) = 2x^4 + 6x^3 + 5x^2 - 45; a = -3$ **0**

Ⓑ **Apply Your Skills**

34. **Reasoning** A polynomial $P(x)$ is divided by a binomial $x - a$. The remainder is zero. What conclusion can you draw? Explain. **$P(a) = 0$; $x - a$ is a factor of $P(x)$.**

35. **Error Analysis** A student represented the product of three linear factors as $x^3 - x^2 - 2x$. She used $x - 1$ as one of the factors. Use division to prove that the student made an error.

35. $x - 1$ is not a factor
of $x^3 - x^2 - 2x$
because it does
not divide into
$x^3 - x^2 - 2x$ evenly.

20. $3x^2 + 8x - 3$
52. $x^3 - x^2 + 1$
53. $x^3 - 2x^2 - 2x + 4$,
    R −35
54. $x^3 - 2x^2 - x + 6$
55. $x^3 - 4x^2 + x$

56a. $x + 1$
  b. $x^2 + x + 1$
  c. $x^3 + x^2 + x + 1$
  d. $(x - 1)(x^4 + x^3 + x^2 + x + 1)$

57a. $x^2 - x + 1$
  b. $x^4 - x^3 + x^2 - x + 1$
  c. $x^6 - x^5 + x^4 - x^3 + x^2 - x + 1$

36. Open-Ended Write a polynomial division that has a quotient of $x + 3$ and a remainder of 2. **Answers may vary. Sample: $(x^2 + x - 4) \div (x - 2)$**

Divide.

37. $x^2 + 4x + 5$

38. $x^3 - 3x^2 + 12x - 35$, R 109

39. $x^4 - x^3 + x^2 - x + 1$

37. $(2x^3 + 9x^2 + 14x + 5) \div (2x + 1)$

38. $(x^4 + 3x^2 + x + 4) \div (x + 3)$

39. $(x^5 + 1) \div (x + 1)$

40. $(x^4 + 4x^3 - x - 4) \div (x^3 - 1)$
$x + 4$

41. $(3x^4 - 5x^3 + 2x^2 + 3x - 2) \div (3x - 2)$
$x^3 - x^2 + 1$

Determine whether each binomial is a factor of $x^3 + x^2 - 16x - 16$.

42. $x + 2$ **no**

43. $x - 4$ **yes**

44. $x + 1$ **yes**

45. $x - 1$ **no**

46. $x - 2$ **no**

47. $x + 4$ **yes**

Homework Video Tutor
Visit: PHSchool.com
Web Code: age-0603

Use synthetic division to determine whether each binomial is a factor of $3x^3 + 10x^2 - x - 12$.

GPS 48. $x + 3$ **yes**

49. $x - 1$ **yes**

50. $x + 2$ **no**

51. $x - 4$ **no**

Divide using synthetic division. 52–55. See margin p. 324.

52. $(x^4 - 2x^3 + x^2 + x - 1) \div (x - 1)$

53. $(x^4 - 6x^2 - 27) \div (x + 2)$

54. $(x^4 - 5x^2 + 4x + 12) \div (x + 2)$

55. $\left(x^4 - \frac{9}{2}x^3 + 3x^2 - \frac{1}{2}x\right) \div \left(x - \frac{1}{2}\right)$

C Challenge

56. **Reasoning** Divide. Look for patterns in your answers. **a–d. See margin p. 324.**
 a. $(x^2 - 1) \div (x - 1)$ b. $(x^3 - 1) \div (x - 1)$ c. $(x^4 - 1) \div (x - 1)$
 d. Using the patterns, factor $x^5 - 1$.

57. Divide. Look for patterns in your answers. **a–d. See margin pp. 324–325.**
 a. $(x^3 + 1) \div (x + 1)$ b. $(x^5 + 1) \div (x + 1)$ c. $(x^7 + 1) \div (x + 1)$
 d. Using the patterns, factor $x^9 + 1$.

58. **Critical Thinking** Explain why a polynomial of degree n, divided by a polynomial of degree 1, yields a quotient of degree $n - 1$ and a remainder that is a constant. **See margin.**

59. Use synthetic division to find $(x^2 + 4) \div (x - 2i)$. **$x + 2i$**

 60. **Writing** Suppose 3, -1, and 4 are zeros of a cubic polynomial function. Sketch a graph of the function. Could there be more than one graph? Explain.
See margin.

 Test Prep

Multiple Choice

61. What is the remainder when $x^2 - 5x + 7$ is divided by $x + 1$? **D**
 A. -13 **B.** -1 **C.** 1 **D.** 13

62. Which binomial is NOT a factor of $x^3 - x^2 - 17x - 15$? **J**
 F. $x - 5$ **G.** $x + 1$ **H.** $x + 3$ **J.** $x + 5$

63. Which of the following, when multiplied by $x - 1$, results in a cubic polynomial whose standard form has three terms? **B**
 A. $(x - 1)^2$ **B.** $x^2 - x$ **C.** $x^2 - 1$ **D.** $x - 1$

Short Response

64. One factor of $x^3 - 7x^2 - x + 7$ is $x - 1$. What are all the zeros of the related polynomial function? Show your work. **See back of book.**

d. $(x + 1)(x^8 - x^7 + x^6 - x^5 + x^4 - x^3 + x^2 - x + 1)$

58. By dividing it by a polynomial of degree 1, you are reducing the

degree-n polynomial by one, to $n - 1$. The remainder will be constant because it is not divisible by the variable.

60. Yes; the graph could rise to the right and fall to the left or it could fall to the right and rise to the left.

PowerPoint
Lesson Quiz

11. a. Divide using long division.
 $(9x^3 - 48x^2 + 13x + 3)$
 $\div (x - 5)$
 $9x^2 - 3x - 2$, R -7
 b. Is $x - 5$ a factor of
 $9x^3 - 48x^2 + 13x + 3$? **no**

2. Divide using synthetic division.
 $(6x^3 - 4x^2 + 14x - 8)$
 $\div (x + 2)$
 $6x^2 - 16x + 46$, R -100

3. Use synthetic division and the given factor $x - 4$
 to completely factor
 $x^3 - 37x + 84$.
 $(x + 7)(x - 3)(x - 4)$

4. Use synthetic division and the Remainder Theorem to find
 $P(-2)$ when $P(x) =$
 $x^4 - 2x^3 + 4x^2 + x + 1$. **47**

Alternative Assessment

Group students in pairs. Have each group write two cubic polynomials and a polynomial of degree 4, all with integer coefficients. Each pair then works together using synthetic division to divide each polynomial by $x - 2$ and $x + 2$. Have them determine whether 2 and -2 are zeros of each polynomial.

Test Prep

Resources
For additional practice with a variety of test item formats:
• Standardized Test Prep, p. 363
• Test-Taking Strategies, p. 358
• Test-Taking Strategies with Transparencies

325

Mixed Review

GO for Help

Lesson 6-2 Write a polynomial function in standard form with the given zeros.   65–68. See margin.

65. $3, -5$ **66.** $0, 1, 8$ **67.** $-1, 2, 5$ **68.** 1, multiplicity 4

Lesson 5-6 Simplify each expression.

69. $(-4i)(6i)$ **24**   **70.** $(2 + i)(2 - i)$ **5**   **71.** $(4 - 3i)(5 + i)$ $23 - 11i$

Lesson 4-6 Find the inverse of each matrix, if it exists. 72–74. See margin.

72. $\begin{bmatrix} 1 & 0 & 3 \\ 1 & 1 & 0 \\ -1 & 0 & -1 \end{bmatrix}$ **73.** $\begin{bmatrix} 1 & 2 & 0 \\ 0 & 2 & -2 \\ 1 & 0 & 2 \end{bmatrix}$ **74.** $\begin{bmatrix} 2 & 1 & 0 \\ -1 & 1 & -2 \\ 3 & -2 & 4 \end{bmatrix}$

Checkpoint Quiz 1   Lessons 6-1 through 6-3

1. Write a polynomial function with at least three zeros that are negative, one of which has multiplicity 2.   **Answers may vary. Sample:**
$y = (x + 1)^2(x + 2)(x + 3)$

Write each polynomial in standard form. Then classify it by degree and by number of terms.

2. $-2x^3 + 6 - x^3 + 5x$ **3.** $\frac{1}{2}x + x^4 - 3x^2 + 2x$ **4.** $3(x - 1)(x + 4)$

2. $-3x^3 + 5x + 6$; degree 3, 3 terms

3. $x^4 - 3x^2 + \frac{5}{2}x$; degree 4, 3 terms

4. $3x^2 + 9x - 12$; degree 2, 3 terms

For each function, determine the zeros and their multiplicity.

5. $y = (x - 2)^2(x - 1)$ **6.** $y = (2x + 1)(x - 4)$ **7.** $y = x^3(x - 3)(x + 1)^2$
1, 2 (mult. 2) $-\frac{1}{2}$, 4   0 (mult. 3), 3, −1 (mult. 2)

Divide.

8. $(x^3 + 3x^2 + 3x + 1) \div (x + 1)$ **9.** $(2x^3 - 7x^2 + 7x - 2) \div (x - 2)$
$x^2 + 2x + 1$ $2x^2 - 3x + 1$

10. Use synthetic division to find $P(4)$ for $P(x) = 2x^4 - 3x^2 + 4x - 1$.
479

Algebra at Work

· · · · · · · · · · · · · · · · · · · **Quality Control Engineer**

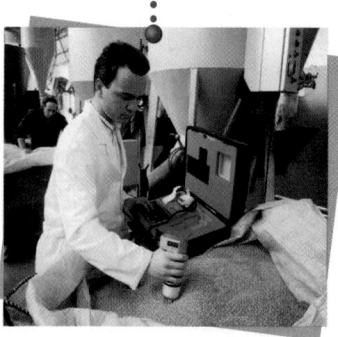

Quality control engineers establish procedures for assuring that products meet minimum standards of quality such as length or purity. Each product is sampled regularly. Data relating to each standard are collected and analyzed. All samples must fall within certain limiting parameters. Quality is further controlled by requiring that a significant portion of the samples fall within even stricter limiting parameters.

Go Online
PHSchool.com   **For:** Information about quality control
                  Web Code: agb-2031

Solving Polynomial Equations

1. Plan

What You'll Learn

- To solve polynomial equations by graphing
- To solve polynomial equations by factoring

. . . And Why

To calculate the dimensions of a portable kennel, as in Example 2

 Check Skills You'll Need

GO for Help Lessons 3-1 and 5-4

Graph each system. Find any points of intersection. 1–3. See back of book.

1. $\begin{cases} y = 3x + 1 \\ y = -2x + 6 \end{cases}$

2. $\begin{cases} -2x + 3y = 0 \\ x + 3y = 3 \end{cases}$

3. $\begin{cases} 2y = -x + 8 \\ x + 2y = -6 \end{cases}$

Factor each expression.

4. $x^2 - 2x - 15$
$(x - 5)(x + 3)$

5. $x^2 - 9x + 14$
$(x - 7)(x - 2)$

6. $x^2 + 6x + 5$
$(x + 5)(x + 1)$

New Vocabulary • sum of cubes • difference of cubes

Objectives
1. To solve polynomial equations by graphing
2. To solve polynomial equations by factoring

Examples
1. Solving by Graphing
2. Real-World Connection
3. Factoring a Sum or Difference of Cubes
4. Solving a Polynomial Equation
5. Factoring by Using a Quadratic Pattern
6. Solving a Higher-Degree Polynomial Equation

---

1. Solving Equations by Graphing

You can solve a polynomial equation by graphing each side of the equation separately and finding the x values at the point(s) of intersection.

1 EXAMPLE Solving by Graphing

Solve $x^3 + 3x^2 = x + 3$ by graphing.

Step 1 Graph $y_1 = x^3 + 3x^2$ and $y_2 = x + 3$ on a graphing calculator.

Step 2 Use the Intersect feature to find the x values at the points of intersection.

The solutions are -3, -1, and 1.

Check Show that each solution makes the original equation a true statement.

$x^3 + 3x^2 = x + 3$
$(-3)^3 + 3(-3)^2 \overset{?}{=} -3 + 3$
$-27 + 27 \overset{?}{=} -3 + 3$
$0 = 0 ✓$

$x^3 + 3x^2 = x + 3$
$(-1)^3 + 3(-1)^2 \overset{?}{=} -1 + 3$
$-1 + 3 \overset{?}{=} -1 + 3$
$2 = 2 ✓$

$x^3 + 3x^2 = x + 3$
$(1)^3 + 3(1)^2 \overset{?}{=} 1 + 3$
$1 + 3 \overset{?}{=} 1 + 3$
$4 = 4 ✓$

Graphing Calculator Hint

You can also solve the equation in Example 1 by graphing the related function $y = x^3 + 3x^2 - x - 3$ and finding its zeros.

1.
$y = x^3 - 2x^2$

Quick Check ① Graph and solve $x^3 - 2x^2 = -3$. Check your answers. $x = -1$. See left for graph.

Lesson 6-4 Solving Polynomial Equations **327**

Math Background

Mathematicians throughout history have looked for formulas, similar to the quadratic formula, for the solutions to higher degree equations. Such formulas exist for cubic and quartic equations but are not as straightforward as the quadratic formula. However, some higher degree equations can be solved with techniques already familiar to students.

More Math Background: p. 304C

Lesson Planning and Resources

See p. 304E for a list of the resources that support this lesson.

 PowerPoint

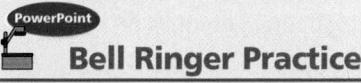 **Bell Ringer Practice**

Check Skills You'll Need
For intervention, direct students to:

Graphing Systems of Equations
Lesson 3-1: Example 1
Extra Skills and Word Problems Practice, Ch. 3

Factoring Quadratic Expressions
Lesson 5-4: Examples 2–4
Extra Skills and Word Problems Practice, Ch. 5

Differentiated Instruction Solutions for All Learners

Special Needs L1
In Example 5, help students recognize how x^4 can be rewritten as $(x^2)^2$, so that both first and middle terms share a common factor, x^2. Have students write the statement "let $a = x^2$" for their *temporary* substitution. Emphasize that x^2 must be substituted back for a. **learning style: verbal**

Below Level L2
Draw graphs and discuss with students why equations of odd degree must have at least one real root while equations of even degree may have only imaginary roots.

learning style: visual

1 EXAMPLE **Technology Tip**

Have students use the method suggested in the Calculator Hint to the left of Example 1. If they use Zoom Decimal, they can use the Trace feature to find that the solutions are −3, −1, and 1. Students can also press 2nd [TABLE] and find where the values in Y_1 and Y_2 are the same.

2 EXAMPLE **Alternative Method**

You do not need to multiply $(x + 7)x(x − 1)$. Have students enter Y_2 in its factored form and note that the results are the same. Discuss the reasonable domain with the students. Since x is the width, the domain is positive, and it must be of a size that is manageable to carry.

PowerPoint

Additional Examples

1 Graph and solve $x^3 − 19x = −2x^2 + 20$. **−5, −1, 4**

Xmin=−8 Ymin=−50
Xmax=8   Ymax=50
Xscl=2   Yscl=10

2 The dimensions in inches of the cubicle area inside a doghouse can be expressed as width x, length $x + 4$, and height $x − 3$. The volume is 15.9 ft³. Find the dimensions of the inside of the doghouse. **about 34 in. by 30 in. by 27 in.**

Real-World **Connection**

International regulations specify the allowable dimensions of pet transportation carriers.

You can write and solve a polynomial equation that models a real-world situation.

2 EXAMPLE **Real-World** **Connection**

Pet Transportation The dimensions in inches of a portable kennel can be expressed as width x, length $x + 7$, and height $x − 1$. The volume is 5.9 ft³. Find the portable kennel's dimensions.

$5.9 \text{ ft}^3 \cdot \dfrac{12^3 \text{ in.}^3}{\text{ft}^3} = 10{,}195.2 \text{ in.}^3$ **Convert the volume to cubic inches.**

$V = \ell \cdot w \cdot h$ **Write the formula for volume.**

$10{,}195.2 = (x + 7)x(x − 1)$ **Substitute.**

Graph $y_1 = 10{,}195.2$ and $y_2 = (x + 7)x(x − 1)$. Use the Intersect feature of the calculator. When $y = 10{,}195.2$, $x \approx 20$. So $x + 7 \approx 27$ and $x − 1 \approx 19$.

The dimensions of the portable kennel are about 27 in. by 20 in. by 19 in.

Intersection
X=19.954686 Y=10195.2

✓ **Quick Check** **2** Find the dimensions of a carrier with volume 7 ft³, width x inches, length $(x + 3)$ inches, and height $(x − 2)$ inches.
22.7125 in., 25.7125 in., 20.7125 in.

---

2 **Solving Equations by Factoring**

Recall that a quadratic *difference of squares* has a special factoring pattern. A cubic **sum of cubes** and **difference of cubes** also have special factoring patterns.

🔑 **Key Concepts**

Properties	Sum and Difference of Cubes
	$a^3 + b^3 = (a + b)(a^2 − ab + b^2)$ $a^3 − b^3 = (a − b)(a^2 + ab + b^2)$

You can verify the patterns by multiplying. Here are steps for the sum of cubes:

$(a + b)(a^2 − ab + b^2) = a(a^2 − ab + b^2) + b(a^2 − ab + b^2)$
$= a^3 − a^2b + ab^2 + a^2b − ab^2 + b^3$
$= a^3 + b^3$

3 EXAMPLE **Factoring a Sum or Difference of Cubes**

Test-Taking Tip

Remembering patterns may help you find answers more quickly.

Multiple Choice If you factor $x^3 − 8$ in the form $(x − A)(x^2 + Bx + C)$, what is the value of A?

Ⓐ 2   Ⓑ −2   Ⓒ 4   Ⓓ −4

$x^3 − 8 = (x)^3 − (2)^3$ **Rewrite the expression as the difference of cubes.**
$= (x − 2)(x^2 + 2x + (2)^2)$ **Factor.**
$= (x − 2)(x^2 + 2x + 4)$ **Simplify.**

The answer is choice A.

✓ **Quick Check** **3** Factor $8x^3 − 1$. **$(2x − 1)(4x^2 + 2x + 1)$**

Differentiated Instruction **Solutions for All Learners**

Advanced Learners L4
Have students create polynomial equations by multiplying factors with both real and complex roots. Have pairs solve each other's equations.

learning style: verbal

English Language Learners ELL
Have students write the names along with the general forms for these special cases of factoring: *sum of cubes, difference of cubes, difference of squares,* and *perfect square trinomials.* Ask students how the factored forms can help them remember their names.

learning style: visual

In Chapter 5, you found the complex roots of quadratic equations. You can do the same with polynomial equations of higher degree.

4 EXAMPLE Solving a Polynomial Equation

Solve $27x^3 + 1 = 0$. Find all complex roots.

$$27x^3 + 1 = (3x)^3 + (1)^3 \qquad \text{Rewrite the cubic expression as the sum of cubes.}$$
$$= (3x + 1)((3x)^2 - 3x + 1) \quad \text{Factor.}$$
$$= (3x + 1)(9x^2 - 3x + 1) \quad \text{Simplify.}$$

Since $3x + 1$ is a factor, $x = -\frac{1}{3}$ is a root.

The quadratic expression $9x^2 - 3x + 1$ cannot be factored, so use the Quadratic Formula to solve the related quadratic equation $9x^2 - 3x + 1 = 0$.

$$x = \frac{-b \pm \sqrt{b^2 - 4ac}}{2a} \qquad \text{Quadratic Formula}$$
$$= \frac{-(-3) \pm \sqrt{(-3)^2 - 4(9)(1)}}{2(9)} \qquad \text{Substitute 9 for } a, -3 \text{ for } b, \text{ and 1 for } c.$$
$$= \frac{3 \pm \sqrt{-27}}{18} \qquad \text{Use the Order of Operations.}$$
$$= \frac{3 \pm 3i\sqrt{3}}{18} \qquad \text{Simplify.}$$
$$= \frac{1 \pm i\sqrt{3}}{6}$$

- The roots are $-\frac{1}{3}$ and $\frac{1 \pm i\sqrt{3}}{6}$.

Vocabulary Tip

$\sqrt{-1} = i$

✓ Quick Check ④ Solve each equation.

a. $x^3 + 8 = 0$
$-2, 1 \pm i\sqrt{3}$

b. $27x^3 - 1 = 0$
$\frac{1}{3}, \frac{-1 \pm i\sqrt{3}}{6}$

You can sometimes factor a polynomial of higher degree by using the techniques you have used in solving polynomials of lower degree.

5 EXAMPLE Factoring by Using a Quadratic Pattern

Factor $x^4 - 2x^2 - 8$.

Step 1 You can write $x^4 - 2x^2 - 8$ in the pattern of a quadratic expression, so you can factor it like one. Make a temporary substitution of variables.

$$x^4 - 2x^2 - 8 = (x^2)^2 - 2(x^2) - 8 \qquad \begin{array}{l}\text{Rewrite in the pattern of} \\ \text{a quadratic expression.}\end{array}$$
$$= a^2 - 2a - 8 \qquad \text{Substitute } a \text{ for } x^2.$$

Step 2 Factor $a^2 - 2a - 8$.

$$a^2 - 2a - 8 = (a - 4)(a + 2)$$

Step 3 Substitute back to the original variable.

$$(a - 4)(a + 2) = (x^2 - 4)(x^2 + 2) \qquad \text{Substitute } x^2 \text{ for } a.$$
$$= (x + 2)(x - 2)(x^2 + 2) \quad \text{Factor completely.}$$

- The factored form of $x^4 - 2x^2 - 8$ is $(x + 2)(x - 2)(x^2 + 2)$.

✓ Quick Check ⑤ Factor each expression.

a. $x^4 + 7x^2 + 6$ $(x^2 + 6)(x^2 + 1)$

b. $x^4 - 3x^2 - 10$ $(x^2 - 5)(x^2 + 2)$

Guided Instruction

3 EXAMPLE Teaching Tip

Point out that memorizing the factorization formulas for the sum and difference of two cubes makes it easy to factor quickly. Tell students that if they forget the formulas, they can use synthetic division to find the quadratic factor. To do so, they need to remember that $a^3 - b^3$ is divisible by $a - b$ and that $a^3 + b^3$ is divisible by $a + b$.

5 EXAMPLE Error Prevention

Students may forget that the substitution does not provide the solution for the original variable. Encourage them to highlight, circle, or underline the substituted variable as a reminder to resubstitute the original variable expression and solve to give solutions for the original variable.

PowerPoint

Additional Examples

3 Factor $x^3 - 125$.
$(x - 5)(x^2 + 5x + 25)$

4 Solve $8x^3 + 125 = 0$. Find all complex roots. $-\frac{5}{2}, \frac{5 \pm 5i\sqrt{3}}{4}$

5 Factor $x^4 - 6x^2 - 27$.
$(x + 3)(x - 3)(x^2 + 3)$

6 Solve $x^4 - 4x^2 - 45 = 0$. ± 3, $\pm i\sqrt{5}$

Resources
• Daily Notetaking Guide 6-4 **L3**

Closure

Have students describe two methods for solving polynomial equations that have a degree greater than two. One method is to solve by graphing. To do this, graph both sides of the equation on a graphing calculator. Then use the Intersect feature to find the x-coordinates of the points where the graphs intersect. Another method is to write the equation in the form $P(x) = 0$. Factor $P(x)$ and use the Zero Product Property to solve.

3. Practice

Assignment Guide

▼1 A B 1–11, 33–41, 61–68

▼2 A B 12–32, 42–60

C Challenge   69–71

Test Prep   72–75
Mixed Review   76–82

Homework Quick Check·

To check students' understanding of key skills and concepts, go over Exercises 11, 20, 37, 54, 62, 68.

Error Prevention!

Exercises 24–26 Students may treat all the factors as linear expressions and only get two solutions (and those are generally not correct). Point out that some of the factors are not linear but quadratic.

Differentiated Instruction Resources

GPS Guided Problem Solving	**L3**
Enrichment	**L4**
Reteaching	**L2**
Practice	**L3**

330

---

6 EXAMPLE Solving a Higher-Degree Polynomial Equation

Solve $x^4 - x^2 = 12$.

$$x^4 - x^2 = 12$$

$$x^4 - x^2 - 12 = 0 \qquad \text{Rewrite so one side of the equation is equal to zero.}$$

$$(x^2)^2 - (x^2) - 12 = 0 \qquad \begin{array}{l}\text{Write in the form of a quadratic expression. Think} \\ \text{of the expression as } a^2 - a - 12, \text{ which factors as} \\ (a - 4)(a + 3).\end{array}$$

$$(x^2 - 4)(x^2 + 3) = 0$$

$$(x - 2)(x + 2)(x^2 + 3) = 0$$

$$x = 2 \quad \text{or} \quad x = -2 \quad \text{or} \quad x^2 = -3 \qquad \text{Use the Factor Theorem.}$$

$$x = \pm 2 \quad \text{or} \quad x = \pm\sqrt{-3} \qquad \text{Solve for } x.$$

$$x = \pm 2 \quad \text{or} \quad x = \pm i\sqrt{3} \qquad \text{Simplify.}$$

● The solutions are $2, -2, i\sqrt{3},$ and $-i\sqrt{3}$.

✓ Quick Check ⑥ Solve $x^4 + 11x^2 + 18 = 0$. $3i, -3i, i\sqrt{2}, -i\sqrt{2}$

EXERCISES

For more exercises, see *Extra Skill and Word Problem Practice*.

Practice and Problem Solving

Ⓐ Practice by Example

Examples 1 and 2
(pages 327 and 328)

GO for Help

5. $0, -1, -2$

6. $0, -3.5, 1$

Solve each equation by graphing. Check your answers.

1. $x^3 - 4x^2 - 7x = -10$ $-2, 1, 5$ **2.** $3x^3 - 6x^2 - 9x = 0$ $-1, 0, 3$ **3.** $4x^3 - 8x^2 + 4x = 0$ $0, 1$

4. $6x^2 = 48x$ $0, 8$ **5.** $x^3 + 3x^2 + 2x = 0$ **6.** $2x^3 + 5x^2 = 7x$

7. $4x^3 = 4x^2 + 3x$ $0, -0.5, 1.5$ **8.** $2x^4 - 5x^3 - 3x^2 = 0$ $-0.5, 0, 3$ **9.** $x^2 - 8x + 7 = 0$ $1, 7$

10. Savings The polynomial $1600x^3 + 1200x^2 + 800x$ represents your savings, with interest, from a summer job after three years. The annual interest rate equals $x - 1$. Find the interest rate needed so that you will have $4000 at the end of three years. **4.8%**

11. Geometry The volume V of a container is modeled by the function $V(x) = x^3 - 3x^2 - 4x$. Let $x, x + 1,$ and $x - 4$ represent the width, the length, and the height respectively. The container has a volume of 70 ft^3. Find the container's dimensions. **about 5.78 ft × 6.78 ft × 1.78 ft**

Example 3
(page 328)

Factor each expression. **12–14. See margin.**

12. $x^3 + 64$ **13.** $x^3 - 1000$ **14.** $125x^3 - 27$

Example 4
(page 329)

Solve each equation. **15–20. See margin.**

15. $x^3 - 27 = 0$ **16.** $x^3 + 64 = 0$ **17.** $x^3 - 125 = 0$

18. $2x^3 + 2 = 0$ **19.** $8x^3 - 1 = 0$ **20.** $64x^3 + 8 = 0$

Example 5
(page 329)

Factor each expression. **21–26. See margin.**

21. $x^4 - 8x^2 + 7$ **22.** $x^4 + 8x^2 - 20$ **23.** $x^4 - 7x^2 + 12$

24. $x^4 - 5x^2 + 4$ **25.** $x^4 - 1$ **26.** $4x^4 - 6x^2 + 2$

---

12. $(x + 4)(x^2 - 4x + 16)$

13. $(x - 10)(x^2 + 10x + 100)$

14. $(5x - 3)(25x^2 + 15x + 9)$

15. $3, \dfrac{-3 \pm 3i\sqrt{3}}{2}$

16. $-4, 2 \pm 2i\sqrt{3}$

17. $5, \dfrac{-5 \pm 5i\sqrt{3}}{2}$

18. $-1, \dfrac{1 \pm i\sqrt{3}}{2}$

19. $\dfrac{1}{2}, \dfrac{-1 \pm i\sqrt{3}}{4}$

20. $-\dfrac{1}{2}, \dfrac{1 \pm i\sqrt{3}}{4}$

21. $(x^2 - 7)(x - 1)(x + 1)$

22. $(x^2 + 10)(x^2 - 2)$

23. $(x^2 - 3)(x - 2)(x + 2)$

24. $(x - 2)(x + 2)(x - 1)(x + 1)$

25. $(x - 1)(x + 1)(x^2 + 1)$

26. $2(2x^2 - 1)(x + 1)(x - 1)$

Example 6
(page 330)

Solve each equation.   27–29. See margin.

27. $x^4 - 10x^2 + 9 = 0$ **28.** $x^4 - 8x^2 + 16 = 0$ **29.** $x^4 - 12x^2 - 64 = 0$

30. $x^4 + 7x^2 - 18 = 0$ **31.** $x^4 + 4x^2 - 12 = 0$ **32.** $x^4 + 8x^2 + 15 = 0$
$\pm 3i, \pm\sqrt{2}$ $\pm\sqrt{2}, \pm i\sqrt{6}$ $\pm i\sqrt{5}, \pm i\sqrt{3}$

B Apply Your Skills

 Solve each equation by graphing. Where necessary, round to the nearest hundredth.

33. 3.24, −1, −1.24

35. −3, −2, 1, 2

36. 1.71, 0.83

33. $x^3 - x^2 - 6x - 4 = 0$ **34.** $2x^4 + 18x^3 = 0$ **−9, 0**

35. $x^4 + 2x^3 - 7x^2 - 8x = -12$ **36.** $x^4 + x^3 = 4x^2 + 4x - 5$

37. $x^3 + 13x = 10x^2$ **38.** $x^3 - 6x^2 + 6x = 0$ **39.** $12x^3 = 60x^2 + 75x$
0, 1.54, 8.46   **0, 1.27, 4.73**   **−1.04, 0, 6.04**

40. The product of three consecutive integers $n - 1, n,$ and $n + 1$ is 210. Write and solve an equation to find the numbers. $(n - 1)(n)(n + 1) = 210;$ 5, 6, 7

Real-World 🌐 Connection

The vacuum bottle, or Dewar flask, was invented by the chemist James Dewar for storing liquefied gases.

41. Multiple Choice The chamber in the container below consists of a cylinder on top of a hemisphere. The chamber holds 500 cm³. What is the radius of the chamber, to the nearest hundredth of a centimeter? **D**

Ⓐ 2.75 cm   Ⓑ 3.12 cm   Ⓒ 3.32 cm   Ⓓ 3.58 cm

10 cm

Solve each equation.   42–53. See margin.

42. $125x^3 + 216 = 0$ **43.** $81x^3 - 192 = 0$ **44.** $x^4 - 64 = 0$

45. $-2x^4 + 46x^2 = -100$ **46.** $27 = -x^4 - 12x^2$ **47.** $x^5 - 5x^3 + 4x = 0$

48. $x^4 - 100 = 0$ **49.** $5x^3 = 5x^2 + 12x$ **50.** $64 - x^3 = 0$

51. $x^3 - 6x^2 + 6x = 0$ **52.** $2x^3 = 5x^2 + 12x$ **53.** $3x^4 + 12x^2 - 15 = 0$

54. $x^3 + 3x^2 - 4x - 12 = 0$ **−3, −2, 2**   **55.** $x^3 - 5x^2 + 3x + 9 = 0$ **−1, 3, 3**

56. $4x^3 - 16x^2 + 12x = 0$ **0, 1, 3**   **57.** $2x^4 - 14x^3 + 12x^2 = 0$ **0, 0, 1, 6**

58. $4x^4 - 2x^2 - 4 = 2$ $\pm\sqrt{\frac{3}{2}}, \pm i$ **59.** $9x^4 - 9x^2 + 2 = 20$ $\pm\sqrt{2}, \pm i$

60. Open-Ended To solve a polynomial equation, you can use any combination of graphing, factoring, and the Quadratic Formula. Write and solve an equation to illustrate each method. **Check students' work.**

61. $V = x^2(4x - 2),$ 4 in. by 4 in. by 16 in.

 For Exercises 61 and 62, write a polynomial function to describe each volume. Then graph your function to solve each problem.

⬜ 61. Geometry Suppose a 2-in. slice is cut from one face of the cheese block as shown. The remaining solid has a volume of 224 in.³. Find the dimensions of the original block.

GO for Help

For a guide to solving Exercise 61, see p. 333.

See left.
⬜ 62. Geometry The width of a box is 2 m less than the length. The height is 1 m less **GPS** than the length. The volume is 60 m³. Find the length of the box.
$x =$ length, $V = x(x - 1)(x - 2),$ 5 meters

27. $\pm 3, \pm 1$

28. ± 2

29. $\pm 4, \pm 2i$

42. $-\frac{6}{5}, \frac{3 \pm 3i\sqrt{3}}{5}$

43. $\frac{4}{3}, \frac{-2 \pm 2i\sqrt{3}}{3}$

44. $\pm 2\sqrt{2}, \pm 2i\sqrt{2}$

45. $\pm 5, \pm i\sqrt{2}$

46. $\pm 3i, \pm i\sqrt{3}$

47. $0, \pm 2, \pm 1$

48. $\pm\sqrt{10}, \pm i\sqrt{10}$

4. Assess & Reteach

PowerPoint
🖥 **Lesson Quiz**

1. Solve $x^3 - 2x^2 - 3 = x - 4$ by graphing. Where necessary, round to the nearest hundredth. **−0.80, 0.55, 2.25**

Factor each expression.

2. $216x^3 - 1$
$(6x - 1)(36x^2 + 6x + 1)$

3. $8x^3 + 125$
$(2x + 5)(4x^2 - 10x + 25)$

4. $x^4 - 5x^2 + 4$
$(x + 1)(x - 1)(x + 2)(x - 2)$

Solve each equation.

5. $x^3 + 125 = 0$ $-5, \frac{5 \pm 5i\sqrt{3}}{2}$

6. $x^4 + 3x^2 - 28 = 0$
$\pm 2, \pm i\sqrt{7}$

Alternative Assessment

Write one polynomial from each Exercise section on the board, one at a time. After you write each polynomial, instruct students to solve by graphing or factoring, whichever method they prefer. Students compare their solutions with others who chose the same method and a different method.

Exercise 41 Make sure students know that a *hemisphere* is half of a sphere.

49. $0, \frac{1}{2} \pm \frac{\sqrt{265}}{10}$

50. $4, -2 \pm 2i\sqrt{3}$

51. $0, 3 \pm \sqrt{3}$

52. $-\frac{3}{2}, 0, 4$

53. $-1, 1, \pm i\sqrt{5}$

331

Resources

For additional practice with a variety of test item formats:
- Standardized Test Prep, p. 363
- Test-Taking Strategies, p. 358
- Test-Taking Strategies with Transparencies

63. $-\frac{5}{2}$, 1;

$y = (2x + 5)(x - 1)$

64. ± 3, ± 1;

$y = (x - 1)(x + 1)$
$(x - 3)(x + 3)$

65. $-1, 2, 2$;

$y = (x + 1)(x - 2)^2$

66. $-2, 1, 3$;

$y = (x + 2)(x - 1)(x - 3)$

67. $-4, -1, 3$;

$y = (x + 4)(x + 1)(x - 3)$

69a. Answers may vary.

Sample: $x^4 - 9 = 0$,
$\pm\sqrt{3}$, $\pm i\sqrt{3}$

b. No; two of the roots are imaginary.

70. Answers may vary.

Sample: The pink block has volume $a^2(a - 3)$, the orange block has volume $9(a - 3)$, the blue block has volume $3a(a - 3)$, and the purple block has volume 27. Thus $a^3 - 27 = a^2(a - 3) + 3a(a - 3) + 9(a - 3) = (a^2 + 3a + 9)(a - 3)$.

74. [2] $\frac{a^3}{b^6} + \frac{1}{8} = \left(\frac{a}{b^2}\right)^3 + \left(\frac{1}{2}\right)^3$

[1] attempts to write each of the terms as a cube

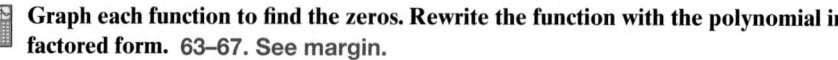

Graph each function to find the zeros. Rewrite the function with the polynomial in factored form. 63–67. See margin.

GO Online
Homework Video Tutor
Visit: PHSchool.com
Web Code: age-0604

63. $y = 2x^2 + 3x - 5$ 64. $y = x^4 - 10x^2 + 9$ 65. $y = x^3 - 3x^2 + 4$

66. $y = x^3 - 2x^2 - 5x + 6$ 67. $y = x^3 + 2x^2 - 11x - 12$

68. **Error Analysis** A student claims that 1, 2, 3, and 4 are the zeros of a cubic polynomial function. Explain why the student is mistaken. **A cubic can only have 3 zeros.**

C Challenge

69. **a. Open-Ended** Write and solve a fourth-degree polynomial equation that includes the difference of squares.   **a–b. See margin.**

b. **Critical Thinking** Are all the roots real numbers? Justify your answer.

70. **Writing** From a large cube with edges a units long, you cut a smaller cube with edges three units long. Explain how the diagram at the right illustrates that $a^3 - 27 = (a - 3)(a^2 + 3a + 9)$.
See margin.

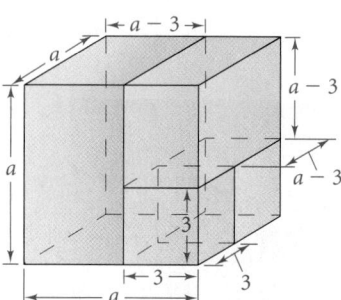

71. **a.** The sum of two positive numbers is 4 and the sum of their cubes is 28. What is the sum of their squares? **10**

b. The product of two positive numbers is 96 and the sum of their squares is 208. What are the two numbers? **8 and 12**

Test Prep

Multiple Choice

72. Which expression is a factor of $x^4 - 18x^2 + 81$? **A**

A. $x^2 - 9$ B. $x^2 + 6x - 9$ C. $x^2 - 6x - 9$ D. $x^2 + 9$

73. Which value is NOT a solution of $x^4 - 3x^2 - 54 = 0$? **H**

F. -3 G. 3   H. $-3i$ J. $-i\sqrt{6}$

Short Response

74. Show how you can rewrite $\frac{a^3}{b^6} + \frac{1}{8}$ as a sum of two cubes. **See margin.**

Extended Response

75. What are all the solutions to $8x^3 - 27 = 0$? Show your work.
See back of book.

Mixed Review

GO for Help

Lesson 6-3

Divide.

76. $(x^3 - 2x^2 - 13x - 10) \div (x + 1)$ 77. $(2x^3 - 7x^2 - 7x + 14) \div (x - 4)$
    $x^2 - 3x - 10$ $2x^2 + x - 3$, **R 2**

Lesson 5-5

Solve each equation by factoring or by taking square roots.

78. $n^2 - 4n = 12$ **$-2, 6$**   79. $n^2 + 1 = 37$ **± 6**   80. $2n^2 - 5n - 3 = 0$
                                                                        $-\frac{1}{2}, 3$

Lesson 4-7

Solve each matrix equation. If the coefficient matrix has no inverse, write *no unique solution*.

no unique solution

81. $\begin{bmatrix} 2 & -1 \\ -3 & 2 \end{bmatrix}\begin{bmatrix} x \\ y \end{bmatrix} = \begin{bmatrix} 5 \\ -10 \end{bmatrix}\begin{bmatrix} 0 \\ -5 \end{bmatrix}$ 82. $\begin{bmatrix} 1 & 4 \\ -2 & -8 \end{bmatrix}\begin{bmatrix} x \\ y \end{bmatrix} = \begin{bmatrix} 2 \\ -4 \end{bmatrix}$

Understanding Word Problems Read the problem below. Then let Ian's thinking guide you through the solution. Check your understanding with the exercises at the bottom of the page.

Geometry Suppose a 2-in. slice is cut from one face of the cheese block as shown. The remaining solid has a volume of 224 in.^{3}. Find the dimensions of the original block.

Understanding Word Problems

Students solve a cubic polynomial to find the original dimensions of a block of cheese.

Guided Instruction

Point out to students that the width and the height of the block are both represented by x, so x gets substituted into the equation twice.

What Ian Thinks

From the diagram, it looks like the widths and heights of the two blocks are equal. I can subtract the amount cut off from the total length to find the length left.

The problem tells me that the volume of the leftover block is 224 in.^{3}. I can write a relationship, substitute, and simplify.

The polynomial equation is a cubic, and the problem asks me to solve by graphing. I'll graph two equations and find their intersection.

I'll enter the equations as Y_1 and Y_2, and I'll change my window values to accommodate a y-value of 224.

Next, I'll use the INTERSECT feature. When $y = 224$, $x = 4$. OK! Now I know x.

I can use x to find the dimensions of the original block.

What Ian Writes

$$\text{length of leftover block} = 4x - \text{length of cut block}$$

$$= 4x - 2$$

$$\text{volume of leftover block} = \ell wh = 224$$

$$V = (4x - 2)(x)(x) = 224$$

$$(4x - 2)(x^2) = 224$$

$$4x^3 - 2x^2 = 224$$

$$Y1 = 4x^3 - 2x^2$$
$$Y2 = 224$$

Xmin=−10
Xmax=10
Xscl=1
Ymin=−100
Ymax=300
Yscl=50

Intersection
X=4   Y=224

Width = Height = $x = 4$
Length = $4x = 4(4) = 16$

The block of cheese measured
16 in. × 4 in. × 4 in.

Technology

In order for students to see the line $y = 224$, the y range in the WINDOW menu must have a maximum greater than 224.

To use the INTERSECT feature, press [2nd] [CALC] 5. Students then must press [ENTER] three times to get the calculator to find the value.

Exercises

Remind students to clear the equations from the Y= list before they enter equations to solve the problem.

EXERCISES

1. Slices of wood $\frac{1}{4}$-in. thick are cut from opposite sides of a cube of wood. The remaining solid has a volume of 151.25 in.^{3}. Find the dimensions of the original block of wood. $5\frac{1}{2}$ in. × $5\frac{1}{2}$ in. × $5\frac{1}{2}$ in.

2. The water level in a fish tank is 4 in. from the top. The depth of the water is the same as the width of the tank, which is half of its length. The volume of the water in the tank is 4394 in.^{3}. What is the capacity of the fish tank? **5746 in.^{3}**

Continuous and Discrete

Students explore the math terms *continuous* and *discrete* in everyday and math/science contexts.

Guided Instruction

English Language Learners ELL

Help students distinguish between *discrete* and *discreet,* which sound alike. *Discreet* means to show good judgment in conduct or speech.

2 EXAMPLE Special Needs L1

Ask: *Why is the amount you pay discrete?* Sample: The smallest unit of money that can be paid is the penny.

Advanced Learners L4

For Exercises 7-10, challenge students to find as many quantities as they can for each situation.

Technology Tip

Most graphing calculators have an LCD screen that is 95 pixels by 63 pixels. This limited number of "spots on the screen" can make graphs of functions look jagged. In fact, the graph is a discrete graph because the calculator only computes and graphs a certain number of ordered pairs. To better illustrate a discrete function, change the mode from Connected to Dot.

Resources

Vocabulary and Study Skills
    Worksheet

1–4, 6. Reasoning may vary. Samples are given.

1. Discrete; airplanes are distinct objects that you can count.

Continuous and *discrete* are two rather sophisticated mathematics words that you can use in everyday conversations. Their mathematical and everyday meanings are compatible:

Continuous means unbroken.

Discrete means separate and distinct.

1 EXAMPLE

On a number line,
- real numbers are continuous,
- but integers are discrete.

2 EXAMPLE

At the gas pump,
- gas pumped and value of gas are continuous;
- the amount you pay is discrete.

EXERCISES

Is the quantity continuous or discrete? Explain. 1–6. See margin.

1. number of airplanes at an airport
2. altitude of an airplane
4. height of a growing flower
4. number of flowers in a garden
5. length of lead in a pencil
6. number of beans in a beanbag

You can use different quantities to describe different aspects of a situation. Name one continuous quantity and one discrete quantity for each situation.
7–10. See back of book.

7. a train ride between two cities
8. a soccer game
9. plowing a field
10. the weather today

Sometimes a situation itself can be described as continuous or discrete. Which word would you use to describe each situation below? Explain.
11–14. See back of book.

11. milk pouring into a glass
12. walking to school
13. bacteria living in a culture
14. Earth-to-sun distance

Is the mathematical object continuous or discrete? Explain. 15–18. See back of book.

15. the graph of a linear function
16. the graph of an absolute value function
17. a scatter plot of 100 data points
18. the zeros of a third-degree polynomial function

19. **Motion Pictures** Film editors watch for *continuity* from one scene to the next (both of which may have needed several "takes"). They want to avoid having a tennis racket suddenly switch from a left hand to a right hand or, worse yet, disappear entirely. Research and describe a continuity error found in a movie. **Check students' work.**

---

2. Continuous; airplane altitude changes smoothly, in an unbroken manner.

3. Continuous; a flower grows continuously, without breaks.

4. Discrete; flowers are distinct objects that you can count.

5. Answers may vary. Sample: Discrete; the length of the lead changes in distinct jumps when the pencil breaks.

6. Discrete; beans are distinct objects that you can count.

Theorems About Roots of Polynomial Equations

What You'll Learn

- To solve equations using the Rational Root Theorem
- To use the Irrational Root Theorem and the Imaginary Root Theorem

. . . And Why

To find all the roots of a polynomial equation, as in Example 2

 Check Skills You'll Need   **GO for Help** Lessons 1-1, 5-1, and 5-6

List all the integer factors of each number. 1–4. See margin p. 337.

1. 12   **2.** 24   **3.** 36   **4.** 48

Multiply.   6. $x^3 + 2x^2 - 3x - 6$

5. $(x - 5)(x^2 + 7)$ $x^3 - 5x^2 + 7x - 35$ **6.** $(x + 2)(x + \sqrt{3})(x - \sqrt{3})$

Define each set of numbers. 7–9. See margin p. 337.

7. rational   **8.** irrational   **9.** imaginary

🔊 **New Vocabulary** • Rational Root Theorem • conjugates
                       • Irrational Root Theorem • complex conjugates
                       • Imaginary Root Theorem

---

1 The Rational Root Theorem

Vocabulary Tip

A polynomial equation has <u>roots</u>. A polynomial function has <u>zeros</u>.

You have learned several methods for finding the roots of a polynomial equation. Another method involves analyzing one or more integer coefficients of the polynomial in the equation.

Consider the equivalent equations $x^3 - 5x^2 - 2x + 24 = 0$ and $(x + 2)(x - 3)(x - 4) = 0$, which have $-2, 3$, and 4 as roots. The product of $2, 3$, and 4 is 24. Notice that all the roots are factors of the constant term, 24. In general, if the coefficients (including the constant term) in a polynomial equation are integers, then any integer root of the equation is a factor of the constant term.

A similar pattern applies to rational roots. Consider the equivalent equations $24x^3 - 22x^2 - 5x + 6 = 0$ and $\left(x + \frac{1}{2}\right)\left(x - \frac{2}{3}\right)\left(x - \frac{3}{4}\right) = 0$, which have $-\frac{1}{2}, \frac{2}{3}$, and $\frac{3}{4}$ as roots. The numerators $1, 2$, and 3 all are factors of the constant term, 6. The denominators $2, 3$, and 4 are factors of the leading coefficient, 24.

Both the constant term and the leading coefficient of a polynomial can play a key role in identifying the rational roots of the related polynomial equation. This role is expressed in the Rational Root Theorem.

 Key Concepts

Theorem	**Rational Root Theorem**

If $\frac{p}{q}$ is in simplest form and is a rational root of the polynomial equation $a_nx^n + a_{n-1}x^{n-1} + \ldots + a_1x + a_0 = 0$ with integer coefficients, then p must be a factor of a_0 and q must be a factor of a_n.

---

1. Plan

Objectives

1 To solve equations using the Rational Root Theorem
2 To use the Irrational Root Theorem and the Imaginary Root Theorem

Examples

1 Finding Rational Roots
2 Using the Rational Root Theorem
3 Finding Irrational Roots
4 Finding Imaginary Roots
5 Writing a Polynomial Equation from Its Roots

 Professional Development

Math Background

An interesting consequence of the rational root theorem is that $\sqrt{p}$ is irrational for p a prime number. If $\sqrt{p}$ were rational, the rational root theorem would guarantee that it is a factor of p since $\sqrt{p}$ is a root of $x^2 - p = 0$. Since p's only factors are one and itself, $\sqrt{p}$ must be irrational.

More Math Background: p. 304D

Lesson Planning and Resources

See p. 304E for a list of the resources that support this lesson.

 PowerPoint

🔊 **Bell Ringer Practice**

✓ **Check Skills You'll Need**
For intervention, direct students to:

Properties of Real Numbers
Lesson 1-1: Example 1
Extra Skills and Word
  Problems Practice, Ch. 1

Complex Numbers
Lesson 5-6: Example 5
Extra Skills and Word
  Problems Practice, Ch. 5

Differentiated Instruction Solutions for All Learners

Special Needs L1
Before teaching the lesson, review the terms *integer, rational, coefficient,* and *root.* To introduce conjugates, have students solve $x^2 - 4 = 0$ by factoring. Discuss what is special about its factors, $(x + 2)(x - 2)$, and roots, ± 2.

learning style: verbal

Below Level L2
Have students multiply binomials of the form $ax + b$ together and then compare the known roots to the possible values of $\frac{p}{q}$.

learning style: verbal

1 EXAMPLE **Alternative Method**

A graphing calculator can quickly do the work for Step 2. Enter the possible rational roots in list L1. Enter $Y_1 = x^3 + x^2 - 3x - 3$ on the Y= list. On the home screen, type Y1(L1)→L2 and press ENTER. Then press STAT 1. The values of Y1 for the possible rational roots are displayed in L2.

2 EXAMPLE **Teaching Tip**

Point out that you could also use synthetic division to test roots. This will also be done in Lesson 6-6, Example 2.

PowerPoint

Additional Examples

1 Find the rational roots of $3x^3 - x^2 - 15x + 5 = 0$. $\frac{1}{3}$

2 Find the roots of $5x^3 - 24x^2 + 41x - 20 = 0$. $\frac{4}{5}, 2 \pm i$

You can use the Rational Root Theorem to find any rational roots of a polynomial equation with integer coefficients.

1 EXAMPLE **Finding Rational Roots**

Find the rational roots of $x^3 + x^2 - 3x - 3 = 0$.

Step 1 List the possible rational roots.

The leading coefficient is 1. The constant term is -3. By the Rational Root Theorem, the only possible rational roots of the equation have the form $\frac{\text{factor of } -3}{\text{factor of } 1}$.

The factors of -3 are ± 1 and ± 3. The factors of 1 are ± 1. The only possible rational roots are ± 1 and ± 3.

Step 2 Test each possible rational root.

Test 1: $x^3 + x^2 - 3x - 3 = (1)^3 + (1)^2 - 3(1) - 3$
$$= -4 \neq 0$$

Test 3: $x^3 + x^2 - 3x - 3 = (3)^3 + (3)^2 - 3(3) - 3$
$$= 24 \neq 0$$

Test -1: $x^3 + x^2 - 3x - 3 = (-1)^3 + (-1)^2 - 3(-1) - 3$
$$= 0 \quad \textbf{So } -1 \textbf{ is a root.}$$

Test -3: $x^3 + x^2 - 3x - 3 = (-3)^3 + (-3)^2 - 3(-3) - 3$
$$= -12 \neq 0$$

The only rational root of $x^3 + x^2 - 3x - 3 = 0$ is -1.

✓ Quick Check **1** Find the rational roots of $x^3 - 4x^2 - 2x + 8 = 0$. **4**

You can often use the Rational Root Theorem to find all the roots of a polynomial equation.

2 EXAMPLE **Using the Rational Root Theorem**

Find the roots of $2x^3 - x^2 + 2x - 1 = 0$.

Step 1 List the possible rational roots.

The leading coefficient is 2. The constant term is -1. By the Rational Root Theorem, the only possible rational roots of the equation have the form $\frac{\text{factor of } -1}{\text{factor of } 2}$.

The factors of -1 are ± 1. The factors of 2 are ± 1 and ± 2. So the only possible rational roots are ± 1 and $\pm \frac{1}{2}$.

Step 2 Test each possible rational root until you find a root.

Test 1: $2x^3 - x^2 + 2x - 1 = 2(1)^3 - (1)^2 + 2(1) - 1$
$$= 2 \neq 0$$

Test $\frac{1}{2}$: $2x^3 - x^2 + 2x - 1 = 2\left(\frac{1}{2}\right)^3 - \left(\frac{1}{2}\right)^2 + 2\left(\frac{1}{2}\right) - 1$
$$= 0 \quad \textbf{So } \frac{1}{2} \textbf{ is a root.}$$

336 Chapter 6 Polynomials and Polynomial Functions

Differentiated Instruction Solutions for All Learners

Advanced Learners **L4**
Have students create polynomial equations with imaginary coefficients. Have them exchange their work and solve the equations.

learning style: verbal

English Language Learners **ELL**
Help students relate the everyday meaning of *conjugate* with its mathematical meaning. A conjugate is an adjective used to describe two items having features in common, but inverses or opposites in some aspect.

learning style: verbal

Step 3 Use synthetic division with the root you found in Step 2 to find the quotient.

$$
\begin{array}{r|rrrr}
\tfrac{1}{2} & 2 & -1 & 2 & -1 \\
 & & 1 & 0 & 1 \\
\hline
 & 2 & 0 & 2 & 0 \\
\end{array}
$$

$$2x^2 \qquad +2 \qquad \text{Remainder}$$

Step 4 Find the roots of $2x^2 + 2 = 0$.

$$2x^2 + 2 = 0$$
$$2(x^2 + 1) = 0 \qquad \textbf{Factor out the GCF, 2.}$$
$$x^2 + 1 = 0$$
$$x^2 = -1$$
$$x = \pm i$$

● The roots of $2x^3 - x^2 + 2x - 1 = 0$ are $\tfrac{1}{2}$, i, and $-i$.

2a. $\pm\sqrt{5}, 2$

b. $-1, \dfrac{1 \pm i\sqrt{2}}{3}$

✓ **Quick Check** ❷ Find the roots of each equation. **See left.**

a. $x^3 - 2x^2 - 5x + 10 = 0$ **b.** $3x^3 + x^2 - x + 1 = 0$

2   Irrational Root Theorem and Imaginary Root Theorem

In Chapter 5 you learned to find irrational solutions to quadratic equations. For example, by the Quadratic Formula, the solutions of $x^2 - 4x - 1 = 0$ are $2 + \sqrt{5}$ and $2 - \sqrt{5}$. Number pairs of the form $a + \sqrt{b}$ and $a - \sqrt{b}$ are called **conjugates**.

You can often use conjugates to find the irrational roots of a polynomial equation.

 Key Concepts

Theorem	Irrational Root Theorem
Let a and b be rational numbers and let $\sqrt{b}$ be an irrational number. If $a + \sqrt{b}$ is a root of a polynomial equation with rational coefficients, then the conjugate $a - \sqrt{b}$ also is a root.	

❸ EXAMPLE   **Finding Irrational Roots**

A polynomial equation with integer coefficients has the roots $1 + \sqrt{3}$ and $-\sqrt{11}$. Find two additional roots.

By the Irrational Root Theorem, if $1 + \sqrt{3}$ is a root, then its conjugate $1 - \sqrt{3}$ is also a root. If $-\sqrt{11}$ is a root, then its conjugate $\sqrt{11}$ also is a root.

● The additional roots are $1 - \sqrt{3}$ and $\sqrt{11}$.

✓ **Quick Check** ❸ **a.** A polynomial equation with rational coefficients has the roots $2 - \sqrt{7}$ and $\sqrt{5}$. Find two additional roots. **$2 + \sqrt{7}, -\sqrt{5}$**

b. Critical Thinking One of the roots of a polynomial equation is $4 - \sqrt{2}$. Can you be certain that $4 + \sqrt{2}$ also is a root of the equation? Explain. **No; the Irrational Root Theorem does not apply unless you know that all of the coefficients of the polynomial are rational.**

Lesson 6-5   Theorems About Roots of Polynomial Equations   **337**

Guided Instruction

❺ EXAMPLE   **Error Prevention**

Some students may write -3 as a root. Be sure students understand that if a is a nonzero real number root of a polynomial equation, $-a$ is not necessarily a root.

PowerPoint

Additional Examples

❸ A polynomial equation with rational coefficients has the roots $2 - \sqrt{5}$ and $\sqrt{7}$. Find two additional roots. **$2 + \sqrt{5}$ and $-\sqrt{7}$**

❹ A polynomial equation with real coefficients has the roots $2 + 9i$ and $7i$. Find two additional roots. **$2 - 9i$ and $-7i$**

❺ Find a third degree polynomial equation with rational coefficients that has roots -2, and $2 - i$. **$x^3 - 2x^2 - 3x + 10 = 0$**

Resources
• Daily Notetaking Guide 6-5 **L3**

Closure

Ask: *If a polynomial equation has integer coefficients, how can you find any rational roots the equation might have?* Apply the Rational Root Theorem and test each possible root. *If you find one irrational or imaginary root, how can you find another one?* Write the conjugate.

page 335   **Check Skills You'll Need**

1. $\pm1, \pm2, \pm3, \pm4, \pm6, \pm12$

2. $\pm1, \pm2, \pm3, \pm4, \pm6, \pm8, \pm12, \pm24$

3. $\pm1, \pm2, \pm3, \pm4, \pm6, \pm9, \pm12, \pm18, \pm36$

4. $\pm1, \pm2, \pm3, \pm4, \pm6, \pm8, \pm12, \pm16, \pm24, \pm48$

7. A rational number can be written as the quotient of two integers, $\tfrac{a}{b}$ where $b \neq 0$.

8. Irrational numbers cannot be written as quotients of integers.

9. An imaginary number is a nonreal number of the form $a + bi$, where $b \neq 0$.

Assignment Guide

▼1 A B 1-12, 25-28, 32-34

▼2 A B 13-24, 29-31, 35-39
C Challenge   40-43

Test Prep   44-47
Mixed Review   48-56

Homework Quick Check

To check students' understanding of key skills and concepts, go over Exercises 7, 20, 29, 32, 37.

Error Prevention!

Exercises 1–12, 25-28 Students may recall the Rational Root Theorem incorrectly and check rational numbers $\frac{p}{q}$ for which p is a factor of the leading coefficient and q is a factor of the constant term. Suggest to students that they think about the solution $x = \frac{4}{3}$ of a linear equation like $9x - 12 = 0$. p (4 here) is a factor of the constant term and q (3 here) is a factor of the leading coefficient.

Number pairs of the form $a + bi$ and $a - bi$ are **complex conjugates.** You can use complex conjugates to find an equation's imaginary roots.

🔑 **Key Concepts**

Theorem	Imaginary Root Theorem

If the imaginary number $a + bi$ is a root of a polynomial equation with real coefficients, then the conjugate $a - bi$ also is a root.

4 EXAMPLE Finding Imaginary Roots

A polynomial equation with integer coefficients has the roots $3 - i$ and $2i$. Find two additional roots.

By the Imaginary Root Theorem, if $3 - i$ is a root, then its complex conjugate $3 + i$ also is a root. If $2i$ is a root, then its complex conjugate $-2i$ also is a root.

● The additional roots are $3 + i$ and $2i$.

✓ **Quick Check** ④ **a.** If a polynomial equation with real coefficients has $3i$ and $-2 + i$ among its roots, then what two other roots must it have? $-3i, -2 - i$
b. Critical Thinking Describe the degree of the equation. **4 or greater**

You can often use the Irrational Root Theorem and the Imaginary Root Theorem to write a polynomial equation if you know some of its roots.

5 EXAMPLE Writing a Polynomial Equation from Its Roots

Find a third-degree polynomial equation with rational coefficients that has roots 3 and $1 + i$.

Step 1 Find the other root using the Imaginary Root Theorem.

Since $1 + i$ is a root, then its complex conjugate $1 - i$ also is a root.

Step 2 Write the factored form of the polynomial using the Factor Theorem.

$(x - 3)(x - (1 + i))(x - (1 - i))$

Step 3 Multiply the factors.

$(x - 3)[x^2 - x(1 - i) - x(1 + i) + (1 + i)(1 - i)]$ Multiply $(x - (1 + i))$ $(x - (1 - i))$.

$(x - 3)(x^2 - x + ix - x - ix + 1 - i^2)$ Simplify.

$(x - 3)(x^2 - x - x + 1 + 1)$

$(x - 3)(x^2 - 2x + 2)$ Multiply.

$x^3 - 5x^2 + 8x - 6$

A third-degree polynomial equation with rational coefficients and roots 3 and $1 + i$ is $x^3 - 5x^2 + 8x - 6 = 0$.

✓ **Quick Check** ⑤ **a.** Find a third-degree polynomial equation with rational coefficients that has roots -1 and $2 - i$. $x^3 - 3x^2 + x + 5 = 0$
b. Find a fourth-degree polynomial equation with rational coefficients that has roots i and $2i$. $x^4 + 5x^2 + 4 = 0$

338   Chapter 6 Polynomials and Polynomial Functions

Exercises

1. $\pm1, \pm2$; 1

2. $\pm1, \pm2, \pm3, \pm6$; 1, $-2, -3$

3. $\pm1, \pm2, \pm4$; -1

4. $\pm\frac{1}{2}, \pm1, \pm2, \pm4, \pm8$; no rational roots

5. $\pm1, \pm2, \pm4, \pm8, \pm16$; -2

6. $\pm1, \pm3, \pm5, \pm15$; no rational roots

8. $5, \pm i\sqrt{7}$

9. $-3, 1, \frac{7}{2}$

10. $-5, \frac{1 \pm \sqrt{3}}{2}$

11. $\pm\frac{1}{2}, \pm3$

12. $1, -2, \frac{1 \pm \sqrt{7}}{3}$

EXERCISES

For more exercises, see *Extra Skill and Word Problem Practice.*

Practice and Problem Solving

A Practice by Example

Example 1
(page 336)

Use the Rational Root Theorem to list all possible rational roots for each polynomial equation. Then find any actual rational roots. 1–6. See margin p. 338.

1. $x^3 - x^2 + 2x - 2 = 0$

2. $x^3 + 4x^2 + x - 6 = 0$

3. $x^3 + x^2 + 4x + 4 = 0$

4. $2x^3 - 9x^2 - 11x + 8 = 0$

5. $x^3 + 2x^2 - 8x - 16 = 0$

6. $x^4 + 2x^2 - 15 = 0$

Example 2
(pages 336–337)

Find the roots of each polynomial equation. 8–12. See margin p. 338.

7. $x^3 - 2x^2 + 5x - 10 = 0$ **2, $\pm i\sqrt{5}$**

8. $x^3 - 5x^2 + 7x - 35 = 0$

9. $2x^4 - 5x^3 - 17x^2 + 41x - 21 = 0$

10. $4x^3 + 16x^2 - 22x - 10 = 0$

11. $4x^4 - 37x^2 + 9 = 0$

12. $9x^4 + 3x^3 - 30x^2 + 6x + 12 = 0$

Examples 3 and 4
(pages 337 and 338)

13. $-\sqrt{5}, \sqrt{13}$

A polynomial equation with rational coefficients has the given roots. Find two additional roots.

$4 + \sqrt{6}, -\sqrt{3}$ $1 + \sqrt{10}, 2 - \sqrt{2}$

13. $\sqrt{5}$ and $-\sqrt{13}$

14. $4 - \sqrt{6}$ and $\sqrt{3}$

15. $1 - \sqrt{10}$ and $2 + \sqrt{2}$

16. $1 + i$ and $-5i$
$1 - i, 5i$

17. $2 + 3i$ and $6i$
$2 - 3i, -6i$

18. $4 - i$ and $3 + 7i$
$4 + i, 3 - 7i$

Example 5
(page 338)

Find a third-degree polynomial equation with rational coefficients that has the given numbers as roots. 19–22. See margin.

19. 1 and $3i$

20. -5 and $1 - i$

21. 2 and $-4i$

22. $3 + i$ and -3

23. $-2i$ and 6
$x^3 - 6x^2 + 4x - 24 = 0$

24. -1 and $i + 1$
$x^3 - x^2 + 2 = 0$

B Apply Your Skills

29. $x^4 - 6x^3 + 14x^2 - 24x + 40 = 0$

30. $x^4 - 2x^3 - x^2 + 6x - 6 = 0$

31. $x^4 - 6x^3 + 2x^2 + 30x - 35 = 0$

32. Never true; 5 is not a factor of 8, so by the Rational Root Theorem, 5 is not a root of the equation.

Use the Rational Root Theorem to list all possible rational roots for each polynomial equation. Then find any actual rational roots. 25–28. See margin.

25. $12x^3 - 32x^2 + 25x - 6 = 0$

26. $10x^3 - 49x^2 + 68x - 20 = 0$

27. $6x^4 - 5x^3 - 65x^2 + 85x - 21 = 0$

28. $8x^3 - 28x^2 + 14x + 15 = 0$

Find a fourth-degree polynomial equation with integer coefficients that has the given numbers as roots.

 29. $3 + i$ and $-2i$

30. $\sqrt{3}$ and $1 - i$

31. $3 + \sqrt{2}$ and $\sqrt{5}$

In each equation, r, s, and t represent integers. Indicate whether the statement is *sometimes*, *always*, or *never* true. Explain your answer. 33–36. See margin pp. 339–340.

32. A root of the equation $3x^3 + rx^2 + sx + 8 = 0$ is 5.

33. A root of the equation $3x^3 + rx^2 + sx + 8 = 0$ is -2.

34. If a is a root of $x^3 + rx^2 + sx + t = 0$, then a is a factor of t.

35. $\sqrt{5}$ and $-\sqrt{5}$ are roots of $x^3 + rx^2 + sx + t = 0$.

36. $2 + i$ and $-2 - i$ are roots of $x^3 + rx^2 + sx + t = 0$.

37. **Multiple Choice** A fourth-degree polynomial with integer coefficients has zeros at 1 and $3 + \sqrt{5}$. Which number CANNOT also be a zero of this polynomial? **D**

Ⓐ 1   Ⓑ -3 Ⓒ $3 - \sqrt{5}$ Ⓓ $3 + \sqrt{2}$

19. $x^3 - x^2 + 9x - 9 = 0$

20. $x^3 + 3x^2 - 8x + 10 = 0$

21. $x^3 - 2x^2 + 16x - 32 = 0$

22. $x^3 - 3x^2 - 8x + 30 = 0$

25. $\pm\frac{1}{12}, \pm\frac{1}{6}, \pm\frac{1}{4}, \pm\frac{1}{2}, \pm\frac{1}{3}, \pm\frac{2}{3}, \pm\frac{3}{4}, \pm1, \pm\frac{3}{2}, \pm2, \pm3, \pm6; \frac{1}{2}, \frac{3}{2}, \frac{2}{3}$

26. $\pm\frac{1}{10}, \pm\frac{1}{5}, \pm\frac{2}{5}, \pm\frac{1}{2}, \pm\frac{4}{5}, \pm1, \pm2, \pm\frac{5}{2}, \pm4, \pm5, \pm10, \pm20; 2, \frac{2}{5}, \frac{5}{2}$

4. Assess & Reteach

PowerPoint
Lesson Quiz

1. Use the Rational Root Theorem to list all possible rational roots of $3x^3 + x^2 - 15x - 5 = 0$. Then find any actual rational roots. $\pm1, \pm5, \pm\frac{1}{3}, \pm\frac{5}{3}, -\frac{1}{3}$

2. Find the roots of $10x^4 + x^3 + 7x^2 + x - 3 = 0$. $-\frac{3}{5}, \frac{1}{2}, \pm i$

3. A polynomial equation with rational coefficients has the roots $\sqrt{7}$ and $-5i$. Find two additional roots. $-\sqrt{7}, 5i$

4. Find a third-degree polynomial equation with integer coefficients that has the roots 8 and $3i$. $x^3 - 8x^2 + 9x - 72 = 0$

Alternative Assessment

Have students work in pairs. Together they construct a cubic polynomial that uses coefficients selected from the numbers $0, \pm1, \pm2, \pm3,$ and ±6. One student selects the coefficient for x^3, the other selects the coefficient for x^2, and so on. They work together to find all roots of any equation generated in this way that has at least one rational root. Students complete this work for at least six such equations.

Exercise 37 Some students may overlook CANNOT and select choice C. Remind them to read the problem carefully and consider each answer choice.

27. $\pm\frac{7}{3}, \pm\frac{1}{6}, \pm\frac{1}{2}, \pm\frac{1}{3}, \pm\frac{7}{6}, \pm1, \pm\frac{3}{2}, \pm3, \pm\frac{7}{2}, \pm7, \pm\frac{21}{2}, \pm21; \frac{1}{3}, -\frac{7}{2}, 1, 3$

28. $\pm\frac{1}{4}, \pm\frac{5}{4}, \pm\frac{1}{2}, \pm\frac{3}{4}, \pm\frac{1}{8}, \pm\frac{5}{8}, \pm\frac{3}{8}, \pm\frac{15}{4}, \pm\frac{5}{2}, \pm1, \pm\frac{3}{2}, \pm\frac{15}{8}, \pm\frac{15}{2}, \pm15, \pm3, \pm5; -\frac{1}{2}, \frac{3}{2}, \frac{5}{2}$

33. Sometimes true; since -2 is a factor of 8, -2 is a possible root of the equation.

339

Resources

For additional practice with a variety of test item formats:
- Standardized Test Prep, p. 363
- Test-Taking Strategies, p. 358
- Test-Taking Strategies with Transparencies

34. Always true; use the Rational Root Theorem with $p = a$ and $q = 1$.

35. Sometimes true; since $\sqrt{5}$ and $-\sqrt{5}$ are conjugates, they can be roots of a polynomial equation with integer coefficients.

36. Never true; since $2 + i$ and $-2 - i$ are not conjugates, they cannot be the only imaginary roots of a polynomial equation with integer coefficients. If their conjugates were also roots, there would be four roots and the equation would have to be of fourth degree.

40a. 2 real, 2 imaginary; 4 imaginary; 4 real

b. 5 real; 3 real, 2 imaginary; 4 imaginary, 1 real

c. Answers may vary. Sample: It has an odd number of real solutions, but it must have at least one real solution.

39. Answers may vary. Sample:
$x^4 - x^2 - 2 = 0$;
roots are $\pm\sqrt{2}$ and $\pm i$.

 Challenge

41. Answers may vary. Sample: You cannot use the Irrational Root Theorem unless the equation has rational coefficients.

38. Error Analysis A student claims that $2i$ is the only imaginary root of a polynomial equation that has real coefficients. Explain the student's mistake.
If $2i$ is a root, then so is $-2i$.

39. Open-Ended Write a fourth-degree polynomial equation with integer coefficients that has two irrational roots and two imaginary roots. **See left.**

40. a. Using *real* and *imaginary* as types of roots, list all possible combinations of root type for a fourth-degree polynomial equation. **a–c. See margin.**
b. Repeat the process for a fifth-degree polynomial equation.
c. Make a Conjecture Make a conjecture about the number of real roots of an odd-degree polynomial equation.

41. Writing A student states that $2 + \sqrt{3}$ is a root of $x^2 - 2x - (3 + 2\sqrt{3}) = 0$. The student claims that $2 - \sqrt{3}$ is another root of the equation by the Irrational Root Theorem. Explain how you would respond to the student.

42. What polynomial equation with complex coefficients and no multiple roots has $-4i$ and $2 + 3i$ as its only roots? $x^2 + (-2 + i)x + 12 - 8i = 0$

43. a. Find a polynomial equation in which $1 + \sqrt{2}$ is the only root.
b. Find a polynomial equation with root $1 + \sqrt{2}$ of multiplicity 2.
c. Find c such that $1 + \sqrt{2}$ is a solution of $x^2 - 2x + c = 0$.
a–c. Answers may vary. Samples:
a. $x - 1 - \sqrt{2} = 0$ **b.** $x^2 - 2(1 + \sqrt{2})x + (1 + \sqrt{2})^2 = 0$ **c.** -1

 Test Prep

Multiple Choice

44. Three roots of a polynomial equation with rational coefficients are $5 + \sqrt{3}$, -17, and $2 - \sqrt{4}$. Which number also is a root of the equation? **D**
A. 17   **B.** $2 + \sqrt{4}$ **C.** $4 - \sqrt{2}$ **D.** $5 - \sqrt{3}$

45. Two roots of a cubic polynomial equation with real coefficients are -3 and $-4i$. If the leading coefficient of the polynomial is 1, what is the equation?
F. $x^3 - 3x^2 + 16x - 48 = 0$ **G.** $x^3 - 3x^2 - 16x + 48 = 0$ **H**
H. $x^3 + 3x^2 + 16x + 48 = 0$ **J.** $x^3 + 3x^2 - 16x - 48 = 0$

Short Response

46. According to the Rational Root Theorem, what is the relationship between the polynomial equation $2x^4 - x^3 - 7x^2 + 3x + 3 = 0$ and rational roots of the form $\frac{p}{q}$, where $\frac{p}{q}$ is in simplest form? **See margin.**

Extended Response

47. A third-degree polynomial equation with rational coefficients has roots -4 and $-4i$. If the leading coefficient of the equation is $\frac{3}{2}$, what is the equation? Show your work. **See back of book.**

Mixed Review

 GO for Help

Lesson 6-4

Solve each equation. **48.** $-\frac{3}{2}, \frac{3 \pm 3i\sqrt{3}}{4}$

48. $8x^3 + 27 = 0$ **49.** $x^4 - x^2 - 20 = 0$ **50.** $2x^4 - 50 = 0$
$\pm\sqrt{5}, \pm 2i$ $\pm\sqrt{5}, \pm i\sqrt{5}$

Lesson 5-7

Solve each equation by completing the square.

51. $x^2 - 6x - 7 = 0$ **52.** $p^2 + 4p = -8$ **53.** $4x^2 - 11 = 12x$
$-1, 7$ $-2 \pm 2i$ $\frac{3}{2} \pm \sqrt{5}$

Lesson 4-8

Use Cramer's Rule to solve each system.

54. $\begin{cases} -3x + y = -7 \\ 5x + 2y = -3 \end{cases}$ **55.** $\begin{cases} x - 3y = -12 \\ 2x + 7y = 2 \end{cases}$ **56.** $\begin{cases} 2x - 8y = 10 \\ -3x + y = -15 \end{cases}$
$(1, -4)$ $(-6, 2)$ $(5, 0)$

46. [2] p is a factor of 3, so
$p = \pm 1$ or ± 3
q is a factor of 2, so
$q = \pm 1$ or ± 2

[1] relates p and q to the coefficients or the constant of the polynomial

6-6 The Fundamental Theorem of Algebra

What You'll Learn

• To use the Fundamental Theorem of Algebra in solving polynomial equations with complex roots

. . . And Why

To find all the zeros of a polynomial function, as in Example 2

✓ **Check Skills You'll Need**

GO for Help Lessons 5-8 and 6-1

Find the degree of each polynomial.

1. $3x^2 - x + 5$ **2**
2. $-x + 3 - x^3$ **3**
3. $-4x^5 + 1$ **5**

Solve each equation using the quadratic formula.

4. $x^2 + 16 = 0$ **±4i**
5. $x^2 - 2x + 3 = 0$ **$1 \pm i\sqrt{2}$**
6. $2x^2 + 5x + 4 = 0$ **$\frac{-5 \pm i\sqrt{7}}{4}$**

🔊 **New Vocabulary** • **Fundamental Theorem of Algebra**

---

1 The Fundamental Theorem of Algebra

3. A fourth-degree polynomial function has 4 zeros regardless of type.

Activity: Counting Zeros

In this activity you will find the solutions to polynomial equations, identify the types of solutions, and then count the number of solutions.

1. a. Find the solutions of $x^4 - 5x^2 + 4 = 0$. **−2, −1, 1, 2**
   b. Identify each solution as *real* or *imaginary*. **all real**
   c. How many solutions are there? **4**

2. a. Find the solutions of $x^4 + 7x^2 + 12 = 0$. **$\pm i\sqrt{3}, \pm 2i$**
   b. Identify each solution as *real* or *imaginary*. **all imaginary**
   c. How many solutions are there? **4**

3. Make a conjecture about the number of zeros of a fourth-degree polynomial function, regardless of the types of zeros. **See left.**

You have solved polynomial equations and found that their roots are included in the set of complex numbers. That is, the roots have been integers, rational numbers, irrational numbers, and imaginary numbers. But can all polynomial equations be solved using complex numbers?

In 1799, the German mathematician Carl Friedrich Gauss (1777–1855) proved that the answer to this question is yes. The roots of every polynomial equation, even those with imaginary coefficients, are complex numbers. The answer is so important that his theorem is called the **Fundamental Theorem of Algebra.**

A corollary to the Fundamental Theorem of Algebra describes the relationship between the degree of a polynomial and the number of zeros of the related polynomial function.

Real-World 🌐 Connection

Germany issued this stamp in honor of the bicentennial of the birth of Gauss.

Lesson 6-6 The Fundamental Theorem of Algebra   **341**

Differentiated Instruction Solutions for All Learners

Special Needs L1
In the Activity, have students use cubic equations that they can easily factor. For example, $x^3 + 4x^2 - 5x = 0$ gives $x(x + 5)(x - 1) = 0$ with solutions of 0, 1, −5; and $x^3 + x = 0$ gives $x(x^2 + 1) = 0$ with solutions of 0, ±i.

learning style: verbal

Below Level L2
Make sure that students understand that the number of roots is equal to the number of factors, and that multiple roots are a result of identical factors.

learning style: verbal

6-6

1. Plan

Objectives

1 To use the Fundamental Theorem of Algebra in solving polynomial equations with complex roots and find all zeros of a polynomial function

Examples

1 Using the Fundamental Theorem of Algebra
2 Finding All Zeros of a Polynomial Function

Math Background

The Fundamental Theorem of Algebra guarantees the existence of a complex root, and as a consequence the number of roots, but does not provide a means for finding them. Students will need to combine the techniques learned in previous lessons to find all complex zeros of a polynomial function.

More Math Background: p. 304D

Lesson Planning and Resources

See p. 304E for a list of the resources that support this lesson.

PowerPoint

🖥 **Bell Ringer Practice**

✓ **Check Skills You'll Need**
For intervention, direct students to:

The Quadratic Formula
Lesson 5-8: Examples 1 and 2
Extra Skills and Word Problems Practice, Ch. 5

Polynomial Functions
Lesson 6-1: Example 1
Extra Skills and Word Problems Practice, Ch. 6

341

2. Teach

Guided Activity

Activity
Each of these equations has four complex roots. In connection with Question 3, help students see that the Factor Theorem implies that a polynomial equation of degree n cannot have more than n zeros.

1 EXAMPLE Teaching Tip

Suggest students review the Imaginary Root Theorem and the Rational Root Theorem before they begin this example.

2 EXAMPLE Teaching Tip

Be sure students understand that "$x^2 - x + 1$ cannot be factored" means there are no linear factors that have only *real* coefficients.

Additional Examples

1 For the equation $x^4 - 3x^3 + 4x + 1 = 0$, find the number of complex roots, the possible number of real roots, and the possible rational roots.
4; 0, 2, or 4; ±1

2 Find the number of complex zeros of $f(x) = x^5 + 3x^4 - x - 3$. Find all the zeros. 5 zeros; ±1, −3, ±i

Resources
• Daily Notetaking Guide 6-6 **L3**

Closure

Ask: *How can you determine how many roots there are for a polynomial equation?* Find the degree of the related polynomial. This degree gives the number of roots, including multiple roots.

 Key Concepts

Theorem	Fundamental Theorem of Algebra

If $P(x)$ is a polynomial of degree $n \geq 1$ with complex coefficients, then $P(x) = 0$ has at least one complex root.

Vocabulary Tip

A <u>corollary</u> of a theorem is itself a theorem. It may be easily and immediately deduced from the original theorem.

Corollary

Including complex roots and multiple roots, an nth degree polynomial equation has exactly n roots; the related polynomial function has exactly n zeros.

In other words, the corollary says that you can factor a polynomial of degree n into n linear factors. The number n includes multiple roots. For example, the equation $x^3 = 0$ should have three roots by the corollary to the Fundamental Theorem of Algebra. Since $x^3 = 0$ can be rewritten as $x \cdot x \cdot x = 0$ or $(x - 0)(x - 0)(x - 0) = 0$, the equation has three linear factors and three roots, all of which are zero.

1 EXAMPLE Using the Fundamental Theorem of Algebra

For the equation $x^3 + 2x^2 - 4x - 6 = 0$, find the number of complex roots, the possible number of real roots, and the possible rational roots.

By the corollary to the Fundamental Theorem of Algebra, $x^3 + 2x^2 - 4x - 6 = 0$ has three complex roots.

By the Imaginary Root Theorem, the equation has either no imaginary roots or two imaginary roots (one conjugate pair). So the equation has either three real roots or one real root.

By the Rational Root Theorem, the possible rational roots of the equation are ±1, ±2, ±3, and ±6.

✓ Quick Check **1** For the equation $x^4 - 3x^3 + x^2 - x + 3 = 0$, find the number of complex roots, the possible number of real roots, and the possible rational roots.
4 complex roots, number of real roots: 0, 2, or 4, possible rational roots: ±1, ±3

You can often find all the zeros of a polynomial function by using some combination of graphing, the Factor Theorem, polynomial division, the Remainder Theorem, and the Quadratic Formula.

2 EXAMPLE Finding All Zeros of a Polynomial Function

Find the number of complex zeros of $f(x) = x^3 + x^2 - x + 2$. Find all the zeros.

By the corollary to the Fundamental Theorem of Algebra, there are three complex zeros. You can use synthetic division to find a rational zero.

Step 1 Find a rational root from the possible roots of ±1 and ±2. Use synthetic division to test each possible root until you get a remainder of zero.

$$
\begin{array}{r|rrrr}
-2 & 1 & 1 & -1 & 2 \\
   &   & -2 & 2 & -2 \\
\hline
   & 1 & -1 & 1 & 0 \\
   & \downarrow & \downarrow & \downarrow & \\
   & 1x^2 & -1x & +1 &
\end{array}
$$

So −2 is one of the roots.

Differentiated Instruction Solutions for All Learners

Advanced Learners **L4**
The equation $y = x^2 - 4x + 4$ has only 2 as a zero. Have students explain how this can be reconciled with the corollary to the Fundamental Theorem of Algebra.

learning style: verbal

English Language Learners **ELL**
Ask students for the everyday meaning of *fundamental*. Relate its definition to the importance of the Fundamental Theorem of Algebra that states all polynomial equations can be solved using complex numbers.

learning style: verbal

Step 2 Since the expression $x^2 - x + 1$ cannot be factored, use the Quadratic Formula to solve the related quadratic equation $x^2 - x + 1 = 0$.

$$x = \frac{-b \pm \sqrt{b^2 - 4ac}}{2a}$$

$$x = \frac{-(-1) \pm \sqrt{(-1)^2 - 4(1)(1)}}{2(1)}$$

$$x = \frac{1 \pm \sqrt{-3}}{2}$$

$$x = \frac{1 \pm i\sqrt{3}}{2}$$

The polynomial function $f(x) = x^3 + x^2 - x + 2$ has one real zero of $x = -2$, and two complex zeros of $x = \frac{1 + i\sqrt{3}}{2}$ and $x = \frac{1 - i\sqrt{3}}{2}$.

 Quick Check 2 **a.** Find all zeros of $y = x^3 - 2x^2 + 4x - 8$. **2, ±2i**
b. Which zeros can you verify on a graphing calculator? Explain.
You can verify the real zeros by graphing the function. You can verify the complex zeros by substituting the values into the function.

EXERCISES

For more exercises, see *Extra Skill and Word Problem Practice*.

Practice and Problem Solving

 A Practice by Example

Example 1
(page 342)

 GO for Help

For each equation, state the number of complex roots, the possible number of real roots, and the possible rational roots. **1–8. See margin.**

1. $x^3 + 4x^2 + 5x - 1 = 0$
2. $3x^2 - 7 = 0$
3. $-x^4 = 0$
4. $2x^5 - 4x^4 - 4x^2 + 5 = 0$
5. $x^7 - x^3 - 2x - 3 = 0$
6. $4x + 8 = 0$
7. $-2x^6 - x^2 + x - 7 = 0$
8. $x^{10} + x^8 - x^4 + 3x^2 - x + 1 = 0$

Example 2
(pages 342–343)

Find all the zeros of each function.

9. $y = 2x^3 + x^2 + 1$ $-1, \frac{1 \pm i\sqrt{7}}{4}$
10. $f(x) = x^3 - 3x^2 + x - 3$ **3, ±i**
11. $g(x) = x^3 - 5x^2 + 5x - 4$ $4, \frac{1 \pm i\sqrt{3}}{2}$
12. $y = x^3 - 2x^2 - 3x + 6$ **2, ±√3**
13. $y = x^4 - 6x^2 + 8$ **±2, ±√2**
14. $f(x) = x^4 - 3x^2 - 4$ **±2, ±i**
15. $y = x^3 - 3x^2 - 9x$ $0, \frac{3 \pm 3\sqrt{5}}{2}$
16. $y = x^3 + 6x^2 + x + 6$ **−6, ±i**

B Apply Your Skills

For each equation, state the number of complex roots, the possible number of real roots, and the possible rational roots. **17–20. See back of book.**

25. $\frac{1}{2}, \pm 2i\sqrt{5}$

26. $\frac{2}{5}, \frac{-1 \pm i\sqrt{11}}{6}$

17. $2x^4 - x^3 + 2x^2 + 5x - 26 = 0$
18. $x^5 - x^3 - 11x^2 + 9x + 18 = 0$
19. $-12 + x + 10x^2 + 3x^3 = 0$
20. $4x^6 - x^5 - 24 = 0$

Find all the zeros of each function.

GO Online
Homework Video Tutor
Visit: PHSchool.com
Web Code: age-0606

GPS **21.** $y = x^3 - 4x^2 + 9x - 36$ **4, ±3i**
22. $f(x) = x^3 + 2x^2 - 5x - 10$ $-2, \pm\sqrt{5}$
23. $y = 2x^3 + 14x^2 + 13x + 6$ $-6, \frac{-1 \pm i}{2}$
24. $y = 4x^3 + 9x^2 + 22x + 5$ $-\frac{1}{4}, -1 \pm 2i$
25. $g(x) = x^3 - \frac{1}{2}x^2 + 20x - 10$
26. $y = 15x^3 - x^2 + 3x - 2$

27. Open-Ended Write a polynomial function that has four possible rational zeros but no actual rational zeros. **Answers may vary. Sample:** $y = x^4 + 3x^2 + 2$

Assignment Guide

1 A B 1-27
C Challenge   28-31

Test Prep   32-39
Mixed Review   40-45

Homework Quick Check
To check students' understanding of key skills and concepts, go over Exercises 7, 15, 20, 21, 22.

Error Prevention!

Exercise 3 Remind students to take the multiplicity of roots into account.

Differentiated Instruction **Resources**

GPS Guided Problem Solving — L3
Enrichment — L4
Reteaching — L2
Practice — L3

possible rational roots:
$\pm\frac{1}{4}, \pm\frac{1}{2}, \pm 1, \pm 2, \pm 4, \pm 8$

7. 6 complex roots
number of real roots: 0, 2, 4, or 6
possible rational roots:
$\pm\frac{1}{2}, \pm 1, \pm\frac{7}{2}, \pm 7$

8. 10 complex roots
number of real roots: 0, 2, 4, 6, 8, or 10
possible rational roots: ±1

---

1. 3 complex roots
number of real roots: 1 or 3
possible rational roots: ±1

2. 2 complex roots
number of real roots: 0 or 2
possible rational roots:
$\pm\frac{1}{3}, \pm\frac{7}{3}, \pm 1, \pm 7$

3. 4 complex roots
number of real roots: 0, 2, or 4
possible rational roots: 0

4. 5 complex roots; number of real roots: 1, 3, or 5
possible rational roots:
$\pm\frac{1}{2}, \pm 1, \pm\frac{5}{2}, \pm 5$

5. 7 complex roots
number of real roots: 1, 3, 5, or 7
possible rational roots:
±1, ±3

6. 1 complex root
number of real roots: 1

343

Lesson Quiz

For each equation, state the number of complex roots, the possible number of real roots, and the possible rational roots.

1. $x^4 - 13x^3 + x^2 - 5 = 0$
   4; 0, 2, or 4; ±1, ±5

2. $x^7 - x^5 + x^2 - 3x + 3 = 0$ 7;
   1, 3, 5, or 7; ±1, ±3

Find all the zeros of each function.

3. $x^3 - 3x^2 - 8x - 10 = 0$
   5, −1±i

4. $x^3 + 3x^2 - 2x - 6 = 0$ −3,
   ±$\sqrt{2}$

5. $x^4 - 29x^2 + 100 = 0$ ±2, ±5

Alternative Assessment

Say: *Write an equation with integer coefficients that has 3 roots—one real root, and two imaginary roots.* Students trade equations to check. Repeat the process, but this time students write an equation with 4 roots—two rational roots and two imaginary roots.

Test Prep

Resources

For additional practice with a variety of test item formats:
• Standardized Test Prep, p. 363
• Test-Taking Strategies, p. 358
• Test-Taking Strategies with Transparencies

 C Challenge   **Graph each function. Approximate the real zeros to the nearest hundredth.**

28. $f(x) = x^4 + 3x^2 - 2$ 29. $f(x) = x^4 + 2x^3 - 2x^2 + 4x - 8$
28–29. See margin.

30. **Writing**   Using the Rational Root Theorem, explain why the following statement is false: If a polynomial has no constant term, then the corresponding polynomial equation has only the number 0 as a possible rational root.
See margin.

31. **Critical Thinking** Consider a polynomial with integer coefficients in which the leading coefficient is not equal to 1. Can the related polynomial equation have a rational root that is an integer? Explain. **Yes; for example,**
$2x^2 - 11x + 5 = 0$ **has roots 0.5 and 5.**

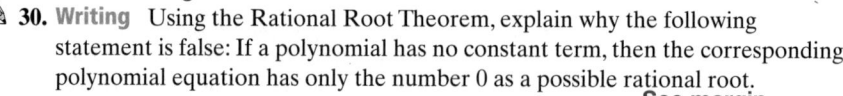 **Test Prep**

Multiple Choice   32. Which number is a root of $f(x) = x^3 + 6x^2 + 9x$ that has multiplicity 1? **C**
    A. 3   B. 1   C. 0   D. −3

33. Three roots of a polynomial equation with real coefficients are 3, 5 − 3i, and −3i. Which number MUST also be a root of the equation?   **H**
    I. −3   II. 5 + 3i III. 3i
    F. II only   G. I and II only   H. II and III only   J. I, II, and III

34. One root of the equation $x^3 + x^2 - 2 = 0$ is 1. What are the other two roots?   **B**
    A. 1 ± 2i B. −1 ± i C. ±1 + 2i D. ±1 − i

35. A polynomial with real coefficients has 3, 2i, and –i as three of its zeros. What is the least possible degree of the polynomial?   **H**
    F. 3   G. 4   H. 5   J. 6

36. How many times does the graph of $x^3 + 27$ cross the x-axis?   **B**
    A. 0   B. 1   C. 2   D. 4

Short Response   37. Find all roots of the equation $x^4 = 256$. Show your work.   **37–39. See back of book.**

38. One root of the equation $x^4 - 4x^3 - 6x^2 + 4x + 5 = 0$ is –1.
    a. Find the number of complex roots.
    b. Find all the roots.

39. List the possible rational roots of the equation $x^4 - 2x^3 + 6x^2 - 2x + 5 = 0$. Do not solve the equation. Explain how you made your list.

Mixed Review

 GO for Help

Lesson 6-5   40. Find a fourth-degree polynomial equation with integer coefficients that has 2i and −3 + i as roots. $x^4 + 6x^3 + 14x^2 + 24x + 40 = 0$

Lesson 5-8   **Solve each equation using the Quadratic Formula.**

41. $x^2 - 6x + 9 = 0$ 42. $2x^2 + 5x = -9$ 43. $2(x^2 + 2) = 3x$
    3 (mult. 2) $\dfrac{-5 \pm i\sqrt{47}}{4}$ $\dfrac{3 \pm i\sqrt{23}}{4}$

Lesson 5-1   **Find a quadratic model for each function.**

44. $f(-1) = 0, f(2) = 3, f(1) = 4$ 45. $f(-4) = 11, f(-5) = 5, f(-6) = 3$
    $f(x) = -x^2 + 2x + 3$ $f(x) = 2x^2 + 24x + 75$

---

28. ±0.75

29. −3.24, 1.24

30. If you have no constant, then all terms have an x that can be factored out. The resulting expression will have a constant that can be used in the Rational Root Theorem.

Permutations and Combinations

1. Plan

What You'll Learn

- To count permutations
- To count combinations

. . . And Why

To find the number of ways you can vote for candidates, as in Example 5

✓ **Check Skills You'll Need**

 GO for Help Lesson 1-2

Simplify each expression.

1. $10 \cdot 9 \cdot 8 \cdot 7 \cdot 6$ **30, 240** **2.** $\frac{4 \cdot 3 \cdot 2}{6 \cdot 5}$ $\frac{4}{5}$

3. $\frac{7 \cdot 6 \cdot 5 \cdot 4 \cdot 3 \cdot 2 \cdot 1}{4 \cdot 3 \cdot 2 \cdot 1}$ **210**

Let $a * b = 2a(a + b)$. Evaluate each expression.

4. $3 * 4$ **42** **5.** $2 * 7$ **36** **6.** $5 * 1$ **60** **7.** $6 * 10$ **192**

🔊 **New Vocabulary** • **permutation** • ***n* factorial** • **combination**

Objectives

1 To count permutations
2 To count combinations

Examples

1 Finding Permutations
2 Real-World Connection
3 Finding Combinations
4 Real-World Connection
5 Real-World Connection

Math Background

The branch of mathematics known as combinatorial analysis begins with questions of the form "In how many ways is it possible to arrange . . . ?" and "In how many ways is it possible to select . . . ?" Questions of the first type deal with permutations, and questions of the second type deal with combinations. Combinatorial analysis is important in algebra, probability, and many other branches of mathematics.

More Math Background: p. 304D

Lesson Planning and Resources

See p. 304E for a list of the resources that support this lesson.

---

1 Permutations

A **permutation** is an arrangement of items in a particular order. You can often find the number of permutations of some set of items by using the Multiplication Counting Principle.

You can use the Multiplication Counting Principle when you plan to choose all of the items of a particular set. Suppose you want to find the number of permutations for three items. There are three ways to choose the first item, two ways to choose the second item, and only one way to choose the third item. By the Multiplication Counting Principle, there are $3 \cdot 2 \cdot 1$ permutations.

Using factorial notation, you can write $3 \cdot 2 \cdot 1$ as 3!, read "three factorial."

 Key Concepts

Definition	***n* Factorial**

For any positive integer n, $n! = n(n - 1) \cdot \ldots \cdot 3 \cdot 2 \cdot 1$.
For $n = 0$, $n! = 1$.

 Graphing Calculator Hint

To calculate factorials, press MATH and then choose the PRB menu and the ! option.

1 EXAMPLE Finding Permutations

In how many different orders can ten dogs line up to be groomed?

Since all ten dogs are being groomed, you are using all the items from the original set. You can use the Multiplication Counting Principle or factorial notation.

There are ten ways to select the first dog in line, nine ways to select the next dog, and so on. The total number of permutations is $10 \cdot 9 \cdot \ldots \cdot 2 \cdot 1 = 10!$.

$10! = 3,628,800$

● The ten dogs can line up in 3,628,800 different orders.

✓ **Quick Check** ❶ In how many ways can you arrange six trophies on a shelf? **720**

PowerPoint
 Bell Ringer Practice

✓ **Check Skills You'll Need**
For intervention, direct students to:

Algebraic Expressions
Lesson 1-2: Example 1
Extra Skills and Word Problems Practice, Ch. 1

Differentiated Instruction Solutions for All Learners

Special Needs
Have students get three different objects such as a pencil, an eraser, and a calculator. Ask them to place the objects in groups that have a different order. Point out that when finding combinations, each of these groups is the same.

learning style: tactile

Below Level
Tell students to think of a permutation as a way to award medals in the Olympics. The order in which the athletes finish races does affect the medal they are awarded.

learning style: verbal

1 EXAMPLE Tactile Learners

Have students write the letters A, B, and C each on its own index card. Then lay the cards out from left to right. Have students arrange the cards in all possible orders and keep a list of the arrangements. Ask them what the value of 3! is. **6** Let students repeat the process for the letters A, B, C, and D and compare the result to 4!. **24** Ask: *Which would be easier to do, manually arrange cards representing 10 dogs or find 10!?* **find 10!**

2 EXAMPLE Alternative Method

One way to remember how to calculate permutations is using the phrase "possible choices times possible choices times possible choices." You say "possible choices" for each time there is a choice to make—three times for this example since there are three places awarded prizes.

PowerPoint

Additional Examples

1 In how many orders can six people line up from left to right for a group photo?
720 orders

2 How many 4-letter codes can be made if no letter can be used twice? **358,800 codes**

Some permutations do not use all the items available in a set. You can still use the Multiplication Counting Principle or factorial notation. The relationship between permutations and factorials can be summarized with a formula.

Key Concepts

Definition	Number of Permutations

The number of permutations of n items of a set arranged r items at a time is $_nP_r$.

$$_nP_r = \frac{n!}{(n-r)!} \text{ for } 0 \le r \le n$$

Example $\quad _{10}P_4 = \frac{10!}{(10-4)!} = \frac{10!}{6!} = 5040$

Real-World Connection

In how many ways can these boats finish first, second, and third?

2 EXAMPLE Real-World Connection

Boating Seven yachts enter a race. First, second, and third places will be given to the three fastest yachts. How many arrangements of first, second, and third places are possible with seven yachts?

Method 1 Use the Multiplication Counting Principle.
$$7 \cdot 6 \cdot 5 = 210$$

Method 2 Use the permutation formula. Since there are seven yachts arranged three at a time, $n = 7$ and $r = 3$.

$$_7P_3 = \frac{7!}{(7-3)!} = \frac{7!}{4!} = 210$$

There are 210 possible arrangements of first, second, and third places.

Quick Check **2** How many arrangements of first, second, and third places are possible with ten yachts? **720**

2 Combinations

In Example 2, you found the number of ways in which three of seven yachts can finish first, second, and third in a race. Each yacht would have a unique place. Consider a situation in which the three fastest yachts win the race with equal status, that is, without first, second, and third places. In that case, the *order* in which the three winning yachts cross the finish line does not matter. A selection in which order does not matter is a **combination.**

As with permutations, you can calculate the number of combinations of n items chosen r at a time by using a formula.

Key Concepts

Definition	Number of Combinations

The number of combinations of n items of a set chosen r items at a time is $_nC_r$.

$$_nC_r = \frac{n!}{r!(n-r)!} \text{ for } 0 \le r \le n$$

Example $\quad _5C_3 = \frac{5!}{3!(5-3)!} = \frac{5!}{3! \cdot 2!} = \frac{120}{6 \cdot 2} = 10$

346 Chapter 6 Polynomials and Polynomial Functions

Differentiated Instruction Solutions for All Learners

Advanced Learners L4
Have students explain how a tree diagram of probabilities reflects the Multiplication Counting Principle.

learning style: verbal

English Language Learners ELL
For Example 5, have a student volunteer explain about student governments and/or student councils. Discuss what is meant by *seats in the student government.*

learning style: verbal

Video Tutor Help
Visit: PhSchool.com
Web Code: age-0775

Graphing Calculator Hint

To find permutations and combinations, press MATH , and then choose the PRB menu.

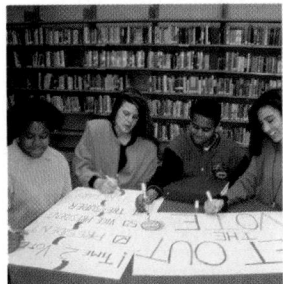

The National Association of Student Councils has more than 18,000 member schools.

3 EXAMPLE Finding Combinations

Evaluate $_{12}C_3$.

$$_{12}C_3 = \frac{12!}{3!(12-3)!}$$ Use the formula $_nC_r = \frac{n!}{r!(n-r)!}$.

$$= \frac{12!}{3! \cdot 9!}$$ Simplify.

$$= \frac{12 \cdot 11 \cdot 10 \cdot 9 \cdot 8 \cdot 7 \cdot 6 \cdot 5 \cdot 4 \cdot 3 \cdot 2 \cdot 1}{3 \cdot 2 \cdot 1 \cdot 9 \cdot 8 \cdot 7 \cdot 6 \cdot 5 \cdot 4 \cdot 3 \cdot 2 \cdot 1}$$ Simplify each factorial.

$$= \frac{12 \cdot 11 \cdot 10}{3 \cdot 2 \cdot 1}$$

$$= 220$$

Quick Check 3 Evaluate each expression.
    a. $_{10}C_5$ **252**   **b.** $_8C_2$ **28**   **c.** $_{25}C_7$ **480,700**

You can use a graphing calculator to find combinations.

4 EXAMPLE Real-World Connection

Literature A reading list for a course in world literature has 20 books on it. In how many ways can you choose four books to read?

Relate 20 books chosen 4 books at a time

Define Let n = total number of books.

         Let r = number of books chosen at a time.

Write $_nC_r = _{20}C_4$

```
20 nCr 4
■              4845
```

Use the $_nC_r$ feature of your calculator.

You can choose four books in 4845 different ways.

Quick Check 4 Of the 20 books, in how many ways can you choose seven books? Twelve books? **77,520; 125,970**

5 EXAMPLE Real-World Connection

Multiple Choice Ten candidates are running for three seats in the student government. You may vote for as many as three candidates. In how many ways can you vote for three or fewer candidates?

  Ⓐ 6   Ⓑ 120   Ⓒ 176   Ⓓ 216

You may vote for 3 people, 2 people, 1 person, or none.

                  $_{10}C_3$ $_{10}C_2$ $_{10}C_1$ $_{10}C_0$
                   120   45   10   1

The total number of ways to vote is $120 + 45 + 10 + 1 = 176$.

There are 176 ways to cast your ballot. The correct choice is C.

Quick Check 5 In how many ways can you vote for five or fewer people? **638**

Lesson 6-7 Permutations and Combinations   **347**

Stress that the value of n must always be specified before selecting nCr from the PRB menu.

PowerPoint

Additional Examples

3 Evaluate $_{10}C_4$. **210**

4 A disk jockey wants to select 5 songs from a new CD that contains 12 songs. How many 5-song selections are possible? **792 selections**

5 A pizza menu allows you to select 4 toppings at no extra charge from a list of 9 possible toppings. In how many ways can you select 4 or fewer toppings? **256 ways**

Resources
• Daily Notetaking Guide 6-7 L3

Closure

Ask: *How is a combination of n items chosen r at a time different from a permutation of n items chosen r at a time?* In the combination, the only important thing is which items are selected. In the permutation, both the items and their order of selection are important.

Assignment Guide

1 A B 1-20, 33-41, 56-66, 68

2 A B 21-32, 42-55, 67

C Challenge 69-73

Test Prep 74-80
Mixed Review 81-94

Homework Quick Check
To check students' understanding
of key skills and concepts, go over
Exercises 27, 32, 40, 55, 60.

Error Prevention!

Exercises 7, 8 Students who use a
graphing calculator to evaluate
these expressions must remember
to use parentheses around the
entire denominator.

Exercise 9 Not all permutations
are recommended for radial tires.

Exercise 39 Make sure students
understand that a number can be
repeated, such as 11111, and that
each number has $2^5 = 32$
different number codes.

33. true because of the
Comm. Prop. of Add.

34. true because of the
Assoc. Prop. of Mult.

EXERCISES

For more exercises, see *Extra Skill and Word Problem Practice.*

Practice and Problem Solving

A Practice by Example

Example 1
(page 345)

Evaluate each expression.

1. 5! **120**
2. 10! **3,628,800**
3. 13! **6,227,020,800**
4. 5!3! **720**
5. $\frac{12!}{6!}$ **665,280**
6. 5(4!) **120**
7. $\frac{10!}{7!3!}$ **120**
8. $\frac{15!}{10!5!}$ **3003**

9. **Automobiles** You should rotate tires on a car at regular intervals.
   a. In how many ways can four tires be arranged on a car? **24**
   b. If the spare tire is included, how many arrangements are possible? **120**

Example 2
(page 346)

Evaluate each expression.

10. $_8P_1$ **8**
11. $_8P_2$ **56**
12. $_8P_3$ **336**
13. $_8P_4$ **1680**
14. $_3P_2$ **6**
15. $_5P_4$ **120**
16. $_9P_6$ **60,480**
17. $_5P_3$ **60**

18. Fifteen students ask to visit a college admissions counselor. Each visit includes one student. In how many ways can ten time slots be assigned? **10,897,286,400**

19. How many different nine-player batting orders can be chosen from a baseball squad of 16? **4,151,347,200**

20. The prom committee has four sites available for the banquet and three sites for the dance. How many arrangements are possible for the banquet and dance? **12**

Examples 3 and 4
(page 347)

Evaluate each expression.

21. $_6C_2$ **15**
22. $_8C_5$ **56**
23. $_4C_4$ **1**
24. $_4C_3$ **4**
25. $_7C_3$ **35**
26. $3(_5C_4)$ **15**
27. $_6C_2 + _6C_3$ **35**
28. $\frac{_7C_4}{_9C_4}$ **$\frac{5}{18}$**

29. **Sports** How many different teams of 11 players can be chosen from a soccer squad of 16? **4368**

30. Suppose you find seven articles related to the topic of your research paper. In how many ways can you choose five articles to read? **21**

Example 5
(page 347)

31. For a band camp, you can choose two or three roommates from a group of 25 friends. In how many ways can you choose? **2600**

32. A salad bar offers eight choices of toppings for lettuce. In how many ways can you choose four or five toppings? **126**

B Apply Your Skills

Assume a and b are positive integers. Decide whether each statement is *true* or *false*. If it is true, explain why. If it is not true, give a counterexample. 35–38. See margin.

33. $a! + b! = b! + a!$
34. $a!(b!c!) = (a!b!)c!$
35. $(a + b)! = a! + b!$
36. $(ab)! = a!b!$
37. $(a!)! = (a!)^2$
38. $(a!)^b = a^{(b!)}$

39. **Multiple Choice** A car door lock has a five-button keypad. Each button has two numerals. How many different five-button patterns are possible? You can use a button more than once. **C**

   Ⓐ 120 Ⓑ 720 Ⓒ 3125 Ⓓ 5555

The entry code 21914 uses the same button sequence as the code 11023.

1/2 3/4 5/6 7/8 9/0

---

35. False; answers may vary. Sample: $(3 + 2)! = 120$ and $3! + 2! = 8$

36. False; answers may vary. Sample: $(3 \times 2)! = 720$ and $3! \times 2! = 12$

37. False; answers may vary. Sample: $(3!)! = 720$ and $(3!)^2 = 36$

38. False; answers may vary. Sample: $(3!)^2 = 36$ and $3^{(2!)} = 9$

Real-World **Connection**

Careers Consumer researchers use formulas to compare and rate products.

46. permutation
47. permutation

55c. Answers may vary. Sample: Each time you choose 3 of the 8 points to use as vertices of a △, the 5 remaining points could be used to form a pentagon.

Homework Video Tutor

Visit: PHSchool.com
Web Code: age-0607

40. **Consumer Issues** A consumer magazine rates televisions by identifying two levels of price, five levels of repair frequency, three levels of features, and two levels of picture quality. How many different ratings are possible? **60**

41. **Writing** In how many ways is it possible to arrange the two numbers *a* and *b* in an ordered pair? Explain why such a pair is called an *ordered* pair.
2 ways, because order matters

Evaluate each expression.

42. $\frac{_{50}C_5}{_{50}C_{10}}$ $\frac{4}{19,393} \approx .000206$ 43. $\frac{1}{3}(_{10}C_5)$ **84**   44. $\frac{_{25}C_2}{_{50}C_2}$ $\frac{12}{49}$ 45. $\frac{_6C_2}{3}$ **5**

Indicate whether each situation involves a combination or a permutation.

46. 5 runners crossing the finish line   47. 12 books arranged on a shelf

48. 4 books pulled at random from a shelf **combination**

49. 3 flavors of juice selected from a variety pack **combination**

How many combinations of four can you make from each set? **50. 330,791,175**

50. 300 people in a club   51. $\{0, 1, 2, 3, 4, 5, 6, 7, 8, 9\}$ **210**

52. 25 baseball cards **12,650** 53. a rose, a daisy, a peony, a daffodil, and a tulip **5**

54. Each line in the [MODE] screen of a graphing calculator shows two or more choices. In how many different ways can you set the mode of this calculator? **9504**

55. a. **Geometry** Eight points lie on a circle. How many triangles can you make using three of the points as vertices? **56**
   b. How many pentagons can you make using five points as vertices? **56**
   c. **Reasoning** Explain why your answers to parts (a) and (b) should be the same. **See left.**

How many four-letter permutations can you form from the letters of each word?

56. MODEL **120**   57. EQUATIONS **3024**   58. LINEAR **360**   59. REAL **24**

60. MATRICES **1680**   61. FORMULA **840**   62. CONJUGATES **5040**   63. SUM **0**

Open-Ended Write a problem that can be solved using each technique.
64–67. Check students' work.
64. the Multiplication Counting Principle   65. a single factorial

66. the permutation formula   67. the combination formula

68. a. Refer to the cartoon below. How many different sets of answers are possible if the test includes eleven true-or-false questions? **2048**
   b. Do you agree with the statement in the last frame? Justify your answer.
Answers may vary. Sample: No, because there are too many possible solutions.

PowerPoint
Lesson Quiz

Evaluate each expression.

1. 8! **40,320**   2. $\frac{14!}{10!4!}$ **1001**
3. $_7C_3$ **35**   4. $_9P_5$ **15,120**
5. There are 12 students waiting to enter a van to go on a trip to the science museum. In how many orders can they enter the van? **479,001,600 orders**
6. You have 8 shopping trips to make this week. You have time to make any 4 of them today. In how many ways can you select the four that you make today? **70 ways**
7. You want to hang 6 pictures in a row on a wall. You have 11 pictures from which to choose. How many picture arrangements are possible? **332,640 arrangements**

Alternative Assessment

Have each student write a real-world problem that can be solved by using permutations or combinations. Students exchange problems. Each student solves the problems written by three other students. They compare their answers and resolve any disagreements about answers.

A sheet of blank grids is available in Test-Taking Strategies with Transparencies booklet. Give this sheet to students for practice with filling in the grids.

📁 **Resources**

For additional practice with a variety of test item formats:
- Standardized Test Prep, p. 363
- Test-Taking Strategies, p. 358
- Test-Taking Strategies with Transparencies

69a. The graph for $y = {}_xC_{x-2}$ is identical to the graph for $y = {}_xC_2$ because ${}_2C_{2-2} = {}_2C_2$, ${}_3C_{3-2} = {}_3C_2$, ${}_4C_{4-2} = {}_4C_2$, ${}_5C_{5-2} = {}_5C_2$, etc.

b. Answers may vary. Sample: The function is defined only at discrete whole-number values of x, and not over a smooth range of points as in a continuous function.

81. 3 complex roots
number of real roots: 1 or 3
possible rational roots: $\pm\frac{1}{12}, \pm\frac{1}{6}, \pm\frac{1}{4}, \pm\frac{1}{3}, \pm\frac{1}{2}, \pm\frac{2}{3}, \pm1, \pm2$

83. $-x^3 - 3x^2 + 6$; cubic trinomial

84. $2x^2 - 4x + 8$; quadratic trinomial

85. $5t^2 - 3t$; quadratic binomial

86. $x^4 - 100$; quartic binomial

87. $x^3 - 4x$; cubic binomial

88. $t^4 - 2t^3 + t^2$; quartic trinomial

350

 C **Challenge**

69. a. The graph at the right shows the function $y = {}_xC_2$. Use it to graph the function $y = {}_xC_{x-2}$.
b. Critical Thinking Explain why the graph consists of discrete points rather than a continuous curve.
a–b. See margin.

70. a. In how many ways can you choose three flags from a collection of seven different flags? **35**
b. Once you choose three flags, in how many different orders can you arrange them? **6**

✏️ **c. Writing** You want to arrange three flags from a group of seven. Explain how you can use ${}_7C_3 \cdot 3!$ to create the permutation formula. **See left.**

70c. ${}_7C_3 = \frac{7!}{3!\,4!}$, so ${}_7C_3 \cdot 3! = \frac{7!}{4!}$, which is the permutation formula for ${}_7P_3$.

71a. All the terms contain the factors 2 and 5. Since multiplication is commutative, $2 \times 5 = 10$ and 10 times any integer ends in zero.

📱 **71.** In the sequence $1!, 2!, 3!, 4!, 5!, 6!, \ldots$, the first term that ends with a zero is 5!.
a. Explain why 5! and all the terms following 5! end with a zero. **See left.**
b. Find the number of zeros with which 100! ends. **24 zeros**

72. Find a number n for which entering $n!$ in your calculator causes overflow error. **Answers may vary. Sample: 99**

🌐 **73. Data Analysis** The bar graph at the right shows the results of 40 responses to a survey.
a. How many people said they squeeze the toothpaste from the middle of the tube? **18 people**
b. Use your answer to part (a). Find the number of possible combinations of five people who said they squeeze the toothpaste from the middle of the tube. **8568**
c. Suppose five people are chosen at random from all the people who responded to the survey. How many combinations of five people are possible? **658,008**
d. Probability What is the probability that the five people selected at random all squeeze toothpaste from the middle of the tube? **about 0.013 or 1.3%**

Toothpaste Survey Results

Gridded Response

74. Find the value of 7!. **5040**

75. What is the value of $\frac{6!}{8!}$? Give your answer as a fraction in simplest terms. **1/56**

76. What is the value of ${}_7C_2$? **21**

77. Find the value of $(3 + 2)! - (4 - 2)!$. **118**

78. How many ways are there to select 25 books from a collection of 27 books? **351**

79. What is the value of the sum $\frac{2!}{3!} + \frac{3!}{4!} + \frac{4!}{5!}$? Express your answer to three decimal places. **.783**

80. A box has 10 items, and you select 3 of them. What is the value of $P - C$, if P represents the number of permutations possible when selecting 3 of the items, and C is the number of combinations possible when selecting 3 of the items? **600**

Checkpoint Quiz

Use this Checkpoint Quiz to check students' understanding of the skills and concepts of Lessons 6-4 through 6-7.

Resources
Grab & Go
• Checkpoint Quiz 2

 for Help

Lesson 6-6

81. For the equation $12x^3 - 17x^2 + 3x + 2 = 0$, find the number of complex roots, the possible number of real roots, and the possible rational roots. **See margin p. 350.**

82. Find all the zeros of the function $f(x) = x^3 - 2x^2 + 6x - 12$. **2, $\pm i\sqrt{6}$**

Lesson 6-1

Write each polynomial in standard form. Then classify it by degree and by number of terms. **83–88. See margin p. 350.**

83. $-3x^2 + 6 - x^3$ **84.** $2(x-1)^2 + 6$ **85.** $t^2 - 3t + 4t^2$

86. $-100 + x^4$ **87.** $x(x+2)(x-2)$ **88.** $(t^2 - t)^2$

Lesson 5-4

Factor each expression completely.

89. $4x^2 - 8x + 4$ **90.** $-x^2 - 6x - 9$ **91.** $3x^2 - 75$
$4(x-1)^2$ $-(x+3)^2$ $3(x-5)(x+5)$

Lesson 5-2

Determine whether the function has a maximum or minimum value. Then find the value.

92. $y = x^2 + 4x - 8$ **93.** $y = -2x^2 + 5x + 1$ **94.** $y = 4x^2 - 7$
minimum; −12 maximum; 4.125 minimum; −7

Checkpoint Quiz 2 **Lessons 6-4 through 6-7**

Solve each equation.

1. $x^3 - 2x^2 = 5x - 6$ **2.** $27x^3 - 1 = 0$ **3.** $x^4 - 4x^2 - 45 = 0$
1, 3, −2 $\frac{1}{3}, \frac{-1 \pm i\sqrt{3}}{6}$ $\pm 3, \pm i\sqrt{5}$

Use the Rational Root Theorem to find all the roots of each equation.

4. $2x^3 + x^2 + x - 1 = 0$ $\frac{1}{2}, \frac{-1 \pm i\sqrt{3}}{2}$ **5.** $3x^3 + 4x^2 - 12x - 16 = 0$
$-2, 2, -\frac{4}{3}$

6. Two roots of a polynomial equation with real coefficients are $3 - 5i$ and $\sqrt{2}$.
   a. Find two additional roots. **$3 + 5i$, $-\sqrt{2}$**
   b. Describe the degree of the polynomial. **Degree must be ≥ 4.**

7. How many roots does a fifth-degree polynomial equation have? Explain.
   5; by the corollary to the Fundamental Theorem of Algebra

8. Evaluate each expression.
   a. $_4P_3 + _6P_5$ **744** **b.** $_4C_3 + _6C_5$ **10**

 9. Food Preparation The students at a culinary arts school are learning to prepare seven different items. In how many ways can you choose each number of items?
   a. two items **21** **b.** three items **35** **c.** four items **35** **d.** five items **21**

10. Advertising Use the ad and the telephone keypad shown below. Find the last seven digits of this phone number. How many seven-number arrangements can be made with these digits? **5040**

351

Students use a geometric pattern to develop Pascal's Triangle. Pascal's Triangle is used in Lesson 6-8 to expand binomials being raised to a power.

Guided Instruction

The numbers at the middle of the triangle quickly become too large to conveniently count the number of paths on the grid. Students may become frustrated as the number of paths increases and the paths become more complex. Help students see that the total number of paths to a given corner in the grid is the sum of the number of paths to the corner directly above the given corner and the corner to the left of the given corner.

Error Prevention!

Students may miscount the number of ways to move to different points because they fail to move right first and then down. Students may not realize that they can move right on the top line of the grid. Demonstrate on the board the different number of ways to reach points B3 and D2 from point A1 to help students count properly.

Resources

Grid paper, markers or colored pencils

Activity Lab

Pascal's Triangle

FOR USE WITH LESSON 6-8

Suppose you are standing at the corner of the grid shown below (point A1). You are allowed to travel down or to the right only.

The only way you can get to point A2 is by traveling down one unit. You can get to point B1 by traveling to the right one unit. The numbers of ways you can get to points A2, B1, and B2 are written next to these points.

6. Answers may vary. Sample: The outer edges are all ones. Row 2 and Column B are consecutive positive integers. The number of paths counted at any point equals the sum of the paths counted at the points one unit above and one unit to the left.

1. The number 2 is written next to point B2. What are the two different ways you can get from point A1 to point B2? **From A1 to A2 to B2 or from A1 to B1 to B2**

2. Copy the grid. Travel only down or to the right. In how many ways can you get from point A1 to point A3? **1**

3. Use your copy of the grid from Exercise 2. In how many ways can you get from point A1 to point C2? **3**

4. In how many ways can you get to the fountain at point E6 from your starting point at A1? **126**

5. Mark the number of ways you can get to each point from point A1. **See back of book.**

6. **Reasoning** Describe any patterns you see in the numbers on the grid. **See above.**

7. **a.** Make a copy of your completed grid. Color the numbers that are multiples of 2. (You may need to extend the grid to see a pattern.) **a–b. See back of book.**
   b. The pattern you see in part (a) is called the Sierpinski triangle. Find another way to describe how to obtain this pattern.

 8. **Writing** The completed grid is called Pascal's Triangle. Rotate your copy of the grid 45° clockwise so that point A1 is at the top. Explain why the grid is called a triangle.
   Answers may vary. Sample: The numbers in the grid form a triangular shape.

The Binomial Theorem

What You'll Learn

• To use Pascal's Triangle

• To use the Binomial Theorem

. . . And Why

To find probabilities associated with basketball, as in Example 4

✓ Check Skills You'll Need

GO for Help   Lessons 5-1 and 6-7

Multiply.

1. $(x + 2)^2$ **2.** $(2x + 3)^2$ **3.** $(x - 3)^3$ **4.** $(a + b)^4$
$x^2 + 4x + 4$ $4x^2 + 12x + 9$ $x^3 - 9x^2 + 27x - 27$

Evaluate.

5. $_5C_0$ 1   **6.** $_5C_1$ 5   **7.** $_5C_2$ 10   **8.** $_5C_3$ 10   **9.** $_5C_4$ 5

🔊 **New Vocabulary**   • expand   • Pascal's Triangle   • Binomial Theorem

4. $a^4 + 4a^3b + 6a^2b^2 + 4ab^3 + b^4$

Objectives

1 To use Pascal's Triangle
2 To use the Binomial Theorem

Examples

1 Using Pascal's Triangle
2 Expanding a Binomial
3 Using the Binomial Theorem
4 Real-World Connection

Math Background

The expansion of $(a + b)^n$ is given by adding together multiples of all possible terms of the form $a^{n-k}b^k$, for any integer k where $0 \le k \le n$. The coefficient of each term is given by $_nC_k$. This is also the number of ways of getting a term of the form $a^{n-k}b^k$.

More Math Background: p. 304D

---

1   Binomial Expansion and Pascal's Triangle

You have learned to multiply binomials using the FOIL method and the Distributive Property. If you are raising a *single* binomial to a power, you have another option for finding the product.

Consider the expansion of several binomials. To **expand** a binomial being raised to a power, first multiply; then write the result as a polynomial in standard form.

$(a + b)^2 = (a + b)(a + b) = a^2 + 2ab + b^2$

$(a + b)^3 = (a + b)(a + b)(a + b) = a^3 + 3a^2b + 3ab^2 + b^3$

In the first case, the coefficients of the product are 1, 2, 1. In the second case, they are 1, 3, 3, 1. Notice that each set of coefficients matches a row of **Pascal's Triangle** below. Pascal's Triangle is a triangular array of numbers formed by first lining the border with 1's, and then placing the sum of two adjacent numbers within a row between and underneath the two original numbers.

Coefficients of an Expansion (Pascal's Triangle)

$(a + b)^0$ ──────────────→   1

$(a + b)^1$ ──────────────→   1   1

$(a + b)^2$ ─────────────→   1   2   1

$(a + b)^3$ ────────────→   1   3   3   1

$(a + b)^4$ ───────────→   1   4   6   4   1

$(a + b)^5$ ───→   1   5   10   10   5   1

Real-World 🌐 **Connection**

In addition to his famous triangle, Pascal made many contributions to math, physics, and philosophy. In 1642 he built the first mechanical digital calculating machine.

The earliest known version of Pascal's Triangle was developed between 300 and 200 B.C. by the Indian mathematician Halayudha. Although other cultures were aware of the triangle, it has been named for Blaise Pascal (1623−1662), a French mathematician.

Each row of Pascal's Triangle contains coefficients for the expansion of $(a + b)^n$. For example, when $n = 6$, you can find the coefficients for the expansion of $(a + b)^6$ in the row that begins 1, 6, 15, . . .

Lesson Planning and Resources

See p. 304E for a list of the resources that support this lesson.

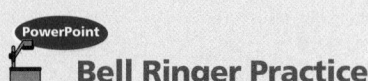

🔊 Bell Ringer Practice

✓ Check Skills You'll Need

For intervention, direct students to:

Permutations and Combinations
Lesson 6-7: Example 3
Extra Skills and Word
   Problems Practice, Ch. 6

Modeling Data With Quadratic Functions
Lesson 5-1: Example 1
Extra Skills and Word
   Problems Practice, Ch. 5

Differentiated Instruction   **Solutions for All Learners**

Special Needs L1
Have students copy Pascal's triangle on a sheet of paper. Have them draw diagonal lines separating each set of diagonal numbers. Extend the diagonals to leave room for at least five more rows.

learning style: visual

Below Level L2
Combination notation is not essential to the Binomial Theorem. Have students check that the fifth row of Pascal's Triangle corresponds to $_5C_0$, $_5C_1$, and so on.

learning style: verbal

2. Teach

Guided Instruction

1 EXAMPLE Teaching Tip

Point out the symmetry in the string of coefficients. When the exponents of *a* and *b* are interchanged, the coefficients remain the same.

PowerPoint

Additional Examples

1 Use Pascal's Triangle to expand $(a + b)^5$. $a^5 + 5a^4b + 10a^3b^2 + 10a^2b^3 + 5ab^4 + b^5$

2 Use Pascal's Triangle to expand $(x - 3)^4$.
$x^4 - 12x^3 + 54x^2 - 108x + 81$

Guided Instruction

3 EXAMPLE Technology Tip

To calculate the coefficients quickly without referring to Pascal's Triangle, enter Y1= 4 nCr X on the Y= list. Press [2nd] [TBLSET], use TblStart = 0 and ▵Tbl = 1. Then press [2nd] [TABLE].

PowerPoint

Additional Examples

3 Use the Binomial Theorem to expand $(x - y)^9$. $x^9 - 9x^8y + 36x^7y^2 - 84x^6y^3 + 126x^5y^4 - 126x^4y^5 + 84x^3y^6 - 36x^2y^7 + 9xy^8 - y^9$

4 Refer to Example 4. Find the probability that Dawn Staley makes exactly 7 out of 12 consecutive free throws.
about 0.38%

Resources

• Daily Notetaking Guide 6-8 **L3**

Closure

Ask: *What is the coefficient of $a^{n-k}b^k$ in the binomial expansion of $(a + b)^n$?* $_nC_k$

Pascal's Triangle

```
              1
            1   1
          1   2   1
        1   3   3   1
      1   4   6   4   1
    1   5  10  10   5   1
  1   6  15  20  15  (6)  1
1   7  21 (35  35) 21   7   1
1   8  28  56  70  56  28   8   1
```

1 EXAMPLE Using Pascal's Triangle

Use Pascal's Triangle to expand $(a + b)^6$.

Use the row that has 6 as its second number.

The exponents for *a* begin with 6 and decrease to 0. ⌐

$$1a^6b^0 + 6a^5b^1 + 15a^4b^2 + 20a^3b^3 + 15a^2b^4 + 6a^1b^5 + 1a^0b^6$$

The exponents for *b* begin with 0 and increase to 6. ⌐

In simplest form, the expansion is
$a^6 + 6a^5b + 15a^4b^2 + 20a^3b^3 + 15a^2b^4 + 6ab^5 + b^6$.

✓ Quick Check 1 Use Pascal's Triangle to expand $(a + b)^8$.
$a^8 + 8a^7b + 28a^6b^2 + 56a^5b^3 + 70a^4b^4 + 56a^3b^5 + 28a^2b^6 + 8ab^7 + b^8$

Sometimes the terms of the binomial have coefficients other than 1. You can still base the expansion to standard form on the pattern for $(a + b)^n$.

2 EXAMPLE Expanding a Binomial

Use Pascal's Triangle to expand $(x - 2)^3$.

First write the pattern for raising a binomial to the third power.

$$\begin{array}{cccc} 1 & 3 & 3 & 1 \\ \downarrow & \downarrow & \downarrow & \downarrow \end{array} \quad \text{coefficients from Pascal's Triangle}$$

$(a + b)^3 = a^3 + 3a^2b + 3ab^2 + b^3$

Since $(x - 2)^3 = (x + (-2))^3$, substitute *x* for *a* and -2 for *b*.

$(x + (-2))^3 = x^3 + 3x^2(-2) + 3x(-2)^2 + (-2)^3$

$\qquad\qquad = x^3 - 6x^2 + 12x - 8$

The expansion of $(x - 2)^3$ is $x^3 - 6x^2 + 12x - 8$.

✓ Quick Check 2 Use Pascal's Triangle to expand $(x - 2)^4$. $x^4 - 8x^3 + 24x^2 - 32x + 16$

---

2 The Binomial Theorem

You can also use combinations to help find the terms of a binomial expansion. For example, if you evaluate the combinations $_4C_0, _4C_1, _4C_2, _4C_3$, and $_4C_4$, you can see a pattern. The results, 1, 4, 6, 4, and 1 match the row of Pascal's Triangle that you would use to expand $(a + b)^4$. You can use the **Binomial Theorem** as a general formula for expanding a binomial.

Key Concepts

Theorem	Binomial Theorem
For every positive integer n, $(a + b)^n =$ $_nC_0a^n + {}_nC_1a^{n-1}b + {}_nC_2a^{n-2}b^2 + \ldots + {}_nC_{n-1}ab^{n-1} + {}_nC_nb^n$	

Notice that the sequence of exponents decreases for *a* while it increases for *b*.

Differentiated Instruction Solutions for All Learners

Advanced Learners **L4**
Have students use the binomial theorem to write the seventh entry in the tenth row of Pascal's triangle.

learning style: verbal

English Language Learners **ELL**
Invite a volunteer to explain to the class what a *free throw* is and when it is awarded. Clarify that only 1 or 2 free throws are awarded at any given moment, and the 10 consecutive free throws discussed happen over a period of time during a game.

learning style: verbal

Graphing Calculator Hint

To evaluate a combination, use the MATH feature, the PRB menu, and the $_nC_r$ option.

Use the Binomial Theorem to expand $(g + h)^4$.

Write the pattern for raising a binomial to the fourth power.

$(a + b)^4 = {}_4C_0a^4 + {}_4C_1a^3b + {}_4C_2a^2b^2 + {}_4C_3ab^3 + {}_4C_4b^4$

Substitute g for a and h for b. Evaluate each combination.

$(g + h)^4 = {}_4C_0g^4 + {}_4C_1g^3h + {}_4C_2g^2h^2 + {}_4C_3gh^3 + {}_4C_4h^4$
$= g^4 + 4g^3h + 6g^2h^2 + 4gh^3 + h^4$

● The expansion of $(g + h)^4$ is $g^4 + 4g^3h + 6g^2h^2 + 4gh^3 + h^4$.

 Quick Check ❸ Use the Binomial Theorem to expand each binomial.
 a. $(v + w)^9$
 b. $(c - 2)^5$ $c^5 - 10c^4 + 40c^3 - 80c^2 + 80c - 32$

3a. $v^9 + 9v^8w + 36v^7w^2 + 84v^6w^3 + 126v^5w^4 + 126v^4w^5 + 84v^3w^6 + 36v^2w^7 + 9vw^8 + w^9$

You can use the Binomial Theorem to solve probability problems. Suppose an event has a probability of success p and a probability of failure q. Each term in the expansion of $(p + q)^n$ represents a probability. For example, $_{10}C_2 p^8q^2$ represents the probability of exactly eight successes in ten trials.

Real-World Connection

WNBA star Dawn Staley makes about 90% of the free throws she attempts.

❹ **EXAMPLE** Real-World Connection

Sports Refer to the photo. Assume that Dawn's probability of success on any single shot is the same as her cumulative record to date. Find the probability that she will make exactly 6 out of 10 consecutive free throws.

Since you want 6 successes (and 4 failures), use the term containing p^6q^4. This term has the coefficient $_{10}C_4$.

Probability (6 out of 10) $= {}_{10}C_4p^6q^4$
$= \frac{10!}{4! \cdot 6!} \cdot (0.9)^6(0.1)^4$ **The probability p of success = 90%, or 0.9.**

$= 0.011160261$ **Simplify.**

Dawn Staley has about a 1% chance of making exactly 6 out of 10 consecutive free throws.

 Quick Check ❹ **a.** Find the probability that Dawn Staley will make exactly 9 out of 10 consecutive free throw attempts. **about 0.387**
 b. Find the probability that she will make exactly 10 out of 10 attempts. **about 0.349**

EXERCISES

For more exercises, see *Extra Skill and Word Problem Practice*.

Practice and Problem Solving

3–6. See back of book.

 A Practice by Example

Examples 1 and 2
(page 354)

GO for Help

Use Pascal's Triangle to expand each binomial. 7–12. See margin.

1. $(a + b)^3$ $a^3 + 3a^2b + 3ab^2 + b^3$ **2.** $(x - y)^2$ $x^2 - 2xy + y^2$ **3.** $(a + b)^4$
4. $(x - y)^5$ **5.** $(a - b)^6$ **6.** $(x - y)^7$
7. $(x + y)^8$ **8.** $(d + 1)^9$ **9.** $(x - 3)^3$
10. $(a + 3b)^4$ **11.** $(x - 2)^6$ **12.** $(x - 4)^8$

3. Practice

Assignment Guide

❶ A B 1-12, 23-42, 59

❷ A B 13-22, 43-58, 60-64
C Challenge   65-68

Test Prep   69-74
Mixed Review   75-85

Homework Quick Check

To check students' understanding of key skills and concepts, go over Exercises 11, 21, 43, 46, 58, 59, 60.

Error Prevention!

Exercises 2–12 Suggest students make sure each binomial is written in the form $(a + b)$ before using Pascal's Triangle to write the expansion.

Differentiated Instruction Resources

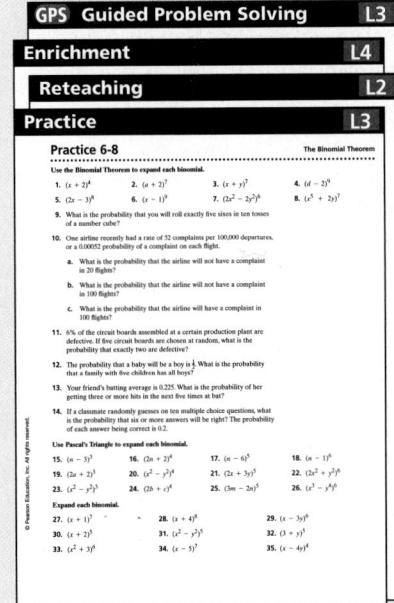

GPS Guided Problem Solving   L3
Enrichment   L4
Reteaching   L2
Practice   L3

7. $x^8 + 8x^7y + 28x^6y^2 + 56x^5y^3 + 70x^4y^4 + 56x^3y^5 + 28x^2y^6 + 8xy^7 + y^8$

8. $d^9 + 9d^8 + 36d^7 + 84d^6 + 126d^5 + 126d^4 + 84d^3 + 36d^2 + 9d + 1$

9. $x^3 - 9x^2 + 27x - 27$

10. $a^4 + 12a^3b + 54a^2b^2 + 108ab^3 + 81b^4$

11. $x^6 - 12x^5 + 60x^4 - 160x^3 + 240x^2 - 192x + 64$

12. $x^8 - 32x^7 + 448x^6 - 3584x^5 + 17,920x^4 - 57,344x^3 + 114,688x^2 - 131,072x + 65,536$

4. Assess & Reteach

Lesson Quiz

Use Pascal's Triangle to expand each binomial.

1. $(x - y^5)^3$
$x^3 - 3x^2y^5 + 3xy^{10} - y^{15}$

2. $(2a + b)^5$
$32a^5 + 80a^4b + 80a^3b^2$
$+ 40a^2b^3 + 10ab^4 + b^5$

3. Use the Binomial Theorem to expand $(3x - 2y)^4$.
$81x^4 - 216x^3y + 216x^2y^2 -$
$96xy^3 + 16y^4$

4. What is the coefficient of a^4b^6 in the expansion of $(a + b)^{10}$? **210**

Alternative Assessment

Have students work in groups of three or four. A student names two whole numbers greater than 2 and less than 10. Suppose the numbers are h and k. All students in the group find the coefficient of $a^h b^k$ in the expansion of $(a + b)^{h + k}$. Students check one another's work and correct errors, if any. Another student picks a different pair of whole numbers, and the activity continues as before, until each student has had two turns selecting a pair of whole numbers for the group to use.

13. $x^4 + 4x^3y + 6x^2y^2 + 4xy^3$
$+ y^4$

14. $w^5 + 5w^4 + 10w^3 + 10w^2$
$+ 5w + 1$

15. $s^2 - 2st + t^2$

16. $x^6 - 6x^5 + 15x^4 - 20x^3$
$+ 15x^2 - 6x + 1$

17. $x^4 - 4x^3y + 6x^2y^2 - 4xy^3$
$+ y^4$

18. $p^7 + 7p^6q + 21p^5q^2$
$+ 35p^4q^3 + 35p^3q^4$
$+ 21p^2q^5 + 7pq^6 + q^7$

19. $x^5 - 15x^4 + 90x^3 - 270x^2$
$+ 405x - 243$

20. $64 - 48x + 12x^2 - x^3$

356

Example 3
(page 355)

Use the Binomial Theorem to expand each binomial. 13–20. See margin.

13. $(x + y)^4$
14. $(w + 1)^5$
15. $(s - t)^2$
16. $(x - 1)^6$
17. $(x - y)^4$
18. $(p + q)^7$
19. $(x - 3)^5$
20. $(4 - x)^3$

Example 4
(page 355)

21. **Probability** A coin is tossed ten times. The probability of heads on each toss is 0.5. Evaluate each probability.
   a. exactly 5 heads **about 25%**
   b. exactly 6 heads **about 21%**
   c. exactly 7 heads **about 12%**

22. A calculator contains four batteries. With normal use, each battery has a 90% chance of lasting for one year. Find the probability that all four batteries will last a year. **about 66%**

B Apply Your Skills

Expand each binomial. 23–42. See margin pp. 356–357.

23. $(x + y)^7$
24. $(x - 5y)^8$
25. $(3x - y)^4$
26. $(x - 4y)^5$
27. $(7 - 2x)^6$
28. $(2x + 3y)^3$
29. $(x^2 + y^2)^2$
30. $(x^2 - 2y)^3$
31. $(x + 1)^6$
32. $(x - 1)^6$
33. $(x + 2)^5$
34. $(x - 2)^5$
35. $(2x + 3y)^4$
36. $(3x + 5y)^3$
37. $(2x - 2y)^6$
38. $(3x + 2y)^4$
39. $(2x + y)^5$
40. $(3x + y)^7$
41. $(x - 3y)^6$
42. $(x + 5y)^3$

54. $-823,680x^8y^7$
55. $314,928x^7$
56. $29,568x^{10}y^6$
57. $1716x^{12}y^{14}$

43. **Genetics** A family has five children. Assume that the probability of having a boy is 0.5. Write the term in the expansion of $(b + g)^5$ for each outcome described. Then evaluate each probability.
   a. exactly 3 boys **about 31%**
   b. exactly 4 boys **about 16%**
   c. exactly 4 girls **about 16%**

44. In the expansion of $(m + n)^9$, one of the terms contains m^3.
   a. What is the exponent of n in this term? **6**
   b. What is the coefficient of this term? **84**

45. Suppose $_8C_3x^5y^3$ is a term of a binomial expansion. Write the next term. $_8C_4x^4y^4$

46. The term $126c^4d^5$ appears in the expansion of $(c + d)^n$. Find n. **9**

47. The coefficient of the second term in the expansion of $(r + s)^n$ is 7. Find the value of n, and write the complete term. **7, $7r^6s$**

Find the specified term of each binomial expansion.

48. Third term of $(x + 3)^{12}$ **$594x^{10}$**
49. Fourth term of $(x + 2)^5$ **$80x^2$**
50. Second term of $(x + 3)^9$ **$27x^8$**
51. Third term of $(x - 2)^{12}$ **$264x^{10}$**
52. Twelfth term of $(2 + x)^{11}$ **x^{11}**
53. Seventh term of $(x - 2y)^6$ **$64y^6$**
54. Eighth term of $(x - 2y)^{15}$
55. Third term of $(3x - 2)^9$
56. Seventh term of $(x^2 - 2y)^{11}$
57. Eighth term of $(x^2 + y^2)^{13}$
   54–57. See above left.

Real-World Connection

Worldwide, about 51.4% of babies born are male.

60. The exponent of q should be 5 because the exponent of q should be the degree (7) minus the exponent of p.

GO Online
Homework Video Tutor
Visit: PHSchool.com
Web Code: age-0608

58. **Writing** Explain why the terms of $(a - 4)^6$ have alternating positive and negative signs. See margin p. 357.

59. **Geometry** A cube has sides of length s. Suppose each of the dimensions of the cube is increased by 0.5.
   a. Write a binomial expression for the volume of the new cube. **$(s + 0.5)^3$**
   b. Expand the binomial. **$s^3 + 1.5s^2 + 0.75s + 0.125$**

60. **Error Analysis** A student claims that $_7C_5p^2q^4$ is a term in a binomial expansion. Explain the student's error. **See left.**

356 Chapter 6 Polynomials and Polynomial Functions

23. $x^7 + 7x^6y + 21x^5y^2$
$+ 35x^4y^3 + 35x^3y^4$
$+ 21x^2y^5 + 7xy^6 + y^7$

24. $x^8 - 40x^7y + 700x^6y^2$
$- 7000x^5y^3 + 43,750x^4y^4$
$- 175,000x^3y^5 + 437,500x^2y^6$
$- 625,000xy^7 + 390,625y^8$

25. $81x^4 - 108x^3y + 54x^2y^2$
$- 12xy^3 + y^4$

26. $x^5 - 20x^4y + 160x^3y^2$
$- 640x^2y^3 + 1280xy^4$
$- 1024y^5$

State the number of terms in each expansion and give the first two terms.

61. $(d + e)^{12}$ **62.** $(x - y)^{15}$ **63.** $(2a + b)^5$ **64.** $(x - 3y)^7$

 Challenge

61. 13, d^{12}, $12d^{11}e$

62. 16, x^{15}, $-15x^{14}y$

63. 6, $32a^5$, $80a^4b$

64. 8, x^7, $-21x^6y$

65. a. Expand $(1 + i)^4$.   **−4**
     b. Verify that $1 - i$ is a fourth root of -4 by repeating the process in part (a) for $(1 - i)^4$. $(1 - i)^4 = 1 - 4i - 6 + 4i + 1 = -4$ ✓   **See margin.**

66. Verify that $-1 + \sqrt{3}i$ is a cube root of 8 by expanding $(-1 + \sqrt{3}i)^3$.

67. Open-Ended Write a probability problem for which $_5C_3(0.5)^2(0.5)^3$ is the solution. **See back of book.**

68. a. Show that $(k + 1)! = (k + 1) \cdot k!$. **a–c. See back of book.**
     b. Show that $_nC_k + {_nC_{k + 1}} = {_{n + 1}C_{k + 1}}$.
     c. Suppose $n = 4$ and $k = 2$. What entries in Pascal's Triangle are represented by $_nC_k, {_nC_{k + 1}}$, and $_{n + 1}C_{k + 1}$? Verify that the equation in part (b) is true for these entries.

Test Prep

Multiple Choice

69. What is the expanded form of $(a - b)^3$?   **D**
     A. $a^3 + a^2b + ab^2 + b^3$ **B.** $a^3 + 3a^2b + 3ab^2 + b^3$
     C. $a^3 - a^2b + ab^2 - b^3$ **D.** $a^3 - 3a^2b + 3ab^2 - b^3$

70. What is the third term in the expansion of $(a - b)^7$?   **J**
     F. $-21a^5b^2$ **G.** $-7a^6b$ **H.** $7a^6b$ **J.** $21a^5b^2$

71. What is the coefficient of the third term in the expansion of $(2a - b)^5$?   **D**
     A. -80 **B.** 32   **C.** 40   **D.** 80

72. Which term in the expansion of $(2a - 3b)^6$ has coefficient 2160?   **G**
     F. second term   **G.** third term
     H. fourth term   **J.** fifth term

Short Response

73. One term of a binomial expansion is $_7C_2x^5y^2$. What is the term just before that term? **See back of book.**

Extended Response

74. Explain how you can use the Binomial Theorem to find the sixth term in the expansion of $(2x - 3y)^7$. **See back of book.**

Mixed Review

 for Help

Lesson 6-7   **Simplify each expression.**

75. $_5P_2$ 20   **76.** 4!   24   **77.** $_7C_3$ 35

78. 11!   39,916,800   **79.** $\dfrac{7!}{3!(7 - 3)!}$ 35   **80.** $_5C_2 + {_5C_3}$ 20

Lesson 6-2   **Find the relative maximum, relative minimum, and zeros of each function.**

81. $f(x) = x^3 - 2x^2 - 11x + 12$ **82.** $f(x) = -x^3 - x^2 + 25x + 25$
     20.75; −12.60; −3, 1, 4   65.67; −32.49; −5, −1, 5

Lesson 5-3   **Write each function in vertex form.**

83. $y = x^2 - 6x + 2$ **84.** $y = x^2 + 7x - 1$ **85.** $y = -4x^2 + 9$
     $y = (x - 3)^2 - 7$ $y = (x + 3.5)^2 - 13.25$ $y = -4(x - 0)^2 + 9$

Online lesson quiz, PHSchool.com, Web Code: aga-0608   Lesson 6-8   The Binomial Theorem   **357**

---

27. $117{,}649 - 201{,}684x + 144{,}060x^2 - 54{,}880x^3 + 11{,}760x^4 - 1344x^5 + 64x^6$

28. $8x^3 + 36x^2y + 54xy^2 + 27y^3$

29. $x^4 + 2x^2y^2 + y^4$

30. $x^6 - 6x^4y + 12x^2y^2 - 8y^3$

31. $x^6 + 6x^5 + 15x^4 + 20x^3 + 15x^2 + 6x + 1$

32. $x^6 - 6x^5 + 15x^4 - 20x^3 + 15x^2 - 6x + 1$

33. $x^5 + 10x^4 + 40x^3 + 80x^2 + 80x + 32$

34. $x^5 - 10x^4 + 40x^3 - 80x^2 + 80x - 32$

Test Prep

Resources
For additional practice with a variety of test item formats:
- Standardized Test Prep, p. 363
- Test-Taking Strategies, p. 358
- Test-Taking Strategies with Transparencies

35. $16x^4 + 96x^3y + 216x^2y^2 + 216xy^3 + 81y^4$

36. $27x^3 + 135x^2y + 225xy^2 + 125y^3$

37. $64x^6 - 384x^5y + 960x^4y^2 - 1280x^3y^3 + 960x^2y^4 - 384xy^5 + 64y^6$

38. $81x^4 + 216x^3y + 216x^2y^2 + 96xy^3 + 16y^4$

39. $32x^5 + 80x^4y + 80x^3y^2 + 40x^2y^3 + 10xy^4 + y^5$

40. $2187x^7 + 5103x^6y + 5103x^5y^2 + 2835x^4y^3 + 945x^3y^4 + 189x^2y^5 + 21xy^6 + y^7$

41. $x^6 - 18x^5y + 135x^4y^2 - 540x^3y^3 + 1215x^2y^4 - 1458xy^5 + 729y^6$

42. $x^3 + 15x^2y + 75xy^2 + 125y^3$

58. Answers may vary. Sample: Since one of the terms is negative and it is alternately raised to odd and even powers, the term is negative when raised to an odd power and positive when raised to an even power.

66. $(-1 + \sqrt{3} \cdot i)^3 = -1 + 3i\sqrt{3} + 9 - 3i\sqrt{3} = 8$ ✓

Drawing a Diagram

This feature demonstrates to students how drawing a diagram can help them solve problems that would otherwise be very complex.

Guided Instruction

1 EXAMPLE Teaching Tip

Students may be tempted to use the INTERSECT function of the graphing calculator to find the real solution to this problem. They only need to know the *number* of real and complex solutions.

Tactile Learners

Suggest students use manipulatives as an alternative to drawing diagrams for Example 2. Students could use blue beads to represent the people, and green beads to indicate whether the person is president or vice-president.

Resources

SAT® and ACT® correlations are on page 236B.

Test-Taking Strategies with Transparencies
• Transparency 7
• Practice sheet p. 30

Test-Taking Strategies with Transparencies

Test-Taking Strategy: Drawing a Diagram

If a test problem does not already have a diagram, you can draw one.

$A(-1, 3)$, $B(3, 3)$, $C(3, -2)$, and $D(-1, -2)$ are the vertices of rectangle $ABCD$. What is the area of this rectangle?

It is difficult to compute the side lengths of this rectangle because some of the coordinates are negative. Draw a diagram of rectangle $ABCD$ on a coordinate grid to find the side lengths.

With the diagram, it is easy to see that the width of the rectangle is 5 and the length is 4. Since $A = \ell w$, the area is 5×4 or 20 square units.

Practice drawing diagrams to solve these problems.

1. $Q(-2, -3)$, $R(1, 1)$, and $S(3, -3)$ are the vertices of triangle QRS. What is the area of this triangle?

2. If $X(-2, -3)$ is the center of a circle that has a radius of 3, which of these points lies on the circle?

   A. $(1, 0)$ B. $(0, 1)$ C. $(-1, 4)$ D. $(-8, 1)$

Solutions

1. 10 square units

2. B

Transparency 6

358

 Test-Taking Strategies · Drawing a Diagram

A picture or a graph can help you solve a problem. If a test problem does not already have a diagram, you can draw one.

1 EXAMPLE

How many real and how many imaginary solutions does the equation $x^5 = x + 1$ have?

The question asks for the number of solutions, not the solutions themselves. Graph $y_1 = x^5$ and $y_2 = x + 1$. There is just one point of intersection. So the equation has just one real solution. Since the related function $y = x^5 - x - 1$ is a fifth-degree function with five zeros, the other four solutions must be imaginary.

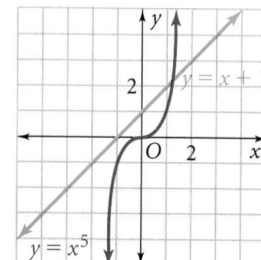

● The equation $x^5 = x + 1$ has one real and four imaginary solutions.

2 EXAMPLE

In how many ways can a president, vice-president, and treasurer be selected from 5 people?

Method 1 Assign titles to people. Draw 5 spaces to represent the 5 people. Assign president (P) to the first person. Then you can assign vice-president (V) to any of the remaining 4, and treasurer (T) to any of the remaining 3. There are $4 \cdot 3$, or 12, ways to assign the titles V and T, if the first person is president. Since P can be assigned to 5 people, there are $5 \cdot 12$ ways to assign the titles.

The answer is 60 ways.

Method 2 Assign people to titles. Draw 3 spaces to represent the 3 titles. Five people can be assigned to the first title, 4 to the second title, and 3 to the third title. There are $5 \cdot 4 \cdot 3$ ways to assign people to titles.

● Again, the answer is 60 ways.

EXERCISES

Find the number of real solutions.

1. $x + 3 = (x - 5)^2$ **2**

2. $x^4 = x - 10$ **0**

3. $x^3 = 5 - x$ **1**

4. In how many ways can two cars be assigned to two of six people, if no car can be assigned to more than one person, and no person can be assigned to more than one car? **30 ways**

5. Is it easier to draw a diagram that assigns 3 jobs to 3 of 100 people, or to draw a diagram that assigns 100 people to 3 jobs? Explain. **100 people to 3 jobs; it requires that only 3 spaces be drawn, rather than 100.**

358 Test-Taking Strategies Drawing a Diagram

Chapter Review

Vocabulary Review

Binomial Theorem (p. 354)
combination (p. 346)
complex conjugates (p. 338)
conjugates (p. 337)
degree (p. 307)
degree of a polynomial (p. 307)
difference of cubes (p. 328)
expand (p. 353)
Factor Theorem (p. 315)

Fundamental Theorem of Algebra
  (p. 341)
Imaginary Root Theorem (p. 338)
Irrational Root Theorem (p. 337)
multiple zero (p. 316)
multiplicity (p. 316)
n factorial (p. 345)
Pascal's Triangle (p. 353)
permutation (p. 345)
polynomial (p. 307)

polynomial function (p. 307)
Rational Root Theorem (p. 335)
relative maximum (p. 315)
relative minimum (p. 315)
Remainder Theorem (p. 323)
standard form of a polynomial (p. 307)
sum of cubes (p. 328)
synthetic division (p. 321)

Go Online
PHSchool.com

For: Vocabulary quiz
Web Code: agj-0651

Choose the correct vocabulary word or phrase to complete each sentence.

1. The exponent of the variable in a term determines its __?__. **degree**

2. The __?__ has terms written in descending order by degree. **standard form of a polynomial**

3. The number of appearances of a zero of a polynomial function describes the __?__ of that zero. **multiplicity**

4. The numbers $a + bi$ and $a - bi$ are called __?__. **complex conjugates**

5. Order is not important when counting __?__. **combinations**

Skills and Concepts

6-1 Objectives

▼ To classify polynomials (p. 306)

▼ To model data using polynomial functions (p. 308)

A **polynomial** is a monomial or a sum of monomials with whole-number exponents. The exponent of the variable in a term is the **degree** of that term. The **degree of a polynomial** is the largest degree of any term of the polynomial. When the terms of a polynomial are in descending order by degree, the polynomial is in standard form. You can classify a polynomial by the number of terms it contains or by its degree. A **polynomial function** in one variable can be written in the form $P(x) = a_n x^n + a_{n-1} x^{n-1} + \ldots + a_1 x + a_0$, where $n \geq 0$ and the coefficients $a_n, \ldots, a_0$ are complex numbers.

You can use a calculator to find cubic or quartic polynomial functions to model data, just as you have done with linear and quadratic polynomial functions.

6. $3p^3 - 2p$; cubic binomial

7. $-5x^9 + 3$; degree 9, binomial

8. $-x^5 - x^3 + x$; quintic trinomial

9. $4x^3 + 2x^2 + 2x$; cubic trinomial

10. $x^7 + x^4 - x^2 + x + 5$; degree 7, 5 terms

Write each polynomial in standard form. Then classify it by degree and by number of terms. 6–10. See left.

6. $p^3 - 2p + 2p^3$

7. $3 - 5x^9$

8. $x - x^3 - x^5$

9. $3x + 2x^2 - x + 4x^3$

10. $5 + x + x^4 - x^2 + x^7$

11. s **s; linear monomial**

12. Find both a cubic and a quartic model for the set of values. Graph each model. Compare the two models to determine which is a better fit. **See margin.**

x	1.2	1.4	1.6	1.8	2.0	2.2
y	3.1	−4.2	4.1	7.5	−8.9	10

12. cubic: $y = 62.2685x^3 - 303.194x^2 + 481.8148x - 248.522$;
quartic: $y = 984.375x^4 - 6631.481x^3 + 16{,}498.68x^2 - 17{,}954.685x + 7208.88$;

The quartic model better fits the data.

Resources

Student Edition
Extra Skills and Word Problems
  Practice, Ch. 6, p. 846
English/Spanish Glossary, p. 899
Properties and Formulas, p. 893
Table of Symbols, p. 889

Differentiated Instruction Resources

Vocabulary and Study Skills
  worksheet 6D
Spanish Vocabulary and Study
  Skills worksheet 6D
Interactive Textbook Audio
  Glossary
Online Vocabulary Quiz

Success ⚙ **Tracker™**
Online at PHSchool.com

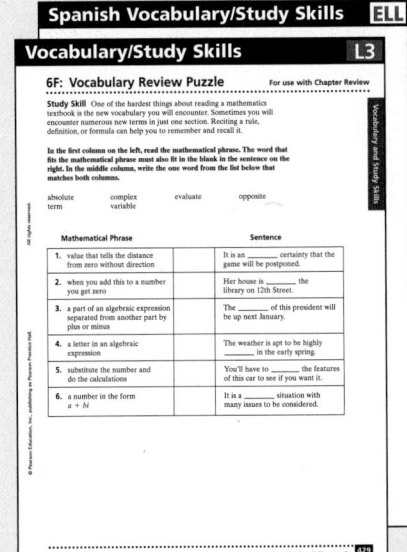

20. $x^2 + 5x + 8$, R 12; check students' work.

21. $x^3 - x^2 + x - 2$, R 4; check students' work.

34. $(x - 2)(x^2 + 2x + 4)$; 2, $-1 \pm i\sqrt{3}$

35. $t^4(2t - 1)(2t + 1)$; $0, \frac{1}{2}, -\frac{1}{2}$

36. $(2x + 1)(4x^2 - 2x + 1)$; $-\frac{1}{2}, \frac{1 \pm i\sqrt{3}}{4}$

37. $x(x - 4)(x - 1)$; 0, 1, 4

38. $x(x^2 - 2x - 5)$; $0, 1 \pm \sqrt{6}$

39. $(x + 2)^2(x^2 - 2x + 4)^2$; $-2, 1 \pm i\sqrt{3}$

6-2 and 6-3 Objectives

▼ To analyze the factored form of a polynomial (p. 313)

▼ To write a polynomial function from its zeros (p. 315)

▼ To divide polynomials using long division (p. 320)

▼ To divide polynomials using synthetic division (p. 321)

13. $f(x) = x(x - 4)(x + 3)$; $-3, 0, 4$; rel. max. $\approx$ 12.60, rel. min. $\approx$ -20.75

14. $g(x) = (2 - x)(2 + x)$; $-2, 2$; rel. max. $= 4$; no rel. min.

15. $y = x^3(x + 2)^4$; 0 (mult. 3), -2 (mult. 4); rel. max. $= 0$, rel. min. $\approx$ -1.07

16. $f(x) = x^4 + 3x^3 - 4x^2 - 12x$

17. $f(x) = x^3 - 4x^2 + 5x - 2$

18. $f(x) = x^4 + 2x^3 - 3x^2$

19. $f(x) = x^3 + 6x^2 + 12x + 8$

A polynomial can be factored into linear factors. The **Factor Theorem** states that the expression $x - a$ is a linear factor of a polynomial if and only if a is a zero of the related polynomial function. Then a is an x-intercept of the polynomial function and is a solution of the related polynomial equation.

If the zeros of a polynomial function are known, a polynomial function can be determined by finding the product of the corresponding linear factors. If $x - a$ is repeated as a factor k times, then a is a **multiple zero** of the polynomial—a zero of **multiplicity** k.

When you consider only neighboring points on a graph, the greatest y-value occurs at a **relative maximum** and the least y-value occurs at a **relative minimum**.

You can divide a polynomial by one of its factors to find another factor. When you divide by a linear factor, you can simplify this division by writing only the coefficients of each term. This process is called **synthetic division**. The **Remainder Theorem** guarantees that $P(a)$ is the remainder when $P(x)$ is divided by $x - a$.

Write each polynomial function in factored form. List the zeros of the function, and their multiplicity. Find any relative maximum or relative minimum values. Round to the nearest hundredth if necessary.

13. $f(x) = x^3 - x^2 - 12x$ **14.** $g(x) = 4 - x^2$ **15.** $y = x^3(x + 2)^4$

Write a polynomial function in standard form with the given zeros.

16. $-3, -2, 0, 2$ **17.** $1, 1, 2$ **18.** $-3, 0, 0, 1$ **19.** $-2, -2, -2$

Divide. Use both long division and synthetic division. Show your work.

20. $(x^3 + 3x^2 - 2x - 4) \div (x - 2)$ **21.** $(x^4 - x + 2) \div (x + 1)$
20–21. See margin.

Use synthetic division and the given factor to completely factor each polynomial.

22. $x^3 - 3x^2 - x + 3; x + 1$ **23.** $x^3 - 4x^2 - 3x + 18; x - 3$
$(x + 1)(x - 3)(x - 1)$ $(x - 3)^2(x + 2)$

Use synthetic division and the Remainder Theorem to find $P(a)$.

24. $P(x) = x^4 + x^3 - x^2 - 2x; a = 3$ 93 **25.** $P(x) = 4 - x - x^5; a = 2$ -30

26. $P(x) = 5x^4 - x^2 + 1; a = -2$ 77 **27.** $P(x) = x^3 - 8x^2 + 5x - 7; a = 1$ -9

6-4 Objectives

▼ To solve polynomial equations by graphing (p. 327)

▼ To solve polynomial equations by factoring (p. 328)

28. $-1, 1.38, 3.62$

29. -1.78

30. 0

You can solve polynomial equations by graphing or by factoring. The **sum of cubes** and the **difference of cubes** have factor formulas. Sometimes you can factor polynomial expressions of higher degree by rewriting the expression in the standard form of a quadratic equation.

Solve each equation by graphing. If necessary, round to the nearest hundredth.

28. $x^3 - 4x^2 + 5 = 0$ **29.** $x - 3 = 4 - x^2 + x^3$ **30.** $x^3 + x = 3x^2 - 3x^3$

31. $x^3 + x + 5 = 0$ **32.** $-5 = 2 - x^2 + x^3$ **33.** $x^3 + 4 = x^3 - 3x^2$
-1.52 -1.63 no real solution

Factor the expression on the left side of each equation. Then solve each equation.

34. $x^3 - 8 = 0$ **35.** $4t^6 - t^4 = 0$ **36.** $8x^3 + 1 = 0$

37. $x^3 - 5x^2 + 4x = 0$ **38.** $x^3 - 2x^2 - 5x = 0$ **39.** $x^6 + 16x^3 + 64 = 0$
34–39. See margin.

Alternative Assessment   L4

Alternative Assessment   C
Chapter 6

TASK 1
a. Draw the related graph of $x^2 - ax = bx - ab$. Determine the multiplicity of each root.
b. Draw the related graph of $(x - a)^2(x - b) = 0$. Determine the multiplicity of each root.
c. Rewrite the equations found in parts a and b in standard form.
d. Given the equation $ax^3 + bx^2 = -cx$, find the roots of this equation in terms of a, b, and c.

TASK 2
a. Use division to find the remaining roots of $y = \frac{1}{3}x^3 + \frac{1}{3}x^2 - 3x - 4$.

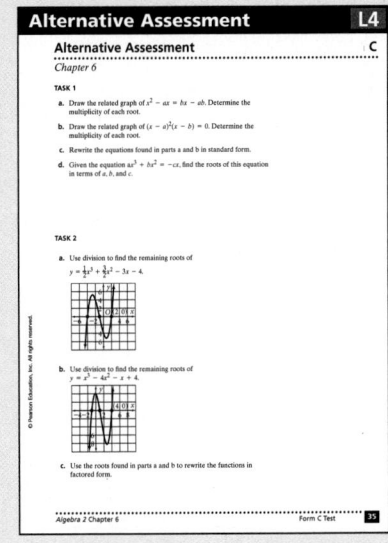

b. Use division to find the remaining roots of $y = x^3 - 4x^2 - x + 4$.

c. Use the roots found in parts a and b to rewrite the functions in factored form.

Algebra 2 Chapter 6   Form C Test   35

6-5 and 6-6 Objectives

▼ To solve equations using the Rational Root Theorem (p. 335)

▼ To use the Irrational Root Theorem and the Imaginary Root Theorem (p. 337)

▼ To use the Fundamental Theorem of Algebra (p. 341)

▼ To solve polynomial equations with complex zeros (p. 342)

The **Rational Root Theorem** identifies all possible rational roots of a polynomial equation with integer coefficients. A rational root of a polynomial equation is the quotient of a factor of the constant term and a factor of the leading coefficient.

Number pairs of the form $a + \sqrt{b}$ and $a - \sqrt{b}$ are called **conjugates,** while those of the form $a + bi$ and $a - bi$ are called **complex conjugates**. The **Irrational Root Theorem** states that irrational roots of a polynomial equation with rational coefficients occur in conjugate pairs. Similarly, the **Imaginary Root Theorem** states that imaginary roots of a polynomial equation with real coefficients occur in complex conjugate pairs.

The **Fundamental Theorem of Algebra** and its corollary assert that an nth degree polynomial equation, where $n \geq 1$, has exactly n complex roots.

For each equation, state the number of complex roots, the possible number of real roots, and the possible rational roots. Then find all the roots. 40–45. See margin.

40. $x^3 - 6x^2 + 11x - 6 = 0$

41. $10x^4 - 13x^3 - 21x^2 + 10x + 8 = 0$

42. $x^4 - 6x^2 + 7 = 0$

43. $x^4 + 6x^3 + 13x^2 + 12x + 4 = 0$

44. $x^3 - 3x^2 + x + 5 = 0$

45. $x^4 - 2x^3 - 7x^2 + 18x - 18 = 0$

Write a polynomial equation of least possible degree, with integer coefficients, that has the given numbers as roots.

46. $x^3 - 2x^2 + x - 2 = 0$

47. $x^4 - 16x^3 + 91x^2 - 216x + 182 = 0$

48. $x^4 - 10x^3 + 39x^2 - 70x + 50 = 0$

46. $2, i, -i$

47. $4 + \sqrt{2}, 4 - \sqrt{3}$

48. $3 + i, 2 - i$

49. $0, -2i, 3 + \sqrt{2}$
$x^5 - 6x^4 + 11x^3 - 24x^2 + 28x = 0$

50. $1 + 2i, 3 - \sqrt{3}$
$x^4 - 8x^3 + 23x^2 - 42x + 30 = 0$

51. $\sqrt{5}, -\sqrt{7}$
$x^4 - 12x^2 + 35 = 0$

6-7 and 6-8 Objectives

▼ To count permutations (p. 345)

▼ To count combinations (p. 346)

▼ To use Pascal's Triangle (p. 353)

▼ To use the Binomial Theorem (p. 354)

The notation $n!$, read **"n factorial,"** means $n(n - 1)(n - 2) \cdot \ldots \cdot 3 \cdot 2 \cdot 1$, and $0! = 1$.

A **permutation** is an arrangement of items in a particular order. You can count permutations using the Multiplication Counting Principle or factorial notation. To compute the number of permutations of n objects chosen r at a time, you can also use the formula $_nP_r = \frac{n!}{(n - r)!}$, for $0 \leq r \leq n$.

A selection in which order does not matter is a **combination**. The number of combinations of n objects chosen r at a time is $_nC_r = \frac{n!}{r!(n - r)!}$, for $0 \leq r \leq n$.

Use the **Binomial Theorem** to **expand** a binomial raised to a power. For $n \geq 0$,
$(a + b)^n = {}_nC_0a^n + {}_nC_1a^{n-1}b + {}_nC_2a^{n-2}b^2 + \ldots + {}_nC_{n-1}ab^{n-1} + {}_nC_nb^n$. The coefficients in the expansion of $(a + b)^n$ are found in **Pascal's Triangle.** You can also use the Binomial Theorem to find probabilities when an event has only two possible outcomes.

Evaluate each expression.

52. $3(4!)$ **72**   **53.** $_4P_3$ **24**   **54.** $_7C_4$ **35**   **55.** $_5P_2 + {}_5C_3$ **30**   **56.** $\frac{6^{C_3}}{5^{C_3}}$ **2**

57. In how many ways can you arrange 5 different canisters in a row on a shelf? **120**

58. Find the fourth term in the binomial expansion of $(2x + 3y)^6$. **$4320x^3y^3$**

59. A coin is tossed seven times. Find the probability of getting exactly four heads. **about 27%**

Chapter 6   Chapter Review   **361**

40. 3 complex roots;
number of real roots:
3 or 1;
possible rational roots:
$\pm1, \pm2, \pm3, \pm6$;
roots: 1, 2, 3

41. 4 complex roots;
number of real roots:
4, 2, or 0;
possible rational roots:
$\pm1, \pm2, \pm4, \pm8, \pm\frac{1}{2}, \pm\frac{1}{5}, \pm\frac{2}{5}, \pm\frac{4}{5}, \pm\frac{8}{5}, \pm\frac{1}{10}$;
roots: $-1, -\frac{1}{2}, \frac{4}{5}, 2$

42. 4 complex roots;
number of real roots:
4, 2, or 0;
possible rational roots:
$\pm1, \pm7$;
roots: $\pm1.26, \pm2.10$

43. 4 complex roots;
number of real roots:
4, 2, or 0;
possible rational roots:
$\pm1, \pm2, \pm4$;
roots: $-1, -2$

44. 3 complex roots;
number of real roots:
3 or 1;
possible rational roots:
$\pm1, \pm5$;
roots: $-1, 2 \pm i$

45. 4 complex roots;
number of real roots:
4, 2, or 0;
possible rational roots:
$\pm1, \pm2, \pm3, \pm6, \pm9, \pm18$;
roots: $\pm3, 1 \pm i$

Go Online
PHSchool.com
For: Chapter Test
Web Code: aga-0652

Write each polynomial in standard form. Then classify it by degree and by number of terms. 1–2. See margin.

1. $3x^2 - 7x^4 + 9 - x^4$

2. $11x^2 + \frac{3}{8}x - 3x^2$

3. $2x(x - 3)(x + 2)$ $2x^3 - 2x^2 - 12x$; **cubic trinomial**

4. $(t - 2)(t + 1)(t + 1)$
   $t^3 - 3t - 2$; **cubic trinomial**

Graph each function. Approximate the real zeros to the nearest hundredth. 5–9. See back of book.

5. $P(x) = -x^3 - x^2 + x$

6. $P(x) = (x + 1)(x + 2)(x^2 + 4x - 5)$

7. $f(x) = x^4 + 3x^3 - 1$

8. $g(x) = -x^6 - x^3 + 2$

9. $f(x) = x^3 - 3x^2 + 2$

Write a polynomial function with rational coefficients in standard form with the given zeros.

10. $x = 1, 2, \frac{3}{5}$ $y = x^3 - \frac{18}{5}x^2 + \frac{19}{5}x - \frac{6}{5}$

11. $x = -2, 0, \sqrt{3}$ $y = x^4 + 2x^3 - 3x^2 - 6x$

12. $x = -4, -4, -4$ $y = x^3 + 12x^2 + 48x + 64$

13. $x = -1, 1, 1$ $y = x^3 - x^2 - x + 1$

14. $x = \sqrt{2}, -i$ $y = x^4 - x^2 - 2$

15. $x = 3 + i, 1 - \sqrt{5}$
    $y = x^4 - 8x^3 + 18x^2 + 4x - 40$

16. **Open-Ended** Write a polynomial function with real coefficients that has an imaginary zero and an irrational zero. **See margin.**

Solve each equation. $-2, -\frac{2}{3}, \frac{7}{8}, \frac{3}{2}$

17. $(2x - 3)(3x + 2)(x + 2)(x + 2)\left(x - \frac{7}{8}\right) = 0$

18. $(x^2 - 3)(x^2 + 3x - 4) = 0$ $\pm\sqrt{3}, -4, 1$

19. $\left(x + \frac{2}{3}\right)(x^2 + 5x + 1) = 0$ $-\frac{2}{3}, \frac{-5 \pm \sqrt{21}}{2}$

20. $x^3 - 2x^2 + x = 0$ **0, 1**

21. $x^3 + 3x^2 - 5x - 4 = 0$ $\frac{1 \pm \sqrt{5}}{2}, -4$

Divide using long division.

22. $(x^2 + 3x - 4) \div (x - 1)$ $x + 4$

23. $(x^3 + 7x^2 - 5x - 6) \div (x + 2)$
    $x^2 + 5x - 15$, **R 24**

Divide using synthetic division.

24. $(3x^2 - 3x + 4) \div (x + 1)$ $3x - 6$, **R 10**

25. $(x^3 + x^2 + x - 14) \div (x + 2)$ $x^2 - x + 3$, **R −20**

Use synthetic division and the Remainder Theorem to find $P(a)$.

26. $P(x) = 6x^4 + 19x^3 - 2x^2 - 44x - 24; a = \frac{-2}{3}$ **0**

27. $P(x) = -x^3 - x^2 + x; a = 0$ **0**

28. $P(x) = 2x^3 - 2x^2 - 12x; a = 3$ **0**

29. $P(x) = x^4 + 3x^3 - 7x^2 - 9x + 12; a = 3$ **84**

30. $P(x) = x^3 + 3x^2 - 5x - 4; a = -1$ **3**

Evaluate each expression. **35. 19,958,400**

31. $6!$ **720**   32. $\frac{6!}{4!2!}$ **15**

33. $_7C_3$ **35**   34. $_5P_2$ **20**

35. $_{11}P_9$ 36. $_9C_8$ **9**

37. $2(_5C_4) - _3C_2$ **7**

Indicate whether each situation involves a combination or a permutation. Then solve.

38. How many ways are there to select five actors from a troupe of nine to improvise a scene?
    combination, 126

39. How many different three-student study groups can be formed from a class of 15? **combination, 455**

40. You are looking for a new apartment. There are five apartments available. In how many ways can you inspect the apartments? **permutation, 120**

Use the Binomial Theorem to expand each binomial.

41. $(x + z)^5$ **See margin.**   42. $(1 - 2t)^2$
    $1 - 4t + 4t^2$

43. A weighted coin has $P(\text{heads}) = \frac{2}{5}$. The coin is tossed seven times. Find the probability of getting exactly six heads. **about 1.7%**

44. **Writing** Describe how to use combinations to produce row n of Pascal's Triangle. **See margin.**

45. **Geometry** The volume V of a prism is modeled by $V = 2\ell^3 - 2\ell$, where ℓ is the length of the prism. The width of the prism equals $\ell - 1$. Find the height of the prism. $2\ell + 2$

1. $-8x^4 + 3x^2 + 9$; **quartic trinomial**

2. $8x^2 + \frac{3}{8}x$; **quadratic binomial**

16. Answers may vary.
    Sample: Using $\pm i$ and $\pm\sqrt{2}$, $y = x^4 - x^2 - 2$.

41. $x^5 + 5x^4z + 10x^3z^2 + 10x^2z^3 + 5xz^4 + z^5$

44. Combinations can be used by starting with $_nC_0$ for the first term. Then the second term would be $_nC_1$, the third $_nC_2$,

and so forth until you reach $_nC_{n-1}$, and finally $_nC_n$.

Standardized Test Prep

Multiple Choice

For Exercises 1–10, choose the correct letter.

1. For which function is 5 a zero?
A
Ⓐ $y = (x - 5)^2$ Ⓑ $y = (x + 5)^2$
Ⓒ $y = (x - 1)^2 + 5$ Ⓓ $y = (x + 1)^2 - 5$

2. The graph of which line is perpendicular to the
G graph of $y = 2x + 1$?
Ⓕ $y = \frac{1}{2}x + 7$ Ⓖ $x + 2y = 4$
Ⓗ $y = -2x - 5$ Ⓙ $x - 2y = 10$

3. What is the equation of the function $y = x^2$
B translated 3 units up and 4 units left?
Ⓐ $y = (x - 3)^2 - 4$ Ⓑ $y = (x + 4)^2 + 3$
Ⓒ $y = (x - 4)^2 + 3$ Ⓓ $y = (x + 3)^2 - 4$

4. What is the axis of symmetry of the graph of a
F quadratic function with vertex at $(5, -1)$?
Ⓕ $x = 5$ Ⓖ $x = -5$
Ⓗ $y = -1$ Ⓙ $y = 1$

5. What is the solution of the matrix equation?
B
$$\begin{bmatrix} -1 & 0 & 2 \\ -3 & 1 & 1 \\ -5 & 4 & 0 \end{bmatrix} X = \begin{bmatrix} -0 & -1 & -20 \\ -2 & -2 & -27 \\ 22 & -5 & -22 \end{bmatrix}$$

Ⓐ $\begin{bmatrix} -1 & 3 & -2 \\ -1 & 0 & -1 \\ -7 & 2 & -6 \end{bmatrix}$ Ⓑ $\begin{bmatrix} -2 & -1 & 6 \\ -3 & -0 & 2 \\ -1 & -1 & 7 \end{bmatrix}$

Ⓒ $\begin{bmatrix} -2 & 3 & 1 \\ -1 & 0 & 1 \\ -6 & 2 & 7 \end{bmatrix}$ Ⓓ $\begin{bmatrix} -2 & 0 & -7 \\ -3 & 1 & -1 \\ -1 & 2 & -6 \end{bmatrix}$

6. Which relation is NOT a function?
H
Ⓕ $y = 3\sqrt{x} - 1$ Ⓖ $y = |x - 7|$
Ⓗ $y = \pm 3x$ Ⓙ $y = 1 - x^3$

7. Which is a factor of $x^4 + 2x^3 - 3x^2 - 4x + 4$?
C   I. $x + 2$ II. $x - 1$ III. $x + 1$
Ⓐ I only   Ⓑ II only
Ⓒ I and II   Ⓓ II and III

8. Which ordered pair is a solution of this system?
J
$\begin{cases} y \leq 2x + 3 \\ y > |x + 1| \\ y < -x + 4 \end{cases}$ I. (0, 2)
          II. (1, -3)
          III. (-1, 4)
Ⓕ II and III   Ⓖ II only
Ⓗ I and II   Ⓙ I only

9. At which point is the cost function
C $C = 3x + y$ minimized for the restrictions
$x + y \geq 1, x \geq 0$, and $y \geq 0$?
Ⓐ (3, 1)   Ⓑ (1, 0)   Ⓒ (0, 1)   Ⓓ (0, 0)

10. What are the solutions of $x^3 + 4x^2 + x - 6 = 0$?
H
Ⓕ $-1, -2, 3$ Ⓖ $-1, 2, -3$
Ⓗ $1, -2, -3$ Ⓙ $-1, 2, 3$

11. Solve $|2 - 4x| + 9 < 19$.
B
Ⓐ $-3 < x < 2$ Ⓑ $-2 < x < 3$
Ⓒ $x < -3$ and $x > 2$ Ⓓ $x < -2$ and $x > 3$

12. Which expression is NOT equivalent to
F $(3 - (2 - x)) - 2(1 + x)$?
Ⓕ $1 + x$ Ⓖ $-x - 1$
Ⓗ $(1 + x) - (2 + 2x)$ Ⓙ $-(-(-1 - x))$

13. Which inequality has a graph that is shaded
A below the boundary?
Ⓐ $y < |x + 7| + 1$ Ⓑ $y + 4x > 20$
Ⓒ $x - y < -2$ Ⓓ $3y - 6x + 16 > -8$

14. For which system of equations can you eliminate
F the variable y by first multiplying one equation
by 2 and then adding the equations?
Ⓕ $\begin{cases} 3x - 4y = 7 \\ x + 2y = 9 \end{cases}$ Ⓖ $\begin{cases} 2x + 6y = 1 \\ 2x - 4y = -3 \end{cases}$
Ⓗ $\begin{cases} x + y = 2 \\ x - y = 1 \end{cases}$ Ⓙ $\begin{cases} 2.5x + 6y = 0 \\ 5x - 9y = 14 \end{cases}$

Gridded Response

15. Find 7!. **5040**

16. Find $_3P_2 - _3C_2$. **3**

17. What is the coefficient of a^2b^3 in the expansion
of $(a + b)^5$? **10**

Short Response   18–19. See back of book.

18. An employer is selecting 4 out of 30 workers as
employees of the month.
  a. Does this situation involve a combination or a
permutation? Explain.
  b. How many different selections are possible?

Extended Response

19. Open-Ended Graph a polygon. Use matrices to
find the image of the polygon after a reflection
in the x-axis followed by a rotation of 90°
counterclockwise. Show your work.

Students must be able to extract
information from reading
passages, answer multiple choice
questions, and construct responses
in order to be successful on current
state and national assessments.

Multiple Choice: Items 1–14
Gridded Response: Items 15–17
Short Response: Item 18
Extended Response: Item 18

Resources

Test Prep Workbook

Grab & Go
• **L3** Cumulative Review

ExamView CD-ROM
• Standardized Test Practice

Differentiated Instruction Resources

Progress Monitoring Assessments
• Benchmark Test
   • Test 3
• Quarter 2 Test
   • **L3** Forms A & B
   • **L2** Forms D & E
• Mid-Course Test
   • **L3** Forms A & B
   • **L2** Forms D & E

Spanish Assessment Resources
• **L3** Spanish Cumulative Review
• Spanish Quarter 2 Test
   • **L3** Forms A & B
• Spanish Mid-Course Test
   • **L3** Forms A & B

Item	1	2	3	4	5	6	7	8	9	10	11	12	13	14	15	16	17	18	19
Lesson	6-2	2-2	5-3	5-2	4-6	2-1	6-2	3-3	3-4	6-4	1-5	1-2	2-7	3-2	6-7	6-7	6-8	6-7	4-4

As the Ball Flies

In these activities students apply their knowledge of parabolas and quadratic equations.

Activating Prior Knowledge

Have students share what they know about the game of soccer, and famous soccer players. Have volunteers describe the rules and objectives of the game of soccer, including various kinds of kicks and what the various objectives for each kind of kick might be.

Guided Instruction

Have a volunteer read the introductory paragraph. Ask: *If you were not ignoring the effects of wind and air resistance, what difference might these factors make in how a player plans a kick?* **Accept all reasonable answers.**

Teaching Tip

Ask a volunteer to review, perhaps using a simple drawing on the board, what a vector represents and how vectors can show the result of two forces acting on one object.

Connection to Science

Have students research information about the gravitational constant, including comparing the force of gravity on Earth and on the moon.

Activity Lab

As the Ball Flies

Applying Quadratic Functions   Have you ever wondered how far a soccer player can kick a ball? Ignoring wind and air resistance, you can use a linear function and a quadratic function to describe the path of a soccer ball. These functions depend on two factors that are within the soccer player's control: velocity of the kick (v_k) and angle of the kick (θ). A good high-school soccer player can kick the ball at speeds ranging from 50 to 60 mi/h. A strong professional player can kick the ball at nearly 80 mi/h.

Activity 1

a. Use the information in the diagram on the facing page to calculate the horizontal and vertical velocities of a ball kicked at a 35° angle with an initial velocity of 60 mi/h. Convert the velocities to ft/s.

b. The equations $x(t) = v_x t$ and $y(t) = v_y t + 0.5gt^2$ describe the x- and y-coordinates of a soccer ball as a function of time. (The gravitational constant g is described on the facing page.) Use the second equation to calculate the time the ball will take to complete its path.

c. Use the first equation to calculate how far the ball will travel horizontally from its original position.

The Soccer Ball

The easily recognized form of a soccer ball is due to its unique combination of pentagons and hexagons.

Men's Soccer

Jurgen Klinsmann is one of Germany's most successful strikers. He led his team to the 1996 European Championship.

Activity 1

a. $v_x \approx 72.1$ ft/s,
   $v_y \approx 50.5$ ft/s

b. about 3.15 s

c. about 227.4 ft

In practice, air resistance and wind play a role in determining the ball's path, but these factors make the equations more complex.

A ball in flight follows a parabolic path.

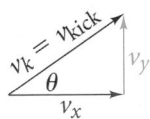

Vectors

The vectors at the left describe the initial velocity of the soccer ball as the combination of a vertical and a horizontal velocity.

$v_x = v_k \cos \theta$
$v_y = v_k \sin \theta$

Gravity

The constant g represents the acceleration of any object as a result of Earth's gravity. The value of g near the surface of Earth is about -32 ft/s^2.

Activity 2

a. Use the technique developed in Activity 1 to calculate the horizontal distance of the kick for angles in 5° increments from 5° to 90°. (You may find a spreadsheet helpful for making these calculations.)

b. Graph the horizontal distance of the kick as a function of the angle of the kick. Which angle gives the greatest distance?

Activity 3

Suppose you played soccer on the moon, where the gravitational acceleration is about one sixth of its value on Earth. What are the maximum height and maximum horizontal distance you could kick the ball by giving it an initial velocity of 48 mi/h?

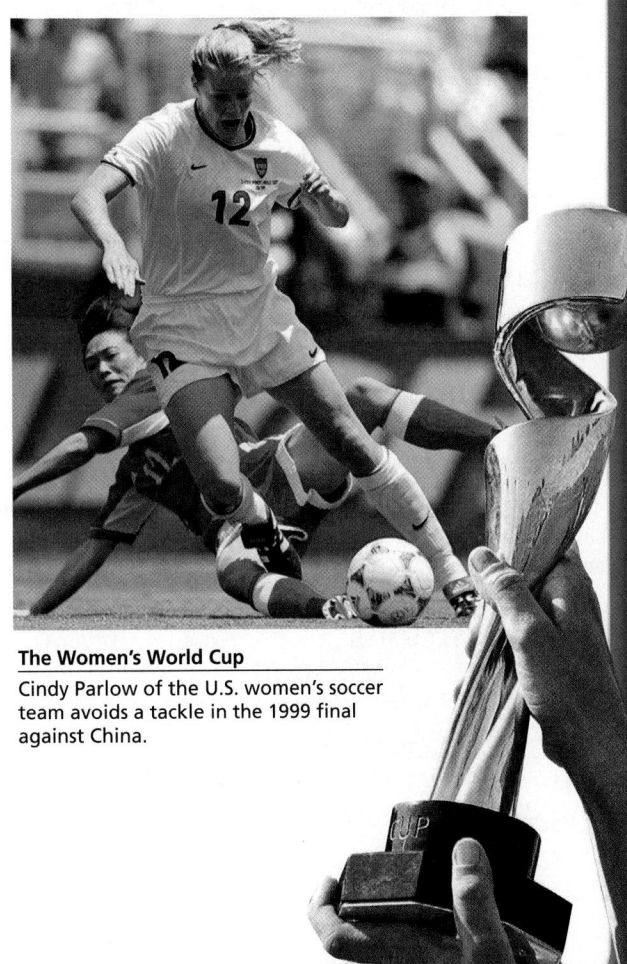

The Women's World Cup
Cindy Parlow of the U.S. women's soccer team avoids a tackle in the 1999 final against China.

Go Online
PHSchool.com

For: Information about soccer
Web Code: age-0653

365

Activity 1

Materials: paper and pencil

Special Needs   L1
Help students organize their work by estimating the form and units for each of the answers in Activity 1.

Activity 2

Materials: paper and pencil, graph paper, spreadsheet (optional)

Teaching Tip
If a spreadsheet program is not available, divide the calculations among various members of the team, or among teams and then have them combine the results.

Scoring Rubric

This scoring rubric can be used for evaluating student work on each activity. Share this scoring rubric with students before they begin work.

4 Equations and calculations (and graphs, if required) are correct.
Steps are neat, accurate, and clearly show the mathematics. Responses are clearly indicated and give the appropriate units.

3 Equations, calculations, and graphs are mostly correct, with some minor errors. Steps are neat and mostly accurate. Units are not completely accurate.

2 Equations, calculations, and graphs contain both major and minor errors.

1 Correct answer, but no work is shown.

Activity 2

a.

Angle	Distance
5	42.02
10	82.77
15	121.00
20	155.55
25	185.38
30	209.58

Angle	Distance
35	227.41
40	238.32
45	242.00
50	238.32
55	227.41
60	209.58

Angle	Distance
65	185.38
70	155.55
75	121.00
80	82.77
85	42.02
90	0.00

b.

45°

Activity 3

max. height: about 232 ft;
max. distance: about 465 ft

Radical Functions and Rational Exponents

Chapter at a Glance

Lesson Titles, Objectives, and Features	Assessment	NCTM Standards	Local Standards
Algebra 1 Review: Properties of Exponents **7-1 Roots and Radical Expressions** • Simplifying *n*th roots	Lesson Quiz	1, 2, 7, 10	
7-2 Multiplying and Dividing Radical Expressions • Multiplying radical expressions • Dividing radical expressions	Lesson Quiz	1, 2, 10	
7-3 Binomial Radical Expressions • Adding and subtracting radical expressions • Multiplying and dividing binomial radical expressions	Lesson Quiz Checkpoint Quiz 1	1, 2, 7, 10	
7-4 Rational Exponents • Simplifying expressions with rational exponents	Lesson Quiz	1, 2	
7-5 Solving Square Root and Other Radical Equations • Solving square root and other radical equations **Geometry Review:** Radical Expressions in Formulas	Lesson Quiz	1, 2, 6	
7-6 Function Operations • Adding, subtracting, multiplying, and dividing functions • Finding the composite of two functions **GPS:** Understanding Word Problems	Lesson Quiz Checkpoint Quiz 2	2, 6, 10	
7-7 Inverse Relations and Functions • Finding the inverse of a relation or function **Activity Lab:** Technology: Graphing Inverses	Lesson Quiz	1, 2, 3, 7	
7-8 Graphing Square Root and Other Radical Functions • Graphing square root and other radical functions **Activity Lab:** Technology: Radical Inequalities	Lesson Quiz	2, 9	

NCTM Standards 2000

1 Number and Operations	**2** Algebra	**3** Geometry	**4** Measurement	**5** Data Analysis and Probability
6 Problem Solving	**7** Reasoning and Proof	**8** Communication	**9** Connections	**10** Representation

Correlations to Standardized Tests

All content for these tests is contained in *Prentice Hall Algebra 2*. This chart reflects coverage in this chapter only.

	7-1	7-2	7-3	7-4	7-5	7-6	7-7	7-8
SAT®								
Number and Operations Operations, ratio & proportions, complex numbers, counting, elementary number theory, matrices, sequences	✔							
Algebra and Functions Expressions, equations, inequalities, representation and modeling, properties of functions (linear, polynomial, rational, exponential)	✔	✔	✔	✔	✔	✔	✔	✔
Geometry and Measurement *Plane Euclidean/Measurement Coordinate* Lines, parabolas, circles, symmetry, transformations *Three-dimensional* Solids, surface area & volume (cylinders, cones, pyramids, spheres, prisms) *Trigonometry* Right triangles, identities								
Data Analysis, Statistics, and Probability Mean, median, mode, range, interquartile range, graphs and plots, regression, probability								
ACT®								
Pre-Algebra Basic operations using whole numbers, decimals, fractions, and integers; place value; square roots and approximations; the concept of exponents; scientific notation; factors, ratio, proportion, and percent; linear equations in one variable; absolute value and ordering numbers by value; elementary counting techniques and simple probability; data collection, representation, and interpretation; and understanding simple descriptive statistics.								
Elementary Algebra Properties of exponents and square roots, evaluation of algebraic expressions through substitution, using variables to express functional relationships, understanding algebraic operations, and solving quadratic equations by factoring.	✔	✔	✔	✔	✔	✔	✔	✔
Intermediate Algebra Understanding of the quadratic formula, rational and radical expressions, absolute value equations and inequalities, sequences and patterns, systems of equations, quadratic inequalities, functions, modeling, matrices, roots of polynomials, and complex numbers.	✔	✔	✔	✔	✔	✔	✔	✔
Coordinate Geometry Graphing and the relations between equations and graphs, including points, lines, polynomials, circles, and other curves; graphing inequalities; slope; parallel and perpendicular lines; distance; midpoints; and conics.							✔	✔
Plane Geometry Properties and relations of plane figures, including angles and relations among perpendicular and parallel lines; properties of circles, triangles, rectangles, parallelograms, and trapezoids; transformations; the concept of proof and proof techniques; volume; and applications of geometry to three dimensions.								
Trigonometry Understanding trigonometric relations in right triangles; values and properties of trigonometric functions; graphing trigonometric functions; modeling using trigonometric functions; use of trigonometric identities; and solving trigonometric equations.								
NAEP								
Number Sense, Properties, and Operations	✔			✔				
Measurement								
Geometry and Spatial Sense								
Data Analysis, Statistics, and Probability								
Algebra and Functions	✔	✔	✔	✔	✔	✔	✔	✔

SAT® The College Board, SAT® Reasoning Test   **ACT®** The ACT Assessment® Test   **NAEP** National Assessment of Educational Progress, 2005 Mathematics Objectives

Math Background

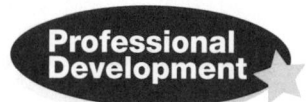

Skills Trace

BEFORE Chapter 7
In previous chapters, students solved polynomial equations, and graphed translations of functions.

DURING Chapter 7
Students perform operations on radical expressions and functions, solve square root and other radical equations, and graph transformations of square root and other radical functions.

AFTER Chapter 7
Students will graph and model data with exponential and trigonometric functions, and solve related equations.

Chapter Overview

Chapter 7 introduces nth roots of real numbers and relates them to nth powers and rational exponents. Students learn to perform operations on radical expressions, simplify radical expressions, and solve radical equations.

Operations on functions are examined, including function composition. Next, inverse relations and inverse functions are discussed. Finally, students graph radical functions.

Roots and Radical Expressions 7-1

When simplifying radical expressions, many students have difficulty with when the absolute value symbol is required and when it is not required. The distinction lies in the difference between odd and even powers. Given $\sqrt[n]{x}$ where x is positive, the expression has two values when n is a positive even number, but only one value when n is odd. To help students see that $\sqrt{x^2}$ is equal to $|x|$ rather than to x, you can ask students to graph $y = \sqrt{x^2}$, $y = |x|$, and $y = x$ and compare their graphs. They will see that the graphs of $y = \sqrt{x^2}$ and $y = |x|$ are the same.

A further complication is given by this example: $\sqrt{x^4 y^6} = x^2 |y^3|$. Notice that x and y can be either positive, negative, or zero, but both x^4 and y^6 are always nonnegative. This means $\sqrt{x^4 y^6}$ is always a nonnegative real value. So, to ensure the simplification $x^2 |y^3|$ is always a nonnegative real value, the absolute value symbol is added to y^3 because it is an odd power (and a negative value of y would result in a negative value for y^3). The x^2 is left alone because it is is an even power (and is always nonnegative).

Multiplying and Dividing Radical Expressions 7-2

Help students understand why restrictions on the values of variables are necessary for multiplying and dividing radical expressions. For $\sqrt[n]{a} \cdot \sqrt[n]{b} = \sqrt[n]{ab}$, $\sqrt[n]{a}$ and $\sqrt[n]{b}$ must be real numbers because $\sqrt[n]{ab}$ would be complex if either a or b (but not both) were negative. For $\dfrac{\sqrt[n]{a}}{\sqrt[n]{b}} = \sqrt[n]{\dfrac{a}{b}}$, $\sqrt[n]{a}$ and $\sqrt[n]{b}$ must be real numbers as well as $b \neq 0$ because division by zero is undefined.

This lesson makes the assumption that the variable under the radical sign is a positive number. This relieves students from determining whether or not an absolute value symbol is required in the answer.

Binomial Radical Expressions 7-3

Like radicals are comparable to like polynomials terms. Like radicals have the same radicand to the same index, and like polynomial terms have the same variables to the same powers. Once like terms have been determined, adding, subtracting, and multiplying radicals involves a straightforward application of earlier skills.

Rationalizing the denominator in expressions such as $\dfrac{3}{1 + \sqrt{2}}$ or $\dfrac{7}{\sqrt{5} - \sqrt{3}}$ is not difficult after one or two examples. Some students need help recognizing that different types of denominators require different multipliers. The goal is to find a multiplier that eliminates the radicals in denominators. The multiplier that will always work is the conjugate of the denominator.

Rational Exponents 7-4

Point out to students that the definitions for rational exponents are designed to be consistent with the earlier definitions and rules for integer exponents. Furthermore, all previous properties of exponents apply for rational number exponents.

Some students confuse negative bases and negative exponents. A negative exponent flips the base such as $27^{-\frac{4}{3}} = \frac{1}{27^{\frac{4}{3}}} = \frac{1}{81}$. A negative base such as $(-27)^{\frac{4}{3}}$ is simply carried through any computations, so $(-27)^{\frac{4}{3}} = (\sqrt[3]{-27})^4 = (-3)^4 = 81$.

It is essential that students recognize the convention that an exponent only applies to the quantity immediately next to it. So $(-8)^{\frac{2}{3}} = (\sqrt[3]{-8})^2 = (-2)^2 = 4$ but $-8^{\frac{2}{3}} = -(\sqrt[3]{8})^2 = -4$ because the negative sign is not included for $-8^{\frac{2}{3}}$.

Solving Square Root and Other Radical Equations   7-5

Similar to solving an equation for a variable, solving a radical equation involves isolating a radical on one side of the equation. The process of squaring both sides of the equation might produce extraneous roots, so students must check each possible solution in the original equation. Also, students can be encouraged to recognize equations that will have no real number solution, such as $\sqrt{x + 2} = -5$.

Function Operations   7-6

The notation $f \circ g$ for the composition of function f with function g looks similar to the notation for the product of f and g. Point out that the operations are quite different. Also point out that function multiplication is commutative, but function composition is not; so $f(x) \cdot g(x) = g(x) \cdot f(x)$ while in general $(f \circ g)(x) \neq (g \circ f)(x)$.

Inverse Relations and Functions   7-7

Students may have difficulty understanding why saying "the inverse of the function f is f^{-1}," is not the same as saying "f and f^{-1} are inverse functions." The first statement should be

interpreted in light of the fact that f can have an inverse relation that is denoted by f^{-1}. The second statement is true only if this inverse relation f^{-1} also happens to be a function. It may help students to recall that the graph of a relation and its inverse are reflections of each other in $y = x$. The inverse relation f^{-1} must satisfy the vertical line test before one can call it an inverse function. A corresponding horizontal line test can be used to test whether a function has an inverse that is also a function.

Horizontal Line Test: If it is possible for a horizontal line to intersect a graph at more than one point, then the graph of the inverse is not the graph of a function.

So, if a graph of a function passes the horizontal line test, then the graph of the inverse passes the vertical line test and is also the graph of a function.

You may wish to show students that, in all cases, there is a connection between the inverse relationship and the identity for the relation. For example, $a \cdot \frac{1}{a} = 1$ means the product of a number and its multiplicative inverse is the multiplicative identity. The composition of a function and its inverse is the identity function $I = f \circ f^{-1} = f^{-1} \circ f$. This is the exception in which composition is commutative: when f and g are inverse functions $(f \circ g)(x) = (g \circ f)(x) = I(x)$ where $I(x)$ is the identity function $I(x) = x$.

Graphing Square Root and Other Radical Functions   7-8

The procedures for graphing radical functions and transformations of graphs of radical functions are similar to those presented for other functions. Students can use graphing calculators to examine the graphs of radical functions for the solutions to problems.

Additional Professional Development Opportunities

Math Background notes for Chapter 7: Every lesson has a Math Background in the PLAN section.

Research Overview, Mathematical Strands
Additional support for these topics and more is in the front of this Teacher's Edition.

Lesson Lab
Lesson Lab, a Pearson Education company, offers comprehensive, facilitated professional development designed to help teachers improve student achievement. To learn more, please visit lessonlab.com

Chapter 7 Resources

Print Resources		7-1	7-2	7-3	7-4	7-5	7-6	7-7	7-8	For the Chapter
L3	Practice	●	●	●	●	●	●	●	●	
L3	Guided Problem Solving	●	●	●	●	●	●	●	●	
L2	Reteaching	●	●	●	●	●	●	●	●	
L4	Enrichment	●	●	●	●	●	●	●	●	
L3	Daily Notetaking Guide	●	●	●	●	●	●	●	●	
L3	Vocabulary and Study Skills Worksheets	●	●		●		●	●		●
L3	Chapter Project									●
L3	Hands On Activities	●				●				
L3	Checkpoint Quiz			●			●			
L2	Below Level Chapter Test									●
L3	Chapter Test									●
L4	Alternative Assessment									●
L3	Cumulative Review									●
L4	Connections to Precalculus Masters	●	●	●	●	●	●	●	●	
L3	Technology Activities								●	

Spanish Resources ELL		7-1	7-2	7-3	7-4	7-5	7-6	7-7	7-8	For the Chapter
L3	Practice	●	●	●	●	●	●	●	●	
L3	Vocabulary and Study Skills Worksheets	●	●		●		●	●		●
L3	Checkpoint Quiz			●			●			
L2	Below Level Chapter Test									●
L3	Chapter Test									●
L4	Alternative Assessment									
L3	Cumulative Review									●

Transparencies	7-1	7-2	7-3	7-4	7-5	7-6	7-7	7-8	For the Chapter
Check Skills You'll Need	●	●	●	●	●	●	●	●	
Additional Examples	●	●	●	●	●	●	●	●	
Problem of the Day	●	●	●	●	●	●	●	●	
Classroom Aid						●			
Student Edition Answers	●	●	●	●	●	●	●	●	●
Lesson Quiz	●	●	●	●	●	●	●	●	
Test-Taking Strategies									●

Technology	7-1	7-2	7-3	7-4	7-5	7-6	7-7	7-8	For the Chapter
TI 83/84 Plus Activities							●		
Interactive Textbook Online	●	●	●	●	●	●	●	●	●
Student Express CD-ROM	●	●	●	●	●	●	●	●	●
TI Navigator, Instant Check System	●	●	●	●	●	●	●	●	
Success Tracker	●	●	●	●	●	●	●	●	●
ExamView CD-ROM with Quick Take	●	●	●	●	●	●	●	●	●
Teacher Express CD-ROM	●	●	●	●	●	●	●	●	●
Presentation Express CD-ROM	●	●	●	●	●	●	●	●	●
Mindpoint Quiz Show CD-ROM	●	●	●	●	●	●	●	●	●
Prentice Hall Web site: PHSchool.com	●	●	●	●	●	●	●	●	●

Also available: Prentice Hall Assessment System (Progress Monitoring Assessments, Skills and Concepts Review, Test Prep Workbook)　Solution Key　Student Workbook
Student Workbook, Adapted Version　Data Analysis and Probability Workbook　Math Notes Study Folder　Spanish Cumulative Assessment

Where You Can Use the Lesson Resources

Here is a suggestion, following the four-step teaching plan, for how you can incorporate Differentiated Instruction Resources into your teaching.

	Instructional Resources L3	**Differentiated Instruction Resources**
1. Plan		
Check Skills You'll Need Assign these exercises to review prerequisite skills. **New Vocabulary** Help students pre-read the lesson by pointing out the new terms introduced in the lesson.	**Math Background** **Transparencies & Presentation Express CD** Check Skills You'll Need **Resources** Vocabulary and Study Skills	**Spanish Support** ELL Vocabulary and Study Skills
2. Teach		
L3 **Guided Instruction** Teach each Example. After each Example, assign the Quick Check exercise for that Example.	**Student Edition** Activity Lab **Resources** Daily Notetaking Guide Activity Lab TI-83/84 Activities CD-ROM **Transparencies & Presentation Express CD** Additional Examples Classroom Aids **ExamView CD-ROM with QuickTake** **TI Navigator Instant Check System**	**Teacher's Edition** Every lesson includes suggestions for working with students who need special attention. L1 Special Needs L2 Below Level L4 Advanced Learners ELL English Language Learners
3. Practice		

Assignment Guide
 	
Homework Exercises
Assign the exercises cited in each lesson's Assignment Guide.
  A Practice by Example
  B Apply Your Skills
  C Challenge
  Test Prep
  Mixed Review
 	
Homework Quick Check
Discuss in class the exercises cited in each lesson's Assignment Guide.
	Transparencies & Presentation Express CD
	Student Answers
	
	Resources
	Practice
	Guided Problem Solving
	Vocabulary and Study Skills
	Activity Lab
	
	ExamView CD-ROM with QuickTake
		Spanish Support
		ELL Practice
		ELL Vocabulary and Study Skills
		
		Resources
		L4 Enrichment

4. Assess & Reteach		
Lesson Quiz Assign the Lesson Quiz to assess students' mastery of the lesson content. **Checkpoint Quiz** Use the Checkpoint Quiz to assess student progress over several lessons.	**Transparencies & Presentation Express CD** Lesson Quiz **Resources** Checkpoint Quiz	**Resources** L2 Reteaching ELL Checkpoint Quiz Success Tracker **ExamView CD-ROM with QuickTake**

KEY   L1 Special Needs   L2 Below Level   L3 For All Students   L4 Advanced, Gifted   ELL English Language Learners

Chapter 7

Radical Functions and Rational Exponents

Check Your Readiness

Answers are in the back of the textbook.

For intervention, direct students to:

Multiplying Binomials
Lesson 6-2: Example 1
Extra Skills and Word
  Problems Practice, Ch. 6

Simplifying Exponential Expressions
Skills Handbook: page 873
Examples 2-4

Solve by Factoring
Lesson 5-5: Example 1
Lesson 6-4: Example 5
Extra Skills and Word
  Problems Practice, Ch. 5, 6

Finding the Domain and Range of Functions
Graphing Quadratic Functions
Lesson 2-1: Example 2
Lesson 5-3: Example 1
Extra Skills and Word
  Problems Practice, Ch. 2, 5

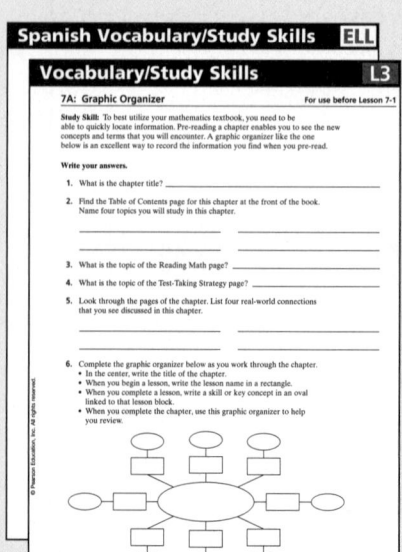

What You've Learned

- In Chapter 2, you learned about relations and functions and their domains and ranges. You also learned to draw graphs of relations and functions on the coordinate plane.

- In Chapter 5, you reviewed square roots and the multiplication and division of square roots. Then you used these skills in graphing and solving quadratic equations.

- In Chapter 6, you learned to graph polynomial functions and solve polynomial equations.

 Check Your Readiness   **for Help** to the Lesson in green.

Multiplying Binomials (Lesson 6-2)

Multiply.

1. $(3y - 2)(y - 4)$
$3y^2 - 14y + 8$

2. $(7a + 10)(7a - 10)$
$49a^2 - 100$

3. $(x - 3)(x + 6)(x + 1)$
$x^3 + 4x^2 - 15x - 18$

Simplifying Exponential Expressions (Skills Handbook p. 880)

Simplify each expression. Use only positive integer exponents.

4. $(3x^3)^2$ $9x^6$ **5.** $(2b^{-2})(4b^5)$ $8b^3$ **6.** $(xy^{-3})^2$ $\dfrac{x^2}{y^6}$ **7.** $\dfrac{18a^2}{3a^{-4}}$ $6a^6$ **8.** $\dfrac{4ab^{-3}}{6a^2b^3}$ $\dfrac{2}{3ab^6}$

Solving by Factoring (Lessons 5-5 and 6-4)

Solve each equation by factoring.

9. $x^2 - 5x - 14 = 0$ $-2, 7$ **10.** $2x^2 - 11x + 15 = 0$ $\frac{5}{2}, 3$ **11.** $3x^2 + 10x - 8 = 0$ $-4, \frac{2}{3}$

12. $12x^2 - 12x + 3 = 0$ $\frac{1}{2}$ **13.** $8x^2 - 98 = 0$ $\pm\frac{7}{2}$ **14.** $x^4 - 14x^2 + 49 = 0$ ± 2.65

Finding the Domain and Range of Functions (Lesson 2-1)

Find the domain and range of each function. **15–16. See margin.**

15. $\{(1, 2), (2, 3), (3, 4), (4, 5)\}$

16. $\{(1, 2), (2, 2), (3, 2), (4, 2)\}$

17. $f(x) = -x - 1$ **domain** $\{x \,|\, x \in \mathbb{R}\}$, **range** $\{y \,|\, y \in \mathbb{R}\}$

18. $f(x) = 2x^2 + 3$ **domain** $\{x \,|\, x \in \mathbb{R}\}$, **range** $\{y \,|\, y \in \mathbb{R} \text{ and } y \geq 3\}$

Graphing Quadratic Functions (Lesson 5-3)

Graph each function. **19–24. See back of book.**

19. $y = 2x^2 - 4$ **20.** $y = -3(x^2 + 1)$ **21.** $y = \frac{1}{2}(x - 3)^2 + 1$

22. $y = -(x + 4)^2 - 5$ **23.** $y = \frac{1}{4}(x + 2)^2 - 1$ **24.** $y = 7 - (5 - x)^2$

15. domain {1, 2, 3, 4},
    range {2, 3, 4, 5}

16. domain {1, 2, 3, 4},
    range {2}

Radical Functions and Rational Exponents

LESSONS

))) Key Vocabulary

What You'll Learn Next

- In Chapter 7, you will extend your knowledge of roots to include cube roots, fourth roots, fifth roots, and so on.

- You will learn to add, subtract, multiply, and divide radical expressions, including binomial radical expressions.

- You will solve radical equations, and graph translations of radical functions and their inverses.

Real-World Connection Applying what you learn, on page 386 you will solve a problem involving space travel.

Chapter 7 Overview

Students begin the chapter with an introduction to roots and radical expressions. Next students learn how to multiply and divide radical expressions. Students then study binomial radical expressions and rational exponents. Subsequently, students learn how to solve radical equations, and are introduced to function operations. The chapter concludes with lessons on inverse relations and functions, and graphing radical functions.

Activating Prior Knowledge

Ask:
- *What is the square root of a number?*

Student answers should include that a square root of a number is a number which when multiplied by itself results in the original number. So, the square roots of 16 are 4 and −4 because $4 \cdot 4 = 16$ and $(-4)(-4) = 16$.

Ask:
- *What is the cube root of a number?*

A cube root of a number is the number which when multiplied by itself three times gives the original number. So, the cube root of 8 is 2 because $2 \cdot 2 \cdot 2 = 8$.

Tell students that in this chapter they will simplify and manipulate *n*th roots, which are also known as radical expressions.

Properties of Exponents

Students will find it helpful to review simplifying expressions with integer exponents before they study rational exponents in Lesson 7-4.

Guided Instruction

EXAMPLE

Remind students that all the properties used to simplify expressions with whole number exponents apply when the exponents are integers. Be sure students understand that for $a \neq 0$ and any integer exponent n, $a^{-n} = \frac{1}{a^n}$.

Error Prevention!

Make sure students understand that to write expressions in simplified form, they must be sure that all exponents are positive.

Resources

Exam View CD-ROM, Chapter 00, Integer, Decimal, and Fraction Operations

25. Answers may vary.
Sample:
$15^0 = 1$
$\frac{4^5}{4^3} = 4^{5-3} = 4^2 = 16$
$(2 \cdot 5)^2 = 2^2 \cdot 5^2 = 4 \cdot 25 = 100$
$\left(\frac{2}{3}\right)^5 = \frac{2^5}{3^5}$
$2^3 \cdot 2^5 = 2^{3+5} = 2^8$
$4^{-3} = \frac{1}{4^3} = \frac{1}{64}$
$(3^2)^3 = 3^{2 \cdot 3} = 3^6 = 729$
In $(ab)^m = a^m b^m$ and $\left(\frac{a}{b}\right)^m = \frac{a^m}{b^m}$ the exponent is distributed to both factors and to both the numerator and the denominator.

Exponents are used to indicate powers. Their properties are listed below. Assume throughout your work that no denominator is equal to zero and that m and n are integers.

- $a^0 = 1, a \neq 0$
- $a^{-n} = \frac{1}{a^n}$
- $a^m \cdot a^n = a^{m+n}$
- $\frac{a^m}{a^n} = a^{m-n}$
- $(ab)^n = a^n b^n$
- $\left(\frac{a}{b}\right)^n = \frac{a^n}{b^n}$
- $(a^m)^n = a^{mn}$

EXAMPLE

Simplify and rewrite each expression using only positive exponents.

a. $(7a^2)(-2a^{-5})$

$(7a^2)(-2a^{-5})$

$= 7(-2)a^{2+(-5)}$

$= -14a^{-3}$

$= \frac{-14}{a^3}$, or $-\frac{14}{a^3}$

b. $(-2x^{-1}y^2)^3$

$(-2x^{-1}y^2)^3$

$= (-2)^3(x^{-1})^3(y^2)^3$

$= -8x^{-3}y^6$

$= \frac{-8y^6}{x^3}$, or $-\frac{8y^6}{x^3}$

c. $\frac{2ab^5c^2}{a^3bc^2}$

$\frac{2ab^5c^2}{a^3bc^2}$

$= 2a^{1-3}b^{5-1}c^{2-2}$

$= 2a^{-2}b^4c^0$

$= \frac{2b^4}{a^2}$

EXERCISES

Simplify each expression. Use only positive exponents.

1. $(3a^2)(4a^6)$ $12a^8$

2. $(-4x^2)(-2x^{-2})$ 8

3. $(4x^3y^5)^2$ $16x^6y^{10}$

4. $(2x^{-5}y^4)^3$ $\frac{8y^{12}}{x^{15}}$

5. $\frac{8a^5}{2a^2}$ $4a^3$

6. $\frac{6x^7y^5}{3x^{-1}}$ $2x^8y^5$

7. $\frac{(4x^2)^0}{2xy^5}$ $\frac{1}{2xy^5}$

8. $\left(\frac{3x^2}{2}\right)^2$ $\frac{9x^4}{4}$

9. $(-6m^2n^2)(3mn)$ $-18m^3n^3$

10. $(3x^4y^5)^{-3}$ $\frac{1}{27x^{12}y^{15}}$

11. $\frac{(2r^{-1}s^2t^0)^{-2}}{2rs}$ $\frac{r}{8s^5}$

12. $x^5(2x)^3$ $8x^8$

13. $\frac{x^4x^{-2}}{x^{-5}}$ x^7

14. $\frac{(12x^2y^6)^2}{8x^4y^7}$ $18y^5$

15. $(4p^2q)(p^2q^3)$ $4p^4q^4$

16. $\frac{4x^3}{2x}$ $2x^2$

17. $(p^2)^{-2}$ $\frac{1}{p^4}$

18. $\frac{-15x^4}{3x}$ $-5x^3$

19. $\frac{r^2s^3t^4}{r^2s^4t^{-4}}$ $\frac{t^8}{s}$

20. $\frac{xy^2}{2} \cdot \frac{6x}{y^2}$ $3x^2$

21. $(s^2t)^3(st)$ s^7t^4

22. $(3x^{-3}y^{-2})^{-2}$ $\frac{x^6y^4}{9}$

23. $(h^4k^5)^0$ 1

24. $\frac{s^2t^3}{r} \cdot \frac{sr^3}{t}$ $r^2s^3t^2$

25. Writing Write a numerical example for each property of exponents shown above. Which properties could be called distributive properties for exponents? Explain. **See margin.**

7-1

Roots and Radical Expressions

What You'll Learn

• To simplify *n*th roots

. . . And Why

To solve a packaging problem, as in Example 4

 Check Skills You'll Need

GO for Help Lesson 5-4

Write each number as a square of a number.

1. 25 5^2

2. 0.09 0.3^2

3. $\frac{4}{49}$ $\left(\frac{2}{7}\right)^2$

Write each expression as a square of an expression.

4. x^{10} $(x^5)^2$

5. $x^4 y^2$ $(x^2 y)^2$

6. $169 x^6 y^{12}$ $(13x^3 y^6)^2$

◀)) **New Vocabulary** • *n*th root • radicand • index • principal root

Objective

1 To simplify *n*th roots

Examples

1 Finding All Real Roots
2 Finding Roots
3 Simplifying Radical Expressions
4 Real-World Connection

---

1 Roots and Radical Expressions

Since $5^2 = 25$, 5 is a square root of 25.

Since $5^3 = 125$, 5 is a cube root of 125.

Since $5^4 = 625$, 5 is a fourth root of 625.

Since $5^5 = 3125$, 5 is a fifth root of 3125.

This pattern leads to the definition of *n*th root.

🔑 **Key Concepts**

Definition	**nth Root**

For any real numbers a and b, and any positive integer n, if $a^n = b$,

then a is an **nth root** of b.

Math Background

The real number *a* is an *n*th root of the real number *b* if and only if $a^n = b$, and *n* is a positive integer greater than or equal to 2. Every real number *b* has exactly one *n*th root if *n* is odd. In cases where *n* is even, the situation is more complicated. If *b* is positive, then *b* has a positive and a negative *n*th root. If *b* is 0, then 0 is the only *n*th root of *b*. If *b* is negative, then the *n*th roots are imaginary. In this chapter, we consider only real *n*th roots.

More Math Background: p. 366C

Vocabulary Tip

The term <u>root</u> is used in more than one way in mathematics:
   root of an equation
   root of a number.

The roots of the equation $y^4 = 16$ are the fourth roots of 16.

Since $2^4 = 16$ and $(-2)^4 = 16$, both 2 and -2 are fourth roots of 16.

Since there is no real number x such that $x^4 = -16$, -16 has no real fourth root.

Since -5 is the only real number whose cube is -125, -5 is the only real cube root of -125.

Some roots, such as the square roots of 10, are irrational numbers. Nevertheless, there is a positive square root and a negative square root of 10.

Here is a summary of the number of possible real roots of a real number.

Type of Number	Number of Real *n*th Roots When *n* Is Even	Number of Real *n*th Roots When *n* Is Odd
positive	2	1
0	1	1
negative	none	1

Lesson Planning and Resources

See p. 366E for a list of the resources that support this lesson.

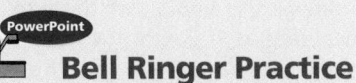
Bell Ringer Practice

✓ **Check Skills You'll Need**
For intervention, direct students to:

Factoring Quadratic Expressions
Lesson 5-4: Example 7
Extra Skills and Word
   Problems Practice, Ch. 5

Differentiated Instruction Solutions for All Learners

Special Needs L1
Ask: *What is the sign of* $(-2)(-2)$? *of* (-2) *raised to any even exponent, or* $(-2)^{even}$? **positive** *What is the sign of* $(-2)(-2)(-2)$? *of* $(-2)^{odd}$? **negative** *For which nth roots, odd or even, are absolute value signs needed?* **even roots such as** $\sqrt[4]{x^4} = |x|$

learning style: verbal

Below Level L2
Ask students to square and then to cube 2, -2, 3, and -3. Discuss the need for absolute value notation when taking the square roots and cube roots of the results.

learning style: verbal

Guided Instruction

Math Tip
State that every positive real number has two square roots. However, the principal square root given by the symbol $\sqrt{\ }$ indicates only one root, its positive square root. To indicate both positive and negative roots, use the $\pm$ symbol, or $\pm\sqrt{\ }$.

2 EXAMPLE Teaching Tip

Have students practice identifying the index, radicand, and principle root for each question in the example.

Error Prevention!

Help students recognize when the absolute value is needed. Because a variable can be positive, negative, or zero, sometimes the absolute value is needed when simplifying variable expressions. Ask:

- When is $\sqrt[n]{x^n} = x$? when the index n is odd or when the index is even and $x > 0$

- When is $\sqrt[n]{x^n} = |x|$? when the index n is even and $x < 0$

3 EXAMPLE Alternative Method

If students do not understand why absolute value signs must be used for some roots, give them the following example. Ask them to evaluate each side of the equation $\sqrt{x^6} = x^3$ for $x = -2$. This results in the false statement $8 = -8$ since $\sqrt{(-2)^6} = \sqrt{64} = 8$ and $(-2)^3 = -8$. Even though 64 has two square roots, -8 and 8, the radical sign signifies the principal square root, which is always positive. Therefore we must write $\sqrt{x^6} = |x^3|$. The absolute value sign ensures that the equation is true.

1 EXAMPLE Finding All Real Roots

Find all the real roots.

a. the cube roots of 0.008, -1000, and $\frac{1}{27}$

Since $(0.2)^3 = 0.008$, 0.2 is the cube root of 0.008.
Since $(-10)^3 = -1000$, -10 is the cube root of -1000.
Since $\left(\frac{1}{3}\right)^3 = \frac{1}{27}$, $\frac{1}{3}$ is the cube root of $\frac{1}{27}$.

b. the fourth roots of 1, -0.0001, and $\frac{16}{81}$

Since $1^4 = 1$ and $(-1)^4 = 1$, 1 and -1 are fourth roots of 1.
There is no real number with a fourth power of -0.0001.
Since $\left(\frac{2}{3}\right)^4 = \frac{16}{81}$ and $\left(-\frac{2}{3}\right)^4 = \frac{16}{81}$, $\frac{2}{3}$ and $-\frac{2}{3}$ are fourth roots of $\frac{16}{81}$.

✓ **Quick Check** ❶ **a.** Find all the real fifth roots of 0, -1, and 32. **0; −1; 2**
b. Find all the real square roots of 0.0001, -1, and $\frac{36}{121}$.
0.01 and −0.01, no real square root, $\frac{6}{11}$ and $-\frac{6}{11}$

Vocabulary Tip

Like the word *radish*, radical comes from the Latin word for root.

A radical sign is used to indicate a root. The number under the radical sign is the **radicand**. The **index** gives the degree of the root.

When a number has two real roots, the positive root is called the **principal root** and the radical sign indicates the principal root. The principal fourth root of 16 is written as $\sqrt[4]{16}$.

The principal fourth root of 16 is 2 because $\sqrt[4]{16}$ equals $\sqrt[4]{2^4}$. The other fourth root of 16 is written as $-\sqrt[4]{16}$, which equals -2.

2 EXAMPLE Finding Roots

Find each real-number root.

a. $\sqrt[3]{-8}$

$\sqrt[3]{-8} = \sqrt[3]{(-2)^3}$ Rewrite -8 as the third power of a number.
$= -2$ Simplify.

b. $\sqrt{-100}$

There is no real number whose square is -100.

✓ **Quick Check** ❷ Find each real-number root.

a. $\sqrt[3]{-27}$ **−3**   **b.** $\sqrt[4]{81}$ **3**   **c.** $\sqrt{49}$ **7**

Notice that when $x = 5$, $\sqrt{x^2} = \sqrt{5^2} = \sqrt{25} = 5 = x$, and when $x = -5$, $\sqrt{x^2} = \sqrt{(-5)^2} = \sqrt{25} = 5 \neq x$.

Key Concepts

Property	*n*th Root of a^n, $a < 0$
For any negative real number a, $\sqrt[n]{a^n} = |a|$ when n is even.	

Differentiated Instruction Solutions for All Learners

Advanced Learners L4
The equation for the period of a simple pendulum is $T = 2\pi\sqrt{\frac{\ell}{g}}$. Ask students to find several more formulas involving radicals.

learning style: verbal

English Language Learners ELL
Review the terms *radicand*, *index*, and *radical sign*. Write a variety of *n*th roots on the board, such as $\sqrt[3]{27}$, $\sqrt{64}$, $\sqrt[5]{32}$, and $\sqrt[4]{625}$, and have students identify the terms for each expression and find its principle root.

learning style: visual

3 EXAMPLE Simplifying Radical Expressions

Simplify each radical expression.

a. $\sqrt{4x^6}$

$$\sqrt{4x^6} = \sqrt{2^2(x^3)^2} = \sqrt{(2x^3)^2} = 2|x^3|$$

Absolute value symbols ensure that the root is positive when x is negative.

b. $\sqrt[3]{a^3b^6}$

$$\sqrt[3]{a^3b^6} = \sqrt[3]{a^3(b^2)^3} = \sqrt[3]{(ab^2)^3} = ab^2$$

Absolute value symbols must not be used here. If a is negative, then the radicand is negative and the root must also be negative.

c. $\sqrt[4]{x^4y^8}$

$$\sqrt[4]{x^4y^8} = \sqrt[4]{x^4(y^2)^4} = \sqrt[4]{(xy^2)^4} = |x|y^2$$

Absolute value symbols ensure that the root is positive when x is negative. They are not needed for y because y^2 is never negative.

✓ **Quick Check** ③ Simplify each radical expression. Use absolute value symbols when needed.

a. $\sqrt{4x^2y^4}$ $2|x|y^2$ **b.** $\sqrt[3]{-27c^6}$ $-3c^2$ **c.** $\sqrt[4]{x^8y^{12}}$ $x^2|y^3|$

For: Simplifying Activity
Use: Interactive Textbook, 7-1

4 EXAMPLE Real-World Connection

Packaging A citrus grower wants to ship a select grade of oranges that weigh from 8 to 9 ounces in gift cartons. Each carton will hold three dozen oranges, in 3 layers of 3 oranges by 4 oranges.

The weight of an orange is related to its diameter by the formula $w = \frac{d^3}{4}$, where d is the diameter in inches and w is the weight in ounces. Cartons can be ordered in whole-inch dimensions. What size cartons should the grower order?

Find the diameters of the oranges.

$8 \le$	w	≤ 9	**Write an inequality.**
$8 \le$	$\frac{d^3}{4}$	≤ 9	**Substitute for w in terms of d.**
$32 \le$	d^3	≤ 36	**Multiply by 4.**
$\sqrt[3]{32} \le$	$\sqrt[3]{d^3}$	$\le \sqrt[3]{36}$	**Take cube roots.**
$3.17 \le$	d	≤ 3.30	**The diameters range from 3.17 in. to 3.30 in.**

The length of a row of 4 of the largest oranges is $4(3.30 \text{ in.}) = 13.2$ in. The length of a row of 3 of the largest oranges is $3(3.30 \text{ in.}) = 9.90$ in. The grower should order cartons that are 14 in. long by 10 in. wide by 10 in. high to accommodate three dozen of the largest oranges.

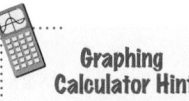

Graphing Calculator Hint

Use the $\sqrt[3]{\ }$ feature in the MATH menu to find cube roots. For other roots, type the index first and then select the $\sqrt[x]{\ }$ feature.

✓ **Quick Check** ④ Use the formula in Example 4 to find the diameter of each orange.

a. 3 oz **2.29 in.**   **b.** 5.5 oz **2.8 in.**   **c.** 6.25 oz **2.92 in.**

Additional Examples

① Find all the real roots.
a. the cube roots of 0.027, −125, and $\frac{1}{64}$ 0.3, −5, $\frac{1}{4}$

b. the fourth roots of 625, −0.0016, and $\frac{81}{625}$ ±5, none, $\pm\frac{3}{5}$

② Find each real-number root.
a. $\sqrt[3]{-1000}$ −10
b. $\sqrt{-81}$ none

③ Simplify each radical expression.
a. $\sqrt{9x^{10}}$ $3|x^5|$
b. $\sqrt[3]{a^3b^3}$ ab
c. $\sqrt[4]{x^{16}y^4}$ $x^4|y|$

④ A cheese manufacturer wants to ship cheese balls that weigh from 10 to 11 ounces in cartons that will have 3 layers of 3 cheese balls by 4 cheese balls. The weight of a cheese ball is related to its diameter by the formula $w = \frac{d^3}{5}$, where d is the diameter in inches and w is the weight in ounces. What size cartons should be used? Assume whole-inch dimensions.
16 in. long by 12 in. wide by 12 in. high

Resources
• Daily Notetaking Guide 7-1 **L3**

Closure

Ask students to explain what is meant by the nth root of a number, where n is a positive integer and $n \ge 2$. Have them explain under what conditions it is necessary to use absolute value in simplifying expressions involving nth roots. A real number a is an nth root of a nonnegative real number b if $a^n = b$. If n is even and a can have negative values then $\sqrt[n]{a^n}$ must be simplified to $|a|$.

Homework Quick Check
To check students' understanding of key skills and concepts, go over Exercises 25, 30, 38, 57, 59.

Error Prevention!

Exercises 21–28 Urge students to be especially cautious with the use of absolute value signs.

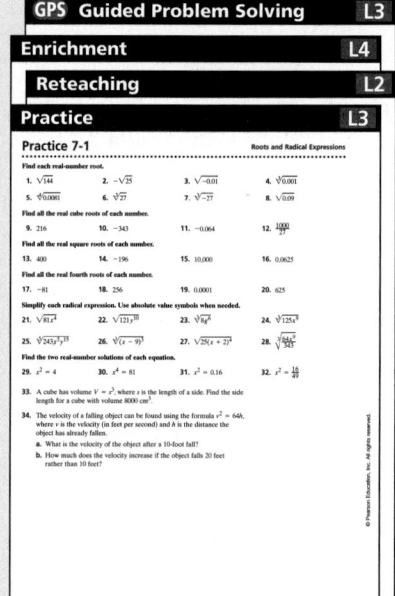

Differentiated	Instruction	Resources

GPS Guided Problem Solving	L3
Enrichment	L4
Reteaching	L2
Practice	L3

Practice 7-1 worksheet image

22. $0.5|x^3|$

23. $x^4|y^9|$

24. $8b^{24}$

44. $3\sqrt[3]{3xy^2}$

45. $12y^2z^2|x|\sqrt{xz}$

46. y^4

47. $-y^4$

48. k^3

49. $-k^3$

EXERCISES

For more exercises, see *Extra Skill and Word Problem Practice*.

Practice and Problem Solving

A Practice by Example

Example 1
(page 370)

Find all the real square roots of each number.

1. 225   15, −15   **2.** 0.0049   0.07, −0.07   **3.** $-\frac{1}{121}$ none   **4.** $\frac{64}{169}$ $\frac{8}{13}$, $-\frac{8}{13}$

Find all the real cube roots of each number.

5. −64 −4   **6.** 0.125 0.5   **7.** $-\frac{27}{216}$ $-\frac{1}{2}$ **8.** 0.000343 0.07

Find all the real fourth roots of each number.

9. 16 2, −2   **10.** −16 none   **11.** 0.0081   0.3, −0.3   **12.** $\frac{10,000}{81}$ $\frac{10}{3}$, $-\frac{10}{3}$

Example 2
(page 370)

Find each real-number root.

13. $\sqrt{36}$ 6   **14.** $-\sqrt{36}$ −6   **15.** $\sqrt{-36}$ no real root   **16.** $\sqrt{0.36}$ 0.6

17. $-\sqrt[3]{64}$ −4   **18.** $\sqrt[3]{-64}$ −4   **19.** $-\sqrt[4]{81}$ −3   **20.** $\sqrt[4]{-81}$ no real root

Example 3
(page 371)

22–24. See margin.

Simplify each radical expression. Use absolute value symbols when needed.

21. $\sqrt{16x^2}$ $4|x|$ **22.** $\sqrt{0.25x^6}$ **23.** $\sqrt{x^8y^{18}}$ **24.** $\sqrt{64b^{48}}$

25. $\sqrt[3]{-64a^3}$ −4a   **26.** $\sqrt[3]{27y^6}$ $3y^2$ **27.** $\sqrt[4]{x^8y^{12}}$ $x^2|y^3|$ **28.** $\sqrt[5]{32y^{10}}$ $2y^2$

Example 4
(page 371)

Geometry The formula for the volume of a sphere is $V = \frac{4}{3}\pi r^3$. Find the radius to the nearest hundredth of a sphere with each volume.

29. 10 in.^{3} 1.34 in.   **30.** 20 ft^3 1.68 ft   **31.** 0.45 cm^3 0.48 cm   **32.** 0.002 mm^3 0.08 mm

B Apply Your Skills

Find the two real-number solutions of each equation.

33. $x^2 = 100$ 10, −10   **34.** $x^4 = 1$ 1, −1   **35.** $x^2 = 0.25$ 0.5, −0.5   **36.** $x^4 = \frac{16}{81}$ $\frac{2}{3}$, $-\frac{2}{3}$

37. Arrange the numbers $\sqrt[3]{-64}$, $-\sqrt[3]{-64}$, $\sqrt{64}$, and $\sqrt[6]{64}$ in order from least to greatest. $\sqrt[3]{-64}$, $\sqrt[6]{64}$, $-\sqrt[3]{-64}$, $\sqrt{64}$

38. Boat Building Boat builders share an old rule of thumb for sailboats. The maximum speed K in knots is 1.35 times the square root of the length L in feet of the boat's waterline.
   a. A customer is planning to order a sailboat with a maximum speed of 8 knots. How long should the waterline be? ≈35 ft
   b. How much longer would the waterline have to be to achieve a maximum speed of 10 knots? ≈20 ft longer

44–50. See margin.

Simplify each radical expression. Use absolute value symbols when needed.

39. $\sqrt[3]{0.125}$ 0.5   **40.** $\sqrt[3]{\frac{8}{216}}$ $\frac{1}{3}$ **41.** $\sqrt[4]{0.0016}$ 0.2   **42.** $\sqrt[4]{\frac{1}{256}}$ $\frac{1}{4}$

43. $\sqrt[4]{16c^4}$ $2|c|$ **44.** $\sqrt[3]{81x^3y^6}$ **45.** $\sqrt{144x^3y^4z^5}$ **46.** $\sqrt[5]{y^{20}}$

47. $\sqrt[5]{-y^{20}}$ **48.** $\sqrt[5]{k^{15}}$ **49.** $\sqrt[5]{-k^{15}}$ **50.** $\sqrt{(x+3)^2}$

Real-World Connection

The waterline of a boat is the intersection of the boat with the surface of the water when the boat is at rest.

51. $\sqrt{(x+1)^4}$ $(x+1)^2$ **52.** $\sqrt[2n]{x^{2n}}$ $|x|$ **53.** $\sqrt[2n]{x^{4n}}$ x^2 **54.** $\sqrt[2n]{x^{6n}}$ $|x^3|$

55. Open-Ended Find three radical expressions that simplify to $-2x^2$. See margin.

50. $|x + 3|$

55. Answers may vary.
   Sample: $\sqrt[3]{-8x^6}$, $-\sqrt[4]{16x^8}$, $\sqrt[5]{-32x^{10}}$

Homework Video Tutor
Visit: PHSchool.com
Web Code: age-0701

56. Critical Thinking For what positive integers n is each of the statements true?
   a. If $x^n = b$, then x is an nth root of b.   **b.** If $x^n = b$, then $x = \sqrt[n]{b}$.
   a–b. See left.

57. Writing Is 10 a first root of 10? Explain.
   Yes, because 10 is really 10^1.

Tell whether each equation is true for *all*, *some*, or *no values* of the variable.
Explain your answers. 58–61. See margin.

58. $\sqrt{x^4} = x^2$ **59.** $\sqrt{x^6} = x^3$ **60.** $\sqrt[3]{x^8} = x^2$ **61.** $\sqrt[3]{x^3} = |x|$

C Challenge

Simplify each radical expression. n is an even number.

62. $\sqrt[n]{m^n}$ $|m|$ **63.** $\sqrt[n]{m^{2n}}$ m^2 **64.** $\sqrt[n]{m^{3n}}$ $|m^3|$ **65.** $\sqrt[n]{m^{4n}}$ m^4

Simplify each radical expression. n is an odd number.

66. $\sqrt[n]{m^n}$ m **67.** $\sqrt[n]{m^{2n}}$ m^2 **68.** $\sqrt[n]{m^{3n}}$ m^3 **69.** $\sqrt[n]{m^{4n}}$ m^4

56a. for all positive integers
b. for all odd positive integers

Test Prep

Multiple Choice

70. Which equation has more than one real-number solution? **B**
 A. $x^2 = 0$ **B.** $x^2 = 1$ **C.** $x^2 = -1$ **D.** $x^3 = -1$

71. Which number is greatest? **J**
 F. $\sqrt{0.5}$ **G.** $\sqrt[3]{0.5}$ **H.** $\sqrt[4]{0.5}$ **J.** $\sqrt[5]{0.5}$

72. Which statement is NOT true? **B**
 A. $-3 = -\sqrt{9}$ **B.** $-3 = -\sqrt{-9}$
 C. $-3 = \sqrt[3]{-27}$ **D.** $-3 = -\sqrt[4]{81}$

73. Absolute value symbols are needed when you simplify some of these expressions. Which ones are they? **H**
 I. $\sqrt[3]{-x^3y^6}$ **II.** $\sqrt{x^2y^4}$ **III.** $\sqrt[4]{x^8y^{12}}$ **IV.** $\sqrt{x^4y^6}$
 F. II and III only   **G.** II and IV only
 H. II, III and IV only   **J.** I, II, III and IV

Short Response

74. For what values of x and y does $\sqrt{x^2y^4}$ equal $\sqrt[3]{x^3y^6}$? Explain your answer.
   See back of book.

Mixed Review

Lesson 6-8 Expand each binomial. 75–78. See margin.

75. $(x + y)^5$ **76.** $(2 - 3y)^4$ **77.** $(3x - 5)^6$ **78.** $(2a - b)^7$

Lesson 6-2 Write each function in factored form. Check by multiplying.

79. $y = x(2x - 7)(2x + 7)$ **79.** $y = 4x^3 - 49x$ **80.** $y = 81x^2 + 36x + 4$
80. $y = (9x + 2)^2$ **81.** $y = 4x^3 + 8x^2 + 4x$ **82.** $y = 12x^3 + 14x^2 + 2x$
                $y = 4x(x + 1)^2$ $y = 2x(6x + 1)(x + 1)$

Lesson 5-3 Rewrite each equation in vertex form.

85. $y = \frac{1}{4}(x + 4)^2 - 5$ **83.** $y = 3x^2 - 7$ **84.** $y = -2x^2 + x - 10$ **85.** $y = \frac{x^2}{4} + 2x - 1$
             $y = 3(x - 0)^2 - 7$ $y = -2\left(x - \frac{1}{4}\right)^2 - \frac{79}{8}$

58. All; x^2 is always positive.
59. Some; they are equal for $x \geq 0$.
60. Some; they are equal for $x = -1, 0, 1$.
61. Some; they are equal for $x \geq 0$.
75. $x^5 + 5x^4y + 10x^3y^2 + 10x^2y^3 + 5xy^4 + y^5$
76. $16 - 96y + 216y^2 - 216y^3 + 81y^4$
77. $729x^6 - 7290x^5 + 30{,}375x^4 - 67{,}500x^3 + 84{,}375x^2 - 56{,}250x + 15{,}625$
78. $128a^7 - 448a^6b + 672a^5b^2 - 560a^4b^3 + 280a^3b^4 - 84a^2b^5 + 14ab^6 - b^7$

1. Plan

Objectives
1 To multiply radical expressions
2 To divide radical expressions

Examples
1 Multiplying Radicals
2 Simplifying Radical Expressions
3 Multiplying Radical Expressions
4 Dividing Radicals
5 Rationalizing the Denominator
6 Real-World Connection

Math Background

The properties for multiplying and dividing radicals, presented in this lesson, both actually hold under less restrictive conditions on $\sqrt[n]{a}$ and $\sqrt[n]{b}$, but more restrictive conditions on n. Students can investigate these conditions using their knowledge of imaginary numbers from Chapter 5. Both properties aid in simplifying radical expressions. To simplify radical expressions that involve fractions, write the expressions so that no denominator contains a radical and no radicand contains a fraction.

More Math Background: p. 366C

Lesson Planning and Resources

See p. 366E for a list of the resources that support this lesson.

✓ **Check Skills You'll Need**
For intervention, direct students to:

Finding Factors
Algebra 1 Review: Page 368

What You'll Learn
• To multiply radical expressions
• To divide radical expressions

. . . Any Why
To transform a famous formula, as in Example 6

✓ **Check Skills You'll Need**

GO for Help   page 368

Find each missing factor.

1. $150 = 5^2(\blacksquare)$ **6**
2. $54 = (\blacksquare)^3(2)$ **3**
3. $48 = 4^2(\blacksquare)$ **3**
4. $x^5 = (\blacksquare)^2(x)$ x^2
5. $3a^3b^4 = (\blacksquare)^3(3b)$ ab
6. $75a^7b^8 = (\blacksquare)^2(3a)$ $5a^3b^4$

◀)) **New Vocabulary**   • rationalize the denominator

---

1 Multiplying Radical Expressions

To multiply radicals consider the following.

$\sqrt{16} \cdot \sqrt{9} = 4 \cdot 3 = 12$ and $\sqrt{16 \cdot 9} = \sqrt{144} = 12$.
So $\sqrt{16} \cdot \sqrt{9} = \sqrt{16 \cdot 9}$.

$\sqrt[3]{-8} \cdot \sqrt[3]{27} = -2 \cdot 3 = -6$ and $\sqrt[3]{-8 \cdot 27} = \sqrt[3]{-216} = -6$.
So $\sqrt[3]{-8} \cdot \sqrt[3]{27} = \sqrt[3]{-8 \cdot 27}$.

In general, the product of the principal nth roots of two numbers equals the principal nth root of their product.

 Key Concepts

Property   **Multiplying Radical Expressions**
If $\sqrt[n]{a}$ and $\sqrt[n]{b}$ are real numbers, then $\sqrt[n]{a} \cdot \sqrt[n]{b} = \sqrt[n]{ab}$.

1 EXAMPLE   **Multiplying Radicals**

Multiply. Simplify if possible.

a. $\sqrt{2} \cdot \sqrt{8}$

$\sqrt{2} \cdot \sqrt{8} = \sqrt{2 \cdot 8} = \sqrt{16} = 4$

b. $\sqrt[3]{-5} \cdot \sqrt[3]{25}$

$\sqrt[3]{-5} \cdot \sqrt[3]{25} = \sqrt[3]{-125} = \sqrt[3]{(-5)^3} = -5$

c. $\sqrt{-2} \cdot \sqrt{8}$

The property for multiplying radicals does *not* apply. $\sqrt{-2}$ is not a real number.

✓ **Quick Check** ❶ Multiply. Simplify if possible.
a. $\sqrt{3} \cdot \sqrt{12}$ **6**   b. $\sqrt[3]{3} \cdot \sqrt[3]{-9}$ **−3**   c. $\sqrt[4]{4} \cdot \sqrt[4]{-4}$ **not possible**

Differentiated Instruction **Solutions for All Learners**

Special Needs **L1**
Show students how a fraction can be rewritten in many equivalent forms using multiplication by 1.
$\frac{1}{2} \cdot \left(\frac{5}{5}\right) = \frac{5}{10}$ $\frac{1}{\sqrt{3}} \cdot \left(\frac{\sqrt{3}}{\sqrt{3}}\right) = \frac{\sqrt{3}}{3}$
Show how a similar procedure can be applied to radical fractions to rationalize the denominator
learning style: visual

Below Level **L2**
Have students write out the properties for multiplying and dividing radical expressions using several different numerical examples.

learning style: verbal

$2\sqrt[3]{3}$ is considered to be a simplified form of $\sqrt[3]{24}$. You can use the property for multiplying radical expressions to simplify some radical expressions.

2 EXAMPLE Simplifying Radical Expressions

Simplify each expression. Assume that all variables are positive. Then absolute value symbols are never needed in the simplified expression.

a. $\sqrt{72x^3}$

$$\sqrt{72x^3} = \sqrt{6^2 \cdot 2 \cdot x^2 \cdot x} \quad \text{Factor into perfect squares.}$$
$$= \sqrt{6^2 x^2} \cdot \sqrt{2x} \quad \sqrt[n]{a} \cdot \sqrt[n]{b} = \sqrt[n]{ab}$$
$$= 6x\sqrt{2x} \quad \text{Simplify.}$$

b. $\sqrt[3]{80n^5}$

$$\sqrt[3]{80n^5} = \sqrt[3]{2^3 \cdot 10 \cdot n^3 \cdot n^2} \quad \text{Factor into perfect cubes.}$$
$$= \sqrt[3]{2^3 n^3} \cdot \sqrt[3]{10n^2} \quad \sqrt[n]{a} \cdot \sqrt[n]{b} = \sqrt[n]{ab}$$
$$= 2n\sqrt[3]{10n^2} \quad \text{Simplify.}$$

✓ **Quick Check** **2** Simplify $\sqrt{50x^4}$ and $\sqrt[3]{18x^4}$. Assume that x is positive.
$$5x^2\sqrt{2}; \; x\sqrt[3]{18x}$$

Simplify the products of radicals as much as possible.

3 EXAMPLE Multiplying Radical Expressions

Multiply and simplify $\sqrt[3]{54x^2y^3} \cdot \sqrt[3]{5x^3y^4}$. Assume that all variables are positive.

$$\sqrt[3]{54x^2y^3} \cdot \sqrt[3]{5x^3y^4} = \sqrt[3]{54x^2y^3 \cdot 5x^3y^4} \quad \sqrt[n]{a} \cdot \sqrt[n]{b} = \sqrt[n]{ab}$$
$$= \sqrt[3]{3^3 x^3 (y^2)^3 \cdot 10x^2y} \quad \text{Factor into perfect cubes.}$$
$$= \sqrt[3]{3^3 x^3 (y^2)^3} \cdot \sqrt[3]{10x^2y} \quad \sqrt[n]{a} \cdot \sqrt[n]{b} = \sqrt[n]{ab}$$
$$= 3xy^2\sqrt[3]{10x^2y} \quad \text{Simplify.}$$

✓ **Quick Check** **3** Multiply and simplify $3\sqrt{7x^3} \cdot 2\sqrt{21x^3y^2}$. Assume that all variables are positive.
$$42x^3y\sqrt{3}$$

2 **Dividing Radical Expressions**

To divide radicals, consider the following.

$$\frac{\sqrt{36}}{\sqrt{25}} = \frac{6}{5} \text{ and } \sqrt{\frac{36}{25}} = \sqrt{\left(\frac{6}{5}\right)^2} = \frac{6}{5}. \text{ So } \frac{\sqrt{36}}{\sqrt{25}} = \sqrt{\frac{36}{25}}.$$

In general, the quotient of the principal nth roots of two numbers equals the principal nth root of their quotient.

🔑 **Key Concepts**

Property	Dividing Radical Expressions
If $\sqrt[n]{a}$ and $\sqrt[n]{b}$ are real numbers and $b \neq 0$, then $\dfrac{\sqrt[n]{a}}{\sqrt[n]{b}} = \sqrt[n]{\dfrac{a}{b}}$.	

Guided Instruction

2 EXAMPLE Math Tip

Point out that to simplify an nth root, you need to look for nth powers that are factors of the radicand. For example, if $n = 2$, then look for factors of the radicand that are perfect squares.

PowerPoint

Additional Examples

1 Multiply. Simplify if possible.
a. $\sqrt{3} \cdot \sqrt{12}$ 6
b. $\sqrt[3]{-16} \cdot \sqrt[3]{4}$ -4
c. $\sqrt{-4} \cdot \sqrt{16}$ The property for multiplying radicals does not apply.

2 Simplify each expression. Assume all variables are positive.
a. $\sqrt{50x^5}$ $5x^2\sqrt{2x}$
b. $\sqrt[3]{54n^8}$ $3n^2\sqrt[3]{2n^2}$

3 Multiply and simplify $\sqrt[3]{25xy^8} \cdot \sqrt[3]{5x^4y^3}$. Assume all variables are positive. $5xy^3\sqrt[3]{x^2y^2}$

Advanced Learners L4
Point out to students that rationalizing a denominator is a necessary algebraic skill in some higher mathematics.

learning style: verbal

English Language Learners ELL
Review for students the different processes they are using: multiplication, division, and simplification (finding roots). Clarify that *rationalizing the denominator* is a simplification process that involves rewriting the radical in an equivalent form.

learning style: verbal

375

5 EXAMPLE Alternative Method

The expression in part b is simplified using Method II. However, the expression can also be simplified with Method I by rewriting the expression as the square root of a fraction.

Additional Examples

④ Divide and simplify. Assume all variables are positive.

a. $\dfrac{\sqrt[3]{-81}}{\sqrt[3]{3}}$ -3

b. $\dfrac{\sqrt[3]{192x^8}}{\sqrt[3]{3x}}$ $4x^2\sqrt[3]{x}$

⑤ Rationalize the denominator of each expression. Assume all variables are positive.

a. $\dfrac{\sqrt{3}}{\sqrt{5}}$ $\dfrac{\sqrt{15}}{5}$

b. $\dfrac{\sqrt{x^5}}{\sqrt{3x^2y}}$ $\dfrac{x\sqrt{3xy}}{3y}$

c. $\sqrt[3]{\dfrac{5}{4y}}$ $\dfrac{\sqrt[3]{10y^2}}{2y}$

⑥ The distance d in meters that an object will fall in t seconds is given by $d = 4.9t^2$. Express t in terms of d and rationalize the denominator. $t = \dfrac{\sqrt{10d}}{7}$

Resources
• Daily Notetaking Guide 7-2 **L3**

Closure

Ask students to describe how to multiply and divide two nth roots, both of which are real numbers. To multiply the nth roots, take the nth root of the product of the radicands. To divide the nth roots, take the nth root of the quotient of the radicands.

---

4 EXAMPLE Dividing Radicals

Divide and simplify. Assume that all variables are positive.

a. $\dfrac{\sqrt[3]{32}}{\sqrt[3]{-4}}$

$$\dfrac{\sqrt[3]{32}}{\sqrt[3]{-4}} = \sqrt[3]{\dfrac{32}{-4}} = \sqrt[3]{-8} = -2$$

b. $\dfrac{\sqrt[3]{162x^5}}{\sqrt[3]{3x^2}}$

$$\dfrac{\sqrt[3]{162x^5}}{\sqrt[3]{3x^2}} = \sqrt[3]{\dfrac{162x^5}{3x^2}} = \sqrt[3]{54x^3} = \sqrt[3]{3^3x^3 \cdot 2} = \sqrt[3]{3^3x^3} \cdot \sqrt[3]{2} = 3x\sqrt[3]{2}$$

✓ **Quick Check** ④ Divide and simplify. Assume that all variables are positive.

a. $\dfrac{\sqrt{243}}{\sqrt{27}}$ 3

b. $\dfrac{\sqrt{12x^4}}{\sqrt{3x}}$ $2x\sqrt{x}$

c. $\dfrac{\sqrt[4]{1024x^{15}}}{\sqrt[4]{4x}}$ $4x^3\sqrt[4]{x^2}$

To **rationalize the denominator** of an expression, rewrite it so there are no radicals in any denominator and no denominators in any radical.

Rationalizing the denominator of a numerical expression makes it easier to calculate its decimal approximation. For example, $\dfrac{1}{\sqrt{2}} = \dfrac{\sqrt{2}}{2}$ and it is easier to divide by 2 than by $\sqrt{2}$.

5 EXAMPLE Rationalizing the Denominator

Rationalize the denominator of each expression. Assume that all variables are positive.

a. $\dfrac{\sqrt{2}}{\sqrt{3}}$

Method 1

$$\dfrac{\sqrt{2}}{\sqrt{3}} = \sqrt{\dfrac{2}{3}} = \sqrt{\dfrac{2 \cdot 3}{3 \cdot 3}} = \sqrt{\dfrac{6}{3^2}} = \dfrac{\sqrt{6}}{\sqrt{3^2}} = \dfrac{\sqrt{6}}{3}$$

Rewrite as a square root of a fraction. Then make the denominator a perfect square.

Method 2

$$\dfrac{\sqrt{2}}{\sqrt{3}} = \dfrac{\sqrt{2} \cdot \sqrt{3}}{\sqrt{3} \cdot \sqrt{3}} = \dfrac{\sqrt{6}}{3}$$

Multiply the numerator and denominator by $\sqrt{3}$ so the denominator becomes a whole number.

b. $\dfrac{\sqrt{x^3}}{\sqrt{5xy}}$

$$\dfrac{\sqrt{x^3}}{\sqrt{5xy}} = \dfrac{\sqrt{x^3} \cdot \sqrt{5xy}}{\sqrt{5xy} \cdot \sqrt{5xy}} = \dfrac{\sqrt{5x^4y}}{5xy} = \dfrac{x^2\sqrt{5y}}{5xy} = \dfrac{x\sqrt{5y}}{5y}$$

c. $\sqrt[3]{\dfrac{2}{3x}}$

$$\sqrt[3]{\dfrac{2}{3x}} = \sqrt[3]{\dfrac{2 \cdot 3^2x^2}{3x \cdot 3^2x^2}} = \sqrt[3]{\dfrac{18x^2}{3^3x^3}} = \dfrac{\sqrt[3]{18x^2}}{3x}$$

Rewrite the fraction so the denominator is a perfect cube.

✓ **Quick Check** ⑤ Rationalize the denominator of each expression. Assume that the variables are positive.

a. $\sqrt{\dfrac{7}{5}}$ $\dfrac{\sqrt{35}}{5}$

b. $\dfrac{\sqrt{2x^3}}{\sqrt{10xy}}$ $\dfrac{x\sqrt{5y}}{5y}$

c. $\dfrac{\sqrt[3]{4}}{\sqrt[3]{6x}}$ $\dfrac{\sqrt[3]{18x^2}}{3x}$

376 Chapter 7 Radical Functions and Rational Exponents

6 EXAMPLE Real-World 🌎 Connection

Einstein's famous formula $E = mc^2$ relates energy E, mass m, and the speed of light c. Express c in terms of E and m and rationalize the denominator.

$$E = mc^2$$

$$c^2 = \frac{E}{m}$$

$$c = \sqrt{\frac{E}{m}} = \sqrt{\frac{Em}{m^2}} = \frac{\sqrt{Em}}{\sqrt{m^2}} = \frac{\sqrt{Em}}{m}$$

 Quick Check ⑥ The formula $a = \frac{d}{t^2}$ relates the acceleration a of a moving object to the distance d it moves in the time t. Solve the formula for t and rationalize the denominator.

$$t = \frac{\sqrt{da}}{a}$$

EXERCISES

For more exercises, see *Extra Skill and Word Problem Practice*.

Practice and Problem Solving

 Practice by Example

Example 1 (page 374)

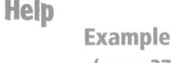 **GO for Help**

Multiply, if possible. Then simplify.

1. $\sqrt{8} \cdot \sqrt{32}$ 16
2. $\sqrt[3]{4} \cdot \sqrt[3]{16}$ 4
3. $\sqrt[3]{9} \cdot \sqrt[3]{-81}$ −9
4. $\sqrt[4]{8} \cdot \sqrt[4]{32}$ 4
5. $\sqrt{-5} \cdot \sqrt{5}$ not possible
6. $\sqrt[3]{-5} \cdot \sqrt[3]{-25}$ 5
7. $\sqrt[3]{9} \cdot \sqrt[3]{-24}$ −6
8. $\sqrt[3]{-12} \cdot \sqrt[3]{-18}$ 6

Example 2 (page 375)

Simplify. Assume that all variables are positive. 9–12. See margin.

9. $\sqrt{20x^3}$
10. $\sqrt[3]{81x^2}$
11. $\sqrt{50x^5}$
12. $\sqrt[3]{32a^5}$

13. $\sqrt[3]{54y^{10}}$ $3y^3\sqrt[3]{2y}$
14. $\sqrt{200a^6b^7}$ $10a^3b^3\sqrt{2b}$
15. $\sqrt[3]{-250x^6y^5}$ $-5x^2y\sqrt[3]{2y^2}$
16. $\sqrt[4]{64x^3y^6}$ $2y\sqrt[4]{4x^3y^2}$

Example 3 (page 375)

Multiply and simplify. Assume that all variables are positive.

17. $\sqrt[3]{6} \cdot \sqrt[3]{16}$ $2\sqrt[3]{12}$
18. $\sqrt{8y^5} \cdot \sqrt{40y^2}$ $8y^3\sqrt{5y}$
19. $\sqrt{7x^5} \cdot \sqrt{42xy^9}$ $7x^3y^4\sqrt{6y}$
20. $4\sqrt{2x} \cdot 5\sqrt{6xy^2}$ $40xy\sqrt{3}$
21. $3\sqrt[3]{5y^3} \cdot 2\sqrt[3]{50y^4}$ $30y^2\sqrt[3]{2y}$
22. $-\sqrt[3]{2x^2y^2} \cdot 2\sqrt[3]{15x^5y}$ $-2x^2y\sqrt[3]{30x}$

Example 4 (page 376)

Divide and simplify. Assume that all variables are positive.

23. $\frac{\sqrt{500}}{\sqrt{5}}$ 10
24. $\frac{\sqrt{48x^3}}{\sqrt{3xy^2}}$ $\frac{4x}{y}$
25. $\frac{\sqrt{56x^5y^5}}{\sqrt{7xy}}$ $2x^2y^2\sqrt{2}$
26. $\frac{\sqrt[3]{250x^7y^3}}{\sqrt[3]{2x^2y}}$ $5x\sqrt[3]{x^2y^2}$

Example 5 (page 376)

Rationalize the denominator of each expression. Assume that all variables are positive. 30–34. See margin.

27. $\frac{\sqrt{x}}{\sqrt{2}}$ $\frac{\sqrt{2x}}{2}$
28. $\frac{\sqrt{5}}{\sqrt{8x}}$ $\frac{\sqrt{10x}}{4x}$
29. $\frac{\sqrt[3]{x}}{\sqrt[3]{2}}$ $\frac{\sqrt[3]{4x}}{2}$
30. $\sqrt[3]{\frac{5}{3x}}$

31. $\frac{\sqrt[4]{2}}{\sqrt[4]{5}}$
32. $\frac{15\sqrt{60x^5}}{3\sqrt{12x}}$
33. $\frac{\sqrt{3xy^2}}{\sqrt{5xy^3}}$
34. $\frac{\sqrt{5x^4y}}{\sqrt{2x^2y^3}}$

Example 6 (page 377)

35. **Physics** The formula $F = \frac{Gm_1m_2}{r^2}$ relates the gravitational force F between an object of mass m_1 and an object of mass m_2 separated by distance r. G is a constant known as the constant of gravitation. Solve the formula for r. Rationalize the denominator. $r = \frac{\sqrt{Gm_1m_2F}}{F}$

Practice (margin answers)

9. $2x\sqrt{5x}$

10. $3\sqrt[3]{3x^2}$

11. $5x^2\sqrt{2x}$

12. $2a\sqrt[3]{4a^2}$

30. $\frac{\sqrt[3]{45x^2}}{3x}$

31. $\frac{\sqrt[4]{250}}{5}$

32. $5x^2\sqrt{5}$

33. $\frac{\sqrt{15y}}{5y}$

34. $\frac{x\sqrt{10}}{2y}$

---

3. Practice

Assignment Guide

❶ A B 1–22, 37–45, 56–59

❷ A B 23–36, 46–55, 60

C Challenge 61–68

Test Prep 69–75
Mixed Review 76–95

Homework Quick Check

To check students' understanding of key skills and concepts, go over Exercises 25, 35, 36, 55, 57, 59.

Error Prevention!

Exercises 9–16 Remind students that they do not need to use absolute value signs since the variables are positive.

Connection to Physics

Exercise 35 You may wish to point out that the distance r is the distance between the centers of the objects.

Assume that all variables are positive.

1. Multiply. Simplify if possible.
   a. $\sqrt{5} \cdot \sqrt{45}$ 15
   b. $\sqrt[3]{4} \cdot \sqrt[3]{2000}$ 20

2. Simplify.
   a. $\sqrt{8x^5}$ $2x^2\sqrt{2x}$
   b. $\sqrt[3]{-243x^3y^{10}}$ $-3xy^3\sqrt[3]{9y}$

3. Multiply and simplify.
   a. $\sqrt{18x^3} \cdot \sqrt{2x^2y^3}$
      $6x^2y\sqrt{xy}$
   b. $\sqrt[3]{10x^2y^4} \cdot \sqrt[3]{4x^2y}$
      $2xy\sqrt[3]{5xy^2}$

4. Divide and simplify.
   a. $\dfrac{\sqrt{128x^3}}{\sqrt{2xy}}$ $\dfrac{8x\sqrt{y}}{y}$
   b. $\dfrac{\sqrt[3]{270x}}{\sqrt[3]{10xy^2}}$ $\dfrac{3\sqrt[3]{y}}{y}$

5. Rationalize the denominator of each expression.
   a. $\dfrac{\sqrt{7x}}{\sqrt{3}}$ $\dfrac{\sqrt{21x}}{3}$
   b. $\dfrac{\sqrt[3]{x^2}}{\sqrt[3]{4}}$ $\dfrac{\sqrt[3]{2x^2}}{2}$

Alternative Assessment

Have students work in pairs. Each student should make up a problem similar to those in each of Examples 1–5. Then have students work each other's problems and check each other's work.

36a. $\dfrac{\sqrt{6} + 3}{15}$

   b. $\dfrac{\sqrt{6} + 3}{15}$

   c. Answers may vary. Sample: First simplify the denominator. Since $\sqrt{98} = \sqrt{2 \cdot 49} = 7\sqrt{2}$, to rationalize the denominator, multiply the fraction by $\dfrac{\sqrt{2}}{\sqrt{2}}$. This yields $\dfrac{\sqrt{2 \cdot 2} + \sqrt{3 \cdot 2}}{7\sqrt{2 \cdot 2}} = \dfrac{2 + \sqrt{6}}{14}$.

36. a. Simplify $\dfrac{\sqrt{2} + \sqrt{3}}{\sqrt{75}}$ by multiplying the numerator and denominator by $\sqrt{75}$.
    b. Simplify the expression in (a) by multiplying by $\sqrt{3}$ instead of $\sqrt{75}$.
    c. Explain how you would simplify $\dfrac{\sqrt{2} + \sqrt{3}}{\sqrt{98}}$. **a–c. See margin.**

Simplify each expression. Rationalize all denominators. Assume that all variables are positive.

40. $20x^2y^3\sqrt{y}$

41. $10 + 7\sqrt{2}$

42. $15 + 3\sqrt{21}$

43. $5 + 5\sqrt{3}$

37. $\sqrt{5} \cdot \sqrt{40}$ $10\sqrt{2}$
38. $\sqrt[3]{4} \cdot \sqrt[3]{80}$ $4\sqrt[3]{5}$
39. $\sqrt{x^5y^5} \cdot 3\sqrt{2x^7y^6}$ $3x^6y^5\sqrt{2y}$

40. $5\sqrt{2xy^6} \cdot 2\sqrt{2x^3y}$
41. $\sqrt{2}(\sqrt{50} + 7)$
42. $3(5 + \sqrt{21})$

43. $\sqrt{5}(\sqrt{5} + \sqrt{15})$
44. $\sqrt[3]{2x} \cdot \sqrt[3]{4} \cdot \sqrt[3]{2x^2}$ $2x\sqrt[3]{2}$
45. $\sqrt[3]{3x^2} \cdot \sqrt[3]{x^2} \cdot \sqrt[3]{9x^3}$ $3x^2\sqrt[3]{x}$

46. $\dfrac{\sqrt{5x^4}}{\sqrt{2x^2y^3}}$ $\dfrac{x\sqrt{10y}}{2y^2}$
47. $\dfrac{5\sqrt{2}}{3\sqrt{7x}}$ $\dfrac{5\sqrt{14x}}{21x}$
48. $\dfrac{1}{\sqrt[3]{9x}}$ $\dfrac{\sqrt[3]{3x^2}}{3x}$

49. $\dfrac{10}{\sqrt[3]{5x^2}}$ $\dfrac{2\sqrt[3]{25x}}{x}$
50. $\dfrac{\sqrt[3]{14}}{\sqrt[3]{7x^2y}}$ $\dfrac{\sqrt[3]{2xy^2}}{xy}$
51. $\dfrac{3\sqrt{11x^3y}}{-2\sqrt{12x^4y}}$ $\dfrac{\sqrt{33x}}{-4x}$

52. $-2(\sqrt[3]{32} + \sqrt[3]{54})$
    $-4\sqrt[3]{4} - 6\sqrt[3]{2}$
53. $\dfrac{3 + \sqrt{5}}{\sqrt{5}}$ $\dfrac{3\sqrt{5} + 5}{5}$
54. $\dfrac{\sqrt{3} - \sqrt{2}}{\sqrt{8}}$ $\dfrac{\sqrt{6} - 2}{4}$

55. **Satellites** The circular velocity v, in miles per hour, of a satellite orbiting Earth is given by the formula $v = \sqrt{\dfrac{1.24 \times 10^{12}}{r}}$, where r is the distance in miles from the satellite to the center of Earth. How much greater is the velocity of a satellite orbiting at an altitude of 100 mi than one orbiting at an altitude of 200 mi? (The radius of Earth is 3950 mi.) **about 212 mi/h greater**

56. **Geometry** A rectangular shelf is $\sqrt{440}$ cm by $\sqrt{20}$ cm. Find its area.

57. **Error Analysis** Explain the error in this simplification of radical expressions.
    $\sqrt{-2} \cdot \sqrt{-8} = \sqrt{-2(-8)} = \sqrt{16} = 4$ **56–57. See margin.**

58. **Physics** A freely falling object hit the ground in $\sqrt{18a^5}$ seconds. It fell h feet. Use the formula $h = 16t^2$ to find h in terms of a. **288 a^5 ft**

59. **Writing** Does $\sqrt{x^3} = \sqrt[3]{x^2}$ for all, some, or no values of x? Explain.
    See margin.

60. **Open-Ended** Of the equivalent expressions $\sqrt{\dfrac{2}{3}}, \dfrac{\sqrt{2}}{\sqrt{3}}$, and $\dfrac{\sqrt{6}}{3}$, which do you prefer to use for finding a decimal approximation with a calculator? Justify your reasoning. **Check students' work.**

Real-World Connection
A satellite being launched from the cargo bay of the space shuttle

Simplify each expression. Rationalize all denominators. Assume that all variables are positive.

61. $\sqrt{\sqrt{16x^4y^4}}$ $2xy$
62. $\sqrt[3]{\sqrt{64x^6y^{12}}}$ $2xy^2$
63. $\sqrt{\sqrt[3]{8000}}$ $2\sqrt{5}$

64. $\sqrt[3]{x^{-1}y^{-2}}$ $\dfrac{\sqrt[3]{x^2y}}{xy}$
65. $\sqrt[5]{x^{-4}y}$ $\dfrac{\sqrt[5]{yx}}{x}$
66. $\sqrt[6]{\dfrac{y^{-3}}{x^{-4}}}$ $\dfrac{\sqrt[6]{x^4y^3}}{y}$

67. $a = -2c, b = -6d$

67. **Critical Thinking** When $\sqrt{x^ay^b}$ is simplified, the result is $\dfrac{1}{x^cy^{3d}}$, where c and d are positive integers. Express a in terms of c, and b in terms of d.

68. **Critical Thinking** In Example 3 you saw that $\sqrt[3]{54x^2y^3} \cdot \sqrt[3]{5x^3y^4}$ simplifies to $3xy^2\sqrt[3]{10x^2y}$, if you assume that all the variables are positive. Now assume that the variables represent any real numbers. What changes must be made in the answer? Explain. **See margin.**

56. $20\sqrt{22}$ cm³

57. A product of two square roots can be simplified in this way only if the square roots are real numbers. $\sqrt{-2}$ and $\sqrt{-8}$ are not.

59. For some values, it is easy to see that the equation is true if $x = 0$ or $x = 1$. But when $x < 0$, $\sqrt{x^3}$ is not a real number, although $\sqrt[3]{x^2}$ is.

68. No changes need to be made; since they are both odd roots, there is no need for absolute value symbols.

Multiple Choice

69. Which expression does NOT simplify to -10? **C**

    A. $-\sqrt[3]{1000}$ **B.** $\sqrt{25} \cdot \sqrt[3]{-8}$

    C. $-\sqrt{25} \cdot \sqrt[5]{-32}$ **D.** $\sqrt[3]{-125} \cdot \sqrt[4]{16}$

70. How can you write $\sqrt[3]{\dfrac{5}{2xy}}$ with a rationalized denominator? **H**

    F. $\dfrac{\sqrt[3]{5}}{2xy}$ **G.** $\dfrac{\sqrt[3]{20}}{2xy}$ **H.** $\dfrac{\sqrt[3]{20x^2y^2}}{2xy}$ **J.** $\dfrac{\sqrt[3]{4x^2y^2}}{2xy}$

71. What is the simplified form of $\dfrac{3 - \sqrt{5}}{\sqrt{5}}$? **A**

    A. $\dfrac{3\sqrt{5} - 5}{5}$ **B.** $\dfrac{5\sqrt{3} - 5}{5}$

    C. $\dfrac{3\sqrt{3} - \sqrt{15}}{5}$ **D.** $\dfrac{14 - 6\sqrt{5}}{5}$

72. To rationalize the denominator of $\sqrt[3]{\dfrac{2}{9}}$, by what number would you multiply the numerator and denominator of the fraction? **G**

    F. 2   **G.** 3   **H.** 6   **J.** 9

73. Which of the following expressions is in simplest form? **D**

    A. $\sqrt{20x^3}$ **B.** $\sqrt[3]{81x}$ **C.** $\sqrt{\dfrac{6}{2}}$ **D.** $\dfrac{\sqrt{2}}{5}$

Short Response

74. For what values of x is $\sqrt{x} \cdot \sqrt{-x}$ a real number? Explain. 74–75. See margin.

Extended Response

75. Rationalize the denominator of $\sqrt[3]{\dfrac{3}{2x}}$. Explain your steps.

Mixed Review

Lesson 7-1

Simplify each radical expression. Use absolute value symbols as needed.

76. $\sqrt{121a^{90}}$ $11|a^{45}|$ **77.** $-\sqrt{81c^{48}d^{64}}$ $-9c^{24}d^{32}$

78. $\sqrt[3]{-64a^{81}}$ $-4a^{27}$ **79.** $\sqrt[5]{32y^{25}}$ $2y^5$

80. $\sqrt{0.25x^6}$ $0.5|x^3|$ **81.** $\sqrt[7]{x^{14}y^{35}}$ x^2y^5

82. $\sqrt[4]{16x^{36}y^{96}}$ $2|x^9|y^{24}$ **83.** $\sqrt{0.0064x^{40}}$ $0.08x^{20}$

Lesson 6-3

Divide. Tell whether each divisor is a factor of the dividend.

84. $(y^3 - 64) \div (y + 4)$ **85.** $(x^3 + 27) \div (x + 3)$

86. $(6a^3 + a^2 - a + 4) \div (2a + 1)$ **87.** $(2x^4 - 3x^3 - 4x + 10) \div (x - 2)$

84–87. See margin.

Lesson 5-7

Complete the square.

88. $x^2 + 10x + \blacksquare$ 25   **89.** $x^2 - 10x + \blacksquare$ 25

90. $x^2 + 11x + \blacksquare$ $\dfrac{121}{4}$ **91.** $x^2 - 11x + \blacksquare$ $\dfrac{121}{4}$

92. $x^2 - \dfrac{x}{3} + \blacksquare$ $\dfrac{1}{36}$ **93.** $x^2 + 0.3x + \blacksquare$ 0.0225

94. $x^2 - \dfrac{3}{4}x + \blacksquare$ $\dfrac{9}{64}$ **95.** $x^2 + \dfrac{3}{5}x + \blacksquare$ $\dfrac{9}{100}$

Right margin

📁 **Resources**

For additional practice with a variety of test item formats:
- Standardized Test Prep, p. 427
- Test-Taking Strategies, p. 422
- Test-Taking Strategies with Transparencies

74. **[2]** $\sqrt{x}$ is a real number if $x \geq 0$ and $\sqrt{-x}$ is a real number if $x \leq 0$. So the only value that makes $\sqrt{x} \cdot \sqrt{-x}$ a real number is $x = 0$.

  [1] answer only OR error describing value(s) of variables

75. **[4]** You should multiply $\sqrt[3]{\dfrac{3}{2x}}$ by $\dfrac{\sqrt[3]{4x^2}}{\sqrt[3]{4x^2}}$ because

$\sqrt[3]{\dfrac{3}{2x}} \cdot \dfrac{\sqrt[3]{4x^2}}{\sqrt[3]{4x^2}} =$

$\dfrac{\sqrt[3]{3}}{\sqrt[3]{2x}} \cdot \dfrac{\sqrt[3]{4x^2}}{\sqrt[3]{4x^2}} =$

$\dfrac{\sqrt[3]{12x^2}}{\sqrt[3]{8x^3}} = \dfrac{\sqrt[3]{12x^2}}{2x}$,

which has a denominator without a radical.

  [3] appropriate methods, but with one minor error

  [2] major error, but subsequent steps consistent with that error

  [1] correct final expression, but no work shown

84. $y^2 - 4y + 16$, R -128, not a factor

85. $x^2 - 3x + 9$, a factor

86. $3a^2 - a$, R 4, not a factor

87. $2x^3 + x^2 + 2x$, R 10, not a factor

Objectives

1 To add and subtract radical expressions
2 To multiply and divide binomial radical expressions

Examples

1 Adding and Subtracting Radical Expressions
2 Real-World Connection
3 Simplifying Before Adding or Subtracting
4 Multiplying Binomial Radical Expressions
5 Multiplying Conjugates
6 Rationalizing Binomial Radical Denominators

Math Background

Radical expressions play an important role in many applications. Learning how to simplify radical expressions is a key tool in expressing answers exactly.

More Math Background: p. 366C

Lesson Planning and Resources

See p. 366E for a list of the resources that support this lesson.

Bell Ringer Practice

✓ Check Skills You'll Need
For intervention, direct students to:

To Identify Quadratic Functions
Lesson 5-1: Example 1
Extra Skills and Word Problems Practice, Ch. 5

Binomial Radical Expressions

What You'll Learn

- To add and subtract radical expressions
- To multiply and divide binomial radical expressions

. . . And Why

To find the dimensions of a window design, as in Example 2

✓ Check Skills You'll Need **for Help** Lesson 5-1 or Skills Handbook page 881

Multiply.

1. $(5x + 4)(3x - 2)$ $15x^2 + 2x - 8$
2. $(-8x + 5)(3x - 7)$ $-24x^2 + 71x - 35$
3. $(x + 4)(x - 4)$ $x^2 - 16$
4. $(4x + 5)(4x - 5)$ $16x^2 - 25$
5. $(x + 5)^2$ $x^2 + 10x + 25$
6. $(2x - 9)^2$ $4x^2 - 36x + 81$

🔊 **New Vocabulary** • like radicals

---

1 Adding and Subtracting Radical Expressions

Like radicals are radical expressions that have the same index and the same radicand. To add or subtract like radicals, use the Distributive Property.

1 EXAMPLE Adding and Subtracting Radical Expressions

Add or subtract if possible.

a. $5\sqrt[3]{x} - 3\sqrt[3]{x}$

$\quad 5\sqrt[3]{x} - 3\sqrt[3]{x} = (5 - 3)\sqrt[3]{x}$ **Distributive Property with like radicals**

$\quad\quad\quad\quad\quad\quad = 2\sqrt[3]{x}$ **Simplify.**

b. $4\sqrt{2} + 5\sqrt{3}$

The radicals are not like radicals. They cannot be combined.

✓ Quick Check ❶ Add or subtract if possible.
a. $2\sqrt{7} + 3\sqrt{7}$ $5\sqrt{7}$
b. $7\sqrt[4]{5} - 2\sqrt[3]{5}$ **cannot combine**
c. $4\sqrt{xy} + 5\sqrt{xy}$ $9\sqrt{xy}$

2 EXAMPLE Real-World 🌐 Connection

2. $60\sqrt{2}$ in. or about 84.9 in.

Gridded Response In the stained-glass window design at the left, the side of each small square is 5 in. Find the perimeter of the window to the nearest tenth of an inch.

The diagonal of a square with side s is $s\sqrt{2}$. So the window's height is $2(5\sqrt{2})$ in., or $10\sqrt{2}$ in. The length is $3(5\sqrt{2})$ in., or $15\sqrt{2}$ in. The perimeter is $2(10\sqrt{2} + 15\sqrt{2})$in., or $50\sqrt{2}$ in. To the nearest tenth of an inch, the perimeter is 70.7 in.

✓ Quick Check ❷ Find the perimeter of the window if each small square is 6 in. on a side.

380 Chapter 7 Radical Functions and Rational Exponents

Differentiated Instruction Solutions for All Learners

Special Needs L1

For Example 1 Quick Check, have students circle indexes that are the same and underline radicands that are the same. Once like radicals are determined, students simply add coefficients as with combining like polynomial expressions.

learning style: visual

Below Level L2

Remind students of the meaning of the terms "index" and "radicand." Ask them to give examples of like and unlike radicals.

learning style: verbal

Simplify radicals before adding or subtracting so you can find all the like radicals.

Test-Taking Tip

A gridded response for an answer that contains a radical has to be an approximation.

3 EXAMPLE **Simplifying Before Adding or Subtracting**

Simplify $6\sqrt{18} + 4\sqrt{8} - 3\sqrt{72}$.

$$6\sqrt{18} + 4\sqrt{8} - 3\sqrt{72} = 6\sqrt{3^2 \cdot 2} + 4\sqrt{2^2 \cdot 2} - 3\sqrt{6^2 \cdot 2} \quad \text{Factor each radicand.}$$
$$= 6 \cdot 3\sqrt{2} + 4 \cdot 2\sqrt{2} - 3 \cdot 6\sqrt{2} \quad \text{Simplify each radical.}$$
$$= 18\sqrt{2} + 8\sqrt{2} - 18\sqrt{2} \quad \text{Multiply.}$$
$$= (18 + 8 - 18)\sqrt{2} \quad \text{Distributive Property}$$
$$= 8\sqrt{2}$$

 Quick Check ③ Simplify $\sqrt{50} + 3\sqrt{32} - 5\sqrt{18}$. $2\sqrt{2}$

2 Multiplying and Dividing Binomial Radical Expressions

Video Tutor Help
Visit: PHSchool.com
Web Code: age-0775

Multiply radical expressions that are in the form of binomials by using FOIL.

4 EXAMPLE **Multiplying Binomial Radical Expressions**

Multiply $(3 + 2\sqrt{5})(2 + 4\sqrt{5})$.

$$(3 + 2\sqrt{5})(2 + 4\sqrt{5}) = 3 \cdot 2 + 3 \cdot 4\sqrt{5} + 2 \cdot 2\sqrt{5} + 2\sqrt{5} \cdot 4\sqrt{5} \quad \text{Use FOIL.}$$
$$= 6 + 12\sqrt{5} + 4\sqrt{5} + 40 \quad \text{Multiply.}$$
$$= 6 + (12 + 4)\sqrt{5} + 40 \quad \text{Combine like radicals.}$$
$$= 46 + 16\sqrt{5}$$

 Quick Check ④ Multiply $(\sqrt{2} - \sqrt{3})^2$. $5 - 2\sqrt{6}$

GO for Help

To review conjugates, go to Lesson 6-5.

Conjugates are expressions, such as $\sqrt{a} + \sqrt{b}$ and $\sqrt{a} - \sqrt{b}$, that differ only in the sign of the second terms. If a and b are rational numbers, then the product of these conjugates is a rational number.

Let a and b represent rational numbers.
$$(\sqrt{a} + \sqrt{b})(\sqrt{a} - \sqrt{b}) = (\sqrt{a})^2 - (\sqrt{b})^2 \quad \text{The product is the difference of squares.}$$
$$= a - b \quad \text{Simplify.}$$
The difference of the rational numbers a and b is a rational number. So the product of the conjugates is a rational number.

5 EXAMPLE **Multiplying Conjugates**

Multiply $(2 + \sqrt{3})(2 - \sqrt{3})$.

$$(2 + \sqrt{3})(2 - \sqrt{3}) = 2^2 - (\sqrt{3})^2 \quad (a + b)(a - b) = a^2 - b^2$$
$$= 4 - 3$$
$$= 1$$

 Quick Check ⑤ Multiply $(\sqrt{5} + \sqrt{2})(\sqrt{5} - \sqrt{2})$. 3

Guided Instruction

Additional Examples

① Add or subtract if possible.
a. $7\sqrt{xy} + 3\sqrt{xy}$ $10\sqrt{xy}$
b. $2\sqrt[3]{x} - 2\sqrt[3]{5}$ not possible

② The rectangular window shown below is made up of three equilateral triangles and two right triangles. The equilateral triangles have sides of length 4 feet. What is the perimeter of the window? $16 + 4\sqrt{3}$ ft, or about 22.9 ft

③ Simplify $3\sqrt{20} - \sqrt{45} + 4\sqrt{80}$. $19\sqrt{5}$

Guided Instruction

Additional Examples

④ Multiply $(2 + 4\sqrt{3})(1 - 5\sqrt{3})$. $-58 - 6\sqrt{3}$

⑤ Multiply $(3 + \sqrt{7})(3 - \sqrt{7})$. 2

⑥ Rationalize the denominator of $\frac{2 - \sqrt{3}}{4 + \sqrt{3}}$. $\frac{11 - 6\sqrt{3}}{13}$

Resources
- Daily Notetaking Guide 7-3 **L3**

Closure

Ask students what must be true of radical expressions in order to add them, but not to multiply them. **They must be like to add them, but not to multiply them.**

Advanced Learners **L4**

Ask students to rationalize $\frac{1}{\sqrt[3]{7}}$ and $\frac{1}{\sqrt[4]{2}}$. Discuss whether $\frac{1}{1 - \sqrt[3]{7}}$ can be rationalized.

learning style: verbal

English Language Learners **ELL**

Using non-examples such as $2xy^3$, $5xy$, xy^2, and $-3x$, review *like terms* for polynomial expressions as having both the same variable(s) and exponent. Then show examples of *like radicals* as having both the same index and radicand.

learning style: visual

Assignment Guide

⓵ A B 1-12, 27-32, 45-47, 50

⓶ A B 13-26, 33-44, 48, 49
  C Challenge   51-55

Test Prep   56-62
Mixed Review   63-76

Homework Quick Check

To check students' understanding of key skills and concepts, go over Exercises 10, 15, 45, 46, 47.

Error Prevention!

Exercises 7–12 Remind students to first simplify the radical expressions they want to add or subtract. Otherwise, they will not always find all the like terms.

Visual Learners

Exercise 50 Have students draw a sketch of the rectangle with its sides labeled accordingly. Then have students write the multiplication expression for the area and work systematically to simplify and manipulate it into one of the answer choices.

Sometimes you need to rationalize the denominator of a fraction when the denominator is a binomial radical expression. Multiply the numerator and denominator of the fraction by the conjugate of the denominator.

6 EXAMPLE **Rationalizing Binomial Radical Denominators**

Rationalize the denominator of $\frac{3 + \sqrt{5}}{1 - \sqrt{5}}$.

$\frac{3 + \sqrt{5}}{1 - \sqrt{5}} = \frac{3 + \sqrt{5}}{1 - \sqrt{5}} \cdot \frac{1 + \sqrt{5}}{1 + \sqrt{5}}$ $1 + \sqrt{5}$ is the conjugate of $1 - \sqrt{5}$.

$= \frac{(3 + \sqrt{5})(1 + \sqrt{5})}{(1 - \sqrt{5})(1 + \sqrt{5})}$ **Multiply.**

$= \frac{3 + 3\sqrt{5} + \sqrt{5} + (\sqrt{5})^2}{1^2 - (\sqrt{5})^2}$ **Simplify.**

$= \frac{8 + 4\sqrt{5}}{-4}$

$= \frac{8}{-4} + \frac{4\sqrt{5}}{-4}$

$= -2 - \sqrt{5}$

✓ **Quick Check** ⑥ Rationalize the denominator of $\frac{6 + \sqrt{15}}{4 - \sqrt{15}}$. $39 + 10\sqrt{15}$

EXERCISES

For more exercises, see *Extra Skill and Word Problem Practice*.

Practice and Problem Solving

 Practice by Example

Examples 1 and 2
(page 380)

Add or subtract if possible.

cannot combine

1. $5\sqrt{6} + \sqrt{6}$ $6\sqrt{6}$ **2.** $6\sqrt[3]{3} - 2\sqrt[3]{3}$ $4\sqrt[3]{3}$ **3.** $4\sqrt{3} + 4\sqrt[3]{3}$

4. $3\sqrt{x} - 5\sqrt{x}$ $-2\sqrt{x}$ **5.** $14\sqrt{x} + 3\sqrt{y}$ **6.** $7\sqrt[3]{x^2} - 2\sqrt[3]{x^2}$
                          cannot combine $5\sqrt[3]{x^2}$

GO for Help

Example 3
(page 381)

Simplify.

7. $6\sqrt{18} + 3\sqrt{50}$ $33\sqrt{2}$ **8.** $14\sqrt{20} - 3\sqrt{125}$ $13\sqrt{5}$ **9.** $\sqrt{18} + \sqrt{32}$ $7\sqrt{2}$

10. $\sqrt[3]{54} + \sqrt[3]{16}$ $5\sqrt[3]{2}$ **11.** $3\sqrt[3]{81} - 2\sqrt[3]{54}$ **12.** $\sqrt[4]{32} + \sqrt[4]{48}$
                                  $9\sqrt[3]{3} - 6\sqrt[3]{2}$ $2\sqrt[4]{2} + 2\sqrt[4]{3}$

Example 4
(page 381)

Multiply.

13. $(3 + \sqrt{5})(1 + \sqrt{5})$ $8 + 4\sqrt{5}$ **14.** $(2 + \sqrt{7})(1 + 3\sqrt{7})$ $23 + 7\sqrt{7}$

15. $(3 - 4\sqrt{2})(5 - 6\sqrt{2})$ $63 - 38\sqrt{2}$ **16.** $(\sqrt{3} + \sqrt{5})^2$ $8 + 2\sqrt{15}$

17. $(\sqrt{13} + 6)^2$ $49 + 12\sqrt{13}$ **18.** $(2\sqrt{5} + 3\sqrt{2})^2$ $38 + 12\sqrt{10}$

Example 5
(page 381)

Multiply each pair of conjugates.

19. $(5 - \sqrt{11})(5 + \sqrt{11})$ 14 **20.** $(4 - 2\sqrt{3})(4 + 2\sqrt{3})$ 4

21. $(2\sqrt{6} + 8)(2\sqrt{6} - 8)$ -40 **22.** $(\sqrt{3} + \sqrt{5})(\sqrt{3} - \sqrt{5})$ -2

Example 6
(page 382)

Rationalize each denominator. Simplify the answer. **23–26. See margin.**

23. $\frac{4}{1 + \sqrt{3}}$ **24.** $\frac{4}{3\sqrt{3} - 2}$ **25.** $\frac{5 + \sqrt{3}}{2 - \sqrt{3}}$ **26.** $\frac{3 + \sqrt{8}}{2 - 2\sqrt{8}}$

23. $-2 + 2\sqrt{3}$ **25.** $13 + 7\sqrt{3}$

24. $\frac{12\sqrt{3} + 8}{23}$ **26.** $\frac{11 + 8\sqrt{2}}{-14}$

B **Apply Your Skills**

Simplify. Rationalize all denominators. Assume that all the variables are positive.

27. $\sqrt{72} + \sqrt{32} + \sqrt{18}$ $13\sqrt{2}$

28. $\sqrt{75} + 2\sqrt{48} - 5\sqrt{3}$ $8\sqrt{3}$

29. $5\sqrt{32x} + 4\sqrt{98x}$ $48\sqrt{2x}$

30. $\sqrt{75} - 4\sqrt{18} + 2\sqrt{32}$

GO **Online**
Homework Video Tutor
Visit: PHSchool.com
Web Code: age-0703

31. $4\sqrt{216y^2} + 3\sqrt{54y^2}$ **30–38. See margin.**

32. $3\sqrt[3]{16} - 4\sqrt[3]{54} + \sqrt[3]{128}$

33. $(\sqrt{3} - \sqrt{7})(\sqrt{3} + 2\sqrt{7})$

34. $(2\sqrt{5} + 3\sqrt{2})(5\sqrt{5} - 7\sqrt{2})$

35. $(1 + \sqrt{72})(5 + \sqrt{2})$

36. $(2 - \sqrt{98})(3 + \sqrt{18})$

37. $(\sqrt{x} + \sqrt{3})(\sqrt{x} + 2\sqrt{3})$

38. $(2\sqrt{y} - 3\sqrt{2})(4\sqrt{y} - 5\sqrt{2})$

Real-World **Connection**

The golden ratio is found in the growth patterns of many plants. $\frac{AC}{CD} = \frac{BC}{BD} = \frac{1 + \sqrt{5}}{2}$

39. $\frac{4 + \sqrt{27}}{2 - 3\sqrt{27}}$ $\frac{89 + 42\sqrt{3}}{-239}$

40. $\frac{4 + \sqrt{6}}{\sqrt{2} + \sqrt{3}}$ $2\sqrt{3} - \sqrt{2}$

41. $\frac{5 - \sqrt{21}}{\sqrt{3} - \sqrt{7}}$ $\frac{\sqrt{3} - \sqrt{7}}{2}$

42. $\frac{3 + \sqrt[3]{2}}{\sqrt[3]{2}}$ $\frac{2 + 3\sqrt[3]{4}}{2}$

43. $\frac{5 + \sqrt[4]{x}}{\sqrt[4]{x}}$ $\frac{x + 5\sqrt[4]{x^3}}{x}$

44. $\frac{4 - 2\sqrt[3]{6}}{\sqrt[3]{4}}$ $2\sqrt[3]{2} - \sqrt[3]{12}$

45. The golden ratio is $\frac{1 + \sqrt{5}}{2}$. Find the difference between the golden ratio and its **GPS** reciprocal. **See margin.**

46. **Critical Thinking** Describe the possible values of a such that $\sqrt{72} + \sqrt{a}$ can be simplified to a single term. **a must be twice a perfect square.**

47. **Writing** Discuss the advantages and disadvantages of first simplifying $\sqrt{72} + \sqrt{32} + \sqrt{18}$ in order to estimate its decimal value. **See margin.**

48. **Physics** An object is moving at a speed of $(3 + \sqrt{2})$ ft/s. How long will it take the object to travel 20 ft? $\frac{60 - 20\sqrt{2}}{7}$ **s, or about 4.53 s**

49. **Open-Ended** Find two pairs of conjugates with a product of 3. **See margin.**

50. **Multiple Choice** The length of a rectangle is $(3 + \sqrt{5})x$. The height is $(1 + 2\sqrt{5})y$. Which expression best describes the area of a rectangle? **D**

    (A) $(4 + 3\sqrt{5})(x + y)$

    (B) $13xy$

    (C) $(6 + 2\sqrt{5})x + (2 + 4\sqrt{5})y$

    (D) $(13 + 7\sqrt{5})xy$

C **Challenge**

Add or subtract.

51. $\frac{1}{1 - \sqrt{5}} + \frac{1}{1 + \sqrt{5}}$ $-\frac{1}{2}$

52. $\frac{4}{\sqrt{5} - \sqrt{3}} - \frac{4}{\sqrt{5} + \sqrt{3}}$ $4\sqrt{3}$

53. For what values of a and b does $\sqrt{a} + \sqrt{b} = \sqrt{a + b}$? **($a = 0$ and $b \geq 0$) or ($b = 0$ and $a \geq 0$)**

54. **Error Analysis** A student used the steps shown below to simplify an expression. Find the student's error and explain why the step is incorrect.

$$\frac{1}{(1 - \sqrt{2})^2} = (1 - \sqrt{2})^{-2}$$

$$= 1^{-2} - (\sqrt{2})^{-2}$$

$$= \frac{1}{1^2} - \frac{1}{(\sqrt{2}^2)} = \frac{1}{1} - \frac{1}{2} = \frac{1}{2}$$

In the second step the exponent was incorrectly distributed: $(a - b)^x \neq a^x - b^x$.

55a. **m and n can be any positive integers.**

b. **m must be even or n must be odd.**

55. In the expression $\sqrt[n]{x^m}$, m and n are positive integers and x is a real number. The expression can be simplified.

    a. If $x > 0$, what are the possible values for m and n?

    b. If $x < 0$, what are the possible values for m and n?

    c. If $x < 0$ and an absolute value symbol is needed in the simplified expression, what are the possible values of m and n? **m must be even, and n can be any positive integer.**

30. $5\sqrt{3} - 4\sqrt{2}$

31. $33y\sqrt{6}$

32. $-2\sqrt[3]{2}$

33. $-11 + \sqrt{21}$

34. $8 + \sqrt{10}$

35. $17 + 31\sqrt{2}$

36. $-36 - 15\sqrt{2}$

37. $x + 3\sqrt{3x} + 6$

38. $8y - 22\sqrt{2y} + 30$

---

4. Assess & Reteach

PowerPoint
Lesson Quiz

Simplify.

1. $6\sqrt{10} - 4\sqrt{10}$ $2\sqrt{10}$

2. $8\sqrt[3]{x} + 5\sqrt[3]{x}$ $13\sqrt[3]{x}$

3. $2\sqrt{27} + \sqrt{48}$ $10\sqrt{3}$

4. $\sqrt[3]{128} - \sqrt[3]{54}$ $\sqrt[3]{2}$

5. Multiply $(7 + 2\sqrt{3})(5 - \sqrt{3})$. $29 + 3\sqrt{3}$

6. Rationalize the denominator in $\frac{3 - 2\sqrt{7}}{10 - \sqrt{7}}$. $\frac{16 - 17\sqrt{7}}{93}$

Alternative Assessment

Have students write two addition problems and two subtraction problems that involve radicals and that have an answer of $3\sqrt{5}$. Then have them write a multiplication problem and a division problem, each involving two binomial radical expressions that have an answer of $2 + \sqrt{5}$. Have students share their problems with another student to check their work.

45. **The reciprocal is** $\frac{-1 + \sqrt{5}}{2}$**, which is one less than** $\frac{1 + \sqrt{5}}{2}$**.**

47. **Answers may vary. Sample: Without simplifying first, you must estimate three separate square roots, and then add the estimates. If they are first simplified, then they can be combined as** $13\sqrt{2}$**. Then only one square root need be estimated.**

49. **Answers may vary. Sample:** $(\sqrt{7} + 2)(\sqrt{7} - 2)$ $(2\sqrt{2} + \sqrt{5})(2\sqrt{2} - \sqrt{5})$

383

Resources

For additional practice with a variety of test item formats:

- Standardized Test Prep, p. 427
- Test-Taking Strategies, p. 422
- Test-Taking Strategies with Transparencies

Checkpoint Quiz

Use this Checkpoint Quiz to check students' understanding of the skills and concepts of Lessons 7-1 through 7-3.

Resources

Grab & Go

- Checkpoint Quiz 1

61. [2] $(1 - \sqrt[3]{8})(1 + \sqrt[3]{8}) =$
$(1 - 2)(1 + 2) =$
$1 - 4 = -3$, which is rational.

[1] the value -3 only OR yes only OR minor error in calculation

62. [4] $\dfrac{2}{5 + 2\sqrt{2}} - \dfrac{3}{5 - 2\sqrt{2}} =$

$\dfrac{2}{5 + 2\sqrt{2}} \cdot \dfrac{5 - 2\sqrt{2}}{5 - 2\sqrt{2}} -$

$\dfrac{3}{5 - 2\sqrt{2}} \cdot \dfrac{5 + 2\sqrt{2}}{5 + 2\sqrt{2}}$

$= \dfrac{10 - 4\sqrt{2}}{25 - 4 \cdot 2} - \dfrac{15 + 6\sqrt{2}}{25 - 4 \cdot 2}$

$= \dfrac{10 - 4\sqrt{2}}{17} - \dfrac{15 + 6\sqrt{2}}{17}$

$= \dfrac{10 - 4\sqrt{2} - 15 - 6\sqrt{2}}{17}$

$= \dfrac{-5 - 10\sqrt{2}}{17}$

[3] minor error, but appropriate method

384

Test Prep

Multiple Choice

56. Which expression does NOT simplify to one term? **B**
- **A.** $-4\sqrt{8} + \sqrt{18}$
- **B.** $\sqrt{27} - \sqrt{8}$
- **C.** $\sqrt{32} + 3\sqrt{8}$
- **D.** $\sqrt{12} - \sqrt{75}$

57. What is an expression for $\sqrt{20} - \sqrt{80} + \sqrt{125}$? **J**
- **F.** $\sqrt{65}$
- **G.** $13\sqrt{5}$
- **H.** $11\sqrt{5}$
- **J.** $3\sqrt{5}$

58. Which expression is NOT equal to 13? **D**
- **A.** $(4 + \sqrt{3})(4 - \sqrt{3})$
- **B.** $(5 - 2\sqrt{3})(5 + 2\sqrt{3})$
- **C.** $(6 + \sqrt{23})(6 - \sqrt{23})$
- **D.** $(7 - \sqrt{6})(7 + \sqrt{6})$

59. How can you write $\dfrac{1 + \sqrt{3}}{5 - \sqrt{3}}$ with a rationalized denominator? **J**
- **F.** -1
- **G.** $-2 - 3\sqrt{3}$
- **H.** $4 + 3\sqrt{3}$
- **J.** $\dfrac{4 + 3\sqrt{3}}{11}$

60. Which of the following is equivalent to $(2 + 3\sqrt{5})(3 + 3\sqrt{5})$? **D**
- **A.** 51
- **B.** $6 + 9\sqrt{5}$
- **C.** $6 + 24\sqrt{5}$
- **D.** $51 + 15\sqrt{5}$

Short Response

61. Is the product $(1 - \sqrt[3]{8})(1 + \sqrt[3]{8})$ a rational number? Explain. **See margin.**

Extended Response

62. What is the value of $\dfrac{2}{5 + 2\sqrt{2}} - \dfrac{3}{5 - 2\sqrt{2}}$? Show your work. **See margin.**

Mixed Review

GO for Help

Lesson 7-2

Simplify each expression. Rationalize all denominators. Assume that all variables are positive.

63. $\sqrt[3]{3} \cdot \sqrt[3]{18}$ $3\sqrt[3]{2}$
64. $\sqrt{3x} \cdot \sqrt{5x}$ $x\sqrt{15}$
65. $\dfrac{\sqrt{32}}{\sqrt{2}}$ 4
66. $\dfrac{\sqrt{62}}{\sqrt{6}}$ $\dfrac{\sqrt{93}}{3}$

67. $\sqrt[3]{2x^2} \cdot \sqrt[3]{4x}$ $2x$
68. $\sqrt{7x} \cdot \sqrt{14x^3}$ $7x^2\sqrt{2}$
69. $\dfrac{\sqrt{6m}}{\sqrt{2mn}}$ $\dfrac{\sqrt{3n}}{n}$
70. $\sqrt[3]{\dfrac{4}{5x}}$ $\dfrac{\sqrt[3]{100x^2}}{5x}$

Lesson 6-4

Solve each equation.

71. $2x^3 - 16 = 0$ $2, -1 \pm i\sqrt{3}$
72. $x^3 + 1000 = 0$ $-10, 5 \pm 5i\sqrt{3}$
73. $125x^3 - 1 = 0$ $\dfrac{1}{5}, \dfrac{-1 \pm i\sqrt{3}}{10}$

74. $x^4 - 14x^2 + 49 = 0$ $\pm\sqrt{7}$
75. $25x^4 - 40x^2 + 16 = 0$ $\dfrac{\pm2\sqrt{5}}{5}$
76. $81x^4 - 1 = 0$ $\pm\dfrac{i}{3}, \pm\dfrac{1}{3}$

Checkpoint Quiz 1

Lessons 7-1 through 7-3

Simplify each radical expression. Use absolute value symbols when needed.

1. $\sqrt[4]{b^4c^8}$ $|b|c^2$
2. $\sqrt[5]{x^5y^{10}}$ xy^2
3. $\sqrt[3]{-a^3}$ $-a$
4. $\sqrt[5]{-y^{10}}$ $-y^2$

Simplify each expression. Rationalize all denominators. Assume that all variables are positive.

5. $\sqrt{8}(\sqrt{24} + 3\sqrt{8})$ $8\sqrt{3} + 24$
6. $2\sqrt{5x^3} \cdot 3\sqrt{28x^3y^2}$ $12x^3y\sqrt{35}$

7. $4\sqrt[3]{81} - 3\sqrt[3]{54}$ $12\sqrt[3]{3} - 9\sqrt[3]{2}$
8. $\dfrac{4\sqrt{2xy}}{9\sqrt{5x^2y}}$ $\dfrac{4\sqrt{10x}}{45x}$

9. $(\sqrt{5} + 2\sqrt{3})(\sqrt{5} - 2\sqrt{3})$ -7
10. $\dfrac{5}{4\sqrt{7} + 5}$ $\dfrac{20\sqrt{7} - 25}{87}$

---

[2] correct method, but finds $\dfrac{10 - 4\sqrt{2}}{17} +$

$\dfrac{15 + 6\sqrt{2}}{17}$ and gets

$\dfrac{25 + 2\sqrt{2}}{17}$

[1] answer only, no work shown

Rational Exponents

What You'll Learn

• To simplify expressions with rational exponents

...And Why

To model simulated gravity in a spacecraft, as in Example 3

 Check Skills You'll Need

 for Help page 368

Simplify.

1. 2^{-4} $\frac{1}{16}$

2. $(3x)^{-2}$ $\frac{1}{9x^2}$

3. $(5x^2y)^{-3}$ $\frac{1}{125x^6y^3}$

4. $2^{-2} + 4^{-1}$ $\frac{1}{2}$

5. $(2a^{-2}b^3)^4$ $\frac{16b^{12}}{a^8}$

6. $(4a^3b^{-1})^{-2}$ $\frac{b^2}{16a^6}$

New Vocabulary • rational exponent

---

1 Simplifying Expressions With Rational Exponents

Another way to write a radical expression is to use a **rational exponent.** See the examples at the right.

Like the radical form, the exponent form always indicates the principal root.

Vocabulary Tip

Exponent comes from the Latin word meaning "place outside."

Radical form		Exponent form
$\sqrt{25}$	$=$	$25^{\frac{1}{2}}$
$\sqrt[3]{27}$	$=$	$27^{\frac{1}{3}}$
$\sqrt[4]{16}$	$=$	$16^{\frac{1}{4}}$

1 EXAMPLE Simplifying Expressions With Rational Exponents

Simplify each expression.

a. $125^{\frac{1}{3}}$

$125^{\frac{1}{3}} = \sqrt[3]{125}$ **Rewrite as a radical.**

$\qquad = \sqrt[3]{5^3}$ **Rewrite 125 as a cube.**

$\qquad = 5$ **Simplify.**

b. $5^{\frac{1}{2}} \cdot 5^{\frac{1}{2}}$

$5^{\frac{1}{2}} \cdot 5^{\frac{1}{2}} = \sqrt{5} \cdot \sqrt{5}$ **Rewrite as radicals.**

$\qquad = 5$ **By definition, $\sqrt{5}$ is the number whose square is 5.**

c. $10^{\frac{1}{3}} \cdot 100^{\frac{1}{3}}$

$10^{\frac{1}{3}} \cdot 100^{\frac{1}{3}} = \sqrt[3]{10} \cdot \sqrt[3]{100}$ **Rewrite as radicals.**

$\qquad = \sqrt[3]{10 \cdot 100}$ **Property for multiplying radical expressions**

$\qquad = \sqrt[3]{10^3}$ **Rewrite the radicand as a cube.**

$\qquad = 10$ **Simplify.**

Quick Check ❶ Simplify each expression.

a. $16^{\frac{1}{4}}$ **2**

b. $2^{\frac{1}{2}} \cdot 2^{\frac{1}{2}}$ **2**

c. $2^{\frac{1}{2}} \cdot 8^{\frac{1}{2}}$ **4**

---

1. Plan

Objective

1 To simplify expressions with rational exponents

Examples

1 Simplifying Expression With Rational Exponents

2 Converting to and From Radical Form

3 Real-World Connection

4 Simplifying Numbers With Rational Exponents

5 Writing Expressions in Simplest Form

 Professional Development

Math Background

Recall that the use of a nonzero integer exponent represents repeated multiplication, such as $2^3 = 2 \cdot 2 \cdot 2 = 8$ or $2^{-3} = \frac{1}{2} \cdot \frac{1}{2} \cdot \frac{1}{2} = \frac{1}{8}$. The use of a positive or negative rational exponent of the form $\frac{1}{n}$, represents the nth root of the base or the nth root of the multiplicative inverse of the base, respectively. These ideas can be combined to understand rational exponents of the form $\frac{m}{n}$, where m and n are integers.

More Math Background: p. 366C

Lesson Planning and Resources

See p. 366E for a list of the resources that support this lesson.

 PowerPoint

Bell Ringer Practice

Check Skills You'll Need

For intervention, direct students to:

Integer Exponents

Algebra 1 Review: Page 368

Differentiated Instruction Solutions for All Learners

Special Needs L1

Watch for students who confuse the meaning of negative and rational exponents. Consider introducing the rule $a^{-\frac{m}{n}} = \frac{1}{a^{\frac{m}{n}}}$ to clarify how the sign of the exponent amounts to finding a reciprocal.

learning style: verbal

Below Level L2

Review the properties of exponents and provide students with more examples of when to add or subtract exponents and when to multiply them.

learning style: verbal

2. Teach

Guided Instruction

 1 EXAMPLE **Auditory Learners**

Students may find it helpful to say to themselves in words what is shown symbolically in the equations. For example, in part a, they can say, "125 to the one-third power is equal to the cube root of 125." Hearing the words helps reinforce the concept.

2 EXAMPLE **Math Tip**

Remind students that terminating or repeating decimals are rational numbers. To write the expression $y^{-2.5}$ in radical form, first rewrite the exponent as a fraction.

4 EXAMPLE **Math Tip**

In part a, students may wonder if they could find $(-32)^{\frac{3}{5}}$ by first finding $(-32)^3$ and then raising the result to the one-fifth power. The expression can be simplified in this way, but a calculator is necessary. The method in the textbook requires only pencil and paper.

A rational exponent may have a numerator other than 1. The property $(a^m)^n = a^{mn}$ shows how to rewrite an expression with an exponent that is an improper fraction.

$$25^{\frac{3}{2}} = 25^{(3 \cdot \frac{1}{2})} = (25^3)^{\frac{1}{2}} = \sqrt{25^3} \quad \text{or} \quad 25^{\frac{3}{2}} = 25^{(\frac{1}{2} \cdot 3)} = (25^{\frac{1}{2}})^3 = (\sqrt{25})^3$$

 Key Concepts

Definition	Rational Exponents

If the nth root of a is a real number and m is an integer, then

$$a^{\frac{1}{n}} = \sqrt[n]{a} \quad \text{and} \quad a^{\frac{m}{n}} = \sqrt[n]{a^m} = (\sqrt[n]{a})^m. \qquad \text{If } m \text{ is negative, } a \neq 0.$$

2c. If m is negative, $a^{\frac{m}{n}} = \frac{1}{(\sqrt[n]{a})^{-m}}$, and

if $a = 0$, then the denominator of the fraction would be zero. Since this cannot happen, $a \neq 0$.

 2 EXAMPLE **Converting to and From Radical Form**

a. Write the exponential expressions $x^{\frac{3}{5}}$ and $y^{-2.5}$ in radical form.

$$x^{\frac{3}{5}} = \sqrt[5]{x^3} \text{ or } (\sqrt[5]{x})^3 \qquad\qquad y^{-2.5} = y^{-\frac{5}{2}} = \frac{1}{\sqrt{y^5}} \text{ or } \frac{1}{(\sqrt{y})^5}$$

b. Write the radical expressions $\sqrt{a^3}$ and $(\sqrt[5]{b})^2$ in exponential form.

$$\sqrt{a^3} = a^{\frac{3}{2}} \qquad\qquad (\sqrt[5]{b})^2 = b^{\frac{2}{5}}$$

✓ **Quick Check** **2 a.** Write the expressions $y^{-\frac{3}{8}}$ and $z^{0.4}$ in radical form. $\frac{1}{\sqrt[8]{y^3}}, \sqrt[5]{z^2}$

b. Write the expressions $\sqrt[3]{x^2}$ and $(\sqrt{y})^3$ in exponential form. $x^{\frac{2}{3}}, y^{\frac{3}{2}}$

c. Critical Thinking Refer to the definition of rational exponents. Explain the need for the following restriction: If m is negative, $a \neq 0$. **See left.**

 3 EXAMPLE **Real-World** **Connection**

Space Travel Bone loss for astronauts on lengthy space voyages may be prevented with a bedlike apparatus that rotates to simulate the effect of gravity. In the formula $N = \frac{a^{0.5}}{2\pi r^{0.5}}$, N is the rate of rotation in revolutions per second, a is the simulated acceleration in m/s², and r is the radius of the apparatus in meters. How fast would an apparatus with a radius of 1.7 m have to rotate to simulate the acceleration of 9.8 m/s² that is due to Earth's gravity?

> **Graphing Calculator Hint**
>
> Use the △ key to enter an exponent. If the exponent is a fraction, enclose it in parentheses. For example, $729^{\frac{2}{3}}$ is entered as 729 △ (2 ÷ 3).

$$N = \frac{a^{0.5}}{2\pi r^{0.5}} \qquad \text{Write the formula.}$$

$$= \frac{9.8^{0.5}}{2\pi(1.7)^{0.5}} \qquad \text{Substitute for } a \text{ and } r.$$

$$\approx 0.382 \qquad \text{Use a calculator.}$$

3. about 0.270 revolutions per second, or about 16 revolutions per minute

The apparatus would have to rotate about 0.382 revolutions per second, or about 23 revolutions per minute.

✓ **Quick Check** **3** Calculate the rate of rotation needed for the apparatus in Example 3 to simulate a gravitational acceleration half as strong as Earth's. **See left.**

386 Chapter 7 Radical Functions and Rational Exponents

 Differentiated Instruction **Solutions for All Learners**

Advanced Learners L4	**English Language Learners** ELL
Have students approximate $2^{\frac{7\pi}{11}}$, then compare their approximation with their calculator answer.	For Example 3, make sure students understand terms such as *apparatus, rate of rotation, artificial acceleration,* and *acceleration due to Earth's gravity.*
learning style: verbal	learning style: verbal

All of the properties of integer exponents also apply to rational exponents. Here is a summary.

Key Concepts

GO for Help

Refer to the properties of integer exponents on p. 368.

Summary	Properties of Rational Exponents

Let m and n represent rational numbers. Assume that no denominator equals 0.

Property	Example
$a^m \cdot a^n = a^{m+n}$	$8^{\frac{1}{3}} \cdot 8^{\frac{2}{3}} = 8^{\frac{1}{3}+\frac{2}{3}} = 8^1 = 8$
$(a^m)^n = a^{mn}$	$\left(5^{\frac{1}{2}}\right)^4 = 5^{\frac{1}{2}\cdot 4} = 5^2 = 25$
$(ab)^m = a^m b^m$	$(4 \cdot 5)^{\frac{1}{2}} = 4^{\frac{1}{2}} \cdot 5^{\frac{1}{2}} = 2 \cdot 5^{\frac{1}{2}}$
$a^{-m} = \dfrac{1}{a^m}$	$9^{-\frac{1}{2}} = \dfrac{1}{9^{\frac{1}{2}}} = \dfrac{1}{3}$
$\dfrac{a^m}{a^n} = a^{m-n}$	$\dfrac{\pi^{\frac{3}{2}}}{\pi^{\frac{1}{2}}} = \pi^{\frac{3}{2}-\frac{1}{2}} = \pi^1 = \pi$
$\left(\dfrac{a}{b}\right)^m = \dfrac{a^m}{b^m}$	$\left(\dfrac{5}{27}\right)^{\frac{1}{3}} = \dfrac{5^{\frac{1}{3}}}{27^{\frac{1}{3}}} = \dfrac{5^{\frac{1}{3}}}{3}$

You can simplify a number with a rational exponent by using the properties of exponents or by converting the expression to a radical expression.

4 EXAMPLE Simplifying Numbers With Rational Exponents

GO Online

Video Tutor Help

Visit: PHSchool.com
Web Code: age-0775

Simplify each number.

a. $(-32)^{\frac{3}{5}}$

Method 1	Method 2
$(-32)^{\frac{3}{5}} = ((-2)^5)^{\frac{3}{5}}$	$(-32)^{\frac{3}{5}} = \left(\sqrt[5]{-32}\right)^3$
$\quad = (-2)^{5 \cdot \frac{3}{5}}$	$\quad = \left(\sqrt[5]{(-2)^5}\right)^3$
$\quad = (-2)^3$	$\quad = (-2)^3$
$\quad = -8$	$\quad = -8$

b. $4^{-3.5}$

Method 1	Method 2
$4^{-3.5} = 4^{-\frac{7}{2}}$	$4^{-3.5} = 4^{-\frac{7}{2}}$
$\quad = (2^2)^{-\frac{7}{2}}$	$\quad = \dfrac{1}{4^{\frac{7}{2}}}$
$\quad = 2^{2 \cdot -\frac{7}{2}}$	$\quad = \dfrac{1}{(\sqrt{4})^7}$
$\quad = 2^{-7}$	$\quad = \dfrac{1}{2^7}$
$\quad = \dfrac{1}{2^7}$	$\quad = \dfrac{1}{128}$
$\quad = \dfrac{1}{128}$	

 Quick Check 4 Simplify each number.

a. $25^{-\frac{3}{2}}$ $\dfrac{1}{125}$ **b.** $32^{\frac{3}{5}}$ 8 **c.** $(-32)^{\frac{4}{5}}$ 16

PowerPoint

Additional Examples

1 Simplify each expression.
a. $64^{\frac{1}{3}}$ 4   **b.** $7^{\frac{1}{2}} \cdot 7^{\frac{1}{2}}$ 7
c. $5^{\frac{1}{3}} \cdot 25^{\frac{1}{3}}$ 5

2 **a.** Write the exponential expressions $x^{\frac{2}{7}}$ and $y^{-0.4}$ in radical form. $\sqrt[7]{x^2}$ or $\left(\sqrt[7]{x}\right)^2$, $\dfrac{1}{\sqrt[5]{y^2}}$ or $\dfrac{1}{\left(\sqrt[5]{y}\right)^2}$
b. Write the radical expressions $\sqrt[4]{c^3}$ and $\left(\sqrt[3]{b}\right)^5$ in exponential form. $c^{\frac{3}{4}}$, $b^{\frac{5}{3}}$

3 The time t in hours needed to cook a pot roast that weighs p pounds can be approximated by using the equation $t = 0.89p^{0.6}$. To the nearest hundredth of an hour, how long would it take to cook a pot roast that weighs 13 lb? **4.15 h**

4 Simplify each number.
a. $(-27)^{\frac{2}{3}}$ 9   **b.** $25^{-2.5}$ $\dfrac{1}{3125}$

5 Write $(243a^{-10})^{\frac{2}{5}}$ in simplest form. $\dfrac{9}{a^4}$

Resources
• Daily Notetaking Guide 7-4 **L3**

Closure

Have students use a radical expression to explain the meaning of $a^{\frac{m}{n}}$, where m and n are integers, the nth root of a is a real number, and $a \neq 0$ if m is negative.
$a^{\frac{m}{n}}$ means $\sqrt[n]{a^m}$ or $\left(\sqrt[n]{a}\right)^m$.

Assignment Guide

1 A B 1-80
C Challenge   81-87

Test Prep   88-96
Mixed Review   97-108

Homework Quick Check
To check students' understanding of key skills and concepts, go over Exercises 34, 46, 62, 69, 77.

Error Prevention!

Exercises 18–21 Be sure students recall that the index for a square root expression is 2.

Exercise 63 Students may incorrectly apply the fractional exponent to the power of 10 and not apply it to 46 as well. Show how $[46 \times (10)^4]^{\frac{4}{3}}$ is of the form $(ab)^m = a^m b^m$.

Exercises 65–76 You may need to remind students that the expressions in each final answer should contain only positive exponents.

To write an expression with rational exponents in simplest form, write every exponent as a positive number.

5 EXAMPLE   **Writing Expressions in Simplest Form**

Write $(16y^{-8})^{-\frac{3}{4}}$ in simplest form.

$$(16y^{-8})^{-\frac{3}{4}} = (2^4 y^{-8})^{-\frac{3}{4}}$$
$$= 2^{4 \cdot (-\frac{3}{4})} \cdot y^{-8 \cdot (-\frac{3}{4})}$$
$$= 2^{-3} y^6$$
$$= \frac{y^6}{2^3}$$
$$= \frac{y^6}{8}$$

 Quick Check **5** Write $(8x^{15})^{-\frac{1}{3}}$ in simplest form. $\frac{1}{2x^5}$

EXERCISES

For more exercises, see *Extra Skill and Word Problem Practice*.

Practice and Problem Solving

A **Practice by Example**

GO for Help

Example 1
(page 385)

Simplify each expression.

1. $36^{\frac{1}{2}}$ 6   **2.** $27^{\frac{1}{3}}$ 3   **3.** $49^{\frac{1}{2}}$ 7

4. $10^{\frac{1}{2}} \cdot 10^{\frac{1}{2}}$ 10   **5.** $(-3)^{\frac{1}{3}} \cdot (-3)^{\frac{1}{3}} \cdot (-3)^{\frac{1}{3}}$ −3   **6.** $3^{\frac{1}{2}} \cdot 12^{\frac{1}{2}}$ 6

7. $2^{\frac{1}{2}} \cdot 32^{\frac{1}{2}}$ 8   **8.** $3^{\frac{1}{3}} \cdot 9^{\frac{1}{3}}$ 3   **9.** $3^{\frac{1}{4}} \cdot 27^{\frac{1}{4}}$ 3

Example 2
(page 386)

Write each expression in radical form.

10. $x^{\frac{1}{6}}$ $\sqrt[6]{x}$ **11.** $x^{\frac{1}{5}}$ $\sqrt[5]{x}$ **12.** $x^{\frac{2}{7}}$ $\sqrt[7]{x^2}$ or $(\sqrt[7]{x})^2$ **13.** $y^{\frac{2}{5}}$

13. $\sqrt[5]{y^2}$ or $(\sqrt[5]{y})^2$

14. $y^{-\frac{9}{8}}$ $\frac{1}{\sqrt[8]{y^9}}$ or $\frac{1}{(\sqrt[8]{y})^9}$ **15.** $t^{-\frac{3}{4}}$ $\frac{1}{\sqrt[4]{t^3}}$ or $\frac{1}{(\sqrt[4]{t})^3}$ **16.** $x^{1.5}$ $\sqrt{x^3}$ or $(\sqrt{x})^3$ **17.** $y^{1.2}$

17. $\sqrt[5]{y^6}$ or $(\sqrt[5]{y})^6$

Write each expression in exponential form.

18. $\sqrt{-10}$ $(-10)^{\frac{1}{2}}$ **19.** $\sqrt{7x^3}$ $7^{\frac{1}{2}} x^{\frac{3}{2}}$ **20.** $\sqrt{(7x)^3}$ $(7x)^{\frac{3}{2}}$ **21.** $\left(\sqrt{7x}\right)^3$ $(7x)^{\frac{3}{2}}$

22. $\sqrt[3]{a^2}$ $a^{\frac{2}{3}}$ **23.** $\left(\sqrt[3]{a}\right)^2$ $a^{\frac{2}{3}}$ **24.** $\sqrt[4]{c^2}$ $c^{\frac{1}{2}}$ **25.** $\sqrt[3]{(5xy)^6}$ $25x^2y^2$

Example 3
(page 386)

The optimal height h of the letters of a message printed on pavement is given by the formula $h = \frac{0.00252 d^{2.27}}{e}$. Here d is the distance of the driver from the letters and e is the height of the driver's eye above the pavement. All of the distances are in meters. Find h for the given values of d and e.

26. $d = 100$ m, $e = 1.2$ m ≈**72.8 m**   **27.** $d = 50$ m, $e = 1.2$ m ≈**15.1 m**

28. $d = 50$ m, $e = 2.3$ m ≈**7.9 m**   **29.** $d = 25$ m, $e = 2.3$ m ≈**1.6 m**

Example 4
(page 387)

Simplify each number.

30. $8^{\frac{2}{3}}$ 4   **31.** $64^{\frac{2}{3}}$ 16   **32.** $(-8)^{\frac{2}{3}}$ 4   **33.** $(-32)^{\frac{6}{5}}$ 64

34. $(32)^{-\frac{4}{5}}$ $\frac{1}{16}$ **35.** $4^{1.5}$ 8   **36.** $16^{1.5}$ 64   **37.** $10,000^{0.75}$ 1000

Left margin answers:

40. $\dfrac{1}{3x^{\frac{2}{3}}}$

41. $\dfrac{5}{x^{\frac{2}{3}}}$

45. $x^{\frac{13}{3}}$

Example 5
(page 388)

Write each expression in simplest form. Assume that all variables are positive.

38. $\left(x^{\frac{2}{3}}\right)^{-3}$ $\dfrac{1}{x^2}$ **39.** $\left(x^{-\frac{4}{7}}\right)^7$ $\dfrac{1}{x^4}$ **40.** $\left(3x^{\frac{2}{3}}\right)^{-1}$ **41.** $5\left(x^{\frac{2}{3}}\right)^{-1}$

42. $\left(-27x^{-9}\right)^{\frac{1}{3}}$ $-\dfrac{3}{x^3}$ **43.** $\left(-32y^{15}\right)^{\frac{1}{5}}$ $-2y^3$ **44.** $\left(\dfrac{x^3}{x^{-1}}\right)^{-\frac{1}{4}}$ $\dfrac{1}{x}$ **45.** $\left(\dfrac{x^2}{x^{-11}}\right)^{\frac{1}{3}}$

46. $\left(x^{\frac{1}{2}}y^{-\frac{2}{3}}\right)^{-6}$ $\dfrac{y^4}{x^3}$ **47.** $\left(x^{\frac{2}{3}}y^{-\frac{1}{6}}\right)^{-12}$ $\dfrac{y^2}{x^8}$ **48.** $\left(\dfrac{x^{\frac{1}{4}}}{y^{-\frac{3}{4}}}\right)^{12}$ x^3y^9 **49.** $\left(\dfrac{x^{-\frac{2}{3}}}{y^{-\frac{1}{3}}}\right)^{15}$ $\dfrac{y^5}{x^{10}}$

B **Apply Your Skills**

Simplify each number.

50. $(-343)^{\frac{1}{3}}$ -7 **51.** $(-243)^{\frac{1}{5}}$ -3 **52.** $32^{1.2}$ 64 **53.** $243^{1.2}$ 729

54. $64^{3.5}$ $2{,}097{,}152$ **55.** $100^{4.5}$ $1{,}000{,}000{,}000$ or 10^9 **56.** $32^{-0.4}$ $\dfrac{1}{4}$ **57.** $64^{-0.5}$ $\dfrac{1}{8}$

58. $(-216)^{-\frac{2}{3}}$ $\dfrac{1}{36}$ **59.** $2(16)^{\frac{3}{4}}$ 16 **60.** $-(-27)^{-\frac{4}{3}}$ $-\dfrac{1}{81}$ **61.** $\dfrac{1000^{\frac{4}{3}}}{100^{\frac{3}{2}}}$ 10

Real-World **Connection**

Archaeologists estimate the ages of artifacts and fossils by using exponential functions.

73. $\dfrac{1}{x^{\frac{13}{36}}}$ **74.** $\dfrac{1}{x^{\frac{7}{24}}}$

75. $\dfrac{1}{x^{\frac{1}{3}}}$ **76.** $\dfrac{1}{(xy)^{\frac{1}{2}}}$

GO Online
Homework Video Tutor
Visit: PHSchool.com
Web Code: age-0704

62. Archaeology The ratio R of radioactive carbon to nonradioactive carbon left **GPS** in a sample of an organism that died T years ago can be approximated by the formula $R = A(2.7)^{-\frac{T}{8033}}$. Here A is the ratio of radioactive carbon to nonradioactive carbon in the living organism. What percent of A is left after 2000 years? After 4000 years? After 8000 years? **about 78%, 61%, 37%**

63. Multiple Choice The expression $0.036m^{\frac{3}{4}}$ is used in the study of fluids. Which best represents the value of the expression for $m = 46 \times 10^4$? **A**

    Ⓐ 636   Ⓑ 1460   Ⓒ 1660   Ⓓ 16,600

64. Physics In the expression $PV^{\frac{7}{5}}$, P represents the pressure and V represents the volume of a sample of a gas. Evaluate the expression for $P = 6$ and $V = 32$.
768

Simplify each expression. Assume that all variables are positive.

65. $x^{\frac{2}{7}} \cdot x^{\frac{3}{14}}$ $x^{\frac{1}{2}}$ **66.** $y^{\frac{1}{2}} \cdot y^{\frac{3}{10}}$ $y^{\frac{4}{5}}$ **67.** $x^{\frac{3}{5}} \div x^{\frac{1}{10}}$ $x^{\frac{1}{2}}$ **68.** $y^{\frac{5}{7}} \div y^{\frac{3}{14}}$ $y^{\frac{1}{2}}$

69. $\dfrac{x^{\frac{2}{3}}y^{-\frac{1}{4}}}{x^{\frac{1}{2}}y^{-\frac{1}{2}}}$ $x^{\frac{1}{6}}y^{\frac{1}{4}}$ **70.** $\dfrac{x^{\frac{1}{2}}y^{-\frac{1}{3}}}{x^{\frac{3}{4}}y^{\frac{1}{2}}}$ $\dfrac{1}{x^{\frac{1}{4}}y^{\frac{5}{6}}}$ **71.** $\left(\dfrac{16x^{14}}{81y^{18}}\right)^{\frac{1}{2}}$ $\dfrac{4x^7}{9y^9}$ **72.** $\left(\dfrac{81y^{16}}{16x^{12}}\right)^{\frac{1}{2}}$ $\dfrac{9y^8}{4x^6}$

73. $\left(x^{\frac{1}{2}} \cdot x^{\frac{5}{12}}\right)^{\frac{1}{3}} \div x^{\frac{2}{3}}$ **74.** $\left(x^{\frac{3}{4}} \div x^{\frac{1}{8}}\right) \cdot x^{-\frac{1}{6}}$ **75.** $\left[\left(x^{-\frac{1}{2}}\right)^2\right]^{\frac{1}{3}}$ **76.** $\left[\left(\sqrt{x^3y^3}\right)^{\frac{1}{3}}\right]^{-1}$

77. Writing Explain why $(-64)^{\frac{1}{3}} = -64^{\frac{1}{3}}$ and $(-64)^{\frac{1}{2}} \neq -64^{\frac{1}{2}}$. **See margin.**

78. Error Analysis Explain why the following simplification is incorrect.
$$5\left(4 - 5^{\frac{1}{2}}\right) = 5(4) - 5\left(5^{\frac{1}{2}}\right) = 20 - 25^{\frac{1}{2}} = 15$$ **See margin.**

79. Open-Ended Find three nonzero numbers a such that $a\left(4 + 5^{\frac{1}{2}}\right)$ is a rational number. Can a itself be a rational number? Explain.

80. a. Reasoning Show that $\sqrt[4]{x^2} = \sqrt{x}$ by using the definition of fourth root.

   b. Reasoning Show that $\sqrt[4]{x^2} = \sqrt{x}$ by rewriting $\sqrt[4]{x^2}$ in exponential form.
a–b. See margin.

C **Challenge**

79. Answers may vary.
Sample: $4 - 5^{\frac{1}{2}}$,

$2\left(4 - 5^{\frac{1}{2}}\right)$, $\dfrac{4 - 5^{\frac{1}{2}}}{2}$; no, if a is rational and the product is rational, then $4 + 5^{\frac{1}{2}}$ must be rational.

Exponents that are irrational numbers can be defined so that all the properties of rational exponents are also true for irrational exponents. Use those properties to simplify each expression.

81. $\left(7^{\sqrt{2}}\right)^{\sqrt{2}}$ 49 **82.** $\dfrac{3^{3+\sqrt{5}}}{3^{1+\sqrt{5}}}$ 9 **83.** $\dfrac{x^{4\pi}}{x^{2\pi}}$ $x^{2\pi}$

84. $5^{2\sqrt{3}} \cdot 25^{-\sqrt{3}}$ 1 **85.** $9^{\frac{1}{\sqrt{2}}}$ $3^{\sqrt{2}}$ **86.** $\left(3^{2+\sqrt{2}}\right)^{2-\sqrt{2}}$ 9

Online lesson quiz, PHSchool.com, Web Code: aga-0704   Lesson 7-4 Rational Exponents   **389**

77. The cube root of -64 is -4, which equals $-(64)^{\frac{1}{3}}$. The square root of -64 is not a real number, but $-(64)^{\frac{1}{2}} = -\sqrt{64} = -8$.

78. The exponent $\frac{1}{2}$ applies only to the 5, not to the 25.

80a. $\sqrt{x} \cdot \sqrt{x} \cdot \sqrt{x} \cdot \sqrt{x} = x \cdot x$
$= x^2$, so $\sqrt[4]{x^2} = \sqrt{x}$

b. $\sqrt[4]{x^2} = (x^2)^{\frac{1}{4}} = x^{\frac{2}{4}} =$
$x^{\frac{1}{2}} = \sqrt{x}$

4. Assess & Reteach

Lesson Quiz

1. Simplify each expression.
   a. $100^{\frac{1}{2}}$ **10** **b.** $(-64)^{\frac{1}{3}}$ **-4**

2. Write each expression in radical form.
   a. $x^{\frac{1}{7}}$ $\sqrt[7]{x}$
   b. $y^{\frac{4}{5}}$ $\sqrt[5]{y^4}$ or $\left(\sqrt[5]{y}\right)^4$
   c. $k^{1.8}$ $\sqrt[5]{k^9}$ or $\left(\sqrt[5]{k}\right)^9$
   d. $a^{-\frac{1}{6}}$ $\dfrac{1}{\sqrt[6]{a}}$

3. A container with curved sides is 10 ft tall. When water is in the container to a depth of h ft, the number of cubic feet of water can be approximated by using the formula $V = 0.95h^{2.9}$. Find the amount of water in the container when the depth of the water is 7.5 ft. Round to the nearest hundredth. **327.64 ft³**

4. Simplify each number.
   a. $(-64)^{\frac{4}{3}}$ **256**
   b. $81^{0.75}$ **27**

5. Write $\left(x^{\frac{2}{3}}y^{-\frac{1}{4}}\right)^{-4}$ in simplest form.
   $\dfrac{y}{x^{\frac{8}{3}}}$

Alternative Assessment

Have students work in pairs. Each student should write a new exercise similar to those in each exercise group in Practice and Problem Solving, Section A (pages 382–383). Students trade exercises and solve the exercises that his or her partner wrote. Students check each other's work and discuss any discrepancies.

100. $15 - 4\sqrt{14}$

101. $\dfrac{4 + 6\sqrt{5} + 2\sqrt{10} + 15\sqrt{2}}{-41}$

102. $\dfrac{10 - 8\sqrt{2}}{7}$

103. $4x(x^2 - 2x + 4)$

104. $(x + 2)^2$

105. $(x - 9)^2$

106. $(4a - 3b)(4a + 3b)$

107. $(5x - 4y)^2$

108. $(3x + 8)^2$

95. [2] $\dfrac{3x^2\sqrt{x}}{y^3}$
[1] minor error

96. [2] $(1 + \sqrt{2})$, or any rational number times $(1 + \sqrt{2})$, and a reasonable explanation
[1] no explanation

94. [2] $x = \dfrac{1}{16}$
[1] minor error

 87. Weather Using data for the effect of temperature and wind on an exposed face, the National Weather Service uses the following formula.

$$\text{Wind Chill Index} = 35.74 + 0.6215T - 35.75V^{0.16} + 0.4275TV^{0.16}$$

T is the temperature in degrees Fahrenheit and V is the velocity of the wind in miles per hour. Frostbite occurs in about 15 minutes when the wind chill index is about -20. Find the wind speed that produces a wind chill index of -20 when the temperature is 5°F. **33.13 mph**

Test Prep

Multiple Choice

88. Which expression is NOT equivalent to $\sqrt[4]{4n^2}$? **B**

A. $(4n^2)^{\frac{1}{4}}$ **B.** $2n^{\frac{1}{2}}$ **C.** $(2n)^{\frac{1}{2}}$ **D.** $\sqrt{2n}$

89. Which expression is NOT equivalent to $\sqrt[6]{81x^4y^8}$? **H**

F. $(3xy^2)^{\frac{2}{3}}$ **G.** $(3x)^{\frac{2}{3}}y^{\frac{4}{3}}$ **H.** $(3x^2y^4)^{\frac{1}{3}}$ **J.** $\sqrt[3]{9x^2y^4}$

90. Which equation represents a property of exponents? **C**

A. $(a^m)^n = a^{m+n}$ **B.** $\left(\dfrac{a}{b}\right)^m = \dfrac{a^m}{b}$ **C.** $a^{-m} = \dfrac{1}{a^m}$ **D.** $a^m \cdot a^n = a^{mn}$

91. Which expression is equivalent to $\left(\dfrac{1}{64}\right)^{-\frac{1}{6}}$? **H**

F. $\left(\dfrac{1}{2}\right)^{-6}$ **G.** 4^3 **H.** 2 **J.** 64^6

92. Which expression is equivalent to $\left(n^{\frac{3}{2}} \div n^{-\frac{1}{6}}\right)^{-3}$? **D**

A. n^{27} **B.** n^{-27} **C.** n^{-4} **D.** n^{-5}

93. Which number is closest to $(81n^2)^{0.75}$ for $n = 2$? **G**

F. 45.4   **G.** 76.4   **H.** 243.0   **J.** 2061.9

Short Response

94. What is the value of x if $32^{0.8}x = 1$? Simplify the answer. **See left.**

95. For $x > 0$ and $y > 0$, write $\sqrt{9x^5y^{-6}}$ in simplest form. **95–96. See above left.**

96. Find a nonzero number q such that $q(1 - \sqrt{2})$ is a rational number. Explain.

Mixed Review

GO for Help

Lesson 7-3

Simplify. Rationalize all denominators.

$1 + 3\sqrt{5}$

97. $6\sqrt[3]{3} - 2\sqrt[3]{3}$ $4\sqrt[3]{3}$ **98.** $3\sqrt{18} + 2\sqrt{72}$ $21\sqrt{2}$ **99.** $(\sqrt{5} - 1)(\sqrt{5} + 4)$

100. $(\sqrt{8} - \sqrt{7})^2$ **101.** $\dfrac{2 + \sqrt{10}}{2 - 3\sqrt{5}}$ **102.** $\dfrac{-2 + \sqrt{8}}{-3 - \sqrt{2}}$

Lesson 5-4

Factor each expression. **100–108. See margin.**

103. $4x^3 - 8x^2 + 16x$ **104.** $x^2 + 4x + 4$ **105.** $x^2 - 18x + 81$

106. $16a^2 - 9b^2$ **107.** $25x^2 - 40xy + 16y^2$ **108.** $9x^2 + 48x + 64$

Solving Square Root and Other Radical Equations

What You'll Learn

• To solve square root and other radical equations

. . . And Why

To find the power from a circular solar cell, as in Example 3

 Check Skills You'll Need

Solve by factoring.

1. $x^2 = -x + 6$ **-3, 2**
2. $x^2 = 5x + 14$ **-2, 7**
3. $2x^2 + x = 3$ **1, $-\frac{3}{2}$**
4. $3x^2 - 2 = 5x$ **$-\frac{1}{3}$, 2**
5. $4x^2 = -8x + 5$ **$-\frac{5}{2}$, $\frac{1}{2}$**
6. $6x^2 = 5x + 6$ **$-\frac{2}{3}$, $\frac{3}{2}$**

 for Help Lesson 5-5

New Vocabulary • radical equation • square root equation

Objectives

1 To solve square root and other radical equations

Examples

1 Solving Square Root Equations
2 Solving Radical Equations With Rational Exponents
3 Real-World Connection
4 Checking for Extraneous Solutions
5 Solving Equations With Two Rational Exponents

1 | Solving Radical Equations

A **radical equation** is an equation that has a variable in a radicand (or a variable with a fractional exponent). If the radical has index 2, the equation is a **square root equation**. In this lesson, you may assume that all radicals have real-number values.

$3 + \sqrt{x} = 10$ **square root equation** $\sqrt{3} + x = 10$ **not a square root equation**

To solve a radical equation, isolate the radical on one side of the equation and then raise both sides of the equation to the same power.

If $\sqrt[n]{x} = k$, then $(\sqrt[n]{x})^n = k^n$ and $x = k^n$.

1 EXAMPLE | Solving Square Root Equations

Solve $2 + \sqrt{3x - 2} = 6$.

$2 + \sqrt{3x - 2} = 6$

$\sqrt{3x - 2} = 4$ **Isolate the radical.**

$(\sqrt{3x - 2})^2 = 4^2$ **Square each side.**

$3x - 2 = 16$

$3x = 18$

$x = 6$

Check $2 + \sqrt{3x - 2} = 6$

$2 + \sqrt{3(6) - 2} \stackrel{?}{=} 6$

$2 + \sqrt{16} \stackrel{?}{=} 6$

$2 + 4 \stackrel{?}{=} 6$

$6 = 6$ ✓

 Quick Check **1** Solve $\sqrt{5x + 1} - 6 = 0$. **7**

 Professional Development

Math Background

Equations of the form $x^{\frac{m}{n}} = k$ can be solved by raising each side of the equation to the $\frac{n}{m}$ power since $\left(x^{\frac{m}{n}}\right)^{\frac{n}{m}} = x^{\frac{mn}{nm}} = x^1 = x$ or $|x|$. Raising both sides of an equation to a power may introduce extraneous solutions. For instance, if we square both sides of $x^3 = -8$ we find $x^6 = 64$. The original equation has $x = -2$ as its only solution, whereas the second equation has $x = \pm 2$ as solutions. Thus, checking solutions is important. This may be done by direct substitution or by graphing both sides of the original equation and finding all intersection points.

More Math Background: p. 366D

Lesson Planning and Resources

See p. 366E for a list of the resources that support this lesson.

 PowerPoint

Bell Ringer Practice

Check Skills You'll Need
For intervention, direct students to:

Quadratic Equations
Lesson 5-5: Example 1
Extra Skills and Word
  Problems Practice, Ch. 5

Differentiated Instruction Solutions for All Learners

Special Needs L1
Discuss how solving square root equations is similar to solving any equation: the goal is to isolate the variable on one side of the equation using inverse operations. The inverse operation for $\sqrt{x}$ is to square each side, because $(\sqrt{x})^2 = x$ or $|x|$.

learning style: verbal

Below Level L2
Review the products of reciprocals. In Example 5, students may need to convert the decimal exponents to fractions.

learning style: verbal

Guided Instruction

① **EXAMPLE** **Alternative Method**

You may want to have students use a graphing calculator to graph $Y_1 = 2 + \sqrt{3x - 2}$ and $Y_2 = 6$. The x-coordinate of the point of intersection of the graphs is the solution of the given equation.

④ **EXAMPLE** **Teaching Tip**

Point out that if you start with $x = 4$ and square both sides to get $x^2 = 16$, you go from an equation with one solution, 4, to one with two solutions, −4 and 4. Since the original equation only had one possible solution, an extraneous solution has been added.

⑤ **EXAMPLE** **Technology Tip**

To check the solutions quickly, you can press 3 [÷] 4 [STO▶] [X,T,θ,n] [ENTER] to store the value $\frac{3}{4}$ (0.75) as the value of x. Next, type the expression on the left side of the equation and press [ENTER].The calculator will display 0 as the value of the expression for $x = \frac{3}{4}$. If you repeat this process and use −1 as the value of x, the calculator will give you an error message telling you that the result is not real.

Technology Activity
This activity shows how graphing can help you determine how many solutions a radical equation has. It helps eliminate extraneous solutions.

You can solve equations of the form $x^{\frac{m}{n}} = k$ by raising each side of the equation to the power $\frac{n}{m}$, the reciprocal of $\frac{m}{n}$. If the nth root of x is a real number, then $(x^{\frac{m}{n}})^{\frac{n}{m}} = |x|$.

② **EXAMPLE** **Solving Radical Equations With Rational Exponents**

Solve $2(x - 2)^{\frac{2}{3}} = 50$.

$$2(x - 2)^{\frac{2}{3}} = 50$$

$$(x - 2)^{\frac{2}{3}} = 25 \qquad \text{Divide each side by 2.}$$

$$\left((x - 2)^{\frac{2}{3}}\right)^{\frac{3}{2}} = 25^{\frac{3}{2}} \qquad \text{Raise each side to the } \tfrac{3}{2} \text{ power.}$$

$$|x - 2|^1 = 25^{\frac{3}{2}} \qquad \text{Simplify.}$$

$$x - 2 = \pm 125 \qquad \text{Simplify.}$$

$$x = 127 \text{ or } x = -123$$

Check
$$2(x - 2)^{\frac{2}{3}} = 50 \qquad\qquad 2(x - 2)^{\frac{2}{3}} = 50$$
$$2(127 - 2)^{\frac{2}{3}} \stackrel{?}{=} 50 \qquad 2(-123 - 2)^{\frac{2}{3}} \stackrel{?}{=} 50$$
$$2(5^3)^{\frac{2}{3}} \stackrel{?}{=} 50 \qquad\quad 2(-125)^{\frac{2}{3}} \stackrel{?}{=} 50$$
$$2(5)^2 \stackrel{?}{=} 50 \qquad\qquad 2(-5)^2 \stackrel{?}{=} 50$$
$$50 = 50 \checkmark \qquad\qquad\quad 50 = 50 \checkmark$$

✓ Quick Check **②** Solve $2(x + 3)^{\frac{3}{2}} = 54$. **6**

③ **EXAMPLE** **Real-World** **Connection**

Multiple Choice The power P in watts that a circular solar cell produces and the radius of the cell in centimeters are related by the square root equation

$r = \sqrt{\dfrac{P}{0.02\pi}}$. About how much power is produced by a cell with a radius of 10 cm?

Ⓐ 0.13 watt   Ⓑ 0.63 watt   Ⓒ 1.3 watts   Ⓓ 6.3 watts

$$r = \sqrt{\frac{P}{0.02\pi}}$$

$$10 = \sqrt{\frac{P}{0.02\pi}} \qquad \text{Substitute 10 for } r.$$

$$100 = \frac{P}{0.02\pi} \qquad \text{Square each side.}$$

$$100(0.02\pi) = P \qquad \text{Multiply each side by } 0.02\pi.$$

$$6.3 \approx P \qquad \text{Simplify. Round to one decimal place.}$$

A cell with radius 10 cm produces about 6.3 watts of power. The correct choice is D.

Real-World **Connection**

Solar cells convert sunlight directly into electricity. They power calculators, emergency road signs, satellites, and experimental vehicles.

✓ Quick Check **③** How much power is produced by a cell with radius 20 cm? How does this compare with the power produced by a 10-cm cell? **about 25.1 watts; it is 4 times the power of a 10-cm cell.**

Differentiated Instruction **Solutions for All Learners**

Advanced Learners **L4**
Challenge students to solve
$\sqrt{x + 1} + \sqrt{2x} = \sqrt{5x + 3}$.
1

English Language Learners **ELL**
For Example 3, have a student volunteer explain the terms *solar cell* and *power in watts* so that students understand the problem. Discuss how light bulbs are rated using watts, and that a 6.3 watt bulb would be a nightlight.

learning style: verbal   learning style: verbal

Extraneous solutions can be introduced when you raise both sides of an equation to a power. So check all possible solutions in the original equation.

4 EXAMPLE Checking for Extraneous Solutions

GO for Help

To review extraneous solutions, go to Lesson 1-5.

Solve $\sqrt{x - 3} + 5 = x$. Check for extraneous solutions.

$$\sqrt{x - 3} + 5 = x$$

$\sqrt{x - 3} = x - 5$	Isolate the radical.
$(\sqrt{x - 3})^2 = (x - 5)^2$	Square each side.
$x - 3 = x^2 - 10x + 25$	Simplify.
$0 = x^2 - 11x + 28$	Combine like terms.
$0 = (x - 4)(x - 7)$	Factor.
$x - 4 = 0$ or $x - 7 = 0$	Zero Product Theorem
$x = 4$ or $x = 7$	

Check

$$\sqrt{x - 3} + 5 = x \qquad\qquad \sqrt{x - 3} + 5 = x$$
$$\sqrt{4 - 3} + 5 \overset{?}{=} 4 \qquad\qquad \sqrt{7 - 3} + 5 \overset{?}{=} 7$$
$$\sqrt{1} + 5 \overset{?}{=} 4 \qquad\qquad \sqrt{4} + 5 \overset{?}{=} 7$$
$$6 \neq 4 \qquad\qquad\qquad 7 = 7$$

● The only solution is 7.

✓ Quick Check ④ Solve $\sqrt{5x - 1} + 3 = x$. Check for extraneous solutions. **10**

If an equation contains two radical expressions (or two terms with rational exponents), isolate one of the radicals (or one of the terms).

5 EXAMPLE Solving Equations With Two Rational Exponents

Test-Taking Tip

When you check a solution on a test, use the equation printed on the test rather than the one you've written on your paper. You could have copied the equation incorrectly.

Solve $(2x + 1)^{0.5} - (3x + 4)^{0.25} = 0$. Check for extraneous solutions.

$$(2x + 1)^{0.5} - (3x + 4)^{0.25} = 0$$

$(2x + 1)^{0.5} = (3x + 4)^{0.25}$	
$((2x + 1)^{0.5})^4 = ((3x + 4)^{0.25})^4$	Raise each side to the 4th power.
$(2x + 1)^2 = 3x + 4$	Simplify exponents.
$4x^2 + 4x + 1 = 3x + 4$	Simplify.
$4x^2 + x - 3 = 0$	Combine like terms.
$(4x - 3)(x + 1) = 0$	Factor.
$x = \frac{3}{4}$ or $x = -1$	Zero Product Theorem

Check
$$(2x + 1)^{0.5} - (3x + 4)^{0.25} = 0 \qquad\qquad (2x + 1)^{0.5} - (3x + 4)^{0.25} = 0$$
$$\left(2 \cdot \tfrac{3}{4} + 1\right)^{0.5} - \left(3 \cdot \tfrac{3}{4} + 4\right)^{0.25} \overset{?}{=} 0 \qquad (2(-1) + 1)^{0.5} - (3(-1) + 4)^{0.25} \overset{?}{=} 0$$
$$\left(\tfrac{5}{2}\right)^{0.5} - \left(\tfrac{25}{4}\right)^{0.25} \overset{?}{=} 0 \qquad\qquad\qquad (-1)^{0.5} - (1)^{0.25} \overset{?}{=} 0$$
$$\left(\tfrac{5}{2}\right)^{0.5} - \left(\left(\tfrac{5}{2}\right)^2\right)^{0.25} \overset{?}{=} 0 \qquad\qquad (-1)^{0.5} \text{ is not a real number.}$$
$$\left(\tfrac{5}{2}\right)^{0.5} - \left(\tfrac{5}{2}\right)^{0.5} = 0$$

● The only solution is $\frac{3}{4}$.

✓ Quick Check ⑤ Solve $\sqrt{3x + 2} - \sqrt{2x + 7} = 0$. Check for extraneous solutions. **5**

Lesson 7-5 Solving Square Root and Other Radical Equations **393**

PowerPoint

Additional Examples

① Solve $-10 + \sqrt{2x + 1} = -5$. **12**

② Solve $3(x + 1)^{\frac{3}{5}} = 24$. **31**

③ An artist wants to make a plastic sphere for a sculpture. The plastic weighs 0.8 ounce per cubic inch. The maximum weight of the sphere is to be 80 pounds. The formula for the volume V of a sphere is $V = \frac{4}{3}\pi r^3$, where r is the radius of the sphere. What is the maximum radius the sphere can have? **about 2.88 in.**

④ Solve $\sqrt{x + 2} - 3 = 2x$. Check for extraneous solutions. **−1**

⑤ Solve $(x + 1)^{\frac{2}{3}} - (9x + 1)^{\frac{1}{3}} = 0$. Check for extraneous solutions. **0, 7**

Resources
• Daily Notetaking Guide 7-5 L3

Closure

Have students describe the procedure for solving a radical equation. **Answers may vary. Sample: Isolate a radical expression on one side of the equation. Next, raise both sides to the power that is the index of this radical. Simplify. Repeat for any remaining radical. Solve the final polynomial equation, and check for extraneous solutions.**

Assignment Guide

▼ **A B** 1-52

C Challenge   53-58

Test Prep   59-64
Mixed Review   65-90

Homework Quick Check

To check students' understanding of key skills and concepts, go over Exercises 11, 13, 32, 33, 39.

Teaching Tip

Exercises 15–20 Remind students that *extraneous* solutions are *extra* solutions. When substituted into the equation they do not make the statement true.

Error Prevention!

Exercise 33 Encourage students to write an equation for the area, $A = s^2 = 32$, and solve for the side length.

Differentiated Instruction Resources

GPS Guided Problem Solving	L3
Enrichment	L4
Reteaching	L2
Practice	L3

Technology Activity: Checking for Extraneous Solutions

You can use a graphing calculator to check for extraneous solutions.

1. a. Solve $x = \sqrt{x + 7} + 5$. How many apparent solutions do you get? **2**

   b. Any or all of the apparent solutions may be extraneous. One way to find out is to let y_1 equal the left side of the equation and let y_2 equal the right side. Graph the two equations. In how many points do they intersect? **1**   **1c. 2 is extraneous.**

   c. The *x*-values of the points of intersection are solutions of the original equation. Are any of the apparent solutions extraneous?

   d. Substitute the apparent solutions in the original equation. Does this algebraic check agree with the calculator check? **yes**

2. Use a graphing calculator to determine the number of solutions of each equation.

   a. $\sqrt{x} = x - 2$ **1**   b. $\sqrt{x^2 + 3} = 2x - 1$ **1**   c. $x + 8 = 4\sqrt{x + 5}$ **2**

EXERCISES

For more exercises, see *Extra Skill and Word Problem Practice*.

Practice and Problem Solving

Ⓐ Practice by Example

Example 1
(page 391)

GO for Help

Solve.

1. $3\sqrt{x} + 3 = 15$ **16**   2. $4\sqrt{x} - 1 = 3$ **1**

3. $\sqrt{x + 3} = 5$ **22**   4. $\sqrt{3x + 4} = 4$ **4**

5. $\sqrt{2x + 3} - 7 = 0$ **23**   6. $\sqrt{6 - 3x} - 2 = 0$ $\frac{2}{3}$

Example 2
(page 392)

Solve.

7. $(x + 5)^{\frac{2}{3}} = 4$ **3, −13**   8. $(x - 2)^{\frac{2}{3}} = 9$ **29, −25**

9. $3(x - 2)^{\frac{3}{4}} = 24$ **18**   10. $3(x + 3)^{\frac{3}{4}} = 81$ **78**

11. $(x + 1)^{\frac{3}{2}} - 2 = 25$ **8**   12. $3 + (4 - x)^{\frac{3}{2}} = 11$ **0**

Example 3
(page 392)

13. **Volume** A spherical water tank holds 15,000 ft³ of water. Find the diameter of the tank. (*Hint:* $V = \frac{\pi}{6}d^3$)   **about 30.6 ft**

14. **Hydraulics** The maximum flow of water in a pipe is modeled by the formula $Q = Av$, where A is the cross-sectional area of the pipe and v is the velocity of the water. Find the diameter of a pipe that allows a maximum flow of 50 ft³/min of water flowing at a velocity of 600 ft/min. Round your answer to the nearest inch. **4 in.**

Example 4
(page 393)

Solve. Check for extraneous solutions.

15. $\sqrt{11x + 3} - 2x = 0$ **3**   16. $(5x + 4)^{\frac{1}{2}} - 3x = 0$ **1**

17. $\sqrt{3x + 13} - 5 = x$ **−3, −4**   18. $\sqrt{x + 7} + 5 = x$ **9**

19. $(x + 3)^{\frac{1}{2}} - 1 = x$ **1**   20. $(5 - x)^{\frac{1}{2}} = x + 1$ **1**

Example 5
(page 393)

Solve. Check for extraneous solutions.

21. $\sqrt{3x} = \sqrt{x+6}$ **3**

22. $(x+5)^{\frac{1}{2}} - (5-2x)^{\frac{1}{4}} = 0$ **−2**

23. $(7x+6)^{\frac{1}{2}} = (9+4x)^{\frac{1}{2}}$ **1**

24. $\sqrt{3x+7} = x - 1$ **6**

25. $\sqrt{x+7} - x = 1$ **2**

26. $\sqrt{-3x-5} = x + 3$ **−2**

27. $(3x+2)^{\frac{1}{2}} - (2x+7)^{\frac{1}{2}} = 0$ **5**

28. $x + 8 = (x^2+16)^{\frac{1}{2}}$ **−3**

29. $(2x)^{\frac{1}{2}} = (x+5)^{\frac{1}{2}}$ **5**

30. $1 = (3+x)^{\frac{1}{2}}$ **−2**

B **Apply Your Skills**

31. a. Form a pair of simultaneous equations by letting y_1 equal the left side and y_2 equal the right side of $\sqrt{5} - x = 1$. Graph the equations. **a–d. See margin.**
   b. Repeat part (a) with the equivalent equation $\sqrt{5} = x + 1$.
   c. Repeat part (a) with the equivalent equation $\sqrt{5} - x - 1 = 0$.
   d. Writing Describe the similarities and differences among the graphs of the three sets of simultaneous equations.

32. a. Package Design The formula for the area A of a hexagon with a side s units long is $A = \frac{3s^2\sqrt{3}}{2}$. See the figure below. Solve the formula for s and rationalize the denominator. $s = \frac{\sqrt{2\sqrt{3}A}}{3}$

b. A package designer wants the hexagonal base of a hat box to have an area of about 200 in.^{2}. About how long is each side? **about 8.8 in.**
   c. What is the distance between opposite sides of the hat box? **about 15.2 in.**

33. Multiple Choice Your can find the area A of a square whose side is s units as $A = s^2$. Find the best estimate for the side of a square with an area of 32 m^2. **B**

   Ⓐ 4.2 m   Ⓑ 5.7 m   Ⓒ 8.0 m   Ⓓ 16 m

Solve. Check for extraneous solutions.

34. $3\sqrt{2x} - 3 = 9$ **8**

35. $2(2x)^{\frac{1}{3}} + 1 = 5$ **4**

36. $\sqrt{2x-1} - 3 = 0$ **5**

37. $(2x+3)^{\frac{1}{2}} - 7 = 0$ **23**

38. $\sqrt{x^2+3} = x + 1$ **1**

39. $(2x+3)^{\frac{3}{4}} - 3 = 5$ **6.5**

40. $2(x-1)^{\frac{4}{3}} + 4 = 36$ **9, −7**

41. $x^{\frac{1}{2}} - (x-5)^{\frac{1}{2}} = 2$ **$\frac{81}{16}$**

42. $\sqrt{x} = \sqrt{x-8} + 2$ **9**

GO Online
Homework Video Tutor
Visit: PHSchool.com
Web Code: age-0705

For each equation, let Y1 = left side and Y2 = right side. Display a graphing calculator table of X, Y1, and Y2 values. Find where Y1 = Y2. Use the Technology Activity steps on page 394 to check that you've found all solutions.

43. $\sqrt{5x+1} - \sqrt{4x+3} = 0$ **2**

44. $\sqrt{x+10} + \sqrt{3-x} = 5$ **−1, −6**

45. $(3x+2)^{\frac{1}{2}} = 8(3x+2)^{-\frac{1}{2}}$ **2**

46. $\sqrt{4x-10} = 3\sqrt{x-5}$ **7**

47. $(x-9)^{\frac{1}{2}} + 1 = x^{\frac{1}{2}}$ **25**

48. $\sqrt{10x} - 2\sqrt{5x-25} = 0$ **10**

49. $(2x+1)^{\frac{1}{3}} = (2+3x)^{\frac{1}{3}}$ **−1**

50. $(2x-1)^{\frac{1}{3}} = (x+1)^{\frac{1}{6}}$ **$\frac{5}{4}$**

PowerPoint
Lesson Quiz

Solve each equation. Check for extraneous solutions.

1. $7 + \sqrt{2x-1} = 10$ **5**

2. $4(x-9)^{\frac{1}{3}} = 8$ **17**

3. $\sqrt{2x-1} = x - 8$ **13**

4. $(4x+3)^{\frac{2}{3}} = (16x+44)^{\frac{1}{3}}$ $-\frac{7}{4}, \frac{5}{4}$

5. A circular table is to be made that will have a top covered with material that costs \$3.50 per square foot. The covering is to cost no more than \$60. What is the maximum radius for the top of the table? **about 2.34 ft**

Alternative Assessment

Ask students to select a whole number and then *work backward* to write two radical equations that have that whole number as a solution. One equation should involve square roots and the other cube roots. Students may need to experiment to find a whole number for which they can most easily write radical equations. Have students share their equations within small groups and solve each equation.

d. The graph of each pair consists of two straight lines, one of which is horizontal. They intersect at different points, but these points have the same x-value, about 1.236.

395

31a.

b.

c.

A sheet of blank grids is available in the Test-Taking Strategies with Transparencies booklet. Give this sheet to students for practice with filling in the grids.

 Resources

For additional practice with a variety of test item formats:
• Standardized Test Prep, p. 427
• Test-Taking Strategies, p. 422
• Test-Taking Strategies with Transparencies

57. Plan 1: Use a calculator to evaluate $\sqrt{2}$ and record it. Add 2, take the square root, and record it. Add 2, take the square root, and record it. Continue this procedure about seven times until it becomes clear that the values are approaching 2. Plan 2: The given equation is equivalent to $x = \sqrt{2 + x}$. Solve this equation to find that $x = 2$.

85. 3, 4

86. 3, 5

87. −5, −4

88. −2, −$\frac{2}{3}$

89. −$\frac{1}{3}$, −$\frac{4}{3}$

90. −2, −$\frac{3}{4}$

---

51. Physics The velocity v of an object dropped from a tall building is given by the formula $v = \sqrt{64d}$, where d is the distance the object has dropped. Solve the formula for d. $d = \frac{v^2}{64}$

52. Open-Ended Write an equation that has two radical expressions and no real roots. **Answers may vary. Sample:** $\sqrt{x - 3} = \sqrt{3x + 5}$

C Challenge

Solve. Check for extraneous solutions.

53. $\sqrt{x + 1} + \sqrt{2x} = \sqrt{5x + 3}$ **1**   **54.** $\sqrt{x + \sqrt{2x}} = \sqrt{2x}$ **0, 2**

55. $\sqrt{x + \sqrt{2x}} = 2$ **2**

56. $\sqrt{\sqrt{x + 25}} = \sqrt{x + 5}$ **0**

57. Critical Thinking Devise a plan to find the value of x. **See margin.**
$$x = \sqrt{2 + \sqrt{2 + \sqrt{2 + \ldots}}}$$

58. Critical Thinking You have solved equations containing square roots by squaring both sides. You were using the property that if $a = b$ then $a^2 = b^2$. Show that the following statements are *not* true for all real numbers.
a. If $a^2 = b^2$ then $a = b$. **a.** A counterexample is $a = 3, b = -3$.
b. If $a < b$ then $a^2 < b^2$. **b.** A counterexample is $a = -5, b = 3$.

Test Prep

Gridded Response

59. Solve $\sqrt{4x - 23} - 3 = 2$. **12**

60. Solve $(x + 2)^{\frac{3}{4}} = 27$. **79**

61. Solve $\sqrt{2x + 1} - \sqrt[4]{x + 11} = 0$. **5/4, or 1.25**

62. Solve $5\sqrt{x} + 7 = 8$. **1/25, or 0.04**

63. Solve $-\sqrt[3]{x} + 3 = 0$. **27**

64. Solve $\sqrt{x + 2} = x$. **2**

Mixed Review

 for Help

Lesson 7-4

Simplify each expression.

65. $64^{\frac{2}{3}}$ **16**   **66.** $25^{1.5}$ **125**   **67.** $6^{\frac{1}{2}} \cdot 12^{\frac{1}{2}}$ **$6\sqrt{2}$**   **68.** $8^{\frac{1}{2}} \cdot 40^{\frac{1}{2}}$ **$8\sqrt{5}$**   **69.** $3^{\frac{1}{3}} \cdot 18^{\frac{1}{3}}$ **$3\sqrt[3]{2}$**

70. $81^{-0.25}$ **$\frac{1}{3}$**   **71.** $4^{3.5}$ **128**   **72.** $125 \cdot 125^{-\frac{1}{3}}$ **25**   **73.** $32 \cdot 256^{-\frac{1}{2}}$ **2**   **74.** $100^{-\frac{3}{2}} \cdot 0.01^{\frac{3}{2}}$ **$\frac{1}{10^6}$**

Lesson 6-7

Evaluate each expression.

75. $_7P_1$ **7**   **76.** $_7P_3$ **210**   **77.** $_5P_3$ **60**   **78.** $_8P_4$ **1680**   **79.** $_4P_4$ **24**

80. $_5C_2$ **10**   **81.** $_7C_5$ **21**   **82.** $_5C_5$ **1**   **83.** $_6C_5$ **6**   **84.** $_7C_1$ **7**

Lesson 5-5

Solve each equation by factoring. 85–90. See margin.

85. $x^2 - 7x + 12 = 0$ **86.** $x^2 - 8x + 15 = 0$ **87.** $x^2 + 9x + 20 = 0$

88. $3x^2 + 8x + 4 = 0$ **89.** $9x^2 + 15x + 4 = 0$ **90.** $4x^2 + 11x + 6 = 0$

Radical Expressions in Formulas

FOR USE WITH LESSON 7-5

You frequently need to use radical expressions in geometry formulas.

EXAMPLE

The cube at the right fits in (is inscribed in) the sphere. How much more than the cube does the sphere hold?

A. 25% more   **B.** 50% more   **C.** 100% more   **D.** 150% more

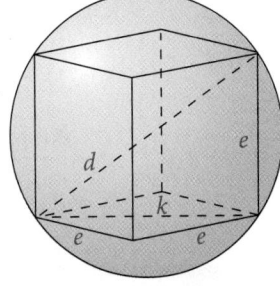

Step 1 Find k.

k is the diagonal of the square that is the base of the cube. Use the Pythagorean Theorem.

$$k^2 = e^2 + e^2$$
$$= 2e^2$$
$$k = e\sqrt{2}$$

Step 2 Find the radius of the sphere.

The diameter d of the sphere is also the diagonal of the cube and the hypotenuse of a right triangle with legs k and e.

$$d^2 = k^2 + e^2$$
$$= (e\sqrt{2})^2 + e^2$$
$$= 2e^2 + e^2$$
$$= 3e^2$$
$$d = e\sqrt{3}.$$

So the radius of the sphere is $\frac{d}{2}$ or $\frac{e\sqrt{3}}{2}$.

Step 3 Find the ratio of the volume of the sphere to the volume of the cube.

The volume of a sphere is $V = \frac{4}{3}\pi r^3$.

The volume of the cube is e^3.

$$\frac{\text{volume of sphere}}{\text{volume of cube}} = \frac{\frac{4}{3}\pi\left(\frac{e\sqrt{3}}{2}\right)^3}{e^3}$$

$$= \frac{4\pi \cdot 3e^3\sqrt{3}}{3 \cdot 8 \cdot e^3}$$

$$= \frac{\pi\sqrt{3}}{2} \approx 2.7$$

The sphere holds about 2.7 times as much as the cube, so it holds 1.7 times more, or 170% more than the cube. If you chose answer D, you are a very good estimator!

EXERCISES

1. a. The cube at the right is inscribed in a cylinder. Estimate the percent **about 57% more volume** by which the volume of the cylinder exceeds the volume of the cube. Then compute the percent. (For the volume of a cylinder: $V = \pi r^2 h$.)

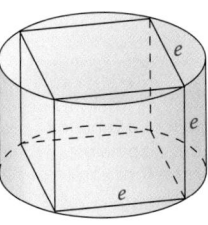

b. Estimate the percent by which the surface area of the cylinder exceeds the surface area of the cube. Then compute the percent. (The formula for the surface area of a cylinder is S.A. $= 2\pi r^2 + 2\pi rh$.)
about 26% more surface area

2. Estimate the percent by which the surface area of a sphere exceeds the surface area of its inscribed cube. Then compute the percent. (The formula for the surface area of a sphere is S.A. $= 4\pi r^2$.) **about 57% more surface area**

3. Estimate the percent by which the area and circumference of a circle exceed the area and perimeter of its inscribed square. Then compute the percents. **See margin.**

4. In the Example, suppose a smaller sphere is inscribed in the cube. Estimate the percent by which the volume of the outer sphere exceeds the volume of the inner sphere. Then compute the percent. **Estimates may vary; 420%.**

Using Radical Expressions in Formulas

This review will give students insight into the important role that radical expressions play in the study of geometric figures.

Guided Instruction

1 EXAMPLE **Teaching Tip**

Urge students to read the question carefully. It asks how *much more* the sphere holds than the cube. This is quite different from asking how *many times more* the sphere holds than the cube. They should also note that the choices make it clear that an estimate is desired, not an exact answer.

Error Prevention!

Exercise 2 Students should be careful to use the correct formula for the surface area of the cube, S.A. $= 6e^2$.

Resources

Technology
ExamView CD-ROM, Chapter 00, Geometry and Measurement

3. The area of the circle exceeds the area of the square by about 57%. The circumference of the circle exceeds the perimeter of the square by about 11%.

397

7-6

Function Operations

1. Plan

Objectives
1 To add, subtract, multiply, and divide functions
2 To find the composite of two functions

Examples
1 Adding and Subtracting Functions
2 Multiplying and Dividing Functions
3 Composition of Functions
4 Real-World Connection

Math Background

Beginning by first using functions with finite, rather than infinite, domains can be helpful. For instance, define two functions f and g which each contain only three ordered pairs. Have two common elements in the domains of f and g, and one element in the range of g that is an element in the domain of f. Then, find $f + g$, $f - g$, $f \cdot g$, $\frac{f}{g}$, $f \circ g$, and $g \circ f$. Discuss the domains of each.

More Math Background: p. 366D

Lesson Planning and Resources

See p. 366E for a list of the resources that support this lesson.

Bell Ringer Practice

✓ **Check Skills You'll Need**
For intervention, direct students to:

Relations and Functions
Lesson 2-1: Examples 2 and 6
Extra Skills and Word Problems Practice, Ch. 2

What You'll Learn
• To add, subtract, multiply, and divide functions
• To find the composite of two functions

. . . And Why
To find successive discounts, as in Example 4

✓ Check Skills You'll Need

GO ▶ **for Help** Lesson 2-1

Find the domain and range of each function. 1–4. See back of book.
1. $\{(0, -5), (2, -3), (4, -1)\}$
2. $\{(-1, 0), (0, 0), (1, 0)\}$
3. $f(x) = 2x - 12$
4. $g(x) = x^2$

Evaluate each function for the given value of x.
5. Let $f(x) = 3x + 4$. Find $f(2)$. **10**
6. Let $g(x) = 2x^2 - 3x + 1$. Find $g(-3)$. **28**

◀)) **New Vocabulary** • composite function

---

1 Operations With Functions

If an airplane has an airspeed of 415 mi/h, then $f(x) = 415x$ represents the distance traveled by the plane in still air in x hours. If the wind speed is 30 mi/h, then $g(x) = 30x$ represents the motion of the wind, and $f(x) + g(x) = 415x + 30x$ represents the distance traveled by the airplane flying with the wind.

You can add, subtract, multiply, and divide functions.

 Key Concepts

1. $(f + g)(x) = 5x^2 + x + 1$, domain: all real numbers; $(f - g)(x) = 5x^2 - 9x - 1$, domain: all real numbers

Definition	Function Operations
Addition	$(f + g)(x) = f(x) + g(x)$
Multiplication	$(f \cdot g)(x) = f(x) \cdot g(x)$
Subtraction	$(f - g)(x) = f(x) - g(x)$
Division	$\left(\dfrac{f}{g}\right)(x) = \dfrac{f(x)}{g(x)}, g(x) \neq 0$

Vocabulary Tip

The <u>domain</u> of a function is the set of all possible inputs of the function.

The <u>range</u> of a function is the set of all possible outputs of the function.

The domains of the sum, difference, product, and quotient functions consist of the x-values that are in the domains of both f and g. However, the domain of a quotient function does not contain any x-value for which $g(x) = 0$.

1 EXAMPLE Adding and Subtracting Functions

Let $f(x) = 3x + 8$ and $g(x) = 2x - 12$. Find $f + g$ and $f - g$ and their domains.

$(f + g)(x) = f(x) + g(x) = (3x + 8) + (2x - 12) = 5x - 4$
$(f - g)(x) = f(x) - g(x) = (3x + 8) - (2x - 12) = x + 20$

● The domain of both $f + g$ and $f - g$ is the set of real numbers.

✓ **Quick Check** ① Let $f(x) = 5x^2 - 4x$ and $g(x) = 5x + 1$. Find $f + g$ and $f - g$ and their domains.
See above left.

Differentiated Instruction **Solutions for All Learners**

Special Needs L1
Point out that when evaluating the composition of two functions, students evaluate the inner function first. Lead students to recognize the similarity between this and evaluating within parentheses first in the order of operations.

learning style: verbal

Below Level L2
Remind students to read $f(x)$ as 'f of x.' The notation for composition of functions also resembles multiplication. Make sure students understand that $(g \circ f)(x) \neq g(x) \cdot f(x)$.

learning style: verbal

2 EXAMPLE Multiplying and Dividing Functions

Let $f(x) = x^2 - 1$ and $g(x) = x + 1$. Find $f \cdot g$ and $\frac{f}{g}$ and their domains.

$$(f \cdot g)(x) = f(x) \cdot g(x) = (x^2 - 1)(x + 1) = x^3 + x^2 - x - 1$$

$$\left(\frac{f}{g}\right)(x) = \frac{f(x)}{g(x)} = \frac{x^2 - 1}{x + 1} = \frac{(x + 1)(x - 1)}{x + 1} = x - 1, x \neq -1$$

The domains of f and g are the set of real numbers, so the domain of $f \cdot g$ is also.

The domain of $\frac{f}{g}$ does not include -1 because $g(-1) = 0$.

2. $(f \cdot g)(x) = 12x^3 + 8x^2 - 17x + 5$, domain: all real numbers; $\left(\frac{f}{g}\right)(x) = 3x + 5$, domain: all real numbers except $\frac{1}{2}$

✓ **Quick Check** ② Let $f(x) = 6x^2 + 7x - 5$ and $g(x) = 2x - 1$. Find $f \cdot g$ and $\frac{f}{g}$ and their domains.
See left.

2 Composition of Functions

The diagram below shows what happens when you apply one function $g(x)$ after another function $f(x)$.

The output from the first function becomes the input for the second function. When you combine two functions as in the diagram above, you form a **composite function.**

Key Concepts

Definition	Composition of Functions

The composition of function g with function f is written as $g \circ f$ and is defined as $(g \circ f)(x) = g(f(x))$. The domain of $g \circ f$ consists of the values a in the domain of f for which $f(a)$ is in the domain of g.

$$(g \circ f)(x) = g(f(x))$$

① **Evaluate the inner function $f(x)$ first.**

② **Then use your result as the input of the outer function $g(x)$.**

3 EXAMPLE Composition of Functions

Let $f(x) = x - 2$ and $g(x) = x^2$. Find $(g \circ f)(-5)$.

Method 1

$(g \circ f)(x) = g(f(x)) = g(x - 2) = (x - 2)^2$

$(g \circ f)(-5) = (-5 - 2)^2$

$= (-7)^2$

$= 49$

Method 2

$(g \circ f)(x) = g(f(x))$

$g(f(-5)) = g(-5 - 2)$

$= g(-7)$

$= (-7)^2 = 49$

3b. No; the order in which operations are performed changes between $(f \circ g)$ and $(g \circ f)$, which changes what each composition equals.

✓ **Quick Check** ③ **a.** Find $(f \circ g)(x)$ and evaluate $(f \circ g)(-5)$ for the functions f and g defined in Example 3. $(f \circ g)(x) = x^2 - 2$, $(f \circ g)(-5) = 23$
b. Critical Thinking Is a composition of functions commutative? Explain.
See left.

Lesson 7-6 Function Operations **399**

Guided Instruction

2 EXAMPLE Auditory Learners

You may want to have a volunteer explain to the class in words how to find $f \cdot g$ and $\frac{f}{g}$.

PowerPoint

Additional Examples

① Let $f(x) = -2x + 6$ and $g(x) = 5x - 7$. Find $f + g$ and $f - g$ and their domains.
$(f + g)(x) = 3x - 1$,
$(f - g)(x) = -7x + 13$;
both domains: all real numbers

② Let $f(x) = x^2 + 1$ and $g(x) = x^4 - 1$. Find $f \cdot g$ and $\frac{f}{g}$ and their domains.
$(f \cdot g)(x) = x^6 + x^4 - x^2 - 1$,
$\left(\frac{f}{g}\right)(x) = \frac{1}{x^2 - 1}$; domain of $f \cdot g$: all real numbers; domain of $\frac{f}{g}$: all real numbers except -1 and 1

Guided Instruction

3 EXAMPLE Alternative Method

You can use a graphing calculator to calculate $(g \circ f)(-5)$. First enter the given functions on the Y= list. For f, use $Y_1 = x - 2$. For g, use $Y_2 = x^2$. On the home screen, type $Y_2(Y_1(-5))$. When you press ENTER, the calculator will display 49.

4 EXAMPLE Diversity

Some students may never have used coupons. Explain why businesses offer coupons and how they are used.

Additional Examples

3 Let $f(x) = x^3$ and $g(x) = x^2 + 7$. Find $(g \circ f)(2)$. **71**

4 A store offers a 20% discount on all items. You have a coupon worth $3.

a. Use functions to model discounting an item by 20% and to model applying the coupon.
$f(x) = 0.8x$, $g(x) = x - 3$

b. Use a composition of your two functions to model how much you would pay for an item if the clerk applies the discount first and then the coupon. $(g \circ f)(x) = 0.8x - 3$

c. Use a composition of your two functions to model how much you would pay for an item if the clerk applies the coupon first and then the discount.
$(f \circ g)(x) = 0.8x - 2.4$

d. How much more is any item if the clerk applies the discount first?
$.60

Resources
• Daily Notetaking Guide 7-6 **L3**

Closure

Have students assume that $f(x)$ and $g(x)$ are two functions. Ask them to explain how to find the value of $f + g$, $f - g$, $f \cdot g$, $\frac{f}{g}$, and $g \circ f$ when $x = 5$, given that the domain of each of the functions is the set of all real numbers. Answers may vary. Sample: First find $f(5)$ and $g(5)$. Suppose these values are a and b respectively, and $b \neq 0$. The values of $f + g$, $f - g$, $f \cdot g$, and $\frac{f}{g}$ for $x = 5$ are $a + b$, $a - b$, $a \cdot b$, and $\frac{a}{b}$, respectively. To find the value of $(g \circ f)$ when $x = 5$, find the value of $g(a)$.

13. $2x^2 + 2x - 4$;
    domain: all real numbers

14. $-2x^2 + 2$;
    domain: all real numbers

15. $2x^2 - 2$;
    domain: all real numbers

16. $2x^3 - x^2 - 4x + 3$;
    domain: all real numbers

400

4a. Let $f(x) = 0.9x$ and $g(x) = 0.75x$. Then $(g \circ f)(x) = g(0.9x) = 0.75(0.9x)$.

b. $(f \circ g)(x) = f(0.75x) = 0.9(0.75)x$.

 Quick Check

17. $2x + 3$;
    domain: all real numbers except 1

18. $\frac{1}{2x + 3}$; domain: all real numbers except $-\frac{3}{2}$ and 1

19. $27x^2$, domain: all real numbers; 3, domain: all real numbers except 0

---

4 **EXAMPLE** **Real-World** **Connection**

Consumer Issues Suppose you are shopping in the store in the photo. You have a coupon worth $5 off any item.

a. Use functions to model discounting an item by 20% and to model applying the coupon.
   Let x = the original price.
   Cost with 20% discount:
   $$f(x) = x - 0.2x = 0.8x$$
   Cost with a coupon for $5:
   $$g(x) = x - 5$$

b. Use a composition of your two functions to model how much you would pay for an item if the clerk applies the discount first and then the coupon.
   $(g \circ f)(x) = g(f(x))$ **applying the discount first**
   $= g(0.8x)$
   $= 0.8x - 5$

c. Use a composition of your two functions to model how much you would pay for an item if the clerk applies the coupon first and then the discount.
   $(f \circ g)(x) = f(g(x))$ **applying the coupon first**
   $= f(x - 5)$
   $= 0.8(x - 5)$
   $= 0.8x - 4$

d. How much more is any item if the clerk applies the coupon first?
   $(f \circ g)(x) - (g \circ f)(x) = (0.8x - 4) - (0.8x - 5)$ **Subtract the functions.**
   $= 1$

   Any item will cost $1 more.

● **Quick Check** **4** A store is offering a 10% discount on all items. In addition, employees get a 25% discount. **a–b. See left.**
   a. Write a composite function to model taking the 10% discount first.
   b. Write a composite function to model taking the 25% discount first.
   c. Suppose you are an employee. Which discount would you prefer to take first? **It makes no difference.**

EXERCISES

For more exercises, see *Extra Skill and Word Problem Practice*.

Practice and Problem Solving

A **Practice by Example**

Examples 1 and 2
(pages 398 and 399)

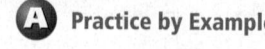 **for Help**

Let $f(x) = 3x + 5$ and $g(x) = x^2$. **Perform each function operation.**

1. $f(x) + g(x)$ $x^2 + 3x + 5$
2. $g(x) - f(x)$ $x^2 - 3x - 5$
3. $f(x) - g(x)$ $-x^2 + 3x + 5$
4. $f(x) \cdot g(x)$ $3x^3 + 5x^2$
5. $\frac{f(x)}{g(x)}$ $\frac{3x + 5}{x^2}$
6. $\frac{g(x)}{f(x)}$ $\frac{x^2}{3x + 5}$
7. $(f + g)(x)$ $x^2 + 3x + 5$
8. $(f - g)(x)$ $-x^2 + 3x + 5$
9. $(g - f)(x)$ $x^2 - 3x - 5$
10. $(f \cdot g)(x)$ $3x^3 + 5x^2$
11. $\left(\frac{f}{g}\right)(x)$ $\frac{3x + 5}{x^2}$
12. $\left(\frac{g}{f}\right)(x)$ $\frac{x^2}{3x + 5}$

400 Chapter 7 Radical Functions and Rational Exponents

Let $f(x) = 2x^2 + x - 3$ and $g(x) = x - 1$. Perform each function operation and then find the domain.   13–19. See margin.

13. $f(x) + g(x)$ **14.** $g(x) - f(x)$ **15.** $f(x) - g(x)$

16. $f(x) \cdot g(x)$ **17.** $\dfrac{f(x)}{g(x)}$ **18.** $\dfrac{g(x)}{f(x)}$

19. Let $f(x) = 9x$ and $g(x) = 3x$. Find $(f \cdot g)(x)$ and $\left(\dfrac{f}{g}\right)(x)$ and their domains.

Example 3
(page 399)

Use each diagram to find $(g \circ f)(x)$. Then evaluate $(g \circ f)(3)$ and $(g \circ f)(-2)$.

20.

$f(x) = 2x$ $g(x) = x + 3$ $2x + 3; 9, -1$

21.
$f(x) = x^2$ $g(x) = |x + 5|$ $x^2 + 5; 14, 9$

Let $g(x) = 2x$ and $h(x) = x^2 + 4$. Evaluate each expression.

22. $(h \circ g)(1)$ 8   **23.** $(h \circ g)(-5)$ 104   **24.** $(h \circ g)(-2)$ 20

25. $(g \circ h)(-2)$ 16   **26.** $(g \circ h)(0)$ 8   **27.** $(g \circ h)(-1)$ 10

28. $(g \circ g)(3)$ 12   **29.** $(h \circ h)(2)$ 68   **30.** $(h \circ h)(-4)$ 404

Let $f(x) = x^2$ and $g(x) = x - 3$. Find each value or expression.

31. $(g \circ f)(-2)$ 1   **32.** $(f \circ g)(-2)$ 25   **33.** $(g \circ f)(0)$ −3

34. $(f \circ g)(0)$ 9   **35.** $(g \circ f)(3.5)$ 9.25   **36.** $(f \circ g)(3.5)$ 0.25

37. $(f \circ g)\left(\dfrac{1}{2}\right)$ 6.25   **38.** $(g \circ f)\left(\dfrac{1}{2}\right)$ −2.75   **39.** $(f \circ g)(c)$ $c^2 - 6c + 9$

40. $(g \circ f)(c)$ $c^2 - 3$ **41.** $(f \circ g)(-a)$ $a^2 + 6a + 9$ **42.** $(g \circ f)(-a)$ $a^2 - 3$

Example 4
(page 400)

43. Sales A car dealer offers a 10% discount off the list price x for any car on the lot. At the same time, the manufacturer offers a $2000 rebate for each purchase of a car.
   a. Write a function $f(x)$ to represent the price after the discount. $f(x) = 0.9x$
   b. Write a function $g(x)$ to represent the price after the $2000 rebate.
   c. Suppose the list price of a car is $18,000. Use a composite function to find the price of the car if the discount is applied before the rebate. $14,200
   d. Suppose the list price of a car is $18,000. Use a composite function to find the price of the car if the rebate is applied before the discount. $14,400

43b. $g(x) = x - 2000$

Real-World Connection

International companies must often compute their costs in many currencies.

44. Economics Suppose the function $f(x) = 0.12x$ represents the number of U.S. dollars equivalent to x Chinese yuan and the function $g(x) = 9.14x$ represents the number of Mexican pesos equivalent to x U.S. dollars.
   a. Write a composite function that represents the number of Mexican pesos equivalent to x Chinese yuan. $(g \circ f)(x) = 1.0968x$
   b. Find the value in Mexican pesos of an item that costs 15 Chinese yuan.
                 16.45 pesos

3. Practice

Assignment Guide

▼1 A B   1-19, 45-56, 71, 73, 74

▼2 A B   20-44, 57-70, 72, 75, 76

C   Challenge   77-84

Test Prep   85-94
Mixed Review   95-112

Homework Quick Check
To check students' understanding of key skills and concepts, go over Exercises 19, 44, 57, 71, 76.

Error Prevention!

Exercises 31–42 Some students may assume that exercises such as Exercises 31 and 32 have the same answer. Caution students that composition of functions is not a commutative operation.

Differentiated Instruction Resources

GPS Guided Problem Solving	L3
Enrichment	L4
Reteaching	L2
Practice	L3

401

Connection to Geometry

Exercise 62 If you draw a diagram representing the circles at 2 s and at 4 s, you would be drawing *concentric circles*. Concentric circles are in the same plane and have the same center.

In the function $r(x)$, the input for x is in seconds. In the function $A(x)$, the input is in inches. Students may be confused about the seemingly dual use of x in $(A \circ r)(x)$. You can draw a diagram like the one on page 393 for a composition of functions. The input x for the function r is x seconds. The output, $12.5x$, is in inches and this is the input for the function A. The output from the second function, $(12.5x)^2$, is in square inches. In the notation $(A \circ r)(x)$, x refers to the first input which is in seconds.

51. $-3x^2 + 2x + 16$, domain: all real numbers

52. $3x^2 - 12$, domain: all real numbers

53. $3x^3 + 8x^2 - 4x \oplus 16$, domain: all real numbers

54. $-9x^3 - 24x^2 + 12x + 48$, domain: all real numbers

55. $3x - 4$, domain: all real numbers except -2

56. $15x - 20$, domain: all real numbers except -2

57. 7; answers may vary. Sample: First evaluate $f(3)$ since the expression is $(g \circ f)(3)$, and that means $g(f(3))$. Then evaluate $g(6)$.

69a. Answers may vary. Sample: $g(x) = 0.12x$

b. $f(x) = 9.50x$

c. $(g \circ f)(x) = 1.14x$; your savings will be $1.14 for each hour you work.

72a. $g(x)$ is the bonus earned when x is the amount of sales over $5000. $h(x)$ is the excess of x sales over $5000.

402

B Apply Your Skills

45. $x^2 - x + 7$

47. $x^2 - 5x - 3$

Let $f(x) = 2x + 5$ and $g(x) = x^2 - 3x + 2$. Perform each function operation.

45. $f(x) + g(x)$
46. $3f(x) - 2$ **6x + 13**
47. $g(x) - f(x)$

48. $-2g(x) + f(x)$ **$-2x^2 + 8x + 1$**
49. $f(x) - g(x) + 10$ **$-x^2 + 5x + 13$**
50. $4f(x) + 2g(x)$ **$2x^2 + 2x + 24$**

Let $f(x) = 3x^2 + 2x - 8$ and $g(x) = x + 2$. Perform each function operation and then find the domain. **51–56. See margin.**

51. $-f(x) + 4g(x)$
52. $f(x) - 2g(x)$
53. $f(x) \cdot g(x)$

54. $-3f(x) \cdot g(x)$
55. $\dfrac{f(x)}{g(x)}$
56. $\dfrac{5f(x)}{g(x)}$

57. **Writing** Evaluate $(g \circ f)(3)$, when $f(x) = 2x$ and $g(x) = x + 1$. Explain what you do first and why. **See margin.**

Let $g(x) = 3x + 2$ and $f(x) = \dfrac{x - 2}{3}$. Find each value.

58. $f(g(1))$ **1**
59. $g(f(-4))$ **-4**
60. $f(g(0))$ **0**
61. $g(f(2))$ **2**

GO for Help

For a guide to solving Exercise 62a, see p. 405.

62a. ≈ 1963; the area after 2 seconds is about 1963 in.^{2}.

65. $12x^2 + 2$, $6x^2 + 4$

66. $x - 3$, $x - 6$

67. $-4x - 7$, $-4x - 28$

68. $\dfrac{x^2 + 5}{2}$, $\dfrac{x^2 + 10x + 25}{4}$

62. **Geometry** You toss a pebble into a pool of water and watch the circular ripples radiate outward. You find that the function $r(x) = 12.5x$ describes the radius r in inches of a circle x seconds after it was formed. The function $A(x) = \pi x^2$ describes the area A of a circle with radius x.
   a. Find $(A \circ r)(x)$ when $x = 2$. Interpret your answer. **See left.**
   b. Find the area of a circle 4 seconds after it was formed. $\approx$**7854 in.^{2}**

For each pair of functions, find $f(g(x))$ and $g(f(x))$.

63. $f(x) = 3x, g(x) = x^2$ **$3x^2$, $9x^2$**
64. $f(x) = x + 3, g(x) = x - 5$ **$x - 2$, $x - 2$**

65. $f(x) = 3x^2 + 2, g(x) = 2x$
66. $f(x) = \dfrac{x - 3}{2}, g(x) = 2x - 3$

67. $f(x) = -x - 7, g(x) = 4x$
68. $f(x) = \dfrac{x + 5}{2}, g(x) = x^2$

69. **Open-Ended** Write a function rule that approximates each value.
   a. The amount you save is a percent of what you earn. (You choose the percent.)
   b. The amount you earn depends on how many hours you work. (You choose the hourly wage.) **a–c. See margin.**
   c. Write and simplify a composite function that expresses your savings as a function of the number of hours you work. Interpret your results.

70. a. **Technology** Suppose $f(x) = 3x$ and $g(x) = x^2 + 3$. In the spreadsheet, values for x are in Column A. What do the formulas in B and C represent? **$f(x)$ and $g(x)$**

GO Online
Homework Video Tutor
Visit: PHSchool.com
Web Code: age-0706

	A	B	C	D	E
1		=3*A1	=A1^2+3		
2	0				
3	5				
4	10				

   b. If the formulas in columns B and C are copied down the columns, what numbers will appear? **0, 15, 30; 3, 28, 103**
   c. Find $(f \circ g)(x)$. **$3x^2 + 9$**
   d. Complete column D for $(f \circ g)(x)$. **3*A1^2 + 9, 9, 84, 309**
   e. Find $(g \circ f)(x)$. **$9x^2 + 3$**
   f. Complete column E for $(g \circ f)(x)$. **9*A1^2 + 3, 3, 228, 903**

---

b. $(g \circ h)(x)$ because you first need to find the excess sales over $5000 to calculate bonus.

73. $(f + g)(x)$
   $= f(x) + g(x)$ Def. of Function Add.
   $= 3x - 2 + (x^2 + 1)$ Substitution
   $= x^2 + 3x - 2 + 1$ Comm. Prop.
   $= x^2 + 3x - 1$ Arithmetic

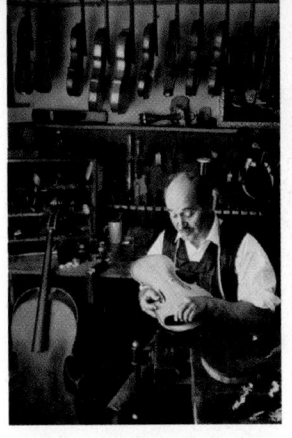

71. Profit A craftsman makes and sells violins. The function $C(x) = 1000 + 700x$ represents his cost in dollars to produce x violins. The function $I(x) = 5995x$ represents the income in dollars from selling x violins.
  a. Write and simplify a function $P(x) = I(x) - C(x)$. $P(x) = 5295x - 1000$
  b. Find $P(30)$, the profit earned when he makes and sells 30 violins.
$157,850

72. Writing A salesperson earns a 3% bonus on weekly sales over $5000.

$$g(x) = 0.03x$$
$$h(x) = x - 5000$$

  a. Explain what each function above represents. **a–b. See margin p. 402.**
  b. Which composition, $(h \circ g)(x)$ or $(g \circ h)(x)$, represents the weekly bonus? Explain.

Real-World **Connection**

Careers A craftsman and business owner uses math to find profit.

Let $f(x) = 3x - 2$ and $g(x) = x^2 + 1$. **Perform each function operation and use the properties of real numbers to justify each step in simplifying your answer.**

73. $(f + g)(x)$ **74.** $(f - g)(x)$ **75.** $(f \circ g)(x)$
73–75. See margin pp. 402–403.

76. Grades Suppose your teacher offers to give the whole class a bonus if everyone passes the next math test. The teacher says she will (1) give everyone a 10-point bonus and (2) increase everyone's grade by 9% of their score.
  a. Let x represent the original test scores. Write statements (1) and (2) as the functions $f(x)$ and $g(x)$, respectively. **a–c. See margin p. 404.**
  b. Explain the meaning of $f(g(x))$. Evaluate $f(g(75))$.
  c. Explain the meaning of $g(f(x))$. Evaluate $g(f(75))$.
  d. Does $g(f(x)) = f(g(x))$? **no**

C **Challenge**

Let $f(x) = x^4 + 2x^3 - 5x^2 - 10x$ and $g(x) = x^3 - 3x^2 - 5x + 15$. **Perform each function operation and simplify, and then find the domain.** **77–79. See margin p. 404.**
77. $f(x) \cdot g(x)$ **78.** $\dfrac{f(x)}{g(x)}$ **79.** $\dfrac{g(x)}{f(x)}$

Find each composition of functions. Simplify your answer.

80. Let $f(x) = \frac{1}{x}$. Find $f(f(x))$. **x**

81. Let $f(x) = \frac{1}{x}$. Find $f(f(f(x)))$. $\frac{1}{x}$

82. Let $f(x) = 1 - \frac{x}{2}$. Find $f(f(f(x)))$. $\frac{6 - x}{8}$

83. Let $f(x) = 2x - 3$. Find $\dfrac{f(1 + h) - f(1)}{h}, h \neq 0$. **2**

84. Let $f(x) = 4x - 1$. Find $\dfrac{f(a + h) - f(a)}{h}, h \neq 0$. **4**

Test Prep

Multiple Choice

85. Let $f(x) = -4x + 1$ and $g(x) = 2x - 6$. Find $(g - f)(x)$. **B**
  A. $6x - 5$ **B.** $6x - 7$ **C.** $-6x + 5$ **D.** $-6x + 7$

86. If $f(x) = 2x^2$ and $g(x) = 3x$, what is $(g \circ f)(x)$? **F**
  F. $6x^2$ **G.** $9x^2$ **H.** $18x^2$ **J.** $8x^4$

87. Let $f(x) = 2x - 3$ and $g(x) = -x^2 - 1$. Find $(g \circ f)(x)$. **B**
  A. $-2x^3 + 3x^2 - 2x + 3$ **B.** $-4x^2 + 12x - 10$
  C. $-x^2 + 2x - 4$ **D.** $-x^2 - 2x + 2$

---

74. $(f - g)(x) = f(x) - g(x)$ **Def. of Function subtraction**
  $= 3x - 2 - (x^2 + 1)$ **Substitution**
  $= 3x - 2 - x^2 - 1$ **Opp. of Sum Prop.**
  $= -x^2 + 3x - 2 - 1$ **Comm. Prop.**
  $= -x^2 + 3x - 3$ **Arithmetic**

75. $(f \circ g)(x)$
  $= f(g(x))$
  $= f(x^2 + 1)$ **Def. of Comp. Functions**
  $= 3(x^2 + 1) - 2$ **Substitution**
  $= 3x^2 + 3 - 2$ **Dist. Prop.**
  $= 3x^2 + 1$ **Arithmetic**

Checkpoint Quiz

Use this Checkpoint Quiz to check students' understanding of the skills and concepts of Lessons 7-4 through 7-6.

Resources
Grab & Go
• Checkpoint Quiz 2

88. If $(f \circ g)(x) = x^2 - 6x + 8$ and $g(x) = x - 3$, which expression could represent $f(x)$? **H**

   F. $x - 4$ **G.** $x - 1$ **H.** $x^2 - 1$ **J.** $x^2 - 6x + 5$

89. Let $g(x) = x - 3$ and $h(x) = x^2 + 6$. Find $(h \circ g)(1)$. **D**

   A. -14 **B.** 4 **C.** 5 **D.** 10

90. If $f(x) = 3 - x$ and $g(x) = x^2 - 3$, which expression has the greatest value? **H**

   F. $(g \circ f)(-3)$ **G.** $(f \circ g)(-3)$ **H.** $(f \cdot g)(-3)$ **J.** $(g - f)(-3)$

91. If $f(x) = x^2$ and $g(x) = x - 1$, which statement is true? **C**

   A. $(f \circ g)(x) \geq (g \circ f)(x)$ for all values of x.
   B. $(f \circ g)(x) \leq (g \circ f)(x)$ for all values of x.
   C. $(f \circ g)(x) = (g \circ f)(x)$ only for $x = 1$.
   D. $(f \circ g)(x) \neq (g \circ f)(x)$ for any value of x.

92. [2] $(f \circ g)(-1) =$
$f(-1 - 6) = f(-7)$
$= 2(-7) + 9 = -5$

[1] one minor computational error, OR no work shown

Short Response

93. [2] $\left(\dfrac{g}{h}\right)(x) = \dfrac{x^2 - 4}{4x - 6}$

[1] Minor error

92. Let $f(x) = 2x + 9$ and $g(x) = x - 6$. Find $(f \circ g)(-1)$. Show your work. See left.

93. Let $g(x) = x^2 - 4$ and $h(x) = 4x - 6$. Find $\left(\dfrac{g}{h}\right)(x)$. See left.

94. If $f(x) = 3x - 4$ and $g(x) = x + 3$, what does $(f \cdot g)(x)$ mean? What is $(f \cdot g)(x)$? Simplify the answer. See margin.

Mixed Review

76a. $f(x) = x + 10$;
$g(x) = 1.09x$

  b. Each grade is increased 9% before adding the 10-point bonus; 91.75.

  c. Add the 10-point bonus and then increase the sum by 9%; 92.65.

77. $x^7 - x^6 - 16x^5 + 10x^4 + 85x^3 - 25x^2 - 150x$; domain: all real numbers

78. $\dfrac{x^2 + 2x}{x - 3}$; domain: all real numbers except 3, $\sqrt{5}$, and $-\sqrt{5}$

79. $\dfrac{x - 3}{x^2 + 2x}$; domain: all real numbers except 0, -2, $\sqrt{5}$, and $-\sqrt{5}$

94. [2] $(f \cdot g)(x)$ means $f(x)$ times $g(x)$ or in this case $(3x - 4)(x + 3)$. The expression for $(f \cdot g)(x)$ is $3x^2 + 5x - 12$.

[1] only $3x^2 + 5x - 12$ OR minor error in explanation

101. $x^8 + 32x^7 + 448x^6 + 3584x^5 + 17,920x^4 + 57,344x^3 + 114,688x^2 + 131,072x + 65,536$

102. $x^6 + 6x^5y + 15x^4y^2 + 20x^3y^3 + 15x^2y^4 + 6xy^5 + y^6$

Lesson 7-5

Solve. Check for extraneous solutions.

95. $\sqrt{x^2 + 3} = x + 1$ **1**   96. $x + 8 = (x^2 + 16)^{\frac{1}{2}}$ **−3**   97. $\sqrt{x^2 + 9} = x + 1$ **4**

98. $(x^2 - 9)^{\frac{1}{2}} - x = -3$ **3**   99. $\sqrt{x^2 + 12} - 2 = x$ **2**   100. $(3x)^{\frac{1}{2}} = (x + 6)^{\frac{1}{2}}$ **3**

Lesson 6-8

Expand each binomial. 101–108. See margin.

101. $(x + 4)^8$ 102. $(x + y)^6$ 103. $(2x - y)^4$ 104. $(2x - 3y)^7$

105. $(9 - 2x)^5$ 106. $(4x - y)^5$ 107. $(x^2 + x)^4$ 108. $(x^2 + 2y^3)^6$

Lesson 5-6

Simplify each expression.

109. $(2 - 3\sqrt{-4}) + (4 + 2\sqrt{-16})$ **6 + 2i**   110. $3\sqrt{-50} - (2 - \sqrt{-32})$ **−2 + 19i√2**

111. $(6 + \sqrt{-20}) - (-7 - \sqrt{-45})$ **13 + 5i√5**   112. $(5 - \sqrt{-9})(2 - \sqrt{-36})$ **−8 − 36i**

Checkpoint Quiz 2   Lessons 7-4 through 7-6

Simplify each expression.

1. $(-27x^3)^{\frac{4}{3}}$ **81x⁴**   2. $(32y^5)^{-0.4}$ $\dfrac{1}{4y^2}$

Solve each equation.

3. $\sqrt{3x + 1} - 4 = 0$ **5**   4. $(5x + 2)^{\frac{2}{3}} = 9$ $5, -\dfrac{29}{5}$

Solve each equation. Check for extraneous solutions.

5. $\sqrt{3x + 3} - 3 = 3x$ $-\dfrac{2}{3}, -1$ 6. $(2 - x)^{0.5} - x = 4$ **−2**

Let $f(x) = 2x + 3$ and $g(x) = x^2 - x$. Find each value.

7. $(f + g)\left(\dfrac{1}{2}\right)$ $\dfrac{15}{4}$ 8. $(f \cdot g)(1)$ **0**   9. $\left(\dfrac{f}{g}\right)(2)$ $\dfrac{7}{2}$ 10. $(f \circ g)(5)$ **43**

404   Chapter 7 Radical Functions and Rational Exponents

103. $16x^4 - 32x^3y + 24x^2y^2 - 8xy^3 + y^4$

104. $128x^7 - 1344x^6y + 6048x^5y^2 - 15,120x^4y^3 + 22,680x^3y^4 - 20,412x^2y^5 + 10,206xy^6 - 2187y^7$

105. $59,049 - 65,610x + 29,160x^2 - 6480x^3 + 720x^4 - 32x^5$

106. $1024x^5 - 1280x^4y + 640x^3y^2 - 160x^2y^3 + 20xy^4 - y^5$

107. $x^8 + 4x^7 + 6x^6 + 4x^5 + x^4$

108. $x^{12} + 12x^{10}y^3 + 60x^8y^6 + 160x^6y^9 + 240x^4y^{12} + 192x^2y^{15} + 64y^{18}$

Guided Problem Solving

Understanding Word Problems Read the problem below. It has two parts. Let the explanations guide you through both solutions. Check your understanding with the exercises at the bottom of the page.

Geometry You toss a pebble into a pool of water and watch the circular ripples radiate outward. You find that the function $r(x) = 12.5x$ describes the radius r in inches of a circle x seconds after it was formed. The function $A(x) = \pi x^2$ describes the area A of a circle with radius x.

a. Find $(A \circ r)(x)$ when $x = 2$. Interpret your answer.

The problem uses function notation. Here is the way to read function notation.

Write $A(x)$ $A(r(x))$ $(A \circ r)(x) = A(r(x))$

Read A of x A of r of x The composition of A with r equals A of r of x.

Solve   For $A(x) = \pi x^2$ and $r(x) = 12.5x$, find $(A \circ r)(2)$.

$$(A \circ r)(2) = A(r(2))$$
$$r(2) = 12.5(2) = 25 \quad \text{Find } r(2) \text{ first.}$$
$$A(25) = \pi(25)^2 \quad \begin{array}{l}\text{Use the output } r(2) = 25 \\ \text{as the input for } A(x).\end{array}$$
$$= 625\pi \approx 1963$$

$$r \qquad\qquad A$$
$$2 \rightarrow 12.5(2) \rightarrow 25 \rightarrow \pi(25)^2 \rightarrow 625\pi$$

To interpret your answer is to explain what your answer means in terms of the problem. The problem tells you that $A(x)$ is the area of a circle with radius x and that $r(x)$ is the radius of a circle x seconds after it was formed.

So $(A \circ r)(2)$ is the area of a circle after 2 seconds. The area is about 1963 in.^{2}.

b. Find the area of a circle 4 seconds after it was formed.

Similar to part (a), $(A \circ r)(4)$ is the area. Using part (a) as a guide,

$$(A \circ r)(4) = A(r(4))$$
$$r(4) = 12.5(4) = 50$$
$$A(50) = \pi(50)^2$$
$$= 2500\pi \approx 7854$$

The area of a circle after 4 seconds is about 7854 in.^{2}.

EXERCISES

1. You toss a pebble into a pool of water and watch the circular ripples radiate outward. You find that the function $r(x) = 12.5x$ describes the radius of the first circle r in inches after x seconds. The function $C(x) = 2\pi x$ describes the circumference C of a circle with radius x. Find $(C \circ r)(x)$ when $x = 3$. Interpret your answer. **75π; 3 seconds after it is formed, a ripple will have a circumference of 75π in.**

2. A tanker leaks a small amount of crude oil into the bay. The function $d(x) = 2.3x$ models the length d, in kilometers, of the oval oil slick after x hours. $A(x) = \frac{3}{8}\pi x^2$ models the area of a slick x km long. Find the area of the oil slick after 10.5 hours. **about 28.45 km^2**

Understanding Word Problems

Students learn how to read and interpret the symbols and parentheses in function notation. Students use what they have learned to solve a problem in function notation.

Guided Instruction

You may want to write several more examples of function notation on the chalkboard or overhead projector and have students practice reading them aloud.

Work through the example in which students find $(A \circ r)(x)$ until students understand that $(A \circ r)(x)$ is equivalent to $A(r(x))$.

Tell students to look back at the original problem when they are trying to interpret the answer. The explanation of the answer is often a restatement of the question in the original problem.

Auditory Learners

Place students in pairs. Have one student write several functions ($f(x) = 3x$ for example) and then say the functions aloud. The other student then records the functions and compares them to the original functions written by the first student.

Exercise Remind students that the circumference of a circle is different from the area, which was the quantity they were asked to find in the example.

Inverse Relations and Functions

1. Plan

Objective
1 To find the inverse of a relation or function

Examples
1 Finding the Inverse of a Relation
2 Interchanging *x* and *y*
3 Graphing a Relation and Its Inverse
4 Finding an Inverse Function
5 Real-World Connection
6 Composition of Inverse Functions

Math Background

The function $g(x) = x$ is the identity function over the real numbers. That is, given any real number *a* it maps *a* onto itself, $g(a) = a$. If functions *f* and *g* are inverses, then their compositions give the identity function. In other words, $(g \circ f)(x) = (f \circ g)(x) = x$. Thus, if *f* acts on *a* and takes it to *b*, or $f(a) = b$, then *g* acts on *b* and maps it to *a*, or $g(b) = a$, and vice versa. Hence, the domain of *f* equals the range of *g* and the range of *f* equals the domain of *g*.

More Math Background: p. 366D

Lesson Planning and Resources

See p. 366E for a list of the resources that support this lesson.

Bell Ringer Practice

✓ **Check Skills You'll Need**
For intervention, direct students to:

Relations and Functions
Lesson 3-1: Example 1
Extra Skills and Word Problems Practice, Ch. 3

What You'll Learn
• To find the inverse of a relation or function

. . . And Why
To estimate the speed of a car, as in Example 5

✓ **Check Skills You'll Need**

 GO for Help Lesson 3-1

Graph each pair of functions on a single coordinate plane. **1–6. See back of book.**

1. $y = x - 6$
   $y = x + 6$

2. $y = \dfrac{x - 7}{2}$
   $y = 2x + 7$

3. $y = 3x - 1$
   $y = \dfrac{x + 1}{3}$

4. $y = 0.5x + 1$
   $y = 2x - 2$

5. $y = -x + 4$
   $y = \dfrac{-x + 4}{-1}$

6. $y = \dfrac{x + 4}{5}$
   $y = 5x - 4$

🔊 **New Vocabulary** • inverse relation • inverse functions

1 The Inverse of a Function

Activity: Inverses

• Function *f* doubles the input and then subtracts 8. $f(x) = 2x - 8$

• Function *g* adds 8 to the input and then divides by 2. $g(x) = \dfrac{x + 8}{2}$

1. a. Find $f(10)$ and $g(f(10))$. **12, 10**
   b. Find $f(0)$ and $g(f(0))$. **−8, 0**
   c. Find $f(-7)$ and $g(f(-7))$. **−22, −7**
   d. Without computing, use the pattern in parts (a)–(c) to find $g(f(-1496))$. **−1496**

2. a. Find $g(6)$ and $f(g(6))$. **7, 6**
   b. Find $g(0)$ and $f(g(0))$. **4, 0**
   c. Find $g(-32)$ and $f(g(-32))$. **−12, −32**
   d. Without computing, use the pattern in parts (a)–(c) to find $f(g(\pi))$. **π**

3. a. Interchange the *x* and *y* variables in $y = 2x - 8$ and solve for *y*.
   b. Graph your two equations in part (a) on the same coordinate axes. Fold your graph paper so the two lines coincide. How are the two graphs related? **a–b. See left.**

3a. $y = \dfrac{x + 8}{2}$

b.

They are reflections of each other in the line $y = x$.

Differentiated Instruction Solutions for All Learners

Special Needs L1
Name ordered pairs. Choose students to say the ordered pair that is the inverse of the one you named.

Below Level L2
Review the definition of a function, display graphs of functions and non functions, and review the vertical line test.

learning style: verbal   learning style: verbal

If a relation pairs element *a* of its domain to element *b* of its range, the **inverse relation** pairs *b* with *a*. So, if (a, b) is an ordered pair of a relation, then (b, a) is an ordered pair of its inverse.

This diagram shows a relation *r* and its inverse.

The range of the relation is the domain of the inverse, and the domain of the relation is the range of the inverse.

Relation *r*

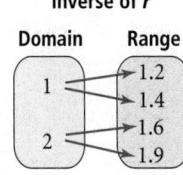

Inverse of *r*

1 EXAMPLE Finding the Inverse of a Relation

a. Find the inverse of relation *s*.

Relation *s*

x	1	2	3	4
y	−1	0	1	1

Interchange the *x* and *y* values to get the inverse.

Inverse of Relation *s*

x	−1	0	1	1
y	1	2	3	4

1a. The line $y = x$ is the perpendicular bisector of each segment connecting a point in *s* to the corresponding point in the inverse of *s*. The graph of the inverse of *s* is a reflection in the line $y = x$ of the graph of *s*.

b. Graph *s* and its inverse.

Relation *s*

Reversing the Ordered Pairs

Inverse of *s*

 Quick Check **1 a.** Describe how the line $y = x$ is related to the graphs of *s* and its inverse.
b. In Example 1, is relation *s* a function? Is the inverse of *s* a function?
yes; no

As shown in Example 1, the graph of the inverse of a relation is the reflection in the line $y = x$ of the graph of the relation. If a relation or function is described by an equation in *x* and *y*, you can interchange *x* and *y* to get the inverse.

2a. Yes; no; for every *x*-value except 3 in the domain of the inverse there are two *y*-values.

b. $y = \frac{1}{3}x + \frac{10}{3}$; it is a function because for each value of *x* there is only one *y*-value.

2 EXAMPLE Interchanging *x* and *y*

Find the inverse of $y = x^2 + 3$.

$$y = x^2 + 3$$
$$x = y^2 + 3 \quad \text{Interchange } x \text{ and } y.$$
$$x - 3 = y^2 \quad \text{Solve for } y.$$
$$\pm\sqrt{x - 3} = y \quad \text{Find the square root of each side.}$$

 Quick Check **2 a.** Does $y = x^2 + 3$ define a function? Is its inverse a function? Explain.
b. Find the inverse of $y = 3x - 10$. Is the inverse a function? Explain.

Lesson 7-7 Inverse Relations and Functions **407**

2. Teach

Guided Instruction

Activity
The functions *f* and *g* in this investigation undo one another in the sense that $g(f(x)) = x$ and $f(g(x)) = x$. After discovering this property of the functions, students discover that the graphs of the functions are reflection images of one another with respect to the line $y = x$.

1 EXAMPLE Tactile Learners

Provide students with a greatly enlarged grid. Have students place small objects such as dimes or number cubes at the points for the relation and its inverse.

PowerPoint

Additional Examples

1 Relation *m*

x	−1	0	1	2
y	−2	−1	−1	−2

a. Find the inverse of relation *m*.

x	−2	−1	−1	−2
y	−1	0	1	2

b. Graph *m* and its inverse on the same graph.

2 Find the inverse of $y = x^2 - 2$.
$$y = \pm\sqrt{x + 2}$$

Advanced Learners **L4**
Discuss with students why, if a function's inverse is a function, the composition of the function and its inverse is always commutative.

learning style: verbal

English Language Learners **ELL**
Have students look in a dictionary or thesaurus for *inverse, invert,* and *reverse.* Help students understand that reversing the ordered pairs means interchanging the *x*- and *y*-coordinates.

learning style: verbal

3.

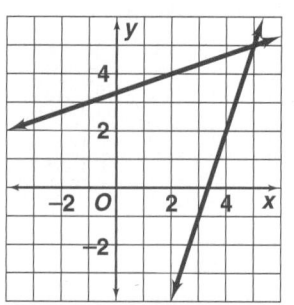

3 EXAMPLE Graphing a Relation and Its Inverse

Graph $y = x^2 + 3$ and its inverse, $y = \pm\sqrt{x - 3}$.

The graph of $y = x^2 + 3$ is a parabola that opens upward with vertex $(0, 3)$. The reflection of the parabola in the line $y = x$ is the graph of the inverse.

You can also find points on the graph of the inverse by reversing the coordinates of points on $y = x^2 + 3$.

✓ **Quick Check** ❸ Graph $y = 3x - 10$ and its inverse. **See left.**

The inverse of function f is denoted by f^{-1}. Read f^{-1} as "the inverse of f" or as "f inverse." The notation $f(x)$ is used for functions, but the relation f^{-1} may not even be a function.

4 EXAMPLE Finding an Inverse Function

Consider the function $f(x) = \sqrt{x + 1}$.

a. Find the domain and range of f.

Since the radicand cannot be negative, the domain is the set of numbers greater than or equal to -1. Since the principal square root is nonnegative, the range is the set of nonnegative numbers.

b. Find f^{-1}.

$$f(x) = \sqrt{x + 1}$$
$$y = \sqrt{x + 1} \qquad \text{Rewrite the equation using } y.$$
$$x = \sqrt{y + 1} \qquad \text{Interchange } x \text{ and } y. \text{ Since } x \text{ equals a principal square root, } x \geq 0.$$
$$x^2 = y + 1 \qquad \text{Square both sides.}$$
$$y = x^2 - 1 \qquad \text{Solve for } y.$$

So, $f^{-1}(x) = x^2 - 1$, $x \geq 0$.

c. Find the domain and range of f^{-1}.

The domain of f^{-1} equals the range of f, which is the set of nonnegative numbers. Since $x^2 \geq 0$, $x^2 - 1 \geq -1$. Thus the range of f^{-1} is the set of numbers greater than or equal to -1. Note that the range of f^{-1} is the same as the domain of f.

d. Is f^{-1} a function? Explain.

For each x in the domain of f^{-1}, there is only one value of $f^{-1}(x)$. So f^{-1} is a function.

✓ **Quick Check** ❹ Let $f(x) = 10 - 3x$. Find each of the following. **a–c. See margin p. 409.**
a. the domain and range of f **b.** f^{-1}
c. the domain and range of f^{-1} **d.** $f^{-1}(f(3))$ **3**
e. $f(f^{-1}(2))$ **2**

408 Chapter 7 Radical Functions and Rational Exponents

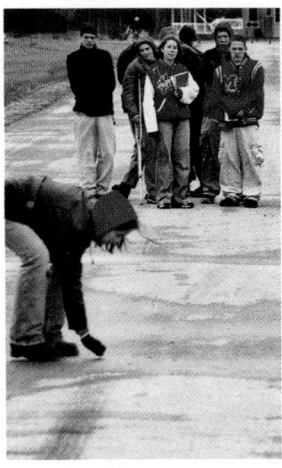

Functions that model real-life situations are frequently expressed as formulas with letters that remind you of the variables they represent. When finding the inverse of a formula, it would be very confusing to interchange the letters. Keep the letters the same and just solve the formula for the other variable.

5 EXAMPLE Real-World 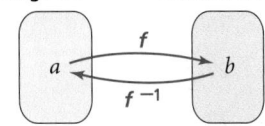 Connection

Multiple Choice The function $d = \frac{r^2}{24}$ is a model for the distance d in feet that a car with locked brakes skids in coming to a complete stop from a speed of r mi/h. Find the inverse of the function. What is the best estimate of the speed of a car that made skid marks 114 feet long?

   Ⓐ 5 mi/h   Ⓑ 12 mi/h   Ⓒ 23 mi/h   Ⓓ 52 mi/h

$d = \frac{r^2}{24}$

$r^2 = 24d$ **Solve for r. Do not interchange the variables.**

$r = \sqrt{24d}$ **Rate of speed must be positive.**

$= \sqrt{24 \cdot 114}$ **Substitute 114 for d.**

≈ 52 **Use a calculator.**

 The car was traveling about 52 mi/h. The correct choice is D.

 Quick Check **5** The function $d = \frac{v^2}{64}$ is a model relating the distance d a stone has fallen in feet to its velocity v in feet per second (ft/s). Find the inverse of the function and use it to find the velocity of a stone that has fallen 30 ft. $v = 8\sqrt{d}$; ≈ 44 ft/s

Real-World 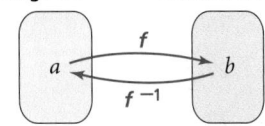 Connection

Many safe driving programs include experience with braking distance.

If f and f^{-1} are both functions, and if f maps a to b, then f^{-1} must map b to a.

Domain of f Range of f
Range of f^{-1} Domain of f^{-1}

$$a \xrightarrow{\;\;\;f\;\;\;} b$$
$$a \xleftarrow{\;\;f^{-1}\;\;} b$$

If f and f^{-1} are functions, they are called **inverse functions.** For inverse functions, $f^{-1}(f(x)) = x$ and $f(f^{-1}(x)) = x$.

Key Concepts

Property	Composition of Inverse Functions

If f and f^{-1} are inverse functions, then

$(f^{-1} \circ f)(x) = x$ and $(f \circ f^{-1})(x) = x$.

6 EXAMPLE Composition of Inverse Functions

For the function $f(x) = \frac{x-7}{6}$, find $(f^{-1} \circ f)(374)$ and $(f \circ f^{-1})(-99\pi)$.

Since f is a linear function with nonzero slope, f^{-1} is also a linear function.

 So $(f^{-1} \circ f)(374) = 374$ and $(f \circ f^{-1})(-99\pi) = -99\pi$.

 Quick Check **6** For $f(x) = 5x + 11$, find $(f^{-1} \circ f)(777)$ and $(f \circ f^{-1})(-5802)$.   **777, −5802**

4a. **D: all real numbers,**
    R: all real numbers

  b. $f^{-1}(x) = \frac{-x + 10}{3}$

  c. **D: all real numbers,**
     R: all real numbers

PowerPoint

Additional Examples

③ Graph $y = -x^2 - 2$ and its inverse $y = \pm\sqrt{-x - 2}$.

④ Consider the function $f(x) = \sqrt{2x + 2}$.

a. Find the domain and range of f. **domain: all numbers greater than or equal to −1; range: all nonnegative numbers**

b. Find f^{-1}. $f^{-1}(x) = \frac{x^2 - 2}{2}, x \geq 0$

c. Find the domain and range of f^{-1}. **domain: all nonnegative numbers; range: all numbers greater than or equal to −1**

d. Is f^{-1} a function? Explain. **Yes; for each x in the domain of f^{-1}, there is only one value of $f^{-1}(x)$.**

⑤ The function $d = 16t^2$ models the distance d in feet that an object falls in t seconds. Find the inverse of the function. Use the inverse to estimate the time it takes an object to fall 50 ft. $t = \frac{1}{4}\sqrt{d}$; **about 1.77 s**

⑥ For the function $f(x) = \frac{1}{2}x + 5$, find $(f^{-1} \circ f)(652)$ and $(f \circ f^{-1})(-\sqrt{86})$. **652, $-\sqrt{86}$**

Resources
• Daily Notetaking Guide 7-7 **L3**

Closure

Ask students how they can find an equation that models the inverse of a relation or function if they have an equation in x and y for the original relation or function. **Interchange the variables x and y in the original equation. Solve the resulting equation for y.**

Homework Quick Check

To check students' understanding of key skills and concepts, go over Exercises 9, 25, 41, 44, 45.

Error Prevention!

Exercises 1–4 Check that the graphs of the relation and its inverse are reflections over the line $y = x$.

Differentiated Instruction Resources

GPS Guided Problem Solving	L3
Enrichment	L4
Reteaching	L2
Practice	L3

5. $y = \frac{1}{3}x - \frac{1}{3}$; yes

6. $y = \frac{1}{2}x + \frac{1}{2}$; yes

7. $y = -\frac{1}{3}x + \frac{4}{3}$; yes

8. $y = \pm\sqrt{\frac{5-x}{2}}$; no

9. $y = \pm\sqrt{x-4}$; no

10. $y = \pm\sqrt{\frac{x+5}{3}}$; no

11. $y = \pm\sqrt{x-1}$; no

410

EXERCISES

For more exercises, see *Extra Skill and Word Problem Practice.*

Practice and Problem Solving

A Practice by Example

Example 1 (page 407)

GO for Help

Find the inverse of each relation. Graph the given relation and its inverse.

1.

x	1	2	3	4
y	0	1	0	2

1–4. See back of book.

2.

x	1	2	3	4
y	0	1	2	3

3.

x	0	1	2	3
y	0	1	4	9

4.

x	−3	−2	−1	0
y	2	2	2	2

Example 2 (page 407)

Find the inverse of each function. Is the inverse a function? 5–13. See margin.

5. $y = 3x + 1$
6. $y = 2x - 1$
7. $y = 4 - 3x$

8. $y = 5 - 2x^2$
9. $y = x^2 + 4$
10. $y = 3x^2 - 5$

11. $y = (x + 1)^2$
12. $y = (3x - 4)^2$
13. $y = (1 - 2x)^2 + 5$

Example 3 (page 408)

Graph each relation and its inverse. 14–22. See back of book.

14. $y = 2x - 3$
15. $y = 3 - 7x$
16. $y = -x$

17. $y = 3x^2$
18. $y = -x^2$
19. $y = 4x^2 - 2$

20. $y = (x - 1)^2$
21. $y = (2 - x)^2$
22. $y = (3 - 2x)^2 - 1$

Example 4 (page 408)

For each function f, find f^{-1} and the domain and range of f and f^{-1}. Determine whether f^{-1} is a function. 23–28. See back of book.

23. $f(x) = 3x + 4$
24. $f(x) = \sqrt{x - 5}$

25. $f(x) = \sqrt{x + 7}$
26. $f(x) = \sqrt{-2x + 3}$

27. $f(x) = 2x^2 + 2$
28. $f(x) = -x^2 + 1$

Example 5 (page 409)

29. The formula for converting from Celsius to Fahrenheit temperatures is $C = \frac{9}{5}F + 32$.

   a. $F = \frac{5}{9}(C - 32)$; yes
   a. Find the inverse of the formula. Is the inverse a function?
   b. Use the inverse to find the Fahrenheit temperature that corresponds to 25°C.
   −3.89°F

30. **Geometry** The formula for the volume of a sphere is $V = \frac{4}{3}\pi r^3$.

   a. Find the inverse of the formula. Is the inverse a function? $r = \sqrt[3]{\frac{3V}{4\pi}}$; yes
   b. Use the inverse to find the radius of a sphere that has a volume of 35,000 ft³.
   20.29 ft

Example 6 (page 409)

For Exercises 31–34, $f(x) = 10x - 10$. Find each value.

31. $(f^{-1} \circ f)(10)$ **10**
32. $(f \circ f^{-1})(-10)$ **−10**

33. $(f^{-1} \circ f)(0.2)$ **0.2**
34. $(f \circ f^{-1})(d)$ **d**

B Apply Your Skills

Find the inverse of each function. Is the inverse a function? 35–43. See margin.

35. $f(x) = 1.5x^2 - 4$
36. $f(x) = \frac{3x^2}{4}$
37. $f(x) = \sqrt{2x - 1} + 3$

38. $f(x) = (x + 1)^2$
39. $f(x) = (2x - 1)^2$
40. $f(x) = (x + 1)^2 - 1$

41. $f(x) = x^3$
42. $f(x) = x^4$
43. $f(x) = \frac{2x^2}{5} + 1$

12. $y = \frac{\pm\sqrt{x} + 4}{3}$; no

13. $y = \frac{1 \pm \sqrt{x - 5}}{2}$; no

35. $f^{-1}(x) = \pm\sqrt{\frac{2x + 8}{3}}$; no

36. $f^{-1}(x) = \pm 2\sqrt{\frac{x}{3}}$; no

37. $f^{-1}(x) = \frac{x^2 - 6x + 10}{2}$, $x \geq 3$; yes

38. $f^{-1}(x) = \pm\sqrt{x} - 1$; no

39. $f^{-1}(x) = \frac{1 \pm \sqrt{x}}{2}$; no

40. $f^{-1}(x) = -1 \pm \sqrt{x + 1}$; no

41. $f^{-1}(x) = \sqrt[3]{x}$; yes

42. $f^{-1}(x) = \pm\sqrt[4]{x}$; no

43. $f^{-1}(x) = \pm\sqrt{\frac{5x - 5}{2}}$; no

Real-World **Connection**

Water towers are tall because each foot of height provides 0.43 lb/in.² of pressure. A typical tower holds about a one-day supply for users.

61. $n = s\sqrt{2}; 3\sqrt{2}$ in. ≈ 4.2 in.

Homework Video Tutor
Visit: PHSchool.com
Web Code: age-0707

44. Water Supply The velocity of the water that flows from an opening at the base of a tank depends on the height of water above the opening. The function $v(x) = \sqrt{2gx}$ models the velocity v in feet per second where g, the acceleration due to gravity, is about 32 ft/s² and x is the height in feet of the water. Find the inverse function and use it to find the depth of water when the flow is 40 ft/s, and when the flow is 20 ft/s. $x = \frac{v^2}{64}$; **25 ft, 6.25 ft**

45. Writing Explain how you can find the range of the inverse of $f(x) = \sqrt{x-1}$ without finding the inverse itself. **The range of the inverse is the domain of f, which is $x \geq 1$.**

46. A function consists of the pairs $(2, 3)$, $(x, 4)$ and $(5, 6)$. What values, if any, may x not assume? **2 and 5**

For each function f, find f^{-1}, the domain and range of f and f^{-1}, and determine whether f^{-1} is a function. **47–58. See back of book.**

47. $f(x) = -\sqrt{x}$ **48.** $f(x) = \sqrt{x} + 3$ **49.** $f(x) = \sqrt{-x+3}$

50. $f(x) = \sqrt{x+2}$ **51.** $f(x) = \frac{x^2}{2}$ **52.** $f(x) = \frac{1}{x^2}$

53. $f(x) = (x-4)^2$ **54.** $f(x) = (7-x)^2$ **55.** $f(x) = \frac{1}{(x+1)^2}$

56. $f(x) = 4 - 2\sqrt{x}$ **57.** $f(x) = \frac{3}{\sqrt{x}}$ **58.** $f(x) = \frac{1}{\sqrt{-2x}}$

59. a. Copy the mapping diagram at the right. Complete it by writing members of the domain and range and connecting them with arrows so that r is a function and r^{-1} is not a function. **a–b. See margin.**
     b. Repeat part (a) so that r is not a function and r^{-1} is a function.

Relation r
Domain   Range

60. Critical Thinking Relation r has one element in its domain and two elements in its range. Is r a function? Is the inverse of r a function? Explain. **See margin.**

61. Geometry Write a function that gives the length of the hypotenuse of an isosceles right triangle with side length s. Evaluate the inverse of the function to find the side length of an isosceles right triangle with a hypotenuse of 6 in.

62. Open-Ended Write a function f such that the graph of f^{-1} lies in Quadrants III and IV. **Check students' work.**

C **Challenge**

Find the inverse of each function. Is the inverse a function? **63–65. See margin.**

63. $f(x) = \frac{1}{5}x^3$ **64.** $f(x) = \sqrt[3]{x-5}$ **65.** $f(x) = \frac{\sqrt[3]{x}}{3}$

66. $f(x) = (x-2)^3$ **67.** $f(x) = \sqrt[4]{x}$ **68.** $f(x) = 1.2x^4$
$f^{-1}(x) = 2 + \sqrt[3]{x}$; yes $f^{-1}(x) = x^4$, $f^{-1}(x) = \pm\sqrt[4]{\frac{5x}{6}}$; no
                 $x \geq 0$; yes

Test Prep

Multiple Choice

69. What is the inverse of $y = 5x - 1$? **B**
     A. $y = 5x + 1$ **B.** $y = \frac{x+1}{5}$ **C.** $y = \frac{x}{5} + 1$ **D.** $y = \frac{x}{5} - 1$

70. If $f(x) = 4x - 3$, what is $(f^{-1} \circ f)(10)$? **G**
     F. $\frac{13}{4}$ **G.** 10   **H.** 37   **J.** $\frac{481}{4}$

59a–b. Answers may vary. Sample:
a.
$-2 \to 0$
$0 \to 4$
$2 \to 16$
4

b.
$0 \to -4$
$5 \to -2$
$9 \to 0$
4

60. r is not a function because there are two y-values for one x-value. r^{-1} is a function because each of its x-values has one y-value.

63. $f^{-1}(x) = \sqrt[3]{5x}$; yes
64. $f^{-1}(x) = x^3 + 5$; yes
65. $f^{-1}(x) = 27x^3$; yes

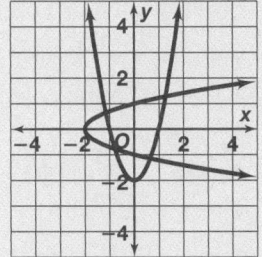

📁 **Resources**
For additional practice with a variety of test item formats:
- Standardized Test Prep, p. 427
- Test-Taking Strategies, p. 422
- Test-Taking Strategies with Transparencies

72. [2] $y^2 = \frac{x-5}{4}$, and

$y = \pm\frac{\sqrt{x-5}}{2}$.

The inverse has values that are real numbers when $x \geq 5$.

[1] $y = \pm\frac{\sqrt{x-5}}{2}$ OR $x \geq 5$ OR minor error

73. [4] $x = y^2 - 2y + 1$ or $x = (y-1)^2$. Then $y - 1 = \pm\sqrt{x}$ or $y = \pm\sqrt{x} + 1$. It is not a function because each positive value of x gives two values of y.

[3] minor error in finding inverse

[2] attempt to find inverse and a statement that the inverse is not a function

[1] attempt to find inverse OR a statement that the inverse is not a function

88. $\pm1, \pm2, \pm3, \pm4, \pm6, \pm12, \pm\frac{1}{2}, \pm\frac{3}{2}$; roots are $-\frac{3}{2}$, ±2.

89. $\pm1, \pm2, \pm4, \pm\frac{1}{3}, \pm\frac{2}{3}, \pm\frac{4}{3}$; roots are $\frac{2}{3}$, 2, −1.

90. $\pm1, \pm2, \pm3, \pm4, \pm6, \pm12, \pm\frac{1}{3}, \pm\frac{2}{3}, \pm\frac{4}{3}$; roots are 1, $-\frac{4}{3}$, −3.

91. $\pm1, \pm2, \pm3, \pm5, \pm6, \pm10, \pm15, \pm30, \pm\frac{1}{2}, \pm\frac{3}{2}, \pm\frac{5}{2}, \pm\frac{15}{2}$; roots are 5, $-\frac{3}{2}$, 2.

92. $\pm1, \pm2, \pm3, \pm6$; roots are 1, 2, 3.

93. $\pm1, \pm2, \pm3, \pm4, \pm6, \pm12$; roots are −2, 2, −3.

71. What is the inverse of $y = x^2 - 3$? **C**
   A. $y = \pm\sqrt{x} + 3$ **B.** $y = \pm\sqrt{x} - 3$
   C. $y = \pm\sqrt{x+3}$ **D.** $y = \pm\sqrt{x-3}$

Short Response

72. What is the inverse of $y = 4x^2 + 5$? For what values of x is the inverse a real number? **See margin.**

Extended Response

73. What is the inverse of $y = x^2 - 2x + 1$? Is the inverse a function? Explain.
See margin.

Mixed Review

Lesson 7-6

Let $f(x) = 4x$, $g(x) = \frac{1}{2}x + 7$, and $h(x) = |-2x + 4|$. Simplify each function.

74. $(f \circ g)(x)$ **2x + 28**   **75.** $(g \circ f)(x)$ **2x + 7**   **76.** $(h \circ g)(x)$ **|−x − 10|**

77. $g(x) + g(x)$ **x + 14**   **78.** $(h \circ (g \circ f))(x)$ **|−4x − 10|**   **79.** $(f \circ g)(x) + h(x)$ **2x + 28 + |−2x + 4|**

Lesson 7-1

Find each indicated root if it is a real number.

not a real number

80. $\sqrt[4]{16}$ **2**   **81.** $-\sqrt[4]{16}$ **−2**   **82.** $\sqrt[4]{-16}$ **83.** $\sqrt[5]{243}$ **3**

84. $-\sqrt[5]{243}$ **−3**   **85.** $\sqrt[5]{-243}$ **−3**   **86.** $\sqrt[3]{0.064}$ **0.4**   **87.** $\sqrt[4]{810,000}$ **30**

Lesson 6-5

List all possible rational roots for each equation. Then use the Rational Root Theorem to find each root. **88–93. See margin.**

88. $2x^3 + 3x^2 - 8x - 12 = 0$ **89.** $3x^3 - 5x^2 - 4x + 4 = 0$

90. $3x^3 + 10x^2 - x - 12 = 0$ **91.** $2x^3 - 11x^2 - x + 30 = 0$

92. $x^3 - 6x^2 + 11x - 6 = 0$ **93.** $x^3 + 3x^2 - 4x - 12 = 0$

Algebra at Work

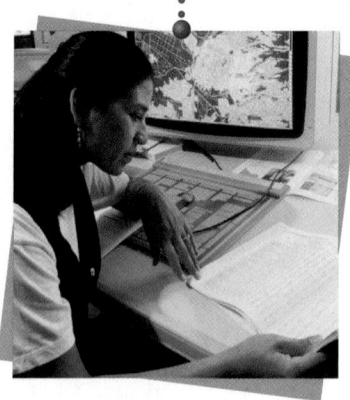

·················· **Demographer**

Demographers study human populations. They collect, analyze, and present data relating to the basic life cycle: birth, marriage, divorce, family formation, employment, aging, migration, and death.
Demographers draw on the related disciplines of sociology, economics, political science, anthropology, psychology, public health, and ecology.
Demography is also concerned with the broader nature of social and economic change and its impact on the natural environment. It includes studying family structure, the role of women, and the value of children, as well as the social, cultural, and institutional context of demographic change. Demography is an essential component of many activities, such as planning government policies and market research.

Go Online
PHSchool.com   **For:** Information about demography
Web Code: agb-2031

Graphing Inverses

Technology

You can graph inverses of functions on a graphing calculator by using the DrawInv feature or by using parametric equations. It takes more keystrokes to set up parametric equations, but once you do you can easily change from one function to another and quickly see the graphs of the new function and its inverse.

ACTIVITY

Graph $y = 0.3x^2 + 1$ and its inverse.

Method 1 Use the DrawInv feature.

Step 1 Press Y= and enter the equation. Press ZOOM 5 to see a graph of the function with equal x- and y-intervals.

Step 2 Press 2nd DRAW 8. You will see DrawInv followed by a flashing cursor. Select equation Y_1 by pressing VARS ▶ 1 1. Press ENTER to see the graph of the function and its inverse.

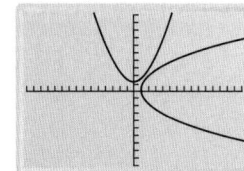

Method 2 Use parametric equations.

Step 1 Set to parametric mode. Press MODE, select **Par**, and press 2nd QUIT.

Step 2 Enter the given equation in parametric form. Press Y= and enter the equations $X_{1T} = T$ and $Y_{1T} = .3T^2 + 1$.

Step 3 Now use $X_{2T} = Y_{1T}$ and $Y_{2T} = X_{1T}$ to interchange the x- and y-values of the first parametric equation. Press Y= and move the cursor to follow $X_{2T} =$. Select Y_{1T} by pressing VARS ▶ 2 2. Enter the equation $Y_{2T} = X_{1T}$ in a similar fashion.

Step 4 Press ZOOM 5. Adjust the Window so that Tmin and Tmax approximately agree with Xmin and Xmax. Press GRAPH to see the graph of the function and its inverse.

5. The third graph would be the same as the first. Interchanging the pairs twice restores the original pairs.

EXERCISES

Graph each function and its inverse with a graphing calculator. Then sketch the graphs. **1.** See back of book. **2–4.** See margin.

1. $y = x^2 - 5$ **2.** $y = (x - 3)^2$ **3.** $y = 0.01x^4$ **4.** $y = 0.5x^3 - 3$

5. Critical Thinking In Method 2, suppose you added a third pair of parametric equations that interchanged the x- and y-values of the second pair ($X_{3T} = Y_{2T}$ and $Y_{3T} = X_{2T}$). What would be the effect on the graphs? Explain.   **See above.**

6. Writing Change the parametric equation $X_{2T} = Y_{1T}$ in Method 2, Step 3 to $X_{2T} = -Y_{1T}$. Describe the graph that results. **The graph is the reflection of the first graph in the x-axis.**

7. Explain how, once you set up parametric equations, you can change from one function to another and quickly see the graphs of the new function and its inverse.
Answers may vary. Sample: Using parametric equations, you only have to change Y_{1T} to see a new function and its inverse.

Activity Lab   Graphing Inverses   **413**

Activity Lab

Graphing Inverses

Students use a graphing calculator to explore two ways of graphing a function and its inverse.

Guided Instruction

Using the DrawInv feature to display the graph of the inverse is faster than using parametric equations. However, it has the disadvantage that you cannot use Trace to trace the graph of the inverse.

Error Prevention!

Students should press WINDOW to check the window settings. Be sure students understand how the Tmin, Tmax, and Tstep values can affect the graph display. If students have little or no experience with parametric graphing, you may want to allow some extra time for experimenting with different settings.

Resources

Students may use any graphing calculator that has a DrawInv feature and parametric graphing capabilities.

2.

3.

4.

Graphing Square Root and Other Radical Functions

1. Plan

Objective

1 To graph square root and other radical functions

Examples

1 Translating Square Root Functions Vertically
2 Translating Square Root Functions Horizontally
3 Graphing Square Root Functions
4 Graphing Cube Root Functions
5 Solving Square Root Equations by Graphing
6 Rewriting Radical Functions

Math Background

Graphs whose equations have the form $y = a(x - h)^2 + k$ are translations h units horizontally and k units vertically of the graph of $y = ax^2$, as seen in Lesson 5-3. The same holds true for functions of the form $y = a\sqrt[n]{x - h} + k$; the graphs are translations of the graph of the parent function $y = \sqrt[n]{x}$.

More Math Background: p. 366D

Lesson Planning and Resources

See p. 366E for a list of the resources that support this lesson.

✓ Check Skills You'll Need

For intervention, direct students to:

Translating Parabolas
Lesson 5-3: Example 1
Extra Skills and Word Problems Practice, Ch. 5

414

What You'll Learn

• To graph square root and other radical functions

... And Why

To estimate the mass of a giraffe, as in Example 5

✓ Check Skills You'll Need

GO for Help Lesson 5-3

Graph each equation. **1–6. See back of book.**

1. $y = (x + 2)^2$
2. $y = (x - 3)^2$
3. $y = -(x + 4)^2$
4. $y = -x^2 - 1$
5. $y = -(x + 1)^2 + 1$
6. $y = 3x^2 + 3$

◀)) New Vocabulary

• radical function • square root function

---

1 Radical Functions

A horizontal line can intersect the graph of $f(x) = x^2$ in two points. For example, $f(-2) = f(2)$. Therefore, a vertical line can intersect the graph of the inverse of $f(x) = x^2$ in two points, and f^{-1} is *not* a function.

GO for Help

To review the vertical line test, go to Lesson 2-1.

$f(x) = x^2$ $f^{-1}(x) = \pm\sqrt{x}$

You can restrict the domain of f so that its inverse is a function.

$f(x) = x^2, x \geq 0$ $f^{-1}(x) = \sqrt{x}$

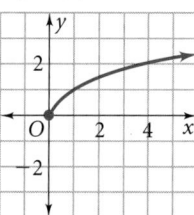

The inverse of $g(x) = x^3$ is a function.

$g(x) = x^3$ $g^{-1}(x) = \sqrt[3]{x}$

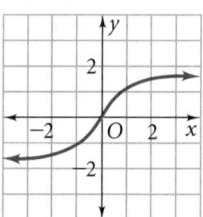

414 Chapter 7 Radical Functions and Rational Exponents

Differentiated Instruction Solutions for All Learners

Special Needs L1

Students may make mistakes because they are not careful in determining what is and what is not within the radical sign. For Example 3, write $y = -2\sqrt{x + 1} - 3$ and $y = -2\sqrt{x + 1} - 3$ on the board and ask students to identify how they are different. **learning style: visual**

Below Level L2

Graph $f(x) = x^2 - 4$ using a graphing calculator. Use the DRAW function to draw the inverse and observe that the inverse is not a function.

learning style: visual

Inverses of functions of the form $y = x^n$ (with domains restricted as needed) form parent functions $y = \sqrt[n]{x}$ of families of **radical functions.** In particular, $f(x) = \sqrt{x}$ is the parent for the family of **square root functions.** Members of this family have the form $f(x) = a\sqrt{x - h} + k$.

 Key Concepts

Summary	**Families of Radical Functions Including the Square Root Function**	
	Square Root	**Radical**
Parent function:	$y = \sqrt{x}$	$y = \sqrt[n]{x}$
Reflection in x-axis:	$y = -\sqrt{x}$	$y = -\sqrt[n]{x}$
Stretch $(a > 1)$, shrink $(0 < a < 1)$ by factor a:	$y = a\sqrt{x}$	$y = a\sqrt[n]{x}$
Reflection in x-axis:	$y = -a\sqrt{x}$	$y = -a\sqrt[n]{x}$
Translation: Horizontal by h	$y = \sqrt{x - h}$	$y = \sqrt[n]{x - h}$
Vertical by k	$y = \sqrt{x} + k$	$y = \sqrt[n]{x} + k$
Combined:	$y = \sqrt{x - h} + k$	$y = \sqrt[n]{x - h} + k$

1.

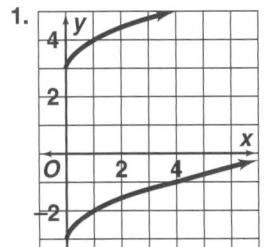

1 **EXAMPLE** **Translating Square Root Functions Vertically**

Graph $y = \sqrt{x} + 2$ and $y = \sqrt{x} - 1$.

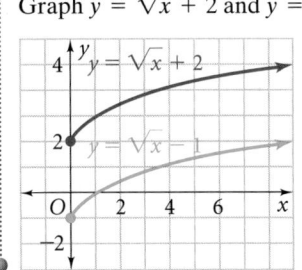

The graph of $y = \sqrt{x} + 2$ is the graph of $y = \sqrt{x}$ shifted up 2 units. The graph of $y = \sqrt{x} - 1$ is the graph of $y = \sqrt{x}$ shifted down 1 unit.

The domains of both functions are the set of nonnegative numbers, but their ranges differ.

✓ **Quick Check** **1** Graph $y = \sqrt{x} - 3$ and $y = \sqrt{x} + 3$. **See left.**

The graph of $y = \sqrt{x - h}$ is a horizontal translation of $y = \sqrt{x}$. If h is positive, translate h units to the right. If h is negative, translate $|h|$ units to the left.

2 **EXAMPLE** **Translating Square Root Functions Horizontally**

Graph $y = \sqrt{x + 3}$ and $y = \sqrt{x - 2}$.

2.

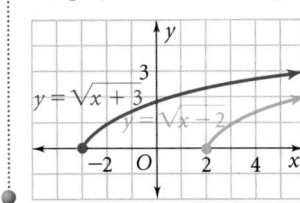

The graph of $y = \sqrt{x + 3}$ is the graph of $y = \sqrt{x}$ shifted left 3 units. The graph of $y = \sqrt{x - 2}$ is the graph of $y = \sqrt{x}$ shifted right 2 units.

The ranges of both functions are the set of nonnegative numbers, but their domains differ.

✓ **Quick Check** **2** Graph $y = \sqrt{x - 1}$ and $y = \sqrt{x + 4}$. **See left.**

Lesson 7-8 Graphing Square Root and Other Radical Functions **415**

Guided Instruction

3 **EXAMPLE** **Special Needs** **L1**

For students who have difficulty reading small type, you may want to enlarge the graphs on a copier.

PowerPoint

Additional Examples

1 Graph $y = \sqrt{x} + 5$ and $y = \sqrt{x} - 7$.

2 Graph $y = \sqrt{x + 7}$ and $y = \sqrt{x - 5}$.

Advanced Learners **L4**

Ask students to use a graphing calculator to graph the function $y = \sqrt[3]{x} - 4$ and find the root of the equation. Discuss the domain and range of the function.

learning style: verbal

English Language Learners **ELL**

Review the terms *domain* and *range* in the context of transformations. Ask for the domain and range of each function before and after the transformation. For students who confuse the domain and range, state x comes before y just as d comes before r.

learning style: verbal

Additional Examples

③ Graph $y = 3\sqrt{x + 2} - 1$.

④ Graph $y = 2\sqrt[3]{x + 2} - 2$.

⑤ The speed v of an object in meters per second can be modeled by $v = \sqrt{\frac{2KE}{m}}$, where KE is its kinetic energy in Joules and m its mass in kilograms. Find the kinetic energy for a 70 kilogram bicycle and rider traveling at a speed of 10 meters per second. **3500 Joules**

⑥ Rewrite $y = \sqrt{9x + 18}$ to make it easy to graph using transformations. Describe the graph.
$y = 3\sqrt{x + 2}$; The graph of $y = 3\sqrt{x + 2}$ is the graph of $y = 3\sqrt{x}$ translated 2 units left.

Resources
• Daily Notetaking Guide 7-8 **L3**

Closure

Ask students to give examples that illustrate how the graphs of radical equations can be translated, stretched, or compressed vertically by modifying the parent functions $y = \sqrt{x}$ and $y = \sqrt[3]{x}$. **Check students' work.**

416

3.

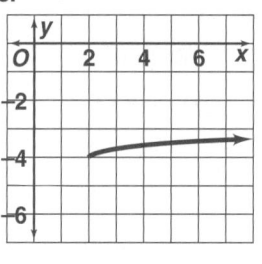

For the combined transformation $y = a\sqrt{x - h} + k$, a indicates a vertical stretch ($a > 1$) or shrink ($0 < a < 1$). A negative sign indicates reflection in the x-axis.

③ **EXAMPLE** **Graphing Square Root Functions**

Graph $y = -2\sqrt{x + 1} - 3$.

The graph of $y = -2\sqrt{x}$ is a stretch of $y = \sqrt{x}$ by a factor of 2 and a reflection across the x-axis (in black). Then translate left 1 unit and down 3 units.

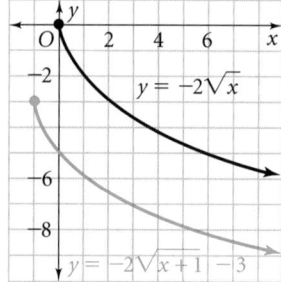

✓ **Quick Check** ③ Graph $y = \frac{1}{4}\sqrt{x - 2} - 4$. **See left.**

The pattern for graphing square root functions applies to other radical functions.

④ **EXAMPLE** **Graphing Cube Root Functions**

Graph $y = 2\sqrt[3]{x + 3} - 1$.

The graph of $y = 2\sqrt[3]{x + 3} - 1$ is the graph of $y = 2\sqrt[3]{x}$ translated 3 units left and 1 unit down.

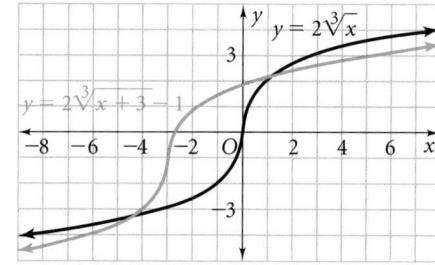

✓ **Quick Check** ④ Graph $y = 3 - \sqrt[3]{x + 1}$. **See margin.**

⑤ **EXAMPLE** **Solving Square Root Equations by Graphing**

Physics You can model the time t, in seconds, an object takes to reach the ground falling from height H, in meters, by $t(H) = \sqrt{\frac{2H}{g}}$. The value of g is 9.81 m/s². From what height does an object fall if it takes 7 seconds to reach the ground?

For $t = 7$, solve the equation $7 = \sqrt{\frac{2H}{9.81}}$.

Graph Y1 $= \sqrt{(2X/9.81)}$ and Y2 $= 7$. Adjust the window to find where the graphs intersect. Use the Intersect feature to find the x-coordinate of the intersection.

The height for a 7-second fall is about 240 m.

✓ **Quick Check** ⑤ How far does an object fall if it takes 3.5 seconds to reach the ground? How does this compare with the height of a 7-second fall?
about 60 m; it is about $\frac{1}{4}$ the height.

page 416 Quick Check

4.

pages 417–419 Exercises

24.

31. $y = 3\sqrt{x - 1}$; the graph is the graph of $y = 3\sqrt{x}$ translated 1 unit to the right.

For: Radical Functions Activity
Use: Interactive Textbook, 7-8

Sometimes you have to rewrite a radical function so you can graph it using transformations.

6 EXAMPLE Rewriting Radical Functions

Rewrite $y = \sqrt{4x - 12}$ to make it easy to graph using transformations. Describe the graph.

$$y = \sqrt{4x - 12} = \sqrt{4(x - 3)} = 2\sqrt{x - 3}$$

● The graph of $y = \sqrt{4x - 12}$ is the graph of $y = 2\sqrt{x}$ translated 3 units right.

 Quick Check ❻ Rewrite $y = \sqrt[3]{8x - 24} + 3$ to make it easy to graph using transformations. Describe the graph. $y = 2\sqrt[3]{x - 3} + 3$; the graph is the graph of $y = 2\sqrt[3]{x}$ translated 3 units right and 3 units up.

EXERCISES

For more exercises, see *Extra Skill and Word Problem Practice.*

Practice and Problem Solving

A Practice by Example

Examples 1 and 2
(page 415)

 for Help

Graph each function. 1–8. See back of book.

1. $y = \sqrt{x} + 1$ **2.** $y = \sqrt{x} - 2$ **3.** $y = \sqrt{x} - 4$ **4.** $y = \sqrt{x} + 5$
5. $y = \sqrt{x - 3}$ **6.** $y = \sqrt{x + 1}$ **7.** $y = \sqrt{x + 6}$ **8.** $y = \sqrt{x - 4}$

Example 3
(page 416)

Graph each function. 9–17. See back of book.

9. $y = 3\sqrt{x}$ **10.** $y = -0.25\sqrt{x}$ **11.** $y = \frac{1}{3}\sqrt{x}$

12. $y = -\sqrt{x} - 1$ **13.** $y = -5\sqrt{x + 2}$ **14.** $y = -0.75\sqrt{x} + 3$

15. $y = -\sqrt{x - 3} + 2$ **16.** $y = \frac{1}{4}\sqrt{x + 2} - 1$ **17.** $y = 3\sqrt{x + 1} + 4$

Example 4
(page 416)

Graph each function. 18–23. See back of book.

18. $y = \sqrt[3]{x} + 5$ **19.** $y = \sqrt[3]{x} - 4$ **20.** $y = \sqrt[3]{x + 2} - 7$

21. $y = -\sqrt[3]{x + 3} - 1$ **22.** $y = 2\sqrt[3]{x - 6} - 9$ **23.** $y = \frac{1}{2}\sqrt[3]{x - 1} + 3$

24. Agriculture A center-pivot irrigation system can water from 1 to 130 acres of crop land. The length ℓ in feet of rotating pipe needed to irrigate A acres is given by the function $\ell = 117.75\sqrt{A}$. **a. See margin p. 416.**
a. Graph the equation on your calculator. Make a sketch of the graph.
b. Find the lengths of pipe needed to irrigate 40, 80, and 130 acres.
≈745 ft, ≈1053 ft, ≈1343 ft

Example 5
(page 416)

Solve each square root equation by graphing. Round the answer to the nearest hundredth if necessary. If there is no solution, explain why. 25–30. See back of book.

25. $\sqrt{x - 3} = 12$ **26.** $\sqrt{2x - 3} = 4$ **27.** $3\sqrt{3 - x} = 10$

28. $2.5\sqrt{2x - 1.3} = -1$ **29.** $2\sqrt{x + 4} = 3\sqrt{x - 1}$ **30.** $\sqrt{2x + 5} = \sqrt{2 - x}$

Example 6
(page 417)

Rewrite each function to make it easy to graph using transformations of its parent function. Describe the graph. 31–36. See margin pp. 416–417.

31. $y = \sqrt{9x - 9}$ **32.** $y = -\sqrt{16x + 32}$ **33.** $y = -2\sqrt{49x + 49}$

34. $y = \sqrt[3]{64x + 128}$ **35.** $y = \sqrt{64x - 128} - 3$ **36.** $y = \sqrt[3]{27x - 54} + 1$

Lesson 7-8 Graphing Square Root and Other Radical Functions **417**

32. $y = -4\sqrt{x + 2}$; the graph is the graph of $y = -4\sqrt{x}$ translated 2 units to the left.

33. $y = -14\sqrt{x + 1}$; the graph is the graph of $y = -14\sqrt{x}$ translated 1 unit to the left.

34. $y = 4\sqrt[3]{x + 2}$; the graph is the graph of $y = 4\sqrt[3]{x}$ translated 2 units to the left.

35. $y = 8\sqrt{x - 2} - 3$; the graph is the graph of $y = 8\sqrt{x}$ translated 2 units to the right and 3 units down.

36. $y = 3\sqrt[3]{x - 2} + 1$; the graph is the graph of $y = 3\sqrt[3]{x}$ translated 2 units to the right and 1 unit up.

Graph each function on the same graph.

1. $y = \sqrt{x} - 6$

2. $y = \sqrt{x} + 8$

3. $y = \frac{2}{3}\sqrt{x}$

4. $y = \sqrt[3]{x} - 2 + 5$

5. The formula $t = 2\pi\sqrt{\frac{L}{9.8}}$ can be used to estimate the number of seconds t it takes a pendulum of length L meters to make one complete swing. Graph the equation on a graphing calculator. Then use the graph to estimate the values of t for pendulums of lengths 1.5 meters and 2.5 meters. **about 2.46 s, about 3.17 s**

6. Rewrite $y = 2\sqrt{9x - 27}$ to make it easy to graph using a translation. $y = 6\sqrt{x - 3}$

Alternative Assessment

Have students work individually. For each of the parent functions $y = \sqrt{x}$ and $y = \sqrt[3]{x}$, have students write an equation for a vertical translation, a horizontal translation, and a stretch or compression of the graph of the parent function. Then have them use a graphing calculator to help sketch the graph of each function.

B Apply Your Skills

37–51. See back of book.

Graph. Find the domain and the range of each function.

37. $y = \sqrt{x} + 7$

38. $y = \sqrt{x} - 6$

39. $y = \sqrt{x - 6}$

40. $y = -3\sqrt{x} + 2$

41. $y = -\frac{4}{5}\sqrt{x}$

42. $y = 7 - \sqrt{2x - 1}$

43. $y = 4\sqrt[3]{x - 2} + 1$

44. $y = \frac{1}{2}\sqrt{x - 1} + 3$

45. $y = -3\sqrt[3]{x - 4} - 3$

46. $y = -\sqrt{x + \frac{1}{2}}$

47. $y = -\sqrt[3]{8x} + 5$

48. $y = -2\sqrt[3]{x - 4}$

49. $y = -1 - \sqrt{4x + 20}$

50. $y = 4 - \sqrt[3]{x + 2.5}$

51. $y = -3\sqrt{x - \frac{3}{4}} + 7$

52. Circus The time t in seconds for a trapeze to complete one full cycle is given by the function $t = 1.11\sqrt{\ell}$, where ℓ is the length of the trapeze in feet.
  a. Graph the equation on your calculator. Make a sketch of the graph.
  b. How long is a full cycle if the trapeze is 15 ft. long? 30 ft. long?
  a–b. See margin.

53. a. Graph $y = \sqrt{x - 2} - 2$.   **a, d. See margin.**
  b. Find the domain and the range.   **D: $x \geq 2$, R: $y \geq -2$**
  c. At what coordinate point does the graph start?   **(2, −2)**
  d. Critical Thinking What is the relationship of the point at which the graph starts to the domain and the range?

54. a. The graph of $y = \sqrt{x}$ is translated five units to the right and two units down. Write an equation of the translated function. $y = \sqrt{x - 5} - 2$
  b. The translated graph from part (a) is again translated, this time four units left and three units down. Write an equation of the translated function.
    $y = \sqrt{x - 1} - 5$

55. a. Graph $y = \sqrt{x - 2} + 1$ and $y = -\sqrt{x - 2} + 1$.
  b. Find the domain and the range of each function.
  a–b. See back of book.

Rewrite each function to make it easy to graph using transformations of its parent function. Describe the graph.   **56–61. See back of book.**

56. $y = \sqrt{25x - 100} - 1$ **57.** $y = \sqrt{36x + 108} + 4$ **58.** $y = -\sqrt[3]{8x - 2}$

59. $y = \sqrt{\frac{x - 1}{4}} - 2$ **60.** $y = 10 - \sqrt[3]{\frac{x + 3}{27}}$ **61.** $y = \sqrt{\frac{x}{9} + 1} + 5$

62. Open-Ended Write a cube root function in which the vertical translation of $y = \sqrt[3]{x}$ is twice the horizontal translation.

63. Electronics The size of a television screen is the length of the screen's diagonal d in inches. The equation $d = \sqrt{2A}$ models the length of a diagonal of a television screen with area A.
  a. Graph the equation on your calculator.   **See margin p. 419.**
  b. Suppose you want to buy a new television that has twice the area of your old television. Your old television has an area of 100 in.^{2}. What size screen should you buy?   **20 in.**

64. Writing Explain the effect that a has on the graph of $y = a\sqrt{x}$.
    See back of book.

C Challenge

Rewrite each function to make it easy to graph using transformations of its parent function. Describe the graph. Find the domain and the range of each function.

65. $y = -\sqrt{2x + 8}$ **66.** $y = -\sqrt{2(4x - 3)}$

67. $y = \sqrt{3x - 5} + 6$ **68.** $y = -3 - \sqrt{12x + 18}$
65–68. See back of book.

Real-World Connection

The length of the pendulum formed by an aerialist on a trapeze depends on how far he hangs below the bar.

62. Answers may vary.
  Sample:
  $y = \sqrt[3]{x - 2} + 4$

pages 417–419   **Exercises**

52a.

b. ≈4.3 s; ≈6.1 s

53a.

d. The domain is based on the x-coordinate of that point, and the range is based on the y-coordinate.

69. a. Graph $y = \sqrt{-x}$, $y = \sqrt{1 - x}$, and $y = \sqrt{2 - x}$.

  b. Make a Conjecture How does the graph of $y = \sqrt{h - x}$ differ from the graph of $y = \sqrt{x - h}$? **a–b. See back of book.**

70. For what positive integers n are the domain and range of $y = \sqrt[n]{x}$ the set of real numbers? Assume that x is a real number. **for all odd positive integers**

Test Prep

Multiple Choice

71. How is the graph of $y = \sqrt{x + 7}$ translated from the graph of $y = \sqrt{x}$? **A**
  A. shifted 7 units left
  B. shifted 7 units right
  C. shifted 7 units up
  D. shifted 7 units down

72. How is the graph of $y = \sqrt{x} - 5$ translated from the graph of $y = \sqrt{x}$? **J**
  F. shifted 5 units left
  G. shifted 5 units right
  H. shifted 5 units up
  J. shifted 5 units down

73. The graph of $y = -\sqrt{x}$ is shifted 4 units up and 3 units right. Which equation represents the new graph? **B**
  A. $y = -\sqrt{x - 4} + 3$
  B. $y = -\sqrt{x - 3} + 4$
  C. $y = -\sqrt{x + 3} + 4$
  D. $y = -\sqrt{x + 4} + 3$

74. Which equation shows $y + 3 = \sqrt{\frac{x}{16} + 2}$ rewritten in the form $y = a\sqrt{x - h} + k$? **H**
  F. $y = \frac{3}{4}\sqrt{x - (-2)}$
  G. $y = \frac{1}{4}\sqrt{x - (-2)} + (-3)$
  H. $y = \frac{1}{4}\sqrt{x - (-32)} + (-3)$
  J. $y = \frac{1}{8}\sqrt{x + 32} + (-3)$

Use the graph at the right with Exercises 75 and 76.

Short Response

75. How are the graphs of $f(x) = \sqrt{x - 1}$ and $g(x) = \sqrt{x} - 1$ like the graph shown, and how are they different?

Extended Response

76. Compare the domains and ranges of the functions $f(x) = \sqrt{x - 1}$ and $g(x) = \sqrt{x} - 1$.
75–76. See margin.

Mixed Review

Lesson 7-7

Find the inverse of each function. Is the inverse a function? **77–82. See margin.**

77. $f(x) = 4x - 1$
78. $f(x) = \frac{2}{3}x - 3$
79. $f(x) = 2.4x^2 + 1$

80. $f(x) = \sqrt{x + 3} - 4$
81. $f(x) = (2x + 1)^2$
82. $f(x) = 2x^3$

Lesson 7-2

Rationalize the denominator of each expression. Assume that all variables are positive. **83–86. See margin.**

83. $\dfrac{\sqrt{36x^3}}{\sqrt{12x}}$
84. $\sqrt[3]{\dfrac{3x}{2y}}$
85. $\dfrac{\sqrt[3]{x}}{\sqrt[3]{3y}}$
86. $\sqrt[5]{\dfrac{3x^3}{2y}}$

Lesson 5-8

Solve using the Quadratic Formula. **87–92. See margin.**

87. $5x^2 + x = 3$
88. $3x^2 + 9x = 27$
89. $x^2 - 9x + 15 = 0$

90. $x^2 + 10x + 11 = 0$
91. $x^2 - 12x + 25 = 0$
92. $8x^2 + 2x - 15 = 0$

63.

75. [2] Both graphs have the same shape as the graph of $y = \sqrt{x}$. The graph of $f(x) = \sqrt{x - 1}$ is the graph of $y = \sqrt{x}$ moved 1 unit to the right, and the graph of $g(x) = \sqrt{x} - 1$ is the graph of $y = \sqrt{x}$ moved 1 unit down.

[1] minor error in either direction

📁 **Resources**
For additional practice with a variety of test item formats:
- Standardized Test Prep, p. 427
- Test-Taking Strategies, p. 422
- Test-Taking Strategies with Transparencies

76. [4] For $f(x) = \sqrt{x} - 1$ the domain is $x \geq 1$ and the range is $y \geq 0$. For $g(x) = \sqrt{x} - 1$ the domain is $x \geq 0$ and the range is $y \geq -1$.

  [3] minor error in one of the descriptions of domains or ranges

  [2] correct domains or ranges

  [1] some attempt to describe the domains

77. $y = \frac{x + 1}{4}$; yes

78. $y = \frac{3(x + 3)}{2}$; yes

79. $y = \pm\sqrt{\frac{x - 1}{2.4}}$; no

80. $y = (x + 4)^2 - 3$, $x \geq -4$; yes

81. $y = \frac{-1 \pm \sqrt{x}}{2}$; no

82. $y = \sqrt[3]{\frac{x}{2}}$; yes

83. $x\sqrt{3}$

84. $\dfrac{\sqrt[3]{12xy^2}}{2y}$

85. $\dfrac{\sqrt[3]{9xy^2}}{3y}$

86. $\dfrac{\sqrt[5]{48x^3y^4}}{2y}$

87. $\dfrac{-1 \pm \sqrt{61}}{10}$

88. $\dfrac{-3 \pm 3\sqrt{5}}{2}$

89. $\dfrac{9 \pm \sqrt{21}}{2}$

90. $-5 \pm \sqrt{14}$

91. $6 \pm \sqrt{11}$

92. $\frac{5}{4}, -\frac{3}{2}$

419

Activity Lab

Radical Inequalities

Solving radical inequalities can be challenging. The domain considerations can be subtle. Algebraic processes can introduce extraneous solutions.

1 ACTIVITY

Can a number be smaller than its own square root?

Many people rely on their number sense and answer "no" to this question. In their minds, they run through a table of values like the one shown here.

Plot1 Plot2 Plot3
\Y1 ⊟X
\Y2 ⊟√(X)
\Y3 =
\Y4 =
\Y5 =
\Y6 =
\Y7 =

X	Y1	Y2
0	0	0
1	1	1
2	2	1.4142
3	3	1.7321
4	4	2
5	5	2.2361
6	6	2.4495
X=0		

1. Why is there no need to start this table with an x-value less than zero?
   The domain of $y = \sqrt{x}$ is $x \geq 0$.
2. For the table above, $y_1 = x$ and $y_2 = \sqrt{x}$.   **the difference between a**
   a. Enter a third function $Y_3 = Y_1 - Y_2$. What will this function show? **number and its square root**
   b. Turn off Y_1 and Y_2. Then view a table of Y_3 values. Scroll down. What happens to Y_3 values as the value of X increases? **Y_3 values increase**

3. In the table above and in your Y_3 table, the first two rows are unique. They may lead you to wonder what happens between $x = 0$ and $x = 1$.   **x-values are less than**
   a. To find out, go to TBLSET. Change ΔTbl to 0.2 and view a $Y_1 - Y_2$ table. **$\sqrt{x}$ values.**
      How do the values of x and $\sqrt{x}$ compare for values of x between 0 and 1?
   b. What would you expect to see in the Y_3 table? Check your conjecture. **negative values**

In Exercise 3, you should have discovered some numbers that are smaller than their own square roots. But can you find them all? It helps to compare $Y_1 = X$ and $Y_2 = \sqrt{(X)}$ graphically.

4. a. Use the window settings shown at the right. Graph Y_1 and Y_2.
   b. Give a convincing argument that only numbers between 0 and 1 are smaller than their own square roots.
   c. What would you expect to see in a graph of Y_3? Check your conjecture. (*Hint:* You'll have to change your window settings.)
   a–c. Check students' work.

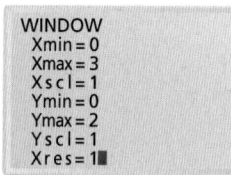

```
WINDOW
 Xmin = 0
 Xmax = 3
 Xscl = 1
 Ymin = 0
 Ymax = 2
 Yscl = 1
 Xres = 1▪
```

2 ACTIVITY

A graphing calculator provides a practical way to solve radical inequalities. However, you must be careful to use appropriate table or window settings.

5. a. What are the domains of $Y_1 = f(x) = \sqrt{x - 3}$ and $Y_2 = g(x) = \sqrt{7 - x}$? **$x \geq 3$; $x \leq 7$**
   b. What are the only values of x that you have to consider to solve the radical inequality
      $\sqrt{x - 3} \leq \sqrt{7 - x}$? (*Hint:* Both expressions must be real numbers.) **$3 \leq x \leq 7$**
   c. Graph Y_1 and Y_2. Solve the inequality. **$3 \leq x \leq 5$**
   d. Let TblStart = 2 and ΔTbl = 1. Predict what a table will show, then check. **Check students' work.**

12a. These restrictions ensure the radicands are nonnegative.
   b. The graph will show part of $y = 1$ above the domain of the inequality.
   c. The solution will be x-values for which Y_2 is beneath Y_3, within the interval shown by Y_1.

6. You can square both sides of the inequality $\sqrt{x-3} \le \sqrt{7-x}$ and simplify to $x \le 5$. Are there any x-values that satisfy $x \le 5$ but are not solutions of $\sqrt{x-3} \le \sqrt{7-x}$? **yes, $x < 3$**

3 ACTIVITY

A **truth function** for an equation or inequality in x is a function whose domain is a set of real numbers and whose range is the two numbers 0 and 1. Domain values are the real numbers that can be used in place of x in the equation or inequality. If a value for x makes the equation or inequality true, the truth-function value is 1. Otherwise, it is 0.

You can solve an inequality graphically by viewing the graph of its truth function.

7. With your calculator in DOT mode, enter $Y_1 = \sqrt{x-3} \le \sqrt{7-x}$. (Find "$\le$" in the TEST menu.) Graph the truth function Y_1 as shown here. **Check students' work.**

8. Explain how the screen on the right shows where $\sqrt{x-3} \le \sqrt{7-x}$ is true. Based on the graph, for what values of x is the inequality true? Does this agree with your result in Exercise 6(c)? **The screen shows a horizontal segment at $y = 1$; $3 \le x \le 5$; yes**

9. For what values of x is the inequality false? How can you tell from the graph? **$5 < x \le 7$; the graph does not show $y = 1$ for these x-values.**

10. Solve the inequality $\sqrt{8+x} + \sqrt{4x} \ge 3 + \sqrt{5-x}$ in two ways.
 a. by graphing it as a truth function **a–b. $1 \le x \le 5$**
 b. by graphing and comparing the two related functions
 c. Compare your solutions from parts (a) and (b). **Check students' work.**

11. Solve the inequality $\sqrt{x} - \sqrt{x-3} \le \sqrt{6-x}$ in two ways.
 a. by graphing it as a truth function **a–b. $3 \le x \le 5.4$**
 b. algebraically
 c. Explain why a truth function might be less useful for solving this inequality.
 Answers may vary. Sample: it is difficult to find the endpoint of the true section of the graph.

4 ACTIVITY

You can find the LOGIC menu next to the TEST menu. The **logical operators** in the LOGIC menu can help you find the domain of an equation or inequality—that is, the values of x to which the solutions of an equation or inequality are restricted. **Answers may vary. See margin for samples.**

12. Use the inequality $\sqrt{x} - \sqrt{x-3} \le \sqrt{6-x}$ from Exercise 11.
 a. For $\sqrt{x} - \sqrt{x-3} \le \sqrt{6-x}$ it must be true that $x \ge 0, x-3 \ge 0$, and $6-x \ge 0$. Why?
 b. The truth function Y_1 in the screen at the right uses the logical operator *and*. Explain why the graph of Y_1 will show the domain of the inequality $\sqrt{x} - \sqrt{x-3} \le \sqrt{6-x}$.
 c. How can graphing $Y_1, Y_2 = \sqrt{x} - \sqrt{x-3}$, and $Y_3 = \sqrt{6-x}$ in the same window help you solve the inequality $\sqrt{x} - \sqrt{x-3} \le \sqrt{6-x}$?

Activity Lab   Radical Inequalities   **421**

Math Tip
Clarify that the truth function has only two values in its range, 0 and 1. By convention, 0 represents false and 1 true.

Advanced Learners   L4
Have students extend their examination of the square root function to its inverse, $y = x^2$, $x \ge 0$.
• *Ask: Can a number be larger than its own square?* **Yes, $x > x^2$ for $0 < x < 1$**
• *Does your result seem logical? Explain.* **Yes, the relationship observed for $y = x^2$ is the inverse relationship found for $y = \sqrt{x}$.**

Finding Multiple Correct Answers

This feature introduces students to the fact that in some types of multiple choice questions, more than one answer might be correct.

 EXAMPLE

The main difference between these types of problems and standard multiple-choice problems is the fact that there are multiple expressions to evaluate. Only when students have evaluated all three expressions (I, II, and III) should they investigate the answer choices.

2 EXAMPLE

Suggest that students circle, highlight, or otherwise mark the expressions that are correct as they evaluate them. This makes choosing the correct answer choice easier.

Resources

SAT® and ACT® correlations are on page 366B.

Test-Taking Strategies with Transparencies
• Transparency 7
• Practice sheet p. 31

Test-Taking Strategies with Transparencies

Test-Taking Strategy: Finding Multiple Correct Answers

Examine each choice to see which one(s) are true.

Example Which of the following are true about the graph of the line $y = -4x - 5$?

 I. The slope is 4.
 II. The y-intercept is −5.
 III. The point $(1, -9)$ is on the line.

 A. None   B. II only   C. III only   D. II and III only

The line is in slope-intercept form: $y = mx + b$, so its slope is −4 and its y-intercept is −5.

So, choice I is false, and choice II is true.

Notice, $-9 = -4(1) - 5$, so choice III is true.

The answer is II and III only are true, or choice D.

Find the answer. Explain your reasoning.

1. If $3x + 4 < 5$, which of the following are true?
 I. $6x + 8 < 10$ II. $-6x - 8 < -10$ III. $-3x > -1$
 A. None   B. I only   C. III only   D. I and III only

2. Use the data: 3, 5, 7, 10, 15. Which of the following are true?
 I. The mean is 8.   II. The median is 7.   III. The range is 12.
 F. None   G. I and II only   H. II only   I. All

Solutions

1. D
2. I

Transparency 7

422

In some multiple-choice questions, there may be several correct answers.

1 EXAMPLE

Which of the following are true for all values of x?

I. $\sqrt[3]{2^x} = \left(\sqrt[3]{2}\right)^x$ II. $\sqrt{x^2} = \sqrt[3]{x^3}$ III. $\sqrt{x^2 + 1} = |x| + 1$

Ⓐ I only   Ⓑ III only   Ⓒ I and II only   Ⓓ I and III only   Ⓔ II and III only

Determine whether each statement is true for all values of x.

Equation I $\sqrt[3]{2^x} = (2^x)^{\frac{1}{3}} = \left(2^{\frac{1}{3}}\right)^x = \left(\sqrt[3]{2}\right)^x$ *True*

Equation II $\sqrt{x^2} = |x| \neq x = \sqrt[3]{x^3}$ *False*

Equation III   Square each side to get
$x^2 + 1 = x^2 + 2|x| + 1$,
or $0 = 2|x|$, which is true only for $x = 0$.   *False*

● Only statement I is true for all values of x. The correct choice is A.

2 EXAMPLE

Which of the following are equal to x for all nonzero values of x?

I. $\sqrt{x^2}$ II. $\sqrt[3]{x^3}$ III. $\dfrac{\sqrt[3]{x^4}}{\sqrt[3]{x}}$

Ⓐ I only   Ⓑ II only   Ⓒ I and II only   Ⓓ II and III only   Ⓔ I, II, and III

Rewrite each statement.

Expression I $\sqrt{x^2} = x$ only when x is positive.

Expression II $\sqrt[3]{x^3} = x$ for all values of x.

Expression III $\dfrac{\sqrt[3]{x^4}}{\sqrt[3]{x}} = \dfrac{x^{\frac{4}{3}}}{x^{\frac{1}{3}}} = x^{\frac{4}{3} - \frac{1}{3}} = x$ when $x \neq 0$.

● Expressions II and III are correct choices. The correct choice is D.

EXERCISES

1. Test each equation in Example 1 with $x = 2$ and $x = -2$. What do your results show about each of the three equations? **Only statement I is true.**

2. **Critical Thinking** Test each equation in Example 1 with $x = 0$ and $x = 1$. Explain whether these values help you answer the question. **Equation III is not true for $x = 1$, eliminating choices B, D, and E.**

3. Suppose Example 2 asked, "Which of the following are equal to x for some nonzero values of x?" What would be the correct answer choice? **E**

4. Which of the following equations are true? **A**

I. $\left(\sqrt[4]{\sqrt{3}}\right)^8 = 3$ II. $\left(\sqrt[4]{\sqrt{3}}\right)^6 = 3$ III. $\dfrac{1}{\left(\frac{3}{5}\right)^{-1}} = \dfrac{5}{3}$

Ⓐ I only   Ⓑ II only   Ⓒ I and II only   Ⓓ I and III only   Ⓔ II and III only

Chapter Review

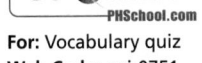
Vocabulary Review

- composite function (p. 399)
- index (p. 370)
- inverse functions (p. 409)
- inverse relation (p. 407)

- like radicals (p. 380)
- nth root (p. 369)
- principal root (p. 370)
- radical equation (p. 391)
- radical function (p. 415)

- radicand (p. 370)
- rational exponent (p. 385)
- rationalize the denominator (p. 376)
- square root equation (p. 391)
- square root function (p. 415)

Choose the correct vocabulary term to complete each sentence.

1. In the expression $\sqrt[3]{8}$, 8 is called the *(principal root, radicand)*. **radicand**

2. In the expression $\sqrt[3]{8}$, 3 is called the *(principal root, index)*. **index**

3. When you rewrite an expression so there are no radicals in any denominator and no denominators in any radical, you *(rationalize the denominator, compose two functions)*. **rationalize the denominator**

4. The expressions $\sqrt{x}$ and $\sqrt[5]{x}$ *(are, are not)* examples of like radicals. **are not**

5. The definition of *(rational exponents, inverse functions)* allows us to write $7^{\frac{2}{3}} = \sqrt[3]{7^2}$. **rational exponents**

6. If $g(x) = x - 4$ and $h(x) = x^2$, $(g \circ h)(x) = x^2 - 4$ is a *(radical function, composite function)*. **composite function**

7. To multiply expressions you sometimes add *(radicands, rational exponents)*. **rational exponents**

8. If f and f^{-1} are *(composite functions, inverse functions)*, then $(f \circ f^{-1})(x) = x$ and $(f^{-1} \circ f)(x) = x$. **inverse functions**

9. $(x - 7)^{\frac{1}{2}} + 2 = x$ is an example of *(a radical equation, an inverse relation)*. **a radical equation**

10. The positive even root of a number is called the *(principal root, rational exponent)*. **principal root**

Go Online
PHSchool.com
For: Vocabulary quiz
Web Code: agj-0751

Skills and Concepts

7-1 and 7-2 Objectives

▼ To simplify nth roots (p. 369)

▼ To multiply radical expressions (p. 374)

▼ To divide radical expressions (p. 375)

For any real numbers a and b, and any positive integer n, if $a^n = b$, then a is an nth root of b. The **principal root** of a number with two real roots is the positive root. The principal nth root of b is written as $\sqrt[n]{b}$. b is the **radicand** and n is the **index** of the radical.

For any negative real number a, $\sqrt[n]{a^n} = |a|$ when n is even.

If $\sqrt[n]{a}$ and $\sqrt[n]{b}$ are real numbers, then $\sqrt[n]{a} \cdot \sqrt[n]{b} = \sqrt[n]{ab}$, and, if $b \neq 0$, then $\dfrac{\sqrt[n]{a}}{\sqrt[n]{b}} = \sqrt[n]{\dfrac{a}{b}}$.

To **rationalize the denominator** of an expression, rewrite it so there are no radicals in any denominator and no denominators in any radical.

Resources

Student Edition
Extra Skills and Word Problems
    Practice, Ch. 7, p. 848
English/Spanish Glossary, p. 899
Properties and Formulas, p. 893
Table of Symbols, p. 889

Vocabulary and Study Skills
    worksheet 7D
Spanish Vocabulary and Study
    Skills worksheet 7D
Interactive Textbook Audio
    Glossary
Online Vocabulary Quiz

Success Tracker
Online at PHSchool.com

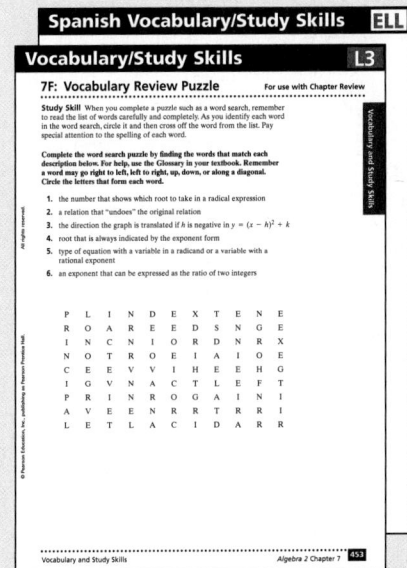

Find each indicated root if it is a real number.

11. $\sqrt{144}$ **12**   **12.** $\sqrt[3]{-0.064}$ **13.** $\sqrt[4]{7^4}$ **7**   **14.** $\sqrt{0.25}$ **0.5**   **15.** $-\sqrt[3]{27}$ **−3**
                           −0.4

Simplify each radical expression. Use absolute value symbols as needed.

16. $\sqrt{49x^2y^{10}}$ $7|xy^5|$ **17.** $\sqrt[3]{-64y^9}$ $-4y^3$ **18.** $\sqrt{(a-1)^4}$ $(a-1)^2$

19. $\sqrt[5]{243x^{15}}$ $3x^3$ **20.** $\sqrt[3]{(y+3)^6}$ $(y+3)^2$ **21.** $\sqrt{32x^9y^5}$ $4x^4y^2\sqrt{2xy}$

24. $10x^2y\sqrt[3]{12y^2}$

25. $7x^2\sqrt{2}$

26. $15x^3y^2\sqrt{x}$

27. $6xy\sqrt[4]{2y}$

31. $6xy\sqrt{3x}$

32. $3a^2b\sqrt[3]{b}$

37. $\dfrac{y\sqrt[3]{150x}}{10x^2}$

Simplify each expression. Assume that all variables are positive.

22. $\sqrt{10}\cdot\sqrt{40}$ **20**   **23.** $\sqrt[3]{12}\cdot\sqrt[3]{36}$ $6\sqrt[3]{2}$ **24.** $2\sqrt[3]{2x^2y}\cdot 5\sqrt[3]{6x^4y^4}$

25. $\sqrt{7x^3}\cdot\sqrt{14x}$ **26.** $\sqrt{5x^4y^3}\cdot\sqrt{45x^3y}$ **27.** $3\sqrt[4]{4x^3}\cdot\sqrt[4]{8xy^5}$

28. $\dfrac{\sqrt{128}}{\sqrt{8}}$ **4**   **29.** $\dfrac{\sqrt[3]{56y^5}}{\sqrt[3]{7y}}$ $2y\sqrt[3]{y}$ **30.** $\dfrac{\sqrt{75x^3}}{\sqrt{3x}}$ $5x$ **31.** $\dfrac{\sqrt{216x^3y^2}}{\sqrt{2}}$ **32.** $\dfrac{\sqrt[3]{81a^8b^5}}{\sqrt[3]{3a^2b}}$

Simplify each expression. Rationalize all denominators. Assume that all variables are positive.

33. $\dfrac{\sqrt{8}}{\sqrt{6}}$ $\dfrac{2\sqrt{3}}{3}$ **34.** $\dfrac{\sqrt{3x^5}}{\sqrt{8x^2}}$ $\dfrac{x\sqrt{6x}}{4}$ **35.** $\dfrac{\sqrt[3]{5}}{\sqrt[3]{x^4}}$ $\dfrac{\sqrt[3]{5x^2}}{x^2}$ **36.** $\dfrac{\sqrt{2a^7b^2}}{\sqrt{32b^3}}$ **37.** $\dfrac{\sqrt[3]{6x^2y^4}}{2\sqrt[3]{5x^7y}}$

                                                        $\dfrac{a^3\sqrt{ab}}{4b}$

7-3 and 7-4 Objectives

▼ To add and subtract radical expressions (p. 380)

▼ To multiply and divide binomial radical expressions (p. 381)

▼ To simplify expressions with rational exponents (p. 385)

Like radicals have the same index and the same radicand. Use the distributive property to add or subtract them. Simplify radicals to find all the like radicals.

Use FOIL to multiply binomial radical expressions.

Binomials such as $a + b$ and $a - b$ are called conjugate expressions.

If the denominator of a fraction is a binomial radical expression, multiply both the numerator and denominator of the fraction by the conjugate of the denominator to rationalize the denominator.

The definition of **rational exponents** states that if the nth root of a is a real number and m is an integer, then $a^{\frac{1}{n}} = \sqrt[n]{a}$ and $a^{\frac{m}{n}} = \sqrt[n]{a^m} = \left(\sqrt[n]{a}\right)^m$. If m is negative, $a \neq 0$. The usual properties of exponents hold for rational exponents.

Simplify each expression.

38. $\sqrt{27} + \sqrt{75} - \sqrt{12}$ **39.** $\left(5 + \sqrt{3}\right)\left(2 - \sqrt{3}\right)$ **40.** $\left(7 - \sqrt{6}\right)\left(7 + \sqrt{6}\right)$
          $6\sqrt{3}$ $7 - 3\sqrt{3}$ **43**

Simplify each expression. Rationalize all denominators. Assume that all variables are positive.

41. $\sqrt{2x} - \sqrt{8x} + \sqrt{18x}$ **42.** $\dfrac{6}{7 + 2\sqrt{3}}$ $\dfrac{42 - 12\sqrt{3}}{37}$ **43.** $\dfrac{\sqrt{2}}{1 - \sqrt{5}}$ $-\dfrac{\sqrt{2} + \sqrt{10}}{4}$
       $2\sqrt{2x}$

Write each expression in radical form.

44. $3^{\frac{1}{5}}$ $\sqrt[5]{3}$ **45.** $x^{\frac{2}{3}}$ $\sqrt[3]{x^2}$ **46.** $2^{-\frac{3}{4}}$ $\sqrt[4]{\dfrac{1}{8}}$ **47.** $3^{0.2}$ $\sqrt[5]{3}$ **48.** $p^{-2.25}$ $\sqrt[4]{\dfrac{1}{p^9}}$

53. $\dfrac{y^4}{x^6}$

Simplify each expression. Assume that all variables are positive.

49. $(243)^{\frac{4}{5}}$ **81**   **50.** $36^{\frac{3}{2}}$ **216**   **51.** $\left(x^{\frac{3}{4}}\right)^{\frac{4}{3}}$ x **52.** $x^{\frac{1}{6}} \cdot x^{\frac{2}{3}}$ $x^{\frac{5}{6}}$ **53.** $\left(x^{-\frac{3}{8}}y^{\frac{1}{4}}\right)^{16}$

7-5 Objective

▼ To solve square root and other radical equations (p. 391)

To solve a **square root equation** or any **radical equation,** isolate a radical on one side of the equation. Then raise both sides of the equation to the same power. Check all possible solutions in the original equation to eliminate extraneous solutions.

Solve each equation. Check for extraneous solutions.

54. $\sqrt[3]{3x + 1} = -5$
-42

55. $\sqrt{x + 7} = x + 1$
2

56. $x^{\frac{1}{2}} - 3 = 8$
121

7-6 and 7-7 Objectives

▼ To add, subtract, multiply, and divide functions (p. 398)

▼ To find the composite of two functions (p. 399)

▼ To find the inverse of a relation or function (p. 406)

The following are definitions of function operations.

Addition $(f + g)(x) = f(x) + g(x)$ Subtraction $(f - g)(x) = f(x) - g(x)$

Multiplication $(f \cdot g)(x) = f(x) \cdot g(x)$ Division $\left(\dfrac{f}{g}\right)(x) = \dfrac{f(x)}{g(x)}, g(x) \neq 0$

The composition of function g with function f is written as $g \circ f$ and is defined as $(g \circ f)(x) = g(f(x))$. The domain of the **composite function** $g \circ f$ consists of the values a in the domain of f such that $f(a)$ is in the domain of g.

If (a, b) is an ordered pair of a relation, then (b, a) is an ordered pair of its **inverse relation.** If a relation or function is described by an equation in x and y, you can interchange x and y to get the inverse. The inverse of a function is denoted by f^{-1}.

If f and f^{-1} are both functions, they are called **inverse functions,** and $(f^{-1} \circ f)(x) = x$ and $(f \circ f^{-1})(x) = x$.

Let $f(x) = 2x + 5$ **and** $g(x) = x^2 - 3x + 2$. **Perform each function operation.**

57. $x^2 - x + 7$

58. $-x^2 + 5x + 3$

59. $2x^3 - x^2 - 11x + 10$

60. $x^2 - 5x - 3$

61. $\dfrac{x^2 - 3x + 2}{2x + 5}, x \neq -\dfrac{5}{2}$

57. $(f + g)(x)$ **58.** $f(x) - g(x)$ **59.** $g(x) \cdot f(x)$ **60.** $(g - f)(x)$ **61.** $\dfrac{g(x)}{f(x)}$

Let $f(x) = x^2$ **and** $g(x) = x - 3$. **Evaluate each expression.**

62. $(g \circ f)(-2)$ **63.** $(f \circ g)(-2)$ **64.** $(f \circ g)(0)$ **65.** $(g \circ g)(7)$ **66.** $(f \circ g)(c)$
1 25 9 1 $c^2 - 6c + 9$

Find the inverse of each function. Is the inverse a function?

67. $y = 6x + 2$ **68.** $y = 2x^3 + 1$ **69.** $y = (x - 2)^4$ **70.** $y = \sqrt{x + 2}$
67–70. See margin.

Let $f(x) = 3x + 1$. **Find each value.**

71. $(f^{-1} \circ f)(5)$ **72.** $(f^{-1} \circ f)(-5)$ **73.** $(f^{-1} \circ f)(6)$ **74.** $(f^{-1} \circ f)(t)$
5 -5 6 t

7-8 Objective

▼ To graph square root and other radical functions (p. 414)

The parent function $f(x) = \sqrt{x}$ defines a family of **square root functions** $f(x) = a\sqrt{x - h} + k$. The graph of $f(x) = a\sqrt{x}$ is a stretch $(a > 0)$ or a shrink $(0 < a < 1)$ of the parent function. The graph of $y = a\sqrt{x - h} + k$ is a translation h units horizontally and k units vertically of $y = a\sqrt{x}$.

Graph each function.   75–78. See margin.

75. $y = \sqrt{x} + 3$

76. $y = \sqrt{x} - 1$

77. $y = -3\sqrt{x} + 6$

78. $y = \sqrt{x + 7} - 2$

67. $y = \dfrac{1}{6}x - \dfrac{1}{3}$; yes

68. $y = \left(\dfrac{x - 1}{2}\right)^{\frac{1}{3}}$; yes

69. $y = \pm\sqrt[4]{x} + 2$; no

70. $y = x^2 - 2, x \geq 0$; yes

75.

76.

77.

78.

Go Online
PHSchool.com
For: Chapter Test
Web Code: aga-0752

Simplify each radical expression. Use absolute value symbols when they are needed.

1. $\sqrt[3]{-0.027}$ **−0.3**

2. $\sqrt{54x^3y^5}$ $3|x|y^2\sqrt{6xy}$

3. $\sqrt[5]{-64x^{14}y^{20}}$ $-2x^2y^4\sqrt[5]{2x^4}$

4. $\sqrt{(x-2)^4}\,(x-2)^2$

Simplify each expression. Rationalize all denominators. Assume that all variables are positive.

5. $\sqrt{7x^3}\cdot\sqrt{14x}$ $7x^2\sqrt{2}$

6. $\sqrt{3y^3}\cdot\sqrt{4xy^4}\cdot\sqrt{6x^5y^2}$ $6x^3y^4\sqrt{2y}$

7. $\dfrac{\sqrt{7x^4y}}{\sqrt{63xy^2}}$ $\dfrac{x\sqrt{xy}}{3y}$

8. $\dfrac{1-\sqrt{3x}}{\sqrt{6x}}$ $\dfrac{\sqrt{6x}-3x\sqrt{2}}{6x}$

9. $\sqrt{48}+2\sqrt{75}+5\sqrt{12}$ $24\sqrt{3}$

10. $\sqrt{98}+\sqrt{50}-\sqrt{5}$ $12\sqrt{2}-\sqrt{5}$

11. $(3+2\sqrt{5})(1-\sqrt{20})$ $-17-4\sqrt{5}$

12. $(7+\sqrt{3})(3+5\sqrt{3})$ $36+38\sqrt{3}$

13. $\dfrac{5}{3-2\sqrt{6}}$ $-1-\tfrac{2}{3}\sqrt{6}$

14. $\dfrac{1+\sqrt{3}}{\sqrt{3}-\sqrt{2}}$ $3+\sqrt{2}+\sqrt{3}+\sqrt{6}$

Simplify each expression. Assume that all variables are positive.

15. $(125)^{-\frac{2}{3}}$ $\tfrac{1}{25}$

16. $x^{\frac{1}{6}}\cdot x^{\frac{1}{3}}$ $x^{\frac{1}{2}}$

17. $\left(\dfrac{8x^9y^3}{27x^2y^{12}}\right)^{\frac{2}{3}}$ $\dfrac{4x^4\sqrt[3]{x^2}}{9y^6}$

Solve each equation. Check for extraneous solutions.

18. $\sqrt{x-3}=x-5$ **7**

19. $\sqrt{x+4}=\sqrt{3x}$ **2**

20. $(3x+4)^{\frac{1}{3}}=-5$ **−43**

21. $x-6=(x-4)^{\frac{1}{2}}$ **8**

Let $f(x)=x-2$ **and** $g(x)=x^2-3x+2.$ **Perform each function operation and then find the domain. 22–27. See margin.**

22. $g(x)-f(x)$

23. $-2g(x)+f(x)$

24. $\dfrac{g(x)}{f(x)}$

25. $-f(x)\cdot g(x)$

For each pair of functions, find $f(g(x))$ **and** $g(f(x)).$

26. $f(x)=x^2-2,\,g(x)=4x+1$

27. $f(x)=2x^2+x-7,\,g(x)=-3x-1$

28. Writing Explain why -108 has no real 6th roots.
See margin.

29. Discounts While purchasing a pair of shoes on sale for 50% off, you noticed that the price on the cash register was only 25% off. The cashier then took another 25% off that price.
  a. Write a function $f(x)$ to represent the 50%-off price of the shoes. $f(x)=0.5x$
  b. Write a function $g(x)$ to represent the price the cash register rang up the first time. $g(x)=0.75x$
  c. Write a composite function to represent the price of the shoes after the cashier's solution to the problem. $g(g(x))=0.5625x$
  d. Compare the result of the cashier's solution to the correct price of the shoes. **See margin.**

Rewrite each function to make it easy to graph using a translation. Describe the graph.

30. $y=\sqrt{16x+80}-1$ **See margin.**

31. $y=\sqrt{9x+3}$ **See margin p. 427.**

Graph. Find the domain and range of each function.

32. $y=2\sqrt{x}+3$

33. $y=\sqrt{2x+3}$

34. $y=-\tfrac{1}{2}\sqrt{x-4}$

35. $y=\sqrt{x+3}-4$

32–35. See back of book.

Let $f(x)=x^3+1$ **and** $g(x)=7x-4.$ **Find each value.**

36. $f(g(-2))$ **−5831**

37. $g(f(3))$ **192**

38. $f(g(0))$ **−63**

Find the inverse of each function. Is the inverse a function? 39–42. See margin p. 427.

39. $f(x)=3x^3-2$

40. $g(x)=\sqrt{x+3}-1$

41. $g(x)=\sqrt{2x+1}$

42. $f(x)=\tfrac{1}{4}x^4$

43. a. Geometry For a sphere, $V=\tfrac{4}{3}\pi r^3.$ Find the volume of a sphere with radius 4 in.
  b. Solve the formula in part (a) for $r.$
  c. Find to the nearest hundredth the radius of a sphere of volume 100 in.^{3}. **a–c. See margin p. 427.**

44. Open-Ended Write a relation rule that is not a function, but whose inverse is a function.
  Check students' work.

45. Measurement The time t in seconds for a swinging pendulum to complete one full cycle is given by the function $t=0.2\sqrt{\ell}$, where ℓ is the length of the pendulum in cm. How long is a full cycle if the pendulum is 10 cm long? 20 cm long?
  $\approx$**0.6 second;** $\approx$**0.9 second**

---

24. $x-1,$ domain: $\{x\,|\,x\neq 2\}$

25. $-x^3+5x^2-8x+4,$ domain: all real numbers

26. $16x^2+8x-1,\,4x^2-7$

27. $18x^2+9x-6,$ $-6x^2-3x+20$

28. The sixth power of a real number is always nonnegative.

29d. The cashier's solution is too high by 6.25% of the original price.

30. $y=4\sqrt{x+5}-1;$ $y=4\sqrt{x}$ translated 5 units left and 1 unit down

22. $x^2-4x+4;$ domain: all real numbers

23. $-2x^2+7x-6;$ domain: all real numbers

Standardized Test Prep

Reading Comprehension Read the passage below. Then answer the questions on the basis of what is *stated* or *implied* in the passage.

> **Boxing Match** You can make an open box from a piece of flat cardboard. First, cut congruent squares from the four corners of the cardboard. Then, fold and tape the sides.
>
> Let *x* equal the side length of each square. As *x* increases, so does the depth of the box. The usable area of cardboard decreases as *x* increases, and so do the length and width of the box.
>
> What happens to the volume of the box? Does it increase or decrease as *x* increases? Would the answer *both* surprise you?
>
> What size squares should you cut from the corners to maximize the volume of your box?

For Questions 1–6, consider a box made from a piece of cardboard that is 80 centimeters by 54 centimeters.

1. What are the dimensions of the box in
C centimeters?
   - Ⓐ $80 - x$, $54 - x$, x
   - Ⓑ $80 - 2x$, $54 - 2x$, $2x$
   - Ⓒ $80 - 2x$, $54 - 2x$, x
   - Ⓓ $x - 80$, $x - 54$, x

2. Which function models the area of the
H cardboard after the corners are cut away?
   - Ⓕ $A(x) = (80 - 2x)(54 - 2x)$
   - Ⓖ $A(x) = (80 - 2x)(54 - 2x) + 4x^2$
   - Ⓗ $A(x) = 4320 - 4x^2$
   - Ⓙ $A(x) = 4320 - 4(2x)^2$

3. By how much does the area of the
B cardboard decrease when *x* changes from 8 cm to 9 cm?
   - Ⓐ 145 cm^2
   - Ⓑ 68 cm^2
   - Ⓒ 26 cm^2
   - Ⓓ 17 cm^2

4. Which function models the volume of the box?
H
   - Ⓕ $V(x) = (80 - x)(54 - x)x$
   - Ⓖ $V(x) = (80 - x)(54 - x) + x$
   - Ⓗ $V(x) = (80 - 2x)(54 - 2x)x$
   - Ⓙ $V(x) = (80 - 2x) + (54 - 2x) + x$

5. What is a reasonable domain for *x*?
A
   - Ⓐ $0 < x < 27$
   - Ⓑ $0 < x < 40$
   - Ⓒ $0 < x < 54$
   - Ⓓ all real numbers

6. Which is the best value for the maximum volume
G of the box?
   - Ⓕ about $20{,}440 \text{ cm}^3$
   - Ⓖ about $20{,}444 \text{ cm}^3$
   - Ⓗ about $20{,}450 \text{ cm}^3$
   - Ⓙ about $20{,}452 \text{ cm}^3$

For Questions 7–9, consider a box made from a piece of cardboard that is 18 inches square.

7. Write a function that models the volume of the box. $V(x) = (18 - 2x)^2 x$

8. What is a reasonable domain for *x*? $0 < x < 9$

9. Find the maximum volume. Is this the maximum of the volume function? Explain. **See margin.**

10. **Open-Ended** Find the dimensions of three different rectangular pieces of cardboard you could use to make a box with volume 432 unit³.
    Check students' work.

To answer the questions, students apply skills and concepts from this chapter and previous chapters.
Multiple Choice: Items 1–6
Free Response: Items 7–9
Extended Response: Item 10

Resources

Test Prep Workbook

Grab & Go
- **L3** Cumulative Review

ExamView CD-ROM
- Standardized Test Practice

Differentiated Instruction Resources

Spanish Assessment Resources
- **L3** Spanish Cumulative Review

Standardized Test Prep

31. $y = 3\sqrt{x} + \frac{1}{3}$; $y = 3\sqrt{x}$ translated $\frac{1}{3}$ unit left

39. $y = \sqrt[3]{\frac{x + 2}{3}}$; yes

40. $y = (x + 1)^2 - 3$, $x \geq -1$; yes

41. $y = \frac{x^2 - 1}{2}$, $x \geq 0$; yes

42. $y = \pm\sqrt[4]{4x}$, $x \geq 0$; no

43. a. $V = \frac{256\pi}{3} \approx 268.08$

    b. $r = \left(\frac{3V}{4\pi}\right)^{\frac{1}{3}}$

    c. $r \approx 2.88$ in.

9. 432 in.²; no; as *x* gets bigger, $(18 - 2x)$ becomes a larger negative, so $(18 - 2x)^2 x$ is a large positive number.

Exponential and Logarithmic Functions

Chapter at a Glance

Lesson Titles, Objectives, and Features	Assessment	NCTM Standards	Local Standards
8-1 Exploring Exponential Models • Modeling exponential growth • Modeling exponential decay **Activity Lab:** Technology: Fitting Exponential Curves to Data	Lesson Quiz	1, 2, 7	
8-2 Properties of Exponential Functions • Identifying the role of constants in $y = ab^{cx}$ • Using e as a base	Lesson Quiz Checkpoint Quiz 1	1, 2	
8-3 Logarithmic Functions as Inverses • Writing and evaluating logarithmic expressions • Graphing logarithmic functions **GPS:** Understanding Word Problems	Lesson Quiz	1, 2, 3, 7	
8-4 Properties of Logarithms • Using the properties of logarithms **Vocabulary Builder:** Reasonable Context	Lesson Quiz	1, 2, 9	
8-5 Exponential and Logarithmic Equations • Solving exponential equations • Solving logarithmic equations **Activity Lab:** Technology: Linear and Exponential Models	Lesson Quiz Checkpoint Quiz 2	1, 2, 6	
8-6 Natural Logarithms • Evaluating natural logarithmic expressions • Solving equations using natural logarithms **Activity Lab:** Technology: Exponential and Logarithmic Inequalities	Lesson Quiz	1, 2, 9, 10	
Activity Lab: Applying Exponential Functions			

NCTM Standards 2000

1 Number and Operations	**2** Algebra	**3** Geometry	**4** Measurement	**5** Data Analysis and Probability
6 Problem Solving	**7** Reasoning and Proof	**8** Communication	**9** Connections	**10** Representation

Correlations to Standardized Tests

All content for these tests is contained in *Prentice Hall Algebra 2*. This chart reflects coverage in this chapter only.

	8-1	8-2	8-3	8-4	8-5	8-6
SAT®						
Number and Operations Operations, ratio & proportions, complex numbers, counting, elementary number theory, matrices, sequences						
Algebra and Functions Expressions, equations, inequalities, representation and modeling, properties of functions (linear, polynomial, rational, exponential)	✔	✔	✔	✔	✔	✔
Geometry and Measurement *Plane Euclidean/Measurement Coordinate* Lines, parabolas, circles, symmetry, transformations *Three-dimensional* Solids, surface area & volume (cylinders, cones, pyramids, spheres, prisms) *Trigonometry* Right triangles, identities						
Data Analysis, Statistics, and Probability Mean, median, mode, range, interquartile range, graphs and plots, regression, probability						
ACT®						
Pre-Algebra Basic operations using whole numbers, decimals, fractions, and integers; place value; square roots and approximations; the concept of exponents; scientific notation; factors, ratio, proportion, and percent; linear equations in one variable; absolute value and ordering numbers by value; elementary counting techniques and simple probability; data collection, representation, and interpretation; and understanding simple descriptive statistics.						
Elementary Algebra Properties of exponents and square roots, evaluation of algebraic expressions through substitution, using variables to express functional relationships, understanding algebraic operations, and solving quadratic equations by factoring.	✔	✔	✔	✔	✔	✔
Intermediate Algebra Understanding of the quadratic formula, rational and radical expressions, absolute value equations and inequalities, sequences and patterns, systems of equations, quadratic inequalities, functions, modeling, matrices, roots of polynomials, and complex numbers.	✔	✔	✔	✔	✔	✔
Coordinate Geometry Graphing and the relations between equations and graphs, including points, lines, polynomials, circles, and other curves; graphing inequalities; slope; parallel and perpendicular lines; distance; midpoints; and conics.	✔	✔	✔		✔	
Plane Geometry Properties and relations of plane figures, including angles and relations among perpendicular and parallel lines; properties of circles, triangles, rectangles, parallelograms, and trapezoids; transformations; the concept of proof and proof techniques; volume; and applications of geometry to three dimensions.						
Trigonometry Understanding trigonometric relations in right triangles; values and properties of trigonometric functions; graphing trigonometric functions; modeling using trigonometric functions; use of trigonometric identities; and solving trigonometric equations.						
NAEP						
Number Sense, Properties, and Operations						
Measurement						
Geometry and Spatial Sense						
Data Analysis, Statistics, and Probability						
Algebra and Functions	✔	✔	✔	✔	✔	✔

SAT® The College Board, SAT® Reasoning Test　　**ACT®** The ACT Assessment® Test　　**NAEP** National Assessment of Educational Progress, 2005 Mathematics Objectives

Math Background

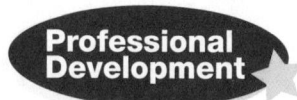
Skills Trace

BEFORE Chapter 8

In previous chapters, students applied properties of exponents and studied inverse functions.

▼

DURING Chapter 8

Students find and apply exponential and logarithmic function models, solve exponential and logarithmic equations, and apply properties of logarithms.

▼

AFTER Chapter 8

Students will graph and model data with rational and trigonometric functions.

Chapter Overview

Most of the functions studied so far have involved a variable quantity raised to a power, as in $y = x^2$, $y = 4x^3$, and $y = x^{\frac{2}{5}}$. In such functions, there is a variable base and an exponent that is a constant. For exponential functions, these roles are reversed: the base is a constant and the exponent varies, as in $y = 2^x$ and $y = \left(\frac{1}{2}\right)^x$. The most basic exponential functions have the form $y = b^x$, where $b > 0$ and $b \neq 1$. Inverses of such functions are also functions and are called *logarithmic functions*.

Important applications of exponential functions include population growth, depreciation, compound interest, and radioactive decay. Logarithmic functions are useful in describing the loudness of sounds and pH levels in chemistry.

Exploring Exponential Models   8-1

In Lesson 7-4, positive and negative rational exponents were defined. Now the possible exponents are extended to include irrational exponents, so that any exponential expression b^x, where $b > 0$, is defined for all real numbers x. This allows for the definition of an *exponential function*. Exponential functions have the form $y = ab^x$, where $a \neq 0$, $b > 0$, and $b \neq 1$. When $b > 1$ and

$x > 0$, the function *grows* exponentially. When $0 < b < 1$ and $x > 0$, the function *decays* exponentially. A function also decays exponentially when $b > 1$ and $x < 0$. Thus, $y = \left(\frac{1}{2}\right)^x = 2^{-x}$.

It is important that students understand the difference between growth by a constant *amount* and growth by a constant rate. When a function increases by a constant amount (in equal intervals of the domain), the function grows linearly. When a function grows at a constant rate, the function grows exponentially by a constant multiplier or growth factor. Thus, the phrase "constant growth" is not clear by itself because it does not distinguish between linear growth and exponential growth.

Properties of Exponential Functions   8-2

The irrational number e is defined as the limit of $\left(1 + \frac{1}{x}\right)^x$ as the value of x increases without bound. This limit is called e in honor of Swiss mathematician Leonhard Euler (1707–1783), who established it. (Incidentally, Euler's approval of the Greek letter π—another irrational number—for the ratio of the circumference to the diameter of a circle led to its conventional use.) Students can experiment with the definition of e by computing values for larger and larger values of x.

Students often wonder what is so special about e. The most straightforward answer is that it is like π in that it appears in many unexpected places. Also, in calculus students will learn that $y = e^x$ is the only function that is both its own integral and its own derivative. This means the area under the curve of $y = e^x$ up to $x = 0$ is the same as the slope of the graph at $x = 0$, which is the same as its corresponding function value ($y = e^0 = 1$).

Logarithmic Functions as Inverses   8-3

Since the exponential function passes the horizontal line test, it is clear that its inverse is a function. The logarithmic function $y = \log_b x$ is defined as the inverse of an exponential function of the form $y = b^x$, where $b > 0$ and $b \neq 1$. Therefore, the equations $y = b^x$ and $\log_b y = x$ are equivalent statements. From this, students should recognize that a logarithm is simply an exponent.

Logarithms were discovered by John Napier (1550–1617) in response to the need to simplify complicated, time-consuming calculations that arose in astronomy and navigation. With graphing calculators, the user no longer has to be concerned with the complexities of the calculations, but the calculator itself uses logarithms to perform many of its internal calculations. Logarithms also remain of great importance because of their mathematical properties and the role they play in modeling real-world situations. Logarithmic scales are used to measure pH levels, decibel levels of sounds, and brightness of stars.

By making tables and graphs of the inverse functions $y = \log_2 x$ and $y = 2^x$, students can understand the properties of logarithmic functions. For instance, logarithms only exist for positive numbers, but its output can be any real number: positive, zero, or negative. A common logarithm has 10 as its base. Whenever the base is not indicated, as in $\log 1000 = 3$, the base is assumed to be 10. Common logarithms are particularly convenient because we use a base 10 number system.

Properties of Logarithms   8-4

Students may be helped to a deeper understanding of the relationships between exponents and logarithms by discussing the table below. Note that x and y must be positive numbers and $a \neq 0$.

Properties of Logarithms	Properties of Exponents
$\log_a (x \cdot y) = \log_a x + \log_a y$	$a^m \cdot a^n = a^{m+n}$
$\log_a\left(\frac{x}{y}\right) = \log_a x - \log_a y$	$\dfrac{a^m}{a^n} = a^{m-n}$
$\log_a x^p = p \cdot \log_a x$	$(a^m)^n = a^{m \cdot n}$

As with Properties of Exponents, students should be able to move comfortably in either direction with Properties of Logarithms. For example, students should be able to rewrite a single logarithm as a sum as well as rewrite a difference as a single logarithm.

Students may also benefit from the following additional properties. Students can prove each of the following statements using the definition of a logarithm and the above properties.

Properties of Exponents	Properties of Logarithms
$b^0 = 1$	$\log_b 1 = 0$
$b^1 = b$	$\log_b b = 1$
$b^{\log_b x} = x$	$\log_b b^x = x$

Exponential and Logarithmic Equations   8-5

A function is called a *one-to-one* function if it has an inverse that is also a function. The strategies of "taking the log of" both sides of an exponential equation and "exponentiating" both sides of a logarithmic equation are justified by the one-to-oneness of the logarithmic and exponential functions. It is true that:

For any positive real numbers a, x, and y, with $a \neq 1$, $x = y$ is true if $\log_a x = \log_a y$ or if $a^x = a^y$.

The Change of Base Formula $\log_b M = \dfrac{\log_c M}{\log_c b}$, where $b \neq 1$ and $c \neq 1$, allows students to compute the logarithm for any base by using base 10 logarithms that are readily obtained from calculators. For example, $\log_5 39 = \dfrac{\log_{10} 39}{\log_{10} 5}$. Students are often amazed when they realize that they can now graph $y = \log_3 x$ by entering $y = \dfrac{\log x}{\log 3}$. Also, by rearranging the Change of Base Formula, students can obtain some interesting results: $\log_b M = \dfrac{1}{\log_M b}$ and $(\log_c b)(\log_b M) = \log_c M$.

Natural Logarithms   8-6

Natural logarithms often represent natural phenomena more effectively than base 10 logarithms. The mathematical importance of natural logarithms will become much clearer to those students who go on to study calculus.

Students must understand that $\ln x$ means $\log_e x$ and that natural logarithms obey all of the same rules as any other logarithm. Also, ln is pronounced "ell-enn" or "lahn."

Additional Professional Development Opportunities

Math Background notes for Chapter 8: Every lesson has a Math Background in the PLAN section.

Research Overview, Mathematical Strands Additional support for these topics and more is in the front of this Teacher's Edition.

Lesson Lab Lesson Lab, a Pearson Education company, offers comprehensive, facilitated professional development designed to help teachers improve student achievement. To learn more, please visit lessonlab.com

Chapter 8 Resources

	8-1	8-2	8-3	8-4	8-5	8-6	For the Chapter
Print Resources							
L3 Practice	•	•	•	•	•	•	
L3 Guided Problem Solving	•	•	•	•	•	•	
L2 Reteaching	•	•	•	•	•	•	
L4 Enrichment	•	•	•	•	•	•	
L3 Daily Notetaking Guide	•	•	•	•	•	•	
L3 Vocabulary and Study Skills Worksheets	•						•
L3 Chapter Project							•
L3 Hands On Activities	•				•		
L3 Checkpoint Quiz		•			•		
L2 Below Level Chapter Test							•
L3 Chapter Test							•
L4 Alternative Assessment							•
L3 Cumulative Review							•
L4 Connections to Precalculus Masters	•	•	•	•	•	•	
L3 Technology Activities	•	•			•	•	
Spanish Resources ELL							
L3 Practice	•	•	•	•	•	•	
L3 Vocabulary and Study Skills Worksheets	•						•
L3 Checkpoint Quiz		•			•		
L2 Below Level Chapter Test							•
L3 Chapter Test							•
L4 Alternative Assessment							
L3 Cumulative Review							•
Transparencies							
Check Skills You'll Need	•	•	•	•	•	•	
Additional Examples	•	•	•	•	•	•	
Problem of the Day	•	•	•	•	•	•	
Classroom Aid	•	•	•				
Student Edition Answers	•	•	•	•	•	•	•
Lesson Quiz	•	•	•	•	•	•	
Test-Taking Strategies							•
Technology							
TI 83/84 Plus Activities	•	•					
Interactive Textbook Online	•	•	•	•	•	•	•
Student Express CD-ROM	•	•	•	•	•	•	•
TI Navigator, Instant Check System	•	•	•	•	•	•	
Success Tracker	•	•	•	•	•	•	•
ExamView CD-ROM with Quick Take	•	•	•	•	•	•	•
Teacher Express CD-ROM	•	•	•	•	•	•	•
Presentation Express CD-ROM	•	•	•	•	•	•	•
Mindpoint Quiz Show CD-ROM	•	•	•	•	•	•	•
Prentice Hall Web site: PHSchool.com	•	•	•	•	•	•	•

Also available: Prentice Hall Assessment System (Progress Monitoring Assessments, Skills and Concepts Review, Test Prep Workbook)   Solution Key   Student Workbook
Student Workbook, Adapted Version   Data Analysis and Probability Workbook   Math Notes Study Folder   Spanish Cumulative Assessment

Where You Can Use the Lesson Resources

Here is a suggestion, following the four-step teaching plan, for how you can incorporate Differentiated Instruction Resources into your teaching.

	Instructional Resources L3	**Differentiated Instruction Resources**
1. Plan		
Check Skills You'll Need Assign these exercises to review prerequisite skills. **New Vocabulary** Help students pre-read the lesson by pointing out the new terms introduced in the lesson.	**Math Background** **Transparencies & Presentation Express CD** Check Skills You'll Need **Resources** Vocabulary and Study Skills	**Spanish Support** ELL Vocabulary and Study Skills
2. Teach		
L3 **Guided Instruction** Teach each Example. After each Example, assign the Quick Check exercise for that Example.	**Student Edition** Activity Lab **Resources** Daily Notetaking Guide Activity Lab TI-83/84 Activities CD-ROM **Transparencies & Presentation Express CD** Additional Examples Classroom Aids **ExamView CD-ROM with QuickTake** **TI Navigator Instant Check System**	**Teacher's Edition** Every lesson includes suggestions for working with students who need special attention. L1 Special Needs L2 Below Level L4 Advanced Learners ELL English Language Learners
3. Practice		

Assignment Guide
 	
Homework Exercises
Assign the exercises cited in each lesson's Assignment Guide.
  A Practice by Example
  B Apply Your Skills
  C Challenge
  Test Prep
  Mixed Review
 	
Homework Quick Check
Discuss in class the exercises cited in each lesson's Assignment Guide.
	Transparencies & Presentation Express CD
	Student Answers
	
	Resources
	Practice
	Guided Problem Solving
	Vocabulary and Study Skills
	Activity Lab
	
	ExamView CD-ROM with QuickTake
		Spanish Support
		ELL Practice
		ELL Vocabulary and Study Skills
		
		Resources
		L4 Enrichment

4. Assess & Reteach		
Lesson Quiz Assign the Lesson Quiz to assess students' mastery of the lesson content. **Checkpoint Quiz** Use the Checkpoint Quiz to assess student progress over several lessons.	**Transparencies & Presentation Express CD** Lesson Quiz **Resources** Checkpoint Quiz	**Resources** L2 Reteaching ELL Checkpoint Quiz Success Tracker **ExamView CD-ROM with QuickTake**

KEY   L1 Special Needs   L2 Below Level   L3 For All Students   L4 Advanced, Gifted   ELL English Language Learners

Exponential and Logarithmic Functions

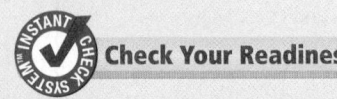
Check Your Readiness

Answers are in the back of the textbook.

For intervention, direct students to:

Evaluating Expressions
Lesson 1-2: Example 2
Extra Skills and Word
  Problems Practice, Ch. 1

Using Linear Models
Lesson 2-4: Example 1
Extra Skills and Word
  Problems Practice, Ch. 2

Using Quadratic Models
Lesson 5-1: Example 3
Extra Skills and Word
  Problems Practice, Ch. 5

Graphic Translations
Lesson 5-3: Example 4
Extra Skills and Word
  Problems Practice, Ch. 5

Graphing Inverse Functions
Lesson 7-7: Example 3
Extra Skills and Word
  Problems Practice, Ch. 7

Spanish Vocabulary/Study Skills **ELL**

Vocabulary/Study Skills **L3**

8A: Graphic Organizer   For use before Lesson 8-1

Study Skill Be sure to read with pencil and paper in hand. Take notes and draw sketches as you look at the new chapter. Formulate questions you might have as you look at each section of the chapter.

Write your answers.

1. What is the chapter title? _____

2. Find the Table of Contents page for this chapter at the front of the book. Name four topics you will study in this chapter.
   _____
   _____

3. What is the topic of the Reading Math page? _____

4. What is the topic of the Test-Taking Strategy page? _____

5. Look through the pages of the chapter. List four real-world connections that you see discussed in this chapter.
   _____
   _____

6. Complete the graphic organizer below as you work through the chapter.
   • In the center, write the title of the chapter.
   • When you begin a lesson, write the lesson name in a rectangle.
   • When you complete a lesson, write a skill or key concept in an oval linked to that lesson block.
   • When you complete the chapter, use this graphic organizer to help you review.

What You've Learned

- In Chapters 1 and 2, you learned to model linear functions and to solve linear equations.

- In Chapter 5, you learned to model quadratic functions and to solve quadratic equations.

- In Chapter 6, you learned to model polynomial functions and to solve polynomial equations.

- In Chapter 7, you learned to find and graph the inverse of a function.

Check Your Readiness

for Help to the Lesson in green.

Evaluating Expressions (Lesson 1-2)

Evaluate each expression for $x = -2, -1, 0, 1,$ and 2.

1. 10^{x+1} **0.1, 1, 10, 100, 1000**   **2.** $\left(\frac{3}{2}\right)^x$ $\frac{4}{9}, \frac{2}{3}, 1, \frac{3}{2}, \frac{9}{4}$ **3.** $x^4 - x^2$ **12, 0, 0, 0, 12**

Using Linear Models (Lesson 2-4)

4a. $n = 3d$

4. Each day, a squirrel buries three acorns.
   a. Write and graph a function to model the number n of acorns the squirrel buries in d days.
   b. Use your function to find the number of acorns buried in four weeks. **b. 84 acorns**
   c. Suppose the squirrel had started out with nine acorns already buried. Explain how this would change your function and its graph. **The function would be $n = 9 + 3d$ and the graph would shift 9 units upward.**

Using Quadratic Models (Lesson 5-1)

Find a quadratic function to model each set of values. Then graph the function.

5. $\{(0, 0), (2, -4), (3, -3)\}$ **6.** $\{(0, 7), (2, 15), (5, 72)\}$
5–6. See margin.

Graphing Transformations (Lesson 5-3)

Identify the parent function of each equation. Graph each equation as a transformation of its parent function. **7–11. See margin pp. 428–429.**

7. $y = -(x - 1)^2 + 4$ **8.** $y = 3(x + 2)^2 - 1$

Graphing Inverse Functions (Lesson 7-7)

Graph each function and its inverse on a coordinate plane.

9. $y = -5x$ **10.** $y = \sqrt{5x + 12}$ **11.** $y = 2x^3$

5. $y = x^2 - 4x$

6. $y = 3x^2 - 2x + 7$

7. $y = -x^2$

8. $y = 3x^2$

Exponential and Logarithmic Functions

Chapter 8

🔊 **Key Vocabulary**

- asymptote (p. 433)
- Change of Base Formula (p. 461)
- common logarithm (p. 447)
- continuously compounded interest formula (p. 441)
- decay factor (p. 433)
- exponential equation (p. 461)
- exponential function (p. 430)
- growth factor (p. 430)
- logarithm (p. 447)
- logarithmic equation (p. 463)
- logarithmic function (p. 448)
- natural logarithmic function (p. 470)

Chapter 8 Overview

Students begin the chapter by exploring exponential models and properties of exponential functions. These lessons are followed by logarithmic functions as inverses, and properties of logarithms. Students continue in the chapter by learning about exponential and logarithmic equations, and conclude with a lesson on natural logarithms.

Activating Prior Knowledge

Ask:
- *What is the general form of a quadratic function?*

Answers should be of the form $y = ax^2 + bx + c$ with $a \neq 0$.

Ask:
- *What is the general form of the square root function?*

Answers should be of the form $y = a\sqrt{x}$ or $y = ax^{\frac{1}{2}}$ with $a \neq 0$, $x \geq 0$.

Instead of a variable x raised to a constant exponent, such as 2 or $\frac{1}{2}$, you can take a constant term and raise it to a variable exponent, such as in $y = 2^x$ or $y = \left(\frac{1}{2}\right)$. These are called exponential functions, and students will study them in this chapter.

What You'll Learn Next

- In Chapter 8, you will learn to use exponential functions to model real-world data.

- You will learn to graph exponential functions and their inverses, logarithmic functions.

- You will learn to solve exponential and logarithmic equations.

 Activity Lab Applying what you learn, on pages 484–485 you will do activities involving world population.

429

9.

10.

11.

1. Plan

Objectives
1 To model exponential growth
2 To model exponential decay

Examples
1 Graphing Exponential Growth
2 Real-World Connection
3 Writing an Exponential Function
4 Analyzing a Function
5 Graphing Exponential Decay
6 Real-World Connection

Math Background

Exponential functions model data that have a constant percent increase or a constant percent decrease. This should not be confused with a constant rate of change, which linear functions have. Informally, a constant percent increase or decrease guarantees that the data grow or decay rapidly.

More Math Background: p. 428C

Lesson Planning and Resources

See p. 428E for a list of the resources that support this lesson.

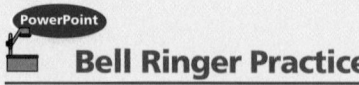

Bell Ringer Practice

☑ Check Skills You'll Need
For intervention, direct students to:

Algebraic Expressions
Lesson 1-2: Examples 1, 2
Extra Skills and Word Problems Practice, Ch. 1

430

What You'll Learn

- To model exponential growth
- To model exponential decay

. . . And Why

To model a car's depreciation, as in Example 6

☑ Check Skills You'll Need

Evaluate each expression for the given value of x.

1. 2^x for $x = 3$ **8**
2. 4^{x+1} for $x = 1$ **16**
3. 2^{3x+4} for $x = -1$ **2**

4. $3^x 3^{x-2}$ for $x = 2$ **9**
5. $\left(\frac{1}{2}\right)^x$ for $x = 0$ **1**
6. 2^x for $x = -2$ **$\frac{1}{4}$**

GO for Help Lesson 1-2

◀)) **New Vocabulary**
- exponential function
- growth factor
- decay factor
- asymptote

---

1 **Exponential Growth**

For some data, the best model is a function that uses the independent variable as an exponent. An **exponential function** is a function with the general form $y = ab^x$, where x is a real number, $a \neq 0$, $b > 0$, and $b \neq 1$.

You can use an exponential function with $b > 1$ to model growth. When $b > 1$, b is the **growth factor.**

Exponential Growth

Growth factor $b > 1$

1a.

b.
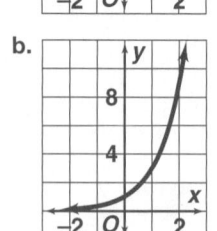

1 **EXAMPLE** Graphing Exponential Growth

Graph $y = 2^x$.

Step 1 Make a table of values.

x	2^x	y
-3	2^{-3}	$\frac{1}{8} = 0.125$
-2	2^{-2}	$\frac{1}{4} = 0.25$
-1	2^{-1}	$\frac{1}{2} = 0.5$
0	2^0	1
1	2^1	2
2	2^2	4
3	2^3	8

Step 2 Graph the coordinates. Connect the points with a smooth curve.

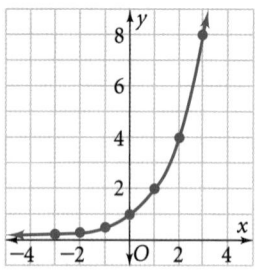

☑ **Quick Check** ① Graph each function. a–b. See left.

a. $y = 4(2)^x$

b. $y = 3^x$

---

430 Chapter 8 Exponential and Logarithmic Functions

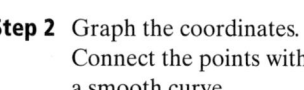
Differentiated **Instruction** **Solutions for All Learners**

Special Needs L1
For Example 3, write $y = 1.24^x$ on the board and tell students that they will jump the distance y in feet for each year of the growth function. Have a volunteer calculate y for each round starting with $x = 0$, and record it on the board. After 8 years (rounds), students cannot jump the distance. **learning style: tactile**

Below Level L2
Have students use their graphing calculators to graph $y = 2^x$ and $y = \left(\frac{1}{2}\right)^x$. How do these graphs compare? Are they inverses of each other? Discuss growth and decay factors. **learning style: visual**

You can use an exponential function to model population growth. If you know the rate of increase r, you can find the growth factor by using the equation $b = 1 + r$.

2 EXAMPLE Real-World Connection

Multiple Choice Refer to the graph. In 2000, the annual rate of increase in the U.S. population was about 1.24%. Suppose the rate of increase continues to be 1.24%. Which function best models U.S. population growth, in millions, after 2000?

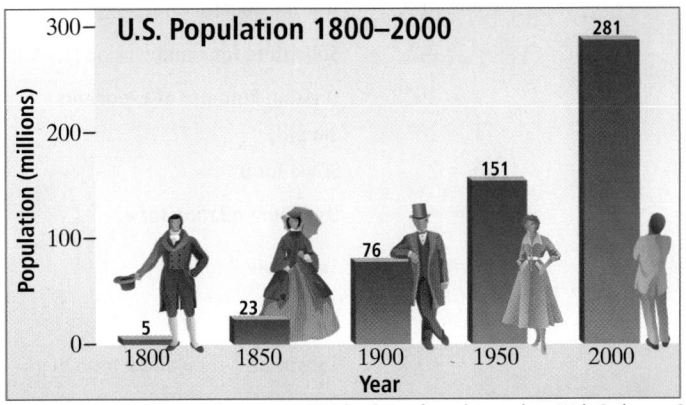

U.S. Population 1800–2000

SOURCE: U.S. Census Bureau. Go to **www.PHSchool.com** for a data update. Web Code: agg-9041

Ⓐ $281 + 1.0124^x$ Ⓑ $281(1.24)^x$ Ⓒ $281(1.024)^x$ Ⓓ $281(1.0124)^x$

First, find the growth factor.

$b = 1 + r$
$\quad = 1 + 0.0124$ **Substitute 1.24%, or 0.0124, for r.**
$\quad = 1.0124$ **Simplify.**

Then write a function.

Relate The population increases exponentially, so use the general form of an exponential function, $p(x) = ab^x$.

Define Let x = number of years after 2000.

Let $p(x)$ = the population in millions.

Write $p(x) = a(1.0124)^x$

$281 = a(1.0124)^0$ **To find a, substitute the 2000 values: $p(x) = 281$, $x = 0$.**
$281 = a \cdot 1$ **Any nonzero number to the zero power equals 1.**
$281 = a$ **Simplify.**
$p(x) = 281(1.0124)^x$ **Substitute a and b into $p(x) = ab^x$.**

● The function $p(x) = 281(1.0124)^x$ models U.S. population growth. The answer is D.

✓ Quick Check ② **a.** Predict U.S. population in 2015 to the nearest million.   **about 338 million**
b. *Critical Thinking* Explain why the model and your prediction may not be valid for 2015.   **The growth factor may change.**
c. Suppose the rate of population increase changes to 1.4%. Write a function to model population growth and use it to predict the 2015 population to the nearest million.   **$y = 281 (1.014)^x$; about 346 million**

Real-World Connection

The United States counts its population every 10 years.

Test-Taking Tip

A percent increase is added to 100%. A 1.24% increase results in a quantity that is 101.24% of, or 1.0124 times, the original quantity.

2. Teach

Guided Instruction

① **EXAMPLE** Alternative Method

Rather than having students sketch the graph, ask them to use a graphing calculator to graph the function. Then ask them to draw on graph paper what they see in the viewing window. They can use the TABLE feature to find points on the curve.

 Additional Examples

① Graph $y = 3^x$.

② The population of the United States in 1994 was about 260 million with an average annual rate of increase of about 0.7%.
a. Find the growth factor for that year. **1.007**
b. Suppose the rate of growth had continued to be 0.7%. Write a function to model this population growth. **$y = 260(1.007)^x$ (in millions)**

Advanced Learners 🔲 **L4**
Some futurists predict that information growth will become so rapid no one can keep up. Students may be interested in researching this idea.

English Language Learners **ELL**
Have students use a dictionary or thesaurus to look up synonyms for *decay*. **Samples: decline, decrease, rot** Explain that the mathematical meaning of this word—decrease—is the opposite of growth. Thus, a decaying population is decreasing.

learning style: verbal

learning style: verbal

Guided Instruction

Activity

Make sure students understand that two teams compete in each game. Also tell students that only teams that win go on to play in the following round. In other words, 64 teams pair off to play 32 games in the first round. Then 32 teams pair off to play the second round. This pattern repeats. There must be a winner for each game, so there are no ties.

Activity

2a.

After Round x	Number of Teams Left in Tournament (y)
0	64
1	32
2	16
3	8
4	4
5	2
6	1

b.

You can write an exponential function from two points on the function's graph.

3 EXAMPLE **Writing an Exponential Function**

Write an exponential function $y = ab^x$ for a graph that includes $(2, 2)$ and $(3, 4)$.

$y = ab^x$	Use the general form.
$2 = a \cdot b^2$	Substitute for x and y using (2, 2).
$\frac{2}{b^2} = a$	Solve for a.
$y = ab^x$	Use the general form.
$4 = \frac{2}{b^2} b^3$	Substitute for x and y using (3, 4) and for a using $\frac{2}{b^2}$.
$4 = 2b^{3-2}$	Division Property of Exponents
$4 = 2b$	Simplify.
$b = 2$	Solve for b.
$a = \frac{2}{b^2}$	Use your equation for a.
$a = \frac{2}{2^2}$	Substitute 2 for b.
$a = \frac{1}{2}$	Simplify.
$y = \frac{1}{2} \cdot 2^x$	Substitute $\frac{1}{2}$ for a and 2 for b in $y = ab^x$.

● The exponential function for a graph that includes $(2, 2)$ and $(3, 4)$ is $y = \frac{1}{2} \cdot 2^x$.

 Quick Check **3** Write an exponential function $y = ab^x$ for a graph that includes $(2, 4)$ and $(3, 16)$.
$y = 0.25(4)^x$

2 Exponential Decay

Real-World Connection

On a day in March, the NCAA announces the selection of 64 teams for its annual tournament.

4. No; the change from one point to the next is not constant.

Activity: Tournament Play

The National Collegiate Athletic Association (NCAA) holds an annual basketball tournament. The top 64 teams in Division I are invited to play each spring. When a team loses, it is out of the tournament.

1. How many teams are left in the tournament after the first round of basketball games? **32 teams**

2. a. Copy, complete, and extend the table until only one team is left. **a–b. See margin.**
   b. Graph the points from your table on graph paper.

After Round x	Number of Teams Left in Tournament (y)
0	64
1	■
2	■

3. How many rounds are played in the tournament? **6 rounds**

4. Does the graph represent a linear function? Explain.

5. How does the number of teams left in each round compare to the number of teams in the previous round? **There are half as many teams as in the previous round.**

You can use an exponential function with $0 < b < 1$ to model decay. When $b < 1$, b is a **decay factor**.

Exponential Decay

Decay factor $b < 1$

4 EXAMPLE Analyzing a Function

Without graphing, determine whether the function $y = 14(0.95)^x$ represents exponential growth or exponential decay.

In $y = 14(0.95)^x$, $b = 0.95$. Since $b < 1$, the function represents exponential decay.

✓ **Quick Check** ④ Without graphing, determine whether each function represents exponential growth or exponential decay.

a. $y = 100(0.12)^x$ **b.** $y = 0.2(5)^x$ **c.** $y = 16\left(\frac{1}{2}\right)^x$

exponential decay   **exponential growth**   **exponential decay**

An **asymptote** is a line that a graph approaches as x or y increases in absolute value.

Vocabulary Tip

Asymptote comes from the Greek word *asymptotos,* meaning "not meeting."

5 EXAMPLE Graphing Exponential Decay

Graph $y = 24\left(\frac{1}{2}\right)^x$. Identify the horizontal asymptote.

Step 1 Make a table of values.

x	-3	-2	-1	0	1	2	3
y	192	96	48	24	12	6	3

5a.

Step 2 Graph the coordinates. Connect the points with a smooth curve.

As *x* increases, *y* approaches 0.

The asymptote is the x-axis, $y = 0$.

✓ **Quick Check** ⑤ Graph each decay function. Identify the horizontal asymptote. **For graphs, see left.**

a. $y = 24\left(\frac{1}{3}\right)^x$ **y = 0**   **b.** $y = 100(0.1)^x$ **y = 0**

5 EXAMPLE Teaching Tip

Discuss the fact that as the *y*-values decrease, the graph approaches the asymptote without ever touching it. Have students substitute 0 for *y* to get $0 = 24\left(\frac{1}{4}\right)^x$. The next step in solving for *x* is to divide 0 by 24, resulting in $0 = \left(\frac{1}{4}\right)^x$. Ask students what power of $\frac{1}{4}$ equals 0. No power of $\frac{1}{4}$ equals 0. Thus, *y* cannot equal 0, and the graph will never intercept the *x*-axis.

PowerPoint

Additional Examples

④ Without graphing, determine whether the function $y = 3\left(\frac{2}{3}\right)^x$ represents exponential growth or exponential decay. **decay**

⑤ Graph $y = 36(0.5)^x$. Identify the horizontal asymptote. **y = 0**

433

Depreciation is the decline in an item's value resulting from age or wear. When an item loses about the same percent of its value each year, you can use an exponential function to model the depreciation.

6 EXAMPLE Real-World Connection

Depreciation The exponential decay graph shows the expected depreciation for a car over four years. Estimate the value of the car after six years.

The decay factor b equals $1 + r$, where r is the annual rate of decrease. The initial value of the car is $20,000. After one year the value of the car is about $17,000.

Expected Decrease in Value

$r = \dfrac{\text{final value} - \text{initial value}}{\text{initial value}}$ Write an equation for r.

$= \dfrac{17,000 - 20,000}{20,000}$ Substitute.

$= -0.15$ Simplify.

$b = 1 + r$ Use r to find b.

$= 1 + (-0.15) = 0.85$ Simplify.

Write a function, and then evaluate it for $x = 6$.

Relate The value of the car decreases exponentially; $b = 0.85$.

Define Let x = number of years. Let y = value of the car.

Write $y = ab^x$

$20,000 = a(0.85)^0$ Substitute using (0, 20,000).

$20,000 = a$ Solve for a.

$y = 20,000(0.85)^x$ Substitute a and b into $y = ab^x$.

$y = 20,000(0.85)^6$ Evaluate for $x = 6$.

≈ 7542.99 Simplify.

• The car's value after six years will be about $7540.

✓ Quick Check **6** Estimate the value of the car from Example 6 after 10 years. **about $3900**

EXERCISES

For more exercises, see *Extra Skill and Word Problem Practice.*

Practice and Problem Solving

A Practice by Example

GO for Help

Example 1
(page 430)

Example 2
(page 431)

Graph each function. 1–8. See margin.

1. $y = 6^x$ **2.** $y = 3(10)^x$ **3.** $y = 1000(2)^x$ **4.** $y = 9(3)^x$

5. $f(x) = 2(3)^x$ **6.** $s(t) = 1.5^t$ **7.** $y = 8(5)^x$ **8.** $y = 2^{2x}$

9. Population The world population in 2000 was approximately 6.08 billion. The annual rate of increase was about 1.26%.
  a. Find the growth factor for the world population. **1.0126**
  b. Suppose the rate of increase continues to be 1.26%. Write a function to model world population growth. $y = 6.08(1.0126)^x$, where $x = 0$ corresponds to 2000

434   Chapter 8   Exponential and Logarithmic Functions

5.

6.

7.

8.

Example 3
(page 432)

Write an exponential function $y = ab^x$ for a graph that includes the given points.

$y = 8(1.5)^x$

10. $(4, 8), (6, 32)$ $y = 0.5(2)^x$ **11.** $(2, 122.5), (3, 857.5)$ **12.** $(2, 18), (5, 60.75)$
$y = 2.5(7)^x$

13. $\left(-1, 8\frac{1}{3}\right), (2, 1.8)$ **14.** $(-3, 24), (-2, 12)$ **15.** $(0, 24), \left(3, \frac{8}{9}\right)$
$y = 5(0.6)^x$ $y = 3(0.5)^x$ $y = 24\left(\frac{1}{3}\right)^x$

Example 4
(page 433)

Without graphing, determine whether each function represents exponential growth or exponential decay. 16–23. See below left.

16. $y = 129(1.63)^x$ **17.** $f(x) = 2(0.65)^x$ **18.** $y = 12\left(\frac{17}{10}\right)^x$ **19.** $y = 0.8\left(\frac{1}{8}\right)^x$

20. $f(x) = 4\left(\frac{5}{6}\right)^x$ **21.** $y = 0.45 \cdot 3^x$ **22.** $y = \frac{1}{100}\left(\frac{4}{3}\right)^x$ **23.** $f(x) = 2^{-x}$

Example 5
(page 433)

Graph each function. 24–31. See back of book.

24. $y = (0.75)^x$ **25.** $y = 2(0.5)^x$ **26.** $y = (0.25)^x$ **27.** $g(x) = 5(0.2)^x$

28. $f(x) = \left(\frac{1}{5}\right)^x$ **29.** $y = 81\left(\frac{1}{3}\right)^x$ **30.** $s(t) = \left(\frac{1}{10}\right)^t$ **31.** $y = \frac{1}{2}\left(\frac{1}{2}\right)^x$

Example 6
(page 434)

Write an exponential function for each graph. Evaluate the function for $x = 6$.

32.

33.

34.

$y = 100(0.5)^x; 1.5625$ $y = 12,000(0.9)^x; 6377$ $y = 12,000(0.1)^x; 0.012$

35. Business A computer valued at $6500 depreciates at the rate of 14.3% per year.
a. Write a function that models the value of the computer. $y = 6500(0.857)^x$
b. Find the value of the computer after three years. $4091.25

 Apply Your Skills

For each function, find the percent increase or decrease that the function models. 36–41. See margin.

36. $y = 1298(1.63)^x$ **37.** $y = 0.65(1.3)^x$ **38.** $f(x) = 2(0.65)^x$

39. $y = 12\left(\frac{17}{10}\right)^x$ **40.** $y = 0.8\left(\frac{1}{8}\right)^x$ **41.** $y = 16\left(\frac{1}{4}\right)^x$

42. Multiple Choice According to the projected growth rate, how will these regions rank from largest to smallest populations in 2015? **D**

World's Largest Metropolitan Regions Outside the U.S.

Rank in 2000	City	2000 Population	Projected Average Annual Growth
1	Tokyo, Japan	34,450,000	0.51%
2	Mexico City, Mexico	18,066,000	1.47%
3	Mumbai (Bombay), India	17,099,000	1.39%
4	Saõ Paulo, Brazil	16,086,000	2.62%

SOURCE: United Nations, Department for Economic and Social Information and Policy Analysis

Ⓐ Tokyo, Mexico City, Saõ Paulo, Mumbai
Ⓑ Tokyo, Mexico City, Mumbai, São Paulo
Ⓒ Tokyo, Mumbai, São Paulo, Mexico City
Ⓓ Tokyo, São Paulo, Mexico City, Mumbai

---

16. exponential growth
17. exponential decay
18. exponential growth
19. exponential decay
20. exponential decay
21. exponential growth
22. exponential growth
23. exponential decay

36. 63% increase
37. 30% increase
38. 35% decrease
39. 70% increase
40. 87.5% decrease
41. 75% decrease

---

3. Practice

Assignment Guide

▼**1** A B 1-12, 36, 37, 39, 42, 46, 47, 50, 52-55

▼**2** A B 13-35, 38, 40, 41, 43-45, 48, 49, 51

C Challenge 56-59

Test Prep 60-64
Mixed Review 65-81

Homework Quick Check

To check students' understanding of key skills and concepts, go over Exercises 5, 34, 43, 45, 54.

Exercise 42 Help students understand that they must calculate the populations for each city in 2015 and compare these amounts.

Error Prevention!

Exercises 46–53 Students may write the growth or decay factor for the percent of increase or decrease. Stress that the growth and decay factors represent the percent of the original amount *present after one change*, not the percent of change.

Lesson Quiz

Sketch the graph of each function. Identify the horizontal asymptote.

1. $y = (0.8)^x$ $y = 0$

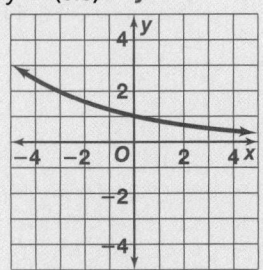

2. $y = \left(\frac{1}{4}\right)^x$ $y = 0$

Without graphing, determine whether each equation represents exponential growth or decay.

3. $y = 15(7)^x$ growth

4. $y = 1285(0.5)^x$ decay

Write an exponential function for a graph that includes the given points.

5. (0, 0.5), (1, 3) $y = 0.5(6)^x$

6. (−1, 5), (0.5, 40) $y = 20(4)^x$

Alternative Assessment

List various growth and decay functions. Instruct each student to write down whether the function is for growth or decay, and then sketch the function. Let students compare answers. Repeat.

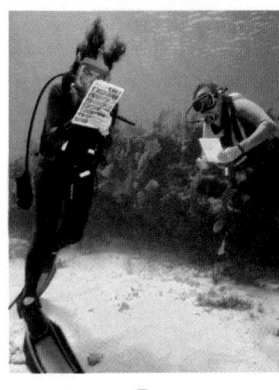

Real-World Connection

Careers Oceanographers model conditions on the ocean floor, interactions between plant and animal life, and the impact of pollution on seawater.

44a. Answers will vary.
Sample:
$y = 30,000(0.7)^x$ for car 1, $y = 15,000(0.8)^x$ for car 2; car 2 will be worth more.

45a. $y = 80(0.965)^x$

b.

about 47 years

GO Online
Homework Video Tutor
Visit: PHSchool.com
Web Code: age-0801

C Challenge

54. $y = 34(1.22)^x$, where x represents the number of years since 1995.

43. Oceanography The function $y = 20 \cdot 0.975^x$ models the intensity of sunlight beneath the surface of the ocean. The output y represents the percent of surface sunlight intensity that reaches a depth of x feet. The model is accurate from about 20 feet to about 600 feet beneath the surface.   **about 5.6%**
a. Find the percent of sunlight 50 feet beneath the surface of the ocean.
b. Find the percent of sunlight at a depth of 370 ft.   **about 0.0017%**

44. a. Depreciation Each graph below shows the expected decrease in a car's value over the next five years. Write a function to model each car's depreciation. Determine which car will be worth more after 10 years.
See below left.

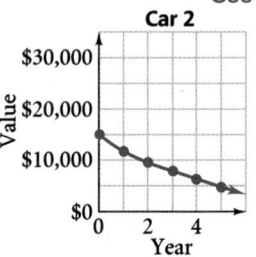

b. Data Collection Find the initial value and the expected decrease in value of your favorite type of car. Write an exponential function to model the car's depreciation.   **Check students' work.**

45. The population of a certain animal species decreases at a rate of 3.5% per year. You have counted 80 of the animals in the habitat you are studying. **a–b. See left.**
a. Write a function that models the change in the animal population.
b. Graph the function. Estimate the number of years until the population first drops below 15 animals.

For each annual rate of change, find the corresponding growth or decay factor.

46. +70% **1.70**   **47.** +500% **6**   **48.** −75% **0.25**   **49.** −55% **0.45**

50. +12.5% **1.125**   **51.** −0.1% **0.999**   **52.** +0.1% **1.001**   **53.** +100% **2**

54. Communications
Cellular phone usage grew about 22% each year from 1995 (about 34 million) to 2003. Write a function to model U.S. cellular phone usage over that time period. **See left.**

55. Open-Ended Write a problem that could be modeled with $y = 20(1.1)^x$.
Check students' work.

56. The value of an industrial machine has a decay factor of 0.75 per year. After six years, the machine is worth $7500. What was the original value of the machine?   **about $42,140**

U.S. Cellular Phone Usage, 1995–2003

SOURCE: The CTIA Semi-Annual Wireless Survey

57. Zoology Determine which situation best matches the graph.
A. A population of 120 cougars decreases 98.75% yearly.
B. A population of 125 cougars increases 1.25% yearly.
C. A population of 115 cougars decreases 1.25% yearly.
D. A population of 200 cougars decreases 50% yearly.

C

59a. A negative growth rate would be represented by adding the negative rate to 1.

b. Armenia: $y = 11.8(1.099)^x$,
Canada: $y = 958.7(1.017)^x$,
Germany: $y = 2271(.999)^x$,
Venezuela: $y = 117.9(0.908)^x$.

x in each equation represents the number of years since 2003.

c. Armenia: $18.9 billion,
Canada: $1043 billion,
Germany: $2260 billion,
Venezuela: $72.8 billion.

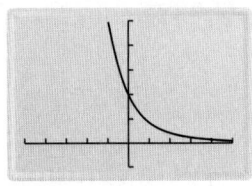

58. B; the graph shows a decreasing function, which eliminates A. The y-values are all positive, which eliminates C.

58. Critical Thinking Analyze the graph at the left to determine which function the graph represents. Explain your reasoning. **See left.**

A. $y = \left(\frac{1}{3}\right)2^x$ **B.** $y = 2\left(\frac{1}{3}\right)^x$ **C.** $y = -2\left(\frac{1}{3}\right)^x$

 59. Economics The table gives the 2003 gross domestic product and the real growth rate for several countries.

  a. Writing Explain how a negative growth rate affects the equation for an exponential model.

  b. Write a function for each country to model the GDP.

  c. Suppose the given real growth rates continue. Predict the gross domestic product for each country in 2008. **a–c. See margin p. 436.**

Domestic Product Growth Rates

Country	2003 Gross Domestic Product (billions)	2003 Real Growth Rate
Armenia	$11.8	9.9%
Canada	$958.7	1.7%
Germany	$2271	−0.1%
Venezuela	$117.9	−9.2%

SOURCE: CIA, *The World Factbook*

Test Prep

Multiple Choice

60. Which function represents exponential growth? **C**

  A. $y = 35x^{1.35}$ **B.** $y = 35 \cdot (0.35)^x$

  C. $y = 35 \cdot (1.35)^x$ **D.** $y = 35 \div (1.35)^x$

61. Which function represents the value after x years of a delivery van that was purchased new for $17,500 and depreciates 11% each year? **H**

  F. $y = -11(17{,}500)^x$ **G.** $y = 17{,}500(0.11)^x$

  H. $y = 17{,}500(0.89)^x$ **J.** $y = 17{,}500(1.11)^x$

62. What is the equation of the asymptote of $y = 15 \cdot \left(\frac{1}{3}\right)^x$? **B**

  A. $y = 1$ **B.** $y = 0$ **C.** $y = x$ **D.** $y = \frac{1}{3}$

Short Response

63. Sketch the graph of the function $y = 2 \cdot \left(\frac{1}{4}\right)^x$. **See back of book.**

Extended Response

64. Write an exponential equation in the form $y = ab^x$ for a graph that includes $(2, 54)$ and $\left(\frac{1}{2}, 2\right)$. Show your work. **See back of book.**

Mixed Review

GO for Help

Lesson 7-8

Graph each function. **65–67. See margin.**

65. $y = \sqrt{x + 2}$ **66.** $y = -2\sqrt[3]{x} + 4$ **67.** $y = \sqrt{9x - 153} - 5$

Lesson 7-2

Simplify each expression.

68. $\sqrt{180n^5}$ **69.** $3\sqrt[3]{72r^5} \cdot 2\sqrt[3]{343r^3}$ **70.** $\frac{\sqrt{64x^4}}{\sqrt{144x^5}}$ $\frac{2\sqrt{x}}{3x}$

  $6n^2\sqrt{5n}$ $84r^2\sqrt[3]{9r^2}$

Lesson 6-2

Construct a polynomial function with the given zeros. **Answers may vary. Samples are given.**

71. $x = 0, 1, 4$ **72.** $x = -2, -1, 3$ **73.** $x = 5, 0, 2$

  $y = x^3 - 5x^2 + 4x$ $y = x^3 - 7x - 6$ $y = x^3 - 7x^2 + 10x$

Lesson 5-2

Each point lies on a parabola with vertex $(0, 2)$. Write the equation of the parabola.

74–81. See margin.

74. $(1, 3)$ **75.** $(1, -3)$ **76.** $(-1, 4)$ **77.** $(2, 42)$

78. $(-2, 8)$ **79.** $(-1, 5)$ **80.** $(2, 0)$ **81.** $(2, -2)$

Test Prep

Resources

For additional practice with a variety of test item formats:
- Standardized Test Prep, p. 483
- Test-Taking Strategies, p. 478
- Test-Taking Strategies with Transparencies

65.

66.

67.

74. $y = x^2 + 2$

75. $y = -5x^2 + 2$

76. $y = 2x^2 + 2$

77. $y = 10x^2 + 2$

78. $y = \frac{3}{2}x^2 + 2$

79. $y = 3x^2 + 2$

80. $y = -\frac{1}{2}x^2 + 2$

81. $y = -x^2 + 2$

Fitting Exponential Curves to Data

Fitting Exponential Curves to Data

Students use a graphing calculator to find the exponential function that best fits a given set of data points.

Guided Instruction

Technology Tip

Remind students to clear the lists before starting a new plot. To plot the points in Step 2, students must turn on Plot 1, and tell the calculator to use a scatter plot.

Error Prevention!

Have students work with a partner. After each step, such as entering a list, or plotting points, encourage partners to compare windows to make sure that they have not made an error.

Resources

Students may use any graphing calculator.

You can use your graphing calculator to fit an exponential curve to data and find the exponential function.

ACTIVITY

The table at the right shows the number of degrees above room temperature for a cup of coffee after x minutes of cooling. Graph the data. Find the best-fitting exponential function.

Step 1 Press STAT ENTER to enter the data in lists.

Step 2 Use the **STAT PLOT** feature to draw a scatter plot.

Step 3 Find the equation for the best-fitting exponential function. Press STAT ▶ 0 ENTER to use the **ExpReg** feature. The line of best fit can be approximated by $f(x) = 133.458(0.942)^x$.

```
ExpReg
 y=a*b^x
 a=133.4584506
 b=.942405561
 r=-.9997925841
```

Step 4 Graph the function. Press Y= CLEAR VARS 5 ▶ ▶ ENTER to enter the **ExpReg** results. Press GRAPH to display the function and the scatter plot together.

Press ZOOM 9 to automatically adjust the window.

Go Online
PHSchool.com
For: Graphing calculator procedures
Web Code: age-2123

Cooling Coffee

Time (min)	°F Above Room Temperature
0	135
5	100
10	74
15	55
20	41
25	30
30	22
35	17
40	12
45	9
50	7
55	5
60	4

EXERCISES

Use a graphing calculator to find the exponential function that best fits each set of data. Graph each function. Sketch your graph. 1–4. See margin.

1.

x	−3	−2	−1	0	1	2
y	50	25	12.5	6.25	3.13	1.56

2.

x	0	1	2	3	4	5
y	2	2.4	2.88	3.46	4.15	5

3.

x	1	2	3	4	5	6
y	1.2	4.8	19.2	76.8	307.2	1228.8

4.

x	−10	−9	−8	−7	−6	−5
y	0.03	0.07	0.14	0.27	0.55	1.09

5. As the temperature of the coffee approaches the temperature of the room, the room temperature ceases to affect the coffee temperature.

5. **Writing** In the example above, the function appears to level off. Explain why this happens. **See right.**

6. **a.** Find a linear function that models the data in Exercise 3. $y = 202.94x - 437.28$
   b. Which is a better fit, the linear function or the exponential function? Explain. **exponential; it is an exact fit.**

438 Activity Lab Fitting Exponential Curves to Data

1. $y = 6.25(0.5)^x$

2. $y = 2.0(1.2)^x$

3. $y = 0.3(4)^x$

4. $y = 38.7(2.0)^x$

Properties of Exponential Functions

What You'll Learn

• To identify the role of constants in $y = ab^{cx}$

• To use e as a base

. . . And Why

To model the half-life of a radioactive substance, as in Example 3

 Check Skills You'll Need

 for Help Lessons 2-6, 5-3, and 7-4

Write an equation for each translation. **1–4. See below.**

1. $y = |x|$, 1 unit up, 2 units left

2. $y = -|x|$, 2 units down

3. $y = x^2$, 2 units down, 1 unit right

4. $y = -x^2$, 3 units up, 1 unit left

Write each equation in simplest form. Assume that all variables are positive.

5. $y = \left(x^{-\frac{5}{4}}\right)^4$ $y = \frac{1}{x^5}$

6. $y = \left(x^{-\frac{1}{7}}\right)^{-7}$ $y = x$

7. $y = \left(x^{\frac{5}{6}}\right)^6$ $y = x^5$

8. Use the formula for simple interest $I = Prt$. Find the interest for a principal of $550 at a rate of 3% for 2 years. **$33**

🔊 **New Vocabulary** • continuously compounded interest formula

1. $y = |x + 2| + 1$ 2. $y = -|x| - 2$
3. $y = (x - 1)^2 - 2$ 4. $y = -(x + 1)^2 + 3$

1 | Comparing Graphs

The function $f(x) = b^x$ is the parent of a family of exponential functions for each value of b. The factor a in $y = ab^x$ stretches, shrinks, and/or reflects the parent.

 for Help

To review function families, see Lesson 2-6 for absolute value functions, and Lesson 5-3 for quadratic functions.

1a.

b.

1 **EXAMPLE** Graphing $y = ab^x$ for $0 < |a| < 1$

Graph $y = \frac{1}{2} \cdot 2^x$ and $y = -\frac{1}{2} \cdot 2^x$. Label the asymptote of each graph.

Step 1 Make a table of values.

Step 2 Graph the functions.

x	$y = \frac{1}{2} \cdot 2^x$	$y = -\frac{1}{2} \cdot 2^x$
−2	$\frac{1}{8}$	$-\frac{1}{8}$
−1	$\frac{1}{4}$	$-\frac{1}{4}$
0	$\frac{1}{2}$	$-\frac{1}{2}$
1	1	−1
2	2	−2
3	4	−4

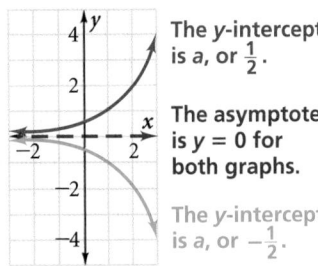

The y-intercept is a, or $\frac{1}{2}$.

The asymptote is y = 0 for both graphs.

The y-intercept is a, or $-\frac{1}{2}$.

$y = \frac{1}{2} \cdot 2^x$ shrinks $y = 2^x$ by a factor of $\frac{1}{2}$.

$y = -\frac{1}{2} \cdot 2^x$ reflects $y = \frac{1}{2} \cdot 2^x$ in the x-axis.

 Quick Check **1** Graph each function.   **a.** $y = -4(2)^x$ **b.** $y = -3^x$ **See left.**

A horizontal shift $y = ab^{x-h}$ is the same as the vertical stretch or shrink $y = (ab^{-h})b^x$. A vertical shift $y = ab^x + k$ also shifts the horizontal asymptote from $y = 0$ to $y = k$.

Lesson 8-2 Properties of Exponential Functions **439**

Objectives

1 To identify the role of constants in $y = ab^{cx}$
2 To use e as a base

Examples

1 Graphing $y = ab^x$ for $0 < |a| < 1$
2 Translating $y = ab^x$
3 Real-World Connection
4 Evaluating e^x
5 Real-World Connection

Math Background

The number e plays an important role in modeling exponential functions with continuous growth or decay. It is an irrational number whose value is given by the limiting value of $y = \left(1 + \frac{1}{x}\right)^x$ as x increases without bound. It is also a transcendental number—like π, e is not the root of any polynomial with rational coefficients.

More Math Background: p. 428C

Lesson Planning and Resources

See p. 428E for a list of the resources that support this lesson.

PowerPoint

Bell Ringer Practice

✓ **Check Skills You'll Need**
For intervention, direct students to:

Translations
Lesson 2-6: Example 8
Extra Skills and Word
  Problems Practice, Ch. 2

Translating Parabolas
Lesson 5-3: Example 2
Extra Skills and Word
  Problems Practice, Ch. 5

Rational Exponents
Lesson 7-4: Example 5
Extra Skills and Word
  Problems Practice, Ch. 7

Differentiated **Instruction** **Solutions for All Learners**

Special Needs **L1**
To demonstrate exponential decay and half life, have all students move to one side of the classroom. Direct one half of the students to move to the other side, and repeat until less than 3 students remain. Point out how smaller amounts decay in each successive half life. **learning style: tactile**

Below Level **L2**
Review the translation forms when $x - h$ is substituted for x and $y - k$ is substituted for y.

learning style: verbal

Guided Instruction

2 EXAMPLE **Auditory Learning**

Have a student explain informally the effect of h on the graph. Have another student explain the effect of k on the graph. Help students associate h with *horizontal* movement.

3 EXAMPLE **Tactile Learning**

Demonstrate exponential decay and half-life by having all students move to one side of the room. If there is an odd number of students, you may participate in the activity. Then direct one half to move to their seats. Continue by asking one half of the remaining group also to move to their seats, taking part yourself or not, as needed for an even number. Repeat until fewer than four persons remain.

PowerPoint
Additional Examples

1 Graph $y = 3 \cdot 2^x$ and $y = -3 \cdot 2^x$. Label the asymptote of each.

2 Graph $y = 6\left(\frac{1}{2}\right)^x$ and $y = 6\left(\frac{1}{2}\right)^{x-3} - 2$. See back of book.

For: Exponential Activity
Use: Interactive Textbook, 8-2

2 EXAMPLE **Translating $y = ab^x$**

Graph the stretch $y = 8\left(\frac{1}{2}\right)^x$ and then the translation $y = 8\left(\frac{1}{2}\right)^{x+2} + 3$.

Step 1 Graph $y = 8\left(\frac{1}{2}\right)^x$. The horizontal asymptote is $y = 0$.

Step 2 For $y = 8\left(\frac{1}{2}\right)^{x+2} + 3$, $h = -2$ and $k = 3$. So shift the $y = 8\left(\frac{1}{2}\right)^x$ graph 2 units left and 3 units up. The horizontal asymptote is $y = 3$.

Quick Check **2** Graph the stretch $y = 9(3)^x$ and then each translation.

a. $y = 9(3)^{x+1}$
b. $y = 9(3)^x - 4$
c. $y = 9(3)^{x-3} - 1$

a–c. See back of book.

Some exponential functions are of the form $y = ab^{cx}$, where c is a nonzero constant.

3 EXAMPLE **Real-World Connection**

Medicine The half-life of a radioactive substance is the time it takes for half of the material to decay. A hospital prepares a 100-mg supply of technetium-99m, which has a half-life of 6 hours. Make a table showing the amount of technetium-99m that remains at the end of each 6-hour interval for 36 hours. Then write an exponential function to find the amount of technetium-99m that remains after 75 hours.

The amount of technetium-99m is reduced by one half each 6 hours.

Number of 6-h Intervals	0	1	2	3	4	5	6
Number of Hours Elapsed	0	6	12	18	24	30	36
Technetium-99m (mg)	100	50	25	12.5	6.25	3.13	1.56

Relate The amount of technetium-99m is an exponential function of the number of half-lives. The initial amount is 100 mg. The decay factor is $\frac{1}{2}$. One half-life equals 6 h.

Define Let y = the amount of technetium-99m.

Let x = the number of hours elapsed. Then $\frac{1}{6}x$ = the number of half-lives.

Write $y = 100\left(\frac{1}{2}\right)^{\frac{1}{6}x}$

$y = 100\left(\frac{1}{2}\right)^{\frac{1}{6} \cdot 75}$ **Substitute 75 for x.**

$= 100\left(\frac{1}{2}\right)^{12.5}$ **Simplify.**

≈ 0.017 **Use a calculator.**

After 75 hours, about 0.017 mg of technetium-99m remains.

Quick Check **3** Arsenic-74 is used to locate brain tumors. It has a half-life of 17.5 days. Write an exponential decay function for a 90-mg sample. Use the function to find the amount remaining after 6 days. $y = 90\left(\frac{1}{2}\right)^{\frac{2}{35}x}$; about 71 mg

Real-World Connection

As technetium-99m decays, it emits low-energy gamma rays. The rays are detected by a gamma camera to produce images like the one above.

440 Chapter 8 Exponential and Logarithmic Functions

Key Concepts

Summary	Families of Exponential Functions
Parent function:	$y = b^x$
Stretch ($\lvert a \rvert > 1$) Shrink ($0 < \lvert a \rvert < 1$) Reflection ($a < 0$) in x-axis	$y = ab^x$
Translation (horizontal by h; vertical by k):	$y = b^{x-h} + k$
Combined:	$y = ab^{x-h} + k$

2 The Number e

At the right is part of the graph of the function $y = \left(1 + \frac{1}{x}\right)^x$. One of the graph's asymptotes is $y = e$, where e is an irrational number approximately equal to 2.71828.

Exponential functions with a base of e are useful for describing continuous growth or decay. Your graphing calculator has a key for e^x.

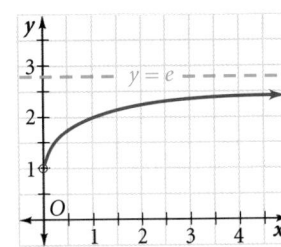

4 EXAMPLE Evaluating e^x

Graph $y = e^x$. Evaluate e^2 to four decimal places.

Step 1 Graph $y = e^x$.

Step 2 Find y when $x = 2$.

Graphing Calculator Hint

After graphing e^x, press TRACE 2 ENTER to find y for $x = 2$.

● The value of e^2 is about 7.3891.

✓ Quick Check ④ Use the graph of $y = e^x$ to evaluate each expression to four decimal places.

a. e^4 54.5982 **b.** e^{-3} 0.0498 **c.** $e^{\frac{1}{2}}$ 1.6487

In past courses, you studied simple and compound interest. The more frequently interest is compounded, the more quickly the amount in an account increases. The formula for *continuously* compounded interest uses the number e.

 Key Concepts

Definition	Continuously Compounded Interest Formula

amount in account   rate of interest (annual)

$$A = Pe^{rt} \longleftarrow \text{time in years}$$

principal

Lesson 8-2 Properties of Exponential Functions **441**

---

③ Using the fact that technetium-99*m* has a half-life of 6 hours, find the amount of technetium-99*m* that remains from a 50-mg supply after 25 hours. **about 2.784 mg**

Guided Instruction

 Connection to Analysis

The number e occurs also in this very famous equation: $e^{i\pi} + 1 = 0$. This equation is sometimes called Euler's Equation or The Famous Five because it contains the basic five constants of mathematics.

PowerPoint

Additional Examples

④ Use the graph of $y = e^x$ to evaluate e^3 to four decimal places. **20.0855**

⑤ Suppose you invest $100 at an annual interest rate of 4.8% compounded continuously. How much will you have in the account after three years? **about $115**

Resources
• Daily Notetaking Guide 8-2 **L3**

Closure

Ask students to explain how h and k in $y = e^{x-h} + k$ affect the graph of the exponential function $y = e^x$. **h translates the graph horizontally, and k translates the graph vertically.** Also ask how you can find the approximate value of e^6. **Answers may vary. Sample: To find e^6, graph $y = e^x$. Then, press CALC, set x equal to 6 and press ENTER.**

3. Practice

Assignment Guide

▼**1** A B 1-17, 27-29, 31-35, 38, 39

▼**2** A B 18-26, 30, 36, 37, 40-47

C Challenge   48-50

Test Prep   51-55
Mixed Review   56-81

Homework Quick Check

To check students' understanding of key skills and concepts, go over Exercises 16, 25, 30, 34, 38.

Error Prevention!

Exercises 11–14 Suggest that students circle the operation sign in the exponent to help them remember that the horizontal translation is the direction opposite to this sign.

Test-Taking Tip

Remember to change the interest rate from percent to a decimal to use it in a formula.

5 EXAMPLE Real-World Connection

Gridded Response Suppose you invest $1050 at an annual interest rate of 5.5% compounded continuously. How much money, to the nearest dollar, will you have in the account after five years?

$A = Pe^{rt}$

$= 1050 \cdot e^{0.055(5)}$ **Substitute 1050 for P, 0.055 for r, and 5 for t.**

$= 1050 \cdot e^{0.275}$ **Simplify.**

$\approx 1050(1.316531)$ **Evaluate $e^{0.275}$.**

≈ 1382.36 **Simplify.**

You will have about $1382 in the account.

Quick Check 5 Suppose you invest $1300 at an annual interest rate of 4.3% compounded continuously. Find the amount you will have in the account after three years.
$1479.00

EXERCISES

For more exercises, see *Extra Skill and Word Problem Practice.*

Practice and Problem Solving

A Practice by Example

Example 1 (page 439)

Graph each function. Label the asymptote of each graph. 1–8. See margin pp. 442–443.

1. $y = -5^x$ **2.** $y = -\left(\frac{1}{2}\right)^x$ **3.** $y = -2(4)^x$ **4.** $y = -9(3)^x$

5. $y = -3(2)^x$ **6.** $y = -24\left(\frac{1}{2}\right)^x$ **7.** $y = -4^x$ **8.** $y = -\left(\frac{1}{3}\right)^x$

Example 2 (page 440)

Graph each function as a transformation of its parent function. 9–14. See back of book.

9. $y = 8^x + 5$ **10.** $y = 15\left(\frac{4}{3}\right)^x - 8$ **11.** $y = -(0.3)^{x-2}$

12. $y = -2(5)^{x+3}$ **13.** $y = 52\left(\frac{2}{13}\right)^{x-1} + 26$ **14.** $y = 9\left(\frac{1}{3}\right)^{x+7} - 3$

Example 3 (page 440)

15. Botany Phosphorus-32 is used to study a plant's use of fertilizer. It has a half-life of 14.3 days. Write the exponential decay function for a 50-mg sample. Find the amount of phosporus-32 remaining after 84 days. $y = 50\left(\frac{1}{2}\right)^{\frac{1}{14.3}x}$; 0.85 mg

16. Public Works Iodine-131 is used to find leaks in water pipes. It has a half-life of 8.14 days. Write the exponential decay function for a 200-mg sample. Find the amount of iodine-131 remaining after 72 days. $y = 200\left(\frac{1}{2}\right)^{\frac{1}{8.14}x}$; 0.43 mg

17. Archaeology Carbon-14 is used to determine the age of artifacts in carbon dating. It has a half-life of 5730 years. Write the exponential decay function for a 24-mg sample. Find the amount of carbon-14 remaining after 30 millennia (1 millennium = 1000 years). $y = 24\left(\frac{1}{2}\right)^{\frac{1}{5730}x}$; 0.64 mg

Example 4 (page 441)

Use the graph of $y = e^x$ to evaluate each expression to four decimal places.

18. e^3 **19.** e^6 **20.** e^{-2} **21.** e^0 **22.** $e^{\frac{5}{2}}$ **23.** e^e
20.0855 403.4288 0.1353 1 12.1825 15.1543

Example 5 (page 442)

Find the amount in a continuously compounded account for the given conditions.

24. principal: $2000
annual interest 5.1%
time: 3 yr **$2330.65**

25. principal: $400
annual interest 7.6%
time: 1.5 yr **$448.30**

26. principal: $950
annual interest 6.5%
time: 10 yr **$1819.76**

1–8. Asymptote is $y = 0$.

1.

2.

3.

4.

5.

B **Apply Your Skills**

27. Find the value of a for which the graph of $y = ab^x$ is a horizontal line. **0**

28. Find the value of b for which the graph of $y = ab^x$ is a horizontal line. **1**

29. Assume that a is positive and $b \geq 1$. Describe the effects of $c < 0$, $c = 0$, and $c > 0$ on the graph of the function $y = ab^{cx}$. **See margin.**

Real-World Connection

A savings plan can be an important part of preparing for college.

33. $y = -3^x$;

$y = -3^{x-8} + 2$

35. $y = -3\left(\frac{1}{3}\right)^x$;

$y = -3\left(\frac{1}{3}\right)^{x+5} - 1$

38. A deficit that is growing exponentially is modeled by $y = ab^{cx}$, where $a < 0$, and either $b > 1$ and $c > 0$ or $0 < b < 1$ and $c < 0$.

30. Savings A student wants to save $8000 for college in five years. How much should be put into an account that earns 5.2% annual interest compounded continuously? **$6168.41**

31. When $a < 0$ and $b > 1$, $y = ab^x$ models negative exponential growth.
   a. Open-Ended Write an exponential function that models negative growth.
   b. Give an example of a situation that could be modeled by your function.
   c. Critical Thinking Explain one difference between negative exponential growth and exponential decay. **a–c. See margin.**

The parent function for each graph below is of the form $y = ab^x$. Write the parent function. Then write a function for the translation indicated.

32.

 $y = 4\left(\frac{1}{2}\right)^x$;

$y = 4\left(\frac{1}{2}\right)^{x+4} + 3$

translation: left 4 units, up 3 units

33.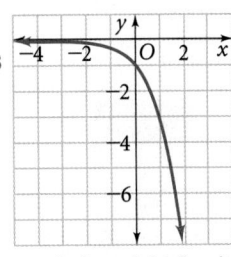

translation: right 8 units, up 2 units

34.

 $y = \frac{1}{2}(2)^x$;

$y = \frac{1}{2}(2)^{x-6} - 7$

translation: right 6 units, down 7 units

35.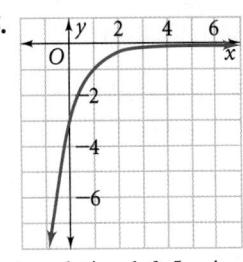

translation: left 5 units, down 1 unit

 36. Physics At a constant temperature, the atmospheric pressure p in pascals is given by the formula $p = 101.3e^{-0.001h}$, where h is the altitude in meters. Find p at an altitude of 300 m. **75.0 pascals**

Vocabulary Tip

The pascal is the metric unit of pressure.

 37. Investment How long would it take to double your principal at an annual interest rate of 8% compounded continuously? **8.7 yr**

 38. Writing Like a debt, a deficit is a negative amount of money. Explain how you would model a deficit that is growing exponentially. In $y = ab^{cx}$, would the values of a and c be positive or negative? Would the value of b be greater than 1 or less than 1? **See above left.**

39. Multiple Choice The gross domestic product, or GDP, of the United States was about $10.99 trillion in 2003. Assume that GDP grows 3.1% each year. Use an exponential model to find which percent best describes the GDP growth that occurs over 18 years. **B**

Ⓐ 19.0%   Ⓑ 74.7%   Ⓒ 129.1%   Ⓓ 173.2%

 GO Online
Homework Video Tutor
Visit: PHSchool.com
Web Code: age-0802

Teaching Tip
Exercise 31 Students may be confused by the opposite meanings of the words *negative* and *growth* in the term *negative exponential growth*. Have pairs of students draw a representation of what they think negative exponential growth means. Let the students discuss their drawings with the class and decide on the correct definition.

Exercise 39 Explain that the *gross domestic product*, or GDP, is the value of all the goods and services produced in a country. The GDP is independent of whether a company producing goods has foreign ownership.

29. If $c < 0$, the graph models exponential decay. If $c = 0$, the graph is a horizontal line. If $c > 0$, the graph models exponential growth.

31a. Answers may vary. Sample: $y = -2(1.3)^x$

b. Answers may vary. Sample: I am in debt for $2 and my debt is growing at a rate of 30% per year.

c. The graph of exponential decay approaches the asymptote $y = 0$ as x increases. The graph of negative exponential growth approaches the asymptote $y = 0$ as x decreases.

6.

7.

8.

443

4. Assess & Reteach

PowerPoint

Lesson Quiz

Describe how the graph of each function relates to its parent function. Then graph the function.

1. $y = -5^x - 1$ reflected over the x-axis and translated down 1

2. $y = 3(5)^{x-2} + 1$ rises more steeply, is translated 2 to the right and up 1

3. Use the formula $A = Pe^{rt}$ to find the amount in a continuously compounded account where the principal is $2000 at an annual interest rate of 5% for 3 years. **about $2324**

4. Use the graph of $y = e^x$ to evaluate $e^{\frac{1}{3}}$ to four decimal places. **1.3956**

Alternative Assessment

Give each student a laminated coordinate plane and a pipe cleaner. Write $y = 2^x$ on the board. Ask the students to model its graph using the pipe cleaner. Now make changes to the function that reflect and/or translate the graph. Instruct students to move the pipe cleaner to match the changes to the function. Walk around the classroom during the whole process to assess student success.

444

Problem Solving Hint

The compound interest formula is

$A = P\left(1 + \frac{r}{n}\right)^{nt}$,

where n is the number of times per year the interest is compounded.

 Challenge

48a. $y = 8001 - 3^x$, where y is the number of uninfected people and x represents days.

Real-World **Connection**

Careers Psychologists use models to evaluate and predict learning rates.

---

40. Suppose you invest $2000 at an annual interest rate of 4.5%, compounded quarterly.
   a. How much will you have in the account after five years? **$2501.50**
   b. Determine how much more you would have if the interest were compounded continuously. **$3.15 more**

41. An investor withdraws all $525 from an account that was neglected for 8 years. It earned 3.4% annual interest, compounded continuously. How much was the initial deposit? **$399.97**

Without graphing, determine whether each equation represents exponential growth or exponential decay. 42–47. See margin.

42. $s(t) = 5e^t$
43. $y = \frac{1}{6}e^x$
44. $y = \left(\frac{1}{e}\right)^x$
45. $y = \frac{7}{5}\left(\frac{e}{2}\right)^x$
46. $f(x) = \left(\frac{e}{3.7}\right)^x$
47. $y = -70e^t$

48. **Biology** A new flu virus is introduced when a stranger visits an isolated village of 8000 people. Every infected person infects two more each day.
   a. Write an exponential function to model the number of *uninfected* people.
   b. Determine how many people remain uninfected after one week. **5814 people**
   c. After how many days will the entire population be infected? **about 9 days**

49. **Psychology** Psychologists use an exponential model of the learning process, $f(t) = c(1 - e^{-kt})$, where c is the total number of tasks to be learned, k is the rate of learning, t is time, and $f(t)$ is the number of tasks learned.
   a. Suppose you move to a new school, and you want to learn the names of 30 classmates in your homeroom. If your learning rate for new tasks is 20% per day, how many complete names will you know after 2 days? After 8 days?
   b. Graph the function on your graphing calculator. How many days will it take to learn everyone's name? Explain. **a–c. See margin.**
   c. **Open-Ended** Does this function seem to describe your own learning rate? If not, how could you adapt it to reflect your learning rate?

50. Work begins on digging a moat on the perimeter of a property. After the first weekend, the first worker recruits a friend to help. After every succeeding weekend, each moat-digger recruits another friend. One person can dig 15 m³ of dirt per weekend. The moat should be 4 m wide and 3 m deep, and it must lie entirely within the 60 m-by-70 m property. **2928 m³**
   a. **Geometry** Determine the volume of dirt that must be removed for the moat.
   b. Write an exponential function to model the volume of dirt remaining to be shoveled after x weekends. $V = 2928 - 15(2^x - 1)$
   c. On which weekend will the moat be completed? **eighth weekend**

Test Prep

Multiple Choice

51. How is the graph of $y = 4 \cdot \left(\frac{1}{2}\right)^{x-3}$ translated from the graph of $y = 4 \cdot \left(\frac{1}{2}\right)^x$? **A**
   A. 3 units right   **B.** 3 units left   **C.** 3 units down   **D.** 3 units up

52. How is the graph of $y = 4 \cdot \left(\frac{1}{2}\right)^x + 3$ translated from the graph of $y = 4 \cdot \left(\frac{1}{2}\right)^x$? **J**
   F. 3 units right   **G.** 3 units left   **H.** 3 units down   **J.** 3 units up

444 Chapter 8 Exponential and Logarithmic Functions

---

42. exponential growth
43. exponential growth
44. exponential decay
45. exponential growth
46. exponential decay
47. exponential growth

49a. about 10 names; about 24 names

b. Graphically, it will never happen; the graph has $y = 30$ as an asymptote. (In reality, you would be close to knowing all the names in about 21 days.)

c. Answers may vary. Sample: I learn names pretty quickly; my learning rate might be 0.4.

53. A savings account earns 4.62% annual interest, compounded continuously. After approximately how many years will a principal of $500 double?   **C**
   A. 2 years   **B.** 10 years   **C.** 15 years   **D.** 44 years

54. Sodium-24 has a half-life of 15 hours. How much sodium-24 will you have after 60 hours if your original sample is 64 mg?   **F**
   F. 4 mg   **G.** 16 mg   **H.** 32 mg   **J.** 64 mg

Short Response   **55.** How much should you invest in a continuously compounded account at an annual interest rate of 6% if you want exactly $8000 after four years? Show how you got your answer.   **See margin.**

Resources
For additional practice with a variety of test item formats:
• Standardized Test Prep, p. 483
• Test-Taking Strategies, p. 478
• Test-Taking Strategies with Transparencies

Mixed Review

Lesson 8-1   **Write an exponential equation $y = ab^x$ for a graph that includes the given points.**

56. $(0, 1), (1, 3)$ $y = 3^x$ **57.** $(1, -8), (2, -32)$ **58.** $(0, -5), (2, -20)$

59. $(-1, 16), (3, 1)$ **60.** $(-3, 0.07), (-1, 7)$ **61.** $(2, 6400), (4, 4096)$
$y = 8(0.5)^x$ $y = 70(10)^x$ $y = 10,000(0.8)^x$

Lesson 7-3   **Simplify each expression.**

57. $y = -2(4)^x$ **62.** $5\sqrt{5} + \sqrt{5}$ **63.** $\sqrt[3]{4} - 2\sqrt[3]{4}$ $= -\sqrt[3]{4}$ **64.** $\sqrt{75} + \sqrt{125}$ **65.** $\sqrt[4]{32} + \sqrt[4]{128}$

58. $y = -5(2)^x$ **66.** $5\sqrt{3} - 2\sqrt{12}$ **67.** $3\sqrt{63} + \sqrt{28}$ **68.** $(3 - \sqrt{6})^2$ $15 - 6\sqrt{6}$ **69.** $\dfrac{-2 - 2\sqrt{5}}{1 - \sqrt{5}}$
   $\sqrt{3}$ $11\sqrt{7}$ $3 + \sqrt{5}$

Lesson 6-3   **Divide using either long division or synthetic division.**

62. $6\sqrt{5}$ **70.** $(x^2 - 3x - 1) \div x$ $x - 3\,R\,{-1}$ **71.** $(x^3 - 2x^2 - 5x + 6) \div (x - 1)$

65. $2(\sqrt[4]{2} + \sqrt[4]{8})$ **72.** $(x^3 + 4x^2 - x - 4) \div (x + 4)$ **73.** $(x^3 - 4x^2 - 4x - 5) \div (x - 5)$

   74. $(13x^2 - 51x - 4) \div (x - 4)$ **75.** $(9x^3 - 18x^2 - x + 2) \div (3x + 1)$
   $13x + 1$ $3x^2 - 7x + 2$

Lesson 3-5   **Find the equations of the traces of each graph.**

71. $x^2 - x - 6$ **76.** $x - y + z = 5$ **77.** $x + y + 4z = -2$ **78.** $3x + 3y - 6z = 24$

72. $x^2 - 1$ **79.** $x - y + 2z = 8$ **80.** $3x + y + 9z = -18$ **81.** $-2x + y - 5z = 10$

73. $x^2 + x + 1$ 76–81. See margin.

✓ Checkpoint Quiz 1   Lessons 8-1 through 8-2

Identify each function as modeling either exponential growth or exponential decay. What percent of increase or decrease does the function model?   1–4. See margin.

   1. $y = 15(1.45)^x$ **2.** $y = 0.32(0.99)^x$ **3.** $y = 0.1(1.7)^x$ **4.** $y = 7.3(0.8)^x$

Graph each function.   5–7. See margin. 8. See back of book.

   5. $y = 3^x$ **6.** $y = 2^x + 1$ **7.** $y = (0.25)^x$ **8.** $y = 4^x - 5$

   9. Open-Ended Describe a real-world problem that you could model with an exponential growth function. **See back of book.**

   10. Chemistry An element has a half-life of 30 hours. Write the exponential decay function for a 100-mg sample. Use the function to find the amount of the element remaining after 100 hours. $y = 100\left(\frac{1}{2}\right)^{\frac{1}{30}x}$; **about 9.9 mg**

Checkpoint Quiz

Use this Checkpoint Quiz to check students' understanding of the skills and concepts of Lessons 8-1 through 8-2.

Resources
Grab & Go
• Checkpoint Quiz 1

Checkpoint Quiz

1. exponential growth; 45% increase

2. exponential decay; 1% decrease

3. exponential growth; 70% increase

4. exponential decay; 20% decrease

5.

6.

7.

---

55. [2] $A = Pe^{rt}$
   $8000 = Pe^{(0.06)(4)}$
   $\dfrac{8000}{e^{(0.06)(4)}} = P$
   $P = \$6293.02$

   [1] answer only, without work shown

76. $x - y = 5, x + z = 5,$
   $-y + z = 5$

77. $x + y = -2, x + 4z = -2,$
   $y + 4z = -2$

78. $x + y = 8,$
   $x - 2z = 8,$
   $y - 2z = 8$

79. $x - y = 8, x + 2z = 8,$
   $-y + 2z = 8$

80. $3x + y = -18,$
   $x + 3z = -6,$
   $y + 9z = -18$

81. $-2x + y = 10, -2x - 5z = 10, y - 5z = 10$

445

8-3

Logarithmic Functions as Inverses

1. Plan

Objectives
1 To write and evaluate logarithmic expressions
2 To graph logarithmic functions

Examples
1 Real-World Connection
2 Writing in Logarithmic Form
3 Evaluating Logarithms
4 Real-World Connection
5 Graphing a Logarithmic Function
6 Translating $y = \log_b x$

Math Background

Functions of the form $f(x) = b^x$ are one-to-one if $b > 0$ and $b \neq 1$. This means that each y-value on the graph of $f(x) = b^x$ has a unique x-value. This is useful when solving equations such as $2^4 = 2^{3x}$. It allows us to conclude that $4 = 3x$.

More Math Background: p. 428C

Lesson Planning and Resources

See p. 428E for a list of the resources that support this lesson.

Bell Ringer Practice

☑ **Check Skills You'll Need**
For intervention, direct students to:

Solving Equations
Lesson 6-4: Example 4
Extra Skills and Word Problems Practice, Ch. 6

Graphing a Relation and Its Inverse
Lesson 7-7: Example 3
Extra Skills and Word Problems Practice, Ch. 7

446

What You'll Learn

- To write and evaluate logarithmic expressions
- To graph logarithmic functions

. . . And Why

To compare the acidities of milk and lemon juice, as in Example 4

☑ **Check Skills You'll Need**
 for Help Lessons 6-4 and 7-7

Solve each equation.
1. $8 = x^3$ **2**
2. $x^{\frac{1}{4}} = 2$ **16**
3. $27 = 3^x$ **3**
4. $4^6 = 4^{3x}$ **2**

Graph each relation and its inverse on a coordinate plane.
5. $y = 5x$
6. $y = 2x^2$
7. $y = -x^3$
8. $y = \frac{1}{2}x$
5–8. See back of book.

◀)) **New Vocabulary** • logarithm • common logarithm • logarithmic function

---

1 Writing and Evaluating Logarithmic Expressions

The magnitude of an earthquake is a measure of the amount of energy released at its source. The Richter scale is an exponential measure of earthquake magnitude. An earthquake of magnitude 5 releases about 30 times as much energy as an earthquake of magnitude 4.

The Richter Scale

magnitude: $+1$

| 0 | 1 | 2 | 3 | 4 | 5 | 6 | 7 | 8 | 9 |

E $E{\cdot}30$ $E{\cdot}30^2$ $E{\cdot}30^3$ $E{\cdot}30^4$ $E{\cdot}30^5$ $E{\cdot}30^6$ $E{\cdot}30^7$ $E{\cdot}30^8$ $E{\cdot}30^9$

energy released: $\times 30$

Real-World Connection

The earthquake that struck Washington in 2001 measured 6.8 on the Richter scale.

1 EXAMPLE **Real-World Connection**

Seismology In 1995, an earthquake in Mexico registered 8.0 on the Richter scale. In 2001, an earthquake of magnitude 6.8 shook Washington state. Compare the amounts of energy released in the two earthquakes.

$\dfrac{E \cdot 30^{8.0}}{E \cdot 30^{6.8}}$ Write a ratio.

$= \dfrac{30^{8.0}}{30^{6.8}}$ Simplify.

$= 30^{8.0 - 6.8}$ Division Property of Exponents

$= 30^{1.2}$ Simplify.

≈ 59.2 Use a calculator.

The earthquake in Mexico released about 59 times as much energy as the earthquake in Washington.

☑ **Quick Check** ❶ In 1997, an earthquake in Alabama registered 4.9 on the Richter scale. In 1999, one in California registered 7.0. Compare the energy released in the two quakes.
See back of book.

Differentiated Instruction Solutions for All Learners

Special Needs L1
Before Example 4, review terms with negative exponents. Write the sequence 10^3, 10^2, 10^1, 10^0, 10^{-1}, 10^{-2}, 10^{-3}. Underneath it, write 1000, 100, 10, and 1. Have students study the pattern and then complete it. Remind students that $x^{-n} = \frac{1}{x^n}$.
$\frac{1}{10}, \frac{1}{100}, \frac{1}{10,000}$
learning style: verbal

Below Level L2
Have students use their calculators to graph $y = 10^x$, then use the Draw Inv function to plot the inverse. Next, graph the function $y = \log(x)$. Discuss how the graphs compare.
learning style: visual

The exponents used by the Richter scale shown in Example 1 are called logarithms, or logs.

 Key Concepts

Definition	Logarithm

The **logarithm** to the base b of a positive number y is defined as follows:

$$\text{If } y = b^x, \text{ then } \log_b y = x.$$

Vocabulary Tip

Read $\log_b y$ as "log base b of y."

The exponent x in the exponential expression b^x is the logarithm in the equation $\log_b y = x$. The base b in b^x is the same as the base b in the logarithm. In both cases, $b \neq 1$ and $b > 0$.

A positive number b raised to any power x cannot equal a number y less than or equal to zero. Therefore, the logarithm of a negative number or zero is undefined.

2 EXAMPLE Writing in Logarithmic Form

Write $25 = 5^2$ in logarithmic form.

If $y = b^x$, then $\log_b y = x$.   **Write the definition.**

If $25 = 5^2$, then $\log_5 25 = 2$.   **Substitute.**

The logarithmic form of $25 = 5^2$ is $\log_5 25 = 2$.

✓ **Quick Check** ② Write each equation in logarithmic form.
a. $729 = 3^6$ $\log_3 729 = 6$ b. $\left(\frac{1}{2}\right)^3 = \frac{1}{8}$ $3 = \log_{\frac{1}{2}} \left(\frac{1}{8}\right)$ c. $10^0 = 1$ $0 = \log_{10} 1$

To evaluate logarithms, you can write them in exponential form.

Video Tutor Help
Visit: PHSchool.com
Web Code: age-0775

3 EXAMPLE Evaluating Logarithms

Evaluate $\log_8 16$.

$\log_8 16 = x$ **Write an equation in logarithmic form.**

$16 = 8^x$ **Convert to exponential form.**

$2^4 = \left(2^3\right)^x$ **Write each side using base 2.**

$2^4 = 2^{3x}$ **Power Property of Exponents**

$4 = 3x$ **Set the exponents equal to each other.**

$\frac{4}{3} = x$ **Solve for x.**

So $\log_8 16 = \frac{4}{3}$.

✓ **Quick Check** ③ Evaluate each logarithm.
a. $\log_{64} \frac{1}{32}$ $-\frac{5}{6}$ b. $\log_9 27$ $\frac{3}{2}$ c. $\log_{10} 100$ 2

A **common logarithm** is a logarithm that uses base 10. You can write the common logarithm $\log_{10} y$ as $\log y$.

Guided Instruction

2 EXAMPLE Tactile Learners

Have students write the equation components y, b, x, log and $=$ on different colored pieces of paper. Direct students to arrange the papers to form the equation $y = b^x$. Then have them rearrange the papers to form $x = \log_b y$.

3 EXAMPLE Teaching Tip

Show students how to use estimation to check their answers. Tell students to first ask themselves, *What power of 8 is equal to 16?* They can use the powers they know for the estimation. For example, they know that 8 to the power of 1 is 8. Also, 8 to the power of 2 is 64. Sixteen is between 8 and 64 so students can expect the power to be a value between 1 and 2.

PowerPoint
Additional Examples

① Compare the amount of energy released in an earthquake that registered 6 on the Richter scale with one that registers 3. The first released about 27,000 times as much energy as the second.

② Write $32 = 2^5$ in logarithmic form. $\log_2 32 = 5$

③ Evaluate $\log_3 81$. 4

Lesson 8-3 Logarithmic Functions as Inverses **447**

Advanced Learners L4
Ask students to find out about several other scientific quantities typically measured on a logarithmic scale and discuss why this might be helpful.

learning style: verbal

English Language Learners ELL
Emphasize for students that a *logarithm* is simply an *exponent*. For Example 3, $\log_8 16$ represents the exponent x that satisfies $8^x = 16$.

learning style: verbal

Additional Example

4 The pH of an apple is about 3.3 and that of a banana is about 5.2. Recall that the pH of a substance equals $-\log[H^+]$, where $[H^+]$ is the concentration of hydrogen ions. Find the concentration of hydrogen ions in each fruit. Which is more acidic? **apple: 5.0×10^{-4}, banana: 6.3×10^{-6}; The apple is more acidic.**

Guided Instruction

5 **EXAMPLE** Visual Learners

Suggest students turn the book so that $y = x$ is vertical. This may help some students see that the two graphs are reflections of each other. .

6 **EXAMPLE** Error Prevention

Some students may try to find a value for y when $x \leq 2$. Remind students that the log of zero or a negative number is undefined. Also have students note that only powers of 6 are used for x in the table. By definition of a logarithm, this makes calculating y an easier task.

Additional Examples

5 Graph $y = \log_4 x$.

6 Graph $y = \log_5(x - 1) + 2$.

Real-World **Connection**

You can use pH strips to measure the acidity of a water solution. The pH scale ranges from 0 to 14.

Scientists use common logarithms to measure acidity, which increases as the concentration of hydrogen ions in a substance increases. The pH of a substance equals $-\log[H^+]$, where $[H^+]$ is the concentration of hydrogen ions.

4 **EXAMPLE** Real-World Connection

Chemistry The pH of lemon juice is 2.3, while the pH of milk is 6.6. Find the concentration of hydrogen ions in each substance. Which substance is more acidic?

Lemon juice	Milk
$pH = -\log[H^+]$	$pH = -\log[H^+]$
$2.3 = -\log[H^+]$	$6.6 = -\log[H^+]$
$\log[H^+] = -2.3$	$\log[H^+] = -6.6$
$[H^+] = 10^{-2.3}$	$[H^+] = 10^{-6.6}$
$\approx 5.0 \times 10^{-3}$	$\approx 2.5 \times 10^{-7}$

The $[H^+]$ of lemon juice is about 5.0×10^{-3}. The $[H^+]$ of milk is about 2.5×10^{-7}. Lemon juice has a higher concentration of hydrogen ions, so it is more acidic.

✓ Quick Check **4** Find the concentration of hydrogen ions in seawater of pH 8.5. **3.2×10^{-9}**

---

2 Graphing Logarithmic Functions

5.

Online active math

For: Log Functions Activity
Use: Interactive Textbook, 8-3

A **logarithmic function** is the inverse of an exponential function. The graph shows $y = 10^x$ and $y = \log x$. Note that $(0, 1)$ and $(1, 10)$ lie on the graph of $y = 10^x$, and that $(1, 0)$ and $(10, 1)$ lie on the graph of $y = \log x$.

Recall that the graph of a function is symmetric to the graph of its inverse over the line $y = x$. You can graph $y = \log_b x$ as the inverse of $y = b^x$.

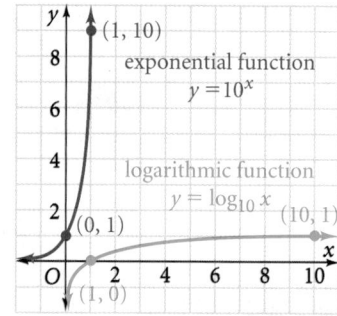

5 **EXAMPLE** Graphing a Logarithmic Function

Graph $y = \log_2 x$.

By the definition of logarithm, $y = \log_2 x$ is the inverse of $y = 2^x$.

Step 1 Graph $y = 2^x$.

Step 2 Draw $y = x$.

Step 3 Choose a few points on $y = 2^x$. Reverse the coordinates and plot the points of $y = \log_2 x$.

✓ Quick Check **5** Graph $y = \log_3 x$. **See above left.**

Resources
• Daily Notetaking Guide 8-3 **L3**

Closure

Ask: *What is the relationship between a logarithm and an exponent? What does the graph of $y = \log_{10} x$ look like?* **A logarithm is an exponent. The graph of $y = \log_{10} x$ is the graph of $y = 10^x$ reflected over $y = x$.**

The function $y = \log_b x$ is the inverse of $y = b^x$. Since $(0, 1)$ and $(1, b)$ are points on the graph of $y = b^x$, $(1, 0)$ and $(b, 1)$ are points on the graph of $y = \log_b x$. Since the x-axis is an asymptote for $y = b^x$, the y-axis is an asymptote for $y = \log_b x$. Using these facts, you can sketch the graph of $y = \log_b x$.

You can graph $y = \log_b (x - h) + k$ by translating the graph of $y = \log_b x$ horizontally by h and vertically by k.

 Key Concepts

Summary	Families of Logarithmic Functions	
Parent function:		$y = \log_b x, b > 0, b \neq 1$
Stretch ($|a| > 1$) Shrink ($0 < |a| < 1$) Reflection ($a < 0$) in x-axis		$y = a \log_b x$
Translation (horizontal by h; vertical by k):		$y = \log_b(x - h) + k$
Combined:		$y = a \log_b (x - h) + k$

6 **EXAMPLE** **Translating** $y = \log_b x$

Graph $y = \log_6 (x - 2) + 3$.

Step 1 Make a table of values for the parent function.

Vocabulary Tip

A parent function is the simplest function in a family of functions.

x	$\log_6 x$	y
6	$\log_6 6 = 1$	1
1	$\log_6 1 = 0$	0
$\frac{1}{6}$	$\log_6 \frac{1}{6} = -1$	-1
$\frac{1}{36}$	$\log_6 \frac{1}{36} = -2$	-2
$\frac{1}{216}$	$\log_6 \frac{1}{216} = -3$	-3

Step 2 Graph the function by shifting the points from the table to the right 2 units and up 3 units.

Quick Check **6** Graph $y = \log_3 (x + 3)$.

EXERCISES

For more exercises, see *Extra Skill and Word Problem Practice*.

Practice and Problem Solving

 A **Practice by Example**

Example 1
(page 446)

GO for Help

Seismology In 1812, an earthquake of magnitude 7.9 shook New Madrid, Missouri. Compare the amount of energy released by that earthquake to the amount of energy released by each earthquake below. 1–5. See margin.

1. magnitude 7.7 in San Francisco, California, in 1906

2. magnitude 9.5 in Valdivia, Chile, in 1960

3. magnitude 3.2 in Charlottesville, Virginia, in 2001

4. magnitude 6.9 in Kobe, Japan, in 1995

5. magnitude 9.2 in Prince William Sound, Alaska, in 1964

Lesson 8-3 Logarithmic Functions as Inverses **449**

1. The earthquake in Missouri released about 1.97 times more energy.

2. The earthquake in Chile released about 231 times more energy.

3. The earthquake in Missouri released about 8,759,310 times more energy.

4. The earthquake in Missouri released about 30 times more energy.

5. The earthquake in Alaska released about 83 times more energy.

3. Practice

Assignment Guide

1 A B 1-34, 41-51, 53-72

2 A B 35-40, 52, 73-84

C Challenge 85-90

Test Prep 91-98
Mixed Review 99-111

Homework Quick Check
To check students' understanding of key skills and concepts, go over Exercises 14, 40, 50, 51, 70

Connection to Geology

Exercises 1–5 An earthquake is caused by rapid movement of the Earth's outer layer. This happens when energy that is usually stored within the Earth in the form of stress in rocks, suddenly releases. This energy is transmitted to the surface of the Earth by earthquake waves. Several hundred earthquakes occur every day around the world. Very large earthquakes, such as the Alaskan one in Exercise 5, occur once every few years. Moderate earthquakes occur about 20 times a year worldwide.

Differentiated Instruction Resources

	GPS Guided Problem Solving	L3
Enrichment		L4
Reteaching		L2
Practice		L3

6. $\log_7 49 = 2$

7. $3 = \log 1000$

8. $\log_5 625 = 4$

9. $\log \frac{1}{10} = -1$

26. 6.3×10^{-6}

27. 6.3×10^{-3}

28. 1.0×10^{-8}

29. 7.9×10^{-4}

30. 5.0×10^{-7}

31. 1.3×10^{-5}

35.

36.

37.

38.

39.

Example 2
(page 447)

Write each equation in logarithmic form. 6–9. See margin.

6. $49 = 7^2$
7. $10^3 = 1000$
8. $625 = 5^4$
9. $\frac{1}{10} = 10^{-1}$

10. $8^2 = 64$
$2 = \log_8 64$
11. $4 = \left(\frac{1}{2}\right)^{-2}$
$-2 = \log_{\frac{1}{2}} 4$
12. $\left(\frac{1}{3}\right)^3 = \frac{1}{27}$
$3 = \log_{\frac{1}{3}}\left(\frac{1}{27}\right)$
13. $10^{-2} = 0.01$
$-2 = \log 0.01$

Example 3
(page 447)

Evaluate each logarithm.

14. $\log_2 16$ 4
15. $\log_4 2$ $\frac{1}{2}$
16. $\log_8 8$ 1
17. $\log_4 8$ $\frac{3}{2}$

20. undefined

18. $\log_2 8$ 3
19. $\log_{49} 7$ $\frac{1}{2}$
20. $\log_5 (-25)$
21. $\log_3 9$ 2

22. $\log_2 2^5$ 5
23. $\log_{\frac{1}{2}} \frac{1}{2}$ 1
24. $\log 10{,}000$ 4
25. $\log_5 125$ 3

Example 4
(page 448)

The pH of each food is given. Find the concentration of hydrogen ions [H$^+$].

26–31. See margin.

26. maple syrup, 5.2
27. lime juice, 2.2
28. egg white, 8.0

29. cider vinegar, 3.1
30. condensed milk, 6.3
31. soy sauce, 4.9

32. tomato juice, 4.0
1.0×10^{-4}
33. watermelon, 5.4
4.0×10^{-6}
34. mustard, 3.6
2.5×10^{-4}

Examples 5 and 6
(pages 448 and 449)

Graph each logarithmic function. 35–40. See margin.

35. $y = \log_4 x$
36. $y = \log_5 x$
37. $y = \log_8 x$

38. $y = \log_5 x + 1$
39. $y = \log_7 (x - 2)$
40. $y = \log_3 (x - 5) + 3$

B **Apply Your Skills**

41. 0.6990; 0

42. −4.2147; −5

43. −1.0969; −2

 for Help

For a guide to solving Exercise 49, see p. 453.

Use your calculator to evaluate each logarithm to four decimal places. Then find the largest integer that is less than the value of the logarithm.

41. $\log 5$
42. $\log (6.1 \times 10^{-5})$
43. $\log 0.08$
44. $\log 200$
2.3010; 2

45. $\log \frac{1}{6}$
−0.7782; −1
46. $\log 17.52$
1.2435; 1
47. $\log (1.3 \times 10^7)$
7.1139; 7
48. $\log \frac{13}{4}$
0.5119; 0

🌐 **49. Chemistry** The pH scale ranges from 0 to 14. A pH level of 7 is neutral. A level greater than 7 is basic, and a level less than 7 is acidic. The table shows the hydrogen ion concentration [H$^+$] for selected foods. Find the pH of each item. Determine whether it is basic or acidic. See margin.

50. Error Analysis Find the error in the following **GPS** evaluation of $\log_{27} 3$. Then evaluate the logarithm correctly.

$$\log_{27} 3 = x$$
$$27 = x^3$$
$$3 = x$$
$$\log_{27} 3 = 3$$

The error is in the second line. It should read $3 = 27^x$; the correct answer is $\frac{1}{3}$.

Approximate [H$^+$] of Foods

Food	[H$^+$]
Apple juice	3.2×10^{-4}
Buttermilk	2.5×10^{-5}
Cream	2.5×10^{-7}
Ketchup	1.3×10^{-4}
Shrimp sauce	7.9×10^{-8}
Strained peas	1.0×10^{-6}

51. First rewrite $y = \log_1 x$ as $1^y = x$. For any real number y, $x = 1$.

✏️ **51. Writing** Explain why the base b in $y = \log_b x$ cannot equal 1.

52. Open-Ended Write a logarithmic function of the form $y = \log_b x$. Find its inverse function. Graph both functions on one set of axes. See margin p. 451.

 nline
Homework Video Tutor
Visit: PHSchool.com
Web Code: age-0803

Write each equation in exponential form.

53. $\log_2 128 = 7$ $128 = 2^7$
54. $\log 0.0001 = -4$
$0.0001 = 10^{-4}$
55. $\log_7 16{,}807 = 5$
$16{,}807 = 7^5$

56. $\log_6 6 = 1$ $6 = 6^1$
57. $\log_4 1 = 0$ $1 = 4^0$
58. $\log_3 \frac{1}{9} = -2$ $\frac{1}{9} = 3^{-2}$

59. $\log_2 \frac{1}{2} = -1$
$\frac{1}{2} = 2^{-1}$
60. $\log 10 = 1$ $10 = 10^1$
61. $\log_2 8192 = 13$
$8192 = 2^{13}$

40.

49. apple juice: 3.5, acidic;
buttermilk: 4.6, acidic;
cream: 6.6, acidic;
ketchup: 3.9, acidic;
shrimp sauce: 7.1, basic;
strained peas: 6, acidic

450

Real-World **Connection**

Samples are loaded into a linear accelerator for carbon dating.

62. Archaeology One method of dating artifacts is radiocarbon dating. The artifacts in the table were found at a dig site near Kit Carson, Colorado. An artifact's age t in years is $t = 1.904 \times 10^4 \cdot \log\left(\frac{13.7}{R}\right)$, where R is the number of beta radiation emissions per minute per gram of carbon in the artifact.

Beta Emissions of Artifacts

Object	Mass of Carbon (g)	Beta Emissions per Minute
Buffalo bone	400	1640 ± 30
Bone fragment	15	61.5 ± 1.5
Pottery shard	25	342 ± 7
Charcoal	10	41.0 ± 1.3
Spear shaft	250	1020 ± 30

a. For each artifact, use the range of beta emissions to find the artifact's maximum and minimum ages. **a–b. See margin.**

b. **Critical Thinking** Which artifact is significantly different in age from the others? Give two possible explanations for the difference.

63. Multiple Choice Which function or functions are the inverse of $y = -\log_{0.25} x$?

I. $y = 4^x$ **II.** $y = 4^{-x}$ **III.** $y = \left(\frac{1}{4}\right)^{-x}$ **C**

A II only B III only C I and III D II and III

Find the inverse of each function.

64. $y = \log_4 x$ $y = 4^x$ **65.** $y = \log_{0.5} x$ $y = 0.5^x$ **66.** $y = \log_{10} x$ $y = 10^x$

68. $y = 10^x - 1$

69. $y = 10^{x-1}$

67. $y = \log_2 2x$ $y = 2^{x-1}$ **68.** $y = \log(x + 1)$ **69.** $y = \log 10x$

70. $y = \log(x - 2)$ $y = 10^x + 2$ **71.** $y = \log_5 x^2$ $y = 5^{\frac{x}{2}}$ **72.** $y = \log_a(x - b)$ $y = a^x + b$

Graph each logarithmic function. **73–84. See margin p. 452.**

73. $y = \log 2x$ **74.** $y = 2\log_2 x$ **75.** $y = \log_4(2x + 3)$

Find the domain and the range of each function.

76. $y = \log_5 x$ **77.** $y = 3\log x$ **78.** $y = \log_2(x - 3)$

79. $y = 1 + \log x$ **80.** $y = \log(x - 2) + 1$ **81.** $y = \log_6(x + 1)$

82. $y = \log_8 x - 2$ **83.** $y = \log_2 x + \frac{1}{3}$ **84.** $y = \log(x - t)$

C Challenge **Sound** The loudness in decibels (dB) of a sound is defined as $10\log\frac{I}{I_0}$.

I is the intensity of the sound. I_0 is 10^{-12}, the intensity of a barely audible sound. Complete the table.

Loudness of Sounds

	Type of Sound	Intensity (W/m^2)	Loudness (dB)
	Pain-producing	1	120
85.	Jackhammer	10^{-2}	■ 100
86.	Busy street	10^{-5}	■ 70
87.	Conversation	10^{-6}	■ 60
88.	Whisper	10^{-10}	■ 20
89.	Rustle of leaves	10^{-11}	■ 10
	Barely audible sound	10^{-12}	0

PowerPoint
Lesson Quiz

Evaluate each logarithm.

1. $\log_2 32$ **5**

2. $\log_{10}(-100)$ **undefined**

3. $\log_5 \frac{1}{25}$ **−2**

Write each equation in exponential form.

4. $\log 0.01 = -2$ $10^{-2} = 0.01$

5. $\log_3 27 = 3$ $3^3 = 27$

6. Graph $y = \log_6(x - 3) + 1$.

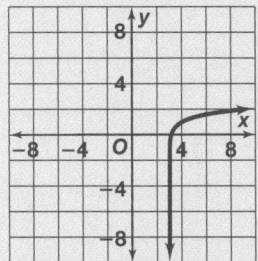

Alternative Assessment

Organize students into groups of four. Have each student write a logarithmic function in the form of $y = \log_b x$. Direct students to pass their papers to the right. This student makes a table of x- and y-values and passes the paper to the right. This student graphs the function, and then rewrites the function to include a translation before passing the paper to the right. The last student graphs the translation. Have students pick 2 of their group's functions to review together to make sure all is correct. If there is time, let groups review all of their functions.

to 10,242 years old, spear shaft: 9776 to 10,263 years old

b. The pottery shard; answers may vary. Samples: the pottery may be from a later civilization, or the mass or the beta radiation emissions may have been measured incorrectly.

52. Answers may vary. Sample: $y = \log_3 x$; $y = 3^x$

62a. buffalo bone: 9826 to 10,128 years old, bone fragment: 9776 to 10,180 years old, pottery shard: 0 to 183 years old, charcoal: 9718

451

Resources

For additional practice with a
variety of test item formats:
- Standardized Test Prep, p. 483
- Test-Taking Strategies, p. 478
- Test-Taking Strategies with
  Transparencies

90. Match each function with the graph of its inverse.

   a. $y = \log_3 x$ **II**   **b.** $y = \log_2 4x$ **III**   **c.** $y = \log_{\frac{1}{2}} x$ **I**

   I.   **II.**   **III.**

Test Prep

Multiple Choice

91. What is the ratio of $(65 \cdot 3^{17})$ to $(65 \cdot 3^{14})$? **D**

  A. 17 to 14   **B.** 3 to 1   **C.** 9 to 1   **D.** 27 to 1

92. What is the logarithmic form of the exponential equation $2^4 = 16$? **J**

  F. $\log_{16} 2 = 4$ **G.** $\log_{16} 4 = 2$ **H.** $\log_4 16 = 2$ **J.** $\log_2 16 = 4$

93. Which function is the inverse of $f(x) = 2^{x-1}$? **D**

  A. $f^{-1}(x) = \log_2 (x - 1)$.   **B.** $f^{-1}(x) = \log_2 (x + 1)$

  C. $f^{-1}(x) = \log_2 x - 1$ **D.** $f^{-1}(x) = \log_2 x + 1$

94. Which function is a shrink of $y = \log x$ by a factor of $\frac{1}{2}$? **F**

  F. $\log \sqrt{x}$ **G.** $\log x^2$ **H.** $\log \left(x - \frac{1}{2}\right)$ **J.** $\log \left(x + \frac{1}{2}\right)$

95. Which of the following relationships is
best represented by the graph at the right? **B**

  A. $y = \log_4 (x - 1) + 5$

  B. $y = \log_4 (x - 2) - 2$

  C. $y = \log_4 (x + 2) - 2$

  D. $y = \log_4 (x - 1) - 1$

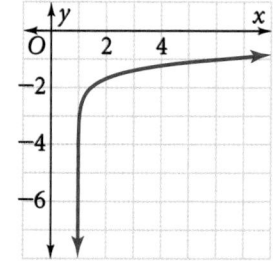

Short Response

96. Evaluate $\log_2 \frac{1}{32}$ without using a calculator.
Show your work. **96–98. See back of book.**

97. Solve the equation $\log_6 y = 3$.

98. Solve the equation $\log_b 9 = \frac{1}{2}$.

Mixed Review

 GO for Help

Lesson 8-2

Sketch the graph of each function. Then locate the asymptote of the curve.

99. $y = 5^x - 100$ **100.** $y = -10(4)^{x+2}$ **101.** $y = -27(3)^{x-1} + 9$
99–101. See margin pp. 452–453.

Lesson 7-4

Write each expression in radical form.

102. $t^{\frac{2}{3}}$ $\sqrt[3]{t^2}$ **103.** $(16w^3)^{\frac{1}{2}}$ $4\sqrt{w^3}$ **104.** $z^{\frac{8}{5}}$ $\sqrt[5]{z^8}$ **105.** $x^{\frac{p}{n}}$ $\sqrt[n]{x^p}$

Lesson 6-4

Solve each equation by graphing. If necessary, round to the nearest thousandth.

106. $3x^2 + 18x + 24 = 0$ **107.** $1 - x = x^2 - 7x$ **108.** $x^4 = 7x^3 + 10x^2$

   $-2, -4$ $-0.162, 6.162$ $-1.217, 0, 8.217$

Lesson 5-4

Factor each expression.

109. $4x^2 - 8x + 3$ **110.** $\frac{1}{4}b^2 - 4$ **111.** $5x^2 + 13x - 6$

   $(2x - 3)(2x - 1)$ $\left(\frac{1}{2}b - 2\right)\left(\frac{1}{2}b + 2\right)$ $(5x - 2)(x + 3)$

452   Chapter 8 Exponential and Logarithmic Functions

Understanding Word Problems Read the problem below. Let the explanations guide you through the use of the data table. Check your understanding with the exercise at the bottom of the page.

Chemistry The pH scale ranges from 0 to 14. A pH level of 7 is neutral. A level greater than 7 is basic, and a level less than 7 is acidic. The table shows the hydrogen ion concentration $[H^+]$ for selected foods. Find the pH of each item. Determine whether it is basic or acidic.

Approximate [H+] of Selected Foods

Food	[H+]
Apple Juice	3.2×10^{-4}
Buttermilk	2.5×10^{-5}
Cream	2.5×10^{-7}
Ketchup	1.3×10^{-4}
Shrimp Sauce	7.9×10^{-8}
Strained Peas	1.0×10^{-6}

A table is a tool for organizing data.

The title of the table indicates the type of → **Approximate [H+] of Selected Foods**
data represented.

Food	[H+]
Apple Juice	3.2×10^{-4}
Buttermilk	2.5×10^{-5}

← **Each row represents a different item. Row 1 contains data for apple juice.**

Each column represents a different category of data. Column 2 lists the [H+] of each food.

Now you can use the table.

$$pH = -\log [H^+]$$
Refer to page 448 for the formula for pH.

$$pH \text{ of apple juice} = -\log ([H^+] \text{ of apple juice})$$ Use the formula.

$$= -\log (3.2 \times 10^{-4})$$ Substitute.

$$\approx 3.49$$ Simplify.

Since the pH of apple juice is less than 7, it is acidic.

The problem asks you to find the pH and whether the item is basic or acidic. To organize the information, you can add two columns to the table.

Food	[H+]	pH	Acid or Base
Apple Juice	3.2×10^{-4}	3.49	Acid

EXERCISE

Copy and complete the table below.

	[H+]	pH	Acid or Base	
7.34				base
2.43	4.6×10^{-8}	■	■	acid
3.74	3.7×10^{-3}	■	■	acid
	1.8×10^{-4}	■	■	

Understanding Word Problems

Students learn how to read and interpret data from a table of values. Once students understand the given information, students then use the data to perform calculations to solve problems.

Guided Instruction

Point out to students that the hydrogen ion concentration $[H^+]$ *is not* the same as the pH. Students must use the $[H^+]$ values listed in the table to find the pH for each food, and then they can determine whether the food is acidic or basic.

Foods that are acidic usually have a sour taste and foods that are basic usually have a bitter taste.

Because pH values are always positive and hydrogen ion concentrations are almost always fractional, it is very important for students to remember to find the negative log of the hydrogen ion concentration when finding pH.

Visual Learners

Suggest that students use the data in the table to create a graph that has $[H^+]$ ion concentration on one axis, and pH on another axis. Have students draw conclusions about the relationship between $[H^+]$ ion concentration and pH based on the graph

Exercise

The question asks students to fill in the pH and corresponding acidity. Remind students that the acidity depends on the pH value.

101. $y = 9$

1. Plan

Objectives

1 To use the properties of logarithms

Examples

1 Identifying the Properties of Logarithms
2 Simplifying Logarithms
3 Expanding Logarithms
4 Real-World Connection

Math Background

Many students want to believe that $\log_b (M + N) = \log_b M + \log_b N$. However, this would be equivalent to adding the exponents in expressions such as $x^2 + x^3$, which cannot be done. Thus, it is reasonable that there is *no* property for the logarithm of a sum. Do not confuse this with the valid property for a logarithm of a product, $\log_b (MN) = \log_b M + \log_b N$.

More Math Background: p. 428C

Lesson Planning and Resources

See p. 428E for a list of the resources that support this lesson.

Bell Ringer Practice

✓ **Check Skills You'll Need**
For intervention, direct students to:

Evaluating Logarithmic Functions
Lesson 8-3: Example 3
Extra Skills and Word
    Problems Practice, Ch. 8

Algebraic Expressions
Lesson 1-2: Examples 1, 2
Extra Skills and Word
    Problems Practice, Ch. 1

454

What You'll Learn

- To use the properties of logarithms

. . . And Why

To relate sound intensity and decibel level, as in Example 4

✓ **Check Skills You'll Need**   **GO for Help** Lessons 8-3 and 1-2

Simplify each expression.

1. $\log_2 4 + \log_2 8$ **5**
2. $\log_3 9 - \log_3 27$ **−1**
3. $\log_2 16 \div \log_2 64$ $\frac{2}{3}$

Evaluate each expression for $x = 3$.

4. $x^3 - x$ **24**
5. $x^5 \cdot x^2$ **2187**
6. $\frac{x^6}{x^9}$ $\frac{1}{27}$
7. $x^3 + x^2$ **36**

---

1   Using the Properties of Logarithms

1. 0, 0.301, 0.477, 0.602, 0.699, 0.778, 0.845, 0.903, 0.954, 1, 1.176, 1.301

2. The sum of the logarithms equals the log of the product.

Activity: Properties of Logarithms

1. Complete the table. Round to the nearest thousandth.

x	1	2	3	4	5	6	7	8	9	10	15	20
log x	■	■	■	■	■	■	■	■	■	■	■	■

2. Complete each pair of statements. What do you notice? **See left.**
  a. log 3 + log 5 = ■ and log (3 · 5) = ■ **1.176, 1.176**
  b. log 1 + log 7 = ■ and log (1 · 7) = ■ **0.845, 0.845**
  c. log 2 + log 4 = ■ and log (2 · 4) = ■ **0.903, 0.903**
  d. log 10 + log 2 = ■ and log (10 · 2) = ■ **1.301, 1.301**

3. Complete the statement: log M + log N = ■. **log (MN)**

4. a. Make a Conjecture How could you rewrite the expression $\log \frac{M}{N}$ using the expressions log M and log N? $\log \frac{M}{N} = \log M - \log N$
  b. Use your calculator to verify your conjecture for several values of M and N. **Check students' work.**

The properties of logarithms are summarized below.

 Key Concepts

Properties	Properties of Logarithms
For any positive numbers, M, N, and b, $b \neq 1$,	
$\log_b MN = \log_b M + \log_b N$	**Product Property**
$\log_b \frac{M}{N} = \log_b M - \log_b N$	**Quotient Property**
$\log_b M^x = x \log_b M$	**Power Property**

Differentiated Instruction   Solutions for All Learners

Special Needs L1
Students who wear hearing aids, or who have difficulty hearing, may be sensitive about a discussion of noise levels and decibels. However, if these students are comfortable with the topic, invite them to contribute some of their special knowledge.
                                    learning style: verbal

Below Level L2
Have students state the Properties of Logarithms in words. Give illustrations using those words. Discuss whether these agree with the Property chosen.

                                    learning style: verbal

You can use the properties of logarithms to rewrite logarithmic expressions.

① EXAMPLE Identifying the Properties of Logarithms

State the property or properties used to rewrite each expression.

a. $\log_2 8 - \log_2 4 = \log_2 2$

Quotient Property: $\log_2 8 - \log_2 4 = \log_2 \frac{8}{4} = \log_2 2$

b. $\log_b x^3 y = 3 \log_b x + \log_b y$

Product Property: $\log_b x^3 y = \log_b x^3 + \log_b y$

Power Property: $\log_b x^3 + \log_b y = 3 \log_b x + \log_b y$

✓ Quick Check ① State the property or properties used to rewrite each expression.
a. $\log_5 2 + \log_5 6 = \log_5 12$ **Product Property**
b. $3 \log_b 4 - 3 \log_b 2 = \log_b 8$ **Power Property, Quotient Property**

You can write the sum or difference of logarithms with the same base as a single logarithm.

② EXAMPLE Simplifying Logarithms

Video Tutor Help
Visit: PHSchool.com
Web Code: age-0775

Write each logarithmic expression as a single logarithm.

a. $\log_3 20 - \log_3 4$

$\log_3 20 - \log_3 4 = \log_3 \frac{20}{4}$ **Quotient Property**

$ = \log_3 5$ **Simplify.**

b. $3 \log_2 x + \log_2 y$

$3 \log_2 x + \log_2 y = \log_2 x^3 + \log_2 y$ **Power Property**

$ = \log_2 (x^3 y)$ **Product Property**

So $\log_3 20 - \log_3 4 = \log_3 5$, and $3 \log_2 x + \log_2 y = \log_2 (x^3 y)$.

✓ Quick Check ② **a.** Write $3 \log 2 + \log 4 - \log 16$ as a single logarithm.   **log 2**
b. Critical Thinking Can you write $3 \log_2 9 - \log_6 9$ as a single logarithm? Explain.   **No; they do not have the same base.**

3a. $\log_2 7 + \log_2 b$

b. $2 \log y - 2 \log 3$

c. $3 \log_7 a + 4 \log_7 b$

You can sometimes write a single logarithm as a sum or difference of two or more logarithms.

③ EXAMPLE Expanding Logarithms

Vocabulary Tip

In mathematics, to expand means "to show the full form of."

Expand each logarithm.

a. $\log_5 \frac{x}{y}$

$ = \log_5 x - \log_5 y$ **Quotient Property**

b. $\log 3r^4$

$ = \log 3 + \log r^4$ **Product Property**

$ = \log 3 + 4 \log r$ **Power Property**

✓ Quick Check ③ Expand each logarithm.   **See above left.**
a. $\log_2 7b$ **b.** $\log \left(\frac{y}{3}\right)^2$ **c.** $\log_7 a^3 b^4$

Guided Instruction

Activity
Teaching Tip
Remind students that a logarithm is an exponent. Therefore, it seems reasonable that there are properties for operations with logarithms that are similar to the properties for operations with exponents.

② EXAMPLE Math Tip

Point out to students that the bases are the same within each expression in part (a) and within each expression in part (b). The properties for logarithms do not apply unless the bases are the same.

PowerPoint

Additional Examples

① State the property or properties used to rewrite each expression.

a. $\log 6 = \log 2 + \log 3$
Product Property

b. $\log_b \frac{x^2}{y} = 2 \log_b x - \log_b y$

Quotient Property and Power Property

② Write each expression as a single logarithm.
a. $\log_4 64 - \log_4 16$ $\log_4 4$ or 1
b. $6 \log_5 x + \log_5 y$ $\log_5 (x^6 y)$

Advanced Learners L4
Ask students to explain how the properties of Logarithms on page 454 are similar to and how they are different from the properties of exponents.

learning style: verbal

English Language Learners ELL
Emphasize the correct reading of a logarithmic expression. For $\log_b 2$, students should say "log base b of 2." Also, clarify that the term *log* by itself is meaningless. You cannot say $y = \log$ just as you cannot say $y = \sqrt{}$.

learning style: verbal

Logarithms are used to model sound. The intensity of a sound is a measure of the energy carried by the sound wave. The greater the intensity of a sound, the louder it seems. This apparent loudness L is measured in decibels. You can use the formula $L = 10 \log \frac{I}{I_0}$, where I is the intensity of the sound in watts per square meter (W/m^2). I_0 is the lowest-intensity sound that the average human ear can detect.

Loudness of Sounds

150 dB — Jet engine
100 dB
Motorcycle
80 dB — Vacuum cleaner
Hum of refrigerator
45 dB
Breathing
Threshold of hearing — 10 dB
0 dB

Real-World Connection

The workers who direct planes at airports must wear ear protection.

4 EXAMPLE Real-World Connection

Noise Control A shipping company has started flying cargo planes out of the city airport. Residents in a nearby neighborhood have complained that the cargo planes are too loud. Suppose the shipping company hires you to design a way to reduce the intensity of the sound by half. By how many decibels would the loudness of the sound be decreased?

Relate The reduced intensity is one half of the present intensity.

Define Let I_1 = present intensity.
Let I_2 = reduced intensity.
Let L_1 = present loudness.
Let L_2 = reduced loudness.

Write $I_2 = 0.5 I_1$

$$L_1 = 10 \log \frac{I_1}{I_0}$$

$$L_2 = 10 \log \frac{I_2}{I_0}$$

$$L_1 - L_2 = 10 \log \frac{I_1}{I_0} - 10 \log \frac{I_2}{I_0} \quad \text{Find the decrease in loudness } L_1 - L_2.$$

$$= 10 \log \frac{I_1}{I_0} - 10 \log \frac{0.5 I_1}{I_0} \quad \text{Substitute } I_2 = 0.5 I_1.$$

$$= 10 \log \frac{I_1}{I_0} - 10 \log \left(0.5 \cdot \frac{I_1}{I_0} \right)$$

$$= 10 \log \frac{I_1}{I_0} - 10 \left(\log 0.5 + \log \frac{I_1}{I_0} \right) \quad \text{Product Property}$$

$$= 10 \log \frac{I_1}{I_0} - 10 \log 0.5 - 10 \log \frac{I_1}{I_0} \quad \text{Distributive Property}$$

$$= -10 \log 0.5 \quad \text{Combine like terms.}$$

$$\approx 3.0 \quad \text{Use a calculator.}$$

4. about 6 decibels

The decrease in loudness would be about three decibels.

 Quick Check **4** Suppose the shipping company wants you to reduce the sound intensity to 25% of the original intensity. By how many decibels would the loudness be reduced?

1. **Product Property**
2. **Quotient Property**
3. **Power Property**
4. **Power Property**
5. **Power Property, Quotient Property**
6. **Power Property**
7. **Power Property, Quotient Property**
8. **Power Property, Product Property**
9. **Power Property, Quotient Property**
10. **Power Property, Product Property**

EXERCISES

For more exercises, see *Extra Skill and Word Problem Practice*.

Practice and Problem Solving

3. Practice

Assignment Guide

1 A B 1-87
C Challenge   88-90

Test Prep   91-95
Mixed Review   96-108

Ⓐ Practice by Example

Example 1
(page 455)

for Help

1–10. See margin
p. 456.

State the property or properties used to rewrite each expression.

1. $\log 4 + \log 5 = \log 20$

2. $\log_3 32 - \log_3 8 = \log_3 4$

3. $\log z^2 = 2 \log z$

4. $\log_6 \sqrt[n]{x^p} = \frac{p}{n} \log_6 x$

5. $8 \log 2 - 2 \log 8 = \log 4$

6. $\log \sqrt[3]{3x} = \frac{1}{3} \log 3x$

7. $3 \log_4 5 - 3 \log_4 3 = \log_4 \left(\frac{5}{3}\right)^3$

8. $2 \log w + 4 \log z = \log w^2 z^4$

9. $2 \log_2 m - 4 \log_2 n = \log_2 \frac{m^2}{n^4}$

10. $\log_b \frac{1}{8} + 3 \log_b 4 = \log_b 8$

Example 2
(page 455)

Write each logarithmic expression as a single logarithm.

11. $\log 7 + \log 2$ **log 14**

12. $\log_2 9 - \log_2 3$ **$\log_2 3$**

13. $5 \log 3 + \log 4$ **log 972**

14. $\log 8 - 2 \log 6 + \log 3$ **$\log \frac{2}{3}$**

15. $4 \log m - \log n$ **$\log \frac{m^4}{n}$**

16. $\log 5 - k \log 2$ **$\log \frac{5}{2^k}$**

17. $\log_6 5 + \log_6 x$ **$\log_6 5x$**

18. $\log_7 x + \log_7 y - \log_7 z$ **$\log_7 \frac{xy}{z}$**

Example 3
(page 455)

Expand each logarithm.   19–30. See margin.

19. $\log x^3 y^5$

20. $\log_7 22xyz$

21. $\log_4 5\sqrt{x}$

22. $\log 3m^4 n^{-2}$

23. $\log_5 \frac{r}{s}$

24. $\log_3 (2x)^2$

25. $\log_3 7(2x - 3)^2$

26. $\log \frac{a^2 b^3}{c^4}$

27. $\log \sqrt{\frac{2x}{y}}$

28. $\log_8 8\sqrt{3a^5}$

29. $\log \frac{s\sqrt{7}}{t^2}$

30. $\log_b \frac{1}{x}$

Example 4
(page 456)

31. One brand of ear plugs claims to block the sound of snoring as loud as 22 dB. A second brand claims to block snoring that is eight times as intense. If the claims are true, for how many more decibels is the second brand effective?   **9 dB**

32. A sound barrier along a highway reduced the intensity of the noise reaching a community by 95%. By how many decibels was the noise reduced?   **13 dB**

Homework Quick Check
To check students' understanding of key skills and concepts, go over Exercises 25, 32, 56, 57, 72, 75.

Diversity
Exercise 32 Some students may not know what a sound barrier along a highway looks like. Ask students to bring pictures, draw a sketch, or tell where one can be seen nearby. Discuss the fact that highway sound barriers are often built to prevent highway noise from affecting neighborhoods.

Ⓑ Apply Your Skills

Use the properties of logarithms to evaluate each expression.

33. $\log_2 4 - \log_2 16$ **−2**

34. $3 \log_2 2 - \log_2 4$ **1**

35. $\log_3 3 + 5 \log_3 3$ **6**

36. $\log 1 + \log 100$ **2**

37. $\log_6 4 + \log_6 9$ **2**

38. $2 \log_8 4 - \frac{1}{3} \log_8 8$ **1**

39. $2 \log_3 3 - \log_3 3$ **1**

40. $\frac{1}{2} \log_5 1 - 2 \log_5 5$ **−2**

41. $\log_9 \frac{1}{3} + 3 \log_9 3$ **1**

42. The coefficient $\frac{1}{2}$ is missing in $\log_4 s$;
$\log_4 \sqrt{\frac{t}{s}} = \frac{1}{2} \log_4 \frac{t}{s} =$
$\frac{1}{2}(\log_4 t - \log_4 s) =$
$\frac{1}{2} \log_4 t - \frac{1}{2} \log_4 s$.

42. Error Analysis Explain why the expansion below of $\log_4 \sqrt{\frac{t}{s}}$ is incorrect. Then do the expansion correctly.   **See left.**

$$\log_4 \sqrt{\frac{t}{s}} = \frac{1}{2} \log_4 \frac{t}{s}$$
$$= \frac{1}{2} \log_4 t - \log_4 s$$

43. Open-Ended Write $\log 150$ as a sum or difference of two logarithms.
Answers may vary. Sample: $\log 150 = \log 15 + \log 10$.

Differentiated Instruction Resources

GPS Guided Problem Solving	L3
Enrichment	L4
Reteaching	L2
Practice	L3

---

19. $3 \log x + 5 \log y$

20. $\log_7 22 + \log_7 x + \log_7 y + \log_7 z$

21. $\log_4 5 + \frac{1}{2} \log_4 x$

22. $\log 3 + 4 \log m - 2 \log n$

23. $\log_5 r - \log_5 s$

24. $2 \log_3 2 + 2 \log_3 x$

25. $\log_3 7 + 2 \log (2x - 3)$

26. $2 \log a + 3 \log b - 4 \log c$

27. $\frac{1}{2} \log 2 + \frac{1}{2} \log x - \frac{1}{2} \log y$

28. $1 + \frac{1}{2} \log_8 3 + \frac{5}{2} \log_8 a$

29. $\log s + \frac{1}{2} \log 7 - 2 \log t$

30. $-\log_b x$

4. Assess & Reteach

PowerPoint

Lesson Quiz

Write each expression as a single logarithm. State the property you used.

1. $\log 12 - \log 3$ **log 4; Quotient Property**

2. $3\log_{11}5 + \log_{11}7$
$\log_{11}(5^3 \cdot 7)$; **Power Property and Product Property**

Expand each logarithm.

3. $\log_c \frac{a}{b}$ $\log_c a - \log_c b$

4. $\log_3 x^4$ $4\log_3 x$

Use the properties of logarithms to evaluate each expression.

5. $\log 0.001 + \log 100$ -1

6. $\frac{1}{2}\log_y y$ $\frac{1}{2}$

Alternative Assessment

Have students work in small groups to prepare an informal proof of an expanded logarithm from Exercises 79–87. They should justify each step, using the Properties of Logarithms. Then ask each group to present their proof at the board, and encourage class discussion of the proof.

Assume that $\log 4 \approx 0.6021$, $\log 5 \approx 0.6990$, and $\log 6 \approx 0.7782$. Use the properties of logarithms to evaluate each expression. Do not use your calculator.

44. $\log 24$ **1.3803** **45.** $\log 30$ **1.4772** **46.** $\log 16$ **1.2042**

47. $\log 125$ **2.097** **48.** $\log 1.5$ **0.1761** **49.** $\log 0.8$ **−0.0969**

50. $\log \frac{1}{4}$ **−0.6021** **51.** $\log \frac{1}{25}$ **−1.398** **52.** $\log 25$ **1.398**

53. $\log \frac{1}{6}$ **−0.7782** **54.** $\log 36$ **1.5564** **55.** $\log \sqrt{5}$ **0.3495**

56. Noise Control New components reduce the sound intensity of a certain model of vacuum cleaner from 10^{-4} W/m^2 to 6.31×10^{-6} W/m^2. By how many decibels do these new components reduce the vacuum cleaner's loudness? **12 dB**

57. Reasoning If $\log x = 5$, what is the value of $\frac{1}{x}$? **0.00001**

Real-World Connection

Decibel meters are used to measure sound levels.

Write *true* or *false* for each statement. Justify your answer. **58–67. See margin.**

58. $\log_2 4 + \log_2 8 = 5$

59. $\log_3 \frac{3}{2} = \frac{1}{2}\log_3 3$

60. $\log_3 8 = 3\log_3 2$

61. $\log_5 16 - \log 2 = \log_5 8$

62. $\log(x-2) = \frac{\log x}{\log 2}$

63. $\frac{\log_b x}{\log_b y} = \log_b \frac{x}{y}$

64. $(\log x)^2 = \log x^2$

65. $\log_4 7 - \log_4 3 = \log_4 4$

66. $\log x + \log(x^2+2) = \log(x^3+2x)$

67. $\log_2 3 + \log_3 2 = \log_6 6$

68. $\log_2 x - 4\log_2 y = \log_2 \frac{x}{y^4}$
68–69. See margin p. 459.

69. $\log_b \frac{1}{8} + 3\log_b 4 = \log_b 8$

70. Construction Suppose you are the supervisor on a road construction job. Your team is blasting rock to make way for a roadbed. One explosion has an intensity of 1.65×10^{-2} W/m^2. What is the loudness of the sound in decibels? (Use $I_0 = 10^{-12}$ W/m^2.) **102 dB**

71. Critical Thinking Can you expand $\log_3(2x+1)$? Explain.

71. No; the expression $(2x + 1)$ is a sum, so it is not covered by the Product, Quotient, or Power properties.

72. Writing Explain why $\log(5 \cdot 2) \neq \log 5 \cdot \log 2$. **See margin p. 459.**

Write each logarithmic expression as a single logarithm. **73–78. See left.**

73. $\log_3 \sqrt[4]{2x}$

74. $\log_x \frac{2\sqrt{y}}{z^3}$

75. $\log \frac{27}{2}$

76. $\log_4 \frac{m^x n^{\frac{1}{y}}}{p}$

77. $\log_b \frac{\sqrt[3]{x^2}\sqrt[4]{y^3}}{z^5}$

78. $\log \frac{\sqrt[4]{z}}{\sqrt[4]{3}\sqrt{x^5}}$

73. $\frac{1}{4}\log_3 2 + \frac{1}{4}\log_3 x$

74. $\frac{1}{2}\big(\log_x 4 + \log_x y\big) - 3\log_x z$

75. $2\log 3 - \frac{1}{2}\log 4 + \frac{1}{2}\log 9$

76. $x\log_4 m + \frac{1}{y}\log_4 n - \log_4 p$

77. $\left(\frac{2\log_b x}{3} + \frac{3\log_b y}{4}\right) - 5\log_b z$

78. $\frac{\log z - \log 3}{4} - 5\frac{\log x}{2}$

GO Online

Homework Video Tutor

Visit: PHSchool.com
Web Code: age-0804

Expand each logarithm. **79–87. See back of book.**

79. $\log\left(\frac{2\sqrt{x}}{5}\right)^3$

80. $\log \frac{m^3}{n^4 p^{-2}}$

81. $\log 2\sqrt{\frac{4r}{s^2}}$

82. $\log_b \frac{\sqrt{x}\sqrt[3]{y^2}}{\sqrt[5]{z^2}}$

83. $\log_4 \frac{\sqrt{x^5 y^7}}{zw^4}$

84. $\log \frac{\sqrt{x^2-4}}{(x+3)^2}$

85. $\log \sqrt{\frac{x\sqrt{2}}{y^2}}$

86. $\log_3 \left[(xy)^{\frac{1}{3}} \div z^2\right]^3$

87. $\log_7 \frac{\sqrt{r+9}}{s^2 t^{\frac{1}{3}}}$

458 Chapter 8 Exponential and Logarithmic Functions

58. True; $\log_2 4 = 2$ and $\log_2 8 = 3$.

59. False; $\frac{1}{2}\log_3 3 = \log_3 3^{\frac{1}{2}}$, not $\log_3 \frac{3}{2}$.

60. True; it is an example of the Power Property since $8 = 2^3$.

61. False; the two logs have different bases.

62. False; this is not an example of the Quotient Property. $\log(x-2) \neq \log x - \log 2$.

63. False; $\log_b \frac{x}{y} = \log_b x - \log_b y$.

64. False; the exponent on the left means $\log x$, quantity squared, not the log of x^2.

65. False; $\log_4 7 - \log_4 3 = \log_4 \frac{7}{3}$, not $\log_4 4$.

66. True; $\log x + \log(x^2+2) = \log x(x^2+2)$, which equals $\log(x^3+2x)$.

67. False; the three logs have different bases.

458

88. Let $u = \log_b M$, and let $v = \log_b N$. Prove the Product Property of Logarithms by completing the equations below.

88. $v = \log_b N$
$b^v = N$
$MN = b^u \cdot b^v =$
b^{u+v}
$\log_b MN = u + v$
$\log_b MN = \log_b M$
$+ \log_b N$

Statement	Reason
$u = \log_b M$	Given
$b^u = M$	Rewrite in exponential form.
$v = \blacksquare$	Given
$b^v = \blacksquare$	Rewrite in exponential form.
$MN = b^u b^v = b^{\blacksquare}$	Apply the Product Property of Exponents.
$\log_b MN = \blacksquare$	Take the logarithm of each side.
$\log_b MN = \log_b \blacksquare + \log_b \blacksquare$	Substitute $\log_b M$ for u and $\log_b N$ for v.

89. Let $u = \log_b M$. Prove the Power Property of logarithms. **See margin.**

90. Let $u = \log_b M$ and $v = \log_b N$. Prove the Quotient Property of logarithms.
See margin.

Test Prep

Multiple Choice

91. Which statement is NOT correct? **B**
A. $\log_2 25 = 2 \cdot \log_2 5$ **B.** $\log_3 16 = 2 \cdot \log_3 8$
C. $\log_5 27 = 3 \cdot \log_5 3$ **D.** $\log_8 10{,}000 = 4 \cdot \log_8 10$

92. Which expression is equal to $\log_7 5 + \log_7 3$? **G**
F. $\log_7 8$ **G.** $\log_7 15$ **H.** $\log_7 125$ **J.** $\log_{49} 15$

93. Which expression is equal to $\log_5 x + 4 \cdot \log_5 y - 2 \cdot \log_5 z$? **D**
A. $\log_5(-8xyz)$ **B.** $-\log_5 \frac{4xy}{2z}$ **C.** $\log_5 \frac{(xy)^4}{z^2}$ **D.** $\log_5 \frac{xy^4}{z^2}$

Short Response

94. $\log_5 10 \approx 1.4307$ and $\log_5 20 \approx 1.8614$. Find the value of $\log_5\left(\frac{1}{2}\right)$ without using a calculator. Explain how you found the value. **See margin.**

Extended Response

95. Use the properties of logarithms to write log 12 in four different ways. Name each property you use. **See back of book.**

Mixed Review

GO for Help

Lesson 8-3

Write each equation in logarithmic form.

                                                      $-3 = \log_5 \frac{1}{125}$

96. $49 = 7^2$ **97.** $5^3 = 125$ **98.** $\frac{1}{4} = 8^{-\frac{2}{3}}$ **99.** $5^{-3} = \frac{1}{125}$
$\log_7 49 = 2$ $3 = \log_5 125$ $\log_8 \frac{1}{4} = -\frac{2}{3}$

Lesson 7-5

Solve each equation. Check for extraneous solutions.

100. $\sqrt[3]{y^4} = 16$ $8, -8$ **101.** $\sqrt[3]{7x} - 4 = 0$ $\frac{64}{7}$ **102.** $2\sqrt{w - 1} = \sqrt{w + 2}$ 2

Lesson 6-5

A polynomial equation with integer coefficients has the given roots. What additional roots can you identify?

103. $\sqrt{3}, -\sqrt{5}$ $-\sqrt{3}, \sqrt{5}$ **104.** $-i, 4i$ $i, -4i$ **105.** $2i, -4 + i$ $-2i, -4 - i$

106. $\sqrt{2}, i - 1$ **107.** $-\sqrt{7}, -\sqrt{11}$ $\sqrt{7}, \sqrt{11}$ **108.** $-2i + 3, i$ $2i + 3, -i$
$-\sqrt{2}, -i - 1$

68. True; the power and quotient properties are used correctly.

69. True; the left side equals $\log_b\left(\frac{1}{8} \cdot 4^3\right)$, which equals $\log_b 8$.

72. The log of a product is equal to the sum of the logs. $\log(MN) = \log M + \log N$. So $\log(5 \cdot 2) = \log 10 = 1$, $\log 5 \cdot \log 2 \approx (0.7)(0.3) = 0.21$, which is not equal to 1.

Test Prep

📁 **Resources**
For additional practice with a variety of test item formats:
- Standardized Test Prep, p. 483
- Test-Taking Strategies, p. 478
- Test-Taking Strategies with Transparencies

89. 1. $u = \log_b M$ (Given)
2. $b^u = M$ (Rewrite in exponential form.)
3. $(b^u)^x = M^x$ (Raise each side to x power.)
4. $b^{ux} = M^x$ (Power Property of Exponents)
5. $\log_b b^{ux} = \log_b M^x$ (Take the log of each side.)
6. $ux = \log_b M^x$ (Simplify.)
7. $\log_b M^x = x \cdot \log_b M$ (Substitution)

90. 1. $u = \log_b M$ (Given)
2. $b^u = M$ (Rewrite in exponential form.)
3. $v = \log_b N$ (Given)
4. $b^v = N$ (Rewrite in exponential form.)
5. $\frac{M}{N} = \frac{b^u}{b^v} = b^{u-v}$ (Quotient Property of Exponents)
6. $\log_b \frac{M}{N} = \log_b b^{u-v}$ (Take the log of each side.)
7. $\log_b \frac{M}{N} = u - v$ (Simplify.)
8. $\log_b \frac{M}{N} = \log_b M - \log_b N$ (Substitution)

94. [2] By the Quotient Property, $\log_5\left(\frac{1}{2}\right) = \log_5\left(\frac{10}{20}\right) \approx 1.4307 - 1.8614 = -0.4307$.
[1] correct answer, without work shown

459

Vocabulary Builder

Reasonable Context

Students determine whether an answer is reasonable based on the given context. Checking for reasonableness can be a valuable test-taking skill.

Guided Instruction

Diversity

Share pictures from magazines with students who may not be familiar with hot-air balloons.

Teaching Tip

Point out that assessing whether an answer is reasonable often requires background knowledge of the context. For instance, some students may not be familiar with hot-air balloons to guess their approximate size.

 English Language Learners ELL

Make sure students understand that a *reasonable domain and range* is context specific. In this context, more that one domain can be reasonable, as explored in Exercises 2-6.

Teaching Tip

Ask: *Why might checking for reasonableness be helpful when using a calculator?* Sample: If a wrong key is pressed and there is no check for reasonableness, an incorrect answer may not be corrected.

Resources

Vocabulary Masters with Study Skills

3.8028

 Reasonable Context

One quick check of a solution to a real-world problem is determining whether the answer is *reasonable* for the given context. The *context* is the situational setting for the problem.

1 EXAMPLE **Reasonableness of a Solution**

The class had to solve a cubic equation to find an approximate radius of the hot air balloon. Here are some students' answers:

Ro: 5 ft   Sal: 15 ft   Tim: 25 ft   Una: 100 ft

Which answers are *unreasonable*?

Ro's answer is unreasonable because hot air balloons are much larger than the people who ride in them.

Una's answer is unreasonable because a balloon with a 100 ft radius would be two-thirds the size of a football field.

The context also helps you determine a reasonable domain and range for a function.

2 EXAMPLE **Reasonable Domain and Range Values**

The quadratic function $h(t) = -16t^2 + 96t + 112$ models the height in feet of a projectile at time t. Give a *reasonable* domain and range for the function h.

The function h is quadratic, so its mathematical domain is the set of real numbers. The graph opens downward, so the function reaches a maximum value at its vertex where

$t = -\frac{b}{2a} = -\frac{96}{2(-16)} = 3$, and $h(3) = -16(3)^2 + 96(3) + 112 = 256$.

The mathematical range of the function is $h(t) \le 256$.

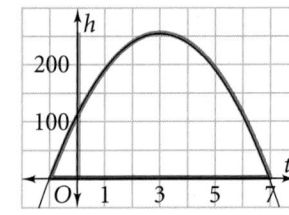

There is not enough information—namely a context—to give a specific domain and range. You can state a reasonable assumed context, however, to give a reasonable domain and range:

Assuming the projectile starts and ends on the ground ($h = 0$), a reasonable domain is $-1 \le t \le 7$ and a reasonable range is $0 \le h(t) \le 256$.

EXERCISES

1. Two other student answers for the radius of the hot air balloon in Example 1 were 8 ft and 50 ft. Is either of these answers unreasonable? Explain. **See margin.**

For Example 2, there are situations possible in which the projectile could have begun its flight at $t = 0$, $t = 3.5$, or even $t = -2$. Give a context for which each set of values below would be a reasonable domain. 2–6. Check student's work.

2. $0 \le t \le 7$ 3. $0 \le t \le 8$ 4. $0 \le t \le 6$ 5. $3.5 \le t \le 7$ 6. $-2 \le t \le 3$

7. Suppose an answer is reasonable in context. Does this provide a check that the answer is correct? **See margin.**

460   Vocabulary Builder   Reasonable Context

1. Answers may vary. Sample: 50 ft; the balloon with a 50-ft radius would have to be as tall as a ten story building.

7. Answers may vary. Sample: no; You might have made a computational error.

460

8-5 Exponential and Logarithmic Equations

What You'll Learn

- To solve exponential equations
- To solve logarithmic equations

. . . And Why

To model animal populations, as in Example 5

✓ Check Skills You'll Need

GO for Help Lessons 8-3 and 7-4

Evaluate each logarithm.

1. $\log_9 81 \cdot \log_9 3$ **1**
2. $\log 10 \cdot \log_3 9$ **2**
3. $\log_2 16 \div \log_2 8$ **$\frac{4}{3}$**
4. Simplify $125^{-\frac{2}{3}}$. **$\frac{1}{25}$**

🔊 New Vocabulary

- exponential equation
- logarithmic equation
- Change of Base Formula

Objectives
1 To solve exponential equations
2 To solve logarithmic equations

Examples
1 Solving an Exponential Equation
2 Solving an Exponential Equation by Graphing
3 Solving an Exponential Equation by Tables
4 Real-World Connection
5 Using the Change of Base Formula
6 Solving a Logarithmic Equation
7 Using Logarithmic Properties to Solve an Equation

---

1 Solving Exponential Equations

An equation of the form $b^{cx} = a$, where the exponent includes a variable, is an **exponential equation.** If m and n are positive and $m = n$, then $\log m = \log n$. You can therefore solve an exponential equation by taking the logarithm of each side of the equation.

1 EXAMPLE Solving an Exponential Equation

Solve $7^{3x} = 20$.

$$7^{3x} = 20$$

$\log 7^{3x} = \log 20$ **Take the common logarithm of each side.**

$3x \log 7 = \log 20$ **Use the power property of logarithms.**

$x = \dfrac{\log 20}{3 \log 7}$ **Divide each side by 3 log 7.** $20\log \div 7\log = \div 3 =$

≈ 0.5132 **Use a calculator.**

Check $7^{3x} = 20$

$7^{3(0.5132)} \approx 20.00382 \approx 20$ ✓

✓ Quick Check ① Solve each equation. Round to the nearest ten-thousandth. Check your answers.
a. $3^x = 4$ **1.2619**   b. $6^{2x} = 21$ **0.8496**   c. $3^{x+4} = 101$ **0.2009**

2 EXAMPLE Solving an Exponential Equation by Graphing

Solve $6^{2x} = 1500$.

Graph the equations $y_1 = 6^{2x}$ and $y_2 = 1500$. Find the point of intersection.

The solution is $x \approx 2.0408$.

> Intersection
> X=2.040793 ⎽⎽⎽ Y=1500 ⎽⎽⎽

✓ Quick Check ② Solve $11^{6x} = 786$ by graphing. **0.4634**

Math Background

The Change of Base Formula allows you to rewrite any logarithm in terms of a logarithm to any desired base.

More Math Background: p. 428D

Lesson Planning and Resources

See p. 428E for a list of the resources that support this lesson.

Bell Ringer Practice

✓ Check Skills You'll Need
For intervention, direct students to:

Logarithmic Functions as Inverses
Lesson 8-3: Example 3
Extra Skills and Word Problems Practice, Ch. 8

Rational Exponents
Lesson 7-4: Example 4
Extra Skills and Word Problems Practice, Ch. 7

Differentiated Instruction Solutions for All Learners

Special Needs L1
Clarify for students that the goal in solving an exponential equation is the same as for any equation, to isolate the variable on one side of the equal sign. However, because the variable is an exponent, students must take the logarithm of both sides.
learning style: verbal

Below Level L2
When solving an exponential equation by taking the logarithm of both sides, the Power Property of Logarithms is used to solve for the variable. Review the Power Property.
learning style: verbal

Guided Instruction

 EXAMPLE Math Tip

Point out that you can take the common logarithm (using base 10) of both sides of the equation no matter what base occurs in the equation. This means that you can use the feature of a calculator that finds the common logarithm.

② **EXAMPLE** Error Prevention

When you enter $y = 6^{2x}$, be sure to use parentheses to enter it as 6^(2x).

④ **EXAMPLE** Connection to Biology

Although the mathematical model may indicate a population in the single digits, the reality of living creatures will not fit the mathematical model exactly. There is a minimum population level below which an endangered species will probably not be able to survive.

 GO for Help

To review solving equations by tables, see Lesson 5-5.

③ **EXAMPLE** Solving an Exponential Equation by Tables

Solve the equation $2(1.5^x) = 6$ to the nearest hundredth.

Enter $y_1 = 2(1.5^x) - 6$. Use tabular zoom-in to find the sign change, as shown at the right.

X	Y1
2.7060	-.0085
2.7070	-.0061
2.7080	-.0037
2.7090	-.0012
2.7100	.0012
2.7110	.0036
2.7120	.0061
X=2.709	

● The solution is $x \approx 2.71$.

Quick Check ③ Solve $11^{6x} = 786$ using tables. Compare your result with your solution in Quick Check 2. **0.4634**

④ **EXAMPLE** Real-World Connection

Zoology Refer to the photo. Write an exponential equation to model the decline in the population. If the decay rate remains constant, in what year might only five peninsular bighorn sheep remain in the United States?

Real-World Connection

The U.S. population of peninsular bighorn sheep was 1170 in 1971. By 1999, only 335 remained.

Step 1 Enter the data into your calculator. Let 0 represent the initial year, 1971.

Step 2 Use the **ExpReg** feature to find the exponential function that fits the data.

ExpReg
y = a*b^x
a = 1170
b = .9563175045

Step 3 Graph the function and the line $y = 5$.

Step 4 Find the point of intersection.

Intersection
X=122.13778 Y=5

The solution is $x \approx 122$, and $1971 + 122 = 2093$, so there may be only five peninsular bighorn sheep in 2093.

Quick Check ④ The population of peninsular bighorn sheep in Mexico was approximately 6200 in 1971. By 1999, about 2300 remained. Determine the year by which only 200 peninsular bighorn sheep might remain in Mexico. **2068**

2 Solving Logarithmic Equations

To evaluate a logarithm with any base, you can use the **Change of Base Formula**.

 Key Concepts

Property	Change of Base Formula

For any positive numbers, M, b, and c, with $b \neq 1$ and $c \neq 1$,

$$\log_b M = \frac{\log_c M}{\log_c b}$$

Differentiated Instruction Solutions for All Learners

Advanced Learners L4
Have students research what form of radioactive dating is most useful for charcoal that is less than 50,000 years old.

learning style: verbal

English Language Learners ELL
In Exercise 51, have a student volunteer explain the meaning of *toxic*. Discuss the pronunciation of *protactinium*, with help from the chemistry teacher or a dictionary.

learning style: visual

5 EXAMPLE Using the Change of Base Formula

Use the Change of Base Formula to evaluate $\log_3 15$. Then convert $\log_3 15$ to a logarithm in base 2.

$$\log_3 15 = \frac{\log 15}{\log 3} \qquad \text{Use the Change of Base Formula.}$$

$$\approx 2.4650 \qquad \text{Use a calculator.}$$

$$\log_3 15 = \log_2 x \qquad \text{Write an equation.}$$

$$2.4650 \approx \log_2 x \qquad \text{Substitute } \log_3 15 \approx 2.4650.$$

$$x \approx 2^{2.4650} \qquad \text{Write in exponential form.}$$

$$\approx 5.5212 \qquad \text{Use a calculator.}$$

● The expression $\log_3 15$ is approximately equal to 2.4650, or $\log_2 5.5212$.

✓**Quick Check** **5 a.** Evaluate $\log_5 400$ and convert it to a logarithm in base 8. **3.7227, $\log_8 2301$**
b. Critical Thinking Consider the equation $2.465 \approx \log_2 x$ from Example 2. How could you solve the equation without using the Change of Base Formula?
Answers may vary. Sample: Use a calculator to raise 2 to the 2.465 power.

An equation that includes a logarithmic expression, such as $\log_3 15 = \log_2 x$ in Example 5, is called a **logarithmic equation**.

6 EXAMPLE Solving a Logarithmic Equation

Solve $\log (3x + 1) = 5$.

Method 1 $\log (3x + 1) = 5$

$$3x + 1 = 10^5 \qquad \text{Write in exponential form.}$$

$$3x + 1 = 100,000$$

$$x = 33,333 \qquad \text{Solve for } x.$$

Method 2 Graph the equations $y_1 = \log (3x + 1)$ and $y_2 = 5$. Use Xmin = 30000, Xmax = 40000, Ymin = 4.9, Ymax = 5.1.

Find the point of intersection.

The solution is $x = 33,333$.

Method 3 Enter $y_1 = \log (3x + 1) - 5$.
Use tabular zoom-in to find the sign change.
Use the information from Methods 1 or 2 to help you with your TblSet values.

The solution is $x = 33,333$.

X	Y1
33330	-4E-5
33331	-3E-5
33332	-1E-5
33333	0.0000
33334	1.3E-5
33335	2.6E-5
33336	3.9E-5

Y1=0

Check $\qquad \log (3x + 1) = 5$

$$\log (3 \cdot 33,333 + 1) \overset{?}{=} 5$$

$$\log 100,000 \overset{?}{=} 5$$

$$\log 10^5 = 5 \checkmark$$

✓**Quick Check** **6** Solve $\log (7 - 2x) = -1$. Check your answer. **3.45**

Lesson 8-5 Exponential and Logarithmic Equations **463**

Assignment Guide

1 A B 1-24, 48-54, 58, 60-63, 66, 76-81, 85, 87, 89-91, 93, 95, 96

2 A B 25-47, 55-57, 59, 64, 65, 67-75, 82-84, 86, 88, 92, 94

C Challenge   97-105

Test Prep   106-112
Mixed Review   113-127

Homework Quick Check
To check students' understanding of key skills and concepts, go over Exercises 14, 47, 49, 64, 77, 87.

Differentiated Instruction Resources

Sometimes the properties of logarithms will help solve an equation.

7 EXAMPLE Using Logarithmic Properties to Solve an Equation

Solve $2 \log x - \log 3 = 2$.

$2 \log x - \log 3 = 2$

$\log\left(\frac{x^2}{3}\right) = 2$ **Write as a single logarithm.**

$\frac{x^2}{3} = 10^2$ **Write in exponential form.**

$x^2 = 3(100)$ **Multiply each side by 3.**

$x = \pm 10\sqrt{3}$, or about ± 17.32

● Log x is defined only for $x > 0$, so the solution is $10\sqrt{3}$, or about 17.32.

Quick Check **7** Solve $\log 6 - \log 3x = -2$.

200

EXERCISES

For more exercises, see *Extra Skill and Word Problem Practice*.

Practice and Problem Solving

A Practice by Example

Solve each equation. Round to the nearest ten-thousandth. Check your answers.

Example 1
(page 461)

1. $2^x = 3$ **1.5850**   **2.** $4^x = 19$ **2.1240**   **3.** $5^x = 81.2$ **2.7320**   **4.** $3^x = 27.3$ **3.0101**

5. $8 + 10^x = 1008$ **3**   **6.** $5 - 3^x = -40$ **3.4650**   **7.** $9^{2y} = 66$ **0.9534**   **8.** $4^{2z} = 40$ **1.330**

9. $14^{x+1} = 36$ **0.3579**   **10.** $12^{y-2} = 20$ **3.2056**   **11.** $25^{2x+1} = 144$ **0.2720**   **12.** $2^{3x-4} = 5$ **2.1073**

Example 2
(page 461)

Solve by graphing. Round to the nearest ten-thousandth.

13. $4^{7x} = 250$ **0.5690**   **14.** $5^{3x} = 500$ **1.2871**   **15.** $6^x = 4565$ **4.7027**   **16.** $1.5^x = 356$ **14.4894**

Example 3
(page 462)

Use a table to solve each equation. Round to the nearest hundredth.

17. $2^{x+3} = 512$ **6**   **18.** $3^{x-1} = 72$ **4.89**   **19.** $6^{2x} = 10$ **0.64**

20. $3^{x-2} = 12x - 1$ **0.09, 5.86**   **21.** $4^{2x+1} = x^2$ **-0.73**   **22.** $2^{2x-1} = 3^x$ **2.41**

Example 4
(page 462)

23. An investment of $2000 earns 5.75% interest, which is compounded quarterly. After approximately how many years will the investment be worth $3000? **about 7.1 years**

24. The equation $y = 281(1.0124)^x$ models the U.S. population y, in millions of people, x years after the year 2000. Graph the function on your graphing calculator. Estimate when the U.S. population will reach 350 million. **about 2018**

Example 5
(page 463)

Use the Change of Base Formula to evaluate each expression. Then convert it to a logarithm in base 8. **25–32. See margin.**

25. $\log_2 9$ **26.** $\log_4 8$ **27.** $\log_3 54$ **28.** $\log_5 62$

29. $\log_3 33$ **30.** $\log_2 7$ **31.** $\log_5 510$ **32.** $\log_4 1.116$

Example 6
(page 463)

Solve each equation. Check your answers.

33. $\log 2x = -1$ **0.05**   **34.** $2 \log x = -1$ $\frac{\sqrt{10}}{10}$ or about 0.3162   **35.** $\log(3x + 1) = 2$ **33**

36. $\log x + 4 = 8$ **10,000**   **37.** $\log 6x - 3 = -4$ $\frac{1}{60}$, or ≈0.0167   **38.** $\log(x - 2) = 1$ **12**

39. $3 \log x = 1.5$ $\sqrt{10}$, or about 3.1623   **40.** $2 \log(x + 1) = 5$ $100\sqrt{10} - 1$, or ≈ 315.2   **41.** $\log(5 - 2x) = 0$ **2**

---

25. 3.1699; $\log_8 729$

26. 1.5; $\log_8 22.627$

27. 3.6309; $\log_8 1901.3$

28. 2.5643; $\log_8 206.93$

29. 3.1827; $\log_8 748.56$

30. 2.8074; $\log_8 343$

31. 3.8737; $\log_8 3149.6$

32. 0.0792; $\log_8 1.1790$

Example 7
(page 464)

Solve each equation.

42. $\log x - \log 3 = 8$ **3 × 10⁸**

44. $2 \log x + \log 4 = 2$ **5**

46. $3 \log x - \log 6 + \log 2.4 = 9$
1357.2

100,000√5, or about 223,606.8
43. $\log 2x + \log x = 11$

45. $\log 5 - \log 2x = 1$ $\frac{1}{4}$

47. $\log (7x + 1) = \log (x - 2) + 1$ **7**

 Apply Your Skills

48. Consider the equation $2^{\frac{x}{3}} = 80$.   **a–c. See margin.**
   a. Solve the equation by taking the logarithm in base 10 of each side.
   b. Solve the equation by taking the logarithm in base 2 of each side.
   c. Writing Compare your result in parts (a) and (b). What are the advantages of either method? Explain.

49. Seismology An earthquake of magnitude 7.9 occurred in 2001 in Gujarat, India. It was 11,600 times as strong as the greatest earthquake ever to hit Pennsylvania. Find the magnitude of the Pennsylvania earthquake. (*Hint*: Refer to the Richter Scale on page 446.)   **5.1**

Write an equation. Then solve the equation without graphing.

50. A parent raises a child's allowance by 20% each year. If the allowance is $8 now, when will it reach $20?   **20 = 8(1.2)ˣ, 5 years**

51. Protactinium-234*m*, a toxic radioactive metal with no known use, has a half-life of 1.17 minutes. How long does it take for a 10-mg sample to decay to 2 mg?   **See margin.**

52. Multiple Choice As a town gets smaller, the population of its high school decreases by 12% each year. The student body has 125 students now. In how many years will it have about 75 students?   **A**

   Ⓐ 4 years   Ⓑ 7 years   Ⓒ 10 years   Ⓓ 11 years

Mental Math Solve each equation.

53. $2^x = \frac{1}{2}$ **−1**   **54.** $3^x = 27$ **3**   **55.** $\log_9 3 = x$ $\frac{1}{2}$ **56.** $\log_4 64 = x$ **3**

57. $\log_8 2 = x$ $\frac{1}{3}$ **58.** $10^x = \frac{1}{100}$ **−2**   **59.** $\log_7 343 = x$ **3**   **60.** $25^x = \frac{1}{5}$ $-\frac{1}{2}$

 Population Use this "Most Populous States" table for Exercises 61–63.

Most Populous States

Rank in 2000	State	2000 Population	Average Annual Percentage Increase Since 1990
1	California	33,871,648	1.30%
2	Texas	20,851,820	2.08%
3	New York	18,976,457	0.54%
4	Florida	15,982,378	2.13%

Sᴏᴜʀᴄᴇ: U.S. Census Bureau. Go to **www.PHSchool.com** for a data update. Web Code: agg-9041

61. a. Determine the growth factors for Florida and New York. Then write an equation to model each state's population growth.   **a–b. See left.**
   b. Estimate when Florida's population might exceed New York's population.

62. a. Determine the growth factors for Texas and California. Then write an equation to model each state's population growth.
   b. Estimate when Texas's population might exceed California's population.   **2063**

63. Critical Thinking Is it likely that Florida's population will exceed that of Texas? Explain your reasoning.   **See margin.**

Real-World 🌐 **Connection**

Careers Seismologists use models to determine the source, nature, and size of seismic events.

61a. Let x equal the number of years after 2000. Florida growth factor = 1.0213, $y = 15{,}982{,}378 \cdot (1.0213)^x$; New York growth factor = 1.0054, $y = 18{,}976{,}457 \cdot (1.0054)^x$

b. 2011

62a. Texas growth factor = 1.0208, $y = 20{,}851{,}820 \cdot (1.0208)^x$; California growth factor = 1.013, $y = 33{,}871{,}648 \cdot (1.013)^x$

Exercise 52 Show students that they can simply multiply the initial population of 125 by the multiplier $1 - 0.12 = 0.88$, and determine the number of multiplications needed to get around 75. Alternatively, students can write an exponential equation that represents the situation and solve it.

Alternative Method

Exercise 53 Organize students in groups of 3. Have each student in the group try a different method: making a table to show successive values, graphing, or solving without graphing. Then have them discuss the relative merits of each method.

63. Since Florida's growth rate is larger than Texas's growth rate, in theory, given constant conditions, Florida would exceed Texas in about 543 years. However, since no state has unlimited capacity for growth, it is unrealistic to predict over a long period of time.

48a. 18.9658

   b. 18.9658

c. **Answers may vary. Sample:** You don't have to use the change of base formula with the base-10 method, but there are fewer steps with the base-2 method.

51. $2 = 10\left(\frac{1}{2}\right)^{\frac{x}{1.17}}$, about 2.7 min

Exercise 67 This exercise can make the Change of Base Formula seem less like an arbitrary rule, thereby making it easier to remember.

Auditory Learners

Exercise 97 Ask a volunteer to find a picture of piano strings (or actually take the class to see a piano if one is nearby) and discuss how the relative length of the strings relates to the pitch of each note on the keyboard. You could also use a guitar or a zither to demonstrate this.

65. Answers may vary.
Sample: $\log x = 1.6$
$10^{1.6} = x$, $x \approx 39.81$

66. Answers may vary.
Sample: A possible model is
$y = 1465(1.0838)^x$ where
$x = 0$ represents 1991;
the growth is probably exponential and
$1465(1.0838)^{10} \approx 3276$;
using this model, there will be 10,000 manatees in about 2015.

67a. $x = \dfrac{\log b}{\log a}$

b. $x = \log_a b = \dfrac{\log b}{\log a}$

c. Substituting the result from part (a) into the results from part (b), or vice versa, yields
$\log_a b = \dfrac{\log b}{\log a}$. This justifies the Change of Base Formula.

77a. top up: 10^{-5} W/m²,
top down: $10^{-2.5}$ W/m²

b. 99.68%

Real-World Connection

Many Florida manatees die after collisions with motorboats.

75. $\dfrac{\log (x + 1)}{\log x}$

GO Online

Homework Video Tutor

Visit: PHSchool.com
Web Code: age-0805

64. Error Analysis What is wrong with the "proof" below that $2 = 1$?

$$2 = \tfrac{2}{1} = \frac{\log 10^2}{\log 10^1} = \log 10^{2-1} = \log 10^1 = 1 \qquad \frac{\log 10^2}{\log 10^1} \neq \log 10^{2-1}$$

65. Open-Ended Write and solve a logarithmic equation. **See margin.**

66. Zoology Conservation efforts have increased the endangered Florida manatee population from 1465 in 1991 to 3276 in 2001. If this growth rate continues, when might there be 10,000 manatees? Explain the reasoning behind your choice of a model. **See margin.**

67. Consider the equation $a^x = b$.
a. Solve the equation by using log base 10. **a–c. See margin.**
b. Solve the equation by using log base a.
c. Use your results in parts (a) and (b) to justify the Change of Base Formula.

Write each logarithm as the quotient of two common logarithms. Do not simplify the quotient.

68. $\log_7 2$ $\dfrac{\log 2}{\log 7}$ **69.** $\log_3 8$ $\dfrac{\log 8}{\log 3}$ **70.** $\log_5 140$ $\dfrac{\log 140}{\log 5}$ **71.** $\log_9 3.3$ $\dfrac{\log 3.3}{\log 9}$

72. $\log_4 3x$ $\dfrac{\log 3x}{\log 4}$ **73.** $\log_6 (1 - x)$ $\dfrac{\log (1 - x)}{\log 6}$ **74.** $\log_x 5$ $\dfrac{\log 5}{\log x}$ **75.** $\log_x (x + 1)$
See left.

Acoustics In Exercises 76–78, the loudness measured in decibels (dB) is defined by loudness $= 10 \log \dfrac{I}{I_0}$, where I is the intensity and $I_0 = 10^{-12}$ W/m².

76. The human threshold for pain is 120 dB. Instant perforation of the eardrum occurs at 160 dB.
a. Find the intensity of each sound. 10^0 (or 1) W/m², 10^4 W/m²
b. How many times as intense is the noise that will perforate an eardrum as the noise that causes pain? **10,000 times as intense**

77. The noise level inside a convertible driving along the freeway with its top up is 70 dB. With the top down, the noise level is 95 dB. **a–b. See margin.**
a. Find the intensity of the sound with the top up and with the top down.
b. By what percent does leaving the top up reduce the intensity of the sound?

78. A screaming child can reach 90 dB. A launch of the space shuttle produces sound of 180 dB at the launch pad.
a. Find the intensity of each sound. 10^{-3} W/m², 10^6 W/m²
b. How many times as intense as the noise from a screaming child is the noise from a shuttle launch? 10^9 **times more intense**

Solve each equation. If necessary, round to the nearest ten-thousandth.

79. $8^x = 444$ 2.9315   **80.** $14^{9x} = 146$ 0.2098

81. $3^{7x} = 120$ 0.6225   **82.** $\tfrac{1}{2} \log x + \log 4 = 2$ 625

83. $4 \log_3 2 - 2 \log_3 x = 1$ 2.3094   **84.** $\log x^2 = 2$ 10

85. $9^{2x} = 42$ 0.8505   **86.** $\log_8 (2x - 1) = \tfrac{1}{3}$ 1.5

87. $1.3^x = 7$ 7.4168   **88.** $\log (5x - 4) = 3$ 200.8

89. $2.1^x = 9$ 2.9615   **90.** $12^{4-x} = 20$ 2.7944

91. $5^{3x} = 125$ 1   **92.** $\log 4 + 2 \log x = 6$ 500

93. $4^{3x} = 77.2$ 1.0451   **94.** $\log_7 3x = 3$ 114.$\overline{3}$

95. $3^x + 0.7 = 4.9$ 1.3063   **96.** $7^x - 1 = 371$ 3.0417

Bassoon
Guitar
Harp
Violin
Viola
Cello
Bass

−10 −5 0 5 10

4. Assess & Reteach

PowerPoint
Lesson Quiz

Use mental math to solve each equation.

1. $2^x = \frac{1}{8}$ −3
2. $\log_4 2 = x$ $\frac{1}{2}$
3. $10^{6x} = 1$ 0
4. Solve $5^{2x} = 125$. $\frac{3}{2}$

C Challenge

97a. bassoon, guitar, harp, violin, viola, cello

b. bassoon, guitar, harp, cello, bass

c. harp, violin

d. harp, violin

97. Music The pitch, or frequency, of a piano note is related to its position on the keyboard by the function $F(n) = 440 \cdot 2^{\frac{n}{12}}$, where F is the frequency of the sound wave in cycles per second and n is the number of piano keys above or below Concert A, as shown above. If $n = 0$ at Concert A, which of the instruments shown in the diagram can sound notes of the given frequency?

    a. 590   **b.** 120   **c.** 1440   **d.** 2093

98. Astronomy The brightness of an astronomical object is called its magnitude. A decrease of five magnitudes increases the brightness exactly 100 times. The sun is magnitude −26.7, and the full moon is magnitude −12.5. The sun is about how many times brighter than the moon? **478,630 times**

99. Archaeology A scientist carbon-dates a piece of fossilized tree trunk that is thought to be over 5000 years old. The scientist determines that the sample contains 65% of the original amount of carbon-14. The half-life of carbon-14 is 5730 years. Is the reputed age of the tree correct? Explain. **No; solving**
$0.65 = (0.5)^{\frac{x}{5730}}$ **for x, the age in years of the sample,**

Solve each equation. **yields an age of about 3561 yr.**

100. $\log_7 (2x - 3)^2 = 2$ **−2, 5**   **101.** $\log_2 (x^2 + 2x) = 3$ **−4, 2**

102. $\log_4 (x^2 - 17) = 3$ **−9, 9**   **103.** $\frac{3}{2} \log_2 4 - \frac{1}{2} \log_2 x = 3$ **1**

104. 20,031 m above sea level

104. In the formula $P = P_0(\frac{1}{2})^{\frac{h}{4795}}$, P is the atmospheric pressure in millimeters of mercury at elevation h meters above sea level. P_0 is the atmospheric pressure at sea level. If P_0 equals 760 mm, at what elevation is the pressure 42 mm?

105b. 0.928 mg or 1.061 mg

c. Estimate in hours is more accurate; the days have a larger rounding error.

105. Chemistry A technician found 12 mg of a radon isotope in a soil sample. After 24 hours, another measurement revealed 10 mg of the isotope.
  a. Estimate the length of the isotope's half-life to the nearest hour and to the nearest day. **91 hours or 4 days**
  b. For each estimate, determine the amount of the isotope after two weeks.
  c. Compare your answers to part (b). Which is more accurate? Explain.

Test Prep

Gridded Response

Use a calculator to solve each equation. Enter each answer to the nearest hundredth.

                                                               2.19
106. $7^{2x} = 75$ **1.11**   **107.** $11^{x-5} = 250$ **7.30**   **108.** $1080 = 15^{3x-4}$

Alternative Assessment

Have a class discussion. Ask students to talk about which aspect of solving exponential and logarithmic equations they found most confusing or difficult, citing specific examples from the lesson. Have other students give tips and explanations to help clarify the topics. Be sure each student contributes to the discussion.

Test Prep

A sheet of blank grids is available in the Test-Taking Strategies with Transparencies booklet. Give this sheet to students for practice with filling in the grids.

Resources
For additional practice with a variety of test item formats:
• Standardized Test Prep, p. 483
• Test-Taking Strategies, p. 478
• Test-Taking Strategies with Transparencies

Use this Checkpoint Quiz to check students' understanding of the skills and concepts of Lessons 8-3 through 8-5.

Resources
Grab & Go
• Checkpoint Quiz 2

113. $\log 2 + 3 \log x - 2 \log y$

114. $\log_3 x - \log_3 y$

115. $3 \log_2 3 + 3 \log_2 x$

116. $\log_3 7 + 2 \log_3 (2x - 3)$

117. $\log_4 5 + \frac{1}{2} \log_4 x$

118. $\log_2 5 + \log_2 a - 2 \log_2 b$

Checkpoint Quiz

1.

2.

4. $2 \log_6 3 + 2 \log_6 x + 2 \log_6 y$

5. $\log_6 4 + \frac{1}{2} \log_6 x$

10. Rewrite $\log_2 10$ as $\frac{\log 10}{\log 2}$ and evaluate it to get ≈ 3.322. Then set $3.322 = \log_3 x$. Rewrite to get $3.322 = \frac{\log x}{\log 3}$ and solve. Convert $\log x = 1.585$ to $10^{1.585} = x$ or $x \approx 38.46$. So $\log_2 10 \approx \log_3 38.46$.

468

Gridded Response Use the Change of Base Formula to solve each equation. Enter the answer to the nearest tenth.

109. $\log_5 x = \log_3 20$ **80.5**

110. $\log_9 x = \log_6 15$ **27.7**

Solve each equation.

111. $\log (1 + 3x) = 3$ **333**

112. $\log (x - 3) = 2$ **103**

Mixed Review

Lesson 8-4 **Expand each logarithm.** 113–118. See margin.

113. $\log 2x^3 y^{-2}$

114. $\log_3 \frac{x}{y}$

115. $\log_2 (3x)^3$

116. $\log_3 7(2x - 3)^2$

117. $\log_4 5\sqrt{x}$

118. $\log_2 \left(\frac{5a}{b^2}\right)$

Lesson 7-6 **Let $f(x) = 3x$ and $g(x) = x^2 - 1$. Perform each function operation.**

119. $(f + g)(x)$
$x^2 + 3x - 1$

120. $(g - f)(x)$
$x^2 - 3x - 1$

121. $(f \cdot g)(x)$
$3x^3 - 3x$

Lesson 6-6 **Find all the zeros of each function.**

122. $y = x^3 - x^2 + x - 11, \pm i$

123. $f(x) = x^4 - 16 \; \pm 2, \pm 2i$

124. $f(x) = x^4 - 5x^2 + 6 \pm \sqrt{2}, \pm \sqrt{3}$

125. $y = 3x^3 - 21x - 18 \; -2, -1, 3$

Lesson 1-3 **Write an equation to solve each problem.**

126. A customer at a hardware store mentions that he is buying fencing for a vegetable garden that is 12 ft longer than it is wide. He buys 128 ft of fencing. What is the width of the garden? $2(x) + 2(x + 12) = 128;$ **26 ft**

127. A bowler has an average of 133. In a set of games one night, her scores are 135, 127, 119, 142, and 156. What score must she bowl in the sixth game to maintain her average? $\frac{679 + x}{6} = 133;$ **119**

Checkpoint Quiz 2

Lessons 8-3 through 8-5

Graph each logarithmic function. 1–2. See margin.

1. $y = \log_6 x$

2. $y = \log (x - 2)$

Expand each logarithm. 4–5. See margin.

3. $\log \frac{s^3}{r^5}$ $3 \log s - 5 \log r$

4. $\log_6 (3xy)^2$

5. $\log_6 4\sqrt{x}$

Solve each equation.

6. $7 - 2^x = -1$ **3**

7. $\log 5x = 2$ **20**

8. $3 \log x = 9$ **1000**

9. $\log 2 \approx 0.3010,$
$\log_3 2 \approx 0.6309,$
$\log_2 3 \approx 1.5850,$
$2^3 = 8,$
$3^2 = 9$

9. Evaluate the expressions below and order them from least to greatest.
$2^3 \qquad \log_2 3 \qquad \log_3 2 \qquad 3^2 \qquad \log 2$

10. **Writing** Explain how to use the Change of Base Formula to rewrite $\log_2 10$ as a logarithmic expression with base 3. **See margin.**

Activity Lab

Linear and Exponential Models

FOR USE WITH LESSON 8-5

You can transform an exponential function into a linear function by taking the logarithm of each side. Since linear models are easy to recognize, you can then determine whether an exponential function is a good model for a set of values.

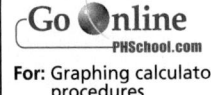

For: Graphing calculator procedures
Web Code: age-2117

$y = ab^x$ **Write the general form of an exponential function.**

$\log y = \log ab^x$ **Take the logarithm of each side.**

$\log y = \log a + x(\log b)$ **Product Property and Power Property**

$\log y = (\log b)x + \log a$ **Rewrite.**

If $\log b$ and $\log a$ are constants, then $\log y = (\log b)x + \log a$ is a linear equation in slope-intercept form. To confirm that $\log b$ is a constant, check that the graph of $\log y = (\log b)x + \log a$ is a line.

ACTIVITY

Determine whether an exponential function is a good model for the values in the table.

x	0	2	4	6	8	10
y	3.0	5.1	8.6	14.5	24.5	41.4

Step 1 Enter the values into STAT lists L_1 and L_2. To enter the values of $\log y$, place the cursor in the heading of L_3 and press LOG L_2 ENTER.

Step 2 To graph $\log y$, access the STAT PLOT feature and press 1. Then enter L_3 next to Ylist:. Then press ZOOM 9.

L1	L2	L3	1
0	3	0.47712	
2	5.1	0.70757	
4	8.6	0.9345	
6	14.5	1.1614	
8	24.5	1.3892	
10	41.4	1.617	

L1(1) = 0

Since the graph of $\log y = (\log b)x + \log a$ is linear, the slope $\log b$ is constant, and b also is constant. An exponential function therefore is a suitable model.

Step 3 Press STAT ▶ 0 ENTER to find the exponential function: $y = 3(1.3)^x$.

EXERCISES

For each set of values, determine whether an exponential function is a good model. If so, find the function.

1.

x	1	3	5	7	9
y	6	22	54	102	145

not a good model

2.

x	−1	0	1	2	3
y	40.2	19.8	9.9	5.1	2.5

$y = 20.0(0.50)^x$

3. Writing Explain how you could determine whether a logarithmic function is a good model for a set of values. **Answers may vary. Sample: Use Change of Base Formula to get $\log x = \frac{\log b}{a} y$. Let $L_1 = x$, $L_2 = y$, and $L_3 = \log x$. Graph L_2 and L_3. If it is linear, then the equation is logarithmic.**

Activity Lab   Linear and Exponential Models   **469**

Activity Lab

Linear Models of Exponential Behavior

Students use a graphing calculator to transform an exponential function into a linear function. The linear form makes it easier to recognize whether the function is a good model for a given set of data points.

Guided Instruction

Error Prevention!

Students may get frustrated when they get an error message and can't find what they are doing incorrectly. Suggest that students work with a partner and compare their work at each step.

Remind students to clear all lists before they begin each exercise.

Resources

Students may use any graphing calculator tomake tales and graphs.

Objectives
1 To evaluate natural logarithmic expressions
2 To solve equations using natural logarithms

Examples
1 Simplifying Natural Logarithms
2 Real-World Connection
3 Solving a Natural Logarithmic Equation
4 Solving an Exponential Equation
5 Real-World Connection

Math Background

Natural logarithms, or logarithms with base e, occur in many problems involving the growth and decay of natural organisms. In fact, natural logarithms arise in those problems which model continuous growth and decay as discussed in Lesson 8-2.

More Math Background: p. 428D

Lesson Planning and Resources

See p. 428E for a list of the resources that support this lesson.

Bell Ringer Practice

✓ **Check Skills You'll Need**
For intervention, direct students to:

Properties of Exponential Functions
Lesson 8-2: Example 4
Extra Skills and Word Problems Practice, Ch. 8

Exponential and Logarithmic Equations
Lesson 8-5: Example 6
Extra Skills and Word Problems Practice, Ch. 8

What You'll Learn
• To evaluate natural logarithmic expressions
• To solve equations using natural logarithms

. . . And Why
To model the velocity of a rocket, as in Example 2

✓ **Check Skills You'll Need**

Use your calculator to evaluate each expression to the nearest thousandth.

1. e^5 148.413   2. $2e^3$ 40.171   3. e^{-2} 0.135   4. $\frac{1}{e}$ 0.368   5. $4.2e$ 11.417

Solve.

6. $\log_3 x = 4$ 81   7. $\log_{16} 4 = x$ $\frac{1}{2}$ 8. $\log_{16} x = 4$ 65,536

🔊 **New Vocabulary** • natural logarithmic function

---

1 Natural Logarithms

In Lesson 8-2, you learned that the number $e \approx 2.71828$ can be used as a base for exponents. The function $y = e^x$ has an inverse, the **natural logarithmic function.**

🔑 **Key Concepts**

| **Definition** | **Natural Logarithmic Function** |

If $y = e^x$, then $\log_e y = x$, which is commonly written as $\ln y = x$.

The natural logarithmic function is the inverse, written as $y = \ln x$.

① $y = e^x$
② $y = \ln x$

Vocabulary Tip

$\ln y$ means "the natural logarithm of y." The l stands for "logarithm" and the n stands for "natural."

The properties of common logarithms apply to natural logarithms also.

 1 EXAMPLE Simplifying Natural Logarithms

Write $3 \ln 6 - \ln 8$ as a single natural logarithm.

$3 \ln 6 - \ln 8 = \ln 6^3 - \ln 8$ **Power Property**

$= \ln \frac{6^3}{8}$ **Quotient Property**

$= \ln 27$ **Simplify.**

✓ **Quick Check** 1 Write each expression as a single natural logarithm.

a. $5 \ln 2 - \ln 4$ ln 8   b. $3 \ln x + \ln y$ ln $x^3 y$ c. $\frac{1}{4} \ln 3 + \frac{1}{4} \ln x$ ln $\sqrt[4]{3x}$

Differentiated Instruction Solutions for All Learners

Special Needs L1
In Example 4, students may fail to take the natural logarithm of both sides. Stress that if any logarithm is taken on one side of the equation, the same logarithm must be applied to the other side. Ask: *Why was the natural logarithm used?* **base is e**

learning style: verbal

Below Level L2
Review the general formula for growth or decay, $N = N_0 e^{kt}$ and the formula for continuously compounded interest, $A = Pe^{rt}$. Compare the meanings of corresponding variables.

learning style: verbal

Natural logarithms are useful because they help express many relationships in the physical world.

2 EXAMPLE Real-World Connection

Space A spacecraft can attain a stable orbit 300 km above Earth if it reaches a velocity of 7.7 km/s. The formula for a rocket's maximum velocity v in kilometers per second is $v = -0.0098t + c \ln R$. The booster rocket fires for t seconds and the velocity of the exhaust is c km/s. The ratio of the mass of the rocket filled with fuel to its mass without fuel is R. Suppose a rocket used to propel a spacecraft has a mass ratio of 25, an exhaust velocity of 2.8 km/s, and a firing time of 100 s. Can the spacecraft attain a stable orbit 300 km above Earth?

Let $R = 25, c = 2.8$, and $t = 100$. Find v.

$v = -0.0098t + c \ln R$	**Use the formula.**
$= -0.0098(100) + 2.8 \ln 25$	**Substitute.**
$\approx -0.98 + 2.8(3.219)$	**Use a calculator.**
≈ 8.0	**Simplify.**

The maximum velocity of 8.0 km/s is greater than the 7.7 km/s needed for a stable orbit. Therefore, the spacecraft can attain a stable orbit 300 km above Earth.

Real-World Connection

The space shuttle is launched into orbit.

✓ **Quick Check** ❷ **a.** A booster rocket for a spacecraft has a mass ratio of about 15, an exhaust velocity of 2.1 km/s, and a firing time of 30 s. Find the maximum velocity of the spacecraft. Can the spacecraft achieve a stable orbit 300 km above Earth? **≈5.4 km/s; no**

b. Critical Thinking Suppose a rocket, as designed, cannot provide enough velocity to achieve a stable orbit. Look at the variables in the velocity formula. What alterations could be made to the rocket so that a stable orbit could be achieved? **One could increase its mass ratio or its exhaust velocity.**

2 Natural Logarithmic and Exponential Equations

You can use the properties of logarithms to solve natural logarithmic equations.

3 EXAMPLE Solving a Natural Logarithmic Equation

Solve $\ln (3x + 5)^2 = 4$.

$\ln (3x + 5)^2 = 4$	
$(3x + 5)^2 = e^4$	**Rewrite in exponential form.**
$(3x + 5)^2 \approx 54.60$	**Use a calculator.**
$3x + 5 \approx \pm \sqrt{54.60}$	**Take the square root of each side.**
$3x + 5 \approx 7.39$ or -7.39	**Use a calculator.**
$x \approx 0.797$ or -4.130	**Solve for x.**

Check $\ln (3 \cdot 0.797 + 5)^2 \overset{?}{=} 4$ $\qquad$ $\ln (3 \cdot (-4.130) + 5)^2 \overset{?}{=} 4$
$\qquad\qquad\quad \ln 54.6 \overset{?}{=} 4$ $\qquad\qquad\qquad\qquad \ln 54.6 \overset{?}{=} 4$
$\qquad\qquad\quad 4.000 \approx 4 ✓$ $\qquad\qquad\qquad\qquad 4.000 \approx 4 ✓$

✓ **Quick Check** ❸ Solve each equation. Check your answers.
a. $\ln x = 0.1$ **1.105** $\qquad$ **b.** $\ln (3x - 9) = 21$ **439,605,247.8** $\qquad$ **c.** $\ln \left(\frac{x + 2}{3}\right) = 12$ **488,262.4**

Lesson 8-6 Natural Logarithms **471**

2. Teach

Guided Instruction

2 EXAMPLE **Teaching Tip**

Point out that the speed is in kilometers per second. To put this in more familiar units so students can get a sense of how fast the rocket is moving, suggest that they convert this speed to km/h or mi/h.

PowerPoint
Additional Examples

❶ Write $2 \ln 12 - \ln 9$ as a single natural logarithm. **ln 16**

❷ Find the velocity of a spacecraft whose booster rocket has a mass ratio of 22, an exhaust velocity of 2.3 km/s, and a firing time of 50 s. Can the spacecraft achieve a stable orbit 300 km above Earth? **about 6.6 km/s; no**

Guided Instruction

3 EXAMPLE **Error Prevention**

Remind students that the parentheses in $\ln (3x + 5)$ are necessary in order to show that you are taking the natural logarithm of the entire binomial.

Advanced Learners **L4**
Ask students to solve $3 \cdot 7^{2x} + 3 = 14$ by taking logs to the base 7 and using the change of base formula.

English Language Learners **ELL**
Help students make the connection between natural logarithms and the math term **ln**. Discuss the pronunciation of ln as the letters sound, or "ell n." Write $\ln x = \log_e x$ on the board and have students read it to emphasize the meaning of natural logarithms. **learning style: verbal**

learning style: verbal

③ Solve ln $(2x - 4)^3 = 6$.
about 5.695

④ Use natural logarithms to
solve $4e^{3x} + 1.2 = 14$. about 0.388

⑤ An initial investment of $200
is now valued at $254.25. The
interest rate is 6%, compounded
continuously. How long has the
money been invested?
about 4 years

④ **EXAMPLE** Technology Tip

Have students check to see if their
calculator has separate keys for
LOG and LN.

Resources
• Daily Notetaking Guide 8-6 **L3**

Closure

Ask students to compare and
contrast natural and common
logarithms. **Answers may
vary. Sample:** They are both
exponents; they both obey the
same properties of exponents
and logarithms; they use a
different base. The base for
common logarithms is the
rational number 10; for natural
logarithms, it is the irrational
number e.

You can use natural logarithms to solve exponential equations.

④ **EXAMPLE** Solving an Exponential Equation

Use natural logarithms to solve $7e^{2x} + 2.5 = 20$.

$7e^{2x} + 2.5 = 20$	
$7e^{2x} = 17.5$	Subtract 2.5 from each side.
$e^{2x} = 2.5$	Divide each side by 7.
$\ln e^{2x} = \ln 2.5$	Take the natural logarithm of each side.
$2x = \ln 2.5$	Simplify.
$x = \frac{\ln 2.5}{2}$	Solve for x.
$x \approx 0.458$	Use a calculator.

 Quick Check ④ Use natural logarithms to solve each equation.

a. $e^{x+1} = 30$ **2.401**　　　　　　b. $e^{\frac{2x}{5}} + 7.2 = 9.1$ **1.605**

⑤ **EXAMPLE** Real-World Connection

Multiple Choice An investment of $100 is now valued at $149.18. The interest rate
is 8%, compounded continuously. About how long has the money been invested?
　Ⓐ 2 years　　　　　Ⓑ 5 years　　　　　Ⓒ 7 years　　　　　Ⓓ 19 years

$A = Pe^{rt}$	Continuously compounded interest formula
$149.18 = 100e^{0.08t}$	Substitute 149.18 for A, 100 for P, and 0.08 for r.
$1.4918 = e^{0.08t}$	Divide each side by 100.
$\ln 1.4918 = \ln e^{0.08t}$	Take the natural logarithm of each side.
$\ln 1.4918 = 0.08t$	Simplify.
$\frac{\ln 1.4918}{0.08} = t$	Solve for t.
$5 \approx t$	Use a calculator.

The money has been invested for about five years. The answer is B.

 Quick Check ⑤ An initial investment of $200 is worth $315.24 after seven years of continuous
compounding. Find the interest rate. **6.5%**

Test-Taking Tip

If you perform an
operation on one side
of an equation,
remember to perform
the same operation on
the other side.

EXERCISES
For more exercises, see *Extra Skill and Word Problem Practice*.

Practice and Problem Solving

Ⓐ **Practice by Example**

Example 1
(page 470)

GO for Help

Example 2
(page 471)

Write each expression as a single natural logarithm.

1. $3 \ln 5$ **ln 125**　　　　**2.** $\ln 9 + \ln 2$ **ln 18**　　　　**3.** $\ln 24 - \ln 6$ **ln 4**

4. $4 \ln 8 + \ln 10$ **ln 40,960**　**5.** $\ln 3 - 5 \ln 3$ **ln $\frac{1}{81}$**　**6.** $2 \ln 8 - 3 \ln 4$ **ln 1**

7. $5 \ln m - 3 \ln n$ **ln $\frac{m^5}{n^3}$**　**8.** $\frac{1}{3}(\ln x + \ln y) - 4 \ln z$ **ln $\frac{\sqrt[3]{xy}}{z^4}$**　**9.** $\ln a - 2 \ln b + \frac{1}{2} \ln c$ **ln $\frac{a\sqrt{c}}{b^2}$**

Find the value of y for the given value of x.

10. $y = 15 + 3 \ln x$, for $x = 7.2$ **20.92**　　**11.** $y = 0.05 - 10 \ln x$, for $x = 0.09$ **24.13**

For Exercises 12 and 13, use $v = -0.0098t + c \ln R$.

12. **Space** Find the velocity of a spacecraft whose booster rocket has a mass ratio of 20, an exhaust velocity of 2.7 km/s, and a firing time of 30 s. Can the spacecraft achieve a stable orbit 300 km above Earth? **7.79 km/s; yes**

13. A rocket has a mass ratio of 24 and an exhaust velocity of 2.5 km/s. Determine the minimum firing time for a stable orbit 300 km above Earth. **25 s**

Example 3 (page 471)

Solve each equation. Check your answers.

14. $\ln 3x = 6$ **134.476**

15. $\ln x = -2$ **0.135**

16. $\ln (4x - 1) = 36$ **1.078 × 10¹⁵**

17. **1488.979**

17. $\ln (2m + 3) = 8$

18. $\ln (t - 1)^2 = 3$ **5.482, −3.482**

19. $1.1 + \ln x^2 = 6$ **±11.588**

20. $\ln \frac{x - 1}{2} = 4$ **110.196**

21. $\ln 4r^2 = 3$ **±2.241**

22. $2 \ln 2x^2 = 1$ **±0.908**

Example 4 (page 472)

Use natural logarithms to solve each equation.

23. $e^x = 18$ **2.890**

24. $e^{2x} = 10$ **1.151**

25. $e^{x + 1} = 30$ **2.401**

26. $e^{\frac{x}{5}} + 4 = 7$ **5.493**

27. $e^{2x} = 12$ **1.242**

28. $e^{\frac{x}{9}} - 8 = 6$ **23.752**

Example 5 (page 472)

29. **Investing** An initial deposit of $200 is now worth $331.07. The account earns 8.4% interest, compounded continuously. Determine how long the money has been in the account. **6 years**

30. An investor sold 100 shares of stock valued at $34.50 per share. The stock was purchased at $7.25 per share two years ago. Find the rate of continuously compounded interest that would be necessary in a banking account for the investor to make the same profit. **78%**

 Apply Your Skills

Mental Math **Simplify each expression.**

31. $\ln e$ **1**

32. $\ln e^2$ **2**

33. $\ln e^{10}$ **10**

34. $10 \ln e$ **10**

35. $\ln 1$ **0**

36. $\frac{\ln e}{4}$ **¼**

37. $\frac{\ln e^2}{2}$ **1**

38. $\ln e^{83}$ **83**

 for Help

For Gridded Responses, see Test-Taking Strategies, page 46.

39. **Gridded Response** The battery power available to run a satellite is given by the formula $P = 50 e^{-\frac{t}{250}}$, where P is power in watts and t is time in days. For how many days can the satellite run if it requires 15 watts? **301**

40. **Space** Use the formula for maximum velocity $v = -0.0098t + c \ln R$. Find the mass ratio of a rocket with an exhaust velocity of 3.1 km/s, a firing time of 50 s, and a maximum shuttle velocity of 6.9 km/s. **10.8**

Determine whether each statement is *always* true, *sometimes* true, or *never* true.

41. $\ln e^x > 1$ **sometimes**

42. $\ln e^x = \ln e^x + 1$ **never**

43. $\ln t = \log_e t$ **always**

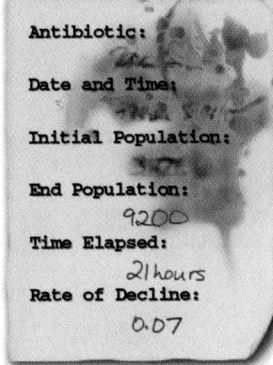

Antibiotic:

Date and Time:

Initial Population:

End Population: 9200

Time Elapsed: 21 hours

Rate of Decline: 0.07

Biology For Exercises 44–46, use the formula $H = \left(\frac{1}{r}\right)(\ln P - \ln A)$. H is the number of hours, r is the rate of decline, P is the initial bacteria population, and A is the reduced bacteria population.

44. A scientist determines that an antibiotic reduces a population of 20,000 bacteria to 5000 in 24 hours. Find the rate of decline caused by the antibiotic. **about 5.8% per hour**

45. A laboratory assistant tests an antibiotic that causes a rate of decline of 0.14. How long should it take for a population of 8000 bacteria to shrink to 500? **about 19.8 h**

46. A scientist spilled coffee on the lab report shown at the left. Determine the initial population of the bacteria. **about 40,000 bacteria**

Online lesson quiz, PHSchool.com, Web Code: aga-0806

Lesson 8-6 Natural Logarithms **473**

3. Practice

Assignment Guide

1 A B 1-13, 31-38

2 A B 14-30, 39-62

C Challenge 63-66

Test Prep 67-70
Mixed Review 71-80

Homework Quick Check
To check students' understanding of key skills and concepts, go over Exercises 8, 18, 30, 39, 44, 56.

Alternative Method
Exercises 31–38 Suggest that students ask themselves the question in a different form. For example, for Exercise 32 ask: *What power of the base e gives me the number e^2?*

4. Assess & Reteach

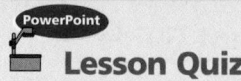

Lesson Quiz

1. Write $4 \ln 6 - 2 \ln 3$ as a single natural logarithm.
   ln 144

2. Solve $e^{3x} = 15$. about 0.903

3. Simplify $\ln e^7$. 7

Alternative Assessment

Ask students to discuss with a partner the differences in the procedures and answers for solving these two equations:
$\ln x - \ln (x - 1) = 2$ and
$\log x - \log (x - 1) = 2$.
Then have each pair write a paragraph that summarizes their discussion. The procedures are the same. If b is the base for the logarithm, then the answer for both equations is $b^2 \div (b^2 - 1)$. However, for the first equation, $b = e$ and for the second equation, $b = 10$. The answers are about 1.157 and about 1.010.

63. No; using the Change of Base Formula would result in one of the log expressions being written as a quotient of logs, which couldn't then be combined with the other expression to form a single logarithm.

64d. $t = \dfrac{\ln\left(\dfrac{y}{300}\right)}{0.241}$, where y is the number of Internet users in millions and t is time in years.

e. Substitute the number of users found in (b) and (c) into the equation in (d). Determine whether your answers in years are the same as t for each.

474

🌐 **Savings** Suppose you invest $500 at 5% interest compounded continuously. Copy and complete the table to find how long it will take to reach each amount.

	Amount (A)	Time (years)		
47.	$600	■	47.	3.6
48.	$700	■	48.	6.7
49.	$800	■	49.	9.4
50.	$900	■	50.	11.8
51.	$1000	■	51.	13.9
52.	$1100	■	52.	15.8
53.	$1200	■	53.	17.5
54.	$1300	■	54.	19.1

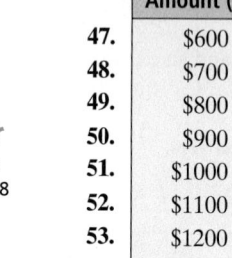

GO Online
Homework Video Tutor
Visit: PHSchool.com
Web Code: age-0808

Solve each equation.

58. 81.286

59. 1.2639

60. no solution

542.31
55. $\ln x - 3 \ln 3 = 3$

56. $\ln (2x - 1) = 0$ 1

57. $4e^{x+2} = 32$ 0.0794

58. $\ln (5x - 3)^{\frac{1}{3}} = 2$

59. $2e^{3x-2} + 4 = 16$

60. $2e^{x-2} = e^x + 7$

61. $\frac{1}{3} \ln x + \ln 2 - \ln 3 = 3$ 27,347.9

62. $\ln (x + 2) - \ln 4 = 3$ 78.342

Ⓒ **Challenge**

63. **Critical Thinking** Can $\ln 5 + \log_2 10$ be written as a single logarithm? Explain.
    See margin.

64. In 2000, there were about 300 million Internet users. That number is projected to grow to 1 billion in 2005. $y = 300e^{0.241t}$
    a. Let t represent the time, in years, since 2000. Write a function of the form $y = ae^{ct}$ that models the expected growth in the population of Internet users.
    b. In what year might there be 500 million Internet users? **2002**
    c. In what year might there be 1.5 billion Internet users? **2006**
    d. Solve your equation for t. **d–e. See margin.**
    e. **Writing** Explain how you can use your equation from part (d) to verify your answers to parts (b) and (c).

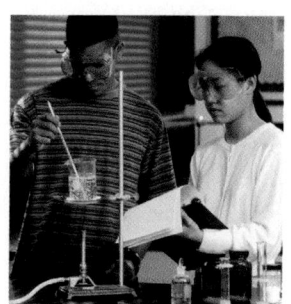

🌐 65. **Physics** The function $T(t) = T_r + (T_i - T_r)e^{kt}$ models Newton's Law of Cooling. $T(t)$ is the temperature of a heated substance t minutes after it has been removed from a heat (or cooling) source. T_i is the substance's initial temperature, k is a constant for that substance, and T_r is room temperature.
    a. The initial surface temperature of a beef roast is 236°F and room temperature is 72°F. If $k = -0.041$, how long will it take for this roast to cool to 100°F?
    b. Write and graph an equation that you can use to check your answer to part (a). Use your graph to complete the table below. **a–b. See margin.**

Temperature (°F)	225	200	175	150	125	100	75
Minutes Later	■	■	■	■	■	■	■

1.7   6.0   11.3   18.1   27.6   43.1   97.6

66. **Open-Ended** Write a real-world problem that you can answer using Newton's Law of Cooling. Then answer it. **Check students' work.**

Test Prep

Multiple Choice

67. Which expression is equal to $3 \ln 4 - 5 \ln 2$? **C**
    A. $\ln (-18)$
    B. $\ln \left(\frac{6}{5}\right)$
    C. $\ln 2$
    D. $\ln 32$

65a. about 43 min

b. $t = \dfrac{-1}{0.041} \ln\left(\dfrac{T-72}{164}\right)$

68. What is the value of x if $17e^{4x} = 85$? **H**

F. $\frac{5}{4}$ G. $\frac{\ln 85}{17 \cdot \ln 4}$ H. $\frac{\ln 5}{4}$ J. $\frac{\ln 85 - \ln 17}{\ln 4}$

69. An investment of $750 will be worth $1500 after 12 years of continuous compounding at a fixed interest rate. What is that interest rate? **B**
A. 2.00%   B. 5.78%   C. 6.93%   D. 200%

Extended Response   **70.** The table shows the values of an investment after the given number of years of continuously compounded interest.

Years	0	1	2	3	4
Value	$500.00	$541.64	$586.76	$635.62	$688.56

a. What is the rate of interest? **a–c. See margin.**
b. Write an equation to model the growth of the investment.
c. To the nearest year, when will the investment be worth $1800?

Mixed Review

Lesson 8-5   **Solve each equation.**

71. $3^{2x} = 6561$ **4**   **72.** $7^x - 2 = 252$ **2.846**   **73.** $25^{2x+1} = 144$ **0.272**

74. $\log 3x = 4$ **3333.$\overline{3}$**   **75.** $\log 5x + 3 = 3.7$ **1.002** **76.** $\log 9 - \log x + 1 = 6$
  9.0×10^{-5}

Lesson 7-7   **Find the inverse of each function. Is the inverse a function?** **77–79. See margin.**

77. $y = 5x + 7$ **78.** $y = 2x^3 + 10$ **79.** $y = -x^2 + 5$

Lesson 6-7   **80.** The Nut Shop carries 30 different types of nuts. The shop special is the Triple Play, a made-to-order mixture of any three different types of nuts. How many different Triple Plays are possible?   **4060 possible combinations**

······· **A Point in Time**

+————+————+————+————+————+————+———→
1500   1600   1700   1800   1900   2000

The first manned moon landing on July 20, 1969, gave scientists a unique opportunity to test their theories about the moon's geologic history.

A logarithmic function was used to date lunar rocks. Radioactive rubidium-87 decays into stable strontium-87 at a fixed rate. The ratio r of the two isotopes in a sample can be measured and used in the equation $T = -h \frac{\ln(r + 1)}{\ln 0.5}$, where T is the age in years and h is the half-life of rubidium-87, 4.7×10^{10} years. For the lunar sample, r was measured at 0.0588, giving an approximate age of 3.87 billion years.

 For: Information about space exploration
PHSchool.com **Web Code:** age-2032

Lesson 8-6 Natural Logarithms   **475**

Test Prep

 Resources
For additional practice with a variety of test item formats:
• Standardized Test Prep, p. 483
• Test-Taking Strategies, p. 478
• Test-Taking Strategies with Transparencies

70.[4] **a.** 8%

  b. $A = Pe^{rt} = 500\,e^{0.08t}$

  c. $1800 = 500\,e^{0.08t}$
   $3.6 = e^{0.08t}$
   $\ln 3.6 = 0.08t$
   $\frac{\ln 3.6}{0.08} = t$
   $16 \approx t$
   about 16 years

  [3] correct model, computation error in (b) or (c)

  [2] incorrect model, solved correctly

  [1] correct model, but without work shown in (c)

77. $y = \frac{x - 7}{5}$; yes

78. $y = \sqrt[3]{\frac{x - 10}{2}}$; yes

79. $y = \pm\sqrt{5 - x}$; no

Activity Lab

Exponential and Logarithmic Inequalities

This feature guides students in solving exponential and logarithmic inequalities using tables and graphs on a graphing calculator.

Guided Instruction

Discuss the problem situation in Activity 1 and make sure students understand what is being asked.

Error Prevention!

For Question 1a, watch for students who incorrectly write $V(x) = 2^x$ instead of $V(x) = 2^{x-1}$. Ask:

- *What does x represent and what is its first value?* **day of the month starting with 1**
- *What is the value of the silver coin on the first day?* **1 denarius**
- *What number for the exponent results in a value of 1?* **0**

Teaching Tip

For Question 3, inform students that 300 kilograms is about 660 pounds.

Advanced Learners [L4]

Challenge students to explain why the total value of the coins is exactly 1 less than twice the value of the 16th day, and whether this applies if the total number of days changes. **The sum of the preceding days is always one less than the following day no matter how may days are included; sample: 1 + 2 + 4 + 8 = 16 − 1**

Resources

Students may use any graphing calculator to make tables and graphs.

You can solve problems using exponential equations and inequalities.

1 ACTIVITY

Legend tells of a Roman general who was so successful in his campaigns that the emperor offered the general his choice of reward. The general asked the emperor for all the silver that he could carry out of the imperial treasury in one month. The emperor agreed, but offered a condition.

On the first day, the general would receive 1 silver denarius. On the second day, he would receive a coin valued at 2 denarii. Each day, the general was to come to the treasury and the treasurer would mint a special coin that would be twice as heavy and worth twice as much as the coin the general got a day earlier.

1. a. What function $V(x)$ gives the value of the coin that the general received on day x? $V(x) = 2^{x-1}$
  b. What is the domain of this function? **positive integers**

One denarius coin weighed about 0.006 kg.

2. Write a function $M(x)$ that gives the mass of each coin in kilograms as a function of day x. $M(x) = 0.006(2^{x-1})$

The largest object the general could carry or roll without help could weigh no more than 300 kg.

3. a. Use $M(x)$ from Exercise 2 to write an inequality that describes the mass of a coin that the general could carry or roll out of the treasury. $0 < 0.006(2^{x-1}) \le 300$
  b. Make a table of values of this function. **Tables may vary.**
  c. Use the table to solve the inequality. $1 \le x \le 16$

b.

x	M(x)
13	24.576
14	49.152
15	98.304
16	196.608
17	393.216

4. What is the total value of the coins that the general would receive? **65,535 denarii**

2 ACTIVITY

Scientists are growing bacteria in a laboratory. They start with a known population of bacteria and measure how long it takes this population to double.

5. Sample A starts with 200,000 bacteria. The population doubles every hour. Write an exponential function that models the population in Sample A as a function of time in hours. $A(t) = 200{,}000(2)^t$

6. Sample B starts with 50,000 bacteria. The population doubles every half hour. Write an exponential function that models the population growth in Sample B as a function of time in hours. $B(t) = 50{,}000(2)^{2t}$

7. a. Write an inequality that models the population in Sample B overtaking the population in Sample A. $200{,}000(2)^t < 50{,}000(2)^{2t}$
  b. Use a graphing calculator to solve the inequality. $t > 2$

You can also use logarithmic equations and inequalities to solve problems.

3 ACTIVITY

Average barometric pressure varies with the altitude of a location. The greater the altitude is, the lower the pressure. The altitude A is measured in feet above sea level. The barometric pressure P is measured in inches of mercury (in. Hg). The altitude can be modeled by the function $A(P) = 90,000 - 26,500 \ln P$.

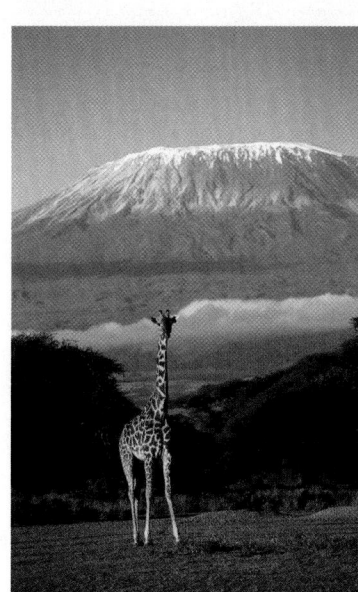

8. What is the reasonable domain of the function? What is the range of the function? **positive real numbers; real numbers**

9. Use a graphing calculator to make a table of function values. Use TblStart = 30 and ΔTbl = −1. **See margin.**

10. Write an equation to find what average pressure the model predicts at sea level, or $A = 0$. Use your table to solve the equation. **$0 = 90,000 - 26,500 \ln P$; about 29.85 in.**

11. Kilimanjaro is a mountain in Tanzania that formed from three extinct volcanoes. The base of the mountain is at 3000 ft above sea level. The peak is at 19,340 ft above sea level. On Kilimanjaro, $3000 \le A(P) \le 19,340$ is true for the altitude. Write an inequality from which you can find minimum and maximum values of normal barometric pressure on Kilimanjaro. Use a table and solve the inequality for P.
$3000 \le 90,000 - 26,500 \ln P \le 19,340$; $14.4 \le P \le 26.7$

12. Denver, Colorado, is nicknamed the "Mile High City" because its elevation is about 1 mile, or 5280 ft, above sea level. The lowest point in Phoenix, Arizona, is 1070 ft above sea level. Write an inequality that describes the range of $A(P)$ as you drive from Phoenix to Denver. Then solve the inequality for P.
$1070 \le 90,000 - 26,500 \ln P \le 5280$; $24.5 \le P \le 28.7$

4 ACTIVITY

Carbon-14 is a radioisotope that is produced when cosmic radiation penetrates Earth's atmosphere. Plants absorb carbon-14 with carbon dioxide from the air. Animals ingest carbon-14 when they eat plants.

The concentration of carbon-14 in a living organism is the same as its concentration in the atmosphere. When an organism dies, it stops replacing carbon-14. The remaining carbon-14 begins to decay. Scientists use the ratio of the concentration of the remaining carbon-14 to its original concentration to estimate the age of organic material. Let r represent this ratio.

13. The age of a fossil $g(r)$, in years, can be modeled as a function of r as $g(r) = -5730 \log_2 r$ or $g(r) = -8266.64 \ln r$. What is the domain of the function? What is the range of the function? **$0 < r < 1$; positive real numbers**

14. Graph the function. **See margin.**

15. Describe the behavior of the function as r becomes very small. **See margin.**

16. A paleontologist found an animal bone fossil and measured r to be 0.01. What is the approximate age of the bone to the nearest thousand years? **38,000 years**

17. Write an inequality that models the carbon-14 ratio in fossils that are more than 50,000 years old. Then solve the inequality by graphing the corresponding function on your calculator. What does your solution mean?
$-8266.64 \ln r > 50,000$; $r \le 0.00236$; the ratio of remaining C-14 to original is about 0.00236.

Activity Lab   Exponential and Logarithmic Inequalities   **477**

9.

X	Y1
30.000	−131.7
29.000	766.66
28.000	1696.6
27.000	2660.3
26.000	3660.4
25.000	4699.8
24.000	5781.6
X=30	

14.

WINDOW
Xmin = 0
Xmax = 1
Xscl = .1
Ymin = 0
Ymax = 50000
Yscl = 10000
Xres = 1▪

Testing Multiple Choices

Many assessment tests include multiple-choice problems. Sometimes testing each answer choice in the problem can be an efficient way to make a selection.

Resources

SAT® and ACT® correlations are on page 428B.

Test-Taking Strategies with Transparencies
- Transparency 8
- Practice sheet, p. 32

Guided Instruction

Use the transparency for more instruction on working backward.

Assign the worksheet to give students more practice with working backward to find the correct answer choice.

Special Needs   **L1**

Exercise 3 Everyone processes information in their own way. Suggest that students learn and practice strategies such as working backwards, and experiment with other strategies to find the ones that best fit their way of thinking.

Test-Taking Strategies with Transparencies

Test-Taking Strategy: Testing Multiple Choices

When you take a multiple-choice test, one of the answer choices is always correct. You can solve a problem by testing the answer choices to find the correct one.

Solve $5^x + 12 = 637$.

A. 2   B. 3   C. 4   D. 5

Work backward by substituting each answer choice for x.

$5^2 + 12 = ?$
$25 + 12 = 37$ not correct

$5^3 + 12 = ?$
$125 + 12 = 137$ not correct

$5^4 + 12 = ?$
$625 + 12 = 637$ correct

You do not have to continue substituting answer choices once you find the correct choice.

The answer is C, 4.

Solve these problems by working backward.

1. Solve $4^x - 7 = 4089$.

   A. 5   B. 6   C. 7   D. 8

2. Solve $y^4 - 24 = 57$.

   A. 7   B. 5   C. 3   D. 1

Solutions

1. B

2. C

Transparency 8

478

One advantage of multiple-choice tests is that the correct answer is among the choices. A frequently useful strategy is to test a choice in the original problem.

EXAMPLE

What number is the solution to $\left(\frac{1}{4}\right)^x = 8$?

  (A) -2 (B) $-\frac{3}{2}$ (C) 0 (D) $\frac{1}{2}$ (E) 16

You can answer the question without solving the equation. Substitute each answer choice into the equation until you find the right one.

If $x = -2$, then $\left(\frac{1}{4}\right)^x = \left(\frac{1}{4}\right)^{-2} = 4^2 = 16$. Since $16 \neq 8$, answer A is wrong.

If $x = -\frac{3}{2}$, then $\left(\frac{1}{4}\right)^x = \left(\frac{1}{4}\right)^{-\frac{3}{2}} = 4^{\frac{3}{2}} = 8$. Since $8 = 8$, the correct answer is B.

You don't have to test the three other choices.

When answering a multiple-choice question that involves solving a difficult equation, you often can save time and effort by working backward from the answers to the question.

EXERCISES   1–2. See right.

1. Refer to the Example. Explain how you can eliminate choices C–E before trying A and B.

2. Algebraically solve the equation in the Example to show that B is the correct answer.

Answer each question by testing the choices. Then solve each equation algebraically.

3. What is the solution to $\log_x (3x + 2) = x + 1$?   **C**

   (A) 0 (B) 1 (C) 2 (D) 6 (E) 10

4. What is the solution to $2^{x+1} + 2x + 1 = 0$?   **E**

   (A) 2 (B) 1 (C) 0 (D) $-\frac{1}{2}$ (E) -1

5. What is the solution to $\ln \sqrt{x + 2} + \ln \sqrt{3x + 4} = \ln 15$?   **E**

   (A) -1 (B) 0 (C) 1 (D) 3 (E) 7

6. What is the solution to $\log (\log (3x - 2)) = 0$?   **D**

   (A) $\frac{2}{3}$ (B) 1 (C) 2 (D) 4 (E) 34

7. What is the solution to $\log_x \frac{1}{2} = \frac{1}{2}$?   **A**

   (A) $\frac{1}{4}$ (B) $\frac{1}{2}$ (C) 0 (D) 1 (E) 2

8. Use the formula for continuously compounded interest, $A = Pe^{rt}$, to find the annual interest rate for an $8000 investment that earns $410.17 in one year.   **C**

   (A) 7% (B) 6% (C) 5% (D) 4% (E) 3%

---

1. Answers may vary.
   Sample: $a^0 = 1$ for every nonzero a, so $x \neq 0$.
   $\left(\frac{1}{4}\right)^x < 1$ for all $x > 0$, so $x \neq \frac{1}{2}$ or 16.

2. $\log \left(\frac{1}{4}\right)^x = \log 8$
   $x = \dfrac{\log 8}{\log \left(\frac{1}{4}\right)} =$
   $-1.5 = -\frac{3}{2}$

Chapter Review

Vocabulary Review

🔊 asymptote (p. 433)
Change of Base Formula (p. 462)
common logarithm (p. 447)
continuously compounded interest
formula (p. 441)

decay factor (p. 433)
exponential equation (p. 461)
exponential function (p. 430)
growth factor (p. 430)
logarithm (p. 447)

logarithmic equation (p. 463)
logarithmic function (p. 448)
natural logarithmic function (p. 470)

Resources

Student Edition
Extra Skills and Word Problems
Practice, Ch. 8, p. 850
English/Spanish Glossary, p. 899
Properties and Formulas, p. 893
Table of Symbols, p. 889

Go Online
PHSchool.com
For: Vocabulary quiz
Web Code: agj-0851

Choose the correct term to complete each sentence.

1. In the exponential function $y = ab^x$, when $b > 1$, b is the _?_. **growth factor**

2. A _?_ is a logarithm that uses base 10. **common logarithm**

3. The line $x = 2$ is a(n) _?_ of the function $f(x) = \frac{2}{x-2}$. **asymptote**

4. The Change of Base Formula can be used to evaluate a _?_ with any base.
  logarithm

5. An _?_ can be solved by taking the logarithm of each side of the equation.
  exponential equation

Differentiated Instruction **Resources**

Vocabulary and Study Skills
worksheet 8D
Spanish Vocabulary and Study
Skills worksheet 8D
Interactive Textbook Audio
Glossary
Online Vocabulary Quiz

Success Tracker™
Online at PHSchool.com

Skills and Concepts

8-1 Objectives

▼ To model exponential
growth (p. 430)

▼ To model exponential
decay (p. 432)

The general form of an **exponential function** is $y = ab^x$, where x is a real number, $a \neq 0$, $b > 0$, and $b \neq 1$. When $b > 1$, the function models exponential growth, and b is the **growth factor**. When $0 < b < 1$, the function models exponential decay, and b is the **decay factor**.

Determine whether each equation represents exponential growth or exponential decay. Find the rate of increase or decrease for each model. Graph each equation.

6. $y = 5^x$　　　**7.** $y = 2(4)^x$　　　**8.** $y = 0.2(3.8)^x$　　**9.** $y = 3(0.25)^x$
6–9. See margin.

Write an exponential equation whose graph passes through the given points.

10. $y = \frac{25}{7}\left(\frac{7}{5}\right)^x$

11. $y = 0.0015(10)^x$

12. $y = 2.25\left(\frac{1}{3}\right)^x$

13. $y = \left(\frac{1}{3}\right)^x$

10. $(1, 5), (2, 7)$　　**11.** $(3, 1.5), (4, 15)$　　**12.** $\left(-1, 6\frac{3}{4}\right), \left(2, \frac{1}{4}\right)$　**13.** $(-2, 9), (0, 1)$

Write an exponential function to model each situation. Find the value of each function after five years, to the nearest dollar.

14. A \$12,500 car depreciates 9% each year. $y = 12{,}500(0.91)^x$; \$7800

15. A baseball card bought for \$50 increases 3% in value each year.
　　　　　　　　　　　　$y = 50(1.03)^x$; \$58

Write an exponential equation for each graph. Evaluate the equation for $x = 4$.

16.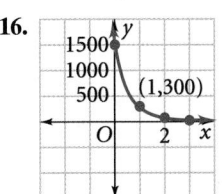

$y = 1500(0.2)^x$; 2.4

17.

$y = 2(1.4)^x$; 7.6832

6. exponential growth; 400%

7. exponential growth; 300%

8. exponential growth; 280%

9. exponential decay; −75%

18. $y = 3^x$ reflected over the x-axis and translated up 1 unit

19. $y = 8^x$ translated down 1 unit

20. $y = 2(2)^x$ translated left 1 unit and up 3 units

21. $y = 2\left(\frac{1}{3}\right)^x$ reflected over the x-axis and translated right 2 units

40.

41.

42.

43.

8-2 Objectives

▼ To identify the role of constants in $y = ab^{cx}$ (p. 439)

▼ To use e as a base (p. 441)

Exponential functions can be translated, stretched, shrunk, and reflected. The graph of $y = ab^{x-h} + k$ is the graph of $y = b^x$ stretched by a factor $|a|$, and translated $|h|$ units horizontally and $|k|$ units vertically.

The **continuously compounded interest** formula is $A = Pe^{rt}$, where P is the principal, r is the annual rate, and t is time in years.

Describe how the graph of each function relates to the graph of its parent function. Then graph each function. 18–21. See margin.

18. $y = -3^x + 1$

19. $y = 8^x - 1$

20. $y = 2(2)^{x+1} + 3$

21. $y = -2\left(\frac{1}{3}\right)^{x-2}$

Find the amount in a continuously compounded account for the given conditions.

22. principal: $1000, annual interest rate: 4.8%, time: 2 yr **$1100.76**

23. principal: $250, annual interest rate: 6.2%, time: 2.5 yr **$291.91**

24. principal: $500, annual interest rate: 8.5%, time: 3 yr **$645.23**

Evaluate to four decimal places.

25. e^1 **2.7183**

26. e^{-1} **0.3679**

27. e^5 **148.4132**

28. $e^{-\frac{1}{2}}$ **0.6065**

29. Physics Radium has a half-life of 1620 years. Write the decay function for a 3-mg sample. Find the amount of radium remaining after 50 years.
$y = 3\left(\frac{1}{2}\right)^{\frac{x}{1620}}$; $\approx$**2.937 mg**

8-3 Objectives

▼ To write and evaluate logarithmic expressions (p. 446)

▼ To graph logarithmic functions (p. 448)

If $y = b^x$, then $\log_b y = x$. The **logarithmic function** is the inverse of the exponential function, so the graphs of the functions are reflections of one another over the line $y = x$. Logarithmic functions can be translated, stretched, shrunk, and reflected.

When $b = 10$, the logarithm is called a **common logarithm**, which you can write as $\log y$.

30. Chemistry The pH of a substance equals $-\log[H^+]$, where $[H^+]$ is the concentration of hydrogen ions. A sample of well water has a pH of 5.7. Find the concentration of hydrogen ions in the sample. **2.0×10^{-6}**

31. The concentration of hydrogen ions in water is 10^{-7}. Find the pH of water. **7**

Write each equation in logarithmic form.

32. $6^2 = 36$ **$2 = \log_6 36$**

33. $2^{-3} = 0.125$ **$-3 = \log_2 0.125$**

34. $3^3 = 27$ **$3 = \log_3 27$**

35. $10^{-3} = 0.001$ **$-3 = \log 0.001$**

Evaluate each logarithm.

36. $\log_2 64$ **6**

37. $\log_3 \frac{1}{9}$ **-2**

38. $\log 0.00001$ **-5**

39. $\log_2 1$ **0**

Graph each logarithmic function. 40–43. See margin.

40. $y = \log_3 x$

41. $y = \log(x + 2)$

42. $y = \log_2 2x$

43. $y = \log_5(x + 1)$

8-4 Objective

▼ To use the properties of logarithms (p. 454)

For any positive numbers, M, N, and $b, b \neq 1$, each of the following statements is true. Each can be used to rewrite a logarithmic expression.

- $\log_b MN = \log_b M + \log_b N$, by the Product Property
- $\log_b \frac{M}{N} = \log_b M - \log_b N$, by the Quotient Property
- $\log_b M^x = x \log_b M$, by the Power Property

Write each logarithmic expression as a single logarithm.

48. $2 \log_4 x + 3 \log_4 y$; Product and Power Properties

49. $\log 4 + 4 \log S + \log t$; Product and Power Properties

50. $\log_3 2 - \log_3 x$; Quotient Property

51. $2 \log (x + 3)$; Power Property

44. $\log 8 + \log 3$ **log 24**

45. $\log_2 5 - \log_2 3$ $\log_2 \frac{5}{3}$

46. $4 \log_3 x + \log_3 7$ $\log_3 7x^4$

47. $\log z - \log y$ $\log \frac{z}{y}$

Expand each logarithm. State the properties of logarithms that you use.

48. $\log_4 x^2 y^3$ **49.** $\log 4s^4 t$ **50.** $\log_3 \frac{2}{x}$ **51.** $\log (x + 3)^2$

52. Use the formula $L = 10 \log \frac{I}{I_0}$. Suppose the sound intensity of a fan must be reduced by one third. By how many decibels would the loudness be decreased? **about 1.76 dB**

8-5 Objectives

▼ To solve exponential equations (p. 461)

▼ To solve logarithmic equations (p. 463)

An equation in the form $b^{cx} = a$, where the exponent includes a variable, is called an **exponential equation**. You can solve exponential equations by taking the logarithm of each side of the equation. An equation that includes a logarithmic expression is called a **logarithmic equation**.

Solve each equation. Round your answers to the nearest hundredth.

53. $4^x = 27$ **2.38**   **54.** $3^x = 36$ **3.26**   **55.** $7^{x-3} = 25$ **4.65** **56.** $5^x = 9$ **1.37**

Solve by graphing.

57. $5^{2x} = 25$ **1**   **58.** $3^{7x} = 160$ ≈ 0.66 **59.** $6^{3x+1} = 215$ ≈ 0.67 **60.** $0.5^x = 0.12$ ≈ 3.06

Solve each logarithmic equation. Leave your answer in exact form.

61. $\log 3x = 1$ $\frac{10}{3}$ **62.** $\log_2 4x = 5$ **8**

63. $\log x = \log 2x^2 - 2$ **50**   **64.** $2 \log_3 x = 54$ **7,625,597,484,987**

65. Convert $\log_2 7$ to a logarithm in base 5. $\log_5 91.68$

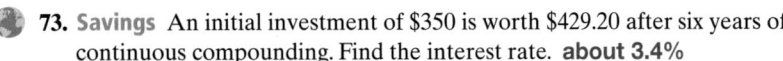 **66. Biology** A culture of 10 bacteria is started, and the number of bacteria will double every hour. In about how many hours will there be 3,000,000 bacteria? **about 18.2 h**

8-6 Objectives

▼ To evaluate natural logarithmic expressions (p. 470)

▼ To solve equations using natural logarithms (p. 471)

The inverse of $y = e^x$ is the **natural logarithmic function** $y = \log_e x = \ln x$. You solve natural logarithm equations in the same way as common logarithm equations.

Solve each equation.

67. $e^{3x} = 12$ **0.83**   **68.** $\ln x + \ln(x + 1) = 2$ **2.26**   **69.** $2 \ln x + 3 \ln 2 = 5$ **4.31**

70. $\ln 4 - \ln x = 10$ **0.00018**   **71.** $4e^{(x-1)} = 64$ **3.77**   **72.** $3 \ln x + \ln 5 = 7$ **6.03**

73. Savings An initial investment of \$350 is worth \$429.20 after six years of continuous compounding. Find the interest rate. **about 3.4%**

Chapter 8   Chapter Review   **481**

Chapter Test

Go Online
PHSchool.com
For: Chapter Test
Web Code: aga-0852

Evaluate each function to the nearest hundredth for for $x = 0, 1, 2, 3, 4, 5$. Graph each function.

1. $y = 3(0.25)^x$ **2.** $f(x) = -(6)^x$

3. $y = 0.1(10)^x$ **4.** $f(x) = 100(2)^x$

1–4. See back of book.

5. Open-Ended Give an example of an exponential function that models exponential growth and an example of an exponential function that models exponential decay. **See margin.**

Write an exponential function of the form $y = ab^x$ that has a graph through the given points.

6. $(1, 1), (2, 3)$ $y = \frac{1}{3}(3)^x$

7. $\left(-2, \frac{2}{25}\right), (1, 10)$ $y = 2(5)^x$

8. $\left(-3, \frac{1}{16}\right), (-1, 1)$ $y = 4(4)^x$

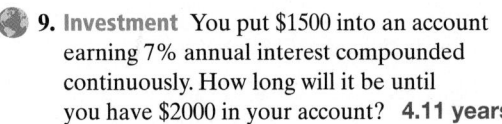 **9. Investment** You put $1500 into an account earning 7% annual interest compounded continuously. How long will it be until you have $2000 in your account? **4.11 years**

Describe how the graph of each function is related to the graph of its parent function.

10. $y = 3^x + 2$ $y = 3^x$ translated up 2 units

11. $y = \left(\frac{1}{2}\right)^{x+1}$ $y = \left(\frac{1}{2}\right)^x$ translated left 1 unit

12. $y = 5^{x-2} - 1$

13. $y = -(2)^{x+2}$ **12–13. See margin.**

Evaluate each logarithm.

14. $\log_2 8$ **3**   **15.** $\log_7 7$ **1**

16. $\log_5 25$ **2**   **17.** $\log_3 27$ **3**

18. $\log_{11} 1$ **0**   **19.** $\log_4 256$ **4**

Graph each logarithmic function.

20. $y = \log_9 x$ **20–23. See back of book.**

21. $y = \log_3 (x - 1)$

22. $y = \frac{1}{2} \log_3 (x + 2)$

23. $y = 1 - \log_2 x$

Use the properties of logarithms to rewrite each logarithmic expression. **24–27. See margin.**

24. $\log_2 4 + 3 \log_2 9$ **25.** $3 \log a - 2 \log b$

26. $\log_7 \frac{a}{b}$ **27.** $\log 3x^3 y^2$

Use the properties of logarithms to evaluate each expression.

28. $\log_3 27 - \log_3 9$ **1**

29. $2 \log_2 64 + \log_2 2$ **13**

30. $-\log_4 \frac{1}{16} - \log_4 64$ **-1**

31. $2 \log 5 + \log 40$ **3**

32. Writing Show that solving the equation $3^{2x} = 4$ by taking common logarithms of both sides is equivalent to solving it by taking logarithms to the base 3 of both sides.
See back of book.

Solve each equation.

33. $\left(\frac{3}{4}\right)^x = 81$ **-15.28**   **34.** $3^{x-1} = 24$ **3.89**

35. $\log 4x = 3$ **250**   **36.** $2 \log x = -4$ **0.01**

Use the Change of Base Formula to rewrite each expression using common logarithms.

37. $\log_3 16$ $\frac{\log 16}{\log 3}$

38. $\log_2 10$ $\frac{1}{\log 2}$

39. $\log_7 8$ $\frac{\log 8}{\log 7}$

Use the properties of logarithms to simplify each equation and solve it. Round to thousandths.

40. $\ln 2 + \ln x = 1$ **1.359**

41. $\ln (x + 1) + \ln (x - 1) = 4$ **7.456**

42. $\ln (2x - 1)^2 = 7$ **17.058, -16.058**

43. $3 \ln x - \ln 2 = 4$ **4.780**

 44. Physics Seawater absorbs light. In some instances, this relationship is modeled by $\ln I = \ln I_0 - 0.014d$. I_0 is the intensity of the light at the surface of the water, and I is the intensity at a depth of d cm. At what depth will the intensity of the light in the water be 25% of the surface intensity? **about 99 cm**

5. Answers may vary. Both answers should be of the form $y = ab^x$. For the growth model, $b > 1$. For the decay model, $0 < b < 1$.

12. $y = 5^x$ translated right 2 units and down 1 unit

13. $y = 2^x$ translated left 2 units and reflected over the x-axis

24. $\log_2 2916$

25. $\log \frac{a^3}{b^2}$

26. $\log_7 a - \log_7 b$

27. $\log 3 + 3 \log x + 2 \log y$

Standardized Test Prep

Standardized Test Prep

Multiple Choice

For Exercises 1–12, choose the correct letter.

1. What can you tell about the roots of
A $3x^2 + 4x - 1 = 0$ from the discriminant?
   - Ⓐ There are two real roots.
   - Ⓑ There are two imaginary roots.
   - Ⓒ There is one real and one imaginary root.
   - Ⓓ There are no roots.

2. Which expressions are equivalent to
G $\log a - 3\log b$?
   - I. $\log ab^3$
   - II. $\log \frac{a}{b^3}$
   - III. $\log a - \log b^3$
   - IV. $\log (ab)^3$

   - Ⓕ I and II
   - Ⓖ II and III
   - Ⓗ III and IV
   - Ⓙ I and IV

3. What is the factored form of $2x^3 + 5x^2 - 12x$?
A
   - Ⓐ $x(2x - 3)(x + 4)$
   - Ⓑ $(2x^2 - 3)(x + 4)$
   - Ⓒ $x(2x + 4)(x - 3)$
   - Ⓓ $(2x - 4)(x + 3)$

4. Which is NOT a solution of the system?
J $\begin{cases} 2x - y > 3 \\ 2x + y \geq 5 \end{cases}$
   - Ⓕ (3, 0)
   - Ⓖ (4, −1)
   - Ⓗ (6, 1)
   - Ⓙ (0, −3)

5. How is the graph of $y = (x - 4)^2 + 1$ translated
D from the graph of $y = x^2$?
   - Ⓐ left 1, up 4
   - Ⓑ left 4, down 1
   - Ⓒ right 1, down 4
   - Ⓓ right 4, up 1

6. What is the inverse of $\begin{bmatrix} 3 & -5 \\ 1 & 4 \end{bmatrix}$?
J
   - Ⓕ $\begin{bmatrix} 4 & 5 \\ -1 & 3 \end{bmatrix}$
   - Ⓖ $\begin{bmatrix} -2 & 5 \\ -1 & -3 \end{bmatrix}$
   - Ⓗ $\begin{bmatrix} -3 & 5 \\ -1 & -4 \end{bmatrix}$
   - Ⓙ $\frac{1}{17}\begin{bmatrix} 4 & 5 \\ -1 & 3 \end{bmatrix}$

7. Solve the system. $\begin{cases} 2x + 3y - 2z = -2 \\ 2x - 4y + 2z = 18 \\ 5x + 2y - 6z = 8 \end{cases}$
C
   - Ⓐ $x = 3, y = 1, z = 2$
   - Ⓑ $x = -3, y = 2, z = -1$
   - Ⓒ $x = 4, y = -3, z = 1$
   - Ⓓ $x = -1, y = 3, z = 2$

8. Let $f(x) = -5x$ and $g(x) = 1 - 2x^2$. Find $(g \circ f)(1)$.
F
   - Ⓕ −49
   - Ⓖ −5
   - Ⓗ 5
   - Ⓙ 51

9. Which polynomials have both −2 and 3 as zeros?
C I. $x^3 - 2x^2 - 5x + 2$ II. $x^3 - 3x^2 - 4x + 12$
   III. $x^3 + 3x^2 - 4x - 12$

   - Ⓐ I only
   - Ⓑ I and II
   - Ⓒ II only
   - Ⓓ I, II, and III

10. Multiply $(3\sqrt{6} - 3\sqrt{2})(\sqrt{6} - 3\sqrt{2})$.
F
   - Ⓕ $36 - 24\sqrt{3}$
   - Ⓖ 6
   - Ⓗ $6 - 12\sqrt{3}$
   - Ⓙ 9

11. Solve $3 + (x - 1)^{\frac{3}{4}} = 30$.
D
   - Ⓐ 9
   - Ⓑ 11
   - Ⓒ 81
   - Ⓓ 82

12. $(\ln x)^2 = 1$. What are possible values of x?
J I. e II. $-e$ III. e^{-1} IV. 1
   - Ⓕ I only
   - Ⓖ I and II
   - Ⓗ IV only
   - Ⓙ I and III

Gridded Response

13. Solve $3^x = 7$. Round your answer to the nearest hundredth. **1.77**

14. What is the discriminant of $2x^2 - 8x + 8 = 0$? **0**

15. Evaluate $\log_4 8$. **3/2 or 1.5**

Short Response **16–17. See back of book.**

16. Write $\log \frac{x^2 y^3}{z^6}$ in expanded form.

17. Solve $5^{2x + 1} = 62$. Round your answer to the nearest hundredth. Show your work.

18. Graph the function $y = 10^{x + 1} - 3$ as a translation of its parent function.
   See back of book.

Extended Response

19. Suppose you put $1000 in an account earning 5.5% interest compounded continuously. How much will be in the account after one year? After four years? **See back of book.**

20. What is the determinant of $\begin{bmatrix} 1 & 2 & 3 \\ 2 & 1 & 3 \\ 2 & 3 & 1 \end{bmatrix}$?

   Show your work. **See back of book.**

To answer the questions, students apply skills and concepts from this chapter and previous chapters.
Multiple Choice: Items 1–12
Gridded Response: Items 13–15
Short Response: Items 16–18
Extended Response: Items 19–20

Resources

Test Prep Workbook

Grab & Go
- **L3** Cumulative Review

ExamView CD-ROM
- Standardized Test Practice

Differentiated Instruction Resources

Progress Monitoring Assessments
- Benchmark Test 4

Spanish Assessment Resources
- **L3** Spanish Cumulative Review

Chapter 8   Standardized Test Prep   **483**

Item	1	2	3	4	5	6	7	8	9	10	11	12	13	14	15	16	17	18	19	20
Lesson	5-8	8-4	6-2	3-3	5-3	4-5	3-6	7-6	6-2	7-2	8-5	8-6	8-5	5-8	8-4	8-4	8-5	8-1	8-1	4-6

A Crowded House

In this activity students apply their knowledge of exponential functions, graphs, and lines of best fit, as well as logarithms.

Activating Prior Knowledge

Ask students to describe what must be true for a given population to have a zero growth rate or a negative growth rate. Have students compare and give examples of linear growth and exponential growth.

Guided Instruction

Have a volunteer read the introductory paragraph. Have them discuss some of the consequences for a country, and for the world, of zero, negative, linear, and exponential population growth rates.

Teaching Tip

Suggest that students gather information about the population growth rate for their town or state over the last 100 years.

Connection to Demographics

Have students use the Internet to research recent population growth rates for various countries around the world, and color groups of countries on a world map to show the various rates. Ask them to form conjectures about possible patterns on this map.

English Language Learners ELL

Ask a volunteer to explain the meaning of *population density.* Make sure that all students understand the meaning of *doubled* and *tripled.*

484

 Activity Lab

A Crowded House

Applying Exponential Functions The number of people in the world has more than tripled since 1900—from less than 2 billion to more than 6 billion. In 2000, an average of about 360,000 babies were born each day. That means that there were four babies born every second.

Old South Meeting House

Historical Site
Old South Meeting House, in Boston, Massachusetts, (left about 1903, right in 2002), was built in 1730. At the time, it was the tallest building in Boston. Note that the time on the clock is 1:43 in both photos.

Proportional Populations
These maps of China, the United States, and Australia are drawn so that their sizes are proportional to their populations.

United States, population about 284,500,000

China, population about 1,273,300,000

About one of every five people in the world lives in China.

Australia, population about 19,400,000

484 All photographs © Dorling Kindersley Limited unless otherwise credited on acknowledgments page

---

Activity

a.
$$P(n) = 2515k^n$$
$$\ln(P(n)) = \ln(2515k^n)$$
$$= \ln(2515) + \ln(k^n)$$
$$= \ln(2515) + n\ln(k)$$

b.

n	P(n)	ln P(n)
0	2,515,000,000	21.65
10	3,019,000,000	21.83
20	3,698,000,000	22.03
30	4,450,000,000	22.22
40	5,284,000,000	22.39
50	6,080,000,000	22.53

c–d.

Population Densities

All cities are crowded, but some are more crowded than others. Hong Kong Island is so closely packed that if it were divided into tennis courts, there would be 25 people on each court. London would have only one person on each court.

London: 1 person in an area the size of a tennis court

Hong Kong Island: 25 people in an area the size of a tennis court. A tennis court covers 2,808 sq ft. (261 sq m)

Activity

The population graph shows that population growth since 1950 has been exponential. You can use the data to write the equation $P(n) = 2515k^n$, where n = the number of years since 1950, k = the growth factor, and $P(n)$ is the population in millions. You will use this equation to estimate population.

a. Show that taking the natural log of each side of the equation yields the equation $\ln (P(n)) = \ln 2515 + n \ln k$.

b. Use the population graph. Make a table of the data for n and $P(n)$. Add a third column to the table to show $\ln (P(n))$.

c. Examine the structure of the equation in part (a). If you think of the parts in black as constants and the parts in red as variables, then this is the slope-intercept form of a linear equation relating $\ln (P(n))$ to n. Graph these two variables on a coordinate plane.

d. Draw a line of best fit and calculate the slope of the line.

e. Look closely at the slope-intercept equation in part (a). Which quantity represents the slope of the line?

f. Use the slope to determine the approximate growth factor k of the world's population since 1950.

g. Use your growth factor to write an exponential equation that models the population growth.

h. Estimate the population in the years 2005 and 2010.

Go Online
PHSchool.com

For: Information about population growth
Web Code: age-0853

World population in 2000: 6,080,000,000

World population in 1990: 5,284,000,000

World population in 1980: 4,450,000,000

World population in 1970: 3,698,000,000

World population in 1960: 3,019,000,000

World population in 1950: 2,515,000,000

World population in 1900: 1,633,000,000

World population in 1850: 1,094,000,000

World population in 1800: 954,000,000

World population in 1700: 679,000,000

World population in 1600: 579,000,000

1500 1600 1700 1800 1900 2000

485

Teaching Tip

Before students begin the activity, discuss the illustrations and their captions. Have students work in pairs or in small groups to complete the activity. Have them read it before beginning.

Activity

Materials: paper and pencil, ruler, graph paper

Connection to Social Studies

Have students research and report on current population density of a number of different states in the United States of America. Ask them to compare density in various areas, for example, on the coasts and for inland western states.

Scoring Rubric

This scoring rubric can be used for evaluating student work on both activities. Share this scoring rubric with students before they begin work.

4 Equations, calculations, and graphs are correct. Steps are neat, accurate, and clearly show the mathematics. Responses are clearly indicated and give the appropriate units.

3 Equations, calculations, and graphs are mostly correct, with some minor errors. Steps are neat and mostly accurate. Units are not completely accurate.

2 Equations, calculations, and graphs contain both major and minor errors.

1 Correct answer, but no work is shown.

e. $\ln k$

f–h. Answers may vary. Samples are given.

f. about 1.02

g. $P(n) = 2515(1.02^n)$

h. 2005: $\approx$ 7,474,000,000
2010: $\approx$ 8,252,000,000

Rational Functions

Chapter at a Glance

Lesson Titles, Objectives, and Features	Assessment	NCTM Standards	Local Standards
9-1 Inverse Variation • Using inverse variation • Using joint and other variations	Lesson Quiz	1, 2, 10	
Activity Lab: Technology: Graphing Rational Functions **9-2 The Reciprocal Function Family** • Graphing reciprocal functions • Graphing translations of reciprocal functions	Lesson Quiz	1, 2, 3	
9-3 Rational Functions and Their Graphs • Identifying properties of rational functions • Graphing rational functions	Lesson Quiz Checkpoint Quiz 1	1, 2, 3	
9-4 Rational Expressions • Simplifying rational expressions • Multiplying and dividing rational expressions	Lesson Quiz	1, 2, 6	
9-5 Adding and Subtracting Rational Expressions • Adding and subtracting rational expressions • Simplifying complex fractions	Lesson Quiz Checkpoint Quiz 2	1, 2, 6	
Activity Lab: Extraneous Solutions **9-6 Solving Rational Equations** • Solving rational equations • Using rational equations in solving problems **Activity Lab:** Technology: Rational Inequalities **GPS:** Understanding Word Problems	Lesson Quiz	1, 2, 6	
9-7 Probability of Multiple Events • Finding the probability of the event *A and B* • Finding the probability of the event *A or B*	Lesson Quiz	1, 2, 5, 6	

NCTM Standards 2000

1 Number and Operations	**2** Algebra	**3** Geometry
6 Problem Solving	**7** Reasoning and Proof	**8** Communication

4 Measurement	**5** Data Analysis and Probability
9 Connections	**10** Representation

Correlations to Standardized Tests

All content for these tests is contained in *Prentice Hall Algebra 2*. This chart reflects coverage in this chapter only.

	9-1	9-2	9-3	9-4	9-5	9-6	9-7
SAT®							
Number and Operations Operations, ratio & proportions, complex numbers, counting, elementary number theory, matrices, sequences							
Algebra and Functions Expressions, equations, inequalities, representation and modeling, properties of functions (linear, polynomial, rational, exponential)	✔	✔	✔	✔	✔	✔	✔
Geometry and Measurement *Plane Euclidean/Measurement Coordinate* Lines, parabolas, circles, symmetry, transformations *Three-dimensional* Solids, surface area & volume (cylinders, cones, pyramids, spheres, prisms) *Trigonometry* Right triangles, identities							
Data Analysis, Statistics, and Probability Mean, median, mode, range, interquartile range, graphs and plots, regression, probability							✔
ACT®							
Pre-Algebra Basic operations using whole numbers, decimals, fractions, and integers; place value; square roots and approximations; the concept of exponents; scientific notation; factors, ratio, proportion, and percent; linear equations in one variable; absolute value and ordering numbers by value; elementary counting techniques and simple probability; data collection, representation, and interpretation; and understanding simple descriptive statistics.							✔
Elementary Algebra Properties of exponents and square roots, evaluation of algebraic expressions through substitution, using variables to express functional relationships, understanding algebraic operations, and solving quadratic equations by factoring.	✔	✔	✔	✔	✔	✔	
Intermediate Algebra Understanding of the quadratic formula, rational and radical expressions, absolute value equations and inequalities, sequences and patterns, systems of equations, quadratic inequalities, functions, modeling, matrices, roots of polynomials, and complex numbers.	✔	✔	✔	✔	✔	✔	
Coordinate Geometry Graphing and the relations between equations and graphs, including points, lines, polynomials, circles, and other curves; graphing inequalities; slope; parallel and perpendicular lines; distance; midpoints; and conics.		✔	✔				
Plane Geometry Properties and relations of plane figures, including angles and relations among perpendicular and parallel lines; properties of circles, triangles, rectangles, parallelograms, and trapezoids; transformations; the concept of proof and proof techniques; volume; and applications of geometry to three dimensions.							
Trigonometry Understanding trigonometric relations in right triangles; values and properties of trigonometric functions; graphing trigonometric functions; modeling using trigonometric functions; use of trigonometric identities; and solving trigonometric equations.							
NAEP							
Number Sense, Properties, and Operations							
Measurement							
Geometry and Spatial Sense							
Data Analysis, Statistics, and Probability							✔
Algebra and Functions	✔	✔	✔	✔	✔	✔	

SAT® The College Board, SAT® Reasoning Test   **ACT®** The ACT Assessment® Test   **NAEP** National Assessment of Educational Progress, 2005 Mathematics Objectives

Math Background

Skills Trace

BEFORE Chapter 9

In previous chapters, students examined direct variation and factored and simplified polynomial expressions.

▼

DURING Chapter 9

Students simplify rational expressions, graph transformations of reciprocal functions, solve rational equations, and find probabilities for multiple events.

▼

AFTER Chapter 9

Students will graph conic sections and translations of conic sections.

Chapter Overview

A rational function is a function that can be written in the form $y = \frac{P(x)}{Q(x)}$ where $P(x)$ and $Q(x)$ are polynomials and $Q(x) \neq 0$. If $Q(x)$ is a nonzero constant, then the function is also a polynomial function. Since students have already studied polynomial functions, this chapter concentrates on rational functions that are not polynomial functions.

The simplest rational functions are inverse variations, which have the form $y = \frac{k}{x}$, where k is a nonzero constant. Graphs of inverse variations have the x- and y-axes as asymptotes. Students see that graphs of more complicated rational functions may have many asymptotes. They may also have holes, where a single point is missing. Students learn how to find such points of discontinuity and how to use asymptotes in sketching graphs.

Students see that simplifying rational expressions and performing operations on them are similar in many ways to the corresponding processes for ordinary fractions in arithmetic. They learn to solve rational equations and check for extraneous solutions.

The chapter concludes with another look at probability. This time students calculate probabilities of multiple events.

Inverse Variation   9-1

Students learned about direct variation in Chapter 2. In a direct variation, the variables are *directly* related: as one variable increases, the other variable increases; and as one variable decreases, the other variable decreases. For an inverse variation, the variables are *inversely* related: as one variable increases, the other variable decreases; and as one variable decreases, the other variable increases. In some contexts, students may see *inverse* variation referred to as *indirect* variation.

Students should be able to identify direct and inverse relationships between variables. Finding everyday examples of quantities (variables) that change directly as well as quantities that change inversely can help students make these relationships concrete. For example, the amount of milk in a carton and time are inversely related (the milk is consumed over a few days), but the amount of air in a milk carton and time are directly related.

Both direct variation and inverse variation describe relationships between variables. Given three or more variables, both relationships can occur simultaneously in what is called a combined variation. As with direct and inverse variations, combined variations have a constant of variation. Direct, inverse, and combined variations can include negative x-values. However, most real-world applications are restricted to positive numbers.

The Reciprocal Function Family   9-2

The reciprocal function models inverse variations. The graph of the parent reciprocal function $y = \frac{1}{x}$ is a hyperbola, but it is not identified as such in the text. The asymptotes are the x- and y-axes, so the hyperbola has been rotated from the vertical or horizontal format presented in Lesson 10-5. Each of the two parts of its graph is called a branch and they exhibit self-symmetry for the line $y = x$ and symmetry between the branches for the line $y = -x$.

The general form of the translated reciprocal function is $y = \frac{a}{x - h} + k$ where $x \neq h$ and (h, k) is the center point where the asymptotes intersect. Graphs of translated reciprocal functions have point or rotational symmetry with a center of rotation of (h, k).

Students may be helped by a discussion of the meaning of having no y-intercept. For instance, in Example 3, if a pipe has no length, it clearly will produce no sound. Students must also understand that the graphs of reciprocal functions are discontinuous, having a "break" in the domain where one x-value (the asymptote) is undefined.

Rational Functions and Their Graphs 9-3

When working with rational functions, we assume that the denominator cannot equal zero because the function would then be undefined. The graphs of rational functions can be either continuous or discontinuous, with discontinuous graphs having holes and/or vertical asymptotes. Graphs of rational functions have at most one horizontal asymptote when the degree of the numerator is less than or equal to the degree of the denominator.

In addition to horizontal and vertical asymptotes, students may enjoy using polynomial division to find the nonhorizontal linear asymptotes that occur in graphing rational functions whose numerator is one degree greater than its denominator.

Rational Expressions 9-4

Students should understand that the restrictions on the variable come from the denominators of each initial expression (before they are simplified). The text lists all possible restrictions. Sometimes the convention is to list only restrictions that are not still included in the simplified expression. Thus, 4 would *not* be listed as a restriction for the simplified expression $\frac{5x}{x-4}$ because it is obviously a restriction since at least one factor of $x-4$ was not eliminated.

Have students look over the exercises and discuss which of the exercises can be more easily simplified by multiplying numerator and denominator by the LCD and which are more easily simplified by multiplying the numerator by the reciprocal of the denominator.

Adding and Subtracting Rational Expressions 9-5

Students can use the formula $\frac{a}{b} \pm \frac{c}{d} = \frac{ad \pm bc}{bd}$ to add or subtract rational expressions. While this technique will always provide an answer, students should be aware of the following two shortcomings:

- If more than two fractions are to be added or subtracted, it is tiresome to have to apply this formula over and over again.

- When the formula is applied to rational expressions whose denominators have a common factor, it sometimes becomes difficult for students to write a solution in simplest form.

Solving Rational Equations 9-6

No extraneous solutions can be introduced when solving an equation using the addition property of equality because both of the following are true for all numbers:

If $a = b$, then $a + c = b + c$.

If $a + c = b + c$, then $a = b$.

However, extraneous solutions can be introduced when solving an equation using the multiplication property of equality.

If $a = b$, then $a \cdot c = b \cdot c$ is true for all numbers a, b, and c.

But if $a \cdot c = b \cdot c$, then $a = b$ may not be true if $c = 0$.

This means that solutions of the derived equation may not be solutions of the original equation. It is essential to check solutions to equations that are solved using the multiplication property because the procedure can introduce extraneous (wrong) answers.

Probability of Multiple Events 9-7

This lesson defines independent, dependent, and mutually exclusive events. Students may have an intuitive grasp of independent events, but you may wish to point out to them that the algebraic definition is sometimes the only guarantee of independence.

Students should understand that if two events are mutually exclusive, they cannot be independent and vice versa. For example, a student cannot be both male and female, nor can they be aged 15 and 17 (mutually exclusive events). However, a student can be both male and 15, or both female and 17 (independent events). Students will continue their study of probability in Chapter 12.

Additional Professional Development Opportunities

Math Background notes for Chapter 9: Every lesson has a Math Background in the PLAN section.

Research Overview, Mathematical Strands
Additional support for these topics and more is in the front of this Teacher's Edition.

Lesson Lab
Lesson Lab, a Pearson Education company, offers comprehensive, facilitated professional development designed to help teachers improve student achievement. To learn more, please visit lessonlab.com

Chapter 9 Resources

Print Resources

		9-1	9-2	9-3	9-4	9-5	9-6	9-7	For the Chapter
L3	Practice	●	●	●	●	●	●	●	
L3	Guided Problem Solving	●	●	●	●	●	●	●	
L2	Reteaching	●	●	●	●	●	●	●	
L4	Enrichment	●	●	●	●	●	●	●	
L3	Daily Notetaking Guide	●	●	●	●	●	●	●	
L3	Vocabulary and Study Skills Worksheets	●							●
L3	Chapter Project								●
L3	Hands On Activities		●		●				
L3	Checkpoint Quiz			●		●			
L2	Below Level Chapter Test								●
L3	Chapter Test								●
L4	Alternative Assessment								●
L3	Cumulative Review								●
L4	Connections to Precalculus Masters	●	●	●	●	●	●	●	
L3	Technology Activities			●					

Spanish Resources ELL

		9-1	9-2	9-3	9-4	9-5	9-6	9-7	For the Chapter
L3	Practice	●	●	●	●	●	●	●	
L3	Vocabulary and Study Skills Worksheets	●							●
L3	Checkpoint Quiz			●		●			
L2	Below Level Chapter Test								●
L3	Chapter Test								●
L4	Alternative Assessment								●
L3	Cumulative Review								●

Transparencies

	9-1	9-2	9-3	9-4	9-5	9-6	9-7	For the Chapter
Check Skills You'll Need	●	●	●	●	●	●	●	
Additional Examples	●	●	●	●	●	●	●	
Problem of the Day	●	●	●	●	●	●	●	
Classroom Aid		●	●					
Student Edition Answers	●	●	●	●	●	●	●	●
Lesson Quiz	●	●	●	●	●	●	●	
Test-Taking Strategies								●

Technology

	9-1	9-2	9-3	9-4	9-5	9-6	9-7	For the Chapter
TI 83/84 Plus Activities		●						
Interactive Textbook Online	●	●	●	●	●	●	●	●
Student Express CD-ROM	●	●	●	●	●	●	●	●
TI Navigator, Instant Check System	●	●	●	●	●	●	●	
Success Tracker	●	●	●	●	●	●	●	●
ExamView CD-ROM with Quick Take	●	●	●	●	●	●	●	●
Teacher Express CD-ROM	●	●	●	●	●	●	●	●
Presentation Express CD-ROM	●	●	●	●	●	●	●	●
Mindpoint Quiz Show CD-ROM	●	●	●	●	●	●	●	●
Prentice Hall Web site: PHSchool.com	●	●	●	●	●	●	●	●

Also available: Prentice Hall Assessment System (Progress Monitoring Assessments, Skills and Concepts Review, Test Prep Workbook)   Solution Key   Student Workbook
Student Workbook, Adapted Version   Data Analysis and Probability Workbook   Math Notes Study Folder   Spanish Cumulative Assessment

Where You Can Use the Lesson Resources

Here is a suggestion, following the four-step teaching plan, for how you can incorporate Differentiated Instruction Resources into your teaching.

	Instructional Resources L3	**Differentiated** Instruction **Resources**
1. Plan		
Check Skills You'll Need Assign these exercises to review prerequisite skills. **New Vocabulary** Help students pre-read the lesson by pointing out the new terms introduced in the lesson.	**Math Background** **Transparencies & Presentation Express CD** Check Skills You'll Need **Resources** Vocabulary and Study Skills	**Spanish Support** **ELL** Vocabulary and Study Skills
2. Teach		
L3 Guided Instruction Teach each Example. After each Example, assign the Quick Check exercise for that Example.	**Student Edition** Activity Lab **Resources** Daily Notetaking Guide Activity Lab TI-83/84 Activities CD-ROM **Transparencies & Presentation Express CD** Additional Examples Classroom Aids **ExamView CD-ROM with QuickTake** **TI Navigator Instant Check System**	**Teacher's Edition** Every lesson includes suggestions for working with students who need special attention. **L1** Special Needs **L2** Below Level **L4** Advanced Learners **ELL** English Language Learners
3. Practice		
Assignment Guide **Homework Exercises** Assign the exercises cited in each lesson's Assignment Guide. A Practice by Example B Apply Your Skills C Challenge Test Prep Mixed Review **Homework Quick Check** Discuss in class the exercises cited in each lesson's Assignment Guide.	**Transparencies & Presentation Express CD** Student Answers **Resources** Practice Guided Problem Solving Vocabulary and Study Skills Activity Lab **ExamView CD-ROM with QuickTake**	**Spanish Support** **ELL** Practice **ELL** Vocabulary and Study Skills **Resources** **L4** Enrichment
4. Assess & Reteach		
Lesson Quiz Assign the Lesson Quiz to assess students' mastery of the lesson content. **Checkpoint Quiz** Use the Checkpoint Quiz to assess student progress over several lessons.	**Transparencies & Presentation Express CD** Lesson Quiz **Resources** Checkpoint Quiz	**Resources** **L2** Reteaching **ELL** Checkpoint Quiz Success Tracker **ExamView CD-ROM with QuickTake**

KEY **L1** Special Needs **L2** Below Level **L3** For All Students **L4** Advanced, Gifted **ELL** English Language Learners

Chapter 9

Rational Functions

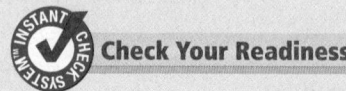

Check Your Readiness

Answers are in the back of the textbook.

For intervention, direct students to:

Finding Theoretical Properties
Lesson 1-6: Example 3
Extra Skills and Word
   Problems Practice, Ch. 1

Using Direct Variation
Lesson 2-3: Example 2
Extra Skills and Word
   Problems Practice, Ch. 2

Factoring Quadratic Expressions
Lesson 5-4: Example 1
Extra Skills and Word
   Problems Practice, Ch. 5

Solving Quadratic Equations
Lesson 5-5: Example 1
Extra Skills and Word
   Problems Practice, Ch. 5

Spanish Vocabulary/Study Skills | **ELL**

Vocabulary/Study Skills | **L3**

9A: Graphic Organizer | For use before Lesson 9-1

Study Skill: As you approach the latter part of the book, take a minute to flip back through the chapters that you have already learned. Think about some of the things that you have already learned. What was your favorite chapter? What was your least favorite? How do you think you will use what you've already learned in this chapter? Record your responses in your notebook.

Write your answers.

1. What is the chapter title? _____

2. Find the Table of Contents page for this chapter at the front of the book. Name four topics you will study in this chapter.
   _____
   _____

3. What is the topic of the Reading Math page? _____

4. What is the topic of the Test-Taking Strategy page? _____

5. Look through the pages of the chapter. List four real-world connections that you see discussed in this chapter.
   _____
   _____

6. Complete the graphic organizer below as you work through the chapter.
   • In the center, write the title of the chapter.
   • When you begin a lesson, write the lesson name in a rectangle.
   • When you complete a lesson, write a skill or key concept in an oval linked to that lesson block.
   • When you complete the chapter, use this graphic organizer to help you review.

What You've Learned

● In Chapter 1, you learned to find theoretical probabilities for random events.

● In Chapter 2, you learned to write and interpret direct variation equations to solve real-world problems.

● In Chapter 5, you learned to factor quadratic expressions and to solve quadratic equations.

Check Your Readiness   **GO** for **Help** to the Lesson in green.

Finding Theoretical Probabilities (Lesson 1-6)

A bookshelf contains 18 math books, 27 science books, 21 history books, and 15 grammar books. You pick one book at random from the shelf. Find each theoretical probability.

1. P(history) $\frac{7}{27}$ **2.** P(science) $\frac{1}{3}$ **3.** P(math or science) $\frac{5}{9}$

4. P(math or science or history) **5.** P(not grammar) $\frac{22}{27}$ **6.** P(not math and not science) $\frac{12}{27}$
$\frac{22}{27}$

Using Direct Variation (Lesson 2-3)

For each direct variation, find the constant of variation. Then find the value of y when $x = -3$.

7. $y = 4$ when $x = 3$ $\frac{4}{3}$; -4 **8.** $y = 1$ when $x = -1.5$ $-\frac{2}{3}$; 2

9. $y = -5$ when $x = \frac{3}{2}$ $-\frac{10}{3}$; 10 **10.** $y = -16$ when $x = 7$ $-\frac{16}{7}$; $\frac{48}{7}$

Factoring Quadratic Expressions (Lesson 5-4)

Factor each expression.

11. $x^2 + x - 6$ $(x + 3)(x - 2)$ **12.** $4x^2 + 17x + 15$ $(4x + 5)(x + 3)$ **13.** $9x^2 - 25$ $(3x - 5)(3x + 5)$

14. $x^2 - 12x + 36$ $(x - 6)^2$ **15.** $3x^2 + 10x + 8$ **16.** $x^2 - 5x + 6$ $(x - 3)(x - 2)$
$(3x + 4)(x + 2)$

Solving Quadratic Equations (Lesson 5-5)

Solve each equation.

17. $x^2 + 7x - 8 = 0$ $1, -8$ **18.** $\frac{1}{4}x^2 + \frac{7}{2}x = -12$ $-6, -8$ **19.** $3x^2 = 18x - 24$ $4, 2$

20. $9x^2 + 6x = 0$ $0, -\frac{2}{3}$ **21.** $4x^2 + 16 = 34x$ $8, \frac{1}{2}$ **22.** $x^2 - 13x - 30 = 0$ $15, -2$

486 Chapter 9

Rational Functions

What You'll Learn Next

- In Chapter 9, you will learn to use inverse variation and the graphs of inverse variations to solve real-world problems.

- You will learn to identify properties of rational functions.

- You will learn to simplify rational expressions and to solve rational equations.

Real-World Connection Applying what you learn, on page 515 you will solve a problem involving photography.

🔊 Key Vocabulary

- branch (p. 495)
- complex fraction (p. 516)
- dependent events (p. 531)
- independent events (p. 531)
- inverse variation (p. 488)
- joint variation (p. 490)
- mutually exclusive events (p. 533)
- point of discontinuity (p. 501)
- rational function (p. 501)
- reciprocal function (p. 495)
- simplest form (p. 509)

Chapter 9 Overview

Students begin the chapter by exploring the concept of inverse variation, and learning how to graph inverse variations. Students then study rational functions and their graphs. Students then study how to multiply, divide, add, and subtract rational expressions. They then study how to solve rational equations. Students conclude the chapter by exploring finding the probability of multiple events.

Activating Prior Knowledge

Ask:
- *What is the general form of a polynomial function?*

Answers should be of the form $y = a_n x^n + a_{n-1} x^{n-1} + \cdots + a_1 x + a_0$ where n is a nonnegative integer and $a_n, \cdots, a_0$ are real numbers.

Ask:
- *What if the exponent n was a negative integer, such as $y = x^{-1}$? Can you rewrite this with a positive exponent?*

Answers should indicate that $y = x^{-1}$ is by definition not a polynomial function. Guide students to rewrite the function as $y = \frac{1}{x}$.

Tell students that $y = \frac{1}{x}$ is called a reciprocal function, and that they will study them in this chapter.

487

Objectives

1 To use inverse variation
2 To use joint and other variations

Examples

1 Modeling Inverse Variation
2 Identifying Direct and Inverse Variations
3 Real-World Connection
4 Real-World Connection
5 Finding a Formula

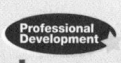

Math Background

In Chapter 2, students learned that in a direct variation $y = kx$, $(k > 0)$, the y-values increase as the x-values increase. The opposite is true for an inverse variation, $y = \frac{k}{x}$. The y-values decrease as the x-values increase. Students will learn later that the graph is a hyperbola.

More Math Background: p. 486C

Lesson Planning and Resources

See p. 486E for a list of the resources that support this lesson.

✓ Check Skills You'll Need

For intervention, direct students to:

Direct Variation
Lesson 2-3: Example 4
Extra Skills and Word
Problems Practice, Ch. 2

Inverse Variation

What You'll Learn

- To use inverse variation
- To use joint and other variations

. . . And Why

To find the life spans of mammals, as in Example 3

✓ Check Skills You'll Need

 for Help Lesson 2-3

In Exercises 1–3, y varies directly with x.
1. Given that $x = 2$ when $y = 4$, find y when $x = 5$. **10**
2. Given that $x = 1$ when $y = 5$, find y when $x = 3$. **15**
3. Given that $x = 10$ when $y = 3$, find y when $x = 4$. **1.2**

🔊 **New Vocabulary** • inverse variation • joint variation

---

1 Using Inverse Variation

In Chapter 2, you studied direct variation. You can model a direct variation with an equation of the form $y = kx$, where $k \neq 0$. You can model an **inverse variation** with any of the equations $xy = k$, $y = \frac{k}{x}$, or $x = \frac{k}{y}$, where $k \neq 0$. As with direct variation, k is the constant of variation.

The table and graph below show the times needed to ride a bike 24 miles at different rates.

Rate (mi/h)	Time (h)
3	8
6	4
12	2
24	1

Notice that as the rate increases, the time decreases. Doubling the rate halves the time. The inverse variation $rt = 24$, or $t = \frac{24}{r}$, models this situation.

1 EXAMPLE Modeling Inverse Variation

Suppose that x and y vary inversely, and $x = 3$ when $y = -5$. Write the function that models the inverse variation.

$$y = \frac{k}{x} \qquad \text{\textit{x} and \textit{y} vary inversely.}$$

$$-5 = \frac{k}{3} \qquad \text{Substitute the given values of \textit{x} and \textit{y}.}$$

$$-15 = k \qquad \text{Find \textit{k}.}$$

$$y = \frac{-15}{x} \qquad \text{Use the value of \textit{k} to write the function.}$$

Vocabulary Tip

You can describe an <u>inverse variation</u> as "y varies inversely as x" or as "y is inversely proportional to x."

488 Chapter 9 Rational Functions

Differentiated Instruction Solutions for All Learners

Special Needs L1
Review the formula distance = rate × time and relate it to the opening table and graph. Show that many combinations of rate and time have a product of 24 miles. Then ask: *As the rate values get larger, what happens to the time values?* smaller

learning style: verbal

Below Level L2
If students are unsure whether a function is a direct variation or indirect variation, suggest that they consider substituting in both $y = kx$ and $y = \frac{k}{x}$.

learning style: verbal

Quick Check **1** Suppose that x and y vary inversely, and $x = 0.3$ when $y = 1.4$. Write the function that models the inverse variation. $y = \frac{0.42}{x}$

2 **EXAMPLE** Identifying Direct and Inverse Variations

For: Variation Activity
Use: Interactive Textbook, 9-1

Is the relationship between the variables in each table a direct variation, an inverse variation, or neither? Write functions to model the direct and inverse variations.

a.

x	0.5	2	6
y	1.5	6	18

As x increases, y increases. Since each y-value is 3 times the corresponding x-value, y varies directly with x, the constant of variation is 3, and the function is $y = 3x$.

b.

x	0.2	0.6	1.2
y	12	4	2

As x increases, y decreases. The product of each pair of x- and y-values is 2.4. y varies inversely with x and the constant of variation is 2.4. So $xy = 2.4$ and the function is $y = \frac{2.4}{x}$.

c.

x	1	2	3
y	2	1	0.5

As x increases, y decreases, but this is not an inverse variation. Not all the products of x and y are the same ($2 \cdot 1 \ne 3 \cdot 0.5$). This is neither a direct variation nor an inverse variation.

 Quick Check **2** Is the relationship between the values in each table a direct variation, an inverse variation, or neither? Write functions to model the direct and inverse variations.

a.

x	0.8	0.6	0.4
y	0.9	1.2	1.8

b.

x	2	4	6
y	3.2	1.6	1.1

c.

x	1.2	1.4	1.6
y	18	21	24

2a. inverse; $y = \frac{0.72}{x}$

b. neither

c. direct; $y = 15x$

3 **EXAMPLE** Real-World Connection

Zoology Heart rates and life spans of most mammals are inversely related. Use the data to write a function that models this inverse variation. Use your function to estimate the average life span of a cat with a heart rate of 126 beats/min.

Heart Rate and Life Span

Mammal	Heart rate (beats/min)	Life span (min)
Mouse	634	1,576,800
Rabbit	158	6,307,200
Lion	76	13,140,000
Horse	63	15,768,000

SOURCE: *The Handy Science Answer Book*

Relate $\boxed{\text{heart rate}} \cdot \boxed{\text{life span}} = \boxed{\text{a constant}}$

Define Let $\boxed{r}$ = heart rate (beats/min).

Let $\boxed{s}$ = life span (min).

Let $\boxed{k}$ = constant of variation (beats in a life span).

Write $\boxed{r}\ \boxed{s} = \boxed{k}$

For each of the four mammals in the table, $rs \approx 1,000,000,000$.

$rs = 1,000,000,000$ **Substitute 1,000,000,000 for k.**

$126s = 1,000,000,000$ **Substitute 126 for r.**

$s \approx 8,000,000$

A cat's life span is about 8 million minutes, or about 15.2 years.

Real-World Connection

Horses have a life span of about 30 years.

3a. about 5,000,000 min, or about 10 yr

Quick Check **3** **a.** A squirrel's heart rate is 190 beats per minute. Estimate its life span.
b. An elephant's life span is about 70 years. Estimate its average heart rate.
about 27 beats per min

---

2. Teach

Guided Instruction

1 **EXAMPLE** Math Tip

Point out that in any inverse variation function, the values of x and y are never zero. Ask students why. The definition of an inverse variation says $k \ne 0$. So, if $xy = k$, neither x nor y can be 0.

PowerPoint

Additional Examples

1 Suppose that x and y vary inversely, and $x = 7$ when $y = 4$. Write the function that models the inverse variation. $y = \frac{28}{x}$

2 Is the relationship between the variables in each table a direct variation, an inverse variation, or neither? Write functions to model the direct and inverse variations.

a.

x	2	4	14
y	0.7	0.35	0.1

inverse variation; $y = \frac{1.4}{x}$

b.

x	−2	−1.3	7
y	6	5	−4

neither

c.

x	−2	4	6
y	5	−10	−15

direct variation; $y = -2.5x$

3 The pressure P of a sample of gas at a constant temperature varies inversely as the volume V. Use the data in the table to write a function that models this inverse variation. Use your equation to estimate the pressure when the volume is 6 in.^{3}. $P = \frac{96}{V}$; 16 lb/in.^{2}

Pressure (lb/in.^{2})	Volume (in.^{3})
3	32
5	19.2
8	12

Advanced Learners L4
If the temperature of an enclosed gas is held constant, the pressure and volume vary inversely. Discuss the volume if the pressure is doubled or halved.

learning style: verbal

English Language Learners ELL
For Example 3, explain the terms *zoology, heart rate, life span,* and *mammal,* or have a student find their definitions. Ask: *For a life span of 75 years, what heart rate would you expect?* **around 25 beats/min**

learning style: verbal

489

4 EXAMPLE **Connection to Physics**

You may want to tell students that the constant G has a value of about 6.672×10^{-11} N $\frac{m^2}{kg^2}$, where N stands for the unit of force called the *newton*.

Additional Examples

4 The mass m of a moving object is related to its kinetic energy k and its velocity v by the formula $m = \frac{2k}{v^2}$. Describe the relationship as a combined variation. *m varies directly as the kinetic energy k and inversely as the square of the velocity v.*

5 The area of an equilateral triangle varies directly as the square of the radius r of its circumscribed circle. The area of an equilateral triangle for which $r = 2$ is $3\sqrt{3}$. Find the formula for the area A of an equilateral triangle in terms of r.
$A = \frac{3\sqrt{3}}{4}r^2$

Resources
• Daily Notetaking Guide 9-1 **L3**

Closure

Ask students to write an equation that shows what it means for a quantity w to vary jointly as x and y and inversely as z. *$w = \frac{kxy}{z}$, where k is a nonzero constant*

Quantities can vary with respect to each other in different ways. For example, y can vary directly with x^3 ($y = kx^3$) or inversely with x^2 ($y = \frac{k}{x^2}$).

It is possible for three or more variables to be related. When one quantity varies with respect to two or more other quantities, the result is a combined variation. For example, a variable z can vary directly with both x and y. You can model such a **joint variation** with the equation $z = kxy$, where $k \neq 0$.

Vocabulary Tip

z varies jointly with x and y means z varies directly with the product of x and y.

Examples of Combined Variations

Combined Variation	Equation Form
z varies jointly with x and y.	$z = kxy$
z varies jointly with x and y and inversely with w.	$z = \frac{kxy}{w}$
z varies directly with x and inversely with the product wy.	$z = \frac{kx}{wy}$

Test-Taking Tip

Use dimensional analysis to check that a formula makes sense. For example, in.^{2} • in. = in.^{3} suggests that $V = Bh$ is correct.

4 EXAMPLE **Real-World Connection**

Physics Newton's Law of Universal Gravitation is modeled by the formula $F = \frac{Gm_1m_2}{d^2}$. F is the gravitational force between two objects with masses m_1 and m_2, and d is the distance between the objects. G is the gravitational constant. Describe Newton's law as a combined variation.

$F = \frac{Gm_1m_2}{d^2}$ ← F varies jointly with the masses m_1 and m_2, and
              ← F varies inversely with the square of the distance d.

✓ **Quick Check** **4** **Geometry** The formula for the area of a trapezoid is $A = \frac{1}{2}h(b_1 + b_2)$. Describe this relationship as a combined variation. ***A varies jointly with the height and the sum of the bases.***

5 EXAMPLE **Finding a Formula**

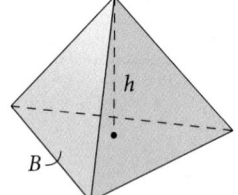

Multiple Choice The volume V of a tetrahedron varies jointly with its altitude h and base area B. A tetrahedron with a 5-cm altitude and 6-in.^{2} base has volume of 10 cm^3. Which formula models this joint variation?

   Ⓐ $V = 3Bh$ Ⓑ $V = \frac{1}{3}Bh$ Ⓒ $h = \frac{1}{12}VB$ Ⓓ $Vh = 5B$

$V = kBh$ **V varies jointly with B and h.**

$10 = k(6)(5)$ **Substitute given values for V, B, and h.**

$\frac{1}{3} = k$ **Solve for k.**

$V = \frac{1}{3}Bh$ **Substitute the value for k.**

The correct choice is B.

✓ **Quick Check** **5** The volume of a square pyramid with congruent edges varies directly as the cube of the length of an edge. The volume of a square pyramid with edge length 4 is $\frac{32\sqrt{2}}{3}$. Find the formula for the volume of a square pyramid with congruent edges.

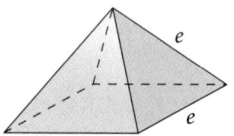

$V = \frac{\sqrt{2}}{6}e^3$

EXERCISES

For more exercises, see *Extra Skill and Word Problem Practice*.

Practice and Problem Solving

 Practice by Example

Example 1
(page 488)

 for Help

Suppose that x and y vary inversely. Write a function that models each inverse variation.

1. $x = 1$ when $y = 11$ $\quad y = \frac{11}{x}$

2. $x = -13$ when $y = 100$ $\quad y = -\frac{1300}{x}$

3. $x = 1$ when $y = 1$ $\quad y = \frac{1}{x}$

4. $x = 28$ when $y = -2$ $\quad y = -\frac{56}{x}$

5. $x = 1.2$ when $y = 3$ $\quad y = \frac{3.6}{x}$

6. $x = 2.5$ when $y = 100$ $\quad y = \frac{250}{x}$

Example 2
(page 489)

Is the relationship between the values in each table a direct variation, an inverse variation, or neither? Write equations to model the direct and inverse variations.

7.

x	3	8	10	22
y	15	40	50	110

7. direct; $y = 5x$

8.

x	3	5	7	10.5
y	14	8.4	6	4

8. inverse; $y = \frac{42}{x}$

9.

x	0.5	2.1	3.5	11
y	1	4.2	7	22

9. direct; $y = 2x$

10.

x	0.1	3	6	24
y	3	0.1	0.05	0.0125

10. inverse; $y = \frac{0.3}{x}$

11.

x	7	3	1	$\frac{1}{5}$
y	$\frac{1}{7}$	$\frac{1}{3}$	1	5

inverse; $y = \frac{1}{x}$

12.

x	10	12	20	23
y	2	$2\frac{2}{5}$	4	$5\frac{3}{5}$

neither

Example 3
(page 489)

Suppose that x and y vary inversely. Write a function that models each inverse variation and find y when $x = 10$.

13. $x = 20$ when $y = 5$
$y = \frac{100}{x}$; 10

14. $x = 20$ when $y = -4$
$y = -\frac{80}{x}$; -8

15. $x = 5$ when $y = -\frac{1}{3}$
$y = -\frac{5}{3x}$; $-\frac{1}{6}$

Example 4
(page 490)

Describe the combined variation that is modeled by each formula.

16. $A = \pi r^2$

17. $A = 0.5bh$

18. $h = \frac{2A}{b}$

19. $V = \frac{Bh}{3}$

20. $V = \pi r^2 h$

21. $h = \frac{V}{\pi r^2}$

22. $V = \ell w h$

23. $\ell = \frac{V}{wh}$

16–23. See margin.

Example 5
(page 490)

Write the function that models each variation. Find z when $x = 4$ and $y = 9$.

24. z varies directly with x and inversely with y. When $x = 6$ and $y = 2$, $z = 15$.
$z = \frac{5x}{y}$; $\frac{20}{9}$

25. $z = 10xy$; 360

25. z varies jointly with x and y. When $x = 2$ and $y = 3$, $z = 60$.

26. z varies directly with the square of x and inversely with y. When $x = 2$ and $y = 4$, $z = 3$. $z = \frac{3x^2}{y}$; $\frac{16}{3}$

27. $z = \frac{4}{xy}$; $\frac{1}{9}$

27. z varies inversely with the product of x and y. When $x = 2$ and $y = 4$, $z = 0.5$.

 Apply Your Skills

28. a. The spreadsheet shows data that could be modeled by an equation of the form $PV = k$. Estimate the value of k. **14,000**
b. Estimate P when $V = 62$. **226**

Each ordered pair is from an inverse variation. Find the constant of variation.

29. $(6, 3)$ 18

30. $(0.9, 4)$ 3.6

31. $\left(\frac{3}{8}, \frac{2}{3}\right)$ $\frac{1}{4}$

32. $\left(\sqrt{2}, \sqrt{18}\right)$ 6

33. $\left(\sqrt{3}, \sqrt{27}\right)$ 9

34. $\left(\sqrt{8}, \sqrt{32}\right)$ 16

	A	B
	P	V
1	P	V
2	140.00	100
3	147.30	95
4	155.60	90
5	164.70	85
6	175.00	80
7	186.70	75

Lesson 9-1 Inverse Variation **491**

16. A varies directly with the square of r.

17. A varies jointly with b and h.

18. h varies directly with A and inversely with b.

19. V varies jointly with B and h.

20. V varies jointly with h and the square of r.

21. h varies directly with V and inversely with the square of r.

22. V varies jointly with ℓ, w, and h.

23. ℓ varies directly with V and inversely with the product of w and h.

3. Practice

Assignment Guide

1 A B 1-15, 28-35, 37-48

2 A B 16-27, 36, 49-55

C Challenge 56-59

Test Prep 60-64
Mixed Review 65-74

Homework Quick Check

To check students' understanding of key skills and concepts, go over Exercises 14, 26, 35, 53, 55.

Error Prevention!

Exercises 43–48 Students may try setting up and solving a proportion. For instance, in Exercise 43, they may write $\frac{7}{3} = \frac{y}{8}$ and conclude that $y = \frac{56}{3}$. Point out that for direct variation, the ratio of y-values to x-values is constant, but for inverse variation, the *product* of y-values and x-values is constant.

Auditory Learners

Exercises 49–51 Students may find it helpful to use different words to say to themselves what each variation statement means. For example, for Exercise 49, they can say, "y equals some constant divided by the square of x."

Differentiated Instruction Resources

GPS **Guided Problem Solving** L3
Enrichment L4
Reteaching L2
Practice L3

491

4. Assess & Reteach

PowerPoint

Lesson Quiz

1. Suppose x and y vary inversely, and $x = 5$ when $y = 1.6$.
   a. Write a function that models the inverse variation. $y = \frac{8}{x}$
   b. Find y when $x = 32$. **0.25**

Tell whether the relationship between the variables in each table is a direct variation, an inverse variation, or neither. Write functions to model the direct and inverse variations.

2.

x	0.1	1.5	4
y	3	2	1.6

neither

3.

x	48	−4	8
y	2	−24	12

inverse variation; $y = \frac{96}{x}$

4.

x	3	7	−10
y	21	49	−70

direct variation; $y = 7x$

5. Describe the combined variation modeled by the formula $V = \frac{1}{3}\pi r^2 h$.
   V varies jointly as the square of r and h.

6. Suppose z varies directly as x and inversely as the square of y. When $x = 35$ and $y = 7$, the value of z is 50. Write the function that models the relationship and find z when $x = 5$ and $y = 10$. $z = \frac{70x}{y^2}$, **3.5**

Alternative Assessment

Have students work in pairs. Each student should create a table of values in which y and x vary directly, one in which y and x vary inversely, and one in which z varies jointly as x and y. Students trade tables. Each student writes an equation that models the variation for each table.

492

GO Online
Homework Video Tutor
Visit: PHSchool.com
Web Code: age-0901

Exercise 52

C Challenge

35. **Mechanics** Gear A drives Gear B. Gear A has a teeth and speed r_A in revolutions per minute (rpm). Gear B has b teeth and speed r_B. The quantities are related by the formula $ar_A = br_B$. Gear A has 60 teeth and speed 5400 rpm. Gear B has 45 teeth. Find the speed of Gear B. **7200 rpm**

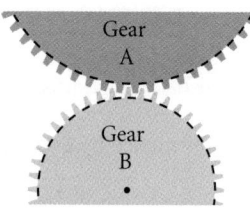

36. **Physics** The force F of gravity on a rocket varies directly with its mass m and inversely with the square of its distance d from Earth. Write a model for this combined variation. $F = k\frac{m}{d^2}$

Each pair of values is from a direct variation. Find the missing value.

37. $(3, 7), (8, y)$ **$18\frac{2}{3}$**   38. $(2, 5), (4, y)$ **10**   39. $(4, 6), (x, 3)$ **2**

40. $(9, 5), (x, 3)$ **5.4**   41. $(8.3, 7.1), (5, y)$ **4.277**   42. $(2.6, 4.5), (x, 6.3)$ **3.64**

Each pair of values is from an inverse variation. Find the missing value.

43. $(3, 7), (8, y)$ **2.625**   44. $(2, 5), (4, y)$ **2.5**   45. $(4, 6), (x, 3)$ **8**

46. $(9, 5), (x, 3)$ **15**   47. $(8.3, 7.1), (5, y)$ **11.786**   48. $(2.6, 4.5), (x, 6.3)$ **1.857**

49. Suppose that y varies inversely with the square of x, and $y = 50$ when $x = 4$. Find y when $x = 5$. **32**

50. Suppose that c varies jointly with d and the square of g, and $c = 30$ when $d = 15$ and $g = 2$. Find d when $c = 6$ and $g = 8$. **$\frac{3}{16}$**

51. Suppose that d varies jointly with r and t, and $d = 110$ when $r = 55$ and $t = 2$. Find r when $d = 40$ and $t = 3$. **$\frac{40}{3}$**

52. **Construction** A concrete supplier sells premixed concrete in 300-ft^3 truckloads. The area A that the concrete will cover is inversely proportional to the depth d of the concrete.
   a. Write a model for the relationship between the area and the depth of a truckload of poured concrete. $A = \frac{300}{d}$
   b. What area will the concrete cover if it is poured to a depth of 0.5 ft? A depth of 1 ft? A depth of 1.5 ft? **600 ft^2; 300 ft^2; 200 ft^2**
   c. When the concrete is poured into a circular area, the depth of the concrete is inversely proportional to the square of the radius r. Write a model for this relationship. $d = \frac{300}{\pi r^2}$

53. Suppose that y varies directly with x and inversely with z^2, and $x = 48$ **GPS** when $y = 8$ and $z = 3$. Find x when $y = 12$ and $z = 2$. **32**

54. Suppose that t varies directly with s and inversely with the square of r. How is the value of t changed when the value of s is doubled? Is tripled? **doubled; tripled**

55. Suppose that x varies directly with the square of y and inversely with z. How is the value of x changed if the value of y is halved? Is quartered? **quartered; divided by 16**

56. **Writing** Explain why 0 cannot be in the domain of an inverse variation. **Division by zero is undefined.**

57. **Critical Thinking** Suppose that (x_1, y_1) and (x_2, y_2) are values from an inverse variation. Show that $\frac{x_1}{x_2} = \frac{y_2}{y_1}$. **See margin.**

58. **Open-Ended** The height h of a cylinder varies directly with its volume V and inversely with the square of its radius r. Find at least four ways to change the volume and radius of a cylinder so that its height is quadrupled. **See margin.**

492   Chapter 9   Rational Functions

57. $x_1y_1 = k$ and $x_2y_2 = k$
   def. of inverse variation
   $x_1y_1 = x_2y_2$ transitivity
   $\frac{x_1}{x_2} = \frac{y_2}{y_1}$ Divide both
   sides by x_2y_1.

58. Answers may vary.
   Sample: Quadruple the volume and leave the radius constant, halve the radius and leave the volume constant, multiply the volume by 16 and double the radius, and multiply the volume and radius by $\frac{1}{4}$.

59. Health Health care professionals use the body mass index (BMI) to establish guidelines for determining any possible risks of their patients and for planning any useful preventative programs. The BMI varies directly with weight and inversely with the square of height. Use this portion of the BMI chart to determine the BMI formula. $BMI \approx \dfrac{705\,w}{h^2}$

Weights and Body Mass Index (BMI)

Height	Range of Weight (pounds)			
	BMI 19–24.9	BMI 25–29.9	BMI 30–39.9	BMI ≥ 40
5'6"	118–154	155–185	186–246	≥247
5'7"	121–158	159–190	191–254	≥255
5'8"	125–163	164–196	197–261	≥262
5'9"	128–168	169–202	203–269	≥270
5'10"	132–173	174–208	209–277	≥278
5'11"	136–178	179–214	215–285	≥286
6'0"	140–183	184–220	221–293	≥294

Test Prep

Multiple Choice

60. Which equation does NOT represent inverse variation between x and z?   **B**

A. $x = \dfrac{y}{z}$ **B.** $x = \dfrac{-15z}{y}$

C. $z = \dfrac{-15y}{x}$ **D.** $xz = 5y$

61. If p and q vary inversely, and $p = 10$ when $q = -4$, what is q when $p = -2$?   **F**

F. 20   **G.** $\dfrac{4}{5}$ **H.** $-\dfrac{4}{5}$ **J.** -20

62. Which equation shows that z varies directly with the square of x and inversely with the cube of y?   **A**

A. $z = \dfrac{x^2}{y^3}$ **B.** $z = \dfrac{x^3}{y^2}$ **C.** $z = \dfrac{y^2}{x^3}$ **D.** $z = \dfrac{y^3}{x^2}$

Short Response

63. Describe how the variables A and r vary in the formula for the area of a circle, $A = \pi r^2$.   **See margin.**

Extended Response

64. Which data set shows inverse variation: (24.4, 4.8) and (9.6, 12.2), or (24.0, 4.5) and (18.0, 6.5)? Explain.   **See margin.**

Mixed Review

Lesson 8-6   Solve each equation.

65. $\ln 4 + \ln x = 5$
$\dfrac{e^5}{4} \approx 37.1$

66. $\ln x - \ln 3 = 4$
$3e^4 \approx 163.79$

67. $2 \ln x + 3 \ln 4 = 4$
$\dfrac{e^2}{8} \approx 0.92$

Lesson 7-2   Multiply and simplify. Assume that all variables are positive.

68. $-5\sqrt{6x} \cdot 3\sqrt{6x^2}$
$-90x\sqrt{x}$

69. $3\sqrt[3]{4x^2} \cdot 7\sqrt[3]{12x^4}$
$42x^2\sqrt[3]{6}$

70. $\sqrt{5x^3} \cdot \sqrt{40xy^7}$
$10x^2y^3\sqrt{2y}$

Lesson 7-1   Simplify each radical expression. Use absolute value bars where they are needed.

71. $\sqrt{x^{10}y^{100}}$
$|x^5|y^{50}$

72. $\sqrt[3]{-64a^3b^6}$
$-4ab^2$

73. $\sqrt[4]{64m^8n^4}$
$2m^2|n|\sqrt[4]{4}$

74. $\sqrt[4]{x^4}$ $|x|$

Test Prep

 Resources
For additional practice with a variety of test item formats:
- Standardized Test Prep, p. 543
- Test-Taking Strategies, p. 538
- Test-Taking Strategies with Transparencies

63. **[2]** *A* varies directly with the square of *r* OR *r* varies directly with the square root of *A*.

[1] incomplete answer

64. **[4]** (24.4, 4.8) and (9.6, 12.2); in both pairs the product is 117.12, so *k* is the same for both. In the other 2 pairs *k* is not equal.

[3] appropriate methods, but one computational error

[2] incomplete explanation

[1] answer only, with no explanation

Guided Instruction

Technology Tip

Graphing calculators often display a graph that mistakenly includes vertical asymptotes. Using Dot mode is one way to get around this difficulty. The window settings can have a significant effect on the appearance of the graph of a rational function. You may want students to experiment with different settings.

Error Prevention!

Caution students to be careful with the use of parentheses when they enter the functions on the Y= list. Except for Exercise 3, the entire denominator of each fraction should be in parentheses.

Resources

Students may use any graphing calculator for this activity.

You can use your graphing calculator to graph members of the reciprocal function family and other rational functions. It is sometimes preferable to use the Dot plotting mode rather than the Connected plotting mode. The Connected mode can join branches of a graph that should be separated. Try both modes to get the best graph.

EXAMPLE

Graph $y = \frac{4}{x-3} - 1.5$.

Step 1 Press the MODE key. Scroll down to highlight the word Dot. Then press ENTER .

Step 2 Enter the function. Use parentheses to enter the denominator accurately.

Step 3 Graph the function.

EXERCISES

1. a. Graph the parent reciprocal function $y = \frac{1}{x}$. Sketch the graph on paper. **a–c. See margin.**

   b. Examine both negative and positive values of x. Describe what happens to the y-values as x approaches zero.

   c. What happens to the y-values as x increases? As x decreases?

2. a. Change the mode on your graphing calculator to **Connected**. Graph the function from the example. Sketch the graph. **a–c. See margin.**

   b. Press the TRACE key and trace the function. What happens between $x \approx 2.9$ and $x \approx 3.2$?

   c. **Critical Thinking** How does your graph differ from the graph in the example? Explain the differences.

Use a graphing calculator to graph each function. Then sketch the graph. **3–14. See back of book.**

3. $y = \frac{7}{x}$

4. $y = \frac{3}{x+4} - 2$

5. $y = \frac{x+2}{(x+1)(x+3)}$

6. $y = \frac{4x+1}{x-3}$

7. $y = \frac{2}{x-2}$

8. $y = \frac{1}{x+2} + 3$

9. $y = \frac{2x}{x+3}$

10. $y = \frac{x^2}{x^2-5}$

11. $y = \frac{20}{x^2+5}$

12. $y = \frac{1}{x-3} - 6$

13. $y = \frac{10}{x^2-5x-10}$

14. $y = \frac{x}{x^2-1}$

494   Activity Lab   Graphing Rational Functions

1a.

b. If x is negative and approaches 0, the y values approach $-\infty$. If x is positive and approaches 0, the y values approach $+\infty$.

c. As x increases, the y values approach 0; as x decreases, the y values approach 0.

494

2a.

b. Answers may vary. Sample: The y values change from very large negative values to very large positive values.

c. In connected mode, the calculator will try to connect the values for $x \approx 2.9$ and $x \approx 3.2$.

The Reciprocal Function Family

What You'll Learn

- To graph reciprocal functions
- To graph translations of reciprocal functions

. . . And Why

To analyze musical pitch and the size of the instrument, as in Example 3

✓ **Check Skills You'll Need**

GO **for Help** Lesson 2-6

Each of the following equations is a translation of $y = |x|$. Describe each translation.

1. $y = |x| + 2$ 2 units up
2. $y = |x + 2|$ 2 units left
3. $y = |x| - 3$ 3 units down
4. $y = |x - 3|$ 3 units right
5. $y = |x + 4| - 5$
   4 units left and 5 units down
6. $y = |x - 10| + 7$
   10 units right and 7 units up

🔊 **New Vocabulary** • reciprocal function • branch

Objectives

1 To graph reciprocal functions
2 To graph translations of reciprocal functions

Examples

1 Graphing an Inverse Variation
2 Graphing Reciprocal Functions
3 Real-World Connection
4 Graphing a Translation
5 Writing the Equation of a Transformation

---

1 Graphing Reciprocal Functions

Functions that model inverse variations belong to a family whose parent is the **reciprocal function** $f(x) = \frac{1}{x}$, where $x \neq 0$. The general form of a family member is $y = \frac{a}{x - h} + k$, with a single real number h missing from its domain.

The inverse variations $y = \frac{a}{x}$ are the stretches and shrinks of the parent reciprocal function.

1.

1 EXAMPLE Graphing an Inverse Variation

Sketch a graph of $y = \frac{6}{x}, x \neq 0$.

Make a table of values that includes positive and negative values of x.

x	−12	−6	−3	−2	−1	−$\frac{1}{2}$	$\frac{1}{2}$	1	2	3	6	12
y	−$\frac{1}{2}$	−1	−2	−3	−6	−12	12	6	3	2	1	$\frac{1}{2}$

Graph the points. Connect them with a smooth curve to the left of where $x = 0$ and another smooth curve to the right of where $x = 0$. Each part of the graph is called a **branch.**

The x-axis is a horizontal asymptote.

The y-axis is a vertical asymptote.

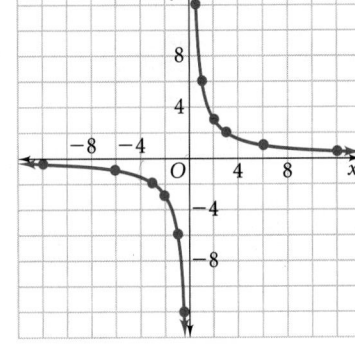

Vocabulary Tip

In a graph, a <u>branch</u> is a distinct part of a curve, just as, in nature, a branch is a distinct part of a river.

✓ **Quick Check** 1 Sketch a graph of $y = \frac{16}{x}$. **See left.**

Math Background

Graphs of inverse variations have two parts. However, many real-world applications are represented by only one of these parts, such as Example 3. Students should be careful to consider the domain relative to each problem situation.

More Math Background: p. 486C

Lesson Planning and Resources

See p. 486E for a list of the resources that support this lesson.

Bell Ringer Practice

✓ **Check Skills You'll Need**
For intervention, direct students to:

Vertical and Horizontal Translations
Lesson 2-6: Example 7
Extra Skills and Word
    Problems Practice, Ch. 2

Differentiated Instruction Solutions for All Learners

Special Needs L1
Have students test the translated function in Example 5. Students first sketch the translated graphs. Then they substitute coordinates into the equations and check that the points are on the graphs they sketched.

learning style: visual

Below Level L2
Review why certain values are excluded from the domain of a function. Discuss how asymptotes help you graph a function.

learning style: verbal

Guided Instruction

Point out that a wide variety of Andean panpipe music is available in libraries and record stores. The craftspeople that build such instruments understand the relationship between the length of a pipe and its pitch.

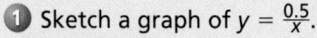

Additional Examples

1 Sketch a graph of $y = \frac{0.5}{x}$.

2 Compare the graphs of $y = \frac{1}{x}$ and $y = \frac{0.25}{x}$ shown below. What points on the graphs are closest to the origin?

The axes are asymptotes for both; both are symmetric with respect to $y = x$ and to $y = -x$. The graph of the second function is closest to the axes. The points $(1, 1)$, $(-1, -1)$, $(0.5, 0.5)$, and $(-0.5, -0.5)$ are closest to the origin.

Vocabulary Tip

Quadrant II	Quadrant I
Quadrant III	Quadrant IV

The branches of $y = \frac{1}{x}$ are in Quadrants I and III. Stretches of the parent function have the form $y = \frac{a}{x}$, where $a > 0$, and remain in Quadrants I and III. Their reflections, $y = \frac{-a}{x}$, are in Quadrants II and IV.

2 EXAMPLE Graphing Reciprocal Functions

Draw the graph of $f(x) = \frac{-4}{x}$. Describe properties of the graph.

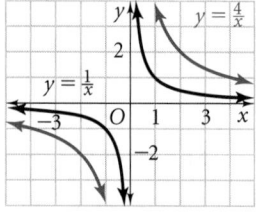

The graph of $y = \frac{4}{x}$ is a stretch of $y = \frac{1}{x}$ by a factor of 4.

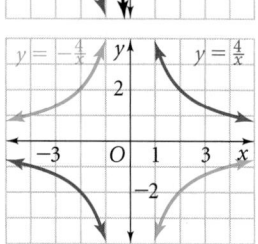

The graph of $y = \frac{-4}{x}$ is a reflection of $y = \frac{4}{x}$ in the x-axis.

The axes are asymptotes for each graph. Each graph is symmetric with respect to $y = x$ and $y = -x$.

✓ Quick Check **2** Use a graphing calculator. Set Xmin = −3, Xmax = 3, Ymin = −2, and Ymax = 2. Draw and compare the graphs of $y = \frac{1}{x}$, $y = \frac{2}{x}$, $y = \frac{-2}{x}$, $y = \frac{0.5}{x}$, and $y = \frac{-0.5}{x}$.
See back of book.

A situation in which an increase in one quantity is related to a proportional decrease in another quantity suggests inverse variation.

3 EXAMPLE Real-World Connection

Music A musical pitch is determined by the frequency of vibration of the sound waves reaching the ear. The greater the frequency, the higher is the pitch. Frequency is measured in vibrations per second, or hertz (Hz).

The pitch y produced by a panpipe varies inversely with the length x of the pipe. The function $y = \frac{564}{x}$ models the inverse variation where x is the length in feet. Find the length of the pipe that produces a pitch of 277 Hz.

Graph the functions $y = \frac{564}{x}$ and $y = 277$. Use the **Intersect** feature.

Xmin=0	Ymin=−75
Xmax=40	Ymax=300
Xscl=5	Yscl=50

Intersection
X=2.0361011 Y=277

The pipe should be about 2.0 ft long.

✓ Quick Check **3 a.** Pitches of 247 Hz, 311 Hz, and 370 Hz form a musical chord. Find the length of pipe that will produce each pitch. **2.28 ft, 1.81 ft, 1.52 ft**
b. **Writing** The asymptotes of $y = \frac{564}{x}$ are $x = 0$ and $y = 0$. Explain why this makes sense in terms of the panpipe. **As the pipe becomes very short, the pitch becomes very high (great frequency). As the pipe becomes very long, the pitch becomes low (frequency near 0).**

Real-World Connection

The length, not the diameter, of a panpipe or organ pipe determines its pitch.

496 Chapter 9 Rational Functions

Differentiated Instruction Solutions for All Learners

Advanced Learners L4
Have students compute the distance from the graph of Example 5 to the point $(2, -3)$ (the translated origin), and compare their methods.

learning style: verbal

English Language Learners ELL
Review *asymptotes* as lines a graph approaches but never reaches. Emphasize that an asymptote is not part of the graph. Contrast this with a *branch*, or part of a graph that has 2 or more parts.

learning style: verbal

The graphs at the right show the parent function $y = \frac{1}{x}$ and two of its translations, $y = \frac{1}{x-1}$ and $y = \frac{1}{x+2}$.

The vertical asymptotes of the graphs are $x = 0$, $x = 1$, and $x = -2$.

The graphs at the right show the parent function $y = \frac{1}{x}$ and two of its translations, $y = \frac{1}{x} + 1$ and $y = \frac{1}{x} - 2$.

The horizontal asymptotes of the graphs are $y = 0$, $y = 1$, and $y = -2$.

 Key Concepts

Summary	The Reciprocal Function Family

Parent function: $\qquad$ $y = \frac{1}{x}, x \neq 0$

$\left. \begin{array}{l} \text{Stretch } (|a| > 1) \\ \text{Shrink } (0 < |a| < 1) \\ \text{Reflection } (a < 0) \text{ in } x\text{-axis} \end{array} \right\}$ $\qquad y = \frac{a}{x}$

Translation (horizontal by h; vertical by k) with vertical asymptote $x = h$, horizontal asymptote $y = k$: $\quad y = \frac{1}{x-h} + k$

Combined: $\qquad\qquad\qquad\qquad\qquad y = \frac{a}{x-h} + k$

You can use asymptotes to graph translations of the parent function.

4 EXAMPLE Graphing a Translation

Sketch the graph of $y = \frac{1}{x-2} - 3$.

Step 1 Draw the asymptotes.
For $y = \frac{1}{x-2} + (-3)$,
$h = 2$ and $k = -3$.
The vertical asymptote is $x = 2$.
The horizontal asymptote is $y = -3$.

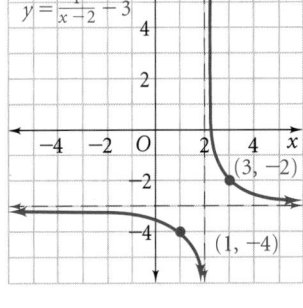

Step 2 Translate $y = \frac{1}{x}$.
The graph of $y = \frac{1}{x}$ includes $(1, 1)$ and $(-1, -1)$. Translate these points 2 units to the right and 3 units down to $(3, -2)$ and $(1, -4)$. Draw the branches through these points.

 Quick Check 4 Find the asymptotes and sketch the graph of $y = -\frac{1}{x+7} - 3$. **See back of book.**

Lesson 9-2 The Reciprocal Function Family $\quad$ **497**

 PowerPoint
Additional Examples

3 The frequency f in hertz of a sound wave varies inversely with its wavelength w. The function $f = \frac{343}{w}$ models the relationship between f and w for a wave with a velocity of 343 m/s. Find the wavelength of a sound wave with a frequency of 440 Hz. **about 0.78 m**

Guided Instruction

 PowerPoint
Additional Examples

4 Sketch the graph of $y = \frac{1}{x+2} + 2$.

5 Write an equation for the translation of $y = -\frac{7}{x}$ that has asymptotes at $x = 8$ and $y = -4$. $y = -\frac{7}{x-8} - 4$

Resources
• Daily Notetaking Guide 9-2 **L3**

Closure

Ask students to describe the graph of an inverse variation $y = \frac{k}{x}$. Ask them to write an equation for a translation of the graph a units to the right and b units up. Finally, ask them to write equations for the asymptotes of the translated graph. **Answers may vary. Sample: The graph will be in Quadrants I and III or else in Quadrants II and IV, depending on the sign of k. It will be symmetric with respect to $y = x$ and $y = -x$ and will have the axes as asymptotes; $y = \frac{k}{x-a} + b; x = a, y = b$**

 Online active math
For: Translation Activity
Use: Interactive Textbook, 9-2

Assignment Guide

1 A B 1-13, 25, 27-38

2 A B 14-24, 26, 39-47
C Challenge   48-52

Test Prep   53-59
Mixed Review   60-72

Homework Quick Check
To check students' understanding of key skills and concepts, go over Exercises 7, 19, 39, 45, 47.

Error Prevention!

Exercises 23, 24 Students may use the wrong operation sign in the denominator of their equation. Remind them that the *x*-value determining the vertical asymptote must be subtracted from *x* in the denominator of the equation for the translated graph.

Differentiated Instruction Resources

GPS Guided Problem Solving	L3
Enrichment	L4
Reteaching	L2
Practice	L3

If you know the translations or asymptotes of a stretch or shrink, $y = \frac{a}{x}$, then you can write its equation.

5 EXAMPLE **Writing the Equation of a Transformation**

Write an equation for the translation of $y = \frac{5}{x}$ that has asymptotes at $x = -2$ and $y = 3$.

$$y = \frac{5}{x - h} + k \qquad \text{Use the general form of a translation.}$$

$$= \frac{5}{x - (-2)} + 3 \qquad \text{Substitute } -2 \text{ for } h \text{ and } 3 \text{ for } k.$$

$$= \frac{5}{x + 2} + 3 \qquad \text{Simplify.}$$

An equation for the translation is $y = \frac{5}{x + 2} + 3$.

✓ Quick Check **5** **a.** Write an equation for the translation of $y = -\frac{1}{x}$ that is 4 units left and 5 units up.
b. Check your work by graphing your solution to part (a).
a. $y = -\frac{1}{x + 4} + 5$
b. See back of book.

EXERCISES

For more exercises, see *Extra Skill and Word Problem Practice*.

Practice and Problem Solving

A Practice by Example

1–3. See back of book.
Make a table of values. Then sketch a graph of each inverse variation.

  for Help

Example 1
(page 495)

1. $y = \frac{2}{x}$ **2.** $y = \frac{10}{x}$ **3.** $y = -\frac{10}{x}$

Example 2
(page 496)

4–9. See back of book.
Draw a graph of each function. Describe properties of the graph.

4. $y = \frac{0.2}{x}$ **5.** $y = \frac{-3}{x}$ **6.** $y = \frac{8}{x}$

7. $y = \frac{-5}{x}$ **8.** $y = \frac{100}{x}$ **9.** $y = \frac{-0.1}{x}$

Example 3
(page 496)

The weight P in pounds that a beam can safely carry is inversely proportional to the distance D in feet between the supports of the beam. For a certain type of wooden beam, $P = \frac{9200}{D}$. Use a graphing calculator and the Intersect feature to find the distance between supports that is needed to carry each given weight.

10. 500 lb 18.4 ft **11.** 1200 lb 7.67 ft **12.** 2400 lb 3.83 ft **13.** 5000 lb 1.84 ft

Example 4
(page 497)

Sketch the asymptotes and the graph of each equation. 14–21. See back of book.

14. $y = \frac{1}{x} - 3$ **15.** $y = \frac{-2}{x} - 3$ **16.** $y = \frac{1}{x - 2} + 5$ **17.** $y = \frac{1}{x - 3} + 4$

18. $y = \frac{2}{x + 6} - 1$ **19.** $y = \frac{-10}{x + 1} - 8$ **20.** $y = \frac{1}{x} + 2$ **21.** $y = \frac{-8}{x + 5} - 6$

Example 5
(page 498)

Write an equation for the translation of $y = \frac{2}{x}$ that has the given asymptotes.

22. $x = 0$ and $y = 4$ **23.** $x = -2$ and $y = 3$ **24.** $x = 4$ and $y = -8$
$y = \frac{2}{x} + 4$ $y = \frac{2}{x + 2} + 3$ $y = \frac{2}{x - 4} - 8$

B Apply Your Skills **25.** **Budgeting** A high school spends $750 each year on student academic achievement awards. The amount spent per award depends on how many awards are given. Write and graph a function that models the relationship between the number a of awards given and the cost c of each award. What are a reasonable domain and range for the function? **See back of book.**

26. Open-Ended Write an equation for a horizontal translation of $y = \frac{2}{x}$. Then write an equation for a vertical translation of $y = \frac{2}{x}$. Identify the horizontal and vertical asymptotes of the graph of each function. **Check students' work.**

Write each equation in the form $y = \frac{k}{x}$.

27. $y = \frac{1}{2x}$ $y = \frac{0.5}{x}$ **28.** $y = \frac{3}{4x}$ $y = \frac{0.75}{x}$ **29.** $y = -\frac{25}{3x}$ $y = -\frac{8.\overline{3}}{x}$

30. $xy = -0.01$ $y = -\frac{0.01}{x}$ **31.** $3xy = 12$ $y = \frac{4}{x}$ **32.** $-7 = 5xy$ $y = -\frac{1.4}{x}$

Sketch the graph of each function.   33–38. See back of book.

33. $xy = 3$ **34.** $xy + 5 = 0$ **35.** $3xy = 1$

36. $5xy = 2$ **37.** $10xy = -4$ **38.** $3xy = -17$

39. Writing Explain how knowing the asymptotes of a translation of $y = \frac{k}{x}$ can help you graph the function. Include an example. **See left.**

40. Multiple Choice The formula $p = \frac{69.1}{a + 2.3}$ models the relation between atmospheric pressure p in inches of mercury and altitude a in miles.

Use the data shown with the photo. At which location does the model predict the pressure to be about 23.93 in. of mercury? **B**

  Ⓐ Sahara Desert
  Ⓑ Kalahari Desert
  Ⓒ Mt. Kilimanjaro
  Ⓓ Vinson Massif

Sahara Desert
average alt. 1500 ft

Kalahari Desert
average alt. 3100 ft

Mt. Kilimanjaro
alt. 19,340 ft

Vinson Massif
alt. 16,860 ft

Graph each pair of functions. Find the approximate point(s) of intersection.
41–46. See back of book.

41. $y = \frac{6}{x - 2}, y = 6$ **42.** $y = -\frac{1}{x - 3} - 6, y = 6.2$

43. $y = \frac{3}{x + 1}, y = -4$ **44.** $y = -\frac{2}{x^2}, y = -10$

45. $y = -\frac{1}{x - 4}, y = 4.2$ **46.** $y = \frac{4}{x^2} + 2, y = 9$

🌐 **47. a. Gasoline Mileage** Suppose you drive an average of 10,000 miles each year.
  GPS Your gasoline mileage (mi/gal) varies inversely with the number of gallons of gasoline you use each year. Write and graph a model for your average mileage m in terms of the gallons g of gasoline used.
  b. After you begin driving on the highway more often, you use 50 gal less per year. Write and graph a new model to include this information.
  c. Calculate your old and new mileage assuming that you originally used 400 gal of gasoline per year. **25 mi/gal, 28.57 mi/gal**

Ⓒ Challenge

Critical Thinking Compare each pair of graphs and find any points of intersection.

48. $y = \frac{1}{x}$ and $y = \left|\frac{1}{x}\right|$ **49.** $y = \frac{1}{x}$ and $y = \frac{1}{x^2}$ **50.** $y = \left|\frac{1}{x}\right|$ and $y = \frac{1}{x^2}$

51. Find two reciprocal functions such that the minimum distance from the origin to the graph of each function is $4\sqrt{2}$. $y = \frac{16}{x}, y = -\frac{16}{x}$

39. Answers may vary. Sample: The graph of the translation looks similar to the graph of $y = \frac{k}{x}$, so knowing the asymptotes helps to position the translation; check students' work.

GO Online
Homework Video Tutor
Visit: PHSchool.com
Web Code: age-0902

47a–b. See back of book.

48–50. See back of book.

PowerPoint
Lesson Quiz

1. Draw a graph of $y = \frac{12}{x}$.

2. Compare the graphs of $y = \frac{6}{x}$ and $y = \frac{12}{x}$. **Answers may vary. Sample: Both graphs lie in Quadrants I and III. Both have the axes as asymptotes. Both are symmetric with respect to $y = x$ and $y = -x$.**

3. A group of college students rents a large two-story house. The amount of rent in dollars that each student pays per month is inversely proportional to the number of students. The rent r per month for one student is related to the number of students n by the equation $r = \frac{1200}{n}$. Find the monthly rent each student pays if there are 8 students in the house. **$150**

4. Sketch the asymptotes and the graph of $y = -\frac{0.5}{x + 2} - \frac{1}{2}$.

5. Write an equation for the translation of $y = \frac{13}{x}$ that has asymptotes at $x = 5$ and $y = -8$. $y = \frac{13}{x - 5} - 8$

Error Prevention!

Exercise 40 Remind students that *altitude* refers to height above sea level. Make sure students convert the given altitudes in feet into miles to apply the pressure formula.

499

Alternative Assessment

Have students work individually and roll a number cube to determine three numbers a, b, and c. Have them sketch the graphs of $y = \frac{a}{x}$, $y = -\frac{a}{x}$, $y = \frac{a}{x + b} + c$, and $y = -\frac{a}{x - b} - c$ and identify the asymptotes of each graph.

Test Prep

Resources

For additional practice with a variety of test item formats:
• Standardized Test Prep, p. 543
• Test-Taking Strategies, p. 538
• Test-Taking Strategies with Transparencies

a–f. See back of book.

52. Write each equation in the form $y = \frac{k}{x - b} + c$, and sketch the graph.

a. $y = \dfrac{2}{3x - 6}$ b. $y = \dfrac{1}{2 - 4x}$ c. $y = \dfrac{3 - x}{x + 2}$

d. $y = \dfrac{2x + 1}{2x - 1}$ e. $xy + 2x = 1$ f. $xy - y = 1$

Test Prep

Multiple Choice

53. Which point is NOT on the graph of $y = -\frac{2}{x}$?   **D**

A. $\left(-\frac{1}{2}, 4\right)$ B. $(-1, 2)$

C. $(2, -1)$ D. $\left(8, -\frac{1}{16}\right)$

54. Which equation is a line of symmetry for $xy = -7$ and does NOT intersect the branches of the graph?   **H**

F. $x = 0$ G. $y = 0$

H. $y = x$ J. $y = -x$

55. What are the asymptotes of the graph of $y = \frac{10}{x - 5}$? **B**

A. $x = 0$, $y = 5$ B. $x = 5$, $y = 0$

C. $x = 5$, $y = 10$ D. $x = 10$, $y = 5$

56. What are the asymptotes of the graph of $y = \frac{10}{x} + 5$?   **F**

F. $x = 0$, $y = 5$ G. $x = 5$, $y = 5$

H. $x = 5$, $y = 10$ J. $x = 10$, $y = 5$

57. What is an equation for the translation of $y = \frac{2}{x}$ that has asymptotes at $x = 3$ and $y = -5$?   **A**

A. $y = \dfrac{2}{x - 3} - 5$ B. $y = \dfrac{2}{x + 3} + 5$

C. $y = \dfrac{2}{x + 5} - 3$ D. $y = \dfrac{2}{x - 5} + 3$

Short Response

58. Explain how to find the asymptotes of $y = -\frac{3}{x - 2} + 11$. **See back of book.**

Extended Response

59. Explain how to find an equation for the translation of $y = \frac{-3}{x}$ that has asymptotes at $x = -5$ and $y = -13$. **See margin.**

Mixed Review

Lesson 9-1

Describe the variation that is modeled by each formula.

60. $V = \dfrac{s^2 h}{3}$ **61.** $h = \dfrac{3V}{s^2}$ **62.** $B = \dfrac{3V}{h}$ **63.** $w = \dfrac{V}{\ell h}$ **64.** $b = \dfrac{2A}{h}$

60–64. See back of book.

Lesson 8-1

Identify each function as exponential growth or decay, and find the growth or decay factor.

65. $y = 3 \cdot 4^x$ **66.** $y = 0.1 \cdot 2^x$ **67.** $y = 5 \cdot (0.8)^x$ **68.** $y = 3 \cdot \left(\frac{1}{2}\right)^x$

      growth, 4   growth, 2   decay, 0.8   decay, 0.5

Lesson 7-3

Multiply.

69. $(5\sqrt{3} - 2)^2$ $79 - 20\sqrt{3}$ **70.** $(\sqrt{3} + \sqrt{5})(\sqrt{3} - \sqrt{5})$ -2

71. $(3\sqrt{5} + 2\sqrt{10})(2\sqrt{5} + \sqrt{10})$ **72.** $(4 + 2\sqrt{3})(6 - 3\sqrt{3})$ 6

      $50 + 35\sqrt{2}$

---

59. [4] The general form of a translation of $y = \frac{-3}{x}$ is $y = \frac{-3}{x - b} + c$. For asymptotes at $x = -5$ and $y = -13$, $b = -5$ and $c = -13$.

Substituting, $y = \dfrac{-3}{x - (-5)} - 13$, or $y = \dfrac{-3}{x + 5} - 13$.

[3] minor error, such as a sign error

[2] several errors OR major error, such as writing $y = \dfrac{-3}{x - 13} + (-5)$

[1] answer only, with no explanation

Rational Functions and Their Graphs

What You'll Learn

- To identify properties of rational functions
- To graph rational functions

. . . And Why

To find the average cost of producing CD-ROMs, as in Example 5

 Check Skills You'll Need

GO for Help Lessons 5-4 and 5-5

Factor.
1. $x^2 + 5x + 6$ $(x + 3)(x + 2)$
2. $x^2 - 6x + 8$ $(x - 4)(x - 2)$
3. $x^2 - 12x + 27$ $(x - 3)(x - 9)$
4. $2x^2 + x - 28$ $(2x - 7)(x + 4)$
5. $2x^2 - 11x + 15$ $(2x - 5)(x - 3)$
6. $2x^2 - 19x + 24$ $(2x - 3)(x - 8)$

Solve.
7. $x^2 + x - 12 = 0$ $3, -4$
8. $x^2 - 3x - 28 = 0$ $-4, 7$
9. $x^2 - 9x + 18 = 0$ $3, 6$

New Vocabulary • rational function • point of discontinuity

Objectives
1 To identify properties of rational functions
2 To graph rational functions

Examples
1 Finding Points of Discontinuity
2 Finding Vertical Asymptotes
3 Finding Horizontal Asymptotes
4 Sketching Graphs of Rational Functions
5 Real-World Connection

1 Properties of Rational Functions

Members of the reciprocal function family are rational functions.

 Key Concepts

| **Definition** | **Rational Function** |

A **rational function** $f(x)$ is a function that can be written as

$$f(x) = \frac{P(x)}{Q(x)},$$

where $P(x)$ and $Q(x)$ are polynomial functions. The domain of $f(x)$ is all real numbers except those for which $Q(x) = 0$.

Vocabulary Tip

A rational function is a ratio of functions, just as a rational number is a ratio of numbers.

The graphs of the rational functions $y = \frac{-2x}{x^2 + 1}$, $y = \frac{1}{x^2 - 4}$, and $y = \frac{(x + 2)(x - 1)}{x + 1}$ are shown below.

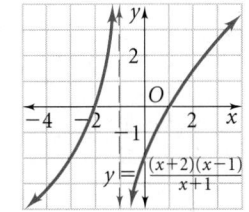

In the first rational function, there is no value of x that makes the denominator 0. The graph is continuous because it has no jumps, breaks, or holes in it. It can be drawn with a pencil that never leaves the paper.

In the second rational function, x cannot be 2 or -2. In the third, x cannot be -1. The last two graphs are discontinuous.

If a is a real number for which the denominator of a rational function f is zero, then a is not in the domain of f. The graph of f is not continuous at $x = a$ and the function has a **point of discontinuity** at $x = a$.

 Professional Development

Math Background

Rational is related to *ratio*. A rational expression is the ratio of two polynomials. Students will draw on all they know about polynomials.

More Math Background: p. 486C

Lesson Planning and Resources

See p. 486E for a list of the resources that support this lesson.

PowerPoint

Bell Ringer Practice

Check Skills You'll Need
For intervention, direct students to:

Factoring Quadratic Expressions
Lesson 5-4: Examples 2–6
Extra Skills and Word Problems Practice, Ch. 5

Quadratic Equations
Lesson 5-5: Example 1
Extra Skills and Word Problems Practice, Ch. 5

 Differentiated Instruction Solutions for All Learners

Special Needs **L1**
Sketch examples of continuous graphs as well as graphs containing jumps, breaks, or holes. Call attention to these different kinds of discontinuities. Note that when you graph a discontinuous function, you lift the pencil from the paper.

learning style: visual

Below Level **L2**
Rational functions can be written as the ratio of two polynomial functions. Point out that it is not necessary to simplify rational functions in order to graph them.

learning style: verbal

Guided Instruction

1 EXAMPLE Math Tip

In part (b), there is another way to see that the function is defined for all real numbers. The value of x^2 is always greater than or equal to 0. Therefore, $x^2 + 1$ is always positive. You may want to have students graph the functions in both parts of the example on a graphing calculator to analyze the behavior of the graphs in more detail.

2 EXAMPLE Teaching Tip

In part (c), note the common factor $x + 4$ in the numerator and denominator. So there is a hole at $x = -4$. The factor $x - 3$ occurs once in the numerator but twice in the denominator. So it follows that $x = 3$ is an asymptote.

To find points of discontinuity, find the values of x that make the denominator 0.

1 EXAMPLE Finding Points of Discontinuity

For each rational function, find any points of discontinuity.

a. $y = \dfrac{1}{x^2 + 2x + 1}$

The function is undefined at value(s) of x for which $x^2 + 2x + 1 = 0$.

$x^2 + 2x + 1 = 0$ **Set the denominator equal to zero.**

$(x + 1)(x + 1) = 0$ **Solve by factoring or using the Quadratic Formula.**

$x + 1 = 0$ **Zero Product Property**

$x = -1$ **Solve for x.**

There is a point of discontinuity at $x = -1$.

b. $y = \dfrac{-x + 1}{x^2 + 1}$

The function is undefined at value(s) of x for which $x^2 + 1 = 0$.

$x^2 + 1 = 0$ **Set the denominator equal to zero.**

$x^2 = -1$ **Solve for x.**

$x = \pm \sqrt{-1}$

Since $\sqrt{-1}$ is not a real number, there is no real value for x for which the function $y = \dfrac{-x + 1}{x^2 + 1}$ is undefined. There is no point of discontinuity.

 Quick Check **1** For each rational function, find any points of discontinuity.

a. $y = \dfrac{1}{x^2 - 16}$ **-4, 4**   **b.** $y = \dfrac{x^2 - 1}{x^2 + 3}$ **none**   **c.** $y = \dfrac{x + 1}{x^2 + 2x - 8}$

-4, 2

The graph of $y = \dfrac{x + 1}{(x - 1)(x + 2)}$ is shown at the right. The zeros of the denominator are 1 and -2. The graph has vertical asymptotes at those points.

Graphing Calculator Hint

A hole in a graph is not displayed on a graphing calculator.

2 is a zero of both the numerator and the denominator of the rational function $y = \dfrac{(x - 2)(x + 1)}{x - 2}$. The graph of this function is the same as the graph of $y = x + 1$, except it has a hole at $x = 2$.

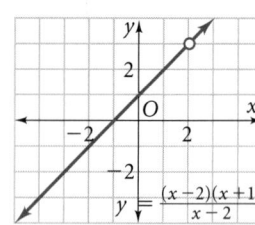

2 is a zero of both the numerator and the denominator of the rational function $y = \dfrac{x - 2}{(x - 2)(x - 1)}$. The graph of this function is the same as the graph of $y = \dfrac{1}{x - 1}$, except it has a hole at $x = 2$.

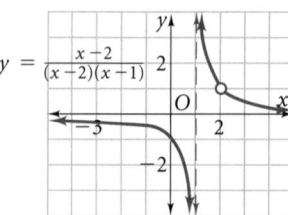

502 Chapter 9 Rational Functions

Differentiated Instruction Solutions for All Learners

Advanced Learners **L4**
Have students investigate the behavior of an expression such as $y = a^x$. Does it have any horizontal or vertical asymptotes?

learning style: verbal

English Language Learners **ELL**
Emphasize that a *rational function* is a *ratio* of two polynomial functions. Unlike polynomial functions, rational functions can have discontinuities or undefined values when a value of x causes the denominator to be zero.

learning style: verbal

2 is a zero of both the numerator and the denominator of the rational function $y = \frac{x-2}{(x-2)^2}$.

The graph of this function is exactly the same as the graph of $y = \frac{1}{x-2}$. The vertical asymptote is $x = 2$ and there is no hole.

Key Concepts

Properties	Vertical Asymptotes

The rational function $f(x) = \frac{P(x)}{Q(x)}$ has a point of discontinuity for each real zero of $Q(x)$.

If $P(x)$ and $Q(x)$ have no common real zeros, then the graph of $f(x)$ has a vertical asymptote at each real zero of $Q(x)$.

If $P(x)$ and $Q(x)$ have a common real zero a, then there is a hole in the graph or a vertical asymptote at $x = a$.

2a. Since 1 and −3 are the zeroes of the denominator and neither is a zero of the numerator, $x = 1$ and $x = -3$ are vertical asymptotes.

b. The graph of this function is the same as the graph of $y = \frac{1}{x+3}$, except that it has a hole at $x = 2$. The vertical asymptote is $x = -3$.

c. The graph of this function is the same as the graph of $y = x - 1$, except that it has a hole at $x = -1$.

PowerPoint

Additional Examples

1 For each rational function, find any points of discontinuity.

a. $y = \frac{3}{x^2 - x - 12}$ points of discontinuity at $x = -3$, $x = 4$

b. $y = \frac{2x}{3x^2 + 4}$ none

2 Describe the vertical asymptotes and holes for the graph of each rational function.

a. $y = \frac{x-7}{(x+1)(x+5)}$ vertical asymptotes $x = -1$, $x = -5$

b. $y = \frac{x(x+3)}{x+3}$ hole at $x = -3$

c. $y = \frac{(x-6)(x+9)}{(x+9)(x+9)(x-6)}$ hole at $x = 6$, vertical asymptote at $x = -9$

2 EXAMPLE   Finding Vertical Asymptotes

Describe the vertical asymptotes and holes for the graph of each rational function.

a. $y = \frac{x+1}{(x-2)(x-3)}$

Since 2 and 3 are the zeros of the denominator and neither is a zero of the numerator, $x = 2$ and $x = 3$ are vertical asymptotes.

b. $y = \frac{(x-2)(x-1)}{x-2}$

The graph of this function is the same as the graph of $y = x - 1$, except it has a hole at $x = 2$.

c. $y = \frac{(x-3)(x+4)}{(x-3)(x-3)(x+4)}$

The graph of this function is the same as the graph of $y = \frac{1}{x-3}$, except it has a hole at $x = -4$. The vertical asymptote is $x = 3$.

Quick Check **2** Describe the vertical asymptotes and holes for the graph of each rational function.

a. $y = \frac{x-2}{(x-1)(x+3)}$ **b.** $y = \frac{x-2}{(x-2)(x+3)}$ **c.** $y = \frac{x^2-1}{x+1}$

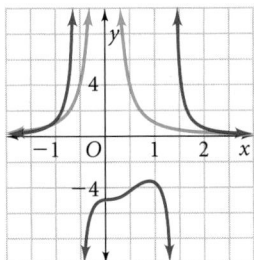

For the graphs of rational functions such as $y = \frac{1}{x}$ and $y = \frac{1}{x^2}$, the horizontal asymptote is $y = 0$. As shown at the left, when the absolute value of x is large, the graph of $y = \frac{2x^2 - x + 10}{5x^4 - 7x^3 + x^2 - 2}$ is very close to the graph of $y = \frac{1}{x^2}$. So $y = 0$ is the horizontal asymptote of both graphs.

In fact, $y = 0$ is the horizontal asymptote of the graph of any rational function, if the degree of the denominator is greater than the degree of the numerator.

If the degree of the numerator equals the degree of the denominator, then the horizontal asymptote can be found as shown in Example 3.

③ **EXAMPLE**   **Finding Horizontal Asymptotes**

Find the horizontal asymptote of $y = \frac{3x + 5}{x - 2}$.

Divide the numerator by the denominator as shown at the right. The function $y = \frac{3x + 5}{x - 2}$ can be written as $y = \frac{11}{x - 2} + 3$.

$$\begin{array}{r} 3 \\ x - 2 \overline{)3x + 5} \\ 3x - 6 \\ \hline 11 \end{array}$$

Its graph is a translation of $y = \frac{1}{x}$. The horizontal asymptote of the graph of $y = \frac{3x + 5}{x - 2}$ is $y = 3$.

✓ **Quick Check** ③ Find the horizontal asymptote of the graph of each rational function.
   a. $y = \frac{-2x + 6}{x - 1}$ $y = -2$ **b.** $y = \frac{2x^2 + 5}{x^2 + 1}$ $y = 2$

🔑 **Key Concepts**

Properties	Horizontal Asymptotes

The graph of a rational function has at most one horizontal asymptote.

The graph of a rational function has a horizontal asymptote at $y = 0$ if the degree of the denominator is greater than the degree of the numerator.

If the degrees of the numerator and the denominator are equal, then the graph has a horizontal asymptote at $y = \frac{a}{b}$. a is the coefficient of the term of highest degree in the numerator and b is the coefficient of the term of highest degree in the denominator.

If the degree of the numerator is greater than the degree of the denominator, then the graph has no horizontal asymptote.

2   Graphing Rational Functions

You can use asymptotes to sketch the graphs of rational functions.

④ **EXAMPLE**   **Sketching Graphs of Rational Functions**

Sketch the graph of $y = \frac{x + 2}{(x + 3)(x - 4)}$.

The degree of the denominator is greater than the degree of the numerator, so the y-axis is the horizontal asymptote. When $x > 4$, y is positive. So as x increases, the graph approaches the y-axis from above. When $x < -3$, y is negative. So as x decreases, the graph approaches the y-axis from below.

Since -2 is the zero of the numerator, the x-intercept is at -2. Since -3 and 4 are the zeros of the denominator, the vertical asymptotes are at $x = -3$ and $x = 4$.

Calculate the values of y for values of x near the asymptotes. Plot those points and sketch the graph.

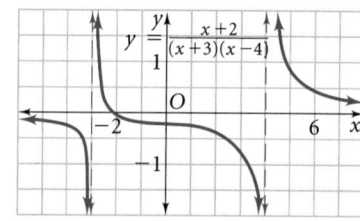

✓ **Quick Check** ④ Sketch the graph of $y = \frac{x + 3}{(x - 1)(x - 5)}$.   **See back of book.**

5 EXAMPLE Real-World 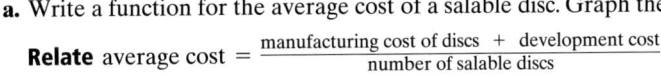 Connection

Business The CD-ROMs for a computer game can be manufactured for $.25 each. The development cost is $124,000. The first 100 discs are samples and will not be sold.

a. Write a function for the average cost of a salable disc. Graph the function.

Relate average cost = $\dfrac{\text{manufacturing cost of discs} + \text{development cost}}{\text{number of salable discs}}$

Define Let x = number of CD-ROMs produced.
Let y = average cost of one saleable disc.

Write $y = \dfrac{0.25x + 124{,}000}{x - 100}$

Graph the function. Adjust the viewing window.

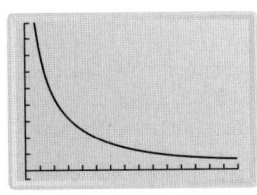

Xmin=0   Ymin=–10
Xmax=15000 Ymax=100
Xscl=1000   Yscl=10

Real-World Connection

Careers Video game programmers need a strong background in computer programming.

b. What is the average cost if 2000 discs are produced? If 12,800 discs are produced?

Use the **CALC** feature to evaluate the function at $x = 2000$ and at $x = 12{,}800$. If 2000 discs are produced, the average cost will be about $65.53. If 12,800 discs are produced, the average cost will be about $10.02.

✓ **Quick Check** **5 a. Critical Thinking** How could you find the number of discs that must be produced to bring the average cost under $8? **See back of book.**
b. What is the vertical asymptote of the graph of the function in Example 5? What is the horizontal asymptote? $x = 100$; $y = 0.25$
c. Describe how the asymptotes are related to the information given in Example 5. **See back of book.**

EXERCISES

For more exercises, see *Extra Skill and Word Problem Practice.*

Practice and Problem Solving

A Practice by Example

Example 1
(page 502)

GO for Help

Find any points of discontinuity for each rational function. **1–18. See margin.**

1. $y = \dfrac{2x^2 + 5}{x^2 - 2x}$

2. $y = \dfrac{x^2 + 2x}{x^2 + 2}$

3. $y = \dfrac{3x - 3}{x^2 - 1}$

4. $y = \dfrac{6 - 3x}{x^2 - 5x + 6}$

5. $y = \dfrac{x^2 + 5x + 6}{x^2 + 6x + 9}$

6. $y = \dfrac{x^2 + 4x + 3}{2x^2 + 5x - 7}$

7. $y = \dfrac{x^3 - 8}{x^3 - 8}$

8. $y = \dfrac{x^2}{x^2 + 1}$

9. $y = \dfrac{1}{2x^2 + 3x - 7}$

Example 2
(page 503)

Describe the vertical asymptotes and holes for the graph of each rational function.

10. $y = \dfrac{3}{x + 2}$

11. $y = \dfrac{x + 5}{x + 5}$

12. $y = \dfrac{x + 3}{(2x + 3)(x - 1)}$

13. $y = \dfrac{(x + 3)(x - 2)}{(x - 2)(x + 1)}$

14. $y = \dfrac{x^2 - 4}{x + 2}$

15. $y = \dfrac{x + 5}{x^2 + 9}$

16. $y = \dfrac{9 - x^2}{x^2 - 9}$

17. $y = \dfrac{2x^2}{2x^2 + 2}$

18. $y = \dfrac{6x^2 + x - 2}{3x^2 + 17x + 10}$

1. $x = 0, x = 2$
2. none
3. $x = 1, x = -1$
4. $x = 2, x = 3$
5. $x = -3$
6. $x = -\frac{7}{2}, x = 1$
7. $x = 2$
8. none
9. $x = -2.77, x = 1.277$
10. vertical asymptote at $x = -2$
11. hole at $x = -5$
12. vertical asymptotes at $x = -\frac{3}{2}$ and $x = 1$

Assignment Guide

1 A B 1-24, 41-43

2 A B 25-40
C Challenge   44-45

Test Prep   46-50
Mixed Review   51-59

Homework Quick Check
To check students' understanding of key skills and concepts, go over Exercises 13, 28, 38, 41, 42.

Error Prevention!

Exercise 14 Students may not factor the numerator of the fraction. This will lead them to think that $x = -2$ is a vertical asymptote. Remind students that a common factor in the numerator and denominator can signal a hole.

Differentiated Instruction Resources

GPS Guided Problem Solving	L3
Enrichment	L4
Reteaching	L2
Practice	L3

13. vertical asymptote at $x = -1$, hole at $x = 2$

14. hole at $x = -2$

15. none

16. holes at $x = \pm 3$

17. none

18. vertical asymptote at $x = -5$, hole at $x = -\frac{2}{3}$

505

Careers

Exercise 45 Point out that knowledge of changes in wages and labor resources is important for people who work in the field of economics. Economists frequently use mathematical models for planning.

25.

26.

27.

28.

29.

30.

31a. $y = \dfrac{0.19x + 210{,}000}{x - 500}$

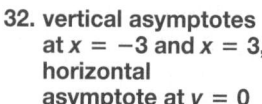

506

Example 3
(page 504)

Find the horizontal asymptote of the graph of each rational function.

19. $y = \dfrac{5}{x + 6}$ $y = 0$ **20.** $y = \dfrac{x + 2}{2x^2 - 4}$ $y = 0$ **21.** $y = \dfrac{x + 1}{x + 5}$ $y = 1$

22. $y = \dfrac{x^2 + 2}{2x^2 - 1}$ $y = \frac{1}{2}$ **23.** $y = \dfrac{5x^3 + 2x}{2x^5 - 4x^3}$ $y = 0$ **24.** $y = \dfrac{3x - 4}{4x + 1}$ $y = \frac{3}{4}$

Example 4
(page 504)

Sketch the graph of each rational function. 25–30. See margin.

25. $y = \dfrac{x^2 - 4}{3x - 6}$ **26.** $y = \dfrac{4x}{x^3 - 4x}$ **27.** $y = \dfrac{x + 4}{x - 4}$

28. $y = \dfrac{x(x + 1)}{x + 1}$ **29.** $y = \dfrac{x + 6}{(x - 2)(x + 3)}$ **30.** $y = \dfrac{3x}{(x + 2)^2}$

Example 5
(page 505)

31. Business CDs can be manufactured for $.19 each. The development cost is $210,000. The first 500 discs are samples and will not be sold.
   a. Write a function for the average cost of a salable disc. Graph the function. **See margin.**
   b. What is the average cost if 5000 discs are produced? If 15,000 discs are produced? **$46.88; $14.68**
   c. How many discs must be produced to bring the average cost under $10? **more than 21,916 discs**
   d. What are the vertical and horizontal asymptotes of the graph of the function? **$x = 500, y = 0.19$**

B **Apply Your Skills**

Find the vertical and horizontal asymptotes, if any, of the graph of each rational function.

32. vertical asymptotes at $x = -3$ and $x = 3$, horizontal asymptote at $y = 0$

33. vertical asymptote at $x = -2$

34. horizontal asymptote at $y = 0$

32.

33.

34.

Sketch the graph of each rational function. 35–40. See back of book.

35. $y = \dfrac{2x + 3}{x - 5}$ **36.** $y = \dfrac{x^2 + 6x + 9}{x + 3}$ **37.** $y = \dfrac{4x^2 - 100}{2x^2 + x - 15}$

38. $y = -\dfrac{x}{(x - 1)^2}$ **39.** $y = \dfrac{2x}{3x - 1}$ **40.** $y = \dfrac{2}{x^2 - 4}$

41. Answers may vary. Sample: There is no value of x for which the denominator equals 0.

 41. Writing Describe the conditions that will produce a rational function with a graph that has no vertical asymptotes.

42. Basketball A basketball player has made 21 of her last 30 free throws—an average of 70%. To model the player's rate of success if she makes x more consecutive free throws, use the function $y = \dfrac{21 + x}{30 + x}$.
   a. Graph the function. **See margin.**
   b. Use the graph to find the number of consecutive free throws the player needs to raise her success rate to 75%. **6 free throws**

43. Data Analysis The president of XYZ Company earns $200,000 a year. Each of the other x employees earns $20,000 a year.
   a. Write and graph a function that models the average salary of all employees of XYZ. **See back of book.**
   b. What is the average salary if there are three employees? If there are 30 employees? **$65,000; $25,806.45**
   c. Critical Thinking Is the average salary the best measure of the workers' pay? Explain. What other measure could you use?
   Answers may vary. Sample: No; the president's salary throws off the average; the median or mode would be a better measure.

Homework Video Tutor
Visit: PHSchool.com
Web Code: age-0903

506 Chapter 9 Rational Functions

42a.

```
WINDOW FORMAT
Xmin=0
Xmax=100
Xscl=10
Ymin=.5
Ymax=1
Yscl=.1
```

44. Reasoning Look for a pattern in the sequence of shells below.

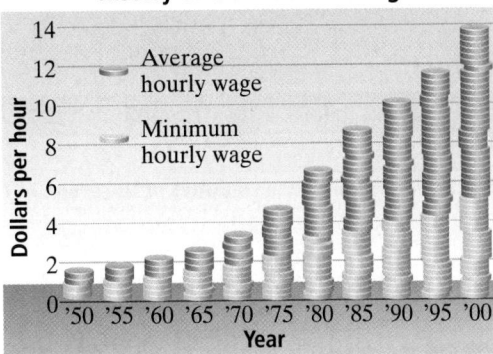

44a. $P(n) = 4n^2$

b. $R(n) = 4n + 1$

c. $y = \frac{4n^2}{4n + 1}; \frac{64}{17};$ check students' work.

a. Write a model for the number of purple shells $P(n)$ at each step n.
b. Write a model for the number of red shells $R(n)$ at each step n.
c. Write a model for the ratio of $P(n)$ to $R(n)$. Use it to predict the ratio of purple shells to red shells in the next figure. Verify your answer.

45. Wage Policy The graph below compares the average hourly wage for production workers and the minimum hourly wage from 1950 to 2000.

History of the Minimum Wage

SOURCE: Bureau of Labor Statistics.
Go to **www.PHSchool.com** for a data update.
Web Code: agg-9041

45a. The increase in production workers' average hourly wage is greater.

c. $R(x) = \frac{M(x)}{A(x)}$

a. How has the comparison of the minimum wage to the production workers' wage changed over the years?
b. If the minimum wage and the production workers' wage are modeled by polynomials, what type of function would model their ratio? **rational**
c. The quadratic function $M(x) = 0.00081x^2 + 0.049x + 0.68$ models the minimum wage, where x is the number of years since 1950. The quadratic function $A(x) = 0.0043x^2 + 0.04x + 1.21$ models the average wage. Write a model for the ratio of these two functions.
d. Graph your model. If the present trends continue, when will the minimum wage decrease to 25% of the average wage? **See back of book.**

Test Prep

Multiple Choice

46. What are the points of discontinuity for $y = \frac{(2x + 3)(x - 5)}{(x + 5)(2x - 1)}$? **C**

    A. $-5, 1$ **B.** $-\frac{3}{2}, 5$ **C.** $-5, \frac{1}{2}$ **D.** $5, -\frac{1}{2}$

47. How many points of discontinuity does the function $y = \frac{2x}{x^2 + 4}$ have? **F**

    F. 0   **G.** 1   **H.** 2   **J.** 4

Exercises, p.508

49. [2]
$$\begin{array}{r} 5 \\ x + 3 \overline{)5x + 7} \\ 5x + 15 \\ \hline -8 \end{array}$$

So $y = \frac{5x + 7}{x + 3}$ can be written as $y = \frac{-8}{x + 3} + 5$.
As x becomes larger, the fraction approaches 0 and y approaches the asymptote at 5.

[1] answer only, with no explanation

4. Assess & Reteach

Lesson Quiz

1. Find any points of discontinuity for the rational function $y = \frac{x + 7}{x^2 + 5x - 14}$.
$x = 2, x = -7$

2. Describe the vertical asymptotes and holes for the graph of $y = \frac{x + 5}{(x - 3)(x + 5)}$.
vertical asymptote at $x = 3$; hole at $x = -5$

3. Find the horizontal asymptote of $y = \frac{x^2 - 9}{3x^2 + 5}$.
$y = \frac{1}{3}$

4. Sketch the graph of $y = \frac{x^2 - 9}{x(x^2 + 2x - 15)}$.

5. The cost in dollars of publishing x copies of a certain book is modeled by $30{,}000 + 10x + 0.0001x^2$.
a. Write a function for the average cost per book. Graph the function.
$f(x) = \frac{30{,}000 + 10x + 0.0001x^2}{x}$

Xmin=0   Ymin=0
Xmax=50000   Ymas=30
Xscl=5000   Yscl=5

b. What is the average cost per book if 12,000 copies are published? if 15,000 copies are published? **$13.70; $13.50**

Alternative Assessment

Ask each student to write three rational functions with the numerator and denominator in factored form: one with two vertical asymptotes and no horizontal asymptote; another with one vertical asymptote, one hole, and no horizontal asymptote; and the third with both vertical and horizontal asymptotes. Students check one another's work.

Use this Checkpoint Quiz to check students' understanding of the skills and concepts of Lessons 9-1 through 9-3.

Resources
Grab & Go
- Checkpoint Quiz 1

48. Which graph *cannot* be the graph of a rational function? **B**

A.   B.

C.   D.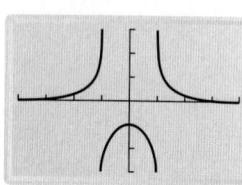

Short Response **49.** Find the horizontal asymptote of $y = \frac{5x + 7}{x + 3}$ by dividing the numerator by the denominator. Explain your steps. **See margin p. 507.**

50. Find the points of discontinuity of $y = \frac{x(2x - 1)(x + 1)}{(x + 5)(x + 1)}$. **[2]** $x = -5, x = -1$ **[1]** one point found

Mixed Review

GO for Help

Lesson 9-2 Find the asymptotes of the graph of each equation. **51–56. See margin.**

51. $y = \frac{3}{x} + 4$ **52.** $y = \frac{2}{x + 3}$ **53.** $y = \frac{-1}{x + 1} + 1$

54. $y = \frac{5}{x - 7} - 3$ **55.** $y = \frac{5}{2 - x}$ **56.** $y = \frac{-2}{5 - x} - 6$

Lesson 8-2 Describe how the graph of each function relates to the graph of $y = 4(0.8)^x$.

57. $y = 4(0.8)^{x-1}$ **58.** $y = 4(0.8)^x + 3$ **59.** $y = 4(0.8)^{x+1} - 5$
   1 unit right   **3 units up**   **1 unit left and 5 units down**

Checkpoint Quiz 1   Lessons 9-1 through 9-3

If $z = 30$ when $x = 3$ and $y = 2$, write the function that models each relationship.

1. z varies jointly with x and y. $z = 5xy$

2. z varies directly with x and inversely with y. $z = \frac{20x}{y}$

3. z varies inversely with the product of x and y. $z = \frac{180}{xy}$

Explain how the graph of y_2 is related to the graph of y_1. **4–6. See margin.**

4. $y_1 = \frac{4}{x}$ and $y_2 = \frac{9}{x}$ **5.** $y_1 = \frac{1}{x}$ and $y_2 = \frac{1}{x} + 5$

6. $y_1 = \frac{1}{x - 1} + 2$ and $y_2 = \frac{1}{x + 1} - 2$

Sketch the graph of each rational function. **7–8, 10. See margin.**

7. $y = \frac{x^2 - 9}{2x + 6}$ **8.** $y = \frac{3x}{x^3 - x}$ **9.** $y = \frac{x + 3}{x - 3}$ **10.** $y = \frac{x^2 - 2x}{x - 2}$
                                                    See back of book.

508   Chapter 9   Rational Functions

51. vertical: $x = 0$, horizontal: $y = 4$

52. vertical: $x = -3$, horizontal: $y = 0$

53. vertical: $x = -1$, horizontal: $y = 1$

54. vertical: $x = 7$, horizontal: $y = -3$

55. vertical: $x = 2$, horizontal: $y = 0$

56. vertical: $x = 5$, horizontal: $y = -6$

page 508   Checkpoint Quiz 1

4. Answers may vary. Sample: Both have vertical asymptote $x = 0$ and horizontal asymptote $y = 0$. $y_1 = \frac{4}{x}$ is closer to the axes.

5. Answers may vary. Sample: $y_2 = \frac{1}{x} + 5$ is a vertical translation of $y_1 = \frac{1}{x}$ up 5 units.

6. Answers may vary. Sample: $y_1 = \frac{1}{x - 1} + 2$ has vertical asymptote $x = 1$ and horizontal asymptote $y = 2$. $y_2 = \frac{1}{x + 1} - 2$ has vertical asymptote $x = -1$ and horizontal asymptote $y = -2$.

7.

8.

10.

Rational Expressions

What You'll Learn

- To simplify rational expressions
- To multiply and divide rational expressions

. . . And Why

To compute ratios of volume to surface area, as in Example 2

 Check Skills You'll Need

GO **for Help** 5-4 and Skills Handbook page 871

Factor.

1. $2x^2 - 3x + 1$ **(2x − 1)(x − 1)**

2. $4x^2 - 9$ **(2x + 3)(2x − 3)**

3. $5x^2 + 6x + 1$ **(5x + 1)(x + 1)**

4. $10x^2 - 10$ **10(x + 1)(x − 1)**

Multiply or divide.

5. $\frac{3}{8} \cdot \frac{5}{6}$ $\frac{5}{16}$

6. $\frac{1}{2} \cdot \frac{4}{6}$ $\frac{1}{3}$

7. $\frac{8}{3} \cdot \frac{2}{16}$ $\frac{1}{3}$

8. $\frac{2}{5} \cdot \frac{3}{7}$ $\frac{6}{35}$

9. $\frac{5}{8} \div 4$ $\frac{5}{32}$

10. $\frac{3}{4} \div \frac{1}{2}$ $\frac{3}{2}$

11. $\frac{9}{16} \div \frac{3}{4}$ $\frac{3}{4}$

12. $\frac{5}{4} \div \frac{15}{8}$ $\frac{2}{3}$

◀)) **New Vocabulary** • simplest form

Objectives
1 To simplify rational expressions
2 To multiply and divide rational expressions

Examples
1 Simplifying Rational Expressions
2 Real-World Connection
3 Multiplying Rational Expressions
4 Dividing Rational Expressions

 Professional Development

Math Background

Simplifying a rational expression depends on factoring polynomials.

More Math Background: p. 486C

Lesson Planning and Resources

See p. 486E for a list of the resources that support this lesson.

---

1 Simplifying Rational Expressions

A rational expression is in **simplest form** when its numerator and denominator are polynomials that have no common divisors.

In simplest form

$$\frac{x}{x-1} \qquad \frac{2}{x^2+3}$$

Not in simplest form

$$\frac{x}{x^2} \qquad \frac{\frac{1}{x}}{x+1} \qquad \frac{2(x-3)}{3(x-3)}$$

You can simplify some expressions by dividing out common factors.

1 EXAMPLE Simplifying Rational Expressions

Simplify $\frac{x^2 + 10x + 25}{x^2 + 9x + 20}$. State any restrictions on the variable.

$$\frac{x^2 + 10x + 25}{x^2 + 9x + 20} = \frac{(x+5)(x+5)}{(x+4)(x+5)}$$ **Factor the polynomials. Notice that x ≠ −4 or −5.**

$$= \frac{(\overset{1}{\cancel{x+5}})(x+5)}{(x+4)(\underset{1}{\cancel{x+5}})}$$ **Divide out common factors.**

$$= \frac{x+5}{x+4}$$

The simplified expression is $\frac{x+5}{x+4}$ for $x \neq -4$ or -5. The restrictions on x are needed to prevent the denominator of the original expression from being zero.

1a. $-\frac{3}{x}$; $x \neq 0, y \neq 0$

b. $\frac{-3(x+2)}{(x-2)(x-4)}$; $x \neq 2$ or 4

c. $\frac{2x+1}{x-3}$; $x \neq 2$ or 3

✓ **Quick Check** ① **1.** Simplify each expression. State any restrictions on the variables.

a. $\frac{-27x^3y}{9x^4y}$

b. $\frac{-6 - 3x}{x^2 - 6x + 8}$

c. $\frac{2x^2 - 3x - 2}{x^2 - 5x + 6}$

 Differentiated Instruction **Solutions for All Learners**

Special Needs **L1**
For Example 2, write on the board "Surface Area = 20" and "Volume = 15." Have students find the ratio of volume to surface area, 15 : 20, and simplify it to 3 : 4. Explain that the amounts 15 and 20 are replaced by polynomials in Example 2.

learning style: verbal

Below Level **L2**
Compare simplifying, multiplying, and dividing rational expressions to the same operations with rational numbers.

learning style: verbal

2. Teach

Guided Instruction

Additional Examples

1 Simplify $\frac{x^2 - 6x - 16}{x^2 + 5x + 6}$. State any restrictions on the variable. $\frac{x - 8}{x + 3}$; $x \neq -2, -3$

2 Compare the ratio of the volume to surface area of a sphere with radius r with the ratio of volume to surface area of a sphere with radius $2r$. The first ratio is $\frac{r}{3}$; the second ratio is $\frac{2r}{3}$. The second ratio is twice the first.

Guided Instruction

Additional Examples

3 Multiply $\frac{3x^2 + 5x - 2}{x - 5}$ and $\frac{x^2 - 25}{3x^2 - 7x + 2}$. State any restrictions on the variable. $\frac{x^2 + 7x + 10}{x - 2}$; $x \neq \frac{1}{3}, 2, 5$

4 Divide $\frac{3 - y}{(2x - 1)(x + 5)}$ by $\frac{6(y - 3)}{(2x - 1)(x - 7)}$. State any restrictions on the variables. $\frac{-x + 7}{6x + 30}$; $x \neq -5, \frac{1}{2}, 7, y \neq 3$

Resources
• Daily Notetaking Guide 9-4 **L3**

Closure

Ask students to explain how to simplify, multiply, and divide rational expressions. To simplify a rational expression, divide the numerator and denominator by their common factors. To multiply, divide out common factors of the numerators and denominators of both expressions. To divide, multiply by the reciprocal of the divisor, then divide out common factors.

Real-World Connection

Crystal Bridge botanical gardens in Oklahoma City

---

2 EXAMPLE Real-World Connection

Architecture One factor in designing a structure is the need to maximize the volume (space for working) for a given surface area (material needed for construction). Compare the ratio of the volume to surface area of a cylinder with radius r and height r to a cylinder with radius r and height $2r$.

Use the formulas for volume and surface area of a cylinder.

$$\text{Volume } (V) = \pi r^2 h$$
$$\text{Surface Area (S.A.)} = 2\pi rh + 2\pi r^2$$

Cylinder with height r Cylinder with height $2r$

$\frac{V}{\text{S.A.}} = \frac{\pi r^2 h}{2\pi rh + 2\pi r^2}$ $\frac{V}{\text{S.A.}} = \frac{\pi r^2 h}{2\pi rh + 2\pi r^2}$ **Write a ratio.**

$= \frac{\pi r^2(r)}{2\pi r(r) + 2\pi r^2}$ $= \frac{\pi r^2(2r)}{2\pi r(2r) + 2\pi r^2}$ **Substitute for h.**

$= \frac{\pi r^3}{2\pi r^2 + 2\pi r^2}$ $= \frac{2\pi r^3}{4\pi r^2 + 2\pi r^2}$ **Simplify.**

$= \frac{\pi r^3}{4\pi r^2}$ $= \frac{2\pi r^3}{6\pi r^2}$ **Combine like terms.**

$= \frac{r}{4}$ $= \frac{r}{3}$ **Simplify.**

For a given radius, the ratio of volume to surface area is greater for the cylinder with a height of $2r$.

✓ Quick Check **2 a.** Find the ratio of volume to surface area of a cylinder whose height is $4r$. $\frac{2r}{5}$
b. Critical Thinking Let mr be the height of a cylinder of radius r, with m a positive number. Describe how the ratio of volume to surface area changes as m changes. **As m gets larger, the ratio gets larger.**

---

2   Multiplying and Dividing Rational Expressions

You can use what you know about simplifying rational expressions when you multiply and divide them.

3 EXAMPLE Multiplying Rational Expressions

Multiply $\frac{2x^2 + 7x + 3}{x - 4}$ and $\frac{x^2 - 16}{x^2 + 8x + 15}$. State any restrictions on the variable.

$\frac{2x^2 + 7x + 3}{x - 4} \cdot \frac{x^2 - 16}{x^2 + 8x + 15} = \frac{(2x + 1)(x + 3)}{x - 4} \cdot \frac{(x - 4)(x + 4)}{(x + 3)(x + 5)}$ **Factor.**

$= \frac{(2x + 1)\overset{1}{\cancel{(x + 3)}}}{\cancel{x - 4}} \cdot \frac{\overset{1}{\cancel{(x - 4)}}(x + 4)}{\cancel{(x + 3)}(x + 5)}$ **Divide out common factors.**

$= \frac{(2x + 1)(x + 4)}{x + 5}$

3. $\frac{a - 2}{a(a - 1)}$;
$a \neq 0, 1, -1, \text{ or } -2$

The product is $\frac{(2x + 1)(x + 4)}{x + 5}$ for $x \neq 4, -3, \text{ or } -5$.

✓ Quick Check **3** Multiply $\frac{a^2 - 4}{a^2 - 1}$ and $\frac{a + 1}{a^2 + 2a}$. State any restrictions on the variable. **See left.**

Differentiated Instruction   **Solutions for All Learners**

Advanced Learners **L4**
In Example 1, challenge students to explain why $x \neq -5$ in the original expression, though $x = -5$ is not a restriction in the derived expression.

learning style: verbal

English Language Learners **ELL**
For Example 2, review the geometric terms *volume*, *surface area*, and *cylinder*. Then discuss what it means for the ratio of volume to surface area to be larger. Given a larger ratio $\frac{V}{\text{S.A.}}$, more space is enclosed for each square foot of surface area.

learning style: verbal

GO for Help

For practice in dividing fractions, go to p. 871.

GO Online

Video Tutor Help

Visit: PHSchool.com
Web Code: age-0775

To divide rational expressions, remember to multiply by the reciprocal of the divisor, just as you did when dividing rational numbers.

4 EXAMPLE Dividing Rational Expressions

Divide $\dfrac{4 - x}{(3x + 2)(x - 2)}$ by $\dfrac{5(x - 4)}{(x - 2)(7y - 5)}$. State any restrictions on the variables.

$$\dfrac{4 - x}{(3x + 2)(x - 2)} \div \dfrac{5(x - 4)}{(x - 2)(7y - 5)}$$

$$= \dfrac{4 - x}{(3x + 2)(x - 2)} \cdot \dfrac{(x - 2)(7y - 5)}{5(x - 4)}$$ **Multiply by the reciprocal.**

$$= \dfrac{-(x - 4)}{(3x + 2)(x - 2)} \cdot \dfrac{(x - 2)(7y - 5)}{5(x - 4)}$$ **Divide out common factors.**

$$= \dfrac{-1}{3x + 2} \cdot \dfrac{7y - 5}{5}$$ **Rewrite the expression.**

$$= \dfrac{-(7y - 5)}{5(3x + 2)}$$ **Multiply.**

The quotient is $\dfrac{-(7y - 5)}{5(3x + 2)}$ for $x \neq -\frac{2}{3}$, 2, or 4, and $y \neq \frac{5}{7}$.

✓ Quick Check ④ Divide $\dfrac{a^2 + 2a - 15}{a^2 - 16}$ by $\dfrac{a + 1}{3a - 12}$. State any restrictions on the variable. $\dfrac{3(a + 5)(a - 3)}{(a + 1)(a + 4)}$; $a \neq -1$, -4, or 4

EXERCISES

Practice and Problem Solving

For more exercises, see *Extra Skill and Word Problem Practice*.

Ⓐ **Practice by Example**

Examples 1 and 2
(pages 509–510)

for Help

10. $\dfrac{4(x + 6)}{3(3x + 8)}$; $x \neq 3$ or $-\frac{8}{3}$

12. 1; $x \neq -2, -1, 2,$ or 3

Example 3
(page 510)

Example 4
(page 511)

Simplify each rational expression. State any restrictions on the variable.

1. $\dfrac{2x}{4x^2 - 2x}$ $\dfrac{1}{2x - 1}$; $x \neq 0$ or $\frac{1}{2}$

2. $\dfrac{6c^2 + 9c}{3c}$ $2c + 3$; $c \neq 0$

3. $\dfrac{b^2 - 1}{b - 1}$ $b + 1$; $b \neq 1$

4. $\dfrac{z^2 - 49}{z + 7}$ $z - 7$; $z \neq -7$

5. $\dfrac{2x + 10}{x^2 + 10x + 25}$ $\dfrac{2}{x + 5}$; $x \neq -5$

6. $\dfrac{x^2 + 8x + 16}{x^2 - 2x - 24}$ $\dfrac{x + 4}{x - 6}$; $x \neq 6$ or -4

Multiply. State any restrictions on the variables.

7. $\dfrac{4x^2}{5y} \cdot \dfrac{7y}{12x^4}$ $\dfrac{7}{15x^2}$; $x \neq 0$, $y \neq 0$

8. $\dfrac{2x^4}{10y^2} \cdot \dfrac{5y^3}{4x^3}$ $\dfrac{xy}{4}$; $x \neq 0$, $y \neq 0$

9. $\dfrac{8y - 4}{10y - 5} \cdot \dfrac{5y - 15}{3y - 9}$ $\dfrac{4}{3}$; $y \neq \frac{1}{2}$ or 3

10. $\dfrac{2x + 12}{3x - 9} \cdot \dfrac{2x - 6}{3x + 8}$

11. $\dfrac{x^2 - 4}{x^2 - 1} \cdot \dfrac{x + 1}{x^2 + 2x}$ $\dfrac{x - 2}{x(x - 1)}$; $x \neq 0$, 1, -1, or -2

12. $\dfrac{x^2 - 5x + 6}{x^2 - 4} \cdot \dfrac{x^2 + 3x + 2}{x^2 - 2x - 3}$

Divide. State any restrictions on the variables. 16–18. See margin.

13. $\dfrac{7x}{4y^3} \div \dfrac{21x^3}{8y}$ $\dfrac{2}{3x^2y^2}$; $x \neq 0$, $y \neq 0$

14. $\dfrac{3x^3}{5y^2} \div \dfrac{6x^5}{5y^3}$ $\dfrac{y}{2x^2}$; $x \neq 0$, $y \neq 0$

15. $\dfrac{6x + 6y}{x - y} \div \dfrac{18}{5x - 5y}$ $\dfrac{5(x + y)}{3}$; $x \neq y$

16. $\dfrac{3y - 12}{2y + 4} \div \dfrac{6y - 24}{4y + 8}$

17. $\dfrac{x^2}{x^2 + 2x + 1} \div \dfrac{3x}{x^2 - 1}$

18. $\dfrac{y^2 - 5y + 6}{y^3} \div \dfrac{y^2 + 3y - 10}{4y^2}$

3. Practice

Assignment Guide

① **A B** 1-6, 19-21, 23-26, 33-35, 37

② **A B** 7-18, 22, 27-32, 36
C Challenge   38-41

Test Prep   42-47
Mixed Review   48-56

Homework Quick Check

To check students' understanding of key skills and concepts, go over Exercises 5, 15, 23, 25, 26, 37.

Error Prevention!

Exercises 13–18 When students state restrictions on the variables, they may forget that values that make the numerator of the divisor equal to 0 must also be excluded. Remind them that any value that makes a factor of the numerator or the denominator of the divisor equal to 0 must be excluded.

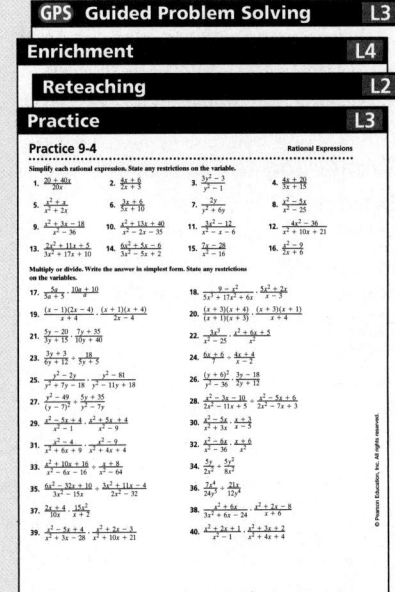

16. 1; $y \neq -2$ or 4

17. $\dfrac{x(x - 1)}{3(x + 1)}$; $x \neq -1$, 1, or 0

18. $\dfrac{4(y - 3)}{y(y + 5)}$; $y \neq 2$, -5, or 0

511

B **Apply Your Skills**

Simplify each rational expression. State any restrictions on the variables.

19. $\frac{(x-8)}{(x-10)}$; $x \neq -3$
or 10

19. $\frac{x^2 - 5x - 24}{x^2 - 7x - 30}$

20. $\frac{2y^2 + 8y - 24}{2y^2 - 8y + 8}$

21. $\frac{xy^3 - 9xy}{12xy^2 + 12xy - 144x}$

Lesson Quiz

20. $\frac{(y+6)}{(y-2)}$; $y \neq 2$

21. $\frac{y(y+3)}{12(y+4)}$; $x \neq 0$,
$y \neq -4$ or 3

22. **Write an expression for the area of the rectangle at the right.** $\frac{6(a+1)}{a-3}$

23. **Error Analysis** A student claims that $x = 2$ is the only solution of the equation $\frac{x}{x-2} = \frac{1}{2} + \frac{2}{x-2}$. Is the student correct? Explain. **See margin.**

Simplify. State any restrictions on the variable.

1. $\frac{x^2 + x - 6}{x^2 + 3x} \cdot \frac{x-2}{x}$; $x \neq -3, 0$

2. $\frac{4x^2 - 25}{2x^2 + 3x - 20} \cdot \frac{2x + 5}{x + 4}$;
$x \neq -4, \frac{5}{2}$

24. **Check students' work.**

24. **Open-Ended** Write three rational expressions that simplify to $\frac{x}{x+1}$.

25. **Writing** How can you tell whether a rational expression is in simplest form? Include an example with your explanation. **See margin.**

3. **Multiply. State any restrictions on the variable.**
$\frac{x^2 + 6x - 7}{x^2 + 5x} \cdot \frac{3x^2 + 16x + 5}{2x^2 + 7x - 9}$
$\frac{3x^2 + 22x + 7}{2x^2 + 9x}$; $x \neq -5, -\frac{9}{2}$,
0, 1

Exercise 26

26. **Industrial Design** A storage tank will have a circular base of radius r and a height of r. The tank can be either cylindrical or hemispherical (half a sphere).
a. Write and simplify an expression for the ratio of the volume of the hemispherical tank to its surface area (including the base). For a sphere, $V = \frac{4}{3}\pi r^3$ and S.A. $= 4\pi r^2$. **a–d. See margin.**
b. Write and simplify an expression for the ratio of the volume of the cylindrical tank to its surface area (including the bases).
c. Compare the ratios of volume to surface area for the two tanks.
d. Compare the volumes of the two tanks.

4. **Divide. State any restrictions on the variable.**
$\frac{y^2 + 5y + 4}{y^2 - 49} \div \frac{2y^2 + 5y - 12}{y^2 + 9y + 14}$
$\frac{y^2 + 3y + 2}{2y^2 - 17y + 21}$; $y \neq -7, -4$,
$-2, \frac{3}{2}, 7$

27–35. See margin
pp. 512–513.

Multiply or divide. State any restrictions on the variable.

27. $\frac{a+3}{a^2 + a - 12} \div \frac{a^2 - 9}{a^2 + 7a + 12}$

28. $\frac{b^2 - 25}{(b+5)^2} \div \frac{2b + 10}{4b + 20}$

29. $\frac{6x^3 - 6x^2}{x^4 + 5x^3} \div \frac{3x^2 - 15x + 12}{2x^2 + 2x - 40}$

30. $\frac{2x^2 - 6x}{x^2 + 18x + 81} \cdot \frac{9x + 81}{x^2 - 9}$

Alternative Assessment

Have students work in pairs. Ask one student to write three problems using Exercises 1, 12, and 17 as models. Ask the other student to write three problems using Exercises 3, 11, and 18 as models. Have each student work the problems written by the other. Then have students check one another's work.

31. $\frac{x^2 - x - 2}{2x^2 - 5x + 2} \div \frac{x^2 - x - 12}{2x^2 + 5x - 3}$

32. $\frac{2x^2 + 5x + 2}{4x^2 - 1} \cdot \frac{2x^2 + x - 1}{x^2 + x - 2}$

Simplify. State any restrictions on the variables.

33. $\frac{(x^2 - x)^2}{x(x-1)^{-2}(x^2 + 3x - 4)}$

34. $\frac{2x + 6}{(x-1)^{-1}(x^2 + 2x - 3)}$

35. $\frac{54x^3 y^{-1}}{3x^{-2}y}$

Connection to Physics

Exercise 37 Be sure students understand the distinction between velocity and acceleration. Velocity is the rate of change of distance with respect to time. Acceleration is the rate of change of velocity with respect to time.

36. The width of the rectangle at the right is $\frac{a+10}{3a+24} \cdot \frac{2(a+8)}{2a+5}$. Write an expression for the length of the rectangle.

$A = \frac{2a+20}{6a+15}$

37. **Physics** The acceleration of an object is a measure of how much its velocity changes in a given period of time.

$$\text{acceleration} = \frac{\text{final velocity} - \text{initial velocity}}{\text{time}}$$

Suppose you are riding a bicycle at 6 m/s. You step hard on the pedals and increase your speed to 12 m/s in about 5 s.
a. Find your acceleration in m/s². **1.2 m/s²**
b. A sedan can go from 0 to 60 mi/h in about 10 s. What is the acceleration in m/s²? (*Hints:* 1 mi $\approx$ 1609 m; 1 h = 3600 s.) **2.68 m/s²**

GO Online
Homework Video Tutor
Visit: PHSchool.com
Web Code: age-0904

C **Challenge**

38. **a.** **Critical Thinking** Simplify $\frac{(2x^n)^2 - 1}{2x^n - 1}$, where x is an integer and n is a positive integer. (*Hint:* Factor the numerator.) **$2x^n + 1$**
b. Use the result from part (a) to show that the value of the given expression is always an odd integer. **2 is a factor of $2x^n$, so $2x^n$ is even, and $2x^n + 1$ is odd.**

23. **The student is not correct; $x = 2$ will make the denominator of $\frac{x}{x-2}$ equal 0, so $x = 2$ is not a solution.**

25. **The numerator and the denominator have no common factors; check students' work.**

26a. $\frac{\frac{2}{3}\pi r^3}{2\pi r^2 + \pi r^2} = \frac{2r}{9}$

b. $\frac{\pi r^2(r)}{2\pi r^2 + 2\pi r(r)} = \frac{r}{4}$

c. **The ratio for the cylindrical tank is always larger.**

d. **For a given value of r, the cylindrical tank will have a larger volume.**

27. $\frac{a+3}{(a-3)(a-3)}$; $a \neq -4$,
-3, or 3

512

Use the fact that $\dfrac{\frac{a}{b}}{\frac{c}{d}} = \dfrac{a}{b} \div \dfrac{c}{d}$ to simplify each rational expression. State any restrictions on the variables.

39. $\dfrac{\frac{8x^2y}{x+1}}{\frac{6xy^2}{x+1}}$

$\dfrac{4x}{3y}$; $x \neq 0$ or -1, $y \neq 0$

40. $\dfrac{\frac{3a^3b^3}{a-b}}{\frac{4ab}{b-a}}$

$-\dfrac{3a^2b^2}{4}$; $a \neq 0$ or b, $b \neq 0$

41. $\dfrac{\frac{9m+6n}{m^2n^2}}{\frac{12m+8n}{5m^2}}$

$\dfrac{15}{4n^2}$; $m \neq 0$ or $-\frac{2}{3}n$, $n \neq 0$

Test Prep

Multiple Choice

42. Which expression can be simplified to $\dfrac{x-1}{x-3}$? **D**

A. $\dfrac{x^2 - x - 6}{x^2 - x - 2}$

B. $\dfrac{x^2 - 2x + 1}{x^2 + 2x - 3}$

C. $\dfrac{x^2 - 3x - 4}{x^2 - 7x + 12}$

D. $\dfrac{x^2 - 4x + 3}{x^2 - 6x + 9}$

43. Which expression is in simplest form? **G**

F. $\dfrac{x^2 - x}{x^2 - 1}$

G. $\dfrac{x^2 - 1}{x^2 + 1}$

H. $\dfrac{x^2 - 1}{x + 1}$

J. $\dfrac{x + 3}{x^2 + 4x + 3}$

44. What is the product of $\dfrac{4x^2 - 1}{2x^2 - 5x - 3}$ and $\dfrac{x^2 - 6x + 9}{2x^2 + 5x - 3}$? **D**

A. 1

B. $x - 3$

C. $x + 3$

D. $\dfrac{x - 3}{x + 3}$

45. What are the restrictions on x when $\dfrac{x^2 - x - 2}{x^2 - 9}$ is divided by $\dfrac{x - 8}{x^2 + 10x + 25}$? **H**

F. $x \neq -3$ or -5

G. $x \neq 3, -3,$ or -5

H. $x \neq 3, -3, -5,$ or 8

J. $x \neq 2, 9, 8,$ or -25

Short Response

46. Let $f(x)$, $g(x)$, $h(x)$, and $k(x)$ be rational expressions. Explain how to find all the restrictions for $\dfrac{f(x)}{g(x)} \div \dfrac{h(x)}{k(x)}$. **See margin.**

47. The product of $\dfrac{x^2 - 11x + 28}{x^2 - 2x - 35}$ and a second rational expression $\dfrac{f(x)}{g(x)}$ is $\dfrac{x + 4}{x + 5}$. What is the second rational expression? Show each step of your work. **See margin.**

50. hole at $x = 4$, vertical asymptote at $x = -3$

Mixed Review

Lesson 9-3

Describe the vertical asymptotes and holes for the graph of each rational function.

48. $y = \dfrac{x - 3}{x - 3}$
hole at $x = 3$

49. $y = \dfrac{x - 1}{(3x + 2)(x + 1)}$
vertical asymptotes at $x = -\frac{2}{3}$ and $x = -1$

50. $y = \dfrac{(x - 4)(x + 5)}{(x + 3)(x - 4)}$
See above.

Lesson 8-3

Evaluate each logarithm.

51. $\log_4 64$ 3

52. $\log_2 \frac{1}{32}$ -5

53. $\log_5 5\sqrt{5}$ $\frac{3}{2}$

54. $\log_{16} 8$ $\frac{3}{4}$

Lesson 7-5

Solve each equation.

55. $\sqrt{x + 3} - 1 = 4$ $x = 22$

56. $\sqrt{7x + 1} - \sqrt{6x + 7} = 0$ $x = 6$

Resources

For additional practice with a variety of test item formats:
• Standardized Test Prep, p. 543
• Test-Taking Strategies, p. 538
• Test-Taking Strategies with Transparencies

28. $\dfrac{2(b - 5)}{b + 5}$; $b \neq -5$

29. $\dfrac{4}{x}$; $x \neq 0, -5, 4,$ or 1

30. $\dfrac{18x}{(x + 9)(x + 3)}$; $x \neq -9, -3,$ or 3

31. $\dfrac{x + 1}{x - 4}$; $x \neq -3, \frac{1}{2}, 2,$ or 4

32. $\dfrac{x + 1}{x - 1}$; $x \neq -\frac{1}{2}, \frac{1}{2}, 1,$ or -2

33. $\dfrac{x(x - 1)^3}{(x + 4)}$, $x \neq -4, 0, 1$

34. 2, $x \neq -3, 1$

35. $\dfrac{18x^5}{y^2}$, $y \neq 0$

46. [2] $\dfrac{f(x)}{g(x)} \div \dfrac{h(x)}{k(x)} = \dfrac{f(x)}{g(x)} \cdot \dfrac{k(x)}{h(x)}$

The restrictions are all the values of x that make any denominator equal zero, so the restrictions are that $g(x) \neq 0$, $k(x) \neq 0$, and $h(x) \neq 0$.

[1] incomplete answer

47. [2]

$\dfrac{x^2 - 11x + 28}{x^2 - 2x - 35} \cdot \dfrac{f(x)}{g(x)} = \dfrac{x + 4}{x + 5}$

$\dfrac{f(x)}{g(x)} = \dfrac{x + 4}{x + 5} \div \dfrac{x^2 - 11x + 28}{x^2 - 2x - 35}$

$= \dfrac{x + 4}{x + 5} \cdot \dfrac{x^2 - 2x - 35}{x^2 - 11x + 28}$

$= \dfrac{x + 4}{x + 5} \cdot \dfrac{(x - 7)(x + 5)}{(x - 7)(x - 4)}$

$= \dfrac{x + 4}{x - 4}$

[1] answer only, with no work shown OR one mistake, such as in factoring

513

9-5

Adding and Subtracting Rational Expressions

1. Plan

Objectives
1 To add and subtract rational expressions
2 To simplify complex fractions

Examples
1 Real-World Connection
2 Finding Least Common Multiples
3 Adding Rational Expressions
4 Subtracting Rational Expressions
5 Simplifying Complex Fractions

Math Background

Addition and subtraction of rational expressions is much like addition and subtraction of rational numbers. First find the least common denominator for the rational expressions. Next, rewrite both expressions using this common denominator. Finally, add or subtract the fractions and simplify the result.

More Math Background: p. 486D

Lesson Planning and Resources

See p. 486E for a list of the resources that support this lesson.

Bell Ringer Practice

✓ **Check Skills You'll Need**
For intervention, direct students to:

Operations with Fractions
Skills Handbook: page 871

What You'll Learn

- To add and subtract rational expressions
- To simplify complex fractions

. . . And Why

To find the focal length of a camera lens, as in Example 1

✓ **Check Skills You'll Need**

Find the least common multiple of the two numbers.

1. 7, 21 **21**   **2.** 6, 10 **30**   **3.** 11, 17 **187**   **4.** 30, 105 **210**

Add or subtract.

5. $\frac{5}{19} + \frac{7}{38}$ $\frac{17}{38}$ **6.** $\frac{2}{15} + \frac{3}{25}$ $\frac{19}{75}$ **7.** $\frac{7}{24} - \frac{5}{36}$ $\frac{11}{72}$ **8.** $\frac{11}{12} - \frac{7}{45}$ $\frac{137}{180}$

🔊 **New Vocabulary** • complex fraction

---

1 Adding and Subtracting Rational Expressions

> **Activity:** Adding Fractions—Extended
>
> **1.** Add. Simplify where possible.
>
>   **a.** $\frac{2}{x} + \frac{3}{x}$ $\frac{5}{x}$ **b.** $\frac{4}{3x} + \frac{2}{3x}$ $\frac{2}{x}$ **c.** $\frac{3c}{2c-1} + \frac{5c+1}{2c-1}$ $\frac{8c+1}{2c-1}$
>
> **2.** Explain the steps you followed in Question 1.
>
> **3.** How is adding rational expressions similar to adding fractions?
>
>   2–3. See back of book.

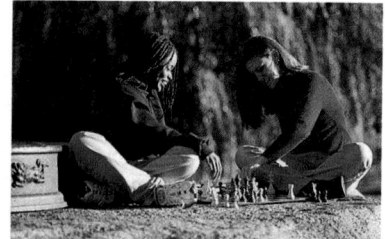

To produce a clear photograph, light rays must be focused on the film. The focal length of a camera lens is the distance from the lens to the point where parallel rays of light are focused.

When you focus a camera, you change the distance from the lens to the film.

The lens equation is $\frac{1}{f} = \frac{1}{d_i} + \frac{1}{d_o}$.

f = focal length of the lens

d_i = distance from the lens to the film

d_o = distance from the lens to the object

Differentiated Instruction **Solutions for All Learners**

Special Needs L1
Write $\frac{2}{3} + \frac{3}{4}$ on the board. Invite a student to simplify the expression by using the LCD. Clarify that the numerator and denominator must be multiplied by the same factor. Leave the solved problem on the board as you work Example 3, showing how the steps are similar. **learning style: visual**

Below Level L2
Review the definitions of least common multiple (LCM) and least common denominator (LCD).

learning style: verbal

Test-Taking Tip

Make sure your answer is in terms of the unit of measure requested in the direction lines.

1 EXAMPLE Real-World Connection

Gridded Response An object is 15 cm from a camera lens. The object is in focus on the film when the lens is 10 cm from the film. Find the focal length of the lens in centimeters.

$\frac{1}{f} = \frac{1}{d_i} + \frac{1}{d_o}$ Use the lens equation.

$\frac{1}{f} = \frac{1}{10} + \frac{1}{15}$ Substitute.

$= \frac{3}{30} + \frac{2}{30}$ Write equivalent fractions with the LCD.

$= \frac{5}{30} = \frac{1}{6}$ Add and simplify.

Since $\frac{1}{f} = \frac{1}{6}$, the focal length of the lens is 6 cm.

 Quick Check ① Suppose an object is 20 cm from a camera lens. When the object is properly focused, the lens is 5 cm from the film. Find the focal length of the lens. **4 cm**

For practice in adding and subtracting fractions, go to p. 871.

To add or subtract rational expressions with different denominators, it is easiest to use the least common multiple of the denominators as a common denominator.

2 EXAMPLE Finding Least Common Multiples

Find the least common multiple of $4x^2 - 36$ and $6x^2 + 36x + 54$.

Step 1 Find the prime factors of each expression.

$4x^2 - 36 = 4(x^2 - 9) = (2)(2)(x - 3)(x + 3)$

$6x^2 + 36x + 54 = 6(x^2 + 6x + 9) = (2)(3)(x + 3)(x + 3)$

Step 2 Write each prime factor the greatest number of times it appears in either expression. Simplify where possible.

$(2)(2)(3)(x - 3)(x + 3)(x + 3) = 12(x - 3)(x + 3)^2$

The least common multiple is $12(x - 3)(x + 3)^2$.

Quick Check ② Find the least common multiple of each pair of expressions.
a. $3x^2 - 9x - 30$ and $6x + 30$
$6(x - 5)(x + 5)(x + 2)$
b. $5x^2 + 15x + 10$ and $2x^2 - 8$
$10(x + 2)(x - 2)(x + 1)$

3 EXAMPLE Adding Rational Expressions

Simplify $\frac{1}{x^2 + 5x + 4} + \frac{5x}{3x + 3}$.

$\frac{1}{x^2 + 5x + 4} + \frac{5x}{3x + 3} = \frac{1}{(x + 1)(x + 4)} + \frac{5x}{3(x + 1)}$ Factor the denominators.

$= \frac{1}{(x + 1)(x + 4)} \cdot \frac{3}{3} + \frac{5x}{3(x + 1)} \cdot \frac{x + 4}{x + 4}$ identity for multiplication

$= \frac{3}{3(x + 1)(x + 4)} + \frac{5x(x + 4)}{3(x + 1)(x + 4)}$ Multiply.

$= \frac{3 + 5x(x + 4)}{3(x + 1)(x + 4)}$ Add.

$= \frac{5x^2 + 20x + 3}{3(x + 1)(x + 4)}$ Simplify the numerator.

Lesson 9-5 Adding and Subtracting Rational Expressions **515**

2. Teach

Guided Instruction

Activity
Teaching Tip

For each part of Question 1, point out that both expressions have the same denominator. Ask students to make a conjecture about how they might add rational expressions with different denominators.

3 EXAMPLE Teaching Tip

Write $\frac{2}{3} + \frac{3}{4}$ on the board. Invite a volunteer to write the steps for adding the fractions on the board. Have the student explain the work. Help students understand that the steps in Example 3 are the same as the steps on the board.

PowerPoint

Additional Examples

① An object is 24 cm from a camera lens. The object is in focus on the film when the lens is 12 cm from the film. Find the focal length of the lens. **8 cm**

② Find the least common multiple of $2x^2 - 8x + 8$ and $15x^2 - 60$. $30(x + 2)(x - 2)^2$

③ Simplify $\frac{1}{3x^2 + 21x + 30} + \frac{4x}{3x + 15}$.
$\frac{4x^2 + 8x + 1}{3(x + 2)(x + 5)}$

✓ **Quick Check** ③ Simplify $\dfrac{1}{x^2 - 4x - 12} + \dfrac{3x}{4x + 8}$. $\dfrac{3x^2 - 18x + 4}{4(x - 6)(x + 2)}$

④ **EXAMPLE** Subtracting Rational Expressions

Simplify $\dfrac{7y}{5y^2 - 125} - \dfrac{4}{3y + 15}$.

$\dfrac{7y}{5y^2 - 125} - \dfrac{4}{3y + 15} = \dfrac{7y}{5(y + 5)(y - 5)} - \dfrac{4}{3(y + 5)}$ **Factor the denominators.**

$= \dfrac{7y}{5(y + 5)(y - 5)} \cdot \dfrac{3}{3} - \dfrac{4}{3(y + 5)} \cdot \dfrac{5(y - 5)}{5(y - 5)}$ **identity for multiplication**

$= \dfrac{(3)(7y)}{(3)(5)(y + 5)(y - 5)} - \dfrac{(4)(5)(y - 5)}{(3)(5)(y + 5)(y - 5)}$ **Multiply.**

$= \dfrac{(3)(7y) - (4)(5)(y - 5)}{(3)(5)(y + 5)(y - 5)}$ **Simplify.**

$= \dfrac{y + 100}{15(y + 5)(y - 5)}$ **Simplify.**

✓ **Quick Check** ④ Simplify each expression.

a. $\dfrac{-2}{3x^2 + 36x + 105} - \dfrac{3x}{6x + 30}$
$\dfrac{-3x^2 - 21x - 4}{6(x + 5)(x + 7)}$

b. $\dfrac{x}{3x^2 - 9x + 6} - \dfrac{2x + 1}{3x^2 + 3x - 6}$
$\dfrac{-x^2 + 5x + 2}{3(x - 1)(x - 2)(x + 2)}$

---

2 **Simplifying Complex Fractions**

A **complex fraction** is a fraction that has a fraction in its numerator or denominator or in both its numerator and denominator. Here are some examples.

$$\dfrac{\frac{1}{x}}{y} \qquad \dfrac{3}{1 - \frac{1}{2y}} \qquad \dfrac{\frac{x - 2}{x} - \frac{2}{x + 1}}{\frac{3}{x - 1} - \frac{1}{x + 1}}$$

To simplify a complex fraction such as $\dfrac{\frac{a}{b}}{\frac{c}{d}}$ you can multiply the numerator $\frac{a}{b}$ and denominator $\frac{c}{d}$ by their least common denominator (LCD) bd. Or you can divide the numerator $\frac{a}{b}$ by the denominator $\frac{c}{d}$.

⑤ **EXAMPLE** Simplifying Complex Fractions

Simplify $\dfrac{\frac{1}{x} + 3}{\frac{5}{y} + 4}$.

Method I First find the LCD of all the rational expressions.

$\dfrac{\frac{1}{x} + 3}{\frac{5}{y} + 4} = \dfrac{\left(\frac{1}{x} + 3\right) \cdot xy}{\left(\frac{5}{y} + 4\right) \cdot xy}$ **The LCD is *xy*. Multiply the numerator and denominator by *xy*.**

$= \dfrac{\frac{1}{x} \cdot xy + 3 \cdot xy}{\frac{5}{y} \cdot xy + 4 \cdot xy}$ **Use the Distributive Property.**

$= \dfrac{y + 3xy}{5x + 4xy}$ **Simplify.**

Method 2 First simplify the numerator and denominator.

$$\frac{\frac{1}{x}+3}{\frac{5}{y}+4} = \frac{\frac{1}{x}+\frac{3x}{x}}{\frac{5}{y}+\frac{4y}{y}}$$ Write equivalent expressions with common denominators.

$$= \frac{\frac{1+3x}{x}}{\frac{5+4y}{y}}$$ Add.

$$= \frac{1+3x}{x} \div \frac{5+4y}{y}$$ Divide the numerator fraction by the denominator fraction.

$$= \frac{1+3x}{x} \cdot \frac{y}{5+4y}$$ Multiply by the reciprocal.

$$= \frac{(1+3x)y}{x(5+4y)}$$

$$= \frac{y+3xy}{5x+4xy}$$

✓ **Quick Check** ⑤ Simplify each complex fraction.

a. $\dfrac{\frac{1}{x}}{y}$ $\frac{1}{xy}$

b. $\dfrac{3}{1-\frac{1}{2y}}$ $\frac{6y}{2y-1}$

c. $\dfrac{\frac{x-2}{x}-\frac{2}{x+1}}{\frac{3}{x-1}-\frac{1}{x+1}}$

$\frac{x^3-4x^2+x+2}{2x^2+4x}$

EXERCISES

For more exercises, see *Extra Skill and Word Problem Practice*.

Practice and Problem Solving

 Practice by Example

Example 1
(page 515)

The focal length f of a camera lens is 2 in. The lens equation is $\frac{1}{f} = \frac{1}{d_i} + \frac{1}{d_o}$, where d_i is the distance between the lens and the film and d_o is the distance between the lens and the object.

1. The object to be photographed is 10 ft away. How far should the lens be from the film? $\frac{120}{59} \approx 2.03$ in.

2. The object to be photographed is 20 ft away. How far should the lens be from the film? $\frac{240}{119} \approx 2.02$ in.

3. Critical Thinking Explain why one setting on the camera is used for photographing all objects that are more than 10 ft from the camera.
   For distances greater than 10 ft, d_i is nearly constant.

Example 2
(page 515)

Find the least common multiple of each pair of polynomials. **4–7. See margin.**

4. $9(x+2)(2x-1)$ and $3(x+2)$

5. x^2-1 and x^2+2x+1

6. $(x-2)(x+3)$ and $10(x+3)^2$

7. $12x^2-6x-126$ and $18x-63$

8. $5y^2-80$ and $y+4$
   $5(y+4)(y-4)$

9. $x^2-32x-10$ and $2x+10$
   $2(x+5)(x^2-32x-10)$

Example 3
(page 515)

Simplify each sum.

10. $\frac{1}{2x}+\frac{1}{2x}$ $\frac{1}{x}$

11. $\frac{d-3}{2d+1}+\frac{d-1}{2d+1}$ $\frac{2(d-2)}{2d+1}$

13. $\frac{7x^2+20x-18}{(x-3)(x+3)(x+4)}$

12. $\frac{5y+2}{xy^2}+\frac{2x-4}{4xy}$ $\frac{xy+8y+4}{2xy^2}$

13. $\frac{5x}{x^2-9}+\frac{2}{x+4}$

15. $\frac{5x^2+14x-12}{(x-3)(x+2)^2}$

14. $\frac{-3x}{x^2-9}+\frac{4}{2x-6}$ $\frac{-x+6}{(x-3)(x+3)}$

15. $\frac{5x}{x^2-x-6}+\frac{4}{x^2+4x+4}$

---

3. Practice

Assignment Guide

❶ A B 1-21, 31-43

❷ A B 22-30, 44-53
C Challenge   54-55

Test Prep   56-61
Mixed Review   62-74

Homework Quick Check
To check students' understanding of key skills and concepts, go over Exercises 14, 29, 42, 43, 45, 52.

Exercises 4–9 Remind students to begin by writing each polynomial in factored form

Differentiated Instruction Resources

GPS Guided Problem Solving	L3
Enrichment	L4
Reteaching	L2
Practice	L3

4. $9(x+2)(2x-1)$

5. $(x-1)(x+1)(x+1)$

6. $10(x-2)(x+3)^2$

7. $18(2x-7)(x+3)$

Error Prevention!

Exercises 22–30 Students are sometimes intimidated by the stacks of fractions. You may want to suggest that they change the complex fraction to a division problem of the form (N) ÷ (D), Where N and D are the expressions in the numerator and denominator of the complex fraction. Be sure to tell them to put N and D in tall parentheses. They can then simplify within the tall parentheses, divide, and simplify.

Teaching Tip

Exercise 54 You may need to explain the terms *resistance, parallel circuit,* and *ohms* to students who are not familiar with the terms.

Example 4
(page 516)

Simplify each difference.

16. $\dfrac{-2}{x} - \dfrac{1}{x}$ $-\dfrac{3}{x}$

17. $\dfrac{-5y}{2y-1} - \dfrac{y+3}{2y-1}$ $\dfrac{-3(2y+1)}{2y-1}$

18. $\dfrac{y}{2y+4} - \dfrac{3}{y+2}$ $\dfrac{y-6}{2(y+2)}$

19. $\dfrac{x}{3x+9} - \dfrac{8}{x^2+3x}$ $\dfrac{x^2-24}{3x(x+3)}$

20. $\dfrac{3y}{y^2-25} - \dfrac{8}{y-5}$ $\dfrac{-5(y+8)}{(y-5)(y+5)}$

21. $\dfrac{2x}{x^2-x-2} - \dfrac{4x}{x^2-3x+2}$ $\dfrac{-2x(x+3)}{(x-2)(x-1)(x+1)}$

Example 5
(page 516)

Simplify each complex fraction.

22. $\dfrac{\frac{1}{x}}{\frac{2}{y}}$ $\dfrac{y}{2x}$

23. $\dfrac{1-\frac{1}{4}}{2-\frac{3}{5}}$ $\dfrac{15}{28}$

24. $\dfrac{\frac{2}{x+y}}{3}$ $\dfrac{2}{3(x+y)}$

25. $\dfrac{\frac{1}{3}}{\frac{3}{b}}$ $\dfrac{b}{9}$

26. $\dfrac{1}{1+\frac{x}{y}}$ $\dfrac{y}{x+y}$

27. $\dfrac{3}{\frac{2}{x}+y}$ $\dfrac{3x}{2+xy}$

28. $\dfrac{\frac{2}{x+y}}{\frac{5}{x+y}}$ $\dfrac{2}{5}$

29. $\dfrac{\frac{3}{x-4}}{1-\frac{2}{x-4}}$ $\dfrac{3}{x-6}$

30. $\dfrac{-3}{\frac{5}{x}+y}$ $\dfrac{-3x}{5+xy}$

B Apply Your Skills

Add or subtract. Simplify where possible.

31. $\dfrac{3}{4x} - \dfrac{2}{x^2}$ $\dfrac{3x-8}{4x^2}$

32. $\dfrac{3}{x+1} + \dfrac{x}{x-1}$ $\dfrac{x^2+4x-3}{(x+1)(x-1)}$

33. $\dfrac{2x}{x^2-1} - \dfrac{1}{x^2}$ $\dfrac{2x^3-x^2+1}{x^2(x+1)(x-1)}$

34. $\dfrac{4}{x^2-9} + \dfrac{7}{x+3}$ $\dfrac{7x-17}{(x-3)(x+3)}$

35. $\dfrac{x+2}{x-1} - \dfrac{x-3}{2x+1}$ $\dfrac{x^2+9x-1}{(x-1)(2x+1)}$

36. $\dfrac{x}{2x^2-x} + \dfrac{1}{2x}$ $\dfrac{4x-1}{2x(2x-1)}$

37. $\dfrac{5x^2+6x+12}{(x-3)(x+2)^2}$

37. $\dfrac{5x}{x^2-x-6} - \dfrac{4}{x^2+4x+4}$

38. $3x + \dfrac{x^2+5x}{x^2-2}$ $\dfrac{x(3x^2+x-1)}{x^2-2}$

39. $4y - \dfrac{y+2}{y^2+3y}$ $\dfrac{4y^3+12y^2-y-2}{y(y+3)}$

40. $\dfrac{5y}{y^2-7y} - \dfrac{4}{2y-14} + \dfrac{9}{y}$ $\dfrac{3(4y-21)}{y(y-7)}$

41. **Open-Ended** Write two rational expressions whose sum is $\dfrac{x-2}{x+4}$. **Check students' work.**

42. Factoring is used to determine the least common multiple of the denominators; check students' work.

42. **Writing** Explain how factoring is used when adding or subtracting rational expressions. Include an example in your explanation.

43. Answers may vary. Sample: Substitute 0 for x in the three expressions, and show that $\dfrac{4}{-9} + \dfrac{7}{3} \neq \dfrac{25}{-9}$.

43. **Error Analysis** How would you convince a student that $\dfrac{7x+25}{x^2-9}$ is *not* the sum of $\dfrac{4}{x^2-9}$ and $\dfrac{7}{x+3}$?

Simplify each complex fraction.

44. $\dfrac{\frac{2}{x}+\frac{3}{y}}{\frac{-5}{x}+\frac{7}{y}}$ $\dfrac{3x+2y}{7x-5y}$

45. $\dfrac{\frac{5}{x}-\frac{2}{y}}{\frac{-4}{x}-\frac{6}{y}}$ $\dfrac{2x-5y}{2(3x+2y)}$

46. $\dfrac{1+\frac{2}{x}}{2+\frac{3}{2x}}$ $\dfrac{2(x+2)}{4x+3}$

47. $\dfrac{\frac{1}{xy}-\frac{1}{y^2}}{\frac{1}{x^2y}-\frac{1}{xy^2}}$ x

48. $\dfrac{\frac{2}{x+4}+2}{1+\frac{3}{x+4}}$ $\dfrac{2(x+5)}{x+7}$

49. $\dfrac{\frac{3}{x-2}-5}{2-\frac{4}{x-2}}$ $\dfrac{-5x+13}{2(x-4)}$

GO Online
Homework Video Tutor
Visit: PHSchool.com
Web Code: age-0905

50. **Open-Ended** Write two different complex fractions that simplify to $\dfrac{x-2}{x+4}$. **Check students' work.**

51. **Critical Thinking** What real numbers are not in the domain of function f? Explain.
$$f(x) = \dfrac{\frac{x+1}{x+2}}{\frac{x+3}{x+4}}$$
$x \neq -2, -3, -4$; those values result in division by 0, which is undefined.

Real-World **Connection**

Shortening a guitar string to $\frac{1}{2}$ or $\frac{2}{3}$ its original length produces a sound in harmony with its original pitch.

52. Music The harmonic mean of two numbers a and b equals $\dfrac{2}{\frac{1}{a} + \frac{1}{b}}$. As you vary the length of a violin or guitar string, its pitch changes. If a full-length string is 1 unit long, then many lengths that are simple fractions produce pitches that harmonize, or sound pleasing together. The harmonic mean relates three lengths that produce harmonious sounds. For example, $\frac{1}{3}$ is the harmonic mean of $\frac{1}{2}$ and $\frac{1}{4}$, and strings of these lengths produce harmonious sounds. Find the harmonic mean for strings of lengths 1 and $\frac{1}{2}$, $\frac{3}{4}$ and $\frac{1}{2}$, and $\frac{3}{4}$ and $\frac{3}{5}$. $\frac{2}{3}, \frac{3}{5}, \frac{2}{3}$

53. a. If you jog 12 mi at an average rate of 4 mi/h and walk the same route back at an average rate of 3 mi/h, you have traveled 24 mi in 7 h and your overall rate is $\frac{24}{7}$ mi/h. What is your overall average rate if you travel d mi at 3 mi/h and d mi at 4 mi/h? $\frac{24}{7}$ mi/h

   b. Harmonic Mean Find the harmonic mean (see Exercise 52) of 3 and 4. $\frac{24}{7}$

   c. If you travel any distance at x mi/h and the same distance at y mi/h then your average rate for the trip is the harmonic mean of x and y. Find the average rate of speed if you travel to a distant city at 50 mi/h and return at 40 mi/h.

   d. You travel to a city at x mi/h and the return trip is a mi/h faster. Express your average rate in terms of x and a.

C **Challenge**

53c. $\frac{400}{9}$ mi/h

d. $\dfrac{2x(x + a)}{2x + a}$ mi/h

54a. $\dfrac{R_1 R_2 R_3}{R_1 R_2 + R_1 R_3 + R_2 R_3}$

54. Electricity The total resistance R for a parallel circuit with three bulbs is $R = \dfrac{1}{\frac{1}{R_1} + \frac{1}{R_2} + \frac{1}{R_3}}$.

   a. Simplify the right side of the equation.

   b. Find the total resistance R of a parallel circuit with bulbs that have resistances of 3 ohms, 2.5 ohms, and 2.5 ohms.   **0.88 ohms**

$R_1 = 3$ ohms
$R_2 = 2.5$ ohms
$R_3 = 2.5$ ohms
Battery

55. Physics Use the camera lens equation $\frac{1}{f} = \frac{1}{d_i} + \frac{1}{d_o}$, where d_i is the distance from the lens to the film and d_o is the distance from the lens to an object.

   a. Solve the lens equation for f by taking the reciprocal of each side of the equation. Simplify the equation so it contains no complex fraction.

   b. When an object is in focus, a lens is x cm from the object and $(2x + 1)$ cm from the film. Find the focal length of the lens.

   a. $f = \dfrac{d_i d_o}{d_i + d_o}$

   b. $\dfrac{x(2x + 1)}{3x + 1} = f$

Test Prep

Multiple Choice

56. Find the least common multiple of $x^2 - 1$ and $x^2 - x$.   **B**
   A. $x - 1$
   B. $x(x - 1)(x + 1)$
   C. $x(x - 1)^2(x + 1)$
   D. $(x - 1)^2(x + 1)^2 x^2$

57. Which expression equals $\dfrac{1}{x^2 - 2x - 3} + \dfrac{1}{x^2 - 4x + 3}$?   **H**
   F. $\dfrac{2x - 1}{(x - 1)(x + 3)(x + 1)}$
   G. $\dfrac{2x + 1}{(x - 1)(x + 1)(x - 3)}$
   H. $\dfrac{2x}{(x - 1)(x + 1)(x - 3)}$
   J. $\dfrac{2x}{(x + 3)(x - 1)(x + 1)}$

Online lesson quiz, PHSchool.com, Web Code: aga-0905   Lesson 9-5 Adding and Subtracting Rational Expressions   **519**

PowerPoint
Lesson Quiz

1. The lens equation for a camera is $\frac{1}{f} = \frac{1}{d_i} + \frac{1}{d_o}$, where f is the focal length of the lens, d_i is the distance between the lens and the film, and d_o is the distance between the lens and the object. For a certain camera, an object that is 18 cm from the lens is in focus when the lens is 9 cm from the film. What is the focal length of the lens? **6 cm**

2. Find the least common multiple of $x(x^2 - 5x + 6)$ and $x^3(x^2 + 4x - 21)$.
$x^3(x - 2)(x - 3)(x + 7)$

Simplify.

3. $\dfrac{x}{x^2 - 4} + \dfrac{7}{3x + 6}$ $\dfrac{10x - 14}{3x^2 - 12}$

4. $\dfrac{m}{m + 3} - \dfrac{6m}{m^2 - 9}$ $\dfrac{m^2 - 9m}{m^2 - 9}$

5. $\dfrac{\frac{2y}{2y + 1} - 1}{1 - \frac{2y}{2y - 1}}$ $\dfrac{2y - 1}{2y + 1}$

Alternative Assessment

Have students work individually. Each student writes two rational expressions with binomial numerators. One rational expression should have $x^2 - 4$ as its denominator, and the other should have $x + 2$ as its denominator. They find the sum and difference of their expressions. Then have each student write a complex fraction that has the original expressions as numerator and denominator. The student then simplifies the complex fraction.

Test Prep

Resources
For additional practice with a variety of test item formats:
- Standardized Test Prep, p. 543
- Test-Taking Strategies, p. 538
- Test-Taking Strategies with Transparencies

60. [2] First factor both denominators:
$x^2 - 5x - 6$
$= (x - 6)(x + 1)$
$x^2 - 12x + 36$
$= (x - 6)^2$. The least common denominator would have to include the factors $(x - 6)$, $(x + 1)$ and $(x - 6)^2$, so the LCD is
$(x - 6)^2(x + 1)$
$= x^3 - 11x^2 + 24x + 36$.

[1] answer only, no work shown

61. [2] $y = 2, x = -15$

[1] one of the asymptotes correct OR x and y are switched

---

58. Which expression equals $\frac{5x}{x^2 - 9} - \frac{4x}{x^2 + 5x + 6}$? **C**

A. $\frac{7x}{(x - 3)(x + 3)(x + 2)}$

B. $\frac{x^2 - 2x}{(x - 3)(x + 3)(x + 2)}$

C. $\frac{x^2 + 22x}{(x - 3)(x + 3)(x + 2)}$

D. $\frac{9x^2 - 2x}{(x - 3)(x + 3)(x + 2)}$

59. Simplify $\frac{\frac{2}{x} - 5}{\frac{6}{x} - 3}$.   **F**

F. $\frac{2 - 5x}{6 - 3x}$

G. $\frac{2 + 5x}{6 - 3x}$

H. $\frac{2x - 5}{6x + 3}$

J. $\frac{6 + 3x}{2 - 5x}$

Short Response

60. Find the least common denominator for the rational expressions $\frac{1}{x^2 - 5x - 6}$ and $\frac{1}{x^2 - 12x + 36}$. Show your work.   **See margin.**

61. What are the asymptotes of the graph of $y = \frac{2x - 1}{x + 15}$.   **See margin.**

Mixed Review

Lesson 9-4

Divide. State any restrictions on the variables.

62. $\frac{4x^3}{3y^4} \div \frac{16x^2}{9y^2}$ $\frac{3x}{4y^2}$; $x \neq 0, y \neq 0$

63. $\frac{7ax^3}{8by^2} \div \frac{14ax^4}{4by}$ $\frac{1}{4xy}$; $a \neq 0, b \neq 0, x \neq 0, y \neq 0$

64. $\frac{6x^2}{y} \div \frac{12x^4}{y^3} \cdot \frac{y^2}{2x^2}$; $x \neq 0, y \neq 0$ $\frac{12x}{x + 3}$; $x \neq -3, 2, $ or 3

65. $\frac{3x^2 - 9x}{x - 2} \div \frac{x^2 - 9}{4x - 8}$ $\frac{3(x - 2)}{4(x - 3)}$; $x \neq -2, 2, $ or 3

66. $\frac{3x - 6}{12x + 24} \div \frac{x^2 - 5x + 6}{3x^2 - 12}$ $\frac{3(x + 1)}{2(x + 3)}$; $x \neq 1, -1, $ or -3

67. $\frac{5x + 15}{10x - 10} \div \frac{x^2 + 6x + 9}{3x^2 - 3}$

Lesson 8-4

Write each expression as a single logarithm.

68. $\log_3 y + 4 \log_3 t$ $\log_3 t^4y$

69. $7 \log_{10} p + \log_{10} q$ $\log_{10} p^7q$

70. $\log_5 x - \frac{1}{5} \log_5 y$ $\log_5 \frac{x}{\sqrt[5]{y}}$

Lesson 7-6

Let $f(x) = x^2 + 1$ and $g(x) = 3x$. Find each value.

71. $(g \circ f)(-3)$ 30

72. $(f \circ g)(-3)$ 82

73. $(g \circ f)\left(\frac{1}{2}\right)$ $\frac{15}{4}$

74. $(f \circ f)(3)$ 101

Checkpoint Quiz 2   Lessons 9-4 through 9-5

Simplify each expression.

1. $\frac{3x - 6}{5x - 20} \cdot \frac{x - 8}{5x - 10}$ $\frac{3(x - 8)}{25(x - 4)}$

2. $\frac{14x + 7}{4x - 6} \cdot \frac{8x - 12}{42x + 21}$ $\frac{2}{3}$

3. $\frac{y^2 - 25}{(y + 5)^2} \div \frac{2y - 10}{4y + 20}$ 2

4. $\frac{y^2 - 25}{y^2 - 16} \div \frac{2y + 10}{y^2 - 4y}$ $\frac{y(y - 5)}{2(y + 4)}$

5. $\frac{8}{3x^3y} + \frac{4}{9xy^3}$ $\frac{4(6y^2 + x^2)}{9x^3y^3}$

6. $\frac{7}{5y + 25} + \frac{4}{3y + 15}$ $\frac{41}{15(y + 5)}$

7. $\frac{5x}{2y + 4} - \frac{6}{y^2 + 2y}$ $\frac{5xy - 12}{2y(y + 2)}$

8. $3x - \frac{x^2 + 5x}{x^2 - 2}$ $\frac{3x^3 - x^2 - 11x}{x^2 - 2}$

9. $\frac{\frac{3}{2y}}{\frac{6}{8x}}$ $\frac{2x}{y}$

10. $\frac{\frac{1}{x} + 3}{4 + \frac{5}{y}}$ $\frac{y(3x + 1)}{x(4y + 5)}$

Extraneous Solutions

FOR USE WITH LESSON 9-6

Activity Lab

Extraneous Solutions

This investigation will help students in Lesson 9-6 as they solve rational equations.

Since division by zero is undefined, strange and illogical things can happen when division by zero sneaks unnoticed into algebraic procedures.

Does $2 = 1$? Study the proof below.

① $\qquad a = b$

② $\qquad a^2 = ab$

③ $\qquad a^2 - b^2 = ab - b^2$

④ $\quad (a - b)(a + b) = b(a - b)$

⑤ $\qquad \dfrac{(a - b)(a + b)}{a - b} = \dfrac{b(a - b)}{a - b}$

⑥ $\qquad a + b = b$

⑦ $\qquad b + b = b$

⑧ $\qquad 2b = b$

⑨ $\qquad 2 = 1$

1a. ① given
② Multiply both sides by a.
③ Subtract b^2 from both sides.
④ Factor.
⑤ Divide both sides by $a - b$.
⑥ division property
⑦ Substitute b for a.
⑧ Combine like terms.
⑨ Divide both sides by b.

1. a. Describe each step of the proof.

b. Check equation ① by replacing a and b with a number such as 3. Do the same for each of the other equations. Which equations are true? **①, ②, ③, and ④**

c. Equation ⑤ seems to be derived by using the Division Property of Equality: If $a = b$ and $c \neq 0$, then $\frac{a}{c} = \frac{b}{c}$. Explain why the property is not used correctly. **See margin.**

2. a. Justify each step of the solution to $\frac{1}{x^2} = \frac{2}{x}$.

① $\qquad \dfrac{1}{x^2} = \dfrac{2}{x}$

② $\qquad 2x^2 = x$

③ $\qquad 2x^2 - x = 0$

④ $\qquad x(2x - 1) = 0$

⑤ $\quad x = 0 \text{ or } x = \frac{1}{2}$

① given
② Multiplication Property of Equality
③ Subtract x from both sides.
④ Factor.
⑤ Use the Zero-Product Property.

b. Check the solution $x = \frac{1}{2}$ in equations ④, ③, ②, and ①. **It checks in all four equations.**

c. Check the solution $x = 0$ in equations ④, ③, ②, and ①. **It checks in ④, ③, and ②.**

d. How are the checks different? Explain. **See margin.**

e. If equations ④ and ① have the same solutions, then you can work backward to derive equation ① from ④. What goes wrong when you try? **You divide by 0.**

f. Critical Thinking Explain why equation ③ can be derived from ②, and ② from ③, thereby ensuring that they have the same solutions. **See margin.**

g. Equation ② is derived from equation ① using the Multiplication Property of Equality: If $a = b$ then $ac = bc$. Both sides of equation ① are multiplied by x^3 to obtain equation ②. Is there anything wrong with this step? **no**

h. Critical Thinking Explain why equation ② can be derived from ①, but ① cannot be derived from ②. **② can be derived from ① using the Multiplication Property of Equality. ① cannot be derived from ② because the Division Property of Equality does not allow division by 0.**

Teaching Tip

Relate the work in this investigation to Example 1 in Lesson 9-4. Be sure students understand that when they simplify a fraction by dividing out a common factor from numerator and denominator, the common factor cannot have the value 0.

Error Prevention!

Exercise 1c Students may confuse the variables used to state the Division Property of Equality with the variables in the 9-step "proof" that $2 = 1$. If so, it may help to restate the Division Property of Equality using other variables.

1c. If $a = b$, then $a - b = 0$. The Division Property of Equality does not allow division by 0.

2d. $x = 0$ does not check in ① since division by 0 is undefined.

f. ③ can be derived from ② using the Subtraction Property of Equality. ② can be derived from ③ using the Addition Property of Equality.

1. Plan

Objectives
1 To solve rational equations
2 To use rational equations in solving problems

Examples
1 Solving Rational Equations
2 Solving Rational Equations
3 Real-World Connection
4 Real-World Connection

Math Background

To solve some rational equations, you can multiply each side by the LCD. To solve others that are proportions, you can use cross products. Remind students that cross multiplying is simply an efficient method, equivalent to solving a proportion by multiplying each side by the LCD.

More Math Background: p. 486D

Lesson Planning and Resources

See p. 486E for a list of the resources that support this lesson.

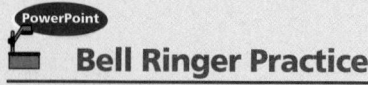

✓ Check Skills You'll Need

For intervention, direct students to:

Operations with Fractions
Skills Handbook: p. 871

Solving Rational Equations

What You'll Learn

• To solve rational equations
• To use rational equations in solving problems

...And Why

To find the average speed of a bicycle trip, as in Example 3

✓ Check Skills You'll Need

Find the LCD of each pair of fractions.

1. $\frac{1}{3t}, \frac{1}{5t^2}$ $15t^2$

2. $\frac{x}{2}, \frac{3x}{8}$ 8

3. $\frac{4}{3h^2}, \frac{2h}{h^3}$ $3h^3$

4. $\frac{4}{y+2}, \frac{3}{y-1}$ $(y+2)(y-1)$

5. $\frac{z}{2z+1}, \frac{1}{z}$ $z(2z+1)$

6. $\frac{1}{k+2}, \frac{3k}{k^2-4}$ $(k+2)(k-2)$

 GO for Help Skills Handbook page 871

---

1 Solving Rational Equations

Extraneous solutions can be introduced when you multiply both sides of an equation by the same algebraic expression. An extraneous solution is a solution of the derived equation, but not of the original equation.

You must check all solutions of the derived equation in the original equation to find whether any of them are not solutions of the original equation.

1 EXAMPLE   Solving Rational Equations

Solve $\frac{5}{2x-2} = \frac{15}{x^2-1}$. Check each solution.

$$\frac{5}{2x-2} = \frac{15}{x^2-1}$$

$5(x^2-1) = 15(2x-2)$ **Write the cross products.**

$5x^2 - 5 = 30x - 30$ **Distributive Property**

$5x^2 - 30x + 25 = 0$ **Write in standard form.**

$x^2 - 6x + 5 = 0$ **Divide each side by 5.**

$(x-1)(x-5) = 0$ **Factor.**

$x = 1 \text{ or } x = 5$ **Zero-Product Property**

Check When $x = 1$, both denominators in the original equation are zero. The original equation is undefined at $x = 1$. So $x = 1$ is not a solution.

When 5 is substituted for x in the original equation, both sides equal $\frac{5}{8}$.

● The solution is $x = 5$.

> **Problem Solving Hint**
>
> In a proportion, the cross products are equal.
> If $\frac{a}{b} = \frac{c}{d}$, then $ad = cb$ ($b \neq 0$, $d \neq 0$).

 Quick Check ❶ Solve each equation. Check each solution.

a. $\frac{-4}{5(x+2)} = \frac{3}{x+2}$ no solution

b. $\frac{-2}{x^2-2} = \frac{2}{x-4}$ −3, 2

Differentiated Instruction Solutions for All Learners

Special Needs L1
For Example 2, make sure students understand that they cannot apply cross products. Show that students need to multiply both sides of the equation by a common denominator, and that the LCD will involve the fewest simplification steps.

learning style: verbal

Below Level L2
Remind students that they can only cross multiply if an equation is a proportion. Other equations require simplifying one or both sides before cross-multiplying.

learning style: verbal

Video Tutor Help

Visit: PHSchool.com
Web Code: age-0775

When an equation has a sum or difference of two rational expressions, you can use the least common denominator (LCD) to simplify the equation.

2 EXAMPLE Solving Rational Equations

Solve $\frac{1}{2x} - \frac{2}{5x} = \frac{1}{2}$.

$$\frac{1}{2x} - \frac{2}{5x} = \frac{1}{2}$$

$$10x\left(\frac{1}{2x} - \frac{2}{5x}\right) = 10x\left(\frac{1}{2}\right) \quad \textbf{Multiply each side by the LCD, 10x.}$$

$$\frac{10x}{2x} - \frac{10x(2)}{5x} = \frac{10x}{2} \quad \textbf{Distributive Property}$$

$$5 - 4 = 5x \quad \textbf{Simplify.}$$

$$x = \frac{1}{5}$$

Since $\frac{1}{5}$ makes the original equation true, the solution is $x = \frac{1}{5}$.

✓ Quick Check ❷ Solve $\frac{4}{x} - \frac{3}{x+1} = 1$. Check your solution. **2, −2**

2 Using Rational Equations

3 EXAMPLE Real-World 🌐 Connection

Real-World 🌐 Connection

This high-performance bicycle has the aerodynamic design of a custom racing bicycle, but is practical enough for everyday riding.

Aerodynamics The aerodynamic covering on this bicycle increases a cyclist's average speed by 10 mi/h. The time for a 75-mi trip is reduced by 2 h. What is the average speed for the trip using the aerodynamic covering?

Relate speed with aerodynamic covering = speed without covering + 10

Define

	Distance (mi)	Rate (mi/h)	Time (h)
Without Covering	75	$\frac{75}{t}$	t
With Covering	75	$\frac{75}{t-2}$	$t - 2$

Write $\frac{75}{t-2} = \frac{75}{t} + 10$

$$\frac{75}{t-2} = \frac{75}{t} + 10$$

$$t(t-2)\left(\frac{75}{t-2}\right) = t(t-2)\left(\frac{75}{t}\right) + t(t-2)(10) \quad \begin{array}{l}\textbf{Multiply by the LCD,}\\ \textbf{t(t − 2).}\end{array}$$

$$t(75) = (t-2)(75) + 10t(t-2) \quad \textbf{Simplify.}$$

$$75t = 75t - 150 + 10t^2 - 20t \quad \textbf{Distributive Property}$$

$$0 = 10t^2 - 20t - 150 \quad \textbf{Simplify.}$$

$$0 = t^2 - 2t - 15 \quad \textbf{Divide each side by 10.}$$

$$0 = (t-5)(t+3) \quad \textbf{Factor.}$$

$$t = 5 \text{ or } t = -3 \quad \text{The time must be positive, so } \frac{75}{t-2} = \frac{75}{5-2} = 25.$$

The average speed with the aerodynamic covering is 25 mi/h.

3. 10 mi/h downhill,
   6 mi/h uphill

✓ Quick Check ❸ Rosa can jog 5 mi downhill in the same time it takes her to jog 3 mi uphill. She jogs downhill 4 mi/h faster than she jogs uphill. Find her jogging rate each way.

Lesson 9-6 Solving Rational Equations **523**

---

2. Teach

Guided Instruction

2 EXAMPLE Technology Tip

After students have studied the algebraic solution, you may want to have them use a graphing calculator to solve the equation. Have them enter the equations $Y_1 = \frac{1}{2x} - \frac{2}{5x}$ and $Y_2 = \frac{1}{2}$ on the Y= list, and then find the x-coordinate of the intersection point. Caution them to use parentheses around the denominators in the first equation. Good settings for the graphing window are Xmin=−3, Xmax=3, Ymin=−1.5, Ymax=1.5.

Additional Examples

❶ Solve $\frac{1}{x-3} = \frac{6x}{x^2-9}$. Check each solution. $\frac{3}{5}$

❷ Solve $\frac{3}{5x} - \frac{4}{3x} = \frac{1}{3}$. $-\frac{11}{5}$

Guided Instruction

Additional Examples

❸ Josefina can row 4 miles upstream in a river in the same time it takes her to row 6 miles downstream. Her rate of rowing in still water is 2 miles per hour. Find the speed of the river current. **0.4 mi/h**

Advanced Learners L4
Have students explore at least 2 ways of using graphing calculators to solve rational equations.

learning style: tactile

English Language Learners ELL
For Example 4, have a student volunteer explain what a *fund-raiser* is and to give examples of fund-raisers they have participated in. Ask: *How many envelopes can Georgia stuff in 1 hour? in 1 minute?* **about 312 per hr; 5.2 per min**

learning style: verbal

523

④ Jim and Alberto have to paint 6000 square feet of hallway in an office building. Alberto works twice as fast as Jim. Working together, they can complete the job in 15 hours. How long would it take each of them working alone? **Alberto: 22.5 h, Jim: 45 h**

Resources
• Daily Notetaking Guide 9-6 **L3**

Closure

Ask students to describe what they must do to find the solutions of a rational equation. Answers may vary. Sample: First, clear the equation of fractions. One way to do this is to simplify both sides and then multiply both sides of the resulting equation by the least common denominator of all expressions. The result will be a polynomial equation. Solve this equation. Check the solutions in the original equation to eliminate extraneous solutions.

---

④ EXAMPLE **Real-World** **Connection**

Volunteerism Tim can stuff envelopes three times as fast as his daughter Georgia. They have to stuff 5000 envelopes for a fund-raiser. Working together, Tim and Georgia can complete the job in about four hours. How many hours would it take each of them working alone?

Relate Tim's rate + Georgia's rate = combined rate

Define

	Time (hr)	Rate (envelopes per hour)
Tim	x	$\frac{5000}{x}$
Georgia	$3x$	$\frac{5000}{3x}$
Combined	4	$\frac{5000}{4} = 1250$

Write $\dfrac{5000}{x} + \dfrac{5000}{3x} = 1250$

Method 1 Use a graphing calculator. Graph $y_1 = \frac{5000}{x} + \frac{5000}{3x}$ and $y_2 = 1250$ in a window with Xmin = 3, Xmax = 10, Ymin = 0, and Ymax = 2000. Then use the INTERSECT feature to find the intersections of the two graphs. The graphs intersect at $x \approx 5.33$.

GO for Help

For help with solving equations by tables, see Lesson 5-5.

Method 2 Use a graphing calculator and $y_1 = \frac{5000}{x} + \frac{5000}{3x} - 1250$. Use the TABLE feature and "zoom in" on the point where the function changes sign. This occurs at $x \approx 5.33$.

Tim could stuff 5000 envelopes in about 5.33 hours.

Georgia could stuff 5000 envelopes in 3(5.33) hours, or about 16 hours.

✓ Quick Check **④ a.** Suppose Maria can stuff envelopes twice as fast as her friend Paco. Together, they can stuff 6750 envelopes in 4.5 hours. How long would it take each of them working alone? **Maria: 6.75 h, Paco: 13.5 h**

b. Suppose Adrian can weed the garden twice as fast as his son Phillip. Together they can weed the garden in 3 hours. How long would it take each of them working alone? **Adrian: 4.5 h, Phillip: 9 h**

EXERCISES

For more exercises, see *Extra Skill and Word Problem Practice*.

Practice and Problem Solving

Ⓐ Practice by Example

GO for Help

Example 1
(page 522)

Solve each equation. Check each solution.

1. $\frac{x}{5} = \frac{x+3}{8}$ **5** 　　**2.** $\frac{1}{5x} = \frac{1}{9x}$ **no solution** 　　**3.** $\frac{4}{3x+3} = \frac{12}{x^2-1}$ **10**

4. $\frac{2}{x-1} = \frac{x+4}{3}$ **2 or −5** **5.** $\frac{3}{x+1} = \frac{1}{x^2-1}$ **$\frac{4}{3}$** **6.** $\frac{4}{2x-3} = \frac{x}{5}$ **$-\frac{5}{2}$ or 4**

7. $\frac{3}{x} = \frac{12}{x+7}$ **$\frac{7}{3}$** 　　**8.** $\frac{10}{6x+7} = \frac{6}{2x+9}$ **3** 　　**9.** $\frac{2}{3x-5} = \frac{4}{x-15}$ **−1**

Example 2
(page 523)

Solve each equation. Check each solution.

10. $\frac{1}{4} - x = \frac{x}{8}$ $\frac{2}{9}$

11. $\frac{y}{5} + \frac{y}{2} = 7$ **10**

12. $\frac{2x}{3} - \frac{1}{2} = \frac{2x + 5}{6}$ **4**

13. $\frac{3x - 2}{12} - \frac{1}{6} = \frac{1}{6}$ **2**

14. $\frac{1}{x} + \frac{x}{2} = \frac{x + 4}{2x}$ **−1 or 2**

15. $\frac{11}{3x} - \frac{1}{3} = \frac{-4}{x^2}$ **−1 or 12**

16. $\frac{3}{2x} - \frac{5}{3x} = 2$ **$-\frac{1}{12}$**

17. $\frac{5x}{4} - \frac{3}{x} = \frac{1}{4}$ **−1.45 or 1.65**

18. $\frac{2}{y} + \frac{1}{2} = \frac{5}{2y}$ **1**

19. $x + \frac{6}{x} = -5$ **−3, −2**

20. $\frac{1}{4x} - \frac{3}{4} = \frac{7}{x}$ **−9**

21. $\frac{5}{2x} - \frac{2}{3} = \frac{1}{x} + \frac{5}{6}$ **1**

Examples 3 and 4
(pages 523 and 524)

22. Carlos can travel 40 mi on his motorbike in the same time it takes Paul to travel 15 mi on his bicycle. If Paul rides his bike 20 mi/h slower than Carlos rides his motorbike, find the speed for each bike. **Carlos: 32 mi/h, Paul: 12 mi/h**

23. A passenger train travels 392 mi in the same time that it takes a freight train to travel 322 mi. If the passenger train travels 20 mi/h faster than the freight train, find the speed of each train. **passenger train: 112 mi/h, freight train: 92 mi/h**

24. Shelley can paint a fence in 8 hours. Karen can do it in 4 hours. How long will it take them to do the job if they work together? **$2\frac{2}{3}$ h**

25. One pump can fill a tank with oil in 4 hours. A second pump can fill the same tank in 3 hours. If both pumps are used at the same time, how long will they take to fill the tank? **$1\frac{5}{7}$ h**

 Apply Your Skills

Solve each equation for the given variable. **27–31. See margin.**

26. $m = \frac{2E}{V^2}$; E **$E = \frac{mV^2}{2}$**

27. $\frac{c}{E} - \frac{1}{mc} = 0$; E

28. $\frac{m}{F} = \frac{1}{a}$; F

29. $\frac{1}{c} - \frac{c}{a^2 - b^2} = 0$; c

30. $\frac{\ell}{T^2} = \frac{g}{4\pi^2}$; T

31. $\frac{q}{m} = \frac{2V}{B^2 r^2}$; B

32. Anita and Fran have volunteered to contact every member of their organization by phone to inform them of an upcoming event. Fran can complete the calls in six days if she works alone. Anita can complete them in four days. How long will they take to complete the calls working together? **$2\frac{2}{5}$ days**

For a guide to solving Exercise 32, see page 530.

33. **Multiple Choice** On the first four tests of the term your average is 84%. You think you can score 96% on each of the remaining tests. How many consecutive test scores of 96% would you need to bring your average up to 90% for the term? **D**

   Ⓐ 1   Ⓑ 2   Ⓒ 3   Ⓓ 4

34. You are planning a school field trip to a local theater. It costs $60 to rent the bus. Each theater ticket costs $5.50. **$c(x) = \frac{5.50x + 60}{x}$**
a. Write a function $c(x)$ to represent the cost per student if x students sign up.
b. How many students must sign up if the cost is to be no more than $10 per student? **14 students**

35a. $L = \frac{24(R - r)}{T}$

b. 32 in., about 28.24 in., about 25.26 in.

🌐 **35.** **Woodworking** A tapered cylinder is made by decreasing the radius of a rod continuously as you move from one end to the other. The rate at which it tapers is the taper per foot. You can calculate the taper per foot using the formula $T = \frac{24(R - r)}{L}$. The lengths R, r, and L are measured in inches.

a. Solve this equation for L.
b. Find L if $R = 4$ in.; $r = 3$ in.; and $T = 0.75, 0.85,$ and 0.95.

Homework Video Tutor
Visit: PHSchool.com
Web Code: age-0906

Lesson 9-6 Solving Rational Equations **525**

27. $E = mc^2$
28. $F = ma$
29. $c = \pm \sqrt{a^2 - b^2}$

30. $T = \pm \sqrt{\frac{4\pi^2 \ell}{g}}$
31. $B = \pm \sqrt{\frac{2Vm}{r^2 q}}$

3. Practice

Assignment Guide

▼1 A B 1-21, 26-31, 39-52

▼2 A B 22-25, 32-38, 53-55
C Challenge 56-58

Test Prep 59-64
Mixed Review 65-74

Homework Quick Check

To check students' understanding of key skills and concepts, go over Exercises 19, 23, 32, 34, 47, 53.

Error Prevention!

Exercises 10–21, 39–52 Students may forget to check for extraneous solutions. Stress that this is an essential step when solving rational equations.

Exercise 33 Have students offer possible solution methods, such as algebra, a graph, or a table. Help students recognize that each method requires they write an equation or function rule.

Exercise 35 You may need to explain the terms *tapered cylinder* and *continuously*.

Differentiated Instruction Resources

GPS) Guided Problem Solving L3
Enrichment L4
Reteaching L2
Practice L3

525

Solve each equation. Check each solution.

1. $\frac{5x}{x^2 - 25} = \frac{2}{x - 5}$ $\frac{10}{3}$

2. $1 + \frac{2}{x} = \frac{3}{x^2}$ $-3, 1$

3. $\frac{x}{x - 1} + x = \frac{4x - 3}{x - 1}$ 3

4. The speed of the current in a river is 5 miles per hour. A boat leaves a dock on the bank of the river, travels upstream 25 miles, and returns to the dock in 12 hours. What is the speed of the boat in still water? **7.5 mi/h**

Alternative Assessment

Ask each student to write two real-world problems about motion (problems that involve distance, speed, and time) that can be modeled by a rational equation. Ask them to write, solve, and check an equation to solve each problem. Students can exchange problems to check each other's work.

36b. $\frac{15,000}{24 + x}(1.60)$

c. $1000 - \frac{15,000}{24 + x}(1.60)$

37. Check students' work.

49. no solution

Real-World Connection

Careers Masons build patterns with brick or stone.

---

36. **Fuel Economy** Suppose you drive an average of 15,000 miles per year, and your car gets 24 miles per gallon. Suppose gasoline costs $1.60 a gallon.
   a. How much money do you spend each year on gasoline? **$1000**
   b. You plan to trade in your car for one that gets x more miles per gallon. Write an expression to represent the new yearly cost of gasoline.
   c. Write an expression to represent your savings on gasoline.
   d. Suppose you save $200 a year with the new car. How many miles per gallon does the new car get? **30 mi/gal**

37. **Open-Ended** Write a rational equation that has the same solution as the question in the cartoon.

38. **Industry** The average hourly wage $H(x)$ of workers in an industry is modeled by the function $H(x) = \frac{16.24x}{0.062x + 39.42}$, where x represents the number of years since 1970. **about 2037**
   a. In what year does the model predict that wages will be $25/h?
   b. **Critical Thinking** Is the prediction reasonable? Explain. Check students' work.

The Family Circus by Bil Keane

4-25

"What's 129 divided by 4?"

Solve each equation. Check each solution.

39. $\frac{15}{x} + \frac{9x - 7}{x + 2} = 9$ 3

40. $\frac{2}{x + 2} - \frac{1}{x} = \frac{-4}{x(x + 2)}$ no solution

41. $\frac{1}{b + 1} + \frac{1}{b - 1} = \frac{2}{b^2 - 1}$ no solution

42. $c - \frac{c}{3} + \frac{c}{5} = 26$ 30

43. $\frac{2}{x - 3} - \frac{4}{x + 3} = \frac{8}{x^2 - 9}$ 5

44. $\frac{1}{8} + \frac{5x}{x + 2} = \frac{5}{2}$ $\frac{38}{21}$

45. $\frac{1}{x - 5} = \frac{x}{x^2 - 25}$ no solution

46. $\frac{k}{k + 1} + \frac{k}{k - 2} = 2$ -4

47. $\frac{3}{x + 5} + \frac{2}{5 - x} = \frac{-4}{x^2 - 25}$ 21

48. $\frac{5}{x + 2} = \frac{-1}{x^2 + 7x + 10} + \frac{3}{-x - 5}$ -4

49. $\frac{5}{x^2 - 7x + 12} - \frac{2}{3 - x} = \frac{5}{x - 4}$

50. $\frac{10}{2y + 8} - \frac{7y + 8}{y^2 - 16} = \frac{-8}{2y - 8}$ 6

51. $\frac{7x + 3}{x^2 - 8x + 15} + \frac{3x}{x - 5} = \frac{1}{3 - x}$ $1, -\frac{2}{3}$

52. $\frac{2}{x + 3} - \frac{3}{4 - x} = \frac{2x - 2}{x^2 - x - 12}$ -1

53. **Landscape Design** Suppose you want to double the area of the patio shown at the right. Find the increase x of both the length and width of the patio. **$x \approx 4.5$ ft**

54. **Writing** Write and solve a problem that can be modeled by a rational equation.
   Check students' work.

55. **Transportation** A plane flies from New York to Chicago (about 700 miles) at a speed of 360 mi/h.
   a. The speed s of the plane is given by $s = \frac{d}{t}$. $t = \frac{d}{s}$ d represents the distance and t is the time. Solve the equation for t.
   b. Find the time for the trip. $\frac{35}{18}$ h
   c. On the return trip from Chicago to New York, a tail wind helps the plane move faster. Write an expression for the speed of the plane on the return trip. Let x represent the speed of the tail wind. $\frac{d}{t} + x$
   d. The total flying time for the round trip is 3.5 h. Write a rational equation for the sum of the flying times. Find the speed x of the tail wind.
   $\frac{700}{360} + \frac{700}{360 + x} = 3.5$; 90 mi/h

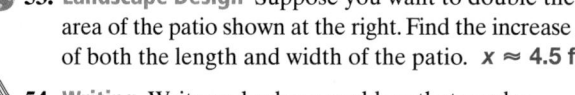

|←—10 ft—→|
|←x→|

12 ft

x

Challenge

56a–c. Check students' work.

56. Open-Ended Write a rational equation that has the following.

   a. one solution   **b.** two solutions   **c.** no real solution

57. A salesman drove from his home to a nearby city at an average speed of 40 mi/h. He returned home at an average speed of 50 mi/h. What was his average speed for the entire trip? **44.44 mi/h**

58. An automatic pitching machine can pitch all its baseballs in $1\frac{1}{4}$ hours. One attendant can retrieve all the baseballs pitched by one machine in $3\frac{1}{2}$ hours. At least how many attendants working at the same rate should be hired so that the baseballs from 10 machines are all retrieved in less than 8 hours? **5 attendants**

Test Prep

Multiple Choice

59. What are all the solutions of $\frac{3}{x^2-1}+\frac{4x}{x+1}=\frac{1.5}{x-1}$? **C**

  A. 1, −1   **B.** 1, 0.375   **C.** 0.375   **D.** 0.375, 3

60. What is the solution of $x+\frac{1}{x}=-2$? **J**

  F. 1 and −1   **G.** 0 only   **H.** $-\frac{1}{2}$ only   **J.** −1 only

61. How many roots does the equation $\frac{2}{x^2}+\frac{1}{x}=0$ have? **B**

  A. 0   **B.** 1   **C.** 2   **D.** 3

62. Solve $\frac{2}{x+7}=\frac{x}{x^2-49}$. **F**

  F. 14 only   **G.** 7 only   **H.** 7 or −7   **J.** −7 only

Short Response

63. A large snowplow can clear a parking lot in 4 hours. A small snowplow needs more time to clear the lot. Working together, they can clear the lot in 3 hours. How long would it take the small plow to clear the lot by itself? Show your work. **See margin.**

Extended Response

64. Solve and check the equation $\frac{x}{3x+9}=\frac{x+2}{x+3}$. Show your work. **See margin.**

Mixed Review

 GO for Help

Lesson 9-5   **Simplify each difference. 65–67. See margin.**

65. $\frac{3y+1}{4y+4}-\frac{2y+7}{2y+2}$ **66.** $\frac{5x}{2y+4}-\frac{6}{y^2+2y}$ **67.** $\frac{x+1}{2x-2}-\frac{2x}{x^2+2x-3}$

Lesson 8-5   **Solve each equation.**

68. $\log_{10} 0.001 = x$ $x = -3$ **69.** $\log_3 27 = 3x+6$ $x = -1$

70. $\log_{0.1}(x+1) = 3$ $x = -0.999$ **71.** $\log_3 \frac{1}{9} = \frac{x}{3}$ $x = -6$

Lesson 7-7   **Find the inverse of each function. Is the inverse a function?**

72. $y = 5 - 2x$ **73.** $y = x^2 + 1$ **74.** $y = x^3 - 4$
   $y = \frac{5-x}{2}$; yes $y = \pm\sqrt{x-1}$; no $y = \sqrt[3]{x+4}$; yes

---

Test Prep

Resources

For additional practice with a variety of test item formats:

- Standardized Test Prep, p. 543
- Test-Taking Strategies, p. 538
- Test-Taking Strategies with Transparencies

63. [2] $\frac{1}{4}+\frac{1}{x}=\frac{1}{3}$

$$12x\left(\frac{1}{4}+\frac{1}{x}\right)=12x\left(\frac{1}{3}\right)$$
$$\frac{12x}{4}+\frac{12x}{x}=\frac{12x}{3}$$
$$3x+12=4x$$
$$12=x$$

It would take the small plow 12 hours to clear the lot by itself.

[1] answer only, with no work shown

64. [4] $\frac{x}{3x+9}=\frac{x+2}{x+3}$

$$\frac{x}{3(x+3)}=\frac{x+2}{x+3}$$
$$x(x+3)=$$
$$3(x+3)(x+2)$$
$$x=3(x+2)$$
$$x=3x+6$$
$$-2x=6$$
$$x=-3$$

However, $x = -3$ makes the denominators in the original equation equal 0, which is undefined. So, the equation has no solution.

[3] one computational error

[2] gets $x = -3$, but does not state that the equation has no solution

[1] answer only, with no work shown

65. $\frac{-y-13}{4(y+1)}$

66. $\frac{5xy-12}{2y(y+2)}$

67. $\frac{x^2+3}{(2x-2)(x+3)}$

527

Rational Inequalities

This feature guides students in solving rational inequalities using tables and graphs with a graphing calculator.

Guided Instruction

Teaching Tip

For Activity 1, guide students in reading Alice's solution for Question 1. Have student volunteers give the justification for each step in the solution process.

Math Tip

For Question 2, consider asking:
- *For which x-values is the inequality not true?* $3 \le x \le 4$
- *For which x-values is the inequality true?* $x < 3$ and $x > 4$

Special Needs   **L1**

For Question 3, have students work with partners, especially those who have difficulty operating graphing calculators or who are unfamiliar with the TABLE feature.

Resources

Students may use any graphing calculator to make tables and graphs.

Activity Lab

Technology

Rational Inequalities

FOR USE WITH LESSON 9-6

You can multiply both sides of a rational inequality by the same algebraic expression just as you have done with equations. However, not only can you introduce extraneous solutions, you can also lose solutions!

1 ACTIVITY

1. Here is Alice's solution of the rational inequality $\frac{N}{4-N} < 3$. Read it carefully.

$$\frac{N}{4-N} < 3$$

$$N < 3(4-N)$$

$$N < 12 - 3N$$

$$4N < 12$$

$$N < 3$$

Alice concluded that the solution consists of all integers less than 3. Or so it would seem. Does Alice's solution appear to be correct? **yes**

2. a. Choose an integer less than 3. Does it make the inequality true? **yes**
  b. Pick an integer greater than 4. Does it make the inequality true? **yes**
  c. What happens to the inequality when $N = 3$? $N = 4$? **not true; left side is undefined.**
  d. Make a conjecture about the solution based on your results in parts (a)–(c). **Check students' work.**

3. Enter the function $y_1 = x/(4-x)$ in your graphing calculator. Set up a table as shown below. Scroll down through the table. All the x-values are integers greater than 3. Find one that fails to satisfy the inequality $\frac{N}{4-N} < 3$. Does this finding agree with your results from Exercise 2? **yes**

```
Plot1 Plot2 Plot3
\Y1 ▪X/(4 − X)
\Y2 =
\Y3 =
\Y4 =
\Y5 =
\Y6 =
\Y7 =■
```

```
TABLE SETUP
 TblStart=20
 ΔTbl=5
Indpnt: Auto  Ask
Depend: Auto  Ask
```

X	Y1
20	−1.25
25	−1.19
30	−1.154
35	−1.129
40	−1.111
45	−1.098
50	−1.087
Y1=−1.25	

2 ACTIVITY

It would appear that Alice's algebraic solution was only partially successful. It correctly concludes that any integer less than 3 satisfies the inequality. Unfortunately, it fails to identify other values that satisfy the inequality.

4. Error Analysis Alice made an error in one step in her solution. Where is the error? What erroneous assumption did Alice make? **from line 1 to line 2; $4 − N > 0$**

5. What is the first change you would make to correct Alice's error. **Check students' work.**

6. Show how the assumption $N > 4$ leads to solutions of the inequality that Alice did not find. (*Hint:* What is important about the value of $4 − N$?) **6–7. See margin.**

7. Now, write a complete solution of the inequality $\frac{N}{4-N} < 3$.

528   Chapter 9   Rational Functions

6. For $N > 4$, $4 − N < 0$.
  So $\frac{N}{4-N} < 0$. Therefore,
  $\frac{N}{4-N} < 3$.

7. $N < 3$ or $N > 4$.

③ ACTIVITY

As you can see, the algebraic solution to the simple-looking rational inequality $\frac{N}{4-N} < 3$ is not all that simple. You might find it easier to solve this inequality (and other rational inequalities) graphically.

8. Graph two functions $y_1 = \frac{x}{4-x}$ and $y_2 = 3$ using the settings at the right. Explain how you can use the graph to solve the inequality $\frac{N}{4-N} < 3$. **See margin.**

9. Graph the function $y_3 = \frac{x}{4-x} - 3$ (or $y_3 = y_1 - y_2$) in the window used in Exercise 8. How can you use this graph to solve the inequality $\frac{N}{4-N} < 3$? **See margin.**

```
WINDOW
 Xmin=-4.7
 Xmax=9.4
 Xscl=1
 Ymin=-8
 Ymax=5
 Yscl=1
 Xres=1▮
```

10. Show how to solve $\frac{N}{4-N} < 3$ by using y_1 and y_2 and tables, or y_3 and tables. **Check students' work.**

EXERCISES

Use the settings from Exercise 8. Solve each of 11–13 using your choice of two graphs (Exercise 8), one graph (Exercise 9), or tables (Exercise 10).

11. $\frac{2}{x-1} < x$ $-1 < x < 1$ or $x > 2$
12. $x + 1 > \frac{x+5}{x+2}$ $x < -3$ or $x > 1$
13. $\frac{2x}{(x-2)(x+3)} < 1$ $x < -3, -2 < x < 2,$ or $x > 3$

14. For Exercises 11–13, check your work by using a different method to solve each inequality. **Check students' work.**

15. **Multiple Choice** Which graph can you use to solve the inequality $\frac{1}{x-2} < -3$ **A**

Ⓐ   Ⓑ   Ⓒ   Ⓓ

16. Mr. Huerta has 600 minutes per week to give individual help to students. He averages 20 min per student. If he reduces the time per student by t min to $(20 - t)$ min, he can meet with $\frac{600}{20-t}$ students. Write an inequality that describes each situation below and solve the inequality.

   a. How many fewer minutes per student will allow Mr. Huerta to work with at least 36 students? $3\frac{1}{3}$ min
   b. How many more minutes per student will allow Mr. Huerta to work with no more than 27 students? $2\frac{2}{9}$ min

17. The equation $d = rt$ relates the distance d you travel, the time t it takes to travel that distance, and the rate r at which you travel. So the time it takes is $t = \frac{d}{r}$. If you increase your rate by a to $r + a$, then it takes less time, $t = \frac{d}{r+a}$. In fact, the time you save by going at the faster rate is $T = \frac{d}{r} - \frac{d}{r+a}$.

   a. You normally take a 500-mi trip, averaging 45 mi/h. You want to increase the rate so that your travel time is at least 1 h shorter. Write an inequality that describes the situation. $\frac{500}{45} - \frac{500}{45+a} \geq 1$
   b. Solve your inequality in part (a). $a \geq 4\frac{41}{91}$

Activity Lab   Rational Inequalities   **529**

8. **Answers may vary.**
   Sample: Look for the part of the graph of y_1 that is below the graph of y_2.

9. **Answers may vary.**
   Sample: Look for the part of the graph of y_3 that is below the x-axis.

529

Visual Learners
For Question 8, point out that $y_1 = \frac{x}{4-x}$ has two distinct branches. State that the algebraic solution in Activity 1 was incomplete because it missed one entire branch, when $x > 4$.

Teaching Tip
Some students may not understand how Question 8 and Question 9 are related. In Question 8, each side of the inequality becomes a different function, and their intersection gives the boundary value for the inequality. In Question 9, a new inequality in which the solution set is less than zero is represented by a single function whose boundary value is given by the zero of the function, or x-intercept of its graph.

English Language Learners ELL
For Exercise 17, remind students that a *rate* is a ratio. The rate in this situation is speed in miles per hour, or $\frac{mi}{h}$.

Error Prevention!
For Exercise 17, some students may be confused that a distance divided by a rate gives time. Show them the following simplification of units in which division is replaced with multiplication by the reciprocal.

$$\text{time} = \frac{\text{distance}}{\text{rate}} = \frac{mi}{\frac{mi}{h}} = mi \div \frac{mi}{h}$$
$$= mi \times \frac{h}{mi} = h$$

Understanding Word Problems

Students solve a rational equation by working through an annotated sample problem. In addition to the worked out problem, students are also given notes about each step in the solution process.

Guided Instruction

Point out that Fran's rate is total work over 6 because she can make the calls in 6 days, and Anita's rate is total work over 4 because she can make the calls in 4 days.

Auditory Learners

Place students in pairs or small groups. Have students take turns working through the steps to solve a problem similar to the one in the example. After each step is completed, the student who did the work explains aloud to the other students what he or she did.

Exercise 1 Make sure students label their answers. The rate will not make sense without a label. Tell students to be mindful of the units. The time units in the example problem was days, and in this problem it is in minutes.

Understanding Word Problems Read the problem below. Then let Ahmed's thinking guide you through the solution. Check your understanding with the exercises at the bottom of the page.

Anita and Fran have volunteered to contact every member of their organization by phone to inform them of an upcoming event. Fran can complete the calls in six days if she works alone. Anita can complete them in four days. How long will they take to complete the calls working together?

What Ahmed Thinks

I'll write the information in my own words.

Work problems involve rates. Even though I don't know the number of calls Fran and Anita are making, maybe I can just consider the entire job, or total amount of work, being done.

I'll define variables, t for time and w for work.

Now I can write an equation.

The variable w is going to cancel out of the equation, so I can just solve for t.

I can write my answer in a sentence now.

What Ahmed Writes

Fran can complete the work in 6 days.
Anita can complete the work in 4 days.

$$\text{rate} = \frac{\text{work being done}}{\text{time}}$$

$$\text{Fran's rate} = \frac{\text{work being done}}{\text{time}} = \frac{\text{total work}}{6}$$

$$\text{Anita's rate} = \frac{\text{work being done}}{\text{time}} = \frac{\text{total work}}{4}$$

$w = \text{total work}$
$t = \text{time working together}$

$$\text{Fran's rate} + \text{Anita's rate} = \text{combined rate}$$

$$\frac{\text{total work}}{6} + \frac{\text{total work}}{4} = \frac{\text{total work}}{\text{time together}}$$

$$\frac{w}{6} + \frac{w}{4} = \frac{w}{t}$$

$$\frac{1}{6} + \frac{1}{4} = \frac{1}{t}$$

$$2t + 3t = 12$$

$$5t = \frac{12}{5} = 2\frac{2}{5}$$

It will take Anita and Fran, working together, $2\frac{2}{5}$ days to complete all the calls.

EXERCISES

1. Charlene can wash a car in 15 minutes, and Robert can wash the same size car in 12 minutes. How long will it take them to wash a car if they work together? $6\frac{2}{3}$ min
2. It takes 12 min to fill a bathtub with the drain closed. If the tap is closed, it takes 20 min to drain the bathtub. How long does it take to fill the bathtub with both the tap and the drain open? **30 min**

530 Guided Problem Solving Understanding Word Problems

Probability of Multiple Events

What You'll Learn

- To find the probability of the event A and B
- To find the probability of the event A or B

. . . And Why

To solve problems involving radio call-in shows, as in Example 2

✓ **Check Skills You'll Need**

GO for Help Lesson 1-6

A bag contains 24 green marbles, 22 blue marbles, 14 yellow marbles, and 12 red marbles. Suppose you pick one marble at random. Find each probability.

1. P(yellow) $\frac{7}{36}$ **2.** P(not blue) $\frac{25}{36}$ **3.** P(green or red) $\frac{1}{2}$

4. Of 300 senior students at Taft High, 150 have taken physics, 192 have taken chemistry, and 30 have taken neither physics nor chemistry. How many students have taken both physics and chemistry? **72**

🔊 **New Vocabulary** • **dependent events** • **independent events**
• **mutually exclusive events**

---

1 Finding P(A and B)

Hands-On Activity: Multiple Events

- Work with a partner to analyze the game Primarily Odd.

- **Partner A:** Roll two standard number cubes. If the sum is either odd *or* a prime number, score a point.

- **Partner B:** Roll two standard number cubes. If the sum is both odd *and* a prime number, score a point.

- Alternate turns rolling the number cubes.

1. a. List all the possible outcomes of rolling two number cubes.   **See margin p. 533.**
   b. How many outcomes result in an odd sum? Calculate the probability of getting an odd sum. **18; $\frac{1}{2}$**
   c. How many outcomes result in a prime sum? Calculate the probability of getting a prime sum. **15; $\frac{5}{12}$**

2. Predict which partner is more likely to score points in Primarily Odd. Justify your reasoning. **See left.**

3. Play the game with your partner. Take 10 turns each. Keep track of each player's score. How do your results compare with the prediction you made in Question 2? **Check students' work.**

2. Partner A is more likely to score points, since that player has more rolls that result in points.

When the outcome of one event affects the outcome of a second event, the two events are **dependent events**. When the outcome of one event does *not* affect the outcome of a second event, the two events are **independent events**.

---

1. Plan

Objectives

1 To find the probability of the event *A and B*

2 To find the probability of the event *A or B*

Examples

1 Classifying Events
2 Real-World Connection
3 Mutually Exclusive Events
4 Real-World Connection
5 Probabilities of Events

Math Background

The use of the word "or" in mathematics is inclusive. If something is in *A or B* it can be in *A* and not *B*, *B* and not *A*, or both *A* and *B*. In general, to find *P(A or B)* we calculate *P(A)* + *P(B)* − *P(A and B)*, subtracting *P(A and B)* so it is not counted twice. If *A* and *B* are mutually exclusive, then *P(A and B)* = 0. *P(A given B)*, or the probability that *A* happens given that *B* is considered the sample space, is just $\frac{P(A \text{ and } B)}{P(B)}$, that is, the ratio of the portion of *A* in *B* to *B*. Thus, *P(A and B)* = *P(B)* · *P(A given B)*. If *A* and *B* are independent, then *P(A given B)* = *P(A)*.

More Math Background: p. 486D

Lesson Planning and Resources

See p. 486E for a list of the resources that support this lesson.

✓ Check Skills You'll Need

For intervention, direct students to:

Probability
Lesson 1-6: Example 3
Extra Skills and Word
   Problems Practice, Ch. 1

Differentiated Instruction **Solutions for All Learners**

Special Needs **L1**
Divide the classroom into 3 regions: "*A*, not *B*", "*B*, not *A*", and "*A* and *B*." Call out pairs of events and have students move into the appropriate region. Examples: (1) *A* is girl; *B* is boy. (2) *A* is girl; *B* is students wearing jeans. (3) *A* rides bus; *B* is boy.
learning style: tactile

Below Level **L2**
Use a bag of marbles similar to the one described in Check Skills You'll Need. Have students select marbles from the bag and discuss the probabilities involved.

learning style: tactile

2. Teach

Guided Instruction

Hands-On Activity

In this Activity, students explore a situation that illustrates the concepts of dependent and independent events. For Questions 1b and 1c, have students count the number of times the event occurs. Then divide by the number of possible outcomes determined in part (a). Tell students to write their probabilities as fractions.

Additional Examples

1 Classify each pair of events as *dependent* or *independent*.
a. Spin a spinner. Then, select a marble from a bag that contains marbles of different colors. **independent**
b. Select a marble from a bag that contains marbles of two colors. Put the marble aside, and select a second marble from the bag. **dependent**

2 A box contains 20 red marbles and 30 blue marbles. A second box contains 10 white marbles and 47 black marbles. If you choose one marble from each box without looking, what is the probability that you get a blue marble and a black marble? $\frac{47}{95}$

---

1 **EXAMPLE** **Classifying Events**

Classify each pair of events as *dependent* or *independent*.

a. Roll a number cube. Then toss a coin.
Since the two events do not affect each other, they are independent.

b. Pick a flower from a garden. Then pick another flower from the same garden.
Picking the first flower affects the possible outcomes of picking the second flower. So the events are dependent.

 Quick Check **1** Suppose you select a marble from a bag of marbles. You replace the marble and then select again. Are your selections dependent or independent events? Explain.
Independent; the number of marbles is the same after the marble is replaced.

You can find the probability that two independent events will both occur by multiplying probabilities.

Key Concepts

Property	Probability of *A* and *B*
If *A* and *B* are independent events, then $P(A \text{ and } B) = P(A) \cdot P(B)$.
Example: If $P(A) = \frac{1}{2}$ and $P(B) = \frac{1}{3}$, then $P(A \text{ and } B) = \frac{1}{2} \cdot \frac{1}{3} = \frac{1}{6}$.	

2 **EXAMPLE** **Real-World Connection**

Radio Suppose your favorite radio station is running a promotional campaign. Every hour, four callers chosen at random get to select two songs each. You call the station once after 7:00 A.M. and again after 3:00 P.M. What is the probability that you will be one of the four callers both times you call?

WKW Radio Statistics

Hour	Calls Received That Hour
7:00 A.M.	125
3:00 P.M.	200

Relate probability of both events is probability of first event times probability of second event

Define Event A = you are one of the four callers after 7:00 A.M. Then $P(A) = \frac{4}{125}$.
Event B = you are one of the four callers after 3:00 P.M. Then $P(B) = \frac{4}{200}$.

Write $P(A \text{ and } B) = P(A) \cdot P(B)$

$P(A \text{ and } B) = \frac{4}{125} \cdot \frac{4}{200}$

$= \frac{16}{25,000}$ **Multiply.**

$= \frac{2}{3125}$ **Simplify.**

The probability of being one of the four callers selected at random both times you call is $\frac{2}{3125}$, or 0.064%.

Real-World Connection

Careers Radio broadcasters try to increase the size of their listening audience so they can increase their advertising rates.

Quick Check **2** Suppose the radio station changes the promotional campaign. Now it chooses five callers at random each hour. **a–b. See margin p. 533.**
a. What is the probability of being one of the five callers after 7 A.M? After 3 P.M.?
b. Find the probability of being one of the five callers both times you call.

532 Chapter 9 Rational Functions

---

2 Finding P(A or B)

When two events cannot happen at the same time, the events are **mutually exclusive events.** If A and B are mutually exclusive events, then $P(A \text{ and } B) = 0$.

3 EXAMPLE Mutually Exclusive Events

Are the events mutually exclusive? Explain.

a. rolling a 2 or a 3 on a number cube

Since you cannot roll a 2 and a 3 at the same time, the events are mutually exclusive.

b. rolling an even number or a multiple of 3 on a number cube

By rolling a 6, you can roll an even number and a multiple of 3 at the same time. So the events are not mutually exclusive.

 Quick Check ③ Are the events mutually exclusive? Explain.

a. rolling an even number and rolling a prime number on a number cube

b. rolling an even number and rolling a number less than 2 on a number cube
Mutually exclusive since no number is both even and less than 2.

 Vocabulary Tip

Events that are not mutually exclusive are sometimes called inclusive events, or non-mutually exclusive events.

3a. Not mutually exclusive since 2 is both even and prime.

You need to determine whether events A and B are mutually exclusive before you can find the probability of (A or B).

Key Concepts

Property	Probability of (A or B)
If A and B are mutually exclusive events, then $P(A \text{ or } B) = P(A) + P(B)$. If A and B are not mutually exclusive events, then $P(A \text{ or } B) = P(A) + P(B) - P(A \text{ and } B)$.	

Many statistical measures are based on probabilities of the form P(A or B).

4 EXAMPLE Real-World Connection

College Enrollment About 53% of U.S. college students are under 25 years old. About 21% of U.S. college students are over 34 years old. What is the probability that a U.S. college student chosen at random is under 25 or over 34?

Since a student cannot be under 25 and over 34, the events are mutually exclusive.

$P(\text{under } 25 \text{ or over } 34) = P(\text{under } 25) + P(\text{over } 34)$ **Use the P(A or B) formula for mutually exclusive events.**

$= 0.53 + 0.21$

$= 0.74$

The probability that a U.S. college student chosen at random is under 25 or over 34 is about 0.74, or about 74%.

4a. about 0.26 or about 26%

b. about 0.47 or about 47%

c. about 0.79 or about 79%

 Quick Check ④ A U.S. college student is chosen at random. Find the probability for each age range of the student.

a. 25−34   **b.** 25−34 or over 34   **c.** 34 or under

Lesson 9-7 Probability of Multiple Events **533**

Hands-On Activity

1a. 1, 1), (1, 2), (1, 3), (1, 4), (1, 5), (1, 6), (2, 1), (2, 2), (2, 3), (2, 4), (2, 5), (2, 6), (3, 1), (3, 2), (3, 3), (3, 4), (3, 5), (3, 6),

(4, 1), (4, 2), (4, 3), (4, 4), (4, 5), (4, 6), (5, 1), (5, 2), (5, 3), (5, 4), (5, 5), (5, 6), (6, 1), (6, 2), (6, 3), (6, 4), (6, 5), (6, 6)

Quick Check

2a. $\frac{1}{25}$ or 4%; $\frac{1}{40}$ or 2.5%

b. $\frac{1}{1000}$ or 0.1%

Guided Instruction

④ **EXAMPLE** Teaching Tip

Point out that the equation $P(A \text{ or } B) = P(A) + P(B) - P(A \text{ and } B)$ also works. Since the events A (under 25) and B (over 34) are mutually exclusive, $P(A \text{ and } B) = 0$.

PowerPoint

Additional Examples

③ Are the events mutually exclusive? Explain.
a. rolling an even number and rolling a number greater than 5 on a number cube no; 6 is even and also greater than 5
b. rolling a prime number or a multiple of 6 on a number cube yes; no prime number is a multiple of 6

④ At a restaurant, customers get to choose one of four vegetables with any main course. About 33% of the customers choose green beans, and about 28% choose spinach. What is the probability that a customer will choose beans or spinach? **0.61**

⑤ A spinner has twenty equal-size sections numbered from 1 to 20. If you spin the spinner, what is the probability that the number you spin will be a multiple of 2 or a multiple of 3? $\frac{13}{20}$

Resources
• Daily Notetaking Guide 9-7 **L3**

Closure

Ask students to explain how they decide whether two events, A and B, are independent or mutually exclusive. Ask them how to find P(A and B) if A and B are independent and if A and B are mutually exclusive. Finally, ask them how to calculate P(A or B). **Events A and B are independent if the outcomes of A do not affect the outcomes of B. The events are mutually exclusive if A and B cannot occur at the same time. For independent events, $P(A \text{ and } B) = P(A) \cdot P(B)$. For mutually exclusive events, $P(A \text{ and } B) = 0$. For any events, $P(A \text{ or } B) = P(A) + P(B) - P(A \text{ and } B)$.**

533

Assignment Guide

1 A B 1-9, 36-40, 45

2 A B 10-35, 41-44, 46, 47
C Challenge   48-52

Test Prep   53-58
Mixed Review   59-70

Homework Quick Check
To check students' understanding of key skills and concepts, go over Exercises 9, 20, 30, 41–44, 45, 47.

Exercise 9 Urge students to read the exercise carefully. The crucial point to note is that the book is put back in the bag.

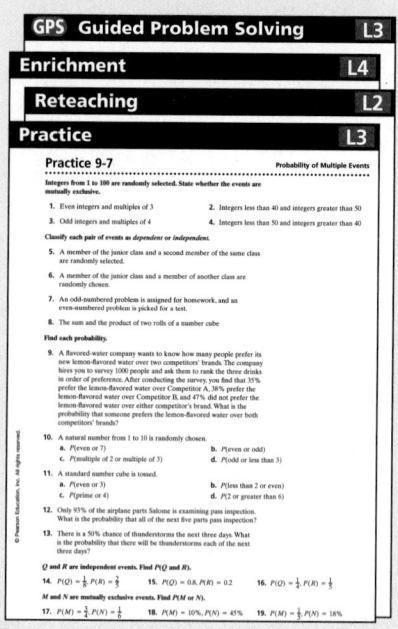

Differentiated Instruction Resources

GPS Guided Problem Solving	**L3**
Enrichment	**L4**
Reteaching	**L2**
Practice	**L3**

10. Not mutually exclusive since 2 is a prime number and less than 4.

11. Mutually exclusive since if the numbers are equal, then the sum is even.

12. Not mutually exclusive since 6·4 = 24, which is greater than 20 and a multiple of 3.

When two events are *not* mutually exclusive, you need to subtract the probability of the common outcomes.

5 **EXAMPLE**   Probabilities of Events

Multiple Choice Suppose you reach into the bowl at the left and select a piece of fruit at random. What is the probability that the fruit is an apple or green?

   Ⓐ $\frac{2}{9}$ Ⓑ $\frac{3}{9}$ Ⓒ $\frac{6}{9}$ Ⓓ $\frac{8}{9}$

$$P(\text{apple or green}) = P(\text{apple}) + P(\text{green}) - P(\text{apple and green})$$
$$= \frac{5}{9} + \frac{3}{9} - \frac{2}{9}$$
$$= \frac{6}{9}$$

The probability of picking a piece of fruit that is an apple or green is $\frac{6}{9}$, or $\frac{2}{3}$. The correct choice is C.

✓ Quick Check **5** Find each probability.   **a.** $P(\text{apple or red})\,\frac{5}{9}$ **b.** $P(\text{green or citrus fruit})\,\frac{2}{3}$

EXERCISES

For more exercises, see *Extra Skill and Word Problem Practice*.

Practice and Problem Solving

Ⓐ **Practice by Example**

Example 1
(page 532)

Classify each pair of events as *dependent* or *independent*.

1. A month is selected at random; a number from 1 to 30 is selected at random. **independent**

2. A month is selected at random; a day of that month is selected at random. **dependent**

3. A letter of the alphabet is selected at random; one of the remaining letters is selected at random. **dependent**

4. The color of a car is selected at random; the type of transmission is selected at random. **independent**

Example 2
(page 532)

Q and R are independent events. Find $P(Q \text{ and } R)$.

5. $P(Q) = \frac{1}{4}, P(R) = \frac{2}{3}$ $\frac{1}{6}$ 6. $P(Q) = \frac{12}{17}, P(R) = \frac{3}{8}$ $\frac{9}{34}$

7. $P(Q) = 0.6, P(R) = 0.9$ **0.54**   8. $P(Q) = \frac{1}{3}, P(R) = \frac{6}{x}$ $\frac{2}{x}$

9. Suppose you have five books in your book bag. Three are novels, one is a biography, and one is a poetry book. Today you grab one book out of your bag without looking, and return it later. Tomorrow you do the same thing. What is the probability that you grab a novel both days? $\frac{9}{25}$

Example 3
(page 533)

Two standard number cubes are tossed. State whether the events are mutually exclusive. Explain your reasoning.   **10–12. See margin.**

10. The sum is a prime number; the sum is less than 4.

11. The numbers are equal; the sum is odd.

12. The product is greater than 20; the product is a multiple of 3.

Example 4
(page 533)

13. **Population** About 30% of the U.S. population is under 20 years old. About 17% of the population is over 60. What is the probability that a person chosen at random is under 20 or over 60?   **47%**

S and T are mutually exclusive events. Find P(S or T).

14. $P(S) = \frac{5}{8}, P(T) = \frac{1}{8}$ $\frac{3}{4}$

15. $P(S) = \frac{3}{5}, P(T) = \frac{1}{3}$ $\frac{14}{15}$

16. $P(S) = 12\%, P(T) = 27\%$ **39%**

17. $P(S) = \frac{1}{7}, P(T) = 60\%$ $\frac{26}{35}$

Example 5
(page 534)

A standard number cube is tossed. Find each probability.

18. $P(3 \text{ or odd})$ $\frac{1}{2}$

19. $P(4 \text{ or even})$ $\frac{1}{2}$

20. $P(\text{even or less than 4})$ $\frac{5}{6}$

21. $P(\text{odd or greater than 2})$ $\frac{5}{6}$

22. $P(\text{odd or prime})$ $\frac{2}{3}$

23. $P(\text{even or prime})$ $\frac{5}{6}$

24. $P(4 \text{ or less than 6})$ $\frac{5}{6}$

25. $P(\text{greater than 1 or less than 5})$ **1**

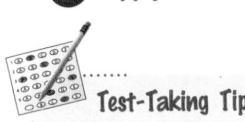

B **Apply Your Skills**

Test-Taking Tip

In $P(C \text{ or } D)$, C or D means that C occurs by itself, D occurs by itself, or possibly both C and D occur together.

C and D are not mutually exclusive events. Copy and complete the table below to find each missing probability.

	P(C)	P(D)	P(C and D)	P(C or D)	
26.	$\frac{4}{9}$	$\frac{4}{9}$	■	$\frac{5}{9}$	$\frac{1}{3}$
27.	$\frac{1}{2}$	$\frac{1}{3}$	$\frac{1}{4}$	■	$\frac{7}{12}$
28.	$\frac{2}{3}$	$\frac{3}{5}$	■	$\frac{13}{15}$	$\frac{2}{5}$
29.	$\frac{3}{7}$	$\frac{1}{4}$	$\frac{1}{8}$	■	$\frac{31}{56}$

30. Multiple Choice Suppose a number from 1 to 100 is selected at random. What is the probability that a multiple of 4 or 5 is chosen? **C**

Ⓐ $\frac{1}{20}$ Ⓑ 0.36   Ⓒ $\frac{2}{5}$ Ⓓ 45%

Real-World Connection

Careers Support personnel keep business and industry running smoothly.

🌐 **Statistics** **The graph at the right shows the types of jobs held by people in the United States. Find each probability.**

31. A person is in a service occupation. **16%**

32. A person is in service or sales. **27.6%**

33. A person is not in production or transportation. **86.9%**

34. A person is neither in sales nor in service, nor in managerial nor professional occupations. **37.6%**

35. A person is neither in service nor in sales. **72.4%**

U.S. Employment, by Occupation

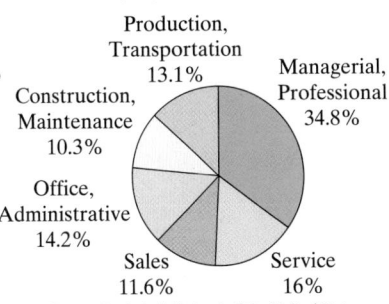

SOURCE: *Statistical Abstract of the United States.*
Go to **www.PHSchool.com** for a data update.
Web Code: agg-9041

GO Online

Homework Video Tutor

Visit: PHSchool.com
Web Code: age-0907

A jar contains four blue marbles and two red marbles. Suppose you choose a marble at random, and do not replace it. Then you choose a second marble. Find the probability of each event.

36. You select a blue marble and then a red marble. $\frac{4}{15}$

37. You select a red marble and then a blue marble. $\frac{4}{15}$

38. One of the marbles you select is blue and the other is red. $\frac{8}{15}$

39. Both of the marbles you select are red. $\frac{1}{15}$

40. You select two red marbles or two blue marbles. $\frac{7}{15}$

Error Prevention!

Exercises 18–25 You may need to remind students that after they add the probabilities, they must subtract $P(A \text{ and } B)$.

Exercise 30 Help students recognize that they need to find three probabilities to calculate the probability for a multiple of 4 or 5, because $P(4 \text{ or } 5) = P(4) + P(5) - P(4 \text{ and } 5)$.

535

Lesson Quiz

1. Classify each pair of events as dependent or independent.
   a. Flip a quarter. Then flip a penny. **independent**
   b. Choose a time for a Monday dental appointment. Then choose a time for that same Monday to meet a friend. **dependent**

2. M and N are independent events. If $P(M) = \frac{1}{6}$ and $P(N) = \frac{3}{10}$, find $P(M$ and $N)$. $\frac{1}{20}$

3. Two standard number cubes are tossed. State whether the events are mutually exclusive.
   a. The product is greater than 6; the sum is less than 7. **no**
   b. The sum is odd; the product is odd. **yes**

4. A spinner has ten equal-size sections numbered from 1 to 10. Find the probability of each event when you spin the spinner.
   a. P(even or multiple of 5) $\frac{3}{5}$
   b. P(multiple of 3 or multiple of 4) $\frac{1}{2}$

Alternative Assessment

Have students work individually. Tell students to imagine that they have two spinners. One spinner has five equal-size sections numbered 1 to 5. The other spinner has seven equal-size sections labeled A through G. Ask students to give two examples of independent events X and Y and two examples of mutually exclusive events R and Q that are based on this situation. Then ask them to calculate $P(X$ and $Y)$ and $P(R$ or $Q)$ for the events in their examples.

H and J are not mutually exclusive events. Copy and complete the table below to find each missing probability.

	$P(H)$	$P(J)$	$P(H$ and $J)$	$P(H$ or $J)$	
41.	$\frac{7}{11}$	$\frac{3}{11}$	■	$\frac{9}{11}$	$\frac{1}{11}$
42.	$\frac{1}{2}$	■	$\frac{1}{4}$	$\frac{2}{3}$	$\frac{5}{12}$
43.	■	$\frac{2}{5}$	$\frac{1}{5}$	$\frac{2}{3}$	$\frac{7}{15}$
44.	$\frac{2}{x}$	$\frac{3}{2x}$	$\frac{1}{x}$	■	$\frac{5}{2x}$

45. **Tests** A multiple-choice test has four choices for each answer.
   a. What is the probability that a random guess on a question will yield the correct answer? $\frac{1}{4}$
   b. Suppose you need to make a random guess on three of the ten test questions. What is the probability that you will answer all three correctly? $\frac{1}{64}$

46. **Open-Ended** Describe two events that are not mutually exclusive. Estimate the probability of both events occurring. **Check students' work.**

47. **Error Analysis** Events F and G are mutually exclusive independent events. A student says that $P(F$ and $G)$ is greater than $P(F$ or $G)$. Explain how you can tell that the student is wrong. $P(F$ **and** $G) = 0 \le P(F$ **or** $G)$

C Challenge

Use the tables below for Exercises 48–50. One student from each school is chosen at random to be on a committee. Find each probability.

School A

Freshman	Sophomore	Junior	Senior
30%	27%	25%	18%

School B

Freshman	Sophomore	Junior	Senior
28%	28%	24%	20%

48. a junior from School A and a senior from School B **5%**

49. two juniors **6%**

50. a freshman or sophomore from School A and a senior from School B **11.4%**

51. Two number cubes are rolled. What is the probability that the sum is greater than 9 or less than 6? $\frac{4}{9}$

52. **Critical Thinking** Tatyana has $x + 2$ pens in the pocket of her backpack. Samuel has $2x - 1$ pens in the pocket of his backpack.
   a. Tatyana has 2 blue pens. Find the probability that she pulls out a blue pen at random.
   b. Samuel has $x - 3$ blue pens. Find the probability that he pulls out a blue pen at random.
   c. Find the probability that both Tatyana and Samuel pull out blue pens at random.
   d. Find the probability that either Tatyana or Samuel pulls out a blue pen at random.

52a. $\frac{2}{x + 2}$

b. $\frac{x - 3}{2x - 1}$

c. $\frac{2(x - 3)}{(x + 2)(2x - 1)}$

d. $\frac{x - 1}{2x - 1}$

Test Prep

Use this information for Exercises 53–58.

Bag 1 contains 5 red marbles, 1 blue marble, 3 yellow marbles, and 2 green marbles. Bag 2 contains 1 red pencil, 3 red pens, 2 blue pencils, and 5 blue pens.

Gridded Response

53. One marble is drawn from bag 1. What is the probability that the marble is red or yellow? **8/11**

54. One marble is drawn from bag 1. What is the probability that the marble is blue or not green? **9/11**

55. One marble is drawn from bag 1. What is the probability that it is blue or yellow or green? **6/11**

56. One item is drawn from bag 2. What is the probability that it is red? **4/11**

57. One item is drawn from bag 2. What is the probability that it is a pen or a red pencil? **9/11**

58. One item is drawn from bag 2. What is the probability that it is red or a pencil? **6/11**

Mixed Review

GO for Help

Lesson 9-6 Solve each equation. Check your answer.

59. $\frac{1}{2} - x = \frac{x}{6}$ **3/7**

60. $\frac{2}{2x - 1} = \frac{x}{3} - \frac{3}{2}$ **or 2**

61. $\frac{3}{2x} - \frac{2}{3x} = 5$ **$\frac{1}{6}$**

Lesson 8-6 Solve each equation.

62. $\ln 2x = 3$ $\frac{e^3}{2} \approx 10.04$

63. $\ln x + \ln 2 = 6$ $\frac{e^6}{2} \approx 201.71$

64. $\ln x - \ln 4 = 5$ $4e^5 \approx 593.65$

65. $\ln x^2 + 1 = 5$ $\pm e^2 \approx \pm 7.39$

66. $\ln x^2 + \ln x = 6$ $e^2 \approx 7.39$

67. $e^x = 12$ $\ln 12 \approx 2.48$

68. $e^{x+1} = 8$ $3 \cdot \ln(2) - 1 \approx 1.08$

69. $e^{x^2} = 3$ about ± 1.048

70. $2e^{2x} + 1 = 5$ **0.3466**

Algebra at Work

.... Economist

Economists study the relationship between the supply of a product and public demand for it. A supply curve shows that the number of units a manufacturer produces will increase as the price of the item increases. A demand curve shows that the number of units sold will decrease as the price increases. The curves cross at a point that establishes a stable equilibrium price.

Go Online **For:** Information about economists
PHSchool.com **Web Code:** agb-2031

Lesson 9-7 Probability of Multiple Events **537**

A sheet of blank grids is available in the Test-Taking Strategies with Transparencies booklet. Give this sheet to students for practice with filling in the grids.

Resources
For additional practice with a variety of test item formats:
- Standardized Test Prep, p. 543
- Test-Taking Strategies, p. 538
- Test-Taking Strategies with Transparencies

Eliminating Answers

Many standardized tests are timed, and students cannot spend too much time on one question. It is often possible to save time by looking for easy ways to eliminate some of the choices in multiple choice items.

Resources

SAT® and ACT® correlations are on page 486B.

Test-Taking Strategies with Transparencies
• Transparency 9
• Practice sheet, p. 33

Guided Instruction

Math Tip

For Example 1, you might ask for the approximate value of $\frac{3}{2 - \sqrt{27}}$. Help students see that since $\sqrt{27}$ is close to 5, the denominator is close to -3. Therefore, the value of the fraction is close to -1.

For Exercise 4, help students see that if the answer were 0, getting a red chip and a green chip would be impossible. But that possibility clearly does exist. Likewise, if 1 were the answer, getting a red and a green chip would be unavoidable. That is clearly not the case either.

Test-Taking Strategies with Transparencies

Test-Taking Strategy: Eliminating Answers

The easiest way to narrow down the answer choices in a multiple-choice item is to eliminate obviously wrong answers.

Solve $\frac{|2x + 16|}{x - 8} = 10$.

A. –4   B. 8   C. 10   D. 12

Look at each answer choice to see if it can be eliminated.

–4 If –4 is substituted then the denominator would be negative which would make the quotient negative. The given quotient is positive, so this answer choice can be eliminated.

8 If 8 is substituted, the denominator would be zero and division by zero is undefined. This answer choice can be eliminated.

The answer choice is either C or D. Substitute these choices for x to select the correct one. D is correct.

Solve these problems by eliminating answer choices.

1. Solve $\frac{625}{y} = -125$.

   A. –25   B. –5   C. 5   D. 25

2. Solve $\frac{1295}{b} = 259$.

   A. 5   B. 8   C. 10   D. 12

Solutions
1. B
2. A

Transparency 9

538

Eliminating Answers

Before you try to find the answer to a problem, you may be able to eliminate some answer choices. Cross out the answers you eliminate in the test booklet, NOT on the answer sheet.

1 EXAMPLE

What is the best approximation to $\sqrt{105} - \frac{3}{2 - \sqrt{27}}$?

A –5.1   B 8.3   C 11.2   D 12.5   E 28.3

The denominator of $\frac{3}{2 - \sqrt{27}}$ is a negative number, so $\sqrt{105} - \frac{3}{2 - \sqrt{27}}$ is a positive number. Therefore, you can eliminate A.

Since $\sqrt{105}$ is close to 10, and $-\frac{3}{2 - \sqrt{27}}$ is a positive number close to 1, $\sqrt{105} - \frac{3}{2 - \sqrt{27}}$ is close to 11. You can eliminate B, D and E.

● The correct answer must be C.

2 EXAMPLE

Solve $\frac{2x}{x + 2} = 1 + \frac{x}{x - 2}$.

A $x = \frac{2}{3}, x = -2,$ or $x = 2$

B $x = \frac{2}{3}$

C $x = 2$ or $x = -2$

D $x = \frac{3}{2}$

E $x = \frac{2}{3}$ or $x = \frac{3}{2}$

The equation has denominators $x + 2$ and $x - 2$. Since the denominators cannot equal zero, you know that x cannot equal -2 or 2. You can eliminate A and C.

EXERCISES

1. What is the correct answer to Example 2? **B**

Explain how you can eliminate two or more choices for each problem.   2–4. See margin.

2. Solve $\frac{x}{x - 4} + 2 = \frac{3x}{x + 1}$.

   A $x = \frac{8}{7}$ B $x = 1\frac{1}{2}$ C $x = 4, x = \frac{8}{7}$ D $x = \frac{7}{8}, x = -1$ E $x = \frac{7}{8}$

3. What is the best approximation to $\sqrt{50} + \frac{1}{\sqrt{5} - 3}$?

   A 5.66   B 5.76   C 7.06   D 7.66   E 7.67

4. A jar contains 3 red, 3 green, and 3 yellow chips. Two chips are drawn at random from the jar, without replacement. What is the probability that one chip is red and the other is green?

   A 0   B $\frac{2}{9}$ C $\frac{1}{4}$ D $\frac{2}{3}$ E 1

538   Test-Taking Strategies Eliminating Answers

---

2. The equation has denominators $x - 4$ and $x + 1$. Since the denominators cannot equal zero, you know that $x \neq 4$ or -1. You can eliminate C and D.

3. $\frac{1}{\sqrt{5} - 3}$ is a small negative number, and $\sqrt{50}$ is close to 7. So $\sqrt{50} + \frac{1}{\sqrt{5} - 3}$ is a little smaller than 7. You can eliminate C, D, and E.

4. Since there are red and green chips, you know the probability cannot be 0. Since there are also yellow chips, you know the probability cannot be 1. You can eliminate A and E.

Chapter Review

Vocabulary Review

🔊 branch (p. 495)
complex fraction (p. 516)
dependent events (p. 531)
independent events (p. 531)

inverse variation (p. 488)
joint variation (p. 490)
mutually exclusive events (p. 533)
point of discontinuity (p. 501)

rational function (p. 501)
reciprocal function (p. 495)
simplest form (p. 509)

Choose the correct vocabulary term to complete each sentence.

1. Two events are _?_ if they cannot happen at the same time. **mutually exclusive**

2. When the numerator and denominator of a rational expression are polynomials with no common divisors, the rational expression is in _?_. **simplest form**

3. When the outcome of one event does not affect the outcome of a second event, the two events are _?_. **independent events**

4. A part of the graph of an inverse variation is called a(n) _?_. **branch**

5. If a is a zero of the denominator of a function, the function has a(n) _?_ at $x = a$. **point of discontinuity**

Go **O**nline
PHSchool.com

For: Vocabulary quiz
Web Code: agj-0951

Skills and Concepts

9-1 Objectives

▼ To use inverse variation (p. 488)

▼ To use joint and other variations (p. 490)

An equation in two variables of the form $xy = k$, $y = \frac{k}{x}$, or $x = \frac{k}{y}$, where $k \neq 0$, is an **inverse variation.** Extensions of direct and inverse variations to more complicated relationships are combined variations.

Suppose that x and y vary inversely. Write a function that models each inverse variation. Find y when $x = 5$.

6. $x = 10$ when $y = 15$
$y = \frac{150}{x}$; **30**

7. $x = 30$ when $y = 2$
$y = \frac{60}{x}$; **12**

8. $x = 6$ when $y = 30$
$y = \frac{180}{x}$; **36**

If possible, write direct or inverse variation equations to model each relation.

9.

x	3	4	8
y	24	18	9

$y = \frac{72}{x}$

10.

x	11	13	15
y	15	13	11

not possible

11.

x	5	7	9
y	30	42	54

$y = 6x$

Write the function that models each relationship. Find z when $x = 4$ and $y = 8$.

12. z varies jointly with x and y. When $x = 2$ and $y = 2$, $z = 7$. $z = \frac{7}{4}xy$; **56**

13. z varies directly with x and inversely with y. When $x = 5$ and $y = 2$, $z = 10$.
13. $z = \frac{4x}{y}$; **2**

14. z varies directly with the cube of x and inversely with y. When $x = 3$ and $y = 3$, $z = 9$. $z = \frac{x^3}{y}$; **8**

Describe the variation modeled by each equation.

17. P varies directly with x and inversely with the product of z and the square of y.

15. $R = kmn^2$
R varies jointly with m and the square of n.

16. $W = \frac{k}{d^2}$
W varies inversely with the square of d.

17. $P = \frac{kx}{y^2z}$

18.

19.

20.

21.

25.

about 31,056
headsets

▼ To graph reciprocal
functions (p. 495)

▼ To graph translations of
reciprocal functions
(p. 497)

The graph of an inverse variation has two parts called **branches**. The graph of
$y = \frac{k}{x - b} + c$ is a translation of $y = \frac{k}{x}$ by b units horizontally and c units vertically.
It has a vertical asymptote at $x = b$ and a horizontal asymptote at $y = c$.

Sketch the graph of each equation. 18–21. See margin.

18. $y = \frac{1}{x}$ **19.** $y = \frac{-2}{x^2}$ **20.** $y = \frac{-1}{x} - 4$ **21.** $y = \frac{3}{x - 2} + 1$

Write an equation for the translation of $xy = 4$ **that has the given asymptotes.**

22. $x = 0, y = 3$ **23.** $x = 2, y = 2$ **24.** $x = -3, y = -4$
$y = \frac{4}{x} + 3$ $y = \frac{4}{x - 2} + 2$ $y = \frac{4}{x + 3} - 4$

▼ To identify properties of
rational functions
(p. 501)

▼ To graph rational
functions (p. 504)

The rational function $f(x) = \frac{P(x)}{Q(x)}$ has a **point of discontinuity** for each real zero
of $Q(x)$. If $P(x)$ and $Q(x)$ have no common factors, then the graph of $f(x)$ has a
vertical asymptote when $Q(x) = 0$. If $P(x)$ and $Q(x)$ have a common real zero a,
then there is a hole or a vertical asymptote at $x = a$.

If the degree of $Q(x)$ is greater than the degree of $P(x)$, then the graph of $f(x)$ has a
horizontal asymptote at $y = 0$.

If $P(x)$ and $Q(x)$ have equal degrees, then there is a horizontal asymptote at $y = \frac{a}{b}$,
where a and b are the coefficients of the terms of greatest degree in $P(x)$ and $Q(x)$.

If the degree of $P(x)$ is greater than the degree of $Q(x)$, then there is no
horizontal asymptote.

25. A headset can be manufactured for $.17. The development cost is $150,000.
Graph the function that represents the average cost of a headset. About how
many must be manufactured to result in a cost of less than $5 per headset?
                                                        See margin.

30. $\frac{(x - 1)(x + 1)}{x + 3}$;
$x \neq -4, -3, \text{ or } 6$

31. $\frac{(2x - 1)(x + 1)}{x + 4}$;
$x \neq -4, -1, \text{ or } 0$

**Find any points of discontinuity for each rational function. Sketch the graph.
Describe any vertical or horizontal asymptotes and any holes. 26–29. See margin
pp. 540–541.**

26. $y = \frac{2.5}{x + 7}$ **27.** $y = \frac{x - 1}{(x + 2)(x - 1)}$

28. $y = \frac{x^3 - 1}{x^2 - 1}$ **29.** $y = \frac{2x^2 + 3}{x^2 + 2}$

▼ To simplify rational
expressions (p. 509)

▼ To multiply and divide
rational expressions
(p. 510)

▼ To add and subtract
rational expressions
(p. 514)

▼ To simplify complex
fractions (p. 516)

A rational expression is in **simplest form** when its numerator and denominator
are polynomials that have no common divisors. To add or subtract rational
expressions with different denominators, write each expression with the least
common denominator.

A fraction that has a fraction in its numerator or denominator or in both is called
a **complex fraction**. You can simplify a complex fraction by multiplying the
numerator and denominator by the LCD of all the rational expressions.

                                              30–31. See above left.
Simplify each rational expression. State any restrictions on the variable.

30. $\frac{x^2 - 2x - 24}{x^2 + 7x + 12} \cdot \frac{x^2 - 1}{x - 6}$ **31.** $\frac{4x^2 - 2x}{x^2 + 5x + 4} \div \frac{2x}{x^2 + 2x + 1}$

26. -7 vertical asymptote
$x = -7$, horizontal
asymptote $y = 0$

27. $-2, 1$ vertical asymptote
$x = -2$, horizontal
asymptote $y = 0$,
hole at $x = 1$

32. What is the ratio of the volume of a sphere to its surface area? $\frac{r}{3}$

33. A camera's focal length is 4 cm. If the lens is 6 cm from the film, what is the distance from the lens to an object that is in focus? **12 cm**

Simplify each expression.

34. $\dfrac{3x}{x^2 - 4} + \dfrac{6}{x + 2}$
$\dfrac{3(3x - 4)}{(x - 2)(x + 2)}$

35. $\dfrac{1}{x^2 - 1} - \dfrac{2}{x^2 + 3x}$
$\dfrac{-x^2 + 3x + 2}{x(x + 1)(x - 1)(x + 3)}$

36. $\dfrac{2 - \frac{2}{3}}{3 - \frac{1}{2}}$
$\dfrac{8}{15}$

37. $\dfrac{\frac{1}{x + y}}{4}$
$\dfrac{1}{4(x + y)}$

9-6 Objectives

▼ To solve rational equations (p. 522)

▼ To use rational equations in solving problems (p. 523)

Solving a rational equation often requires multiplying both sides by an algebraic expression. This may introduce an extraneous solution—a solution of a derived equation but not of the original equation. Check all possible solutions in the original equation.

Solve each equation. Check each solution.

38. $\dfrac{1}{x} = \dfrac{5}{x - 4}$ **−1**

39. $\dfrac{2}{x + 3} - \dfrac{1}{x} = \dfrac{-6}{x(x + 3)}$ **no solution**

40. $\dfrac{1}{2} + \dfrac{x}{6} = \dfrac{18}{x}$ **−12, 9**

41. One pump can fill a water cistern twice as fast as a second pump. Working together, the two pumps can fill the cistern in 5 hours. Find how long it takes each pump to fill the cistern when working alone. **7.5 h, 15 h**

9-7 Objectives

▼ To find the probability of the event *A and B* (p. 531)

▼ To find the probability of the event *A or B* (p. 533)

When the occurrence of one event affects the probability of another event, the two events are **dependent events.** When the occurrence of one event does not affect the probability of another event, the two events are **independent events.** When two events cannot happen at the same time, the events are **mutually exclusive events.**

If A and B are independent, then $P(A \text{ and } B) = P(A) \cdot P(B)$.

If A and B are mutually exclusive, then $P(A \text{ and } B) = 0$.

If A and B are mutually exclusive, then $P(A \text{ or } B) = P(A) + P(B)$.

If A and B are not mutually exclusive, then
$P(A \text{ or } B) = P(A) + P(B) - P(A \text{ and } B)$.

Classify each pair of events as *dependent* or *independent*.

42. A student in your algebra class is selected at random. One of the remaining students is selected at random. **dependent**

43. A number 1 through 6 is chosen by tossing a standard number cube. The same number cube is tossed again to select a number 1 through 6. **independent**

Two standard number cubes are tossed. State whether the events are mutually exclusive.

44. One of the numbers is 1 less than the other. The sum is odd.
not mutually exclusive

45. The sum is greater than 10. Six is one of the numbers.
not mutually exclusive

A standard number cube is tossed. Find each probability.

46. a 5 or a 6 $\frac{1}{3}$

47. an even number or a number greater than 4 $\frac{2}{3}$

48. an odd number or a number less than or equal to 5 $\frac{5}{6}$

---

28. 1, −1

vertical asymptote
$x = -1$, **hole at** $x = 1$

---

29. no points of discontinuity

horizontal asymptote
$y = 2$

541

Chapter 9

Chapter Test

Go Online
PHSchool.com
For: Chapter Test
Web Code: aga-0952

Write a function that models each variation. $y = \frac{-16}{x}$

1. $x = 2$ when $y = -8$. y varies inversely with x.

2. $x = 0.2$ and $y = 3$ when $z = 2$. z varies jointly with x and y. $z = \frac{10}{3}xy$

3. $x = \frac{1}{3}, y = \frac{1}{5}$, and $r = 3$ when $z = \frac{1}{2}$. z varies directly with x and inversely with the product of r^2 and y. $z = \frac{2.7x}{r^2 y}$

Is the relationship between the values in each table a direct variation, an inverse variation, or neither? Write an equation to model any direct or inverse variation.

4.

x	3	5	7	9
y	6	8	10	12

neither

5.

x	4	6	8	10
y	10	8	6	4

neither

6.

x	4	8	16	32
y	32	16	8	4

inverse variation; $y = \frac{128}{x}$

Graph the translation of $y = \frac{7}{x}$ with the given asymptotes. Write the equation of the translation.

7. $x = 1; y = 2$ **8.** $x = -3; y = -2$

7–8. See back of book.

For each rational function, identify any holes, or horizontal or vertical asymptotes of its graph.

9. $y = \frac{x+1}{x-1}$ **10.** $y = \frac{x+3}{x+3}$

11. $y = \frac{x-2}{(x+1)(x-2)}$ **12.** $y = \frac{2x^2}{x^2-4x}$

13. $y = \frac{1}{x+2} - 3$ **14.** $y = \frac{5}{x-2} + 1$

15. $y = \frac{x^2+5}{x-5}$ **16.** $y = \frac{x+2}{(x+2)(x-3)}$

9–16. See margin.

Simplify each rational expression. State any restrictions on the variable.

17. $\frac{x^2+7x+12}{x^2-9}$ $\frac{x+4}{x-3}; x \neq -3$ or 3

18. $\frac{(x+3)(2x-1)}{x(x+4)} \div \frac{(-x-3)(2x+1)}{x}$ See back of book.

19. Open-Ended Write a function whose graph has a horizontal asymptote but no vertical asymptote.
Check students' work.

Find the least common multiple of each pair of polynomials.

20. $3x + 5$ and $9x^2 - 25$ $9x^2 - 25$

21. $5(x + 3)(x + 1)$ and $2(x + 1)(x - 3)$
$10(x + 3)(x + 1)(x - 3)$

Simplify each sum or difference.

22. $\frac{x+2}{(x-3)(x+1)} + \frac{(x-1)(x+2)}{x-3}$ $\frac{x^2(x+2)}{(x-3)(x+1)}$

23. $\frac{x^2-1}{(x-2)(3x-1)} - \frac{x+1}{x+3}$ $-\frac{(x+1)(2x^2-9x+5)}{(x-2)(3x-1)(x+3)}$

24. $\frac{x(x+4)}{x-2} + \frac{x-1}{x^2-4}$ $\frac{x^3+6x^2+9x-1}{x^2-4}$

Simplify each complex fraction.

25. $\frac{\frac{2}{x}}{1 - \frac{1}{y}}$ $\frac{2y}{x(y-1)}$ **26.** $\frac{3 - \frac{3}{4}}{\frac{1}{2} - \frac{1}{4}}$ 9

Solve each equation. Check each solution.

27. $\frac{x}{2} = \frac{x+1}{4}$ 1 **28.** $\frac{3}{x-1} = \frac{4}{3x+2}$ -2

29. $\frac{3x}{x+1} = 0$ 0 **30.** $\frac{3}{x+1} = \frac{1}{x^2-1}$ $\frac{4}{3}$

31. $\frac{1}{x} + \frac{1}{3} = \frac{6}{x^2}$ -6 or 3 **32.** $\frac{1}{x} + \frac{x}{x+2} = 1$ 2

33. Almir can seal a driveway in 4 hours. Working together, he and Louis can seal it in 2.3 hours. How long would it take Louis to seal it working alone? ≈ 5.4 h

Two standard number cubes are tossed. State whether the events are mutually exclusive. Then find $P(A \text{ or } B)$.

34. A means their sum is 12; B means both are odd   mutually exclusive; $\frac{5}{18}$

35. A means they are equal; B means their sum is a multiple of 3   not mutually exclusive; $\frac{4}{9}$

36. a. Writing Suppose you select a number at random from the set $\{90, 91, 92, \ldots, 99\}$. Event A is selecting a multiple of 3. Event B is selecting a multiple of 4. Are these two events mutually exclusive? Explain.
b. Find $P(A \text{ and } B)$. $\frac{1}{10}$
c. Find $P(A \text{ or } B)$. $\frac{1}{2}$

a. No; 96 is a multiple of both 3 and 4.

9. vertical asymptote $x = 1$, horizontal asymptote $y = 1$

10. hole at $x = -3$

11. hole at $x = 2$, vertical asymptote $x = -1$, horizontal asymptote $y = 0$

12. hole at $x = 0$, vertical asymptote $x = 4$, horizontal asymptote $y = 2$

13. vertical asymptote $x = -2$, horizontal asymptote $y = -3$

14. vertical asymptote $x = 2$, horizontal asymptote $y = 1$

15. vertical asymptote $x = 5$

16. hole at $x = -2$, vertical asymptote $x = 3$; horizontal asymptote at $y = 0$

Standardized Test Prep

Standardized Test Prep

Reading Comprehension Read the passage below. Then answer the questions on the basis of what is *stated* or *implied* in the passage.

> **Payback** Buying a house is the biggest investment most people ever make. So it's important to know how mortgage loans work.
>
> Suppose you borrow $80,000 for a 30-year mortgage with an annual interest rate of 7.8%. The bank calculates a *monthly* interest rate (7.8% ÷ 12 = 0.0065) and uses it to calculate a monthly payment of $575.90. Each month, the bank adds the monthly interest to the current principal to get the balance, and then subtracts the payment to get the new principal.
>
> | End of Month | Current Principal | Amount of Interest | Balance | Payment | New Principal |
> |---|---|---|---|---|---|
> | 1 | 80,000.00 | 520.00 | 80,520.00 | 575.90 | 79,944.10 |
> | 2 | 79,944.10 | 519.64 | 80,463.74 | 575.90 | 79,887.84 |
> | 3 | 79,887.84 | 519.27 | 80,407.11 | 575.90 | 79,831.21 |
>
> You can calculate the monthly payment for any mortgage with the formula $P = \dfrac{A \cdot m(1 + m)^{12y}}{(1 + m)^{12y} - 1}$. P is the monthly payment, A is the amount borrowed, m is the monthly interest rate, and y is the length of the mortgage in years.
>
> If you know the monthly payment you want to make, you can use the formula $A = \dfrac{P\left[(1 + m)^{12y} - 1\right]}{m(1 + m)^{12y}}$ to find the total amount you can borrow.

1. For the mortgage loan described above, what will be the 4th month's balance after the interest is added to the principal?
   D
   - (A) $518.90
   - (B) $575.90
   - (C) $79,744.21
   - (D) $80,350.11

2. If the annual interest for a loan is 8.55%, what is the monthly interest rate?
   J
   - (F) 8.8375%
   - (G) 7.125
   - (H) 0.07125%
   - (J) 0.007125

3. Consider a 15-year mortgage for $65,000 with an annual interest rate of 6%. Rewrite the formula $P = \dfrac{A \cdot m(1 + m)^{12y}}{(1 + m)^{12y} - 1}$ by substituting values for A, m, and y. **See margin.**

4. To the nearest cent, what is the monthly payment for a 15-year mortgage loan of $65,000 with an annual interest rate of 6%? **$548.51**

5. To the nearest cent, what is the monthly payment for a 15-year mortgage loan of $65,000 with an annual interest rate of 7.5%? **$602.56**

6. Suppose you want to make a monthly mortgage payment of $675.00. To the nearest hundred dollars, what is the most you can borrow for a 25-yr mortgage with an annual interest rate of 7.2%? **$93,800**

7. Show how to derive the formula
   $$A = \dfrac{P\left[(1 + m)^{12y} - 1\right]}{m(1 + m)^{12y}}$$
   from the formula $P = \dfrac{A \cdot m(1 + m)^{12y}}{(1 + m)^{12y} - 1}$. **See margin.**

Chapter 9   Standardized Test Prep   **543**

3. $P = \dfrac{65{,}000 \cdot 0.005 \,(1.005)^{180}}{(1.005)^{180} - 1}$

7. $P = \dfrac{A \cdot m\,(1 + m)^{12y}}{(1 + m)^{12y} - 1}$

$P[(1 + m)^{12y} - 1] = A \cdot m\,(1 + m)^{12y}$

$\dfrac{P\left[(1 + m)^{12y} - 1\right]}{m(1 + m)^{12y}} = A$

Students must be able to extract information from reading passages, answer multiple choice questions, and construct responses in order to be successful on current state and national assessments.

To answer the questions, students apply skills and concepts from this chapter and previous chapters.
Multiple Choice: Items 1–2
Free Response: Items 3–7

Resources

Test Prep Workbook

Grab & Go
- **L3** Cumulative Review

ExamView CD-ROM
- Standardized Test Practice

Differentiated Instruction Resources

Progress Monitoring Assessments
- Quarter 3 Test
  - **L3** Forms A & B
  - **L2** Forms D & E

Spanish Assessment Resources
- **L3** Spanish Cumulative Review
- Spanish Quarter 3 Test
  - **L3** Forms A & B

Chapter 10

Quadratic Relations and Conic Sections

Chapter at a Glance

Lesson Titles, Objectives, and Features	Assessment	NCTM Standards	Local Standards
Activity Lab: Hands-On: Conic Sections **10-1 Exploring Conic Sections** • Graphing conic sections • Identifying conic sections **Activity Lab: Technology:** Graphing Conic Sections	Lesson Quiz	2, 3, 10	
10-2 Parabolas • Writing the equation of a parabola • Graphing parabolas	Lesson Quiz	2, 3, 6	
10-3 Circles • Writing and graphing the equation of a circle • Finding the center and radius of a circle and using them to graph the circle **Activity Lab: Technology:** Using Parametric Equations	Lesson Quiz Checkpoint Quiz 1	2, 3, 6	
10-4 Ellipses • Writing the equation of an ellipse • Finding the foci of an ellipse and graphing an ellipse	Lesson Quiz	2, 3, 6	
10-5 Hyperbolas • Graphing hyperbolas • Finding and using the foci of a hyperbola **GPS:** Understanding Math Problems	Lesson Quiz Checkpoint Quiz 2	2, 3, 6	
10-6 Translating Conic Sections • Writing the equation of a translated conic section • Identifying a translated conic section from an equation **Activity Lab: Technology:** Solving Quadratic Systems	Lesson Quiz	2, 3, 6	
Activity Lab: Applying Conic Sections			

NCTM Standards 2000

1 Number and Operations	**2** Algebra	**3** Geometry	**4** Measurement	**5** Data Analysis and Probability
6 Problem Solving	**7** Reasoning and Proof	**8** Communication	**9** Connections	**10** Representation

Correlations to Standardized Tests

All content for these tests is contained in *Prentice Hall Algebra 2*. This chart reflects coverage in this chapter only.

	10-1	10-2	10-3	10-4	10-5	10-6
SAT®						
Number and Operations Operations, ratio & proportions, complex numbers, counting, elementary number theory, matrices, sequences						
Algebra and Functions Expressions, equations, inequalities, representation and modeling, properties of functions (linear, polynomial, rational, exponential)	✔	✔	✔	✔	✔	✔
Geometry and Measurement *Plane Euclidean/Measurement Coordinate* Lines, parabolas, circles, symmetry, transformations *Three-dimensional* Solids, surface area & volume (cylinders, cones, pyramids, spheres, prisms) *Trigonometry* Right triangles, identities	✔	✔	✔	✔	✔	✔
Data Analysis, Statistics, and Probability Mean, median, mode, range, interquartile range, graphs and plots, regression, probability						
ACT®						
Pre-Algebra Basic operations using whole numbers, decimals, fractions, and integers; place value; square roots and approximations; the concept of exponents; scientific notation; factors, ratio, proportion, and percent; linear equations in one variable; absolute value and ordering numbers by value; elementary counting techniques and simple probability; data collection, representation, and interpretation; and understanding simple descriptive statistics.						
Elementary Algebra Properties of exponents and square roots, evaluation of algebraic expressions through substitution, using variables to express functional relationships, understanding algebraic operations, and solving quadratic equations by factoring.	✔	✔	✔	✔	✔	✔
Intermediate Algebra Understanding of the quadratic formula, rational and radical expressions, absolute value equations and inequalities, sequences and patterns, systems of equations, quadratic inequalities, functions, modeling, matrices, roots of polynomials, and complex numbers.	✔	✔	✔	✔	✔	✔
Coordinate Geometry Graphing and the relations between equations and graphs, including points, lines, polynomials, circles, and other curves; graphing inequalities; slope; parallel and perpendicular lines; distance; midpoints; and conics.	✔	✔	✔	✔	✔	✔
Plane Geometry Properties and relations of plane figures, including angles and relations among perpendicular and parallel lines; properties of circles, triangles, rectangles, parallelograms, and trapezoids; transformations; the concept of proof and proof techniques; volume; and applications of geometry to three dimensions.						
Trigonometry Understanding trigonometric relations in right triangles; values and properties of trigonometric functions; graphing trigonometric functions; modeling using trigonometric functions; use of trigonometric identities; and solving trigonometric equations.						
NAEP						
Number Sense, Properties, and Operations						
Measurement						
Geometry and Spatial Sense	✔	✔	✔	✔	✔	✔
Data Analysis, Statistics, and Probability						
Algebra and Functions	✔	✔	✔	✔	✔	✔

SAT® The College Board, SAT® Reasoning Test   **ACT®** The ACT Assessment® Test   **NAEP** National Assessment of Educational Progress, 2005 Mathematics Objectives

Math Background

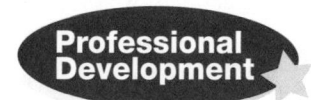

Skills Trace

BEFORE Chapter 10

In previous chapters, students graphed quadratic functions, applied properties of parabolas, and solved quadratic equations.

DURING Chapter 10

Students identify and graph conic sections including translated conics, and write equations of conic sections.

AFTER Chapter 10

Students will calculate measures of central tendency and variation.

Chapter Overview

The ancient Greeks defined a conic section as the intersection of a plane and a double cone. Much later, it was shown how to give simple definitions using loci and two-dimensional coordinate geometry. The definitions used in most present-day textbooks are analytic geometry definitions thanks to the work of Germinal Pierre Dandelin, a 19th century French mathematician who studied the connections between the three-dimensional and two-dimensional approaches.

Conic sections are extremely important in astronomy and in many parts of physics and technology. A number of interesting applications of conic sections are presented in the chapter.

Exploring Conic Sections   10-1

A plane that contains the vertex of a double cone will intersect the cone in a pair of intersecting lines (a degenerate hyperbola), a single line (a degenerate parabola), or a single point (the vertex of the cone, a degenerate ellipse). Other planes will intersect the cone in a parabola, an ellipse (which may be a circle), or a hyperbola. The degenerate cases are often excluded from lists of conic sections, but most students find them interesting. The names ellipse, parabola, and hyperbola are attributed to the Greek geometer and astronomer Apollonius of Perga or Perge (c. 262-190 BC).

In the Cartesian coordinate plane, the graph of a quadratic equation in two variables is always a conic section. Students explore these curves by graphing equations that describe them.

Parabolas   10-2

Students have learned that the graph of a quadratic function is a parabola. Here the standard locus definition is presented by applying the distance formula. The first example shows how the locus definition yields a quadratic function. Students must become familiar with the terms focus and directrix and relate these terms to equations and graphs. Students should recognize that the orientation of the directrix as horizontal or vertical determines whether the parabola opens up/down or right/left, respectively.

Students write equations and make graphs of parabolas given the focus and directrix, focus and vertex, and vertex and directrix. In each situation, student must identify whether the graph opens up/down or left/right by the relationships between each pair of given facts.

Circles   10-3

A locus definition of an circle is presented. The standard form of an equation of a circle $(x - h)^2 + (y - k)^2 = r^2$ follows directly from the distance formula, and students should be expected to reproduce this equation by memory or derivation. Once this equation is known, the other conics can be more easily recalled by comparison to the equation of a circle.

Students must recognize that the center of the translated circle $(x - h)^2 + (y - k)^2 = r^2$ is simply (h, k) and the radius is r. Students often overlook finding the square root of r^2 to find the radius when graphing a given equation of a circle. Students should also recognize that positive values for h and k give translations right and up respectively; negative values for h and k give translations left and down respectively

Ellipses   10-4

You may wish to suggest that interested students use the distance formula to show how to obtain the standard-form equation for the ellipse with center at the origin and foci at $(-4, 0)$ and $(4, 0)$, given that the sum of the distances from a point on the ellipse to the foci is 10. Students must become familiar with the terms foci, major axis, minor axis, vertices, and co-vertices of an ellipse. By convention, the length of the major axis is $2a$ and the length of the minor axis is $2b$. This gives two standard forms for an equation of an ellipse based on the orientation of the major axis:

$\frac{x^2}{a^2} + \frac{y^2}{b^2} = 1$ for a horizontal major axis and $\frac{x^2}{b^2} + \frac{y^2}{a^2} = 1$ for a vertical major axis.

A circle is a special case of an ellipse in which the major axis and the minor axis have the same length. So, $a = b$ and $c = 0$, and the foci of a circle centered at the origin are at the origin, which is also the center of the circle. The radius a or b is usually called r. The degenerate special cases of an ellipse include a line segment and a point.

Hyperbolas   10-5

The work with hyperbolas parallels closely that for ellipses. Instead of the *sum* of the distances from a point to two foci being a constant, the *difference* between the distances from a point to two foci are a constant. Again, the foci and vertices lie on the "major" axis known as the transverse axis. The central rectangle whose diagonals give the asymptotes measures $2a$ by $2b$. This gives two standard forms for an equation of an ellipse based on the orientation of the transverse axis:

$\frac{x^2}{a^2} - \frac{y^2}{b^2} = 1$ for a horizontal transverse axis and $\frac{y^2}{a^2} - \frac{x^2}{b^2} = 1$ for a vertical transverse axis.

Students should include the asymptotes to help sketch graphs of hyperbolas.

To make a connection between the equation of a rectangular hyperbola and an equation in standard form, consider the hyperbola $xy = 1$. Its center is at $(0, 0)$ and the vertices are $(1, 1)$ and $(-1, -1)$. Students might recognize that this is the parent reciprocal function $y = \frac{1}{x}$. Explain to students that, in future courses, they will learn to use trigonometric functions to re-orient (rotate) such a hyperbola, so that its equation can then be written in a standard form with $a = b = \sqrt{2}$. Note that this is the distance from the origin to the vertex in either form.

Translating Conic Sections   10-6

It can be shown that the graphs of second-degree equations of the form $Ax^2 + Bxy + Cy^2 + Dx + Ey + F = 0$ (A and C not both 0) are either conics, degenerate conics, two parallel lines, or the null set. The determining fact is the value of $B^2 - 4AC$. Suppose A, B, and C are not all 0, and the graph is not degenerate. (Note B is the coefficient of xy, not of y^2, as in the lesson.)

- If $B^2 - 4AC < 0$, then the graph is a circle or an ellipse. (For a circle, $A = C$ and $B = 0$.)

- If $B^2 - 4AC = 0$, then the graph is a parabola.

- If $B^2 - 4AC > 0$, then the graph is hyperbola.

Some students may observe that in this text, it is always true that $B = 0$. Assure them that later work using trigonometry to rotate graphs will convince them that this causes no loss of generality.

Additional Professional Development Opportunities

Math Background notes for Chapter 10: Every lesson has a Math Background in the PLAN section.

Research Overview, Mathematical Strands Additional support for these topics and more is in the front of this Teacher's Edition.

Lesson Lab Lesson Lab, a Pearson Education company, offers comprehensive, facilitated professional development designed to help teachers improve student achievement. To learn more, please visit lessonlab.com

Chapter 10 Resources

	10-1	10-2	10-3	10-4	10-5	10-6	For the Chapter
Print Resources							
L3 Practice	•	•	•	•	•	•	
L3 Guided Problem Solving	•	•	•	•	•	•	
L2 Reteaching	•	•	•	•	•	•	
L4 Enrichment	•	•	•	•	•	•	
L3 Daily Notetaking Guide	•	•	•	•	•	•	
L3 Vocabulary and Study Skills Worksheets	•						•
L3 Chapter Project							•
L3 Hands On Activities				•	•		
L3 Checkpoint Quiz			•		•		
L2 Below Level Chapter Test							•
L3 Chapter Test							•
L4 Alternative Assessment							•
L3 Cumulative Review							•
L4 Connections to Precalculus Masters	•	•	•	•	•	•	
L3 Technology Activities	•	•		•	•		
Spanish Resources ELL							
L3 Practice	•	•	•	•	•	•	
L3 Vocabulary and Study Skills Worksheets	•						•
L3 Checkpoint Quiz			•		•		
L2 Below Level Chapter Test							•
L3 Chapter Test							•
L4 Alternative Assessment							•
L3 Cumulative Review							•
Transparencies							
Check Skills You'll Need	•	•	•	•	•	•	
Additional Examples	•	•	•	•	•	•	
Problem of the Day	•	•	•	•	•	•	
Classroom Aid						•	
Student Edition Answers	•	•	•	•	•	•	•
Lesson Quiz	•	•	•	•	•	•	
Test-Taking Strategies							•
Technology							
TI 83/84 Plus Activities							
Interactive Textbook Online	•	•	•	•	•	•	•
Student Express CD-ROM	•	•	•	•	•	•	•
TI Navigator, Instant Check System	•	•	•	•	•	•	
Success Tracker	•	•	•	•	•	•	•
ExamView CD-ROM with Quick Take	•	•	•	•	•	•	•
Teacher Express CD-ROM	•	•	•	•	•	•	•
Presentation Express CD-ROM	•	•	•	•	•	•	•
Mindpoint Quiz Show CD-ROM	•	•	•	•	•	•	•
Prentice Hall Web site: PHSchool.com	•	•	•	•	•	•	•

Also available: Prentice Hall Assessment System (Progress Monitoring Assessments, Skills and Concepts Review, Test Prep Workbook)   Solution Key   Student Workbook
Student Workbook, Adapted Version   Data Analysis and Probability Workbook   Math Notes Study Folder   Spanish Cumulative Assessment

Where You Can Use the Lesson Resources

Here is a suggestion, following the four-step teaching plan, for how you can incorporate Differentiated Instruction Resources into your teaching.

	Instructional Resources L3	**Differentiated** Instruction **Resources**
1. Plan		
Check Skills You'll Need Assign these exercises to review prerequisite skills. **New Vocabulary** Help students pre-read the lesson by pointing out the new terms introduced in the lesson.	**Math Background** **Transparencies & Presentation Express CD** Check Skills You'll Need **Resources** Vocabulary and Study Skills	**Spanish Support** ELL Vocabulary and Study Skills
2. Teach		
L3 **Guided Instruction** Teach each Example. After each Example, assign the Quick Check exercise for that Example.	**Student Edition** Activity Lab **Resources** Daily Notetaking Guide Activity Lab TI-83/84 Activities CD-ROM **Transparencies & Presentation Express CD** Additional Examples Classroom Aids **ExamView CD-ROM with QuickTake** **TI Navigator Instant Check System**	**Teacher's Edition** Every lesson includes suggestions for working with students who need special attention. L1 Special Needs L2 Below Level L4 Advanced Learners ELL English Language Learners
3. Practice		
Assignment Guide **Homework Exercises** Assign the exercises cited in each lesson's Assignment Guide. A Practice by Example B Apply Your Skills C Challenge Test Prep Mixed Review **Homework Quick Check** Discuss in class the exercises cited in each lesson's Assignment Guide.	**Transparencies & Presentation Express CD** Student Answers **Resources** Practice Guided Problem Solving Vocabulary and Study Skills Activity Lab **ExamView CD-ROM with QuickTake**	**Spanish Support** ELL Practice ELL Vocabulary and Study Skills **Resources** L4 Enrichment
4. Assess & Reteach		
Lesson Quiz Assign the Lesson Quiz to assess students' mastery of the lesson content. **Checkpoint Quiz** Use the Checkpoint Quiz to assess student progress over several lessons.	**Transparencies & Presentation Express CD** Lesson Quiz **Resources** Checkpoint Quiz	**Resources** L2 Reteaching ELL Checkpoint Quiz Success Tracker **ExamView CD-ROM with QuickTake**

KEY   L1 Special Needs   L2 Below Level   L3 For All Students   L4 Advanced, Gifted   ELL English Language Learners

Chapter 10

Quadratic Relations and Conic Sections

 Check Your Readiness

Answers are in the back of the textbook.

For intervention, direct students to:

Modeling Data with Quadratic Functions
Lesson 5-1: Example 1
Extra Skills and Word
  Problems Practice, Ch. 5

Properties of Parabolas
Lesson 5-2: Examples 1 and 2
Extra Skills and Word
  Problems Practice, Ch. 5

Completing the Square
Lesson 5-7: Examples 2 and 6
Extra Skills and Word
  Problems Practice, Ch. 5

Theorems About Roots of Polynomial Equations
Lesson 6-5: Example 2
Extra Skills and Word
  Problems Practice, Ch. 6

Exploring Exponential Models
Lesson 8-1: Example 5
Extra Skills and Word
  Problems Practice, Ch. 8

What You've Learned

● In Chapter 5, you learned to write and graph the equation of a parabola.

● In Chapter 5, you also learned to rewrite a quadratic equation by completing the square.

● In Chapter 8, you learned to locate the asymptote of the graph of an exponential function.

 Check Your Readiness   GO **for Help** to the Lesson in green.

Identifying Quadratic Functions (Lesson 5-1)

Determine whether each function is linear or quadratic. Identify the quadratic, linear, and constant terms. **1–6. See margin.**

1. $y = 6x - x^2 + 1$ **2.** $f(x) = -2(3 + x)^2 + 2x^2$ **3.** $y = 2x - y - 13$

4. $y = 4x(7 - 2x)$ **5.** $g(x) = -2x^2 - 3(x - 2)$ **6.** $y = x - 2(x + 5)$

Graphing Quadratic Functions (Lesson 5-2)

Graph each function. **7–10. See margin.**

7. $y = -x^2$ **8.** $y = \frac{1}{3}x^2$ **9.** $y = 2x^2 + 5$ **10.** $y = x^2 + 6x + 8$

Completing the Square (Lesson 5-7)

Complete the square.

11. $x^2 + 8x + \blacksquare$ 16   **12.** $x^2 - 5x + \blacksquare$ $\frac{25}{4}$ **13.** $x^2 + 14x + \blacksquare$ 49

Rewrite each function in vertex form. Then graph the function. **14–16. See margin p. 545 for graphs.**

14. $y = x^2 + 6x + 7$ **15.** $y = 2x^2 - 4x + 10$ **16.** $y = -3x^2 + x$
  $y = (x + 3)^2 - 2$ $y = 2(x - 1)^2 + 8$ $y = -3\left(x - \frac{1}{6}\right)^2 + \frac{1}{12}$

Solving Polynomial Equations (Lesson 6-5)

Find all the roots of each polynomial equation.

17. $2x^3 - x^2 + 10x - 5 = 0$ $\frac{1}{2}, \pm i\sqrt{5}$ **18.** $2x^3 - 5x^2 + 4x - 1 = 0$ $\frac{1}{2}, 1$

Graphing Exponential Decay (Lesson 8-1) **19–21. See back of book.**

Sketch the graph for each decay function. Label the asymptote.

19. $y = 8\left(\frac{1}{2}\right)^x$ **20.** $y = 2(0.4)^x$ **21.** $y = \left(\frac{3}{4}\right)^x$

1. quadratic; $-x^2$, $6x$, 1

2. linear; none, $-12x$, -18

3. linear; none, x, $-\frac{13}{2}$

4. quadratic; $-8x^2$, $28x$, none

5. quadratic; $-2x^2$, $-3x$, 6

6. linear; none, $-x$, -10

7.

8.

Quadratic Relations and Conic Sections

Chapter 10

What You'll Learn Next

- In Chapter 10, you will learn to use conic sections to model real-world problems.
- You will learn to graph parabolas, circles, ellipses, and hyperbolas.
- You will learn to identify the equation of a specific conic section by completing the square.

 Activity Lab Applying what you learn, on pages 596–597 you will do activities involving planetary exploration.

LESSONS

10-1 Exploring Conic Sections

10-2 Parabolas

10-3 Circles

10-4 Ellipses

10-5 Hyperbolas

10-6 Translating Conic Sections

◀)) Key Vocabulary

- center (p. 561)
- circle (p. 561)
- conic section (p. 547)
- co-vertices (p. 568)
- directrix (p. 555)
- ellipse (p. 568)
- focus of a parabola (p. 555)
- focus of an ellipse (p. 568)
- focus of a hyperbola (p. 575)
- hyperbola (p. 575)
- major axis (p. 568)
- minor axis (p. 568)
- radius (p. 561)
- standard form of an equation of a circle (p. 561)
- transverse axis (p. 575)
- vertices of an ellipse (p. 568)
- vertices of a hyperbola (p. 575)

545

Chapter 10 Overview

In this chapter, students learn that conic sections are curves that can be formed by intersecting a plane with a double cone. They learn how to graph parabolas, circles, ellipses, and hyperbolas, as well as how to identify the different conic sections from their equations. Students also learn to apply the same techniques that they used to translate parabolas in Lesson 5-3 to translate circles, ellipses, and hyperbolas.

Activating Prior Knowledge

Have students list everything they can think about circles. Students should include its definition, related vocabulary such as center, radius, diameter, pi, and formulas for its circumference and area:

Ask:
- *Do you think an algebraic equation can be written to represent a circle?*

Allow students time to discuss their answers before informing them that yes, an equation can be written for a circle. Tell students that in this chapter they will learn to write equations, similar to equations for lines, for circles as well as other conic sections: parabolas, ellipses, circles, and hyperbolas.

9.

10.

14.

15.

16.

545

Conic Sections

Students learn that conic sections are curves that lie in a plane and are formed by intersecting a plane with a double cone. The templates and models created in this investigation will provide students with a visual for each of the conic sections studied in the rest of the chapter.

Guided Instruction

Connection to History of Mathematics

An early study of conic sections is credited to the Greek Menaechmus in 350 B.C. In 225 B.C., Appollonius of Perga showed that conic sections could be formed by varying the inclination of a cutting plane to a double cone.

Tactile Learners

Extend the idea in the Activity by challenging students to form the conic sections by cutting foam cones that they may obtain at a craft store. Have students slice the cones and paint the inside surfaces to show the shape of a parabola, an ellipse, and a circle. Students can hold the sections of the cones together by long pins. They may be able to pin two cones together to demonstrate the hyperbola. These sliced cones make excellent class models.

Resources

Students use paper, tape, scissors, and compasses to form cones and templates of conic sections.

Activity Lab

Hands-On

Conic Sections

FOR USE WITH LESSON 10-1

A conic section is a special curve formed by the intersection of a cone and a plane. You can use paper cutouts to investigate conic sections.

Step 1 Draw two circular areas, each one measuring four inches in diameter. Cut out each circular area, and then cut it in half. Roll each half into a cone and secure it with tape.

Step 2 Trace the three templates below onto a sheet of paper. Cut out the parts corresponding to the white areas. The remaining parts corresponding to the blue areas are the templates. Label each one.

Parabola

Ellipse

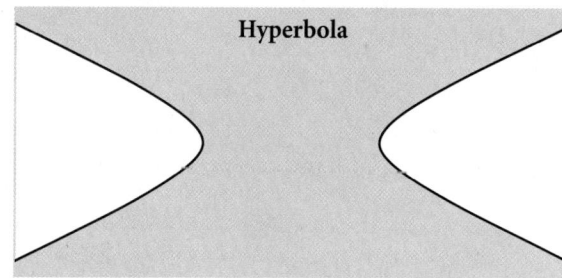
Hyperbola

Step 3 Make a fourth template for a circle. Use a compass or a coin of any size to draw the circle.

Step 4 Fit each template around the cones so that the template stays flat, like a plane. The ellipse is shown at the right. Sketch each result.

EXERCISES

1. **a.** The template for a hyperbola has two parts. Explain how you must position the cones to use this template as a model of a hyperbola.
   b. Suppose you tried to fit your other three templates around a double cone. Would the results change? Explain.

2. **a.** Fold the template for each curve so that two halves coincide. In how many ways can you do this for each of the four templates?
   b. How many axes of symmetry does each template have?

3. Which templates have rotational symmetry? Explain.

1a. Answers may vary. Sample: The individual cones must touch at their vertices, and the axes of the individual cones must align.

  b. Answers may vary. Sample: Yes; the other three templates can fit around either of the two cones that form the double cone.

2a. 2 ways for the ellipse, 1 way for the parabola, 2 ways for the hyperbola, infinitely many ways for the circle

  b. ellipse: 2 axes of symmetry; parabola: 1 axis of symmetry; hyperbola: 2 axes of symmetry; circle: infinitely many axes of symmetry

3. ellipse, hyperbola, circle

Exploring Conic Sections

1. Plan

What You'll Learn

- To graph conic sections
- To identify conic sections

. . . And Why

To analyze Moiré patterns, as in Example 5

✓ Check Skills You'll Need

GO for Help Lessons 2-2, 5-2, and 5-5

Find the *x*- and *y*-intercepts of the graph of each function.

1. $y = 3x + 6$ **−2, 6**   **2.** $2y = −x − 3$ **−3, −1.5**

3. $3x − 4y = −12$ **−4, 3**   **4.** $y = x^2 − 4$ **±2, −4**

5. $y = (x − 3)^2$ **3, 9**   **6.** $y = −4x^2 + 1$ **±0.5, 1**

◀)) **New Vocabulary**   • conic section

Objectives
1   To graph conic sections
2   To identify conic sections

Examples
1   Graphing a Circle
2   Graphing an Ellipse
3   Graphing a Hyperbola
4   Identifying Graphs of Conic Sections
5   Real-World Connection

Math Background

Conic sections are formed by the intersection of a plane and a double cone. An interesting topic for students to investigate is Dandelin spheres. Dandelin spheres help connect the 2- and 3-dimensional descriptions of conics.

More Math Background: p. 544C

Lesson Planning and Resources

See p. 2544E for a list of the resources that support this lesson.

1   Graphing Equations of Conic Sections

A **conic section** is a curve formed by the intersection of a plane and a double cone. By changing the inclination of the plane, you can create a circle, a parabola, an ellipse, or a hyperbola. You can use lines of symmetry to graph a conic section.

Vocabulary Tip

Cone comes from the Indo-European word for "sharpen." Section comes from the word for "cut."

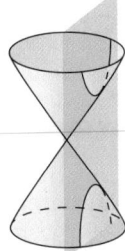

1   EXAMPLE   Graphing a Circle

Graph the equation $x^2 + y^2 = 25$. Describe the graph and its lines of symmetry. Then find the domain and range.

Make a table of values.

x	−5	−4	−3	0	3	4	5
y	0	±3	±4	±5	±4	±3	0

Plot the points and connect them with a smooth curve.

The graph is a circle of radius 5. Its center is at the origin. Every line through the center is a line of symmetry.

Recall from Chapter 2 that you can use set notation to describe a domain or a range. In this example, the domain is $\{x \mid −5 \le x \le 5\}$. The range is $\{y \mid −5 \le y \le 5\}$.

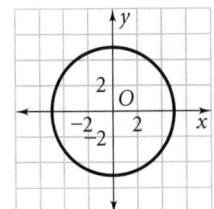

The photograph shows a double cone of illuminated smoke being intersected by a laser to produce a circle.

Bell Ringer Practice

✓ Check Skills You'll Need
For intervention, direct students to:

Linear Equations
Lesson 2-2: Example 2
Extra Skills and Word
   Problems Practice, Ch. 2

Properties of Parabolas
Lesson 5-2: Examples 1, 2
Extra Skills and Word
   Problems Practice, Ch. 5

Quadratic Equations
Lesson 5-5: Example 2
Extra Skills and Word
   Problems Practice, Ch. 5

Differentiated Instruction Solutions for All Learners

Special Needs **L1**
For Example 5, help visually impaired students understand the patterns by having a partner describe each pattern that is overlapped. Then partners guide students' fingers over the shapes of the overlapping patterns and the unintended pattern.

learning style: tactile

Below Level **L2**
Remind students that among the conic sections, only parabolas may be functions.

learning style: verbal

547

Guided Instruction

1 EXAMPLE Math Tip

Clarify that the graph is just the circular boundary. Points in the interior of the circle are not part of the graph. Have students pick any point in the interior of the circle, such as (2, 2), and, by substituting the point into the equation, demonstrate that the point does not satisfy the equation.

2 EXAMPLE Auditory Learners

Ask students to describe how the equation of a circle is different from the equation of an ellipse.

3 EXAMPLE Teaching Tip

Students may have difficulty writing the domain because of the gap between the two branches of the hyperbola. Students must take this gap into consideration when they write the domain. Hint that they can use absolute values to describe the domain.

Additional Examples

1 Graph the equation $x^2 + y^2 = 16$. Describe the graph and its lines of symmetry. Then find the domain and range.

The graph is a circle of radius 4 with center (0, 0). Every line through the center is a line of symmetry; domain: $\{x \mid -4 \leq x \leq 4\}$, range: $\{y \mid -4 \leq y \leq 4\}$

Quick Check **1** **a.** Graph the functions $y = \sqrt{25 - x^2}$ and $y = -\sqrt{25 - x^2}$ on the same screen. Compare this graph to the one in Example 1. **a–b. See back of book.**
b. Explain how you can get the equations in part (a) from $x^2 + y^2 = 25$.
c. **Critical Thinking** Why is there no point on the graph of Example 1 with an x-coordinate of 6? **When $x = 6$, $25 - x^2 = -11$. $\sqrt{-11}$ is not a real number.**

An ellipse is similar to a circle, but it has only two lines of symmetry.

2 EXAMPLE Graphing an Ellipse

Graph the equation $9x^2 + 16y^2 = 144$. Describe the graph and the lines of symmetry. Then find the domain and range.

Make a table of values.

x	−4	−3	0	3	4
y	0	±2.0	±3	±2.0	0

Plot the points and connect them with a smooth curve.

The graph is an ellipse. The center is at the origin. It has two lines of symmetry, the x-axis and the y-axis.

The domain is $\{x \mid -4 \leq x \leq 4\}$.
The range is $\{y \mid -3 \leq y \leq 3\}$.

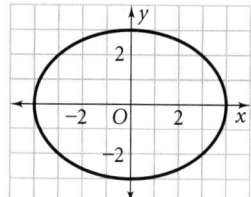

Quick Check **2** **a.** How far are the x-intercepts from the center of the ellipse? How far are the y-intercepts from the center? Describe how an ellipse differs from a circle.
b. The point $(1, 2.9)$ is an approximation of a point on the graph of Example 2. Use symmetry to find three other approximate points on the ellipse.
c. Graph the equation $2x^2 + y^2 = 18$. Describe the graph and give the coordinates of the x- and y-intercepts. **See back of book.**

2a. 4 units; 3 units; an ellipse is oblong instead of round. It has 2 axes of symmetry rather than infinitely many.

b. $(1, -2.9)$, $(-1, 2.9)$, $(-1, -2.9)$

Not all conic sections consist of one smooth curve. Note the unique shape of the hyperbola.

3 EXAMPLE Graphing a Hyperbola

Graph the equation $x^2 - y^2 = 9$. Describe the graph and its lines of symmetry. Then find the domain and range.

Make a table of values.

x	−5	−4	−3	−2	−1	0	1	2	3	4	5
y	±4	±2.6	0	−	−	−	−	−	0	±2.6	±4

Plot the points and connect them with smooth curves.

The graph is a hyperbola that consists of two branches. Its center is at the origin. It has two lines of symmetry, the x-axis and the y-axis.

The domain is $\{x \mid x \leq -3 \text{ or } x \geq 3\}$. The range is all real numbers.

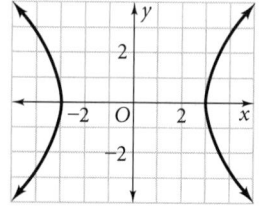

Here the laser intersects the smoke to produce an ellipse.

Here the laser intersects the smoke to produce a hyperbola.

Differentiated Instruction Solutions for All Learners

Advanced Learners L4
Have students research which types of conic sections are represented by orbits of astronomical objects.

English Language Learners ELL
Help students pronounce the names of the conic sections by having them slowly speak the names aloud. Some students might confuse the sounds of *parabola* and *hyperbola*. Also clarify that conic *sections* are flat, two-dimensional, shapes.

learning style: verbal   learning style: verbal

Quick Check ❸ **a.** Does the graph in Example 3 represent a function? Explain.
b. In the table in Example 3, why is the y-value undefined when
$x = -2, -1, 0, 1,$ or 2? **a–b. See back of book.**
c. Critical Thinking What two lines does each branch of this hyperbola get
very close to? What are these lines called? $y = x$ and $y = -x$; asymptotes

2 Identifying Conic Sections

The center and the intercepts are important points to identify on the graph of
some conic sections.

4 EXAMPLE Identifying Graphs of Conic Sections

Identify the center and intercepts of each conic section. Then find the domain and
range. In part (b), each interval on the graph represents one unit.

a.

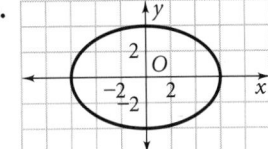

The center of the ellipse is $(0, 0)$. The x-intercepts are $(-6, 0)$ and $(6, 0)$, and
the y-intercepts are $(0, -4)$ and $(0, 4)$. The domain is $\{x \mid -6 \le x \le 6\}$, and the
range is $\{y \mid -4 \le y \le 4\}$.

b.

The center of the hyperbola is $(0, 0)$. The x-intercepts are $(-5, 0)$ and $(5, 0)$, and
there are no y-intercepts. The domain is $\{x \mid x \ge 5 \text{ or } x \le -5\}$, and the range is
all real numbers.

 Quick Check ❹ Identify the center and intercepts of the conic section. Then find the domain and
range. Each interval represents one unit. **center: (0, 0); no x-intercepts,
y-intercepts: -4, 4; domain: all
real numbers, range: all y such that
$y \ge 4$ or $y \le -4$**

You will study each conic section in detail later in this chapter. Even before you
learn the details of the equations of conic sections, you can match the equations
with their graphs.

---

❷ Graph the equation
$9x^2 + 4y^2 = 36$. Describe the
graph and the lines of symmetry.
Then find the domain and range.

 The graph is an
ellipse with center
$(0, 0)$; there are
two lines of
symmetry, the
x-axis and
the y-axis. The domain is
$\{x \mid -2 \le x \le 2\}$. The range is
$\{y \mid -3 \le y \le 3\}$.

❸ Graph the equation
$x^2 - y^2 = 4$. Describe the graph
and its lines of symmetry. Then
find the domain and range.

 The graph is a
hyperbola that
consists of two
branches. Its
center is at the
origin. The lines
of symmetry are the x-axis and
the y-axis. The domain is
$\{x \mid x \le -2 \text{ or } x \ge 2\}$. The range is
all real numbers.

Guided Instruction

Additional Examples

❹ Identify the center and
intercepts of the conic section.

center: $(0, 0)$; x-int: $(\pm 5, 0)$,
y-int: $(0, \pm 4)$

❺ Determine whether each
equation models a circle, an
ellipse, or a hyperbola.

a. $25x^2 + 4y^2 = 100$ ellipse

b. $x^2 + y^2 = 4$ circle

c. $2x^2 - y^2 = 16$ hyperbola

Resources
• Daily Notetaking Guide
   10-1

Closure

Ask students to give an example
of an equation that models a
circle, an ellipse, and a hyperbola.
Then, ask students to explain how
they can identify each conic

section from its equation.
Answers may vary. Sample:
$x^2 + y^2 = 1, 4x^2 + y^2 = 4,$
$x^2 - y^2 = 1.$ **For conic sections
centered at the origin students
should indicate that they can
be written in the form**

$ax^2 + by^2 = c$, where $a = b > 0$
and $c > 0$ for a circle, $a \ne b$ and
$a, b, c > 0$ for an ellipse, and a
and b are of opposite signs with
$c > 0$ for a hyperbola.

549

Assignment Guide

⓵ A B 1-16, 29-32, 35-38

⓶ A B 17-28, 33, 34, 39-46

C Challenge   47-49

Test Prep   50-55
Mixed Review   56-73

Homework Quick Check
To check students' understanding
of key skills and concepts, go over
Exercises 15, 21, 26, 33, 34, 37.

Error Prevention!

Exercises 1, 4 These equations
describe hyperbolas with vertices
on the y-axis, not the x-axis.

Diversity

Exercise 47 Students vary in
their ability to visualize in three
dimensions. Encourage students
to work in pairs to discuss the
figures they visualize. Students
can increase their visualization
skills with practice.

---

5 EXAMPLE Real-World Connection

Design Moiré patterns are formed when two patterns, such as arrays of dots or
lines, overlap to produce a third, unintended pattern. Moiré patterns cause
problems for printers and video technicians. Describe each unintended pattern.
Match it with one of these possible equations: $x^2 - y^2 = 1$, $x^2 + y^2 = 16$, or
$9x^2 + 25y^2 = 225$.

Vocabulary Tip

Moiré is a French word
meaning "watered" or
"wavy."

a.   b.   c.

  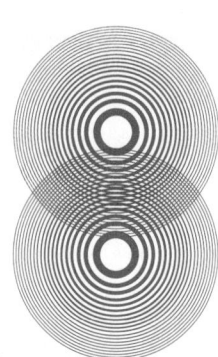

a. Ellipse: The equation $9x^2 + 25y^2 = 225$ represents a conic section with two
sets of intercepts, $(\pm5, 0)$ and $(0, \pm3)$. Since the intercepts are not equidistant
from the center, the equation models an ellipse.

b. Hyperbola: The equation $x^2 - y^2 = 1$ represents a conic section with one set
of intercepts, $(\pm1, 0)$, so the equation must model a hyperbola.

c. Circle: The equation $x^2 + y^2 = 16$ represents a conic section with two sets of
intercepts, $(\pm4, 0)$ and $(0, \pm4)$. Since each intercept is 4 units from the center,
the equation models a circle.

✓ **Quick Check** **5 a.** Critical Thinking What similarities do you notice among the three equations
in Example 5? **a–b. See back of book.**
b. What differences do you notice?

EXERCISES

For more exercises, see *Extra Skill and Word Problem Practice.*

Practice and Problem Solving

A Practice by Example

Examples 1, 2, and 3
(pages 547 and 548)

 for Help

**Graph each equation. Identify the conic section and describe the graph and its
lines of symmetry. Then find the domain and range.** **1–16. See back of book.**

1. $3y^2 - x^2 = 25$ **2.** $2x^2 + y^2 = 36$

3. $x^2 + y^2 = 16$ **4.** $3y^2 - x^2 = 9$

5. $4x^2 + 25y^2 = 100$ **6.** $x^2 + y^2 = 49$

7. $x^2 - y^2 + 1 = 0$ **8.** $x^2 - 2y^2 = 4$

9. $6x^2 + 6y^2 = 600$ **10.** $x^2 + y^2 - 4 = 0$

11. $6x^2 + 24y^2 - 96 = 0$ **12.** $4x^2 + 4y^2 - 20 = 0$

13. $x^2 + 9y^2 = 1$ **14.** $4x^2 - 36y^2 = 144$

15. $4y^2 - 36x^2 = 1$ **16.** $36x^2 + 4y^2 = 144$

550 Chapter 10 Quadratic Relations and Conic Sections

---

17. center (0, 0),
x-intercepts at ±3,
y-intercepts at ±2;
domain: −3 ≤ x ≤ 3,
range: −2 ≤ y ≤ 2

18. center (0, 0), no
x-intercepts,
y-intercepts at ±2;
domain: all real
numbers, range:
y ≤ −2 or y ≥ 2

19. center (0, 0),
x-intercepts at ±3, no
y-intercepts; domain:
x ≤ −3 or x ≥ 3, range:
all real numbers

Example 4
(page 549)

17–22. See margin
pp. 550–551.

Identify the center and intercepts of each conic section. Give the domain and range of each graph. On graphing calculator screens, each interval represents one unit.

17.

18.

19.

20.

21.

22.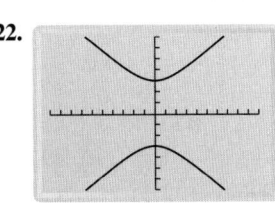

Example 5
(page 550)

Match each equation with a graph in Exercises 17–22.

23. $x^2 - y^2 = 9$ **19**

24. $4x^2 + 9y^2 = 36$ **17**

25. $y^2 - x^2 = 4$ **18**

26. $x^2 + 4y^2 = 64$ **20**

27. $25x^2 + 9y^2 = 225$ **21**

28. $y^2 - x^2 = 9$ **22**

B Apply Your Skills

Graph each equation. Describe the graph and its lines of symmetry. Then find the domain and range. 29–32. See margin.

29. $9x^2 - y^2 = 144$

30. $11x^2 + 11y^2 = 44$

31. $-8x^2 + 32y^2 - 128 = 0$

32. $25x^2 + 16y^2 - 320 = 0$

33. **Light** The light emitted from a lamp with a shade forms a shadow on the wall. **GPS** Explain how you could turn the lamp in relation to the wall so that the shadow cast by the shade forms each conic section. **a–d. See back of book.**
    a. hyperbola   b. parabola   c. ellipse   d. circle

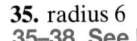

34. a. **Writing** Describe the relationship between the center of a circle and the axes of symmetry of the circle. **a–b. See back of book.**
    b. **Make a Conjecture** Where is the center of an ellipse or a hyperbola located in relation to the axes of symmetry? Verify your conjectures with examples.

Graph each circle so that the center is at the origin. Then write the equation.

35. radius 6   36. radius $\frac{1}{2}$ 37. diameter 8   38. diameter 2.5
35–38. See back of book.

GO Online
Homework Video Tutor
Visit: PHSchool.com
Web Code: age-1001

39. **Multiple Choice** The sharpened part of the pencil at the right meets each painted surface in a curved path. What is the best name for such a path? **D**
    Ⓐ circle   Ⓑ ellipse   Ⓒ parabola   Ⓓ hyperbola

20. center (0, 0),
    x-intercepts at ±8,
    y-intercepts at ±4;
    domain: −8 ≤ x ≤ 8,
    range: −4 ≤ y ≤ 4

21. center (0, 0),
    x-intercepts at ±3,
    y-intercepts at ±5;
    domain: −3 ≤ x ≤ 3,
    range: −5 ≤ y ≤ 5

22. center (0, 0), no
    x-intercepts,
    y-intercepts at ±3;
    domain: all real
    numbers; range:
    y ≤ −3 or y ≥ 3

Exercise 39 Help students understand that each side of the pencil is a portion of a plane. The sharpened part of the pencil is a portion of a cone. If the pencil were a double cone, the plane would intersect both parts, forming a hyperbola.

29.

Hyperbola: center (0, 0), x-intercepts ±4, the lines of symmetry are the x- and y-axes; domain: $x \le -4$ or $x \ge 4$, range: all real numbers.

30.

Circle: center (0, 0), radius 2, x- and y-intercepts at ±2, there are infinitely many lines of symmetry; domain: $-2 \le x \le 2$, range: $-2 \le y \le 2$.

31.

Hyperbola: center (0, 0), y-intercepts at ±2, the lines of symmetry are the x- and y-axes; domain: all real numbers, range: $y \le -2$ or $y \ge 2$.

32.

Ellipse: center (0, 0), x-intercepts at $\pm\frac{8\sqrt{5}}{5}$, y-intercepts at $\pm 2\sqrt{5}$, the lines of symmetry are the x- and y-axes; domain: $-\frac{8\sqrt{5}}{5} \le x \le \frac{8\sqrt{5}}{5}$, range: $-2\sqrt{5} \le y \le 2\sqrt{5}$.

551

4. Assess & Reteach

Lesson Quiz

Graph each equation.
Identify the conic section and
determine its intercepts. Then,
give the domain and range of
each graph.

1. $2y^2 - x^2 = 8$

hyperbola, $(0, \pm 2)$;
domain: all real numbers,
range: $\{y \mid -\infty < y \le -2$ or
$2 \le y < \infty\}$

2. $16x^2 + 25y^2 = 400$

ellipse, x-int: $(\pm 5, 0)$,
y-int: $(0, \pm 4)$;
domain: $\{x \mid -5 \le x \le 5\}$,
range: $\{y \mid -4 \le y \le 4\}$

3. $2x^2 + 2y^2 = 50$

circle, x-int: $(\pm 5, 0)$,
y-int: $(0, \pm 5)$;
domain: $\{x \mid -5 \le x \le 5\}$,
range: $\{y \mid -5 \le y \le 5\}$

Alternative Assessment

Have students make a poster
showing equations and graphs of
a circle, ellipse, and hyperbola.
Then have students write a short
essay comparing and contrasting
the conic sections and their
equations.

Mental Math Each given point is on the graph of the given equation. Use symmetry to find at least one more point on the graph.

40. $(2, -4), y^2 = 8x$ **(2, 4)**

41. $(-\sqrt{2}, 1), x^2 + y^2 = 3$ **$(\sqrt{2}, 1)$**

42. $(2, 2\sqrt{2}), x^2 + 4y^2 = 36$ **$(-2, 2\sqrt{2})$**

43. $(-2, 0), 9x^2 + 9y^2 - 36 = 0$ **(2, 0)**

44. $(-3, -\sqrt{51}), 6y^2 - 9x^2 - 225 = 0$ **$(-3, \sqrt{51})$**

45. $(0, \sqrt{7}), x^2 + 2y^2 = 14$ **$(0, -\sqrt{7})$**

46. Open-Ended Describe any other figures you can imagine that can be formed by the intersection of a plane and other shapes. **Check students' work.**

© Challenge

47a.

c. No intercepts, but
$y = x$ and $y = -x$
are lines of symmetry.

47. a. Graph the equation $xy = 16$. Use both positive and negative values for x.
b. Which conic section does the equation appear to model? **hyperbola**
c. Identify any intercepts and lines of symmetry.
d. Does your graph represent a function? If so, rewrite the equation using function notation. **yes; $f(x) = \frac{16}{x}$**

48. An xy term has an interesting effect on the graph of a conic section. Sketch the graph of each conic section below using your graphing calculator. (*Hint:* To solve for y, you will need to complete a square.)
a. $4x^2 + 2xy + y^2 = 9$ **a–b. See margin.**
b. $4x^2 + 2xy - y^2 = 9$

49. Sound An airplane flying faster than the speed of sound creates a cone-shaped pressure disturbance in the air. This is heard by people on the ground as a sonic boom. What is the shape of the path on the ground? **one branch of a hyperbola**

Test Prep

Multiple Choice

50. The graph of which equation of a circle contains all the points in the table below? **D**

x	−3	0	3
y	0	±3	0

A. $x^2 + y^2 - 4 = 0$ **B.** $x^2 + y^2 = 25$
C. $x^2 + y^2 = 36$ **D.** $6x^2 + 6y^2 = 54$

51. The graph of which ellipse contains all the points in the table below? **F**

x	−4	−2	0	2	4
y	0	±√3	±2	±√3	0

F. $x^2 + 4y^2 = 16$ **G.** $4x^2 + 16y^2 = 144$
H. $4x^2 + 25y^2 = 64$ **J.** $9x^2 + y^2 = 81$

52. Which point is NOT on the graph of $4x^2 - y^2 = 4$? **D**
A. $(-2, -2\sqrt{3})$ **B.** $(-1, 0)$ **C.** $(1, 0)$ **D.** $(2, 2)$

53. Which equation does NOT represent a line of symmetry for the circle with equation $x^2 + y^2 = 100$? **J**
F. $x = 0$ **G.** $y = \frac{1}{2}x$ **H.** $y = x$ **J.** $y = x + 1$

552 Chapter 10 Quadratic Relations and Conic Sections

48a.

b.

54. Which equation represents a line of symmetry for the ellipse with equation $x^2 + 9y^2 = 9$? **B**

    A. $y = -x$ **B.** $y = 0$ **C.** $y = x$ **D.** $xy = 1$

Short Response

55. The graph of the equation $x^2 + y^2 = 121$ is a circle. Describe the graph and its lines of symmetry. Find the domain and the range. **See margin.**

Mixed Review

Lesson 9-7

A standard number cube is tossed. Find each probability.

56. P(5 or greater than 3) $\frac{1}{2}$ **57.** P(even or 6) $\frac{1}{2}$

58. P(even or 7) $\frac{1}{2}$ **59.** P(prime or 2) $\frac{1}{2}$

Lesson 9-1

Suppose z varies jointly with x and y. Write a function that models each relationship. Find the value of z when $x = -2$ and $y = 3$. 60–63. **See margin.**

60. $z = -5$ when $x = -1$ and $y = -1$ **61.** $z = 72$ when $x = 3$ and $y = -6$

62. $z = 32$ when $x = 0.1$ and $y = 8$ **63.** $z = 5$ when $x = -4$ and $y = 2.5$

Lesson 8-1

Write an exponential equation $y = ab^x$ whose graph passes through the given points. 64–73. **See margin.**

64. $(-1, 2)$ and $(3, 32)$ **65.** $\left(0, \frac{1}{2}\right)$ and $(2, 8)$ **66.** $(1, 6)$ and $(2, 12)$

67. $\left(0, \frac{1}{3}\right)$ and $(2, 3)$ **68.** $\left(-1, \frac{2}{3}\right)$ and $(2, 18)$ **69.** $\left(-1, \frac{1}{8}\right)$ and $(4, 4)$

Lesson 6-8

Expand each binomial.

70. $(x - y)^3$ **71.** $(p + q)^6$ **72.** $(x - 2)^4$ **73.** $(3 - x)^5$

⋯⋯⋯⋯ A Point in Time

1500   1600   1700   1800   1900   2000

Titanic was the largest passenger liner that had yet been built. On its maiden voyage in 1912, it struck an iceberg and sank. More than 1500 people died.

In 1985 a French and American team searched for *Titanic*. Research vessels combed the area with sonar. Transmitters aboard each ship sent out powerful spherical sound waves. Each wave reflected off any object in a half-mile-wide strip of ocean floor and returned to a receiver. The receiver then converted the echo to a picture of the object and calculated its depth. Two months after the search began, *Titanic* was discovered lying in two sections at a depth of some 13,000 feet.

Drawing not to scale

Go Online   **For:** Information about *Titanic*
PHSchool.com   **Web Code:** age-2032

Lesson 10-1 Exploring Conic Sections   **553**

Test Prep

📁 **Resources**

For additional practice with a variety of test item formats:
• Standardized Test Prep, p. 595
• Test-Taking Strategies, p. 590
• Test-Taking Strategies with Transparencies

55. **[2]** It is a circle with center at (0, 0) and a radius of 11. The x- and y-intercepts are at ±11. The lines of symmetry are all lines through the origin. The domain is $-11 \le x \le 11$ and the range is $-11 \le y \le 11$.

    [1] includes either description OR domain and range, but not both

60. $z = -5xy$; 30

61. $z = -4xy$; 24

62. $z = 40xy$; −240

63. $y = -\frac{1}{2}xy$; 3

64. $y = 4(2)^x$

65. $y = \frac{1}{2}(4)^x$

66. $y = 3(2)^x$

67. $y = \frac{1}{3}(3)^x$

68. $y = 2(3)^x$

69. $y = \frac{1}{4}(2)^x$

70. $x^3 - 3x^2y + 3xy^2 - y^3$

71. $p^6 + 6p^5q + 15p^4q^2 + 20p^3q^3 + 15p^2q^4 + 6pq^5 + q^6$

72. $x^4 - 8x^3 + 24x^2 - 32x + 16$

73. $243 - 405x + 270x^2 - 90x^3 + 15x^4 - x^5$

Students learn how to use their graphing calculators to graph conic sections. In additon to being able to check their work throughout the chapter, students will find these techniques helpful in Lesson 10-6 when learning how to translate conic sections.

Guided Instruction

Technology Tip
Remind students that they can press ZOOM 5 to have their calculators graph the conic section in the default square viewing window. Then, if the figure is too small, they can change the window.

Technology Tip
Exercise 11 Remind students that $y - 3 = x$ or $y - 3 = -x$. Then, have students solve each equation for y. Help students realize that each equation must be graphed separately. Remind them that the domain is $\{x | x \geq 0\}$. To graph only for $x \geq 0$, students must surround the entire equation with parentheses. After entering the equation, enter the domain in parentheses. (To get $\geq$, press 2nd [TEST] 4).

Resources

Students may use any graphing calculator to graph conic sections.

7a.

b. *x*-intercepts at ±4.5, *y*-intercepts at ±4.5

554

You can use your graphing calculator to graph relations that are not functions.

● ACTIVITY

Graph the ellipse $\frac{x^2}{16} + \frac{y^2}{9} = 1$.

Step 1 Solve the equation for y.

$$\frac{x^2}{16} + \frac{y^2}{9} = 1$$

$$\frac{y^2}{9} = 1 - \frac{x^2}{16}$$

$$y^2 = 9\left(1 - \frac{x^2}{16}\right)$$

$$y = \pm 3\sqrt{1 - \frac{x^2}{16}}$$

Step 2 Enter the equations as Y_1 and Y_2.

Step 3 Select a square window.

Step 4 Graph.

EXERCISES

Graph each conic section. 1–6. See back of book.

1. $x^2 + y^2 = 25$ **2.** $4x^2 + y^2 = 16$ **3.** $9x^2 - 16y^2 = 144$

4. $x^2 - y^2 = 3$ **5.** $\frac{x^2}{4} - \frac{y^2}{9} = 1$ **6.** $x^2 + \frac{y^2}{4} = 16$

7. a. Graph the functions $y = \sqrt{\frac{81}{4} - x^2}$ and $y = -\sqrt{\frac{81}{4} - x^2}$. a–b. See margin.

  b. Estimate the x-intercepts and find the y-intercepts.

  c. Adjust the window to $-9.3 \leq x \leq 9.5$. Verify the x-intercepts. Check students' work.

  d. What conic section does the graph represent? circle with center (0, 0) and radius 4.5

Graph each conic section. Find the x- and y-intercepts. 8–10. See margin for graphs.

8. $4x^2 + y^2 = 25$ ±2.5, ±5 **9.** $x^2 + y^2 = 30$ ±$\sqrt{30}$, ±$\sqrt{30}$ **10.** $9x^2 - 4y^2 = 72$ ±2$\sqrt{2}$, none

 11. Writing Explain how to use a graphing calculator to graph the relation $x = |y - 3|$. **Answers may vary. Sample: Graph $y = (3 - x)$ where $x \geq 0$ and $y = (3 + x)$ where $x \geq 0$, on the same screen.**

12. Critical Thinking Which conic sections can you graph using only one function? Explain. **Parabolas with a vertical axis of symmetry; other conic sections have the x-axis as a line of symmetry, so they fail the vertical line test.**

8.

9.

10.

Parabolas

What You'll Learn

- To write the equation of a parabola
- To graph parabolas

. . . And Why

To model a solar collector, as in Example 3

✓ **Check Skills You'll Need**   **GO** for Help   Skills Handbook pages 872 and 884

Solve for c.

1. $\frac{1}{8} = \frac{1}{c}$ 8
2. $\frac{1}{8} = \frac{1}{2c}$ 4
3. $\frac{1}{12} = \frac{1}{4c}$ 3
4. $2 = \frac{1}{4c}$ $\frac{1}{8}$

Find the distance between the given points.

5. $(2, 3)$ and $(4, 1)$ $2\sqrt{2}$
6. $(4, 6)$ and $(3, -2)$ $\sqrt{65}$
7. $(-1, 5)$ and $(2, -3)$ $\sqrt{73}$

◀)) **New Vocabulary** • focus of a parabola • directrix

Objectives
1 To write the equation of a parabola
2 To graph parabolas

Examples
1 Using the Definition of a Parabola
2 Writing the Equation of a Parabola
3 Real-World Connection
4 Identifying Focus and Directrix
5 Graphing the Equation of a Parabola

1 Writing the Equation of a Parabola

In Chapter 5 you learned that a parabola is the graph of a quadratic equation. By definition, a parabola is the set of all points in a plane that are the same distance from a fixed line and a fixed point not on the line. The fixed point is the **focus of a parabola.** The fixed line is the **directrix.** The line through the focus and perpendicular to the directrix is the axis of symmetry.

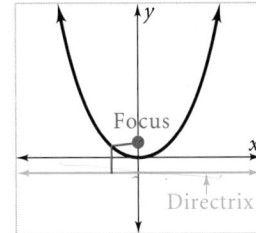

Math Background

Parabolas play an important role in many applications. In this lesson, students learn how to model solar collectors. In physics, students learn that light beams, which approach a parabolic surface parallel to the axis of symmetry are reflected to the focus of the parabola. These facts are used in the construction of objects such as solar collectors and flashlights.

More Math Background: p. 544C

Lesson Planning and Resources

See p. 544E for a list of the resources that support this lesson.

PowerPoint

Bell Ringer Practice

✓ **Check Skills You'll Need**
For intervention, direct students to:

Ratios and Proportions
Skills Handbook: p. 872

Distance Formula
Skills Handbook: p. 884

1 EXAMPLE   Using the Definition of a Parabola

Write an equation for a graph that is the set of all points in the plane that are equidistant from the point $F(0, 3)$ and the line $y = -3$.

You need to find all points $P(x, y)$ such that FP and the distance from P to the given line are equal.

$$FP = PQ$$
$$\sqrt{(x - 0)^2 + (y - 3)^2} =$$
$$\sqrt{(x - x)^2 + (y - (-3))^2}$$
$$x^2 + (y - 3)^2 = 0^2 + (y + 3)^2$$
$$x^2 + y^2 - 6y + 9 = y^2 + 6y + 9$$
$$x^2 = 12y$$
$$y = \frac{1}{12}x^2$$

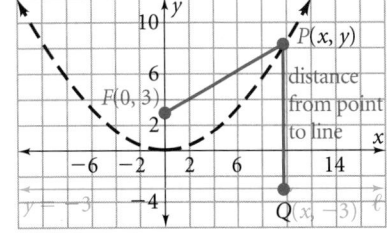

Problem Solving Hint

The distance between $P_1(x_1, y_1)$ and $P_2(x_2, y_2)$ is $\sqrt{(x_2 - x_1)^2 + (y_2 - y_1)^2}$.

An equation of the set of all points equidistant from $F(0, 3)$ and $y = -3$ is $y = \frac{1}{12}x^2$.

✓ **Quick Check** 1 Write an equation for a graph that is the set of all points in the plane that are equidistant from the point $F(2, 0)$ and the line $x = -2$. $x = \frac{1}{8}y^2$

Differentiated Instruction Solutions for All Learners

Special Needs L1
Make a sketch for each of the four parabolas on p. 556. Hang them in four corners of the classroom. Have students move to the parabola(s) for which a stated fact applies. Examples of facts: opens right, $a > 0$, directrix is parallel to the y-axis, focus on the x-axis, equation of form $y = ax^2$. **learning style: tactile**

Below Level L2
Review the distance formula, and discuss how to find the distance from a line to a point not on it. Also review completing the square.

learning style: verbal

1 EXAMPLE **Auditory Learners**

Encourage students to say, *"A point is on a parabola if its distances from the focus and directrix are equal."* Have students use this sentence along with the graph in Example 1 to write $FP = PQ$.

3 EXAMPLE **Visual Learners**

Bend a sheet of paper into a trough to model the solar collectors in this example. Clarify that you can only see the parabola when you look at a cross section. Point out that this parabolic shape does not extend upward indefinitely.

▣ Additional Examples

1 Write an equation for a graph that is the set of all points in the plane that are equidistant from the point $F(0, 1)$ and the line $y = -1$. $y = \frac{1}{4}x^2$

2 Write an equation of a parabola with a vertex at the origin and a focus at $(0, -7)$. $y = -\frac{1}{28}x^2$

GO for Help

To review graphing parabolas, go to Lesson 5-2.

Test-Taking Tip

When you identify or graph a relation, be sure you correctly match the equation variables and the graph variables.

In Chapter 5 you learned about the special relationship between the value of a and the graph of a quadratic function in the form $y = ax^2$. Now you will learn about the relationship between the value of a and the graph of a quadratic relation in the form $y = ax^2$ or $x = ay^2$.

If c is the distance from the vertex to the focus of a parabola, then $|a| = \frac{1}{4c}$.

Consider any parabola with equation $y = ax^2$ and vertex at the origin.

If $a > 0$, then
- the parabola opens upward
- the focus is at $(0, c)$
- the directrix is $y = -c$

If $a < 0$, then
- the parabola opens downward
- the focus is at $(0, -c)$
- the directrix is at $y = c$

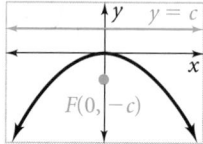

Consider any parabola with equation $x = ay^2$.

If $a > 0$, then
- the parabola opens to the right
- the focus is at $(c, 0)$
- the directrix is at $x = -c$

If $a < 0$, then
- the parabola opens to the left
- the focus is at $(-c, 0)$
- the directrix is at $x = c$

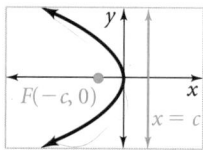

You can use the information above to write an equation of a parabola.

2 EXAMPLE **Writing the Equation of a Parabola**

Multiple Choice Which equation represents a parabola with a vertex at the origin and a focus at $(-5, 0)$?

Ⓐ $y = \frac{1}{20}x^2$ Ⓑ $x = \frac{1}{20}y^2$ Ⓒ $y = -\frac{1}{20}x^2$ Ⓓ $x = -\frac{1}{20}y^2$

Step 1 Determine the orientation of the parabola. Make a sketch. Since the focus is located to the left of the vertex, the parabola must open to the left. Use $x = ay^2$.

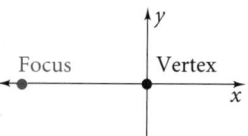

Step 2 Find a.

$$|a| = \frac{1}{4c}$$
$$= \frac{1}{4(5)} \quad \text{Since the focus is a distance of 5 units from the vertex, } c = 5.$$
$$= \frac{1}{20}$$

Since the parabola opens to the left, a is negative. So $a = -\frac{1}{20}$.

An equation for the parabola is $x = -\frac{1}{20}y^2$. The correct choice is D.

✓ Quick Check **2** Write an equation of a parabola with a vertex at the origin and a focus at $\left(\frac{1}{2}, 0\right)$.

$$x = \frac{1}{2}y^2$$

Differentiated Instruction   Solutions for All Learners

Advanced Learners   L4
Have students explore the definitions of an ellipse and a hyperbola in terms of foci and directrices, and share their results with the class.

learning style: verbal

English Language Learners   ELL
To help students learn the terms *vertex*, *focus*, and *directrix*, have them draw a parabola with each term identified in their sketch. Stress that the vertex and focus are points but the directrix is a line and thus has a linear equation.

learning style: verbal

You can find the equation of a parabola that models a real-world situation.

3 EXAMPLE Real-World 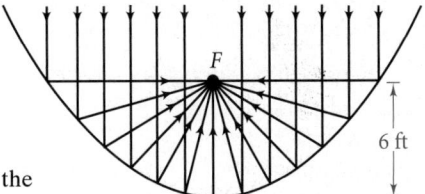 Connection

Solar Energy In some solar collectors, a mirror with a parabolic cross section is used to concentrate sunlight on a pipe, which is located at the focus of the mirror.

Real-World Connection

Parabolic solar mirrors focus the sun's energy to produce steam that drives electric generators.

a. Suppose the pipe is located 6 ft from the vertex of the mirror. Write an equation of the parabola that models the cross section of the mirror.

6 ft

The distance from the vertex to the focus is 6 ft, so $c = 6$. Find the value of a.

$$a = \frac{1}{4c}$$

$$= \frac{1}{4(6)}$$

$$= \frac{1}{24} \qquad \text{Since the parabola opens upward, } a \text{ is positive.}$$

The equation of the parabola is $y = \frac{1}{24}x^2$.

b. Suppose you stretch the equation of the mirror (and the mirror itself upward) by a factor of 2 to become $y = \frac{1}{12}x^2$. How should you move the pipe so that it remains at the focus?

In $a = \frac{1}{4c}$, if a doubles, the value of c must halve. The distance to the focus would change from 6 ft to 3 ft.

✓ **Quick Check** ③ Suppose the pipe is located 8.25 ft from the vertex of the mirror. Write an equation of the parabola to model the cross section of the mirror. $y = \frac{1}{33}x^2$

---

2 Graphing Parabolas

You can use the value of a to identify the focus and directrix of a parabola.

4 EXAMPLE Identifying Focus and Directrix

Identify the focus and the directrix of the graph of the equation $y = -\frac{1}{16}x^2$.

The parabola is of the form $y = ax^2$, so the vertex is at the origin and the parabola has a vertical axis of symmetry. Since $a < 0$, the parabola opens downward.

Test-Taking Tip

Forgetting a negative sign is one of the most common mistakes on tests.

$$\left| a \right| = \frac{1}{4c}$$

$$\left| -\frac{1}{16} \right| = \frac{1}{4c} \qquad \text{Substitute } -\frac{1}{16} \text{ for } a.$$

$$4c = 16 \qquad \text{Solve for } c.$$

$$c = 4$$

The focus is at $(0, -4)$. The equation of the directrix is $y = 4$.

✓ **Quick Check** ④ Identify the focus and the directrix of the graph of the equation $y = \frac{1}{12}x^2$.
$(0, 3), y = -3$

Lesson 10-2 Parabolas **557**

PowerPoint

Additional Example

③ A parabolic mirror has a focus that is located 4 in. above the vertex of the mirror. Write an equation of the parabola that models the cross section of the mirror. $y = \frac{1}{16}x^2$

Guided Instruction

PowerPoint

Additional Examples

④ Identify the focus and directrix of the graph of the equation $x = -\frac{1}{8}y^2$. $(-2, 0), x = 2$

⑤ Identify the vertex, the focus, and the directrix of the graph of the equation $x^2 + 4x + 8y - 4 = 0$. Then graph the parabola. $(-2, 1)$, $(-2, -1), y = 3;$

Resources
• Daily Notetaking Guide 10-2 **L3**

Closure

Ask students to explain how to write the equation of a parabola and how to graph a parabola. An equation of a parabola is determined by the set of all points that are equidistant from a fixed line called a directrix and a fixed point not on the line called a focus. The graph can be determined from the vertex and two other points.

557

3. Practice

Assignment Guide

1 A B 1-15, 36-41, 43-45, 52-57

2 A B 16-35, 42, 46-51

C Challenge 58-61

Test Prep 62-67
Mixed Review 68-77

Exercises 1–6 Encourage students to begin by determining whether the graphs open upward, downward, right, or left. Have them verify their findings with their equations.

Error Prevention!

Exercise 57 Encourage students to make a quick sketch of the parabola using the vertex and focus. Their sketch shows the parabola opens left and is translated up 3 units.

Differentiated Instruction Resources

GPS Guided Problem Solving	L3
Enrichment	L4
Reteaching	L2
Practice	L3

1. $y = \frac{1}{8}x^2$

2. $y = -\frac{1}{4}x^2$

3. $x = -\frac{1}{12}y^2$

558

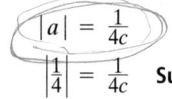

Online
active math

For: Parabolas Activity
Use: Interactive Textbook, 10-2

GO for Help

To review completing the square, go to page 281 and Lesson 5-7.

5. $(-3, -1)$, $(-3, -1.75)$,
   $y = -\frac{1}{4}$

4. $y = -\frac{1}{32}x^2$

5. $y = \frac{1}{8}x^2 + 2$

6. $x = \frac{1}{2}y^2$

You can use the focus and directrix to graph the equation of a parabola.

5 EXAMPLE Graphing the Equation of a Parabola

Identify the vertex, the focus, and the directrix of the graph of the equation $y^2 - 4x - 4y + 16 = 0$. Then graph the parabola.

$$y^2 - 4x - 4y + 16 = 0$$

$4x = y^2 - 4y + 16$	Solve for x, since x is in only one term.
$4x = (y^2 - 4y + 4) + 16 - 4$	Complete the square in y.
$x = \frac{1}{4}(y^2 - 4y + 4) + 4 - 1$	Divide both sides of the equation by 4.
$x = \frac{1}{4}(y - 2)^2 + 3$	vertex form

The parabola is of the form $x = a(y - k)^2 + h$. This is a translation of $x = ay^2$. All of the graph's features—axis of symmetry, vertex, focus, and directrix—translate with the parabola. The parabola has a horizontal axis of symmetry. $a > 0$, so the parabola opens to the right. Its vertex is at $(h, k) = (3, 2)$.

$\|a\| = \frac{1}{4c}$	
$\left\|\frac{1}{4}\right\| = \frac{1}{4c}$	Substitute $\frac{1}{4}$ for a.
$4c = 4$	Solve for c.
$c = 1$	

The focus is at $(4, 2)$. The directrix is $x = 2$.

Locate one or more points on the parabola. Select a value for y, such as 4. The point on the parabola with a y-value of 4 is $(4, 4)$. Use the symmetric nature of a parabola to find the corresponding point, $(4, 0)$.

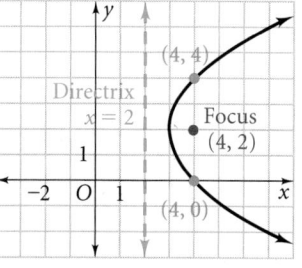

✓ Quick Check **5** Identify the vertex, the focus, and the directrix of the graph of $x^2 + 6x + 3y + 12 = 0$. Then graph the equation. **See left.**

EXERCISES

For more exercises, see *Extra Skill and Word Problem Practice*.

Practice and Problem Solving

A Practice by Example

Example 1
(page 555)

GO for Help

Example 2
(page 556)

Example 3
(page 557)

Write an equation for a graph that is the set of all points in the plane that are equidistant from the given point and the given line. **1–9. See margin.**

1. $F(0, 2), y = -2$ **2.** $F(0, -1), y = 1$ **3.** $F(-3, 0), x = 3$

4. $F(0, -8), y = 8$ **5.** $F(0, 4), y = 0$ **6.** $F\left(\frac{1}{2}, 0\right), x = -\frac{1}{2}$

Write an equation of a parabola with a vertex at the origin and the given focus.

7. focus at $(6, 0)$ **8.** focus at $(0, -4)$ **9.** focus at $(0, 7)$

10. focus at $(-1, 0)$ **11.** focus at $(2, 0)$ **12.** focus at $(0, -5)$
   $x = -\frac{1}{4}y^2$ $x = \frac{1}{8}y^2$ $y = -\frac{1}{20}x^2$

Write an equation of a parabola opening upward with a vertex at the origin.

13. focus 1.5 units from vertex **14.** focus $\frac{1}{8}$ of a unit from vertex
   $y = \frac{1}{6}x^2$ $y = 2x^2$

7. $x = \frac{1}{24}y^2$

8. $y = -\frac{1}{16}x^2$

9. $y = \frac{1}{28}x^2$

15. Answers may vary.
Sample: $y = x^2$

The light produced by the bulb will reflect off the parabolic mirror in parallel rays.

15. Optics A cross section of a flashlight reflector is a parabola. The bulb is located at the focus. Suppose the bulb is located $\frac{1}{4}$ in. from the vertex of the reflector. Model a cross section of the reflector by writing an equation of a parabola that opens upward and has its vertex at the origin. What is an advantage of this parabolic design?   **See margin p. 558.**

Example 4
(page 557)

16–23.
Identify the focus and the directrix of the graph of each equation. See margin.

16. $y = \frac{1}{4}x^2$ **17.** $y = x^2$ **18.** $y = -\frac{1}{8}x^2$ **19.** $x = \frac{1}{2}y^2$

20. $y = \frac{1}{2}x^2$ **21.** $x = \frac{1}{36}y^2$ **22.** $x = -\frac{1}{18}y^2$ **23.** $y = -2x^2$

Example 5
(page 558)

Identify the vertex, the focus, and the directrix of each graph. Then sketch the graph.
24–35. See back of book.

24. $x = \frac{1}{24}y^2$ **25.** $y = -\frac{1}{4}x^2$ **26.** $x = \frac{1}{12}y^2$

27. $y^2 - 25x = 0$ **28.** $x^2 = 4y$ **29.** $x^2 = -4y$

30. $(x - 2)^2 = 4y$ **31.** $-8x = y^2$ **32.** $(x + 2)^2 = y - 4$

33. $y^2 - 6x = 18$ **34.** $x^2 + 24y - 8x = -16$ **35.** $y^2 - 12x + 2y = -37$

36. $x = \frac{1}{12}y^2$

37. $y = \frac{1}{400}x^2$

38. $y = -\frac{1}{20}x^2$

B **Apply Your Skills**   **Write an equation of a parabola with a vertex at the origin.**   36–38. See left.

36. directrix $x = -3$ **37.** focus at $(0, 100)$ **38.** directrix $y = 5$

39. focus at $(-7, 0)$ **40.** directrix $x = 9$ **41.** directrix $y = 2.8$
$x = -\frac{1}{28}y^2$ $x = -\frac{1}{36}y^2$ $y = -\frac{5}{56}x^2$

42. Earth Science The equation $d = \frac{1}{10}s^2$ relates the depth d (in meters) of the ocean to the speed s (in meters per second) at which tsunamis travel. Graph the equation.   **See margin.**

Use the information in each graph to write the equation for the graph.

43.

$x = -\frac{1}{8}y^2$

44.

$y = \frac{1}{4}x^2$

45.
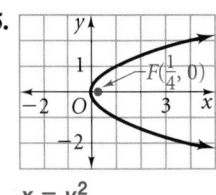
$x = y^2$

Graph each equation.

46. $y^2 - 8x = 0$ **47.** $y^2 - 8y + 8x = -16$ **48.** $2x^2 - y + 20x = -53$

49. $x^2 = 12y$ **50.** $y = 4(x - 3)^2 - 2$ **51.** $(y - 2)^2 = 4(x + 3)$
46–51. See back of book.

Write an equation of a parabola with a vertex at (1, 1).

52. directrix $y = -\frac{1}{2}$ **53.** directrix $x = \frac{3}{2}$ **54.** focus at $(1, 0)$
$y = \frac{1}{6}(x - 1)^2 + 1$ $x = -\frac{1}{2}(y - 1)^2 + 1$ $y = -\frac{1}{4}(x - 1)^2 + 1$

55. Open-Ended Write an equation for a parabola that opens to the left. Give the focus and directrix of the parabola.   **Check students' work.**

56. Writing Explain how to find the distance from the focus to the directrix of the parabola $x = 2y^2$.   **See margin.**

57. Multiple Choice The focus of a parabola is at $(-3, 3)$. The vertex is at $(0, 3)$. What is the equation of the parabola?   **B**

Ⓐ $y - 3 = \frac{1}{12}x^2$ Ⓑ $x = -\frac{1}{12}(y - 3)^2$

Ⓒ $y = -\frac{1}{12}(x - 3)^2$ Ⓓ $x = \frac{1}{12}(y + 3)^2$

16. $(0, 1)$, $y = -1$ **20.** $\left(0, \frac{1}{2}\right)$, $y = -\frac{1}{2}$ **42.**

17. $\left(0, \frac{1}{4}\right)$, $y = -\frac{1}{4}$ **21.** $(9, 0)$, $x = -9$

18. $(0, -2)$, $y = 2$ **22.** $\left(-\frac{9}{2}, 0\right)$, $x = \frac{9}{2}$

19. $\left(\frac{1}{2}, 0\right)$, $x = -\frac{1}{2}$ **23.** $\left(0, -\frac{1}{8}\right)$, $y = \frac{1}{8}$

Real-World **Connection**

Tsunamis are ocean waves that result from an undersea earthquake. As the waves approach shallow water, their height increases and their speed decreases.

GO Online
Homework Video Tutor
Visit: PHSchool.com
Web Code: age-1002

---

4. Assess & Reteach

PowerPoint
Lesson Quiz

1. Write an equation for a graph that is the set of all points in the plane equidistant from the point $F\left(-\frac{1}{8}, 0\right)$ and the line $x = \frac{1}{8}$. $x = -2y^2$

2. Write an equation of a parabola with a vertex at the origin and a focus at $(0, -3)$. $y = -\frac{1}{12}x^2$

3. Identify the vertex, the focus, and the directrix of the equation $y^2 - 4y - 16x + 36 = 0$. Then, graph the parabola.
$(2, 2)$, $(6, 2)$, $x = -2$;

Alternative Assessment

Have students find photos of parabolas in real life such as a suspension bridge, water in a fountain, or a gymnast doing a backbend. Find photos of four different parabolas (opens up, opens down, opens on the right, opens on the left). Write at least four facts for each parabola such as the parabola opens downward, $a > 0$, the directrix is parallel to the y-axis, the focus is on the x-axis, and the equation has the form $y = ax^2$.

56. Answers may vary. Sample: Write the equation in the form $x = \frac{1}{4\left(\frac{1}{8}\right)}y^2$. The distance from the focus to the directrix is $2\left(\frac{1}{8}\right)$, or $\frac{1}{4}$.

559

Test Prep

58. The directrix will have equation $y = k - c$. A point (x, y) is on the parabola if and only if the distance from (x, y) to the directrix is equal to the distance from (x, y) to the focus. So (x, y) is on the parabola if and only if
$$|y - (k - c)| = \sqrt{(x-h)^2 + (y-k-c)^2}$$
Square and simplify to get the equivalent equation $4cy - 4kc = (x-h)^2$, or $(x-h)^2 = 4c(y-k)$.

59.

66. [2] $|a| = \frac{1}{4c}$

$|a| = \frac{1}{4 \cdot 4}$

$|a| = \frac{1}{16}$

so since the focus is at $(0, 4)$ and the directrix is $y = -4$, a is positive. The equation is $y = \frac{1}{16}x^2$.

[1] answer correct, without work shown

67. [2] $|a| = \frac{1}{4c}$

$\left|\frac{1}{36}\right| = \frac{1}{4c}$

$36 = 4c$

$c = 9$

so the focus is at $(0, 9)$ since $a > 0$ and the equation of the directrix is $y = -9$.

[1] answer correct, without work shown

68.

560

60a. the bottom half of the parabola $y^2 = x$

b. domain: all non-negative real numbers, range: all non-positive real numbers

61a. The vertex moves up, and the parabola widens.

b. The vertex moves down, and the parabola narrows.

58. Critical Thinking Use the definition of a parabola to show that the parabola with vertex (h, k) and focus $(h, k + c)$ has the equation $(x - h)^2 = 4c(y - k)$. **58–59. See margin.**

59. Modeling Draw a cross section of a parabolic mirror modeled by the equation $y = 0.002323x^2$.

60. a. What part of a parabola is modeled by the function $y = -\sqrt{x}$?
b. State the domain and range for the function in part (a).

61. The directrix of a parabola is the line $y = -2$. The focus is the point $(0, 2)$.
a. Suppose the directrix remains fixed, but the focus is shifted along the y-axis farther away from the directrix. Explain what happens to the vertex and the shape of the parabola.
b. Suppose the focus moves along the y-axis toward the directrix. Explain what happens to the vertex and the shape of the parabola.
c. What would happen if the focus moved down all the way to the directrix? The parabola would degenerate into the ray with endpoint $(0, -2)$ that passes through the origin.

Test Prep

Multiple Choice

62. What is the distance from $P(2, -5)$ to the line $y = -8$? **B**
A. -6 B. 3   C. 5   D. 10

63. Which point is equidistant from $F(0, 5)$ and the line $y = -5$? **F**
F. $(-10, 5)$ G. $(-5, 0)$ H. $(0, 1)$ J. $(10, 10)$

64. Which equation represents a parabola that opens to the left? **A**
A. $x = -2y^2$ B. $x = 2y^2$ C. $y = -2x^2$ D. $y = 2x^2$

65. Which equation represents a parabola that opens downward? **H**
F. $x = -2y^2$ G. $x = 2y^2$ H. $y = -2x^2$ J. $y = 2x^2$

Short Response

66. What is the equation of a parabola that is the set of all points that are equidistant from $F(0, 4)$ and the line $y = -4$? **See margin.**

67. Find the focus and the directrix of the parabola with equation $y = \frac{1}{36}x^2$. **See margin.**

Mixed Review

GO for Help

Lesson 10-1

Graph each equation. **68–70. See margin.**

68. $x^2 + y^2 = 64$ **69.** $x^2 + 9y^2 = 9$ **70.** $4x^2 - 9y^2 = 36$

Lesson 9-2

Find the asymptotes of the graph of each equation. **71–76. See margin.**

71. $y = \frac{3}{x}$ **72.** $y = \frac{1}{x} + 4$ **73.** $y = \frac{4}{x+1}$

74. $y = -\frac{1}{x-1}$ **75.** $y = \frac{5}{x+5} + 2$ **76.** $y = \frac{2}{x-3} - 1$

Lesson 8-2 🌐 **77. Investing** Suppose you have a continuously compounding account with a beginning principal of $3,800 and an interest rate of 8.1%. What is the balance after 4 years? **$5254.06**

69.

70.

71. the x- and y-axes
72. $x = 0$ and $y = 4$
73. $x = -1$ and $y = 0$
74. $x = 1$ and $y = 0$
75. $x = -5$ and $y = 2$
76. $x = 3$ and $y = -1$

10-3

Circles

What You'll Learn

- To write and graph the equation of a circle
- To find the center and radius of a circle and use it to graph the circle

. . . And Why

To model gears in machinery, as in Example 3

 Check Skills You'll Need **for Help** Lesson 5-7 and Skills Handbook page 883

Simplify.

1. $\sqrt{16}$ 4   2. $\sqrt{49}$ 7   3. $\sqrt{20}$ $2\sqrt{5}$ 4. $\sqrt{48}$ $4\sqrt{3}$ 5. $\sqrt{72}$ $6\sqrt{2}$

Find the missing value to complete the square.

6. $x^2 - 2x + \blacksquare$ 1   7. $x^2 + 4x + \blacksquare$ 4   8. $x^2 - 6x + \blacksquare$ 9

 New Vocabulary • circle • center • radius
• standard form of an equation of a circle

---

1 Writing the Equation of a Circle

Real-World **Connection**

People of many cultures use circular dwellings, like those shown above in Mali, to maximize volume for a given surface area.

A **circle** is the set of all points in a plane that are a distance r from a given point, called the **center.** The distance r is the **radius** of the circle.

In the coordinate plane, if r is the radius of a circle with a center at the origin, then the equation of the circle can be written in the form $x^2 + y^2 = r^2$.

Not every circle has its center at the origin. You can use the distance formula to find an equation of a circle with a radius r and a center at the point (h, k).

Let (x, y) be any point on the circle. The distance from (h, k) to (x, y) is the radius.

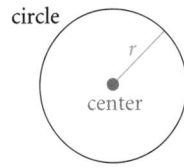

$d = \sqrt{(x_2 - x_2)^2 + (y_2 - y_1)^2}$ **Distance Formula**

$r = \sqrt{(x - h)^2 + (y - k)^2}$ **Substitute r for d, (h, k) for (x_1, y_1), and (x, y) for (x_2, y_2).**

$r^2 = (x - h)^2 + (y - k)^2$ **Square each side.**

This derivation leads to a definition.

Key Concepts

Definition	Standard Form of an Equation of a Circle

The standard form of an equation of a circle with center (h, k) and radius r is

$$(x - h)^2 + (y - k)^2 = r^2.$$

Lesson 10-3 Circles   **561**

Objectives

1 To write and graph the equation of a circle
2 To find the center and radius of a circle and use it to graph the circle

Examples

1 Writing the Equation of a Circle
2 Using Translations to Write an Equation
3 Real-World Connection
4 Finding the Center and Radius
5 Graphing a Circle Using Center and Radius

Professional Development

Math Background

Techniques learned in this lesson will be useful for modeling applications involving circles, and in graphing three-dimensional surfaces in future courses.

More Math Background: p. 544C

Lesson Planning and Resources

See p. 544E for a list of the resources that support this lesson.

PowerPoint

Bell Ringer Practice

Check Skills You'll Need
For intervention, direct students to:

Operations with Radicals
Skills Handbook: p. 883

Completing the Square
Lesson 5-7: Example 2
Extra Skills and Word Problems Practice, Ch. 5

2. Teach

Guided Instruction

1 EXAMPLE Alternative Method

Begin by having students sketch the circle. Have them label the center and a point (x, y) on the circle. Then, have students find the distance from (x, y) to the center.

2 EXAMPLE Math Tip

Point out that they only need to find the equation of the circle with center $(-4, 3)$ with the same radius.

3 EXAMPLE Tactile Learners

To help students understand that the radius of Gear A must be 8 times the radius of Gear B, point out that one rotation of a gear travels a distance equal to the circumference of the circle. Have students use compasses to draw a circle with radius 6 cm and a circle with radius 2 cm, representing two gears. Then, have students cut pieces of string to the size of the circumference of each circle. Have students determine the number of pieces of the small string required to make up the large string. **3** This number represents the number of rotations of the small gear for one rotation of the large gear. It is equal to the ratio of the circumference of the large gear to the circumference of the small gear, or equivalently the ratio of the radius of the large gear to the radius of the small gear.

You can use the center and the radius of a circle to write an equation for a circle.

1 EXAMPLE Writing the Equation of a Circle

Write an equation of a circle with center $(-4, 3)$ and radius 4.

$(x - h)^2 + (y - k)^2 = r^2$ **Use the standard form of the equation of a circle.**

$(x - (-4))^2 + (y - 3)^2 = 4^2$ **Substitute −4 for h, 3 for k, and 4 for r.**

$(x + 4)^2 + (y - 3)^2 = 16$ **Simplify.**

An equation for the circle is $(x + 4)^2 + (y - 3)^2 = 16$.

Check Solve the equation for y and enter both functions into your graphing calculator.

$(x + 4)^2 + (y - 3)^2 = 16$

$(y - 3)^2 = 16 - (x + 4)^2$

$y - 3 = \pm \sqrt{16 - (x + 4)^2}$

$y = 3 \pm \sqrt{16 - (x + 4)^2}$

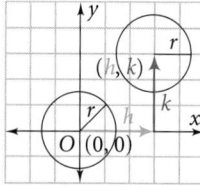

Graphing Calculator Hint

When graphing a conic section, press ZOOM 5 to select a square window. The standard window makes a circle look like an ellipse.

✓ **Quick Check** ① Write an equation for a circle with center at $(5, -2)$ and radius 8. Check your answer. $(x - 5)^2 + (y + 2)^2 = 64$

You can use parameters h and k to translate the circle $x^2 + y^2 = r^2$ with center $(0, 0)$ to the circle $(x - h)^2 + (y - k)^2 = r^2$ with center (h, k). Translate to the right when h is positive; to the left when h is negative. Translate up when k is positive; down when k is negative.

2 EXAMPLE Using Translations to Write an Equation

Write an equation for the translation of $x^2 + y^2 = 9$ four units left and three units up. Then graph the translation.

$(x - h)^2 + (y - k)^2 = r^2$ **Use standard form.**

$(x - (-4))^2 + (y - 3)^2 = 9$ **Substitute −4 for h, 3 for k, and 9 for r^2.**

$(x + 4)^2 + (y - 3)^2 = 9$ **Simplify.**

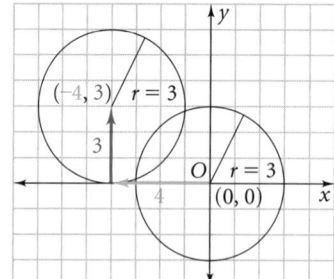

✓ **Quick Check** ② Write an equation for each translation.

a. $x^2 + y^2 = 1$; left 5 and down 3

$(x + 5)^2 + (y + 3)^2 = 1$

b. $x^2 + y^2 = 9$; right 2 and up 3

$(x - 2)^2 + (y - 3)^2 = 9$

Differentiated Instruction Solutions for All Learners

Advanced Learners L4
Have students verify that the standard form of a circle given in the chapter is equivalent to the general form.

learning style: verbal

English Language Learners ELL
For Example 3, have a student volunteer explain the meanings of *shaft* and *gear*. Ideally, a demonstration device would be available to illustrate how shafts and gears of different sizes work together.

learning style: verbal

You can write an equation of a circle to model a real-world situation.

3 EXAMPLE Real-World 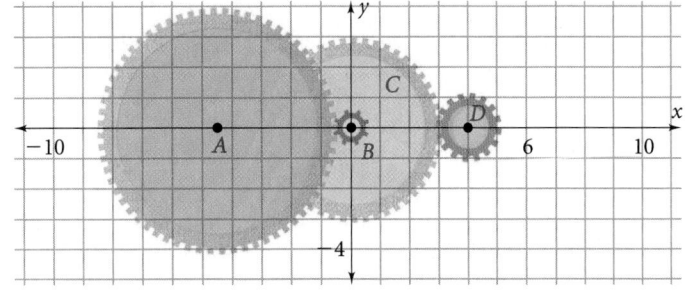 Connection

Machinery The diagram below shows four gears in a motor assembly. Gear B rotates 8 times for each rotation of gear A. Gears B and C share the same shaft, with centers at the origin. The radius of gear C is 6 times the radius of gear B. The radius of gear D is $\frac{1}{3}$ the radius of gear C. Write the equation of the circle that represents each gear.

Real-World 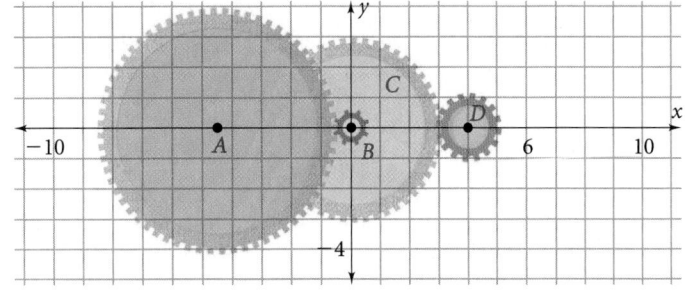 **Connection**

Gears change the rate of rotation of different parts of a machine. The gears shown above are part of a printing press.

Make a table. Let the radius of gear $B = \frac{1}{2}$. The radius of gear A must be 8 times the radius of gear B, or 4.

Gear	(h, k)	r	Equation
A	$\left(-4\frac{1}{2}, 0\right)$	4	$\left(x + \frac{9}{2}\right)^2 + y^2 = 16$
B	$(0, 0)$	$\frac{1}{2}$	$x^2 + y^2 = \frac{1}{4}$
C	$(0, 0)$	3	$x^2 + y^2 = 9$
D	$(4, 0)$	1	$(x - 4)^2 + y^2 = 1$

✓ Quick Check ③ Write the equation of a circle for a gear that is the same size as gear D and has center $(0, -4)$. $x^2 + (y + 4)^2 = 1$

2 Using the Center and Radius of a Circle

You can find the center and radius of a circle by rewriting the equation in the standard form of a circle.

4 EXAMPLE Finding the Center and Radius

Find the center and radius of the circle with equation $(x - 16)^2 + (y + 9)^2 = 144$.

$(x - h)^2 + (y - k)^2 = r^2$	Write the standard form.
$(x - 16)^2 + (y + 9)^2 = 144$	Write the equation.
$(x - 16)^2 + (y - (-9))^2 = 12^2$	Rewrite the equation in standard form.
$h = 16 \quad k = -9 \quad r = 12$	Find h, k, and r.

The center of the circle is $(16, -9)$. The radius is 12.

✓ Quick Check ④ Find the center and radius of the circle with equation $(x + 8)^2 + (y + 3)^2 = 121$.
$(-8, -3)$, 11

Lesson 10-3 Circles **563**

PowerPoint

Additional Examples

① Write an equation of a circle with center $(3, -2)$ and radius 3.
$(x - 3)^2 + (y + 2)^2 = 9$

② Write an equation for the translation of $x^2 + y^2 = 16$ two units right and one unit down.
$(x - 2)^2 + (y + 1)^2 = 16$

③ Suppose Gear B, from Example 3, rotates 10 times for each rotation of Gear A. Assuming all other information from Example 3 remains the same, find the new equation of the circle that represents Gear A.
$\left(x + \frac{11}{2}\right)^2 + y^2 = 25$

Guided Instruction

④ **EXAMPLE** Math Tip

Point out that $r^2 = 144$ has two roots, ± 12. However, a radius of -12 is not possible since distance is always non-negative.

PowerPoint

Additional Examples

④ Find the center and radius of the circle with equation $(x + 4)^2 + (y - 2)^2 = 36$.
$(-4, 2)$; 6

⑤ Graph $(x - 3)^2 + (y + 1)^2 = 4$.

Resources
• Daily Notetaking Guide 10-3   **L3**

Closure

Ask: *What information do you need to write and graph the equation of a circle?* **center and radius** *Given the equation of a circle, how do you determine the center and radius of the circle?* **When written in the form $(x - h)^2 + (y - k)^2 = r^2$, (h, k) represents the center and r represents the radius.**

563

Assignment Guide

1 A B   1-18, 35-54

2 A B   19-34, 55-66

C   Challenge   67-70

Test Prep   71-76
Mixed Review   77-86

Homework Quick Check

To check students' understanding of key skills and concepts, go over Exercises 15, 21, 54, 59, 63.

Error Prevention!

Exercises 1–8 To help avoid sign errors, suggest students place parentheses around the values that they are substituting for h and k.

Exercise 52 Encourage students to first write the standard form of an equation of a circle. Students can then substitute the given information before selecting an answer choice.

You can use the center and the radius to graph a circle.

5 EXAMPLE   Graphing a Circle Using Center and Radius

Graph $(x + 1)^2 + (y - 3)^2 = 25$.

$$(x - h)^2 + (y - k)^2 = r^2 \qquad \text{Find the center and the radius of the circle.}$$
$$(x - (-1))^2 + (y - 3)^2 = 25$$
$$h = -1 \qquad k = 3 \qquad r^2 = 25, \text{ or } r = 5$$

For: Circles Activity
Use: Interactive Textbook, 10-3

Draw the center $(-1, 3)$ and radius 5. Draw a smooth curve.

Quick Check   5   Graph $(x - 4)^2 + (y + 2)^2 = 49$.

EXERCISES

For more exercises, see *Extra Skill and Word Problem Practice.*

Practice and Problem Solving

A Practice by Example

Example 1
(page 562)

Example 2
(page 562)

Example 3
(page 563)

Example 4
(page 563)

GO for Help

Write an equation of a circle with the given center and radius. Check your answers.

1. $(0, 0), 10$ **2.** $(-4, -6), 7$ **3.** $(2, 3), 4.5$ **4.** $(-6, 10), 1$

5. $(1, -3), 10$ **6.** $(-5, -1), 6$ **7.** $(-3, 0), 8$ **8.** $(-1.5, -3), 2$

1–8. See margin.

Write an equation for each translation. **9–14. See margin.**

9. $x^2 + y^2 = 9$; down 1   **10.** $x^2 + y^2 = 1$; left 1

11. $x^2 + y^2 = 25$; right 2 and down 4   **12.** $x^2 + y^2 = 81$; left 1 and up 3

13. $x^2 + y^2 = 100$; down 5   **14.** $x^2 + y^2 = 49$; right 3 and up 2

15. $x^2 + y^2 = 20$; left 6 and up 1   **16.** $x^2 + y^2 = 50$; right 5
$(x + 6)^2 + (y - 1)^2 = 20$ $(x - 5)^2 + y^2 = 50$

Write an equation for each circle. Each interval represents one unit.

17.   **18.**

       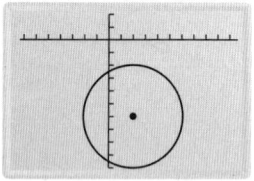

$(x + 3)^2 + (y - 4)^2 = 9$ $(x - 2)^2 + (y + 6)^2 = 16$

For each equation, find the center and radius of the circle.

19. $(x - 1)^2 + (y - 1)^2 = 1$ **(1, 1), 1**   **20.** $(x + 2)^2 + (y - 10)^2 = 4$

21. $(x - 3)^2 + (y + 1)^2 = 36$ **(3, –1), 6**   **22.** $(x + 3)^2 + (y - 5)^2 = 81$

23. $x^2 + (y + 3)^2 = 25$ **(0, –3), 5**   **24.** $(x + 6)^2 + y^2 = 121$ **(–6, 0), 11**

25. $(x + 2)^2 + (y + 4)^2 = 256$ **26.** $(x - 3)^2 + (y - 7)^2 = 96$

20. $(-2, 10), 2$
22. $(-3, 5), 9$
25. $(-2, -4), 16$
26. $(3, 7), 4\sqrt{6}$

564   Chapter 10   Quadratic Relations and Conic Sections

1. $x^2 + y^2 = 100$

2. $(x + 4)^2 + (y + 6)^2 = 49$

3. $(x - 2)^2 + (y - 3)^2 = 20.25$

4. $(x + 6)^2 + (y - 10)^2 = 1$

5. $(x - 1)^2 + (y + 3)^2 = 100$

6. $(x + 5)^2 + (y + 1)^2 = 36$

7. $(x + 3)^2 + y^2 = 64$

8. $(x + 1.5)^2 + (y + 3)^2 = 4$

9. $x^2 + (y + 1)^2 = 9$

10. $(x + 1)^2 + y^2 = 1$

11. $(x - 2)^2 + (y + 4)^2 = 25$

12. $(x + 1)^2 + (y - 3)^2 = 81$

13. $x^2 + (y + 5)^2 = 100$

14. $(x - 3)^2 + (y - 2)^2 = 49$

Example 5
(page 564)

Use the center and the radius to graph each circle.

27. $(x + 9)^2 + (y + 2)^2 = 100$

28. $(x + 4)^2 + (y - 4)^2 = 4$

29. $(x - 6)^2 + y^2 = 64$

30. $(x - 1)^2 + (y + 3)^2 = 16$

31. $x^2 + y^2 = 9$

32. $(x + 3)^2 + (y - 9)^2 = 49$

33. $(x - 7)^2 + (y - 1)^2 = 100$

34. $x^2 + (y + 4)^2 = 144$

27–34. See back of book.

B **Apply Your Skills**

Write the equation of the circle that passes through the given point and has a center at the origin. (*Hint:* You can use the distance formula to find the radius.)

35. $x^2 + y^2 = 16$

36. $x^2 + y^2 = 9$

37. $x^2 + y^2 = 25$

38. $x^2 + y^2 = 3$

39. $x^2 + y^2 = 25$

40. $x^2 + y^2 = 169$

41. $x^2 + y^2 = 169$

42. $x^2 + y^2 = 13$

43. $x^2 + y^2 = 26$

44. $x^2 + y^2 = 52$

35. $(0, 4)$ **36.** $(0, -3)$ **37.** $(-5, 0)$ **38.** $(\sqrt{3}, 0)$ **39.** $(4, -3)$

40. $(-5, -12)$ **41.** $(12, -5)$ **42.** $(-2, 3)$ **43.** $(1, -5)$ **44.** $(-6, -4)$

Use the given information to write an equation of the circle. 45–51. See margin.

45. radius 7, center $(-6, 13)$

46. area 25π, center $(5, -3)$

47. center $(-2, 7.5)$, circumference 3π

48. center $(1, -2)$, through $(0, 1)$

49. center $(2, 1)$, through $(6, 4)$

50. center $(6, 4)$, through $(2, 1)$

51. translation of $(x - 1)^2 + (y + 3)^2 = 36$, 2 units left and 4 units down

52. Multiple Choice Which equation models the circular fountain at the right? **A**

Ⓐ $(x - 24)^2 + (y - 22)^2 = 100$

Ⓑ $(x + 22)^2 + (y + 24)^2 = 100$

Ⓒ $(x - 24)^2 + (y - 22)^2 = 10$

Ⓓ $(x + 24)^2 + (y + 22)^2 = 10$

53. Check students' work.

53. Open-Ended Write two functions that together represent a circle.

54. Error Analysis A student claims that the circle $(x + 7)^2 + (y - 7)^2 = 8$ is a translation of the circle $x^2 + y^2 = 8$, 7 right and 7 down. What is the student's mistake? **See margin.**

60. $(-2, -4), 5\sqrt{2}$

61. $(-3, 5), \sqrt{38}$

63. $(3, 1), \sqrt{6}$

64. $(0, 2), 2\sqrt{5}$

Find the center and the radius of each circle.

55. $x^2 + y^2 = 2$ **(0, 0)**, $\sqrt{2}$

56. $x^2 + (y + 1)^2 = 5$ **(0, -1)**, $\sqrt{5}$

57. $x^2 + y^2 = 14$ **(0, 0)**, $\sqrt{14}$

58. $x^2 + (y - 4)^2 = 11$ **(0, 4)**, $\sqrt{11}$

59. $(x + 5)^2 + y^2 = 18$ **(-5, 0)**, $3\sqrt{2}$

60. $(x + 2)^2 + (y + 4)^2 = 50$

61. $(x + 3)^2 + (y - 5)^2 = 38$

62. $x^2 + 2x + 1 + y^2 = 4$ **(-1, 0)**, **2**

GPS **63.** $x^2 + y^2 - 6x - 2y + 4 = 0$

64. $x^2 + y^2 - 4y - 16 = 0$

Homework Video Tutor
Visit: PHSchool.com
Web Code: age-1003

Graph each pair of equations. Identify the conic section represented by the graph. Then write the equation of the conic section. 65–66. See margin.

65. $y = 3 + \sqrt{16 - (x - 4)^2}$
$y = 3 - \sqrt{16 - (x - 4)^2}$

66. $y = -2 + \sqrt{x - 3}$
$y = -2 - \sqrt{x - 3}$

C **Challenge**

67. Reasoning Let $P(x, y)$ be any point on the circle with center $(0, 0)$ and radius r. Choose a method for proving that $x^2 + y^2 = r^2$. **See back of book.**

45. $(x + 6)^2 + (y - 13)^2 = 49$

46. $(x - 5)^2 + (y + 3)^2 = 25$

47. $(x + 2)^2 + (y - 7.5)^2 = 2.25$

48. $(x - 1)^2 + (y + 2)^2 = 10$

49. $(x - 2)^2 + (y - 1)^2 = 25$

50. $(x - 6)^2 + (y - 4)^2 = 25$

51. $(x + 1)^2 + (y + 7)^2 = 36$

54. Replacing x with $x + 7$ and y with $y - 7$ has the effect of translating the circle 7 units left and 7 units up.

565

A sheet of blank grids is available with the Test-Taking Strategies with Transparencies booklet. Give this sheet to students for practice with filling in the grids.

Resources

For additional practice with a variety of test item formats:
• Standardized Test Prep, p. 595
• Test-Taking Strategies, p. 590
• Test-Taking Strategies with Transparencies

Checkpoint Quiz

Use this Checkpoint Quiz to check students' understanding of the skills and concepts of Lessons 10-1 through 10-3.

Resources
Grab & Go
• Checkpoint Quiz 1

 68. a. **Writing** Explain why $x^2 + y^2 = 0$ does not represent a circle.
  b. **Critical Thinking** What does the equation represent? **point (0, 0)**

68a. The radius would have length 0.

69. The table gives the diameters of four planets.
  a. Use a center of $(0, 0)$ to graph a circle that represents the size of each planet. **a–b. See back of book.**
  b. Write an equation representing the circular cross section through the center of each planet.

Planet	Diameter (miles)
Pluto	1430
Mercury	3031
Mars	4222
Earth	7926

70a. $(x - 3)^2 + (y - 4)^2 = 25$
  b. $y = -\frac{1}{3}x^2 + \frac{10}{3}x$

70. a. A circle contains $(0, 0)$, $(6, 8)$, and $(7, 7)$. Find its equation by solving a system of three equations.
  b. Several parabolas contain the three points of part (a), but only one is described by a quadratic function. Find that function.

Gridded Response

71. What is the radius of the circle with equation $(x + 5)^2 + (y - 3)^2 = 144$? **12**

72. What is the radius of the circle with equation $(x - 2)^2 + 3 + (y + 1)^2 = 7$? $\frac{7}{2}$

73. Circle A has equation $(x + 5)^2 + y^2 = 169$. The diameter of circle B is one fourth as long as the diameter of circle A. What is the radius of circle B? **3.25**

74. What is the distance between $T(9, -5)$ and the center of the circle with equation $(x - 6)^2 + (y + 1)^2 = 10$? **5**

75. Find the distance between the centers of the circles with equations $(x - 5)^2 + (y - 1)^2 = 16$ and $(x + 1)^2 + (y - 9)^2 = 49$. **10**

76. What is the area of the circle whose equation is $(x + 1)^2 + (y + 1)^2 = 1$? Round your answer to the nearest hundredth. **3.14**

Mixed Review

GO for Help

Lesson 10-2

77. Write an equation of a parabola opening left with vertex $(0, 0)$ and focus $(-3, 0)$.
$x = -\frac{1}{12}y^2$

Lesson 9-3 **For each rational function, find any points of discontinuity.**

78. $y = \frac{2}{x + 1}$
$x = -1$

79. $y = \frac{1}{x^2 - 5x + 6}$
$x = 2, x = 3$

80. $y = \frac{2x - 1}{x^2 + 4}$
no discontinuities

Lesson 8-3 **Evaluate each logarithm.**

81. $\log_2 16$ **4**

82. $\log_5 25$ **2**

83. $\log_3 \frac{1}{27}$ **−3**

84. $\log 10,000$ **4**

85. $\log_{36} 6$ $\frac{1}{2}$

86. $\log_{100} 100$ **1**

Checkpoint Quiz 1 **Lessons 10-1 through 10-3**

Identify the vertex, focus, and directrix of each parabola. Then graph the parabola.

1. $y = 3x^2$
2. $x = 4(y + 2)^2$
3. $y + 1 = (x - 3)^2$
1–3. See margin.

4. $(x + 6)^2 + (y - 3)^2 = 64$

4. Write an equation in standard form of the circle with center $(-6, 3)$ and radius 8.

5. What translation of $x^2 + y^2 = 18$ results in $(x + 4)^2 + (y - 6)^2 = 18$?
4 units left and 6 units up

Checkpoint Quiz

1. $(0, 0)$, $\left(0, \frac{1}{12}\right)$, $y = -\frac{1}{12}$;

2. $(0, -2)$, $\left(\frac{1}{16}, -2\right)$, $x = -\frac{1}{16}$;

3. $(3, -1)$, $\left(3, -\frac{3}{4}\right)$, $y = -\frac{5}{4}$;

Activity Lab

1.

Activity Lab

Technology

Using Parametric Equations

FOR USE WITH LESSON 10-3

The graphing calculator program below uses parametric equations (Activity Lab, page 124) to graph a circle. To enter the program, use the **PRGM** **NEW** menu. Name your program **CIRCLE**.

Note that you find the **Disp**, **Prompt**, and **DispGraph** features in the **PRGM** **I/O** menu, and X_{1T} and Y_{1T} in the **VARS** **Y-Vars Parametric** menu. You can find **Par** and **Radian** under **MODE**, and **Tmin**, **Tmax**, and **Tstep** in the **VARS** **Window T/θ** menu.

Use **ALPHA** keys to enter words, quotation marks, and variables H, K, R, and T.

Go Online
PHSchool.com
For: Graphing calculator procedures
Web Code: age-2119

```
PROGRAM:CIRCLE
:Disp "CENTER (H,K)"
:Disp "RADIUS R"
:Prompt H,K,R
:"Rcos(T)+H"→X₁T
■
```

```
PROGRAM:CIRCLE
:"Rsin(T)+K"→Y₁T
:Param
:Radian
:0→Tmin
:2π→Tmax
:.05→Tstep
:DispGraph■
```

The screens below show the program being run for a circle with a center at $(-2, 3)$ and a radius of 5. Enter appropriate square-window values with the calculator in function mode. Then choose the program from the **PRGM** **EXEC** menu.

```
WINDOW
 Xmin=-12
 Xmax=12
 Xscl=1
 Ymin=-8
 Ymax=8
 Yscl=1
 Xres=1■
```

```
prgmCIRCLE
CENTER (H,K)
RADIUS R
H=?-2
K=?3
R=?5■
```

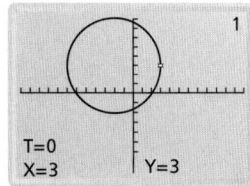

```
T=0
X=3        Y=3
```

Note that you can trace to find the coordinates of points on the circle.

EXERCISES

Use your program to graph each circle. Use an appropriate square window for each graph. 1–6. See margin pp. 566–567. 7–8. See back of book.

1. center $(0, 2)$, radius 4

2. center $(5, -2)$, radius 5

3. center $(-1, 3)$, radius 8

4. $(x - 2)^2 + (y + 1)^2 = 25$

5. $(x + 4)^2 + (y - 3)^2 = 100$

6. $x^2 + (y + 2)^2 = 49$

7. $(x - 1)^2 + (y + 2)^2 = 36$

8. $(x - 6)^2 + y^2 = 100$

9. Open-Ended Use **TRACE** to find four points in Quadrant III that lie on the circle described by the equation $(x + 5)^2 + (y - 2)^2 = 16$. **Check students' work.**

10. Writing Describe how to change your program to work in degrees and plot a point every 5° of rotation. **In the program, change radian to degree, change $2\pi \to T_{max}$ to $360 \to T_{max}$, and change $0.05 \to T_{step}$ to $5 \to T_{step}$.**

Activity Lab   Using Parametric Equations   **567**

2.

3.

 4.

Activity Lab

Using Parametric Equations

Students learn how to write a program for their calculators that will graph a circle when the center and radius are given. This program uses the same information that students needed to graph a circle by hand.

Guided Instruction

Teaching Tip

Students may wish to revisit the Technology Extension for Lesson 3-2 for a review of parametric equations.

Error Prevention!

Exercise 10 Students having difficulty should be encouraged to examine the program and identify the instruction lines that use, or refer to, angles or radians. Students should explain how to rewrite these lines so that they refer to degrees instead of radians.

Resources

Students may use any graphing calculator with parametric graphing capabilities.

5.

6.

567

10-4

Ellipses

Objectives

1 To write the equation of an ellipse

2 To find the foci of an ellipse and to graph an ellipse

Examples

1 Writing the Equation of an Ellipse

2 Real-World Connection

3 Finding the Foci of an Ellipse

4 Using the Foci of an Ellipse

Math Background

Students build on their knowledge of circles to help them develop the techniques necessary to write the equation of an ellipse and graph an ellipse. An interesting application of ellipses is based on the property that when a light or sound wave is emitted at one focus it passes through the other focus. This property is typically studied in science, geometry, and calculus courses. Also, note that a circle is an ellipse whose two foci are coincident.

More Math Background: p. 544D

Lesson Planning and Resources

See p. 544E for a list of the resources that support this lesson.

PowerPoint

Bell Ringer Practice

✓ **Check Skills You'll Need**
For intervention, direct students to:

Quadratic Equations
Lesson 5-5: Examples 1 and 2
Extra Skills and Word Problems Practice, Ch. 5

What You'll Learn

• To write the equation of an ellipse

• To find the foci of an ellipse and to graph an ellipse

...And Why

To model NASA's Transonic Tunnel, as in Example 2

 ✓ **Check Skills You'll Need** **for Help** Lesson 5-5 and Skills Handbook page 874

Solve each equation.

1. $27 = x^2 + 11$ ± 4

2. $x^2 = 48$ $\pm 4\sqrt{3}$

3. $84 = 120 - x^2$ ± 6

Evaluate each expression for $a = 3$ and $b = 5$.

4. $a^2 + b^2$ 34

5. $a^2 - b^2$ -16

6. $b^2 - 2a^2$ 7

🔊 **New Vocabulary** • ellipse • focus of an ellipse • major axis
• vertices of an ellipse • minor axis • co-vertices

---

 1 **Writing the Equation of an Ellipse**

Ellipses play an important role in science. For example, the planets follow elliptical, not circular, orbits around the sun.

 Key Concepts

Definition	**Ellipse**

An **ellipse** is a set of points P in a plane such that the sum of the distances from P to two fixed points F_1 and F_2 is a given constant k.

$$PF_1 + PF_2 = k, \text{ where } k > F_1F_2$$

Vocabulary Tip

Ellipse comes from a Greek word for "smaller." The cutting plane of an ellipse makes a smaller angle with the base than does the side of the cone. See p. 547.

Each fixed point F is a **focus of an ellipse** (plural: foci). The **major axis** is the segment that contains the foci and has its endpoints on the ellipse. The endpoints of the major axis are **vertices of an ellipse.** The midpoint of the major axis is the center of the ellipse. The **minor axis** is perpendicular to the major axis at the center. The endpoints of the minor axis are **co-vertices.**

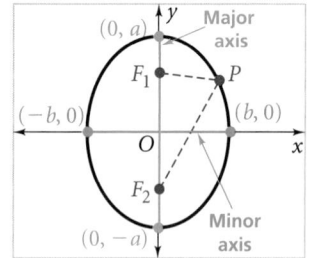

$$\frac{x^2}{a^2} + \frac{y^2}{b^2} = 1$$ ← standard forms of an → $$\frac{x^2}{b^2} + \frac{y^2}{a^2} = 1$$
equation of an ellipse,
major axis: horizontal   with center at the   major axis: vertical
vertices: $(\pm a, 0)$ origin and $a > b > 0$ vertices: $(0, \pm a)$
co-vertices: $(0, \pm b)$ co-vertices: $(\pm b, 0)$

Differentiated Instruction **Solutions for All Learners**

Special Needs L1
Draw an ellipse, labeling the key terms. Show that an ellipse is symmetrical about both the major and minor axes. Thus, the 2 vertices, 2 co-vertices, and 2 foci are paired reflections. Also, the distance from the center to a vertex is half the length of the axis.

learning style: visual

Below Level L2
Show students how to draw an ellipse using two push pins and a piece of string. Ask them to explain how this construction technique relates to the definition of an ellipse.

learning style: tactile

You can write the equation of an ellipse with a center at the origin if you know an *x*-intercept and a *y*-intercept.

1 EXAMPLE Writing the Equation of an Ellipse

Write an equation in standard form of an ellipse that has a vertex at $(0, 5)$, a co-vertex at $(2, 0)$, and a center at the origin.

Since $(0, 5)$ is a vertex of the ellipse, the other vertex is at $(0, -5)$, and the major axis is vertical. Since $(2, 0)$ is a co-vertex, the other co-vertex is at $(-2, 0)$, and the minor axis is horizontal. So $a = 5, b = 2, a^2 = 25$, and $b^2 = 4$.

$\dfrac{x^2}{b^2} + \dfrac{y^2}{a^2} = 1$ **standard form of an equation of an ellipse with a vertical major axis**

$\dfrac{x^2}{4} + \dfrac{y^2}{25} = 1$ **Substitute 4 for b^2 and 25 for a^2.**

● An equation of the ellipse is $\dfrac{x^2}{4} + \dfrac{y^2}{25} = 1$.

✓ **Quick Check** ❶ Write an equation in standard form for an ellipse that has a vertex at $(0, -6)$, a co-vertex at $(3, 0)$, and a center at the origin. $\dfrac{x^2}{9} + \dfrac{y^2}{36} = 1$

You can write an equation for an ellipse with a center at the origin if you know the length of both axes.

2 EXAMPLE Real-World Connection

Aerodynamics Scientists used the Transonic Tunnel at NASA Langley Research Center, Virginia, to study the dynamics of air flow. The elliptical opening of the Transonic Tunnel is 82 ft wide and 58 ft high. Find an equation of the ellipse.

Imagine a large coordinate grid placed over the elliptical opening. Since the widest part of the ellipse is horizontal and the width is 82 ft, place the vertices at $(\pm 41, 0)$. Place the co-vertices at $(0, \pm 29)$.

So $a = 41, b = 29, a^2 = 1681$, and $b^2 = 841$.

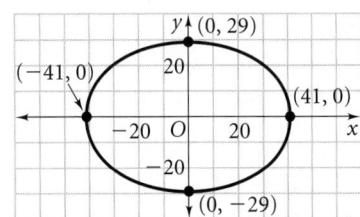

$\dfrac{x^2}{a^2} + \dfrac{y^2}{b^2} = 1$ **standard form for an ellipse with a horizontal major axis**

$\dfrac{x^2}{1681} + \dfrac{y^2}{841} = 1$ **Substitute 1681 for a^2 and 841 for b^2.**

● An equation of the ellipse is $\dfrac{x^2}{1681} + \dfrac{y^2}{841} = 1$.

✓ **Quick Check** ❷ Find an equation of an ellipse centered at the origin that is 12 units wide and 30 units high. $\dfrac{x^2}{36} + \dfrac{y^2}{225} = 1$

Real-World 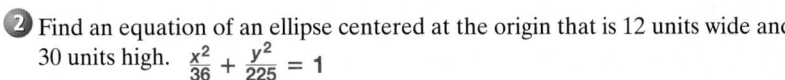 Connection

The guide vanes in the elliptical opening of the Transonic Tunnel allow a smooth flow of air through the passageway.

Guided Instruction

To elaborate on the Definition of an Ellipse, go outside and organize students into groups of three. Give each group a piece of string about 15 ft long and at least 20 colored counters. Have two students stand about 10 ft apart and each hold an end of the string. The third student takes the counters and the middle of the string and walks a few paces until the string is taut. A counter is placed at this spot. Now the student walks around the other two students, sliding the string between the fingers, but always keeping it taut. The student places counters on the ground every couple of paces. Students should see that the counters are forming an ellipse. Students acting as foci may need to duck so that the string does not get caught around their bodies.

PowerPoint

▣ Additional Examples

❶ Write an equation in standard form of an ellipse that has a vertex at $(0, -4)$, a co-vertex at $(3, 0)$, and is centered at the origin. $\dfrac{x^2}{9} + \dfrac{y^2}{16} = 1$

❷ Find an equation of an ellipse centered at the origin that is 20 units wide and 10 units high. $\dfrac{x^2}{100} + \dfrac{y^2}{25} = 1$

Advanced Learners **L4**
Students with an interest in astronomy can look up Kepler's three laws of planetary motion. Have students report their findings to the class.

learning style: verbal

English Language Learners **ELL**
Encourage students to look up the word *focus* in a dictionary or thesaurus. Ask students to list other uses of the word that may or may not be related to the geometric meaning.

learning style: verbal

569

Connection to
3 EXAMPLE Geometry

Students may not see how the relationship for *a*, *b*, and *c* is related to the Pythagorean Theorem. Ask: *Which variables represent the legs? b and c Which variable represents the hypotenuse? a* Write $b^2 + c^2 = a^2$ on the board. Then use the Subtraction Property of Equality to write $c^2 = a^2 - b^2$.

4 EXAMPLE Technology Tip

Students may wish to graph this ellipse and verify their graphs from Example 3 by using their graphing calculators. They can either apply the technique used in Lesson 10-3 Example 1 or modify the circle program created in the Activity Lab for Lesson 10-3. To modify the program, students need to change "Prompt H, K, R" to "Prompt H, K, A, B", "Rcos T + H" to "Acos T + H", and "Rsin T + K" to "Bsin T + K", where (H, K) is the center of the ellipse, A is the distance from the center to a vertex, and B is the distance from the center to a co-vertex.

PowerPoint
Additional Examples

3 Find the foci of the ellipse with the equation $9x^2 + y^2 = 36$. Graph the ellipse. $(0, \pm4\sqrt{2})$

4 Write an equation of the ellipse with foci at $(0, \pm4)$ and co-vertices at $(\pm2, 0)$.
$$\frac{x^2}{4} + \frac{y^2}{20} = 1$$

Resources
- Daily Notetaking Guide 10-4 **L3**

---

2 Finding and Using the Foci of an Ellipse

The foci are important points in an ellipse. For example, the sun is at a focus, not at the center, of Earth's orbit around the sun.

The foci of an ellipse are always on the major axis at *c* units from the center.

There is an important and useful relationship among *a*, *b*, and *c*:
$c^2 = a^2 - b^2$.

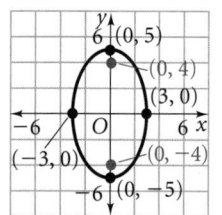

You can use the relationship to find the foci of an ellipse.

3 EXAMPLE Finding the Foci of an Ellipse

Find the foci of the ellipse with the equation $25x^2 + 9y^2 = 225$. Graph the ellipse.

$25x^2 + 9y^2 = 225$

$\quad \frac{x^2}{9} + \frac{y^2}{25} = 1$ **Write in standard form.**

Since $25 > 9$ and 25 is with y^2, the major axis is vertical, $a^2 = 25$, and $b^2 = 9$.

$c^2 = a^2 - b^2$ **Find c.**

$\quad = 25 - 9$ **Substitute 25 for a^2 and 9 for b^2.**

$\quad = 16$

$c = 4$

The major axis is vertical, so the coordinates of the foci are $(0, \pm c)$. The foci are $(0, 4)$ and $(0, -4)$.

The vertices are $(0, \pm5)$. The co-vertices are $(\pm3, 0)$.

Quick Check **3** Find the foci of the ellipse with the equation $x^2 + 9y^2 = 9$. Graph the ellipse.
See back of book.

You can use the relationship among *a*, *b*, and *c* to write the equation of an ellipse.

4 EXAMPLE Using the Foci of an Ellipse

Write an equation of the ellipse with foci at $(\pm7, 0)$ and co-vertices at $(0, \pm6)$.

Since the foci have coordinates $(\pm7, 0)$, the major axis is horizontal.

Since $c = 7$ and $b = 6$, $c^2 = 49$ and $b^2 = 36$.

$c^2 = a^2 - b^2$ **Use the equation to find a^2.**

$49 = a^2 - 36$ **Substitute 49 for c^2 and 36 for b^2.**

$a^2 = 85$ **Simplify.**

$\frac{x^2}{85} + \frac{y^2}{36} = 1$ **Substitute 85 for a^2 and 36 for b^2.**

An equation of the ellipse is $\frac{x^2}{85} + \frac{y^2}{36} = 1$.

Quick Check **4** Write an equation of the ellipse with foci at $(0, \pm\sqrt{17})$ and co-vertices at $(\pm8, 0)$. $\frac{x^2}{64} + \frac{y^2}{81} = 1$

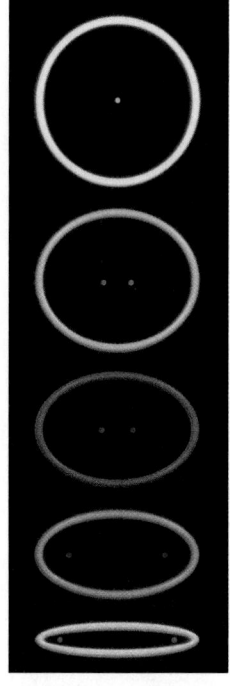
The figure above shows the relationship between the center of a circle and the foci of an ellipse.

Online
active math
For: Ellipse Activity
Use: Interactive Textbook, 10-4

Closure

Have students explain the process for writing the equation of an ellipse, graphing an ellipse, and determining the foci of an ellipse. Assume that the ellipse is centered at the origin. Determine the vertices, co-vertices, and major and minor axes. The equation has the form $\frac{x^2}{a^2} + \frac{y^2}{b^2} = 1$ or $\frac{x^2}{b^2} + \frac{y^2}{a^2} = 1$, where *a* is the distance from the center to a vertex and *b* is the distance from the center to a co-vertex. Use this information to graph the equation. The foci lie on the major axis and are $(\pm c, 0)$ or $(0, \pm c)$, where $c^2 = a^2 - b^2$.

EXERCISES

For more exercises, see *Extra Skill and Word Problem Practice*.

Practice and Problem Solving

A Practice by Example

Example 1
(page 569)

 for Help

Write an equation of an ellipse in standard form with center at the origin and with the given vertex and co-vertex. **1–8. See margin.**

1. $(4,0),(0,3)$ **2.** $(0,1),(2,0)$ **3.** $(3,0),(0,-1)$ **4.** $(0,6),(1,0)$

5. $(0,-7),(4,0)$ **6.** $(-6,0),(0,5)$ **7.** $(-9,0),(0,-2)$ **8.** $(0,5),(-3,0)$

Example 2
(page 569)

Find an equation of an ellipse for each given height and width. Assume that the center of the ellipse is $(0,0)$. **9–17. See back of book.**

9. $h = 1\text{ m}, w = 3\text{ m}$ **10.** $h = 32\text{ ft}, w = 16\text{ ft}$ **11.** $h = 20\text{ ft}, w = 12\text{ ft}$

12. $h = 10\text{ cm}, w = 7\text{ cm}$ **13.** $h = 14\text{ yd}, w = 28\text{ yd}$ **14.** $h = 8\text{ ft}, w = 2\text{ ft}$

15. $h = 15\text{ ft}, w = 32\text{ ft}$ **16.** $h = 40\text{ mi}, w = 60\text{ mi}$ **17.** $h = 5\text{ m}, w = 2\text{ m}$

Example 3
(page 570)

Find the foci for each equation of an ellipse. Then graph the ellipse.

18. $\frac{x^2}{4} + \frac{y^2}{9} = 1$ **19.** $\frac{x^2}{9} + \frac{y^2}{25} = 1$ **20.** $\frac{x^2}{81} + \frac{y^2}{49} = 1$

21. $\frac{x^2}{100} + \frac{y^2}{36} = 1$ **22.** $\frac{x^2}{64} + \frac{y^2}{100} = 1$ **23.** $3x^2 + y^2 = 9$

24. $x^2 + 4y^2 = 16$ **25.** $\frac{x^2}{225} + \frac{y^2}{144} = 1$ **26.** $\frac{x^2}{256} + \frac{y^2}{121} = 1$
18–26. See back of book.

Example 4
(page 570)

Write an equation of an ellipse for the given foci and co-vertices.

27. foci $(\pm 6,0)$, co-vertices $(0,\pm 8)$ **28.** foci $(0,\pm 8)$, co-vertices $(\pm 8,0)$

29. foci $(\pm 5,0)$, co-vertices $(0,\pm 8)$ **30.** foci $(0,\pm 4)$, co-vertices $(\pm 2,0)$

31. foci $(\pm 14,0)$, co-vertices $(0,\pm 7)$ **32.** foci $(\pm 17,0)$, co-vertices $(0,\pm 15)$
27–32. See margin.

B Apply Your Skills

Find the foci for each equation of an ellipse. **33–40. See below left.**

33. $4x^2 + 9y^2 = 36$ **34.** $16x^2 + 4y^2 = 64$ **35.** $36x^2 + 4y^2 = 144$

36. $25x^2 + 4y^2 = 100$ **37.** $36x^2 + 8y^2 = 288$ **38.** $25x^2 + 24y^2 = 600$

39. $25x^2 + 16y^2 + 150x = 160y - 225$ **40.** $2x^2 + 8x + y^2 + 4 = 0$

Vocabulary Tip

Eccentric means "out of center."

41. The eccentricity of an ellipse is a measure of how nearly circular it is. Eccentricity is defined as $\frac{c}{a}$, where c is the distance from the center to a focus and a is the distance from the center to a vertex.
 a. Find the eccentricity of an ellipse with foci $(\pm 9,0)$ and vertices $(\pm 10,0)$.
  GPS Sketch the graph. **a–d. See back of book.**
 b. Find the eccentricity of an ellipse with foci $(\pm 1,0)$ and vertices $(\pm 10,0)$. Sketch the graph.
 c. Describe the shape of an ellipse that has an eccentricity close to 0.
 d. Describe the shape of an ellipse that has an eccentricity close to 1.

33. $(\sqrt{5}, 0), (-\sqrt{5}, 0)$

34. $(0, 2\sqrt{3}), (0, -2\sqrt{3})$

35. $(0, 4\sqrt{2}), (0, -4\sqrt{2})$

36. $(0, \sqrt{21}), (0, -\sqrt{21})$

37. $(0, 2\sqrt{7}), (0, -2\sqrt{7})$

38. $(0, 1), (0, -1)$

39. $(-3, 8), (-3, 2)$

40. $(-2, \sqrt{2}), (-2, -\sqrt{2})$

42. Multiple Choice Which equation represents the ellipse with foci on the x-axis, major axis 9 units long, minor axis 4 units long, and center at the origin? **B**
 A $\frac{x^2}{4} + \frac{y^2}{9} = 1$ **B** $\frac{x^2}{20.25} + \frac{y^2}{4} = 1$ **C** $\frac{x^2}{9} + \frac{y^2}{4} = 1$ **D** $\frac{x^2}{4} + \frac{y^2}{20.25} = 1$

43. a. Critical Thinking An ellipse has foci very close to the center. Its minor axis has length 2. Explain why its shape is close to that of a circle.
 b. Is a circle also an ellipse? Explain. **a–b. See back of book.**

Lesson 10-4 Ellipses **571**

3. Practice

Assignment Guide

1 A B 1-17, 44-49, 51-53, 62, 63

2 A B 18-43, 50, 54-61, 64
C Challenge 65-68

Test Prep 69-72
Mixed Review 73-83

Homework Quick Check

To check students' understanding of key skills and concepts, go over Exercises 15, 29, 41, 48, 62, 64.

Teaching Tip

Exercise 41 Have students look up the word *eccentric* in a dictionary or thesaurus. Suggest additional meanings such as *irregular* or *abnormal* to help students further understand the mathematical meaning of the word.

Exercise 42 Ask: *If the foci are on the x-axis, is the major axis horizontal or vertical?* **horizontal** *How do you know?* **major axis contains the foci**

Differentiated Instruction Resources

GPS Guided Problem Solving	L3
Enrichment	L4
Reteaching	L2
Practice	L3

---

1. $\frac{x^2}{16} + \frac{y^2}{9} = 1$

2. $\frac{x^2}{4} + y^2 = 1$

3. $\frac{x^2}{9} + y^2 = 1$

4. $x^2 + \frac{y^2}{36} = 1$

5. $\frac{x^2}{16} + \frac{y^2}{49} = 1$

6. $\frac{x^2}{36} + \frac{y^2}{25} = 1$

7. $\frac{x^2}{81} + \frac{y^2}{4} = 1$

8. $\frac{x^2}{9} + \frac{y^2}{25} = 1$

27. $\frac{x^2}{100} + \frac{y^2}{64} = 1$

28. $\frac{x^2}{64} + \frac{y^2}{128} = 1$

29. $\frac{x^2}{89} + \frac{y^2}{64} = 1$

30. $\frac{x^2}{4} + \frac{y^2}{20} = 1$

31. $\frac{x^2}{245} + \frac{y^2}{49} = 1$

32. $\frac{x^2}{514} + \frac{y^2}{225} = 1$

1. Write an equation in standard form of an ellipse that has a vertex at $(-4, 0)$, a co-vertex at $(0, 1)$, and is centered at the origin.
$$\frac{x^2}{16} + \frac{y^2}{1} = 1$$

2. Find an equation of an ellipse centered at the origin that is 14 units wide and 8 units high.
$$\frac{x^2}{49} + \frac{y^2}{16} = 1$$

3. Find the foci of an ellipse with the equation $25x^2 + 36y^2 = 900$. Graph the ellipse. $(\pm\sqrt{11}, 0)$

Alternative Assessment

Have students work in pairs. Each student uses one of the two techniques explained in the technology tip for Example 4 to graph an ellipse on their calculator. Students trade calculators and must determine the equation of the ellipse shown, specifically noting the vertices, co-vertices, and foci. Students should check the settings for the viewing window to help them.

Connection to Astronomy

Exercise 66 Challenge interested students to make a table listing the planets and their orbit eccentricities. They may also wish to include details about the orbits of moons and comets.

Connection to Science

Exercise 68 Many science museums have whispering galleries. If a museum near your city has one, encourage students to visit the museum to experience the whispering gallery for themselves.

44. $\frac{x^2}{9} + \frac{y^2}{4} = 1$

45. $\frac{x^2}{16} + y^2 = 1$

46. $x^2 + \frac{y^2}{9} = 1$

47. $\frac{x^2}{4} + \frac{y^2}{16} = 1$

50. $\frac{x^2}{4} + \frac{y^2}{3} = 1$

51. $\frac{x^2}{25} + \frac{y^2}{4} = 1$

52. $\frac{x^2}{121} + \frac{y^2}{81} = 1$

53. $\frac{x^2}{702.25} + \frac{y^2}{210.25} = 1$

54. $\frac{x^2}{169} + \frac{y^2}{144} = 1$

55. $\frac{x^2}{256} + \frac{y^2}{324} = 1$

56. $\frac{x^2}{72.25} + \frac{y^2}{90.25} = 1$

57. $\frac{x^2}{400} + \frac{y^2}{100} = 1$

58. $\frac{x^2}{16} + \frac{y^2}{12} = 1$

59. $\frac{x^2}{16} + \frac{y^2}{25} = 1$

60. $\frac{x^2}{39} + \frac{y^2}{64} = 1$

61. $\frac{x^2}{36} + \frac{y^2}{27} = 1$

62. $\frac{x^2}{4} + \frac{y^2}{9} = 1$

63. $\frac{x^2}{18} + \frac{y^2}{20} = 1$

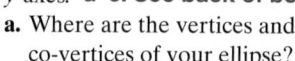

Homework Video Tutor
Visit: PHSchool.com
Web Code: age-1004

Write an equation for each ellipse.

44.

45.

46.

47.
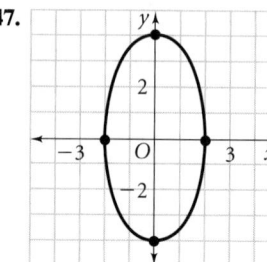

48. **Error Analysis** A student claims that an ellipse has vertices at $(\pm 3, 0)$ and co-vertices at $(0, \pm 7)$. What is the student's error? **See back of book.**

49. **Open-Ended** Find a real-world design that uses ellipses. Place a coordinate grid over the design and write an equation of the ellipse. **Check students' work.**

Write an equation of an ellipse in standard form with center at the origin and with the given characteristics.

50. focus $(1, 0)$, width 4

51. $a = 5$, $b = 2$, width 10

52. vertex $(-11, 0)$, co-vertex $(0, 9)$

53. height 29, width 53

54. focus $(-5, 0)$, co-vertex $(0, -12)$

55. $c^2 = 68$, vertex $(0, -18)$

56. focus $(0, 3\sqrt{2})$, height 19

57. focus $(10\sqrt{3}, 0)$, width 40

58. focus $(2, 0)$, x-intercept 4

59. focus $(0, 3)$, y-intercept 5

60. focus $(0, -5)$, y-intercept 8

61. focus $(3, 0)$, x-intercept -6

62. $a = 3$, $b = 2$, width 4

63. $a = 2\sqrt{5}$, $b = 3\sqrt{2}$, width $6\sqrt{2}$

64. Draw an ellipse by placing two tacks in a piece of graph paper laid over a piece of cardboard. Place a loop of string around the tacks. With your pencil keeping the string taut, draw around the tacks. Mark the center of your ellipse $(0, 0)$ and draw the x- and y-axes. **a–c. See back of book.**
   a. Where are the vertices and co-vertices of your ellipse?
   b. Where are the foci?
   c. Write the equation of your ellipse.

C Challenge 65. **Writing** The area of a circle is πr^2. The area of an ellipse is πab. Explain the connection. **See back of book.**

66a. 3×10^6 mi

b. about 0.016

c. $\dfrac{x^2}{8.649 \times 10^{15}} + \dfrac{y^2}{8.64675 \times 10^{15}} = 1$

66. Astronomy The sun is at a focus of Earth's elliptical orbit.

a. Find the distance from the sun to the other focus.

b. Refer to Exercise 41 for the definition of eccentricity. What is the eccentricity of the orbit?

c. Write an equation of Earth's orbit. Assume that the major axis is horizontal.

Earth sun

9.45×10^7 mi from sun (farthest)

9.15×10^7 mi from sun (nearest)

Resources
For additional practice with a variety of test item formats:
- Standardized Test Prep, p. 595
- Test-Taking Strategies, p. 590
- Test-Taking Strategies with Transparencies

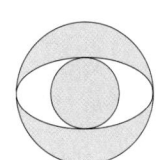

67. An ellipse and two circles share a center. The major axis of the ellipse is twice as long as its minor axis. The diameter of the larger circle is the same length as the major axis of the ellipse. The diameter of the smaller circle is the same length as the minor axis of the ellipse. The area of an ellipse is πab. Compare the areas of the blue and white regions at the left. **area of blue region = 3(area of white region)**

68. Acoustics In "whispering galleries" a sound made at one focus can be clearly heard at the other focus, even though very little can be heard by someone in between. Suppose an elliptical room measures 320 ft long and 150 ft wide. How far would the listener have to be from the source of the sound in order to hear it?

$10\sqrt{799}$ **or about 282.7 ft**

Test Prep

Multiple Choice

69. The point $A(-10, 0)$ is on the ellipse with equation $\dfrac{x^2}{100} + \dfrac{y^2}{64} = 1$. What is the sum of the distances $AF_1 + AF_2$, where F_1 and F_2 are the foci? **D**

A. 10   B. 12   C. 14   D. 20

70. What is the length of the major axis on the graph of $\dfrac{x^2}{100} + \dfrac{y^2}{64} = 1$? **J**

F. 12   G. $2\sqrt{41}$ H. 16   J. 20

71. What is the length of the minor axis of the graph of $\dfrac{x^2}{100} + \dfrac{y^2}{64} = 1$? **C**

A. 12   B. $2\sqrt{41}$ C. 16   D. 20

Short Response

72. Explain how to find an equation for the ellipse, centered at the origin, that is 50 units wide and 40 units high. **See back of book.**

Mixed Review

Lesson 10-3

Write an equation of a circle with the given center and radius.

73. center $(2, -3)$, radius 6
$(x - 2)^2 + (y + 3)^2 = 36$

74. center $(-4, 7)$, radius 11
$(x + 4)^2 + (y - 7)^2 = 121$

Lesson 9-4

Simplify each expression. What are the restrictions on the variable?

75–77. See back of book. **75.** $\dfrac{3x}{6x^2 - 9x^5}$ **76.** $\dfrac{x^2 - 36}{x^2 + 5x - 6}$ **77.** $\dfrac{x^2 - 3x - 10}{x^3 + 8}$

Lesson 8-4

Write each logarithmic expression as a single logarithm.

78. $\log 3 + \log 5$ **log 15**   **79.** $\log_3 12 - \log_3 2$ **$\log_3 6$** **80.** $3 \log 2 - \log 4$ **log 2**

81. $5 \log 2 + \log 10$ **log 320** **82.** $\log x - \log y$ **$\log \frac{x}{y}$**   **83.** $k \log 5 - \log 4$ **$\log \frac{5^k}{4}$**

Hyperbolas

Objectives
1 To graph hyperbolas
2 To find and use the foci of a hyperbola

Examples
1 Graphing a Hyperbola
2 Finding the Foci of a Hyperbola
3 Real-World Connection

Math Background

Students learn that the definition of a hyperbola closely resembles that of an ellipse in that it depends on the distances between a set of points in a plane to two fixed points called foci. Students will revisit graphing hyperbolas in calculus courses as the graphs lend themselves well to the study of limits.

More Math Background: p. 544D

Lesson Planning and Resources

See p. 544E for a list of the resources that support this lesson.

Bell Ringer Practice

✓ **Check Skills You'll Need**
For intervention, direct students to:

Linear Equations
Lesson 2-2: Examples 4–6
Extra Skills and Word Problems Practice, Ch. 2

What You'll Learn

• To graph hyperbolas

• To find and use the foci of a hyperbola

. . . And Why

To write an equation that models the path of Voyager 2 around Saturn, as in Example 3

 Check Skills You'll Need **for Help** Lesson 2-2 and Skills Handbook page 874

Write an equation of a line in slope-intercept form using the given information.

1. rise -5, run 2, through the origin   **2.** through $(3, 1)$ and $(9, 3)$

Solve each equation for y.   **1–5. See margin p. 575.**

3. $\frac{x^2}{4} - \frac{y^2}{16} = 1$ **4.** $\frac{y^2}{9} - \frac{x^2}{25} = 1$ **5.** $\frac{x^2}{36} - \frac{y^2}{81} = 1$

🔊 **New Vocabulary**   • hyperbola   • transverse axis   • focus of a hyperbola
• vertices of a hyperbola

---

1 Graphing Hyperbolas Centered at the Origin

Vocabulary Tip

<u>Hyperbola</u> comes from a Greek word for "greater." The cutting plane of a hyperbola makes a greater angle with the base than does the side of the cone. See p. 547.

1. column 1: 60, 27, 33
column 2: 20, 53, 33
column 3: 48, 14, 34
column 4: 8, 43, 35
column 5: 41, 7, 34
column 6: 20, 54, 34
column 7: 63, 30, 33

Activity: Analyzing Hyperbolas

1. The diagram below shows the shape of a hyperbola. Measure the distances to the nearest millimeter to complete the table. **See left.**

Distance	P_1	P_2	P_3	...
Distance From F_1	■	■	■	■
Distance From F_2	■	■	■	■
$|PF_1 - PF_2|$	■	■	■	■

2. **Make a Conjecture** What is the relationship between the distances from the points F_1 and F_2 to any point on the hyperbola? $|PF_1 - PF_2|$ is constant.

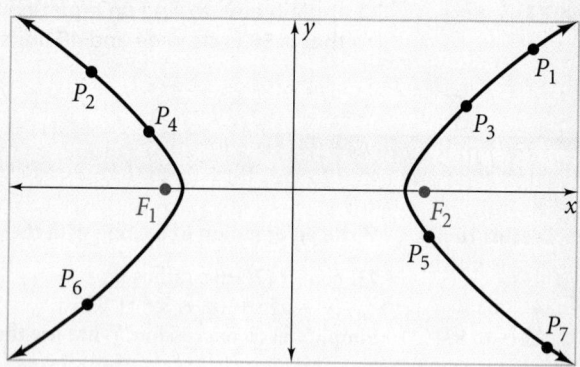

Hyperbolas play an important role in science and navigation. Some comets follow hyperbolic paths.

Differentiated Instruction   **Solutions for All Learners**

Special Needs **L1**
Have a student write the equation of an ellipse on the board. Show how the equation for a hyperbola involves subtraction instead of addition. Then compare equations for ellipses and hyperbolas that are oriented vertically and horizontally.
learning style: visual

Below Level **L2**
Point out to students that the hyperbola is the only conic section with asymptotes. While a parabola may appear to have asymptotes, it does not.
learning style: verbal

Definition   Hyperbola

A **hyperbola** is a set of points P in a plane such that the absolute value of the difference between the distances from P to two fixed points F_1 and F_2 is a constant k.

$$|PF_1 - PF_2| = k, \text{ where } k < F_1F_2.$$

Each fixed point F is a **focus of a hyperbola.** The segment that lies on the line containing the foci and has endpoints on a hyperbola is the **transverse axis.** The endpoints are the **vertices of a hyperbola.** The midpoint of the segment is the center of a hyperbola.

Below are the standard forms of the equation of a hyperbola centered at $(0, 0)$.

Vocabulary Tip

An <u>asymptote</u> is a line that a graph approaches.

$$\frac{x^2}{a^2} - \frac{y^2}{b^2} = 1$$ standard form of an equation of a hyperbola with a horizontal transverse axis

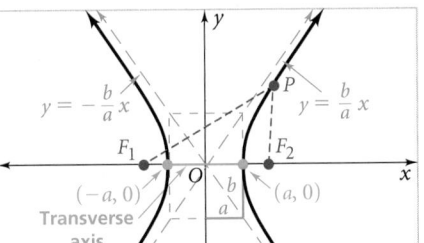

foci: F_1, F_2

vertices: $(\pm a, 0)$

asymptotes: $y = \pm \frac{b}{a}x$

x-intercepts: $\pm a$

y-intercepts: none

$$\frac{y^2}{a^2} - \frac{x^2}{b^2} = 1$$ standard form of an equation of a hyperbola with a vertical transverse axis

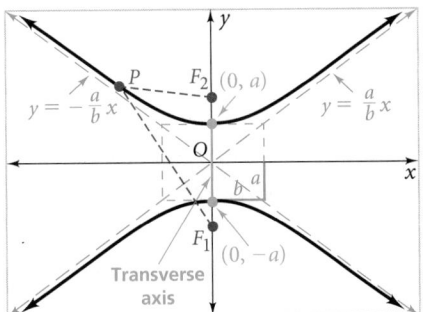

foci: F_1, F_2

vertices: $(0, \pm a)$

asymptotes: $y = \pm \frac{a}{b}x$

x-intercepts: none

y-intercepts: $\pm a$

To graph a hyperbola, use the standard form of the equation to find the values of a and b. You can use a and b to find and graph the vertices and to draw a central rectangle that is used to guide the graph.

Draw the asymptotes through the diagonals of the central rectangle. Then draw the branches of the hyperbola through the vertices so they approach the asymptotes.

Lesson 10-5   Hyperbolas   **575**

---

2. Teach

Guided Instruction

Activity

Tactile Learners

Once students have made all the measurements from the diagram, have them reproduce the diagram on the classroom floor. Challenge a team of students to choose a scale for the model and then convert the distances in the diagram to distances for the floor. They can use different colors of tape or chalk for the axes, the rectangle, and the asymptotes, string for the hyperbola, and different colored counters for the foci and vertices.

Key Concepts

Teaching Tip

The amount of information presented in the diagrams may overwhelm students. Rather than presenting all the facts at once, draw each hyperbola on the board. Then step by step add the details to your diagram. At each step, introduce the facts and formulas one by one. Before you introduce each new fact, ask students questions about the fact you presented.

Check Skills You'll Need

1. $y = -\frac{5}{2}x$

2. $y = \frac{1}{3}x$

3. $y = \pm 2\sqrt{x^2 - 4}$

4. $y = \pm\frac{3}{5}\sqrt{x^2 + 25}$

5. $y = \pm\frac{3}{2}\sqrt{x^2 - 36}$

Advanced Learners L4

Have students research Boyle's law and graph $PV = 36$. What are the asymptotes?

English Language Learners ELL

Note that the term *transverse* does not always apply to the *x*- axis or *y*-axis. In fact, it is not necessarily horizontal or vertical. *Transverse* means to cut across. Students should think of the transverse axis as crossing from one vertex to the other.

learning style: verbal

learning style: verbal

575

Additional Example

1 Graph $4x^2 - 16y^2 = 64$.

Guided Instruction

2 EXAMPLE **Technology Tip**

Graphs may be verified using the graphing calculator. Solve the equation for y to get $y = \pm\frac{1}{3}\sqrt{x^2 - 36}$ and enter both functions into the graphing calculator. Also enter $y = \pm\frac{1}{3}x$, the equations of the asymptotes, as two separate functions. You may also wish to point out that a^2 is not necessarily the larger of the two denominators in the standard form of an equation of a hyperbola as it was for an ellipse. Rather, determining which denominator is a^2 is based on which term is added in the formula.

3 EXAMPLE **Alternative Method**

Some students may feel overwhelmed by the large numbers in this example. Solve a simplified version of this example using $a = 3$ and $c = 5$. Once students understand this example have them use it as a guide for solving Example 3.

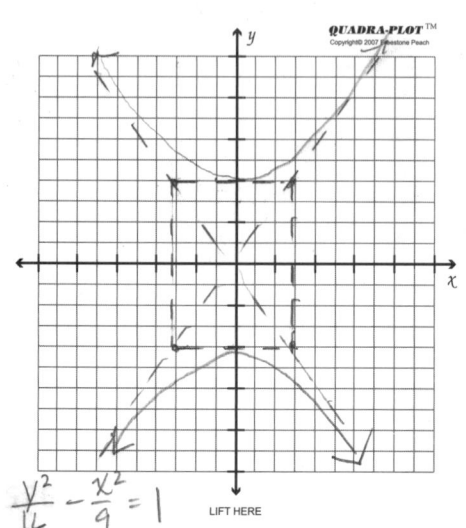

1 EXAMPLE **Graphing a Hyperbola**

Graph $9x^2 - 25y^2 = 225$.

$9x^2 - 25y^2 = 225$

$$\frac{x^2}{25} - \frac{y^2}{9} = 1 \qquad \textbf{Rewrite the equation in standard form.}$$

The equation is of the form $\frac{x^2}{a^2} - \frac{y^2}{b^2} = 1$, so the transverse axis is horizontal. Since $a^2 = 25$ and $b^2 = 9$, $a = 5$ and $b = 3$.

Step 1 Graph the vertices. Since the transverse axis is horizontal, the vertices lie on the x-axis. The coordinates are $(\pm a, 0)$, or $(\pm 5, 0)$.

Step 2 Use the values of a and b to draw the central rectangle. The lengths of its sides are $2a$ and $2b$, or 10 and 6.

Step 3 Draw the asymptotes. The equations of the asymptotes are $y = \pm\frac{b}{a}x$ or $y = \pm\frac{3}{5}x$. The asymptotes contain the diagonals of the central rectangle.

Step 4 Sketch the branches of the hyperbola through the vertices so they approach the asymptotes.

1.

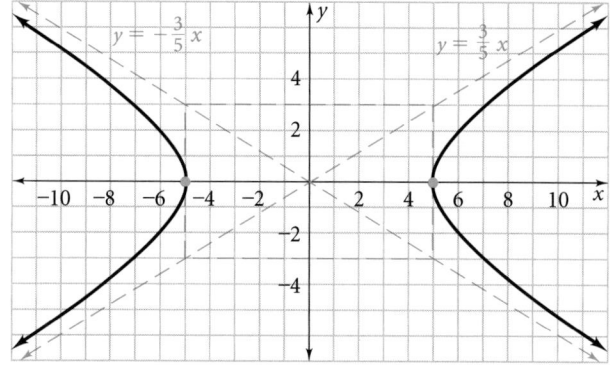

Quick Check **1** Graph the hyperbola with equation $\frac{y^2}{16} - \frac{x^2}{9} = 1$. **See left.**

2 Using the Foci of a Hyperbola

Use $(\pm c, 0)$ for the coordinates of the foci if the transverse axis is horizontal or $(0, \pm c)$ if it is vertical.

The distance between the foci, $2c$, is also the length of the diagonal of the central rectangle.

You can find the value of c using the Pythagorean Theorem.

$$c^2 = a^2 + b^2$$

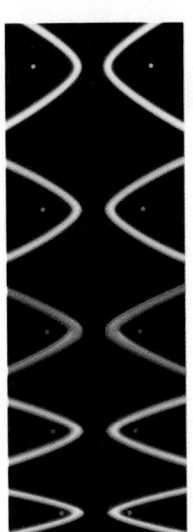

The figures above show how the shape of a hyperbola changes with decreased distances between the foci and the vertices.

Find the foci of the graph $\frac{x^2}{36} - \frac{y^2}{4} = 1$. Draw the graph.

The equation is in the form $\frac{x^2}{a^2} - \frac{y^2}{b^2} = 1$, so the transverse axis is horizontal; $a^2 = 36$ and $b^2 = 4$.

$c^2 = a^2 + b^2$ **Use the Pythagorean Theorem.**

$\quad = 36 + 4$ **Substitute 36 for a^2 and 4 for b^2.**

$\quad c = \sqrt{40} \approx 6.3$ **Find the square root of each side of the equation.**

The foci $(\pm c, 0)$ are approximately $(-6.3, 0)$ and $(6.3, 0)$. The vertices $(\pm a, 0)$ are $(6, 0)$ and $(-6, 0)$. The asymptotes are the lines $y = \pm\frac{b}{a}x$, or $y = \pm\frac{1}{3}x$.

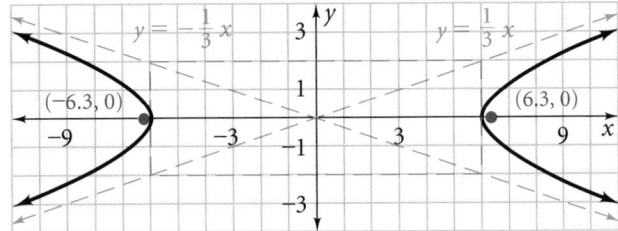

✓ **Quick Check** ❷ Find the foci of $\frac{x^2}{25} - \frac{y^2}{9} = 1$. Draw the graph. **See left.**

You can use the value of c to write the equation of a hyperbola.

3 EXAMPLE Real-World Connection

Space As a spacecraft approaches a planet, the gravitational pull of the planet changes the spacecraft's path to a hyperbola that diverges from its asymptote. Find an equation that models the path of Voyager 2 around Saturn, given that $a = 332{,}965$ km and $c = 492{,}788.2$ km.

Assume that the center of the hyperbola is at the origin and that the transverse axis is horizontal. The equation will be in the form $\frac{x^2}{a^2} - \frac{y^2}{b^2} = 1$.

$c^2 = a^2 + b^2$ **Use the Pythagorean Theorem.**

$(492{,}788.2)^2 = (332{,}965)^2 + b^2$ **Substitute.**

$b^2 = (492{,}788.2)^2 - (332{,}965)^2$ **Solve for b^2.**

$\quad \approx 1.320 \times 10^{11}$ **Use a calculator.**

$\dfrac{x^2}{1.109 \times 10^{11}} - \dfrac{y^2}{1.320 \times 10^{11}} = 1$ **Substitute a^2 and b^2.**

The path of Voyager 2 around Saturn can be modeled by
$$\frac{x^2}{1.109 \times 10^{11}} - \frac{y^2}{1.320 \times 10^{11}} = 1.$$

✓ **Quick Check** ❸ Find an equation that models the path of Voyager 2 around Jupiter, given that $a = 2{,}184{,}140$ km and $c = 2{,}904{,}906.2$ km.
$$\frac{x^2}{4.770 \times 10^{12}} - \frac{y^2}{3.668 \times 10^{12}} = 1$$

Online active math

For: Hyperbola Activity
Use: Interactive Textbook, 10-5

2. $(\sqrt{34}, 0), (-\sqrt{34}, 0)$;

Additional Examples

❷ Find the foci of the graph $\frac{y^2}{4} - \frac{x^2}{9} = 1$. Draw the graph. $(0, \pm\sqrt{13})$

❸ As a spacecraft approaches a planet, the gravitational pull of the planet changes the spacecraft's path to a hyperbola that diverges from its asymptote. Find an equation that models the path of the spacecraft around the planet given that $a = 300{,}765$ km and $c = 424{,}650$ km. Assume that the center of the hyperbola is at the origin and that the transverse axis is horizontal.
$$\frac{x^2}{9.046 \times 10^{10}} - \frac{y^2}{8.987 \times 10^{10}} = 1$$

Resources
• Daily Notetaking Guide 10-5   **L3**

Closure

Ask students to explain how to graph a hyperbola and how to find its foci. Also, explain how the foci can be used to write the equation of a hyperbola. **To graph a hyperbola, use the standard form of the equation to determine the values of a and b. Use a and b to find the vertices and asymptotes. Draw the corresponding central rectangle and use it to guide the graph. The foci can be determined using the formula $c^2 = a^2 + b^2$, where c represents the distance that a focus is from the center of the hyperbola. Thus, given any two values among a, b, and c, this relationship can be used to find the missing value. Then, the equation of the hyperbola can be written using the values of a and b.**

577

Assignment Guide

▼ **1** A B 1-9, 27-31, 33-36, 38, 40-46

▼ **2** A B 10-26, 32, 37, 39
C Challenge 47-48

Test Prep 49-54
Mixed Review 55-63

Homework Quick Check
To check students' understanding of key skills and concepts, go over Exercises 7, 20, 32, 36, 39, 47.

Error Prevention!

Exercise 1–18 Suggest students check their graphs using graphing calculators.

Teaching Tip

Exercise 30–32 Encourage students to ask themselves these questions as they work through each problem:
• What do I know?
• What do I need to know?
• What new information can I find with what I have?

578

EXERCISES

For more exercises, see *Extra Skill and Word Problem Practice*.

Practice and Problem Solving

A Practice by Example

GO for Help

Example 1
(page 576)

Graph each equation. 1–18. See back of book.

1. $\frac{x^2}{16} - \frac{y^2}{4} = 1$ **2.** $\frac{y^2}{169} - \frac{x^2}{16} = 1$ **3.** $\frac{x^2}{25} - \frac{y^2}{36} = 1$

4. $x^2 - 4y^2 = 4$ **5.** $36y^2 - 9x^2 = 324$ **6.** $25x^2 - 16y^2 = 400$

7. $9x^2 - 49y^2 = 441$ **8.** $25x^2 - 35y^2 = 875$ **9.** $81y^2 - 9x^2 = 729$

Example 2
(page 577)

Find the foci of each hyperbola. Then draw the graph.

10. $\frac{y^2}{81} - \frac{x^2}{16} = 1$ **11.** $\frac{y^2}{49} - \frac{x^2}{64} = 1$ **12.** $\frac{x^2}{121} - \frac{y^2}{144} = 1$

13. $\frac{x^2}{64} - \frac{y^2}{36} = 1$ **14.** $\frac{y^2}{25} - \frac{x^2}{100} = 1$ **15.** $\frac{x^2}{36} - \frac{y^2}{169} = 1$

16. $4y^2 - 25x^2 = 100$ **17.** $36x^2 - 8y^2 = 288$ **18.** $14y^2 - 28x^2 = 448$

Example 3
(page 577)

For Exercises 19–21, find the equation of a hyperbola with the given values. Assume that the transverse axis is horizontal. 19–26. See margin.

19. $a = 263, c = 407$ **20.** $b = 100, c = 500$ **21.** $a = 13,872, c = 19,043$

22. Find an equation that models the path of Voyager 2 around Jupiter, given that $a = 1,362,450$ km and $c = 1,543,781$ km.

B Apply Your Skills

Write the equation of a hyperbola with the given foci and vertices.

23. foci $(\pm 5, 0)$, vertices $(\pm 3, 0)$ **24.** foci $(0, \pm 13)$, vertices $(0, \pm 5)$

25. foci $(0, \pm 2)$, vertices $(0, \pm 1)$ **26.** foci $(\pm\sqrt{5}, 0)$, vertices $(\pm 2, 0)$

38. Answers may vary. Sample: axes of symmetry, vertices, asymptotes

Graph each equation. 27–32. See back of book.

27. $5x^2 - 12y^2 = 120$ **28.** $16x^2 - 20y^2 = 560$ **29.** $\frac{y^2}{20} - \frac{x^2}{5} = 1$

Write the equation of a hyperbola from the given information. Graph the equation. Place the center of each hyperbola at the origin of the coordinate plane.

30. Transverse axis is vertical and is 9 units; central rectangle is 9 units by 4 units.

31. Perimeter of central rectangle is 16 units; vertices are at $(0, 3)$ and $(0, -3)$.

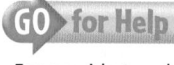
GO for Help

For a guide to solving Exercise 32, see p. 581.

32. (Distance from the center of a hyperbola to a focus)$^2 = 96$; endpoints of the transverse axis are at $\left(-\sqrt{32}, 0\right)$ and $\left(\sqrt{32}, 0\right)$.

 Solve each equation for *y*. Graph each relation on your graphing calculator. Use the TRACE feature to locate the vertices. 33–35. See back of book.

33. $x^2 - 2y^2 = 4$ **34.** $x^2 - y^2 = 1$ **35.** $3x^2 - y^2 = 2$

36. Rewrite the equation $4x^2 - 9y^2 = 36$ in standard form. Then write the equation **GPS** for a translation right 3 units and down 5 units. Draw the graph of each. See back of book.

GO Online
Homework Video Tutor
Visit: PHSchool.com
Web Code: age-1005

37. Open-Ended Choose two points on an axis to be the vertices of a hyperbola. Choose two other points on the same axis to be the foci. Write the equation of your hyperbola and draw its graph. Check students' work.

38. List the properties of a hyperbola that allow you to sketch its graph.
See above left.

---

19. $\frac{x^2}{69,169} - \frac{y^2}{96,480} = 1$

20. $\frac{x^2}{240,000} - \frac{y^2}{10,000} = 1$

21. $\frac{x^2}{192,432,384} - \frac{y^2}{170,203,465} = 1$

22. $\frac{x^2}{1.856 \times 10^{12}} - \frac{y^2}{5.270 \times 10^{11}} = 1$

23. $\frac{x^2}{9} - \frac{y^2}{16} = 1$

24. $\frac{y^2}{25} - \frac{x^2}{144} = 1$

25. $y^2 - \frac{x^2}{3} = 1$

26. $\frac{x^2}{4} - y^2 = 1$

40. $(0, \pm 1), y = \pm x$

41. $(\pm 1, 0), y = \pm\frac{1}{3}x$

42. $(0, \pm 8), y = \pm 2x$

43. $(\pm 5, 0), y = \pm\frac{4}{5}x$

44. $(0, \pm 4), y = \pm 2x$

39. Writing Describe the similarities and differences between hyperbolas and ellipses. **See back of book.**

40–45. See margin pp. 578–579.
Find the vertices and the asymptotes of each hyperbola.

40. $y^2 - x^2 = 1$ **41.** $x^2 - 9y^2 = 1$ **42.** $y^2 - 4x^2 = 64$

43. $16x^2 - 25y^2 = 400$ **44.** $9y^2 - 36x^2 = 144$ **45.** $25x^2 - 49y^2 = 1225$

46. a. Prove that the hyperbola $\frac{y^2}{a^2} - \frac{x^2}{b^2} = 1$ never intersects its asymptotes.

   b. Is $\frac{y^2}{16} - \frac{x^2}{9} = 4$ a hyperbola? Is $\frac{y^2}{16} - \frac{x^2}{9} = -1$ a hyperbola? Explain.
   a–b. See back of book.

C Challenge **47. Air Traffic Control** Suppose you are an air traffic controller directing the pilot of a plane on a hyperbolic flight path. You and another air traffic controller from a different airport send radio signals to the pilot simultaneously. The two airports are 48 km apart. The pilot's instrument panel tells him that the signal from your airport always arrives 100 μs (microseconds) before the signal from the other airport.

   a. To which airport is the plane closer?   **your airport**
   b. If the signals travel at a rate of 300 m/μs, what is the difference in distances from the plane to the two airports?   **30 km**
   c. Write the equation of the flight path. (*Hint:* $k = 2a$) $\frac{x^2}{225} - \frac{y^2}{351} = 1$
   d. Draw the hyperbola. Which branch represents the flight path?   **See margin.**

Real-World Connection

Careers Air traffic controllers coordinate the flow of air traffic by the use of radar and visual observation.

48. The function $y = \sqrt{x^2 - 9}$ represents part of a hyperbola. The tables at the right show the coordinates of several points on the graph.
   a. Explain why ERROR appears for some entries.   **a–d. See back of book.**
   b. Describe the relationship between the x- and y-coordinates as x gets larger.
   c. Critical Thinking Do you think that the x- and y-coordinates will ever be equal? Explain.
   d. Make a Conjecture What are the equations of the asymptotes of this hyperbola? Verify your answer by drawing the complete graph.

X	Y1
0	ERROR
1	ERROR
2	ERROR
3	0
4	2.6458
5	4
6	5.1962
X=0	

X	Y1
10	9.5394
20	19.774
30	29.85
40	39.887
50	49.91
60	59.925
70	69.936
X=10	

Test Prep

Multiple Choice

49. Which hyperbola has ($\pm$6, 0) as its x-intercepts?   **D**
   A. $y^2 - x^2 = 36$ **B.** $\frac{y^2}{36} - \frac{x^2}{49} = 1$ **C.** $\frac{x^2}{25} - \frac{y^2}{36} = 1$ **D.** $\frac{x^2}{36} - \frac{y^2}{4} = 1$

50. Which hyperbola does NOT have (0, $\pm$4) as its y-intercepts?   **H**
   F. $y^2 - x^2 = 16$ **G.** $4y^2 - 16x^2 = 64$
   H. $\frac{x^2}{25} - \frac{y^2}{16} = 1$ **J.** $\frac{y^2}{16} - \frac{x^2}{9} = 1$

51. What are the x-intercepts of $\frac{y^2}{25} - \frac{x^2}{49} = 1$?   **D**
   A. ($\pm$7, 0)   **B.** ($\pm$5, 0)   **C.** (0, $\pm$5)   **D.** none

Short Response

52. What is the standard form of an equation of a hyperbola? Explain how to rewrite $25x^2 - 49y^2 = 1225$ in standard form.   **See back of book.**

45. ($\pm$7, 0), $y = \pm\frac{5}{7}x$

47d.

the branch that contains the vertex closest to your airport

PowerPoint

Lesson Quiz

1. Graph $16y^2 - 9x^2 = 144$.

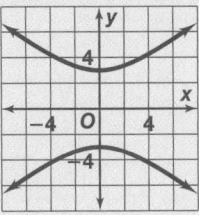

2. Find the foci of the graph $\frac{x^2}{4} - \frac{y^2}{36} = 1$. Draw the graph.   ($\pm 2\sqrt{10}$, 0)

3. Find the equation of a hyperbola that has one focus located at (4, 0) and one vertex located at (-2, 0). Assume that the center of the hyperbola is at the origin. $\frac{x^2}{4} - \frac{y^2}{12} = 1$

Alternative Assessment

Have students work in pairs. On a sheet of paper, each group writes the equations of two hyperbolas centered at the origin, one with a horizontal transverse axis and one with a vertical transverse axis. They both have the same asymptotes and a and b are both integers between 1 and 5 inclusive (or other appropriate integers based on the size of the Geoboards). Students fold the piece of paper and leave it on the desk. Using a Geoboard and rubber bands, each group creates a coordinate system and graphs the asymptotes of their hyperbolas. Groups then switch stations and must write the equations of the two hyperbolas from the asymptotes on the Geoboards. They verify their equations with those written on the piece of paper on the desk.

579

Resources

For additional practice with a variety of test item formats:
- Standardized Test Prep, p. 595
- Test-Taking Strategies, p. 590
- Test-Taking Strategies with Transparencies

 Checkpoint Quiz

Use this Checkpoint Quiz to check students' understanding of the skills and concepts of Lessons 10-4 through 10-5.

Resources
Grab & Go
- Checkpoint Quiz 2

53.
$$\frac{x^2}{1.19 \times 10^{12}} - \frac{y^2}{8.86 \times 10^{11}} = 1$$

54.
$$\frac{x^2}{2.76 \times 10^{10}} - \frac{y^2}{2.05 \times 10^{10}} = 1$$

Read the article below. Then complete Exercises 53 and 54.

Jupiter Bound: Voyager on its Way . . .

Voyager 1 explored the outer planets of our solar system. Its path was a hyperbola that depended on the planet that was closest.
The table below gives the distance c from each planet to the center of the hyperbola and the distance a from the vertex of the hyperbola to the center of the hyperbola. At each vertex, Voyager 1's path was directly between a planet and the center of the hyperbola.

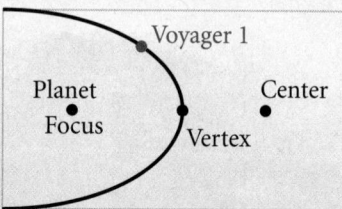

	Jupiter	Saturn
a	1,092,356 km	166,152 km
c	1,441,909.92 km	219,320.64 km

53. Write an equation of the path taken by Voyager 1 around Jupiter.
54. Write an equation of the path taken by Voyager 1 around Saturn.

Mixed Review

 for Help

Lesson 10-4

Find the vertices and co-vertices of each ellipse.

55. $\frac{x^2}{34} + \frac{y^2}{25} = 1$
$(\pm\sqrt{34}, 0), (0, \pm 5)$

56. $3x^2 + 2y^2 = 6$
$(0, \pm\sqrt{3}), (\pm\sqrt{2}, 0)$

57. $25x^2 + 16y^2 = 1600$
$(0, \pm 10), (\pm 8, 0)$

Lesson 9-5

Simplify each expression. 58–60. See margin.

58. $\frac{1}{5x} + \frac{1}{10x}$

59. $\frac{2x}{x^2 - 2x - 3} - \frac{7}{x^2 - 9}$

60. $\frac{4}{2x - 6} + \frac{x + 1}{x - 3}$

Lesson 8-5

Solve each equation.

61. $8^{2x} = 4$ $\frac{1}{3}$

62. $\log 8x = 3$ **125**

63. $2\log_3 x - \log_3 4 = 2$ 6

 Checkpoint Quiz 2   **Lessons 10-4 through 10-5**

Write an equation for each ellipse with the given foci and co-vertices. See left.

1. foci $(\pm 3, 0)$
co-vertices $(0, \pm 4)$

2. foci $(0, \pm 2)$
co-vertices $(\pm 5, 0)$

3. foci $(0, \pm 7)$
co-vertices $(\pm 10, 0)$

1. $\frac{x^2}{25} + \frac{y^2}{16} = 1$

2. $\frac{x^2}{25} + \frac{y^2}{29} = 1$

3. $\frac{x^2}{100} + \frac{y^2}{149} = 1$

10. $\frac{y^2}{64} - \frac{x^2}{12.25} = 1$

Find the foci for each conic section. Then draw the graph. 4–7. See margin.

4. $\frac{x^2}{16} - \frac{y^2}{49} = 1$

5. $\frac{y^2}{100} - \frac{x^2}{36} = 1$

6. $\frac{x^2}{4} - \frac{y^2}{81} = 1$

7. $\frac{y^2}{25} - \frac{x^2}{64} = 1$

Write an equation for a hyperbola centered at the origin with the given characteristics.

8. horizontal transverse axis, $a = 11, c = 15$ $\frac{x^2}{121} - \frac{y^2}{104} = 1$

9. vertices $(\pm 4, 0)$, perimeter of central rectangle 28 units $\frac{x^2}{16} - \frac{y^2}{9} = 1$

10. Transverse axis is vertical, 16 units long; central rectangle is 16 units by 7 units.

58. $\frac{3}{10x}$

59. $\frac{2x^2 - x - 7}{x^3 + x^2 - 9x - 9}$

60. $\frac{x + 3}{x - 3}$

Checkpoint Quiz

4. $(\sqrt{65}, 0), (-\sqrt{65}, 0)$

5. $(0, 2\sqrt{34}), (0, -2\sqrt{34})$

6. $(\sqrt{85}, 0), (-\sqrt{85}, 0)$

7. $(0, \sqrt{89}), (0, -\sqrt{89})$

Understanding Math Problems

Students read an example problem in which the equation of a hyperbola is written from given information. Along with the worked-out problem are explanations for each step of the work.

Understanding Math Problems Read the problem below. Then let Michelle's thinking guide you through the solution. Check your understanding with the exercise at the bottom of the page.

Write the equation of a hyperbola from the given information. Graph the equation. Place the center of the hyperbola at the origin of the coordinate plane.

(Distance from the center of a hyperbola to a focus)^2 = 96; endpoints of the transverse axis are at $\left(-\sqrt{32}, 0\right)$ and $\left(\sqrt{32}, 0\right)$.

What Michelle Thinks

There is a lot of information here. I'll start with the second part. The endpoints of the transverse axis of a hyperbola are its vertices.

I know that the hyperbola opens horizontally, because the transverse axis lies on the *x*-axis. The vertices are at $(-a, 0)$ and $(a, 0)$, so I know the value of a^2.

Now I'll work on the first part of the given information. The distance from the center to the focus is c, which is also half the length of the diagonal of the central rectangle. I'll draw what I know so far.

Knowing c will help me find b! I can use the Pythagorean Theorem.

I'm ready to fill in the rest of the standard form of the equation for the hyperbola. Then I'll graph the hyperbola.

What Michelle Writes

Vertices: $\left(-\sqrt{32}, 0\right)$ and $\left(\sqrt{32}, 0\right)$

The transverse axis is horizontal, so the equation will look like $\dfrac{x^2}{a^2} - \dfrac{y^2}{b^2} = 1$.

$a = \sqrt{32}$, so $a^2 = 32$.

c = distance from center to focus
  = half length of diagonal

$c^2 = 96$, so $c = \sqrt{96}$

$b^2 = c^2 - a^2 = 96 - 32 = 64$

Equation:
$\dfrac{x^2}{32} - \dfrac{y^2}{64} = 1$

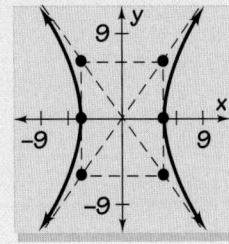

Guided Instruction

Have students explain some of the assumptions in the problem that are not otherwise explained. For example, Michelle states that she knows the transverse axis is the *x*-axis. Ask students to explain why. **The endpoints of the transverse axis both lie on the *x*-axis.**

Technology

Suggest that students use their graphing calculators to graph the hyperbola to check their work.

Exercise

Have students place a piece of blank paper over the "What Michelle Writes" column of the example problem. Then have students work out the Check Understanding problem on this piece of paper, using the clues in the "What Michelle Thinks" column as a guide.

EXERCISE

Write the equation of a hyperbola from the given information. Graph the equation. Place the center of the hyperbola at the origin of the coordinate plane.

(Distance from the center of a hyperbola to a focus)^2 = 40; endpoints of the transverse axis are at $(-4, 0)$ and $(4, 0)$.

$\dfrac{x^2}{16} - \dfrac{y^2}{24} = 1$

See margin for graph.

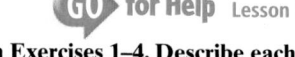

10-6
Translating Conic Sections

10-6

Objectives
1 To write the equation of a translated conic section
2 To identify a translated conic section from an equation

Examples
1 Writing the Equation of a Translated Ellipse
2 Writing the Equation of a Translated Hyperbola
3 Real-World Connection
4 Identifying a Translated Conic Section

Math Background

The techniques used to translate ellipses and hyperbolas are analogous to those used to translate parabolas and circles. In future courses, students will learn that these techniques can also be applied to three-dimensional surfaces.

More Math Background: p. 544D

Lesson Planning and Resources

See p. 544E for a list of the resources that support this lesson.

Bell Ringer Practice

✓ **Check Skills You'll Need**
For intervention, direct students to:

Translating Parabolas
Lesson 5-3: Examples 1 and 4
Extra Skills and Word
   Problems Practice, Ch. 5

What You'll Learn

• To write the equation of a translated conic section

• To identify a translated conic section from an equation

. . . Any Why

To explore the LORAN navigation system, as in Example 3

✓ **Check Skills You'll Need**

GO for Help   Lesson 5-3

Name the parent function for the equations in Exercises 1–4. Describe each equation as a translation of the parent function.   2, 4. See below.

1. $y = x^2 + 4$ $y = x^2$; 4 units up   **2.** $y = (x - 3)^2 - 2$

3. $y - 1 = x^2$ $y = x^2$; 1 unit up   **4.** $y = (x + 5)^2 + 6$

Rewrite each equation in vertex form.

5. $y = x^2 - 6x + 1$ $y = (x - 3)^2 - 8$ **6.** $y = x^2 + 10x - 7$ $y = (x + 5)^2 - 32$

7. $y = 2x^2 + 8x + 5$ $y = 2(x + 2)^2 - 3$ **8.** $y = 4x^2 - 12x + 3$

---

2. $y = x^2$; 3 units right and 2 units down   **8.** $y = 4\left(x - \frac{3}{2}\right)^2 - 6$

4. $y = x^2$; 5 units left, 6 units up

---

1   Writing Equations of Translated Conic Sections

Vocabulary Tip

A <u>translation</u> shifts a graph horizontally, vertically, or both.

1. They are the same size and shape, but their positions are different. Ellipse 2 is 2 units right and 3 units down from ellipse 1.

2. $\dfrac{(x - 2)^2}{36} + \dfrac{(y + 3)^2}{16} = 1$

3. $\dfrac{(x + 4)^2}{9} - \dfrac{(y - 1)^2}{4} = 1$

Technology Activity: Translating Conic Sections

1. Examine the calculator screen at the right. Describe the relationship between the two ellipses. How are they similar? How are they different?

2. The equation of ellipse ① is $\dfrac{x^2}{36} + \dfrac{y^2}{16} = 1$. Use what you know about translations to write the equation of ellipse ②.

Xmin=−9   Ymin=−9
Xmax=12   Ymax=5
Xscl=1   Yscl=1

3. The graph at the right shows the hyperbola with equation $\dfrac{x^2}{9} - \dfrac{y^2}{4} = 1$. Write the equation of the hyperbola that has been shifted four units left and one unit up.

Xmin=−12   Ymin=−8
Xmax=12   Ymax=8
Xscl=1   Yscl=1

Just as you have translated parabolas in Chapter 5 and circles in Lesson 10-3, you can also use parameters h and k to translate ellipses and hyperbolas. A translated ellipse or hyperbola has center (h, k).

---

582   Chapter 10   Quadratic Relations and Conic Sections

Differentiated Instruction   Solutions for All Learners

Special Needs   L1
Have students make a coordinate grid on the floor with masking tape, labeling the x- and y-axes. Then have students form the shapes of conic sections, such as a circle. Students them perform a translation of the conic section.

learning style: tactile

Below Level   L2
Be sure students understand that if there are squared terms in both x and y, they must complete the square for each variable.

learning style: verbal

Key Concepts

Summary	Families of Conic Sections	

Conic Section	Standard Form of Equation	
Parabola	Vertex $(0, 0)$ $y = ax^2$ $x = ay^2$	Vertex (h, k) $y - k = a(x - h)^2$ or $y = a(x - h)^2 + k$ $x - h = a(y - k)^2$ or $x = a(y - k)^2 + h$
Circle	Center $(0, 0)$ $x^2 + y^2 = r^2$	Center (h, k) $(x - h)^2 + (y - k)^2 = r^2$
Ellipse	Center $(0, 0)$ $\dfrac{x^2}{a^2} + \dfrac{y^2}{b^2} = 1$ $\dfrac{x^2}{b^2} + \dfrac{y^2}{a^2} = 1$	Center (h, k) $\dfrac{(x - h)^2}{a^2} + \dfrac{(y - k)^2}{b^2} = 1$ $\dfrac{(x - h)^2}{b^2} + \dfrac{(y - k)^2}{a^2} = 1$
Hyperbola	Center $(0, 0)$ $\dfrac{x^2}{a^2} - \dfrac{y^2}{b^2} = 1$ $\dfrac{y^2}{a^2} - \dfrac{x^2}{b^2} = 1$	Center (h, k) $\dfrac{(x - h)^2}{a^2} - \dfrac{(y - k)^2}{b^2} = 1$ $\dfrac{(y - k)^2}{a^2} - \dfrac{(x - h)^2}{b^2} = 1$

1 EXAMPLE Writing the Equation of a Translated Ellipse

Write an equation of an ellipse with center $(-3, -2)$, vertical major axis of length 8, and minor axis of length 6.

The length of the major axis is $2a$. So $2a = 8$ and $a = 4$. The length of the minor axis is $2b$. So $2b = 6$ and $b = 3$. Since the center is $(-3, -2)$, $h = -3$ and $k = -2$.

The major axis is vertical, so the equation has the form $\dfrac{(x - h)^2}{b^2} + \dfrac{(y - k)^2}{a^2} = 1$.

$\dfrac{(x - (-3))^2}{3^2} + \dfrac{(y - (-2))^2}{4^2} = 1$ **Substitute -3 for h and -2 for k.**

The equation of the ellipse is $\dfrac{(x + 3)^2}{9} + \dfrac{(y + 2)^2}{16} = 1$.

Check Solve the equation for y and graph both equations.

$$\dfrac{(x + 3)^2}{9} + \dfrac{(y + 2)^2}{16} = 1$$
$$16(x + 3)^2 + 9(y + 2)^2 = 144$$
$$9(y + 2)^2 = 144 - 16(x + 3)^2$$
$$(y + 2)^2 = \tfrac{1}{9}(144 - 16(x + 3)^2)$$
$$y + 2 = \pm\sqrt{\tfrac{1}{9}(144 - 16(x + 3)^2)}$$
$$y = -2 \pm \tfrac{1}{3}\sqrt{144 - 16(x + 3)^2}$$

1. $\dfrac{(x - 1)^2}{25} + \dfrac{(y + 4)^2}{4} = 1$

✓ Quick Check **1** Write an equation of an ellipse with center $(1, -4)$, horizontal major axis of length 10, and minor axis of length 4. Check your answer.

Lesson 10-6   Translating Conic Sections   **583**

---

2. Teach

Guided Instruction

Technology Activity
Teaching Tip
Tell students to think about how they translated parabolas and circles. Tell them to apply these methods to the equations of the ellipse and hyperbola.

1 EXAMPLE Alternative Method

You may wish to reinforce ideas that students developed in the Activity or previously. Encourage them to begin by writing the equation of an ellipse with center (0, 0), vertical major axis of length 8, and minor axis of length 6. Then, have students translate this ellipse so that its center is at $(-3, -2)$.

PowerPoint
Additional Examples

1 Write an equation of an ellipse with center $(-2, 4)$, vertical major axis of length 10, and minor axis of length 8.
$\dfrac{(x + 2)^2}{16} + \dfrac{(y - 4)^2}{25} = 1$

584

Problem Solving Hint

The midpoint of the segment joining (x_1, y_1) and (x_2, y_2) is $\left(\dfrac{x_1 + x_2}{2}, \dfrac{y_1 + y_2}{2}\right)$.

2. $\dfrac{(y-3)^2}{16} - \dfrac{(x-2)^2}{33} = 1$

✓ **Quick Check**

Real-World Connection

LORAN stands for *long range navigation*. It uses simultaneously broadcast radio signals from three transmitters to locate the ship's position at the intersection of the red and the blue hyperbolas.

---

② **EXAMPLE**   Writing the Equation of a Translated Hyperbola

Write an equation of a hyperbola with vertices $(0, 1)$ and $(6, 1)$, and foci $(-1, 1)$ and $(7, 1)$.

Draw a sketch. The center is the midpoint of the line joining the vertices. Its coordinates are $(3, 1)$.

The distance between the vertices is $2a$ and the distance between the foci is $2c$. $2a = 6$, so $a = 3$; $2c = 8$, so $c = 4$.

Find b^2 using the Pythagorean Theorem.
$$c^2 = a^2 + b^2$$
$$16 = 9 + b^2$$
$$b^2 = 7$$

The transverse axis is horizontal. The equation has form $\dfrac{(x-h)^2}{a^2} - \dfrac{(y-k)^2}{b^2} = 1$.

● The equation of the hyperbola is $\dfrac{(x-3)^2}{9} - \dfrac{(y-1)^2}{7} = 1$.

② Write an equation of a hyperbola with vertices $(2, -1)$ and $(2, 7)$, and foci $(2, 10)$ and $(2, -4)$.

③ **EXAMPLE**   Real-World ○ Connection

Navigation Some ships navigate using LORAN. The ship's equipment calculates the difference between the arrival times of simultaneously broadcast radio signals. The difference in arrival times indicates how much closer the ship is to one transmitter than to the other. The navigator then locates the ship on a hyperbola shown in red. The process is repeated using a second pair of transmitters to locate the ship on a hyperbola shown in blue.

All points on hyperbola #25800 as shown in the diagram are 48 mi closer to one transmitter than the other. The transmitters, at the foci, are 200 mi apart and are located at $(0, 0)$ and $(200, 0)$. Find the equation of hyperbola #25800.

Step 1 Find c. Since the foci are 200 mi apart, $2c = 200$, $c = 100$, and the center of the hyperbola is at $(100, 0)$.

Step 2 Find a by calculating the difference in the distances from the vertex at $(a + 100, 0)$ to the two foci.
$$48 = (a + 100) - [200 - (a + 100)]$$
$$= 2a$$
$$24 = a$$

Step 3 Find b^2.
$$c^2 = a^2 + b^2$$
$$(100)^2 = (24)^2 + b^2$$
$$10{,}000 = 576 + b^2$$
$$b^2 = 9424$$

● The equation of the hyperbola is $\dfrac{(x-100)^2}{24^2} - \dfrac{y^2}{9424} = 1$ or $\dfrac{(x-100)^2}{576} - \dfrac{y^2}{9424} = 1$.

✓ **Quick Check**   ③ Use the information from Example 3. Find the equation of the hyperbola with all points 56 mi closer to one transmitter than the other.

GO for Help

To review completing the square, go to page 281 and Lesson 5-7.

The equation $Ax^2 + Bxy + Cy^2 + Dx + Ey + F = 0$ is the general equation for all conic sections, where A and C are not both equal to zero. To determine which conic section the equation represents, write the equation in standard form by completing the square for the x- and y-terms.

4 EXAMPLE Identifying a Translated Conic Section

Multiple Choice Identify the conic section with equation
$4x^2 + y^2 - 24x + 6y + 9 = 0$.

Ⓐ circle; center $(3, -3)$ Ⓑ ellipse; foci $(3, -3 - 3\sqrt{3})$ and $(3, -3 + 3\sqrt{3})$
Ⓒ circle; center $(-3\sqrt{3}, 3\sqrt{3})$ Ⓓ ellipse; foci $(0, 3)$ and $(0, -3)$

Complete the square for the x- and y-terms to write the equation in standard form.

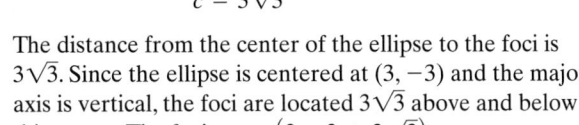

$$4x^2 + y^2 - 24x + 6y + 9 = 0$$

$$4x^2 - 24x + y^2 + 6y = -9 \qquad \text{Group the } x\text{- and } y\text{-terms.}$$

$$4(x^2 - 6x + \blacksquare) + (y^2 + 6y + \blacksquare) = -9 \qquad \text{Complete the square.}$$

$$4(x^2 - 6x + (-3)^2) + (y^2 + 6y + 3^2) = -9 + 4(-3)^2 + 3^2 \qquad \begin{array}{l}\text{Add } 4(-3)^2 \text{ and } 3^2 \\ \text{to each side.}\end{array}$$

$$4(x^2 - 6x + 9) + (y^2 + 6y + 9) = -9 + 36 + 9 \qquad \text{Simplify.}$$

$$4(x - 3)^2 + (y + 3)^2 = 36 \qquad \begin{array}{l}\text{Write the trinomials} \\ \text{as binomials squared.}\end{array}$$

$$\frac{4(x - 3)^2}{36} + \frac{(y + 3)^2}{36} = 1 \qquad \text{Divide each side by 36.}$$

$$\frac{(x - 3)^2}{9} + \frac{(y + 3)^2}{36} = 1 \qquad \text{Simplify.}$$

Test-Taking Tip

For equivalent equations, remember to add the same quantity to both sides.

The equation represents an ellipse. The center is $(3, -3)$. The major axis is vertical. Since $b^2 = 9, b = 3$. Since $a^2 = 36, a = 6$.

$$c^2 = a^2 - b^2 = 36 - 9$$
$$= 27$$
$$c = 3\sqrt{3}$$

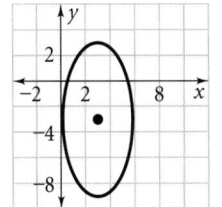

The distance from the center of the ellipse to the foci is $3\sqrt{3}$. Since the ellipse is centered at $(3, -3)$ and the major axis is vertical, the foci are located $3\sqrt{3}$ above and below this center. The foci are at $(3, -3 + 3\sqrt{3})$ and $(3, -3 - 3\sqrt{3})$. The correct choice is B.

4. circle with center $(6, -2)$ and radius $4\sqrt{3}$;

✓ **Quick Check** ④ Identify the conic section represented by $x^2 + y^2 - 12x + 4y = 8$. Sketch the graph. **See left.**

EXERCISES

For more exercises, see *Extra Skill and Word Problem Practice*.

Practice and Problem Solving

Ⓐ **Practice by Example**

GO for Help
Example 1
(page 583)

1–4. See margin.

Write an equation of an ellipse with the given characteristics. Check your answers.

1. center $(-2, 1)$, horizontal major axis of length 6, minor axis of length 4

2. center $(5, 3)$, vertical major axis of length 12, minor axis of length 8

3. center $(0, -4)$, horizontal major axis of length 12, minor axis of length 10

4. center $(3, -6)$, vertical major axis of length 14, minor axis of length 6

Assignment Guide

1 A B 1-11, 27, 29-54

2 A B 12-26, 28

C Challenge   55-58

Test Prep   59-65
Mixed Review   66-75

Homework Quick Check

To check students' understanding of key skills and concepts, go over Exercises 10, 20, 27, 34, 36, 44.

Differentiated Instruction Resources

GPS Guided Problem Solving	L3
Enrichment	L4
Reteaching	L2
Practice	L3

1. $\dfrac{(x + 2)^2}{9} + \dfrac{(y - 1)^2}{4} = 1$

2. $\dfrac{(x - 5)^2}{16} + \dfrac{(y - 3)^2}{36} = 1$

3. $\dfrac{x^2}{36} + \dfrac{(y + 4)^2}{25} = 1$

4. $\dfrac{(x - 3)^2}{9} + \dfrac{(y + 6)^2}{49} = 1$

586

Exercise 26 Ask: *What changes when an ellipse is translated?* **The location of its center, vertices and co-vertices, and foci** *What does not change when an ellipse is translated?* its shape—size and orientation—so that the relationship between all of the points on the ellipse are maintained

Error Prevention!

Exercises 37–48 Clarify that the equations given may represent conic sections that have already been translated from the origin. However, students are to translate these graphs 3 units right and 5 units up.

Careers

Exercise 56 Anthropologists study the beliefs, customs, and origins of people. Analyzing patterns often plays an important role in their work.

24. **Translate the equation** $\frac{x^2}{16} - \frac{y^2}{8} = 1$, **a hyperbola centered at (0, 0), 3 units left.**

27. **The hyperbola originally had center (0, 0) and a horizontal or vertical transverse axis. If the new center is (h, k), then the equations of the new asymptotes are obtained by replacing x with $x - h$ and y with $y - k$ in the equations of the original asymptotes.**

Example 2
(page 584)

Write an equation of a hyperbola with the given characteristics.

5. vertices $(1, -3)$ and $(-7, -3)$, foci $(2, -3)$ and $(-8, -3)$ $\quad \frac{(x + 3)^2}{16} - \frac{(y + 3)^2}{9} = 1$

6. vertices $(4, -1)$ and $(4, -5)$, foci $(4, 3)$ and $(4, -9)$ $\quad \frac{(y + 3)^2}{4} - \frac{(x - 4)^2}{32} = 1$

7. vertices $(2, 2)$ and $(-4, 2)$, foci $(6, 2)$ and $(-8, 2)$ $\quad \frac{(x + 1)^2}{9} - \frac{(y - 2)^2}{40} = 1$

 8. $\frac{(y + 1)^2}{25} - \frac{(x + 1)^2}{56} = 1$ 8. vertices $(-1, 4)$ and $(-1, -6)$, foci $(-1, 8)$ and $(-1, -10)$

9. vertices $(0, -2)$ and $(0, 4)$, foci $(0, 6)$ and $(0, -4)$ $\quad \frac{(y - 1)^2}{9} - \frac{x^2}{16} = 1$

Example 3
(page 584)

For Exercises 10–11, find the equation of each hyperbola described.

10. All points on the hyperbola are 72 units closer to one focus than the other. The foci are located at $(0, 0)$ and $(300, 0)$. $\quad \frac{(x - 150)^2}{1296} - \frac{y^2}{21,204} = 1$

11. All points on the hyperbola are 88 units closer to one focus than the other. The foci are located at $(0, 0)$ and $(350, 0)$. $\quad \frac{(x - 175)^2}{1936} - \frac{y^2}{28,689} = 1$

Example 4
(page 585)

12–23. See back of book.

Identify the conic section represented by each equation by writing the equation in standard form. For a parabola, give the vertex. For a circle, give the center and the radius. For an ellipse or a hyperbola, give the center and the foci. Sketch the graph.

12. $x^2 - 8x - y + 19 = 0$ 13. $x^2 + y^2 + 12x = 45$

14. $3x^2 + 6x + y^2 - 6y = -3$ 15. $x^2 + y^2 - 2x + 6y = 3$

16. $y^2 - x^2 + 6x - 4y = 6$ 17. $x^2 - 4y^2 - 2x - 8y = 7$

18. $x^2 + y^2 + 14y = -13$ 19. $y^2 - 2x - 4y = -10$

20. $4x^2 + 9y^2 + 16x - 54y = -61$ 21. $x^2 - y^2 + 6x + 10y = 17$

22. $x^2 + 4y^2 - 2x - 15 = 0$ 23. $9x^2 - 4y^2 - 24y = 72$

B Apply Your Skills

24. A conic section centered at the origin is translated. Describe the translation that would produce the equation $x^2 - 2y^2 + 6x - 7 = 0$. **See margin.**

25. **Critical Thinking** Use the equation $Ax^2 + Bxy + Cy^2 + Dx + Ey + F = 0$ to identify the shape of the graph that results in each case.
   a. $A = C = D = E = 0, B \neq 0, F \neq 0$ **hyperbola**
   b. $A = B = C = 0, D \neq 0, E \neq 0, F \neq 0$ **line**

26. **Multiple Choice** How does the translation of an ellipse affect the lengths of its axes? **C**
   Ⓐ Both increase in length.   Ⓑ Both decrease in length.
   Ⓒ Both stay the same length.   Ⓓ One increases; the other decreases.

 27. **Writing** Describe how the translation of a hyperbola affects the equations of its asymptotes. **See margin.**

28. **Critical Thinking** Campbell claims that $\frac{x^2}{10} + \frac{y^2}{10} = 1$ represents an ellipse. Monique disagrees. Whom do you support? Give a reasoned argument.
   Check students' work.

Write an equation for each conic section. Then sketch the graph.

29. circle with center $(-6, 9)$ and radius 9   **29–32. See back of book.**

30. ellipse with center $(3, 2)$, vertices $(9, 2)$ and $(-3, 2)$, and co-vertices $(3, 5)$ and $(3, -1)$

31. parabola with vertex $(2, -3)$ and focus $(2, 5)$

32. hyperbola with center $(6, -3)$, one focus $(6, 0)$, and one vertex $(6, -1)$

GO Online
Homework Video Tutor

Visit: PHSchool.com
Web Code: age-1006

33. $\dfrac{(x-1)^2}{9} + \dfrac{(y+1)^2}{16} = 1$

34. $\dfrac{(x-3)^2}{36} - \dfrac{(y+2)^2}{15.84} = 1$

Write the equation of each graph. In Exercise 35, each interval represents one unit.

33.

34.
GPS

35.

$(x+4)^2 + (y+4)^2 = 25$

36.
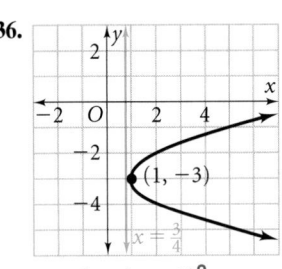
$x - 1 = (y+3)^2$

37. $(x-8)^2 + (y-2)^2 = 4$

38. $\dfrac{(x-6)^2}{64} + \dfrac{(y-2)^2}{36} = 1$

39. $y - 5 = 4(x-3)^2$

40. $\dfrac{(x-3)^2}{16} - \dfrac{(y-5)^2}{9} = 1$

41. $\dfrac{(x-5)^2}{36} - \dfrac{(y-8)^2}{25} = 1$

42. $\dfrac{(x-6)^2}{4} + \dfrac{(y-9)^2}{9} = 1$

43. $\dfrac{(x-2)^2}{16} + \dfrac{(y-7)^2}{9} = 1$

44. $\dfrac{x^2}{16} + \dfrac{(y-5)^2}{4} = 1$

45. $\dfrac{(x-4)^2}{16} - (y-9)^2 = 1$

46. $(x-8)^2 = 12(y-11)$

47. $\dfrac{x^2}{16} + \dfrac{(y-10)^2}{25} = 1$

48. $x^2 - (y-10)^2 = 1$

The graph of each equation is to be translated 3 units right and 5 units up. Write each new equation.   37–48. See left.

37. $(x-5)^2 + (y+3)^2 = 4$

38. $\dfrac{(x-3)^2}{64} + \dfrac{(y+3)^2}{36} = 1$

39. $y = 4x^2$

40. $9x^2 + 3x + 10 = 16y^2 + 154 + 3x$

41. $\dfrac{(x-2)^2}{36} - \dfrac{(y-3)^2}{25} = 1$

42. $\dfrac{(x-3)^2}{4} + \dfrac{(y-4)^2}{9} = 1$

43. $9x^2 + 16y^2 + 18x = 64y + 71$

44. $x^2 + 4y^2 + 6x - 7 = 0$

45. $x^2 - 16y^2 - 2x + 128y = 271$

46. $(x-5)^2 = 12(y-6)$

47. $25x^2 + 16y^2 + 150x = 160y - 225$

48. $x^2 - y^2 + 6x + 10y = 17$

Graph each pair of functions. Identify the conic section represented by the graph and write each equation in standard form.   49–54. See back of book.

49. $y = \sqrt{36 - 4x^2}$
$y = -\sqrt{36 - 4x^2}$

50. $y = \sqrt{4x^2 - 36}$
$y = -\sqrt{4x^2 - 36}$

51. $y = \sqrt{4x^2 + 36}$
$y = -\sqrt{4x^2 + 36}$

52. $y = \sqrt{36 - x^2}$
$y = -\sqrt{36 - x^2}$

53. $y = 0.5\sqrt{36 - x^2}$
$y = -0.5\sqrt{36 - x^2}$

54. $y = \sqrt{x - 4}$
$y = -\sqrt{x - 4}$

C Challenge

55. **Open-Ended** On a graphing calculator, create a design using three translated quadratic relations.   **Check students' work.**

56. **History** Some symbols of the writing system of the Ejagham, people who lived in Nigeria and Cameroon, are shown. The symbol for marriage consists of two parabolic shapes. Reproduce this symbol on a graphing calculator. What equations did you use?
Check students' work.

speech   divorce

discussion   marriage

57. Consider equations of the form $Ax^2 + By^2 + Cx + Dy + E = 0$.
   a. What must be true about A and B for the graph of the equation to be a circle? To be an ellipse? To be a hyperbola? To be a parabola?   **a–b. See margin.**
   b. Suppose $A = 1$ and $B = 1$. Must the graph be a circle? Explain.
   c. Suppose $A = 1, B = -1,$ and $C = D = E = 0$. Describe the graph.
   two intersecting lines ($y = x$ and $y = -x$).

Real-World Connection

This Nigerian cloth combines writing symbols and patterns.

Online lesson quiz, PHSchool.com, **Web Code:** aga-1006

Lesson 10-6 Translating Conic Sections   **587**

57a. $A = B$; $A \neq B$ and A and B have the same sign; A and B have opposite signs; $A = 0$ or $B = 0$, but not both A and B are zero.

b. No; answers may vary. Sample: If $C = D = E = 0$, then the graph will be the single point $(0, 0)$.

PowerPoint
Lesson Quiz

1. Write an equation of an ellipse with center $(-5, -2)$, horizontal major axis of length 6, and minor axis of length 4.
$\dfrac{(x+5)^2}{9} + \dfrac{(y+2)^2}{4} = 1$

2. Find an equation of a hyperbola with vertices $(0, -1)$ and $(4, -1)$, and foci $(-1, -1)$ and $(5, -1)$.
$\dfrac{(x-2)^2}{4} - \dfrac{(y+1)^2}{5} = 1$

3. Identify the conic section with equation $x^2 - 4x + y^2 + 2y = -1$. If it is a parabola, give the vertex. If it is a circle, give the center and radius. If it is an ellipse or a hyperbola, give the center and foci. Sketch the graph. **circle; center: $(2, -1)$, radius: 2**

Alternative Assessment

Arrange the desks in the classroom into rows and columns. Assign a desk near the center of the room to be the origin. Show students where the coordinate axes are and tell them that the desks are separated by units of one. Challenge each student to write down the equation of an ellipse and hyperbola using his or her desk as the center. In either case, students must write down the values that they have chosen for a and b, and find the foci. Have students indicate the general location of each of these points in the room. Finally, have students sketch a graph and discuss the results.

587

Resources

For additional practice with a variety of test item formats:
- Standardized Test Prep, p. 595
- Test-Taking Strategies, p. 590
- Test-Taking Strategies with Transparencies

58a. Earth:

$$\frac{x^2}{(149.60)^2} + \frac{y^2}{(149.58)^2} = 1$$

Mars:

$$\frac{x^2}{(227.9)^2} + \frac{y^2}{(226.9)^2} = 1$$

Mercury:

$$\frac{x^2}{(57.9)^2} + \frac{y^2}{(56.6)^2} = 1$$

WINDOW FORMAT
Xmin=−379.0322...
Xmax=379.03225...
Xscl=1
Ymin=−250
Ymax=250
Yscl=1

 58. Astronomy The dimensions of the elliptical orbits of three planets are given in millions of kilometers in the table. The sun is at one focus. The other focus is on the positive x-axis.

Planet	a	b
Earth	149.60	149.58
Mars	227.9	226.9
Mercury	57.9	56.6

a. Write an equation for each orbit and draw the curves on your graphing calculator. (Remember to adjust the viewing window.) **See margin.**

b. Reasoning Which orbit is most circular? Justify your reasoning. **Earth: $\frac{a}{b}$ is closest to 1 for Earth.**

Test Prep

Multiple Choice

59. An ellipse with center $(-4, -2)$ has a horizontal major axis of length 6 and a minor axis of length 4. Which equation represents the ellipse? **C**

A. $\dfrac{(x-4)^2}{4} - \dfrac{(y-2)^2}{9} = 1$ B. $\dfrac{(x+2)^2}{9} - \dfrac{(y+4)^2}{4} = 1$

C. $\dfrac{(x+4)^2}{9} + \dfrac{(y+2)^2}{4} = 1$ D. $\dfrac{(x+4)^2}{4} + \dfrac{(y+2)^2}{9} = 1$

60. The foci of a hyperbola are $(0, -4)$ and $(0, 8)$. Which additional information would allow you to write an equation for the hyperbola? **G**

   F. location of the center   **G.** location of one vertex

   H. midpoint of transverse axis   **J.** distance from the center to a focus

61. Which of the following is an equation of a parabola? **B**

   A. $2x^2 - 5y^2 + 4x - 36 = 0$ B. $2x^2 - 5y + 4x - 36 = 0$

   C. $2x^2 + 2y^2 + 4x - 12y - 36 = 0$ D. $2x^2 + 5y^2 - 36 = 0$

62. Which conic section is represented by the equation $x^2 + y^2 = 6x - 14y - 9$? **F**

   F. circle   **G.** ellipse   **H.** parabola   **J.** hyperbola

63. Which of the conic sections have more than one focus? **D**

   I. circle   II. parabola   III. ellipse   IV. hyperbola

   A. I and III   **B.** II and III   **C.** I and II   **D.** III and IV

Short Response

64. What are the coordinates of the foci of $4x^2 - 24x = 64 - 25y^2$?

65. A parabola with vertex at the origin and focus at $(-1, 0)$ is translated 3 units to the right and 4 units up. What is the equation of the translated parabola? Show your work. **64–65. See back of book.**

Mixed Review

GO for Help

Lesson 10-5

Find the foci of each hyperbola. Draw the graph. **66–68. See margin.**

66. $\dfrac{x^2}{49} - \dfrac{y^2}{36} = 1$ **67.** $8y^2 - 6x^2 = 72$ **68.** $4y^2 - 100x^2 = 400$

Lesson 9-6

Solve each equation. Check your answers.

69. $\dfrac{1}{3x+1} = \dfrac{1}{x^2-3}$ **−1, 4**   **70.** $\dfrac{2}{x+2} = \dfrac{6}{x^2-4}$ **5**   **71.** $\dfrac{5}{x^2-x} + \dfrac{3}{x-1} = 6$

                                                          about −0.4315, 1.9315

Lesson 8-6

Simplify each expression.

72. $\ln e$ **1**   **73.** $2 \ln e$ **2**   **74.** $\ln e^3$ **3**   **75.** $4 \ln e^2$ **8**

588   Chapter 10   Quadratic Relations and Conic Sections

66. $(\sqrt{85}, 0), (-\sqrt{85}, 0)$ **67.** $(0, \sqrt{21}), (0, -\sqrt{21})$ **68.** $(0, 2\sqrt{26}), (0, -2\sqrt{26})$

Solving Quadratic Systems

Activity Lab

Solving Quadratic Systems

Students solve systems that include quadratic equations both algebraically and graphically.

In Chapter 3 you solved systems of linear equations algebraically and graphically. You can use the same methods to solve systems that include quadratic equations.

1 ACTIVITY Solving Algebraically

Solve the system algebraically. $\begin{cases} x^2 - y^2 = 9 \\ x^2 + 9y^2 = 169 \end{cases}$

$x^2 - y^2 = 9$

$\underline{x^2 + 9y^2 = 169}$

$-10y^2 = -160$ **Subtract like terms to eliminate the x^2 terms.**

$y = 4 \text{ or } y = -4$ **Solve for y.**

$x^2 - (4)^2 = 9$ **Substitute the values of y into** $x^2 - (-4)^2 = 9$

$x^2 = 25$ **one of the original equations.** $x^2 = 25$

$x = 5 \text{ or } x = -5$ **Solve for x.** $x = 5 \text{ or } x = -5$

● The ordered pairs $(5, 4), (-5, 4), (5, -4),$ and $(-5, -4)$ are solutions to the system.

2 ACTIVITY Solving Graphically

Solve the system by graphing. $\begin{cases} x^2 + y^2 = 36 \\ y = (x - 2)^2 - 3 \end{cases}$

$x^2 + y^2 = 36$

$y = \pm\sqrt{36 - x^2}$ **Solve the first equation for y.**

Graph the equations and find the point(s) of intersection.
● The solutions are approximately $(-1.0, 5.9)$ and $(4.6, 3.8)$.

Guided Instruction

Error Prevention!

Some students may initially think that all quadratic systems involve two equations of the form $y = ax^2 + bx + c$, where $a \neq 0$. Point out that quadratic systems can also involve quadratic equations in two variables such as circles, ellipses, and hyperbolas.

Math Tip

Quadratic systems can have from 0 to 4 solutions. Encourage students to sketch graphs to represent each of these situations.

Resources

Students may use any graphing calculator to graph quadratic systems.

EXERCISES

Solve each quadratic system.

3. $\left(\pm\dfrac{21 + \sqrt{41}}{10}, \dfrac{9 - 21\sqrt{41}}{50}\right), \left(\pm\dfrac{21 - \sqrt{41}}{10}, \dfrac{9 + 21\sqrt{41}}{50}\right)$ or about $(\pm2.74, -2.51), (\pm1.46, 2.87)$

1. $\begin{cases} x^2 + 64y^2 = 64 \\ x^2 + y^2 = 64 \end{cases}$ **2.** $\begin{cases} 2x^2 - y^2 = 2 \\ x^2 + y^2 = 25 \end{cases}$ **3.** $\begin{cases} 9x^2 + 25y^2 = 225 \\ y = -x^2 + 5 \end{cases}$ **4.** $\begin{cases} 4x^2 + 4y^2 = 100 \\ 3x^2 + 3y^2 = 27 \end{cases}$

$(-8, 0), (8, 0)$ $(3, 4), (-3, 4), (3, -4), (-3, -4)$ **no solutions**

5. a. **Writing** The system that consists of $y = -3x + 6$ and $y = x^2 - 4x$ is a linear-quadratic system. How would you solve the system algebraically? Graphically? **See margin.**

   b. Solve the system in part (a). $(-2, 12), (3, -3)$

6–9. See margin.

10–13. See back of book.

Identify each system as linear-quadratic or quadratic-quadratic. Then solve.

6. $\begin{cases} y = x - 1 \\ x^2 + y^2 = 25 \end{cases}$ **7.** $\begin{cases} 9x^2 + 4y^2 = 36 \\ x^2 - y^2 = 4 \end{cases}$ **8.** $\begin{cases} -x + y = 4 \\ y = x^2 - 4x + 2 \end{cases}$ **9.** $\begin{cases} 4x^2 + 25y^2 = 100 \\ y = x + 2 \end{cases}$

10. $\begin{cases} y^2 = 5x - 3 \\ 3x^2 - 3y^2 = 1 \end{cases}$ **11.** $\begin{cases} y = 3x + 1 \\ x^2 + y^2 = 3 \end{cases}$ **12.** $\begin{cases} (x - 1)^2 = (y + 2)^2 \\ y = 2x^2 - 4 \end{cases}$ **13.** $\begin{cases} x^2 + y^2 = 25 \\ (x - 3)^2 + (y - 3)^2 = 100 \end{cases}$

5a. Algebraically: substitute $-3x + 6$ for y in $y = x^2 - 4x$, solve for x, and then substitute each of the solutions in $y = -3x + 6$ to find corresponding values for y. Graphically: Graph both relations. Then use the Intersect feature on the CALC menu to find the coordinates of all points where the graphs intersect.

6. linear-quadratic; $(-3, -4), (4, 3)$

7. quadratic-quadratic; $(\pm2, 0)$

8. linear-quadratic; $\left(\dfrac{5 + \sqrt{33}}{2}, \dfrac{13 + \sqrt{33}}{2}\right), \left(\dfrac{5 - \sqrt{33}}{2}, \dfrac{13 - \sqrt{33}}{2}\right)$

9. linear-quadratic; $(0, 2), \left(-\dfrac{100}{29}, -\dfrac{42}{29}\right)$

Choosing *Cannot Be Determined*

This feature helps students understand the importance of carefully examining all of the information given and all answer choices for multiple choice questions, before choosing the answer choice "cannot be determined."

Guided Instruction

Error Prevention!

Exercise 4 Students may initially think that the center of the parabola must be at the origin and that the parabola opens upward. Show students how sketching a picture can help them determine that they can find more than one parabola whose focus is at (0, 3). Hence, the equation of the directrix cannot be determined.

Resources

SAT® and ACT® correlations are on page 544B.

Test-Taking Strategies with Transparencies
- Transparency 10
- Practice sheet, p. 34

Test-Taking Strategies with Transparencies

Test-Taking Strategy: Choosing "Cannot Be Determined"

Several strategies can be used.

Example The wholesale price for a sweater is $19. The retail markup is 175%. On a 25%-off sale, how much profit is made on each sweater?

A. $52.25   B. $39.19   C. $33.25   D. cannot be determined

Compute the markup: 19 × 1.75 = $33.25.

Choice C is $33.25, but this is the full-price profit.

Work backward. Choices A and B are more than $33.25, so they are wrong.

Use mental math. The full price is 19 + 33.25 = $52.25.

Estimate the sale markdown: 52 × 0.25 = $13.

The sale price should be about $52 − $13 = $39, so the sale profit is about 39 − 19 = $20.

The answer is not A, B, or C, so choose D.

Explain why the correct answer cannot be determined.

1. Pam walks 300 yd north and 400 yd east to school. What is the shortest distance from school to home?

A. 300 yd   B. 400 yd   C. 700 yd   D. cannot be determined

2. Juan drove 150 miles in 2.5 hours. At this rate, how long will it take Juan to drive 360 miles?

A. 1 h   B. 4.5 h   C. 7.5 h   D. cannot be determined

Transparency 10

590

Some multiple-choice questions cannot be solved. If so, then one of the answer choices will be *cannot be determined*. Be careful, however. Sometimes the answer choice *cannot be determined* is included as a distractor.

1 EXAMPLE

Find an equation of a circle that passes through the points $(0, 0)$, $(1, 0)$ and $(2, 0)$.

A. $(x - 1)^2 + y^2 = 1$

B. $\left(x - \frac{1}{2}\right)^2 + y^2 = \frac{1}{4}$

C. $\left(x - \frac{3}{2}\right)^2 + y^2 = \frac{1}{4}$

D. cannot be determined

Since the y-coordinates of all three points are zero, the points are collinear. A circle cannot pass through three collinear points. The correct answer is D.

2 EXAMPLE

Which of the following completely describes the graphs of $(x - d)^2 + (y - d)^2 = 2d^2$?

A. circles of radius d with centers on the line $y = x$

B. circles with centers (d, d)

C. circles with centers on the line $y = x$ and passing through $(0, 0)$

D. cannot be determined

The standard form of an equation of a circle is $(x - h)^2 + (y - k)^2 = r^2$, where (h, k) is the center of the circle and r is the radius. So the equation in Example 2 describes circles that have centers at (d, d) and have radius $\sqrt{2d^2}$, or $|d|\sqrt{2}$.

Eliminate choice A, since the radius is incorrect. Since the centers of the circles are (d, d), they all lie on the line $y = x$. Choices B and C could be correct. Test choice C by substituting $x = 0$ and $y = 0$.

$$(0 - d)^2 + (0 - d)^2 \stackrel{?}{=} 2d^2 \qquad \textbf{Substitute (0, 0) for } x \textbf{ and } y.$$
$$(-d)^2 + (-d)^2 \stackrel{?}{=} 2d^2 \qquad \textbf{Simplify.}$$
$$2d^2 = 2d^2$$

The circles pass through the point $(0, 0)$. The correct answer is C. Choice D is a distractor.

EXERCISES

1. Cannot be determined because the radius would be the square root of a negative number.

If the answer to an exercise can be determined, write the answer. If not, write *cannot be determined* and explain your reasoning.

1. Find the radius of the circle defined by $x^2 + y^2 - 4x - 2y + 14 = 0$. **See above.**

2. Find the number of points of intersection of the graphs of $y = x^2$ and $y = 2ax - a^2$. **1**

3. Given that $x^2 - y^2 = 12$, find y when $x = 3$. **Cannot be determined because if $x = 3$, y^2 is a negative number.**

4. The focus of a parabola is $(0, 3)$. Find the equation of the directrix.
 Cannot be determined because many parabolas have (0, 3) as their focus.

Chapter Review

Vocabulary Review

center (p. 561)
circle (p. 561)
conic section (p. 547)
co-vertices (p. 568)
directrix (p. 555)
ellipse (p. 568)

focus of a parabola (p. 555)
focus of an ellipse (p. 568)
focus of a hyperbola (p. 575)
hyperbola (p. 575)
major axis (p. 568)
minor axis (p. 568)

radius (p. 561)
standard form of an equation of a
  circle (p. 561)
transverse axis (p. 575)
vertices of an ellipse (p. 568)
vertices of a hyperbola (p. 575)

Choose the correct vocabulary term to complete each sentence.

1. In the definition of a parabola, the fixed line is the _?_ .   directrix
2. The vertices of an ellipse are on its _?_ .   major axis
3. $(x - h)^2 + (y - k)^2 = r^2$ is the _?_ .   standard form of an equation of a circle
4. The distance from a point on a circle to its center is the _?_ of the circle.   radius
5. The vertices of a hyperbola are on its _?_ .   transverse axis

Go Online
PHSchool.com
For: Vocabulary quiz
Web Code: agj-1051

Skills and Concepts

10-1 Objectives
▼ To graph conic sections (p. 547)
▼ To identify conic sections (p. 549)

A **conic section** is a curve formed by the intersection of a plane and a double cone. Circles, ellipses, parabolas, and hyperbolas are all conic sections.

Graph each equation. Identify the conic section and describe the graph and its lines of symmetry. Then find the domain and range.   6–9. See back of book.

6. $\frac{x^2}{49} + \frac{y^2}{121} = 1$ 7. $x^2 + y^2 = 4$ 8. $\frac{x^2}{25} - \frac{y^2}{4} = 1$ 9. $x = 2y^2 + 5$

Identify the center, the intercepts, and the domain and range of each graph.

10. center (0, 0); (±4, 0);
    domain: $x \geq 4$ or $x \leq -4$
    range: all real numbers

11. center (0, 0); (0, ±2),
    (±3, 0);
    domain: $-3 \leq x \leq 3$
    range: $-2 \leq y \leq 2$

10.

11.

10-2 Objectives
▼ To write the equation of a parabola (p. 555)
▼ To graph parabolas (p. 557)

In a plane, a parabola is the set of all points that are the same distance c from a fixed line, the **directrix,** and a fixed point not on the line, the **focus.**

For $y = ax^2$ when $a > 0$, the parabola opens upward. The focus is $(0, c)$ and the directrix is $y = -c$. When $a < 0$, the parabola opens downward. The focus is $(0, -c)$ and the directrix is $y = c$. For $x = ay^2$, when $a > 0$, the parabola opens to the right. The focus is $(c, 0)$ and directrix is $x = -c$. When $a < 0$, the parabola opens to the left. The focus is $(-c, 0)$ and the directrix is $x = c$. Always, $|a| = \frac{1}{4c}$.

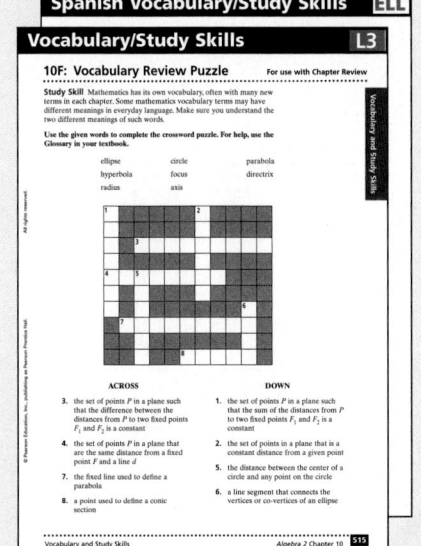

Chapter 10   Chapter Review   **591**

19. $\left(0, \frac{1}{20}\right), y = -\frac{1}{20}$

20. $\left(\frac{1}{8}, 0\right), x = -\frac{1}{8}$

21. $(-2, 0), x = 2$

28. center $(1, 0)$, radius 8

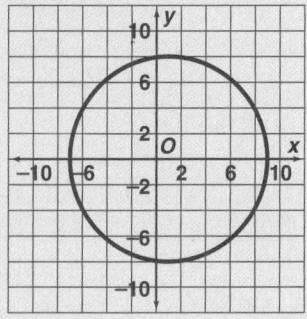

29. center $(-7, -3)$, radius 7

16. $y = \frac{1}{24}x^2$

17. $y = \frac{1}{10}x^2$

18. $y = 3x^2$

Write an equation for a graph that is the set of all points in the plane that are equidistant from the given point and the given line.

12. $F(0, 3), y = -1$ $\quad y = \frac{1}{8}x^2 + 1$ **13.** $F(-2, 0), x = 4$ $\quad x = -\frac{1}{12}y^2 + 1$

Write an equation of a parabola with a vertex at the origin and the given focus.

14. focus at $(5, 0)$ $\quad x = \frac{1}{20}y^2$ **15.** focus at $(0, -5)$ $\qquad\qquad$ **16.** focus at $(0, 6)$
$\qquad\qquad\qquad\qquad\qquad\qquad\qquad y = -\frac{1}{20}x^2$

Write an equation of a parabola opening upward with a vertex at the origin.

17. focus is 2.5 units from the vertex $\qquad$ **18.** focus is $\frac{1}{12}$ of a unit from the vertex

Find the focus and the directrix of the graph of each equation. Sketch the graph.

19. $y = 5x^2$ $\qquad\qquad$ **20.** $x = 2y^2$ $\qquad\qquad$ **21.** $x = -\frac{1}{8}y^2$
19–21. See margin.

10-3 Objectives

▼ To write and graph the equation of a circle (p. 561)

▼ To find the center and radius of a circle and use it to graph the circle (p. 563)

In a plane, a **circle** is the set of all points at a given distance, the **radius** r, from a given point, the **center** (h, k). The **standard form of an equation of a circle** is $(x - h)^2 + (y - k)^2 = r^2$.

Write an equation in standard form of the circle with the given center and radius.

22. center $(0, 0)$, radius 4 $\quad x^2 + y^2 = 16$ **23.** center $(8, 1)$, radius 5
$\qquad\qquad\qquad\qquad\qquad\qquad\qquad\qquad\qquad (x - 8)^2 + (y - 1)^2 = 25$

Write an equation for each translation of $x^2 + y^2 = r^2$ with the given radius.

24. left 3 units, up 2 units; radius 10 **25.** right 5 units, down 3 units; radius 8
$\quad (x + 3)^2 + (y - 2)^2 = 100$ $\qquad\qquad (x - 5)^2 + (y + 3)^2 = 64$

Write an equation for each circle. Each interval represents one unit.

26. $\qquad\qquad\qquad\qquad\qquad\qquad$ **27.**

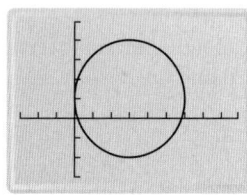

$(x - 3)^2 + (y - 1)^2 = 9$ $\qquad\qquad (x + 1)^2 + y^2 = 4$

Find the center and the radius of each circle. Sketch the graph.

28. $(x - 1)^2 + y^2 = 64$ $\qquad\qquad$ **29.** $(x + 7)^2 + (y + 3)^2 = 49$
28–29. See margin.

10-4 Objectives

▼ To write the equation of an ellipse (p. 568)

▼ To find the foci of an ellipse, and to graph an ellipse (p. 570)

In a plane, an **ellipse** is the set of all points P, the sum of whose distances to two fixed points, the **foci**, is constant. The **major axis** is the segment that contains the foci and has endpoints called the **vertices of an ellipse**. The **minor axis** is perpendicular to the major axis and has endpoints called the **co-vertices**.

There are two standard forms of an ellipse centered at the origin. If $\frac{x^2}{a^2} + \frac{y^2}{b^2} = 1$, the major axis is horizontal with vertices $(\pm a, 0)$ and co-vertices $(0, \pm b)$, where $a > b > 0$.

If $\frac{x^2}{b^2} + \frac{y^2}{a^2} = 1$, the major axis is vertical with vertices $(0, \pm a)$ and co-vertices $(\pm b, 0)$. In either case, you can find the foci c using the relationship $c^2 = a^2 - b^2$.

30. $\frac{x^2}{17} + \frac{y^2}{16} = 1$

31. $\frac{x^2}{25} + \frac{y^2}{29} = 1$

32. $\frac{x^2}{9} + \frac{y^2}{10} = 1$

33. $\frac{x^2}{40} + \frac{y^2}{36} = 1$

Write an equation of an ellipse in standard form with a center at the origin and with the given characteristics.

30. foci $(\pm 1, 0)$, co-vertices $(0, \pm 4)$

31. vertex $(0, \sqrt{29})$, co-vertex $(-5, 0)$

32. focus $(0, 1)$, vertex $(0, \sqrt{10})$

33. foci $(\pm 2, 0)$, co-vertices $(0, \pm 6)$

34. Write the equation of an ellipse centered at the origin with height 8 units and width 16 units. $\frac{x^2}{64} + \frac{y^2}{16} = 1$

35. Graph $\frac{x^2}{4} + \frac{y^2}{9} = 1$. Identify the foci. **See margin.**

10-5 Objectives

▼ To graph hyperbolas (p. 574)

▼ To find and use the foci of a hyperbola (p. 576)

In a plane, a **hyperbola** is the set of all points P such that difference between the distances from P to two fixed points, the **foci**, is constant. The foci lie on the line containing the **transverse axis**. Each branch of a hyperbola intersects the transverse axis at a **vertex of the hyperbola**. Each branch approaches the two asymptotes, which contain the diagonals of the central rectangle.

There are two standard forms of hyperbolas centered at the origin. If $\frac{x^2}{a^2} - \frac{y^2}{b^2} = 1$, the asymptotes are $y = \pm \frac{b}{a}x$, the transverse axis is horizontal with vertices $(\pm a, 0)$, and the foci are $(\pm c, 0)$. If $\frac{y^2}{a^2} - \frac{x^2}{b^2} = 1$, the asymptotes are $y = \pm \frac{a}{b}x$, the transverse axis is vertical with vertices $(0, \pm a)$, and the foci are $(0, \pm c)$. In either case, you can find the value of b using the relationship $c^2 = a^2 + b^2$.

Find the foci of each hyperbola. Draw the graph. **36–38. See margin.**

36. $\frac{x^2}{36} - \frac{y^2}{225} = 1$

37. $\frac{y^2}{400} - \frac{x^2}{169} = 1$

38. $\frac{x^2}{121} - \frac{y^2}{81} = 1$

39. Find an equation that models the path of a spacecraft around a planet if $a = 107{,}124$ and $c = 213{,}125.9$. $\frac{x^2}{1.148 \times 10^{10}} - \frac{y^2}{3.395 \times 10^{10}} = 1$

10-6 Objectives

▼ To write the equation of a translated conic section (p. 582)

▼ To identify the equation of a translated conic section (p. 585)

41. $\frac{(x-6)^2}{9} - \frac{(y-3)^2}{16} = 1$

You can substitute $(x - h)$ for x and $(y - k)$ for y to translate graphs of an ellipse or a hyperbola. A translated ellipse or hyperbola has center (h, k).

Write an equation of a conic section with the given characteristics.

40. an ellipse with center $(3, -2)$, vertical major axis of length 6; minor axis of length 4 $\frac{(x-3)^2}{4} + \frac{(y+2)^2}{9} = 1$

41. a hyperbola with vertices $(3, 3)$ and $(9, 3)$, foci $(1, 3)$ and $(11, 3)$

42. All points on the hyperbola are 81 units closer to one focus than the other. The foci are at $(0, 0)$ and $(155, 0)$. $\frac{(x-77.5)^2}{1640.25} - \frac{y^2}{4366} = 1$

Identify the conic section represented by each equation by writing the equation in standard form. For a parabola, give the vertex. For a circle, give the center and the radius. For an ellipse or a hyperbola, give the center and the foci. Sketch the graph. **43–46. See margin.**

43. $-x^2 + y^2 + 4y - 16 = 0$

44. $x^2 + y^2 + 3x - 4y - 9 = 0$

45. $x^2 + x - y - 42 = 0$

46. $2x^2 + 3y^2 - 4x + 12y - 20 = 0$

Chapter 10 Chapter Review **593**

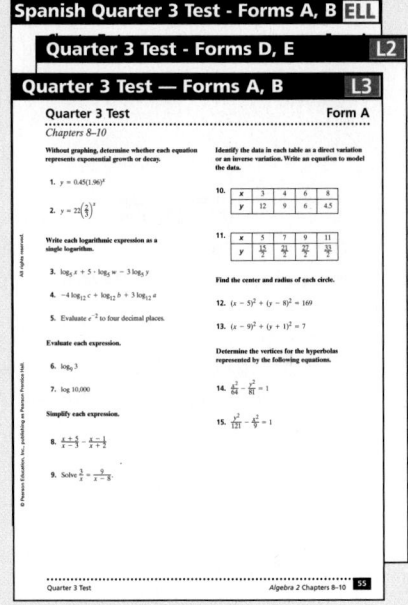
43. **hyperbola; center** $(0, -2)$, **foci** $(0, -2 \pm 2\sqrt{10})$

44. **circle, center** $\left(-\frac{3}{2}, 2\right)$, **radius** $\frac{\sqrt{61}}{2}$

45. **parabola; vertex** $\left(-\frac{1}{2}, -\frac{169}{4}\right)$

46. **ellipse; center** $(1, -2)$, **foci** $\left(\frac{3 \pm \sqrt{51}}{3}, -2\right)$

35.

foci $(0, \pm\sqrt{5})$

36.

foci $(\pm 3\sqrt{29}, 0)$

37.

foci $(0, \pm\sqrt{569})$

38.

foci $(\pm\sqrt{202}, 0)$

593

Chapter Test

Go Online
PHSchool.com
For: Chapter Test
Web Code: aga-1052

Identify the center and intercepts of each conic section. Give the domain and range of each graph. 1–4. See margin.

1.

2.

3.

4.
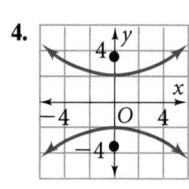

5. Writing Explain how you can tell what kind of conic section a quadratic equation describes without graphing the equation. **Write the equation in standard form.**

Identify the focus and the directrix of the graph of each equation. 6–9. See back of book.

6. $y = 3x^2$

7. $x = -2y^2$

8. $x + 5y^2 = 0$

9. $9x^2 - 2y = 0$

Write an equation of a parabola with a vertex at the origin and the given characteristic. $x = \frac{1}{12}y^2$

10. focus at $(0, -2)$ $y = -\frac{1}{8}x^2$ **11.** focus at $(3, 0)$

12. directrix $x = 7$ **13.** directrix $y = -1$
  $x = -\frac{1}{28}y^2$ $y = \frac{1}{4}x^2$

Find the center and radius of the circle. Sketch the circle. 14–17. See back of book.

14. $(x - 2)^2 + (y - 3)^2 = 36$

15. $(x + 5)^2 + (y + 8)^2 = 100$

16. $(x - 1)^2 + (y + 7)^2 = 81$

17. $(x + 4)^2 + (y - 10)^2 = 121$

Find an equation of an ellipse for each given height and width. Assume that the center of the ellipse is $(0, 0)$. $\frac{x^2}{64} + \frac{y^2}{25} = 1$

18. height 10 units, width 16 units

19. height 2 units, width 12 units $\frac{x^2}{36} + y^2 = 1$

20. height 9 units, width 5 units
  $\frac{x^2}{6.25} + \frac{y^2}{20.25} = 1$

Find the foci for each ellipse. Sketch the ellipse.

21. $\frac{x^2}{81} + \frac{y^2}{36} = 1$ **22.** $\frac{x^2}{25} + \frac{y^2}{121} = 1$

23. $x^2 + \frac{y^2}{49} = 1$ **24.** $4x^2 + y^2 = 4$
21–24. See back of book.

25. Critical Thinking What is the shape of an ellipse whose height and width are equal? **circle**

Find the foci for each hyperbola. Sketch the hyperbola. 26–29. See back of book.

26. $\frac{x^2}{144} - \frac{y^2}{100} = 1$ **27.** $\frac{y^2}{169} - \frac{x^2}{400} = 1$

28. $\frac{x^2}{64} - \frac{y^2}{4} = 1$ **29.** $y^2 - \frac{x^2}{225} = 1$

30. Open-Ended Write the equation of a hyperbola with a transverse axis on the x-axis. **Check students' work.**

Write an equation of an ellipse with the given characteristics. 31–33. See back of book.

31. center $(0, 0)$, vertex $(4, 0)$, co-vertex $(0, -3)$

32. center $(-2, 7)$, horizontal major axis of length 8, minor axis of length 6

33. center $(3, -2)$, vertical major axis of length 12, minor axis of length 10

Write an equation of a hyperbola with the given characteristics. 34–36. See back of book.

34. vertices $(\pm 3, 7)$, foci $(\pm 5, 7)$

35. vertices $(2, \pm 5)$, foci $(2, -7), (2, 7)$

36. vertices $(-3, -1), (-5, -1)$, foci $(0, -1), (-8, -1)$

Identify the conic section represented by each equation. If it is a parabola, give the vertex. If it is a circle, give the center and radius. If it is an ellipse or a hyperbola, give the center and foci. Sketch the graph. 37–40. See back of book.

37. $3y^2 - x - 6y + 5 = 0$

38. $x^2 + y^2 - 4x - 6y + 4 = 0$

39. $4x^2 + y^2 - 16x - 6y + 9 = 0$

40. $4x^2 - y^2 - 16x + 6y - 9 = 0$

1. center $(0, 0)$, intercepts $(\pm 2, 0), (0, \pm 3)$; domain: $-2 \leq x \leq 2$, range: $-3 \leq y \leq 3$

2. center $(0, 0)$, intercepts $(\pm 2, 0)$; domain: $x \leq -2$ or $x \geq 2$, range: all real numbers

3. center $(0, 0)$, intercepts $(\pm 2, 0), (0, \pm 1)$; domain: $-2 \leq x \leq 2$, range: $-1 \leq y \leq 1$

4. center $(0, 0)$, intercepts $(0, \pm 2)$; domain: all real numbers, range: $y \leq -2$ or $y \geq 2$

Standardized Test Prep

Multiple Choice

For Exercises 1–14, choose the correct letter.

1. Which equation represents a circle with center
C $(-3, 8)$ and radius 12?

- Ⓐ $(x - 8)^2 + (y + 3)^2 = 144$
- Ⓑ $(x - 8)^2 - (y + 3)^2 = 144$
- Ⓒ $(x + 3)^2 + (y - 8)^2 = 144$
- Ⓓ $(x - 3)^2 - (y - 8)^2 = 144$

2. Which function has a growth factor of 1.25?
G

- Ⓕ $y = 1.25x$
- Ⓖ $y = 4.1(1.25)^x$
- Ⓗ $y = 1.25(3.7)^x$
- Ⓙ $y = 1.25(0.9)^x$

3. What is the product $\dfrac{x^2(x - 2)}{x + 4} \cdot \dfrac{2(2x + 8)}{x^3 - x^2}$?
D

- Ⓐ $\dfrac{x^4(x - 1)(x - 2) - 4(x + 4)^2}{x^2(x - 1)(x + 4)}$
- Ⓑ $\dfrac{12x^4 + 14x^3 - 32x^2}{x^4 + 2x^3 - 4x^2}$
- Ⓒ $\dfrac{x^4(x - 1)(x - 2)}{4(x + 4)^2}$
- Ⓓ $\dfrac{4(x - 2)}{x - 1}$

4. The equation $y = (x - 4)^2$ represents which
H conic section?

- Ⓕ circle
- Ⓖ ellipse
- Ⓗ parabola
- Ⓙ hyperbola

5. Which events are dependent?
B I. spinning a spinner three times
  II. choosing three students from a class
  III. tossing two coins and a number cube

- Ⓐ I only
- Ⓑ II only
- Ⓒ III only
- Ⓓ I and II

6. The graph below represents which function?
G

- Ⓕ $y = \dfrac{x^2 - 4}{x + 4}$
- Ⓖ $y = x^2 - 4x + 1$
- Ⓗ $y = |x + 4|$
- Ⓙ $y = x^3 + x^2 - 4$

7. Which equation has roots $-3, 0, 1,$ and 2?
A

- Ⓐ $x^4 - 7x^2 + 6x = 0$
- Ⓑ $x^4 - 6x^3 + 11x - 6x = 0$
- Ⓒ $x^4 - 4x^3 + x^2 - 6x = 0$
- Ⓓ $x^4 - 7x^2 - 6 = 0$

8. Solve $4x^2 - 64 = 0$.
G

- Ⓕ $x = \pm 2$
- Ⓖ $x = \pm 4$
- Ⓗ $x = \pm 8$
- Ⓙ $x = \pm 16$

9. Solve $4(9 - x)^{0.5} - 6 = 10$.
B

- Ⓐ 7
- Ⓑ -7
- Ⓒ 5
- Ⓓ -5

10. For what value of c is $x^2 - 5x + c$ a square of a
H binomial?

- Ⓕ 25
- Ⓖ -25
- Ⓗ $\dfrac{25}{4}$
- Ⓙ $-\dfrac{25}{4}$

11. What is the complete solution of
A $\log (6x - 9) = 2 \log x$?

- Ⓐ 3
- Ⓑ -3
- Ⓒ $-3, 3$
- Ⓓ $1, 3$

12. Evaluate $\log_3 81$.
H

- Ⓕ 2
- Ⓖ 3
- Ⓗ 4
- Ⓙ 9

13. Identify the directrix of the graph of
B $6x = x^2 + 8y + 9$.

- Ⓐ $x = 2$
- Ⓑ $y = 2$
- Ⓒ $x = -4$
- Ⓓ $y = -4$

14. Find the distance between the foci of the ellipse
J with the equation $\dfrac{x^2}{36} + \dfrac{(y - 2)^2}{100} = 1$.

- Ⓕ 4
- Ⓖ 8
- Ⓗ 12
- Ⓙ 16

Gridded Response

15. Simplify $\dfrac{1 - \frac{1}{8}}{2 - \frac{3}{4}}$. 0.7

16. A and B are independent but not mutually
exclusive events. $P(A) = \frac{1}{4}$ and $P(B) = \frac{1}{5}$. Find
$P(A \text{ or } B)$.   2/5

Short Response

17. Find $\begin{bmatrix} 1 & 0 \\ 0 & 2 \\ 1 & 3 \end{bmatrix} + \begin{bmatrix} 2 & 1 \\ 1 & 3 \\ 0 & 0 \end{bmatrix}$.   [2] $\begin{bmatrix} 3 & 1 \\ 1 & 5 \\ 1 & 3 \end{bmatrix}$ [1] one or 2 errors

18. Find the zeros of the function $y = x^2 - 2x$.
Show your work. **See back of book.**

Extended Response

19. a. Write an equation of a line perpendicular
to $y = 3x + 2$.
b. Write an equation of a line parallel
to $y = 3x + 2$. **See back of book.**

20. Find $\dfrac{x + 4}{x^2 + 6x + 8} \div \dfrac{x^2 - 16}{x^2 + 8x + 12}$. **See margin.**
What are the restrictions on the variable?

Chapter 10 Standardized Test Prep **595**

Students must be able to extract information from reading passages, answer multiple choice questions, and construct responses in order to be successful on current state and national assessments.

To answer the questions, students apply skills and concepts from this chapter and previous chapters.
Multiple Choice: Items 1–14
Gridded Response: Items 15–16
Short Response: Items 17–18
Free Response: Items 19–20

Resources

Test Prep Workbook

Grab & Go
- **L3** Cumulative Review

ExamView CD-ROM
- Standardized Test Practice

Differentiated Instruction Resources

Progress Monitoring Assessments
- Benchmark Test 5

Spanish Assessment Resources
- **L3** Spanish Cumulative Review

Item	1	2	3	4	5	6	7	8	9	10	11	12	13	14	15	16	17	18	19	20
Lesson	10-3	8-1	9-4	10-1	9-7	9-3	6-5	6-4	7-5	5-7	8-5	8-3	10-2	10-4	9-4	9-7	4-2	6-2	2-2	9-4

Martian Math

In these activities students apply their knowledge of functions, ratios, and conic sections, particularly the ellipse.

Activating Prior Knowledge

Have students discuss what they know about planets, and about Mars in particular. Elicit information about the various ways that scientists have gathered information about the Red Planet.

Guided Instruction

Have a volunteer read the introductory paragraph. Ask: *What characteristics of Mars would help to make it a relatively easy place to land a human space expedition? What characteristics would make this difficult?*

Teaching Tip

Ask a volunteer to review the difference between mass (*constant*) and weight (*varies with gravitational attraction*).

Tactile Learners

Have students use a pencil and a string about 10 inches long, fastened at each end by two tacks that are about 4 inches apart, to draw an ellipse. Ask students to identify the foci for this demonstration (*the two tacks*) and the constant sum of the two distances (*the length of the string*).

English Language Learners ELL

Have a volunteer explain what is meant by the *eccentricity* of a planet's orbit.

Activity Lab

Martian Math

Applying Conic Sections Even though we haven't discovered life on Mars, we know a lot of other things about the planet. Mars has a day about 25 hours long, a pattern of seasons similar to Earth's, and polar icecaps. Mars also has surface temperatures that rarely rise above freezing and almost no oxygen in its atmosphere. Mars is often called the Red Planet because red deserts cover its surface.

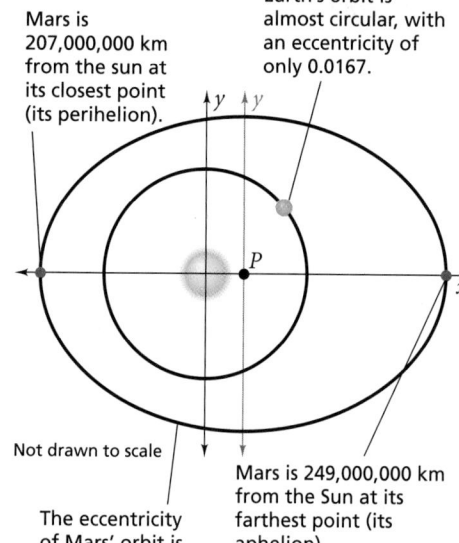

Activity 1

a. Mars travels in an elliptical orbit with the sun at one of its foci. Use the data from the diagram to calculate a, b, and c of this elliptical orbit.

b. Point P is the midpoint between Mars' closest and farthest distances to the sun. Use your values of a and b to write an equation of the elliptical orbit of Mars relative to a coordinate system drawn through point P (y-axis in gray). Use distances in millions of kilometers.

c. It is also useful to define Mars' motion relative to the sun. Imagine a new coordinate system (y-axis in black) with its origin at the center of the sun. Rewrite your equation for the ellipse in this new coordinate system.

d. **Critical Thinking** Explain how the eccentricity of a planet's orbit can affect its annual weather cycle.

Mars is 207,000,000 km from the sun at its closest point (its perihelion).

Earth's orbit is almost circular, with an eccentricity of only 0.0167.

Not drawn to scale

The eccentricity of Mars' orbit is 0.0934.

Mars is 249,000,000 km from the Sun at its farthest point (its aphelion).

Martian sand dunes

Antenna

Deflated air bag

Solar Panels

Ramp for Sojourner

596 All photographs © Dorling Kindersley Limited unless otherwise credited on acknowledgments page

---

Activity 1

a. $a = 228,000,000$ km,
   $b = 227,000,000$ km,
   $c = 21,000,000$ km

b. $\dfrac{x^2}{228^2} + \dfrac{y^2}{227^2} = 1$

c. $\dfrac{(x - 21)^2}{228^2} + \dfrac{y^2}{227^2} = 1$

d. Answers may vary. Sample: For an orbit of high eccentricity, the planet's distance from the sun and the amount of the heat that the planet receives will change.

Activity 2

Astronauts who walked on the moon felt as if they weighed about one sixth of their weight on Earth. This is because the weight of an object is determined by the gravitational attraction between the object and the planet (or moon) it's on. You can use the following formula to estimate the weight of an object on the surface of any of the planets: gravitational force $= \frac{GmM}{r^2}$, where $G =$ universal gravitational constant, $m =$ mass of the object, $M =$ mass of the planet, and $r =$ radius of the planet. For a given object, G and m remain constant, so the force of gravity depends only on the variables M and r.

a. Use the data below. Write a ratio to determine the factor by which you would multiply the weight of a 150-lb person on Earth to find his or her weight on Mars.

b. Find the person's weight on Mars.

c. Repeat parts (a) and (b) for two other planets.

Man on the Moon
On July 20, 1969, U.S. astronauts first set foot on the moon.

Mercury
mass: 5788 Mercurys = 1 Jupiter
radius: 2439 km

Venus
mass: 393 Venuses = 1 Jupiter
radius: 6052 km

Saturn
mass: 3.3 Saturns = 1 Jupiter
radius: 60,268 km

Mars
mass: 2894 Marses = 1 Jupiter
radius: 3397 km

Earth
mass: 317 Earths = 1 Jupiter
radius: 6378 km

Jupiter
mass: 1 Jupiter
radius: 71,942 km

Go Online
PHSchool.com

For: Information about Mars
Web Code: age-1053

Sojourner rover

Bouncing to a Stop
The Pathfinder Probe parachuted onto Mars inside a giant "beach ball"—a set of air bags designed to cushion the probe's landing. The probe bounced 15 times across the rocky ground and rolled to a stop. Its airbags deflated. Three panels then folded out like petals, exposing the probe's instruments and the Sojourner rover to the Martian landscape.

597

Teaching Tip
Before students begin the activity, discuss the illustrations and their captions. Have students work in pairs or in small groups to complete the activities. Have each team read through both activities before beginning to work.

Activity 1

Materials: paper and pencil

Inclusion
Help students review the equation for an ellipse, and the name and meaning of each of the variables.

Activity 2

Materials: paper and pencil

Visual Learners
Have students find or draw a picture of the planets that shows them as circles with the appropriate relative sizes.

Scoring Rubric

This scoring rubric can be used for evaluating student work on both activities. Share this scoring rubric with students before they begin work.

4 Equations and calculations are correct.
   Steps are neat, accurate, and clearly show the mathematics. Responses are clearly indicated and give the appropriate units.

3 Equations and calculations are mostly correct, with some minor errors.
   Steps are neat and mostly accurate. Units are not completely accurate.

2 Equations and calculations contain both major and minor errors.

1 Correct answer, but no work is shown.

Activity 2

a. 0.386

b. 57.9 lb

c. **Answers may vary.**
   Sample: Mercury: 0.3745, 56.2 lb; Jupiter: 2.49, 373.5 lb

Sequences and Series

Chapter at a Glance

Lesson Titles, Objectives, and Features	Assessment	NCTM Standards	Local Standards
11-1 Mathematical Patterns • Identifying mathematical patterns • Using a formula for finding the *n*th term of a sequence	Lesson Quiz	1, 2	
11-2 Arithmetic Sequences • Identifying and generating arithmetic sequences **Activity Lab:** The Fibonacci Sequence	Lesson Quiz	1, 2, 8, 10	
11-3 Geometric Sequences • Identifying and generating geometric sequences **GPS:** Understanding Math Problems	Lesson Quiz Checkpoint Quiz 1	1, 2, 3, 8, 10	
11-4 Arithmetic Series • Writing and evaluating arithmetic series • Using summation notation	Lesson Quiz	1, 2, 10	
Activity Lab: Geometry and Infinite Series **11-5 Geometric Series** • Evaluating a finite geometric series • Evaluating an infinite geometric series **Extension:** Mathematical Induction **Activity Lab:** Technology: Evaluating Series	Lesson Quiz Checkpoint Quiz 2	1, 2, 10	
11-6 Area Under a Curve • Finding area under a curve	Lesson Quiz	2, 3, 4, 7	

NCTM Standards 2000

1 Number and Operations	**2** Algebra	**3** Geometry	**4** Measurement	**5** Data Analysis and Probability
6 Problem Solving	**7** Reasoning and Proof	**8** Communication	**9** Connections	**10** Representation

Correlations to Standardized Tests

All content for these tests is contained in *Prentice Hall Algebra 2*. This chart reflects coverage in this chapter only.

	11-1	11-2	11-3	11-4	11-5	11-6
SAT®						
Number and Operations Operations, ratio & proportions, complex numbers, counting, elementary number theory, matrices, sequences	✔	✔	✔	✔	✔	✔
Algebra and Functions Expressions, equations, inequalities, representation and modeling, properties of functions (linear, polynomial, rational, exponential)	✔	✔	✔	✔	✔	✔
Geometry and Measurement *Plane Euclidean/Measurement Coordinate* Lines, parabolas, circles, symmetry, transformations *Three-dimensional* Solids, surface area & volume (cylinders, cones, pyramids, spheres, prisms) *Trigonometry* Right triangles, identities						
Data Analysis, Statistics, and Probability Mean, median, mode, range, interquartile range, graphs and plots, regression, probability						
ACT®						
Pre-Algebra Basic operations using whole numbers, decimals, fractions, and integers; place value; square roots and approximations; the concept of exponents; scientific notation; factors, ratio, proportion, and percent; linear equations in one variable; absolute value and ordering numbers by value; elementary counting techniques and simple probability; data collection, representation, and interpretation; and understanding simple descriptive statistics.						
Elementary Algebra Properties of exponents and square roots, evaluation of algebraic expressions through substitution, using variables to express functional relationships, understanding algebraic operations, and solving quadratic equations by factoring.					✔	
Intermediate Algebra Understanding of the quadratic formula, rational and radical expressions, absolute value equations and inequalities, sequences and patterns, systems of equations, quadratic inequalities, functions, modeling, matrices, roots of polynomials, and complex numbers.	✔	✔	✔	✔	✔	✔
Coordinate Geometry Graphing and the relations between equations and graphs, including points, lines, polynomials, circles, and other curves; graphing inequalities; slope; parallel and perpendicular lines; distance; midpoints; and conics.						
Plane Geometry Properties and relations of plane figures, including angles and relations among perpendicular and parallel lines; properties of circles, triangles, rectangles, parallelograms, and trapezoids; transformations; the concept of proof and proof techniques; volume; and applications of geometry to three dimensions.						
Trigonometry Understanding trigonometric relations in right triangles; values and properties of trigonometric functions; graphing trigonometric functions; modeling using trigonometric functions; use of trigonometric identities; and solving trigonometric equations.						
NAEP						
Number Sense, Properties, and Operations						
Measurement						✔
Geometry and Spatial Sense						
Data Analysis, Statistics, and Probability						
Algebra and Functions	✔	✔	✔	✔	✔	✔

SAT® The College Board, SAT® Reasoning Test   **ACT®** The ACT Assessment® Test   **NAEP** National Assessment of Educational Progress, 2005 Mathematics Objectives

Math Background

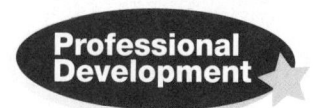
Skills Trace

BEFORE Chapter 11

In previous chapters, students modeled data using linear and exponential functions and solved linear and exponential equations.

DURING Chapter 11

Students identify and generate arithmetic and geometric sequences, write and evaluate arithmetic and geometric series, and find the area under curves.

AFTER Chapter 11

Students will solve probability problems, analyze data using statistics, and work with periodic functions.

Chapter Overview

This chapter introduces sequences as lists of numbers that are generated according to a pattern. Sequences can be defined recursively by telling how the sequence starts and then giving instructions for using known terms as "stepping stones" to get to the next terms. Sequences can also be defined by an explicit formula that gives the value of a term as a function of its position in the sequence. Using either an explicit or a recursive formula to describe a sequence depends on the nature of the problem at hand. Recursive formulas are often useful in programming computers to solve problems, since recursive definitions usually make it easy to create program loops.

Series are defined as expressions for the sum of the terms of a sequence. Students investigate arithmetic and geometric series. They see that under certain conditions an infinite geometric series converges to a finite sum.

The final lesson shows how inscribed rectangles and circumscribed rectangles can be used to approximate the area under a curve. In addition to this brief glimpse at a problem that is treated later in calculus, the chapter has feature pages that discuss the Fibonacci sequence and mathematical induction.

Mathematical Patterns   11-1

In an effort to make sense of the world, humans look for patterns. Examples of patterns in the natural world range from when to reap and sow crops to the shape of a leaf or the anatomy of the shell of the chambered nautilus. Quantifying patterns involves making comparisons or measurements, and this involves putting numbers to quantifiable attributes. Make sure students understand that not all patterns can be expressed mathematically and that not all mathematical patterns can be expressed with a formula.

Students may not realize that in indicating a pattern of a sequence of numbers the ellipsis follows three repetitions of the pattern. This is a generally accepted convention, but it is always possible to find a sequence for which a triple repetition does not determine the pattern—more explicit means must be used to convey the content of such a sequence. For example, for the sequence 2, 4, 8, it is impossible to tell whether 16 (the next power of 2) or 14 (add 2, add 4, add 6,...) is the next term.

A sequence can be thought of as a function whose domain is a subset of the integers, usually natural or whole numbers. For example, consider the sequence of positive even numbers: 2, 4, 6, 8,... . Let the x-coordinate be the number of the term and the y-coordinate be the term itself. Then we can write the function $f = \{(1,2), (2,4), (3,6), (4,8),...\}$. A recursive formula for the even numbers is $a_n = a_{n-1} + 2$, or $a(n) = a(n - 1) + 2$ in function notation where n is a positive integer. The explicit formula for the even numbers is $a_n = 2n$, or $a(n) = 2n$ where n is a positive integer.

Arithmetic Sequences   11-2

The positive even numbers 2, 4, 6, 8,... can be written as the function $f = \{(1,2), (2,4), (3,6), (4,8),...\}$ where the term numbers are the domain and the even numbers are the range. When we graph these ordered pairs, they all fall on the line with equation $y = 2x$. This is no surprise, since the explicit formula of the arithmetic sequence is $a_n = 2n$. Notice that the slope of the line equals the common difference of the sequence. An important distinction to make between the equation and the sequence is that the equation is a *continuous* function while the sequence is a *discrete* function. Thus, the graph of the sequence consists of a set of discrete points, while the graph of the equation consists of every point on the line.

Students have ample experience finding arithmetic means. However, students should also understand the question an arithmetic mean answers: "if all the terms had the same value, what would that value have to be in order to achieve the same total?"

Geometric Sequences 11-3

Students should recognize that the difference between consecutive terms varies for geometric sequences. Furthermore, the relationship between successive terms involves multiplication instead of addition. Thus a constant difference between terms for an arithmetic sequence becomes a constant ratio between terms for an geometric sequence.

Just as an arithmetic sequence is related to a linear function, a geometric sequence is related to an exponential function. For example, consider the sequence of powers of 2: 2, 4, 8, 16, ... Again, consider the sequence as a function. Then we can write the ordered pairs {(1,2), (2,4), (3,8), (4,16),...}. When we graph these points, they all fall on the exponential curve with equation $y = 2^x$. This is no surprise, since the explicit rule of the geometric sequence is $a_n = 2 \cdot 2^{n-1}$, or $a_n = 2^n$. Notice that the base of the exponential equation equals the common ratio r of the sequence. Have students graph equations such as $y = 3^n$ and $y = \left(\frac{1}{3}\right)^n$ to establish that, when $r > 1$, exponential growth is modeled, and that, when $0 < r < 1$, exponential decay is modeled. (Refer back to exponential functions in Chapter 8 as needed.)

Because students are familiar with arithmetic means, they often wonder when a geometric mean would be relevant. Geometric means are often used in business to find average rates of growth. For example, suppose an investment earns 15% the first year, 25% the second year, and 50% the third year. What is its average rate of return, or by what multiplier would the investment need to be multiplied by each year in order to achieve the same final amount? The correct average would be the geometric mean of three numbers, or $\sqrt[3]{1.15 \cdot 1.25 \cdot 1.5}$, which is about 1.29 or 29%. Notice that this is less than the arithmetic mean of $\frac{15\% + 25\% + 50\%}{3} = 30\%$.

Arithmetic Series 11-4

Have students relate the sum of a finite arithmetic series formula $S_n = \frac{n}{2}(a_1 + a_n)$ to the arithmetic mean. Students should recognize the sum formula finds the average term value and multiplies it by

the number of terms, or $S_n = n \cdot \frac{(a_1 + a_n)}{2}$. You may wish to challenge interested students to prove the formula for the sum S_n of an arithmetic series. Students will need summation notation in future math courses.

Geometric Series 11-5

When you discuss convergent and divergent geometric series, ask students whether an infinite *arithmetic* sequence converges or diverges. Examples and reasoning can be used to convince them that it is impossible for an infinite arithmetic series to converge. So, there can be no formula for the sum of an infinite arithmetic series, only infinite geometric series.

Also have students discuss whether or not the sign of the common ratio of a geometric series (negative, positive, or alternating) has an effect on whether or not the series converges or diverges. Students should recognize that the determining factor is the magnitude of the common ratio, or $|r|$, and not the sign of r. Students usually have little difficulty understanding the difference between a *finite* geometric series and an *infinite* geometric series.

Area Under a Curve 11-6

You may want to point out that we are only using portions of curves that touch or lie above the x-axis. Some students may observe that they can improve on the area approximations in this lesson by first using inscribed rectangles, then circumscribed rectangles, and then finding the average of the two approximations. Another more direct way to obtain the same result is to form rectangles that intersect the curve at the middle x-value of its width. Thus, part of the rectangle is inside (underneath) the curve while the other part extends beyond (above) the curve.

Additional Professional Development Opportunities

Math Background notes for Chapter 11: Every lesson has a Math Background in the PLAN section.

Research Overview, Mathematical Strands
Additional support for these topics and more is in the front of this Teacher's Edition.

Lesson Lab
Lesson Lab, a Pearson Education company, offers comprehensive, facilitated professional development designed to help teachers improve student achievement. To learn more, please visit lessonlab.com

Chapter 11 Resources

	11-1	11-2	11-3	11-4	11-5	11-6	For the Chapter
Print Resources							
L3 Practice	●	●	●	●	●	●	
L3 Guided Problem Solving	●	●	●	●	●	●	
L2 Reteaching	●	●	●	●	●	●	
L4 Enrichment	●	●	●	●	●	●	
L3 Daily Notetaking Guide	●	●	●	●	●	●	
L3 Vocabulary and Study Skills Worksheets	●						●
L3 Chapter Project							●
L3 Hands On Activity	●			●			
L3 Checkpoint Quiz			●		●		
L2 Below Level Chapter Test							●
L3 Chapter Test							●
L3 Alternative Assessment							●
L4 Cumulative Review							●
L4 Connections to Precalculus Masters	●	●	●	●	●	●	
L3 Technology Activities					●		
Spanish Resources ELL							
L3 Practice	●	●	●	●	●	●	
L3 Vocabulary and Study Skills Worksheets	●						●
L3 Checkpoint Quiz			●		●		
L2 Below Level Chapter Test							●
L3 Chapter Test							●
L4 Alternative Assessment							
L3 Cumulative Review							●
Transparencies							
Check Skills You'll Need	●	●	●	●	●	●	
Additional Examples	●	●	●	●	●	●	
Problem of the Day	●	●	●	●	●	●	
Classroom Aid							
Student Edition Answers	●	●	●	●	●	●	●
Lesson Quiz	●	●	●	●	●	●	
Test-Taking Strategies							●
Technology							
TI 83/84 Plus Activities							
Interactive Textbook Online	●	●	●	●	●	●	●
Student Express CD-ROM	●	●	●	●	●	●	●
TI Navigator, Instant Check System	●	●	●	●	●	●	
Success Tracker	●	●	●	●	●	●	●
ExamView CD-ROM with Quick Take	●	●	●	●	●	●	●
Teacher Express CD-ROM	●	●	●	●	●	●	●
Presentation Express CD-ROM	●	●	●	●	●	●	●
Mindpoint Quiz Show CD-ROM	●	●	●	●	●	●	●
Prentice Hall Web site: PHSchool.com	●	●	●	●	●	●	●

Also available: Prentice Hall Assessment System (Progress Monitoring Assessments, Skills and Concepts Review, Test Prep Workbook)   Solution Key   Student Workbook
Student Workbook, Adapted Version   Data Analysis and Probability Workbook   Math Notes Study Folder   Spanish Cumulative Assessment

Where You Can Use the Lesson Resources

Here is a suggestion, following the four-step teaching plan, for how you can incorporate Differentiated Instruction Resources into your teaching.

	Instructional Resources L3	**Differentiated** Instruction **Resources**
1. Plan		
Check Skills You'll Need Assign these exercises to review prerequisite skills. **New Vocabulary** Help students pre-read the lesson by pointing out the new terms introduced in the lesson.	**Math Background** **Transparencies & Presentation Express CD** Check Skills You'll Need **Resources** Vocabulary and Study Skills	**Spanish Support** ELL Vocabulary and Study Skills
2. Teach		
L3 **Guided Instruction** Teach each Example. After each Example, assign the Quick Check exercise for that Example.	**Student Edition** Activity Lab **Resources** Daily Notetaking Guide Activity Lab TI-83/84 Activities CD-ROM **Transparencies & Presentation Express CD** Additional Examples Classroom Aids **ExamView CD-ROM with QuickTake** **TI Navigator Instant Check System**	**Teacher's Edition** Every lesson includes suggestions for working with students who need special attention. L1 Special Needs L2 Below Level L4 Advanced Learners ELL English Language Learners
3. Practice		
Assignment Guide **Homework Exercises** Assign the exercises cited in each lesson's Assignment Guide. A Practice by Example B Apply Your Skills C Challenge Test Prep Mixed Review **Homework Quick Check** Discuss in class the exercises cited in each lesson's Assignment Guide.	**Transparencies & Presentation Express CD** Student Answers **Resources** Practice Guided Problem Solving Vocabulary and Study Skills Activity Lab **ExamView CD-ROM with QuickTake**	**Spanish Support** ELL Practice ELL Vocabulary and Study Skills **Resources** L4 Enrichment
4. Assess & Reteach		
Lesson Quiz Assign the Lesson Quiz to assess students' mastery of the lesson content. **Checkpoint Quiz** Use the Checkpoint Quiz to assess student progress over several lessons.	**Transparencies & Presentation Express CD** Lesson Quiz **Resources** Checkpoint Quiz	**Resources** L2 Reteaching ELL Checkpoint Quiz Success Tracker **ExamView CD-ROM with QuickTake**

KEY L1 Special Needs   L2 Below Level   L3 For All Students   L4 Advanced, Gifted   ELL English Language Learners

Sequences and Series

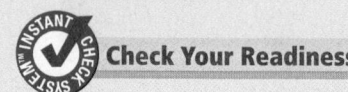 **Check Your Readiness**

Answers are in the back of the textbook.

For intervention, direct students to:

Evaluating Functions
Lesson 2-1: Example 6
Extra Skills and Word
  Problems Practice, Ch. 2

Graphing Quadratic Functions
Lesson 5-2: Example 1
Extra Skills and Word
  Problems Practice, Ch. 5

Evaluating Radical Expressions
Lesson 7-1: Example 2
Extra Skills and Word
  Problems Practice, Ch. 7

Simplifying Complex Fractions
Lesson 9-5: Example 5
Extra Skills and Word
  Problems Practice, Ch. 9

Spanish Vocabulary/Study Skills `ELL`

Vocabulary/Study Skills `L3`

11A: Graphic Organizer   For use before Lesson 11-1

Study Skill Skimming and selective reading are quick and efficient ways for getting what you need from a mathematics textbook or magazine article. It is always important to preview the chapter to see what new concepts are being developed and to link them to previous knowledge.

Write your answers.

1. What is the chapter title? _____

2. Find the Table of Contents page for this chapter at the front of the book. Name four topics you will study in this chapter.

3. What is the topic of the Reading Math page? _____
4. What is the topic of the Test-Taking Strategy page? _____
5. Look through the pages of the chapter. List four real-world connections that you see discussed in this chapter.

6. Complete the graphic organizer below as you work through the chapter.
   • In the center, write the title of the chapter.
   • When you begin a lesson, write the lesson name in a rectangle.
   • When you complete a lesson, write a skill or key concept in an oval linked to that lesson block.
   • When you complete the chapter, use this graphic organizer to help you review.

What You've Learned

- In Chapter 2, you learned to evaluate functions in function notation.
- In Chapter 5, you learned to use parabolas for graphing quadratic functions.
- In Chapter 7, you learned to evaluate radical expressions.
- In Chapter 9, you learned to simplify complex fractions, which are fractions that have fractions in the numerator or denominator or in both the numerator and denominator.

 Check Your Readiness   **GO for Help** to the Lesson in green.

Evaluating Functions (Lesson 2-1)

For each function, find $f(1), f(2), f(3)$, and $f(4)$.

          1, 6, 11, 16   **0.9, 1.1, 1.3, 1.5**
1. $f(x) = 2x + 7$ **2.** $f(x) = 5x - 4$ **3.** $f(x) = 0.2x + 0.7$
9, 11, 13, 15
4. $f(x) = -5x + 3$ **5.** $f(x) = 4x - \frac{2}{3}$ **6.** $f(x) = -3x - 9$
   −2, −7, −12, −17   **$3\frac{1}{3}, 7\frac{1}{3}, 11\frac{1}{3}, 15\frac{1}{3}$**   **−12, −15, −18, −21**

Graphing Quadratic Functions (Lesson 5-2)

Graph each function. **7–9. See margin. 10–12. See back of book.**

7. $y = x^2 + 3$ **8.** $y = -\frac{1}{2}x^2 + 2$ **9.** $y = 4x^2 - 1$

10. $y = 2x^2 - 7x + 3$ **11.** $y = -4x^2 + 8x + 5$ **12.** $y = x^2 + 3x + 4$

Evaluating Radical Expressions (Lesson 7-1)

Find each real-number root.

13. $\sqrt{16}$ **4**   **14.** $-\sqrt{16}$ **−4**   **15.** $\sqrt{0.16}$ **0.4**   **16.** $\sqrt{2500}$ **50**

Simplify each radical expression. Use absolute value symbols as needed.

17. $\sqrt{25x^4}$ **$5x^2$**   **18.** $-\sqrt{0.09y^8}$ **$-0.3y^4$**   **19.** $\sqrt{x^6y^{10}}$ **$|x^3y^5|$**   **20.** $\sqrt{121y^{24}}$ **$11y^{12}$**

Simplifying Complex Fractions (Lesson 9-5)

Simplify each complex fraction.

21. $\dfrac{1 - \frac{1}{3}}{\frac{1}{2}}$ **$\frac{4}{3}$**   **22.** $\dfrac{\frac{1}{3} + \frac{1}{6}}{\frac{2}{3}}$ **$\frac{3}{4}$**   **23.** $\dfrac{1}{1 - \frac{2}{5}}$ **$\frac{5}{3}$**   **24.** $\dfrac{1 - \frac{3}{8}}{2 + \frac{1}{4}}$ **$\frac{5}{18}$**

598 Chapter 11

7.

8.

9.

Sequences and Series

Chapter 11 Overview

This chapter begins to introduce students to sequences and series with a lesson on mathematical patterns. Students are then introduced to arithmetic and geometric series. Finally, students conclude the chapter with a lesson on the area under a curve.

Activating Prior Knowledge

Ask:
- *What are some examples of number patterns?*

Write all suggestions on the board using a comma to separate the numbers.

Ask:
- *What are the next two numbers in each number pattern on the board?*

Accept all reasonable answers. You may want students to describe the procedure or rule they used to obtain the next two numbers.

Inform students that number patterns are called sequences and that they will study different kinds of sequences in this chapter.

◀)) Key Vocabulary

- arithmetic mean (p. 607)
- arithmetic sequence (p. 606)
- arithmetic series (p. 620)
- circumscribed rectangles (p. 635)
- common difference (p. 606)
- common ratio (p. 612)
- converge (p. 627)
- diverge (p. 627)
- explicit formula (p. 602)
- geometric mean (p. 614)
- geometric sequence (p. 612)
- geometric series (p. 626)
- inscribed rectangles (p. 635)
- limit (p. 621)
- recursive formula (p. 602)
- sequence (p. 600)
- series (p. 619)
- term (p. 600)

What You'll Learn Next

- In Chapter 11, you will learn to identify and generate arithmetic sequences and geometric sequences.

- You will learn to evaluate arithmetic series and geometric series.

- You will use rectangles to approximate the area under a curve.

Real-World Connection Applying what you learn, on page 635 you will solve a problem involving the speed of a falcon.

599

11-1

Mathematical Patterns

Objectives
1 To identify mathematical patterns
2 To use a formula for finding the *n*th term of a sequence

Examples
1 Generating a Sequence
2 Real-World Connection
3 Using a Recursive Formula
4 Real-World Connection

Math Background

Sequences are functions whose domain is usually the set of natural or the set of whole numbers. Sometimes a_n is written $a(n)$.

More Math Background: p. 598C

Lesson Planning and Resources

See p. 598E for a list of the resources that support this lesson.

Bell Ringer Practice

✓ **Check Skills You'll Need**
For intervention, direct students to:

Skills Handbook: p. 866

What You'll Learn

• To identify mathematical patterns
• To use a formula for finding the *n*th term of a sequence

...And Why

To predict the height of a bouncing ball, as in Example 2

✓ **Check Skills You'll Need**

GO for Help Skills Handbook p. 866

Find the next two numbers of each pattern. Then write a rule to describe the pattern. 2–6. See back of book.

1. $1, 3, 5, 7, 9, 11, \ldots$ **13, 15; add 2.**
2. $-2, -4, -6, -8, -10, -12, \ldots$
3. $0.2, 1, 5, 25, 125, 625, \ldots$
4. $50, 45, 40, 35, 30, 25, \ldots$
5. $512, 256, 128, 64, 32, 16, \ldots$
6. $2, 5, 8, 11, 14, 17, \ldots$
7. $16, 32, 64, \ldots$ **128, 256; multiply by 2.**
8. $-3, -7, -11, -15, \ldots$ **−19, −23; subtract 4.**

🔊 **New Vocabulary** • sequence • term • recursive formula • explicit formula

1 Identifying Mathematical Patterns

Activity: Generating a Pattern

Suppose each student in your math class has a phone conversation with every other member of the class. What is the minimum number of calls required?

Instead of actually making the calls, you can represent telephone conversations by drawing diagrams like the ones below.

1. How many calls are necessary for two people to have a conversation? **1 call**
2. How many calls are necessary for everyone to talk to everyone else in a group of three people? In a group of four people? **3 calls; 6 calls**
3. Use a diagram to find the number of calls needed for five people. **See back of book.**
4. **Reasoning** Which of the following expressions represents the pattern for numbers of telephone calls? **C**
   A. $2n - 3$
   B. $n(n - 1) - 5$
   C. $\dfrac{n(n - 1)}{2}$
5. Use the expression from Question 4 to find the number of calls needed for a group of seven students. **21**
6. How many calls would be needed for your class? **Check students' work.**

Sometimes steps in a process form a pattern. You can describe some patterns with a **sequence,** or ordered list of numbers. Each number in a sequence is a **term.**

Differentiated Instruction **Solutions for All Learners**

Special Needs **L1**	Below Level **L2**
In Example 4, students may be confused by the two number sequences contained within the spreadsheet. Have students cover up the row for perimeter while they are looking at the row of side lengths.	Have students working in pairs each create a sequence. Then have students exchange sequences and find the next terms in each other's sequences.
learning style: visual	learning style: verbal

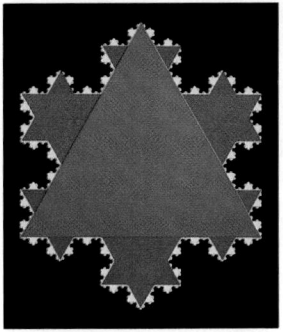

When you apply the construction from Example 1 to an equilateral triangle, you form the Koch snowflake.

1 EXAMPLE Generating a Sequence

a. To create one side of the Koch snowflake, replace each _____ with _/_. Draw the first four figures of the pattern.

b. Write the number of segments in each figure above as a sequence.

$1, 4, 16, 64, \ldots$

c. Predict the next term of the sequence. Explain your choice.

Each term is 4 times the preceding term. The next term is $64 \cdot 4$, or 256. There will be 256 segments in the next figure in the pattern.

 Quick Check ❶ Describe the pattern formed. Find the next three terms.

a. $27, 34, 41, 48, \ldots$
  Add 7; 55, 62, 69.

b. $243, 81, 27, 9, \ldots$
  Divide by 3; 3, 1, $\frac{1}{3}$.

Sometimes you can find the next term in a sequence by using a pattern from the terms that come before it.

2 EXAMPLE Real-World 🌐 Connection

Multiple Choice Suppose you drop a handball from a height of 10 ft. After the ball hits the floor, it rebounds to 85% of its previous height. About how high will the ball rebound after its fourth bounce?

(A) 10 ft   (B) 8.5 ft   (C) 6.1 ft   (D) 5.2 ft

Original height of ball: 10 ft →

After 1st bounce: 85% of $10 = 0.85(10) = 8.5$ →

After 2nd bounce: $0.85(8.5) = 7.225$ →

After 3rd bounce: $0.85(7.225) \approx 6.141$ →

After 4th bounce: $0.85(6.141) \approx 5.220$ →

The ball will rebound about 5.2 ft after the fourth bounce. The correct choice is D.

 Quick Check ❷ **a.** About how high will the ball rebound after the seventh bounce?
b. After what bounce will the rebound height be less than 2 ft?
  a. 3.2 ft   b. 10th bounce

Test-Taking Tip

When you have to repeat a step several times, be careful to use the correct number of steps.

You can use a variable, such as a, with positive integer subscripts to represent the terms in a sequence.

1st term	2nd term	3rd term	...	$n - 1$ term	nth term	$n + 1$ term	...
↓	↓	↓		↓	↓	↓	
a_1	a_2	a_3	...	a_{n-1}	a_n	a_{n+1}	...

Lesson 11-1 Mathematical Patterns   **601**

Ask a volunteer to look up the word *recur* in a dictionary and to read the definition aloud to the class. Discuss how the definition is related to the adjective recursive.

4 EXAMPLE Alternative Method

To help students visually identify the pattern, have them graph each pair (Length of Side, Perimeter). Ask: *What type of pattern is formed?* **linear** Then, have students find an equation to represent the pattern. *p* = 4*n*, where *p* represents the perimeter of a square whose sides measure *n* units. Finally, have students connect this method with the method presented in Example 4.

PowerPoint

Additional Examples

3 a. Describe the pattern that allows you to find the next term in the sequence 2, 6, 18, 54, 162, ... Write a recursive formula for the sequence. **Multiply a term by 3 to get the next term;** $a_n = 3a_{n-1}$, where $a_1 = 2$
b. Find the sixth and seventh terms in the sequence. **486, 1458**
c. Find the value of a_{10} in the sequence. **39,366**

4 The spreadsheet shows the perimeters of regular pentagons with sides from 1 to 4 units long. The numbers in each row form a sequence.

	a1	a2	a3	a4
Length of a Side	1	2	3	4
Perimeter	5	10	15	20

a. For each sequence, find the next term (a_5) and the twentieth term (a_{20}). **row 2: 5, 20; row 3: 25, 100**
b. Write an explicit formula for each sequence. **row 2:** $a_n = n$; **row 3:** $a_n = 5n$

Resources
- Daily Notetaking Guide 11-1   **L3**

602

---

2 Using Formulas to Generate Mathematical Patterns

A **recursive formula** defines the terms in a sequence by relating each term to the ones before it. The pattern in Example 2 was recursive because the height of the ball after each bounce was 85% of its previous height. The recursive formula that describes the ball's height is $a_n = 0.85a_{n-1}$, where $a_1 = 10$.

3 EXAMPLE Using a Recursive Formula

a. Describe the pattern that allows you to find the next term in the sequence 2, 4, 6, 8, 10, . . . Write a recursive formula for the sequence.

The terms of the sequence are the even numbers. Add 2 to a term to find the next term. A recursive formula is $a_n = a_{n-1} + 2$, where $a_1 = 2$.

b. Find the sixth and seventh terms in the sequence.

Since $a_5 = 10$, $a_6 = 10 + 2 = 12$, and $a_7 = 12 + 2 = 14$.

c. Find the value of term a_9 in the sequence.

Term a_9 is the ninth term. $a_9 = a_8 + 2 = (a_7 + 2) + 2 = (14 + 2) + 2 = 18$

Quick Check **3** Find terms a_{11} and a_{15} in the sequence. **22, 30**

Sometimes you can find the value of a term of a sequence without knowing the preceding term. Instead, you can use the number of the term to calculate its value. A formula that expresses the *n*th term in terms of *n* is an **explicit formula.**

4 EXAMPLE Real-World Connection

Geometry The spreadsheet below shows the perimeters of squares with sides from 1 to 6 units long. The numbers in each row form a sequence.

	A	B	C	D	E	F	G	H
1		a1	a2	a3	a4	a5	a6	...
2	Length of a Side	1	2	3	4	5	6	...
3	Perimeter	4	8	12	16	20	24	...

a. For each sequence, find the next term (a_7) and the twenty-fifth term (a_{25}).

In the sequence in row 2, each term is the same as its subscript. Therefore, $a_7 = 7$ and $a_{25} = 25$.

In the sequence in row 3, each term is 4 times its subscript. Therefore, $a_7 = 4(7) = 28$ and $a_{25} = 4(25) = 100$.

b. Write an explicit formula for each sequence.

The explicit formula for the sequence in row 2 is $a_n = n$. The explicit formula for the sequence in row 3 is $a_n = 4n$.

Quick Check **4 a.** Write the first six terms in the sequence showing the areas of the squares in Example 4. Then find a_{20}. **1, 4, 9, 16, 25, 36; 400**
b. Write an explicit formula for the sequence from part (a). $a_n = n^2$
c. Critical Thinking Given the recursive formula $a_n = a_{n-1} + 3$, can you find the fourth term in the sequence? Explain. **No; a_1 is not given.**

602   Chapter 11   Sequences and Series

Closure

Ask students to describe two ways that they might use to completely describe the pattern in a sequence of numbers. **Answers may vary. Sample: Study the** pattern and, if possible, write an explicit formula involving an expression in the variable *n* that can be evaluated to find the value of any term a_n. If you cannot do that, describe how the pattern can be used to get from a previous term to the next term.

EXERCISES

For more exercises, see *Extra Skill and Word Problem Practice*.

Practice and Problem Solving

A Practice by Example

Examples 1 and 2
(page 601)

Describe each pattern formed. Find the next three terms. 3–9. See back of book.

1. $80, 77, 74, 71, 68, \ldots$ **2.** $4, 8, 16, 32, 64, \ldots$ **3.** $0, 3, 7, 12, 18, \ldots$

4. $1, 4, 7, 10, 13, \ldots$ **5.** $100, 10, 1, 0.1, 0.01, \ldots$ **6.** $\frac{1}{2}, \frac{1}{4}, \frac{1}{8}, \frac{1}{16}, \frac{1}{32}, \ldots$

7. $4, -8, 16, -32, 64, \ldots$ **8.** $1, 2, 6, 24, 120, \ldots$ **9.** $0, 1, 0, \frac{1}{3}, 0, \frac{1}{5}, \ldots$

1. Subtract 3; 65, 62, 59.

2. Multiply by 2; 128, 256, 512.

Fractal Geometry **Draw the first four figures of the sequence described.**

10. ——— is replaced by ⎯⎍⎯ . **11.** △ is replaced by △△ .

10–11. See back of book.

Example 3
(page 602)

Write a recursive formula for each sequence. Then find the next term.

12. $-2, -1, 0, 1, 2, \ldots$ **13.** $43, 41, 39, 37, 35, \ldots$ **14.** $40, 20, 10, 5, \frac{5}{2}, \ldots$

15. $6, 1, -4, -9, \ldots$ **16.** $144, 36, 9, \frac{9}{4}, \ldots$ **17.** $\frac{1}{2}, \frac{1}{4}, \frac{1}{8}, \frac{1}{16}, \frac{1}{32}, \ldots$

12–20. See margin.

Example 4
(page 602)

Write an explicit formula for each sequence. Then find a_{12}.

18. $4, 5, 6, 7, 8, \ldots$ **19.** $\frac{1}{2}, \frac{1}{3}, \frac{1}{4}, \frac{1}{5}, \frac{1}{6}, \ldots$ **20.** $4, 7, 10, 13, 16, \ldots$

21. $3, 7, 11, 15, 19, \ldots$ **22.** $-2\frac{1}{2}, -2, -1\frac{1}{2}, -1, \ldots$ **23.** $2, 5, 10, 17, 26, \ldots$
$a_n = 4n - 1; 47$ $a_n = \frac{n-6}{2}; 3$ $a_n = n^2 + 1; 145$

B Apply Your Skills

Decide whether each formula is *explicit* or *recursive*. Then find the first five terms of each sequence. 24–29. See back of book.

24. $a_n = 2a_{n-1} + 3$, where $a_1 = 3$ **25.** $a_n = \frac{1}{2}(n)(n-1)$

26. $(n-5)(n+5) = a_n$ **27.** $a_n = -3a_{n-1}$, where $a_1 = -2$

28. $a_n = -4n^2 - 2$ **29.** $a_n = 2n^2 + 1$

31. recursive; 340, 323, 306, 289, 272

30. $a_n = 5n$ explicit; 5, 10, 15, 20, 25 **31.** $a_n = a_{n-1} - 17$, where $a_1 = 340$

Real-World Connection

Bryan Berg built a 24-ft 4-in. 127-story freestanding house of cards.

32. **Entertainment** Suppose you are building a tower of cards with levels as displayed below. Complete the table, assuming the pattern continues.

Levels	1	2	3	4	5
Cards Needed	2	7	■	■	■

15 26 40

Find the next two terms in each sequence. Write a formula for the *n*th term. Identify each formula as *explicit* or *recursive*. 33–41. See back of book.

33. $5, 8, 11, 14, 17, \ldots$ **34.** $3, 6, 12, 24, 48, \ldots$ **35.** $1, 8, 27, 64, 125, \ldots$

36. $4, 16, 64, 256, 1024, \ldots$ **37.** $49, 64, 81, 100, 121, \ldots$ **38.** $-1, 1, -1, 1, -1, 1, \ldots$

39. $-16, -8, -4, -2, \ldots$ **40.** $-75, -68, -61, -54, \ldots$ **41.** $21, 13, 5, -3, \ldots$

Lesson 11-1 Mathematical Patterns   **603**

---

12. $a_n = a_{n-1} + 1, a_1 = -2; 3$ **15.** $a_n = a_{n-1} - 5, a_1 = 6; -14$ **18.** $a_n = n + 3; 15$

13. $a_n = a_{n-1} - 2, a_1 = 43; 33$ **16.** $a_n = \frac{a_{n-1}}{4}, a_1 = 144; \frac{9}{16}$ **19.** $a_n = \frac{1}{n+1}; \frac{1}{13}$

14. $a_n = \frac{a_{n-1}}{2}, a_1 = 40; \frac{5}{4}$ **17.** $a_n = a_{n-1} \cdot \frac{1}{2}, a_1 = \frac{1}{2}; \frac{1}{64}$ **20.** $a_n = 3n + 1; 37$

---

3. Practice

Assignment Guide

1 A B 1-11, 32, 51

2 A B 12-31, 33-50
C Challenge   52-57

Test Prep   58-62
Mixed Review   63-72

Homework Quick Check

To check students' understanding of key skills and concepts, go over Exercises 8, 16, 32, 40, 43.

Error Prevention!

Exercises 12–17 Students may forget to specify the value of a_1. Remind them that a recursive formula always has two parts.

Diversity

Exercise 42 Some students may not be familiar with the idea of counting sheep as a way to induce sleep. Ask students to describe techniques they use to help them fall asleep.

Tactile Learners

Exercise 51 Students might use plastic or wooden cubes to model the stacks of boxes.

Differentiated Instruction **Resources**

GPS Guided Problem Solving	L3
Enrichment	L4
Reteaching	L2
Practice	L3

603

For Exercises 1 and 2, describe each pattern. Find the next three terms.

1. 5, 15, 25, 35, . . . **Each new term is 10 more than the preceding term; 45, 55, 65**

2. $1, \frac{2}{3}, \frac{4}{9}, \frac{8}{27}, \ldots$ **Each new term is $\frac{2}{3}$ of the preceding term; $\frac{16}{81}, \frac{32}{243}, \frac{64}{729}$**

3. Write a recursive formula for the sequence 7, −1, −9, −17, ... Then find the next term. $a_n = a_{n-1} - 8$, where $a_1 = 7$; **−25**

4. Write an explicit formula for the sequence $1, \frac{1}{4}, \frac{1}{9}, \frac{1}{16}, \ldots$. Then find a_{15}. $a_n = \frac{1}{n^2}$; $\frac{1}{225}$

5. A recursive formula for a sequence is $a_n = a_{n-1} + 2n$, where $a_1 = 1$. Write the first five terms of the sequence. **1, 5, 11, 19, 29**

Alternative Assessment

Have students work individually. Ask students to select two of the sequences from Exercises 12–17. Then, ask students to write an explicit formula for each sequence they picked. Ask them to show work verifying that the explicit formulas generate the same sequences as those given in the exercises. Then ask students to select two sequences from Exercises 18–23 and write a recursive formula for each sequence. Ask them to show work verifying that the recursive formulas generate the same sequences as those given in the exercises.

43. Answers may vary. Sample: A recursive formula requires that the previous term be known to find a given term. An explicit formula only requires the number of the term.

604

44a–c. Answers may vary. Sample:

a. 1, −2, 4, −8...

b. $a_n = -2(a_{n-1})$, where $a_n = 1$; $a_n = (-2)^{n-1}$

45. 28, 53, 89, 138

46. 24, 78, 240, 726

C Challenge

56a. $a_n = a_{n-1} + 5$, $a_1 = 25$; $a_n = 20 + 5n$

---

42. Suppose the cartoon at the right included one sheep to the left and another sheep to the right of the three shown. What "names" would you give these sheep? a_{n-2}, a_{n+2}

43. Writing Explain the difference between a recursive formula and an explicit formula. **See margin.**

44. a. Open-Ended Write four terms of a sequence of numbers that you can describe both recursively and explicitly.
  b. Write a recursive formula and an explicit formula for your sequence.
  c. Find the 20th term of the sequence by evaluating one of your formulas. Use the other formula to check your work. **−524,288**

WHEN MATHEMATICIANS CAN'T SLEEP

Use the given rule to write the 4th, 5th, 6th, and 7th terms of each sequence.

45. $a_1 = -1, a_n = a_{n-1} + n^2$

46. $a_1 = -2, a_n = 3(a_{n-1} + 2)$

47. $a_n = (n + 1)^2$ **25, 36, 49, 64**

48. $a_n = 2(n - 1)^3$ **54, 128, 250, 432**

49. $a_n = \frac{n^2}{n+1}$ $\frac{16}{5}, \frac{25}{6}, \frac{36}{7}, \frac{49}{8}$

50. $a_n = \frac{n+1}{n+2}$ $\frac{5}{6}, \frac{6}{7}, \frac{7}{8}, \frac{8}{9}$

51. Geometry Suppose you are stacking boxes in levels that form squares. The numbers of boxes in successive levels form a sequence. The figure at the left shows the top four levels as viewed from above. **25 boxes**
  a. How many boxes of equal size would you need for the next lower level?
  b. How many boxes of equal size would you need to add three levels? **110 boxes**
  c. Suppose you are stacking a total of 285 boxes. How many levels will you have? **9 levels**

Use each recursive formula to write an explicit formula for the sequence.

52. $a_1 = 10, a_n = 2a_{n-1}$ $a_n = 10 \cdot 2^{n-1}$

53. $a_1 = -5, a_n = a_{n-1} - 1$ $a_n = -n - 4$

54. $a_1 = -2, a_n = \frac{1}{2}a_{n-1}$ $a_n = -2 \cdot \left(\frac{1}{2}\right)^{n-1}$

55. $a_1 = 1, a_n = a_{n-1} + 4$ $a_n = 1 + 4(n - 1)$

56. Finance Use the information in the ad.
  a. Suppose you start a savings account at Mun e-Bank. Write both a recursive formula and an explicit formula for the amount of money you would have in the bank at the end of any week.
  b. How much money would you have in the bank after four weeks? **$40**
  c. Assume the bank pays interest every four weeks. To calculate your interest, multiply the balance at the end of the four weeks by 0.005. Then add that much to your account on the last day of the four-week period. Write a recursive $a_n = (a_{n-1} + \$20) \cdot 1.005, a_1 = \$40.20$ formula for the amount of money you have after each interest payment.
  d. Critical Thinking What is the bank's annual interest rate? **6.5%**

Mun _e_-**Bank**
is offering a **GREAT** deal right now!

Start a savings club account by depositing only $25 today and $5 a week starting next week.

See how easy it is to save!

57a. 15, 21

b. $a_n = a_{n-1} + n$, $a_1 = 1$

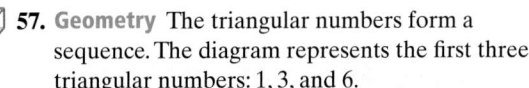

57. Geometry The triangular numbers form a sequence. The diagram represents the first three triangular numbers: 1, 3, and 6.
  a. Find the fifth and sixth triangular numbers.
  b. Write a recursive formula for the nth triangular number.
  c. Is the explicit formula $a_n = \frac{1}{2}(n^2 + n)$ the correct formula for this sequence? How do you know? **Yes; the formula yields the same value as the recursive formula.**

$n = 1$ $n = 2$ $n = 3$

Resources
For additional practice with a variety of test item formats:
• Standardized Test Prep, p. 645
• Test-Taking Strategies, p. 640
• Test-Taking Strategies with Transparencies

Test Prep

Multiple Choice

58. What is the difference between the third term in the sequence whose recursive formula is $a_1 = -5$, $a_n = 2a_{n-1} + 1$ and the third term in the sequence whose recursive formula is $a_1 = -3$, $a_n = -a_{n-1} + 3$? **B**
  A. 2   **B.** 14   **C.** 20   **D.** 32

59. What is a recursive formula for the sequence whose explicit formula is $a_n = (n + 1)^2$? **G**
  F. $a_1 = 1$, $a_n = (a_{n-1} + 1)^2$ **G.** $a_1 = 4$, $a_n = \left(\sqrt{a_{n-1}} + 1\right)^2$
  H. $a_1 = n$, $a_n = a_{n-1} + n$ **J.** $a_1 = n^2$, $a_n = (a_{n-1})^2 + 1$

Use the figure below for Exercises 60–62.

62. [2] $a_n = a_{n-1} + n^2$, $a_1 = 1$; Each term consists of the previous term added to the square of the number of the term.

[1] incorrect formula OR no explanation OR incorrect explanation

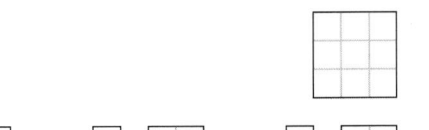

Term 1   Term 2   Term 3   Term 4

60. How many 1×1 squares are in the sixth term of the sequence? **C**
  A. 21   **B.** 36   **C.** 91   **D.** 441

61. Which expressions represent the first three terms of the sequence? **J**
  F. $1^2, 2^2, 3^2, \ldots$ **G.** $1, 1 + 2, 1 + 2 + 3, \ldots$
  H. $1^2, (1 + 2)^2, (1 + 2 + 3)^2, \ldots$ **J.** $1^2, 1^2 + 2^2, 1^2 + 2^2 + 3^2, \ldots$

Short Response

62. Write a recursive formula for the sequence in the figure above. Explain your reasoning. **See left.**

64. $\dfrac{(x + 1)^2}{36} + \dfrac{(y + 2)^2}{36} = 1$

Mixed Review

Lesson 10-6

The graph of each equation is translated 2 units left and 3 units down. Write each new equation.

68. $xy = 27$

72. $xy = 100$

63. $(x + 2)^2 + (y - 1)^2 = 5$ **64.** $\dfrac{(x - 1)^2}{36} + \dfrac{(y - 1)^2}{36} = 1$
  $(x + 4)^2 + (y + 2)^2 = 5$ See above.

Lesson 9-1

Each point is from an inverse variation. Write an equation to model the data.

65. $(1, 20)$ $xy = 20$ **66.** $(5, 2)$ $xy = 10$ **67.** $(9, 13)$ $xy = 117$ **68.** $(-3, -9)$
                           $xy = 72$
69. $(2, 5)$ $xy = 10$ **70.** $(-6, -12)$ **71.** $\left(\frac{1}{2}, -\frac{1}{2}\right)$ $xy = -\frac{1}{4}$ **72.** $(-10, -10)$

Arithmetic Sequences

Objectives
1 To identify and generate arithmetic sequences

Examples
1 Identifying an Arithmetic Sequence
2 Real-World Connection
3 Using the Arithmetic Mean

Professional Development

Math Background

An arithmetic sequence is a special case of a linear function. The domain is the set of natural numbers.

More Math Background: p. 598C

Lesson Planning and Resources

See p. 598E for a list of the resources that support this lesson.

PowerPoint

Bell Ringer Practice

✓ **Check Skills You'll Need**
For intervention, direct students to:

Look for a Pattern
Skills Handbook: p. 866

What You'll Learn
• To identify and generate arithmetic sequences

. . . And Why
To determine the amount of money raised during a fund-raiser, as in Example 2

◀》 **New Vocabulary**

✓ **Check Skills You'll Need**

GO **for Help** Skills Handbook p. 866

Describe the pattern in each sequence. Use at least one of the words *add*, *subtract*, or *difference*.

1. $10, 8, 6, 4, 2, 0, \ldots$ Subtract 2.
2. $100, 117, 134, 151, 168, \ldots$ Add 17.
3. $\frac{5}{7}, \frac{8}{7}, \frac{11}{7}, 2, \ldots$ Add $\frac{3}{7}$.
4. $-\frac{1}{4}, -\frac{1}{2}, -\frac{3}{4}, -1, -\frac{5}{4}, -\frac{3}{2}, \ldots$ Subtract $\frac{1}{4}$.

• arithmetic sequence   • common difference
• arithmetic mean

---

1 **Identifying and Generating Arithmetic Sequences**

Vocabulary Tip

The stress in the noun arithmetic is on the second syllable (uh RITH muh tik). The stress in the adjective arithmetic is on the third syllable (ar ith MET ik).

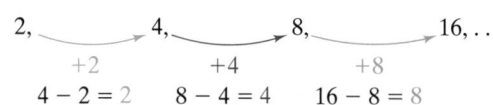
Online
active math

For: Sequences Activity
Use: Interactive Textbook, 11-2

In an **arithmetic sequence,** the difference between consecutive terms is constant. This difference is called the **common difference.** The common difference can be positive (the terms of the sequence are increasing in value) or negative (the terms of the sequence are decreasing in value).

1 **EXAMPLE**   Identifying an Arithmetic Sequence

Is the given sequence arithmetic?

a. $2, 4, 8, 16, \ldots$

$$2, \quad 4, \quad 8, \quad 16, \ldots$$
$$\quad +2 \quad\quad +4 \quad\quad +8$$
$$4 - 2 = 2 \quad 8 - 4 = 4 \quad 16 - 8 = 8$$

There is no common difference. This is *not* an arithmetic sequence.

b. the golf ball pattern at the right

$$6, \quad 12, \quad 18, \ldots$$
$$\quad +6 \quad\quad +6$$
$$12 - 6 = 6 \quad 18 - 12 = 6$$

The common difference is 6. The dots on the golf ball form an arithmetic sequence.

✓ **Quick Check** Is the given sequence arithmetic? If so, identify the common difference.
a. $2, 5, 7, 12, \ldots$ **b.** $48, 45, 42, 39, \ldots$
    no   yes; -3

You can use an explicit formula to find the value of the nth term of an arithmetic sequence when the previous term is unknown.

606   Chapter 11   Sequences and Series

Differentiated Instruction **Solutions for All Learners**

Special Needs **L1**
In Example 1, students with vision difficulties may not be able to count the "dimples" on the golf ball. Draw the pattern using dots on the board or a large sheet of paper.

learning style: visual

Below Level **L2**
Have students list sequences that they already know, and identify the common differences.

learning style: verbal

Key Concepts

Property	**Arithmetic Sequence Formulas**

Recursive Formula   **Explicit Formula**

$a_1 = $ a given value, $a_n = a_{n-1} + d$ $a_n = a_1 + (n-1)d$

In these formulas, a_n is the nth term ($n > 1$), a_1 is the first term, n is the number of the term, and d is the common difference.

Real-World Connection

The AIDSRide raises money for AIDS services in locations across the United States.

2 EXAMPLE   Real-World Connection

Fund-Raising Suppose you participate in a bike-a-thon for charity. The charity starts with $1100 in donations. Each participant must raise at least $35 in pledges. What is the minimum amount of money raised if there are 75 participants?

Find the 76th term of the sequence 1100, 1135, 1170, ...

$a_n = a_1 + (n-1)d$ **Use the explicit formula.**

$a_{76} = 1100 + (76-1)(35)$ **Substitute a_1 = 1100, n = 76, and d = 35.**

$= 1100 + (75)(35)$ **Subtract within parentheses.**

$= 3725$ **Simplify.**

● With 75 participants, the bike-a-thon will raise a minimum of $3725.

✓ **Quick Check** ② **a.** *Critical Thinking* In Example 2, why find the value of the 76th term, not the 75th term? **See margin.**

     b. Use the explicit formula to find the 25th term in the sequence 5, 11, 17, 23, 29, ...
                                                   149

The **arithmetic mean** of any two numbers is the average of the two numbers.

$$\text{arithmetic mean} = \frac{\text{sum of two numbers}}{2}$$

For any three sequential terms in an arithmetic sequence, the middle term is the arithmetic mean of the first and third terms.

Graphs of arithmetic sequences are linear. Two terms of an arithmetic sequence and their arithmetic mean lie on the same line.

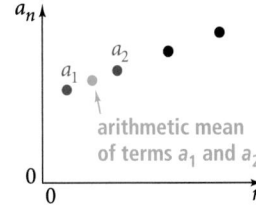

arithmetic mean of terms a_1 and a_2

Video Tutor Help

Visit: PHSchool.com
Web Code: age-0775

You can use the arithmetic mean to find a missing term of an arithmetic sequence.

3 EXAMPLE   Using the Arithmetic Mean

Find the missing term of the arithmetic sequence 84, ■, 110.

arithmetic mean $= \dfrac{84 + 110}{2}$ **Write the average.**

$= 97$ **Simplify.**

● The missing term is 97.

✓ **Quick Check** ③ **a.** Find the missing term of the arithmetic sequence 24, ■, 57. **40.5**

     b. Write an expression for the arithmetic mean of a_6 and a_7. $\dfrac{a_6 + a_7}{2}$

Advanced Learners   **L4**
Have students find examples of sequences that are neither arithmetic nor geometric. One example is the Fibonacci sequence.

English Language Learners   **ELL**
Have students write the words *arithmetic, difference, consecutive, constant,* and *common.* Then have them define each term and write a sentence using them in a mathematical context.

                         learning style: verbal   **learning style: verbal**

---

2. Teach

Guided Instruction

PowerPoint

Additional Examples

① Is the given sequence arithmetic?
a. 7, 10, 13, 16, . . .   yes
b. the sequence of dots in the "triangles" shown below   no

② Suppose you have already saved $75 toward the purchase of a new CD player and speakers. You plan to save at least $12 a week from money you earn at a part-time job. In all, what is the minimum amount you will have after 26 weeks? $387

③ Find the missing term of the arithmetic sequence 50, ■, 92.   71

Resources
• Daily Notetaking Guide 11-2   **L3**

Closure

Ask students how they can write an explicit formula and a recursive formula for an arithmetic sequence with first term a_1 and common difference d. **Answers may vary. Sample: In an arithmetic sequence, you can add the common difference to a term to get to the next term. To get to the nth term, you can start with a_1 and add d a total of $n − 1$ times. So $a_n = a_1 + (n-1)d$. This is an explicit formula. Using $a_n = a_{n-1} + d$ and a_1 = (given number), you have a recursive formula.**

2a. The first term in the sequence, 1100, was the amount of money with *no* participants, so there is one more term than the number of participants.

Homework Quick Check
To check students' understanding of key skills and concepts, go over Exercises 18, 43, 45, 60, 62, 64.

Error Prevention!

Exercises 1–10 When students are deciding whether a sequence is an arithmetic sequence, they should be careful to subtract each term from the term that immediately succeeds it. Subtracting terms from the terms that preceed them will give the wrong common difference for any sequence that is arithmetic.

Technology Tip

Exercise 44 There are several ways to generate arithmetic sequences with a graphing calculator. You may want to suggest that students explore generating sequences with the Table feature, sequence mode, and the seq(feature on the LIST OPS menu.

EXERCISES

For more exercises, see *Extra Skill and Word Problem Practice.*

Practice and Problem Solving

Ⓐ Practice by Example

Example 1
(page 606)

 for Help

Is the given sequence arithmetic? If so, identify the common difference.

1. $1, 4, 9, 16, \ldots$ **no**

2. $10, 20, 30, 40, \ldots$ **yes; 10**

3. $1, 1, 2, 3, 5, 8, \ldots$ **no**

4. $0, 1, 3, 6, 10, \ldots$ **no**

5. $-21, -18, -15, -12, \ldots$ **yes; 3**

6. $97, 86, 75, 64, \ldots$ **yes; −11**

7. $3, 7, 11, 15, \ldots$ **yes; 4**

8. $100, 10, 1, 0.1, \ldots$ **no**

9. $\frac{1}{2}, \frac{1}{4}, \frac{1}{8}, \frac{1}{16}, \ldots$ **no**

10. $-5, 5, -5, 5, -5, \ldots$ **no**

Example 2
(page 607)

Find the 32nd term of each sequence.

11. $34, 37, 40, 43, \ldots$ **127**

12. $-9, -8.7, -8.4, \ldots$ **0.3**

13. $0.1, 0.5, 0.9, 1.3, \ldots$ **12.5**

14. $0.0023, 0.0025, 0.0027, \ldots$ **0.0085**

15. $101, 105, 109, 113, \ldots$ **225**

16. $213, 201, 189, 177, \ldots$ **−159**

17. $3, 1, -1, -3, \ldots$ **−59**

18. $23, 30, 37, 44, \ldots$ **240**

19. $9, 4, -1, -6, -11, \ldots$ **−146**

20. $13, 17, 21, 25, \ldots$ **137**

Example 3
(page 607)

Find the missing term of each arithmetic sequence.

21. $-16, \blacksquare, 1, \ldots$ **−7.5**

22. $14, \blacksquare, 28, \ldots$ **21**

23. $\ldots 5, \blacksquare, 21, \ldots$ **13**

24. $\frac{13}{2}, \blacksquare, \frac{51}{2}, \ldots$ **16**

25. $101, \blacksquare, -115, \ldots$ **−7**

26. $203, \blacksquare, 1117, \ldots$ **660**

27. $25, \blacksquare, -10, \ldots$ **7.5**

28. $\ldots 65, \blacksquare, -60, \ldots$ **2.5**

29. $\ldots a_{10}, \blacksquare, a_{12}, \ldots$ **a_{11}**

30. $\ldots 99, \blacksquare, 66, \ldots$ **82.5**

Ⓑ Apply Your Skills

Find the arithmetic mean a_n of the given terms.

31. $a_{n-1} = 7, a_{n+1} = 1$ **4**

32. $a_{n-1} = 4, a_{n+1} = -3$ $\frac{1}{2}$

33. $a_{n-1} = 21, a_{n+1} = 5$ **13**

34. $a_{n-1} = 100, a_{n+1} = 140$ **120**

35. $a_{n-1} = -18, a_{n+1} = -21$ **−19.5**

36. $a_{n-1} = 0.3, a_{n+1} = 1.9$ **1.1**

37. $a_{n-1} = 9, a_{n+1} = -11$ **−1**

38. $a_{n-1} = \frac{3}{5}, a_{n+1} = 1$ $\frac{4}{5}$

39. $a_{n-1} = r, a_{n+1} = s$ $\frac{r+s}{2}$

40. $a_{n-1} = r, a_{n+1} = r + s$ $\frac{2r+s}{2}$

41. $a_{n-1} = -2x, a_{n+1} = 2x$ **0**

42. $a_{n-1} = x + 3, a_{n+1} = 3x - 1$ $2x + 1$

43. The student assumed that the sequence was $a_n = 2^{n-1}$. However, $a_1 = 2^0 = 1$, not 0 as given in the problem.

43. Error Analysis A student claims that the next term of the arithmetic sequence $0, 2, 4, \ldots$ is 8. What error did the student make?   **See left.**

 44. a. Open-Ended Use your calculator to generate an arithmetic sequence with a common difference of -7. How could you use a calculator to find the 6th term? The 8th term? The 20th term?   **a–b. See margin.**

b. Critical Thinking Explain how your answer to part (a) relates to the explicit formula $a_n = a_1 + (n - 1)d$.

 Online
Homework Video Tutor
Visit: PHSchool.com
Web Code: age-1102

45. Writing Describe some advantages and some disadvantages of a recursive formula and an explicit formula.   **See margin pp. 608–609.**

44a. Answers may vary. Sample: 25, 18, 11, 4, −3, −10...; to find the nth term, multiply $n - 1$ times (-7) and add to a_1.

b. Answers may vary. Sample: Start with the first term and continue to subtract 7 for each term. For each term, you subtract $7 \cdot$ (term number −1) from the first term.

45. Answers may vary. Sample: An advantage of a recursive formula is that only the preceding term must be known to find the next term; a disadvantage is that many calculations

Find the 17th term of each sequence.

46. $a_{16} = 18, d = 5$ **23**

47. $a_{16} = 18, d = -3$ **15**

48. $a_{16} = 18, d = \frac{1}{2}$ **18.5**

49. $a_{18} = 18, d = -4$ **22**

50. $a_{18} = 18, d = 12$ **6**

51. $a_{18} = 18, d = -11$ **29**

Write an explicit and a recursive formula for each sequence.   **52–61. See margin.**

52. $2, 4, 6, 8, 10, \ldots$

53. $0, 6, 12, 18, 24, \ldots$

54. $-5, -4, -3, -2, -1, \ldots$

55. $-4, -8, -12, -16, -20, \ldots$

56. $-2, 5, 12, 19, 26, 33, \ldots$

57. $27, 15, 3, -9, -21, \ldots$

58. $-5, -3.5, -2, -0.5, 1, \ldots$

59. $-32, -20, -8, 4, 16, \ldots$

60. $1, 1\frac{1}{3}, 1\frac{2}{3}, 2, \ldots$

61. $0, \frac{1}{8}, \frac{1}{4}, \frac{3}{8}, \ldots$

🌐 **62. Transportation** Suppose a trolley stops at a certain intersection every 14 min.
GPS The first trolley of the day gets to the stop at 6:43 A.M. How long do you have to wait for a trolley if you get to the stop at 8:15 A.M.? At 3:20 P.M.?   **6 min; 1 min**

Find the missing terms of each arithmetic sequence. (*Hint:* The arithmetic mean of the first and fifth terms is the third term.)

63. $2, ■, ■, ■, -22, \ldots$ **−4, −10, −16**

64. $10, ■, ■, ■, -11.6, \ldots$ **4.6, −0.8, −6.2**

65. $1, ■, ■, ■, -35, \ldots$ **−8, −17, −26**

66. $\ldots \frac{13}{5}, ■, ■, ■, \frac{37}{5}, \ldots$ **$\frac{19}{5}, 5, \frac{31}{5}$**

67. $17, ■, ■, ■, 17, \ldots$ **17, 17, 17**

68. $660, ■, ■, ■, 744, \ldots$ **681, 702, 723**

69. $\ldots -17, ■, ■, ■, 1, \ldots$ **−12.5, −8, −3.5**

70. $\ldots a + 1, ■, ■, ■, a + 17, \ldots$ **$a + 5, a + 9, a + 13$**

🌐 **71. Savings** In February you start a holiday savings account with a deposit of $20. You increase each monthly deposit by five dollars until the end of the year.   **a–b. See margin.**
a. Write the amount in the account after each deposit.
b. Write a recursive formula for the sequence of balances.
c. How much money will you have saved by the end of the year?   **$495**

Graph the arithmetic sequence generated by each formula over the domain $1 \le n \le 10$.   **72–73. See back of book.**

72. $a_1 = -60, a_n = a_{n-1} + 9$

73. $a_n = 50 - 7n$

74. Critical Thinking Suppose you turn the water on in an empty bathtub with vertical sides. After 20 s, the water has reached a level of 1.15 in. You then leave the room. You want to turn the water off when the level in the bathtub is 8.5 in. How many minutes later should you return? (*Hint:* Begin by identifying two terms of an arithmetic sequence.)   **2.46 min or 2 min 28 s**

C **Challenge**

75. The arithmetic mean of two terms in an arithmetic sequence is 42. One term is 30. Find the other term.   **54**

76. The arithmetic mean of two terms in an arithmetic sequence is −6. One term is −20. Find the other term.   **8**

77. In an arithmetic sequence with $a_1 = 4$ and $d = 9$, which term is 184?   **21st term**

78. In an arithmetic sequence with $a_1 = 2$ and $d = -2$, which term is −82?   **43rd term**

Real-World 🌐 Connection

San Francisco's historic cable cars move by gripping and releasing a moving steel cable under the street.

PowerPoint
Lesson Quiz

Is the given sequence arithmetic? If so, identify the common difference.

1. −9, 0, 9, 18, . . .   **yes; 9**

2. 0.1, 0.01, 0.001, 0.0001, . . .   **no**

3. $\frac{1}{6}, \frac{1}{3}, \frac{1}{2}, \frac{2}{3}, \ldots$ **yes; $\frac{1}{6}$**

4. Find the 25th term of the arithmetic sequence 26, 13, 0, −13, ...   **−286**

Find the missing term of each arithmetic sequence.

5. 8, ■, 20, . . .   **14**

6 $3\frac{1}{2}, ■, 12\frac{1}{2}, \ldots$ **8**

Alternative Assessment

Have students work in pairs. Each student should write the first four terms of five sequences. Three of the sequences should be arithmetic and two should be non-arithmetic. Students trade sequences. Have each student classify the sequences he or she receives as arithmetic or non-arithmetic. For each arithmetic sequence, the student should name the common difference and give the values of a_{19} and a_{21}.

59. $a_n = -32 + (n - 1)12$;
$a_n = a_{n-1} + 12$,
$a_1 = -32$

60. $a_n = 1 + (n - 1)\frac{1}{3}$;
$a_n = a_{n-1} + \frac{1}{3}, a_1 = 1$

61. $a_n = \frac{1}{8}(n - 1)$;
$a_n = a_{n-1} + \frac{1}{8}, a_1 = 0$

71a. $20, $45, $75, $110, $150, $195, $245, $300, $360, $425, $495

b. $a_n = a_{n-1} + $20 + $5(n - 1), a_1 = 20

may be required to find a term. An advantage of an explicit formula is that it is easy to find any term.

52. $a_n = 2 + 2(n - 1)$,
$a_n = a_{n-1} + 2, a_1 = 2$

53. $a_n = 0 + 6(n - 1)$,
$a_n = a_{n-1} + 6, a_1 = 0$

54. $a_n = -5 + 1(n - 1)$,
$a_n = a_{n-1} + 1, a_1 = -5$

55. $a_n = -4 - 4(n - 1)$,
$a_n = a_{n-1} - 4, a_1 = -4$

56. $a_n = -2 + (n - 1)7$;
$a_n = a_{n-1} + 7, a_1 = -2$

57. $a_n = 27 - (n - 1)12$;
$a_n = a_{n-1} - 12, a_1 = 27$

58. $a_n = -5 + (n - 1)1.5$;
$a_n = a_{n-1} + 1.5, a_1 = -5$

609

📁 **Resources**

For additional practice with a variety of test item formats:
- Standardized Test Prep, p. 645
- Test-Taking Strategies, p. 640
- Test-Taking Strategies with Transparencies

79. $a_1 = -1, d = 3$

80. $a_1 = -4, d = 4$

81. $a_1 = 52, d = -10$

82. $a_1 = -21\frac{1}{4}, d = 4\frac{1}{4}$

83. $a_1 = -100.5, d = 22$

84. $a_1 = -9, d = 2.2$

Given two terms of each arithmetic sequence, find a_1 and d. See left.

79. $a_3 = 5$ and $a_5 = 11$ 　　　　　80. $a_4 = 8$ and $a_7 = 20$

81. $a_3 = 32$ and $a_7 = -8$ 　　　　82. $a_{10} = 17$ and $a_{14} = 34$

83. $a_4 = -34.5$ and $a_5 = -12.5$ 　84. $a_4 = -2.4$ and $a_6 = 2$

Find the indicated term of each arithmetic series.

85. $a_1 = k, d = k + 4; a_9$ 　9k + 32 　86. $a_1 = k + 7, d = 2k - 5; a_{11}$ 　21k − 43

Test Prep

Multiple Choice

87. Which arithmetic sequence DOES NOT include the term 33? 　B
- **A.** 1, 5, 9, 13, . . . 　　　　　**B.** 1, 11, 21, . . .
- **C.** 3, 9, 15, . . . 　　　　　　**D.** 85, 72, 59, . . .

88. Which arithmetic sequence includes the term 27? 　J
- **I.** $a_1 = 7, a_n = a_{n-1} + 5$ 　**II.** $a_n = 3 + (n-1)4$ 　**III.** $a_n = 57 - 6n$
- **F.** I only 　　**G.** I and II only 　**H.** II and III only 　**J.** I, II, and III

89. The arithmetic mean of the monthly salaries of two people is $2955. One person earns $2760 per month. What is the monthly salary of the other person? 　B
- **A.** $2857.50 　　**B.** $3150 　　**C.** $5520 　　**D.** $5715

90. What is the 30th term of the sequence 7, 16, 25, 34, . . . ? 　H
- **F.** 277 　　　**G.** 270 　　　**H.** 268 　　　**J.** 261

Short Response

91. Explain how to use the arithmetic mean to find the missing terms in the arithmetic sequence 15, ■, ■, ■, 47, . . . See margin.

Extended Response

92. Find the 100th term of the arithmetic sequence 3, 10, 17, 24, 31, . . . Explain your steps. 　See margin.

---

91. **[2]** The third term, 31, is the mean of the first and fifth terms. The second term, 23, is the mean of the first and third terms. The fourth term, 39, is the mean of the third and fifth terms.

[1] incomplete explanation OR incorrect term values

92. **[4]** 696; $a_2 - a_1 = 10 - 3 = 7$, so the common difference is 7. Use $a_1 = 3$, $d = 7$, and $n = 100$ in the formula $a_n = a_1 + (n - 1)d$ to find a_{100}.

[3] explanation correct, but computational error

[2] incomplete explanation

[1] correct number, but no explanation

Mixed Review

Lesson 11-1

GO for Help

93. recursive; −2, −7, −12, −17, −22

Decide whether each formula is *explicit* or *recursive*. Then find the first five terms of each sequence.

93. $a_1 = -2, a_n = a_{n-1} - 5$ 　　　94. $a_n = 3n(n + 1)$ 　explicit; 6, 18, 36, 60, 90

95. $a_n = n^2 - 1$ 　explicit; 0, 3, 8, 15, 24 　96. $a_1 = -121, a_n = a_{n-1} + 13$ 　recursive; −121, −108, −95, −82, −69

Lesson 10-6

98. $(-4\sqrt{2}, 0)$ and $(4\sqrt{2}, 0)$

Find the foci of each ellipse.

97. $\frac{x^2}{4} + \frac{y^2}{9} = 1$ 　$(0, -\sqrt{5})$ and $(0, \sqrt{5})$ 　98. $\frac{x^2}{36} + \frac{y^2}{4} = 1$ 　See left.

99. $\frac{(x-1)^2}{121} + \frac{y^2}{100} = 1$ 　　　100. $\frac{(x-1)^2}{64} + \frac{(y-3)^2}{25} = 1$
$(1 - \sqrt{21}, 0)$ and $(1 + \sqrt{21}, 0)$ 　　　$(1 + \sqrt{39}, 3)$ and $(1 - \sqrt{39}, 3)$

Lesson 7-2 **101.** **Geometry** The formula for volume V of a sphere with radius r is $V = \frac{4}{3}\pi r^3$. Find the radius of a sphere as a function of its volume. Rationalize the denominator. 　$r = \frac{\sqrt[3]{6\pi^2 V}}{2\pi}$

The Fibonacci Sequence

FOR USE WITH LESSON 11-2

One famous mathematical sequence is the Fibonacci sequence. You can find each term of the sequence using addition, but the sequence is not arithmetic. The recursive formula for the Fibonacci sequence is $F_n = F_{n-2} + F_{n-1}$, with $F_1 = 1$ and $F_2 = 1$.

You can use the formula to generate the first five terms of the sequence.

$F_1 = 1$
$F_2 = 1$
$F_3 = F_1 + F_2 = 1 + 1 = 2$
$F_4 = F_2 + F_3 = 1 + 2 = 3$
$F_5 = F_3 + F_4 = 2 + 3 = 5$

The first five terms of the Fibonacci sequence are $1, 1, 2, 3, 5$.

1. **Nature** The numbers of the Fibonacci sequence are often found in other areas, especially in nature. Which term of the Fibonacci sequence does each picture represent?

   a.   b.   c.   d.

   fifth   seventh   sixth   fourth

2. a. Describe a recursive rule for constructing Pascal's Triangle at the right. How is your rule similar to the process for generating the Fibonacci sequence? (*Hint:* How can you find the numbers in the last row?)

   b. Find "diagonals" in Pascal's Triangle by starting with the first 1 in each row and moving one row up and one number to the right. For example, the diagonal starting in the fifth row is 1, 3, 1. The diagonal starting in the sixth row is 1, 4, 3. For each diagonal, write the sum of its entries. What pattern do the sums form?
   a–b. See back of book.

   ```
   1
   1 1
   1 2 1
   1 3 3 1
   1 4 6 4 1
   1 5 10 10 5 1
   1 ▦ ▦ ▦ ▦ ▦ ▦
   ```

3. a. Generate the first ten terms of the Fibonacci sequence. **a–c. See margin.**

   b. Find the sum of the first ten terms of the Fibonacci sequence. Divide the sum by 11. What do you notice?

   c. **Open-Ended** Choose two numbers other than 1 and 1. Generate a Fibonacci-like sequence from them. Write the first ten terms of your sequence, find the sum, and divide the sum by 11. What do you notice?

   d. **Make a Conjecture** What is the sum of the first ten terms of any Fibonacci-like sequence? **It will be 11 times the seventh term.**

4. a. Study the pattern at the right. Write the next line.

   b. Without calculating, use the pattern to predict the sum of squares of the first ten terms of the Fibonacci sequence. **4895**

   c. Verify the prediction you made in part (b). **Check students' work.**

   $$1^2 + 1^2 \qquad\qquad = 2 = 1 \cdot 2$$
   $$1^2 + 1^2 + 2^2 \qquad = 6 = 2 \cdot 3$$
   $$1^2 + 1^2 + 2^2 + 3^2 \quad = 15 = 3 \cdot 5$$
   $$1^2 + 1^2 + 2^2 + 3^2 + 5^2 = 40 = 5 \cdot 8$$
   $$1^2 + 1^2 + 2^2 + 3^2 + 5^2 + 8^2 = 104 = 8 \cdot 13$$

5. Make a table with four columns, as shown as the right. Begin with $n = 2$ and complete the first 8 rows. Make a conjecture suggested by the numbers in the third and fourth columns.
   See back of book.

n	F_n	$(F_n)^2$	$F_{n-1} \cdot F_{n+1}$

The Fibonacci Sequence

Students explore a famous sequence that arises in a variety of situations in mathematics, nature, and the sciences.

Guided Instruction

Teaching Tip
For Exercise 2, it may help students to show Pascal's Triangle in the form shown below. Have students calculate the sum of the numbers on each diagonal, from the top downward.

```
1
1 1
1 2 1
1 3 3 1
1 4 6 4 1
1 5 10 10 5 1
```

Error Prevention!

Exercise 3 For part (c), you may need to explain that the term *Fibonacci-like sequence* means a sequence for which the first two terms are numbers other than 1 and 1 but for which the equation $F_n = F_{n-2} + F_{n-1}$ still holds.

3a. 1, 1, 2, 3, 5, 8, 13, 21, 34, 55

b. 143; 13; the answer is the seventh term.

c. Check students' work; the answer is the seventh term.

11-3

Geometric Sequences

Objectives

1 To identify and generate geometric sequences

Examples

1 Identifying a Geometric Sequence
2 Real-World Connection
3 Real-World Connection

What You'll Learn

• To identify and generate geometric sequences

... And Why

To find the size of a reduced logo, as in Example 2

 for Help Lesson 11-1

✓ Check Skills You'll Need

Find the next term in each sequence.

1. $1, 2, 4, 8, \ldots$ **16**   2. $336, 168, 84, 42, \ldots$ **21**
3. $0.1, 1, 10, 100, \ldots$ **1000**   4. $900, 300, 100, \ldots$ $\frac{100}{3}$

🔊 **New Vocabulary**   • geometric sequence   • common ratio   • geometric mean

Math Background

Arithmetic sequences are based on addition, and geometric sequences are based on multiplication. A geometric sequence is a special case of an exponential function. The domain is the set of natural numbers.

More Math Background: p. 598C

Lesson Planning and Resources

See p. 598E for a list of the resources that support this lesson.

Bell Ringer Practice

✓ Check Skills You'll Need

For intervention, direct students to:

Mathematical Patterns
Lesson 11-1: Examples 3, 4
Extra Skills and Word
   Problems Practice, Ch. 11

---

1 ▸ Identifying and Generating Geometric Sequences

4a. Check students' work.

b. Check students' work; they multiply the previous term by a constant.

c. Check students' work.

d. Check students' work.

Graphing Calculator Hint

Enter the values of n and a_n into lists. Then use the STAT and 2nd STAT PLOT features to graph the sequences.

Activity: Geometric Sequences

• Make a large right isosceles triangle out of colored paper.

• Cut the triangle into two congruent isosceles triangles.

• Place one triangle on top of the other and repeat the previous step.

1. Complete the sequence for the numbers of triangles below.   **1, 2, 4, 8**

$a_1 = \blacksquare$ $a_2 = \blacksquare$ $a_3 = \blacksquare$ $a_4 = \blacksquare$

2. Is the sequence in Question 1 arithmetic? Explain why or why not.
                          No; there is no common difference.
3. a. Find the sixth term, a_6, of the sequence.   **32**
   b. Write a formula for a_6 in terms of a_5. $a_6 = a_5 \cdot 2$
   c. Write a general formula for a_n in terms of a_{n-1}. $a_n = a_{n-1} \cdot 2, a_1 = 1$

4. a. Open-Ended Generate two sequences by multiplying by a constant factor. Write each sequence.
   b. Write a recursive formula for each sequence. What do these formulas and the formula for a_n from Question 3 have in common?
   c. Graph all three sequences. Then sketch each graph.
   d. Compare all three graphs. Write a description of the pattern.

In a **geometric sequence,** the ratio between consecutive terms is constant. This ratio is called the **common ratio.** Unlike in an arithmetic sequence, the difference between consecutive terms varies.

Differentiated Instruction Solutions for All Learners

Special Needs L1
Review the definition of *ratio*. Have a group of students stand to represent a ratio of boys to girls as 3 to 4. Then have students group together to represent the ratio of students with brown hair to students without brown hair.

learning style: tactile

Below Level L2
Have students generate a list of practical applications of geometric sequences, such as depreciation, compound interest, and amortization tables.

learning style: verbal

GO Online

Video Tutor Help

Visit: PHSchool.com
Web Code: age-0775

1a. 5, 15, 45, 135, 405, 1215, 3645, 10,935, 32,805, 98,415; the tenth term is the ninth term times 3.

b. Geometric; the common ratio is −4.

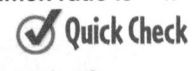 **Quick Check**

c. Arithmetic; the common difference is +12.

Key Concepts

---

1 EXAMPLE Identifying a Geometric Sequence

Is the given sequence geometric? If so, identify the common ratio.

a. 5, 15, 45, 135, . . .

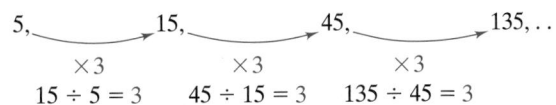

$$15 \div 5 = 3 \qquad 45 \div 15 = 3 \qquad 135 \div 45 = 3$$

There is a common ratio of 3. This is a geometric sequence.

b. 15, 30, 45, 60, . . .

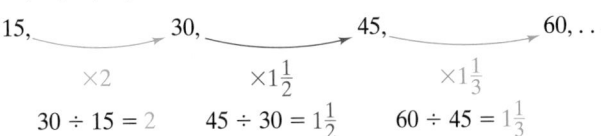

$$30 \div 15 = 2 \qquad 45 \div 30 = 1\frac{1}{2} \qquad 60 \div 45 = 1\frac{1}{3}$$

There is no common ratio. This is *not* a geometric sequence.

Quick Check **1** **a.** Write the first ten terms of the geometric sequence from Example 1. Explain how you found the tenth term in the sequence, a_{10}.
b. Is the sequence 6, −24, 96, −384, . . . *arithmetic, geometric,* or *neither?* Explain.
c. Is the sequence 8, 20, 32, 44, . . . *arithmetic, geometric,* or *neither?* Explain.

Property	**Geometric Sequence Formulas**

Recursive Formula   **Explicit Formula**

$$a_1 = \text{a given value}, a_n = a_{n-1} \cdot r \qquad a_n = a_1 \cdot r^{n-1}$$

In these formulas, a_n is the nth term, a_1 is the first term, n is the number of the term, and r is the common ratio.

As with an arithmetic sequence, you can use an explicit formula to find the value of the nth term when the previous term is unknown.

2 EXAMPLE **Real-World** 🌐 **Connection**

Design Suppose you want a reduced copy of a photograph. The actual length of the photograph is 10 in. The smallest size the copier can make is 64% of the original. Find the length of the photograph after five reductions at 64%.

For five reductions, you need to find the 6th term of the geometric sequence 10, 6.4, . . .

$$
\begin{aligned}
a_n &= a_1 \cdot r^{n-1} & &\text{Use the explicit formula.}\\
a_6 &= 10 \cdot 0.64^{6-1} & &\text{Substitute } a_1 = 10, n = 6, \text{ and } r = 0.64.\\
&= 10 \cdot 0.64^5 & &\text{Simplify the exponent.}\\
&\approx 1.07 & &\text{Use a calculator.}
\end{aligned}
$$

After five reductions of 64%, the photograph is about 1 in. long.

Real-World 🌐 **Connection**

Careers Graphic designers use math to lay out pages of books and magazines.

Quick Check **2** Find the 19th term in each sequence.
a. 11, 33, 99, 297, . . . **4,261,625,379**   **b.** 20, 17, 14, 11, 8, . . . **−34**

Lesson 11-3 Geometric Sequences   **613**

---

2. Teach

Guided Instruction

Activity
Visual Learners
When students copy the sequence in Part 1, encourage them to number each individual triangle within a figure so they can better see the number of triangles in each.

1 EXAMPLE **Teaching Tip**

Make it clear that the common ratio for a geometric sequence cannot be 0. Also, the first term of a geometric sequence cannot be 0.

2 EXAMPLE **Careers**

Show students how graphic designers reduce the pages of the student book and place them in the Teachers' Edition.

3 EXAMPLE **Connection to Physics**

Friction between the swing and child with the air molecules causes the wind resistance. Some students may not realize that the child on the swing is slowing down to a stop. The arc decreases as the swing comes to a stop.

Error Prevention!

In Quick Check 3, the missing term can be either positive or negative depending on the sign of the common ratio. If the common ratio is negative, the sign of the terms alternates from positive to negative.

PowerPoint
Additional Examples

1 Is the given sequence geometric? If so, identify the common ratio.
a. 1, −6, 36, −216, . . . **yes; −6**
b. 2, 4, 6, 8, . . . **no**

2 Suppose you want to enlarge a photo to 120% of its original size. A photo has a length of 10 cm. Find the length of the photo after five enlargements at 120%.
about 25 cm

613

3 A family purchased a home for $150,000. Two years later the home was valued at $188,160. If the value of the home is increasing geometrically, how much was the home worth after one year?
$168,000

Resources
• Daily Notetaking Guide 11-3   **L3**

Closure

Ask students to explain what a geometric sequence is. Then ask them to explain how they can generate a geometric sequence whose first term is 5. A geometric sequence is a sequence in which the ratio between consecutive terms is always the same number. To generate a geometric sequence whose first term is 5, you can pick a nonzero number r and multiply 5 by r repeatedly.

4. yes; -1; -1, 1
5. yes; 0.4; 0.256, 0.1024
6. yes; 0.1; 0.0007, 0.00007
7. yes; $-\frac{1}{3}$; $\frac{2}{9}$, $-\frac{2}{27}$
8. no
9. yes; 1.5; 50.625, 75.9375
13. $a_n = 5 \cdot (-3)^{n-1}$; 5, -15, 45, -135, 405
14. $a_n = 0.0237 \cdot 10^{n-1}$; 0.0237, 0.237, 2.37, 23.7, 237
15. $a_n = \frac{1}{2}\left(\frac{2}{3}\right)^{n-1}$; $\frac{1}{2}$, $\frac{1}{3}$, $\frac{2}{9}$, $\frac{4}{27}$, $\frac{8}{81}$
16. $a_n = 0.5^{n-1}$; 1, 0.5, 0.25, 0.125, 0.0625
17. $a_n = 100(-20)^{n-1}$; 100, -2000, 40,000, $-800,000$, 16,000,000
18. $a_n = 7 \cdot 1^{n-1}$; 7, 7, 7, 7, 7
19. $a_n = 1024(0.5)^{n-1}$; 1024, 512, 256, 128, 64

GO for Help

To review exponential curves, go to Lesson 8–2.

The graphs of arithmetic and geometric sequences have different shapes.

 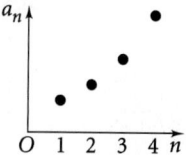

Arithmetic graphs are linear.   Geometric graphs are exponential.

You can find the **geometric mean** of any two positive numbers by taking the positive square root of the product of the two numbers.

$$\text{geometric mean} = \sqrt{\text{product of the two numbers}}$$

You can use the geometric mean to find a missing term of a geometric sequence.

Online active math

For: Sequences Activity
Use: Interactive Textbook, 11-3

3 EXAMPLE   Real-World Connection

Physics When a child swings without being pushed, air resistance causes the length of the arc of the swing to decrease geometrically. Find the missing arc length.

Find the geometric mean of the two arc lengths.

$$\text{geometric mean} = \sqrt{8 \cdot 6\tfrac{1}{8}}$$
$$= \sqrt{49}$$
$$= 7$$

8 ft
$6\frac{1}{8}$ ft

• On the second swing, the length of the arc is 7 ft.

Quick Check **3** Find the missing term of each geometric sequence. It could be the geometric mean or its opposite.
a. 20, ■, 80, ... **40 or −40** b. 3, ■, 18.75, ... **7.5 or −7.5** c. 28, ■, 5103, ... **378 or −378**

EXERCISES

For more exercises, see *Extra Skill and Word Problem Practice*.

Practice and Problem Solving

A Practice by Example

Example 1 (page 613)

GO for Help

4–9. See margin pp. 614–615.

Is the sequence geometric? If so, find the common ratio and the next two terms.
1. $1, 2, 4, 8, \ldots$ **yes; 2; 16, 32**
2. $1, 2, 3, 4, \ldots$ **no**
3. $1, -2, 4, -8, \ldots$ **yes; −2; 16, −32**
4. $-1, 1, -1, 1, \ldots$
5. $10, 4, 1.6, 0.64, \ldots$
6. $7, 0.7, 0.07, 0.007, \ldots$
7. $18, -6, 2, -\frac{2}{3}, \ldots$
8. $1, \frac{1}{2}, \frac{1}{3}, \frac{1}{4}, \ldots$
9. $10, 15, 22.5, 33.75, \ldots$
10. $2, -10, 50, -250, \ldots$ **yes; −5; 1250, −6250**
11. $-1, -6, -36, -216, \ldots$ **yes; 6; −1296, −7776**
12. $\frac{1}{2}, \frac{1}{4}, \frac{1}{6}, \frac{1}{8}, \ldots$ **no**

20. $a_n = 4(0.1)^{n-1}$; 4, 0.4, 0.04, 0.004, 0.0004
21. $a_n = 10(-1)^{n-1}$; 10, −10, 10, −10, 10

Example 2
(page 613)

Write the explicit formula for each sequence. Then generate the first five terms.

13. $a_1 = 5, r = -3$ **14.** $a_1 = 0.0237, r = 10$ **15.** $a_1 = \frac{1}{2}, r = \frac{2}{3}$

16. $a_1 = 1, r = 0.5$ **17.** $a_1 = 100, r = -20$ **18.** $a_1 = 7, r = 1$

19. $a_1 = 1024, r = 0.5$ **20.** $a_1 = 4, r = 0.1$ **21.** $a_1 = 10, r = -1$

13–21. See margin pp. 614–615.

Example 3
(page 614)

Find the missing term of each geometric sequence. It could be the geometric mean or its opposite.

67.5 or −67.5   1530 or −1530 $\frac{4}{15}$ or $-\frac{4}{15}$

22. $5, \blacksquare, 911.25, \ldots$ **23.** $9180, \blacksquare, 255, \ldots$ **24.** $\frac{2}{5}, \blacksquare, \frac{8}{45}, \ldots$

25. $3, \blacksquare, 0.75, \ldots$ **26.** $5, \blacksquare, 2.8125, \ldots$ **27.** $12, \blacksquare, 3, \ldots$

1.5 or −1.5   3.75 or −3.75   6 or −6

 Apply Your Skills

28. geometric; 720, 1440

29. arithmetic; 125, 150

30. geometric; 3, −3

31. arithmetic; 50, 55

32. geometric; −80, 160

33. geometric; 0.125, 0.0625

Identify each sequence as *arithmetic*, *geometric*, or *neither*. Then find the next two terms.

28. $45, 90, 180, 360, \ldots$ **29.** $25, 50, 75, 100, \ldots$ **30.** $3, -3, 3, -3, \ldots$

31. $30, 35, 40, 45, \ldots$ **32.** $-5, 10, -20, 40, \ldots$ **33.** $2, 1, 0.5, 0.25, \ldots$

34. $5, 6, 8, 11, 15, \ldots$ **35.** $2, 2, 2, 2, \ldots$ **36.** $1, 4, 9, 16, \ldots$
neither; 20, 26   either; 2, 2   neither; 25, 36

Find the missing terms of each geometric sequence. (*Hint:* The geometric mean of the first and fifth terms is the third term. Some terms might be negative.)

GPS **37.** $19,683; \blacksquare; \blacksquare; \blacksquare; 243; \ldots$ **38.** $2.5, \blacksquare, \blacksquare, \blacksquare, 202.5, \ldots$ 37–40.

39. $12.5, \blacksquare, \blacksquare, \blacksquare, 5.12, \ldots$ **40.** $-4, \blacksquare, \blacksquare, \blacksquare, -30\frac{3}{8}, \ldots$ See margin.

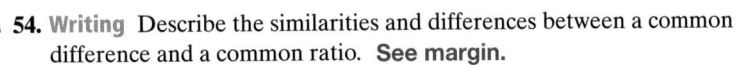

GO for Help

For a guide to solving Exercise 37, see p. 618.

41. a. Open-Ended Choose two positive numbers. Find their geometric mean.
   b. Find the common ratio for a geometric sequence that includes the terms from part (a) in order from least to greatest or from greatest to least.
   c. Find the 9th term of the geometric sequence from part (b).
   d. Find the geometric mean of the term from part (c) and the first term of your sequence. What term of the sequence have you just found?

41a–d. Answers may vary. Sample:

a. 3 and 12; 6

b. 3, 6, 12; 2

c. 768

d. 48; 5th term

For the geometric sequence $3, 12, 48, 192, \ldots$, **find the indicated term.**

42. 5th term   768   **43.** 7th term   12,288   **44.** 10th term   786,432

45. 14th term   201,326,592   **46.** 17th term 3×4^{16} or   **47.** *n*th term $3(4^{n-1})$
$\approx 1.3 \times 10^{10}$

Find the 10th term of each geometric sequence.

GO Online

Homework Video Tutor

Visit: PHSchool.com
Web Code: age-1103

48. $a_9 = 8, r = \frac{1}{2}$ 4   **49.** $a_{11} = 8, r = \frac{1}{2}$ 16

50. $a_9 = -5, r = -\frac{1}{2}$ 2.5   **51.** $a_{11} = -5, r = -\frac{1}{2}$ 10

52. $a_9 = -\frac{1}{3}, r = \frac{1}{2}$ $-\frac{1}{6}$ **53.** $a_{11} = -\frac{1}{3}, r = \frac{1}{2}$ $-\frac{2}{3}$

 54. Writing Describe the similarities and differences between a common difference and a common ratio.   **See margin.**

 Challenge   **55. Banking** Copy and complete the table below. Use the geometric mean. Assume compound interest is earned and no withdrawals are made.

55. $142.79, $613.59,
$28.62, $58.92,
$105.82, $262.94

Period 1	$140.00	$600.00	$25.00	$57.50	$100.00	$250.00
Period 2	$\blacksquare$	$\blacksquare$	$\blacksquare$	$\blacksquare$	$\blacksquare$	$\blacksquare$
Period 3	$145.64	$627.49	$32.76	$60.37	$111.98	$276.55

37. 6561, 2187, 729, or
   −6561, 2187, −729

38. 7.5, 22.5, 67.5, or
   −7.5, 22.5, −67.5

39. 10, 8, 6.4, or
   −10, 8, −6.4

40. −6.64, −11.02, −18.30, or
   6.64, −11.02, 18.30

54. Both the common difference and the common ratio are used to find the next term in a sequence, but a common difference is added and a common ratio is multiplied.

Homework Quick Check

To check students' understanding of key skills and concepts, go over Exercises 20, 26, 38, 41, 54.

Math Tip

Exercise 37-40 The first, third, and fifth terms will always have the same sign. Likewise, the second and fourth terms will always have the same sign, but it will be a different sign from the odd-number terms if the common ratio is negative.

Error Prevention!

Exercise 58 Some students may choose 0.25 as *r*. Help students see that *r* is the same as the decay factor in an exponential function. Therefore, you must subtract 0.25 from 1 to find *r*.

Differentiated Instruction Resources

GPS Guided Problem Solving	L3
Enrichment	L4
Reteaching	L2
Practice	L3

Lesson Quiz

Is the given sequence geometric? If so, identify the common ratio and find the next two terms.

1. 1, 2, 6, 12, . . . no

2. 2, 1, 0.5, 0.25, . . . yes; 0.5; 0.125, 0.0625

3. −9, 81, −729, 6561, . . . yes; −9; −59,049, 531,441

4. Write the explicit formula for the geometric sequence for which $a_1 = 7$ and $r = \frac{1}{3}$. Then generate the first five terms.
$a_n = 7 \cdot \left(\frac{1}{3}\right)^{n-1}$;
$7, \frac{7}{3}, \frac{7}{9}, \frac{7}{27}, \frac{7}{81}$

5. Find the missing term for the geometric sequence
3, ■, 48, . . . 12

Alternative Assessment

Have students work individually. Ask students to write six different geometric sequence formulas. Three of the sequences should be recursive and three should be explicit. Instruct them to find the first four terms of each sequence, and then to find a_6. Finally, ask students to pick two nonzero numbers p and q. Ask them to write an explicit formula for a sequence for which $a_1 = p$ and $a_3 = q$.

Test Prep

Resources

For additional practice with a variety of test item formats:
- Standardized Test Prep, p. 645
- Test-Taking Strategies, p. 640
- Test-Taking Strategies with Transparencies

56a. $d, \frac{1}{2}d, \frac{1}{4}d, \frac{1}{8}d, \frac{1}{16}d, \frac{1}{32}d$

b. Yes; the common ratio is $\frac{1}{2}$.

c. $a_n = a_{n-1} \cdot \frac{1}{2}$

57. Both arithmetic and geometric sequence explicit formulas use the first term a_1, $n - 1$, and a common term. The recursive formulas both use a_{n-1} and a common term.

56. **Golf** Each of the putts misses the hole and continues past it for half the distance.
   a. Write a sequence to represent the ball's distance from the hole before each of his first six putts.
   b. Is this sequence geometric? Explain your reasoning.
   c. Write a recursive formula for the sequence.

57. **Critical Thinking** How are the formulas for a geometric sequence similar to the formulas for an arithmetic sequence?

58. Suppose a balloon is filled with 5000 cm³ of helium. It then loses one fourth of its helium each day.
   a. Write the geometric sequence that shows the amount of helium in the balloon at the start of each day for five days. 5000, 3750, 2812.5, 2109.38, 1582.03
   b. What is the common ratio of the sequence? $\frac{3}{4}$
   c. How much helium will be left in the balloon at the start of the tenth day? 375.42 cm³
   d. Graph the sequence. Then sketch the graph. **See back of book.**
   e. **Critical Thinking** How does the common ratio affect the shape of the graph?
   See margin.

Find a_1 for a geometric sequence with the given terms.

59. $a_5 = 112$ and $a_7 = 448$ 7

60. $a_9 = \frac{1}{2}$ and $a_{12} = \frac{1}{16}$ 128

Test Prep

Multiple Choice

61. Which geometric sequence DOES NOT include the term 100? **A**
   A. 5, 10, 20, . . .
   B. 337.5, 225, 150, . . .
   C. $a_1 = 25$, $a_n = 2a_{n-1}$
   D. $a_n = 4 \cdot 5^n$

62. What is the product of the geometric mean of 2 and 32 and the geometric mean of 1 and 4? **F**
   F. 16   G. 19   H. 32   J. 256

63. Find the common ratio in the geometric sequence 4, 10, 25, 62.5, . . . **B**
   A. 0.4   B. 2.5   C. 15   D. 25

64. What is the geometric mean of 8 and 18? **F**
   F. 12   G. 13   H. 26   J. 36

65. Find the missing term in the geometric sequence 8, ■, 0.5, −0.125, . . . **B**
   A. 2   B. −2   C. 4   D. −4

66. The first term of a geometric sequence is 1 and its common ratio is 6. What is the sixth term? **H**
   F. 31   G. 3176   H. 7776   J. 46,656

67. [2] $-1(-5)^7 = 78,125$
   [1] no work shown

68. [2] $r = \frac{40}{120} = \frac{1}{3}$,
   so $a_1 = \frac{120}{\left(\frac{1}{3}\right)^5} = 29,160$
   [1] no work shown

Short Response

67. The first term of a geometric sequence is −1. The common ratio is −5. Find the eighth term in the sequence. **See left.**

68. The sixth term in a geometric sequence is 120. The seventh term is 40. What is the first term in the sequence? **See left.**

58e. The common ratio $\frac{3}{4}$ is less than one, so the graph is decreasing.

69. [2] geometric mean =
   $\sqrt{4 \cdot 16} = \sqrt{64} = 8$
   arithmetic mean =
   $\frac{4 + 16}{2} = \frac{20}{2} = 10$
   The arithmetic mean is greater.

[1] correct answer with no work shown

69. Which is greater, the geometric mean of 4 and 16 or the arithmetic mean of 4 and 16? Show your work.   See margin p. 616.

Extended Response **70.** In a geometric sequence, $a_1 = 3$ and $a_4 = 192$. Explain how to find a_2 and a_3.   See margin.

Mixed Review

Lesson 11-2   **Write an explicit and a recursive formula for each arithmetic sequence.**

71. $-3, 0, 3, 6, \ldots$ **72.** $17, 8, -1, \ldots$ **73.** $-2, -13, -24, \ldots$
71–76. See margin.

Lesson 10-3   **Write an equation of the circle with the given center and radius. Graph the circle.**

74. center $(0, 0)$, radius 3   **75.** center $(-3, 1)$, radius 5   **76.** center $(1, 1)$, radius 2

Lesson 9-3   **Find the vertical asymptotes of each function.**

77. $y = \frac{x-3}{x+3}$ $x = -3$ **78.** $y = \frac{x-3}{x+1}$ $x = -1$ **79.** $y = \frac{x-3}{x(x-1)}$ $x = 0, 1$

Checkpoint Quiz 1   Lessons 11-1 through 11-3

Identify each sequence as *arithmetic* or *geometric*. Then find the common difference or common ratio.   1–3. See margin.

1. $15, 30, 45, 60, \ldots$ **2.** $2, 6, 18, 54, \ldots$ **3.** $37, 34, 31, 28, 25, \ldots$

4. $700, 350, 175, 87.5, \ldots$ **5.** $8, -4, 2, -1, 0.5, \ldots$ **6.** $4, 2, 0, -2, -4, \ldots$
geometric; 0.5   geometric; -0.5 arithmetic; -2

Find the fifth term of each sequence.

7. $a_1 = 100, a_n = \frac{1}{2}a_{n-1}$ **8.** $a_1 = 2, a_n = 3a_{n-1} - 2$ **9.** $a_n = -n + 6$
6.25   82   1

10. Writing Explain how to compute the arithmetic mean and the geometric mean of two terms of a sequence.   See margin.

A P•int in Time

1000   1200   1400   1600   1800   2000

In 1276, the Chinese astronomer Guo Shoujing built a device to study the sun. A hole in the tower of his observatory faced due south. At noon, a horizontal pole in the tower cast a shadow on a low wall that extended north from the building. Guo Shoujing learned about the sun's movements by studying the geometric pattern of the shadows on the wall.

Go **O**nline
PHSchool.com
For: Information about techniques for measuring the sun's position
Web Code: age-2032

Lesson 11-3 Geometric Sequences   **617**

 Checkpoint Quiz

Use this Checkpoint Quiz to check students' understanding of the skills and concepts of Lessons 11-1 through 11-3.

Resources
Grab & Go
• Checkpoint Quiz 1

73. $a_n = 9 - 11n$; $a_n = a_{n-1} - 11$, $a_1 = -2$

74. $x^2 + y^2 = 9$

75. $(x + 3)^2 + (y - 1)^2 = 25$
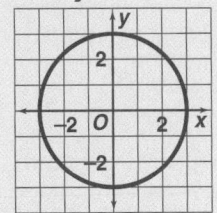

76. $(x - 1)^2 + (y - 1)^2 = 4$

Checkpoint Quiz

1. arithmetic; 15

2. geometric; 3

3. arithmetic; -3

10. To find the arithmetic mean, add the terms and divide by 2. To find the geometric mean, multiply the terms and find the square root of the product.

70. [4] Since $a_4 = a_3 \cdot r = a_2 \cdot r^2 = a_1 \cdot r^3$, $192 = 3 \cdot r^3$. So $r^3 = 64$, and $r = \sqrt[3]{64} = 4$. Then $a_2 = a_1 \cdot r = 3 \cdot 4 = 12$ and $a_3 = a_2 \cdot r = 12 \cdot 4 = 48$.

[3] appropriate methods, but with one computational error

[2] correct answer, but with minimal explanation

[1] correct answer, but with no explanation

71. $a_n = -6 + 3n$; $a_n = a_{n-1} + 3$, $a_1 = -3$

72. $a_n = 26 - 9n$; $a_n = a_{n-1} - 9$, $a_1 = 17$

617

Understanding Math Problems

Students read an example problem in which they are asked to find the missing terms in a geometric sequence. In addition to being worked out, the problem includes notes that explain each step of the work.

Guided Instruction

Suggest that students review the definition of a geometric mean if they have trouble following the sequence of steps taken to solve this problem.

Error Prevention!

Make sure students understand that the first term in the given geometric sequence is 19,683, and not 19, followed by 683.

Exercises

Make sure students label the terms so they can keep track of each term as they find it.

Guided Problem Solving

Understanding Math Problems Read the problem below. Then let Wanda's thinking guide you through the solution. Check your understanding with the exercises at the bottom of the page.

Find the missing terms of the geometric sequence. (*Hint:* The geometric mean of the first and fifth terms is the third term. Some terms might be negative.)

19,683; ■; ■; ■; 243; ...

What Wanda Thinks

In this geometric sequence, the numbers decrease.

The hint tells me information about terms in the sequence. I'll label the terms.

The hint says that the geometric mean of the first and fifth terms is the third term. That makes sense, because the third term is the middle term. I'll write that relationship and substitute.

Perfect. I have the third term in the sequence.

I can rewrite the sequence to include the third term.

Now I can find the 2nd and 4th terms in the same way, because they are between terms I know.

I'll rewrite the sequence with the missing terms filled in.

What Wanda Writes

19,683; ■; ■; ■; 243; ...

1st term = 19,683
2nd term = ■
3rd term = ■
4th term = ■
5th term = 243

Geometric mean of 1st and 5th terms is 3rd term

3rd term = $\sqrt{19,683 \cdot 243}$
3rd term = $\sqrt{4,782,969}$
3rd term = 2187

19,683; ■; 2187; ■; 243; ...

2nd term = $\pm\sqrt{19,683 \cdot 2187}$ = ±6561

4th term = $\pm\sqrt{2187 \cdot 243}$ = ±729

The sequence is
19,683; 6561; 2187; 729; 243; ...
or 19,683; −6561; 2187; −729; 243; ...

EXERCISES

Find the missing terms of each geometric sequence.

1. 12,312; ■; ■; ■; 152; ... ±4104, 1368, ±456

2. 1.7; ■; ■; ■; 11,153.7; ... ±15.3, 137.7, ±1239.3

3. −100; ■; ■; ■; −0.16; ... ±20, −4, ±0.8

4. 5040; ■; ■; ■; $\frac{35}{9}$; ... ±840, 140, $\pm\frac{70}{3}$

5. Critical Thinking Explain why, in the worked example above, the second and fourth terms can be both positive or both negative but the third term must be positive.
Sample: the terms must either all have the same sign, or alternate in sign.

11-4 Arithmetic Series

What You'll Learn

- To write and evaluate arithmetic series
- To use summation notation

...And Why

To find the number of stitches in a cross-stitch pattern, as in Example 2

✓ Check Skills You'll Need

GO for Help Lesson 11-1

Find each sum.

1. $2 + 3.5 + 5 + 6.5 + 8$ **25**

2. $-17 + (-13) + (-9) + (-5) + (-1) + 3$ **−42**

Write an explicit formula for each sequence.

3. $4, 6, 8, 10, 12, \ldots$ $a_n = 2 + 2n$ **4.** $1, 4, 7, 10, 13, 16, \ldots$ $a_n = -2 + 3n$

5. $-17, -23, -29, -35, \ldots$ $a_n = -11 - 6n$ **6.** $10, 1, -8, -17, \ldots$ $a_n = 19 - 9n$

🔊 **New Vocabulary** • series • arithmetic series • limit

---

1 Writing and Evaluating Arithmetic Series

Activity: Arithmetic Series

Use the sequence 1, 2, 3, 4, . . . , 97, 98, 99, 100 to answer each question.

1. Is it *arithmetic, geometric,* or *neither*? Justify your reasoning.

2. a. Add the first and last terms of the sequence and write down the answer. Then add the second and next-to-last terms. Continue adding terms until you get to the middle of the sequence.

   b. Reasoning What patterns do you notice in your answers to part (a)?
   All of the sums are 101.

3. Use your answer to Question 2 to find the sum of the terms of the sequence. **5050**

4. a. Describe a short method for finding the following sum.
   $5 + 10 + 15 + 20 + 25 + 30 + 35 + 40 + 45 + 50$
   b. Find the sum. **275**

1. The sequence is arithmetic because it has a common difference of 1.

2a. $1 + 100 = 101$
$2 + 99 = 101$
⋮ ⋮ ⋮
$50 + 51 = 101$

4a. Add the first and last terms. Multiply this sum by the number of terms divided by 2.

Vocabulary Tip

Ellipsis points, as used here, indicate that the pattern continues.

A **series** is the expression for the sum of the terms of a sequence. Finite sequences and series have terms that you can count individually from 1 to a final whole number *n*. Infinite sequences and series continue without end. You indicate an infinite sequence or series with ellipsis points.

Finite sequence	Finite series
$6, 9, 12, 15, 18$	$6 + 9 + 12 + 15 + 18$

Infinite sequence	Infinite series
$3, 7, 11, 15, \ldots$	$3 + 7 + 11 + 15 + \ldots$

Lesson 11-4 Arithmetic Series   **619**

11-4

1. Plan

Objectives

1 To write and evaluate arithmetic series

2 To use summation notation

Examples

1 Writing and Evaluating a Series

2 Real-World Connection

3 Writing a Series in Summation Notation

4 Finding the Sum of a Series

Math Background

Convergence (the existence of a finite sum) of a series is a classical concern of calculus and analysis, but also has importance in chaos theory.

More Math Background: p. 598D

Lesson Planning and Resources

See p. 598E for a list of the resources that support this lesson.

Bell Ringer Practice

✓ Check Skills You'll Need
For intervention, direct students to:

Mathematical Patterns
Lesson 11-1: Example 4
Extra Skills and Word Problems Practice, Ch. 11

Differentiated Instruction Solutions for All Learners

Special Needs L1
Have students use stackable objects such as pennies or blocks. Students form a stack of objects for each number in a series. Ask: *How do the stacks represent a series?* each stack is a term and the total number of objects is the sum of the series
learning style: tactile

Below Level L2
Have students work in pairs to make up arithmetic series for each other to sum. Then have them write the series using summation notation.
learning style: verbal

619

Guided Instruction

Activity
You may wish to review the definitions of *finite* and *infinite*.

1 EXAMPLE Alternative Method

You may wish to show how to use addition of equations to find the value of the series. Let S be the value of the series. You can write the series with the terms arranged in the given order or in reverse order. Write two equations, add, and solve the resulting equation.

$$\begin{aligned} S = &\ 2 + 11 + 20 + 29 + 38 + 47 \\ S = &\ 47 + 38 + 29 + 20 + 11 +\ 2 \\ \hline 2S = &\ 49 + 49 + 49 + 49 + 49 + 49 \\ 2S = &\ 294 \\ S = &\ 147 \end{aligned}$$

PowerPoint

Additional Examples

1 Use the sequence 5, 9, 13, 17, 21, 25, 29. Write the related series. Evaluate the series.
5 + 9 + 13 + 17 + 21 + 25 + 29; 119

2 A staircase uses same-size cement blocks arranged 4 across, as shown below. Find the total number of blocks in the staircase.
60 blocks

1a. 0.3 + 0.6 + 0.9 + 1.2 + 1.5 + 1.8 + 2.1 + 2.4 + 2.7 + 3.0; 16.5

b. 100 + 125 + 150 + 175 + 200 + 225; 975

Quick Check

---

1 EXAMPLE Writing and Evaluating a Series

Use the finite sequence 2, 11, 20, 29, 38, 47. Write the related series. Then evaluate the series.

Related series → 2 + 11 + 20 + 29 + 38 + 47 = 147 ← **Add to evaluate.**

● The sum of the terms of the sequence is 147.

✓ Quick Check **1** Write the related series for each finite sequence. Then evaluate the series.
a. 0.3, 0.6, 0.9, 1.2, 1.5, 1.8, 2.1, 2.4, 2.7, 3.0   **b.** 100, 125, 150, 175, 200, 225

An **arithmetic series** is a series whose terms form an arithmetic sequence. When a sequence has many terms, or when you know only the first and last terms of the sequence, you can use a formula to evaluate the related series quickly.

Key Concepts

Property	Sum of a Finite Arithmetic Series

The sum S_n of a finite arithmetic series $a_1 + a_2 + a_3 + \ldots + a_n$ is
$$S_n = \frac{n}{2}(a_1 + a_n)$$
where a_1 is the first term, a_n is the nth term, and n is the number of terms.

2 EXAMPLE Real-World 🌐 Connection

Crafts Embroidery such as cross-stitch frequently decorates table linens and clothing, although it was originally used to strengthen and repair woven fabric.

Several rows of cross-stitches make up the green roof. Find the total number of green cross-stitches in the roof.

Relate $\underset{\text{the series}}{\text{sum of}}$ is $\dfrac{\text{number of terms}}{2}$ times $\left(\underset{\text{term}}{\text{the first}}\ \text{plus}\ \underset{\text{term}}{\text{the last}}\right)$

Define Let S_n = total number of cross-stitches,
and let n = the number of rows.
Then a_1 = the number of cross-stitches in the first row,
and a_n = the number of cross-stitches in the last row.

Write $S_n = \frac{n}{2}(a_1 + a_n)$ **Use the formula.**
$= \frac{5}{2}(5 + 13)$ **Substitute** $n = 5$, $a_1 = 5$, **and** $a_n = 13$.
$= 2.5(18)$ **Simplify.**
$= 45$ **Multiply.**

● There are 45 cross-stitches in the green roof.

✓ Quick Check **2** Suppose the pattern from Example 2 extends to 14 rows of cross-stitches.
a. Find the 14th term of the sequence. **31**
b. Use the formula to find the value of the series to the 14th term. **252**

---

620 Chapter 11 Sequences and Series

Differentiated Instruction Solutions for All Learners

Advanced Learners L4
Have students explain why the sum of an infinite arithmetic series is always infinite.

learning style: verbal

English Language Learners ELL
For Example 2, explain the terms *embroidery*, *cross-stitch*, *table linens*, and *woven fabric*. Pass around samples, or perhaps a student can share samples of work they have completed.

learning style: tactile

2 Using Summation Notation

Vocabulary Tip

Σ is the Greek capital letter s<u>igma</u>, the equivalent of the English letter S (for summation).

You can use the summation symbol Σ to write a series. Then you can use limits to indicate how many terms you are adding. **Limits** are the least and greatest integral values of n.

$$\underbrace{\sum_{n=1}^{3}}_{\substack{\text{lower limit,}\\ \text{least value of } n}} \overset{\substack{\text{upper limit,}\\ \text{greatest value of } n}}{\underset{}{(5n+1)}}$$

explicit formula for the sequence

3 EXAMPLE Writing a Series in Summation Notation

Use summation notation to write the series $3 + 6 + 9 + \ldots$ for 33 terms.

$3 \cdot 1 = 3, 3 \cdot 2 = 6, 3 \cdot 3 = 9, \ldots$ **The explicit formula for the sequence is 3n.**

$3 + 6 + 9 + \ldots + 99 = \sum\limits_{n=1}^{33} 3n$ **The lower limit is 1 and the upper limit is 33.**

✓ **Quick Check** ❸ Use summation notation to write each series for the specified number of terms.
  a. $1 + 2 + 3 + \ldots ; n = 6$ **a–b. See left.**
  b. $3 + 8 + 13 + 18 + \ldots ; n = 9$

3a. $\sum\limits_{n=1}^{6} n$

b. $\sum\limits_{n=1}^{9} (5n - 2)$

To expand a series from summation notation, you can substitute each value of n into the explicit formula and add the results.

Video Tutor Help
Visit: PHSchool.com
Web Code: age-0775

4 EXAMPLE Finding the Sum of a Series

Use the series $\sum\limits_{n=1}^{3} (5n + 1)$.

a. Find the number of terms in the series.
  Since the values of n are $1, 2$, and 3, there are three terms in the series.

b. Find the first and last terms of the series.
  The first term of the series is $5n + 1 = 5(1) + 1 = 6$.
  The last term of the series is $5n + 1 = 5(3) + 1 = 16$.

c. Evaluate the series.

$\sum\limits_{n=1}^{3} (5n + 1) = (5(1) + 1) + (5(2) + 1) + (5(3) + 1)$ **Substitute.**

$= 6 + 11 + 16$ **Simplify within parentheses.**

$= 33$ **Add.**

The sum of the series is 33.

✓ **Quick Check** ❹ For each sum, find the number of terms, the first term, and the last term. Then evaluate the series.
  a. $\sum\limits_{n=1}^{10} (n - 3)$ **b.** $\sum\limits_{n=1}^{4} \left(\frac{1}{2}n + 1\right)$ **c.** $\sum\limits_{n=2}^{5} n^2$
  $10, -2, 7; 25$ $4, \frac{3}{2}, 3; 9$ $4, 4, 25; 54$

Lesson 11-4 Arithmetic Series **621**

Guided Instruction

3 EXAMPLE Math Tip

Tell students that they can read $\sum\limits_{n=1}^{33} 3n$ as "the sum of the values of $3n$ from n equals 1 to n equals 33."

4 EXAMPLE Teaching Tip

Ask students how they know that this series is arithmetic. **The value of 5n + 1 increases by 5 if n increases by 1.** You may want to point out that summation notation can be used with any type of series, arithmetic or non-arithmetic. Also, stress that the parentheses around 5n + 1 are essential.

PowerPoint
Additional Examples

❸ Use summation notation to write the series $8 + 16 + 24 + \ldots$ for 50 terms. $\sum\limits_{n=1}^{50} 8n$

❹ Use the series $\sum\limits_{n=1}^{4} (-2n + 3)$.
a. Find the number of terms in the series. **4 terms**
b. Find the first and last terms of the series. **1, −5**
c. Evaluate the series. **−8**

Resources
• Daily Notetaking Guide
  11-4   **L3**

Closure

Ask students what formula they can use to find the sum of the first n terms of an arithmetic sequence with first term a_1 and nth term a_n. Then ask them how they would use the formula to find the value of $\sum\limits_{n=1}^{10} 7n$.

$S_n = \frac{n}{2}(a_1 + a_n)$; The series $\sum\limits_{n=1}^{10} 7n$ is an arithmetic series with $a_1 = 7$ and $a_{10} = 70$. The series has 10 terms. So $\sum\limits_{n=1}^{10} 7n = \frac{10}{2}(7 + 70) = 5(77) = 385$.

621

Assignment Guide

1 A B 1-12, 25-33, 35-41

2 A B 13-24, 34, 42
C Challenge 43-48

Test Prep 49-57
Mixed Review 58-69

Homework Quick Check
To check students' understanding of key skills and concepts, go over Exercises 10, 22, 31, 34, 41.

Error Prevention!

Exercises 13–18 Remind students to use parentheses around the expression following the summation symbol where necessary. For example, the value of $\sum_{n=1}^{8} (n + 7)$ is 92, but the value of $\sum_{n=1}^{8} n + 7$ is 43.

Exercise 41 For part b, explain that *pros and cons* is a phrase meaning "arguments for and against."

Differentiated Instruction **Resources**

GPS Guided Problem Solving	**L3**
Enrichment	**L4**
Reteaching	**L2**
Practice	**L3**

EXERCISES

For more exercises, see *Extra Skill and Word Problem Practice*.

Practice and Problem Solving

A Practice by Example

Example 1
(page 620)

Write the related series for each finite sequence. Then evaluate each series.

1. 21, 18, 15, 12, 9, 6, 3
2. $-5, -15, -25, -35, -45$
3. 100, 99, 98, . . . , 95
4. 0.5, 0.25, 0, . . . , -0.75
5. 17.3, 19.6, 21.9, 24.2, 26.5
6. 4.5, 5.6, 6.7, . . . , 11.1
1–6. See margin.

Example 2
(page 620)

Each sequence has eight terms. Evaluate each related series.

7. $\frac{1}{2}, \frac{3}{2}, \frac{5}{2}, \ldots, \frac{15}{2}$ **32**
8. $1, -1, -3, \ldots, -13$ **−48**
9. $5, 13, 21, \ldots, 61$ **264**
10. $-3.5, -1.25, 1, \ldots, 12.25$ **35**
11. $1765, 1414, 1063, \ldots, -692$ **4292**
12. $-13, -14.5, -16, \ldots, -23.5$ **−146**

Example 3
(page 621)

Use summation notation to write each arithmetic series for the specified number of terms. 13–18. See margin pp. 622–623.

13. $2 + 4 + 6 + \ldots; n = 4$
14. $8 + 9 + 10 + \ldots; n = 8$
15. $5 + 6 + 7 + \ldots; n = 7$
16. $1 + 4 + 7 + 10 + \ldots; n = 11$
17. $7 + 14 + 21 + \ldots; n = 15$
18. $(-3) + (-6) + (-9) + \ldots; n = 5$

Example 4
(page 621)

For each sum, find the number of terms, the first term, and the last term. Then evaluate the series.

5, 1, 9; 25   5, −3, −11; −35   6, 4, −1; 9
19. $\sum_{n=1}^{5} (2n - 1)$
20. $\sum_{n=1}^{5} (-2n - 1)$
21. $\sum_{n=3}^{8} (7 - n)$

22. $\sum_{n=1}^{5} (0.2n - 0.2)$
23. $\sum_{n=2}^{10} \frac{4n}{3}$ 9, $\frac{8}{3}$, $\frac{40}{3}$; 72
24. $\sum_{n=5}^{10} (20 - n)$
5, 0, 0.8; 2   6, 15, 10; 75

B Apply Your Skills

Tell whether each list is a *sequence* or a *series*. Then tell whether it is *finite* or *infinite*.

sequence; finite
25. 1, 2, 4, 8, 16, 32, . . . sequence; infinite **26.** 1, 0.5, 0.25, 0.125, 0.0625
27. $5 + 10 + \ldots + 25$ series; finite
28. $-0.5 - 0.25 - 0.125 - \ldots$
series; infinite
29. $\frac{4}{3}, \frac{7}{3}, \frac{10}{3}, \frac{13}{3}, \frac{16}{3}, \ldots$ sequence; infinite **30.** 2.3 + 4.6 + 9.2 + 18.4
series; finite

Real-World **Connection**

The seats in a theater are staggered so people don't block the view of those in the row behind them.

31. Architecture A 20-row theater has three sections of seating. In each section, the number of seats in a row increases by one with each successive row. The first row of the middle section has 10 seats. The first row of each of the two side sections has 4 seats. **a–c. See margin p. 623.**
  a. Find the total number of chairs in each section. Then find the total seating capacity of the theater.
  b. Write an arithmetic series to represent each section.
  c. After every five rows, the ticket price goes down by $5. Front-row tickets cost $60. What is the total amount of money generated by a full house?

32. a. Consider the finite arithmetic series $10 + 13 + 16 + \ldots + 31$.
  How many terms are in it? Explain. **8; the formula for the corresponding sequence is $a_n = 3n + 7$. Solving $3n + 7 = 31$ for n shows that $n = 8$.**
  b. Evaluate the series. **164**

622 Chapter 11 Sequences and Series

2. $(-5) + (-15) + (-25) + (-35) + (-45); -125$

3. $100 + 99 + 98 + 97 + 96 + 95; 585$

4. $0.5 + 0.25 + 0 + (-0.25) + (-0.5) + (-0.75); -0.75$

5. $17.3 + 19.6 + 21.9 + 24.2 + 26.5; 109.5$

6. $4.5 + 5.6 + 6.7 + 7.8 + 8.9 + 10 + 11.1; 54.6$

13. $\sum_{n=1}^{4} 2n$

14. $\sum_{n=1}^{8} (n + 7)$

15. $\sum_{n=1}^{7} (n + 4)$

1. $21 + 18 + 15 + 12 + 9 + 6 + 3; 84$

33. Education Luis has taken three math tests so far this semester. The spreadsheet shows his grades.

	A	B	C	D
1	Student Name	Test 1	Test 2	Test 3
2	Luis Ortez	75	79	83
3	Marie Bova	78	85	84
4	Lasheha Brown	87	82	91

a. Suppose his test grades continue to improve at the same rate. What will be his grade on the fifth (and final) test? **91**
b. What will his test average be for this grading period? (Assume each test is worth 100 points.) **83**

34. a. A supermarket displays cans in a triangle. Write an explicit formula for the sequence of the number of cans. $a_n = n + 1$
b. Use summation notation to write the related series for a triangle with 10 cans in the bottom row. **b–d. See margin.**
c. Suppose the triangle had 17 rows. How many cans would be in the 17th row?
d. Critical Thinking Could the triangle have 110 cans? 140 cans? Justify your reasoning.

Evaluate each series to the given term.
35. $2 + 4 + 6 + 8 + \ldots$; 10th term **110**   **36.** $-5 - 25 - 45 - \ldots$; 9th term **−765**
37. $2 + 3 + 4 + 5 + \ldots$; 100th term **5150**   **38.** $\frac{5}{2} + 1 - \frac{1}{2} - 2 - \ldots$; 8th term **−22**
39. $0.17 + 0.13 + 0.09 + 0.05 + \ldots$; 12th term **−0.6**
40. $1500 + 1499 + 1498 + 1497 + \ldots$; 1000th term **1,000,500**

41. Technology A school committee has decided to spend a large portion of its annual technology budget on graphing calculators. This year, the technology coordinator bought 75 calculators, and plans to buy 25 new calculators each year from now on.
a. Suppose the school committee has decided that each student in the school should have access to a graphing calculator within seven years. The school population is 500. Will the technology coordinator meet this goal? Explain your reasoning. **No; 75 + 25(6) = 225, which is less than 500.**
b. Writing What are some pros and cons of buying calculators in this manner? If you could change the plan, would you? If so, how would you change it?

41b. Answers may vary.
Sample: Pro: spreading the cost over several years, con: calculators purchased first may be outdated by the time 500 calculators have been purchased; check student's work.

42. a. Open-Ended Write two explicit formulas for arithmetic sequences.
b. Write the first five terms of each related series.
c. Use summation notation to rewrite each series.
d. Evaluate each series.   **a–d. Check students' work.**

 Challenge

Use the values of a_1 and S_n to find the value of a_n.
43. $a_1 = 4$ and $S_{40} = 6080$; a_{40} **300**   **44.** $a_1 = -6$ and $S_{50} = -5150$; a_{50} **−200**

Find a_1 for each arithmetic series.
45. $S_8 = 440$ and $d = 6$ **34**   **46.** $S_{30} = 240$ and $d = -2$ **37**

47. Evaluate S_{10} for the series $x + (x + y) + (x + 2y) + \ldots$ **10x + 45y**
48. Evaluate S_{15} for the series $3x + (3x - 2y) + (3x - 4y) + \ldots$ **45x − 210y**

16. $\sum_{n=1}^{11} (3n - 2)$
17. $\sum_{n=1}^{15} 7n$
18. $\sum_{n=1}^{5} -3n$
31a. 270 chairs on each side, 390 chairs middle, 930 chairs total
b. each side: $\sum_{n=1}^{20} (n + 3)$;
middle: $\sum_{n=1}^{20} (n + 9)$
c. $46,950

PowerPoint
Lesson Quiz

1. Write an addition expression for the finite series represented by $\sum_{n=1}^{8} 10n$. $10 + 20 + 30 + 40 + 50 + 60 + 70 + 80$

Write each finite arithmetic series using summation notation. Then find the sum of each series.

2. $102 + 104 + 106 + 108 + 110 + 112$ $\sum_{n=1}^{6} (100 + 2n)$; 642

3. $10 + 5 + 0 + (-5) + (-10) + (-15)$ $\sum_{n=1}^{6} (15 - 5n)$; −15

4. Write the arithmetic series to the given term using summation notation. Then find the sum of the series.
$3 + 6 + 9 + 12 + \ldots$; 100th $\sum_{n=1}^{100} 3n$; 15,150

Alternative Assessment

Have students work in pairs. Ask each student to write three finite arithmetic series, each with at least six terms. Students trade series. Each student should use summation notation to represent the series he or she received. The student should then evaluate the series. Ask students to check one another's work.

34b. $\sum_{n=1}^{9} (n + 1)$
c. 18 cans
d. No; no; 13 rows have 104 cans, 14 rows have 119 cans, 15 rows have 135 cans, and 16 rows have 152 cans. The number of rows would not be an integer for 110 cans or 140 cans.

623

Resources

For additional practice with a variety of test item formats:
- Standardized Test Prep, p. 645
- Test-Taking Strategies, p. 640
- Test-Taking Strategies with Transparencies

Multiple Choice

49. Which expression represents the sum $10 + 20 + 30 + 40$? **B**

    I. $\displaystyle\sum_{n=1}^{4} 10n$ **II.** $\displaystyle\sum_{n=10}^{40} 10n$ **III.** $10\left(\displaystyle\sum_{n=1}^{4} n\right)$

  A. I and II only   **B.** I and III only   **C.** II and III only   **D.** I, II, and III

50. What is the value of $\displaystyle\sum_{n=1}^{5} (2n - 3)$? **G**

  F. 6   **G.** 15   **H.** 17   **J.** $10n - 15$

51. Which expression defines the series $14 + 20 + 26 + 32 + 38 + 44 + 50$? **C**

  A. $\displaystyle\sum_{n=2}^{8} (7n - 1)$ **B.** $\displaystyle\sum_{n=3}^{8} (6n - 4)$ **C.** $\displaystyle\sum_{n=3}^{9} (6n - 4)$ **D.** $\displaystyle\sum_{n=8}^{14} (n + 6)$

52. Which expression represents a series with 12 terms? **G**

  F. $\displaystyle\sum_{n=3}^{12} 12n$ **G.** $\displaystyle\sum_{n=3}^{14} \left(\frac{n + 4}{2}\right)$ **H.** $\displaystyle\sum_{n=9}^{21} (3n - 6)$ **J.** $\displaystyle\sum_{n=1}^{11} \frac{n}{2}$

53. Which expression represents the sum of the finite series $13 + 10 + 7 + 4$? **A**

    I. $\displaystyle\sum_{n=1}^{4} (16 - 3n)$ **II.** $\displaystyle\sum_{n=3}^{6} (22 - 3n)$ **III.** $\displaystyle\sum_{n=1}^{4} (4 + 3n)$

  A. I and II   **B.** I and III   **C.** II and III   **D.** I, II, and III

54. The first term of an arithmetic series is 123. The common difference is 12, and the sum 1320. How many terms are in the series? **H**

  F. 10   **G.** 9   **H.** 8   **J.** 7

Short Response

55. Write an expression for the sum of a 6-term arithmetic sequence with first term of 3 and a common difference of 4. Then find the sum. **55–57. See back of book.**

56. Evaluate the series $\displaystyle\sum_{n=1}^{40} \left(10 - \frac{n}{2}\right)$ Show your work.

57. The 30th term of a finite arithmetic series is 4.4. The sum of the first 30 terms is 78. What is the first term of the series?

58. $a_n = 2^{n-1}$; 1, 2, 4

59. $a_n = 5^{n-1}$; 1, 5, 25

60. $a_n = -1(-1)^{n-1}$; $-1, 1, -1$

61. $a_n = 3\left(\frac{3}{2}\right)^{n-1}$; $3, \frac{9}{2}, \frac{27}{4}$

62. $a_n = -7(0.1)^{n-1}$; $-7, -0.7, -0.07$

63. $a_n = 20(-0.5)^{n-1}$; $20, -10, 5$

64.

ellipse: x- and y-axes; domain: $-6 \le x \le 6$; range: $-2\sqrt{3} \le y \le 2\sqrt{3}$

65.

hyperbola: x- and y-axes; domain: $x \le -5$ or $x \ge 5$; range: $-\infty \le y \le \infty$

66.

circle: all lines through the origin; domain: $-2 \le x \le 2$; range: $-2 \le y \le 2$

Mixed Review

Lesson 11-3

GO for Help

Write the explicit formula for each geometric sequence. Then generate the first three terms. **58–63. See margin.**

58. $a_1 = 1, r = 2$ **59.** $a_1 = 1, r = 5$ **60.** $a_1 = -1, r = -1$

61. $a_1 = 3, r = \frac{3}{2}$ **62.** $a_1 = -7, r = 0.1$ **63.** $a_1 = 20, r = -0.5$

Lesson 10-1

Graph each equation. Describe each graph and its lines of symmetry. Give the domain and range for each graph. **64–66. See margin.**

64. $x^2 + 3y^2 = 36$ **65.** $x^2 - y^2 = 25$ **66.** $x^2 + y^2 = 4$

Lesson 9-4

Simplify each rational expression. **67–69. See margin.**

67. $\dfrac{x^2 + 4x + 3}{x^2 - 3x - 4}$ **68.** $\dfrac{c^2 - 8c + 12}{c^2 - 11c + 30}$ **69.** $\dfrac{3z^4 + 36z^3 + 60z^2}{3z^3 - 3z^2}$

67. $\dfrac{x + 3}{x - 4}$

68. $\dfrac{c - 2}{c - 5}$

69. $\dfrac{z^2 + 12z + 20}{z - 1}$

Geometry and Infinite Series

FOR USE WITH LESSON 11-5

You can use geometric figures to model some infinite series.

1 ACTIVITY Modeling an Infinite Series

Geometry Draw a geometric figure to model the series.

$$\frac{1}{2} + \left(\frac{1}{2}\right)^2 + \left(\frac{1}{2}\right)^3 + \ldots + \left(\frac{1}{2}\right)^n + \ldots$$

Use a square grid. Shade one half of the grid. Then shade one half of the remaining area. Continue until the grid is full.

So the series

$$\frac{1}{2} + \left(\frac{1}{2}\right)^2 + \left(\frac{1}{2}\right)^3 + \ldots + \left(\frac{1}{2}\right)^n + \ldots$$

appears to have a sum of 1.

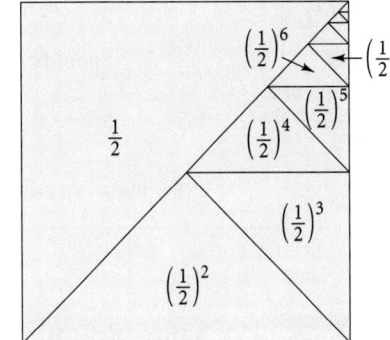

You can write an infinite series from a geometric model.

2 ACTIVITY Writing an Infinite Series

Geometry Write the series modeled by the trapezoids. Estimate the sum of the series. Explain your reasoning.

          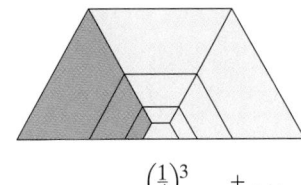

$$\frac{1}{4} \quad + \quad \left(\frac{1}{4}\right)^2 \quad + \quad \left(\frac{1}{4}\right)^3 \quad + \ldots$$

The red area approaches one third of the figure.

So the series $\frac{1}{4} + \left(\frac{1}{4}\right)^2 + \left(\frac{1}{4}\right)^3 + \ldots + \left(\frac{1}{4}\right)^n + \ldots$ appears to have a sum of $\frac{1}{3}$.

EXERCISES 1–3. See margin.

1. **a.** Write the series modeled by the figure at the right.
   b. Evaluate the series. Explain your reasoning.

2. Draw a figure to model the series. Begin with a 10×10 square.
   $$\frac{1}{5} + \left(\frac{1}{5}\right)^2 + \left(\frac{1}{5}\right)^3 + \ldots + \left(\frac{1}{5}\right)^n + \ldots$$

3. **Make a Conjecture** Consider the series
   $$\frac{1}{c} + \left(\frac{1}{c}\right)^2 + \left(\frac{1}{c}\right)^3 + \ldots + \left(\frac{1}{c}\right)^n + \ldots$$
   What is the sum of the series? Explain your reasoning.

Geometry and Infinite Series

In this activity, students use geometric figures to develop an intuitive feel for geometric series that converge to a limit. The ideas explored will be helpful in Lesson 11-5.

Guided Instruction

1 EXAMPLE Math Tip

Be sure students understand that it is not literally possible to shade an infinite number of triangles. So, in a theoretical sense, the grid does not get completely shaded.

Error Prevention!

Exercise 3 Students may not consider all of the possible values of c. Be sure they consider values for which $c \leq 1$.

1a. $\frac{1}{3} + \left(\frac{1}{3}\right)^2 + \left(\frac{1}{3}\right)^3 + \ldots + \left(\frac{1}{3}\right)^n + \ldots$

b. $\frac{1}{2}$; the shaded area approximates one half of the figure.

2. Answers may vary. Sample:

3. Answers may vary. Sample: Where $c > 1$ ($\frac{1}{c} < 1$), the sum of the series is $\frac{1}{c-1}$; the examples and the other exercises seem to suggest that pattern.

Geometric Series

Objectives

1 To evaluate a finite geometric series
2 To evaluate an infinite geometric series

Examples

1 Using the Geometric Series Formula
2 Real-World Connection
3 Determining Divergence and Convergence
4 Real-World Connection

Math Background

The sum $S_n = a_1 + a_2 + a_3 + \ldots + a_n$ of a finite geometric series can be written as $S_n = a_1 + a_1r + a_1r^2 + \ldots + a_1r^{n-1}$. If you multiply both sides by r, you get $rS_n = a_1r + a_1r^2 + a_1r^3 + \ldots + a_1r^n$. When you subtract this equation from the preceding equation, most of the terms on the right side cancel out, and you get $S_n - rS_n = a_1 - a_1r^n$. Factor on both sides to get the equation $S_n(1 - r) = a_1(1 - r^n)$. When you divide both sides by $1 - r$ (assuming $r \neq 1$), you obtain $S_n = \frac{a_1(1 - r^n)}{1 - r}$, which is the formula for the sum of the geometric series.

More Math Background: p. 598D

Lesson Planning and Resources

See p. 598E for a list of the resources that support this lesson.

Bell Ringer Practice

✓ Check Skills You'll Need
For intervention, direct students to:

Adding and Subtracting Rational Expressions
Lesson 9-5: Example 5
Extra Skills and Word Problems Practice, Ch. 9

626

What You'll Learn

• To evaluate a finite geometric series
• To evaluate an infinite geometric series

. . . And Why

To find the length of a chambered nautilus shell, as in Example 4

GO for Help   Lesson 9-5

✓ Check Skills You'll Need

Find each sum or difference.

1. $100 + 50 + 25 + \frac{25}{2} + \frac{25}{4}$ $193\frac{3}{4}$ 2. $3 + 9 + 27 + 81$ **120**
3. $-2 + 4 - 8 + 16 - 32$ **−22**   4. $-5 - 10 - 20 - 40$ **−75**

Simplify each fraction.

5. $\frac{1 - \frac{1}{5}}{\frac{1}{3}}$ $\frac{12}{5}$ 6. $\frac{1}{1 - \frac{1}{4}}$ $\frac{4}{3}$ 7. $\frac{\frac{1}{2} - \frac{1}{3}}{\frac{1}{4}}$ $\frac{2}{3}$ 8. $\frac{2 + \frac{1}{16}}{\frac{1}{3}}$ $\frac{99}{16}$

◄)) New Vocabulary   • geometric series   • converge   • diverge

---

1 ▸ Evaluating a Finite Geometric Series

A **geometric series** is the expression for the sum of the terms of a geometric sequence. As with arithmetic series, you can use a formula to evaluate a finite geometric series.

 Key Concepts

Property	**Sum of a Finite Geometric Series**

The sum S_n of a finite geometric series $a_1 + a_2 + a_3 + \ldots + a_n, r \neq 1$, is

$$S_n = \frac{a_1(1 - r^n)}{1 - r}$$

where a_1 is the first term, r is the common ratio, and n is the number of terms.

1 EXAMPLE   Using the Geometric Series Formula

Use the formula to evaluate the series $3 + 6 + 12 + 24 + 48 + 96$.

The first term is 3, and there are six terms in the series.

The common ratio is $\frac{6}{3} = \frac{12}{6} = \frac{24}{12} = \frac{48}{24} = \frac{96}{48} = 2$.

So $a_1 = 3, r = 2,$ and $n = 6$.

$S_n = \frac{a_1(1 - r^n)}{1 - r}$ **Write the formula.**

$S_6 = \frac{3(1 - 2^6)}{1 - 2}$ **Substitute $a_1 = 3, r = 2,$ and $n = 6$.**

$= \frac{-189}{-1} = 189$ **Simplify.**

● The sum of the series is 189.

GO for Help

For more practice with ratios, see Skills Handbook p. 872.

Differentiated Instruction   Solutions for All Learners

Special Needs L1
In Example 1, students may incorrectly use the order of operations with the sum formula. Emphasize that students should raise r to the nth power before they subtract from 1. Students must also find the difference in the denominator before dividing.
learning style: verbal

Below Level L2
Have students graph arithmetic and geometric sequences. Explain why arithmetic sequences are called linear and geometric sequences are called exponential.
learning style: visual

Quick Check

1 Identify a_1, r, and n for each series. Then evaluate each series.

a. $-45 + 135 - 405 + 1215 - 3645$ **b.** $\frac{1}{3} + \frac{1}{9} + \frac{1}{27} + \frac{1}{81}$

1a. $a_1 = -45, r = -3,$
    $n = 5; -2745$

b. $a_1 = \frac{1}{3}, r = \frac{1}{3}, n = 4;$
   $\frac{40}{81}$

You can use the formula to solve problems involving geometric series.

2 EXAMPLE Real-World Connection

Financial Planning In March, the Floyd family starts saving for a vacation at the end of August. The Floyds expect the vacation to cost $1375. They start with $125. Each month they plan to deposit 20% more than the previous month. Will they have enough money for their trip?

Real-World Connection

Careers Financial planners use math to help families plan savings for college, retirement, and vacations.

Relate $S_n = \dfrac{a_1(1 - r^n)}{1 - r}$ Write the formula for the sum of a geometric series.

Define S_n = total amount saved
$a_1 = 125$ initial amount
$r = 1.2$ common ratio
$n = 6$ number of months (March through August)

Write $S_6 = \dfrac{125(1 - 1.2^6)}{1 - 1.2}$ Substitute.

$= 1241.24$ Simplify.

The final balance will be $1241.24. The Floyds will *not* have enough money for their trip in August.

 Quick Check

2 a. Reasoning Explain how the common ratio 1.2 was found.
b. Suppose each month the Floyds deposit 25% more than the previous month. Describe how this changes the problem. **a–b. See below left.**
c. At this rate of saving, will they have enough money for their trip? Explain. **Yes; they will have $1407.35.**

2 Evaluating an Infinite Geometric Series

2a. To find the amount 20% larger than a given amount, multiply by 1.2, which is equivalent to 120%.
b. The common ratio becomes 1.25.

Vocabulary Tip

In $\displaystyle\sum_{n=1}^{\infty}$, the symbol for infinity ∞ indicates that the series continues without end.

In some cases you can evaluate an infinite geometric series. When $|r| < 1$, the series **converges,** or gets closer and closer, to the sum S. When $|r| \geq 1$, the series **diverges,** or approaches no limit.

3 EXAMPLE Determining Divergence and Convergence

Decide whether each infinite geometric series *diverges* or *converges*. State whether the series has a sum.

a. $1 - \frac{1}{3} + \frac{1}{9} - \ldots$

$a_1 = 1, a_2 = -\frac{1}{3}$
$r = -\frac{1}{3} \div 1 = -\frac{1}{3}$
Since $|r| < 1$, the series converges, and the series has a sum.

b. $\displaystyle\sum_{n=1}^{\infty} 5(2)^{n-1}$

$a_1 = 5(2^0) = 5, a_2 = 5(2^1) = 10$
$r = 10 \div 5 = 2$
Since $|r| \geq 1$, the series diverges, and the series does not have a sum.

 Quick Check

3 Determine whether each infinite series converges or diverges.
a. $1 + \frac{1}{5} + \frac{1}{25} + \ldots$ **converges**   **b.** $4 + 8 + 16 + \ldots$ **diverges**

Lesson 11-5 Geometric Series   **627**

---

2. Teach

Guided Instruction

PowerPoint
Additional Examples

1 Use the formula to evaluate the series
$5 + 15 + 45 + 135 + 405 + 1215.$
1820

2 The Floyd family starts saving for a vacation that is one year away. They start with $125. Each month they save 8% more than the previous month. How much money will they have saved 12 months later? **$2372.14**

Guided Instruction

3 EXAMPLE Math Tip

In part b, call attention to the symbol ∞ above the sigma symbol. Explain that the infinity symbol is used to indicate that there is no upper limit for the number of terms for the summation.

---

4 EXAMPLE Connection to Biology

A classic work on the relation between mathematics and biology is *On Growth and Form* by D'Arcy Wentworth Thompson. This famous book is still in print and is also available in libraries.

Additional Examples

3 Decide whether each infinite geometric series *diverges* or *converges*. State whether the series has a sum.

a. $\sum_{n=1}^{\infty} \left(\frac{2}{3}\right)^n$ converges; has a sum

b. $2 + 6 + 18 + \ldots$ diverges; does not have a sum

4 The weight at the end of a pendulum swings through an arc of 30 inches on its first swing. After that, each successive swing is 85% of the length of the previous swing. What is the total distance the weight will swing by the time it comes to rest? **200 in.**

Resources
• Daily Notetaking Guide 11-5   **L3**

Closure

Ask students what formula they can use to evaluate the sum of the first n terms of a geometric series with first term a_1 and common ratio r ($r \neq 1$). Then ask them how they can tell whether an infinite geometric series converges or diverges. Finally, ask how one can find the sum if the series converges. $S_n = \frac{a_1(1 - r^n)}{1 - r}$; converges if and only if $|r| < 1$; Use $S = \frac{a_1}{1 - r}$.

9. converges; has a sum

10. converges; has a sum

11. converges; has a sum

12. diverges; no sum

13. diverges; no sum

14. converges; has a sum

628

 Key Concepts

Definition	**Sum of an Infinite Geometric Series**

An infinite geometric series with $|r| < 1$ converges to the sum

$$S = \frac{a_1}{1 - r}$$

where a_1 is the first term and r is the common ratio.

You can use the sum formula to evaluate some infinite geometric series.

4 EXAMPLE Real-World Connection

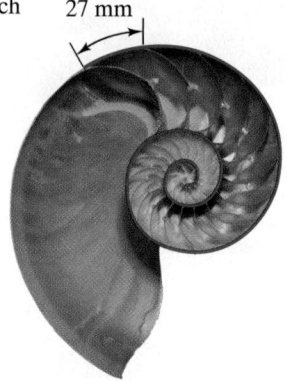

Multiple Choice The length of the outside shell of each closed chamber of a chambered nautilus is 0.9 times the length of the larger chamber next to it. What is the best estimate for the total length of the outside shell for the enclosed chambers?

27 mm

Ⓐ 24.3 mm   Ⓑ 30 mm
Ⓒ 243 mm   Ⓓ 270 mm

The outside edge of the largest enclosed chamber is 27 mm long, so $a_1 = 27$.

$S = \dfrac{a_1}{1 - r}$ **Use the formula.**

$= \dfrac{27}{1 - 0.9}$ **Substitute.**

$= 270$ **Simplify.**

● The estimate for the length is 270 mm. The correct choice is D.

 Quick Check **4** Evaluate each infinite geometric series.

a. $1 + \frac{1}{2} + \frac{1}{4} + \frac{1}{8} + \ldots$ **2**   **b.** $3 - \frac{3}{2} + \frac{3}{4} - \frac{3}{8} + \ldots$ **2**

 Test-Taking Tip

For a word problem, identify the math model that fits. Write the formula you need. Then identify values to use in the formula.

EXERCISES

For more exercises, see *Extra Skill and Word Problem Practice*.

Practice and Problem Solving

 Practice by Example

Examples 1 and 2
(pages 626 and 627)

 for Help

Evaluate the finite series for the specified number of terms.

1. $1 + 2 + 4 + \ldots; n = 8$ **255**

2. $4 + 12 + 36 + \ldots; n = 6$ **1456**

3. $3 + 6 + 12 + \ldots; n = 7$ **381**

4. $7 - 35 + 175 - \ldots; n = 5$ **3647**

5. $-5 - 10 - 20 - \ldots; n = 11$ **-10,235**

6. $-\frac{1}{6} + 1 - 6 + 36 - \ldots; n = 5$ $-\frac{1111}{6}$

7. $\frac{1}{2} + \frac{1}{4} + \frac{1}{8} + \ldots; n = 8$ $\frac{255}{256}$

8. $1 - 3 + 9 - 27 + \ldots; n = 8$ **-1640**

Example 3
(page 627)

Decide whether each infinite geometric series *diverges* or *converges*. State whether each series has a sum. 9–14. See margin.

9. $1 + \frac{1}{4} + \frac{1}{16} + \ldots$

10. $1 - \frac{1}{2} + \frac{1}{4} - \ldots$

11. $4 + 2 + 1 + \ldots$

12. $1 + 2 + 4 + \ldots$

13. $6 + 18 + 54 + \ldots$

14. $-54 - 18 - 6 - \ldots$

15. $1 - 1 + 1 - \ldots$
diverges; no sum

16. $1 + \frac{1}{5} + \frac{1}{25} + \ldots$
converges; has a sum

17. $\frac{1}{4} + \frac{1}{2} + 1 + 2 + \ldots$
diverges; no sum

Example 4
(page 628)

Evaluate each infinite geometric series.

18. $1.1 + 0.11 + 0.011 + \ldots$ $1.\overline{2}$

19. $1.1 - 0.11 + 0.011 - \ldots$ 1

20. $1 - \frac{1}{5} + \frac{1}{25} - \frac{1}{125} + \ldots$ $\frac{5}{6}$

21. $3 + 1 + \frac{1}{3} + \frac{1}{9} + \ldots$ $\frac{9}{2}$

22. $3 + 2 + \frac{4}{3} + \frac{8}{9} + \ldots$ 9

23. $3 - 2 + \frac{4}{3} - \frac{8}{9} + \ldots$ $\frac{9}{5}$

B **Apply Your Skills**

Determine whether each series is *arithmetic* or *geometric*. Then evaluate the finite series for the specified number of terms.

24. geometric; 2046

26. geometric; −1,627,605

27. geometric; ≈96.47

arithmetic; 420

24. $2 + 4 + 8 + 16 + \ldots; n = 10$

25. $2 + 4 + 6 + 8 + \ldots; n = 20$

26. $-5 + 25 - 125 + 625 - \ldots; n = 9$

27. $6.4 + 8 + 10 + 12.5 + \ldots; n = 7$

28. $1 + 2 + 3 + 4 + \ldots; n = 1000$

29. $81 + 27 + 9 + 3 + \ldots; n = 200$
arithmetic; 500,500
geometric; 121.5

 30. Communications Many companies use a telephone chain to notify employees of a closing due to bad weather. Suppose the first person in the chain calls four people. Then each of these people calls four others, and so on.
  a. Make a tree diagram to show the first three stages in the telephone chain. How many calls are made at each stage? **See back of book.**
  b. Write the series that represents the total number of calls made through the first six stages. $4 + 16 + 64 + 256 + 1024 + 4096$
  c. How many employees have been notified after stage six?
  5460

31a. 20, 18, 16.2, 14.58

c. $S = \frac{20}{1 - 0.9} = 200$

31. The graph shows the sum of the first n terms in the series with $a_1 = 20$ and $r = 0.9$.
  a. Write the first four terms of the series.
  b. Use the graph to evaluate the series to the 47th term. ≈**198.59**
  c. Write and evaluate the formula for the sum of the series.
  d. Graph the sum using the window values shown. Use the graph to verify your answer to part (c). **Check students' work.**

X=47   Y=198.58607

Xmin=0   Ymin=0
Xmax=94   Ymax=250
Xscl=10   Yscl=50

Evaluate each infinite series that has a sum.

32. $\sum_{n=1}^{\infty} \left(\frac{1}{5}\right)^{n-1}$ $\frac{5}{4}$

33. $\sum_{n=1}^{\infty} 3\left(\frac{1}{4}\right)^{n-1}$ 4

34. $\sum_{n=1}^{\infty} \left(-\frac{1}{3}\right)^{n-1}$ $\frac{3}{4}$

35. $\sum_{n=1}^{\infty} 7(2)^{n-1}$ **no sum**

36. $\sum_{n=1}^{\infty} (-0.2)^{n-1}$ $0.8\overline{3}$

37. $\sum_{n=1}^{\infty} 2(1.2)^{n-1}$ **no sum**

38. A bouncing ball reaches heights of 16 cm, 12.8 cm, and 10.24 cm on three consecutive bounces.
  a. If the ball started at a height of 25 cm, how many times has it bounced when it reaches a height of 16 cm? **2**
  b. Write a geometric series for the downward distances the ball travels from its release at 25 cm. $25 + 20 + 16 + 12.8 + 10.24 + \ldots$
  c. Write a geometric series for the upward distances the ball travels from its first bounce. $20 + 16 + 12.8 + 10.24 + \ldots$
  d. Find the total vertical distance the ball travels before it comes to rest.
  225 cm

Visit: PHSchool.com
Web Code: age-1105

39. Open-Ended Write an infinite geometric series that converges to 3. Use the formula to evaluate the series. **Check students' work.**

Assignment Guide

1 A B 1-8, 24-30, 43

2 A B 9-23, 31-42, 44
 C Challenge   45-50

Test Prep   51-56
Mixed Review   57-66

Homework Quick Check
To check students' understanding of key skills and concepts, go over Exercises 8, 22, 30, 34, 40, 43.

Error Prevention!

Exercises 12, 13, 17 Students sometimes want to say that a series for which $a_n > 0$ and $r > 1$ converges to ∞. Be sure to point out that we say a series converges *only* if it converges to a real number. The symbol ∞ does not represent a real number.

Exercise 48 You may need to explain the terms *friction* and *pendulum*. Let students tie a small object onto the end of a piece of string to simulate the movement of a pendulum.

Differentiated Instruction Resources

GPS Guided Problem Solving	L3
Enrichment	L4
Reteaching	L2
Practice	L3

1. Find the sum of the geometric series. $3 - 30 + 300 - 3000 + 30{,}000$ **27,273**

2. Find the sum of the first twelve terms of the geometric series. Round your answer to the nearest thousandth. $16 + 8 + 4 + \ldots$ **31.992**

3. How can you tell whether an infinite geometric series converges or diverges? **Check the common ratio r. If $|r| < 1$, the series converges. Otherwise, it diverges.**

4. Find the sum of the infinite geometric series. $16 + 8 + 4 + \ldots$ **32**

5. Find the sum of the infinite geometric series. $15 + 5 + \frac{5}{3} + \frac{5}{9} + \ldots$ **22.5**

Alternative Assessment

Have students work individually. Ask students to write two finite geometric series with at least five terms. Ask them to find the sum of each series. Then ask them to write two infinite geometric series, one that diverges and one that converges. Ask them to find the sum of the series that converges.

Test Prep

A sheet of blank grids is available in the Test-Taking Strategies with Transparencies booklet. Give this sheet to students for practice with filling in the grids.

Resources

For additional practice with a variety of test item formats:
- Standardized Test Prep, p. 645
- Test-Taking Strategies, p. 640
- Test-Taking Strategies with Transparencies

40a. No; the sum of a series of positive numbers will be positive.

b. Your classmate did not check to see if $|r|$ was less than 1.

43. (b); (a) yields $26,000; using the formula for finding the sum of a finite geometric series, (b) yields $1,342,177.26.

49a. $S = \frac{0.142857}{1 - 0.000001} = \frac{0.142857}{0.999999} = \frac{1}{7}$

---

40. **a.** A classmate uses the formula for the sum of an infinite geometric series to evaluate $1 + 1.1 + 1.21 + 1.331 + \ldots$ and gets -10. Is your classmate's answer reasonable? Explain.

    b. Error Analysis What did your classmate fail to check before using the formula?

Critical Thinking Find the specified value for each infinite geometric series.

41. $a_1 = 12, S = 96$; find r. $\frac{7}{8}$

42. $S = 12, r = \frac{1}{6}$; find a_1. **10**

43. **Writing** Suppose you are to receive an allowance each week for the next 26 weeks. Would you rather receive (a) $1000 per week or (b) 2¢ the first week, 4¢ the second week, 8¢ the third week, and so on for the 26 weeks? Justify your answer.

44. The sum of an infinite geometric series is twice its first term.
    a. Error Analysis A student says the common ratio of the series is $\frac{3}{2}$. What is the student's error? **See margin.**
    b. Find the common ratio of the series. $\frac{1}{2}$

 Challenge

Technology Create a spreadsheet to evaluate the first n terms of each series. Determine whether each infinite series converges to a sum. If so, estimate the sum.

45. $\sum_{n=1}^{\infty} \frac{1}{2^n}$ **converges; 1**

46. $\sum_{n=1}^{\infty} \frac{100}{n}$ **diverges**

47. $\sum_{n=1}^{\infty} \frac{1}{(n-1)!}$ **converges; 2.718**

48. **Physics** Because of friction and air resistance, each swing of a pendulum is a little shorter than the previous one. The lengths of the swings form a geometric sequence. Suppose the first swing of a pendulum has a length of 100 cm and the return swing is 99 cm.
    a. On which swing will the arc first have a length less than 50 cm? **70th swing**
    b. Find the total distance traveled by the pendulum until it comes to rest. **10,000 cm**

49. **a.** Show that the infinite geometric series $0.142857 + 0.000000142857 + \ldots$ has a sum of $\frac{1}{7}$.
    b. Find the fraction form of the repeating decimal $0.428571428571\ldots$ $\frac{3}{7}$

50. The function $S(n) = \frac{10(1 - 0.8^n)}{0.2}$ represents the sum of the first n terms of an infinite geometric series.
    a. What is the domain of the function? **a–b. See margin.**
    b. Find $S(n)$ for $n = 1, 2, 3, \ldots, 10$. Sketch the graph of the function.
    c. Find the sum S of the infinite geometric series. **50**

 Test Prep

Gridded Response

51. What is the common ratio for the geometric series $\sum_{n=1}^{10} 7\left(\frac{4}{7}\right)^{n-1}$? Enter your answer as a fraction. **4/7**

52. What is the common ratio in a geometric series if $a_2 = \frac{2}{5}$ and $a_5 = \frac{16}{135}$? Enter your answer as a fraction. **2/3**

630   Chapter 11 Sequences and Series

44a. **Answers may vary. Sample: The student used $r - 1$ instead of $1 - r$ in the formula for the sum of an infinite geometric series.**

50a. **all integers greater than or equal to 1**

b. **10; 18; 24.4; 29.52; 33.62; 36.89; 39.51; 41.61; 43.29; 44.63;**

53. Evaluate the infinite geometric series $\frac{2}{5} + \frac{4}{25} + \frac{8}{125} + \ldots$ Enter your answer as a fraction. **2/3**

54. Find the sum of the two infinite series $\sum\limits_{n=1}^{\infty} \left(\frac{2}{3}\right)^{n-1}$ and $\sum\limits_{n=1}^{\infty} \left(\frac{2}{3}\right)^{n}$. **5**

55. Evaluate the sum $\sum\limits_{n=1}^{3} \left(\frac{1}{n+1}\right)^2$. Enter your answer as a decimal to the nearest hundredth. **0.42**

56. Car 1 cost $22,600 when new and depreciated 14% each year for 5 years. The same year, Car 2 cost $17,500 when new and depreciated 7% each year for 5 years. To the nearest dollar, what was the difference in the values of the two cars after 5 years? **1543**

Mixed Review

Lesson 11-4 **Evaluate each series to the given term.**

57. $12.5 + 15 + 17.5 + 20 + 22.5 + \ldots$; 7th term **140**

58. $-100 - 95 - 90 - 85 - \ldots$; 11th term **−825**

59. $-17 - 11 - 5 + 1 + 7 + 13 + \ldots$; 25th term **1375**

Lesson 10-2 **Identify the focus and directrix of each parabola. Then graph the parabola.**

60. $y = \frac{1}{16}x^2$ **61.** $x = -\frac{1}{4}y^2$ **62.** $x^2 = -9y$
60–62. See margin.

Lesson 9-5 **Add or subtract. Simplify where possible.**

63. $\frac{7}{2c} - \frac{2}{c^2}$ $\frac{7c-4}{2c^2}$ **64.** $\frac{5}{y+3} + \frac{15}{y-3}$

64. $\frac{10(2y+3)}{(y+3)(y-3)}$

65. $\frac{4}{x^2-36} + \frac{x}{x-6}$ $\frac{x^2+6x+4}{(x+6)(x-6)}$ **66.** $\frac{15}{3-d} - \frac{-3}{9-d^2}$ $\frac{-3(5d+16)}{(d+3)(d-3)}$

Checkpoint Quiz 2   Lessons 11-4 through 11-5

Determine whether each series is *arithmetic* or *geometric*. Then evaluate the finite series for the specified number of terms.

1. $1 + 3 + 5 + 7 + \ldots$; $n = 30$ **2.** $1 + 3 + 9 + 27 + \ldots$; $n = 10$

3. $-4 - 2 - 1 - 0.5 - \ldots$; $n = 7$ **4.** $500 + 380 + 260 + 140 + \ldots$; $n = 6$

5. $120 + 60 + 30 + 15 + \ldots$; $n = 8$ geometric; 239.0625   **6.** $-175 - 50 + 75 + 200 + \ldots$; $n = 12$ arithmetic; 6150

1. arithmetic; 900
2. geometric; 29,524
3. geometric; −7.9375
4. arithmetic; 1200

Evaluate each infinite geometric series.

7. $\sum\limits_{n=1}^{\infty} \left(\frac{1}{15}\right)^{n-1}$ $\frac{15}{14}$ **8.** $\sum\limits_{n=1}^{\infty} 2(0.5)^{n-1}$ **4**

9–10. See margin.

9. **Open-Ended** Write a finite geometric series with a sum less than 1.

10. **Critical Thinking** Can an infinite arithmetic series converge? Explain. Do not consider the series $0 + 0 + \ldots = 0$.

60. $(0, 4)$, $y = -4$;

61. $(-1, 0)$, $x = 1$;

62. $\left(0, -\frac{9}{4}\right)$, $y = \frac{9}{4}$;

**Sidebar:**

✓ Checkpoint Quiz

Use this Checkpoint Quiz to check students' understanding of the skills and concepts of Lessons 11-4 through 11-5.

Resources
Grab & Go
• Checkpoint Quiz 2

Checkpoint Quiz

9. Answers may vary.
   Sample:
   $\frac{1}{2} + \frac{1}{4} + \frac{1}{8}$

10. No; the common difference causes arithmetic series to diverge.

Mathematical Induction

Students use the Principle of Mathematical Induction to prove statements are true for all positive integers n.

Guided Instruction

Visual Learners

Set up a domino "chain" and show students how knocking over the first domino results in knocking over all of the dominoes.

Resources

Technology

ExamView CD-ROM, Chapter 00, Extension Topics

Consider the pattern in the following statements.

$$
\begin{aligned}
1 &= 1 \\
1 + 3 &= 4 \\
1 + 3 + 5 &= 9 \\
1 + 3 + 5 + 7 &= 16 \\
1 + 3 + 5 + 7 + 9 &= 25
\end{aligned}
$$

If this pattern continues without end, then the statement

$$1 + 3 + 5 + 7 + \ldots + (2n - 1) = n^2$$

is true for all positive integers n.

The general statement above is true for the first several values of n. There is, however, no number of examples that would prove it true for all positive integers. To prove such a statement true for all positive integers, you can use a method called mathematical induction.

Theorem	Principle of Mathematical Induction

Let S be a statement involving a positive integer n.

Then S is true for all positive integers if the following two conditions hold.

1. S is true for $n = 1$.

2. For any positive integer k, if S is true for k, then S is true for $k + 1$.

The principle of mathematical induction is like a chain reaction in an infinite line of dominoes. Proving that a statement is true for $n = 1$ is like knocking over the first domino. Knowing that if the statement is true for any value of k then it will be true for $k + 1$ is like knowing that if any domino is knocked over the one after it will be knocked over also.

EXAMPLE Using Mathematical Induction

Prove that the following statement is true for all positive integers n.

$$1 + 3 + 5 + \ldots + (2n - 1) = n^2$$

Proof First show that the statement is true for $n = 1$.

$2n - 1 = n^2$	Use the statement.
$2(1) - 1 \stackrel{?}{=} 1^2$	Substitute 1 for n.
$2 - 1 \stackrel{?}{=} 1^2$	Multiply.
$1 = 1 \checkmark$	Simplify.

The statement is true for $n = 1$.

Next, assume that the statement is true for k.

$$1 + 3 + 5 + \ldots + (2k - 1) = k^2$$

From this assumption, prove that the statement is true for $k + 1$.

$$1 + 3 + 5 + \ldots + [2(k + 1) - 1] \stackrel{?}{=} (k + 1)^2 \qquad \text{Write the statement for } k + 1.$$

$$1 + 3 + 5 + \ldots + (2k + 1) \stackrel{?}{=} (k + 1)^2 \qquad \text{Simplify the left side.}$$

$$1 + 3 + 5 + \ldots + (2k - 1) + (2k + 1) \stackrel{?}{=} (k + 1)^2 \qquad \text{Rewrite to show the odd number preceding } (2k + 1).$$

$$k^2 + (2k + 1) \stackrel{?}{=} (k + 1)^2 \qquad \text{Substitute from the assumption.}$$

$$(k + 1)^2 = (k + 1)^2 \checkmark \qquad \text{Factor the left side.}$$

The proof shows that conditions 1 and 2 of the principle of mathematical induction are true. By the principle, then, $1 + 3 + 5 + \ldots + (2n - 1) = n^2$ is true for all positive integers, which is what we wanted to prove.

EXERCISES   1–11. See back of book.

1. Test the statement from the example to verify that it is true for $n = 6, 7,$ and 8.

2. Complete the mathematical induction steps below to prove that
$$2 + 4 + 6 + \ldots + 2n = n(n + 1)$$
is true for all positive integers n.
 a. Show that the statement is true for $n = 1$.
 b. What statement will you assume to be true?
 c. What statement will you prove true using the assumption from part (b)?
 d. Express the sum in your statement from part (c) in terms of what you assumed. Then substitute and simplify to complete the proof.

Use mathematical induction to prove that each statement is true for all positive integers n.

3. $\dfrac{1}{1 \cdot 2} + \dfrac{1}{2 \cdot 3} + \dfrac{1}{3 \cdot 4} + \ldots + \dfrac{1}{n(n + 1)} = \dfrac{n}{n + 1}$

4. $1 + 2 + 3 + \ldots + n = \dfrac{n(n + 1)}{2}$

5. $1 + 4 + 7 + \ldots + (3n - 2) = \dfrac{n(3n - 1)}{2}$

6. $\dfrac{1}{2} + \left(\dfrac{1}{2}\right)^2 + \left(\dfrac{1}{2}\right)^3 + \left(\dfrac{1}{2}\right)^4 + \ldots + \left(\dfrac{1}{2}\right)^n = 1 - \left(\dfrac{1}{2}\right)^n$

7. $n^2 + n$ is divisible by 2.

8. $1 \cdot 2 + 2 \cdot 3 + 3 \cdot 4 + \ldots + n(n + 1) = \dfrac{n(n + 1)(n + 2)}{3}$

9. $1^2 + 2^2 + 3^2 + \ldots + n^2 = \dfrac{n(n + 1)(2n + 1)}{6}$

10. $a_1 + a_1 r + a_1 r^2 + a_1 r^3 + \ldots + a_1 r^{n - 1} = \dfrac{a_1(1 - r^n)}{1 - r}, r \neq 1$
 (This is the formula for the sum of a finite geometric series, page 626.)

11. $1^3 + 2^3 + 3^3 + \ldots + n^3 = (1 + 2 + 3 + \ldots + n)^2$

Extension

Teaching Tip
Let students apply mathematical induction to mathematical rules that they already know.

Evaluating Series

Students use features on the LIST OPS and LIST MATH menus of a graphing calculator to explore two ways of calculating the sum of a series. These ideas can be applied to earlier work on series as well as in Lesson 11-6.

Guided Instruction

Students may want to use the techniques explained here to take another look at sums of arithmetic and geometric series.

Error Prevention!

When students use the procedure from Activity 2, they may forget to identify the variable used in the explicit formula after they enter the formula itself. The calculator will announce a syntax error. Remind students that it is essential to identify the variable.

Resources

Students may use any graphing calculator that has features for automatically generating a sequence and evaluating the corresponding series.

7. **Answers may vary. Sample:** The method from Example 1 is best to use with a short series of numbers; if given a series in summation notation use the method from Example 2, a long series may be converted to summation notation to take advantage of the Example 2 method as well.

You can use a graphing calculator to evaluate finite series.

1 **ACTIVITY** Using the Sum Feature

Find the sum of the terms of the sequence: 15, 30, 45, 60, 75, 90, 105.

Step 1 Enter the sequence in a list. Exit using **QUIT**.

Step 2 Select 5 from the **MATH** menu of the **LIST** feature.

Step 3 Enter the list number. Press **ENTER**.

● The sum of the series 15 + 30 + 45 + . . . + 105 is 420.

2 **ACTIVITY** Evaluating a Finite Series

Use your graphing calculator to evaluate $\sum_{n=1}^{5} \frac{n^2}{2}$.

Step 1 Access the **SUM** feature (Step 2 above).

Step 2 Select 5 from the **OPS** menu of the **LIST** feature.

Step 3 Enter the explicit formula, N, the lower limit, the upper limit, and 1 (to increase N by 1 each time). Press **ENTER**.

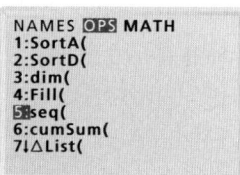

The value of $\sum_{n=1}^{5} \frac{n^2}{2}$ is 27.5.

EXERCISES

Evaluate each series.

1. 595 + 495 + 395 + 295 **1780**
2. 3 + 9 + 27 + 81 **120**
3. $4 + 2 + 1 + \ldots + \frac{1}{8}$ $7\frac{7}{8}$

4. $\sum_{n=1}^{5} (2n^2 - 5)$ **85**
5. $\sum_{x=1}^{5} 2^x$ **62**
6. $\sum_{n=1}^{5} -\sqrt{n^2}$ **−15**

7. Writing Compare the methods in Activities 1 and 2. When would you use the method from Activity 1? When would you use the method from Activity 2? Explain. **See margin.**

Area Under a Curve

What You'll Learn

• To find area under a curve

...And Why

To estimate the distance traveled by a peregrine falcon, as in Example 1

11-6

1. Plan

Objectives

1 To find area under a curve

Examples

1 Real-World Connection
2 Using a Sum to Estimate Area Under a Curve
3 Using a Graphing Calculator

✔ **Check Skills You'll Need** **for Help** Skills Handbook page 875

Find the area of a rectangle with the given length and width.

1. $\ell = 4$ ft, $w = 1$ ft **4 ft^2**

2. $\ell = 5.5$ m, $w = 0.5$ m **2.75 m^2**

3. $\ell = 6.2$ cm, $w = 0.1$ cm **0.62 cm^2**

4. $\ell = 9\frac{1}{2}$ in., $w = 3\frac{5}{8}$ in. **See below.**

🔊 **New Vocabulary** • inscribed rectangles • circumscribed rectangles

4. $34\frac{7}{16}$ in.^{2}

Math Background

In earlier work, students have found the approximate area of an irregularly shaped figure by placing the figure on a grid. In this lesson they approximate the area under a curve by using rectangles.

More Math Background: p. 598D

Lesson Planning and Resources

See p. 598E for a list of the resources that support this lesson.

Bell Ringer Practice

✔ **Check Skills You'll Need**
For intervention, direct students to:

Area and Volume
Skills Handbook: p. 875

1 Finding Area Under a Curve

You can easily calculate the exact area under part of a line parallel to the x-axis, but it is not so easy to calculate the exact area under part of a curve. You can use rectangles to estimate the area under a curve and analyze data.

Inscribed rectangles are completely under the curve. The approximation is less than the area.

 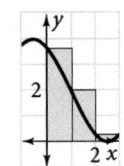

Circumscribed rectangles are partially above the curve. The approximation is greater than the area.

1 EXAMPLE Real-World Connection

Data Analysis The curve at the right approximates the speed of a peregrine falcon during the first 20 s of a high-speed dive.

a. What does the area under the curve represent?

$\text{area} = \frac{\text{meters}}{\text{second}} \cdot \text{seconds}$ **Use dimensional analysis.**

$= \text{meters}$ **Simplify.**

The area under the curve approximates the total distance traveled by the peregrine falcon.

b. Use inscribed rectangles 5 units wide to estimate the area under the curve.

┌─ Width of each rectangle   ┌─ Total area

$5(18) + 5(54) + 5(78) + 5(89) = 1195$

↑   ↑   ↑   ↑

Value of curve at upper edge of each rectangle

The area under the curve is about 1195 units^2. The peregrine falcon traveled about 1195 m during the first 20 s of its dive. The estimate is low because inscribed rectangles were used.

Real-World 🌐 **Connection**

Adult peregrine falcons can reach speeds of 200 mi/h in a dive.

Differentiated Instruction Solutions for All Learners

Special Needs L1
For Example 2, draw a large graph of $y = -x^2 + 5$ on a piece of butcher paper. Make several precut pieces of paper 0.5 units wide and longer than the height of the graph. Have students tape the precut pieces on the graph and cut them to fill in under the curve.
learning style: tactile

Below Level L2
Show that the height of the right-most circumscribed rectangle in Quick Check 1a does not occur at the right or left of the interval.

learning style: verbal

2. Teach

Guided Instruction

Additional Examples

1 The curve shown below approximates the speed of a car during a 12-minute drive.

a. What does the area under the curve represent? **total feet traveled in 12 min**

b. Use inscribed rectangles 2 units wide to estimate the area under the curve. **about 35,000 ft**

2 Estimate the area under the curve $f(x) = -0.5x^2 + 6$ for the domain $0 \le x \le 2$ by evaluating

$A = \sum_{n=1}^{4} (0.5)f(a_n)$, where

$a_1 = 0.5$, $a_2 = 1$, $a_3 = 1.5$, and $a_4 = 2$. **10.125 units²**

3 Use a graphing calculator to graph $f(x) = -x^2 + 4x + 5$. Find the area under the curve for the domain $1 \le x \le 4$. **24 units²**

Resources

- Daily Notetaking Guide 11-6   **L3**

Closure

Ask how the size of the rectangle will affect the approximation of the area under a curve. **Smaller rectangles yield a better approximation.**

636

✓ Quick Check

1a. Answers may vary. Sample: 1545; it is much larger.

b. 1370; the mean is likely the most accurate; it is between the other measures known to be smaller and larger than the actual value.

2a.

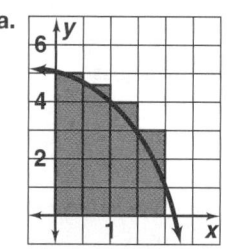

b. The left side values give the height of the circumscribed rectangles.

Online active math

For: Area Under a Curve Activity
Use: Interactive Textbook, 11-6

2c. $0.5(5) + 0.5(4.75) + 0.5(4) + 0.5(2.75) = 8.25$ units²; it is greater than Example 2.

---

1 The graph at the right shows the curve from Example 1, but it shows circumscribed rectangles.

a. Estimate the area under the curve using circumscribed rectangles. How does your answer differ from the answer to Example 1?

b. Critical Thinking Find the mean of the answer using inscribed rectangles and the answer using circumscribed rectangles. Of the three answers, which is likely the most accurate? Explain. **a–b. See left.**

You can use summation notation to represent the area of a series of rectangles and to approximate the area under the curve $f(x)$. Let a_n represent the x-value of a point on the base of the nth rectangle.

$$A = \sum_{n=1}^{b} (w)f(a_n)$$

$b \longleftarrow$ number of rectangles
width of each rectangle $\longrightarrow$ $\quad$ $\longleftarrow$ function value at a_n

The expression $f(a_n)$ gives the height of the nth rectangle.

2 EXAMPLE Using a Sum to Estimate Area Under a Curve

Estimate the area under the curve $f(x) = -x^2 + 5$ for the domain $0 \le x \le 2$ by evaluating the sum A.

$$A = \sum_{n=1}^{4} (0.5)f(a_n)$$

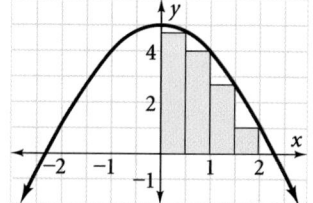

Evaluate the function at the right side of each rectangle.

$a_1 = 0.5, a_2 = 1, a_3 = 1.5, a_4 = 2$ Use the x-values on the right side of each rectangle.

$A = 0.5f(0.5) + 0.5f(1) + 0.5f(1.5) + 0.5f(2)$ **Add the areas of the rectangles.**

$= 0.5(4.75 + 4 + 2.75 + 1)$ total area = $\dfrac{\text{width of}}{\text{each rectangle}} \cdot \dfrac{\text{sum of the}}{\text{heights}}$

$= 0.5(12.5)$ **Add within parentheses.**

$= 6.25$ **Simplify.**

● The indicated area is about 6.25 units².

✓ Quick Check

2 a. Sketch the graph from Example 2 and draw circumscribed rectangles for the domain $0 \le x \le 2$. **a–c. See left.**

b. Critical Thinking To find the area using these rectangles, you should evaluate the function at the left side of each rectangle. Explain why.

c. Use the circumscribed rectangles to write and evaluate a sum that approximates the area under the curve for the domain $0 \le x \le 2$. Compare your answer to the answer in Example 2.

636 Chapter 11 Sequences and Series

You can use a graphing calculator to find the exact area under a curve.

③ EXAMPLE Using a Graphing Calculator

Graph the function $f(x) = -2x^2 + 5$. Find the area under the curve for the domain $-1 \le x \le 1.5$.

Step 1 Input the equation. Adjust the window values.

Step 2 Access the $\int f(x)\,dx$ feature from the CALC menu.

Step 3 Use the lower limit of $x = -1$.

Step 4 Use the upper limit of $x = 1.5$.

Lower Limit?
X=-1   Y=3

Xmin=-4.7   Ymin=-7
Xmax=4.7   Ymax=8
Xscl=1   Yscl=1

$\int f(x)dx=9.5833333$

● The area under the curve between $x = -1$ and $x = 1.5$ is about 9.583 units².

 Graphing Calculator Hint

To move the cursor by tenths along the x-axis, set your x window values to multiples of 4.7 or press ZOOM 4.

✓ **Quick Check** ③ Use the equation from Example 3 and a graphing calculator. Find the area under the curve for each domain.
  a. $0 \le x \le 1$ 4.$\overline{3}$ **b.** $-1 \le x \le 1$ 8.$\overline{6}$ **c.** $-1.5 \le x \le 0$ 5.25

EXERCISES

For more exercises, see *Extra Skill and Word Problem Practice.*

Practice and Problem Solving

 A Practice by Example

Example 1
(page 635)

 GO for Help

Given each set of axes, what does the area under the curve represent?

1. y-axis: production rate, x-axis: time **total produced**

2. y-axis: rate of growth, x-axis: time **amount of growth**

3. y-axis: miles per gallon, x-axis: gallons **miles**

4. y-axis: distance traveled per year, x-axis: years **distance traveled**

5. y-axis: price per pound of gold, x-axis: pounds of gold **total price**

Use the given rectangles to estimate area under the curve.

6.

≈270 units²

7.

100 units²

8. 100

480 units²

Lesson 11-6 Area Under a Curve **637**

Assignment Guide

❶ **A B** 1-41
C Challenge   42-45

Test Prep   46-50
Mixed Review   51-58

Homework Quick Check
To check students' understanding of key skills and concepts, go over Exercises 16, 20, 30, 31, 38.

Teaching Tip

Exercises 1–5 You may need to give a hint if students have trouble knowing what units to use in the answers. Use ideas from dimensional analysis. For instance, in Exercise 1, time × $\frac{\text{units produced}}{\text{time}}$ = units produced.

Error Prevention!

Exercises 24–29 Watch for students who use circumscribed rather than inscribed rectangles. You may need to help them understand the difference.

Differentiated Instruction Resources

GPS Guided Problem Solving	L3
Enrichment	L4
Reteaching	L2
Practice	L3

1. Use circumscribed rectangles to approximate the area under the graph of the function $f(x) = 5 - \frac{1}{4}x^2$, for $0 \le x \le 3$. Use rectangles 1 unit wide. **about 13.75 units²**

2. Use inscribed rectangles to approximate the area under the graph of the function $f(x) = \sqrt{3 + x}$, for $-3 \le x \le 0$. Use rectangles 0.5 units wide. **about 2.96 units²**

3. Evaluate a sum to approximate the area under the graph of the function $f(x) = 3x^2$, for $0 \le x \le 10$. Use inscribed rectangles 2 units wide. **about 720 units²**

4. Use a graphing calculator to find the area under the graph of $y = x^3 - 2x^2 + 3$, for $0 \le x \le 3$. **11.25 units²**

Alternative Assessment

Have students work individually. They will need a graphing calculator. Ask them to construct three functions whose graphs are above the x-axis for $2 \le x \le 5$. Ask them to approximate the area under the graph of each function for this domain by using rectangles of width 0.5. Then have them use the calculator to find each area by using the $\int f(x)dx$ feature on the CALC menu.

32. 9 units²

33. 7.5 units²

34. 15 units²

35. 3.46 units²

36. 8.05 units²

37. 9.75 units²

638

Example 2
(page 636)

Write and evaluate a sum to estimate the area under each curve for the domain $0 \le x \le 2$. 9–17. See back of book.
a. Use inscribed rectangles 1 unit wide.
b. Use circumscribed rectangles 1 unit wide.

9. $f(x) = \frac{1}{2}x^2$
10. $y = -x^2 + 5$
11. $g(x) = x^2 + 1$
12. $y = -x^2 + 4$
13. $y = \frac{2}{3}x^2 + 5$
14. $h(x) = 5x^2$
15. $y = 4 - \frac{1}{4}x^2$
16. $h(x) = -(x - 2)^2 + 5$
17. $y = (x - 2)^2 + 2$

Example 3
(page 637)

18. 1.6̄ units²

B Apply Your Skills

GO Online
Homework Video Tutor
Visit: PHSchool.com
Web Code: age-1106

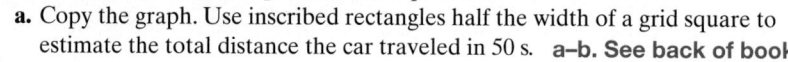

Xmin: 0   Ymin: 0
Xmax: 200 Ymax: 70
Xscl: 25   Yscl: 10

C Challenge

42c. The estimate in (a) is closer to the actual area because there is less area between the curve and the rectangles when more rectangles are used.

Find the area under each curve for the domain $0 \le x \le 1$.
18. $y = -x^2 + 2$
19. $f(x) = x + 2$ **2.5 units²**
20. $y = x^3$ **0.25 units²**
21. $y = -x^4 + 2x^3 + 3$ **3.3 units²**
22. $y = x^5 - x^2 + 2.5$ **2.3̄ units²**
23. $y = -(x - 1)^3 + 3$ **3.25 units²**

Graph each curve. Use inscribed rectangles to approximate the area under the curve for the interval and rectangle width given. 24–29. See back of book.
24. $y = x^2 + 1, 1 \le x \le 3, 0.5$
25. $y = 3x^2 + 2, 2 \le x \le 4, 1$
26. $y = x^2, 3 \le x \le 5, 0.5$
27. $y = 2x^2, 3 \le x \le 5, 1$
28. $y = x^3, 1 \le x \le 3, 0.25$
29. $y = x^2 + 4, -2 \le x \le 2, 0.5$

30. a. Graph the curve $y = \frac{1}{3}x^3$. **a, c–d. See back of book.**
    GPS b. Use inscribed rectangles to approximate the area under the curve for the interval $0 \le x \le 3$ and rectangle width of 1 unit. **3 units²**
    c. Repeat part (b) using circumscribed rectangles.
    d. Find the mean of the areas you found in parts (b) and (c). Of the three estimates, which best approximates the area for the interval? Explain.

31. The graph at the left approximates the speed of a car as it enters a highway from a stopped position and merges with traffic. The x-axis represents time in seconds, and the y-axis represents miles per hour.
    a. Copy the graph. Use inscribed rectangles half the width of a grid square to estimate the total distance the car traveled in 50 s. **a–b. See back of book.**
    b. **Writing** How does your choice of inscribed or circumscribed rectangles in part (a) affect your area estimate?

Evaluate the area under each curve for $-1 \le x \le 2$. 32–37. See margin.
32. $f(x) = -x^2 + 4$
33. $y = (x - 0.5)^2 + 1.75$
34. $g(x) = 2 + 3x^2$
35. $y = \sqrt{1 + x}$
36. $g(x) = 2^x + 1$
37. $y = x^3 + 2$
38. $y = -(x - 1)^2 + 4\frac{1}{3}$ **10 units²**
39. $h(x) = \sqrt{x^2}$ **2.5 units²**
40. $f(x) = -x^4 + 2x^3 + 3$ **9.9 units²**

41. **Open-Ended** Write equations for three curves that are positive for $1 \le x \le 3$. Use your graphing calculator to find the area under each curve for this domain. **Check students' work.**

42. Approximate the area under the curve $f(x) = x^2$ for the interval $0 \le x \le 4$ by evaluating each sum. Use inscribed rectangles.
    a. $\sum_{n=1}^{8} (0.5)f(a_n)$ **17.5 units²**
    b. $\sum_{n=1}^{4} (1)f(a_n)$ **14 units²**
    c. Which estimate is closer to the actual area under the curve? Explain.

43. a. Graph $y = \frac{1}{4}x^3 + 1$ and $y = 1$ over the domain $-4.7 \le x \le 4.7$.
    b. **Critical Thinking** Evaluate the area under each curve for the interval $-1.5 \le x \le 1.5$. What do you notice? Explain. **a–b. See margin.**

43a.

b. The area under both curves is the same, 3 units², over the interval $-1.5 \le x \le 1.5$; this is true because the amount of area *above* $y = \frac{1}{4}x^3 + 1$

and *below* $y = 1$ on the left side of the y-axis is equal to the area *below* $y = \frac{1}{4}x^3 + 1$ and *above* $y = 1$ on the right side of the y-axis.

45b.

23.56 units²

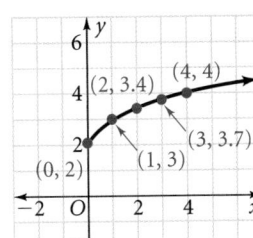

44. Critical Thinking Use your graphing calculator to find the area of the triangle with vertices $(-3, 0)$, $(-1, 3)$, and $(1, 0)$. (*Hint:* First find the function whose graph makes a peak at $(-1, 3)$.) **6 units²**

45. a. Write the equation $\frac{x^2}{25} + \frac{y^2}{9} = 1$ in calculator-ready form. $y = \sqrt{9 - \frac{9x^2}{25}}$

b. Graph the top half of the ellipse. Calculate the area under the curve for the interval $-5 \le x \le 5$. **See left.**

c. Use symmetry to find the area of the entire ellipse. **47.12 units²**

d. Open-Ended Find the area of another symmetric shape by graphing part of it. Sketch your graph and show your calculations. **Check students' work.**

Test Prep

Resources
For additional practice with a variety of test item formats:
- Standardized Test Prep, p. 645
- Test-Taking Strategies, p. 640
- Test-Taking Strategies with Transparencies

Test Prep

Multiple Choice

Use the graph of $f(x) = \sqrt{x} + 2$ for Exercises 46–49.

46. Which series represents the area of four inscribed rectangles? **A**
   A. $(1)(2) + (1)(3) + (1)(3.4) + (1)(3.7)$
   B. $(1)(3) + (1)(3.4) + (1)(3.7) + (1)(4)$
   C. $(1 + 2 + 3 + 4)(0 + 1 + 2 + 3)$
   D. $(1 + 2 + 3 + 4)(3 + 3.4 + 3.7 + 4)$

47. Which series represents the area of four circumscribed rectangles? **G**
   F. $(1)(2) + (1)(3) + (1)(3.4) + (1)(3.7)$
   G. $(1)(3) + (1)(3.4) + (1)(3.7) + (1)(4)$
   H. $(1 + 2 + 3 + 4)(0 + 1 + 2 + 3)$
   J. $(1 + 2 + 3 + 4)(3 + 3.4 + 3.7 + 4)$

48. Which of the following is the most accurate value of the area under $f(x) = \sqrt{x} + 2$ for $0 \le x \le 4$? **B**
   A. 12.1   **B.** 14.1   **C.** 16.1   **D.** 24.0

49. Which expression does NOT represent a reasonable estimate of the area under $f(x) = \sqrt{x} + 2$ for $0 \le x \le 4$? **G**
   F. $\sum_{n=1}^{4} f(a_n)$ **G.** $\sum_{n=1}^{5} (0.2) f(a_n)$ **H.** $\sum_{n=1}^{8} (0.5) f(a_n)$ **J.** $\sum_{n=1}^{10} (0.4) f(a_n)$

Short Response

50. The area under a curve is estimated using inscribed rectangles and circumscribed rectangles. Explain why the mean of these two values might be a more accurate estimate than either one. **See margin.**

50. [2] The mean might be a better estimate since it is between the estimate using inscribed rectangles, which is too low, and the estimate using circumscribed rectangles, which is too high.

[1] incomplete explanation

Mixed Review

GO for Help

Lesson 11-5

Determine whether the sum of each infinite geometric series exists.

51. $4 + 2 + 1 + \frac{1}{2} + \frac{1}{4} + \dots$ **52.** $-972 - 324 - 108 - \dots$
   has a sum   **has a sum**

Lesson 10-5

Write the equation of each hyperbola in standard form. Sketch the graph.

53. $9x^2 - 16y^2 = 144$ **54.** $x^2 - 25y^2 = 25$ **55.** $16x^2 - 10y^2 = 160$
53–55. See margin.

53. $\frac{x^2}{16} - \frac{y^2}{9} = 1$;

54. $\frac{x^2}{25} - \frac{y^2}{1} = 1$;

55. $\frac{x^2}{10} - \frac{y^2}{16} = 1$;

Lesson 9-6

Solve each equation. Check your solution.

56. $\frac{x}{4} = \frac{x - 3}{8} - 3$ **57.** $\frac{5}{2 - x} = \frac{4}{2x + 1}$ $\frac{3}{14}$ **58.** $\frac{x}{x + 1} - \frac{x}{x - 3} = 9$ $\frac{7 \pm 2\sqrt{73}}{9}$

Using Estimation

Estimation is a useful skill in eliminating choices and in checking the reasonableness of answers obtained by using pencil and paper calculations or a calculator.

Guided Instruction

1 EXAMPLE Teaching Tip

A diagram can be very helpful in making sure you have taken all aspects of this situation into consideration. Estimation is helpful in eliminating answer choices A and B. You must be careful when you decide between C and D. Remember that when the ball bounces, it travels up a certain distance and then down that same distance before it bounces again.

Resources

SAT® and ACT® correlations are on page 598B.

Test-Taking Strategies with Transparencies
• Transparency 11
• Practice sheet, p. 35

Estimating the answer to a test question may help you eliminate one or more answers, find the answer, or check your answer.

1 EXAMPLE

A ball drops from a height of 2 m. After it hits the floor, it rebounds to 60% of its previous height. Find the total distance the ball travels before it comes to rest.

   (A) 3 m   (B) 3.5 m   (C) 5 m   (D) 10 m   (E) 20 m

Estimate the distance the ball travels before the second bounce. The ball rebounds about one-half its previous height, so it travels down 2 m, then up about 1 m, and then down about 1 m. Since $2 + 1 + 1 = 4$, the ball travels about 4 m before the second bounce. You can eliminate answer choices A and B.

Since the distance the ball travels on each bounce models a geometric sequence with $r < 1$, the final answer will be closer to 4 than to 10. The answer is C.

2 EXAMPLE

A student jogs 3.8 mi around a local reservoir five afternoons a week. The student claims to have run about 990 mi around the reservoir last year. Is the student correct? Explain.

$3.8 \cdot 5 \cdot 52 \approx 4 \cdot 5 \cdot 50$ **distance · days per week · weeks per year**

$\qquad\qquad = 20 \cdot 50 = 1000$ **Simplify and multiply.**

The student ran about 1000 mi around the reservoir last year. The student is correct.

EXERCISES

1. A square is inscribed in a circle. The square has side length 4 cm. What is the best estimate for the area of the circle? **B**
   (A) 50 cm^2 (B) 25 cm^2 (C) 16 cm^2 (D) 15 cm^2 (E) 12 cm^2

2. Which is the best approximation of the area of the region between the graph of $y = (x - 1)^2$, the x-axis, and the y-axis? **E**
   (A) 2 units^2 (B) 1.5 units^2 (C) 1 units^2 (D) 0.8 units^2 (E) 0.5 units^2

3. Which estimate is closest to the sum $1 + \frac{1}{4} + \frac{1}{16} \cdots + \frac{1}{1024}$? **C**
   (A) 2.00   (B) 1.50   (C) 1.33   (D) 0.5   (E) 0.33

Estimate the answer to each problem.

4. Suppose your aunt gives you $100 on your birthday, along with a promise to give you one half the previous year's amount each year until the amount reaches 1¢. What is the total amount of money that your aunt will give you? **$200**

5. If two numbers a and b are approximately equal, their arithmetic mean and their geometric mean are approximately equal. Use this fact to estimate the value of $\sqrt{56}$. **7.5**

Chapter Review

Vocabulary Review

))

arithmetic mean (p. 607)
arithmetic sequence (p. 606)
arithmetic series (p. 620)
circumscribed rectangles (p. 635)
common difference (p. 606)
common ratio (p. 612)

converge (p. 627)
diverge (p. 627)
explicit formula (p. 602)
geometric mean (p. 614)
geometric sequence (p. 612)
geometric series (p. 626)

inscribed rectangles (p. 635)
limit (p. 621)
recursive formula (p. 602)
sequence (p. 600)
series (p. 619)
term (p. 600)

.Go Online
PHSchool.com

For: Vocabulary quiz
Web Code: agj-1151

Choose the correct vocabulary term to complete each sentence.

1. When using Σ to write a series, you can use __?__ to indicate how many terms you are adding. **limits**

2. Using __?__ to approximate the area under a curve will result in an approximation that is greater than the area. **circumscribed rectangles**

3. An ordered list of terms is a __?__. **sequence**

4. If an infinite geometric series __?__, then it must have a sum. **converges**

5. There is a __?__ between consecutive terms in a geometric sequence. **common ratio**

Skills and Concepts

11-1 Objectives

▼ To identify mathematical patterns (p. 600)

▼ To use a formula for finding the nth term of a sequence (p. 602)

6. $a_n = a_{n-1} + 17, a_1 = 5$;
   73, 90, 107

7. $a_n = -7 \cdot a_{n-1}, a_1 = 1$;
   2401, −16,807, 117,649

8. $a_n = a_{n-1} + 9, a_1 = -2$; 34, 43, 52

A **sequence** is an ordered list of numbers called **terms.** A **recursive formula** gives the first term and defines the other terms in a sequence by relating each term to the one before it. An **explicit formula** expresses the nth term in a sequence in terms of n, where n is a positive integer.

Write a recursive formula for each sequence. Then find the next three terms.

6. 5, 22, 39, 56, . . .   **7.** 1, −7, 49, −343, . . .   **8.** −2, 7, 16, 25, . . .

Write an explicit formula for each sequence. Then find a_{12}.

9. 1, 4, 7, 10, . . .
$a_n = 3n - 2$; 34

10. 2, 4, 8, 16, . . .
$a_n = 2^n$; 4096

11. −24, −6, 24, 66, . . .
$a_n = 6n^2 - 30$; 834

12. Writing Explain how you decide whether a formula is explicit or recursive.
See margin.

11-2 Objectives

▼ To identify and generate arithmetic sequences (p. 606)

In an **arithmetic sequence,** the difference between consecutive terms is constant. The difference is the **common difference.** A recursive formula for an arithmetic sequence is $a_n = a_{n-1} + d$, given a_1. An explicit formula for an arithmetic sequence is $a_n = a_1 + (n - 1)d$. In each case, a_n is the nth term, a_1 is the first term, n is the number of the term, and d is the common difference. The **arithmetic mean** of any two numbers (or terms in a sequence) is the average of the two numbers.

$$\text{arithmetic mean} = \frac{\text{sum of two numbers}}{2}$$

12. Answers may vary. Sample: If the formula uses the previous term, then it is recursive; otherwise it is explicit.

34. $\sum\limits_{n=1}^{5} (13 - 3n)$; 20

35. $\sum\limits_{n=1}^{7} (45 + 5n)$; 455

36. $\sum\limits_{n=1}^{11} (4.6 + 1.4n)$; 143

37. $\sum\limits_{n=1}^{8} (23 - 2n)$; 112

Is each given sequence arithmetic? If so, identify the common difference and find the 32nd term of the sequence.

13. 2, 4, 7, 10, 13, . . . **no**
14. 3, 18, 33, 48, . . .
yes; $d = 15$; $a_{32} = 468$
15. 7, 10, 13, 16, . . .
yes; $d = 3$; $a_{32} = 100$

Find the missing term(s) of each arithmetic sequence.

16. 1, ■, 9, . . . **5**
17. 104, ■, 99, . . . **101.5**
18. −4.6, ■, −5.2, . . . $\overset{-4.9}{}$

19. −1, ■, 11, . . . **5**
20. −13, ■, ■, ■, −3, . . .
−10.5, −8, −5.5
21. 2, ■, ■, ■, −0.4, . . .
1.4, 0.8, 0.2

Find a_n, the arithmetic mean of the given terms.

22. $a_{n-1} = 7, a_{n+1} = 15$ **11**
23. $a_{n-1} = -2, a_{n+1} = 3$ **0.5**

 24. Writing Explain how you can determine if a sequence is arithmetic.
If the terms of the sequence have a common difference, then the sequence is arithmetic.

11-3 Objectives

▼ To identify and generate geometric sequences (p. 612)

In a **geometric sequence,** the ratio of consecutive terms is constant. The ratio is the **common ratio.** You can use recursive or explicit formulas to express a geometric sequence.

A recursive formula for a geometric sequence is $a_n = a_{n-1} \cdot r$, given a_1. An explicit formula for a geometric sequence is $a_n = a_1 \cdot r^{n-1}$. In each case, a_n is the nth term, a_1 is the first term, n is the number of the term, and r is the common ratio.

You can find the geometric mean of two positive numbers by taking the positive square root of the product of the two numbers.

$$\text{geometric mean} = \sqrt{\text{product of two numbers}}$$

25. yes; $r = \frac{1}{2}$, $a_n = 1\left(\frac{1}{2}\right)^{n-1}$, $\frac{1}{16}, \frac{1}{32}$

26. no

27. yes; $r = 1.2$, $a_n = 3(1.2)^{n-1}$, 6.2208, 7.46496

31. ±10, −5, ±2.5

32. $\pm\frac{1}{3}, -\frac{2}{3}, \pm\frac{4}{3}$

33. $\pm 3\frac{1}{2}, 12\frac{1}{4}, \pm 42\frac{7}{8}$

The middle term of any three consecutive terms in a geometric sequence is the geometric mean of the first and third terms.

Is the given sequence geometric? If so, identify the common ratio, write the explicit formula for the sequence, and find the next two terms.

25. 1, $\frac{1}{2}, \frac{1}{4}, \frac{1}{8}$, . . .
26. 1, 3, 5, 7, . . .
27. 3, 3.6, 4.32, 5.184, . . .

Find the missing term(s) of each geometric sequence.

28. 3, ■, 12, . . . **±6**
29. 60, ■, $\frac{20}{3}$, . . . **±20**
30. 0.004, ■, 0.4, . . . $\overset{\pm 0.04}{}$

31. −20, ■, ■, ■, −1.25, . . .
32. $-\frac{1}{6}$, ■, ■, ■, $-2\frac{2}{3}$, . . .
33. 1, ■, ■, ■, $150\frac{1}{16}$, . . .

11-4 Objectives

▼ To write and evaluate arithmetic series (p. 619)

▼ To use summation notation (p. 621)

A **series** is the expression for the sum of the terms of a sequence. Whether the sequence is finite or infinite determines whether the series is finite or infinite.

An **arithmetic series** is the expression for the sum of the terms of an arithmetic sequence. The sum S_n of the first n terms of an arithmetic series is $S_n = \frac{n}{2}(a_1 + a_n)$.

You can use a summation symbol, Σ, and **limits** to write a series. Limits are the least and greatest integral values of n.

Use summation notation to write each arithmetic series for the specified number of terms. Then evaluate the sum. 34–37. See margin.

34. $10 + 7 + 4 + \dots$; $n = 5$
35. $50 + 55 + 60 + \dots$; $n = 7$

36. $6 + 7.4 + 8.8 + \dots$; $n = 11$
37. $21 + 19 + 17 + \dots$; $n = 8$

Find the number of terms in each series, the first term, and the last term. Then evaluate the sum.

38. $\displaystyle\sum_{n=1}^{3}(17n-25)$ **39.** $\displaystyle\sum_{n=2}^{10}\left(\frac{1}{2}n+3\right)$ **40.** $\displaystyle\sum_{n=5}^{15}\left(-\frac{2}{3}n\right)$

11, $-\frac{10}{3}$, -10; $-\frac{220}{3}$

3, −8, 26; 27   **9, 4, 8; 54**

 41. Business Deanna Jones opened a video rental store this year with 400 tapes. She plans to buy 150 new tapes each year from now on. Deanna expects to have 1300 tapes available during her fifth year in business. At her current purchasing rate, will she reach her goal? Explain. **No; she will have only 1150 available by the end of the fifth year.**

11-5 Objectives

▼ To evaluate a finite geometric series (p. 626)

▼ To evaluate an infinite geometric series (p. 627)

A **geometric series** is the sum of the terms of a geometric sequence. The sum S_n of the first n terms of a geometric series is $S_n = \dfrac{a_1(1-r^n)}{1-r}$.

You can find the sum of some infinite geometric series. When $|r| < 1$, the series gets closer and closer, or **converges**, to $S = \dfrac{a_1}{1-r}$. When $|r| \geq 1$, the series **diverges**, or approaches no limit.

Evaluate the finite series for the specified number of terms.

42. $3 + 1 + \frac{1}{3} + \ldots\,; n = 7$ $4\frac{121}{243}$ **43.** $1 + 2 + 4 + \ldots\,; n = 5$ **31**

44. $80 - 40 + 20 - \ldots\,; n = 8$ **53.125**   **45.** $12 + 2 + \frac{1}{3} + \ldots\,; n = 4$ $14\frac{7}{18}$

Decide whether each infinite geometric series *converges* or *diverges*. Then state whether each series has a sum, and if it does, find the sum.

46. converges; S = 187.5

47. diverges; no sum

46. $150 + 30 + 6 + \ldots$ **47.** $2.2 + 2.42 + 2.662 + \ldots$

48. $-10 - 20 - 40 - \ldots$ **49.** $\frac{2}{3} + \frac{4}{9} + \frac{8}{27} + \ldots$

diverges; no sum   **converges; S = 2**

11-6 Objective

▼ To find the area under a curve (p. 635)

You can approximate the area under a curve by using **inscribed rectangles** or **circumscribed rectangles.** If you use inscribed rectangles, the approximation is less than the area under the curve. If you use circumscribed rectangles, the approximation is greater than the area under the curve. You can use summation notation to represent the area of a series of rectangles and the approximate area under a curve $f(x)$:

$$A = \sum_{n=1}^{b}(w)f(a_n),$$

where b is the number of rectangles, w is the width of each rectangle, a_n is the x-value of a point on the base of the nth rectangle, and $f(a_n)$ is the function value at a_n.

Write and evaluate a sum to approximate the area under each curve for the domain $0 \leq x \leq 2$.   50–55. See margin.

a. Use inscribed rectangles 1 unit wide.

b. Use circumscribed rectangles 1 unit wide.

c. Use a graphing calculator to find the area under the curve.

50. $y = x^2$ **51.** $y = x^3 + 1$ **52.** $y = -2x^2 + 8$

53. $y = -x + 5$ **54.** $y = x^3 + 4$ **55.** $y = x^2 + 3$

Chapter 11   Chapter Review   **643**

50. $A = \displaystyle\sum_{n=1}^{2} 1 \cdot f(a_n)$

a. 1 unit²

b. 5 units²

c. $\frac{8}{3}$ units²

51. $A = \displaystyle\sum_{n=1}^{2} 1 \cdot f(a_n)$

a. 3 units²

b. 11 units²

c. 6 units²

52. $A = \displaystyle\sum_{n=1}^{2} 1 \cdot f(a_n)$

a. 6 units²

b. 14 units²

c. $10.\overline{6}$ units²

53. $A = \displaystyle\sum_{n=1}^{2} 1 \cdot f(a_n)$

a. 7 units²

b. 9 units²

c. 8 units²

54. $A = \displaystyle\sum_{n=1}^{2} 1 \cdot f(a_n)$

a. 9 units²

b. 17 units²

c. 12 units²

55. $A = \displaystyle\sum_{n=1}^{2} 1 \cdot f(a_n)$

a. 7 units²

b. 11 units²

c. $8\frac{2}{3}$ units²

Chapter 11

Chapter Test

Go Online
PHSchool.com
For: Chapter Test
Web Code: aga-1152

Write a recursive and an explicit formula for each sequence. Then find a_{12}. 1–3. See margin.

1. $7, 13, 19, 25, 31, \ldots$

2. $10, 20, 40, 80, 160, \ldots$

3. After one month at a new job, you have saved $50. You decide to save $5 more each month.
  a. Write an explicit formula to model the amounts you save each month.
  b. How much will you save in the sixth month?

Determine whether each sequence is *arithmetic*, *geometric*, or *neither*. Then find the tenth term.

4. $23, 27, 31, 35, 39, \ldots$ arithmetic; 59

5. $-12, -5, 2, 9, 16, \ldots$ arithmetic; 51

6. $-5, 15, -45, 135, -405, \ldots$ geometric; 98,415

Find the arithmetic mean a_n of the given terms.

7. $a_{n-1} = 4, a_{n+1} = 12$ **8**

8. $a_{n-1} = -11, a_{n+1} = 23$ **6**

9. Open-Ended Write an arithmetic sequence. Then write an explicit formula for it.
Check students' work.

Determine whether each sequence is *arithmetic* or *geometric*. Then identify the common difference or the common ratio.

10. $1620, 540, 180, 60, 20, \ldots$ geometric; $r = \frac{1}{3}$

11. $78, 75, 72, 69, 66, 63, 60, \ldots$ arithmetic; $d = -3$

12. $\frac{3}{32}, \frac{3}{16}, \frac{3}{8}, \frac{3}{4}, \frac{3}{2}, 3, 6, \ldots$ geometric; $r = 2$

In Exercises 13–16, a_1 is the first term of a sequence, r is a common ratio, and d is a common difference. Write the first five terms. 13–15. See margin.

13. $a_1 = 2, r = -2$

14. $a_1 = 3, d = 7$

15. $a_1 = -100, r = \frac{1}{5}$

16. $a_1 = 19, d = -4$
19, 15, 11, 7, 3

Find the missing term of each geometric sequence.

17. $2, \blacksquare, 0.5, \ldots$ **1**

18. $2, \blacksquare, 8, \ldots$ **4**

Find the sum of each infinite geometric series.

19. $0.5 + 0.05 + 0.005 + \ldots$ $\frac{5}{9}$

20. $1 - \frac{1}{2} + \frac{1}{4} - \ldots$ $\frac{2}{3}$

21. $6 + 5 + \frac{25}{6} + \ldots$ **36**

Determine whether each series is *arithmetic* or *geometric*. Then evaluate the finite series for the specified number of terms.

22. $2 + 7 + 12 + \ldots; n = 8$ arithmetic; 156

23. $5000 + 1000 + 200 + \ldots; n = 15$ geometric; 6250

24. $1 + 0.01 - 0.98 - \ldots; n = 5$ arithmetic; -4.9

For each sum, find the number of terms, the first term, and the last term. Then evaluate the sum.

25. $\sum_{n=1}^{5} (3n + 1)$ 5, 4, 16; 50

26. $\sum_{n=1}^{8} \frac{2n}{3}$ 8, $\frac{2}{3}$, $\frac{16}{3}$; 24

27. $\sum_{n=4}^{10} (0.8n - 0.4)$ 7, 2.8, 7.6; 36.4

28. $\sum_{n=2}^{6} (-2)^{n-1}$ 5, -2, -32; -22

29. Critical Thinking How can you tell whether or not a geometric series converges? Include examples of both types of series. Evaluate the series that converges. **See margin.**

30. Investments A diamond is purchased for $2500. Suppose its value increases 5% each year. Find the value of the diamond after 8 years. **$3693.64**

31. Physics A ball on a pendulum moves 40 cm on its first swing. On each succeeding swing back or forth it moves 90% of the distance of the previous swing. Write the first four terms of the sequence of swing lengths. **40 cm, 36 cm, 32.4 cm, 29.16 cm**

Given each set of axes, what does the area under the curve represent?

32. y-axis: miles per hour, x-axis: hours **miles**

33. y-axis: pounds per in.^{2}, x-axis: in.^{2} **pounds**

34. y-axis: dollars per gallon, x-axis: gallons **dollars**

Use left endpoints in the given interval and inscribed rectangles 1 unit wide to approximate the area under the curve $y = f(x)$. 35–38. See back of book.

35. $y = 2x^2; 0 \le x \le 2$

36. $y = x^3; 1 \le x \le 3$

37. $y = x^2 + 1; -1 \le x \le 2$

38. Writing Explain how you could use circumscribed and inscribed rectangles to estimate the area under a curve.

1. $a_n = a_{n-1} + 6, a_1 = 7,$ $a_n = 1 + 6n$; 73

2. $a_n = a_{n-1} \cdot 2, a_1 = 10,$ $a_n = 10 \cdot 2^{n-1}$; 20,480

3a. savings $= 50 + 5($months $- 1)$

b. $75

13. $2, -4, 8, -16, 32$

14. $3, 10, 17, 24, 31$

15. $-100, -20, -4, -\frac{4}{5}, -\frac{4}{25}$

29. If the absolute value of the common ratio is less than 1, then it will converge; check students' work.

Standardized Test Prep

Reading Comprehension Read the passage below. Then answer the questions on the basis of what is *stated* or *implied* in the passage.

Arcs To cut an arc-topped shape from a rectangular board, carpenters may choose a circular arc or an elliptical arc.

Suppose the length of the board is $2m$ and the height is n.

For a circular arc, the carpenter can find the radius of the circle by using the formula $r = \frac{m^2 + n^2}{2n}$. Using a tack at the center C, and a piece of string of length r, the carpenter can draw a circular arc through points P, T, and Q.

For an elliptical arc, the carpenter can find points A and B on $\overline{PQ}$ that are $\sqrt{m^2 - n^2}$ units from point Z. Using tacks at A and B and a piece of string of length $2m$, the carpenter can draw an elliptical arc through points P, T, and Q.

Students must be able to extract information from reading passages, answer multiple choice questions, and construct responses in order to be successful on current state and national assessments.

To answer the questions, students apply skills and concepts from this chapter and previous chapters.
Multiple Choice: Items 1–5
Extended Response: Items 6–9

Resources

Test Prep Workbook

Grab & Go
• **L3** Cumulative Review

ExamView CD-ROM
• Standardized Test Practice

Differentiated Instruction **Resources**

Spanish Assessment Resources
• **L3** Spanish Cumulative Review

1. What is the value of PQ?
C
(A) $m + n$ (B) $2n$
(C) $2m$ (D) $\sqrt{m^2 + n^2}$

2. For a circular arc, what is the distance from **G** point C to point Z?
(F) r (G) $r - n$
(H) $r - m$ (J) $\frac{m^2 + n^2}{2n}$

3. Suppose $m = 21$ in. and $n = 7$ in. For a **D** circular arc, what length of string should the carpenter use?
(A) 19.8 in.   (B) 22.1 in.
(C) 28 in.   (D) 35 in.

4. Suppose $\overline{PQ}$ is on the x-axis of a coordinate **J** system and $\overline{TZ}$ is on the y-axis. What are the coordinates of the foci of the ellipse needed to draw an elliptical arc?
(F) $(m, 0)$ and $(-m, 0)$
(G) $(0, n)$ and $(0, -n)$
(H) $(\sqrt{m^2 + n^2}, 0)$ and $(-\sqrt{m^2 + n^2}, 0)$
(J) $(\sqrt{m^2 - n^2}, 0)$ and $(-\sqrt{m^2 - n^2}, 0)$

5. Suppose $m = 70$ cm and $n = 9$ cm. For an **C** elliptical arc, what length of string should the carpenter use?
(A) 18 cm   (B) 70.58 cm
(C) 140 cm   (D) 276.72 cm

6. Use the Pythagorean Theorem and a diagram of a circular arc to derive the formula $r = \frac{m^2 + n^2}{2n}$.
See margin.

7. A carpenter wants to cut the largest possible circular arc-topped shape from a board that is 40 in. by 12 in. Find the length of string the carpenter should use. $22\frac{2}{3}$ in.

8. Using a board the same size as the one in Question 7, a carpenter wants to cut the largest possible elliptical arc-topped shape. What length of string should the carpenter use? Where should the carpenter attach the string? **See margin.**

9. A board is 30 in. by 15 in. Compare the largest circular and elliptical arc-topped shapes that can be cut from the board. **They are the same.**

6.

Consider $\triangle ZQC$.
$r^2 = m^2 + (r - n)^2$
$r^2 = m^2 + r^2 - 2nr + n^2$
$r^2 - r^2 + 2nr = m^2 + r^2$
$\quad - 2nr + n^2 - r^2 + 2nr$
$2nr = m^2 + n^2$
$r = \frac{m^2 + n^2}{2n}$

8. 40 in.; one end should be attached 16 in. from point Z along $\overline{PZ}$, and the other end should be attached 16 in. from point Z along $\overline{QZ}$.

Probability and Statistics

Chapter at a Glance

Lesson Titles, Objectives, and Features	Assessment	NCTM Standards	Local Standards
12-1 Probability Distributions • Making a probability distribution • Using a probability distribution in conducting a simulation	Lesson Quiz	2, 5, 10	
12-2 Conditional Probability • Finding conditional probability • Using formulas and tree diagrams **Extension:** Comparing Conditional Probabilities	Lesson Quiz	2, 5, 10	
12-3 Analyzing Data • Calculating measures of central tendency • Drawing and interpreting box-and-whisker plots	Lesson Quiz Checkpoint Quiz 1	2, 4, 5	
12-4 Standard Deviation • Finding the standard deviation of a set of values • Using standard deviation in real-world situations **GPS:** Understanding Math Problems **Activity Lab:** Continuous Probability	Lesson Quiz	2, 4, 5, 10	
12-5 Working With Samples • Finding sample proportions • Finding the margin of error **Vocabulary Builder:** Variable and Parameter	Lesson Quiz	2, 4, 5, 6	
12-6 Binomial Distributions • Finding binomial probabilities • Using binomial distributions	Lesson Quiz Checkpoint Quiz 2	2, 5, 6, 8, 9	
12-7 Normal Distributions • Using a normal distribution • Using the standard normal curve **Activity Lab:** Technology: Area Under a Curve	Lesson Quiz	2, 5, 6, 8, 9	
Activity Lab: Applying Sequences			

NCTM Standards 2000

1 Number and Operations	**2** Algebra	**3** Geometry	**4** Measurement	**5** Data Analysis and Probability
6 Problem Solving	**7** Reasoning and Proof	**8** Communication	**9** Connections	**10** Representation

Correlations to Standardized Tests

All content for these tests is contained in *Prentice Hall Algebra 2*. This chart reflects coverage in this chapter only.

	12-1	12-2	12-3	12-4	12-5	12-6	12-7
SAT®							
Number and Operations Operations, ratio & proportions, complex numbers, counting, elementary number theory, matrices, sequences	✔	✔	✔	✔	✔	✔	✔
Algebra and Functions Expressions, equations, inequalities, representation and modeling, properties of functions (linear, polynomial, rational, exponential)							
Geometry and Measurement *Plane Euclidean/Measurement Coordinate* Lines, parabolas, circles, symmetry, transformations *Three-dimensional* Solids, surface area & volume (cylinders, cones, pyramids, spheres, prisms) *Trigonometry* Right triangles, identities							
Data Analysis, Statistics, and Probability Mean, median, mode, range, interquartile range, graphs and plots, regression, probability	✔	✔	✔	✔	✔		
ACT®							
Pre-Algebra Basic operations using whole numbers, decimals, fractions, and integers; place value; square roots and approximations; the concept of exponents; scientific notation; factors, ratio, proportion, and percent; linear equations in one variable; absolute value and ordering numbers by value; elementary counting techniques and simple probability; data collection, representation, and interpretation; and understanding simple descriptive statistics.			✔	✔	✔		
Elementary Algebra Properties of exponents and square roots, evaluation of algebraic expressions through substitution, using variables to express functional relationships, understanding algebraic operations, and solving quadratic equations by factoring.	✔	✔		✔	✔	✔	✔
Intermediate Algebra Understanding of the quadratic formula, rational and radical expressions, absolute value equations and inequalities, sequences and patterns, systems of equations, quadratic inequalities, functions, modeling, matrices, roots of polynomials, and complex numbers.							
Coordinate Geometry Graphing and the relations between equations and graphs, including points, lines, polynomials, circles, and other curves; graphing inequalities; slope; parallel and perpendicular lines; distance; midpoints; and conics.							
Plane Geometry Properties and relations of plane figures, including angles and relations among perpendicular and parallel lines; properties of circles, triangles, rectangles, parallelograms, and trapezoids; transformations; the concept of proof and proof techniques; volume; and applications of geometry to three dimensions.							
Trigonometry Understanding trigonometric relations in right triangles; values and properties of trigonometric functions; graphing trigonometric functions; modeling using trigonometric functions; use of trigonometric identities; and solving trigonometric equations.							
NAEP							
Number Sense, Properties, and Operations							
Measurement							
Geometry and Spatial Sense							
Data Analysis, Statistics, and Probability	✔	✔	✔	✔	✔	✔	✔
Algebra and Functions							

SAT® The College Board, SAT® Reasoning Test   **ACT®** The ACT Assessment® Test   **NAEP** National Assessment of Educational Progress, 2005 Mathematics Objectives

Math Background

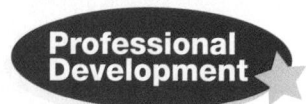

Skills Trace

> ### BEFORE Chapter 12
> In previous chapters, students found experimental and theoretical probabilities and probabilities of multiple events.
>
> ### DURING Chapter 12
> Students make and use probability distributions, find conditional probabilities, and analyze data using measures of central tendency and measures of variation.
>
> ### AFTER Chapter 12
> Students will model data using trigonometric functions and solve real-world problems using the Laws of Sines and Cosines.

Chapter Overview

The study of probability and statistics emerged in the seventeenth and eighteenth centuries. Their development was motivated by studies of games of chance, errors in measurements, and numerical data about political units such as cities and counties. Formal development has continued since then and both have found numerous applications in many fields of human endeavor. This chapter introduces students to probability distributions, ways of organizing and displaying data, and measures of central tendency. Students study measures of variation to describe how data in a data set are spread out. They consider samples and the relationship between sample size and margin of error. Finally, they learn about binomial experiments, binomial distributions, and normal distributions.

Probability Distributions 12-1

Have students discuss what they think is the most likely sum for rolling two number cubes. Students often guess a sum of 7, which is half-way between the maximum and minimum sums of 12 and 2. But why is 7 the most likely sum? A frequency table showing a probability distribution answers this question. The related bar graph nicely illustrates this discrete probability function. Probability distributions are then applied to simulations and will be used in the rest of this chapter.

Conditional Probability 12-2

Deciding the likelihood of an event can be influenced by knowing that some other event has taken place. The *conditional probability* of B, given that event A has taken place, or $P(B \mid A)$, is the fraction of those times when A happens that event B also happens. The definition is an extension of the original definition of a probability as the ratio of favorable outcomes to total possible outcomes. Here, 'total possible outcomes' is the restricted sample space where B occurs. For example, a 6-sided number cube is rolled. If an even number is rolled, what is the probability of the number being a 2? The result shown below indicates the conditional probability is higher than it would be if the other event was not given.

$$P(B \mid A) = \frac{P(A \text{ and } B)}{P(A)} \qquad P(2 \mid \text{even}) = \frac{P(2)}{P(\text{even})} = \frac{\frac{1}{6}}{\frac{1}{2}} = \frac{1}{3}$$

Analyzing Data 12-3

As a society, we are somewhat obsessed with data. Newspaper articles, television news reports, and advertisements are common places to find data and statistics presented as factual support for certain conclusions. Because we are bombarded with so much data, it is important to be able to analyze data, in order to make our own conclusions about the data. The measures of central tendency that are presented in this lesson provide several such ways to analyze data.

The mean is most affected by outliers, and the median and mode are generally not affected by outliers. Because a mode may not be near the center of the data set at all, medians become a particularly helpful measure of central tendency when the data set has outliers. In fact, many statisticians do not include the mode as a measure of *central* tendency. This is understandable because there can be no mode, one mode, and more than one mode. Modes however are helpful with non-numerical data sets, such as finding the most common color for automobiles in a parking lot. Also, modes are always actual data values when the mean and median are not necessarily actual data values.

Standard Deviation 12-4

The *range* of a data set is not to be confused with the *range* of a function or relation. The range of a data set is the distribution statistic that is analogous to the mode for central tendency. This is because the range takes only the maximum and minimum values into account, and gives a rather crude picture of the distribution of data. The interquartile range gives the range of the middle 50% of data values and is analogous to the median for central tendency.

Finally, the standard deviation takes all the data values into account and is analogous to the mean for central tendency.

When we say that the standard deviation for a set of data is large or small, it is important to interpret this qualitatively in relation to the size of the median value. This will become clearer when students study Lesson 12-7 and normal distribution curves; large standard deviations have wide or flat distribution curves while small standard deviations have narrow or tall distribution curves.

Some calculators provide a list of one-variable statistics when a set of data is entered. The statistics may include mean, sum of data values, sum of squared data values, sample standard deviation, population standard deviation, number of data points, minimum value, maximum value, median, first quartile, and third quartile.

Working With Samples   12-5

The term *population* is used in statistics as a carryover from the time when statistics was used mainly to study sociological and economical phenomena. Today, the term is applied to sets or collections of objects, actual or conceptual, and mainly to sets of numbers, measurements, or observations—in any case, the data to be studied. A *sample* is simply part of the population—a subset of the possible data.

Sampling procedures that are based on random processes provide every element of the population with an equal and independent chance of being chosen. Such procedures aim to provide information about the sample that can be generalized to the population. Random sampling procedures can be contrasted with sampling that is not based on random processes—for example, questionnaires, which are more susceptible to *bias*. To illustrate, a person who responds to a questionnaire *voluntarily* provides information and may be more likely to have a strong opinion than a person who chooses not to respond to the questionnaire. In this situation the sample and the total population may differ significantly.

Understanding samples is crucial to interpreting data. In today's world, surveys are commonly used to sway public opinion. The validity of a survey, however, depends on the sample. Being able to understand samples will help students interpret the surveys they hear about on the news or read about in the newspaper.

Binomial Distributions   12-6

When you flip a coin, the outcome is either heads or tails. When you guess someone's birth month, you are either right or wrong. In each situation, the event has two mutually exclusive possible outcomes. One of the possible outcomes can be designated *success* and the other outcome *failure*. Thus, the probability of success p and the probability of failure q must together make 100%, or $p + q = 1$. If the event is repeated for n trials, then a binomial distribution can be used to determine the probability of exactly x successes using combinations and $_nC_x p^x q^{n-x}$. This formula assumes that events have:

- only two possible outcomes,

- mutually exclusive outcomes, and

- repeated independent trials (or randomly selected).

Normal Distributions   12-7

Note that the binomial distribution is not identical to the normal distribution but can only be approximated by it under certain conditions. The greater the number of trials n and the closer the value of the probability of success p is to 0.5, the better the approximation will be. The *standard* normal distribution is the normal distribution with mean 0 and standard deviation 1. You may wish to tell students that the equation for the standard normal distribution is $y = \frac{1}{\sqrt{2\pi}} e^{\frac{-x^2}{2}}$. As is necessary for a probability distribution, the total area between the x-axis and the curve is one—another example of a limiting value, since the curve does not touch the x-axis.

Students can easily compute the exact percentages for the various regions under the normal curve. Some students may observe that $P(z < a) = P(z \le a)$. In terms of area, the inclusion of $z = a$ makes no difference—a line has no width. Various practical problems may or may not include an endpoint of the interval.

Additional Professional Development Opportunities

Math Background notes for Chapter 12: Every lesson has a Math Background in the PLAN section.

Research Overview, Mathematical Strands
Additional support for these topics and more is in the front of this Teacher's Edition.

Lesson Lab
Lesson Lab, a Pearson Education company, offers comprehensive, facilitated professional development designed to help teachers improve student achievement. To learn more, please visit lessonlab.com

Chapter 12 Resources

Print Resources	12-1	12-2	12-3	12-4	12-5	12-6	12-7	For the Chapter
L3 Practice	●	●	●	●	●	●	●	
L3 Guided Problem Solving	●	●	●	●	●	●	●	
L2 Reteaching	●	●	●	●	●	●	●	
L4 Enrichment	●	●	●	●	●	●	●	
L3 Daily Notetaking Guide	●	●	●	●	●	●	●	
L3 Vocabulary and Study Skills Worksheets	●							●
L3 Chapter Project								●
L3 Hands On Activities	●					●		
L3 Checkpoint Quiz			●			●		
L2 Below Level Chapter Test								●
L3 Chapter Test								●
L4 Alternative Assessment								●
L3 Cumulative Review								●
L4 Connections to Precalculus Masters	●	●	●	●	●	●	●	
L3 Technology Activities								

Spanish Resources ELL	12-1	12-2	12-3	12-4	12-5	12-6	12-7	For the Chapter
L3 Practice	●	●	●	●	●	●	●	
L3 Vocabulary and Study Skills Worksheets	●							●
L3 Checkpoint Quiz			●			●		
L2 Below Level Chapter Test								●
L3 Chapter Test								●
L4 Alternative Assessment								
L3 Cumulative Review								●

Transparencies	12-1	12-2	12-3	12-4	12-5	12-6	12-7	For the Chapter
Check Skills You'll Need	●	●	●	●	●	●	●	
Additional Examples	●	●	●	●	●	●	●	
Problem of the Day	●	●	●	●	●	●	●	
Classroom Aid			●					
Student Edition Answers	●	●	●	●	●	●	●	●
Lesson Quiz	●	●	●	●	●	●	●	
Test-Taking Strategies								●

Technology	12-1	12-2	12-3	12-4	12-5	12-6	12-7	For the Chapter
TI 83/84 Plus Activities								
Interactive Textbook Online	●	●	●	●	●	●	●	●
Student Express CD-ROM	●	●	●	●	●	●	●	
TI Navigator, Instant Check System	●	●	●	●	●	●	●	
Success Tracker	●	●	●	●	●	●	●	●
ExamView CD-ROM with Quick Take	●	●	●	●	●	●	●	●
Teacher Express CD-ROM	●	●	●	●	●	●	●	●
Presentation Express CD-ROM	●	●	●	●	●	●	●	●
Mindpoint Quiz Show CD-ROM	●	●	●	●	●	●	●	●
Prentice Hall Web site: PHSchool.com	●	●	●	●	●	●	●	●

Also available: Prentice Hall Assessment System (Progress Monitoring Assessments, Skills and Concepts Review, Test Prep Workbook)   Solution Key   Student Workbook
Student Workbook, Adapted Version   Data Analysis and Probability Workbook   Math Notes Study Folder   Spanish Cumulative Assessment

Where You Can Use the Lesson Resources

Here is a suggestion, following the four-step teaching plan, for how you can incorporate Differentiated Instruction Resources into your teaching.

	Instructional Resources L3	Differentiated Instruction Resources
1. Plan		
Check Skills You'll Need Assign these exercises to review prerequisite skills. **New Vocabulary** Help students pre-read the lesson by pointing out the new terms introduced in the lesson.	**Math Background** **Transparencies & Presentation Express CD** Check Skills You'll Need **Resources** Vocabulary and Study Skills	**Spanish Support** **ELL** Vocabulary and Study Skills
2. Teach		
L3 Guided Instruction Teach each Example. After each Example, assign the Quick Check exercise for that Example.	**Student Edition** Activity Lab **Resources** Daily Notetaking Guide Activity Lab TI-83/84 Activities CD-ROM **Transparencies & Presentation Express CD** Additional Examples Classroom Aids **ExamView CD-ROM with QuickTake** **TI Navigator Instant Check System**	**Teacher's Edition** Every lesson includes suggestions for working with students who need special attention. **L1** Special Needs **L2** Below Level **L4** Advanced Learners **ELL** English Language Learners
3. Practice		

Assignment Guide
 	
Homework Exercises
Assign the exercises cited in each lesson's Assignment Guide.
  A Practice by Example
  B Apply Your Skills
  C Challenge
  Test Prep
  Mixed Review
 	
Homework Quick Check
Discuss in class the exercises cited in each lesson's Assignment Guide.
	Transparencies & Presentation Express CD
	Student Answers
	
	Resources
	Practice
	Guided Problem Solving
	Vocabulary and Study Skills
	Activity Lab
	
	ExamView CD-ROM with QuickTake
		Spanish Support
		ELL Practice
		ELL Vocabulary and Study Skills
		
		Resources
		L4 Enrichment

4. Assess & Reteach		
Lesson Quiz Assign the Lesson Quiz to assess students' mastery of the lesson content. **Checkpoint Quiz** Use the Checkpoint Quiz to assess student progress over several lessons.	**Transparencies & Presentation Express CD** Lesson Quiz **Resources** Checkpoint Quiz	**Resources** **L2** Reteaching **ELL** Checkpoint Quiz Success Tracker **ExamView CD-ROM with QuickTake**

KEY   **L1** Special Needs   **L2** Below Level   **L3** For All Students   **L4** Advanced, Gifted   **ELL** English Language Learners

Chapter 12

Probability and Statistics

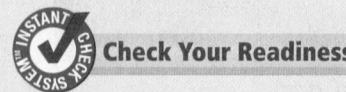
Check Your Readiness

Answers are in the back of the textbook.

For intervention, direct students to:

Evaluating Expressions
Lesson 6-7: Example 3
Extra Skills and Word
  Problems Practice, Ch. 6

Expanding Binomials
Lesson 6-8: Example 2
Extra Skills and Word
  Problems Practice, Ch. 6

Finding Real Roots
Lesson 7-1: Example 1
Extra Skills and Word
  Problems Practice, Ch. 7

Finding Probability
Lesson 9-7: Example 2
Extra Skills and Word
  Problems Practice, Ch. 9

What You've Learned

● In Chapter 1, you learned to find theoretical and experimental probabilities.

● In Chapter 6, you learned to use the Binomial Theorem.

● In Chapter 9, you learned to find the probability of multiple events.

Check Your Readiness   **for Help** to the Lesson in green.

Evaluating Expressions (Lesson 6-7)

Evaluate each expression.

1. $5!$ **120** **2.** $6!$ **720** **3.** $4! \cdot 3!$ **144**

4. $_5C_5$ **1** **5.** $_6C_1$ **6** **6.** $_7C_4$ **35**

Expanding Binomials (Lesson 6-8)

Use Pascal's Triangle or the Binomial Theorem to expand each binomial. **7–10. See margin.**

7. $(a + b)^5$ **8.** $(j + 3k)^3$ **9.** $(m + 0.7)^2$ **10.** $(0.2 + t)^6$

Finding Real Roots (Lesson 7-1)

Find the real square roots of each number. Round to the nearest thousandth.

11. $\frac{1}{100}$ **±0.1** **12.** $\frac{1}{200}$ **±0.071** **13.** $\frac{1}{250}$ **±0.063**
14. $\frac{1}{391}$ **±0.051** **15.** $\frac{1}{435}$ **±0.048** **16.** $\frac{1}{757}$ **±0.036**

Finding Probability (Lesson 9-7)

A and B are independent events. Find $P(A \text{ and } B)$.

17. $P(A) = 0.4, P(B) = 0.2$ **18.** $P(A) = 0.25, P(B) = 0.5$ **19.** $P(A) = 0.85, P(B) = 0.10$
  0.08 **0.125** **0.085**

20. Find $P(A \text{ or } B)$ for the events in Exercise 19. **0.865**

 21. Data Analysis While processing a day's worth of new checkbook orders, a data entry operator notices that thirty percent of customers prefer the leather checkbook cover to the vinyl checkbook cover. Twenty percent prefer script lettering on their checks to any other kind of lettering. Find the probability that an order selected at random is for a leather checkbook cover with script lettering on the checks. **0.06**

646 Chapter 12

7. $a^5 + 5a^4b + 10a^3b^2 + 10a^2b^3 + 5ab^4 + b^5$

8. $j^3 + 9j^2k + 27jk^2 + 27k^3$

9. $m^2 + 1.4m + 0.49$

10. $0.000064 + 0.00192t + 0.024t^2 + 0.16t^3 + 0.6t^4 + 1.2t^5 + t^6$

Probability and Statistics

Key Vocabulary

What You'll Learn Next

- In Chapter 12, you will learn to make and use a probability distribution to conduct a simulation.

- You will learn to use formulas, tree diagrams, and normal distributions to find the probability of an event.

- You will learn to use measures of central tendency and measures of variation to compare data in real-world problems.

Applying what you learn, on pages 706–707 you will do activities involving trains.

Chapter 12 Overview

Students begin their investigation into probability and statistics by learning about probability distributions and conditional probability. Next, students delve into statistics with lessons on analyzing data, standard deviation, and working with samples. The chapter is rounded out with lessons on binomial distributions and normal distributions.

Activating Prior Knowledge

Ask:
- *What is the definition of theoretical probability?*

Students should indicate that theoretical probability is a ratio of the number of outcomes in an event to the number of possible outcomes (known as the sample space).

Ask:
- *What are the possible values for any probability?*

Answers should state probabilities are numbers from 0 and 1, with 0 as impossible and 1 as certain.

Ask:
- *If a probability can be represented by a function, what is its range?*

Answers should indicate the range is between 0 and 1, inclusive. Tell students that they will study probability functions in this chapter.

647

1. Plan

Objectives
1 To make a probability distribution
2 To use a probability distribution in conducting a simulation

Examples
1 Making a Frequency Table
2 Real-World Connection
3 Probability Distributions
4 Real-World Connection
5 Real-World Connection

Math Background

Recalling that the sum of the probabilities for a sample space must total 1 may help students compute cumulative probabilities correctly.

More Math Background: p. 646C

Lesson Planning and Resources

See p. 646E for a list of the resources that support this lesson.

Bell Ringer Practice

✔ **Check Skills You'll Need**
For intervention, direct students to:

Finding Theoretical Probability
Lesson 1-6: Example 3
Extra Skills and Word Problems Practice, Ch. 1

Probability Distributions

What You'll Learn
- To make a probability distribution
- To use a probability distribution in conducting a simulation

... And Why
To conduct market research, as in Example 5

✔ **Check Skills You'll Need** 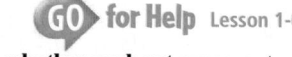 Lesson 1-6

Suppose you roll a standard number cube. State whether each set represents a sample space for the outcomes.

1. {1, 2, 3, 4, 5, 6} **yes**   **2.** {less than 3, 4, 5, 6} **no**   **3.** {even, prime} **no**

Find each probability for two tosses of a number cube.

4. $P(4 \text{ and } 3)$ $\frac{1}{18}$ **5.** $P(\text{two odd numbers})$ $\frac{1}{4}$ **6.** $P(\text{two integers})$ **1**

🔊 **New Vocabulary** • frequency table • cumulative probability
• probability distribution

---

1 Making a Probability Distribution

A **frequency table** is a list of the outcomes in a sample space and the number of times each outcome occurs.

Vocabulary Tip

Scalene comes from the Latin word for uneven.

1 EXAMPLE Making a Frequency Table

Below are three types of triangles: equilateral, isosceles, and scalene. Make a frequency table. For isosceles, use triangles with exactly two congruent sides.

Step 1 Count the number of each type.

Equilateral	𝍸𝍸 𝍸	
Isosceles	𝍸𝍸 𝍸𝍸 𝍸	
Scalene	𝍸𝍸 𝍸𝍸𝍸	
Total number of triangles: 25		

Step 2 Make a table.

Type	Number
Equilateral	6
Isosceles	11
Scalene	8
Total	25

1.
Type	Number
Acute	13
Right	7
Obtuse	5
Total	25

 ● The triangles in Example 1 can also be described as acute, right, and obtuse. Make a frequency table using those categories. **See left.**

Probability over a continuous range of events is **cumulative probability.** You can use a frequency table to find cumulative probability.

Differentiated Instruction **Solutions for All Learners**

Special Needs L1
Have students copy the probability distribution bar graph on a large sheet of paper. Have them label each bar with the sum and its corresponding number pairs. For the sum of 3, the pairs are (1, 2) and (2, 1).

learning style: visual

Below Level L2
Graphs can help students understand frequency distributions. Have students create graphs for frequency tables to help them interpret the data.

learning style: visual

Vocabulary Tip

The <u>experimental probability</u> of an event is the ratio of the number of times the event occurs to the number of trials.

2 EXAMPLE Real-World Connection

Social Science Use the frequency table. Find the probability that an elderly person living alone will have contact with his or her children more than once a week.

Contact Between Children and Elderly Who Live Alone

How Often Contact Is Made	Number of Elderly
7 times per week	680
2–6 times per week	276
1 time per week	236
Less than 1 time per week	199
Total	1391

Source: *Statistical Handbook on the American Family*

$P(7 \text{ times per week}) = \frac{680}{1391}$ **Find the experimental probability for each event in the table that represents contact more than once a week.**

$P(2-6 \text{ times per week}) = \frac{276}{1391}$

$\frac{680}{1391} + \frac{276}{1391} = \frac{956}{1391} \approx 0.687$ **Add to find cumulative probability.**

● The probability of contact more than once a week is about 0.687, or 68.7%.

✓ Quick Check ② Find $P(\text{once a week or more})$. **≈0.857, or 85.7%**

A **probability distribution** is a function that gives the probability of each event in a sample space. You can use a table or a graph to show a probability distribution.

3 EXAMPLE Probability Distributions

Suppose you roll two number cubes. Show the probability distribution for the sum of the numbers.

Method 1 Make a frequency table. Then extend the table to include probabilities.

Rolling Two Number Cubes

Sum	2	3	4	5	6	7	8	9	10	11	12
Frequency	1	2	3	4	5	6	5	4	3	2	1
Probability	$\frac{1}{36}$	$\frac{2}{36}$	$\frac{3}{36}$	$\frac{4}{36}$	$\frac{5}{36}$	$\frac{6}{36}$	$\frac{5}{36}$	$\frac{4}{36}$	$\frac{3}{36}$	$\frac{2}{36}$	$\frac{1}{36}$

→ There are 36 possible outcomes.
→ Divide to find the probability.

Method 2 Draw a graph.

✓ Quick Check ③ Use a table or a graph to show the probability distribution for the roll of one number cube. **See back of book.**

Lesson 12-1 Probability Distributions **649**

1 EXAMPLE Tactile Learners

Suggest that students trace the triangles onto paper. Then they can cut out the triangles and sort them into categories in order to complete a frequency table.

PowerPoint
Additional Examples

❶ Take a survey of your class-mates' eye colors and make a frequency table with the data. **Answers may vary. Sample:**

Eye Color	Number
Brown	15
Green	6
Blue	4
Total	25

❷ Use the frequency table. Find the probability that a student is involved in at least one extra-curricular activity.

Number of Activities	Number of Students
More than one activity	144
One activity	360
No activities	216
Total Students	720

0.7, or 70%

❸ Suppose you spin two spinners. Each spinner has 4 possible outcomes: 1, 2, 3, or 4. Show the probability distribution for the sum of the numbers.

Spinning Two Spinners

Sum	2	3	4	5	6	7	8
Frequency	1	2	3	4	3	2	1
Probability	$\frac{1}{16}$	$\frac{2}{16}$	$\frac{3}{16}$	$\frac{4}{16}$	$\frac{3}{16}$	$\frac{2}{16}$	$\frac{1}{16}$

Advanced Learners L4
Have students discuss the frequency distribution of the heights of all high school seniors, and how the graph might change if only males were included.

learning style: verbal

English Language Learners ELL
Ask students if they know what *accumulate* means. **to increase in amount gradually** Then explain that *cumulative* is an adjective which means increasing in amount by successive (one after another) additions.

learning style: verbal

Additional Example

4 Use information in the chart of inherited gene pairs. Graph the probability distribution for each sample space.

Inherited Gene Pairs from One Recessive and One Hybrid Pea Plant

		Parent Plant	
		r	r
Parent	R	Rr	Rr
Plant	r	rr	rr

RR = dominant gene pair (red flower)
Rr = hybrid gene pair (pink flower)
rr = recessive gene pair (white flower)

a. Genotype Distribution

b. Plant Color Distribution

Guided Instruction

5 EXAMPLE Technology Tip

Students can type the command =INT(RAND()*100+1) into a spreadsheet cell to generate random numbers. Then they press *enter* to get a random number and copy and paste the cell to generate additional random numbers.

Additional Example

5 The probability of an information desk at a community library receiving calls *c* each hour varies according to the following distribution.

Number of Calls Each Hour

c	0	1	2	3	4	5
P(c)	0.05	0.15	0.25	0.3	0.2	0.05

Use random numbers to predict the number of calls received during an eight-hour shift. **Check students' work.**

650

A situation may be described by more than one sample space. In that case, each sample space has its own probability distribution.

4 EXAMPLE **Real-World Connection**

Genetics Use the information in the chart of inherited gene pairs. Graph the probability distribution for each sample space.

Inherited Gene Pairs From Two Hybrid Corn Plants

		Parent Plant	
		G	w
Parent	G	GG	Gw
Plant	w	Gw	ww

GG = dominant gene pair (green plant)
Gw = hybrid gene pair (green plant)
ww = recessive gene pair (white plant)

a. Genotype Distribution
{GG, Gw, ww}

b. Plant Color Distribution
{green, white}

Real-World Connection

Careers Agriculturists experiment to grow different types of crops.

✓ **Quick Check** **4 a. Critical Thinking** Which probability distribution would be more useful to a farmer who wants to avoid raising white corn plants? Explain.
b. Make a probability distribution table for each sample space in Example 4.
a–b. See back of book.

---

2 **Using a Probability Distribution**

You can design a simulation based on a probability distribution. First, use the probabilities to assign numbers to each event in the sample space. For example, if *P*(event) = 0.15, assign 15 out of 100 numbers to that event. Then you can conduct trials by generating random numbers.

5 EXAMPLE **Real-World Connection**

Market Research At a certain store, the number of customers *c* who arrive at the checkout counters each minute varies according to the distribution below. Simulate the number of customers over a ten-minute period.

Number of Customers Each Minute

c	0	1	2	3	4	5	6
P(c)	0.15	0.24	0.28	0.17	0.09	0.05	0.02

Resources
• Daily Notetaking Guide 12-1 **L3**

Closure

Ask students to explain what a probability distribution is and how to use random numbers with it to conduct a simulation.

A probability distribution is a function that gives the probability of each event in the sample space. Assign numbers to each outcome based on its probability. Conduct the simulation and interpret.

Step 1 Define how the simulation will be done. Use random numbers. Assign numbers from 1 to 100 to the events, based on the probability of each event. Use cumulative probabilities to help you assign the numbers.

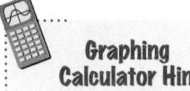
Graphing Calculator Hint

Use the command int(100*rand) + 1 to generate random numbers from 1 to 100. Press MATH and use the int option under the NUM menu and the rand option under the PRB menu.

Event	Probability	Cumulative Probability	Assigned Numbers
0	0.15	0.15	01–15
1	0.24	0.39	16–39
2	0.28	0.67	40–67
3	0.17	0.84	68–84
4	0.09	0.93	85–93
5	0.05	0.98	94–98
6	0.02	1.00	99–100

Since $P(0) = 0.15$, assign 15 numbers to this outcome.

There are 17 numbers from 68 to 84.

Step 2 Conduct the simulation. Model a ten-minute period by generating ten random numbers from 1 to 100.

Minute →	1st	2nd	3rd	4th	5th	6th	7th	8th	9th	10th
Random numbers →	81	29	83	93	18	9	40	97	47	16
Number of customers →	3	1	3	4	1	0	2	5	2	1

The random number 9 is assigned to the outcome 0 customers.

Step 3 Interpret the simulation. Based on this simulation, a total of 22 customers would arrive at checkout counters over a ten-minute period.

✓ **Quick Check** ⑤ Conduct a simulation for Example 5 over a 20-minute period.
Check students' work.

EXERCISES

Practice and Problem Solving

For more exercises, see *Extra Skill and Word Problem Practice*.

Ⓐ Practice by Example

Example 1 (page 648)

GO for Help

In the game Rock-Paper-Scissors, the scissors cut the paper, the rock dulls the scissors, and the paper covers the rock. Use the results below for Exercises 1 and 2.

Rock-Paper-Scissors

Player 1	R	S	P	P	S	R	S	S	R	P	S	S	R	S	P	P	R	S
Player 2	S	P	R	S	P	P	R	S	R	S	R	R	P	P	P	R	S	S

R = Rock   P = Paper   S = Scissors   **Bold** = Winner

1. Make a frequency table for the objects played: rock, paper, or scissors.

2. Make a frequency table for the winning players: Player 1, Player 2, or tie.
1–2. See margin.

Example 2 (page 649)

The table shows the frequency of responses to editorials. Find each probability.

Number of Responses	0	1	2	3	4	5	6 or more	Total
Number of Editorials	20	30	56	38	34	16	6	200

3. $P(5 \text{ or more responses})$
0.11

4. $P(\text{at most 4 responses})$
0.89

5. $P(0\text{–}2 \text{ responses})$
0.53

Lesson 12-1 Probability Distributions **651**

Assignment Guide

❶ A B 1-9, 12-16, 18

❷ A B 10, 11, 17

C Challenge 19-20

Test Prep 21-23
Mixed Review 24-30

Homework Quick Check

To check students' understanding of key skills and concepts, go over Exercises 8, 10, 14, 17, 18.

Error Prevention!

Exercises 10, 11 Caution students that rounding may introduce a slight error.

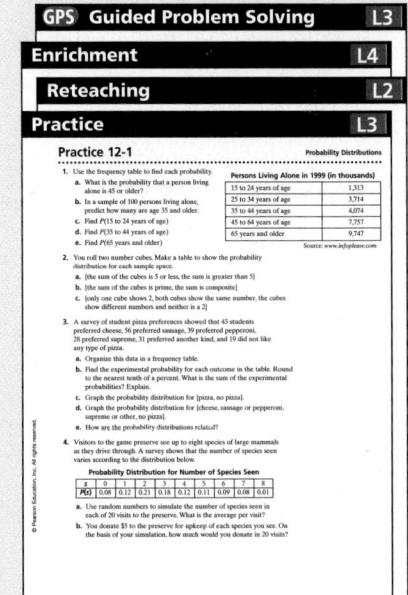
Differentiated Instruction Resources

GPS Guided Problem Solving	L3
Enrichment	L4
Reteaching	L2
Practice	L3

1.

Object	Frequency
Rock	11
Paper	10
Scissors	15
Total	36

2.

Player	Wins
1	7
2	8
Tie	3
Total	18

Lesson Quiz

1. During lunch on Monday, the cafeteria deli sold soft drinks to 32 customers, bottled waters to 12 customers, sandwiches to 16 customers, tacos to 12 customers, salads to 13 customers, and baked potatoes to 9 customers. There were a total of 50 customers during lunch on Monday.
a. Make a frequency table for the data. Extend the table to include probability distribution.

Item	Freq.	Prob.
Soft drinks	32	$\frac{32}{50}$
Bottled Water	12	$\frac{12}{50}$
Sandwiches	16	$\frac{16}{50}$
Tacos	12	$\frac{12}{50}$
Salads	13	$\frac{13}{50}$
Baked potatoes	9	$\frac{9}{50}$
Total customers	50	

b. What is the probability that the next customer will order a drink? **0.88**

2. Given the data on the number of bus rides per week for 100 people surveyed, conduct a simulation for the number of bus rides per week for the next ten people surveyed.

Rides per Week	P(Rides per Week)
0	0.52
1	0.25
2	0.13
3	0.08
4 or more	0.02

See answer below.

Alternative Assessment

Have students make a spinner and conduct 100 spins to create a frequency table for the outcomes. Then, based on the frequency table, have students run a simulation for the outcomes of 10 more spins.

Example 3
(page 649)

6. Use a table and a graph to show the probability distribution for the spinner {red, green, blue, yellow}. **See back of book.**

7. Use a table and a graph to show the probability distribution for the number of days {28, 29, 30, 31} in each of 48 consecutive months. **See margin p. 653.**

Example 4
(page 650)

Suppose you roll two number cubes. Graph the probability distribution for each sample space. 8–9. See back of book.

8. {sum of numbers even, sum of numbers odd}

9. {both numbers even, both numbers odd, one number even and the other odd}

Example 5
(pages 650–651)

10. Design and conduct a simulation to determine the ages of 20 licensed drivers chosen at random in the United States. **See back of book.**

Licensed Drivers in the United States, by Age

a	< 20	20–29	30–39	40–49	50–59	60–69	70–79	≥ 80
P(a)	0.048	0.175	0.199	0.211	0.167	0.102	0.066	0.032

SOURCE: **U.S. Department of Transportation.** Go to **www.PHSchool.com** for a data update. Web Code: agg-9041

11. Design and conduct a simulation to determine the size and type of 30 cars purchased from U.S. car dealerships. **See back of book.**

U.S. Car Sales by Vehicle Size and Type

t	Luxury	Large	Midsize	Small
P(t)	0.165	0.076	0.527	0.232

SOURCE: **Ward's Communications**

B Apply Your Skills

Graph the probability distribution described by each function. 12–13. See margin p. 653.

12. $P(x) = \frac{x}{10}$ for $x = 1, 2, 3,$ and 4

13. $P(x) = \frac{2x + 1}{15}$ for $x = 1, 2,$ and 3

Weather Conditions in Dayton, Ohio

Type of Weather	Days Per Year
Clear	82
Partly Cloudy	118
Mostly Cloudy	34
Rain	75
Light Snow (< 1.5 in.)	45
Snow (≥ 1.5 in.)	11
Total	365

SOURCE: **The USA Today Weather Almanac**

14. **Weather** Refer to the table at the left. **a–c. See back of book.**
a. Make a table showing the probability distribution for weather in Dayton.
b. Define the independent and dependent variables.
c. Find the probability that a day in Dayton will include rain or snow.

15. **Data Collection** Find weather data for a city near you. Draw a graph to show the probability distribution of weather conditions. **Check students' work.**

16. a. **Transportation** Sometimes a probability distribution is shown as a circle graph. Define the independent and dependent variables in the distribution at the right.
b. Draw the distribution as a bar graph.
c. Find P(the tank is at least half full when a driver buys gas). **a–c. See back of book.**

How Full is the Tank When People Buy Gas?

16% — $\frac{3}{4}$ Full
12% — $\frac{1}{2}$ Full
25% — $\frac{1}{4}$ Full
47% — Almost Empty

SOURCE: *The First Really Important Survey of American Habits*

17. **Writing** In a simulation, how do equally likely outcomes help you represent the probability distribution? **See margin p. 653.**

18. **Odds** The odds in favor of an event equal the ratio of the number of times the event occurs to the number of times the event does not occur. The odds in favor of event A are 1 : 4. The odds in favor of event B are 2 : 3. The odds in favor of event C are 1 : 3. The odds in favor of event D are 3 : 17. Graph the probability distribution of events A, B, C, and D. **See margin p. 653.**

Online
Homework Video Tutor
Visit: PHSchool.com
Web Code: age-1201

Lesson Quiz 12-1
2. Answers will vary. Sample: Use random numbers. Assign numbers from 1 to 100 to events based on the probability of each event.

Person Surveyed	1	2	3	4	5	6	7	8	9	10
Random Numbers	40	19	91	92	92	33	38	52	74	4
Rides per week	0	0	3	3	3	0	0	0	1	0

C Challenge

19. Safety The table shows data for 911 calls in a town.
  a. Conduct a simulation for the number of 911 calls over a 24-hour period.
  b. If there are two response teams available, and each response takes about an hour, how many callers in your simulation have to wait?
  c. Find P(caller will have to wait). $\frac{10}{47}$
  d. Critical Thinking Use your simulation to determine whether additional response teams are needed for this town. Explain your reasoning.
  a–b, d. See back of book.

20. Marketing A company includes instant-win tickets with 10,000,000 of its products. Of the prizes offered, one is a large cash prize, 1,600,000 are small cash prizes, and the other prizes are free samples of the company's products.
  a. Find the theoretical probability of winning each type of prize.
  b. Design and conduct a simulation to determine the prizes for 100 products.
  c. Find the experimental probability for winning each type of prize.
  a. 0.0000001, 0.16, ≈0.84
  b–c. Check students' work.

Probability Distribution for Number of 911 Calls Each Hour

c	$P(c)$
0	0.21
1	0.30
2	0.18
3	0.13
4	0.09
5	0.05
6	0.03
7	0.01

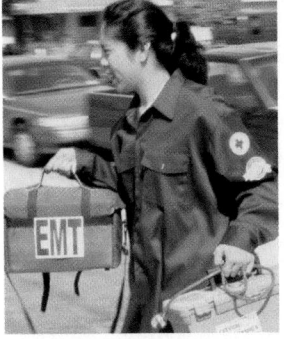

Real-World Connection

More than 93% of the U.S. population is covered by 911 service.

Test Prep

Multiple Choice

The table shows the number of cities in a region of the U.S. that are served by the given number of airlines. Use the table for Exercises 21–22.

Number of Airlines	Number of Cities
1	27
2	14
3	15
4	18
5	14
6	11

21. What is the probability that a city chosen at random is served by exactly 4 airlines? **C**
  A. $\frac{1}{18}$ **B.** $\frac{4}{21}$ **C.** $\frac{2}{11}$ **D.** $\frac{2}{9}$

22. What is the probability that a city chosen at random is served by at least 1 airline? **J**
  F. 0   **G.** $\frac{1}{99}$ **H.** $\frac{3}{11}$ **J.** 1

Extended Response

23. A spinner has 4 sections labeled A, B, C, and D. Can the spinner be designed so $P(A) = \frac{1}{12}$, $P(B) = \frac{1}{6}$, $P(C) = \frac{1}{3}$, and $P(D) = \frac{5}{12}$? If so, explain how.
  See margin.

Mixed Review

GO for Help

Lesson 11-6   Find the area under each curve for the domain $0 \le x \le 1$.
  24. $y = 3$ **3 units²**   **25.** $y = 4x + 2$ **4 units²**   **26.** $y = 4x^3 + 1$ **2 units²**

Lesson 10-6   Sketch the graph of each equation.   **27–28. See margin.**
  27. $x^2 - 4y^2 + 2x + 24y = 51$ **28.** $20y^2 - 40y - x = -25$

Lesson 9-7   Classify each pair of events as *dependent* or *independent*.
  dependent
  29. Choose one item from a buffet. Then choose a different item from the buffet.
  30. Choose a size for your drink. Then select a flavor.   **independent**

nline lesson quiz, PHSchool.com, Web Code: aga-1201   Lesson 12-1 Probability Distributions   **653**

Test Prep

Resources
For additional practice with a variety of test item formats:
• Standardized Test Prep, p. 705
• Test-Taking Strategies, p. 700
• Test-Taking Strategies with Transparencies

17. Answers may vary. Sample: Suppose the events in a probability distribution are *not* equally likely. By assigning the appropriate number of *equally likely* outcomes to each event, you can design a simulation that reflects the actual probabilities expected.

18.

23. [4] Since $\frac{1}{12} + \frac{1}{6} + \frac{1}{3} + \frac{5}{12} = 1$, such a spinner is possible. Divide the spinner into 12 equal parts. Label 1 part A, 2 parts B, 4 parts C, and 5 parts D.
  [3] incorrectly divides the 12 parts
  [2] does not explain answer
  [1] incorrectly adds probabilities

27.

28.

---

7. Number of Days Per Month

Days	28	29	30	31
Frequency	3	1	16	28
Probability	$\frac{3}{48}$	$\frac{1}{48}$	$\frac{16}{48}$	$\frac{28}{48}$

12.

13.

653

Objectives
1 To find conditional probability
2 To use formulas and tree diagrams

Examples
1 Finding Conditional Probability
2 Real-World Connection
3 Real-World Connection
4 Making a Tree Diagram

Math Background

The formula for a conditional probability has the same *description* as that for any probability. It is the ratio of the probability of success to the probability of the sample space.

More Math Background: p. 646C

Lesson Planning and Resources

See p.646E for a list of the resources that support this lesson.

Bell Ringer Practice

☑ **Check Skills You'll Need**
For intervention, direct students to:

Finding Theoretical Probability
Lesson 9-7: Example 2
Extra Skills and Word
   Problems Practice, Ch. 9

Conditional Probability

What You'll Learn

• To find conditional probabilities

• To use formulas and tree diagrams

… And Why

To find the probability of school closings after snowfall, as in Example 4

☑ **Check Skills You'll Need**

 Lesson 9-7

A spinner has four equal sections that are red, blue, green, and yellow. Find each probability for two spins.

1. P(blue, then blue) $\frac{1}{16}$
2. P(red, then yellow) $\frac{1}{16}$
3. P(not yellow, then green) $\frac{3}{16}$
4. P(not blue, then not red) $\frac{9}{16}$
5. P(at least one green) $\frac{7}{16}$
6. P(neither spin red) $\frac{9}{16}$

◀)) **New Vocabulary** • conditional probability

---

1 Finding Conditional Probabilities

A **conditional probability** contains a condition that may limit the sample space for an event. You can write a conditional probability using the notation $P(B \mid A)$, read "the probability of event B, given event A."

1 EXAMPLE **Finding Conditional Probability**

The table shows the results of a class survey. Find P(did a chore | male).

The condition *male* limits the sample space to 15 possible outcomes. Of the 15 males, 7 did a chore. Therefore, P(did a chore | male) equals $\frac{7}{15}$.

Did you do a household chore last night?

	Yes	No
Male	7	8	← 15 males
Female	7	6	← 13 females

☑ **Quick Check** ① Use the data in Example 1 to find P(female | did a chore). $\frac{7}{14}$, or $\frac{1}{2}$

2 EXAMPLE **Real-World 🌎 Connection**

Test-Taking Tip

When using tables, mark on the table to help you keep track of the data you need.

Multiple Choice Americans recycle increasingly more materials through municipal waste collection each year. The table shows recycling data for a recent year. Find the probability that a sample of recycled waste was paper.

Ⓐ 16 %
Ⓑ 28%
Ⓒ 36%
Ⓓ 54%

Municipal Waste Collected (millions of tons)

Material	Recycled	Not Recycled
Paper	36.7	45.1
Metal	6.3	11.9
Glass	2.4	10.1
Plastic	1.4	24.0
Other	21.2	70.1

SOURCE: U.S. Environmental Protection Agency.
Go to www.PHSchool.com for a data update.
Web Code: agg-9041

654 Chapter 12 Probability and Statistics

Differentiated Instruction Solutions for All Learners

Special Needs L1

Have students write P(paper | not recycled) $= \frac{\square}{\square}$.

Then direct students to draw a line from "paper" to the numerator box, and draw another line from "not recycled" to the denominator box.

learning style: visual

Below Level L2
Suggest that students think of conditional probability in terms of deciding what to order at a restaurant. The food you order is going to depend on the type of restaurant.

learning style: verbal

The given condition limits the sample space to *recycled* waste. A favorable outcome is recycled paper.

$$P(\text{paper} \mid \text{recycled}) = \frac{36.7}{36.7 + 6.3 + 2.4 + 1.4 + 21.2}$$
$$\approx 0.54$$

The probability that the recycled waste was paper is about 54%. The correct choice is D.

Quick Check ② Find the probability that a sample of recycled waste was plastic.
about 0.021 or 2.1%

2 Using Formulas and Tree Diagrams

You can use a formula to find conditional probability.

 Key Concepts

Property	Conditional Probability Formula

For any two events A and B from a sample space with $P(A) \neq 0$,

$$P(B \mid A) = \frac{P(A \text{ and } B)}{P(A)}$$

Using the formula, you can calculate a conditional probability from other probabilities.

3 EXAMPLE Real-World Connection

Market Research Researchers asked shampoo users whether they apply shampoo directly to the head, or indirectly using a hand. Find the probability that a respondent applies shampoo directly to the head, given that the respondent is female.

Applying Shampoo

	Directly Onto Head	Into Hand First
Male	2	18
Female	6	24

Relate $P(\text{female}) = \frac{30}{50}$

$P(\text{female } and \text{ applies directly to head}) = \frac{6}{50}$

Define Let A = female.
Let B = applies directly to head.

Write $P(B \mid A) = \dfrac{P(A \text{ and } B)}{P(A)}$

$= \dfrac{\frac{6}{50}}{\frac{30}{50}}$ **Substitute.**

$= \dfrac{6}{30} = \dfrac{1}{5}$ **Simplify.**

The probability that a respondent applies shampoo directly to the head, given that the respondent is female, is $\frac{1}{5}$, or 20%.

Quick Check ③ Eighty percent of an airline's flights depart on schedule. Seventy-two percent of its flights depart and arrive on schedule. Find the probability that a flight that departs on time also arrives on time. **0.9**

Lesson 12-2 Conditional Probability **655**

Advanced Learners **L4**
Make sure students understand under what conditions $P(A \mid B)$ and $P(B \mid A)$ are the same. Have them give an example illustrating their answer.

learning style: verbal

English Language Learners **ELL**
For Example 3, help students understand the term *respondent*. Explain that a *respondent* is a person who responds to (answers questions in) a survey. Ask if any students have been a respondent in a survey.

learning style: verbal

655

---

2. Teach

Guided Instruction

① **EXAMPLE** Math Tip

Have students compare the conditional probability of $P(\text{male} \mid \text{didn't do a chore})$ to $P(\text{didn't do a chore})$ to see that the conditional probability is quantitatively different because of the difference in the sample space.

PowerPoint
Additional Examples

❶ The table shows the results of a class survey. Find $P(\text{own a pet} \mid \text{female})$.

Do You Own a Pet?

	Yes	No
Female	8	6
Male	5	7

$\frac{8}{14}$

❷ Use the data in the table in Example 2 to find the probability that a sample of not-recycled waste was plastic. **about 15%**

Guided Instruction

PowerPoint
Additional Examples

❸ Researchers asked people who exercise regularly whether they jog or walk. Fifty-eight percent of the respondents were male. Twenty percent of all respondents were males who said that they jog. Find the probability that a male respondent jogs. **about 34%**

Additional Example

4 A student made the following observations of the weather in his hometown.
- On 28% of the days, the sky is mostly clear.
- During the mostly clear days, it rained 4% of the time.
- During the cloudy days, it rained 31% of the time.

Use a tree diagram to find the probability that a day will start out clear, and then it will rain. **about 1%**

Resources
- Daily Notetaking Guide 12-2 **L3**

Closure

Ask students to give an example of a sample space and create a conditional probability problem using a subset of the sample space. **Check students' work.**

11.

M = male
F = female
R = right
L = left

0.1, 0.114

12.

$P(W) = 0.55$

You can use tree diagrams to solve problems involving conditional probabilities.

4 EXAMPLE Making a Tree Diagram

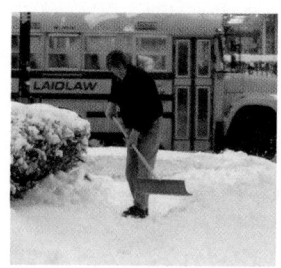

Real-World Connection

During some winters, Buffalo gets more than 100 inches of snow.

A student in Buffalo, New York, made the observations below.
- Of all snowfalls, 5% are heavy (at least 6 in.).
- After a heavy snowfall, schools are closed 67% of the time.
- After a light (less than 6 in.) snowfall, schools are closed 3% of the time.

Find the probability that the snowfall is light and the schools are open.

Make a tree diagram. Use H for heavy snowfall, L for light snowfall, C for schools closed, and O for schools open. Find $P(L \text{ and } O)$.

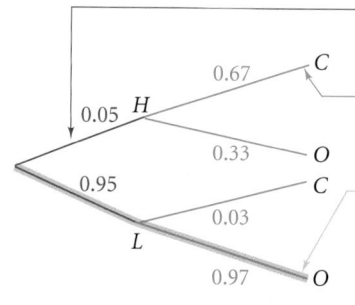

Each first branch represents a simple probability. $P(H) = 0.05$

Each second branch represents a conditional probability. $P(C|H) = 0.67$

The highlighted path represents $P(L \text{ and } O)$.
$$P(L \text{ and } O) = P(L) \cdot P(O|L)$$
$$= 0.95 \cdot 0.97$$
$$= 0.9215$$

• The probability that the snowfall is light and the schools are open is about 92%.

✓ Quick Check **4** Find P(schools open, given heavy snow). **0.33**

EXERCISES

For more exercises, see *Extra Skill and Word Problem Practice*.

Practice and Problem Solving

A Practice by Example

GO for Help

Example 1
(page 654)

Use the table to find each probability.

1. P(has diploma) **0.9**

2. P(has diploma and experience) **0.6**

3. P(has experience | has diploma) **0.6̄**

4. P(has no diploma | has experience) **≈0.085**

Characteristics of Job Applicants

		Has Experience	
		Yes	No
Has High School Diploma	Yes	54	27
	No	5	4

Example 2
(pages 654–655)

Use the table below to find each probability.

5. P(The recipient is male.) **≈0.405**

6. P(The degree is a bachelor's.) **≈0.519**

7. P(The recipient is female, given that the degree is advanced.) **≈0.562**

8. P(The degree is *not* an associate's, given that the recipient is male.) **≈0.784**

Projected Number of Degree Recipients in 2010 (thousands)

Degree	Male	Female
Associate's	245	433
Bachelor's	598	858
Advanced	293	376

SOURCE: U.S. National Center for Education Statistics

Example 3
(page 655)

Use the survey results below for Exercises 9 and 10.

9. Find the probability that a respondent has a pet, given that the respondent has had a pet. **≈45%**

39% have a pet now and have had a pet.

61% do not have a pet now.

86% have had a pet.

14% do not have a pet now and have never had a pet.

10. Find the probability that a respondent has never had a pet, given that the respondent does not have a pet now. **≈23%**

Example 4
(page 656)

11. Make a tree diagram based on the survey results below . Then find P(a female respondent is left-handed) and P(a respondent is both male and right-handed). **11–12. See margin p. 656.**
   - Of all the respondents, 17% are male.
   - Of the male respondents, 33% are left-handed.
   - Of female respondents, 90% are right-handed.

12. A football team has a 70% chance of winning when it doesn't snow, but only a 40% chance of winning when it snows. Suppose there is a 50% chance of snow. Make a tree diagram to find the probability that the team will win.

B Apply Your Skills

13d. The fact that $P(A) = P(A|B)$ illustrates that the probability of A is the same, regardless of the occurrence of B.

13. Suppose A and B are independent events, with $P(A) = 0.60$ and $P(B) = 0.25$.
GPS Find each probability.
   a. $P(A \text{ and } B)$ **0.15**
   b. $P(A \mid B)$ **0.60**
   c. What do you notice about $P(A)$ and $P(A \mid B)$? **$P(A)$ is equal to $P(A \mid B)$**
   d. **Critical Thinking** One way to describe A and B as independent events is *The occurrence of B has no effect on the probability of A*. Explain how the answer to part (c) illustrates this relationship.

Surveys **Conduct a survey in your class. Then find each probability.**
14–18. Check students' work.

14. P(left-handed | left shoe)

15. P(left-handed | not the right shoe)

16. P(left shoe | right-handed)

17. P(first shoe picked up | right-handed)

18. P(don't know)

GO Online
Homework Video Tutor
Visit: PHSchool.com
Web Code: age-1202

Which Shoe Do You Put on First?		Dominant Hand	
		Right	Left
First Shoe Put On	Right	▪	▪
	Left	▪	▪
	First One Grabbed	▪	▪
	Don't Know	▪	▪

Weather **Use probability notation to describe the chance of each event. Let S, C, W, and R represent sunny, cloudy, windy, and rainy weather, respectively.**

19. cloudy weather **$P(C)$**

20. sunny and windy weather **$P(S \text{ and } W)$**

21. rainy weather if it is windy **$P(R \mid W)$**

22. windy weather if it is sunny **$P(W \mid S)$**

C Challenge 🖉

23. a. **Writing** Explain which branches of the tree diagram at the right represent conditional probabilities. Give a specific example.
   b. Are the event of having a license and the event of being an adult independent events? Justify your answer.
   c. **Open-Ended** Estimate probabilities for each branch of the tree diagram for your city or town. Then find $P(L)$. **a–c. See margin.**

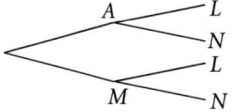

A = adult (21 or older)
M = minor (under 21)
L = licensed driver
N = not licensed to drive

23a. The four right branches represent probabilities conditional upon the person being an adult or a minor. For example, the top branch represents the probability that a person is licensed given that he or she is an adult.

b. No; the probability of a minor being licensed is not the same as the probability of an adult being licensed.

c. Check students' work.

Assignment Guide

1 A B 1-8, 13-22

2 A B 9-12
C Challenge   23-24

Test Prep   25-28
Mixed Review   29-38

Homework Quick Check
To check students' understanding of key skills and concepts, go over Exercises 5-8, 11-13.

Error Prevention!

Exercises 1–13 Urge students to be careful when substituting values into the conditional probability formula. It is important to correctly identify the limited sample space.

Differentiated **Instruction** **Resources**

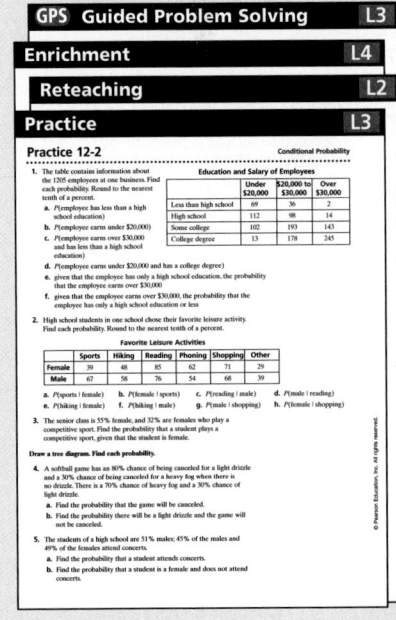

GPS Guided Problem Solving	L3
Enrichment	L4
Reteaching	L2
Practice	L3

PowerPoint
Lesson Quiz

1. A study was conducted at Central High School to find out how much television students watch per night. Thirty eight percent of the respondents were freshmen. Twenty-two percent of all respondents were freshman who said that they watch at least one hour of television per night. Find the probability that a freshman respondent watches at least one hour of television per night. **about 58%**

2. The tree diagram below shows the probabilities that Jose will or will not cook breakfast on weekends or weekdays. Find the probability that Jose will cook breakfast on any given day. **about 38%**

Alternative Assessment

Group students in pairs. Have each student create a tree diagram of a conditional probability problem in Exercises 1–10 or 18–22. Then ask students to share their diagrams with each other. The students should try to interpret each other's diagram, and find one of the conditional probabilities.

Standardized Test Prep

 Resources

For additional practice with a variety of test item formats:
- Standardized Test Prep, p. 705
- Test-Taking Strategies, p. 700
- Test-Taking Strategies with Transparencies

24. **Critical Thinking** Sixty percent of a company's sales representatives have completed training seminars. Of these, 80% have had increased sales. Overall, 56% of the representatives (whether trained or not) have had increased sales. Use a tree diagram to find the probability of increased sales, given that a representative has not been trained. $P(I|N) = 0.2$

Test Prep

Multiple Choice A school library classifies its books as hardback or paperback, fiction or nonfiction, and illustrated or nonillustrated. Use the table at the right for Exercises 25–27.

		Illustrated	Non-illustrated
Hardback	Fiction	420	780
	Nonfiction	590	250
Paperback	Fiction	150	430
	Nonfiction	110	880

25. What is the probability that a book selected at random is a paperback, given that it is illustrated? **C**
   A. $\frac{260}{3610}$ B. $\frac{150}{1270}$ C. $\frac{260}{1270}$ D. $\frac{110}{150}$

26. What is the probability that a book selected at random is nonfiction, given that it is a nonillustrated hardback? **H**
   F. $\frac{250}{2040}$ G. $\frac{780}{1030}$ H. $\frac{250}{1030}$ J. $\frac{250}{780}$

27. What is the probability that a book selected at random is a paperback? **D**
   A. $\frac{1}{1570}$ B. $\frac{260}{1310}$ C. $\frac{1570}{2040}$ D. $\frac{1570}{3610}$

Short Response 28. In a library, the probability that a book is a hardback, given that it is illustrated, is 0.40. The probability that the book is hardback *and* illustrated is 0.20. Find the probability that a book is illustrated. **See margin.**

Mixed Review

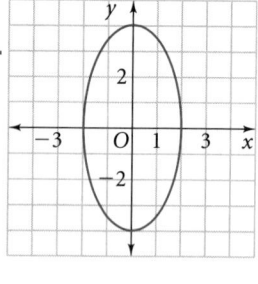

GO for Help

Lesson 12-1 29. Consider a February that is not in a leap year. Graph the probability distribution for the sample space {weekdays, weekend days}. **See back of book.**

Lesson 11-1 30. **Construction** An earthmover purchased for $600,000 loses 18% of its value each year. What is the value of the earthmover after one year? After three years? **$492,000; $330,820.80**

Lesson 10-1 31. Identify the center and intercepts of the conic section at the right. Then find the domain and range. **See margin.**

Lesson 8-5 Solve each equation. If necessary, round to the nearest thousandth.
   32. $2^x = 4$ **2**   33. $4^{2x} = 10$ **0.830**   34. $4^{x+1} = 28$ **1.404**
   35. $7 - 3^x = -38$ **3.465**   36. $\log x = -1$ **0.1**
   37. $2 \log x = 1$ **3.162**   38. $\log(2x + 2) = 2$ **49**

28. **[2]** $P(B \mid A) = \frac{P(A \text{ and } B)}{P(A)}$, where A is "the book is illustrated" and B is "the book is hardback".

   $0.40 = \frac{0.20}{P(A)}$
   $0.40 \cdot P(A) = 0.20$
   $P(A) = 0.5$

   [1] answer only OR minor error

31. center (0, 0)
   x-intercepts (2, 0), (−2, 0)
   y-intercepts (0, 4), (0, −4);
   domain: {x | −2 ≤ x ≤ 2};
   range: {y | −4 ≤ y ≤ 4}

Comparing Conditional Probabilities

You can use a tree diagram like the one at the right to find the conditional probability $P(P \mid D)$, which is the probability that a person with a disease will test positive for it. In this case, $P(P \mid D) = 0.99$.

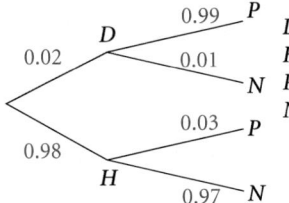

D = person has the disease
H = person is healthy
P = person tests positive
N = person tests negative

Scientists also look at $P(H \mid P)$, the probability of a "false positive," which is the probability that a person who tests positive is actually healthy. Since this probability is not found on a branch in the diagram, you must use the formula for conditional probability.

EXAMPLE

Use the tree diagram above to find $P(H \mid P)$.

Since $P(H \mid P) = \dfrac{P(H \text{ and } P)}{P(P)}$, find $P(H \text{ and } P)$ and $P(P)$.

$P(H \text{ and } P) = 0.98 \cdot 0.03$ $P(P) = P(D \text{ and } P)$ or $P(H \text{ and } P)$
$= 0.0294$ $= 0.02 \cdot 0.99 + 0.98 \cdot 0.03 = 0.0492$

So $P(H \mid P) = \dfrac{P(H \text{ and } P)}{P(P)}$

$= \dfrac{0.0294}{0.0492}$ **Substitute.**
≈ 0.598 **Simplify.**

About 60% of the people who test positive do not actually have the disease.

EXERCISES

Use the tree diagram in the Example to find each probability.

1. $P(N)$ **0.9508**
2. $P(H \text{ and } N)$ **0.9506**
3. $P(H \mid N)$ **0.9998**
4. $P(D \mid N)$ **0.0002**

5. **Transportation** You can take Bus 65 or Bus 79 to get to work. You take the first bus that arrives. The probability that Bus 65 arrives first is 75%. There is a 40% chance that Bus 65 picks up passengers along the way. There is a 60% chance that Bus 79 picks up passengers. Your bus picked up passengers. What is the probability that it was Bus 65? $\frac{2}{3}$ **or about 67%**

The tree diagram relates snowfall and school closings. Find each probability.

H = heavy snowfall
L = light snowfall
C = schools closed
O = schools open

6. $P(C)$ **0.5**
7. $P(H \text{ and } O)$
8. $P(H \mid C)$ **0.64**
9. $P(L \mid O)$
10. $P(L \mid C)$ **0.36**
11. $P(H \mid O)$ **0.16**
7. **0.08**
9. **0.84**
12. **Writing** Explain the difference in meaning between $P(P \mid D)$ and $P(D \mid P)$ for the test in the Example. Compare the values of $P(P \mid D)$ and $P(D \mid P)$. What is the best use for this test? Explain. See margin.

12. $P(P \mid D) = 0.99$, $P(D \mid P) \approx$ 0.402. Answers may vary. Sample: $P(P \mid D)$ is the probability that the test will detect the disease if it is present while $P(D \mid P)$ is the probability that the disease is present if the test is positive. While the test identifies almost all (99%) of the people with the disease, only 40% of those who test positive actually have the disease (the other 60% are "false positives"). The test can be an effective screen, used to identify a smaller population with whom to use a (more expensive) confirming test.

Students learn to compare conditional probabilities using a tree diagram.

Guided Instruction

Students may expect that the probability of a false positive is 0.01 since the given probability of testing positive and having the disease is 0.99. Explain that the "false positive" probability speaks to the reliability of the test. Ask students to comment on the reliability of the test if the person is actually healthy.

Visual Learners
Make sure students write the formula for each probability statement in the exercises before they consult the tree diagram for the probabilities to substitute into the formulas.

Resources

ExamView CD-ROM, Chapter 00, Extension Topics

Objectives

1 To calculate measures of central tendency
2 To draw and interpret box-and-whisker plots

Examples

1 Finding Measures of Central Tendency
2 Real-World Connection
3 Making a Box-and-Whisker Plot
4 Real-World Connection
5 Using Percentiles
6 Identifying an Outlier

Math Background

The mean and the median are the most useful classical measures of central tendency. Box-and-whisker plots were invented by John Tukey in the 1970s.

More Math Background: p. 646C

Lesson Planning and Resources

See p. 646E for a list of the resources that support this lesson.

Bell Ringer Practice

☑️ **Check Skills You'll Need**
For intervention, direct students to:

Finding Theoretical Probability
Lesson 1-1: Example 3
Extra Skills and Word Problems Practice, Ch. 1

Analyzing Data

What You'll Learn

• To calculate measures of central tendency

• To draw and interpret box-and-whisker plots

. . . And Why

To analyze a set of water temperatures, as in Example 2

☑️ **Check Skills You'll Need**

Order each set of values from least to greatest. Then find the middle value.

1. 0.2 0.3 0.6 1.2 0.7 0.9 0.8   **2.** 11 23 15 17 21 18 21

3. 7.8 2.6 3.9 15.6 9.1 11.7 10.4   **4.** 76 89 80 82 86 84 86
1–4. See margin p. 661.

🔊 **New Vocabulary** • measures of central tendency • mean • median • mode
• bimodal • quartiles • box-and-whisker plot • percentiles
• outlier

---

1   Measures of Central Tendency

Statistics is the study of data analysis and interpretation. The mean, the median, and the mode are single, central values that help describe a set of data. They are called **measures of central tendency.**

Key Concepts

Definition	Measures of Central Tendency	
Measure	**Definition**	**Example, using {1, 2, 2, 3, 5, 5}**
Mean	$\dfrac{\text{sum of the data values}}{\text{number of data values}}$	$\dfrac{1 + 2 + 2 + 3 + 5 + 5}{6} = \dfrac{18}{6} = 3$
Median	middle value *or* mean of the two middle values	$\dfrac{2 + 3}{2} = 2.5$
Mode	most frequently occurring value	2 and 5

A **bimodal** data set has two modes. If a data set has more than two modes, then the modes are probably not statistically useful. If no value occurs more frequently than any other, then there is no mode.

Vocabulary Tip

Read $\bar{x}$ as "the mean of x" or "x bar."

1 EXAMPLE   Finding Measures of Central Tendency

Find the mean, median, and mode for these values: 98, 95, 99, 97, 89, 92, 97, 62, 90.

$$\bar{x} = \frac{98 + 95 + 99 + 97 + 89 + 92 + 97 + 62 + 90}{9} = \frac{819}{9} = 91$$ Use the symbol $\bar{x}$ to designate the mean.

62 89 90 92 95 97 97 98 99   Find the median and the mode by
            ↑   ↑ ↑   ordering the values numerically.
          Median Mode

The mean is 91, the median is 95, and the mode is 97.

☑️ **Quick Check** ❶ Find the mean, median, and mode for these values: 2.4, 4.3, 3.7, 3.9, 2.8, 5.4, 2.8.
                                                         ≈3.6, 3.7, 2.8

660   Chapter 12   Probability and Statistics

Differentiated Instruction   Solutions for All Learners

Special Needs L1	**Below Level** L2
Have 7 students stand in a line in front of the class. Ask the middlemost student to step forward. Then have the students arrange themselves in order by height, and have the middlemost student step forward. Ask: *How does this relate to finding the median?* **learning style: tactile**	Suggest that students think of the box portion of a box-and-whisker plot as a fence that surrounds the majority of the data and tells how close together data values fall. **learning style: visual**

You can use a graphing calculator to find the measures of central tendency.

2 EXAMPLE **Real-World** 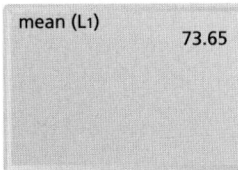 **Connection**

Oceanography Find the mean, the median, and the mode of all the water temperatures listed for the eastern coast of the Gulf of Mexico.

Gulf of Mexico Eastern Coast Water Temperatures (°F)

Location	J	F	M	A	M	J	J	A	S	O	N	D
Pensacola, Florida	56	58	63	71	78	84	85	86	82	74	65	58
St. Petersburg, Florida	62	64	68	74	80	84	86	86	84	78	70	64
Key West, Florida	69	70	75	78	82	85	87	87	86	82	76	72
Dauphin Island, Alabama	51	53	60	70	75	82	84	84	80	72	62	56
Grand Isle, Louisiana	61	61	64	70	77	83	85	85	83	77	70	65

Step 1 Use the STAT feature to enter the data as L1 in your graphing calculator.

Step 2 Use the LIST feature to access the MATH menu. Find the mean.

```
NAMES OPS MATH
1:min(
2:max(
3:mean(
4:median(
5:sum(
6:prod(
7↓stdDev(
```

```
mean (L1)
              73.65
```

Step 3 Return to the same menu to find the median.

```
NAMES OPS MATH
1:min(
2:max(
3:mean(
4:median(
5:sum(
6:prod(
7↓stdDev(
```

```
mean (L1)
              73.65
median (L1)
                 75
```

Step 4 Use the STAT PLOT feature to access **Plot 1**. Choose the histogram, L1, and

```
Plot1 Plot2 Plot3
On  Off
Type: ⊡ ⊿ ⊞
      ⊹ ⊞ ∠
Xlist: L1
Freq: 1
```

```
WINDOW
Xmin = 50
Xmax = 90
Xscl = 1
Ymin = −2
Ymax = 8
Yscl = 1
Xres = 1
```

Frequency 1 options. Then enter an appropriate viewing window.

Step 5 Graph the data. Use the TRACE feature to move the cursor to the highest points of the graph.

On the screen, the mode appears as the minimum value for the cursor. The modes are 70 and 84.

The modes both occur five times in the data.

● The mean is 73.65°F, the median is 75°F, and the modes are 70°F and 84°F.

✓ Quick Check ② Find the mean, median, and mode for the water temperatures in Grand Isle, Louisiana. ≈73.42°F; 73.5°F; 61°F, 70°F, 77°F, 83°F, 85°F

Lesson 12-3 Analyzing Data **661**

Guided Instruction

2 EXAMPLE **Technology Tip**

When finding the mean and the median, press [2nd] 1 to enter L1. When students use the TRACE feature, *min* represents the temperature and *n* represents the number of times that temperature is listed in the table.

PowerPoint
Additional Examples

① Find the mean, median, and mode for these values: 78, 87, 84, 75, 80, 98, 78, 95, 72. 83; 80; 78

② Using the data in the table in Example 2, find the mean, the median, and the mode for the water temperatures in Dauphin Island, AL. 69.1; 71; 84

Check Skills You'll Need

1. 0.2 0.3 0.6 0.7 0.8 0.9 1.2; 0.7

2. 11 15 17 18 21 21 23; 18

3. 2.6 3.9 7.8 9.1 10.4 11.7 15.6; 9.1

4. 76 80 82 84 86 86 89; 84

Advanced Learners [L4]
Around 80% of adult drivers consider themselves above average. Have students discuss whether 80% of drivers can be above the mean, median, or mode.

learning style: verbal

English Language Learners ELL
To help students understand the meaning of *bimodal*, have them list words beginning with the prefix *bi-*, such as *bicycle*, *biplane*, *bifocal*, and *bicultural* and discuss their meanings.

learning style: verbal

Guided Instruction

3 EXAMPLE **Teaching Tip**

Point out to students that not only are the minimum, maximum, median, and quartiles easily visible but also the range of the data.

4 EXAMPLE **Technology Tip**

Students may enter the data for this example in any list; they must then make certain that they select the appropriate list after selecting the type of plot using the STAT PLOT feature.

5 EXAMPLE **Teaching Tip**

Point out to students that scores for the SAT® and ACT® are often reported using percentiles. Ask students why knowing the percentile of their score might be beneficial? **The percentile will show how they scored compared to others who took the tests.**

6 EXAMPLE **Math Tip**

Often, when making a box-and-whisker plot, the "whiskers" of the plot are not extended to any outliers. In such cases, the "whiskers" would be extended only to the least or greatest values that are not outliers.

2 Box-and-Whisker Plots

If you arrange data in increasing order, then the median divides the data set into two equal parts. You can use the median of each of the parts to divide the set further, into four equal parts. The values separating the four parts are called **quartiles.** Quartiles are shown below for the 12 water temperatures from Pensacola in Example 2.

Median of lower part (Q_1) = 60.5   Median of upper part (Q_3) = 83

56   58   58   63   65   71   74   78   82   84   85   86

Median of data set (Q_2) = 72.5

Vocabulary Tip

Quartiles are sometimes called "hinges."

The values Q_1, Q_2, and Q_3 are the first, second, and third quartiles. A **box-and-whisker plot** is a method of displaying data that uses quartiles to form the center box and the minimum and maximum values to form the whiskers.

3 EXAMPLE **Making a Box-and-Whisker Plot**

Make a box-and-whisker plot for these values: 84, 79, 90, 73, 95, 88, 92, 81, 67.

Step 1 Find the quartile values, the minimum value, and the maximum value.

67   73   79   81   84   88   90   92   95

Q_2 = median = 84

When the median is a value of the data set, it is removed for the calculation of Q_1 and Q_3.

67   73   79   81   88   90   92   95

$Q_1 = \dfrac{73 + 79}{2} = 76$ $Q_3 = \dfrac{90 + 92}{2} = 91$

The minimum value is 67, and the maximum value is 95.

Step 2 Draw a number line for the base of your box-and-whisker plot. Above the number line, plot the three quartiles, the minimum value, and the maximum value.

Step 3 Finish your box-and-whisker plot by drawing a box through Q_1 and Q_3, a vertical line through the median, and line segments from the box outward to the minimum and maximum values.

3.

25 30 35 40 45 50

✓ **Quick Check** ③ Make a box-and-whisker plot for these values: 34, 36, 47, 45, 28, 31, 29, 40.
See left.

662 Chapter 12 Probability and Statistics

Online
active math

For: Box Plot Activity
Use: Interactive Textbook, 12-3

Oceanography Use a graphing calculator to find the quartiles of the water temperature data in Example 2.

Use the **STAT PLOT** feature to select a box-and-whisker plot. Enter the window values. Graph the box-and-whisker plot.

● Use the **TRACE** feature to find the quartiles: $Q_1 = 64.5$, $Q_2 = 75$, and $Q_3 = 83.5$.

✓ **Quick Check** 4 Use the data for just the summer months, as shown in the graph below. Find the quartiles by graphing the box-and-whisker plot. **See left.**

4.

$Q_1 = 84$, $Q_2 = 85$,
$Q_3 = 86$

Gulf of Mexico Eastern Coast Water Temperatures (°F)

Pensacola   St. Petersburg   Key West   Dauphin Island   Grand Isle

■ June   ■ July   ■ August

Let x be a value from a data set. A **percentile** is a number from 0 to 100 that you can associate with x to indicate the percent of the data that are less than or equal to x. If x is at the 63rd percentile, then 63% of the data are less than or equal to x.

5 **EXAMPLE** Using Percentiles

Find the values at the 20th and 65th percentiles for the values below.
54 98 45 87 98 64 21 61 71 82 93 65 62 98 87 24 65 97 31 47

Step 1 Order the values.
21 24 31 45 47 54 61 62 64 65 65 71 82 87 87 93 97 98 98 98

Step 2 Find the number of values that fall below the 20th percentile and the number that fall below the 65th percentile.

Of the 20 values, 20% should fall below the 20th percentile and 65% should fall below the 65th percentile.

$20 \cdot 20\% = 20 \cdot 0.20 = 4$ $20 \cdot 65\% = 20 \cdot 0.65 = 13$

Since 47 is greater than 4 values, 47 is at the 20th percentile.   Since 87 is greater than 13 values, 87 is at the 65th percentile.

● The value at the 20th percentile is 47 and the value at the 65th percentile is 87.

✓ **Quick Check** 5 Find the value at each percentile for the data in Example 5.
    a. 0th percentile **21**   **b.** 45th percentile **65**   **c.** 55th percentile **71**

Lesson 12-3 Analyzing Data **663**

Additional Examples

3.

76 78 80 82 84 86 88 90 92 94 96 98 100 102 104 106 108

663

Assignment Guide

🄥 A B 1-3, 12, 20

🄦 A B 4-11, 13-19
C Challenge 21-22

Test Prep 23-27
Mixed Review 28-35

Homework Quick Check

To check students' understanding of key skills and concepts, go over Exercises 2, 6, 8, 13, 16-18, 20.

Error Prevention!

Exercises 1–11 Remind students that data sets must be placed in increasing or decreasing order before finding medians.

Differentiated Instruction **Resources**

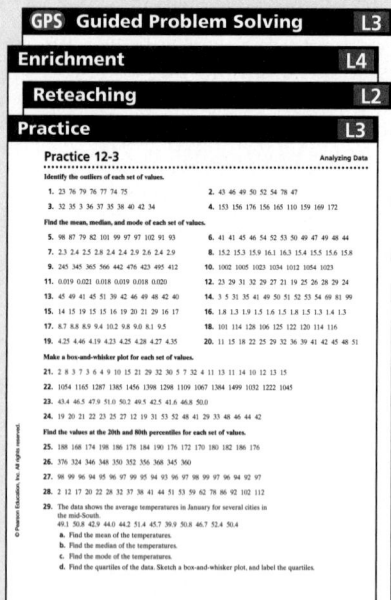

GPS Guided Problem Solving	L3
Enrichment	L4
Reteaching	L2
Practice	L3

4.

10 12 14 16 18 20

5.

100 110 120 130 140 150

6.

20 40 60 80 100

664

6a. Yes; it is unlikely that the water temperature of a lake would change by 25°.

Test-Taking Tip

It is often helpful to arrange a data list in increasing or decreasing order.

✓ **Quick Check**

An **outlier** is an item of data with a value substantially different from the rest of the items in the data set. Sometimes an outlier is an important part of the data. At other times it can represent a false reading. When you think an outlier has resulted from an error, you may remove it from the data set.

6 EXAMPLE Identifying an Outlier

Multiple Choice Which is an outlier for this set of values: 56 65 73 59 98 65 59?
- Ⓐ 42
- Ⓑ 65
- Ⓒ 98
- Ⓓ 59

Order the data.

Find the differences between adjacent values.

● 98 is substantially different, so 98 is an outlier. The correct choice is C.

6 a. Suppose the values in Example 6 are measurements of the water temperature of a lake. Would you discard the outlier? Explain. **a. See above left.**

b. Suppose the data represent the number of customers in a small restaurant each night during one week. Would you discard the outlier? Explain.
No; 98 would represent the busiest night of the week and it may relate to a weekly event.

EXERCISES

For more exercises, see *Extra Skill and Word Problem Practice*.

Practice and Problem Solving

Ⓐ **Practice by Example**

Examples 1 and 2
(pages 660 and 661)

Examples 3 and 4
(pages 662 and 663)

GO for Help

1. 4.$\overline{36}$, 3, 1

2. 338.5, 316, no mode

Find the mean, median, and mode of each set of values. 1–2. See below left.

1. 5 9 1 2 7 3 1 8 8 1 3
2. 307 309 323 304 390 398
3. 475 722 499 572 402 809 499 828 405 499 800 422 672 800
600.3, 535.5, 499

Make a box-and-whisker plot for each set of values. 4–7. See margin.

4. 12 11 15 12 19 20 19
5. 120 145 133 105 117 150
6. 49 57.5 58 49.2 62 22.2 67 52.1 77 99.9 80 51.7 64

7. Weather The table shows the high temperatures for one day at different locations on the island of Maui, Hawaii. Make a box-and-whisker plot of the data.

High Temperatures on Maui

Location	Temperature
Kahului	88°F
Kihei	85°F
Lahaina	86°F
Hana	82°F
Haleakala	66°F
Kula	75°F

Example 5
(page 663)

Find the values at the 30th and 90th percentiles for each set of values.

8. 6283 5700 6381 6274 5700 5896 5972 6075 5993 5581 **5896, 6381**

9. 7 12 3 14 17 20 5 3 17 4 13 2 15 9 15 18 16 9 1 6 **6, 18**

Example 6
(page 664)

Identify the outlier of each set of values.

10. 3.4 4.5 2.3 5.9 9.8 3.3 2.1 3.0 2.9 **9.8**

11. 17 21 19 10 15 19 14 0 11 16 **0**

7.

66 70 74 78 82 86 90

Dilbert

B **Apply Your Skills**

12. a. What percent of the customers in the cartoon are exactly the median age?   **0%**
  b. Must one item from a data set fall exactly at the median? Explain.
  c. Can the company do anything about the shocking discovery? Explain.
  b–c. See margin.

13. Meteorology On May 3, 1999, 59 tornadoes hit Oklahoma in the largest
  GPS tornado outbreak ever recorded in the state. Sixteen of these were classified
  as strong (F2 or F3) or violent (F4 or F5).   **a, c. See margin.**
  a. Make a box-and-whisker plot of the data for length of path.
  b. Identify the outliers. Remove them from the data set and make a revised
  box-and-whisker plot.   **b. See below left.**
  c. Writing How does the removal of the outliers affect the box-and-whisker
  plot? How does it affect the median of the data set?

Identify the outlier of each set of values. Then describe how its value affects the mean of the data.
  103; this value lowers the mean.
14. 947 757 103 619 661 582 626 900 869 728 1001 596 515

15. 87 104 381 215 174 199 233 186 142 228 9 53 117 129
  381; this value raises the mean.

For Exercises 16–18, use the set of values below.
1 1 1 1 1 1 2 3 5 8 13 21 34 55 89 89 89 89 89 89

16. At what percentile is 1? **0th**   **17.** At what percentile is 34? **60th**

18. Error Analysis A student claims that 89 is at the 100th percentile. Explain
  the student's error.   **See margin.**

19. Geology The table below shows the number of major earthquakes (magnitude
  7.0 or greater) worldwide in the ten-year period from 1991 through 2000.

Major Earthquakes Worldwide (Magnitude 7.0 and Greater)

Year	1991	1992	1993	1994	1995	1996	1997	1998	1999	2000
Earthquakes	11	23	16	15	25	22	20	16	23	18

SOURCE: U.S. Geological Survey National Earthquake Information Center

a. Find the mean and the median of the numbers of
  annual earthquakes.   **18.9, 19**
b. Do the data include an outlier that you should
  discard? Explain.   **b–c. See margin.**
c. Compare the box-and-whisker plots at the right.
  One shows the data above. The other shows
  worldwide earthquake data from 1900 through
  2000. What conclusions can you draw about
  recent earthquakes? Justify your reasoning.

Xmin = 0   Ymin = 0
Xmax = 45   Ymax = 1
Xscl = 5   Yscl = 1

Major Tornadoes in Oklahoma, May 3, 1999

Length of Path (miles)	Intensity
6	F3
9	F3
4	F2
37	F5
7	F2
12	F3
8	F2
7	F2
15	F4
39	F4
1	F2
22	F3
15	F3
8	F2
13	F3
2	F2

SOURCE: National Oceanic & Atmospheric Administration

13b. 37, 39

GO Online
Homework Video Tutor
Visit: PHSchool.com
Web Code: age-1203

Connection to Geology

Exercise 19 The magnitudes of earthquakes are measured on the Richter scale. It is a scale from 0 to 9 used to measure the severity of earthquakes according to the amount of energy released, with a higher number indicating stronger tremors. Each increase of magnitude of 1 on the scale represents a release of about 30 times as much energy.

12b. No; if there is an even number of items in a data set, the median may lie between data values.

  c. No; 50% of a data set will always lie at or below the median.

13a.

  0 10 20 30 40

  c. The main effect of removing the outlier is a shortening of the long whisker. The median decreases from 8.5 to 8.

18. Only 14 out of 20 values are below 89, so 89 is at the 70th percentile. For a number to be at the 100th percentile, 100% of the values must be below that number. That is impossible since a number cannot be less than itself.

19b. No; none of the values is significantly less or greater than the others.

  c. Recent earthquakes have been more consistent in their numbers, with fewer light years as well as fewer extremely heavy years; this is indicated by the shorter whiskers on the box-and-whisker plot for 1991 through 2000.

665

Lesson Quiz

1. Marina has the following quiz grades in her Algebra 2 class: 84, 90, 96, 100, 67, 88, 90, 92, 94.
   a. Find the mean, median, and mode for Marina's quiz grades. **89; 90; 90**
   b. Make a box-and-whisker plot for Marina's grades.

   65 70 75 80 85 90 95 100

2. Find the values at the 40th and 70th percentiles for the values below.
   26, 37, 18, 45, 20, 36, 22, 25, 50, 41
   26; 41

3. Identify an outlier for this set of data: 65, 70, 56, 45, 59, 67, 62. **45**

Alternative Assessment

Write several sets of data on the chalkboard or overhead projector. Then give students one box and whisker plot that matches one of the sets of data. Ask students to identify the set of data that the plot represents. Then ask students to describe the median, quartiles, minimum, maximum, and any outliers.

Test Prep

Resources
For additional practice with a variety of test item formats:
• Standardized Test Prep, p. 705
• Test-Taking Strategies, p. 700
• Test-Taking Strategies with Transparencies

---

20. **Critical Thinking** Which measure better represents a data set with several outliers—the mean or the median? Justify your answer. **See margin.**

Challenge

21. **Track and Field** The table shows the 36 best qualifying distances for the shot put events for both men and women during the 2004 Olympics.

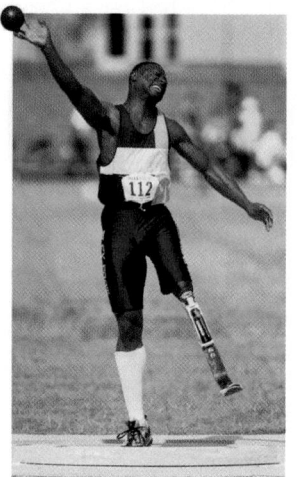

Real-World Connection

The "shot" in shot put refers to cannonballs. For centuries, soldiers used them in throwing contests.

2004 Olympic Qualifying Distances for Shot Put (meters)

Men	21.15	20.78	20.65	20.61	20.53	20.45	20.37	20.32	20.11
	20.06	20.06	20.04	19.69	19.68	19.67	19.60	19.55	19.50
	19.46	19.41	19.40	19.38	19.31	19.25	19.14	19.09	19.09
	19.07	19.04	19.02	19.02	18.91	18.89	18.67	18.52	18.44
Women	19.69	19.10	18.90	18.79	18.65	18.61	18.57	18.52	18.38
	18.33	18.16	18.03	18.00	17.99	17.89	17.78	17.44	17.34
	17.28	17.22	17.17	17.11	16.90	16.58	16.49	16.47	16.45
	16.35	15.99	15.91	15.86	15.33	15.20	15.06	14.88	14.60

a. Using the same number line base for both plots, make a box-and-whisker plot for the men's results and another for the women's results.
b. Writing Compare your box-and-whisker plots. Describe any conclusions you can draw about Olympic-level male and female shot-putters. **a–b. See margin.**

22. **a. Government** Make a box-and-whisker plot for the data from each of the three types of elections shown in the table below. **a–b. See margin p. 667.**

Voter Turnout (percent of voting-age population)

Presidential Year	1976	1980	1984	1988	1992	1996	2000
Voting for President	53.5	52.8	53.3	50.3	55.1	48.9	51.2
Voting for Representatives	48.9	47.6	47.8	44.9	50.8	45.7	47.2
Non-Presidential Year	1978	1982	1986	1990	1994	1998	2002
Voting for Representatives	34.9	38.0	33.5	33.1	36.6	32.7	34.2

SOURCE: **U.S. Census Bureau.** Go to **www.PHSchool.com** for a data update.
Web Code: agg-9041

b. Writing How does a Presidential election in the United States affect the voter turnout rate in elections for the House of Representatives? Use your box-and-whisker plots to describe any effect that you see.

Test Prep

Multiple Choice

A person checked for e-mail four times each day. The table shows the number of new e-mails she received each time she checked during 5 days.

Day 1	Day 2	Day 3	Day 4	Day 5
6, 3, 1, 5	5, 3, 7, 2	6, 7, 3, 2	8, 2, 6, 9	7, 7, 6, 11

23. Which value is the greatest? **D**
   A. the mean number of e-mails for checks made on days 1–3
   B. the mean number of e-mails for checks made on days 2–4
   C. the mean number of e-mails for checks made on days 2–3
   D. the median number of e-mails for checks made on days 3–4

24. Which of the given sets of data has the greatest median? **G**
   F. 1, 1, 2, 3, 4, 5, 6, 7, 8, 8   **G.** 1, 2, 3, 4, 5, 6, 7, 8, 9, 10
   H. 4, 4, 4, 5, 5, 5, 5, 5, 5, 4, 4   **J.** 1, 2, 3, 4, 5, 6, 7, 8

---

20. The median is a better representation for the data; a few outliers can heavily influence the mean without drastically affecting the median.

21a.
Men: ⊏⊐
Women: ⊏⊐
14 15 16 17 18 19 20 21

b. Answers may vary. Sample: The range for women's shot put is greater than men's. The men are more consistent, as indicated by the shorter box and whiskers. Overall the men tend to throw farther.

25. Which statement(s) is (are) true?   **B**

 I. The mean number of e-mails for checks made over the 5 days was 5.3.
 II. The mean number of e-mails for checks made on day 5 was 7.75.
 III. The median number of e-mails for checks made over the 5 days was 6.5.

 A. I only   **B.** I and II only   **C.** II and III only   **D.** I, II, and III

Short Response **26.** Describe how you could find the scores at the 20th and 60th percentiles in a set of 80 scores.   **See margin.**

Extended Response **27.** Draw a box-and-whisker plot for this set of values: 123, 127, 127, 142, 118, 131, 137, 125, 131.   **See margin.**

Mixed Review

Lesson 12-2 **Of all the respondents to a survey, 59% are girls. Of the girls, 61% read horror stories. Of the boys, 49% read horror stories.**

 28. Find P(boy and reads horror stories).   **29.** Find P(reads horror stories).
  ≈ 0.20 ≈ 0.56

Lesson 11-2 **Is the sequence arithmetic? If so, identify the common difference.**

 30. $16, 7, -2, \ldots$ **31.** $34, 51, 68, \ldots$ **32.** $2, 2.2, 2.22, \ldots$ **33.** $1, 1, 1, \ldots$
   yes; -9 yes; 17   no   yes; 0

Lesson 10-2 **Graph each equation.   34–35. See margin.**

 34. $y^2 - x - 2y + 1 = 0$ **35.** $x^2 + 4x + 144y + 4 = 0$

✓ Checkpoint Quiz 1   **Lessons 12-1 through 12-3**

In a poll, gymnasts were asked, "How many seconds long was your longest handstand on the balance beam?" Use the results below for Exercises 1 and 2.

Longest Handstand

Duration (seconds)	0–2	3–5	6–10	11–20	21–30	31–60	> 60	Total
Number of Respondents	14	27	19	18	13	15	24	130

 1. Graph the probability distribution.   **2.** Find $P(6-30$ seconds).
      See margin.   0.385

3. No; when $x = 1$, $P(x) = -\frac{1}{2}$, and probability is never negative.

 3. Writing Could the function $P(x) = \frac{x-2}{2}$ for $x = 1, 2, 3,$ or 4, represent a probability distribution? Explain.   **See left.**

4. $\frac{12}{57} = \frac{4}{19}$

6. $\frac{23}{43}$

Use the table at the right to find each probability.

 4. $P(\text{teacher} \mid \text{yes})$ **5.** $P(\text{no} \mid \text{teacher})$ $\frac{5}{8}$

 6. $P(\text{student} \mid \text{no})$ **7.** $P(\text{yes} \mid \text{student})$ $\frac{45}{68}$

Did You Eat Breakfast Today?

	Yes	No
Teachers	12	20
Students	45	23

Find the mean, median, and mode of each data set.

 8. 7 4 9 3 5 4 4 7 9 10 3 1 8   **5.69, 5, 4**

 9. 1.2 2.1 4.6 2.5 9.7 6.2 2.6 2.4 3.1 3.8   **3.82, 2.85, no mode**

 10. Open-Ended Write a data set that includes an outlier. Make a box-and-whisker plot of your data set with and without the outlier.   **Check students' work.**

22a.

 b. A Presidential election greatly increases voter turnout rate for the House of Representatives. The median turnout increases by 13.4%. The minimum **turnout in a Presidential election year is 6.9% greater than the maximum turnout for a non-Presidential election year.**

✓ Checkpoint Quiz

Use this Checkpoint Quiz to check students' understanding of the skills and concepts of Lessons 12-1 through 12-3.

Resources
Grab & Go
 • Checkpoint Quiz 1

26. **[2] Order the 80 scores from lowest to highest. The 20th percentile is the score that is greater than 20%, or 16, of the values; the 60th percentile is the score that is greater than 60% or 48, of the values.**

 [1] minor error

27. **[4]**

115 120 125 130 135 140 145

 [3] 4 correct values out of 5

 [2] 3 correct values

 [1] 1 correct value

34.

35.

Checkpoint Quiz 1

1.

Longest Handstand bar graph — Probability (0.05–0.25) vs Seconds Duration (0–2, 3–5, 6–10, 11–20, 20–30, 30–60, >60)

667

12-4

1. Plan

Objectives
1 To find the standard deviation of a set of values
2 To use standard deviation in real-world situations

Examples
1 Real-World Connection
2 Finding the Standard Deviation
3 Real-World Connection
4 Real-World Connection
5 Finding the z-score

Math Background

Standard deviation is often very important in scientific experiments. A small standard deviation for measurements in an experiment often signifies that the results are consistent. A large standard deviation often signifies that the experiment is inconclusive. The use of z-scores provides a common measurement standard.

More Math Background: p. 646C

Lesson Planning and Resources

See p. 646E for a list of the resources that support this lesson.

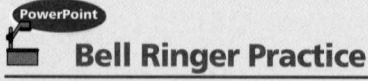

Bell Ringer Practice

☑ **Check Skills You'll Need**
For intervention, direct students to:

Simplifying Expressions with Integers
Skills Handbook: p. 873

668

12-4 Standard Deviation

What You'll Learn

- To find the standard deviation of a set of values
- To use standard deviation in real-world situations

. . . And Why

To analyze energy demand, as in Example 3

 New Vocabulary

☑ **Check Skills You'll Need**

 for Help Skills Handbook page 873

Simplify each expression. If necessary, round to the nearest hundredth.

1. $\frac{34.3}{7}$ **4.9**
2. $\frac{6}{2.4}$ **2.5**
3. $8.4 \cdot 1.25$ **10.5**
4. $12 - 6 \cdot 0.5$ **9**
5. $\frac{1}{3}[(2-6)^2 + (7-6)^2 + (8-6)^2]$ **7**
6. $\sqrt{\frac{1}{2}(4-3)^2 + (5+3)^2}$ **8.03**

- measures of variation
- range of a set of data
- interquartile range
- standard deviation
- z-score

---

1 Finding Standard Deviation

1a. Set 1: 80, 80, 80
Set 2: 80, 80, 80
Set 3: 80, 80, 80
Set 4: 80, 80, 80

b. No; although the measures of central tendency are the same, the data in each set are different.

2. Set 1: 6
Set 2: 120
Set 3: 60
Set 4: 120
These differences tell you only how far apart the min. and max. values are.

3. Set 1: 78.5, 80, 81.5
Set 2: 65, 80, 95
Set 3: 65, 80, 95
Set 4: 35, 80, 125

4. Set 1: 3
Set 2: 30
Set 3: 30
Set 4: 90

Activity: Analyzing Data Spread

1. a. Find the mean, the median, and the mode of each set of data.

Set 1	77	78	79	80	80	81	82	83
Set 2	20	60	70	80	80	90	100	140
Set 3	50	60	70	80	80	90	100	110
Set 4	20	30	40	80	80	120	130	140

b. Are the sets the same? Explain.

2. Find the difference between the greatest and least values in each set of data. What do these differences tell you about each set of data?

3. Find the quartiles of each set of data.

4. For each set, half of the data lie between Q_1 and Q_3. The value $Q_3 - Q_1$ gives you an idea of how the data are spread out. Find $Q_3 - Q_1$ for each set of data.

5. a. Give an example of two sets of data that are spread out differently, though the differences between their extreme values are the same.
b. Give an example of two sets of data that are spread out differently, though their values of $Q_3 - Q_1$ are the same.

5–6. See back of book.
6. a. Summarize the similarities and differences among the four sets in terms of central tendency and spread. Which is the most spread-out set? Which is the least? Explain.
b. Make box-and-whisker plots of the four sets of data. Do the plots support your conclusions from part (a)?

668 Chapter 12 Probability and Statistics

Differentiated Instruction Solutions for All Learners

Special Needs L1
Students may be overwhelmed by the number of new terms in this lesson. Encourage them to make flashcards of the terms with short descriptions on the flipsides.

learning style: tactile

Below Level L2
Make sure students understand that the upper case sigma (Σ) and the lower case sigma (σ) have two different meanings.

learning style: verbal

668

Statisticians use several **measures of variation** to describe how the data in a data set are spread out.

The **range of a set of data** is the difference between the greatest and least values. The **interquartile range** is the difference between the third and first quartiles.

① EXAMPLE **Real-World Connection**

Thirteen men qualified for the 2002 U.S. Men's Alpine Ski Team. Find the range and the interquartile range of their ages at the time of qualification: 27, 28, 29, 23, 25, 26, 26, 28, 22, 23, 23, 21, 25.

greatest value − least value = 29 − 21	**Find the range.**
= 8	

Median   **Find the median.**
↓

21 22 23 23 23 25 **25** 26 26 27 28 28 29
      ↑   ↑

$Q_1 = 23$ $Q_3 = \frac{27+28}{2} = 27.5$ **Find Q_1 and Q_3.**

$Q_3 - Q_1 = 27.5 - 23$ **Find the interquartile range.**
           = 4.5

● The range is 8 years. The interquartile range is 4.5 years.

✓ Quick Check **①** **a.** Seventeen women qualified for the 2002 U.S. Women's Alpine Ski Team. Find the range and the interquartile range of their ages: 24, 30, 29, 21, 22, 22, 28, 21, 16, 17, 25, 22, 21, 18, 19, 18, 19. **range: 14, interquartile range: 6**
b. Critical Thinking Can the variation, or spread, in two sets of data be different, even though they have the same range? Give an example.
c. Can the variation in two sets of data be different, even though they have the same interquartile range? Give an example. **b–c. See back of book.**

Another measure of variation is the **standard deviation,** a measure of how much the values in a data set vary, or deviate, from the mean. The Greek letter σ (sigma) represents standard deviation.

You can use the following procedure to calculate standard deviation.

 Key Concepts

Summary	**Finding Standard Deviation**

- Find the mean of the data set: $\bar{x}$.
- Find the difference between each value and the mean: $x - \bar{x}$.
- Square each difference: $(x - \bar{x})^2$.
- Find the average (mean) of these squares: $\dfrac{\sum(x - \bar{x})^2}{n}$.
- Take the square root to find the standard deviation:

$$\sigma = \sqrt{\frac{\sum(x - \bar{x})^2}{n}}.$$

2. Teach

Guided Instruction

Activity
You may want to have students make box-and-whisker plots for each data set first, before completing steps 4–6a. The visual representation of the data may make the comparisons easier.

PowerPoint
Additional Example

① There are 9 members of the Community Youth Leadership Board. Find the range and interquartile range of their ages: 22, 16, 24, 17, 16, 25, 20, 19, 26
10 years; 8 years

2 Find the mean and standard deviation for the values 78.2, 90.5, 98.1, 93.7, 94.5 **91; about 6.8**

3 Use the information from Example 3 to find the mean and standard deviation for daily energy demand on the *weekends* only. **about 36.1; about 3.6**

2 EXAMPLE **Math Tip**

Greek letters are often used in mathematics as variables or to represent special numbers. Some examples are σ, and π. Explain that the Greek letters have upper- and lower-case forms like the Latin letters we use in English. In the case of sigma, the upper- and lower-case forms have very different meaning in mathematics. The upper-case form, Σ, means summation. The lower-case form, σ, represents standard deviation. Suggest that students record the meanings of Σ, and σ in their notebooks.

3 EXAMPLE **Alternative Method**

The square of the standard deviation, also known as the variance, can be calculated by subtracting the square of the mean from the mean of the squares of the data values. The square root of this value is the standard deviation. Have students use the information displayed in the first three lines by the 1-Var Stats function to calculate the standard deviation for the data given in Example 3 using this alternative method. This value should agree with the value displayed as σx.

670

---

2 EXAMPLE **Finding the Standard Deviation**

Find the mean and the standard deviation for the values: 48.0, 53.2, 52.3, 46.6, 49.9.

$$\bar{x} = \frac{48.0 + 53.2 + 52.3 + 46.6 + 49.9}{5} = 50.0$$ **Find the mean.**

Organize the next steps in a table.

x	$\bar{x}$	$x - \bar{x}$	$(x - \bar{x})^2$
48.0	50.0	-2.0	4.00
53.2	50.0	3.2	10.24
52.3	50.0	2.3	5.29
46.6	50.0	-3.4	11.56
49.9	50.0	-0.1	0.01

Sum: 31.1

$$\sigma = \sqrt{\frac{\sum (x - \bar{x})^2}{n}}$$ **Find the standard deviation.**

$$= \sqrt{\frac{31.1}{5}} \approx 2.5$$

● The mean is 50.0, and the standard deviation is about 2.5.

✓ Quick Check **2** Find the mean and the standard deviation for these values: 50, 60, 70, 80, 80, 90, 100, 110. **80, ≈18.7**

Standard deviation is like a custom-made measuring stick for the variation in a set of data. A small standard deviation (compared to actual data values) indicates that the data are clustered tightly around the mean. As the data become more spread out, the standard deviation increases.

3 EXAMPLE **Real-World Connection**

Vocabulary Tip

The watt is the metric unit of measurement for power. One million watts of power delivered for one hour results in one megawatt-hour (MWh).

Energy Find the mean and the standard deviation of the data for daily energy demand in a small town during August.

Daily Energy Demand During August (MWh)

Sun.	Mon.	Tues.	Wed.	Thurs.	Fri.	Sat.
		53	52	47	50	39
33	40	41	44	47	49	43
39	47	49	54	53	46	36
33	45	45	42	43	39	33
33	40	40	41	42		

Step 1 Use the STAT feature to enter the data as L1.

Step 2 Use the CALC menu of STAT to access the 1-Var Stats option.

The mean is about 43.2 MWh; the standard deviation is about
● 6.0 MWh.

```
1-Var Stats
 x̄=43.16129032        ← mean
 Σx=1338
 Σx²=58872
 Sx=6.116081394
 σx=6.016626288       ← standard
↓n=31                     deviation
```

✓ Quick Check ③ Find the mean and standard deviation for this data set: 2 mm, 3 mm, 4 mm, 6 mm, 7 mm, 9 mm, 10 mm, 12 mm, 13 mm, 14 mm.   **8, about 4.0**

2 Using Standard Deviation

In a data list, every value falls within some number of standard deviations of the mean. When a value falls within one standard deviation of the mean, it is in the range of values from one standard deviation below the mean to one standard deviation above. For example, if the mean is 50 and the standard deviation is 10, then a value x within one standard deviation of the mean must be in the range $40 \le x \le 60$.

④ **EXAMPLE** Real-World Connection

Energy Use the energy demand data from Example 3. Within how many standard deviations of the mean do all of the values fall? How might the company supplying power to the town use this information?

Step 1 Draw a number line. Plot the data values and the mean.

Step 2 Mark off intervals of 6.0 on either side of the mean.

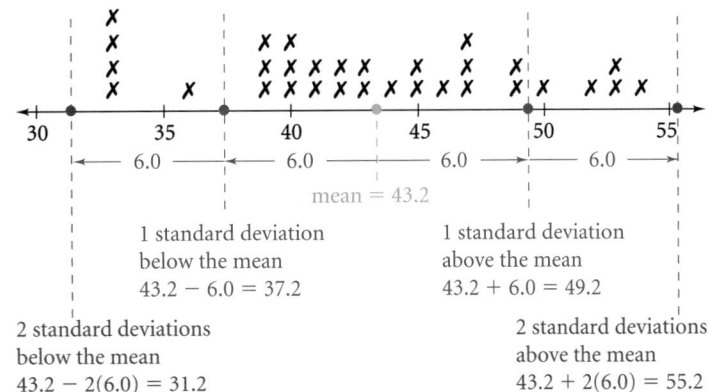

1 standard deviation below the mean
$43.2 - 6.0 = 37.2$

1 standard deviation above the mean
$43.2 + 6.0 = 49.2$

2 standard deviations below the mean
$43.2 - 2(6.0) = 31.2$

2 standard deviations above the mean
$43.2 + 2(6.0) = 55.2$

All of the values fall within two standard deviations of the mean. Therefore, the power company can expect that the daily demand on most days in August will fall within two standard deviations of the mean.

✓ Quick Check ④ **a.** Within how many standard deviations of the mean for August is a demand of 38.5 MWh? **1**

4b. No; three standard deviations from the mean is 46.3, which is less than 48.

b. In May, the mean daily energy demand is 35.8 MWh, with a standard deviation of 3.5 MWh. The power company prepares for any demand within three standard deviations of the mean. Are they prepared for a demand of 48 MWh? Explain.

The **z-score** is the number of standard deviations that a value is from the mean. In Example 4, the value 49.2 is one standard deviation above the mean, so it has a z-score of 1. The value 37.2, which is one standard deviation below the mean, has a z-score of −1.

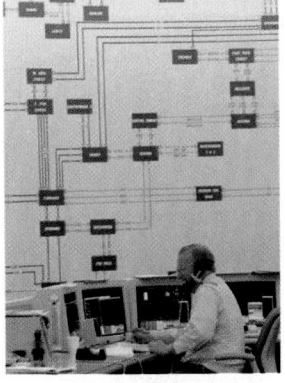

Real-World Connection

Careers Dispatchers coordinate a utility's power supply and demand.

Guided Instruction

④ **EXAMPLE** **Math Tip**

Make sure students understand that two standard deviations on the number line is 12 units. So all of the values are less than 12 units from the mean.

PowerPoint

Additional Examples

④ The number of points that Darden scored in each of 11 basketball games is listed below. Within how many standard deviations of the mean do all of the values fall? What can Darden's coach do with this information? 8, 12, 13, 10, 7, 5, 10, 9, 13, 11, 8
2; The coach can predict that his score in the next game will fall within two standard deviations of the mean.

⑤ A set of values has a mean of 22 and a standard deviation of 5. Find the z-score for a value of 30.
1.6

Resources
• Daily Notetaking Guide 12-4 [L3]

Closure

Give students the following situation: *Suppose two baseball players have the same mean number of hits per game. However, player A's data has a standard deviation of 0.5 and player B's data has a standard deviation of 2. Which one is most likely to get a hit at his next at-bat? Explain.* **Player A. His lower standard deviation means that he is more consistent.**

Assignment Guide

▼**1** A B 1–7, 15–19, 22–26, 28

▼**2** A B 8–14, 20, 21, 27
C Challenge   29–30

Test Prep   31–34
Mixed Review   35–41

Homework Quick Check
To check students' understanding of key skills and concepts, go over Exercises 4, 8, 10, 17–22.

Error Prevention!

Exercises 8, 9 Caution students that they must use the number of standard deviations that includes *all* data values, both above and below the mean.

Differentiated Instruction **Resources**

GPS Guided Problem Solving	L3
Enrichment	L4
Reteaching	L2
Practice	L3

15. 14.6, 52.3; the bird speeds are more spread out than the cat speeds.

16. 4.1, 2.0; the number of buttons is more spread out than the number of pockets.

---

5 **EXAMPLE** Finding the z-score

A set of values has a mean of 85 and a standard deviation of 6. Find the z-score of the value 76.

$$z\text{-score} = \frac{\text{value} - \text{mean}}{\text{standard deviation}}$$

$$= \frac{76 - 85}{6} \quad \textbf{Substitute.}$$

$$= \frac{-9}{6} \quad \textbf{Simplify.}$$

$$= -1.5$$

✓ **Quick Check** **5** Use the mean and standard deviation from Example 5. Find the value that has a z-score of 2.5. **100**

EXERCISES

For more exercises, see *Extra Skill and Word Problem Practice.*

Practice and Problem Solving

Ⓐ **Practice by Example**

GO for **Help**

Example 1
(page 669)

Find the range and the interquartile range of each set of values.

1. 5 6 7 3 4 5 6 7 8 **5, 2.5**   **2.** 56 78 125 34 67 91 20 **105, 57**

3. 724 786 670 760 300 187 190 345 456 732 891 879 324
704, 461

Examples 2 and 3
(page 670)

Find the mean and the standard deviation for each set of values.

4. 78 90 456 673 111 381 21   **5.** 13 15 17 18 12 21 10

4. 258.6, 228.3

5. 15.1, 3.5

6. The Dow Jones Industrial average for the last 24 weeks of 1994: **3816.43; 67.22**

3735.04	3764.50	3747.02	3768.71	3755.11	3881.05
3885.58	3874.81	3933.35	3831.75	3843.19	3797.43
3910.47	3891.30	3930.66	3807.52	3801.47	3815.26
3708.27	3745.62	3691.11	3807.19	3833.43	3834.44

7. The Dow Jones Industrial average for the last 24 weeks of 2004: **10,259.18; 300.28**

9962.22	10,139.71	9815.33	9825.35	10,110.14	10,195.01
10,260.20	10,313.07	10,284.46	10,047.24	10,192.65	10,055.20
9933.38	9757.81	10,027.47	10,387.54	10,539.01	10,456.91
10,522.23	10,592.21	10,543.22	10,649.92	10,827.12	10,783.01

Example 4
(page 671)

Determine the whole number of standard deviations that includes all data values.

8. The mean price of the nonfiction books on a best-sellers list is \$25.07; the standard deviation is \$2.62. **2 standard deviations**
\$26.95, \$22.95, \$24.00, \$24.95, \$29.95, \$19.95, \$24.95, \$24.00, \$27.95, \$25.00

9. The mean length of Beethoven's nine symphonies is 37 minutes; the standard deviation is 12 minutes. **3 standard deviations**
27 min, 30 min, 47 min, 35 min, 30 min, 40 min, 35 min, 22 min, 65 min

Example 5
(page 672)

A data set has mean 25 and standard deviation 5. Find the z-score of each value.

10. 39 **2.8**   **11.** 18 **−1.4**   **12.** 125 **20**   **13.** 25 **0**   **14.** 11 **−2.8**

---

18. The range dropped slightly from 7715 in 2001 to 7611 in 2002. Overall farm income increased slightly, but there was less variability among the states in 2002.

19. 2678.9, 2759.0; The incomes in 2001 clustered more tightly around the mean.

22. ≈10.9; ≈3.3

23. ≈75.8; ≈8.7

24. ≈1.9; ≈1.4

25. ≈0.007; ≈0.08

B **Apply Your Skills** **Find the standard deviation for each data set. Use the standard deviations to compare each pair of data sets.** 15–16. See margin p. 672.

15. fastest recorded speeds of various large wild cats (miles per hour):
70 50 30 40 35 30 30 40 15
fastest recorded speeds of various birds in flight (miles per hour):
217 106 95 56 65 37 50 31 53 25 25 25

16. the number of buttons on selected outfits:
11 5 12 8 3 12 10 10 0 5 0 2 7 10
the number of pockets in the same outfits:
5 5 5 2 2 5 3 2 0 2 0 0 5 5

 Income Use the chart at the right for Exercises 17–20.

17. Find the mean income for each year. 2001: ≈6707; 2002: ≈6738

Real-World **Connection**

The fastest wild cat is the cheetah, which can run as fast as 70 mi/h.

18. **Writing** Use the range of the data for each year to describe how farm income varied from 2001 to 2002. **See margin p. 672.**

19. Find the standard deviation for each year. In which year did farm income cluster more tightly around the mean? **See margin p. 672.**

20. Which state's 2001 income has a z-score of about 1.4? **Iowa**

Farm Income in Midwestern States (millions of dollars)

State	2001	2002
Iowa	10,653	10,834
Kansas	7979	7862
Minnesota	7537	7478
Missouri	4723	4402
Nebraska	9221	9589
North Dakota	2938	3223
South Dakota	3897	3779

SOURCE: U.S. Department of Agriculture

21a. 53.8, ≈3.4   b. 7; 9; 10

 21. a. **Energy** Find the mean and the standard deviation for daily energy usage during ten days in June: 51.8 MWh, 53.6 MWh, 54.7 MWh, 51.9 MWh, 49.3 MWh, 52.0 MWh, 53.5 MWh, 51.2 MWh, 60.7 MWh, 59.3 MWh.
b. How many items in the data set fall within one standard deviation of the mean? Within two standard deviations? Within three standard deviations?

Another measure of variation is *variance*, **which equals** σ^2**. Find the variance and the standard deviation of each data set.**   22–27. See margin.

GPS 22. 12 h 3 h 2 h 4 h 5 h 7 h   23. 60 m 40 m 35 m 45 m 39 m

24. $6.99 $5.50 $7.10 $9.22 $8.99   25. 0.7 g 0.84 g 0.9 g 0.8 g 0.69 g

26. **Critical Thinking** From your results in Exercises 22–25, which do you think is a better measure of variation—variance or standard deviation? Explain.

27. **Error Analysis** Minh says that the data below fall within three standard deviations of the mean. Marsha disagrees, saying that the data fall within six standard deviations of the mean. With whom do you agree? Explain.

mean = 82.5

GO **Online**

Homework Video Tutor

Visit: PHSchool.com
Web Code: aga-1204

GO for Help

For a guide to solving Exercise 21, see p. 675.

26. **Answers may vary. Sample: standard deviation, because it has the same units of measure as the data, and it doesn't magnify the** variation as much as the variance does.

27. **Minh; one standard deviation encompasses all values within one** standard deviation above and below the mean. The graph actually shows that all values are within 3 standard deviations of the mean.

PowerPoint
Lesson Quiz

Use the following set of data for items 1 through 3 below.

13, 10, 11, 8, 14, 13, 13, 14, 30

1. Find the range and interquartile range for the above set of data. **22; 3.5**

2. Find the mean and standard deviation for the above set of data. **14; about 6.0**

3. Within how many standard deviations of the mean do all of the above data values fall? **3**

4. A set of values has a mean of 34 and a standard deviation of 4. Find the z-score of the value 26. **−2**

Careers

Exercises 17–20 Ask students why they think farm income has decreased. Some reasons may be: droughts, floods, or other natural phenomenon. Tell students that the number of farms is decreasing. Some farmers are finding it more profitable to sell their land to community developers or to large farming companies, rather than keep their land as a personal or family farm.

Diversity

Exercise 30 Be sensitive to the disparity between earnings since some students in your class may have family members that work in the listed occupations.

Alternative Assessment

Organize students in pairs or small groups. Have each group toss two number cubes 50 times, recording the results for each trial. Then ask students to find the mean and standard deviation for the data, and compare these results with those of other groups. Based on their comparisons, have students draw conclusions about which numbers are more likely than others to come up on a random toss of the number cubes.

673

29a. men: 14; 22.9; 3.2
women: 12; 25.9; 3.8

b. No; the men's team has a broader range of ages, but a smaller standard deviation than the women's team.

30a. union: $641; $279
nonunion: $564; $317

b. union: $98
nonunion: $92

c. union: 3;
nonunion: 2

d. On average, union workers are paid more than nonunion workers. The pay range is broader for nonunion workers. Union workers' pay is more broadly distributed than nonunion workers'.

35.

36.

40.

41.

28. a. Data Collection Make a table showing the number of siblings of each student in the class.
b. Find the mean and standard deviation of the data. **Check students' work.**

 Challenge

29. a. Use the table at the left to find the range, the mean, and the standard deviation of the ages for each team. **a–b. See margin.**
b. Critical Thinking For two data sets, does the set with the larger range necessarily have the larger standard deviation? Support your answer with your results from part (a).

Ages of the Members of the 2000 U.S. Olympic Soccer Teams

Men		Women	
23	32	32	29
29	23	29	22
23	23	32	28
22	23	25	23
21	18	22	22
19	22	20	24
20	23	32	25
23	21	29	27
26	22	24	22

30. Earnings The table at the right shows the median weekly earnings of union and nonunion workers in various occupations.
a. Find the mean and the range of the data for union workers and for nonunion workers.
b. Find the standard deviation for each set of data.
c. Within how many standard deviations of the mean are earnings of $395 for union workers? For nonunion workers?
d. Writing Compare the wages of union and nonunion workers. Use your results from parts (a) through (c).
a–d. See margin.

Workers' Median Weekly Earnings, 1999

Occupation	Union	Nonunion
Construction	$778	$509
Transportation and public utilities	$748	$613
Trade	$499	$418
Manufacturing	$614	$561
Services	$554	$515
Finance, insurance, and real estate	$582	$599
Mining	$710	$735

SOURCE: U.S. Bureau of Labor Statistics.
Go to www.PHSchool.com for a data update.
Web Code: agg-9041

Test Prep

Gridded Response

For Exercises 31–32, use the following bowling scores for six members of a bowling team: 175, 210, 180, 195, 208, 196.

31. What is the mean of the scores? **194**

32. What is the standard deviation of the scores? **13.0**

33. At a second bowling tournament, the mean of all the scores was 205, with a standard deviation of 14. What was the z-score for a score of 282? **5.5**

34. At the second tournament, a participant had a z-score of −2.5. What was the participant's bowling score? **170**

Mixed Review

GO for Help

Lesson 12-3

Make a box-and-whisker plot for each set of values. 35–36. See margin.

35. 25, 25, 30, 35, 45, 45, 50, 55, 60, 60   **36.** 20, 23, 25, 36, 37, 38, 39, 50, 52, 55

Lesson 11-3

Find the missing positive term in each geometric sequence.

37. 64, ■, 4, … **16**   **38.** 20, ■, 0.05, … **1**   **39.** 29, ■, 65.25, … **43.5**

Lesson 10-3

Graph each circle. 40–41. See margin.

40. $(x - 2)^2 + (y + 1)^2 = 36$ **41.** $(x - 1)^2 + (y - 1)^2 = 4$

Understanding Math Problems

Understanding Math Problems Read the problem below. Let the explanation guide you through analyzing the data. Check your understanding by solving the exercises at the bottom of the page.

a. **Energy** Find the mean and the standard deviation for daily energy usage during ten days in June: 51.8 MWh, 53.6 MWh, 54.7 MWh, 51.9 MWh, 49.3 MWh, 52.0 MWh, 53.5 MWh, 51.2 MWh, 60.7 MWh, 59.3 MWh.

To find the mean, add the data entries and divide by the number of entries.

$$\bar{x} = \frac{51.8 + 53.6 + 54.7 + 51.9 + 49.3 + 52.0 + 53.5 + 51.2 + 60.7 + 59.3}{10} = 53.8$$

The mean energy usage for 10 days is 53.8 MWh.

To simplify finding standard deviation, enter the data into a table.

x	51.8	53.6	54.7	51.9	49.3	52.0	53.5	51.2	60.7	59.3
$\bar{x}$					53.8					
$x - \bar{x}$	−2.0	−0.2	0.9	−1.9	−4.5	−1.8	−0.3	−2.6	6.9	5.5
$(x - \bar{x})^2$	4.00	0.04	0.81	3.61	20.25	3.24	0.09	6.76	47.61	30.25

Now use the definition of standard deviation.

$$\sigma = \sqrt{\frac{\sum (x - \bar{x})^2}{n}}$$

$$= \sqrt{\frac{116.66}{10}}$$

$$\approx 3.4$$

The standard deviation is about 3.4 MWh.

b. How many items in the data set fall within one standard deviation of the mean? Within two standard deviations? Within three standard deviations?

Look at the $x - \bar{x}$ row in your table. Compare its values with the following.

$$1\sigma \approx 3.4 \qquad 2\sigma \approx 6.8 \qquad 3\sigma \approx 10.2$$

7 items are within 1σ of the mean, 9 items are within 2σ, and 10 items are within 3σ.

EXERCISES

Find the mean and the standard deviation of the data. List entries that are more than two standard deviations from the mean.

1. 1.1, 1.8, 2.1, 0.7, 1.8, 0.5, 0.9, 2.9, 5.0, 2.1 **1.89; 1.25; 5.0**

2. 122, 94, 111, 95, 137, 56, 89, 115, 119, 125 **106.3; 22.15; 56**

3. 1635, 1247, 1689, 1496, 1571, 1836, 1652 **1589.4; 170.31; 1247**

4. −0.6, 0.8, 1.1, 0.3, −0.8, −0.3, −1.6, 0.8, 0.4, −0.1 **0; 0.8; none**

Understanding Math Problems

Guided Instruction

This feature guides students in solving a word problem and interpreting the results.

Teaching Tip

Explain that MWh stands for mega watt-hours and is a measure of energy. Point out that a light bulb is measured in watts, and multiplying watts by the number of hours it is on tells how much energy it uses. Also, a household would measure its energy usage in kWh, or kilo watt-hours. This is because kilo is 10^3 and mega is 10^6.

Technology

Suggest that students use a calculator to check their work.

Exercises

Encourage students to guess at which entries are more than two standard deviations before they perform the calculations.

Error Prevention!

Exercise 4 Watch for students who make sign errors when calculating $x - \bar{x}$ for negative values of x.

Activity Lab

Continuous Probability

This feature guides students in finding probabilities for continuous situations.

Guided Instruction

Lead a discussion on the terms *discrete* and *continuous*. Then have a student read the situation presented in the Activity. Ask:
If people and test scores are discrete, what is being measured in this situation that is continuous? **time**

Teaching Tip

Exercise 1 Have students draw a number line to model when the traffic signal is green. Then ask:
- *How long is the traffic signal green?* **20 seconds**
- *During what portion of these 20 seconds will the signal turn yellow within 5 seconds?* **the last 5 seconds**
- *What is the probability that the signal will turn yellow within 5 seconds?*
  $\frac{5}{20} = 0.25$

Exercises

Encourage students to draw diagrams to model each exercise.

Activity Lab

Continuous Probability

FOR USE WITH LESSON 12-4

Most of the probability examples you study in this chapter are about discrete situations. These situations involve whole numbers of people, test scores, money amounts, and so on. You can apply probabilities to continuous situations as well.

ACTIVITY

A traffic signal is green for 20 seconds out of every minute. Find the probability that the signal will be green when you turn the corner and first see it.

You can model the signal's color intervals by using a number line.

Let an interval of 60 represent one cycle of green, yellow, and red. Inside that interval, an interval of 20 represents a green light. You come across the signal at a random point in time, so

$$P(\text{green}) = \frac{\text{time light is green}}{\text{total time of cycle}} = \frac{20}{60} = \frac{1}{3}$$

EXERCISES

1. The traffic signal is green when you first see it. What is the probability that it will turn yellow within 5 seconds?   **0.25**

2. The traffic signal is red when you first see it. What do you need to know to find the probability that it will not turn green for another 15 seconds?
You need to know how long the signal stays red.

The following continuous situations involve functions and conic sections that you have studied to this point. For each, assume that you pick real numbers a and b at random between 0 and 10. Find the probability of each of the following.

3. The line $y = ax$ intersects the segment joining $(0, 10)$ and $(5, 10)$. See graph at the right.   **0.8**

4. The circle $(x - a)^2 + (y - b)^2 = 1$ lies entirely within a square with opposite vertices $(0, 0)$ and $(10, 10)$.   **0.64**

5. The ellipse $\frac{x}{a^2} + \frac{y}{b^2} = 1$ has a vertical major axis.   **0.5**

6. The hyperbola $\frac{x}{a^2} - \frac{y}{b^2} = 1$ has a horizontal transverse axis.   **0.5**

7. The interval from 4 to 6 is a part of the domain of the function $y = \sqrt{x - a} + b$.   **0.4**

8. The function $y = ab^x$ models growth.   **0.9**

9. The function $y = \frac{1}{x - a} + b$ has a horizontal asymptote.   **1**

10. The point (a, b) is in the upper triangle formed by the diagonals of a square whose sides lie on the axes and the lines $x = 10$ and $y = 10$.   **0.25**

Working With Samples

What You'll Learn

- To find sample proportions
- To find the margin of error

. . . And Why

To analyze data from a poll, as in Example 5

✓ **Check Skills You'll Need**

GO for Help Lesson 7-1

Simplify each expression.

1. $\frac{1}{\sqrt{4}}$ $\frac{1}{2}$

2. $-\frac{1}{\sqrt{9}}$ $-\frac{1}{3}$

3. $\frac{1}{\sqrt{36}}$ $\frac{1}{6}$

4. $-\frac{1}{\sqrt{121}}$ $-\frac{1}{11}$

5. $\frac{1}{\sqrt{50}}$ $\frac{\sqrt{2}}{10}$

6. $-\frac{1}{\sqrt{81}}$ $-\frac{1}{9}$

◀)) **New Vocabulary**
- sample
- sample proportion
- random sample
- margin of error

Objectives
1 To find sample proportions
2 To find the margin of error

Examples
1 Find the Sample Proportion
2 Real-World Connection
3 Comparing Sample Sizes
4 Using the Margin of Error
5 Real-World Connection

---

1 Sample Proportions

Suppose you want to know what percent of all teenagers recognize the word that means "to pass the summer in a state of slumber." Since it is too costly and time consuming to ask every teenager, use a sample. A **sample** gathers information from only part of a population.

Using any sample, you can find a sample proportion. The **sample proportion** is the ratio $\frac{x}{n}$, where x is the number of times an event occurs in a sample of size n.

─ Word Wise ─

Which word means "to pass the summer in a state of slumber"?

A. stridulate
B. ruminate
C. estivate
D. somnambulate

1 EXAMPLE Finding the Sample Proportion

In a sample of 350 teenagers, 294 have never made a snow sculpture. Find the sample proportion for those who have never made a snow sculpture. Write the answer as a percent.

sample proportion $= \frac{x}{n}$ **Write the formula.**

$= \frac{294}{350}$ **Substitute 294 for x and 350 for n.**

$= 0.84$ **Simplify.**

● The sample proportion is 84%.

✓ **Quick Check** ➊ In a poll of 1085 voters, 564 favor Candidate A. Find the sample proportion for those who favor Candidate A.   **52%**

Samples vary in how well they reflect the entire population. In a **random sample**, all members of the population are equally likely to be chosen.

Vocabulary Tip

Bias means "slant."

When a part of a population is overrepresented or underrepresented in a sample, the sample is biased. A random sample can help avoid bias in gathering data.

Lesson 12-5 Working With Samples   **677**

Professional Development

Math Background

When it is not practical to collect data on an entire population, a sample, or smaller portion of the population is often surveyed. The data collected from the sample is then assumed to reflect data of the entire population. When using samples, care must be taken to assure that the members of a sample are selected randomly from the members of a population. Also, the size of a sample reflects the reliability of its data. Larger samples tend to more accurately reflect the entire population.

More Math Background: p. 646D

Lesson Planning and Resources

See p. 646E for a list of the resources that support this lesson.

PowerPoint

Bell Ringer Practice

✓ **Check Skills You'll Need**
For intervention, direct students to:

Finding Roots
Lesson 7-1: Example 3
Extra Skills and Word
    Problems Practice, Ch. 7

Differentiated Instruction Solutions for All Learners

Special Needs L1 Have students work in small groups to write their own scenario with 3 sampling methods, as shown in Example 2. Have each group share their scenario and lead a discussion of any bias in their sampling methods. learning style: verbal	**Below Level** L2 Have students discuss what sample of the population it might be useful to choose when trying to predict the outcome of an election. **likely voters** learning style: verbal

Guided Instruction

2 EXAMPLE Teaching Tip

Ask students to conjecture why random sampling techniques might be especially important to minority groups within a community.

PowerPoint

Additional Examples

1 In a sample of 500 teenagers, 328 had never attended a popular music concert. Find the sample proportion for those who have never attended a popular music concert. Write the answer as a percent. **about 66%**

2 The Sunnyvale High School student council dance committee is trying to decide whether to have a band or a DJ for the fall dance. They decided that each of the four committee members should survey the students in their homeroom classes. Identify any bias in this sampling method. **This is a convenience sample that is convenient for the committee members. Four homerooms may not accurately reflect the opinions of the entire school. The opinions of the committee members may influence the opinions of their homeroom students.**

---

2 EXAMPLE Real-World Connection

Public Opinion A news program reports on a proposed school dress code. The purpose of the program is to find out what percent of the population in its viewing area favors the dress code. Identify any bias in each sampling method.

a. Viewers are invited to call the program and express their preferences.

The people who decide to call in may over- or underrepresent some views. For example, members of a group favoring the new dress code might encourage its members to call in. This type of sample is called a "self-selected" sample.

b. A reporter interviews people on the street near the local high school.

This is a "convenience" sample, since it is convenient for the reporter to stay in one place. Because the location is near the school, students may be overrepresented in the sample and the results will be biased.

c. During the program, 300 people are selected at random from the viewing area. Then each person is contacted.

This sampling method contains the least bias. It is a random sample.

✓ Quick Check **2 a.** Suppose the 350 teenagers in Example 1 all live in Florida. Is there bias in this sample? Explain. **a–b. See margin p. 679.**

b. *Critical Thinking* The only way to know a true population proportion is to poll every person in the population. Such a poll is no longer a sample, but a census. Describe a situation in which a sample is unsatisfactory and a census is required.

---

2 Sample Size and Margin of Error

The size of a sample affects its reliability. With a small sample size, you are likely to get a wide range of sample proportions. For example, in some samples, no one will recognize the word that means "to pass the summer in a state of slumber." In other samples, everyone will recognize *estivate*. With larger sample sizes, you are less likely to have a sample containing an "all or nothing" result.

The Law of Large Numbers states that the variation in a data set decreases as the sample size increases. By comparing the variation in samples, you can get an idea of their relative sizes.

3 EXAMPLE Comparing Sample Sizes

Each graph below shows the sample proportions for 20 samples. Match each graph to the most likely sample size.

a. 20 people per sample   **b.** 5 people per sample

Distributions of Sample Proportions

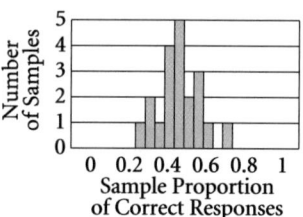

Differentiated Instruction Solutions for All Learners

Advanced Learners **L4**
Have students research the difference between population standard deviation and sample standard deviation.

learning style: verbal

English Language Learners **ELL**
Make sure students understand that a *sample proportion* is an estimate. Ask: *Is a sample proportion an experimental or a theoretical probability?* **experimental because it is based on collected data**

learning style: verbal

a. The graph on the right shows less variation, so it is more likely to be based on samples of a larger size, 20 people per sample.

b. The graph on the left shows more variation, so it is more likely to be based on 5 people per sample.

 Quick Check

3. B; a larger sample has less variation, which corresponds to a smaller standard deviation.

3 A science class measured the heights of blades of grass behind the school. The class took three samples. Use the information in the table below to decide which sample most likely was the greatest in size. Explain your reasoning.

Sample	Standard Deviation (in.)
A	1.45
B	1.09
C	1.26

A sample proportion should be reported with an estimate of error, called the **margin of error.** The margin of error is based on the standard deviation in graphs like those in Example 3. The larger the sample size, the smaller the margin of error.

Key Concepts

Property	Margin of Error Formula

When a random sample of size n is taken from a large population, the sample proportion has a margin of error of approximately $\pm\dfrac{1}{\sqrt{n}}$.

4 EXAMPLE Using the Margin of Error

A poll reports that 56% of voters favor Candidate B, with a margin of error of ±3%. Estimate the number of voters in the poll.

$\text{margin of error} = \pm\dfrac{1}{\sqrt{n}}$	**Write the formula.**
$\pm\sqrt{n} = \dfrac{1}{\text{margin of error}}$	**Rewrite the equation.**
$= \dfrac{1}{0.03}$	**Substitute 0.03 for margin of error.**
≈ 33.33	**Simplify.**
$n \approx 1111$	**Square each side.**

The poll included about 1100 voters.

Quick Check **4** Estimate the sample size for each margin of error.
   a. ±10% 100   **b.** ±4% 625   **c.** ±2% 2500

You can use the margin of error to determine the likely range for the true population proportion. The graph below shows the range for the population in Example 4.

Sample Proportion

← −3% — +3% → ← Margin of error

53%   56%   59% ← Likely range for the true population proportion

---

4 EXAMPLE Math Tip

Explain to students that when solving for n, both sides of the equation are squared, which eliminates the ± sign. Additionally, a negative number of voters would not make sense.

5 EXAMPLE Teaching Tip

Challenge students to use their knowledge of reciprocals to explain what happens to the margin of error as n increases and decreases. **As n increases, the margin of error decreases, and as n decreases, the margin of error increases.**

PowerPoint

Additional Examples

3 In a survey, teenagers were asked to rank the importance of their relationships with their parents. The response scale ranged from 1 to 5, with 5 being extremely important. Use the information in the table to decide which sample was most likely the greatest in size.

Sample	Score	Standard Deviation
A	4.4	1.4
B	4.6	0.6
C	4.6	1.2

Sample B was most likely the greatest in size since it has the smallest standard deviation.

4 An opinion poll about the popularity of the mayor has a margin of error of ±5%. Estimate the number of people who were surveyed. **about 400 people**

Quick Check

2a. Yes; the sample is biased because it overrepresents students who live in a warm climate.

b. Answers may vary. Sample: Every 10 years, the United States conducts a census of the population to find exactly how many people live in the country.

679

Math Tip
Math Tip
The margin of error formula $\pm\frac{1}{\sqrt{n}}$ assumes a 95% confidence level, or 2 standard deviations. A 95% confidence level is so common for polling results, that it is no longer reported. However, in most scientific research a confidence level of 99% or higher is expected, and reporting a margin of error without the confidence level can be misleading.

Additional Example

5 A survey of 528 high school seniors found that 65% already had career plans after high school.
a. Find the margin of error for the sample. **about ±4%**
b. Use the margin of error to find an interval that is likely to contain the true population proportion. **61–69%**

Resources
• Daily Notetaking Guide 12-5 **L3**

Closure

Ask volunteers to compare and contrast the importance of sampling without bias and sample size. Ask: *Is one aspect more important than the other when working with samples?* **Answers may vary. Sample: Sampling without bias is important to get a sample that is representative of the entire population. Size of the sample is important to the reliability of the sample. Both are equally important when working with samples.**

6. If students walk or drive to school, or are involved in other after-school activities, they are underrepresented by this sample method.

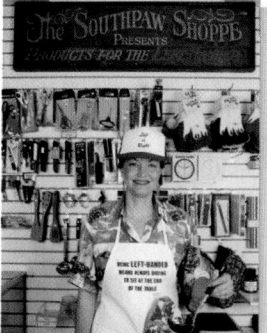

Real-World Connection

Some retail businesses cater to left-handers.

 Quick Check

---

5 **EXAMPLE** **Real-World Connection**

Genetics A survey of 2580 students found that 9% are left-handed.

a. Find the margin of error for the sample.

$$\text{margin of error} = \pm\frac{1}{\sqrt{n}} \qquad \text{Use the formula.}$$

$$= \pm\frac{1}{\sqrt{2580}} \qquad \text{Substitute.}$$

$$\approx \pm 0.0197 \qquad \text{Use a calculator.}$$

The margin of error is about ±2%.

b. Use the margin of error to find an interval that is likely to contain the true population proportion.

The margin of error forms an interval with the sample proportion at its midpoint.

Sample Proportion

7%   9%   11%

The proportion of students who are left-handed is likely to be from 7% to 11%.

5 In a poll of 123 students, 87 have never ridden a ferry. Find the sample proportion, the margin of error, and the interval likely to contain the true population proportion. **71%, ±9%, 62% to 80%**

EXERCISES

For more exercises, see *Extra Skill and Word Problem Practice*.

Practice and Problem Solving

 A **Practice by Example**

Example 1
(page 677)

 GO for Help

For each sample, find the sample proportion. Write it as a percent.

1. 837 out of 1150 insurance applicants have no citations on their driving record. **73%**

2. 27 out of 60 shoppers prefer generic brands when available. **45%**

3. 532 out of 580 households own a color television set. **92%**

Example 2
(page 678)

Identify any bias in each sampling method.

4. A supermarket wants to find the proportion of shoppers who use reduced-price coupons. A manager interviews every shopper entering the greeting card aisle.

5. A maintenance crew wants to estimate how many of 3000 air filters in an office building need replacing. The crew examines five filters chosen at random on each floor of the building. **very little bias**

6. The student government wants to find out how many students have after-school jobs. A pollster interviews students selected at random as they board buses at the end of the school day. **See margin.**

4. This sampling method overrepresents shoppers buying greeting cards.

Example 3
(pages 678–679)

7. C; this sample has the smallest standard deviation, which most likely indicates a larger sample.

7. In a survey, teenagers were asked the importance of "making your own things." The response scale ranged from 1 to 5, with 5 being extremely important. Which sample most likely was largest? Explain.

Sample	Score	Standard Deviation
A	3.6	1.2
B	3.8	1.0
C	3.8	0.5

680 Chapter 12 Probability and Statistics

8. Group B probably was the smaller sample; it has the greater variation in the percentages represented in the graph.

8. The table below shows the results of a poll asking students, "How many hours a week would you say you spend doing academic homework?" Which sample most likely was smaller? Explain.

Example 4
(page 665)

Find the margin of error for the sample proportion, given each sample of size *n*.

9. $n = 200$ **±7%**   **10.** $n = 800$ **±4%**   **11.** $n = 1200$ **±3%**

Find the sample size that produces each margin of error.

12. ±8% **156**   **13.** ±5% **400**   **14.** ±1% **10,000**

Example 5
(page 666)

For each situation, find the margin of error for the sample. Then find an interval likely to contain the true population proportion.

15. Of 750 teenagers polled, 59% think boys and girls are portrayed as equals on television. **±4%; 55% to 63%**

16. Of 400 teenagers surveyed, 62% do not plan to stay in their community after finishing their education. **±5%; 57% to 67%**

B Apply Your Skills 🌐 Surveys **For each sample, find (a) the sample proportion, (b) the margin of error, and (c) the interval likely to contain the true population proportion.**

17. In a random sample of 408 grocery shoppers, 258 prefer one large trip per week **GPS** to several smaller ones. **a. 63% b. ±5% c. 58% to 68%**

18. Of 500 teenagers surveyed, 460 would like to see adults in their community do more to solve drug problems. **a. 92% b. ±4% c. 88% to 96%**

19. In a survey of 32 people, 30 return a milk carton to the refrigerator immediately after using it. **a. 94% b. ±18% c. 76% to 100%**

20. In a survey of 16 people, one person never locks his car.
a. 6% b. ±25% c. 0% to 31%

21. Writing Write a news article describing the sample proportion and margin of error for the poll results shown at the right.
Check students' work.

22. Reasoning How is the margin of error affected if you double the sample size? Explain.
See margin.

23. a. Data Collection Write a survey question to find out the number of students at your school who plan to continue their education after high school
b. Describe the sampling method you would use.
c. Conduct your survey. **a–c. Check students' work.**

24. A sample proportion is an experimental probability; it is based on actual measurements.

24. Critical Thinking A sample proportion provides an estimate for the percent of an entire population that favors an event. Is a sample proportion an experimental or a theoretical probability? Explain.
See left.

GO Online
Homework Video Tutor
Visit: PHSchool.com
Web Code: age-1205

Assignment Guide

1 **A** **B** 1-6, 23-25

2 **A** **B** 7-22, 26-29
C Challenge   30-32

Test Prep   33-37
Mixed Review   38-46

Homework Quick Check

To check students' understanding of key skills and concepts, go over Exercises 6, 12, 16, 17, 21, 22, 25.

Error Prevention!

Exercises 15, 16 Make sure students select an interval centered on the sample proportion.

Differentiated Instruction Resources

GPS Guided Problem Solving	**L3**
Enrichment	**L4**
Reteaching	**L2**
Practice	**L3**

22. Doubling a sample size multiplies the margin of error by $\frac{1}{\sqrt{2}} \approx 0.71$, so the margin is about 71% of its former value.

Lesson Quiz

1. If 412 of 1720 students at a high school participate in extra-curricular sports activities, what is the proportion of the students who participate in sports? Write the proportion as a percent. **about 24%**

2. A radio talk show found that over 90% of listeners who called in were against building a community recreation center. Identify any bias in this sampling method. **This is a self-selected sample, and the people who call in are likely to over- or under-represent certain viewpoints.**

3. A biology class counted the number of microorganisms in drops of water from a nearby pond. The class took three samples. Use the information in the table to decide which sample was largest. Explain your reasoning.

Sample	Standard Deviation
A	1.2
B	1.7
C	2.1

Sample A; Sample A has the lowest standard deviation suggesting that it was the largest sample.

4. A survey of voters found that 61% of voters supported building a new high school, with a margin of error of 2%. Estimate the number of voters in the poll. **about 2500 voters**

5. Jill conducted a survey of 100 drivers and found that 72% thought that improperly timed traffic lights were the city's worst traffic problem. Find the margin of error and the interval that is likely to contain the true population proportion. **±10%; 62–82%**

 25. Computer Use An online advertisement asks you to participate in a survey. The survey asks how much time you spend online each week. Identify any bias in this method. If appropriate, suggest a method more likely to produce a random sample. **See margin.**

An event occurs x times in a sample of size n. Find its sample proportion and margin of error.

26. $x = 96$
$n = 900$
11%, ±3%

27. $x = 20$
$n = 64$
31%, ±13%

28. $x = 100$
$n = 250$
40%, ±6%

29. $x = 273$
$n = 435$
63%, ±5%

 Challenge

30b. **$50,000; more than doubling the cost of the survey has made only a small improvement in the margin of error.**

30. a. It costs $20 to interview each person for a survey. Find the cost to obtain a ±3% margin of error. **$22,220**

b. Critical Thinking Find the cost to obtain a ±2% margin of error. Why do you think polls with smaller margins of error are rare?

31. a. Elections A poll of 150 voters shows that a candidate is preferred by 56% of the voters while 44% prefer the opponent. Should the candidate be concerned? Explain. **a–b. See margin.**

b. A later poll of 600 voters shows the candidate is preferred by 55% of the voters. Should this candidate feel more or less confident, given the results of the second poll? Explain.

32. Wildlife Wild animal populations are often estimated through the use of the capture−tag−recapture method. Several animals are captured, tagged, and released back into the wild. The animals continue to roam freely. Then, some time later at the same site, several more animals are captured, and the number of tagged animals is recorded. An estimate of the population can then be calculated. This method of estimation assumes that the fraction of tagged animals in the second sample is equivalent to the fraction of tagged animals in the entire population.

Exercise 32

$$\frac{\text{tagged animals in second sample}}{\text{animals in second sample}} = \frac{\text{tagged animals in population}}{\text{population } (P)}$$

Use the formula above to predict the black bear population of the northern coastal plain of South Carolina. Researchers tagged fourteen black bears in the fall and captured eleven bears the following summer. Of the eleven bears, three were tagged. **51 black bears**

Test Prep

Multiple Choice

33. In a sample of 625 airline travelers, 485 collected "airline miles" toward free trips. What does the number $\frac{140}{625}$ represent? **B**
A. the probability that a passenger collects airline miles
B. the sample proportion of the travelers who do not collect airline miles
C. the sample proportion of the travelers who collect airline miles
D. the margin of error for the sample

34. A random sample of people answered the question "Do you collect airline miles?" The margin of error for the sample was ±2%. The sample proportion of people who answered no was $\frac{3}{10}$. How many people in the sample answered no? **H**
F. 15
G. 225
H. 750
J. 2500

25. **This method is biased because it overrepresents people who respond to the online advertisement.**

A less biased method could involve surveying a group of people selected at random.

31a. **There is an 8% margin of error; the candidate should be aware that 52% of the voters could actually prefer the opponent.**

35. A research group had a stack of survey responses. The number of respondents was more than 5000 and fewer than 5500. When the researchers divided the respondents into 13 equal groups, there were no extra respondents. Similarly, there were no extra respondents when they divided the responses into 7 equal groups or 11 equal groups. How many respondents were there?   **B**

   A. 1001   **B.** 5005   **C.** 5031   **D.** 500,500

Short Response

36. What is the margin of error for a random sample of size 3600? Show your work.   **See margin.**

Extended Response

37. In a poll of 2750 airline travelers, 138 said they never check their luggage when they fly. Find the sample proportion, the margin of error, and the interval likely to contain the true population proportion.   **See margin.**

Mixed Review

Lesson 12-4

Find the mean and the standard deviation for each data set.

38. 0 km, 1 km, 1 km, 1 km, 2 km, 2 km, 2 km, 3 km, 3 km, 4 km, 5 km, 10 km
                                             ≈2.8, ≈2.5

39. 1 oz, 1 oz, 2 oz, 2 oz, 3 oz, 4 oz, 5 oz, 6 oz, 8 oz, 9 oz, 10 oz, 10 oz, 12 oz, 20 oz
                                             ≈6.6, ≈5.1

Lesson 11-4

Use summation notation to write each arithmetic series for the specified number of terms.   **40–43. See margin.**

40. $3 + 8 + 13 + \ldots; n = 5$ **41.** $41 + 33 + 25 + \ldots; n = 8$

42. $-14 + (-8) + (-2) + \ldots; n = 6$ **43.** $-27 + (-21) + (-15) + \ldots; n = 10$

Lesson 10-4

Find the equation of each ellipse centered at the origin.

44. height: 20 units   **45.** height: 12 units   **46.** height: 24 units
     width: 6 units   width: 10 units   width: 36 units
     $\frac{x^2}{9} + \frac{y^2}{100} = 1$ $\frac{x^2}{25} + \frac{y^2}{36} = 1$ $\frac{x^2}{324} + \frac{y^2}{144} = 1$

Algebra at Work

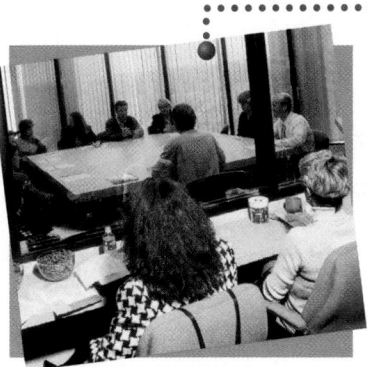

Market Researcher

When questions arise about consumer products or services, a market researcher gathers statistical information to help answer the questions. The information a market researcher collects and analyzes helps companies improve their products and make decisions about their customer base. Quantitative research allows a market researcher to analyze data from a large population of potential customers. Market research strategies for gathering information include the following.

- mail surveys
- focus groups
- telephone surveys
- in-person interviews

For: Information about market research
Web Code: agb-2031

---

b. The candidate should feel more confident after the second poll; it has a margin of error of only 4%, which means this candidate is preferred by at least 51% of voters.

36. [2] For a random sample of size n, the margin of error is approximately $\pm\frac{1}{\sqrt{n}}$.

For $n = 3600$, the margin of error is approximately

$\pm\frac{1}{\sqrt{3600}} = \pm\frac{1}{60} \approx \pm0.02 \approx \pm2\%.$

[1] answer only or a calculation error

---

37. [4] The sample proportion is $\frac{138}{2750} \approx$ 5%. The margin of error is

$\pm\frac{1}{\sqrt{2750}} \approx \pm\frac{1}{52.44} \approx$ $\pm0.019 \approx \pm2\%.$ The interval is (5% − 2%) to (5% + 2%), or 3% to 7%.

[3] minor error, but all parts of the question answered

[2] more than one part of the answer is correct

[1] answer only OR only one part of the question answered correctly

40. $\sum\limits_{n=1}^{5} (-2 + 5n)$

41. $\sum\limits_{n=1}^{8} (49 - 8n)$

42. $\sum\limits_{n=1}^{6} (-20 + 6n)$

43. $\sum\limits_{n=1}^{10} (-33 + 6n)$

Vocabulary Builder

Variable and Parameter

Students learn to distinguish between variables and parameters by applying them to families of functions.

Guided Instruction

Visual Learners

Ask: *Why do you think only one parameter is generally changed when graphing a family of functions?* Sample: The effect of that particular parameter can be best observed when all other factors are held constant.

Math Tip

In statistics, a *parameter* is a quantity that describes a statistical population such as a mean. In this feature, a *parameter* is an arbitrary constant whose value characterizes a family of functions.

Advanced Learners **L4**

Have students research the relationship of *parameter* and *parametric equations*.

Exercises 6–12 Students may be confused by the statement "the outputs are functions." Ask: *What is the independent variable for each function?* a parameter Have students use graphing calculators to examine the effect of each parameter.

Resources

Vocabulary and Study Skills worksheet

6. horizontal translations of the function $f(x) = x^2$; all functions whose graph is a parabola with the vertex on the x-axis.

7. vertical stretches, shrinks, and reflections of the function $f(x) = x^2$; all quadratic functions whose graph is a parabola with the vertex at the origin.

684

For the equation $y = mx + b$, you may have heard x and y described as variables and m and b as parameters. In other situations, however, x and y may be parameters and m and b may be variables. At this time, you can perhaps better understand the distinction between *variable* and *parameter* by considering examples than by reading definitions of these terms.

EXAMPLE **The Family of Quadratic Functions**

Distinguish between the variable x and the parameters a, h, and k as they appear in $f(x) = a(x - h)^2 + k$, the vertex form of a quadratic function.

The variable x represents any value in the domain of the function f. Since the domain of a quadratic function is the set of real numbers, x represents any real number.

The parameters a, h, and k represent real numbers, but they are constant for any specific quadratic function. They give that function the stretch and translation characteristics that relate it to the parent quadratic function $y = x^2$.

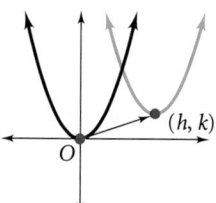

EXERCISES

Describe the values given to the quadratic parameters in each vertex-form quadratic function below.

1. $f(x) = 2(x - 3)^2 + 4$
$a = 2, h = 3, k = 4$

2. $g(x) = -(x + 1)^2 - 2$
$a = -1, h = -1, k = -2$

3. $h(x) = -x^2 + 1$
$a = -1, h = 0, k = 1$

4. You may not have noticed, but the "parent" exponential function $y = b^x$ is itself a family of functions, with each parent defined by the value of the parameter b. (That's why the Key Concepts Summary on page 441 uses the plural "Families" in its title "Families of Exponential Functions.")

    a. What parameter values give the two parent exponential functions shown in the graph? $2, \frac{1}{3}$

    b. Describe the domain of the parameter b for the exponential function $y = b^x$. **all positive real numbers $b \neq 1$**

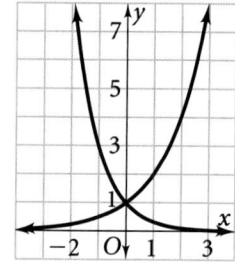

5. The function $V(k) = x^2 + k$ pairs a number k with a member of the family of quadratic functions. In other words, the inputs for V are the parameter values k; the outputs are quadratic functions. Describe this set of quadratic functions by their common characteristics. **vertical translations of the function $f(x) = x^2$**

The domain of each function is a set of real-number parameter values. The outputs are functions. Describe each set of outputs by their common characteristics. 6–11. See margin.

6. $T(h) = (x - h)^2$

7. $S(a) = ax^2$

8. $V(k) = -x^2 + k$

9. $R(h) = \sqrt{x - h}$

10. $L(b) = \log_b x$

11. $V(h) = \pi r^2 h$

12. Probability Suppose k and n are whole numbers with $1 \leq k \leq n$.

    a. If you choose one number at random from 1 through n, what is P(choosing k)? $\frac{1}{n}$

    b. For this situation, you can think of k as a variable and n as a parameter. How is your answer to part (a) affected by the value of the parameter n? **See margin.**

8. vertical translations of the function $f(x) = x^2$; all functions whose graph is a parabola with the vertex on the y-axis.

9. horizontal translations of the function $f(x) = \sqrt{x}$

10. all log functions that pass through the point (1, 0)

11. vertical stretches, shrinks, and reflections of the function $f(r) = r^2$; all

quadratic functions whose graph is a parabola with the vertex at the origin

12b. As n increases, the probability P(choosing k) decreases.

Binomial Distributions

What You'll Learn

• To find binomial probabilities

• To use binomial distributions

. . . And Why

To find the probability of winning a prize, as in Example 2

 Check Skills You'll Need

 for Help Lessons 6-7 and 6-8

Evaluate each expression.

1. $_4C_2$ 6
2. $_3C_3$ 1
3. $_5C_2$ 10

Use the binomial theorem to expand each binomial.   5–9. See back of book.

4. $(x + 2)^3$ $x^3 + 6x^2 + 12x + 8$
5. $(w - y)^4$
6. $(m + n)^3$
7. $(t + 3s)^4$
8. $(a + 2b)^5$
9. $(p + q)^6$

 New Vocabulary   • binomial experiment   • binomial probability

Objectives
1   To find binomial probabilities
2   To use binomial distributions

Examples
1   Designing a Binomial Experiment
2   Real-World Connection
3   Real-World Connection
4   Real-World Connection

Math Background

In statistics, students will learn conditions under which a normal distribution can be used to approximate a binomial distribution. Computers calculate either easily.

More Math Background: p. 646D

Lesson Planning and Resources

See p. 646E for a list of the resources that support this lesson.

 Bell Ringer Practice

Check Skills You'll Need
For intervention, direct students to:

Permutations and Combinations
Lesson 6-7: Examples 3, 4
Extra Skills and Word
  Problems Practice, Ch. 6

The Binomial Theorem
Lesson 6-8: Example 3
Extra Skills and Word
  Problems Practice, Ch. 6

---

1 Finding Binomial Probabilities

2a. Answers may vary. Sample: Generate random integers from 1 to 100. Odd numbers represent a wrong answer. 10 numbers represent one test.

Problem Solving Hint

You can use a coin, a number cube, or random numbers to conduct a simulation.

Activity: Binomial Probability

1. Examine the situations described in the chart below. What do the situations printed in blue have in common?

1. Each situation has only two possible outcomes.

| receive a numerical grade |
| receive a pass/fail grade |
| wear soccer, running, basketball, or street shoes |
| wear shoes with cleats or no cleats |
| guess on a matching test |
| guess on a true/false test |

2. Suppose you guess each answer on a ten-question true-or-false test. Are you likely to get 70% or more right?
   a. Design and conduct a simulation for this situation.
   b. Run your simulation 10 times. Make a frequency table of the scores.   **See back of book.**
   c. Find P(70% or more right).   **20%**

A **binomial experiment** has three important features:

• The situation involves repeated trials.

• Each trial has two possible outcomes (success or failure).

• The probability of success is constant throughout the trials. (The trials are independent.)

Differentiated Instruction   Solutions for All Learners

Special Needs L1
Have students make a tree diagram for Example 3 using the format presented in Example 2.

Below Level L2
Use a tree diagram to calculate the probability of flipping two heads in three trials of the binomial experiment *flip-a-coin*.

learning style: visual

learning style: visual

Guided Instruction

Activity
Teaching Tip

Ask students to list possible outcomes for each situation in order to see that the situations printed in green have only two outcomes.

① EXAMPLE Tactile Learners

Let students use a spinner with five possible outcomes to help them develop their random number tables.

② EXAMPLE Teaching Tip

Students have used tree diagrams to represent conditional probabilities in the past. Have students make a table to write similarities and differences between a tree diagram for a conditional probability and a tree diagram for a binomial probability. The table might include the following:

Conditional probability tree diagram: represents the probability that an outcome occurs, given that there is a condition that limits the sample space; it applies to all conditional events, whether they are independent or dependent; the probabilities may vary for each set of branches, as long as they add up to 1; multiplication is used to compute each probability.

Binomial probability tree diagram: represents an experiment that contains the three important features listed on page 685 (encourage students to list them in their own words); multiplication is used to compute each probability.

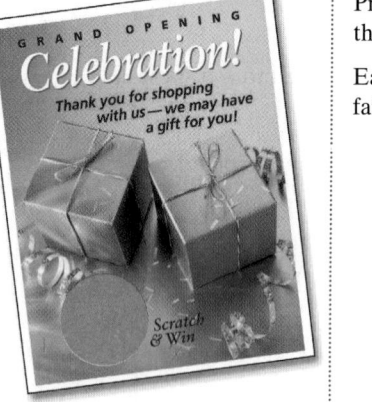

---

① EXAMPLE Designing a Binomial Experiment

Suppose that you guess the answers to three questions of a multiple-choice test. Each question has five choices, with one correct choice.

a. Describe a trial for this situation. How many trials are there?

Each guess is a trial. Since you are guessing three times, there are three trials.

b. Describe a success. What is the probability of success on any single trial?

Each correct answer is a success. Since there are five possible answers, all of them equally likely, the probability of success on any single trial is 0.2.

c. Design and conduct a simulation to determine the probability of getting at least two answers correct. Run the simulation 10 times.

Assign each number from 1 to 5 to an outcome, based on each outcome's probability. Let 1 represent a correct response. Let $2-5$ represent incorrect responses. Generate random numbers from 1 to 5.

Simulation	1	2	3	4	5	6	7	8	9	10
Number Generated, Trial 1	2	4	2	5	5	2	1	5	1	2
Number Generated, Trial 2	1	1	5	4	4	5	1	4	5	1
Number Generated, Trial 3	1	3	1	2	2	5	4	2	3	2
Number of Correct Guesses	2	1	1	0	0	0	2	0	1	1

Two of the simulations result in two or more correct guesses. So the experimental probability of getting at least two answers correct is $\frac{2}{10}$, or 20%.

✓ Quick Check ① Run the simulation an additional 15 times. Use the results of all 25 simulations to find the experimental probability of getting at least two answers correct.
Check students' work.

You can use a tree diagram to analyze binomial probabilities.

② EXAMPLE Real-World 🌐 Connection

Merchandising As part of a promotion, a store is giving away scratch-off cards. Prizes are awarded on 40% of the game cards. Suppose you have three cards. Find the probability that exactly two of the three cards will reveal a prize.

Each card represents a trial with a probability of success of 0.4. The probability of failure is 0.6. The tree diagram below shows the probabilities along each path.

$P(\text{three prizes}) = 1(0.4)^3 = 0.064$

— Number of paths

$P(\text{two prizes}) = 3(0.4)^2(0.6) = 0.288$

$P(\text{one prize}) = \blacksquare(0.4)^{\blacksquare}(0.6)^{\blacksquare} = \blacksquare$

$P(\text{no prize}) = \blacksquare(0.6)^{\blacksquare} = \blacksquare$

The probability that exactly two of the three cards will reveal a prize is 0.288.

Differentiated Instruction Solutions for All Learners

Advanced Learners L4
Have students find out what other probability distribution can be used to calculate the accident rate per mile of highway.

learning style: verbal

English Language Learners ELL
Write the binomial probability formula $_nC_x p^x q^{n-x}$ on the board, and the variables n, x, p, and q underneath. Invite students to explain in their own words what each variable represents and record their explanations.

learning style: visual

Quick Check ② **a.** Complete the tree diagram in Example 2 by finding the probability of receiving one prize and the probability of receiving no prize.

b. Verify your work by adding the probabilities for three, two, one, and no prizes. What answer should you get?   **1**

2a. P (one prize) =
   $3(0.4)^1(0.6)^2 = 0.432$;
   P(no prize) =
   $1(0.6)^3 = 0.216$

The relationships you have seen are summarized in the following formula.

 Key Concepts

Definition	Binomial Probability

Suppose you have repeated independent trials, each with a probability of success p and a probability of failure q (with $p + q = 1$). Then the probability of x successes in n trials is the following product.

$$_nC_x p^x q^{n-x}$$

③ **EXAMPLE** **Real-World** 🌐 **Connection**

Quality Control A calculator contains four batteries. With normal use, each battery has a 90% chance of lasting for one year. What is the probability that all four batteries will last a year?

Relate This is a binomial experiment.

• There are four batteries.

• Each battery may succeed or fail.

• The probability of success is 0.9 for each battery.

Graphing Calculator Hint

$nCr = \dfrac{n!}{r!(n-r)!}$
On a graphing calculator, use
MATH and nCr in the PRB menu.

Define Let $n = 4$.   Let $x = 4$.
Let $p = 0.9$.   Let $q = 0.1$.

Write $_nC_x p^x q^{n-x} = {_4}C_4(0.9)^4(0.1)^0$ **Substitute.**
$= (1)(0.9)^4(1)$ **Simplify.**
$= 0.6561$ **Simplify.**

```
(4 nCr 4) *0.9^4*0.1^0
                  .6561
```

• The probability that all four batteries will last one year is about 66%.

 Quick Check ③ Find the probability of x successes in n trials for the given probability of success p on each trial.

a. $x = 2, n = 5, p = 0.25$
   0.2637

b. $x = 8, n = 10, p = 0.7$
   0.2335

---

2 **Using a Binomial Distribution**

To find the full probability distribution for a binomial experiment, expand the binomial $(p + q)^n$. For example, suppose you guess on four questions of a five-choice multiple choice test. For four questions, $n = 4$, $p = 0.2$, and $q = 0.8$.

	4 correct		3 correct		2 correct		1 correct		0 correct

$(p + q)^4 = \quad 1p^4 \quad + \quad 4p^3q \quad + \quad 6p^2q^2 \quad + \quad 4pq^3 \quad + \quad 1q^4$

$= (0.2)^4 + 4(0.2)^3(0.8) + 6(0.2)^2(0.8)^2 + 4(0.2)(0.8)^3 + (0.8)^4$

$= 0.0016 + \quad 0.0256 \quad + \quad 0.1536 \quad + \quad 0.4096 \quad + 0.4096$

PowerPoint

Additional Examples

❶ Suppose you and a friend flip a coin three times to find out who gets to play an arcade game first. The person who gets two out of three flips wins. Your winning side is heads.
a. Describe a trial for this situation. How many trials are there? **Each flip is a trial and there are three trials.**
b. Describe a success. What is the probability of a success on each trial? **Heads is a success; 0.5**
c. Conduct a simulation to find the probability of getting heads two out of three times. Run the simulation ten times. **Check students' work.**

❷ A fast food restaurant is attaching prize cards to every one of its soft drink cups. The restaurant awards free drinks as prizes on three out of four cards. Suppose you have three cards. Find the probability that exactly one of these cards will reveal a free soft drink as its prize. **about 0.14**

❸ Alicia walks to school with her friend Juana. Juana is on time 80% of the time. What is the probability that Juana will be on time five days in a row? **about 33%**

EXAMPLE 4   **Error Prevention**

Students may make mistakes when expanding the binomial $(p + q)^n$. Help students see the following:

1) The exponent of p decreases as the exponent of q increases.

2) The sum of the exponents in each term must equal n.

3) There is one more term than the power to which the binomial is being raised.

PowerPoint

Additional Example

4 When it rains, there is a 70% chance that Malcolm's soccer practice will be cancelled. If it rains for the next three days, what is the probability that Malcolm's practice will be cancelled on at least one of the days? **about 97%**

Resources
- Daily Notetaking Guide 12-6   **L3**

Closure

Ask students to explain why, for a binomial probability, $p + q$ must equal 1. **In any probability distribution the sum of the probabilities must be 1. Since there are only two possible outcomes, p and q, $p + q$ must equal 1.**

1. **Each guess is a trial. There are 5 trials. Each correct answer is a success. The probability of a success on a single trial is 0.5. Check students' designs and simulations.**

2. **Each voter selected is a trial. There are 10 trials. A vote in favor of the bond is a success. The probability of a success on a single trial is 0.4. Check students' designs and simulations.**

3. **Each shift is a trial. There are 3 trials. Not experiencing a breakdown is a success.**

688

Real-World Connection

Teardrop-shaped balloons collect weather data.

 Quick Check

Of course, you can display a binomial distribution as a graph.

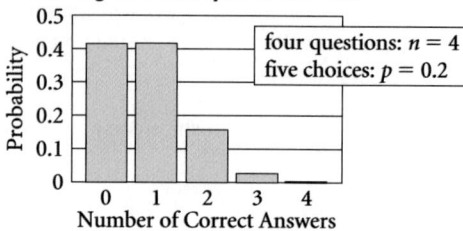

Guessing on a Multiple-Choice Test

four questions: $n = 4$
five choices: $p = 0.2$

EXAMPLE 4   **Real-World Connection**

Weather A scientist hopes to launch a weather balloon on one of the next three mornings. For each morning, there is a 40% chance of suitable weather. What is the probability that there will be at least one morning with suitable weather?

Use the expansion for $(p + q)^n$, with $n = 3$, $p = 0.4$, and $q = 0.6$.

$$\begin{array}{ccccccccc} & & 3\text{ successes} & & 2\text{ successes} & & 1\text{ success} & & 0\text{ successes} \\ (p + q)^3 = & & 1p^3 & + & 3p^2q & + & 3pq^2 & + & 1q^3 \\ = & & (0.4)^3 & + & 3(0.4)^2(0.6) & + & 3(0.4)(0.6)^2 & + & (0.6)^3 \\ = & & 0.064 & + & 0.288 & + & 0.432 & + & 0.216 \end{array}$$

$P(\text{at least 1 success}) = P(1 \text{ success}) + P(2 \text{ successes}) + P(3 \text{ successes})$

$= 0.432 + 0.288 + 0.064$

$= 0.784$

The probability of at least one morning with suitable weather is about 78%.

4 One survey found that 80% of respondents eat corn on the cob in circles rather than from side to side. Assume that this sample accurately represents the population. What is the probability that, out of five people you know, at least two of them eat corn on the cob in circles? **0.9933**

EXERCISES

For more exercises, see *Extra Skill and Word Problem Practice.*

Practice and Problem Solving

A   **Practice by Example**

Example 1
(page 686)

 for Help

For each situation, describe a trial and a success. Then design and run a simulation to find the probability.   **1–3. See margin.**

1. On a true-or-false test, you guess the answers to five questions. Find the probability of guessing the correct answers to exactly three of the five questions.

2. A poll shows that 40% of the voters in a city favor passage of a bond issue to finance park improvements. If ten voters are selected at random, find the probability that exactly four of them will vote in favor of it.

3. A plant production line has a 90% probability of not experiencing a breakdown during an eight-hour shift. Find the probability that three successive shifts will not have a breakdown.

The probability of a success on a single trial is 0.9. Check students' designs and simulations.

21. Each term of a binomial expansion $(p + q)^n$ contains a power of p times a power of q. The coefficient of each term is the number of times that a combination of powers results when $(p + q)^n$ is expanded. In a binomial experiment of n trials, each trial results in success or failure, with probabilities p and q. The probability of each outcome contains n factors, each of which

Example 2
(page 686)

Suppose you guess on a true-or-false test. Use a tree diagram to find each probability.

4. $P(4 \text{ correct in } 4 \text{ guesses})$ **6.25%**
5. $P(1 \text{ correct in } 4 \text{ guesses})$ **25%**
6. $P(3 \text{ correct in } 4 \text{ guesses})$ **25%**
7. $P(6 \text{ correct in } 4 \text{ guesses})$ **0%**

Example 3
(page 687)

Find the probability of x successes in n trials for the given probability of success p on each trial.

8. $x = 3, n = 8, p = 0.3$ **0.2541**
9. $x = 4, n = 8, p = 0.3$ **0.1361**
10. $x = 5, n = 10, p = 0.5$ **0.2461**
11. $x = 5, n = 10, p = 0.1$ **0.0015**

Example 4
(page 688)

Use the binomial expansion of $(p + q)^n$ to calculate and graph each binomial distribution. **12–14. See back of book.**

12. $n = 6, p = 0.3$
13. $n = 6, p = 0.5$
14. $n = 6, p = 0.9$

 B Apply Your Skills   **Marketing** A fruit company guarantees that 90% of the pineapples it ships will be ripe within four days. Find each probability for a case containing 12 pineapples.

15. 0.2824

15. All 12 are ripe within four days.
16. At least 10 are ripe within four days.

16. 0.8891

17. No more than 9 are ripe within four days. **0.1109**

Sociology A study shows that 50% of the families in a community watch television during dinner. Suppose you select 10 families at random from this population. Find each probability.

18. $P(5 \text{ of the 10 families watch television during dinner})$ **0.2461**

19. $P(6 \text{ of the 10 families watch television during dinner})$ **0.2051**

20. $P(\text{at least 5 of the 10 families watch television during dinner})$ **0.6230**

21. Writing Explain how a binomial experiment is related to a binomial expansion. **See margin p. 688.**

22. Quality Control A company claims that 99% of its cereal boxes have at least as **GPS** much cereal by weight as the amount stated on the box.
  a. At a quality control checkpoint, one box out of a random sample of ten boxes falls short of its stated weight. What is the probability of this happening due to chance variation in box weights? **0.0914**
  b. Suppose three of ten boxes fail to have the claimed weight. What would you conclude? Explain why. **See margin.**

23. Data Collection Use the current winning percentage of a local sports team as its probability of success. Find the team's probability of winning at least three of any five games. **Check students' work.**

Real-World **Connection**

Manufacturers ensure the quality of their products by inspecting raw materials, machinery, and procedures, as well as finished products.

24. Genetics About 11% of the general population is left-handed. At a school with an average class size of 30, each classroom contains four left-handed desks. Does this seem adequate? Justify your answer. **See margin.**

25. For a group of 40 people, what is the probability that exactly three people in the group will celebrate their birthdays on a Wednesday this year?
  a. Find the probability by using the binomial probability formula.
  b. Find the probability by designing and running a simulation.
  c. Compare your results for parts (a) and (b). Explain any discrepancy.
  a–c. See back of book.

26. Open-Ended Describe a binomial experiment that can be solved using the expression $_7C_2(0.6)^2(0.4)^5$. **See back of book.**

Online
Homework Video Tutor
Visit: PHSchool.com
Web Code: age-1206

is either p or q. The coefficient of each term is the number of ways that outcome can be achieved.

22b. The probability that 3 boxes would be

underweight is 0.0001. Thus I would conclude that there is a malfunction in the machinery that must be corrected.

24. The probability of a group of 30 students having 4 or fewer left-handed students is 77.05%. This percentage means that more than

three quarters of the classes will have enough left-handed desks; 4 is an adequate number.

3. Practice

Assignment Guide

1 A B 1-11, 18-21, 24, 26

2 A B 12-17, 22, 23, 25
C Challenge 27-29

Test Prep 30-35
Mixed Review 36-48

Homework Quick Check
To check students' understanding of key skills and concepts, go over Exercises 8, 14, 21, 22, 23, 25.

Differentiated Instruction Resources

GPS Guided Problem Solving	L3
Enrichment	L4
Reteaching	L2
Practice	L3

1. North High School's football team has a reputation for losing the first game of every season. In the last 20 years, they have lost 70% of their opening games. What is the probability that they will lose their season opening games for the next three years? **about 34%**

2. Yolanda enjoys fishing even though she only catches fish on about 20% of the days she spends fishing. If Yolanda is going on a 4-day fishing trip, what is the probability that she will catch fish on at least one of the four days? **about 59%**

Alternative Assessment

Instruct each student to write a problem similar to Example 3. Direct students to exchange problems. Have each student describe a trial and success, use a tree diagram to find the probability, then use the binomial expansion of $(p + q)^n$ to check that their tree diagram is correct. Have students graph the binomial distribution.

Test Prep

Resources

For additional practice with a variety of test item formats:
- Standardized Test Prep, p. 705
- Test-Taking Strategies, p. 700
- Test-Taking Strategies with Transparencies

 C Challenge

29a. The graph is symmetrical about the line $x = 3.5$.

b.

x	y
0	0.0078
1	0.0547
2	0.1641
3	0.2734
4	0.2734
5	0.1641
6	0.0547
7	0.0078

33. [2] $_4C_3 (0.8)^3(0.2)^1$
$+ _4C_4(0.8)^4(0.2)^0$
$= 0.4096 + 0.4096$
$= 0.8192$

[1] computational error

Short Response

Extended Response

Statistics **A multiple-choice test has ten questions. Each question has five choices, with only one correct.**

27. Statisticians consider a "rare" event to have less than a 5% chance of occurring. According to this standard, what grades would be rare on this test if you guess? Justify your answer. **See margin.**

28. Design and conduct a simulation to model this situation. Gather results of simulations from your classmates. Do these results confirm the grades you identified as rare in Exercise 27? Explain. **Check students' work.**

29. Enter the binomial probability formula as shown. Set the window and table shown. (To get integer values of x, you may need to adjust your window.)

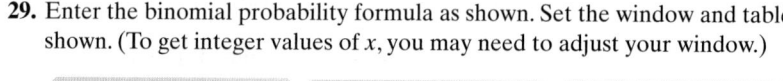

a. Examine the graph of $y = _7C_x(0.5)^x(0.5)^{7-x}$. Describe any symmetry you see in the graph. **a–b. See left.**

b. Verify the symmetry by displaying values of the function in table form.

c. Change the graph to $y = _7C_x(0.6)^x(0.4)^{7-x}$. Does this graph have any symmetry? Explain. **No; the bulge in the graph has shifted right.**

 Test Prep

30. Four percent of the tenants in an apartment building live alone. Suppose five tenants are selected randomly. Which expression represents P(all live alone)? **A**
 A. $(0.04)^5$ **B.** $(0.4)^5$ **C.** $(0.96)^5$ **D.** $(5)^{0.04}$

31. A survey shows that 60% of the adults floss their teeth every day. In a random sample of ten adults, what is the probability that exactly six floss every day? **G**
 F. 11% **G.** 25% **H.** 60% **J.** 100%

32. A multiple-choice quiz contains five questions, each with three answer choices. You select all five answer choices at random. What is the best estimate of the probability that you will get at least four answers correct? **B**
 A. 4.1% **B.** 4.5% **C.** 13.2% **D.** 46.1%

33. A family is planning a four-day campout. The weather forecast shows a 20% chance of rain for each of the four days. Find the probability, to the nearest hundredth, that there will be no rain on at least three of the four days. **See left.**

34. Evaluate $_nC_x p^x q^{n-x}$ for $n = 7$, $x = 4$, $p = 0.2$, and $q = 0.8$. Round your answer to the nearest thousandth. **See margin p. 691.**

35. A bank of track lights contains several bulbs. The chance that some number of the bulbs will last for at least 2 years is given by the expression $_5C_2(0.15)^2 (0.85)^3$. **a–c. See margin p. 691.**
 a. What is the number of bulbs in the track?
 b. How many bulbs should last at least 2 years?
 c. What is the probability that all the bulbs will last at least 2 years?

---

27. Getting 5 or more items right by guessing would be statistically rare. The probability of getting 10, 9, 8, 7, or 6 correct is each less than 1%. The probability of getting 5 right is 2.6%. The probability of getting 4 right is 8.8%.

GO for Help

Lesson 12-5

36. The table contains information from a study of the prices of comparable airline tickets. Which sample most likely was greater in size, A or B? Explain.

Sample B was larger because it had a smaller standard deviation.

Sample	Standard Deviation
A	$10.81
B	$3.97

Lesson 11-5

37. 394.0625

38. ≈18.18

Find the sum of each geometric series to the given term.

37. $8 + 12 + 18 + \ldots; n = 8$

38. $20 + (-2) + 0.2 + \ldots; n = 12$

39. $729 + 243 + 81 + \ldots; n = 9$
1093.$\overline{4}$

40. $\frac{1}{16} + \frac{1}{4} + 1 + \ldots; n = 6$
85.3125

Lesson 10-5

Find the equation of a hyperbola with horizontal transverse axis, centered at the origin, for the given a and c values. 41–42. See margin.

41. $a = 897$ units, $c = 1024$ units

42. $a = 20$ units, $c = 29$ units

Lesson 5-4

Factor each expression. 43–46. See margin.

43. $x^2 + 6x + 9$

44. $x^2 + x - 6$

45. $x^2 - 7x + 10$

46. $3x^2 + 12x + 9$

47. $2x^2 - x - 6$
$(2x + 3)(x - 2)$

48. $5x^2 + 5x - 10$
$5(x - 1)(x + 2)$

Checkpoint Quiz 2   Lessons 12-4 through 12-6

Calculate the mean, range, and standard deviation for each set of data.

1. 34 36 29 45 34 25
33.8$\overline{3}$, 20, 6.20

2. 12 9 10 11 14 10
11, 5, 1.63

3. 1 5 2 1 4 1 3 2
2.375, 4, 1.41

4. A set of values has a mean of 300 and a standard deviation of 60. What value has a z-score of -1.2? **228**

5a. This survey may be biased because it overrepresents people who shop for CDs online and entirely misses those who do not have internet access.

b. Answers may vary. Sample: Survey a random selection of students in homerooms for each grade level.

5. A survey on the Web site of an online CD store includes the question, "Who is your favorite singer?" a–b. See left.
a. Explain why the results of the survey may be biased.
b. Open-Ended Suggest a way to make the survey an unbiased representation of the population of your high school.

 6. Consumer Spending In a survey of 683 car owners selected at random, 235 reported paying cash for their first car.
a. Find the sample proportion. **0.3441 ≈ 34.4%**
b. Find the margin of error. **±3.8%**
c. Find an interval likely to contain the true population proportion.
30.6% to 38.2%

7. Determine the sample size that produces a margin of error of ±20%. **25**

8. Seventy percent of the time, a friend of yours is more than 10 minutes late to meet you for a movie. What is the probability that your friend will be more than 10 minutes late to meet you for all of the next three movies you see?
0.343

Each trial of an experiment has a probability of success p. Find the probability of x successes in n trials.

9. $p = 0.8, x = 4, n = 5$ **0.4096**

10. $p = 0.4, x = 4, n = 5$ **0.0768**

Online lesson quiz, PHSchool.com, Web Code: aga-1206   Lesson 12-6 Binomial Distributions **691**

---

34. [2] $_nC_x p^x q^{n-x} =$
$_7C_4(0.2)^4(0.8)^{7-4} =$
$\frac{7!}{4!3!} \cdot (0.2)^4(0.8)^3 =$
$35(0.0016)(0.512) \approx$
0.029

[1] answer only OR incomplete solution

35. [4] If $_nC_x p^x q^{n-x} =$
$_5C_2(0.15)^2(0.85)^3$, then
$n = 5, x = 2, p = 0.15$, and $q = 0.85$.

a. The number of bulbs in the track is n, or 5, bulbs.

b. The number that are supposed to last at least 2 years is x, or 2, bulbs.

c. The probability that all the bulbs will last at least 2 years is $_5C_5(0.15)^5(0.85)^0$ ≈ 0.000076.

[3] a minor error

[2] at least 1 part correct

[1] answers only OR at least some correct information

41. $\frac{x^2}{804,609} - \frac{y^2}{243,967} = 1$

42. $\frac{x^2}{400} - \frac{y^2}{441} = 1$

43. $(x + 3)(x + 3)$

44. $(x + 3)(x - 2)$

45. $(x - 5)(x - 2)$

46. $3(x + 1)(x + 3)$

Objectives
1 To use a normal distribution
2 To use the standard normal curve

Examples
1 Real-World Connection
2 Real-World Connection
3 Using the Standard Normal Curve
4 Real-World Connection

Math Background

Much of mathematical statistics is directed at relating data sets to a normal distribution. This is because the normal distribution supports hypothesis testing, which depends on the distribution of data within 1, 2, and 3 standard deviations of the mean of a normal distribution.

More Math Background: p. 646D

Lesson Planning and Resources

See p. 646E for a list of the resources that support this lesson.

✓ Check Skills You'll Need
For intervention, direct students to:

Standard Deviation
Lesson 12-4: Example 4
Extra Skills and Word Problems Practice, Ch. 12

Normal Distributions

What You'll Learn
- To use a normal distribution
- To use the standard normal curve

... And Why
To describe the jaws of great white sharks, as in Example 2

 New Vocabulary • normal distribution • standard normal curve

✓ Check Skills You'll Need

 for Help Lesson 12-4

Find the numbers that are one and two standard deviations above and below each given mean. Write these numbers from least to greatest. 1–6. See below left.

1. $\bar{x} = 12, \sigma = 2$ **2.** $\bar{x} = 16.7, \sigma = 1$ **3.** $\bar{x} = 7, \sigma = 1.5$

4. $\bar{x} = 22, \sigma = 1.7$ **5.** $\bar{x} = 17.5, \sigma = 0.9$ **6.** $\bar{x} = 33.1, \sigma = 1.2$

---

1 Using a Normal Distribution

1. 8, 10, 14, 16

2. 14.7, 15.7, 17.7, 18.7

3. 4, 5.5, 8.5, 10

Real-World Connection

Careers Neonatal nurses specialize in the nursing care of newborns and babies up to 30 days old.

4. 18.6, 20.3, 23.7, 25.4

5. 15.7, 16.6, 18.4, 19.3

6. 30.7, 31.9, 34.3, 35.5

A **normal distribution** shows data that vary randomly from the mean. The pattern the data form is a bell-shaped curve called a normal curve.

1 EXAMPLE   Real-World Connection

Medicine The bar graph below gives the birth weights of a population of 100 babies. The red curve shows how the weights are normally distributed about the mean, 3250 g. Estimate the percent of babies weighing 2500–3999 g.

Full-Term Birth Weight Distribution for a Population

Estimate and add the percents for 2500–2999, 3000–3499, and 3500–3999.

$23\% + 42\% + 23\% = 88\%$

About 88% of the babies weigh 2500–3999 g.

✓ Quick Check
1 **a.** Estimate the percent of babies weighing less than 3500 g. **71%**
b. The standard deviation in birth weights is about 500 g. Estimate the percent of babies whose birth weights are within 1.5 standard deviations of the mean. **88%**

692   Chapter 12   Probability and Statistics

Every normal curve has a symmetric bell shape. When outcomes are normally distributed, you can sketch the graph of the distribution.

Real-World Connection

The jaw widths of a population of great white sharks are normally distributed about a mean of 15.7 inches.

2 EXAMPLE Real-World Connection

Biology Refer to the photo. For the given population of sharks, the standard deviation of the jaw widths is 2.8 inches. Sketch a normal curve showing the jaw widths at one, two, and three standard deviations from the mean.

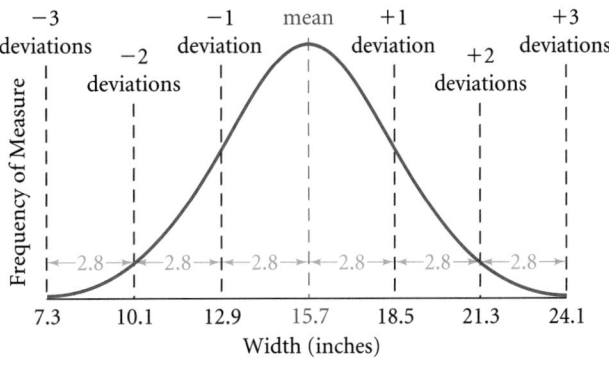

Distribution of Jaw Widths for Great White Sharks

✓ **Quick Check** ❷ Suppose the mean in Example 2 is 15.4 inches and the standard deviation is 3.1 inches. Sketch a normal curve showing the jaw widths at one, two, and three standard deviations from the mean. **See back of book.**

2 Using the Standard Normal Curve

When you show a probability distribution as a bar graph, the height of the bar for each outcome indicates the probability. For a normal curve, however, the area between the curve and the x-axis represents the probability.

The **standard normal curve** is a normal distribution centered on the y-axis. The mean of the standard normal curve is 0. The standard deviation is 1.

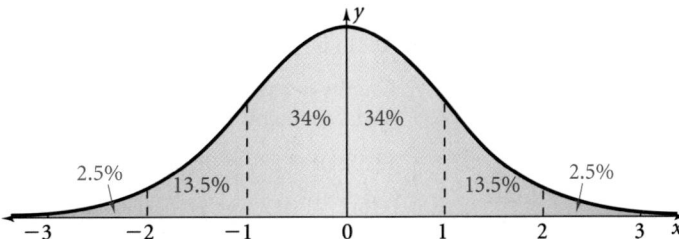

The Standard Normal Curve

Vocabulary Tip

The *z-score* of a value is the number of standard deviations that the value is from the mean.

Every normal curve contains the same probability distribution. When a data set is normally distributed, about 68% of the data fall within one standard deviation of the mean. About 95% of the data fall within two standard deviations of the mean. To find the values that are two standard deviations away from the mean, find the values that have z-scores of -2 and 2.

Guided Instruction

1 EXAMPLE **Visual Learners**

Ask students to bring a bell from home. Encourage all shapes and sizes. Tape a sheet of butcher paper on the board. Have students trace the vertical outline of their bell on the paper.

2 EXAMPLE **Tactile Learners**

Suggest students fold a piece of paper in half lengthwise. Then fold it into thirds lengthwise. They can use the fold lines to mark the standard deviations.

PowerPoint

Additional Examples

❶ Use the data from Example 1 to estimate the number of babies whose birth weights are between one and two standard deviations from the mean. The standard deviation in birth weights is about 500g. **about 10%**

❷ A survey of the employees of the XYZ Corporation found that the mean morning commute time to work was 18 minutes. The standard deviation was 4 minutes. Sketch a normal curve showing the commute times at one, two, and three standard deviations from the mean.

Distribution for Commute Times for XYZ Employees

Advanced Learners L4
Teachers sometimes "curve" grades. Discuss what conditions would be needed for grades to match a normal distribution.

learning style: verbal

English Language Learners ELL
Explain that a bell-shaped curve comes from the physical shape of a bell. Ask: *What are some characteristics of the bell-shaped curve?*
shape is symmetrical about the mean and highest in the middle

learning style: verbal

693

Instruct students to draw an *x*-axis and a *y*-axis on their paper. They can use string to estimate the shape of the bell curve on the paper. Encourage students to use this paper and string when working the Exercises.

Additional Examples

3 In a survey, the responses to the question, "How much time do you spend in the shower every day?" were normally distributed. The mean was 15 minutes; the standard deviation was 2 minutes.
a. What values are one standard deviation from the mean?
13 minutes and 17 minutes
b. What percent of the responses would you expect to find that are less than 13 and greater than 17?
32%

4 Use the distribution from Example 4 to answer the following question. Assume there are 92 students in the lecture class. The professor has found that students who score between one and two standard deviations below the mean need to attend study sessions in order to pass the class. How many students need to attend study sessions? **about 12 students**

Resources
• Daily Notetaking Guide
  12-6   **L3**

Closure

Ask students to list some data that is likely to be normally distributed. Some possibilities are shoe size, test scores, and birth weight. Ask students to explain the definition of the mean and standard deviation as it relates to their data.

---

3 EXAMPLE **Using the Standard Normal Curve**

In a survey, the responses to the question "How much time do you spend at meals in one week?" were normally distributed. The mean was 13 h; the standard deviation was 3 h.

a. What values are one standard deviation from the mean?

Values that are one standard deviation from the mean have *z*-scores of -1 and 1.

$$z\text{-score} = \frac{\text{value} - \text{mean}}{\text{standard deviation}}$$

$$-1 = \frac{v - 13}{3} \qquad\qquad 1 = \frac{u - 13}{3}$$
$$v = 10 \qquad\qquad u = 16$$

The values 10 h and 16 h are one standard deviation away from the mean.

b. What percent of the responses would you expect to find from 10 h to 16 h?

The responses are normally distributed, and 10 h and 16 h are the values that are one standard deviation from the mean. Since 68% of the data are within one standard deviation of the mean, 68% should be values from 10 h to 16 h.

 Quick Check **3 a.** Suppose there were 100 responses to the survey question. How many responses would you expect to be values from 10 h to 16 h? **68 responses**
b. Of 100 responses, how many would you expect to be values from 16 h to 19 h?
13 or 14 responses

4 EXAMPLE **Real-World** **Connection**

Education In a university lecture class with 174 students, the final exam scores have a mean of 68.5 and a standard deviation of 7.3. The grades on the exams are all whole numbers, and the grade pattern follows a normal curve.

a. About how many students receive grades from one to two standard deviations above the mean.

Use the normal curve. About 13.5% of the students receive grades from one to two standard deviations above the mean.

Distribution of Final Exam Scores

2.5%	13.5%	34%	34%	13.5%	2.5%
	53.9	61.2	68.5	75.8	83.1

$0.135(174) = 23.49$ **Find the number of students that corresponds to 13.5%.**

About 23 students receive grades from one to two standard deviations above the mean.

b. About how many students receive grades of 61 or below.

Use the normal curve from part (a). A grade of 61 is about one standard deviation below the mean.

$13.5\% + 2.5\% = 16\%$ **Find the % at least 1 standard deviation below the mean.**

$0.16(174) = 27.84$ **Find the number of students.**

About 28 students receive grades of 61 or below.

4b. 76 is about 1 SD above the mean. About 13.5% + 2.5% should receive grades above 76. 16% of 140 is about 22.

 Quick Check **4 a.** Suppose there are 140 students in the class in Example 4. About how many would receive grades from 69 to 75? **47 or 48 students**
b. *Writing* How do you know that in a class of 140 students, about 22 students receive grades of 76 or higher? **See left.**

EXERCISES

For more exercises, see *Extra Skill and Word Problem Practice.*

Practice and Problem Solving

A Practice by Example

Example 1
(page 692)

GO for Help

Biology The heights of men in a survey are distributed normally about the mean. Use the graph for Exercises 1–4.

Heights of Men Ages 25–34

1. About what percent of men aged 25 to 34 are 69–71 inches tall? **43%**

2. About what percent of men aged 25 to 34 are less than 70 inches tall? **39%**

3. Suppose the survey included data on 100 men. About how many would you expect to be 69–71 inches tall? **43 men**

4. The mean of the data is 70, and the standard deviation is 2.5. About what percent of men are within one standard deviation of the mean in height? **66%**

Example 2
(page 693)

Sketch a normal curve for each distribution. Label the *x*-axis values at one, two, and three standard deviations from the mean. **5–8. See margin.**

5. mean = 45, standard deviation = 5   6. mean = 45, standard deviation = 10

7. mean = 45, standard deviation = 2   8. mean = 45, standard deviation = 3.5

Examples 3 and 4
(page 694)

A set of data with a mean of 62 and a standard deviation of 5.7 is normally distributed. Find each value, given its distance from the mean.

9. +3 standard deviations **79.1**   10. −1 standard deviation **56.3**

A set of data has a normal distribution with a mean of 50 and a standard deviation of 8. Find the percent of data within each interval.

11. from 42 to 58 **68%**   12. greater than 34 **97.5%**   13. less than 50 **50%**

14. **Test Scores** The scores on an exam are normally distributed, with a mean of 85 and a standard deviation of 5. What percent of the scores are from 85 to 95? **47.5%**

B Apply Your Skills

15. The numbers of paper clips in a truckload of boxes are normally distributed, with a mean of 100 and a standard deviation of 5. Find the probability that a box will *not* contain from 95 to 105 clips. **32%**

16. The student's grade is an outlier; 99% of all grades are expected to be within 3 standard deviations of the mean; and this score is 4.4 standard deviations above the mean.

16. **Writing** In a class of 25, one student receives a grade of 100 on a test. The grades are distributed approximately normally, with a mean of 78 and a standard deviation of 5. Do you think the student's grade is an outlier? Explain. **See left.**

Lesson 12-7 Normal Distributions **695**

---

3. Practice

Assignment Guide

1 A B 1-10, 17, 27-28

2 A B 11-16, 18-26, 29
C Challenge 30-31

Test Prep 32-38
Mixed Review 39-50

Homework Quick Check
To check students' understanding of key skills and concepts, go over Exercises 6, 14, 16, 18, 19, 28.

Error Prevention!

Exercises 5–8 Suggest students fold their papers in half to check that their graphs are symmetric.

Differentiated Instruction Resources

GPS Guided Problem Solving L3
Enrichment L4
Reteaching L2
Practice L3

5.
30 35 40 45 50 55 60

6.
15 25 35 45 55 65 75

7.
39 41 43 45 47 49 51

8.
34.5 38 41.5 45 48.5 52 55.5

695

17a. set 2

b–c.

4 5 6 7 8 9 10 11

28a.

b. The data do not fit a normal curve; the data are too skewed to the left.

26. The first plant was in the top 16% of its group.

---

17. a. From the table at the right, select the set of values that appears to be distributed normally.
  b. Using the set you chose in part (a), make a histogram of the values. **a–c. See margin.**
  c. Sketch a normal curve over your graph.

18. **Track** To qualify as a contestant in a race, a runner has to be in the fastest 16% of all applicants. The running times are normally distributed, with a mean of 63 min and a standard deviation of 4 min. To the nearest minute, what is the qualifying time for the race?
59 minutes

19. **Agriculture** To win a prize, a tomato must be greater than 4 in. in diameter. The diameters of a crop of tomatoes grown in a special soil are normally distributed, with a mean of 3.2 in. and a standard deviation of 0.4 in. Find the probability that the crop will contain a winning tomato. **2.5%**

Set 1	Set 2	Set 3
1	5	5
10	7	6
5	7	9
19	7	1
2	7	1
7	4	1
1	11	5
7	7	11
2	7	1
10	7	10
6	9	4
9	7	2
	7	8

A normal distribution has a mean of 100 and a standard deviation of 10. Find the probability that a value selected at random is in the given interval.

20. from 80 to 100 **47.5%**   21. from 70 to 130 **100%**   22. from 90 to 120 **81.5%**

23. at least 100 **50%**   24. at most 110 **84%**   25. at least 80 **97.5%**

26. Two tomato plants were chosen from two groups of plants grown in different soils. Each sample plant produced 23 tomatoes. The mean number of tomatoes for plants in the first soil was 17, with a standard deviation of 5. The mean number of tomatoes for plants in the second soil was 18, with a standard deviation of 6. Determine which plant, if either, is in the top 16% of its group.

27. In a set of data, the value that is -3 standard deviations from the mean is 86. The value that is $+1$ standard deviation from the mean is 250.
  a. Find the mean. **209**
  b. Find the standard deviation. **41**
  c. Find an interval with an end value of 250 that contains about 81.5% of the data. **127–250**

28. **Seismology** The table below shows the number of earthquakes worldwide in 2000.
  a. Draw a histogram to represent the data. **a–b. See margin.**
  b. Does the histogram approximate a normal curve? Explain.

GO nline
Homework Video Tutor
Visit: PHSchool.com
Web Code: age-1207

Worldwide Earthquakes in 2000			
Magnitude	**Number**	**Magnitude**	**Number**
0.1–0.9	6	5.0–5.9	1318
1.0–1.9	1028	6.0–6.9	157
2.0–2.9	3728	7.0–7.9	14
3.0–3.9	4741	8.0–8.9	4
4.0–4.9	8114	≥9.0	0

SOURCE: U.S. Geological Survey

29. Critical Thinking Jake and Elena took the same standardized test, but with different groups of students. They both received a score of 87. In Jake's group, the mean was 80 and the standard deviation was 6. In Elena's group, the mean was 76 and the standard deviation was 4. Did either student score in the top 10% of his or her group? Explain.   **See margin.**

C Challenge **30. Quality Control** Tubs of Better Butter weigh 1.0 lb each, with a standard deviation of 0.06 lb. At a quality control checkpoint, 12 of the tubs taken as samples weighed less than 0.88 lb. Assume that the weights of the samples were normally distributed. How many tubs of butter were taken as samples?

30. 480 tubs

31. Games In the Japanese game pachinko, a player launches small steel balls from the bottom of a playing frame to the top. The balls then fall through pins and bounce around haphazardly. They land in slots at the bottom of the game and form a normal distribution. If a ball falls into a specially marked slot, the player wins additional balls with which to play again in the next round. If a ball does not fall into a marked slot, the player loses that ball.

   a. Suppose that all slots between one and two standard deviations from the center are marked. When a ball lands in one of the marked slots, you win the ball back along with two others. If you begin with 200 balls, how many balls should you have after one round?   **162 balls**

   b. Suppose that there are two sets of marked slots. One set is within one standard deviation of the center and the other set is more than two standard deviations from the center. When a ball lands in one of the slots in the first set, you win the ball back. When a ball lands in one of the slots in the second set, you win the ball back, along with four others. If you begin with 1000 balls, how many balls should you have after one round?   **930 balls**

   c. Open-Ended Using your knowledge of normal distributions, design a pachinko game with both winning and losing slots in which you would theoretically have the same number of balls after each round as when you started. You can adjust the number of balls at the beginning of the game, the placement of the winning slots, and the number balls won per slot.
   Check students' work.

Test Prep

Multiple Choice   For a daily airline flight between two cities, the number of pieces of checked luggage has a mean of 380 and a standard deviation of 20. Use this information for Exercises 32–33.

32. On what percent of the flights would you expect from 340 to 420 pieces of checked luggage?   **D**
   A. 34%   **B.** 47.5%   **C.** 68%   **D.** 95%

33. What number of pieces of checked luggage is 3 standard deviations above the mean?   **H**
   F. 60   **G.** 97.5   **H.** 440   **J.** 1140

34. A set of data is normally distributed with a mean of 44 and a standard deviation of 3.2. Which statements are NOT true?   **A**
   I. 68% of the values are between 37.6 and 50.4
   II. 13.5% of the values are less than 40.8
   III. 5% of the values are lower than 37.6 or higher than 50.4

   A. I and II only   **B.** I and III only   **C.** II and III only   **D.** I, II, and III

Lesson Quiz

1. The bar graph below gives the hours of homework per week of surveyed students.

a. About what percent of students have between 5 and 9 hours of homework per week?   **about 66%**

b. Suppose the survey included 500 students. About how many have between 5 and 9 hours of homework per week?   **about 330 students**

c. The mean of the data is seven hours and the standard deviation is two. About what percentage of students have an amount of homework within 2 standard deviations of the mean?   **about 92%**

2. A biology class did a survey of an open field for the number of visible insects per square foot of ground. The results were normally distributed. The mean was 28 insects and the standard deviation was 5.

a. What values are 1 standard deviation from the mean?   **23 and 33 insects**

b. Suppose the class surveyed 50 one-foot square plots. Find the number of plots that contained a number of insects within one standard deviation of the mean.   **34 plots**

---

29. Elena scored within the top 10% of her group. Her score is 2.75 std. dev. above the mean, which places her in the top 1%.

Jake did not score in the top 10%. His score is 1.16 std. dev. above the mean, or at the 88th percentile.

697

Alternative Assessment

Have students come up with an idea for a survey of students in the school that would collect data that should be normally distributed. Ask them to use the standard normal curve to predict the number of students who should fall within one standard deviation of the mean, two standard deviations of the mean, and so on. Then, if it is feasible, have students conduct the survey and find out if their actual data is normally distributed.

Test Prep

 Resources

For additional practice with a variety of test item formats:
- Standardized Test Prep, p. 705
- Test-Taking Strategies, p. 700
- Test-Taking Strategies with Transparencies

35. [2] For Distribution A, with 50 data values, 25 values are at or below 40, which is the mean. For Distribution B, with 30 data values, 15 values are at or below the mean 40. So Distribution A has more values at or below 40.

　　[1] answer only OR error

39. Answers may vary. Sample: For each trial generate 4 random numbers 1–100. If all 4 numbers are less than or equal to 95, the trial is a success. Repeat for 10 trials.

40. total garbage generated over x years

41. total number of bus passengers over x hours

43. Answers may vary. Sample: $\frac{x^2}{16} + \frac{y^2}{9} = 1$

44. Answers may vary. Sample: $\frac{x^2}{4} - \frac{y^2}{4} = 1$

698

Short Response

35. Distribution A has 50 data values with mean 40 and standard deviation 2.4. Distribution B has 30 data values with mean 40 and standard deviation 2.8. Which distribution has more data values at or below 40? Show your work.　**See margin.**

Read the article below. Then answer Exercises 36–38.

36. [2] $514 - 401 = 113$ or one standard deviation. The probability is 34% or 0.34.
　　[1] minor error

37. [2] $727 - 505 = 222$ or two standard deviations. The probability is 2.5% or 0.025.
　　[1] minor error

38. [2] $505 + 111 <$ math $< 505 + 222$
　　$616 <$ math < 727
　　$514 + 113 <$ verbal $< 514 + 226$
　　$627 <$ verbal < 740
　　$1243 <$ math $+$ verbal < 1467
　　The limits are 1243 and 1467 points
　　[1] minor error

College Entrance Exam Results for 2000

In 2000, over 1.2 million students across the country took college entrance exams. The average score on the verbal section showed no improvement over the average scores of the previous four years. The average score on the mathematics section was three points higher than the previous year's average.

Section	Mean	Standard Deviation
Math	505	111
Verbal	514	113

36. What is the probability that a student's score on the verbal section is from 401 to 514?

37. What is the probability that a student's score on the math section is greater than 727?

38. Both Susanna's math score and her verbal score were more than one standard deviation above the mean, but less than two standard deviations above the mean. What are the lower and upper limits of Susanna's combined score?

Mixed Review

 GO for Help

Lesson 12-6 　**39.** Production　A plant production line has a 95% probability of not experiencing a breakdown during a six-hour shift. The plant managers want to know the probability that four successive shifts will not have a breakdown. Design and run a simulation to find the probability. Include an explanation of what constitutes a trial and a success.　**See margin.**

Lesson 11-6　**For each set of axes, what does the area under the curve represent?** 40–41. See margin.

40. y-axis: tons of garbage generated per year, x-axis: years

41. y-axis: bus passengers per hour, x-axis: hours

Lesson 10-6　**42.** Coordinate Geometry　Write the equation of a circle centered at $(4, -5)$ with radius 7.　$(x - 4)^2 + (y + 5)^2 = 49$

Open-Ended　**Write the equation of a conic section with the given characteristics.**
43–44. See margin.

43. an ellipse with a major axis 8 units long

44. a hyperbola with an asymptote at $y = -x$

Lesson 9-1　**Suppose that x and y vary inversely. Write a function to model inverse variation.**

45. $x = 1$ when $y = 5$　　**46.** $x = -1$ when $y = 10$　　**47.** $x = -3$ when $y = 3$

48. $x = 25$ when $y = -5$　　**49.** $x = 1.8$ when $y = -6$　　**50.** $x = 7.5$ when $y = 50$

45–50. See margin.

698　Chapter 12　Probability and Statistics

---

45. $y = \frac{5}{x}$

46. $y = -\frac{10}{x}$

47. $y = -\frac{9}{x}$

48. $y = -\frac{125}{x}$

49. $y = -\frac{10.8}{x}$

50. $y = \frac{375}{x}$

Area Under a Curve

Statisticians use the function $f(x) = \frac{1}{\sqrt{2\pi}}e^{-\frac{x^2}{2}}$ to model data such as height or birth weight. You can use the area under the graph of the function to find probabilities.

ACTIVITY

In a given population, the weights of babies are normally distributed about the mean, 3250 g. The standard deviation is 500 g. Find the probability that a baby chosen at random weighs from 2250 g to 4250 g.

Step 1 Find the z-scores of the lower and upper limits.

$$z\text{-score} = \frac{\text{value} - \text{mean}}{\text{standard deviation}}$$

$$z_1 = \frac{2250 - 3250}{500} = \frac{-1000}{500} = -2$$

$$z_2 = \frac{4250 - 3250}{500} = \frac{1000}{500} = 2$$

Step 2 Enter $f(x) = \frac{1}{\sqrt{2\pi}}e^{-\frac{x^2}{2}}$ as Y$_1$. Adjust the window values.

```
WINDOW
  Xmin =-4.7
  Xmax= 4.7
  Xscl =1
  Ymin =-.2
  Ymax =.5
  Yscl =.1
  Xres =1
```

Step 3 Use the CALC feature and press 7 to access the $\int f(x)dx$ feature. Move the cursor until the lower limit is $x = -2$. Press ENTER. Move the cursor until the upper limit is $x = 2$. Press ENTER.

The area under the curve from $x = -2$ to $x = 2$ is about 0.95. So the probability that a baby weighs from 2250 g to 4250 g is about 95%.

EXERCISES

Use the data and the function in the example. Find the probability that the weight of a baby chosen at random falls within each interval.

1. 3150–4150 g **0.543**   2. 4300–4500 g **0.012**   3. less than 1800 g **0.002** 4. more than 4550 g **0.005**

5. For Exercises 1–4, estimate the number of babies within each interval from a population of 2400 babies. **1303 babies; 29 babies; 5 babies; 12 babies**

6. **Manufacturing** A battery company manufactures batteries having life spans that are normally distributed, with a mean of 45 months and a standard deviation of 5 months. Find the probability that a battery chosen at random will have each life span.
   a. 45–52 months **0.419**   b. 48–50 months **0.116**

Area Under a Curve

Students use the graphing calculator to graph a normal distribution curve and then use the numerical integral function $\int f(x)dx$ to find an area under the curve. This area represents the probability that a baby weighs within two standard deviations of the given mean birth weight.

Guided Instruction

Students already know that every standard normal curve contains the same probability distribution. So they should expect that 95% of the data should fall within two standard deviations of the mean. When the standard normal curve is centered on the y-axis, the mean of the curve is 0, and the standard deviation is 1. For two standard deviations, the data would fall between x-values of -2 and 2 on the curve.

Connection to Calculus

In this activity, the students learn that the area under the standard normal curve between -2 and 2 on the x-axis is equal to about 0.95, which is also the probability that data will fall within two standard deviations of the mean. Explain that finding the area under a curve involves integrating between two points on the curve. This is a calculus operation represented by the expression $\int f(x)dx$.

Resources

Students may use any graphing calculator.

Answering the Question Asked

This feature helps students devise strategies for carefully identifying the specific question being asked. This is an important strategy because answer choices are often correct for questions that are closely related to the question being asked.

Resources

SAT® and ACT® correlations are on page 646B.

Test-Taking Strategies with Transparencies
- Transparency 12
- Practice sheet, p. 36

Guided Instruction

Ask students if they have ever seen questions on standardized tests where more than one answer seemed correct. Explain that good test questions often include incorrect choices (distracters) that seem to be correct if the student does not read the question carefully. Therefore it is critical that students identify the question being asked.

Test-Taking Strategies with Transparencies

When answering a question, be sure to answer the question that is asked. Read the question carefully and identify the quantity that you are asked to find. Some answer choices are answers to related questions, so you have to be careful that you are answering the right question.

EXAMPLE

There are five puppies in a litter. If the probability that a puppy is male is 0.5, what is the probability that at most one puppy in the litter is male?

(A) 0.15625   (B) 0.1875   (C) 0.5   (D) 0.8125   (E) 0.96875

The problem is asking for the probability of "at most" one male puppy. Do not confuse this with "exactly" or "at least" one male puppy.

$$P(\text{at most one male puppy}) = P(\text{no male puppies}) + P(\text{exactly 1 male puppy})$$
$$= {}_5C_0(0.5)^0(0.5)^5 + {}_5C_1(0.5)^1(0.5)^4$$
$$= 0.03125 + 0.15625 = 0.1875$$

The correct answer is B.

Choices A and E are answers to related, but different, questions.

$$P(\text{exactly one male puppy}) = {}_5C_1(0.5)^1(0.5)^4 = 0.15625$$
$$P(\text{at least one male puppy}) = P(\text{exactly 1 male}) + \ldots + P(\text{exactly 5 males})$$
$$= {}_5C_1(0.5)^1(0.5)^4 + \ldots + {}_5C_5(0.5)^5(0.5)^0$$
$$= 0.15625 + \ldots + 0.03125$$
$$= 0.96875$$

EXERCISES

Identify the quantity that is being asked for. Then answer the question.

1. A box contains four quarters. Exactly two of the quarters have the American eagle on the back. Suppose you draw two quarters with replacement at random from the box.
   a. What is the probability that both have the American eagle on the back?
   b. What is the probability that neither has the American eagle on the back?
   c. What is the probability that at least one has the American eagle on the back? **a–c. See margin.**

2. In a survey, 28% of respondents say they are left-handed, 64% say they are right-handed, and 8% say they are ambidextrous. If the ambidextrous people are omitted, about what percent of those remaining are left-handed? **See margin p. 701.**
   (A) 28%   (B) 30%   (C) 32%   (D) 34%   (E) 36%

3. A student conducted a survey at school and found that 75% of the boys and 65% of the girls like to watch hockey games. There are an equal number of boys and girls in the school. If someone does not like to watch hockey games, what is the approximate probability that the person is a boy? **See margin p. 701.**
   (A) 25%   (B) 42%   (C) 48%   (D) 55%   (E) 75%

1a. Out of the possible pairs of quarters, the pair drawn have the American eagle on the back. $\frac{1}{4}$ or 0.25

b. Out of the possible pairs of quarters, the pair drawn do not have the American eagle on the back. $\frac{1}{4}$ or 0.25

c. Out of the possible pairs of quarters, the pair drawn have at least one quarter with the American eagle on the back. $\frac{3}{4}$ or 0.75

Chapter Review

Vocabulary Review

🔊 bimodal (p. 660)
binomial experiment (p. 685)
binomial probability (p. 687)
box-and-whisker plot (p. 662)
conditional probability (p. 654)
cumulative probability (p. 648)
frequency table (p. 648)
interquartile range (p. 669)
margin of error (p. 679)

mean (p. 660)
measures of central tendency (p. 660)
measures of variation (p. 669)
median (p. 660)
mode (p. 660)
normal distribution (p. 692)
outlier (p. 664)
percentile (p. 663)
probability distribution (p. 649)

quartiles (p. 662)
random sample (p. 677)
range of a set of data (p. 669)
sample (p. 677)
sample proportion (p. 677)
standard deviation (p. 669)
standard normal curve (p. 693)
z-score (p. 671)

Go Online
PHSchool.com
For: Vocabulary quiz
Web Code: agj-1251

Choose the correct term to complete each sentence.

1. A(n) ? is part of a population.   **sample**

2. A(n) ? has a value substantially different from other data in a set.   **outlier**

3. A function that gives the probability of each event in a sample space is a(n) ? .   **probability distribution**

4. A(n) ? involves repeated trials, each of which has two possible outcomes whose probabilities are constant throughout the trials.   **binomial experiment**

5. Dispersion of data in a data set can be described by ? .
measures of variation

Skills and Concepts

12-1 and 12-2 Objectives

▼ To make a probability distribution (p. 648)

▼ To use a probability distribution in conducting a simulation (p. 650)

▼ To find conditional probabilities (p. 654)

▼ To use formulas and tree diagrams (p. 655)

A **probability distribution** is a function that gives the probability of each event in a sample space. A **frequency table** lists outcomes and the number of times each occurs. A frequency table can be used to find **cumulative probability**, which is the probability of a range of events.

A **conditional probability** limits the sample space to a given event. The probability of event A, given event B, is written $P(A \mid B)$. You can find a conditional probability from a table, a tree diagram, or by the conditional probability formula.

$$P(A \mid B) = \frac{P(A \text{ and } B)}{P(B)}$$

6. Use the results in the table below for the Rock-Paper-Scissors game.
   a. Make a frequency table for the winner: Player 1, Player 2, or tie.
   b. Find $P(\text{Player 2 wins})$. $P(\text{Player 2 wins}) = \frac{4}{15}$

6a.

Winner	Freq.
Player 1	8
Player 2	4
Ties	3
Total	15

Rock-Paper-Scissors

Player 1	S	P	P	R	R	P	**P**	**P**	**P**	S	R	S	**P**	S	R
Player 2	P	R	S	**S**	**P**	**S**	R	R	P	**P**	R	**R**	P	**R**	**P**

R = Rock   P = Paper   S = Scissors   **Bold** = Winner

7. Two number cubes are rolled. Use a table to show the probability distribution for the product of the two numbers.   **See back of book.**

Resources

Student Edition
Extra Skills and Word Problems
Practice, Ch. 12, p. 858
English/Spanish Glossary, p. 899
Properties and Formulas, p. 893
Table of Symbols, p. 889

Differentiated Instruction Resources

Vocabulary and Study Skills
worksheet 12F
Spanish Vocabulary and Study
Skills worksheet 12F
Interactive Textbook Audio
Glossary
Online Vocabulary Quiz

Success 𝒰 **Tracker**
Online at PHSchool.com

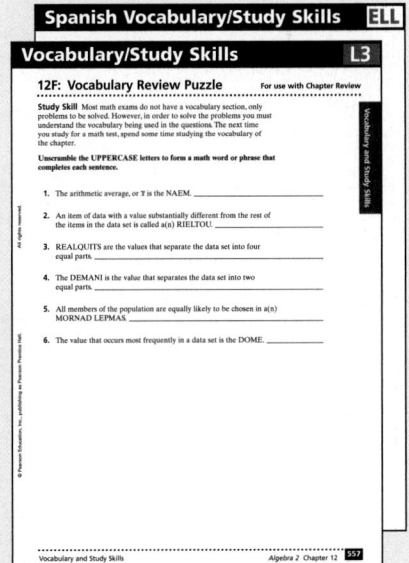

2. of the respondents who are not ambidextrous, the percentage who are left-handed, B

3. of the percentage of students who do not like to watch hockey, the probability that the student will be male, B

11.

Number of Siblings   Have Own Room

0 → 0.9 → Y
0.2 → 0.1 → N
0.6 → 1 → 0.8 → Y
0.2 → N
0.2 → 2 or more → 0.5 → Y
0.5 → N

14. 14.4; 14; 12, 13, 14

15.

$0 \le x \le 20$
$0 \le y \le 10$

16. 20th percentile = 13,
90th percentile = 18

17. 53rd percentile

---

8. At a bank, the number of customers c who arrive at the teller counters each minute varies according to the distribution below. Simulate the number of customers over a ten-minute period. **Check students' work.**

Number of Customers Each Minute

c	0	1	2	3	4	5	6	7
$P(c)$	0.16	0.28	0.25	0.18	0.09	0.02	0.01	0.01

Use the frequency table below for Exercises 9 and 10.

Birthday Months of Respondents to a Survey

Month	J	F	M	A	M	J	J	A	S	O	N	D
Male	0	1	2	1	1	3	2	0	1	1	0	2
Female	0	1	0	1	0	2	1	3	1	0	4	1

9. Find P(birthday in August | female respondent). $\frac{3}{14}$

10. Find P(male respondent | birthday in June). $\frac{3}{5}$

Use these survey results for Exercises 11–13.

- Of all respondents, 60% have 1 sibling and 20% have 2 or more siblings.
- Of the respondents with 0 siblings, 90% have their own room.
- Of the respondents with 1 sibling, 20% do not have their own room.
- Of the respondents with 2 or more siblings, 50% have their own room.

11. Make a tree diagram that reflects the results of the survey. **See margin.**

12. Find P(own room | 0 siblings). **0.9**   **13.** Find P(share room | 1 sibling). **0.2**

12-3 Objectives

▼ To calculate measures of central tendency (p. 660)

▼ To draw and interpret box-and-whisker plots (p. 662)

You can use **measures of central tendency** to analyze data. The **mean** $\bar{x}$ equals the sum of the values divided by the number of values. The **median** is the middle value of a data set in numerical order. If the set has an even number of values, then the median is the mean of the middle two values. The **mode** is the most frequently occurring value. There can be more than one mode or no mode. A **bimodal** distribution has 2 modes. The second quartile is the median of the whole set. The first and third **quartiles** are, respectively, the medians of the values less than and greater than the median. A **box-and-whisker plot** displays data by using the quartiles to form a box and the minimum and maximum values to form whiskers. A **percentile** divides the range of a data set into two parts such that the part lying below the value contains a given percentage of the data. An **outlier** is a data value substantially different from the rest of the data.

Use the following set of values for Exercises 14–19. 14–17. See margin.

13 12 15 18 14 16 18 12 13 14 14 17 15 8 17
16 12 16 14 15 13 13 17 15 14 18 16 12 12 13

14. Find the mean, median, and mode.   **15.** Make a box-and-whisker plot.

16. Find the 20th and 90th percentiles.   **17.** At what percentile is 15?

18. Identify the outlier. **8**   **19.** Find the range without the outlier.
                                                                  6

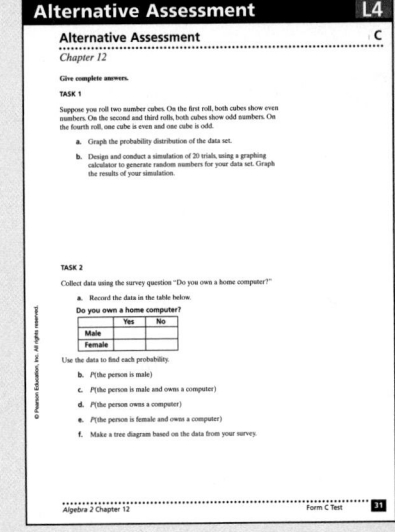
12-4 Objectives

▼ To find the standard deviation of a set of values (p. 668)

▼ To use standard deviation in real-world situations (p. 671)

You can use **measures of variation** to describe the spread of data. The **range of a set of data** is the difference between the maximum and minimum values. The **interquartile range** is the difference between the third and first quartiles. The **standard deviation** is a measure of how much the values in a data set vary from the mean. To find the standard deviation, (1) find the mean, (2) find the difference between each data value and the mean, (3) square each difference, (4) find the mean of the squares, and (5) take the square root of this mean. The **z-score** of a value is the number of standard deviations that value is from the mean.

Use the following set of values for Exercises 20–22.

$1.95 $1.27 $1.81 $1.33 $1.30 $.99 $1.63 $1.49 $1.39 $1.25 $1.50

20. Find the standard deviation. ≈**0.26**

21. Within how many standard deviations of the mean do all of the values fall? **2**

22. Find the z-score of the value $1.85, to the nearest hundredth. ≈**1.56**

12-5 Objectives

▼ To find sample proportions (p. 677)

▼ To find the margin of error (p. 678)

A **sample** is part of a population. For a **random sample**, all members of the population are equally likely to be chosen for the sample. When an event occurs x times in a sample of size n, the **sample proportion** is the ratio $\frac{x}{n}$. When a random sample of size n is taken from a large population, the sample proportion has a **margin of error** of approximately $\pm\frac{1}{\sqrt{n}}$.

23. Of 50 people who rented clubs at a golf course, 38 were right-handed.
  a. Find the sample proportion as a percent. **76%**
  b. Find the margin of error. **±14%**
  c. Find an interval likely to contain the true population proportion. **from 62% to 90%**

12-6 and 12-7 Objectives

▼ To find binomial probabilities (p. 685)

▼ To use binomial distributions (p. 687)

▼ To use a normal distribution (p. 692)

▼ To use the standard normal curve (p. 693)

A **binomial experiment** has repeated independent trials, each trial having two possible outcomes. In a binomial experiment with probability of success p and of failure q (so $p + q = 1$), the probability of x successes in n trials is $_nC_x p^x q^{n-x}$. This value is the **binomial probability**.

A **normal distribution** shows data that vary from the mean in a random manner. The pattern they form is a bell-shaped curve called a normal curve. The **standard normal curve** is a normal distribution centered on the y-axis. The mean is 0 and the standard deviation is 1. When a data set follows the normal curve, about 68% of the data fall within one standard deviation of the mean. About 95% of the data fall within two standard deviations of the mean.

24. A true-or-false quiz contains four questions. Design and describe a simulation you could use to find the probability of guessing three questions correctly. **See margin.**

25. Find the probability of 13 successes in 24 trials, given that the probability of success is 0.6 for each trial. **0.137**

26. Use the binomial expansion of $(p + q)^n$ to write the binomial distribution for $n = 5$ and $p = 0.7$. **See back of book.**

27. Sketch a curve for a normal distribution with mean 10 and standard deviation 4. Label the x-axis at one, two, and three standard deviations from the mean. **See margin.**

Chapter 12 Chapter Review **703**

24. Answers may vary. Sample: Each guess is a trial. There are 4 trials. Since there are 2 equally likely answers, the probability of success is 0.5. Let 1 represent a correct response and 2 an incorrect response. Generate 4 random numbers, either 1 or 2, 10 times. The probability is one tenth the number of times there are exactly three 1's.

27.

Chapter 12

Chapter Test

Go Online
PHSchool.com
For: Chapter Test
Web Code: aga-1252

Differentiated Instruction Resources

- **L3** Ch. 12 Test
- **L2** Below Level Ch. 12 Test
- **L4** Ch. 12 Alternative Assessment
- **L3** Spanish Ch. 12 Test
- **L4** Spanish Ch. 12 Alternative Assessment
- ExamView CD-ROM
  - Ch. 12 Pre-Made Test
  - Make your own Ch. 12 test
- Online Chapter 12 Test at www.PHSchool.com

Graph the probability distribution for each sample space when two number cubes are rolled.

1. {both cubes the same number, each cube a different number} **1–3. See back of book.**

2. {prime sum, composite sum}

3. **Writing** Describe how a situation can have more than one sample space. Include an example.

Use the table below for Exercises 4–8.

How Many Current Music Groups Can You Name?

Age of Respondent	Number of Groups	
	0 – 4	5 or more
< 30	7	18
≥ 30	13	12

4. Make a frequency table for the ages of the respondents. **4–5. See margin.**

5. Make a frequency table for the number of groups named.

6. Find $P(5 \text{ or more})$. $\frac{3}{5}$

7. Find $P(5 \text{ or more} \mid age < 30)$. $\frac{18}{25}$

8. Find $P(age \geq 30 \mid 0\text{–}4)$. $\frac{13}{20}$

9. Find the mean, median, and mode for this set of values: 8, 9, 11, 12, 13, 15, 16, 18, 20. **See margin.**

10. Make a box-and-whisker plot for this set of values: 36, 36, 48, 65, 75, 82, 92, 101. **See margin.**

11. Find the 20th and 60th percentiles for this set of values: 36, 38, 42, 47, 51, 56, 62, 69, 70, 74. **42, 62**

12. Given the set of values below, at what percentiles are 78 and 81?
43 58 64 78 78 81 89 89 91 93
78 at 30th percentile, 81 at 50th percentile

13. Identify the outlier of this set of values: 17, 15, 16, 15, 9, 18, 16. **9**

14. **Open-Ended** Write a set of values that has a range of 10, a mean of 86, and a mode of 85. **See margin.**

15. Find the mean and the standard deviation for this set of values: 15, 17, 19, 20, 14, 23, 12. **See margin.**

16. A data set has a mean 30 and a standard deviation of 3. Find the z-score of the value 38.
z-score ≈ 2.67

Find the margin of error for each sample. Then find an interval likely to contain the true population proportion.   17–18. See margin.

17. 15% of 457 teachers

18. 47% of 296 teens

19. 56% of 87 musicians **±10.7%; 45.3%–66.7%**

20. 23% of 100 bakers **±10%; 13%–33%**

A newspaper wants to take a poll about which candidate voters prefer for President. Identify any bias in each sampling method.

21. The newspaper interviews people at a political debate. **bias toward active voters**

22. The newspaper publishes a number for people to call and express their opinion. **See margin.**

23. The newspaper calls people selected at random from the local telephone book.
bias toward voters with listed numbers

Find the probability of x successes in n trials for the given probability of success p on each trial.

24. $x = 4, n = 10, p = 0.2$ **0.088**

25. $x = 3, n = 8, p = 0.6$ **0.124**

26. At a high school, 30% of the students buy class rings. You select five students at random. Find $P(\text{exactly two buy rings})$ and $P(\text{at least two buy rings})$. **0.309, 0.472**

27. A student guesses the answers to three questions on a true-or-false test. Design and describe a simulation to find the probability that the student guesses at least one of the questions correctly.
See back of book.

A set of data has a normal distribution with a mean of 29 and a standard deviation of 4. Find the percent of data within each interval.

28. from 25 to 33 **68%**   29. from 21 to 25 **13.5%**

30. greater than 29 **50%**   31. less than 21 **2.5%**

32. A data set is normally distributed with a mean of 37 and a standard deviation of 8.1. Sketch a normal curve for the distribution. Label the x-axis values at one, two, and three standard deviations from the mean. **See back of book.**

Below Level Chapter Test **L2**

Chapter Test **L3**

Chapter Test
Chapter 12

1. At a store, you buy 8 plums, 4 bananas, 6 apples, and 12 carrots.
   a. Graph the probability distribution for the items purchased.
   b. Find the probability that one food item chosen at random is a piece of fruit.

Use the results of the survey below to find each conditional probability.

How many pets do you have in your home?

	0 Pets	1 Pet	2 Pets	3+ Pets
Male respondents	5	10	5	2
Female respondents	4	13	6	2

2. P(male | 2 pets)   3. P(2 pets | male)
4. P(0 pets | female)   5. P(0 or 1 pet | male)
6. Which of these is equal to 0.18, according to the tree diagram?
   A. P(C | A)
   B. P(C and B)
   C. P(D | C)
   D. P(A and D)

7. Writing Explain how to find the median of a set of data.

Use the following set of values for Exercises 8–13.
6.3 6.6 6.9 1.3 6.4 6.6 1.2 1.4 1.1 6.2 6.2

8. Find the mean, median, and mode(s) of the data set. Round answers to the nearest hundredth, if necessary.
9. Draw a box-and-whisker plot.
10. Find the range.
11. Find the interquartile range.
12. Find the standard deviation. Round to the nearest hundredth.
13. Find the 25th and 75th percentiles.
14. Open-Ended Write two data sets with a range equal to 35 but with different standard deviations. You do not need to calculate the standard deviations.

Algebra 2 Chapter 12 **27**

4.

AGE	Number of Respondents
< 30	25
≥ 30	25

5.

Number of Groups	Number of Respondents
0–4	20
5 or more	30

9. mean ≈ 13.56, median = 13, no mode

10.
(box-and-whisker plot with scale: 30 40 50 60 70 80 90 100)

14. Answers may vary.
Sample: 82, 85, 85, 92

15. mean ≈ 17.14, standard deviation ≈ 3.523

17. ±4.7%; 10.3%–19.7%

18. ±5.8%; 41.2%–52.8%

22. bias toward newspaper subscribers and people motivated to call

Standardized Test Prep

Standardized Test Prep

Multiple Choice

For Exercises 1–13, choose the correct letter.

1. Which polynomial has $(x - 1)$ as a factor?
C
 Ⓐ $x^2 + 3x + 2$
 Ⓑ $x^2 + 2x + 1$
 Ⓒ $x^3 - x^2 - x + 1$
 Ⓓ $x^3 - 3x - 2$

2. Which is the equation of an inverse variation for which $x = 5$ when $y = -28$?
J
 Ⓕ $y = \frac{-x}{140}$ Ⓖ $y = \frac{-130}{x}$
 Ⓗ $y = \frac{-x}{130}$ Ⓙ $y = \frac{-140}{x}$

3. Which parabola has focus $(3, 0)$ and directrix $x = -3$?
C
 Ⓐ $y = \frac{1}{12}x^2$ Ⓑ $y = -\frac{1}{3}x^2$
 Ⓑ $x = \frac{1}{12}y^2$ Ⓓ $x = \frac{1}{3}y^2$

4. Which is greatest for these data?
F 9 10 10 10 11 12 12 13 15
 Ⓕ mean   Ⓖ median
 Ⓗ range   Ⓙ mode

5. What are the quartiles of these data?
A 18 19 20 20 22 23 25 28 32
 Ⓐ $Q_1 = 19.5, Q_2 = 22, Q_3 = 26.5$
 Ⓑ $Q_1 = 20, Q_2 = 21, Q_3 = 26.5$
 Ⓒ $Q_1 = 20, Q_2 = 22, Q_3 = 25$
 Ⓓ $Q_1 = 19, Q_2 = 22.5, Q_3 = 28$

6. In which interval is the area above the x-axis and under the curve $y = 4x^2 + 1$ greatest?
F
 Ⓕ $-5 \le x \le 1$ Ⓖ $1 \le x \le 3$
 Ⓗ $1 \le x \le 4$ Ⓙ $2 \le x \le 5$

7. What are the foci of $\frac{x^2}{64} + \frac{y^2}{36} = 1$?
B
 Ⓐ $(0, \pm10)$ Ⓑ $(\pm2\sqrt{7}, 0)$
 Ⓒ $(\pm10, 0)$ Ⓓ $(0, \pm2\sqrt{7})$

8. Which graph has an asymptote at $x = 3$?
J
 Ⓕ $y = \frac{1}{x + 3}$ Ⓖ $y = \frac{3}{x - 1}$
 Ⓗ $y = \frac{x - 3}{x + 3}$ Ⓙ $y = \frac{3}{x - 3}$

9. Which function is the inverse of $f(x) = (x - 3)^2$?
C
 Ⓐ $g(x) = \frac{x^2}{(3x - 1)^2}$ Ⓑ $g(x) = \frac{1}{(x - 3)^2}$
 Ⓒ $g(x) = \sqrt{x} + 3$ Ⓓ $g(x) = \sqrt{x - 3}$

10. Which function has an asymptote at $x = -3$?
G
 Ⓕ $y = \log_6 (x - 3) + 1$
 Ⓖ $y = \log_6 (x + 3) + 1$
 Ⓗ $y = \log_6 (x - 1) + 3$
 Ⓙ $y = \log_6 (x - 1) - 3$

11. Solve $2 \log x - \log 4 = 2$.
B
 Ⓐ 200   Ⓑ 20   Ⓒ 2   Ⓓ 0.5

12. You toss a number cube numbered 1 through 6.
H Find P(NOT a prime number).
 Ⓕ $\frac{1}{6}$ Ⓖ $\frac{1}{3}$ Ⓗ $\frac{1}{2}$ Ⓙ $\frac{2}{3}$

13. Which equation represents an ellipse with a
C center at $(-1, 3)$ and a horizontal major axis?
 Ⓐ $\frac{(x + 1)^2}{3^2} + \frac{(y - 3)^2}{12} = 1$
 Ⓑ $\frac{(x - 1)^2}{3^2} + \frac{(y + 3)^2}{12} = 1$
 Ⓒ $\frac{(x + 1)^2}{12} + \frac{(y - 3)^2}{3^2} = 1$
 Ⓓ $\frac{(x - 1)^2}{12} + \frac{(y + 3)^2}{3^2} = 1$

Gridded Response

14. A stain on a page is 4 mm wide. You enlarged the image on a photocopier 6 times with 124% setting. What is the approximate width of the final image of the stain in millimeters? **14.5**

15. Evaluate $\sum_{n=1}^{8} \frac{3n}{2}$. **54**

16. Write the sum of the infinite geometric series as a fraction. $1 - 0.2 + 0.04 - \dots$ **5/6**

Short Response

17. Solve the equation $\frac{x}{6} = \frac{x + 4}{9}$. Check your solution. Show your work. **17–18. See back of book.**

18. State the property or properties used to justify the identity $9 \log 3 - 3 \log 9 = \log 27$.

Extended Response

19. Find the vertices, intercepts, asymptotes, and foci of the hyperbola $\frac{x^2}{16} - \frac{y^2}{9} = 1$. **19–20. See back of book.**

20. Is the series $10,000 + 1000 + 100 + 10 + \dots$ *arithmetic* or *geometric*? Find the sum of the first eight terms.

Resources

Test Prep Workbook

Grab & Go
- **L3** Cumulative Review

ExamView CD-ROM
- Standardized Test Practice

Differentiated **Instruction** **Resources**

Progress Monitoring Assessments

- Quarter 4 Test
  - **L3** Forms A & B
  - **L2** Forms D & E

Spanish Assessment Resources
- **L3** Spanish Cumulative Review
- Spanish Quarter 4 Test
  - **L3** Forms A & B

Item	1	2	3	4	5	6	7	8	9	10	11	12	13	14	15	16	17	18	19	20
Lesson	6-2	9-1	10-2	12-3	12-3	11-6	10-4	9-3	7-7	9-3	8-5	1-6	10-4	8-1	11-4	11-5	9-6	8-4	10-5	11-4/5

Training Day

In these activities students apply their knowledge of geometric and arithmetic sequences and explore transforming a drawing by dilation.

Activating Prior Knowledge

Have students discuss various two-dimensional representations they have seen of three-dimensional objects. Examples could include plans for building model planes, ships, or houses, maps, and pictures of geometric shapes such as cubes and pyramids. Ask students to point out various ways that three dimensions are reduced to two.

Guided Instruction

Have a volunteer read the introductory paragraph. Discuss optical illusions in general. Point out the contrast between what is known (the parallel train tracks do not meet) and the illusion (to create a sense of distance, they do meet in the drawing).

Teaching Tip

Ask students to review the meaning and definition of a geometric sequence, as applied in this activity.

Tactile Learners

Have students use integer lengths for their railroad ties, and have them create a collage picture using spaghetti or thin wood sticks for the ties, glued to a piece of cardboard.

Connection to Art History

Have students research when perspective drawing, with parallel lines meeting in a vanishing point, was first studied and used by famous artists.

English Language Learners ELL

Ask students to point to the *ties* and the *tracks* in the figure, to make sure that everyone understands the difference between these terms.

 Activity Lab

Training Day

Applying Sequences The world is three-dimensional, but drawings are done on a two-dimensional surface. We know that railroad tracks are parallel, but to create a feeling of depth in a drawing, tracks are often drawn as though they meet. The point where they seem to meet is called a vanishing point. This technique is called perspective drawing.

Strong-Armed Laborer
To build the track of the Canadian Pacific railroad, a freight car loaded with crossties was hauled to the end of the trails. Workers carried the crossties farther down the roadbed to extend the rails.

Legendary Locomotive
During the Civil War, this engine was hijacked by Union soldiers who planned to blow up a bridge. Confederate troops pursued them, and after an 18-hour, 139-km (87-mile) chase, caught up with the engine and recaptured it.

Activity 1

Materials: paper and pencil, ruler

a. Draw a set of railroad tracks such that the lengths of the horizontal ties form a geometric sequence.

b. Write the first four terms of the sequence.

c. Write a recursive formula for the sequence.

d. Write an explicit formula for the sequence.

Spanning Three Generations
These three trains represent more than 25 years of development. The original "Bullet Train" (on the right) was built in 1964. Series 300 (on the left) was built in 1992. It has a top speed of 168 mi/h.

Activity 1

a–d. **Check students' work.**

Activity 2

Find a small picture or drawing you want to enlarge. Follow the steps below to enlarge the drawing. Use the diagram below as a guide.

Step 1 Choose a point O to the right of the drawing.

Step 2 Choose and label some key points on the drawing as A, B, C, etc.

Step 3 Lightly draw $\overrightarrow{OA}$.

Step 4 To make a drawing with dimensions that are *three times* the size of the original picture, locate point A' on $\overrightarrow{OA}$ so that $OA' = 3 \cdot OA$.

Step 5 Repeat Steps 3 and 4 for the remaining points on the picture (each ray begins at point O). Use the new points to help you draw the figure with new dimensions. (In this example, the new drawing will have a scale factor of 3.)

Energy for Trains

Before the invention of the steam engine, heavy loads were transported along railroads using human or animal power. Steam locomotives have nearly disappeared in America. Locomotives are now diesel or electric.

Activity 3

a. Begin with a small, simple drawing (perhaps one of your own or a cartoon). Use the method from Activity 2 to create at least two size changes of the original drawing so that the scale factors form an arithmetic sequence. (The original drawing has a scale factor of 1.)

b. Write the first four terms of the arithmetic sequence of scale factors.

c. Write a recursive formula for the sequence.

d. Write an explicit formula for the sequence.

Go Online
PHSchool.com
For: Information about trains
Web Code: age-1253

707

Teaching Tip

Before students begin the activities, discuss the illustrations and their captions. Have students work in pairs or in small groups to complete the activities. Have each team read through all the activities before beginning to work.

Activity 1

Materials: paper and pencil, ruler, small picture or drawing to enlarge

Teaching Tip

Have a student explain the difference between a recursive and an explicit formula for a sequence.

Activity 2

Materials: paper and pencil, ruler, small picture or drawing to enlarge

Teaching Tip

Encourage students to choose a fairly simple line drawing to enlarge.

Activity 3

Materials: large piece of paper, pencil, ruler

Scoring Rubric

This scoring rubric can be used for evaluating student work on each of the activities. Share this scoring rubric with students before they begin work.

4 Drawings, formulas, and calculations are correct. Steps are neat, accurate, and clearly show the mathematics.

3 Drawings, formulas, and calculations are mostly correct, with some minor errors. Steps are neat and mostly accurate.

2 Drawings, formulas, and calculations contain both major and minor errors.

1 Correct answer, but no work is shown.

Activity 2

Check students' work.

Activity 3

Check students' work.

Chapter 13

Periodic Functions and Trigonometry

Chapter at a Glance

Lesson Titles, Objectives, and Features	Assessment	NCTM Standards	Local Standards
13-1 Exploring Periodic Data • Identifying cycles and periods of periodic functions • Finding the amplitude of periodic functions	Lesson Quiz	1, 2, 3, 4, 5	
Geometry Review: Special Right Triangles **13-2 Angles and the Unit Circle** • Working with angles in standard position • Finding coordinates of points on the unit circle	Lesson Quiz	1, 2, 3, 4, 8	
Activity Lab: Hands-On: Measuring Radians **13-3 Radian Measure** • Using radian measure for angles • Finding the length of an arc of a circle	Lesson Quiz Checkpoint Quiz 1	2, 3, 4	
13-4 The Sine Function • Identifying properties of the sine function • Graphing sine curves Activity Lab: Technology: Graphing Trigonometric Functions	Lesson Quiz	2, 3	
13-5 The Cosine Function • Graphing and writing cosine functions • Solving trigonometric equations	Lesson Quiz	2, 3, 7	
13-6 The Tangent Function • Graphing the tangent function GPS: Understanding Math Problems	Lesson Quiz	2, 3, 7, 8	
13-7 Translating Sine and Cosine Functions • Graphing translations of trigonometric functions • Writing equations of translations	Lesson Quiz Checkpoint Quiz 2	2, 3, 7, 8	
13-8 Reciprocal Trigonometric Functions • Evaluating reciprocal trigonometric functions • Graphing reciprocal trigonometric functions	Lesson Quiz	2, 3, 7, 8	

NCTM Standards 2000

1 Number and Operations	**2** Algebra	**3** Geometry	**4** Measurement	**5** Data Analysis and Probability
6 Problem Solving	**7** Reasoning and Proof	**8** Communication	**9** Connections	**10** Representation

Correlations to Standardized Tests

All content for these tests is contained in *Prentice Hall Algebra 2*. This chart reflects coverage in this chapter only.

	13-1	13-2	13-3	13-4	13-5	13-6	13-7	13-8
SAT®								
Number and Operations Operations, ratio & proportions, complex numbers, counting, elementary number theory, matrices, sequences								
Algebra and Functions Expressions, equations, inequalities, representation and modeling, properties of functions (linear, polynomial, rational, exponential)								
Geometry and Measurement *Plane Euclidean/Measurement Coordinate* Lines, parabolas, circles, symmetry, transformations *Three-dimensional* Solids, surface area & volume (cylinders, cones, pyramids, spheres, prisms) *Trigonometry* Right triangles, identities								
Data Analysis, Statistics, and Probability Mean, median, mode, range, interquartile range, graphs and plots, regression, probability								
ACT®								
Pre-Algebra Basic operations using whole numbers, decimals, fractions, and integers; place value; square roots and approximations; the concept of exponents; scientific notation; factors, ratio, proportion, and percent; linear equations in one variable; absolute value and ordering numbers by value; elementary counting techniques and simple probability; data collection, representation, and interpretation; and understanding simple descriptive statistics.								
Elementary Algebra Properties of exponents and square roots, evaluation of algebraic expressions through substitution, using variables to express functional relationships, understanding algebraic operations, and solving quadratic equations by factoring.		✔	✔					
Intermediate Algebra Understanding of the quadratic formula, rational and radical expressions, absolute value equations and inequalities, sequences and patterns, systems of equations, quadratic inequalities, functions, modeling, matrices, roots of polynomials, and complex numbers.	✔			✔	✔	✔	✔	✔
Coordinate Geometry Graphing and the relations between equations and graphs, including points, lines, polynomials, circles, and other curves; graphing inequalities; slope; parallel and perpendicular lines; distance; midpoints; and conics.				✔	✔	✔	✔	✔
Plane Geometry Properties and relations of plane figures, including angles and relations among perpendicular and parallel lines; properties of circles, triangles, rectangles, parallelograms, and trapezoids; transformations; the concept of proof and proof techniques; volume; and applications of geometry to three dimensions.								
Trigonometry Understanding trigonometric relations in right triangles; values and properties of trigonometric functions; graphing trigonometric functions; modeling using trigonometric functions; use of trigonometric identities; and solving trigonometric equations.	✔	✔	✔	✔	✔	✔	✔	✔
NAEP								
Number Sense, Properties, and Operations								
Measurement			✔					✔
Geometry and Spatial Sense								
Data Analysis, Statistics, and Probability								
Algebra and Functions	✔	✔	✔	✔	✔	✔	✔	✔

SAT® The College Board, SAT® Reasoning Test   **ACT®** The ACT Assessment® Test   **NAEP** National Assessment of Educational Progress, 2005 Mathematics Objectives

Math Background

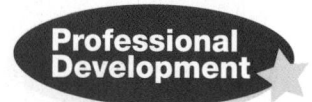

Skills Trace

BEFORE Chapter 13

In previous chapters, students graphed various parent functions and translations of these functions.

DURING Chapter 13

Students explore periodic functions, convert degrees to radians, graph the sine, cosine, and tangent functions, and examine reciprocal trigonometric functions.

AFTER Chapter 13

Students will solve trigonometric equations, verify trigonometric identities, and apply the Laws of Sines and Cosines.

Chapter Overview

Chapter 13 introduces the concept of a periodic function. After a discussion of measures of angles in standard position in the coordinate plane, the sine and cosine functions are defined in terms of the *x*- and *y*-coordinates of points on the unit circle. Students learn about radian measure, examine the graphs of sine and cosine functions, and learn how to find the amplitude and period of such functions.

The tangent function is defined in relation to the unit circle. Students learn about phase shifts and translations of graphs of sine and cosine functions. Finally, they consider the cosecant, secant, and cotangent functions, which are defined using the reciprocals of the sine, cosine, and tangent functions.

Exploring Periodic Data 13-1

The term *periodic* means repetitive or cyclic. Therefore, periodic functions must be somehow cyclic or repetitive, such as the motion of the hands of a clock through time. Thus, the entire graph of a periodic function can be formed from copies of one particular portion—a complete pattern called a *cycle*—that are laid end to end. The horizontal length of this cycle is called the *period*. So, the period is the smallest continuous portion of the domain for which the function completes a cycle. Note that a constant function such as $f(x) = 5$ is technically periodic. Its period is all nonzero real numbers; so, it does not have a smallest continuous portion of the domain.

Many periodic functions cycle through a restricted range. The *amplitude* of a periodic function is the distance between the maximum and minimum values of the function, divided by two. Thus, the amplitude is "half the height" of the function.

As students explore the graphs of periodic functions, make sure they understand how each is repetitive; using non-examples can be particularly helpful to students. The relation to a circle will follow in the next lesson.

Angles and the Unit Circle 13-2

Many geometry courses treat angle measure in such a way that no angle can have a measure greater than 180°. There are many sound reasons for doing so. In trigonometry, it is more helpful to relate angle measure to the concept of rotations, and permit angle measures of *any* size, positive or negative. Emphasize for students that for angles in standard position, a counterclockwise rotation is positive and clockwise rotation is negative. Furthermore, a given angle can be named by an unlimited number of degree measures by simply adding or subtracting 360°.

The unit circle definitions of the sine and cosine functions make it easy to see why these are periodic functions. These definitions are often new to students who associate trigonometric functions only with triangles.

Radian Measure 13-3

Some students are so accustomed to degree measure and unfamiliar with radian measure that it may take a little time for them to appreciate the many advantages of radian measure. Inform students that in trigonometry and calculus, radian measure of an angle is preferred because it simplifies calculations.

Students must understand that the radian measure of an angle is the ratio of the arc length to the radius of a circle. The conversion factor follows directly from this definition because the circumference of a circle is $2\pi r$, so 2π radians is 360°. There is a very convenient relationship between an angle measure in radians and its arc length *s* determined by a central angle θ in a circle, $s = r\theta$.

The Sine Function
13-4

Students should be able to describe how the sine curve goes through one complete period with the unit circle definition of the sine function. It starts at 0 when $\theta = 0$, goes up to 1 when $\theta = 90°$, back down to 0 when $\theta = 180°$, then down to -1 when $\theta = 270°$, and finally back to 0 when $\theta = 360°$. Students should also be able to give this description using radians instead of degrees.

Encourage students to first write out the five equally spaced points for one cycle before sketching the graph. Students should feel comfortable with the pattern of these five points as following a repeating pattern: *zero-max-zero-min-zero*. Students should also recognize the inverse relationship between the number of cycles b in an interval from 0 to 2π and the period $\frac{2\pi}{b}$.

The Activity Lab following the lesson on using graphing calculators to graph sine functions can be helpful for students. Students need to be aware of the mode setting—for degrees or radians—and the corresponding window settings to graph any trigonometric function.

The Cosine Function
13-5

When students have completed this lesson, they should be able to inspect an equation of the form $y = a \cos b\theta$ ($a \neq 0$, $b > 0$, θ in radians), specify its amplitude and period, and sketch a rough graph. Students should recognize that the pattern of equally spaced points: *max-zero-min-zero-max* represents that of the sine function shifted left by one of the key points. The exercises in these lessons will help students appreciate how versatile the sine and cosine functions are in modeling situations involving periodic data.

The Tangent Function
13-6

The tangent function can be defined as the quotient of the sine and cosine functions. Alternatively, the tangent function can be defined as the y-coordinate of the point where the terminal side of an angle in standard position intersects the line $x = 1$ (the line tangent to the unit circle at (1,0)). This lesson uses the second approach since it gives an immediate geometric interpretation and makes it easy to determine the period of the tangent function.

Students should be able to identify properties of the tangent function that differ from those of the sine and cosine functions. For instance, the tangent function has no amplitude, its period is $\frac{\pi}{b}$ (instead of $\frac{2\pi}{b}$), and is undefined where the graph has vertical asymptotes. The five point pattern becomes five elements: *asymptote-($-a$)-zero-(a)-asymptote*.

Translating Sine and Cosine Functions
13-7

By now, many students can probably anticipate what equations for translations of the graphs of $y = a \sin b\theta$ or $y = a \cos b\theta$ will look like. The concepts of phase shifts and vertical shifts fit naturally with what students know about translations. For instance, students will recognize that translations alone do not change the amplitude and period. Using a graphing calculator can be effective in showing how trigonometric graphs can be translated.

Students write sine and cosine functions to model data without using the statistical model feature available on graphing calculators. Students find the amplitude a using the maximum and minimum values, the period to calculate b, and the phase shift h and vertical shift k to write a function model of the form $y = a \cos b(x - h) + k$ defined by these values.

Reciprocal Trigonometric Functions
13-8

The cosecant, secant, and cotangent functions are defined using the respective reciprocals of the sine, cosine, and tangent functions. Some students need to be reminded that the $\sin^{-1}$, $\cos^{-1}$, and $\tan^{-1}$ functions on the calculator are not reciprocals, but rather inverse functions, which they will learn about in Chapter 14. Vertical asymptotes are necessary for the graphs of the tangent, secant, cosecant, and cotangent functions. Students should be encouraged to review the occurrence of vertical asymptotes in the graphs of rational functions. (See Chapter 9.)

Additional Professional Development Opportunities

Math Background notes for Chapter 13: Every lesson has a Math Background in the PLAN section.

Research Overview, Mathematical Strands
Additional support for these topics and more is in the front of this Teacher's Edition.

Lesson Lab
Lesson Lab, a Pearson Education company, offers comprehensive, facilitated professional development designed to help teachers improve student achievement. To learn more, please visit lessonlab.com

Chapter 13 Resources

	13-1	13-2	13-3	13-4	13-5	13-6	13-7	13-8	For the Chapter
Print Resources									
L3 Practice	●	●	●	●	●	●	●		
L3 Guided Problem Solving	●	●	●	●	●	●	●		
L2 Reteaching	●	●	●	●	●	●	●		
L4 Enrichment	●	●	●	●	●	●	●		
L3 Daily Notetaking Guide	●	●	●	●	●	●	●		
L3 Vocabulary and Study Skills Worksheets	●								●
L3 Chapter Project									●
L3 Hands On Activities							●		
L3 Checkpoint Quiz			●				●		
L2 Below Level Chapter Test									●
L3 Chapter Test									●
L4 Alternative Assessment									●
L3 Cumulative Review									●
L4 Connections to Precalculus Masters	●	●	●	●	●	●	●	●	
L3 Technology Activities		●			●				
Spanish Resources ELL									
L3 Practice	●	●	●	●	●	●	●	●	
L3 Vocabulary and Study Skills Worksheets	●								●
L3 Checkpoint Quiz			●				●		●
L2 Below Level Chapter Test									●
L3 Chapter Test									●
L4 Alternative Assessment									●
L3 Cumulative Review									●
Transparencies									
Check Skills You'll Need	●	●	●	●	●	●	●		
Additional Examples	●	●	●	●	●	●	●		
Problem of the Day	●	●	●	●	●	●	●		
Classroom Aid				●	●	●	●		
Student Edition Answers	●	●	●	●	●	●	●		
Lesson Quiz	●	●	●	●	●	●	●		●
Test-Taking Strategies									●
Technology									
TI 83/84 Plus Activities					●		●		
Interactive Textbook Online	●	●	●	●	●	●	●	●	●
Student Express CD-ROM	●	●	●	●	●	●	●	●	●
TI Navigator, Instant Check System	●	●	●	●	●	●	●	●	●
Success Tracker	●	●	●	●	●	●	●	●	●
ExamView CD-ROM with Quick Take	●	●	●	●	●	●	●	●	●
Teacher Express CD-ROM	●	●	●	●	●	●	●	●	●
Presentation Express CD-ROM	●	●	●	●	●	●	●	●	●
Mindpoint Quiz Show CD-ROM	●	●	●	●	●	●	●	●	●
Prentice Hall Web site: PHSchool.com	●	●	●	●	●	●	●	●	●

Also available: Prentice Hall Assessment System (Progress Monitoring Assessments, Skills and Concepts Review, Test Prep Workbook)   Solution Key   Student Workbook
Student Workbook, Adapted Version   Data Analysis and Probability Workbook   Math Notes Study Folder   Spanish Cumulative Assessment

Where You Can Use the Lesson Resources

Here is a suggestion, following the four-step teaching plan, for how you can incorporate Differentiated Instruction Resources into your teaching.

	Instructional Resources L3	**Differentiated** Instruction **Resources**
1. Plan		
Check Skills You'll Need Assign these exercises to review prerequisite skills. **New Vocabulary** Help students pre-read the lesson by pointing out the new terms introduced in the lesson.	**Math Background** **Transparencies & Presentation Express CD** Check Skills You'll Need **Resources** Vocabulary and Study Skills	**Spanish Support** ELL Vocabulary and Study Skills
2. Teach		
L3 **Guided Instruction** Teach each Example. After each Example, assign the Quick Check exercise for that Example.	**Student Edition** Activity Lab **Resources** Daily Notetaking Guide Activity Lab TI-83/84 Activities CD-ROM **Transparencies & Presentation Express CD** Additional Examples Classroom Aids **ExamView CD-ROM with QuickTake** **TI Navigator Instant Check System**	**Teacher's Edition** Every lesson includes suggestions for working with students who need special attention. L1 Special Needs L2 Below Level L4 Advanced Learners ELL English Language Learners
3. Practice		

Assignment Guide
 	
Homework Exercises
Assign the exercises cited in each lesson's Assignment Guide.
  A Practice by Example
  B Apply Your Skills
  C Challenge
  Test Prep
  Mixed Review
 	
Homework Quick Check
Discuss in class the exercises cited in each lesson's Assignment Guide.
	Transparencies & Presentation Express CD
	Student Answers
	
	Resources
	Practice
	Guided Problem Solving
	Vocabulary and Study Skills
	Activity Lab
	
	ExamView CD-ROM with QuickTake
		Spanish Support
		ELL Practice
		ELL Vocabulary and Study Skills
		
		Resources
		L4 Enrichment

4. Assess & Reteach		
Lesson Quiz Assign the Lesson Quiz to assess students' mastery of the lesson content. **Checkpoint Quiz** Use the Checkpoint Quiz to assess student progress over several lessons.	**Transparencies & Presentation Express CD** Lesson Quiz **Resources** Checkpoint Quiz	**Resources** L2 Reteaching ELL Checkpoint Quiz Success Tracker **ExamView CD-ROM with QuickTake**

KEY   L1 Special Needs   L2 Below Level   L3 For All Students   L4 Advanced, Gifted   ELL English Language Learners

Periodic Functions and Trigonometry

 Check Your Readiness

Answers are in the back of the textbook.

For intervention, direct students to:

Analyzing graphs of rational functions
Lesson 9-3; Example 2
Extra Skills and Word
    Problems Practice, Ch. 9

Simplifying complex fractions
Lesson 9-5; Example 5
Extra Skills and Word
    Problems Practice, Ch. 9

Translating conic sections
Lesson 10-6; Example 4
Extra Skills and Word
    Problems Practice, Ch. 10

Writing formulas for sequences
Lesson 11-1; Example 3
Extra Skills and Word
    Problems Practice, Ch. 11

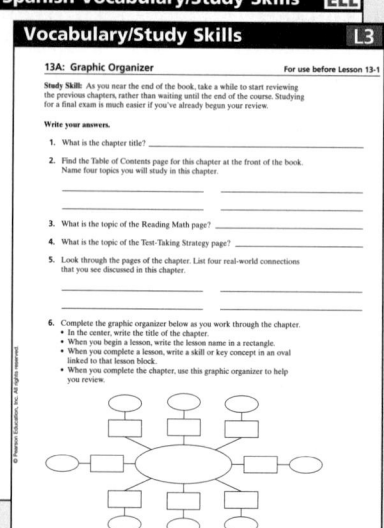

What You've Learned

- In Chapter 9, you learned to graph rational functions, some of which have graphs that are discontinuous in the coordinate plane.

- In Chapter 10, you learned to write and graph equations representing circles, ellipses, hyperbolas, and parabolas.

- In Chapters 11 and 12, you learned about patterns and probability.

 Check Your Readiness   **GO for Help** to the Lesson in green.

Analyzing Graphs of Rational Functions (Lesson 9-3)

Describe the vertical asymptotes and holes for each rational function.

1. $y = \dfrac{2}{x-3}$
    vertical asymptote $x = 3$

2. $y = \dfrac{(x-5)(x-1)}{x-1}$
    hole at $x = 1$

3. $y = \dfrac{x+2}{(2x+1)(x-4)}$
    vertical asymptotes
    $x = -\frac{1}{2}$ and $x = 4$

Simplifying Complex Fractions (Lesson 9-5)

Simplify each complex fraction.

4. $\dfrac{\frac{2}{a}}{\frac{1}{b}}$ $\dfrac{2b}{a}$

5. $\dfrac{5+\frac{1}{2}}{2-\frac{1}{5}}$ $\dfrac{55}{18}$

6. $\dfrac{\frac{3}{c+d}}{2}$ $\dfrac{3}{2(c+d)}$

7. $\dfrac{\frac{1}{4}}{\frac{4}{c}}$ $\dfrac{c}{16}$

8. $\dfrac{\frac{2}{3}}{\frac{6}{c+4}}$ $\dfrac{c+4}{9}$

9. $\dfrac{\frac{4}{x}}{\frac{2}{8}}$ $\dfrac{16}{x}$

10. $\dfrac{3-\frac{1}{2}}{\frac{7}{6}}$ $\dfrac{15}{7}$

11. $\dfrac{\frac{9}{m-n}}{\frac{3}{2m-2n}}$ 6

Translating Conic Sections (Lesson 10-6)

Write an equation for each conic section. Then sketch the graph.   **12–15. See margin.**

12. circle with center at $(1, -4)$ and radius 4

13. ellipse with center at $(2, 5)$, vertices at $(5, 5)$ and $(-1, 5)$, and co-vertices at $(2, 3)$ and $(2, 7)$

14. parabola with vertex at $(0, -3)$ and focus at $(0, 5)$

15. hyperbola with center at $(6, 1)$, one focus at $(6, 6)$, and one vertex at $(6, -2)$

Writing Formulas for Sequences (Lesson 11-1)

Find the next two terms in each sequence. Write a formula for the nth term. Identify each formula as *explicit* or *recursive*.   **16–18. See margin p. 709.**

16. $16, 13, 10, 7, \ldots$

17. $-1, -8, -27, -64, -125, \ldots$

18. $9, 3, 1, \frac{1}{3}, \ldots$

12. $(x-1)^2 + (y+4)^2 = 16;$

13. $\dfrac{(x-2)^2}{9} + \dfrac{(y-5)^2}{4} = 1;$

14. $y = \dfrac{1}{32}x^2 - 3;$

Periodic Functions and Trigonometry

What You'll Learn Next

- In Chapter 13, you will learn how geometric measurement relates to trigonometry.

- You will learn to use radian measure.

- You will learn how to write and graph functions that describe periodic data.

Real-World Connection Applying what you learn, on page 729 you will solve a problem involving a satellite's orbit.

🔊 Key Vocabulary

709

Chapter 13 Overview

This chapter begins with an exploration of periodic data in which students are introduced to cycles, periods, and amplitudes. The chapter continues with lessons that introduce the unit circle and radian measure. Students then complete lessons on the sine, cosine, and tangent functions. The chapter concludes with lessons on translating trigonometric functions and reciprocal trigonometric functions.

Activating Prior Knowledge

Initiate a discussion by asking:
- *Does anyone know what the term trigonometry means?*

The name comes from "trigon" for triangle and "metry" for *measure*.

Ask:
- *How is trigonometry useful?*

Students should recall using trigonometry to find measures of unknown sides or angles in right triangles.

Ask:
- *What are some names for trigonometric functions?*

Answers should include the sine, cosine, and tangent.

Inform students that in this chapter they will study the inverse trigonometric functions of secant, cosecant, and cotangent. They will also define trigonometric functions using circles instead of triangles.

---

15. $\dfrac{(y-1)^2}{9} - \dfrac{(x-6)^2}{16} = 1$;

16. $4, 1$; $a_n = 19 - 3n$, explicit; $a_1 = 16$, $a_n = a_{n-1} - 3$, recursive

17. $-216, -343$; $a_n = -n^3$, explicit

18. $\dfrac{1}{9}, \dfrac{1}{27}$; $a_n = 9\left(\dfrac{1}{3}\right)^{n-1}$, explicit; $a_1 = 9$, $a_n = \dfrac{1}{3} \cdot a_{n-1}$, recursive

Objectives
1 To identify cycles and periods of periodic functions
2 To find the amplitude of periodic functions

Examples
1 Identifying Cycles and Periods
2 Identifying Periodic Functions
3 Finding Amplitude of a Periodic Function
4 Real-World Connection

Math Background

Trigonometric functions are probably the periodic functions most accessible to students, but there are many others. There are machines that display periodic graphs, for example heart monitors and oscilloscopes.

More Math Background: p. 708C

Lesson Planning and Resources

See p. 708E for a list of the resources that support this lesson.

Bell Ringer Practice

✓ **Check Skills You'll Need**
For intervention, direct students to:

Determining Whether Relations are Functions
Lesson 2-1: Example 4
Extra Skills and Word
   Problems Practice, Ch. 2

Exploring Periodic Data

What You'll Learn
- To identify cycles and periods of periodic functions
- To find the amplitude of periodic functions

. . . And Why
To make predictions about sound waves, as in Example 4

✓ **Check Skills You'll Need**

 for Help Lesson 2-1

Determine whether each relation is a function.

1. $\{(2,4),(1,3),(-3,-1),(4,6)\}$ **yes**
2. $\{(2,6),(-3,1),(-2,2)\}$ **yes**
3. $\{(x,y)|\ x=3\}$ **no**
4. $\{(x,y)|\ y=8\}$ **yes**
5. $\{(x,y)|\ x=y^2\}$ **no**
6. $\{(x,y)|\ x^2+y^2=36\}$ **no**
7. $\{(a,b)|\ a=b^3\}$ **yes**
8. $\{(w,z)|\ w=z-36\}$ **yes**

🔊 **New Vocabulary** • periodic function • cycle • period • amplitude

---

1 **Identifying Periodic Functions**

Activity: Periodic Cycles

Use the diagram below. Suppose you and a friend are the last two people seated on a Ferris wheel. Once the ride begins, the wheel moves at a constant speed. It takes 36 seconds to complete one revolution.

1. a. At 0 seconds, when the ride starts, how high above the ground are you? **5 ft**
   b. 25 ft; 45 ft; 25 ft
   b. At what height are you at 9 seconds? At 18 seconds? At 27 seconds?
   c. At what height are you at 126 seconds? How many revolutions have you made? **45 ft; 3.5 revolutions**
   d. Predict where you will be at 3 minutes. **5 ft**

2. Sketch a graph showing the relationship between your height above the ground and the time since the ride began. Use $0 \le t \le 144$ for the domain, where $t = 0$ is the time at which the ride starts. **See back of book.**

3. **Critical Thinking** How far (in feet) have you traveled after one revolution of the wheel? How far have you traveled at 144 seconds? **about 125.66 ft; about 502.65 ft**

710 Chapter 13 Periodic Functions and Trigonometry

Differentiated Instruction Solutions for All Learners

Special Needs L1
Have students stand in a large circle. Ask a student to explain how sports fans perform "the wave." Then perform a wave going around the circle. Explain that one revolution is a period. Perform the wave faster and slower, and discuss how the period changes.
learning style: tactile

Below Level L2
Ask students to explain why the motion of a piston in a cylinder, tides in the oceans, the motion of a pendulum, etc. are periodic.
learning style: verbal

A **periodic function** repeats a pattern of *y*-values (outputs) at regular intervals. One complete pattern is a **cycle.** A cycle may begin at any point on the graph of the function. The **period** of a function is the horizontal length of one cycle.

1 EXAMPLE Identifying Cycles and Periods

Analyze the periodic function below. Identify one cycle in two different ways. Then determine the period of the function.

Begin at any point on the graph. Trace one complete pattern.

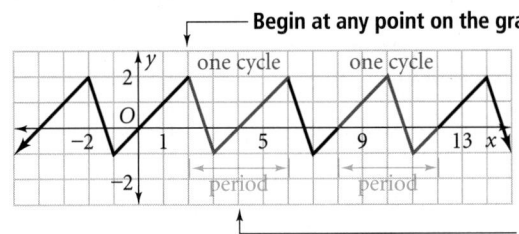

The beginning and ending *x*-values of each cycle determine the period of the function.

● Each cycle is 4 units long. The period of the function is 4.

✓ Quick Check ① For each function, identify one cycle in two different ways. Then determine the period of the function.

a.

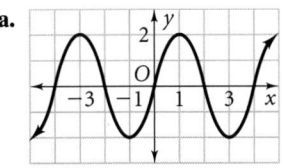

from −3 to 1 or 0 to 4; 4

b.

from −4 to −1 or 0 to 3; 3

You can determine whether a function is periodic by analyzing its graph.

2 EXAMPLE Identifying Periodic Functions

Determine whether each function *is* or *is not* periodic. If it is, find the period.

a.

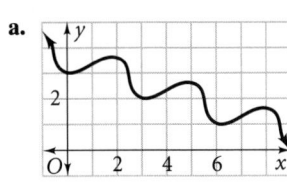

Although the graph shows similar curves, the *y*-values from one section do not repeat in other sections. The function *is not* periodic.

b.

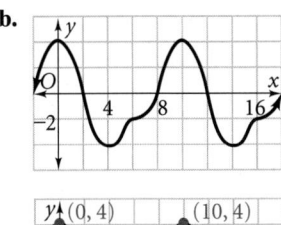

The pattern of *y*-values in one section repeats exactly in other sections. The function *is* periodic.

Find points at the beginning and end of one cycle. Subtract the *x*-values of the points: $10 - 0 = 10$. The pattern in the graph repeats every 10 units, so the period is 10.

Guided Instruction

Activity
Direct students' attention to the diagram of the Ferris wheel. Ask how many revolutions were made after 9 s, 18 s and 27 s. $\frac{1}{4}$, $\frac{1}{2}$, and $\frac{3}{4}$ of a revolution

Suggest that students connect the points with smooth curves rather than straight lines. They may need to plot more points to draw the curves accurately.

PowerPoint
Additional Examples

① Analyze this periodic function. Identify one cycle in two different ways. Then determine the period of the function. A cycle could begin, for example, at (−5, 0) or at (−3, 2). Each cycle is 7 units long; the period is 7.

② Determine whether each function *is* or *is not* periodic. If it is, find the period.

a.

Yes; 2

b.

Yes; 3

Advanced Learners **L4**
A function is periodic if, for some non-zero real number α, $f(x + \alpha) = f(x)$ for every *x* in the domain. Discuss the meaning of the smallest possible value of α.

learning style: verbal

English Language Learners **ELL**
Have students use a dictionary or thesaurus to look up the meaning of *period*. Synonyms for *period* include *cycle, interval,* and *duration.* A period is the length of one cycle. For example, class periods in your school might be consistently 45 minutes.

learning style: verbal

711

Guided Instruction

3 EXAMPLE Error Prevention

Students may incorrectly assume that all periodic functions are symmetric about the *x*-axis. Point out that the line of symmetry for this function is $x = 5$ or any multiple of 5.

4 EXAMPLE Teaching Tip

For simplicity, units of measure are given only for the values of time *t*. The amplitude of sound waves is generally measured in units of pressure, such as *pascals*.

PowerPoint
Additional Examples

3 Find the amplitudes of the two functions in Additional Example 2.
a) 2   b) 3

4 The oscilloscope screen below shows the graph of the alternating current electricity *s*, in volts, supplied to homes in the United States. Find the period and amplitude.

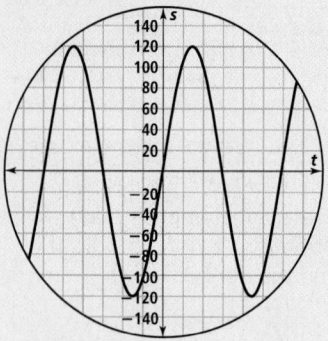

1 unit on the *t*-axis $= \frac{1}{360}$ s
$\frac{1}{60}$ s; 120 volts

Resources
• Daily Notetaking Guide
  13-1   **L3**

Closure

Ask students: *If you know the period and the amplitude of a graph, do you have enough information to sketch the graph?* No, you need to know the shape of the graph during a cycle.

Quick Check **2** Determine whether each function *is* or *is not* periodic. If it is, find the period.

a.   b.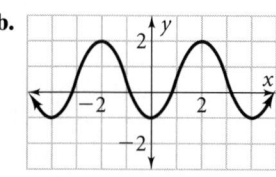

   not periodic   periodic; 4

2 Finding the Amplitude of a Periodic Function

Vocabulary Tip

Amplitude modulation (AM) radio works by varying the amplitude of radio waves.

The amplitude of a periodic function measures the amount of variation in the function values.

Key Concepts

Definition	**Amplitude of a Periodic Function**

The **amplitude** of a periodic function is half the difference between the maximum and minimum values of the function.

3 EXAMPLE Finding Amplitude of a Periodic Function

Find the amplitude of the periodic function at the right.

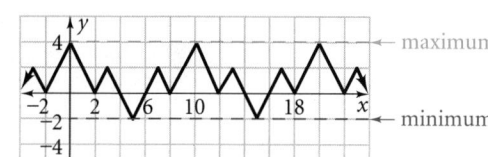

amplitude $= \frac{1}{2}$(maximum value − minimum value)   **Use the definition of amplitude.**

$= \frac{1}{2}[4 - (-2)]$ **Substitute.**

$= \frac{1}{2}(6) = 3$ **Subtract within parentheses and simplify.**

● The amplitude of the function is 3.

Quick Check **3** Find the amplitude of each function.

a.   b.

   1.5   1.5

You can model some data with periodic functions. The rotation of a Ferris wheel, the beating of a heart, and the movement of sound waves are all examples of real-world events that generate periodic data.

Real-World 🌐 **Connection**

A microphone converts sound waves into an electrical signal, which can be shown as a graph on an oscilloscope.

4 EXAMPLE Real-World 🌐 Connection

Sound Waves Sound is produced by periodic changes in air pressure called sound waves. The oscilloscope at the right shows the graph of a pure tone from a tuning fork. Find the period and the amplitude of the sound wave.

1 unit on the *t*-axis = 0.001 s

One cycle of the sound wave occurs from 0.003 s to 0.0075 s. The maximum value of the function is 4, and the minimum value is −4.

period $= 0.0075 − 0.003$ **Use the definitions.**   amplitude $= \frac{1}{2}[4 − (−4)]$

      $= 0.0045$ **Simplify.** $= \frac{1}{2}(8) = 4$

• The period of the sound wave is 0.0045 s. The amplitude is 4.

✓ **Quick Check** ④ Sketch the graph of a sound wave with a period of 0.004 s and an amplitude of 2. **See margin.**

EXERCISES

For more exercises, see *Extra Skill and Word Problem Practice.*

Practice and Problem Solving

 Practice by Example

 for Help

Example 1 (page 711)

Example 2 (page 711)

4. not periodic

5. periodic; 12

6. not periodic

7. not periodic

8. periodic; 8

9. periodic; 7

1–3. See margin.

Identify one cycle in two different ways. Then determine the period of the function.

1.

2.

3.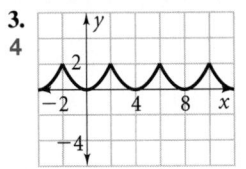

Determine whether each function *is* or *is not* periodic. If it is, find the period.

4.

5.

6.

7.

8.

9.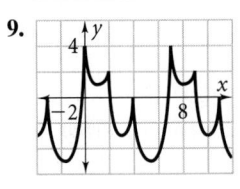

3. Practice

Assignment Guide

1 A B   1-9, 17-20, 23-30

2 A B   10-16, 21, 22

C   Challenge   31-34

Test Prep   35-40
Mixed Review   41-47

Homework Quick Check

To check students' understanding of key skills and concepts, go over Exercises 6, 14, 16, 17, 21.

Error Prevention!

Exercises 1–13, 23–25 Some students may have problems reading the units from small graphs. Some options are to provide a magnifier, make enlarged copies of the page, or have them work with a partner.

Differentiated Instruction Resources

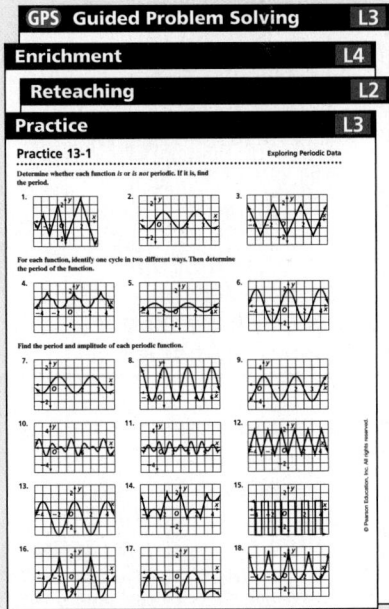

GPS Guided Problem Solving	L3
Enrichment	L4
Reteaching	L2
Practice	L3

Quick Check

4.

1 unit on the x-axis is 0.001 s.

1–3. Answers may vary. Samples are given.

1. $x = −2$ to $x = 3$, $x = 2$ to $x = 7$; 5

2. $x = 0$ to $x = 4$, $x = 5$ to $x = 9$; 4

3. $x = 0$ to $x = 4$, $x = 2$ to $x = 6$; 4

713

Examples 3 and 4
(pages 712 and 713)

Find the amplitude of each periodic function.

10.

11.

12.

13.

B **Apply Your Skills**

Sketch the graph of a sound wave with the given period and amplitude.

14. period 0.02, amplitude 4   **15.** period 0.005, amplitude 9
14–15. See margin.
16. Complete each statement with *x* or *y*.
  a. You use ■-values to compute the amplitude of a function. **y**
  b. You use ■-values to compute the period of a function. **x**

✏️ **Writing** **Could you use a periodic function to represent each situation described below? Explain. 18–19. See margin.**

17. Answers may vary.
Sample: Yes;
average monthly
temperatures for
three years should
be cyclical due to
the variation of the
seasons.

17. the average monthly temperature in your community, recorded every month for three years

18. the population in your community, recorded every year for the last 50 years

19. the number of cars per hour that pass through an intersection near where you live, recorded for two consecutive work days

🌐 **Health** **Use the graph below for Exercises 20 and 21.**

20. A person's pulse rate is the number of times his or her heart beats in one minute. Each cycle in the graph represents one heartbeat. Find the pulse rate.
60 beats per min

RHYTHM STRIP 1 unit (horizontal) = 0.2 s
1 unit (vertical) = 0.5 mV

21. An electrocardiogram (EKG or ECG) measures the electrical activity of a
GPS person's heart in millivolts over time.
  a. What is the period of the EKG shown above? **1 s**
  b. What is the amplitude of the EKG? **1.5 mV**

Real-World 🌐 **Connection**

The carotid artery of the neck is a commonly used pulse point.

22. Open-Ended Sketch a graph of a periodic function that has a period of 3 and an amplitude of 2. **Check students' work.**

Find the maximum, minimum, and period of each periodic function. Then copy the graph and sketch two more cycles. 23–25. See margin.

23.

24.

25.

GO **Online**
Homework Video Tutor
Visit: PHSchool.com
Web Code: age-1301

14.

1 unit on the *x*-axis is 0.005 s.

15.

1 unit on the *x*-axis is 0.001 s.

18. Answers may vary.
Sample: No; population
usually increases or
decreases but is not
cyclical.

19. Answers may vary.
Sample: Yes; traffic
that passes through an
intersection should be
at the same levels for the
same times of day for two
consecutive work days.

23. 3, −3, 4;

24. 5, 0, 8;

25. 4, −4, 8;

Language Arts Functions that repeat over time are common in everyday life. The English language has many words that stand for common periods of time. State the period of time from which each term derives.

26. annual	27. biweekly	28. quarterly	29. hourly	30. circadian
1 yr	**2 weeks**	**3 months**	**1 hour**	**1 day**

C Challenge

31. Suppose f is a periodic function. The period of f is 5 and $f(1) = 2$. Find $f(6)$, $f(11)$, and $f(-4)$. **2, 2, 2**

32. Suppose g is a periodic function. The period of g is 24, $g(3) = 67$, and $g(8) = 70$. Find each function value.
   a. $g(27)$ **67**   **b.** $g(80)$ **70**   **c.** $g(-16)$ **70**   **d.** $g(51)$ **67**

33. **Motion** You are sitting on a pier watching the waves when you notice a bottle in the water. The bottle bobs so that it is between 2.5 ft and 4.5 ft below the pier. You know you can reach 3 ft below the pier. Suppose the bottle reaches its highest point every 5 s.
   a. Sketch a graph of the bottle's distance below the pier for 15 s. Assume that at $t = 0$, the bottle is closest to the pier. **See back of book.**
   b. Find the period and the amplitude of the function. **5 s, 1 ft**
   c. **Estimation** Use your graph to estimate the length of time the bottle is within reach during each cycle. **Answers may vary. Sample: about $1\frac{1}{3}$ s**

34. **Calendar** A day—the time Earth takes to rotate from one noon to the next—is a basic measure of time. A solar year is about 365.2422 days. We try to keep our calendar in step with the solar year.
   a. If every calendar year has 365 days, by how many days would the calendar year and the solar year differ after 100 years? **24.22 days**
   b. If every fourth year has an extra "leap" day added, by how many days would the two systems differ after 100 years? **0.78 day**
   c. If every hundred years the "leap" day is omitted, by how many days would the two systems differ after 100 years? **0.22 day**
   d. **Critical Thinking** Why is it important for the difference between the calendar year and the solar year to be zero? **See margin.**

Real-World 🌐 **Connection**

Coast Guard rescue jumpers time their pickups for the crests of the waves.

Test Prep

Multiple Choice

35. A periodic function goes through 5 complete cycles in 4 min. What is the period of the function? **C**
   A. $\frac{1}{5}$ min   **B.** $\frac{1}{4}$ min   **C.** 48 s   **D.** 75 s

36. The period of a periodic function is 8 s. How many cycles does it go through in 30 s? **G**
   F. $\frac{4}{15}$ cycle   **G.** 3.75 cycles   **H.** 22 cycles   **J.** 240 cycles

37. Which graph is NOT the graph of a periodic function? **B**

       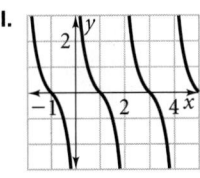

      A. I only   **B.** II only   **C.** III only   **D.** II and III

34d. Answers may vary. Sample:
The calendar year is meant to predict events in the solar year. Keeping the difference between the two minimal is necessary for the calendar year to be useful.

Lesson Quiz

1. Determine whether the function shown is periodic.

         yes

2. Determine whether the function shown is periodic.

         no

Find the period and the amplitude of the periodic functions shown.

3.

6; 1.5

4.

3; 0.5

Alternative Assessment

Have students draw the graph in Example 1 with a period that is double the one shown and with half the original amplitude. Then have them draw the graph with a period that is half the one shown and with twice the amplitude.

Resources

For additional practice with a variety of test item formats:
- Standardized Test Prep, p. 775
- Test-Taking Strategies, p. 770
- Test-Taking Strategies with Transparencies

---

38. The amplitude of a periodic function is 2.5 and its minimum value is 0. What is the function's maximum value? **J**

   F. −2.5   **G.** 0   **H.** 2.5   **J.** 5.0

Short Response

39. A periodic function completes m cycles in n seconds. What is the period of the function? Show your work. **See margin.**

Extended Response

40. A machine begins recording two periodic functions at the same time. The first has a period of 6 s. The second has a period of 7 s. After 20 s, the machine begins recording a third periodic function, with a period of 8 s. How many seconds after the machine begins recording the third function are all three functions at the beginning of their periods? Explain. **See margin.**

Mixed Review

GO for Help

Lesson 12-7

41. Sketch a normal curve for a distribution that has mean 57 and standard deviation 12. Label the x-axis values at one, two, and three standard deviations from the mean. **See back of book.**

Lesson 11-1

Find the next two terms in each sequence. Write a formula for the nth term. Identify each formula as *explicit* or *recursive*. 42–44. See margin.

42. $1, 3, 5, 7, 9, \ldots$ **43.** $4, 6, 8, 10, 12, \ldots$ **44.** $3, 6, 11, 18, 27, \ldots$

Lesson 10-6

Write an equation for each conic section. Then sketch the graph.

45. parabola with vertex $(-3, 2)$ and focus $(-3, 7)$ 45–47. See margin.

46. hyperbola with center $(5, -3)$, one focus at $(5, 0)$, and one vertex at $(5, -1)$

47. ellipse with center $(-2, 1)$, vertices at $(-6, 1)$ and $(2, 1)$, and co-vertices at $(-2, 3)$ and $(-2, -1)$

---

39. [2] A period is the length of 1 cycle, so
$$\frac{n \text{ seconds}}{m \text{ cycles}} = \frac{x \text{ seconds}}{1 \text{ cycle}}.$$
Then $xm = n$, or $x = \frac{n}{m}$. The period is $\frac{n}{m}$ seconds.

[1] answer only with no explanation

40. [4] 64 seconds. The first two functions are at the beginning of their cycles together every $6 \cdot 7 = 42$ seconds: 42, 84, 126, . . . The third function is at the beginning of its cycle every 8 seconds, starting at 20 seconds: 20, 28, 36, 44, 52, 60, 68, 76, 84, . . . The three functions are all at the beginning of their cycles at 84 seconds, which is 64 seconds after the third function begins.

[3] minor error in calculation

[2] incomplete explanation

[1] answer only, with no explanation

42. $11, 13$; $a_n = 2n - 1$, explicit; $a_1 = 1$, $a_n = a_{n-1} + 2$, recursive

43. $14, 16$; $a_n = 2n + 2$, explicit; $a_1 = 4$, $a_n = a_{n-1} + 2$, recursive

44. $38, 51$; $a_1 = 3$, $a_n = a_{n-1} + 2n - 1$, recursive; $a_n = n^2 + 2$, explicit

---

A Point in Time

1500   1600   1700   1800   1900   2000

To human beings, the most important periodic function is the rhythm of the heart. About once per second, a nerve in the heart generates an electrical signal. This causes the heart to contract and force blood through the body.

In 1958, doctors placed the first pacemaker in a patient with a malfunctioning nerve. The creator of the device's control unit was Otis Boykin, an inventor from Dallas, Texas. He began his career testing automatic airplane controls. Today, more than a million pacemakers are helping people worldwide enjoy the normal rhythms of the human heart.

Go Online   **For:** Information about pacemakers
PHSchool.com   **Web Code:** age-2032

45. $(x + 3)^2 = 20(y - 2)$

46. $\dfrac{(y + 3)^2}{4} - \dfrac{(x - 5)^2}{5} = 1$

47. $\dfrac{(x + 2)^2}{16} + \dfrac{(y - 1)^2}{4} = 1$

Special Right Triangles

FOR USE WITH LESSON 13-2

Special Right Triangles

Students review the special right triangles from geometry in preparation for learning about the unit circle and the definitions of trigonometric functions.

In Geometry you learned about two special right triangles, the 45°-45°-90° triangle and the 30°-60°-90° triangle. The figures at the right summarize the relationships among the lengths of the sides of each triangle.

 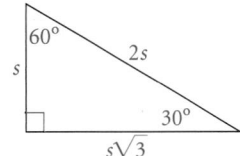

1 EXAMPLE Finding Side Lengths in a 45°-45°-90° Triangle

Find the missing side lengths in each figure.

a.

$$h = \sqrt{2} \cdot 5 \qquad \text{hypotenuse} = \sqrt{2} \cdot \text{leg}$$

$$h = 5\sqrt{2} \qquad \text{Simplify.}$$

b.

$$5 = \sqrt{2} \cdot s$$

$$s = \frac{5}{\sqrt{2}}$$

$$s = \frac{5\sqrt{2}}{2}$$

2 EXAMPLE Finding Side Lengths in a 30°-60°-90° Triangle

Find the missing side lengths in the triangle at the right.

$$4 = \sqrt{3} \cdot s \qquad \text{longer leg} = \sqrt{3} \cdot \text{shorter leg}$$

$$s = \frac{4}{\sqrt{3}} = \frac{4\sqrt{3}}{3} \qquad \text{Divide and simplify.}$$

$$h = 2s \qquad \text{hypotenuse} = 2 \cdot \text{shorter leg}$$

$$= 2 \cdot \frac{4\sqrt{3}}{3} = \frac{8\sqrt{3}}{3} \quad \text{Substitute } \frac{4\sqrt{3}}{3} \text{ for } s \text{ and simplify.}$$

EXERCISES

Use the given information to find the missing side length(s) in each 45°-45°-90° triangle. Rationalize any denominators. 1–4. See right.

1. hypotenuse 1 in.
2. leg 2 cm
3. hypotenuse $\sqrt{3}$ ft
4. leg $2\sqrt{5}$ m

Use the given information to find the missing side lengths in each 30°-60°-90° triangle. Rationalize any denominators. 5–13. See margin.

5. shorter leg 3 in.
6. longer leg 1 cm
7. hypotenuse 1 ft
8. shorter leg $\sqrt{3}$ cm
9. hypotenuse $2\sqrt{2}$ ft
10. longer leg $2\sqrt{3}$ in.
11. hypotenuse $3\sqrt{2}$ m
12. longer leg $\sqrt{5}$ cm
13. shorter leg $\sqrt{13}$ mm

14. What is the ratio of the length to the width of a rectangle whose diagonals form a 90° angle? A 60° angle? **1:1; $\sqrt{3}$:1**

Guided Instruction

1 EXAMPLE Teaching Tip

Remind students that the hypotenuse is always the longest side of a right triangle.

2 EXAMPLE Error Prevention

Suggest to students that, as a memory aid and in order to prevent confusing these two special triangles, they record the two special right triangles in their notebooks. Then they can refer to them in the future for problems involving special triangles.

Connection to Algebra

Remind students that they are rationalizing the denominator in the second step in Example 1b. Rationalizing the denominator means multiplying by 1, here $\frac{\sqrt{2}}{\sqrt{2}}$, in order that roots appear only in the numerator.

Resources

ExamView CD-ROM, Chapter 00, Geometry and Measurement

10. shorter leg: 2 in., hypotenuse: 4 in.
11. shorter leg: $\frac{3\sqrt{2}}{2}$ m, longer leg: $\frac{3\sqrt{6}}{2}$ m
12. shorter leg: $\frac{\sqrt{15}}{3}$ cm, hypotenuse: $\frac{2\sqrt{15}}{3}$ cm
13. hypotenuse: $2\sqrt{13}$ mm, longer leg: $\sqrt{39}$ mm

5. hypotenuse: 6 in., longer leg: $3\sqrt{3}$ in.

6. shorter leg: $\frac{\sqrt{3}}{3}$ cm, hypotenuse: $\frac{2\sqrt{3}}{3}$ cm

7. shorter leg: $\frac{1}{2}$ ft, longer leg: $\frac{\sqrt{3}}{2}$ ft

8. hypotenuse: $2\sqrt{3}$ cm, longer leg: 3 cm

9. shorter leg: $\sqrt{2}$ ft, longer leg: $\sqrt{6}$ ft

1. Plan

Objectives

1 To work with angles in standard position
2 To find coordinates of points on the unit circle

Examples

1 Measuring an Angle in Standard Position
2 Sketching an Angle in Standard Position
3 Real-World Connection
4 Finding the Cosine and Sine of an Angle
5 Finding Exact Values of Cosine and Sine

Math Background

The arrow arc drawn to show the rotation to the terminal side of an angle in standard position is important. It distinguishes between positive and negative coterminal angles, such as an angle of −30° and one of 330°. The arrow can also be used to show an angle that has a measure greater than 360°.

More Math Background: p. 708C

Lesson Planning and Resources

See p. 708E for a list of the resources that support this lesson.

Bell Ringer Practice

✓ **Check Skills You'll Need**
For intervention, direct students to:

Skills Handbook p. 876

The Coordinate Plane
Algebra 1 Review:
Page 54

13-2 Angles and the Unit Circle

What You'll Learn

• To work with angles in standard position
• To find coordinates of points on the unit circle

... And Why

To use an ancient calendar, as in Example 3

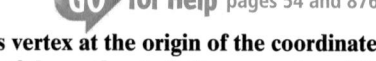

✓ Check Skills You'll Need

GO for Help pages 54 and 876

For each measure, draw an angle with its vertex at the origin of the coordinate plane. Use the positive x-axis as one ray of the angle. 1–6. See margin p. 720.

1. 90°   2. 45°   3. 30°
4. 150°   5. 135°   6. 120°

🔊 New Vocabulary
• standard position • initial side • terminal side
• coterminal angles • unit circle • cosine of θ • sine of θ

---

1 Working With Angles in Standard Position

Vocabulary Tip

<u>Terminal</u> means "at an end" or "forming a boundary."

An angle is in **standard position** when the vertex is at the origin and one ray is on the positive x-axis. The ray on the x-axis is the **initial side** of the angle; the other ray is the **terminal side** of the angle.

Standard Position

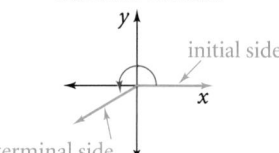

To measure an angle in standard position, find the amount of rotation from the initial side to the terminal side.

1 EXAMPLE Measuring an Angle in Standard Position

Find the measure of the angle at the right.

The angle measures 20° more than a straight angle of 180°.

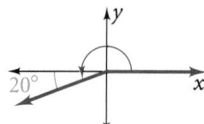

● Since 180 + 20 = 200, the measure of the angle is 200°.

✓ **Quick Check** ❶ One full rotation contains 360 degrees. How many degrees are in one quarter of a rotation? In one half of a rotation? In three quarters of a rotation? **90°; 180°; 270°**

718 Chapter 13 Periodic Functions and Trigonometry

Differentiated Instruction — Solutions for All Learners

Special Needs L1
Have students sit in a circle around a clearly labeled set of x- and y-axes on the floor. Call out an angle and have the student closest to that angle measure stand up. Be sure to call both positive and negative angles.

learning style: tactile

Below Level L2
Have students copy and complete the chart in Exercise 50 on page 723 to help them remember when sines and cosines are positive.

learning style: visual

2a.

85°

b.

−320°

c.

180°

The measure of an angle is positive when the rotation from the initial side to the terminal side is in the counterclockwise direction. The measure is negative when the rotation is clockwise.

+120° Counterclockwise
Clockwise
−120°

2 EXAMPLE Sketching an Angle in Standard Position

Sketch each angle in standard position.

a. 36°   **b.** 315°   **c.** −150°

36°
Counterclockwise

315°
Counterclockwise

−150°
150°
Clockwise

✓ Quick Check **2** Sketch each angle in standard position. **a–c. See left.**
a. 85°   **b.** −320°   **c.** 180°

Two angles in standard position are **coterminal angles** if they have the same terminal side.

135°
−225°

Angles that have measures 135° and −225° are coterminal.

3 EXAMPLE Real-World Connection

History The Aztec calendar stone has 20 divisions for the 20 days in each month of the Aztec year. The yellow angle marks the passage of 11 days. Find the measures of two coterminal angles that coincide with the angle. The terminal side of the angle is $\frac{11}{20}$ of a full rotation from the initial side.

$$\frac{11}{20} \cdot 360° = 198°$$

To find a coterminal angle, subtract one full rotation.

$$198° - 360° = -162°$$

● Two coterminal angle measures for the angle in the photograph are 198° and −162°.

Real-World Connection

Archaeologists assembling a sample of Mesoamerican hieroglyphic text

✓ Quick Check **3 a.** Find another angle coterminal with 198° by adding one full rotation. **558°**
b. Reasoning Are angles with measures of 40° and 680° coterminal? Explain.
c. Make a Conjecture Generalize how the measures of two coterminal angles are related. **b–c. See margin p. 720.**

Lesson 13-2 Angles and the Unit Circle   **719**

2. Teach

Guided Instruction

3 EXAMPLE Diversity

If any students are of Mexican ancestry, they may share what they know of Aztec history. Explain that the Aztec civilization migrated into central Mexico from the north, and then moved by way of Chapultepec to settle in the area that is now Mexico City, around 1325 AD. The Aztecs were in control of most of central Mexico when the Spaniards arrived in 1519.

PowerPoint

Additional Examples

1 Find the measure of the angle.

150°
30°

2 Sketch each angle in standard position.
a. 48°   **b.** 310°

48°
310°

c. −170°

−170°

719

Activity

Some students may need help with using the compass and protractor. Ask a student who is familiar with these to act as a coach. As the students are making their conjectures, point out again that the radius of the circle that they drew is 1 unit.

Additional Examples

③ An angle on the Aztec calendar shows the passage of 16 days. Find the measures of the two coterminal angles that coincide with the angle. **288° and −72°**

Check Skills You'll Need

1.
   90°

2.
   45°

3.
   30°

4.
   150°

5.
   135°

6.
   120°

Quick Check

3b. No; 40° is coterminal with 400° and 760°.

c. Answers may vary.
   Sample: The difference between measures of two coterminal angles is a multiple of 360°.

720

Activity: Angles in a Circle

- Use a compass. Construct a circle with a radius of 1 in. on the coordinate plane. Place the center of the circle at the origin.

- Use a protractor. Draw an angle of 30°. Place one ray along the positive *x*-axis. Place the other ray in Quadrant I. Label the point where the second ray intersects the circle *P(x, y)*.

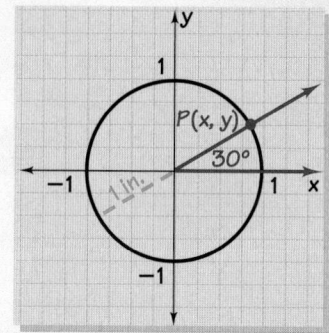

1. **Answers may vary.** Sample: Use a 30°-60°-90° triangle.

3. **0.87, 0.5; these values are the same as those in Question 2.**

4b. **0.707, 0.707; these values are the same as those in part (a).**

c. **The *x*-coordinate of *P* equals the cosine of the angle containing *P*, and the *y*-coordinate equals the sine of the angle.**

1. Identify the methods you could use to find the coordinates of *P*.

2. Choose one method and find the values of *x* and *y*. Express the coordinates in decimal form. **(0.87, 0.5)**

3. Use a calculator to find the values of cos 30° (read "cosine of 30 degrees") and sin 30° (read "sine of 30 degrees"). Compare these values to the values you found in Question 2.

4. a. Repeat the steps above using an angle of 45°. What are the coordinates of the new point *P*? **(0.707, 0.707)**
   b. Find cos 45° and sin 45° using your calculator. How do these values compare to those you found in part (a)?
   c. **Make a Conjecture** What is the relationship between the coordinates of a point *P* on the circle and the values of the sine and cosine of the angle containing *P*?

Vocabulary Tip

The Greek letter θ (pronounced THAY-tuh) is frequently used as a variable for angle measure.

The **unit circle** has a radius of 1 unit and its center at the origin of the coordinate plane. Points on the unit circle are related to periodic functions.

You can use the symbol θ for the measure of an angle in standard position.

 Key Concepts

Definition	**Cosine and Sine of an Angle**

Suppose an angle in standard position has measure θ. The **cosine of θ** (cos θ) is the *x*-coordinate of the point at which the terminal side of the angle intersects the unit circle. The **sine of θ** (sin θ) is the *y*-coordinate.

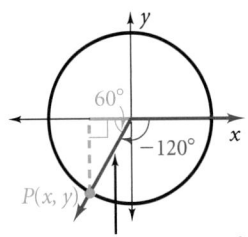
5 **EXAMPLE** **Math Tip**

Since perpendicular lines form right angles, point out that the right triangle is always formed by drawing a line perpendicular to the *x*-axis from the point where the terminal side intersects the unit circle.

4 **EXAMPLE** Finding the Cosine and Sine of an Angle

Find the cosine and sine of 60°.

As the figure suggests, the *x*-coordinate of point *A* is $\frac{1}{2}$, so cos 60° = $\frac{1}{2}$, or 0.5.

Use a 30°-60°-90° right triangle to find sin 60°.

$$\begin{aligned} \text{longer leg} &= \sqrt{3} \cdot \text{shorter leg} \\ &= \sqrt{3} \cdot \tfrac{1}{2} \quad \textbf{Substitute.} \\ &= \tfrac{\sqrt{3}}{2} \quad \textbf{Multiply.} \\ &\approx 0.87 \quad \textbf{Simplify.} \end{aligned}$$

Problem Solving Hint

The coordinates of the point at which the terminal side of a 60° angle intersects the unit circle are $(\frac{1}{2}, \frac{\sqrt{3}}{2})$, so cos 60° = 0.5 and sin 60° = $\frac{\sqrt{3}}{2} \approx 0.87$.

✓ **Quick Check** 4 Draw each angle in a unit circle. Then find the cosine and sine of each angle.
    a. 45°   **b.** 30°   **c.** 120°

4a.
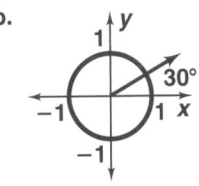

$\frac{\sqrt{2}}{2} \approx 0.707, \frac{\sqrt{2}}{2} \approx 0.707$

b.
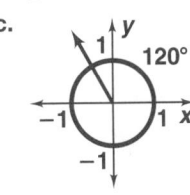

$\frac{\sqrt{3}}{2} \approx 0.87, 0.5$

c.

$-0.5, \frac{\sqrt{3}}{2} \approx 0.87$

You can use right triangles to find the *exact* cosine and sine of an angle whose terminal side is not in Quadrant I.

5 **EXAMPLE** Finding Exact Values of Cosine and Sine

Find the exact values of cos (−120°) and sin (−120°).

Step 1 Sketch an angle of −120° in standard position. Sketch a unit circle.

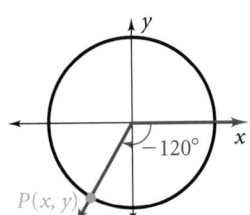

x-coordinate = cos (−120°)
y-coordinate = sin (−120°)

Step 2 Sketch a right triangle. Place the hypotenuse on the terminal side of the angle. Place one leg on the *x*-axis. (The other leg will be parallel to the *y*-axis.)

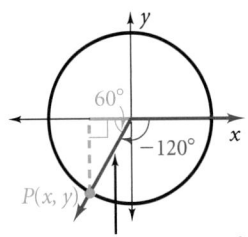

The triangle contains angles of 30°, 60°, and 90°.

Step 3 Find the length of each side of the triangle.

  hypotenuse = 1   **The hypotenuse is a radius of the unit circle.**

  shorter leg = $\frac{1}{2}$ **The shorter leg is half the hypotenuse.**

  longer leg = $\frac{1}{2}\sqrt{3}$ **The longer leg is $\sqrt{3}$ times the short leg.**

          = $\frac{\sqrt{3}}{2}$

Since the point lies in Quadrant III, both coordinates are negative. The shorter leg lies along the *x*-axis, so cos (−120°) = $-\frac{1}{2}$, and sin (−120°) = $-\frac{\sqrt{3}}{2}$.

PowerPoint

Additional Examples

4 Find the cosine and sine of 135°.
about −0.71; about 0.71

5 Find the exact values of cos (−150°) and sin (−150°).
$-\frac{\sqrt{3}}{2}; -\frac{1}{2}$

Resources
• Daily Notetaking Guide
  13-2   L3

Closure

Ask students: *What do the sine and cosine of an angle represent on the unit circle?* The sine is the *y*-coordinate of the point where the terminal side of the angle intersects the unit circle; the cosine is the *x*-coordinate of the point where the terminal side of the angle intersects the unit circle.

3. Practice

Assignment Guide

▼1 A B 1-20, 37-49

▼2 A B 21-36, 50-52
C Challenge   53-62

Test Prep   63-68
Mixed Review   69-77

Homework Quick Check
To check students' understanding
of key skills and concepts, go over
Exercises 8, 22, 50, 51, 52.

Error Prevention!

Exercises 21–28 Tell students
to pay close attention to the
quadrant in which the terminal
side of the angle lies. The
quadrant determines whether
or not the x- and y-coordinates
are negative, and therefore
affects whether the sine and
cosine of the angle are negative.

Teaching Tip

Exercises 29–36 The Greek letter
θ is read as "theta."

Differentiated Instruction Resources

GPS Guided Problem Solving L3
Enrichment L4
Reteaching L2
Practice L3

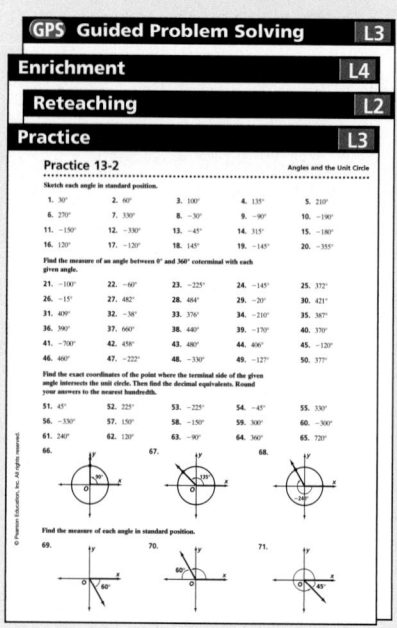

722

5a. −0.5, −0.87; the values
are the rounded
decimal values of
$-\frac{1}{2}$ and $-\frac{\sqrt{3}}{2}$.

5 a. Use a calculator to find cos (−120°) and sin (−120°). How do these values
compare to the exact values found in Example 5?
b. Find the exact values of cos 135° and sin 135°. Use properties of a 45°-45°-90°
triangle. Use a calculator to find the decimal equivalents. $-\frac{\sqrt{2}}{2}, \frac{\sqrt{2}}{2}$;
c. Find the exact values of cos 150° and sin 150°.   ≈ −0.707, ≈ 0.707

c. $-\frac{\sqrt{3}}{2}, \frac{1}{2}$

EXERCISES

For more exercises, see *Extra Skill and Word Problem Practice.*

Practice and Problem Solving

A **Practice by Example**

Find the measure of each angle in standard position.

Example 1
(page 718)

GO for Help

1. −315°
2. −135°
3. 240°

4. 115°
5. −110°
6. −340°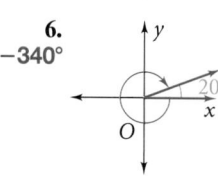

Example 2
(page 719)

Sketch each angle in standard position. 7–11. See back of book.

7. 40°   **8.** −130°   **9.** −270°   **10.** 120°   **11.** 95°

Example 3
(page 719)

Find the measure of an angle between 0° and 360° coterminal with each given angle.

12. 385° **25°**   **13.** 575° **215°**   **14.** −405° **315°**   **15.** −356° **4°**

16. 500° **140°**   **17.** −210° **150°**   **18.** 415° **55°**   **19.** −180° **180°**

20. Telephones Rotary telephones were widely
used until the 1980s. Dialing a higher number
(or 0) took longer because the dial moved
through a larger central angle. Estimate the
measures of two coterminal angles that
coincide with the angle at the right.
Answers may vary. Sample: −135°, 585°

Examples 4 and 5
(page 721)

**Find the exact values of the cosine and sine of each angle. Then find the decimal
values. Round your answers to the nearest hundredth.   23–28. See margin.**

21. $\frac{1}{2}, -\frac{\sqrt{3}}{2}$; 0.50, −0.87

22. $-\frac{\sqrt{2}}{2}, -\frac{\sqrt{2}}{2}$; −0.71,
−0.71

21.
22.
23.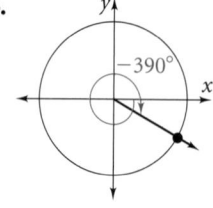

24. −240°   **25.** 390°   **26.** 315°   **27.** −30°   **28.** 135°

23. $\frac{\sqrt{3}}{2}, -\frac{1}{2}$; 0.87, −0.50

24. $-\frac{1}{2}, \frac{\sqrt{3}}{2}$; −0.50, 0.87

25. $\frac{\sqrt{3}}{2}, \frac{1}{2}$; 0.87, 0.50

26. $\frac{\sqrt{2}}{2}, -\frac{\sqrt{2}}{2}$; 0.71, −0.71

27. $\frac{\sqrt{3}}{2}, -\frac{1}{2}$; 0.87, −0.50

28. $-\frac{\sqrt{2}}{2}, \frac{\sqrt{2}}{2}$; −0.71, 0.71

50a.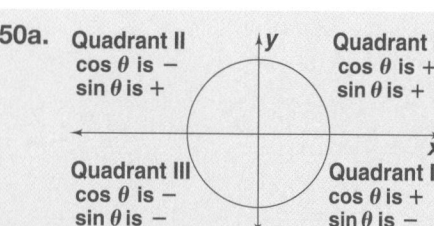

B Apply Your Skills

For each angle θ, find the values of cos θ and sin θ. Round your answers to the nearest hundredth.

29. 0° 1.00, 0.00   **30.** 32° 0.85, 0.53   **31.** −45° 0.71, −0.71   **32.** −210° −0.87, 0.50

33. −95° −0.09, −1.00   **34.** −10° 0.98, −0.17   **35.** 154° −0.90, 0.44   **36.** 90° 0.00, 1.00

Open-Ended Find a positive and a negative coterminal angle for the given angle.

37. 45°   **38.** −125°   **39.** −675°   **40.** 400°

41. −85° 275°, −445°   **42.** −425° 295°, −65°   **43.** 213° 573°, −147°   **44.** −57° 303°, −417°

In which quadrant, or on which axis, does the terminal side of each angle lie?

45. 150° II   **46.** 210° III   **47.** 540° negative x-axis   **48.** −60° IV   **49.** 0° positive x-axis

50. a. Copy and complete the chart at the right. **See margin p. 722.**
(GPS)
b. Suppose you know that cos θ is negative and sin θ is positive. In which quadrant does the terminal side of the angle lie? **II**
c. Writing Summarize how the quadrant in which the terminal side of an angle lies affects the sign of the sine and cosine of that angle. **See margin.**

Quadrant II
cos θ is ■
sin θ is ■

Quadrant I
cos θ is +
sin θ is +

Quadrant III
cos θ is ■
sin θ is ■

Quadrant IV
cos θ is ■
sin θ is ■

51. a. Use a calculator to find the value of each expression: cos 40°, cos 400°, and cos (−320°). **0.77, 0.77, 0.77**
b. Critical Thinking What do you notice about the values you found in part (a)? Explain. **See margin.**

52. Writing Explain how to find the sine and cosine of angles with measures of 0°, 90°, 180°, 270°, and 360° without using a calculator. **See margin.**

C Challenge

Sketch each angle in standard position. Use the unit circle and a right triangle to find exact values of the cosine and the sine of the angle. **53–58. See back of book.**

53. −300°   **54.** 120°   **55.** 225°

56. −780°   **57.** −405°   **58.** 1020°

59. Design Navajo sand paintings like the one at the right have many lines of symmetry. Suppose point A is on a unit circle. Find the coordinates of A. $\left(-\frac{\sqrt{2}}{2}, \frac{\sqrt{2}}{2}\right)$

60. Open-Ended Find the measures of four angles in standard position that have a sine of 0.5. (*Hint:* Use the unit circle and right triangles.)

61. Critical Thinking Suppose θ is an angle in standard position and cos $\theta = -\frac{1}{2}$ and sin $\theta = -\frac{\sqrt{3}}{2}$. Can the value of θ be 60°? Can it be −120°? Draw a diagram and justify your reasoning. **See margin.**

37–44. Answers may vary. Samples:

37. 405°, −315°
38. 235°, −485°
39. 45°, −315°
40. 40°, −320°

nline
Homework Video Tutor
Visit: PHSchool.com
Web Code: age-1302

60. Answers may vary. Sample: 30°, 150°, −210°, 390°

50c. If the terminal side of an angle is in Quadrants I or II, then the sine of the angle is positive; otherwise it is not. If the terminal side of an angle is in Quadrants I or IV,

then the cosine of the angle is positive; otherwise it is not.

51b. The cosines of the three angles are equal because the angles are coterminal.

52. The x-coordinate of a point on the ray defined by angle θ is equal to cos θ; similarly for the y-coordinate and sin θ. The terminal sides of the angles 0°, 180°, and 360°

Sketch each angle in standard position. Use a right triangle to find the exact values of the cosine and sine of the angle.

1. 45° $\frac{\sqrt{2}}{2}$; $\frac{\sqrt{2}}{2}$

2. −120° $-\frac{1}{2}$; $-\frac{\sqrt{3}}{2}$

3. What angle is less than 360° and coterminal with 45°? Answers may vary. Sample: −315°

Alternative Assessment

Have students make a poster showing a unit circle with a central angle with a movable side made of a cardboard strip fastened at the origin with a brad. Have them use the poster to explain how to find the sine and cosine of the special angles 30°, 45°, 60° and their negatives.

lie on the x-axis, and thus their sines are all 0. Then using the unit circle we can find their cosines, which are ±1. The angles 90° and 270° lie on the y-axis, so their cosines are 0 and their sines are 1 and −1 respectively.

61. No; yes; if the sine and cosine are both negative, the angle is in Quadrant III. 60° is in Quadrant I, and −120° is in Quadrant III.

723

Resources
For additional practice with a
variety of test item formats:
- Standardized Test Prep, p. 775
- Test-Taking Strategies, p. 770
- Test-Taking Strategies with
  Transparencies

72.

73.

74. $(0, 2\sqrt{5}), (0, -2\sqrt{5})$

75. $(0, 5\sqrt{5}), (0, -5\sqrt{5})$

 62. Navigation When navigators locate an object, they measure in a clockwise direction from due north. The measure of the angle is called the bearing. Suppose a lighthouse's bearing is 110° from a ship.
  a. Sketch the diagram at the right on a coordinate plane. Place north along the positive y-axis.
  b. Express the location of the lighthouse in terms of an angle in standard position.

a. Check students' work.
b. −20°

Test Prep

Multiple Choice

63. Which angle, in standard position, is NOT coterminal with the others?   **A**
  A. −190°   **B.** −170°   **C.** 190°   **D.** 550°

64. An angle drawn in standard position has a terminal side that passes through the point $(\sqrt{2}, -\sqrt{2})$. What is one possible measure of the angle?
  F. 45°   **G.** 225°   **H.** 315°   **J.** 330°   **H**

65. An angle of 120° is in standard position. What are the coordinates of the point at which the terminal side intersects the unit circle?   **D**
  A. $\left(\frac{1}{2}, \frac{\sqrt{3}}{2}\right)$ **B.** $\left(-\frac{1}{2}, -\frac{\sqrt{3}}{2}\right)$ **C.** $\left(-\frac{\sqrt{3}}{2}, \frac{1}{2}\right)$ **D.** $\left(-\frac{1}{2}, \frac{\sqrt{3}}{2}\right)$

66. An angle of −225° is in standard position. Which points can lie on the terminal side of the angle?   **H**
  I. $\left(\frac{\sqrt{2}}{2}, -\frac{\sqrt{2}}{2}\right)$ **II.** $\left(-\frac{\sqrt{2}}{2}, \frac{\sqrt{2}}{2}\right)$ **III.** $\left(-\frac{\sqrt{2}}{2}, -\frac{\sqrt{2}}{2}\right)$ **IV.** $(-1, 1)$
  F. I and II   **G.** II and III   **H.** II and IV   **J.** I and III

Short Response

67. What is the exact value of $\cos(-210°)$? Show your work. **See back of book.**

Extended Response

68. Use an angle in standard position to find the exact value of $[\sin(-135°)]^2 + [\cos(-135°)]^2$. Show your work.   **See back of book.**

Mixed Review

GO for Help

Lesson 13-1

Determine whether each function *is* or *is not* periodic. If it is, find the period.

69.

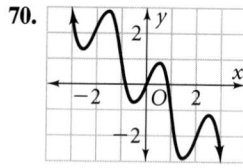

periodic; 3

70.

not periodic

71.

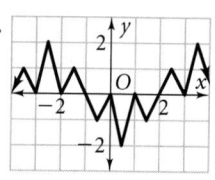

periodic; 6

Lesson 12-1

Graph the probability distribution for each sample space.

72. {two coins heads, two coins tails, one coin heads and the other tails}

73. {the sum of two number cubes a prime number, the sum a composite number}
72–77. See margin.

Lesson 10-5

Find the foci of each hyperbola. Draw the graph.

74. $\frac{y^2}{16} - \frac{x^2}{4} = 1$ **75.** $\frac{y^2}{25} - \frac{x^2}{100} = 1$ **76.** $\frac{x^2}{36} - \frac{y^2}{49} = 1$ **77.** $\frac{x^2}{81} - \frac{y^2}{64} = 1$

76. $(\sqrt{85}, 0), (-\sqrt{85}, 0)$

77. $(\sqrt{145}, 0), (-\sqrt{145}, 0)$

Measuring Radians

In the past, you have used degrees to measure angles. When angles are used in periodic functions, they are often measured in larger units called radians.

1. Measure the diameter of a cylinder and calculate its radius. On a piece of string, mark off a "number line" with each unit equal to the radius. Mark at least seven units. **1–5. Check students' work.**

2. Wrap the string around the cylinder. How many radius units are needed to go around the cylinder one time?

3. Use the end of the cylinder to draw a circle on a sheet of paper. Keep the cylinder in place and wrap the string around it on the paper. Mark an arc of the circle equal to one radius unit of length.

4. Remove the cylinder and string. Use paper folding to locate the center of the circle. (Fold the circle onto itself and crease the paper along a diameter. Repeat to get a second diameter.) Draw a central angle that intercepts one radius unit of arc.

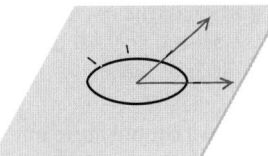

The measure of the angle you drew in Question 4 is 1 radian.

5. Use a protractor to measure the angle from Question 4 in degrees.

6. Critical Thinking The formula $C = 2\pi r$ relates the circumference of a circle C to its radius r. *Exactly* how many radians are in a 360° angle? Explain.

6. 2π; a circle has an angle measure of 360°. Dividing the circumference, $2\pi r$, by the length of a radius, r, we find there are 2π radians in 360°.

The diagram at the right shows that a rotation of 180° is equivalent to π radians.

7. Find the number of degrees in one radian by dividing 180 by π. How does your answer compare to the measurement you made in Question 5? **57.30°; the numbers are very close.**

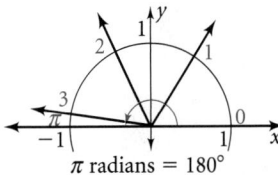

π radians $= 180°$

EXERCISES

Use the proportion $\dfrac{d°}{180°} = \dfrac{r \text{ radians}}{\pi \text{ radians}}$. Find the equivalent degree measure or radian measure.

1. 10° $\frac{\pi}{18}$ radians   **2.** 45° $\frac{\pi}{4}$ radians   **3.** 90° $\frac{\pi}{2}$ radians   **4.** 120° $\frac{2\pi}{3}$ radians   **5.** 270° $\frac{3\pi}{2}$ radians

6. 310° $\frac{31\pi}{18}$ radians   **7.** 50° $\frac{5\pi}{18}$ radians   **8.** 415° $\frac{83\pi}{36}$ radians   **9.** 170° $\frac{17\pi}{18}$ radians **10.** 380° $\frac{19\pi}{9}$ radians

11. $\frac{13\pi}{18}$ radians   **12.** $\frac{3\pi}{8}$ radians   **13.** $\frac{7\pi}{2}$ radians   **14.** $\frac{11\pi}{4}$ radians   **15.** $\frac{5\pi}{6}$ radians
   130°   **67.5°**   **630°**   **495°**   **150°**

Measuring Radians

Students investigate how many times a length of string equal to the radius of a circle will wrap around the circumference of that same circle. This experiential learning leads to a better understanding of the definition of a radian.

Guided Instruction

Math Tip
The number of radians in a central angle of a circle is the measure of the intercepted arc in radian units.

Teaching Tip
Emphasize to students that a radian is a unit used to measure an angle. They may want to think of a degree as measuring an angle by comparing it to the whole *inside* of a circle, while a radian measures an angle by comparing it to the whole *outside* of a circle.

Resources

Cylinder, ruler, string, protractor

Objectives

1 To use radian measure for angles
2 To find the length of an arc of a circle

Examples

1 Using a Proportion
2 Using Dimensional Analysis
3 Finding Cosine and Sine of Radian Measures
4 Finding the Length of an Arc
5 Real-World Connection

Professional Development

Math Background

The radian measure of an angle can also be expressed as a ratio: radian measure of an angle = $\frac{arc\ length}{radius}$. When the arc length is the radius, the value of this ratio is one. When the arc length is the whole circle, or $2\pi r$, then the value of this ratio is 2π.

More Math Background: p. 708C

Lesson Planning and Resources

See p. 708E for a list of the resources that support this lesson.

PowerPoint
Bell Ringer Practice

☑ **Check Skills You'll Need**
For intervention, direct students to:

Finding the Circumference of a Circle
Formulas: p. 898

Radian Measure

What You'll Learn

• To use radian measure for angles
• To find the length of an arc of a circle

...And Why

To solve problems involving the orbits of satellites, as in Example 5

Find the circumference of a circle with the given radius or diameter. Round your answer to the nearest tenth.

1. radius 4 in. **25.1 in.**   2. diameter 70 m **219.9 m**
3. radius 8 mi **50.3 mi**   4. diameter 3.4 ft **10.7 ft**
5. radius 5 mm **31.4 mm**   6. diameter 6.3 cm **19.8 cm**

🔊 **New Vocabulary** • central angle • intercepted arc • radian

---

1 Using Radian Measure

A **central angle** of a circle is an angle with a vertex at the center of a circle. An **intercepted arc** is the portion of the circle with endpoints on the sides of the central angle and remaining points within the interior of the angle.

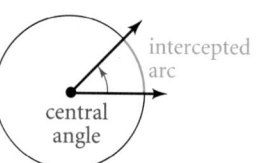
intercepted arc
central angle

Vocabulary Tip

Radian is a shortened form of the phrase *radial angle*.

When a central angle intercepts an arc that has the same length as a radius of the circle, the measure of the angle is defined to be one **radian**. Like degrees, radians measure the amount of rotation from the initial side to the terminal side of an angle.

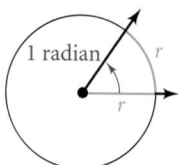
1 radian

Because the circumference of a circle is $2\pi r$, there are 2π radians in any circle. Since 2π radians $= 360°$, and therefore π radians $= 180°$, you can use a proportion such as $\frac{d°}{180°} = \frac{r\ radians}{\pi\ radians}$ to convert between degrees and radians.

Real-World 🌐 **Connection**

Some pendulum rides travel through a complete revolution of 2π radians.

1 EXAMPLE Using a Proportion

a. Find the radian measure of an angle of 60°.

$$\frac{60°}{180°} = \frac{r\ radians}{\pi\ radians}$$ Write a proportion.

$60 \cdot \pi = 180 \cdot r$ Write the cross-products.

$r = \frac{60 \cdot \pi}{180}$ Divide each side by 180.

$= \frac{\pi}{3} \approx 1.05$ Simplify.

An angle of 60° measures about 1.05 radians.

b. Find the degree measure of $\frac{5\pi}{2}$ radians.

Differentiated Instruction **Solutions for All Learners**

Special Needs L1
Have students convert 1 radian into degrees and ask: *Which is larger 1 radian or 1°?* **1 radian is much larger** Note that radians do not have exact degree equivalents. Stress that the degree symbol is not used for radian measures.

learning style: verbal

Below Level L2
Remind students that when an angle measure is reported in radians the unit is normally not written. Since the radian angle measure is a ratio between two lengths, it has no units.

learning style: verbal

$$\frac{\frac{5\pi}{2} \text{ radians}}{\pi \text{ radians}} = \frac{d^\circ}{180^\circ} \qquad \textbf{Write a proportion.}$$

$$\frac{\frac{5\pi}{2}}{\pi} = \frac{d}{180}$$

$$\frac{5\pi}{2} \cdot 180 = \pi \cdot d \qquad \textbf{Write the cross-products.}$$

$$\frac{5\pi \cdot 180}{2 \cdot \pi} = d \qquad \textbf{Divide each side by } \pi.$$

$$d = \frac{5\pi \cdot 180^{90}}{\,{}_1 2 \cdot \pi} \qquad \textbf{Simplify.}$$

$$= 450$$

• An angle of $\frac{5\pi}{2}$ radians measures 450°.

 Quick Check **1** Use a proportion for each conversion.
   a. 85° to radians **≈1.48 radians**   **b.** 2.5 radians to degrees **≈143.24°**

The proportion $\frac{d^\circ}{180^\circ} = \frac{r \text{ radians}}{\pi \text{ radians}}$ leads to the following two convenient conversion factors.

 Key Concepts

Summary	Converting Between Radians and Degrees

To convert degrees to radians, multiply by $\frac{\pi \text{ radians}}{180^\circ}$.

To convert radians to degrees, multiply by $\frac{180^\circ}{\pi \text{ radians}}$.

You can use the conversion factors and dimensional analysis to convert between angle measurement systems.

2 **EXAMPLE** **Using Dimensional Analysis**

a. Find the degree measure of an angle of $-\frac{3\pi}{4}$ radians.

$$-\frac{3\pi}{4} \text{ radians} = -\frac{3\pi}{4} \text{ radians} \cdot \frac{180^\circ}{\pi \text{ radians}} \qquad \textbf{Multiply by } \frac{180^\circ}{\pi \text{ radians}}.$$

$$= -\frac{3\pi}{{}_1 4} \text{ radians} \cdot \frac{{}^{45}180^\circ}{\pi \text{ radians}} \qquad \textbf{Simplify.}$$

$$= -135^\circ$$

An angle of $-\frac{3\pi}{4}$ radians measures $-135°$.

b. Find the radian measure of an angle of 27°.

$$27^\circ = 27^\circ \cdot \frac{\pi}{180^\circ} \text{ radians} \qquad \textbf{Multiply by } \frac{\pi \text{ radians}}{180^\circ}.$$

$$= {}^3 27^\circ \cdot \frac{\pi}{{}_{20}180^\circ} \text{ radians} \qquad \textbf{Simplify.}$$

$$= \frac{3\pi}{20} \text{ radians}$$

• An angle of 27° measures $\frac{3\pi}{20}$ radians.

 Quick Check **2** Use dimensional analysis to convert each degree measure from degrees to radians or from radians to degrees. (Express radian measures in terms of π.)
   a. $\frac{\pi}{2}$ radians **90°**   **b.** 225° $\frac{5\pi}{4}$ **radians**   **c.** 2 radians **≈114.59°**   **d.** 150° $\frac{5\pi}{6}$ **radians**

GO Online

Video Tutor Help
Visit: PHSchool.com
Web Code: age-0775

Lesson 13-3 Radian Measure **727**

2. Teach

Guided Instruction

1 EXAMPLE **Error Prevention**

Suggest that students can find their own errors if they use the basic relationship 360° = 2π radians, or about 6.28 radians, to help them form a rough estimate of the size of the answer before they calculate.

2 EXAMPLE **Auditory Learners**

Ask student volunteers to explain how they decide which form of the unit fraction to use, $\frac{180^\circ}{\pi \text{ radians}}$ or $\frac{\pi \text{ radians}}{180^\circ}$.

3 EXAMPLE **Teaching Tip**

Emphasize that radian measures are often written with fractions. This notation has the advantage of giving exact values instead of decimal approximations. However, when measuring lengths or distances in an actual situation, the decimal value may be required.

PowerPoint
Additional Examples

1 **a.** Find the radian measure of an angle of 45°.
about 0.79 radians
b. Find the degree measure of $\frac{13\pi}{6}$ radians. **390°**

2 **a.** Find the degree measure of an angle of $-\frac{3\pi}{2}$ radians. **−270°**
b. Find the radian measure of an angle of 54°. $\frac{3\pi}{10}$ **radians**

Additional Examples

3 Find the exact values of $\cos\left(\frac{\pi}{3}\text{ radians}\right)$ and $\sin\left(\frac{\pi}{3}\text{ radians}\right)$.

$\frac{1}{2}, \frac{\sqrt{3}}{2}$

Guided Instruction

4 EXAMPLE Teaching Tip

Verify that students understand the meaning of *intercepted arc* by asking them to use a colored pencil to mark this arc on a sketch of the circle.

Additional Examples

4 Use this circle to find length *s* to the nearest tenth.

s 22.0 in.
$\frac{7\pi}{6}$
6 in.

5 A satellite completes one orbit around Earth every 4 h. The satellite orbits 6400 km above Earth's surface. How far does the satellite travel in 1 h?
about 20,100 km

Resources

• Daily Notetaking Guide
13-3 **L3**

Closure

Ask students: *What is a radian and how is it used?* A radian is the measure of a central angle that intercepts an arc equal in length to the radius of a circle. Radians are used to measure angles.

3a. 0.71, 0.71; these values are the rounded decimal equivalent of $\frac{\sqrt{2}}{2}$.

b. π radians = 180°, so $\frac{\pi}{4}$ radians becomes $\frac{180°}{4}$, which is 45°.

 Quick Check

You can find the sine and cosine of angles in radian measure by first converting the radian measure to degrees and then using the unit circle.

3 EXAMPLE Finding Cosine and Sine of Radian Measures

Find the exact values of $\cos\left(\frac{\pi}{4}\text{ radians}\right)$ and $\sin\left(\frac{\pi}{4}\text{ radians}\right)$.

$\frac{\pi}{4}$ radians $\cdot \frac{180°}{\pi\text{ radians}} = 45°$ **Convert radians to degrees.**

Draw the angle. Complete a 45°-45°-90° triangle. Since the hypotenuse has length 1, both legs have length $\frac{\sqrt{2}}{2}$.

Thus, $\cos\left(\frac{\pi}{4}\text{ radians}\right) = \frac{\sqrt{2}}{2}$

and $\sin\left(\frac{\pi}{4}\text{ radians}\right) = \frac{\sqrt{2}}{2}$.

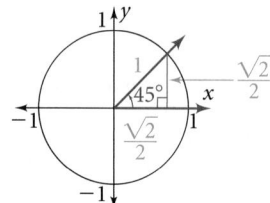

Quick Check **3** **a.** Use a calculator to find $\cos\left(\frac{\pi}{4}\text{ radians}\right)$ and $\sin\left(\frac{\pi}{4}\text{ radians}\right)$. How do these values compare to the coordinates found in Example 3? **a–b. See left.**
b. Explain how to use mental math to convert $\frac{\pi}{4}$ radians to degrees. (*Hint:* Begin with the relationship π radians = 180°.)

2 Finding the Length of an Arc

You can find the length of an intercepted arc by using the proportion

$$\frac{\text{arc length } s}{\text{circumference } 2\pi r} = \frac{\text{central angle measure } \theta \text{ radians}}{2\pi \text{ radians}}.$$

Simplifying this proportion results in the formula below.

Key Concepts

Property	Length of an Intercepted Arc

For a circle of radius *r* and a central angle of measure θ (in radians), the length *s* of the intercepted arc is $s = r\theta$.

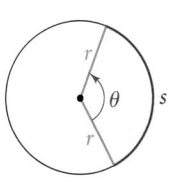

4 EXAMPLE Finding the Length of an Arc

Use the circle at the right. Find length *s* to the nearest tenth.

$s = r\theta$ **Use the formula.**

$= 3 \cdot \frac{5\pi}{6}$ **Substitute 3 for *r* and $\frac{5\pi}{6}$ for θ.**

$= \frac{5\pi}{2}$ **Simplify.**

≈ 7.9 **Use a calculator.**

The arc has a length of about 7.9 in.

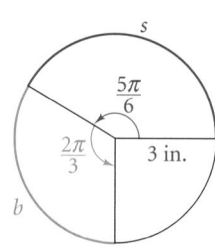

Quick Check **4** Find length *b* in Example 4. Round your answer to the nearest tenth. **6.3 in.**

5 EXAMPLE Real-World 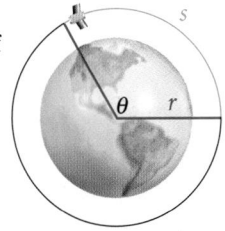 Connection

Weather Satellite A weather satellite in a circular orbit around Earth completes one orbit every 2 h. The radius of Earth is about 6400 km, and the satellite orbits 2600 km above Earth's surface. How far does the satellite travel in 1 h?

Since one complete revolution (orbit) takes 2 h, the satellite completes $\frac{1}{2}$ of a revolution in 1 h.

Step 1 Find the radius of the satellite's orbit.

$r = 6400 + 2600$ Add the radius of Earth and the distance from Earth's surface to the satellite.

$= 9000$ Simplify.

Step 2 Find the measure of the central angle the satellite travels through in 1 h.

$\theta = \frac{1}{2} \cdot 2\pi$ Multiply the fraction of the revolution by the number of radians in one complete revolution.

$= \pi$ Simplify.

Step 3 Find s for $\theta = \pi$.

$s = r\theta$ Use the formula.

$= 9000\pi$ Substitute 9000 for r and π for θ.

$\approx 28{,}274$ Simplify.

● The satellite travels about 28,000 km in 1 h.

 Quick Check **5** Find the length of the arc intercepted by each angle.

a. $\angle AOB$ 5a. ≈ 3.14 units
b. $\angle COD$ b. ≈ 4.19 units
c. $\angle AOC$ c. ≈ 6.28 units
d. $\angle AOD$ d. ≈ 10.47 units

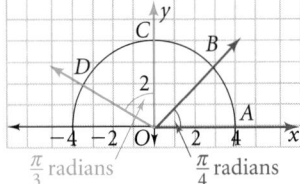

$\frac{\pi}{3}$ radians $\frac{\pi}{4}$ radians

EXERCISES

For more exercises, see *Extra Skill and Word Problem Practice.*

Practice and Problem Solving

 A **Practice by Example**

Examples 1 and 2
(pages 726 and 727)

 GO for Help

Write each measure in radians. Express the answer in terms of π and as a decimal rounded to the nearest hundredth.

1. $-300°$ $-\frac{5\pi}{3}$, -5.24 2. $150°$ $\frac{5\pi}{6}$, 2.62 3. $-90°$ $-\frac{\pi}{2}$, -1.57

4. $-60°$ $-\frac{\pi}{3}$, -1.05 5. $160°$ $\frac{8\pi}{9}$, 2.79 6. $20°$ $\frac{\pi}{9}$, 0.35

Write each measure in degrees. Round your answer to the nearest degree, if necessary.

7. 3π radians $540°$ 8. $\frac{11\pi}{10}$ radians $198°$ 9. $-\frac{2\pi}{3}$ radians $-120°$

10. -3 radians $-172°$ 11. 1.57 radians $90°$ 12. 4.71 radians $270°$

3. Practice

Assignment Guide

▼1 A B   1-19, 31-44, 46, 49

▼2 A B   20-30, 45, 47, 48, 50, 51

C   Challenge   52-57

Test Prep   58-62
Mixed Review   63-74

Homework Quick Check

To check students' understanding of key skills and concepts, go over Exercises 1-6, 28, 30, 49, 50.

Differentiated Instruction Resources

GPS Guided Problem Solving	L3
Enrichment	L4
Reteaching	L2
Practice	L3

37.

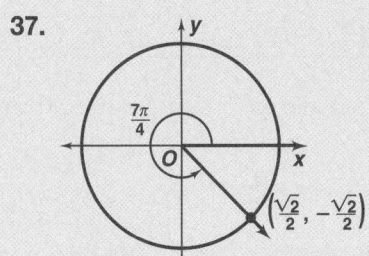

$$\frac{7\pi}{4}$$

$$\left(\frac{\sqrt{2}}{2}, -\frac{\sqrt{2}}{2}\right)$$

0.71, −0.71

38.

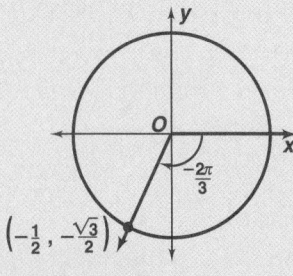

$$-\frac{2\pi}{3}$$

$$\left(-\frac{1}{2}, -\frac{\sqrt{3}}{2}\right)$$

−0.50, −0.87

39.

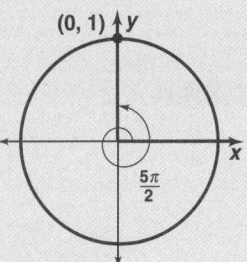

(0, 1)

$$\frac{5\pi}{2}$$

0.00, 1.00

13. Copy and complete the diagram at the right. Fill in the missing measures in radians or degrees.

See back of book.

Example 3
(page 728)

The measure θ of an angle in standard position is given. Find the exact values of $\cos \theta$ and $\sin \theta$ for each angle measure.

14. $\frac{\pi}{6}$ radians

$$14. \ \frac{\sqrt{3}}{2}, \frac{1}{2}$$

15. $\frac{\pi}{3}$ radians

$$15. \ \frac{1}{2}, \frac{\sqrt{3}}{2}$$

16. $\frac{\pi}{2}$ radians **0, 1**

17. $\frac{2\pi}{3}$ radians

$$17. \ -\frac{1}{2}, \frac{\sqrt{3}}{2}$$

18. $\frac{5\pi}{6}$ radians

$$18. \ -\frac{\sqrt{3}}{2}, \frac{1}{2}$$

19. $-\frac{\pi}{2}$ radians **0, −1**

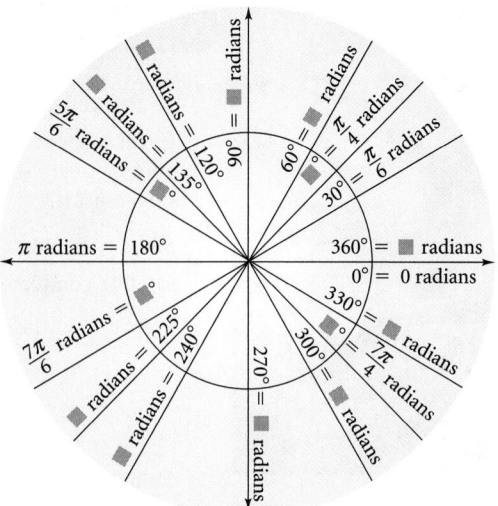

Example 4
(page 728)

Use each circle to find the length of the indicated arc. Round your answer to the nearest tenth.

20.

3.1 cm

$\frac{\pi}{3}$ t

3 cm

21.

c 10.5 m

$\frac{2\pi}{3}$

5 m

22.

51.8 ft

m

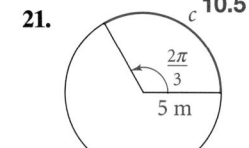

9 ft

$\frac{11\pi}{6}$

23.

a

$\frac{4\pi}{3}$

6 in.

25.1 in.

24.

2 m

$\frac{3\pi}{4}$

w

4.7 m

25.

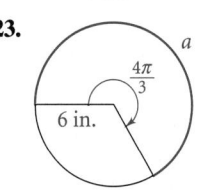

$\frac{5\pi}{4}$ 11 cm

z

43.2 cm

Example 5
(page 729)

Find the length of each arc.

26.

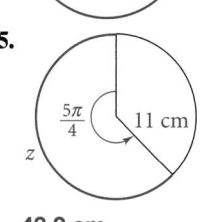

255°

24 in.

≈**107 in.**

27.

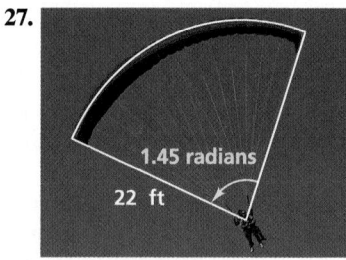

1.45 radians

22 ft

≈**32 ft**

🌐 **28. Space** A geostationary satellite is positioned 35,800 km above Earth's surface. It takes 24 h to complete one orbit. The radius of Earth is about 6400 km.

  a. What distance does the satellite travel in 1 h? ≈**11,048 km**

  b. What distance does the satellite travel in 3 h? ≈**33,144 km**

  c. What distance does the satellite travel in 2.5 h? ≈**27,620 km**

  d. What distance does the satellite travel in 25 h? ≈**276,198 km**

  e. Critical Thinking After how many hours has the satellite traveled 200,000 km?

18.1 h

Apply Your Skills **29. Automobile Design** Suppose a windshield wiper arm has a length of 22 in. and rotates through an angle of 110°. What distance does the tip of the wiper travel as it moves once across the windshield? **≈42.2 in.**

 30. Geography The 24 lines of longitude that approximate the 24 standard time zones are equally spaced around the equator.

30a. 15°, $\frac{\pi}{12}$ radians

a. Suppose you use 24 central angles to divide a circle into 24 equal arcs. Express the measure of each angle in degrees and in radians.
b. The radius of the equator is about 3960 mi. About how wide is each time zone at the equator? **≈1036.7 mi**
c. The radius of the Arctic Circle is about 1580 mi. About how wide is each time zone at the Arctic Circle? **≈413.6 mi**

In which quadrant, or on which axis, does the terminal side of each angle lie?

31. $\frac{4\pi}{3}$ radians **III**
32. $-\frac{5\pi}{4}$ radians **II**
33. $\frac{9\pi}{2}$ radians **positive y-axis**

34. $\frac{5\pi}{6}$ radians **II**
35. $-\pi$ radians **negative x-axis**
36. $\frac{6\pi}{5}$ radians **III**

Draw an angle in standard position with each given measure. Then find the values of the cosine and sine of the angle to the nearest hundredth. **37–42. See margin pp. 730–731.**

37. $\frac{7\pi}{4}$ radians
38. $-\frac{2\pi}{3}$ radians
39. $\frac{5\pi}{2}$ radians

40. -2π radians
41. $\frac{7\pi}{6}$ radians
42. $-\frac{\pi}{5}$ radians

43. a. Geometry Draw a unit circle on the coordinate plane. Then draw five angles in standard position measuring $\frac{\pi}{5}$, $\frac{4\pi}{5}$, $\frac{6\pi}{5}$, $\frac{9\pi}{5}$, and $\frac{3\pi}{10}$ radians.
b. For each angle, complete a right triangle. Place the hypotenuse along the terminal side (from the origin to the unit circle). Place one leg along the x-axis. The other leg will be parallel to the y-axis.
c. Critical Thinking Are the five triangles congruent? Justify your answer by using the values of sin θ and cos θ for each angle. **a–c. See margin.**

44. Open-Ended Draw an angle in standard position. Draw a circle with its center at the vertex of the angle. Find the measure of the angle in radians and degrees. **Check students' work.**

 45. Transportation Suppose the radius of a bicycle wheel is 13 in. (measured to the outside of the tire). Find the number of radians through which a point on the tire turns when the bicycle has moved forward a distance of 12 ft. **≈11 radians**

46. Error Analysis A student wanted to rewrite $\frac{9\pi}{4}$ radians in degrees. The screen shows her calculation. What error did the student make? **The student forgot to include parentheses around 2*π.**

```
9*π/4*360/2*π
        3997.189782
```

Find the length of each arc. Also, assuming each angle to be in standard position, find the measures of two angles coterminal with the given angle.

47. ≈798 ft; 55°, −665°

48. ≈23.6 in.; Sample: $-\frac{7\pi}{6}, \frac{17\pi}{6}$

Homework Video Tutor
Visit: PHSchool.com
Web Code: age-1303

47.

150 ft
−305°

48.
$\frac{5\pi}{6}$ radians
9 in.

Lesson 13-3 Radian Measure **731**

Connection to Geography

Exercise 30 Remind students that lines of longitude are perpendicular to the equator and lines of latitude are parallel to the equator.

40.

(1, 0)
−2π
1.00, 0.00

41.
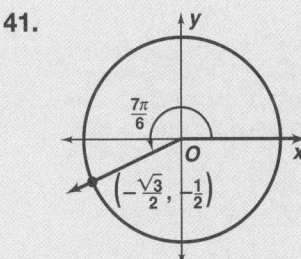
$\frac{7\pi}{6}$
$\left(-\frac{\sqrt{3}}{2}, -\frac{1}{2}\right)$
−0.87, −0.50

42.

(0, 1)
$-\frac{\pi}{5}$
(0.81, −0.59)
0.81, −0.59

43a-b.
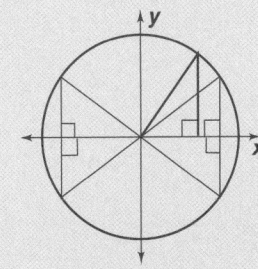

c. All five triangles are congruent by SSS. All have a hypotenuse of 1 unit, a long leg of 0.81 unit, and a short leg of 0.59 unit.

$\cos\frac{\pi}{5} \approx 0.81$, $\sin\frac{\pi}{5} \approx 0.59$;

$\sin\frac{3\pi}{10} \approx 0.81$, $\cos\frac{3\pi}{10} \approx 0.59$;

$\cos\frac{4\pi}{5} \approx -0.81$, $\sin\frac{4\pi}{5} \approx 0.59$;

$\cos\frac{6\pi}{5} \approx -0.81$, $\sin\frac{6\pi}{5} \approx -0.59$;

$\cos\frac{9\pi}{5} \approx 0.81$, $\sin\frac{9\pi}{5} \approx -0.59$

731

Lesson Quiz

1. Rewrite each angle measure using the other unit, either degrees or radians.
   a. 225° $\frac{5\pi}{4}$ radians
   b. $\frac{\pi}{2}$ radians 90°

2. A wrench turns through an angle of 1.5 radians. If the wrench is 14 in. long, what is the distance that the end of the wrench moves?
   21 in.

3. A jogger runs 100 m around a circular track with a radius of 40 m. Through what angle does the jogger move? Express your answer in both radians and degrees. 2.5 radians; about 143.2°

Alternative Assessment

Have students use their completed drawings for Exercises 37–42, and measure each angle, in degrees, with a protractor. Then have them calculate the measure of each angle in degrees by multiplying the radian measure by $\frac{180}{\pi}$. Finally ask them to compare the measured and calculated results to see how close their measurements came to the calculated values.

Test Prep

Resources

For additional practice with a variety of test item formats:
- Standardized Test Prep, p. 775
- Test-Taking Strategies, p. 770
- Test-Taking Strategies with Transparencies

49. If two angles measured in radians are coterminal, the difference of their measures will be evenly divisible by 2π.

56.
$$\frac{\theta}{2\pi} = \frac{s}{2\pi r}$$
$$\frac{\theta}{2\pi} \cdot 2\pi r = \frac{s}{2\pi r} \cdot 2\pi r$$
$$\theta r = s$$
$$s = r\theta$$

57a. 0.5017962; 0.4999646; the first four terms

49. **Writing** Two angles are measured in radians. Explain how to tell whether the angles are coterminal without rewriting their measures in degrees.

50. **Music** A CD with diameter 12 cm spins in a CD player. Calculate how much farther a point on the outside edge of the CD travels in one revolution than a point 1 cm closer to the center of the CD. ≈6.3 cm

51. **Geography** Assume that Earth is a sphere with radius 3960 miles. A town is at latitude 32° N. Find the distance in miles from the town to the North Pole. (*Hint:* Latitude is measured north and south from the equator.) ≈4008.7 mi

C Challenge

The given angle θ is in standard position. Find the radian measure of the angle that results after the given number of revolutions from the terminal side of θ.

52. $\theta = \frac{\pi}{2}$; 1 clockwise revolution $-\frac{3\pi}{2}$ radians

53. $\theta = \frac{\pi}{3}$; 2 clockwise revolutions $-\frac{11\pi}{3}$ radians

54. $\theta = -\frac{2\pi}{3}$; 1 counterclockwise revolution $\frac{4\pi}{3}$ radians

55. $\theta = \frac{5\pi}{6}$; $2\frac{1}{2}$ counterclockwise revolutions $\frac{35\pi}{6}$ radians

56. **Reasoning** Use the proportion $\frac{\text{measure of central angle}}{\text{measure of one complete rotation}} = \frac{\text{length of arc}}{\text{circumference}}$ to derive the formula $s = r\theta$. Use θ for the central angle measure and s for the arc length. Measure the rotation in radians.

57. a. Use the cartoon below. Use a calculator to evaluate the first three terms of Jason's expression to seven decimal places. Then evaluate the first four terms. Which is a better estimate of cos 60°?

FOX TROT by Bill Amend

b. Jason's expression will approximate the cosine of any angle if you know its radian measure. Write a general form of his expression by substituting x for $\frac{\pi}{3}$. 57b. $1 - \frac{x^2}{2!} + \frac{x^4}{4!} - \frac{x^6}{6!} + \frac{x^8}{8!} - \ldots$

c. Use the general formula you wrote in part (b) to estimate $\cos\left(\frac{\pi}{10} \text{ radians}\right)$ to the nearest thousandth. What is the angle measure, in degrees? ≈0.951; 18°

Test Prep

Multiple Choice

58. Which pairs of measurements represent the same angle measures? **C**

I. 240°, $\frac{7\pi}{6}$ radians   II. 135°, $\frac{3\pi}{4}$ radians   III. 150°, $\frac{5\pi}{6}$ radians

A. I and II only   B. I and III only   C. II and III only   D. I, II, and III

59. What is the exact value of $\cos\left(\frac{5\pi}{4} \text{ radians}\right)$? **G**

    F. $-\frac{\sqrt{3}}{2}$ **G.** $-\frac{\sqrt{2}}{2}$ **H.** $-\frac{1}{2}$ **J.** $\frac{\sqrt{2}}{2}$

60. In a circle, an arc of length 8π cm is intercepted by a central angle of $\frac{2\pi}{3}$ radians. What is the radius of the circle? **D**

    A. $\frac{3\pi}{16}$ cm   **B.** $\frac{16\pi}{3}$ cm   **C.** $\frac{16\pi^2}{3}$ cm   **D.** 12 cm

61. Two arcs have the same length. One arc is intercepted by an angle of $\frac{3\pi}{2}$ radians in a circle of radius 15 cm. If the radius of the other circle is 25 cm, what central angle intercepts the arc? **G**

    F. $\frac{3\pi}{2}$ radians   **G.** $\frac{9\pi}{10}$ radians   **H.** $\frac{3\pi}{2}$ radians   **J.** $\frac{5\pi}{3}$ radians

Short Response

62. Describe the relationship between a central angle of one radian and the radius of the circle. **See margin.**

Mixed Review

Lesson 13-2

Sketch each angle in standard position. **63–67. See margin.**

63. 15°   **64.** −75°   **65.** 150°   **66.** −270°   **67.** −85°

Lesson 12-4

Find the mean and the standard deviation for each set of values.

68. 6 1 9 12 4 15 21 7 8 8 **9.1, 5.41**

69. 12 13 15 9 16 5 18 16 12 11 15 **12.9, 3.53**

70. 21 29 35 26 25 28 27 51 24 34 **30, 8.09**

Lesson 10-3

Write an equation of a circle with the given center and radius.

71. $x^2 + y^2 = 64$

72. $x^2 + (y + 5)^2 = 16$

71. center $(0, 0)$, radius 8   **72.** center $(0, -5)$, radius 4

73. center $(3, 7)$, radius 6.5   **74.** center $(-8, 4)$, radius 3
    $(x - 3)^2 + (y - 7)^2 = 42.25$ $(x + 8)^2 + (y - 4)^2 = 9$

✓ Checkpoint Quiz 1   Lessons 13-1 through 13-3

Find the period and the amplitude of each periodic function.

1.

    5, 1

2.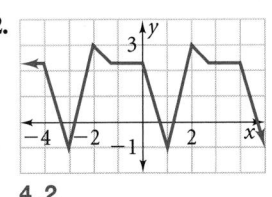

    4, 2

Find the exact values of $\sin\theta$ and $\cos\theta$ for an angle in standard position with each measure θ.

3. −45° $-\frac{\sqrt{2}}{2}, \frac{\sqrt{2}}{2}$ **4.** 210° $-\frac{1}{2}, -\frac{\sqrt{3}}{2}$ **5.** π radians **0, −1**   **6.** $\frac{\pi}{6}$ radians
                                                                        $\frac{1}{2}, \frac{\sqrt{3}}{2}$

Convert each angle measure into its equivalent in radians or degrees.

7. −180°   **8.** 36° $\frac{\pi}{5}$ radians   **9.** π radians **180°**   **10.** $\frac{4\pi}{3}$ radians
    −π radians   **240°**

✓ Checkpoint Quiz

Use this Checkpoint Quiz to check students' understanding of the skills and concepts of Lessons 13-1 through 13-3.

Resources
Grab & Go
• Checkpoint Quiz 1

62. [2] For a central angle of 1 radian, the length of the intercepted arc is the length of the radius.

    [1] incomplete explanation

63.

64.

65.

66.

67.

734

13-4

The Sine Function

What You'll Learn
- To identify properties of the sine function
- To graph sine curves

. . . And Why
To model light waves, as in Example 7

☑ **Check Skills You'll Need**

GO for Help Lesson 13-1

Use the graph. Find the value(s) of each of the following.

1. the period   2
2. the domain   all real numbers
3. the amplitude   1
4. the range   all real numbers between −1 and 1, inclusive

🔊 **New Vocabulary** • sine function • sine curve

---

1 Interpreting Sine Functions

Vocabulary Tip

Sine comes from the Latin word *sinus*, meaning "bay," a reference to the shape of the sine curve.

The **sine function,** $y = \sin \theta$, matches the measure θ of an angle in standard position with the y-coordinate of a point on the unit circle. This point is where the terminal side of the angle intersects the unit circle.

$y = \sin \theta$

1 EXAMPLE Interpreting the Sine Function in Degrees

Use the graph of the sine function.

a. What is the value of $y = \sin \theta$ for $\theta = 270°$?

The value of the function at $\theta = 270°$ is −1.

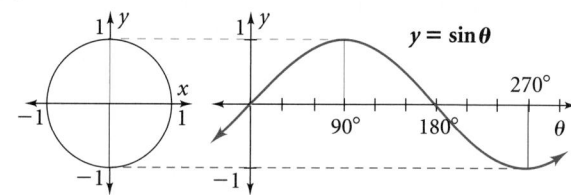

$y = \sin \theta$

1a. yes; at 450°

b. Yes; the y-values repeat at regular intervals.

b. For what value of θ between 0° and 360° does the graph of $y = \sin \theta$ reach the maximum value of 1?

When $y = 1, \theta = 90°$.

☑ **Quick Check** **1** **a.** Extend the graph from Example 1 to include angle measures from 270° to 720°. Will the graph reach the maximum value of 1 again, and if so, where?
b. **Reasoning** Is the sine function a periodic function? Explain.

734 Chapter 13 Periodic Functions and Trigonometry

Real-World 🌐 **Connection**

If you mark a point on one of the blades of an eggbeater and plot the point's horizontal distance over time from the center of the eggbeater, the graph is a sine curve.

As you have seen, an angle measure θ can be expressed in degrees or in radians. In this book, when no unit is mentioned you should use radians.

You can graph the sine function in radians. In the unit circle, you can show radian measures along the circle as lengths of arcs. In the graphs below, the points for 1, 2, and 3 radians are marked on the unit circle and on the θ-axis.

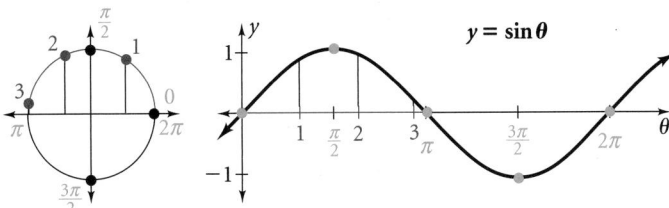

---

2 EXAMPLE **Estimating Sine Values in Radians**

Estimate each value from the graph. Check your estimate with a calculator.

a. sin 2

The sine function reaches its maximum value of 1 at $\frac{\pi}{2} \approx 1.57$. The value of the function at 2 is slightly less than 1, or about 0.9.

$\sin 2 \approx 0.9092974268$ **Use a calculator in radian mode.**

b. sin π

The sine function crosses the x-axis at π, so $\sin \pi = 0$.

$\sin \pi = 0$ **Use a calculator in radian mode.**

✓ **Quick Check** ❷ Use the graphs of sin θ from Examples 1 and 2.
   a. Find the amplitude of the sine function. **1**   **b. 360°, 2π radians**
   b. Express the period of the sine function in degrees and in radians.
   c. What are the domain and range of the sine function?
      domain: all real numbers, range: all real numbers between −1 and 1, inclusive

The graph of a sine function is called a **sine curve**. By varying the period, you get different sine curves.

Online active math

For: Sine Function Activity
Use: Interactive Textbook, 13-4

---

3 EXAMPLE **Finding the Period of a Sine Curve**

Use the graph of $y = \sin 4\theta$ at the right.

a. How many cycles occur in the graph at the right? How is the number of cycles related to the coefficient of θ in the equation?

Xmin=0
Xmax=2π
Xscl=π/2
Ymin=−2
Ymax=2
Yscl=1

The graph shows 4 cycles. The number of cycles is equal to the coefficient of θ.

Vocabulary Tip

The period of a function is the horizontal length of one cycle.

b. Find the period of $y = \sin 4\theta$.

$2\pi \div 4 = \frac{\pi}{2}$ **Divide the interval of the graph by the number of cycles.**

The period of $y = \sin 4\theta$ is $\frac{\pi}{2}$.

Lesson 13-4 The Sine Function   **735**

735

---

2. Teach

Guided Instruction

1 EXAMPLE **Tactile Learners**

To help students see how the points on the sine function represent an unrolling of the circle, have them place one finger on the circle and another on the graph. Then move their fingers simultaneously to see how the points on the circle and graph correspond.

PowerPoint
📖 **Additional Examples**

❶ Use the graph of the sine function shown in Example 1.
   a. What is the value of $y = \sin \theta$ for $\theta = 180°$? **0**
   b. For what other values of θ, on the interval shown, does the graph of sin θ have the same value as for $\theta = 180°$? **0°, 360°**

❷ Estimate each value from the graph shown in Example 2. Check your estimate with a calculator.
   a. sin 3 **about 0.1**
   b. sin $\frac{\pi}{2}$ **1**

❸ Use this graph of $y = \sin 6\theta$, for $0 \le \theta \le 2\pi$.

   a. How many cycles occur in this graph? How is the number of cycles related to the coefficient of θ in the equation? **6; They are equal.**
   b. Find the period of $y = \sin 6\theta$. $\frac{\pi}{3}$

4 EXAMPLE Math Tip

Point out to students that
$y = a \sin x$ is a vertical stretch or
shrink of $y = \sin x$ by a factor of a,
where a is the amplitude. Ask:
- *For which values of a is*
  $y = a \sin x$ a stretch? $a > 1$
- *For which values of a is*
  $y = a \sin x$ a shrink? $0 < a < 1$
- *What happens to $y = a \sin x$*
  when $a < 0$? The graph is a
  reflection of $y = |a| \sin x$
  across the x-axis.

Additional Examples

④ Here is the graph of
$y = a \sin \theta$ for values of $a = \frac{3}{4}$
and $a = 3$.

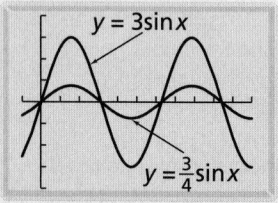

a. Find the amplitude of each
sine curve. How does the value of
a affect the amplitude? $\frac{3}{4}$, 3; The
amplitude is $|a|$.
b. How would a negative value of
a affect each graph? **A negative**
value of a reflects the graph in
the x-axis.

Guided Instruction

5 EXAMPLE Teaching Tip

Remind students to connect the
five points in the pattern with
curves rather than straight lines.

6 EXAMPLE Error Prevention

Students may think that a cycle is
just the part of the curve between
two zero y-values. In this case, the
part of the curve between two
zeros is only half of the cycle.

 Quick Check ③ Find the period of each sine curve below. For each graph, the θ-axis shows values
from 0 to 2π.

a.

2π

b.

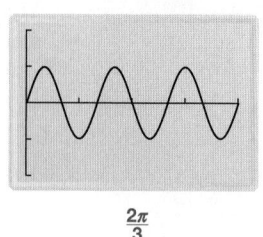

$\frac{2\pi}{3}$

You can also vary the amplitude of a sine curve.

4 EXAMPLE Finding the Amplitude of a Sine Curve

The graphing calculator
screens at the right show
several graphs of
$y = a \sin \theta$. Each θ-axis
shows values from 0 to 2π.

Vocabulary Tip

The <u>amplitude</u> of a
function is half the
difference between
its maximum and
minimum values.

a. Find the amplitude of
each sine curve. How
does the value of a affect the amplitude?

The amplitude of $y = \sin \theta$ is 1, and the amplitude of $y = 2 \sin \theta$ is 2.
The amplitude of $y = -\sin \theta$ is 1, and the amplitude of $y = -2 \sin \theta$ is 2.
In each case, the amplitude of the curve is $|a|$.

b. How does a negative value of a affect the position of the curve?
When a is negative, the graph is a reflection in the x-axis.

 Quick Check ④ Find the amplitude of each sine curve. Each interval on the y-axis
represents one unit.

a.
4

b.
3

The summary box below lists the properties of sine functions.

Key Concepts

Summary	Properties of Sine Functions

Suppose $y = a \sin b\theta$, with $a \neq 0$, $b > 0$, and θ in radians.

- $|a|$ is the amplitude of the function.

- b is the number of cycles in the interval from 0 to 2π.

- $\frac{2\pi}{b}$ is the period of the function.

You can use five points equally spaced through one cycle to sketch a sine curve. For $a > 0$, this five-point pattern is *zero–max–zero–min–zero*.

5 **EXAMPLE** **Sketching a Graph**

a. Sketch one cycle of a sine curve with amplitude 2 and period 4π.

Step 1 Choose scales for the y-axis and the θ-axis that are about equal ($\pi \approx 3$ units). On the θ-axis, mark one period (4π).

zero max zero min zero

$\frac{1}{4}(4\pi) = \pi$ $\frac{1}{2}(4\pi) = 2\pi$ $\frac{3}{4}(4\pi) = 3\pi$

Step 2 Mark equal spaces through one cycle by dividing the period into fourths.

Step 3 Since the amplitude is 2, the maximum is 2 and the minimum is -2. Plot the five points and sketch the curve.

b. Use the form $y = a \sin b\theta$. Write an equation with $a > 0$ for the sine curve in part (a).

The amplitude is 2, and $a > 0$, so $a = 2$.

The period is 4π, and $4\pi = \frac{2\pi}{b}$, so $b = \frac{1}{2}$.

An equation for the function is $y = 2 \sin \frac{1}{2}\theta$.

Quick Check **5** **a.** Sketch one cycle of a sine curve with amplitude 3, period 4, and $a > 0$.
b. **Critical Thinking** Predict the five-point pattern for graphing a sine curve when $a < 0$. **zero-min-zero-max-zero**
c. Sketch one cycle of a sine curve with amplitude 2, period $\frac{2\pi}{3}$, and $a < 0$. **a, c. See left.**

You can also graph sine functions from a given function rule.

6 **EXAMPLE** **Graphing From a Function Rule**

Sketch one cycle of $y = \frac{1}{2} \sin 2\theta$.

$|a| = \frac{1}{2}$, so the amplitude is $\frac{1}{2}$.

$b = 2$, so there are 2 cycles from 0 to 2π.

$\frac{2\pi}{b} = \frac{2\pi}{2} = \pi$, so the period is π.

Divide the period into fourths.

Using the values of the amplitude and period, plot the *zero–max–zero–min–zero* pattern.

zero max zero min zero

Sketch the curve.

Quick Check **6** Sketch one cycle of the graph of each sine function. **a–b. See left.**
a. $y = 1.5 \sin 2\theta$ **b.** $y = 3 \sin \frac{\pi}{2}\theta$

5a.

c.

6a.

b.

5 **a.** Sketch one cycle of a sine curve with amplitude 3 and period 4.

b. Use the form $y = a \sin b\theta$. Write an equation with $a > 0$ for the sine curve in part a.
$y = 3 \sin \frac{\pi}{2} x$

6 Sketch one cycle of $y = \frac{5}{3} \sin 3\theta$.

7 Find the period of the following sine curve. Then write an equation for the curve.

$3; y = 5 \sin \left(\frac{2\pi\theta}{3}\right)$

Resources
• Daily Notetaking Guide 13-4   **L3**

Closure

Ask students: *What have you learned about the graph of the sine function? What does the shape of the sine graph depend on?* The graph of a sine function is a periodic curve. For the function $y = a \sin b\theta$, the amplitude of the graph is $|a|$, and the number of cycles between 0 and 2π is b. The period of the function is $\frac{2\pi}{b}$, $b > 0$.

Assignment Guide

▼1 A B 1-15, 34-39, 42-44, 51, 52

▼2 A B 16-33, 40, 41, 45-50
  C Challenge   53-59

  Test Prep   60-65
  Mixed Review   66-74

Homework Quick Check

To check students' understanding of key skills and concepts, go over Exercises 12, 26, 40, 43, 44, 49.

Differentiated Instruction Resources

GPS Guided Problem Solving	L3
Enrichment	L4
Reteaching	L2
Practice	L3

16.

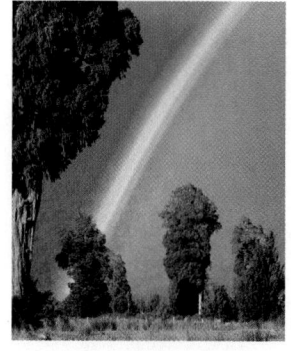

Real-World Connection

Light can be modeled as waves. Changes in wavelength (period) change the color that the eye perceives. Changes in amplitude affect the intensity of the color.

You can use sine functions to model real-world situations.

7 EXAMPLE **Real-World Connection**

Multiple Choice The graph at the right models waves of red, blue, and yellow light. Which equation best models blue light?

Ⓐ $y = \sin 240\pi\theta$ Ⓑ $y = \sin 480\pi\theta$ Ⓒ $y = \sin \frac{\pi}{480}\theta$ Ⓓ $y = \sin \frac{\pi}{240}\theta$

According to the graph, one blue cycle takes 480 nanometers to complete, so the period is 480.

To write an equation, first find b.

$\text{period} = \frac{2\pi}{b}$ Use the relationship between the period and b.

$480 = \frac{2\pi}{b}$ Substitute.

$b = \frac{2\pi}{480}$ Multiply each side by $\frac{b}{480}$.

An equation for blue light is $y = \sin \frac{2\pi}{480}\theta$ or $y = \sin \frac{\pi}{240}\theta$. The correct choice is D.

✓ **Quick Check** 7 Write equations for the sine curves that model the red and yellow light waves in Example 7. $y = \sin \frac{\pi}{320}\theta, y = \sin \frac{\pi}{285}\theta$

EXERCISES

For more exercises, see *Extra Skill and Word Problem Practice*.

Practice and Problem Solving

A Practice by Example

Example 1 (page 734)

Use the graph at the right to find the value of $y = \sin\theta$ for each value of θ.

1. 30° $\frac{1}{2}$ **2.** 45° ≈0.7 **3.** 120° ≈0.9
4. 180° 0 **5.** 240° ≈−0.9 **6.** 300° ≈−0.9

GO for Help

Example 2 (page 735)

Use the graph at the right to find the value of $y = \sin\theta$ for each value of θ.

7. $\frac{\pi}{2}$ radians 1 **8.** 3 radians ≈0.1
9. ≈−0.8
9. 4 radians **10.** 5 radians ≈−1
11. $\frac{3\pi}{2}$ radians−1 **12.** $\frac{7\pi}{4}$ radians ≈−0.7

Examples 3 and 4 (pages 735 and 736)

How many cycles does each sine function have in the interval from 0 to 2π? Find the amplitude and period of each function.

13. 3; 2, $\frac{2\pi}{3}$
14. $\frac{1}{2}$; 1, 4π
15. 2; 3, π

13.

14.

15.

$y = 2 \sin 3\theta$

17.
$y = \frac{1}{3} \sin 2\theta$

18.
$y = 4 \sin \frac{1}{2}\theta$

738 Chapter 13 Periodic Functions and Trigonometry

19.

$y = 3 \sin\theta$

20.

$y = \sin \pi\theta$

21.

$y = \frac{3}{2} \sin \frac{2\pi}{3}\theta$

22.

Example 5
(page 737)

Sketch one cycle of each sine curve. Assume $a > 0$. Write an equation for each graph. **16–21. See margin p. 738.**

16. amplitude 2, period $\frac{2\pi}{3}$

17. amplitude $\frac{1}{3}$, period π

18. amplitude 4, period 4π

19. amplitude 3, period 2π

20. amplitude 1, period 2

21. amplitude 1.5, period 3

Example 6
(page 737)

Sketch one cycle of the graph of each sine function. **22–27. See margin.**

22. $y = 2 \sin \theta$

23. $y = \sin 3\theta$

24. $y = -\sin \frac{\pi}{2}\theta$

25. $y = 2 \sin \pi\theta$

26. $y = 4 \sin \frac{1}{2}\theta$

27. $y = -4 \sin \frac{1}{2}\theta$

Example 7
(page 738)

Find the period of each sine curve. Then write an equation for each sine function.

28. $2\pi; y = 2 \sin \theta$

29. $2\pi; y = -3 \sin \theta$

30. $\pi; y = \frac{5}{2} \sin 2\theta$

31. $\frac{\pi}{3}; y = \frac{1}{2} \sin 6\theta$

28.

29.

30.

31.

32.

33.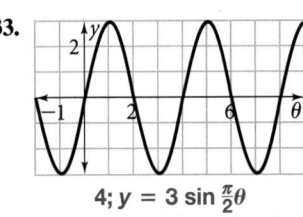

$\pi; y = -\sin 2\theta$

$4; y = 3 \sin \frac{\pi}{2}\theta$

Test-Taking Tip

In a graph of a periodic function, a cycle easiest to see is often one that starts on an axis. Easiest of all is one that starts at the origin.

B Apply Your Skills

How many cycles does each sine function have in the interval from 0 to 2π? Find the amplitude and period of each function.

34. $y = \sin \theta$ 1; 1, 2π

35. $y = \sin 5\theta$ 5; 1, $\frac{2\pi}{5}$

36. $y = \sin \pi\theta$ π; 1, 2

37. $y = 3 \sin \theta$ 1; 3, 2π

38. $y = -5 \sin \theta$ 1; 5, 2π

39. $y = -5 \sin 2\pi\theta$ 2π; 5, 1

40. a. Graph the functions $y = \sin \theta$, $y = 2 \sin \theta$, and $y = 3 \sin \theta$ on the same screen. **a–b. See margin.**

b. Critical Thinking If a is positive, how does the graph of $y = a \sin \theta$ change as the value of a changes?

41. a. Graph the functions $y = 3 \sin \theta$ and $y = -3 \sin \theta$ on the same screen. How are the two graphs related? **a–c. See margin.**

b. Graph the functions $y = \sin 3\theta$ and $y = \sin (-3\theta)$ on the same screen. How are the two graphs related?

c. Critical Thinking How does the graph of $y = a \sin b\theta$ change when a is replaced with its opposite? How does the graph change when b is replaced with its opposite?

42. Use the formula period $= \frac{2\pi}{b}$ to find the period of each sine function.

a. $y = 1.5 \sin 2\theta$ π

b. $y = 3 \sin \frac{\pi}{2}\theta$ 4

Homework Video Tutor
Visit: PHSchool.com
Web Code: age-1304

Lesson 13-4 The Sine Function **739**

Connection to Algebra
Exercise 52c To help students recall the basics of translations, ask: *What equation would you write to translate $y = x^2$ to the right 3 units?* $y = (x - 3)^2$

27.

40a.

b. As a increases, the amplitude of the graph increases.

41a.

They are reflections of each other in the x-axis.

b.

They are reflections of each other in the x-axis.

c. When either a or b is replaced by its opposite, the graph is a reflection of the original graph in the x-axis.

23.

24.

25. (graph)

26.

739

PowerPoint

Lesson Quiz

1. Sketch the graph of $y = 3 \sin 2\theta$ in the interval from 0 to 2π.

2. Write an equation of the sine function for this graph.

$y = \frac{1}{3} \sin \frac{x}{3}$

3. What is the amplitude of the graph in Question 2? $\frac{1}{3}$

Alternative Assessment

Have students use the drawings for Exercises 13–15 and write an equation of the sine function for each graph.
$y = 2 \sin 3\theta$; $y = \sin \frac{1}{2}\theta$, $y = 3 \sin 2\theta$

52b. $y = 4 \sin \theta$

44. • $|a|$ is the amplitude of the function.

• b is the number of cycles in the interval 0° to 360°.

• $\frac{360}{b}$ is the period of the function. The properties relating to number of cycles and period are affected.

45. $\frac{2\pi}{5}$, 3.5

Real-World Connection

Careers Sound engineers working on music videos use sound boards to control hundreds of sound waves.

43. **Music** The sound wave for the note A above middle C can be modeled by the function $y = 0.001 \sin 880\pi\theta$.
   a. What is the period of the function? $\frac{1}{440}$
   b. What is the amplitude of the function? **0.001**
   c. How many cycles of the graph are between 0 and 2π? 880π

44. **Writing** Suppose the independent variable θ is measured in degrees. Restate the properties of the sine function $y = a \sin b\theta$ on page 736 in terms of degrees. Which properties are affected by the conversion to degrees? **See margin.**

Find the period and amplitude of each sine function. Then sketch each function from 0 to 2π. 45–50. See margin pp. 740–741.

45. $y = -3.5 \sin 5\theta$
46. $y = \frac{5}{2} \sin 2\theta$
47. $y = -2 \sin 2\pi\theta$
48. $y = 0.4 \sin 3\theta$
49. $y = 0.5 \sin \frac{\pi}{3}\theta$
50. $y = -1.2 \sin \frac{5\pi}{6}\theta$

51. **Open-Ended** Write the equations of three sine functions with the same amplitude that have periods of 2, 3, and 4. Then sketch all three graphs on the same coordinate axes. **Check students' work.**

52. **Electricity** One type of electric generator consists of a rotating magnetic field surrounded by stationary coils. The voltages produced by the generator can be modeled by sine curves. Suppose three coils are placed symmetrically around a magnetic field. The graph below shows the voltage produced in each coil.

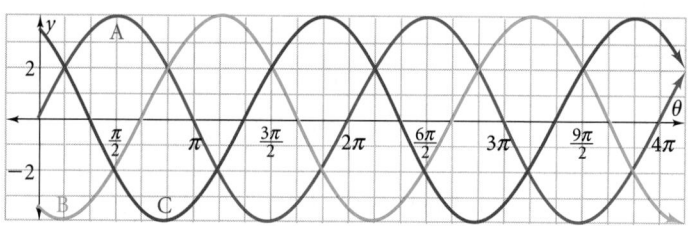

a. Find the amplitude and period of each sine curve. **4, 2π**
b. Write an equation for the graph that models the voltage produced by coil A.
c. **Critical Thinking** One of the graphs has the equation $y = 4 \sin \left(\theta - \frac{2\pi}{3}\right)$. Use your knowledge of translations in the coordinate plane to predict whether this is the equation for coil B or coil C. Check your prediction using a graphing calculator. **coil B**

C Challenge

Sound For sound waves, the period and the frequency of a pitch are reciprocals of each other: period $= \frac{\text{seconds}}{\text{cycle}}$ and frequency $= \frac{\text{cycles}}{\text{second}}$. Write an equation for each pitch. Let $\theta =$ time in seconds. Use $a = 1$.

53. the lowest pitch easily heard by humans: 30 cycles per second $y = \sin 60\pi\theta$

54. the lowest pitch heard by elephants: 15 cycles per second $y = \sin 30\pi\theta$

55. the highest pitch heard by bats: 120,000 cycles per second $y = \sin 240{,}000\pi\theta$

56–58. See margin p. 741.
Find the period and amplitude of each function. Sketch each function from 0 to 2π.

56. $y = \sin (\theta + 2)$
57. $y = \sin (\theta - 3)$
58. $y = \sin (2\theta + 4)$

46. $\pi, \frac{5}{2}$

47. 1, 2

48. $\frac{2\pi}{3}$, 0.4

49. 6, 0.5

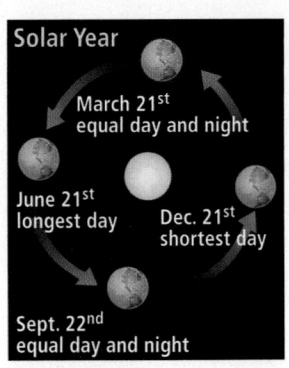

Solar Year

March 21st
equal day and night

June 21st
longest day

Dec. 21st
shortest day

Sept. 22nd
equal day and night

Not drawn to scale

59. Astronomy Sunrise and sunset are defined as the times when someone at sea level sees the uppermost edge of the sun on the horizon. In Houston, Texas, at the spring equinox (March 21), there are 12 hours and 9 minutes of sunlight. Throughout the year, the variation from 12 hours 9 minutes of sunlight can be modeled by a sine function. The longest day (June 21) has 1 hour 55 minutes more sunlight than at the equinox. The shortest day (December 21) has 1 hour 55 minutes less sunlight.

a. Define the independent and dependent variables for a function that models the variation in hours of sunlight in Houston. **a–b. See margin.**

b. What are the amplitude and period of the function measured in days?

c. Write a function that relates the number of days away from the spring equinox to the variation in hours of sunlight in Houston. $y = \frac{23}{12} \sin \frac{2\pi x}{365}$

d. Estimation Use your function from part (c). In Houston, about how much less sunlight does February 14 have than March 21? **1.1 h**

e. Research Find the number of hours of sunlight in your area on June 21 and on December 21. Develop a sunlight model from your data. Use your model to predict the number of hours of sunlight you will have one week from now.
Check students' work.

Test Prep

Multiple Choice

60. Which value is NOT the same as the other three values? **C**
A. sin 100°   B. sin 80°   C. sin −80°   D. sin −260°

61. What is the amplitude of $y = 3 \sin 4\theta$? **G**
F. $\frac{4}{3}$ G. 3   H. 4   J. 2π

62. Which answer choice describes $y = -\sin 2\theta$? **B**
A. amplitude −1, period 4π   B. amplitude 1, period π
C. amplitude 2, period −π   D. amplitude 2π, period 1

63. Which function has a period of 4π and an amplitude of 8? **G**
F. $y = -8 \sin 8\theta$ G. $y = -8 \sin \frac{1}{2}\theta$ H. $y = 8 \sin 2\theta$ J. $y = 4 \sin 8\theta$

Short Response

64. Find the value of θ that is between 90° and 180° such that $\sin \theta = \sin 60°$. Show your work. **See margin.**

Extended Response

65. The period of a sine function is 30° and its amplitude is 1. Write the function in the form $y = a \sin b\theta$, where θ is in radians. Show your work.
See margin.

Mixed Review

Lesson 13-3

Write each measure in radians. Express the answer in terms of π and as a decimal rounded to the nearest hundredth. **66–70. See margin.**

66. −80°   **67.** 150°   **68.** −240°   **69.** 320°   **70.** −450°

Lesson 12-2

71. A poll of teenagers in one town showed that 43% play a team sport. It also showed that 21% play varsity team sports. Find the probability that a teenager plays varsity sports, given that the teenager plays a team sport. **≈49%**

Lesson 11-1

Write an explicit formula for each sequence. Then find a_{15}.

72. 6, 5, 4, 3, . . .
$a_n = 7 - n$; −8

73. 15, 18, 21, 24, . . .
$a_n = 12 + 3n$; 57

74. 0.6, 1.4, 2.2, 3, . . .
$a_n = 0.8n - 0.2$; 11.8

nline lesson quiz, PHSchool.com, Web Code: aga-1304

Lesson 13-4 The Sine Function **741**

Test Prep

Resources

For additional practice with a variety of test item formats:
• Standardized Test Prep, p. 775
• Test-Taking Strategies, p. 770
• Test-Taking Strategies with Transparencies

59a. days from spring equinox, hours of sunlight

b. $\frac{23}{12}$ h, about 365 days

64. **[2]** Since sine is always positive in the first and second quadrants, a value of θ where its sine is equal to the sin 60° would have a reference angle of 60°. 180° − 60° is equal to 120°.

[1] answer only, with no work shown

65. **[4]** The amplitude is 1, so $a = 1$.
$30° \cdot \frac{\pi \text{ radians}}{180°} = \frac{\pi}{6}$ radians, so $b = 2\pi \div \frac{\pi}{6} = 2\pi \cdot \frac{6}{\pi} = 12$. The function is $y = \sin 12\theta$.

[3] one calculation error

[2] incomplete explanation

[1] answer only, with no work shown

66. $-\frac{4\pi}{9}$ radians, −1.40 radians

67. $\frac{5\pi}{6}$ radians, 2.62 radians

68. $-\frac{4\pi}{3}$ radians, −4.19 radians

69. $\frac{16\pi}{9}$ radians, 5.59 radians

70. $-\frac{5\pi}{2}$ radians, −7.85 radians

741

50. $\frac{12}{5}$, 1.2

56. 2π, 1

57. 2π, 1

58. π, 1

Graphing Trigonometric Functions

Students use a graphing calculator to graph both $y = \sin x$ and $y = \cos x$, for x in radians or degrees.

Guided Instruction

1 ACTIVITY

Ask students: *Compare the window setting for Xmin for the two graphs.* They are the same; one is in radians and the other is in degrees.

2 ACTIVITY

If students are having difficulty with graphing correctly, or using the TRACE function, have them work with a partner. Suggest that partners compare screens at each step to find errors.

Connection to History

In the early nineteenth century, French mathematical physicist Joseph Fourier, during his studies of heat flow, showed that many mathematical curves can be considered as the sum of simple sine and cosine functions. This is the basis of the oscilloscope.

Resources

Any graphing calculator

2. 2π radians, 360°; 1

3. $\frac{2\pi}{3}$ radians, 120°; −1

4. 2π radians, 360°; −3

5. 2π radians, 360°; −0.5

6.

The graphs are horizontal translations of each other by $\frac{\pi}{2}$.

742

Activity Lab — Graphing Trigonometric Functions

Technology
FOR USE WITH LESSON 13-4

You can use a graphing calculator to graph trigonometric functions in radians or degrees.

Go Online
PHSchool.com
For: Graphing calculator procedures
Web Code: age-2111

1 ACTIVITY **Comparing Graphs in Radians and Degrees**

Compare the graphs of $y = \cos x$ from −360° to 360° and from −2π to 2π radians.

Step 1 Press MODE to change the mode to degrees. Adjust the window values. Graph the function.

Step 2 Change the mode to radians. Graph the function.

Xmin = −360   Ymin = −1.2
Xmax = 360   Ymax = 1.2
Xscl = 90   Yscl = 1

Xmin = −2π   Ymin = −1.2
Xmax = 2π   Ymax = 1.2
Xscl = π/2   Yscl = 1

The graphs appear to be identical, although in different windows. The function has a period of 360° or 2π radians.

• You can use the TRACE feature to evaluate trigonometric functions.

2 ACTIVITY **Using the Trace Feature**

Graph the function $y = \sin x$. Find sin 30° and sin 150°.

Step 1 Change the mode to degrees. Adjust the window values.

Step 2 Graph the function. Use the TRACE key to find the y-values when $x = 30$ and $x = 150$.

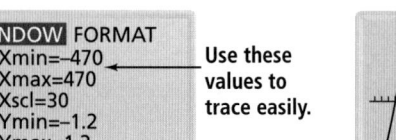

Use these values to trace easily.

EXERCISES

Use appropriate window values to identify the period of each function in radians and in degrees. Then evaluate each function at 90°. 2–8. See margin.

1. $y = \cos x$ **2.** $y = \sin x$ **3.** $y = \sin 3x$ **4.** $y = -3 \sin x$ **5.** $y = \cos (x + 30°)$

2π radians, 360°; 0

Writing **Graph the two functions in the same window. Compare the graphs. How are they similar? How are they different?**

6. $y = \sin x, y = \cos x$ **7.** $y = \sin x, y = \cos \left(x - \frac{\pi}{2}\right)$ **8.** $y = \sin x, y = \cos \left(x + \frac{\pi}{2}\right)$

7.

8.

The graphs are a reflection of each other along the x-axis or horizontal translations of each other by π.

The graphs are the same.

The Cosine Function

What You'll Learn

- To graph and write cosine functions
- To solve trigonometric equations

. . . And Why

To model wave motion, as in Example 3

✓ Check Skills You'll Need

Find the *x*-coordinate of each point on the unit circle at the right.

1. *A* 1
2. *B* 0
3. *C* −1
4. *D* 0

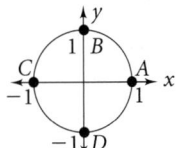

GO for Help Lesson 13-2

◀)) New Vocabulary • cosine function

Objectives
1 To graph and write cosine functions
2 To solve trigonometric equations

Examples
1 Interpreting the Graph of Cos θ
2 Sketching the Graph of a Cosine Function
3 Real-World Connection
4 Solving a Cosine Equation

---

1 Graphing and Writing Cosine Functions

The **cosine function,** $y = \cos \theta$, matches the measure θ of an angle in standard position with the *x*-coordinate of a point on the unit circle. This point is where the terminal side of the angle intersects the unit circle.

 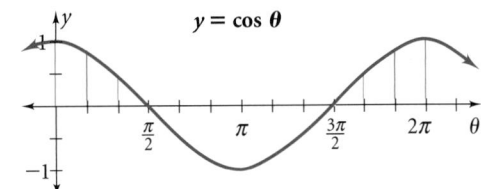

Math Background

The term "cosine" was first used by Edmund Gunter in 1620, who suggested combining the terms "complement" and "sine" into *cosinus* which was anglicized to "cosine." The sine was originally called *jya*, a Hindu word that means half-chord. This word was incorrectly translated (around 1150) into the Latin word *sinus* which is the term we now use in the form sine.

More Math Background: p. 708D

1 EXAMPLE Interpreting the Graph of Cos θ

Use the graph shown above.

a. Find the domain, period, range, and amplitude of the cosine function.

The domain of the function is all real numbers.

The function goes from its maximum value of 1 and back again in an interval from 0 to 2π. The period is 2π.

The function has a maximum value of 1 and a minimum value of −1. The range is $-1 \le y \le 1$.

$$\text{amplitude} = \tfrac{1}{2}(\text{maximum} - \text{minimum})$$
$$= \tfrac{1}{2}[1 - (-1)]$$
$$= 1$$

b. Examine the cycle of the cosine function in the interval from 0 to 2π. Where in the cycle does the maximum value occur? Where does the minimum occur? Where do the zeros occur?

The maximum value occurs at 0 and 2π. The minimum value occurs at π. The zeros occur at $\frac{\pi}{2}$ and $\frac{3\pi}{2}$.

Lesson Planning and Resources

See p. 708E for a list of the resources that support this lesson.

PowerPoint
Bell Ringer Practice

✓ **Check Skills You'll Need**
For intervention, direct students to:

Angles and the Unit Circle
Lesson 13-2: Example 4
Extra Skills and Word Problems Practice, Ch. 13

Real-World 🌎 Connection

The distance over time between the center line of a metronome and a point on the metronome's swinging arm can be modeled with a cosine function.

Differentiated Instruction **Solutions for All Learners**

Special Needs L1
Give pairs of students a length of string. Have them make waves and explore the relationship between *amplitude, period,* and *number of cycles.*

learning style: tactile

Below Level L2
Make sure students understand that because the sine and cosine function are the same curve, shifted $\frac{\pi}{2}$ radians, the functions have the same maximum and minimum values.

learning style: verbal

2. Teach

Guided Instruction

Draw a sine curve on a transparency. Place it on the overhead projector over a transparency with a coordinate system. Ask a student to shift (or translate) the sine curve so that it shows the cosine curve.

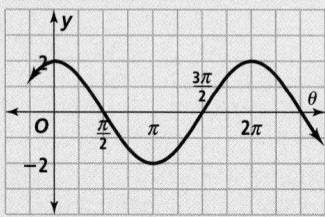

Additional Examples

1 Use the graph shown below.

a. Find the domain, period, range, and amplitude of the cosine function. **all real numbers; 2π; $-2 \le y \le 2$; 2**

b. Examine the cycle of the cosine function in the interval from 0 to 2π. Where in the cycle does the maximum value occur? Where does the minimum occur? Where do the zeros occur? **0, 2π; π; $\frac{\pi}{2}$, $\frac{3\pi}{2}$**

2 Sketch the graph of $y = -2 \cos \pi\theta$ in the interval from 0 to 4.

✓ Quick Check **1** Use the graphs below. How are the graphs of the sine and cosine functions alike? How are they different?

1. They are the same curve translated $\frac{\pi}{2}$ units horizontally.

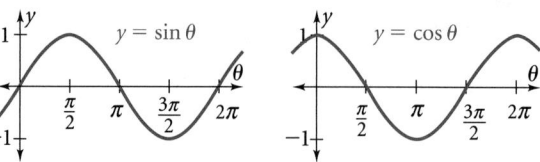

The cosine function has some of the same properties as the sine function.

🔑 Key Concepts

2a.

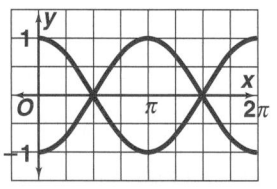

They are reflections of each other over the x-axis.

⬤nline active math

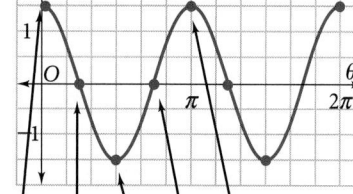

For: Cosine Function Activity
Use: Interactive Textbook, 13-5

Summary	**Properties of Cosine Functions**

Suppose $y = a \cos b\theta$, with $a \ne 0$, $b > 0$, and θ in radians.

- $|a|$ is the amplitude of the function.
- b is the number of cycles in the interval from 0 to 2π.
- $\frac{2\pi}{b}$ is the period of the function.

To graph a cosine function, locate five points equally spaced through one cycle. For $a > 0$, this five-point pattern is *max–zero–min–zero–max*.

2 EXAMPLE Sketching the Graph of a Cosine Function

Sketch the graph of $y = 1.5 \cos 2\theta$ in the interval from 0 to 2π.

$|a| = 1.5$, so the amplitude is 1.5.

$b = 2$, so the graph has two full cycles from 0 to 2π.

$\frac{2\pi}{b} = \pi$, so the period is π.

Divide the period into fourths. Plot five points for the first cycle. Use 1.5 for the maximum and -1.5 for the minimum. Repeat the pattern for the second cycle.

⬤ Sketch the curve.

Choose scales for axes that are about equal $\left(\frac{\pi}{3} \approx 1\right)$.

max zero min zero max

✓ Quick Check **2 a.** Graph the equations $y = \cos x$ and $y = -\cos x$ on the same coordinate plane. Compare the graphs. **a–b. See left.**

2b. min-zero-max-zero-min **b. Critical Thinking** Write the five-point pattern to graph $y = a \cos b\theta$ when $a < 0$.
c. Sketch the cosine curve $y = -\frac{1}{2} \cos \pi\theta$ in the interval from 0 to 2π.
See margin p. 745.

---

2 — Solving Trigonometric Equations

Waves of water show periodic motion. Away from the shore, individual water molecules move up and down, returning to their initial position after a wave passes. Their height can be modeled with a cosine function.

744 Chapter 13 Periodic Functions and Trigonometry

Differentiated Instruction Solutions for All Learners

Advanced Learners L4	**English Language Learners** ELL
Ask students to use the unit circle and the Pythagorean theorem to justify the equation $(\sin \theta)^2 + (\cos \theta)^2 = 1$, and share their justifications.	Help students recognize that the graphs of $y = \cos \theta$ and $y = \sin \theta$ are horizontal translations of one another. Have students graph $y = \cos \left(x - \frac{\pi}{2}\right)$ and $y = \sin x$ on graphing calculators. *Ask: Are the graphs identical?* **yes**
learning style: verbal	**learning style: visual**

Real-World **Connection**

The regular waves in a wave pool can be modeled with a cosine function.

 3 EXAMPLE Real-World Connection

Wave Motion The figures at the right show the vertical motion of a particle in water as a wave moves by. Suppose 10-in. waves occur every 4 s. Write an equation that models the height of the particle as it moves from crest to crest.

The equation will have the form $y = a \cos b\theta$.
Find values for a and b.

$a = \frac{10}{2}$ amplitude $= \frac{\text{maximum} - \text{minimum}}{2}$

$\quad = 5$ Simplify.

period $= \frac{2\pi}{b}$ Use the formula for the period.

$4 = \frac{2\pi}{b}$ The period is 4. Substitute.

$b = \frac{2\pi}{4}$ Multiply each side by $\frac{b}{4}$.

$\quad = \frac{\pi}{2}$ Simplify.

An equation that models the height of the particle is $y = 5 \cos \frac{\pi}{2}\theta$.

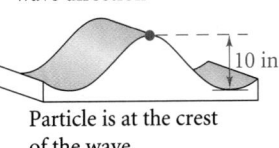
wave direction ⟶
10 in.
Particle is at the crest of the wave.

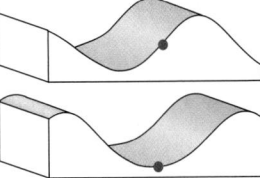
Particle is in the trough of the wave.

✓ **Quick Check** **3** Write a cosine function for each description. Choose $a > 0$.
  a. amplitude 4, period 6π **a.** $y = 4 \cos \frac{1}{3}\theta$
  b. amplitude 2.5, period 8   **b.** $y = 2.5 \cos \frac{\pi}{4}\theta$

You can solve an equation by graphing to find an exact location along a sine or cosine curve.

4 EXAMPLE Solving a Cosine Equation

Suppose you want to find the time t in seconds when the particle from Example 3 is exactly 3 in. above the average height represented by $y = 0$. Solve $5 \cos \frac{\pi}{2}t = 3$ in the interval from 0 to 8.

Step 1 Use two equations. Graph the equations $y = 3$ and $y = 5 \cos \frac{\pi}{2}t$ on the same screen.

Step 2 Use the **Intersect** feature to find the points at which the two graphs intersect.

The graph shows four solutions in the interval. They are $t \approx 0.6$, 3.4, 4.6, and 7.4.

Intersection
X=.59033447 Y=3

Xmin=0
Xmax=8
Xscl=1
Ymin=−8
Ymax=8
Yscl=1

The particle is 3 in. above the average height at about 0.6, 3.4, 4.6, and 7.4 s.

Graphing Calculator Hint

When you use the Intersect feature, move the cursor close to the desired point after the Guess? prompt appears.

✓ **Quick Check** **4** Find all solutions in the interval from 0 to 2π.
  a. $3 \cos 2t = -2$ **a.** 1.2, 2.0, 4.3, 5.1
  b. $-2 \cos \theta = 1.2$ **b.** 2.2, 4.1
  c. Critical Thinking In the interval from 0 to 2π, when is $-2 \cos \theta$ less than 1.2? Greater than 1.2? $0 \le \theta < 2.2$ and $4.1 < \theta \le 2\pi$; $2.2 < \theta < 4.1$

Quick Check

2c.

3 EXAMPLE **Connection to Oceanography**

Tsunami is a Japanese word derived from the characters "harbor" and "wave." Tsunamis are giant waves, usually caused by earthquakes under the ocean. A tsunami with waves as high as 100 feet occurred on December 24, 2004 in the Indian Ocean, and killed well over 200,000 people.

4 EXAMPLE **Tactile Learners**

To model the nature of a wave, bring a few yards of cloth to class. You hold one end of the cloth still while a volunteer generates waves by moving the other end up and down. Have a second volunteer hold a yardstick horizontally to show the average height.

4 EXAMPLE **Technology Tip**

The graphing calculator must be set to radians to use the given window settings.

PowerPoint

Additional Examples

3 Suppose 8-in. waves occur every 6 s. Write an equation that models the height of a water molecule as it moves from crest to crest. $y = 4 \cos \frac{\pi}{3}\theta$.

4 Solve the equation $1 = -2 \cos \left(\frac{2x}{3}\right)$ in the interval from 0 to 10. about 3.14 and 6.28, or π and 2π.

Resources
• Daily Notetaking Guide 13-5   **L3**

Closure

Ask students: *How is the graph of the cosine function different from the graph of the sine function? How is it the same?* The graphs are both the same periodic curve, except the graph of the cosine function is translated 90°, or $\frac{\pi}{2}$ radians to the left of the graph of the sine function.

Assignment Guide

▼**1** A B 1-9, 22-29, 36

▼**2** A B 10-21, 30-35

C Challenge 37-39

Test Prep 40-47
Mixed Review 48-56

Homework Quick Check
To check students' understanding of key skills and concepts, go over Exercises 8, 10, 16, 33, 34, 35.

Error Prevention!

Exercises 5–9 Remind students that these are cosine functions, so the *y*-value at zero radians is the maximum or minimum value for the function, not zero as it is for a sine function.

Careers

Exercise 35 Oceanographers collect many kinds of data every day, such as making measurements of wave heights, tides, and the width of the beach in order to measure erosion over a period of time.

EXERCISES

For more exercises, see *Extra Skill and Word Problem Practice*.

Practice and Problem Solving

A Practice by Example

Example 1
(page 743)

  for Help

1. 2π, 3; max: 0, 2π, min: π, zeros: $\frac{\pi}{2}, \frac{3\pi}{2}$

2. $\frac{2\pi}{3}$, 1; max: 0, $\frac{2\pi}{3}, \frac{4\pi}{3}, 2\pi$
min: $\frac{\pi}{3}, \pi, \frac{5\pi}{3}$
zeros: $\frac{\pi}{6}, \frac{\pi}{2}, \frac{5\pi}{6}, \frac{7\pi}{6}, \frac{3\pi}{2}, \frac{11\pi}{6}$

3. π, 1; max: 0, π, 2π min: $\frac{\pi}{2}, \frac{3\pi}{2}$
zeros: $\frac{\pi}{4}, \frac{3\pi}{4}, \frac{5\pi}{4}, \frac{7\pi}{4}$

4. 2π, 2; max: π, min: 0, 2π
zeros: $\frac{\pi}{2}, \frac{3\pi}{2}$

16. 0.52, 2.62, 3.67, 5.76

17. 1.98, 4.30

18. 0.55, 1.45, 2.55, 3.45, 4.55, 5.45

Example 4
(page 745)

B Apply Your Skills

Find the period and amplitude of each cosine function. At what values of x for $0 \le x \le 2\pi$ do the maximum value(s), minimum value(s), and zeros occur?

1.
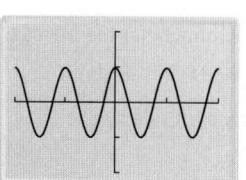
Xmin=−2π
Xmax=2π
Xscl=π
Ymin=−4
Ymax=4
Yscl=1

2.
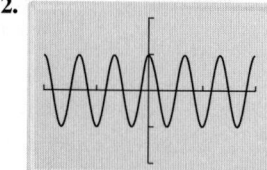
Xmin=−2π
Xmax=2π
Xscl=π
Ymin=−2
Ymax=2
Yscl=1

3.
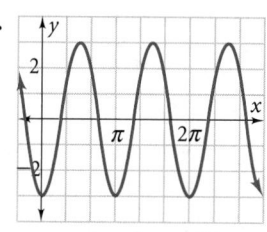
Xmin=−2π
Xmax=2π
Xscl=π
Ymin=−2
Ymax=2
Yscl=1

4.

Xmin=−2π
Xmax=2π
Xscl=π
Ymin=−4
Ymax=4
Yscl=1

Sketch the graph of each function in the interval from 0 to 2π.

5. $y = \cos 2\theta$ **6.** $y = -3 \cos \theta$ **7.** $y = -\cos 3t$ **8.** $y = \cos \frac{\pi}{2}\theta$ **9.** $y = -\cos \pi\theta$
5–9. See margin pp. 746–747.

Write a cosine function for each description. Assume that $a > 0$.

10. amplitude 2, period π
$y = 2 \cos 2\theta$

11. amplitude $\frac{\pi}{2}$, period 3
$y = \frac{\pi}{2} \cos \frac{2\pi}{3}\theta$

12. amplitude π, period 2
$y = \pi \cos \pi\theta$

Write an equation of a cosine function for each graph.

13.
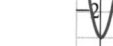

$y = -3 \cos 2\theta$

14.

$y = 2 \cos \frac{\pi}{4}\theta$

15. Wave Motion Suppose 8-in. waves pass every 3 s. Write an equation that models the height of a water molecule as it moves from crest to crest.
$y = 4 \cos \frac{2\pi}{3}\theta$

Solve each equation in the interval from 0 to 2π. Round to the nearest hundredth.

16. $\cos 2t = \frac{1}{2}$ **17.** $20 \cos t = -8$ **18.** $-2 \cos \pi\theta = 0.3$

19. $3 \cos \frac{t}{3} = 2$ 2.52 **20.** $\cos \frac{1}{4}\theta = 1$ 0.00 **21.** $8 \cos \frac{\pi}{3}t = 5$ 0.86, 5.14

Identify the period, range, and amplitude of each function.

22. $y = 3 \cos \theta$ **23.** $y = -\cos 2t$ **24.** $y = 2 \cos \frac{1}{2}t$ **25.** $y = \frac{1}{3} \cos \frac{\theta}{2}$

26. $y = 3 \cos \left(-\frac{\theta}{3}\right)$ **27.** $y = -\frac{1}{2} \cos 3\theta$ **28.** $y = 16 \cos \frac{3\pi}{2}t$ **29.** $y = 0.7 \cos \pi t$
22–29. See margin p. 747.

Solve each equation in the interval from 0 to 2π. Round your answers to the nearest hundredth.

30. $\sin \theta = 0.6$
0.64, 2.50

31. $-3 \sin 2\theta = 1.5$
1.83, 2.88, 4.97, 6.02

32. $\sin \pi\theta = 1$
0.50, 2.50, 4.50

5.

6.

7.

8.

33b. 10.07, 11.92; these values are the sums of the values from part (a) and 2π.

33. a. Solve $-2 \sin \theta = 1.2$ in the interval from 0 to 2π. **3.79, 5.64**
b. Solve $-2 \sin \theta = 1.2$ in the interval $2\pi \le \theta \le 4\pi$. How are these solutions related to the solutions in part (a)?

34. a. Graph the equation $y = 5 \cos \frac{\pi}{2}\theta$ from Example 3. **a–b. See back of book.**
b. The independent variable θ represents time (in seconds). Find four times at which the particle is at the crest of a wave.
c. For how many seconds during each cycle is the particle above the line $y = 0$? Below $y = 0$? **2 s; 2 s**

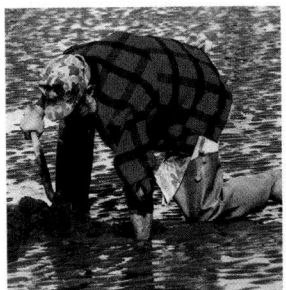

Real-World Connection

Commercial fishermen, including clam diggers, work in relation to the tides.

35a. 5.5 ft; 1.5 ft

b. about 12 h 22 min

35. Tides The table at the right shows the times for high tide and low tide. The markings on the side of a local pier showed a high tide of 7 ft and a low tide of 4 ft on the previous day.

Tide Table	
High tide	4:03 A.M.
Low tide	10:14 A.M.
High tide	4:25 P.M.
Low tide	10:36 P.M.

a. What is the average depth of water at the pier? What is the amplitude of the variation from the average depth? **a–b. See left.**
b. How long is one cycle of the tide?
c. Write a cosine function that models the relationship between the depth of water and the time of day. Use $y = 0$ to represent the average depth of water. Use $t = 0$ to represent the time 4:03 A.M. $y = 1.5 \cos \frac{2\pi t}{742}$
d. Critical Thinking Suppose your boat needs at least 5 ft of water to approach or leave the pier. Between what times could you come and go?
12:17 A.M.–7:49 A.M., 12:39 P.M.–8:11 P.M.

36. Ferris Wheel A Ferris wheel ride (see the Activity on page 710) lets you, in a sense, ride the sine and cosine waves.

a. Recall the unit circle definitions of sine and cosine (pages 734, 743). Which function, sine or cosine, might serve as a better model for a Ferris wheel ride in the sense of riding a wave? Explain. (*Hint:* For a point on the unit circle, which function suggests vertical position?) **a–i. See back of book.**

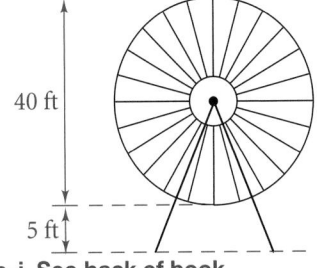

40 ft

5 ft

b. Assume the Ferris wheel pictured turns counterclockwise. For a ride on the unit-circle sine wave, it would be ideal to begin your sine wave ride halfway up on the right side. On a Ferris wheel, however, you begin your ride at the bottom where you board your car. This means that your ride will be $\frac{\pi}{2}$ radians "out of phase" with $\sin x$. Graph Y1 = sin X and Y2 = $\sin\left(X - \frac{\pi}{2}\right)$. Explain the meaning of "out of phase."

c. How does the amplitude of your sine wave ride compare with the amplitude of a unit-circle (1 ft radius) sine wave?
d. How does the center of your Ferris wheel compare with the center of the unit circle?
e. Write a sine function that models your sine-wave Ferris wheel ride.
f. Graph your function using screen dimensions $0 \le x \le 2\pi$ and $0 \le y \le 50$.
g. How could you build the speed of the Ferris wheel into your model?
h. How could you build the speed of the Ferris wheel into your graphical display? (*Hint:* Use parametric mode.)
i. How can you relate the cosine function to a ride on the Ferris wheel?

Online
Homework Video Tutor
Visit: PHSchool.com
Web Code: age-1305

C Challenge

37. a. Graph $y = \cos \theta$ and $y = \cos\left(\theta - \frac{\pi}{2}\right)$ in the interval from 0 to 2π. What translation of the graph of $y = \cos \theta$ produces the graph of $y = \cos\left(\theta - \frac{\pi}{2}\right)$?
b. Graph $y = \cos\left(\theta - \frac{\pi}{2}\right)$ and $y = \sin \theta$ in the interval from 0 to 2π. What do you notice?
c. Critical Thinking Explain how you could rewrite a sine function as a cosine function. **a–c. See margin.**

9.

22. 2π, $-3 \le y \le 3$, 3
23. π, $-1 \le y \le 1$, 1
24. 4π, $-2 \le y \le 2$, 2
25. 4π, $-\frac{1}{3} \le y \le \frac{1}{3}$, $\frac{1}{3}$

26. 6π, $-3 \le y \le 3$, 3
27. $\frac{2\pi}{3}$, $-\frac{1}{2} \le y \le \frac{1}{2}$, $\frac{1}{2}$
28. $\frac{4}{3}$, $-16 \le y \le 16$, 16
29. 2, $-0.7 \le y \le 0.7$, 0.7

Resources

For additional practice with a variety of test item formats:
- Standardized Test Prep, p. 775
- Test-Taking Strategies, p. 770
- Test-Taking Strategies with Transparencies

39. On the unit circle, the x-values of $-\theta$ are equal to the x-values of θ, so $\cos(-\theta) = \cos \theta$. $-\cos \theta$ is the opposite of $\cos \theta$, so these graphs are reflections of each other over the x-axis.

48.

$y = \sin 6\theta$

49.

$y = \frac{5}{2}\sin 2\theta$

50.

$y = 4\sin 2\pi\theta$

54. $a_n = 10 \cdot 3^{n-1}$; 10, 30, 90, 270, 810

55. $a_n = 12(-0.3)^{n-1}$; 12, -3.6, 1.08, -0.324, 0.0972

56. $a_n = 900\left(-\frac{1}{3}\right)^{n-1}$; 900, -300, 100, $-\frac{100}{3}$, $\frac{100}{9}$

---

38. Biology A helix is a three-dimensional spiral. The coiled strands of DNA and the edges of twisted crepe paper are examples of helixes. In the diagram, the y-coordinate of each edge illustrates a cosine function. Write an equation for the y-coordinate of one edge. $y = \cos\frac{\pi}{12}x$ or $y = -\cos\frac{\pi}{12}x$

39. Graph one cycle of $y = \cos\theta$, one cycle of $y = -\cos\theta$, and one cycle of $y = \cos(-\theta)$ on the same set of axes. Use the unit circle to explain any relationships you see among these graphs. **See margin.**

Test Prep

Multiple Choice

40. Which statement(s) is (are) true? **A**
 I. $\cos\theta = \cos(-\theta)$ II. $\cos(\theta + 2\pi) = \cos\theta$ III. $\cos\pi = -\cos\pi$
 A. I and II only   **B.** II only   **C.** I and III only   **D.** I, II, and III

41. Which function has a period of 2π and an amplitude of 4? **J**
 F. $f(x) = 2\cos 4\theta$ **G.** $f(x) = 2\cos\theta$
 H. $f(x) = 4\cos 2\theta$ **J.** $f(x) = 4\cos\theta$

42. Which equation corresponds to the graph shown at the right? The screen dimensions are $-4\pi \le x \le 4\pi$ and $-2 \le y \le 2$. **A**
 A. $y = \frac{1}{2}\cos\frac{x}{4}$ **B.** $y = \frac{1}{2}\cos 4x$
 C. $y = 2\cos\frac{x}{4}$ **D.** $y = 2\cos 4x$

43. Which equation has the same graph as $y = -\cos t$? **H**
 F. $y = \cos(-t)$ **G.** $y = \sin(t - \pi)$ **H.** $y = \cos(t - \pi)$ **J.** $y = -\sin t$

44. How many solutions does the equation $1 = -\sin 2t$ have for $0 \le t < 2\pi$?
 A. 1   **B.** 2   **C.** 3   **D.** 4   **B**

Short Response

45. Find the amplitude and period of $y = -0.2\cos\frac{\pi}{3}\theta$.

46. Solve $75\cos 4t = 12.5$ for t from 0 to 2π. Round your result(s) to the nearest hundredth.

47. For what value(s) of t in the interval from 0 to 2π is the value of $f(t) = 3\cos 2t$ the least?

45. [2] amplitude = 0.2; period = 6
[1] one computational error

46. [2] seven or eight correct: 0.35, 1.22, 1.92, 2.79, 3.49, 4.36, 5.06, 5.93
[1] two to six numbers correct

47. [2] $\frac{\pi}{2}, \frac{3\pi}{2}$
[1] answer only OR one value correct

Mixed Review

 for Help

Lesson 13-4

Sketch one cycle of each sine curve. Assume that $a > 0$. Then write an equation for each graph.   48–50. See margin.

48. amplitude 1, period $\frac{\pi}{3}$ **49.** amplitude 2.5, period π **50.** amplitude 4, period 1

Lesson 12-5

Find the sample size that produces each margin of error.

51. $\pm 3\%$ about 1111   **52.** $\pm 7\%$ about 204   **53.** $\pm 11\%$ about 83

Lesson 11-3

Write the explicit formula for each geometric sequence. List the first five terms.

54. $a_1 = 10, r = 3$ **55.** $a_1 = 12, r = -0.3$ **56.** $a_1 = 900, r = -\frac{1}{3}$
54–56. See margin.

The Tangent Function

What You'll Learn

- To graph the tangent function

. . . And Why

To model the facade of a building, as in Example 3

 Check Skills You'll Need

 GO for Help Lesson 13-3

Use a calculator to find the sine and cosine of each value of θ. Then calculate the ratio $\frac{\sin \theta}{\cos \theta}$.

1. $\frac{\pi}{3}$ radians $\approx 0.87, 0.5; \approx 1.73$
2. 30 degrees $0.5, \approx 0.87; \approx 0.58$
3. 90 degrees $1, 0;$ undefined
4. $\frac{5\pi}{6}$ radians $0.5, \approx -0.87; \approx -0.58$
5. $\frac{5\pi}{2}$ radians $1, 0;$ undefined
6. 0 degrees $0, 1; 0$

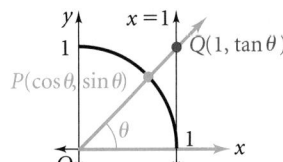 **New Vocabulary** • tangent of θ • tangent function

Objectives
1 To graph the tangent function

Examples
1 Finding Tangent Values From a Graph
2 Graphing a Tangent Function
3 Real-World Connection

Professional Development

Math Background

The sine and cosine functions were first used in the context of astronomy, but the tangent function was developed in response to requirements for practical measurements of heights and distances.

More Math Background: p. 708D

Lesson Planning and Resources

See p. 708E for a list of the resources that support this lesson.

PowerPoint

Bell Ringer Practice

✓ **Check Skills You'll Need**
For intervention, direct students to:

Angles and the Unit Circle
Lesson 13-3: Example 3
Extra Skills and Word Problems Practice, Ch. 13

---

1 **Graphing the Tangent Function**

Vocabulary Tip

A line <u>tangent</u> to a circle intersects the circle at exactly one point.

The sine and cosine of an angle derive from the coordinates of a point on the unit circle. The tangent of an angle derives from the coordinates of a point on a line *tangent* to the unit circle.

For an angle θ in standard position, the **tangent of θ** is the y-coordinate of the point where the line containing the terminal side of the angle intersects the tangent line $x = 1$.

The line containing the terminal side of θ intersects the line $x = 1$ at Q.

The graph below shows one cycle of the **tangent function,** $y = \tan \theta$. Since the period is π, the asymptote that occurs at $\theta = \frac{\pi}{2}$ repeats every π units.

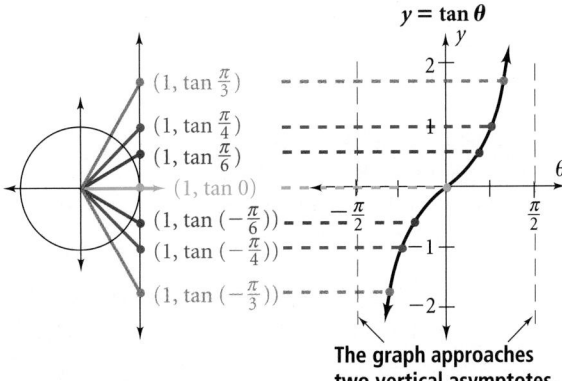

The graph approaches two vertical asymptotes.

You can estimate function values from the graph of the tangent function.

Math Background

2 EXAMPLE Teaching Tip

Some students find graphing tangent functions challenging. Give them the following steps.
- Find the period of the function.
- Find and sketch the asymptotes.
- Plot three points in each cycle.
- Sketch the curves between the marked points.

PowerPoint

Additional Examples

1 Use the graph of the tangent function shown in Example 1 to find each value.
a. tan −45° **−1**
b. tan 0° **0**
c. tan 45° **1**

2 Sketch two cycles of the graph of $y = \tan \frac{\theta}{2}$

3 What is the height of the triangle in the design from Example 3 when $\theta = 18°$? What is the height when $\theta = 20°$? **about 32.5 ft; about 36.4 ft**

Resources
- Daily Notetaking Guide 13-6 **L3**

Closure

Ask students: *How is the graph of the tangent function the same as the graphs of the cosine and sine functions? How is it different?*
The graph of the tangent function is periodic like the sine and cosine functions, but unlike those functions, the graph has vertical asymptotes at $x = \pm\frac{\pi}{2}$ and every odd multiple of $\pm\frac{\pi}{2}$.

Online active math

For: Tangent Function Activity
Use: Interactive Textbook, 13-6

1 EXAMPLE Finding Tangent Values From a Graph

Use the graph of $y = \tan \theta$ at the right to find each value.

a. $\tan\left(-\frac{\pi}{4}\right)$ $\tan\left(-\frac{\pi}{4}\right) = -1$
b. $\tan 0$ $\tan 0 = 0$
c. $\tan \frac{\pi}{4}$ $\tan \frac{\pi}{4} = 1$

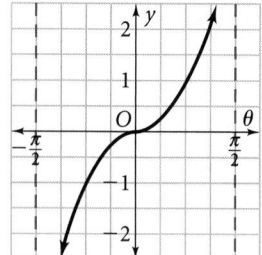

✓ Quick Check

1 a. Use the graph in Example 1 to find $\tan \frac{\pi}{8}$ and $\tan\left(-\frac{\pi}{8}\right)$. **0.4, −0.4**
b. **Critical Thinking** Explain why the terminal side of an angle with measure $\frac{\pi}{2}$ *does not intersect* the tangent line. **The terminal side of $\frac{\pi}{2}$ lies on the line $x = 0$, which cannot intersect $x = 1$.**

The graph in Example 1 shows one cycle of the tangent function, $y = \tan \theta$. Since the period is π, the asymptote that occurs at $\theta = \frac{\pi}{2}$ is repeated every π units.

Key Concepts

Summary	Properties of Tangent Functions

Suppose $y = a \tan b\theta$, with $b > 0$ and θ in radians.
- $\frac{\pi}{b}$ is the period of the function.
- One cycle occurs in the interval from $-\frac{\pi}{2b}$ to $\frac{\pi}{2b}$.
- There are vertical asymptotes at each end of the cycle.

You can use asymptotes and three points to sketch one cycle of a tangent curve. As with sine and cosine, the five elements are equally spaced through one cycle. Use the pattern *asymptote–(−a)–zero–(a)–asymptote*. In the graph at the right, $a = b = 1$.

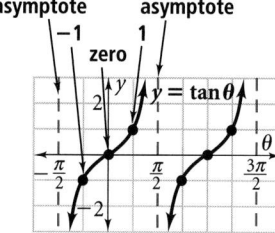

The next example shows how to use the period, asymptotes, and points to graph a tangent function.

2 EXAMPLE Graphing a Tangent Function

Sketch two cycles of the graph of $y = \tan \pi\theta$.

period $= \frac{\pi}{b}$ **Use the formula for the period.**

$= \frac{\pi}{\pi} = 1$ **Substitute π for b and simplify.**

One cycle occurs in the interval from $-\frac{1}{2}$ to $\frac{1}{2}$.
Asymptotes occur every 1 unit, at $\theta = -\frac{1}{2}, \frac{1}{2}$, and $\frac{3}{2}$.
Since $a = 1$, $\left(-\frac{1}{4}, -1\right)$ and $\left(\frac{1}{4}, 1\right)$ are on the graph.
Plot three points in each cycle. Sketch the curve.

750 Chapter 13 Periodic Functions and Trigonometry

✓ **Quick Check** ② Sketch the graph of each tangent curve. **See below left.**
   a. $y = \tan 3\theta, 0 \leq \theta \leq \pi$ **b.** $y = \tan \frac{\pi}{2}\theta, 0 \leq \theta < 3$

You can use the tangent function and a graphing calculator to solve problems involving angles.

③ **EXAMPLE** **Real-World** **Connection**

2a.

b.

Design An architect is designing the front facade of a building to include a triangle, as shown in the figure. The base of the triangle is 200 ft wide. The function $y = 100 \tan \theta$ models the height of the triangle, where θ is the angle indicated. Graph the function in degree mode. What is the height of the triangle when $\theta = 16°$? What is the height when $\theta = 22°$?

Not drawn to scale

Step 1 Graph the function.

Xmin=0
Xmax=470
Xscl=50
Ymin=–300
Ymax=300
Yscl=90

Step 2 Use the TABLE feature.

X	Y1
16	28.675
17	30.573
18	32.492
19	34.433
20	36.397
21	38.386
22	40.403

X=16

When $\theta = 16°$, the height of the triangle is about 28.7 ft. When $\theta = 22°$, the height of the triangle is about 40.4 ft.

✓ **Quick Check** ③ **a.** What is the height of the triangle when $\theta = 25°$? **≈46.6 ft**
   b. Reasoning The architect wants the triangle to be at least one story tall. The average height of a story is 14 ft. What must the measure of θ be for the height of the triangle to be at least 14 ft? **≈8°**

EXERCISES

For more exercises, see *Extra Skill and Word Problem Practice.*

Practice and Problem Solving

Ⓐ **Practice by Example**

Example 1
(page 750)

for
Help

Use the graph of $y = \tan \theta$ to find each value. If the tangent is undefined at that point, write *undefined*.

1. $\tan(-\pi)$ **0**   **2.** $\tan \pi$ **0**
3. $\tan \frac{3\pi}{4}$ **−1**   **4.** $\tan \frac{\pi}{2}$ **undefined**
5. $\tan\left(-\frac{7\pi}{4}\right)$ **1**   **6.** $\tan 2\pi$ **0**
7. $\tan\left(-\frac{3\pi}{4}\right)$ **1**   **8.** $\tan \frac{3\pi}{2}$
                                        undefined

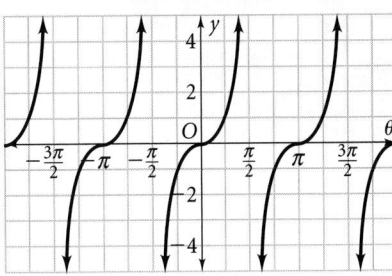

3. Practice

Assignment Guide

▼ A B 1-42
C Challenge   43-46

Test Prep   47-53
Mixed Review   54-68

Homework Quick Check
To check students' understanding of key skills and concepts, go over Exercises 16, 22, 30, 32, 42.

Differentiated Instruction Resources

GPS Guided Problem Solving   L3

Enrichment   L4

Reteaching   L2

Practice   L3

15.

16.

17.

18.

19.

50, undefined, −50

20.

−100, undefined, 100

21.

≈51.8, 125, ≈301.8

22a.

752

Example 2
(page 750)

Each graphing calculator screen shows the interval 0 to 2π. What is the period of each graph?

9.
π

10.
$\frac{\pi}{2}$

11. $\frac{\pi}{5}$, $\theta = -\frac{\pi}{10}, \frac{\pi}{10}$

12. $\frac{2\pi}{3}$, $\theta = -\frac{\pi}{3}, \frac{\pi}{3}$

13. $\frac{\pi}{4}$, $\theta = -\frac{\pi}{8}, \frac{\pi}{8}$

14. $\frac{3\pi^2}{2}$, $\theta = -\frac{3\pi^2}{4}, \frac{3\pi^2}{4}$

Identify the period and tell where two asymptotes occur for each function.

11. $y = \tan 5\theta$ **12.** $y = \tan \frac{3\theta}{2}$ **13.** $y = \tan 4\theta$ **14.** $y = \tan \frac{2}{3\pi}\theta$

Sketch the graph of each tangent curve in the interval from 0 to 2π.

15. $y = \tan \theta$ **16.** $y = \tan 2\theta$ **17.** $y = \tan \frac{2\pi}{3}\theta$ **18.** $y = \tan(-\theta)$
15–18. See margin.

Example 3
(page 751)

Graph each function on the interval $0° < x < 470°$ and $-300 < y < 300$. Evaluate the function at $x = 45°, 90°,$ and $135°$.   **19–21. See margin.**

19. $y = 50 \tan x$ **20.** $y = -100 \tan x$ **21.** $y = 125 \tan \left(\frac{1}{2}x\right)$

22. Suppose the architect in Example 3 reduces the length of the base of the triangle to 100 ft. The function that models the height of the triangle becomes $y = 50 \tan \theta$.
 a. Graph the function on a graphing calculator. **See margin.**
 b. What is the height of the triangle when $\theta = 16°$?   ≈14.3 ft
 c. What is the height of the triangle when $\theta = 22°$?   ≈20.2 ft

B   **Apply Your Skills**

Identify the period for each tangent function. Then graph each function in the interval from -2π to 2π.   **23–25. See margin.**

23. $y = \tan \frac{\pi}{6}\theta$ **24.** $y = \tan 2.5\theta$ **25.** $y = \tan \left(-\frac{3}{2\pi}\theta\right)$

Solve each equation in the interval from 0 to 2π. Round your answers to the nearest hundredth.

26. $\tan \theta = 2$ **27.** $\tan \theta = -2$ **28.** $6 \tan 2\theta = 1$
   1.11, 4.25   **2.03, 5.18**   **0.08, 1.65, 3.22, 4.79**

29. a. Set your graphing calculator to Degree mode. Use window values $0 \le x \le 141$ and $-500 \le y \le 500$. Graph the functions $y = 100 \tan 2x$, $y = 200 \tan 2x$, and $y = 400 \tan 2x$ on the same set of axes. Sketch the graphs.
 b. Choose five values for x. Compare the y values. Explain how doubling the coefficient of the tangent function affects the output.
 c. Without graphing, make a prediction about the difference between the y-values of $y = 200 \tan x$ and $y = 600 \tan x$. Check your prediction on your graphing calculator.   **a–c. See margin p. 753.**

30. Ceramics An artist is creating triangular ceramic tiles for a triangular patio.
GPS The patio will be an equilateral triangle with base 18 ft and height 15.6 ft.
 a. Find the area of the patio in square feet.   **140.4 ft²**
 b. The artist uses tiles that are isosceles triangles with base 6 in. The function $y = 3 \tan \theta$ models the height of the tiles, where θ is the measure of one of the base angles. Graph the function. Find the height of the tile when $\theta = 30°$ and when $\theta = 60°$.   **b–d. See margin p. 753.**
 c. Find the area of one tile in square inches when $\theta = 30°$ and when $\theta = 60°$.
 d. Find the number of tiles the patio will require if $\theta = 30°$ and if $\theta = 60°$.

Real-World Connection

Careers Ceramic artists work with a variety of geometric shapes.

---

23. 6

24. $\frac{2\pi}{5}$

25. $\frac{2\pi^2}{3}$

Homework Video Tutor

Visit: PHSchool.com
Web Code: age-1306

31. **a. Open-Ended** Write a tangent function. **Check students' work.**
    b. Graph the function on the interval -2π to 2π.
    c. Identify the period and the asymptotes of the function.

32. **Writing** Explain how you can find the equations of the asymptotes of
    $y = \tan b\theta$. **See below left.**

Use the function $y = 200 \tan x$ on the interval $0° \le x \le 141°$. Complete each
ordered pair. Round your answers to the nearest whole number.

33. $(45°, \blacksquare)$ 34. $(\blacksquare°, 0)$ 35. $(\blacksquare°, -200)$ 36. $(141°, \blacksquare)$ 37. $(\blacksquare°, 550)$
      200   0   135   -162   70

Write an equation of a tangent function for each graph.

GO for Help

For a guide to solving
Exercise 38, see p. 755.

38.

39.

32. The asymptotes
    occur at $-\frac{\pi}{2b}$ and
    $\frac{\pi}{2b}$; adding or
    subtracting multiples
    of their difference will
    give other asymptote
    values.

40.

41.

38. $y = \tan\left(\frac{1}{2}x\right)$

39. $y = -\tan\left(\frac{1}{2}x\right)$

40. $y = -\tan x$ or
    $y = \tan(-x)$

41. $y = \tan(2x)$

42. **Construction** An architect is designing a hexagonal gazebo. The floor is a
    hexagon made up of six isosceles triangles. The function $y = 4 \tan \theta$ models the
    height of one triangle, where θ is the measure of one of the base angles and the
    base of the triangle is 8 ft long.   **a. See margin.**
    a. Graph the function. Find the height of one triangle when $\theta = 60°$.
    b. Find the area of one triangle in square feet when $\theta = 60°$. **27.7 ft²**
    c. Find the area in square feet covered by the gazebo when the triangles
       forming the hexagon are equilateral. **166.3 ft²**

C Challenge

43a.

43. **Geometry** The base of a square pyramid has
    side length 150 ft. The function $\ell = 75 \tan \theta$
    models the slant height ℓ of the pyramid, where
    θ is the angle indicated in the figure.
    a. Graph the function $\ell = 75 \tan \theta$ as $Y_1 = 75 \tan X$
       on a graphing calculator. Sketch the graph.
    b. Find the slant height of the pyramid when
       $\theta = 60°$. **130 ft**
    c. Find the surface area of the pyramid.
       (*Hint:* Don't forget to include the base
       of the pyramid.) **61,500 ft²**

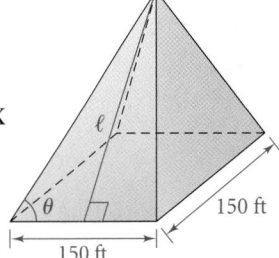
ℓ 150 ft
150 ft

44. **a.** Graph $y = \tan x$, $y = a \tan x$ (with $a > 0$), and $y = a \tan x$ (with $a < 0$) on
       the same coordinate plane.   **Check students' work.**
    b. Critical Thinking Recall the pattern of five elements for graphing a tangent
       function: $asymptote-(-1)-zero-(1)-asymptote$. How does the value of a
       affect this pattern?
       The new pattern is asymptote–(–a)–zero–(a)–asymptote.

29a.

b. **Check students' work;
   doubling the coefficient
   of the tangent function
   also doubles the output.**

c. **Answers may vary. Sample:
   the values of $y = 600 \tan x$
   will be three times greater
   than the values of $y = 200$
   $\tan x$.**

42a.

≈ 6.9 ft

---

4. Assess & Reteach

PowerPoint

Lesson Quiz

1. Sketch the graph of
   $y = \frac{1}{2} \tan 2\theta$ in the interval
   from 0 to 2π.

2. What is the period of the
   graph in Question 1? $\frac{\pi}{2}$

3. Write an equation of a tangent
   function that has an asymptote
   at $x = 2$. **Answers may vary.**
   Sample: $y = \tan \frac{\pi}{4}x$.

Alternative Assessment

Have students in small groups
prepare a presentation, illustrated
by a poster, of the unit circle and
the graph of one of the three
functions: sine, cosine, or tangent.
Then let the groups present their
posters and explanations to
the class.

Test Prep

Resources
For additional practice with a
variety of test item formats:
• Standardized Test Prep, p. 775
• Test-Taking Strategies, p. 770
• Test-Taking Strategies with
  Transparencies

30b.

≈ 1.7 in., ≈ 5.2 in.

c. ≈ 5.2 in.², ≈ 15.6 in.²

d. ≈ 3888 tiles, ≈ 1296 tiles

753

46. 2; for $0 \le x < 2\pi$, x is nonnegative and there are only 2 branches of the graph of the tangent function above the x-axis.

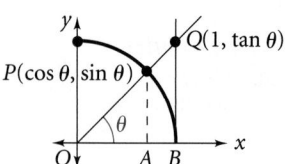

45. Geometry Use the drawing at the right and similar triangles. Justify the statement that $\tan \theta = \frac{\sin \theta}{\cos \theta}$. **See margin.**

46. How many solutions does the equation $x = \tan x$ have for $0 \le x < 2\pi$? Explain.

Test Prep

Multiple Choice

47. Which value is NOT defined? **C**

 A. $\tan 0$ **B.** $\tan \pi$ **C.** $\tan \frac{3\pi}{2}$ **D.** $\frac{1}{\tan \frac{\pi}{4}}$

48. What is the exact value of $\tan \frac{7\pi}{6}$? **H**

 F. $-\sqrt{3}$ **G.** $-\frac{\sqrt{3}}{3}$ **H.** $\frac{\sqrt{3}}{3}$ **J.** $\sqrt{3}$

49. Which pair of values are NOT equal? **D**

 A. $\tan \frac{\pi}{4}$, $-\tan \frac{3\pi}{4}$ **B.** $\tan \frac{\pi}{4}$, $\tan \frac{5\pi}{4}$

 C. $\tan \theta$, $-\tan (-\theta)$ **D.** $\tan \theta$, $\tan (\pi - \theta)$

50. Which equation does NOT represent a vertical asymptote of the graph of $y = \tan \theta$? **G**

 F. $\theta = -\frac{\pi}{2}$ **G.** $\theta = 0$ **H.** $\theta = \frac{\pi}{2}$ **J.** $\theta = \frac{3\pi}{2}$

51. Which function has a period of 4π? **D**

 A. $y = \tan 4\theta$ **B.** $y = \tan 2\theta$ **C.** $y = \tan \frac{1}{2}\theta$ **D.** $y = \tan \frac{1}{4}\theta$

Short Response

52. Explain why there is no discussion of the amplitude of the tangent function in the lesson. **See margin.**

Extended Response

53. Compare the period of $y = \tan \theta$ with the period of $y = \sin \theta$. Use a graph of the two functions to support your statements. **See margin.**

Mixed Review

Lesson 13-5

Solve each equation in the interval from 0 to 2π. Round your answer to the nearest hundredth.

 54. $\cos t = \frac{1}{4}$ **1.32, 4.97**   **55.** $10 \cos t = -2$ **1.77, 4.51**   **56.** $-2 \cos \theta = 0.7$ **1.93, 4.35**

 57. $3 \cos \frac{t}{5} = 1$ **6.15**   **58.** $\cos \frac{3}{4}\theta = -0.6$ **2.95, 5.43**   **59.** $5 \cos \pi t = 0.9$ **0.44, 1.56, 2.44, 3.56, 4.44, 5.56**

Lesson 12-3

Find the mean, median, and mode for each set of values.

 60. 9 6 8 1 3 4 5 2 6 8 4 9 12 3 4 10 7 6 $\approx$**5.9, 6, 4 and 6**

 61. 45 42 39 35 41 45 49 42 43 48 32 51 42 **42.6, 42, 42**

 62. 7.1 8.5 7.0 7.6 8.5 8.1 7.9 8.2 7.3 9.1 8.7 7.9 $\approx$**8, 8, 7.9 and 8.5**

Lesson 11-2

Find the 27th term of each sequence.

 63. 5, 8, 11, ... **83**   **64.** 59, 48, 37, ... **−227**   **65.** 1, 3.5, 6, 8.5, ... **66**

 66. 2.1, 1.7, 1.3, ... **−8.3**   **67.** −11, −5, 1, ... **145**   **68.** 6, −7, −20, ... **−332**

45. Answers may vary.
 Sample: Triangles *OAP* and *OBQ* both share the angle θ and each triangle has a right angle, so they are similar by AA. $\frac{\sin \theta}{\cos \theta} = \frac{AP}{OA} = \frac{BQ}{OB} = \frac{\tan \theta}{1}$. Thus $\frac{\sin \theta}{\cos \theta} = \tan \theta$.

52. [2] There is no discussion of the amplitude of the tangent function because the tangent function has no upper or lower limit.
 [1] incomplete explanation

754

53. [4] (Student graphs $y = \tan \theta$ and $y = \sin \theta$ correctly, showing 2 periods of $y = \tan \theta$ and 1 period of $y = \sin \theta$.) The period of $y = \tan \theta$ is half of the period of $y = \sin \theta$.
 [3] statement correct and graph accurate, but doesn't illustrate 2 periods of $y = \tan \theta$
 [2] accurate graph with incorrect answer OR inaccurate graph with correct answer
 [1] answer only, with no graph

Guided Problem Solving

Understanding Math Problems

Students learn to read and interpret information from problems involving graphs.

Understanding Math Problems Read the problem below. Let the explanation guide you through reading a graph. Check your understanding with the exercises at the bottom of the page.

Write an equation of a tangent function for the graph.

A graph shows data points of a function on a coordinate grid. When you read a graph, you identify information from the graph to help you solve the problem. As you look at a graph, ask yourself the following questions.

What relationship is shown in the graph?

The problem states that the graph shows a tangent function.

What information can I obtain from the graph?

Scale   The scale on the *y*-axis shows that two grid lines represent 3 units. The scale on the *x*-axis shows that four grid lines represent 2π units, which means two grid lines represent π units. Redraw the graph and add labels to the *x*-axis.

Asymptotes   A tangent function has vertical asymptotes. Now that you've added labels, you can see that asymptotes occur at *x*-values of $-\pi, \pi,$ and 3π.

Period   The period is the horizontal distance between asymptotes.

$$\text{period} = \text{distance between asymptotes} = \pi - (-\pi) = 2\pi$$

Now you can use the information you've obtained from the graph to write an equation for the tangent function shown. The standard form for the equation of a tangent function is $y = \tan bx$. Since you know the period, you can find b.

$$\text{period} = \frac{\pi}{b}, \text{ so } b = \frac{\pi}{\text{period}} = \frac{\pi}{2\pi} = \frac{1}{2}$$

Since $\left(-\frac{\pi}{2}, -1\right)$ is on the graph, $a = 1$.

An equation for the tangent function is $y = \tan \frac{1}{2}x$.

EXERCISES

For each graph below (a) identify the asymptotes; (b) identify the period; (c) write an equation for the function, and (d) find the zeros of the function.   See margin.

1.

2.

3.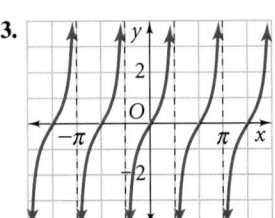

Guided Instruction

Using the graph, show students how to determine the scale on the *x*- and *y*-axes. Explain that not all graphs have each tick mark on the axes labeled, so care must be taken to determine the value represented by each mark. Also tell students to be mindful that the *x*- and *y*-axes may not have the same scale.

Visual Learners

Have students copy the graph and annotate their copy noting the scale, asymptotes, and period. Students may use this annotated copy for future reference.

Exercises

Have students note the differences in scale, asymptotes, and period between each graph.

1. $-\frac{\pi}{2}, \frac{\pi}{2}; \pi; y = \tan x; -\pi, 0, \pi$

2. $\pm\frac{2\pi}{5}, \pm\frac{6\pi}{5}, \pm2\pi; \frac{4\pi}{5}; y = \tan \frac{5}{4}x;$
   $0, \pm\frac{4\pi}{5}, \pm\frac{8\pi}{5}, \pm\frac{12\pi}{5}$

3. $\pm\frac{\pi}{3}, \pm\pi, \pm\frac{5\pi}{3}; \frac{2\pi}{3}; y = \tan \frac{3}{2}x; 0, \pm\frac{2\pi}{3}, \pm\frac{4\pi}{3}$

Objectives

1 To graph translations of trigonometric functions
2 To write equations of translations

Examples

1 Identifying Phase Shifts
2 Graphing Translations
3 Graphing a Combined Translation
4 Graphing a Translation of $y = \sin 2x$
5 Writing a Translation
6 Real-World Connection

Math Background

The trigonometric functions can be defined in a number of different ways, all of which are valid and useful. This chapter emphasizes the functional nature of sine, cosine, and tangent, and defines and explains them by referring to a unit circle and their graphs.

More Math Background: p. 708D

Lesson Planning and Resources

See p. 708E for a list of the resources that support this lesson.

Check Skills You'll Need

For intervention, direct students to:

Vertical and Horizontal Translations
Lesson 2-6: Example 1
Extra Skills and Word Problems Practice, Ch. 2

 Translating Sine and Cosine Functions

What You'll Learn

- To graph translations of trigonometric functions
- To write equations of translations

. . . And Why

To analyze temperature data, as in Example 6

 for Help Lesson 2-6

Graph each pair of equations on the same coordinate plane. Identify each translation as *horizontal, vertical,* or *diagonal.* **1–6. See back of book.**

1. $y = 2x, y = 2x + 5$
2. $g(x) = |x|, f(x) = |x + 3|$
3. $y = -x, y = -x - 1$
4. $g(x) = |x|, h(x) = |x| - 4$
5. $y = -|x|, y = -|x - 2| + 1$
6. $y = x^2, y = (x + 3)^2 - 2$

New Vocabulary • phase shift

---

1 Graphing Translations of Trigonometric Functions

Real-World Connection

A modem (modulator-demodulator) uses phase shifts to convert data between digital signals, which use binary digits, and analog signals, which use waves.

You can translate periodic functions horizontally and vertically using the methods you have used for other functions.

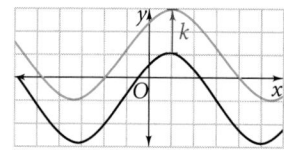

$g(x)$: horizontal translation of $f(x)$ $h(x)$: vertical translation of $f(x)$
$g(x) = f(x - h)$ $h(x) = f(x) + k$

Each horizontal translation of certain periodic functions is a **phase shift.**

When $g(x) = f(x - h)$, the value of h is the amount of the shift left or right. If $h > 0$, the shift is to the right. If $h < 0$, the shift is to the left.

1 EXAMPLE   Identifying Phase Shifts

What is the value of h in each translation? Describe each phase shift (use a phrase such as *3 units to the left*).

a. $g(x) = f(x - 2)$

$\quad h = 2$; the phase shift is 2 units to the right.

b. $y = \cos (x + 4)$
$\quad\quad = \cos (x - (-4))$
$\quad h = -4$; the phase shift is 4 units to the left.

Quick Check ❶ What is the value of h in each translation? Describe each phase shift (use a phrase such as *3 units to the left*).
a. $g(t) = f(t - 5)$ **5; 5 units to the right**
b. $y = \sin (x + 3)$ **−3; 3 units to the left**

Differentiated Instruction **Solutions for All Learners**

Special Needs **L1**
Have students make a poster of the general form of the transformed sine and cosine functions. Students should color code each variable constant and list how each constant transforms the functions.

learning style: visual

Below Level **L2**
Review with students the basic equation for translation, $g(x) = f(x - h) + k$, where h and k are the number of units the graph is moved horizontally and vertically.

learning style: verbal

You can analyze a translation to determine how it relates to the parent function.

2 EXAMPLE Graphing Translations

Use the graph of the parent function $y = \sin x$ at the left. Sketch each translation of the graph in the interval $0 \leq x \leq 2\pi$.

a. $y = \sin x + 3$

Translate the graph of $y = \sin x$ 3 units up.

b. $y = \sin \left(x - \frac{\pi}{2} \right)$

Translate the graph of $y = \sin x$ $\frac{\pi}{2}$ units to the right.

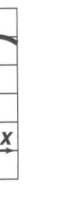 **Quick Check** **2** Use the graph of $y = \sin x$ from Example 2. Sketch each translation of the graph in the interval $0 \leq x \leq 2\pi$. Which translation is a phase shift? **a–b. See back of**
a. $y = \sin x - 2$ **b.** $y = \sin (x - 2)$ **book.**

You can translate both vertically and horizontally to produce combined translations.

3 EXAMPLE Graphing a Combined Translation

Use the graph of the parent function $y = \sin x$ in Example 2. Sketch the translation $y = \sin (x + \pi) - 2$ in the interval $0 \leq x \leq 2\pi$.

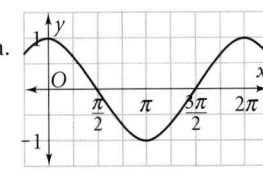

Translate the parent function π units to the left and 2 units down.

 Quick Check **3** The graph at the right shows $y = \cos x$. Use it to graph each combined translation. **a–b. See left.**
a. $y = \cos (x - 2) + 5$
b. $y = \cos (x + 1) + 3$

Lesson 13-7 Translating Sine and Cosine Functions   **757**

2. Teach

Guided Instruction

1 EXAMPLE Math Tip

Make sure that students recall that a translation is one kind of transformation.

2 EXAMPLE Error Prevention

Make sure that students notice the difference that the parentheses make in the meaning of these translations.

PowerPoint

Additional Examples

1 What is the value of h in each translation? Describe each phase shift.
a. $g(x) = f(x + 3)$ $h = -3$; 3 units to the left
b. $y = \sin (x - 2)$ $h = 2$; 2 units to the right

2 Sketch each translation of the graph $y = \sin \theta$ in the interval $0 \leq \theta \leq 2\pi$.
a. $y = \sin \theta + 2$

b. $y = \sin (\theta - \pi)$

Advanced Learners **L4**
Use the basic translation of functions relation to derive a mathematical relation between the sine and cosine functions.

learning style: verbal

English Language Learners **ELL**
Explain how the term *phase shift* applies only to horizontal translations of periodic functions. Because a periodic function repeats, a horizontal translation by an integer multiple of its period will result in an identical graph.

learning style: verbal

757

Video Tutor Help
Visit: PHSchool.com
Web Code: age-0775

Additional Example

③ Use the graph of $y = \sin x$ in Example 2. Sketch the translation $y = \sin\left(x + \frac{\pi}{2}\right) - 1$ in the interval $0 \le x \le 2\pi$.

④ Sketch the graph of $y = \sin 3\left(x - \frac{\pi}{2}\right) - \frac{1}{2}$ in the interval from 0 to 2π.

Guided Instruction

⑥ EXAMPLE **Connection to Meteorology**

Tell the students that data about weather is a particularly rich resource for scientists and mathematicians of all kinds. This is because records have been kept all over the world for a great many years, so there is an enormous database in which to look for patterns.

Online
active math

For: Trig Functions Activity
Use: Interactive Textbook, 13-7

4a.

b.

The translations graphed in Examples 2 and 3 belong to the families of the sine and cosine functions.

🔧 Key Concepts

Summary	Families of Sine and Cosine Functions

Parent Function   **Transformed Function**
$y = \sin x$ $y = a \sin b(x - h) + k$
$y = \cos x$ $y = a \cos b(x - h) + k$

- $|a|$ = amplitude (vertical stretch or shrink)
- $\frac{2\pi}{b}$ = period (when x is in radians and $b > 0$)
- h = phase shift, or horizontal shift
- k = vertical shift

You can use a simpler member of the sine or cosine families to help you graph a more complicated member.

4 EXAMPLE **Graphing a Translation of $y = \sin 2x$**

Sketch the graph of $y = \sin 2\left(x - \frac{\pi}{3}\right) - \frac{3}{2}$ in the interval from 0 to 2π.

Since $a = 1$ and $b = 2$, the graph is a translation of $y = \sin 2x$.

Step 1 Sketch one cycle of $y = \sin 2x$. Use five points in the pattern *zero–max–zero–min–zero*.

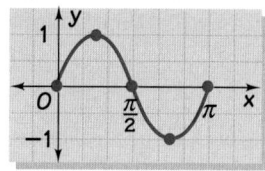

Step 2 Since $h = \frac{\pi}{3}$ and $k = -\frac{3}{2}$, translate the graph $\frac{\pi}{3}$ units to the right and $\frac{3}{2}$ units down. Extend the periodic pattern from 0 to 2π. Sketch the graph.

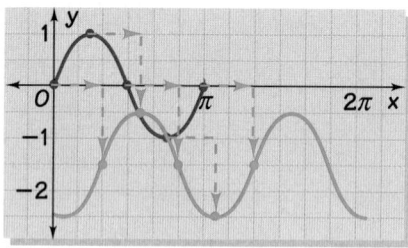

● The blue curve above is the graph of $y = \sin 2\left(x - \frac{\pi}{3}\right) - \frac{3}{2}$.

✓ Quick Check **④** Sketch each graph in the interval from 0 to 2π. **a–b. See left.**
  a. $y = -3 \sin 2\left(x - \frac{\pi}{3}\right) - \frac{3}{2}$
  b. $y = 2 \cos \frac{\pi}{2}(x + 1) - 3$

You can write an equation to describe a translation.

5 EXAMPLE Writing a Translation

Write an equation for each translation.

a. $y = \sin x$, π units down

π units down means $k = -\pi$.

An equation is $y = \sin x - \pi$.

b. $y = -\cos x$, 2 units to the left

2 units to the left means $h = -2$.

An equation is $y = -\cos (x - (-2))$.

✓ **Quick Check** **5** Write an equation for each translation.
a. $y = \cos x$, $\frac{\pi}{2}$ units up $y = \cos x + \frac{\pi}{2}$ **b.** $y = 2 \sin x$, $\frac{\pi}{4}$ units to the right $y = 2 \sin \left(x - \frac{\pi}{4}\right)$

5 Write an equation for each translation.
a. $y = \cos x$, π units up
$y = \cos x + \pi$
b. $y = -\sin x$, 3 units to the right
$y = -\sin (x - 3)$

6 EXAMPLE Real-World Connection

Temperature Cycles The table at the left gives the typical high temperature in New Orleans, Louisiana, on several days of the year (January 1 = 1, February 1 = 32, and so on). Plot the data in the table. Write a cosine model for the data.

Day of Year	Temperature (°F)
16	62
47	65
75	71
106	79
136	85
167	90
197	91
228	90
259	87
289	79
320	70
350	64

Plot the data.

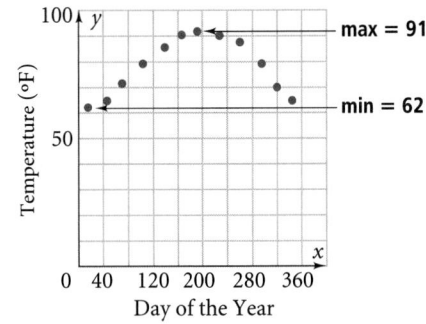

Use the form $y = a \cos b(x - h) + k$. Find values $a, b, h,$ and k.

amplitude $= \frac{1}{2}(\text{max} - \text{min})$

$= \frac{1}{2}(91 - 62)$

$= 14.5$

period $= \frac{2\pi}{b}$

$365 = \frac{2\pi}{b}$ **One complete cycle takes 365 days.**

$b = \frac{2\pi}{365}$

So (choosing $a > 0$), $a = 14.5$.

To find the values h and k, compare $y = 14.5 \cos \frac{2\pi}{365}x$ with the plot of the data.

  phase shift: $h = 197 - 0$

    $= 197$

  vertical shift: $k = 91 - 14.5$

    $= 76.5$

A model for the data is

$y = 14.5 \cos \frac{2\pi}{365}(x - 197) + 76.5$.

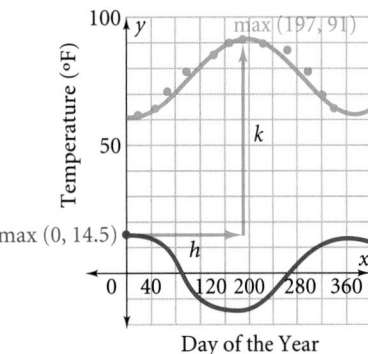

6 Use the following graph, which shows the model for the data given in Example 6, to draw some conclusions about the weather in New Orleans.

Answers may vary. Be sure students mention the highs and lows as well as the fact that the graph shows that fluctuations are moderate and do not go below 50°F nor above 100 degrees.

Resources
• Daily Notetaking Guide 13-7   **L3**

Closure

Ask students: *How do you translate a sine or cosine curve in the coordinate plane? What are the effects of the various parts of the equation* $y = a \cos b(x - h) + k$? The basic shape of a curve remains the same when translated. In the equation above, $|a|$ is the amplitude, $\frac{2\pi}{b}$ is the period, when $b > 0$. The phase shift, or horizontal shift is represented by h and k is the vertical shift.

Assignment Guide

1 A B 1-30

2 A B 31-46
C Challenge   47-54

Test Prep   55-60
Mixed Review   61-72

Homework Quick Check
To check students' understanding
of key skills and concepts, go over
Exercises 28, 37, 43, 44, 46.

Differentiated Instruction Resources

GPS Guided Problem Solving	L3
Enrichment	L4
Reteaching	L2
Practice	L3

1. −1; 1 unit to the left

2. −2; 2 units to the left

3. 1.6; 1.6 units to the right

4. 3; 3 units to the right

5. −π; π units to the left

6. $\frac{5\pi}{7}$; $\frac{5\pi}{7}$ units to the right

760

 Quick Check **a. Estimation** Use the model from Example 6. Estimate the high temperature in New Orleans on September 1 (day 244). **86.5°**

b. Graphing Calculator Graph the model on your calculator. Use it to estimate the first day of the year that the high temperature is likely to reach 75°F. **day 100**

EXERCISES
For more exercises, see *Extra Skill and Word Problem Practice.*

Practice and Problem Solving

A Practice by Example

Example 1
(page 756)

GO for Help

What is the value of *h* in each translation? Describe each phase shift (use a phrase like *3 units to the left*). **1–6. See margin.**

1. $g(x) = f(x + 1)$ **2.** $g(t) = f(t + 2)$

3. $h(z) = g(z − 1.6)$ **4.** $h(x) = f(x − 3)$

5. $y = \sin (x + \pi)$ **6.** $y = \cos \left(x − \frac{5\pi}{7}\right)$

Example 2
(page 757)

Use the function *f(x)* at the right. Graph each translation.

7. $f(x) + 1$ **8.** $f(x) − 3$

9. $f(x + 2)$ **10.** $f(x − 1)$
7–10. See margin pp. 760–761.

Graph each translation of $y = \cos x$ in the interval from 0 to 2π.

11. $y = \cos (x + 3)$ **12.** $y = \cos x + 3$ **13.** $y = \cos x − 4$

14. $y = \cos (x − 4)$ **15.** $y = \cos x + \pi$ **16.** $y = \cos (x − \pi)$
11–16. See back of book.

Example 3
(page 757)

17. 1 unit up

18. 1 unit left and 2 units down

19. $\frac{\pi}{2}$ units left and 2 units up

20. 3 units right and 2 units up

Describe any phase shift and vertical shift in the graph. **17–20. See left.**

17. $y = 3 \sin x + 1$ **18.** $y = 4 \cos (x + 1) − 2$

19. $y = \sin \left(x + \frac{\pi}{2}\right) + 2$ **20.** $y = \cos (x − 3) + 2$

Graph each function in the interval from 0 to 2π.

21. $y = 2 \sin \left(x + \frac{\pi}{4}\right) − 1$ **22.** $y = \sin \left(x + \frac{\pi}{3}\right) + 1$

23. $y = \cos (x − \pi) − 3$ **24.** $y = 2 \sin \left(x − \frac{\pi}{6}\right) + 2$
21–24. See back of book.

Example 4
(page 758)

Graph each function in the interval from 0 to 2π.

25. $y = 3 \sin \frac{1}{2}x$ **26.** $y = \cos 2\left(x + \frac{\pi}{2}\right) − 2$

27. $y = \frac{1}{2} \sin 2x − 1$ **28.** $y = \sin 3\left(x + \frac{\pi}{3}\right)$

29. $y = \sin 2(x + 3) − 2$ **30.** $y = 3 \sin \frac{\pi}{2}(x − 2)$
25–30. See back of book.

Example 5
(page 759)

Write an equation for each translation. **31–36. See margin p. 761.**

31. $y = \sin x, \pi$ units to the left   **32.** $y = \cos x, \frac{\pi}{2}$ units down

33. $y = \sin x, 3$ units up   **34.** $y = \cos x, 1.5$ units to the right

35. $y = \cos x, \frac{3}{2\pi}$ units to the left   **36.** $y = \sin x, 3\pi$ units down

7.

8.

9.

Example 6
(page 759)

37. Temperature The table below shows water temperatures at a buoy in the Gulf of Mexico on several days of the year.

Water Temperatures in the Gulf of Mexico

Day of the Year	16	47	75	106	136	167	197	228	259	289	320	350
Temperature (°F)	71	69	70	73	77	82	85	86	84	82	78	74

SOURCE: *The USA Today Weather Almanac*

a. Plot the data.   **See back of book.**   **b.** Write a cosine model for the data.

$$y = 8.5 \cos \frac{2\pi}{365} (x - 228) + 77.5$$

B **Apply Your Skills**

Write an equation for each translation.

41. $y = 2 \cos \left(x - \frac{\pi}{3}\right) - 1;$
$y = 2 \sin \left(x + \frac{\pi}{6}\right) - 1$

38. $y = \sin x$, 2 units to the right and 4 units down $y = \sin (x - 2) - 4$

39. $y = \cos x$, 3 units to the left and π units up $y = \cos (x + 3) + \pi$

42. $y = -10 \cos \frac{\pi}{10}x;$
$y = 10 \sin \left(\frac{\pi}{10}x - \frac{\pi}{2}\right)$

40. $y = \sin x$, $\frac{\pi}{2}$ units to the right and 3.5 units up $y = \sin \left(x - \frac{\pi}{2}\right) + 3.5$

43a. $\frac{\pi}{2}$; $\sin x = \cos \left(x - \frac{\pi}{2}\right)$

b. $-\frac{\pi}{2}$; $\cos x =$
$\sin \left(x + \frac{\pi}{2}\right)$

Write a cosine function for each graph. Then write a sine function for each graph.

41.

42.

43. The graphs of $y = \sin x$ and $y = \cos x$ are shown at the left.   **a–b. See left.**
GPS **a.** What phase shift will translate the cosine graph onto the sine graph? Write your answer as an equation in the form $\sin x = \cos (x - h)$.
b. What phase shift will translate the sine graph onto the cosine graph? Write your answer as an equation in the form $\cos x = \sin (x - h)$.

44. a. Critical Thinking Use a sine function to model the normal daily high temperature in New Orleans. Use the data given in Example 6 on page 759.
b. Writing How do the sine and cosine models differ?   **a–b. See margin.**
c. Estimation Use your sine model to estimate the high temperature in New Orleans on December 1 (day 334).   **about 66°**
d. Graph your model. Use it to estimate the first day of the year that the high temperature is likely to reach 70°F.   **March 20 (day 79)**

45a. Check students' work.

45. a. Open-Ended Draw a periodic function. Find its amplitude and period. Then sketch a translation of your function 3 units down and 4 units to the left.
b. Critical Thinking Suppose your original function is $f(x)$. Describe your translation using the form $g(x) = f(x - h) + k$. $g(x) = f(x + 4) - 3$

GO **Online**
Homework Video Tutor
Visit: PHSchool.com
Web Code: age-1307

46. a. Write $y = 3 \sin (2x - 4) + 1$ in the form $y = a \sin b(x - h) + k$. (*Hint:* Factor where possible.) $y = 3 \sin 2(x - 2) + 1$
b. Find the amplitude and period. Describe any translations.
3, π; 2 units right and 1 unit up

C **Challenge**

Use a graphing calculator to graph each function in the interval from 0 to 2π. Then sketch each graph.   **47–54. See back of book.**

Graphing Calculator Hint
Change window values between exercises to see each graph clearly.

47. $y = \sin x + x$
48. $y = \sin x + 2x$
49. $y = \sin x - 0.5x$
50. $y = \cos x - x$
51. $y = \cos x - 2x$
52. $y = \cos x + x$
53. $y = \sin (x + \cos x)$
54. $y = \sin (x + 2 \cos x)$

10.

31. $y = \sin (x + \pi)$

32. $y = \cos x - \frac{\pi}{2}$

33. $y = \sin x + 3$

34. $y = \cos (x - 1.5)$

35. $y = \cos \left(x + \frac{3}{2\pi}\right)$

36. $y = \sin x - 3\pi$

4. Assess & Reteach

PowerPoint
Lesson Quiz

1. Sketch the graph of $y = \frac{1}{2} \sin x - 1$ in the interval from 0 to 2π.

2. What is the value of h in the translation $g(x) = f(x + 4)$? $h = -4$

3. Describe the phase shift in the translation $g(x) = f(x + 4)$.
four units to the left

4. Write an equation for the translation of $y = \sin x$, $\frac{\pi}{2}$ units down. $y = \sin x - \frac{\pi}{2}$

Alternative Assessment

Ask students to write a journal page or two about what they have learned in this lesson, including examples and sketches of graphs. Ask them to describe any points about which they are still confused.

Test Prep

Resources
For additional practice with a variety of test item formats:
• Standardized Test Prep, p. 775
• Test-Taking Strategies, p. 770
• Test-Taking Strategies with Transparencies

44a. $14.5 \sin \left(\frac{2\pi}{365}\right.$
$\left.(x - 105.75)\right) + 76.5$

b. The difference between the two models is the sine function is a horizontal shift of the cosine function.

761

Use this Checkpoint Quiz to check students' understanding of the skills and concepts of Lessons 13-4 through 13-7.

Resources
Grab & Go
• Checkpoint Quiz 2

58–59. Answers will vary. Sample:

58. [2] If the function $y = \cos \theta$ is shifted to the right by $\frac{\pi}{2}$ radians, the result is $y = \cos (\theta - \frac{\pi}{2})$, which is the same as $y = \sin \theta$. So $a = 1$, and $b = -\frac{\pi}{2}$.

[1] answer only, with no work shown

59. [2] $y = 4 \sin x$ has an amplitude of 4, but a min. value of -1. Shift the graph up 5 units so the min. value is 4. The function is $y = 4 \sin \theta + 5$.

[1] answer only, with no work shown

60. [4] $\sin \theta = 3 \sin \theta$
$\sin \theta - \sin \theta$
$= 3 \sin \theta - \sin \theta$
$0 = 2 \sin \theta$
$\frac{0}{2} = \frac{2 \sin \theta}{2}$
$0 = \sin \theta$
$\sin \theta = 0$ at $-\pi$, 0, π, and 2π

[3] minor computational error

[2] partial answer, with correct work shown

[1] answer only, with no work shown

61. $\frac{\pi}{6}$; $\theta = -\frac{\pi}{12}, \frac{\pi}{12}$

62. 4π; $\theta = -2\pi, 2\pi$

63. $\frac{2\pi}{3}$; $\theta = -\frac{\pi}{3}, -\frac{\pi}{3}$

64. 6π; $\theta = -3\pi, 3\pi$

Multiple Choice

55. Which function is a phase shift of $y = \sin \theta$ by 5 units to the left? **C**
 A. $y = 5 \sin \theta$ **B.** $y = \sin \theta + 5$ **C.** $y = \sin (\theta + 5)$ **D.** $y = \sin 5\theta$

56. Which function is a translation of $y = \cos \theta$ by 5 units down? **G**
 F. $y = -5 \cos \theta$ **G.** $y = \cos \theta - 5$
 H. $y = \cos (\theta - 5)$ **J.** $y = \cos (-5\theta)$

57. Which function is a translation of $y = \sin \theta$ that is $\frac{\pi}{3}$ units up and $\frac{\pi}{2}$ units to the left? **B**

 A. $y = \sin \left(\theta + \frac{\pi}{3}\right) + \frac{\pi}{2}$ **B.** $y = \sin \left(\theta + \frac{\pi}{2}\right) + \frac{\pi}{3}$

 C. $y = \sin \left(\theta - \frac{\pi}{2}\right) + \frac{\pi}{3}$ **D.** $y = \sin \left(\theta - \frac{\pi}{3}\right) - \frac{\pi}{2}$

Short Response

58. Find values of a and b such that the function $y = \sin \theta$ can be expressed as $y = a \cos (\theta + b)$. **See margin.**

59. Write a function that is a transformation of $y = \sin \theta$ so that its amplitude is 4 and its minimum value is 1. Show your work. **See margin.**

Extended Response

60. Find all the values of θ between $-\pi$ and 2π for which $\sin \theta = 3 \sin \theta$. Show your work. **See margin.**

Mixed Review

Lesson 13-6

GO for Help

Identify the period of each function. Then tell where two asymptotes occur for each function. **61–64. See margin.**

61. $y = \tan 6\theta$ 62. $y = \tan \frac{\theta}{4}$ 63. $y = \tan 1.5\theta$ 64. $y = \tan \frac{\theta}{6}$

Lesson 12-6

For the given probability of success p on each trial, find the probability of x successes in n trials.

65. $x = 4, n = 5, p = 0.2$ **0.0064**   66. $x = 3, n = 5, p = 0.6$ **0.3456**

67. $x = 4, n = 8, p = 0.7$ **≈0.136**   68. $x = 7, n = 8, p = 0.7$ **≈0.198**

Lesson 11-5

Evaluate the finite series for the specified number of terms.

69. $2 + 4 + 8 + \ldots$; $n = 5$ **62**   70. $3 + 12 + 48 + \ldots$; $n = 7$ **16,383**

71. $-1 - 6 - 36 + \ldots$; $n = 8$ 72. $120 - 30 + 7.5 - \ldots$; $n = 5$
                   −335,923   **96.09375**

Checkpoint Quiz 2   **Lessons 13-4 through 13-7**

Graph each function in the interval from -2π to 2π. **1–10. See back of book.**

1. $y = \sin 4x$ 2. $y = 3 \cos x$ 3. $y = -2 \sin \pi x$

4. $y = 2 \cos \frac{\pi}{2}x$ 5. $y = \tan 2x$ 6. $y = -\tan x$

7. $y = \cos (x - 2)$ 8. $y = \sin x + 4$ 9. $y = 3 \tan \frac{\pi}{4}x$

10. Sketch the graph of $y = \sin 3x$ after a translation of 2 units to the right and π units down.

Reciprocal Trigonometric Functions

What You'll Learn

- To evaluate reciprocal trigonometric functions
- To graph reciprocal trigonometric functions

. . . And Why

To find indirect measurements, as in Example 6

 Check Skills You'll Need

GO for Help Lesson 7-8 and page 879

Find the reciprocal of each fraction.

1. $\frac{9}{13}$ $\frac{13}{9}$
2. $\frac{-5}{8}$ $-\frac{8}{5}$
3. $\frac{1}{2\pi}$ 2π
4. $\frac{4m}{15}$ $\frac{15}{4m}$
5. $\frac{14}{-t}$ $-\frac{t}{14}$

Graph each pair of relations on the same coordinate plane. 6–9. See back

6. $y = x, y = -x$
7. $y = x^2, y = \pm\sqrt{x}$ of book.
8. $y = |2x|, y = -|2x|$
9. $y = -6x^2, y = \pm\frac{\sqrt{6x}}{6}$

New Vocabulary • cosecant • secant • cotangent

---

1 Evaluating Reciprocal Trigonometric Functions

In earlier lessons in this chapter, you studied three trigonometric functions—sine, cosine, and tangent. Three other functions—cosecant, secant, and cotangent—are related to reciprocals of the three you have used.

 Key Concepts

Definition	**Cosecant, Secant, and Cotangent Functions**

The cosecant (csc), secant (sec), and cotangent (cot) functions are defined using reciprocals. Their domains do not include the real numbers θ that make a denominator zero.

$$\csc\theta = \frac{1}{\sin\theta} \qquad \sec\theta = \frac{1}{\cos\theta} \qquad \cot\theta = \frac{1}{\tan\theta}$$

You can evaluate reciprocal trigonometric functions by using the definitions.

Graphing Calculator Hint

Caution! The keys for $\sin^{-1}$, $\cos^{-1}$, and $\tan^{-1}$ do not give reciprocals. They represent inverse trigonometric functions, which you will study in Chapter 14.

1 EXAMPLE Using Reciprocals

a. Find csc 60°.

Use a calculator in degree mode.

```
1/sin (60)
          1.154700538
```

Use the definition.
$$\csc 60° = \frac{1}{\sin 60°}$$

b. Suppose $\cos\theta = \frac{5}{13}$. Find sec θ.

$\sec\theta = \frac{1}{\cos\theta}$ **Use the definition.**

$= \frac{1}{\frac{5}{13}}$ **Substitute.**

$= \frac{13}{5}$ **Simplify.**

 Quick Check **a.** Suppose $\sin\theta = \frac{15}{8}$. Find csc θ. $\frac{8}{15}$

b. Find cot 55° to the nearest hundredth.
≈ 0.70

Objectives

1 To evaluate reciprocal trigonometric functions
2 To graph reciprocal trigonometric functions

Examples

1 Using Reciprocals
2 Finding Exact Values
3 Using Radians
4 Sketching a Graph
5 Using Technology to Graph Reciprocals
6 Real-World Connection

 Professional Development

Math Background

Students may have used trigonometric functions previously in problems involving indirect measurement. If so, they know that these functions can also be defined as the ratio of sides in a right triangle. Defining sine as the ratio of the lengths of the leg opposite the acute angle and the hypotenuse makes clear the reciprocal relationship with cosecant.

More Math Background: p. 708D

Lesson Planning and Resources

See p. 708E for a list of the resources that support this lesson.

PowerPoint

Bell Ringer Practice

Check Skills You'll Need
For intervention, direct students to:

Graphing Two-Variable Equations
Skills Handbook: p. 879

Radical Functions
Lesson 7-8:
Extra Skills and Word Problems Practice, Ch. 7

Differentiated Instruction Solutions for All Learners

Special Needs L1
Have students examine the table in Example 4. Ask: *What is the reciprocal of 1?* 1 *What is the reciprocal of 0?* undefined *Where is csc x = sin x?* when sin x = 1 *Where are asymptotes in the graph of* y = csc x? when sin x = 0

learning style: verbal

Below Level L2
Point out to students that the definitions of the reciprocal trig functions are true for all values of A for which both functions are defined. So they are identities.

learning style: verbal

2. Teach

Guided Instruction

1 EXAMPLE Visual Learners

Draw the following chart on the board as a memory aid for the reciprocal relationships.

sin x ←┐
cos x ←┘
tan x ←┐
cot x ←┘
sec x ←
csc x ←

2 EXAMPLE Alternative Method

Since the reciprocal of $\frac{a}{b}$ is always $\frac{b}{a}$ (a and $b \neq 0$), the reciprocal of $\frac{\sqrt{3}}{2}$ can be written directly as $\frac{2}{\sqrt{3}}$. Rationalizing the denominator produces the result csc $60° = \frac{2\sqrt{3}}{3}$.

3 EXAMPLE Technology Tip

Ask students what would happen if you left the calculator in degree mode to do these calculations. The angle $\frac{\pi}{3}$ is interpreted as an angle of a little more than one degree rather than 60 degrees.

PowerPoint
Additional Examples

1 a. Find csc 45°. **about 1.41**
 b. Suppose cos $\theta = \frac{4}{5}$. Find sec θ. $\frac{5}{4}$

2 Find the exact value of csc 45°.
$\sqrt{2}$

3 Use a calculator to evaluate each expression. Round to the nearest thousandth.
a. cot $\frac{\pi}{5}$ **1.376**
b. sec (-2) **−2.403**

You can use what you know about the unit circle to find exact values for reciprocal trigonometric functions.

2 EXAMPLE Finding Exact Values

Multiple Choice Which expression represents the exact value of csc 60°?

(A) $\frac{\sqrt{3}}{3}$ (B) $\frac{\sqrt{3}}{2}$ (C) $\frac{2\sqrt{3}}{3}$ (D) $\sqrt{3}$

Use the unit circle to find the exact value of sin 60°. Then write the reciprocal.

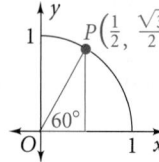

Test-Taking Tip

A point on the unit circle has coordinates (cos x, sin x) for an angle of measure x in standard position.

The y-coordinate of point P is $\frac{\sqrt{3}}{2}$.

$$\csc 60° = \frac{1}{\sin 60°} \quad \text{Use the definition.}$$

$$= \frac{1}{\frac{\sqrt{3}}{2}} \quad \text{Substitute.}$$

$$= \frac{2}{\sqrt{3}} \quad \text{Simplify.}$$

$$= \frac{2\sqrt{3}}{3} \quad \text{Rationalize the denominator.}$$

● The correct choice is C.

✓ **Quick Check** **2** Find each exact value.
a. sec 60° **2**   b. cot 45° **1**   c. csc 30° **2**

You can also evaluate the reciprocal functions in radians.

3 EXAMPLE Using Radians

Evaluate each expression. Use your calculator's radian mode. Round to the nearest thousandth.

a. cot $\frac{\pi}{3}$ b. sec (-1)

$$\cot \frac{\pi}{3} = \frac{1}{\tan \frac{\pi}{3}}$$ $$\sec (-1) = \frac{1}{\cos (-1)}$$

1/tan (π/3)
.5773502692

1/cos (–1)
1.850815718

● cot $\frac{\pi}{3} \approx 0.577$ sec $(-1) \approx 1.851$

✓ **Quick Check** **3** Use a calculator to evaluate each expression. Each angle is given in radians. Round to the nearest thousandth.
a. csc (-1.5) **−1.003**   b. sec 2 **−2.403**   c. cot π **undefined**

Differentiated Instruction Solutions for All Learners

Advanced Learners **L4**
Students who created a table for the trigonometric functions in terms of a right triangle can now expand that table to the reciprocal functions.

learning style: verbal

English Language Learners **ELL**
Students may have difficulty remembering which trig functions are related to which reciprocal trig functions. Tell students that each s is paired with a c. So, secant and cosine are reciprocals, as are sine and cosecant.

learning style: verbal

2 Graphing Reciprocal Trigonometric Functions

The graphs of reciprocal trigonometric functions have asymptotes where their denominators are zero.

4 EXAMPLE Sketching a Graph

Sketch the graphs of $y = \sin x$ and $y = \csc x$ in the interval from 0 to 2π.

Step 1 Make a table of values.

x	0	$\frac{\pi}{6}$	$\frac{\pi}{3}$	$\frac{\pi}{2}$	$\frac{2\pi}{3}$	$\frac{5\pi}{6}$	π	$\frac{7\pi}{6}$	$\frac{4\pi}{3}$	$\frac{3\pi}{2}$	$\frac{5\pi}{3}$	$\frac{11\pi}{6}$	2π
sin x	0	0.5	0.9	1	0.9	0.5	0	−0.5	−0.9	−1	−0.9	−0.5	0
csc x	■	2	1.2	1	1.2	2	■	−2	−1.2	−1	−1.2	−2	■

Step 2 Plot the points and sketch the graphs.

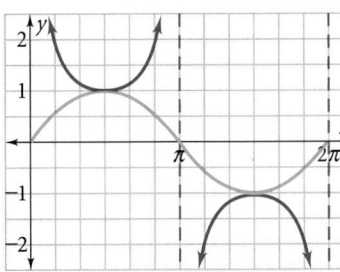

y = csc *x* will have a vertical asymptote wherever its denominator (sin *x*) is 0.

✓ **Quick Check** ④ Graph $y = \tan x$ and $y = \cot x$ in the interval from 0 to 2π. **See left.**

4.

You can use a graphing calculator to graph trigonometric functions quickly.

5 EXAMPLE Using Technology to Graph Reciprocals

Graph $y = \sec x$. Find the value of sec 20°.

Step 1 Use degree mode.
Graph $y = \frac{1}{\cos x}$.

Xmin=−360
Xmax=360
Xscl=30
Ymin=−5
Ymax=5
Yscl=1

Step 2 Use the TABLE feature.

X	Y1
20	1.0642
21	1.0711
22	1.0785
23	1.0864
24	1.0946
25	1.1034
26	1.1126

X=20

sec 20° ≈ 1.0642

✓ **Quick Check** ⑤ Use the graph of the reciprocal trigonometric function to find csc 45°. ≈1.4142

④ **EXAMPLE** Connection to Algebra

Ask where the graph of $y = \sec x$ will have a vertical asymptote in the interval from 0 to 2π. $\frac{\pi}{2}, \frac{3\pi}{2}$

⑥ **EXAMPLE** Teaching Tip

Point out that the units in which the string is measured must be feet because the height of the person is given in feet.

PowerPoint
Additional Examples

④ Graph $y = \cos x$ and $y = \sec x$ in the interval from 0 to 2π.

⑤ Use the graph of $y = \sec x$ in Example 5 to find the value of sec 13°. about 1.0263

⑥ Use the function in Example 6 to find the length of string needed to form an angle of 55°.
about 10.5 ft

Resources
• Daily Notetaking Guide 13-8 **L3**

Closure

Ask: *How can you graph the cotangent, secant, and cosecant functions on the calculator? Where are the asymptotes for these functions?* You can graph these functions by graphing the reciprocals of the tangent, cosine, and sine functions. For example, enter cos(x)/sin(x) to graph cot(x). The asymptotes will be located wherever sin(x) = 0.

3. Practice

Assignment Guide

1 A B 1-28, 42-49, 54-58, 70

2 A B 29-41, 50-53, 59-69

C Challenge   71-74

Test Prep   75-82
Mixed Review   83-92

Homework Quick Check

To check students' understanding of key skills and concepts, go over Exercises 26, 41, 55-58, 60.

Error Prevention!

Exercises 56–58 Make sure students remember that division by zero is undefined.

You can use a reciprocal trigonometric function to solve a real-world problem.

6 EXAMPLE   **Real-World Connection**

Indirect Measurement A handler of a parade balloon holds a line of length y. The length is modeled by the function $y = d \sec \theta$, where d is the distance from the handler of the balloon to the point on the ground just below the balloon, and θ is the angle formed by the line and the ground. Graph the function for $d = 6$. Find the length of line needed to form an angle of 60°.

$y = 6 \sec \theta = 6\left(\dfrac{1}{\cos \theta}\right) = \dfrac{6}{\cos \theta}$ **Use the definition of secant. Simplify.**

Graph the function. Use the **value** feature.

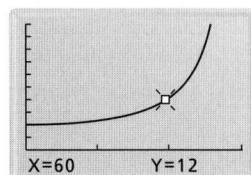

Xmin=0
Xmax=90
Xscl=30
Ymin=0
Ymax=30
Yscl=3

X=60   Y=12

• To form an angle of 60°, the line must be 12 ft long.

Quick Check **6** How long must the line be to form an angle of 30°? Of 45°? Of 85°?
6.9 ft; 8.5 ft; 68.8 ft

Real-World Connection

Some large parade balloons need more than 50 physically fit, trained handlers.

EXERCISES

For more exercises, see *Extra Skill and Word Problem Practice.*

Practice and Problem Solving

A Practice by Example

Example 1
(page 763)

GO for Help

Evaluate each expression. Give your answer as a decimal rounded to the nearest hundredth.

1. csc 100° **1.02**   **2.** csc 80° **1.02**   **3.** cot (−55°) **−0.70** **4.** sec 200° **−1.06**

Evaluate each expression. Write your answer in exact form.

5. Suppose $\tan \theta = \frac{20}{15}$. Find cot θ. $\frac{3}{4}$ **6.** Suppose $\sin \theta = \frac{13}{18}$. Find csc θ. $\frac{18}{13}$

7. Suppose $\cos \theta = -\frac{21}{35}$. Find sec θ. $-\frac{5}{3}$ **8.** Suppose $\tan \theta = -\frac{4}{3}$. Find cot θ. $-\frac{3}{4}$

Example 2
(page 764)

Find the exact value of each expression. If the expression is undefined, write *undefined*.

9. sec 45° $\sqrt{2}$ **10.** cot 60° $\frac{\sqrt{3}}{3}$ **11.** cot 90° **0**   **12.** sec 180° **−1**

13. csc 0° **undefined** **14.** csc 60° $\frac{2\sqrt{3}}{3}$ **15.** cot 0° **undefined** **16.** cot 30° $\sqrt{3}$

17. sec 90° **undefined**   **18.** csc 30° **2**   **19.** sec 60° **2**   **20.** csc 45° $\sqrt{2}$

Example 3
(page 764)

Evaluate each expression to the nearest hundredth. Each angle is given in radians.

21. cot 3 **−7.02**   **22.** sec π **−1**   **23.** csc $\frac{\pi}{2}$ **1**   **24.** sec (−π) **−1**

25. sec 2.5 **−1.25**   **26.** csc (−3.2) **17.13** **27.** cot $\frac{\pi}{6}$ **1.73**   **28.** csc (−4.5) **1.02**

Example 4
(page 765)

Graph each function in the interval from 0 to 2π.   **29–32. See margin.**

29. $y = \sec 2\theta$ **30.** $y = \cot \theta$ **31.** $y = \csc 2\theta - 1$ **32.** $y = \csc 2\theta$

29.

30.

31.

32.

Example 5
(page 765)

Use the graph of the appropriate reciprocal trigonometric function to find each value. Round to four decimal places.

33. sec 30° **1.1547**   **34.** sec 80° **5.7588**   **35.** sec 110° **−2.9238**   **36.** csc 30° **2**

37. csc 70° **1.0642**   **38.** csc 130° **1.3054**   **39.** cot 30° **1.7321**   **40.** cot 60° **0.5774**

Example 6
(page 766)

41. Indirect Measurement A communications tower has wires anchoring it to the ground. Each wire is attached to the tower at a height 20 ft above the ground. The length y of the wire is modeled with the function $y = 20 \csc \theta$, where θ is the measure of the angle formed by the wire and the ground.
  a. Graph the function.   **See back of book.**
  b. Find the length of wire needed to form an angle of 45°.   ≈28.3 ft
  c. Find the length of wire needed to form an angle of 60°.   ≈23.1 ft
  d. Find the length of wire needed to form an angle of 75°.   ≈20.7 ft

B **Apply Your Skills**

Evaluate each expression. Write your answer in exact form. If appropriate, also state it as a decimal rounded to the nearest hundredth. If the expression is undefined, write *undefined*.

42. $\cot(-45°)$ −1
43. $\sec(-30°)$ $\frac{2\sqrt{3}}{3}$; 1.15

44. $\csc(-90°)$ −1
45. $\sec(-180°)$ −1

Graph each function in the interval from 0 to 2π.   **46–49. See margin.**

46. $y = \csc \theta - \frac{\pi}{2}$
47. $y = \sec \frac{1}{4}\theta$

48. $y = -\sec \pi\theta$
49. $y = \cot \frac{\theta}{3}$

Match each function with its graph.

50. $y = \frac{1}{\sin x}$ **B**
51. $y = \frac{1}{\cos x}$ **C**

52. $y = -\frac{1}{\sin x}$ **A**
53. $y = \frac{1}{\tan x}$ **D**

A.

B.

C.

D.
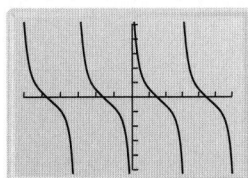

54a. domain: all real numbers except multiples of π; range: all real numbers ≥1 or ≤−1; period 2π

54. a. What are the domain, range, and period of $y = \csc x$?   **See left.**
  b. What is the relative minimum in the interval $0 \le x \le \pi$?   1
  c. What is the relative maximum in the interval $\pi \le x \le 2\pi$?   −1

55. Reasoning Use the relationship $\csc x = \frac{1}{\sin x}$ to explain why each statement is true.   **Reciprocals have the same sign.**
  a. When the graph of $y = \sin x$ is positive, so is the graph of $y = \csc x$.
  b. When the graph of $y = \sin x$ is near a y-value of −1, so is the graph of $y = \csc x$.   **The reciprocal of −1 is −1.**

Homework Video Tutor
Visit: PHSchool.com
Web Code: age-1308

PowerPoint
Lesson Quiz

1. What are the equations of the two lines that define the maximum and minimum values for the graphs of $y = \sin x$ and $y = \cos x$?
$y = 1$ and $y = -1$

2. Which basic trigonometric functions have vertical asymptotes?
$y = \tan x$, $y = \cot x$,
$y = \sec x$, $y = \csc x$

3. What are not in the ranges of $y = \sec x$ and $y = \csc x$?
$-1 < y < 1$

Alternative Assessment

Have students work in small groups to make a poster that includes the graphs of all six of the trigonometric functions. Have groups exchange and check and correct the work before displaying the posters in the classroom.

46.

47.

48.

49.

59a.

b. 63.9 ft

---

56. csc 180° is undefined because sin 180° is 0 and csc $\theta = \frac{1}{\sin \theta}$.

57. sec 90° is undefined because cos 90° is 0 and sec $\theta = \frac{1}{\cos \theta}$.

58. cot 0° is undefined because sin 0° is 0 and cot $\theta = \frac{\cos \theta}{\sin \theta}$.

60a.

b. The domain of $y = \tan x$ is all real numbers except odd multiples of $\frac{\pi}{2}$, which are its asymptotes. The domain of $y = \cot x$ is all real numbers except multiples of π, which are its asymptotes. The range of both functions is all real numbers.

c. The graphs have the same period and range. Their asymptotes are shifted by $\frac{\pi}{2}$.

d. Answers may vary. Sample: $x = \frac{\pi}{4}$, $x = \frac{3\pi}{4}$

71. $y = \sec x$ and $y = \csc x$ are not parabolas because parabolas are not restricted by asymptotes, whereas the curves of $y = \sec x$ and $y = \csc x$ are between asymptotes.

768

✏️ **Writing Explain why each expression is undefined.** 56–58. See margin.

56. csc 180°   **57.** sec 90°   **58.** cot 0°

59a–b. See left.

🌐 **59. Indirect Measurement** The function $y = 60 \sec \theta$ models the length y of a fire ladder as a function of the measure of the angle θ formed by the ladder and the horizontal when the hinge of the ladder is 60 ft from the building.

a. Graph the function.

b. In the photo, $\theta = 20°$. How far is the ladder extended?

c. How far is the ladder extended when it forms an angle of 30°?   **69.3 ft**

d. Suppose the ladder is extended to its full length of 80 ft. What angle does it form with the horizontal? How far up a building can the ladder reach when fully extended? (*Hint:* Use the information in the photo.)   ≈41.4°; 60.9 ft

GPS **60. a.** Graph $y = \tan x$ and $y = \cot x$ on the same axes.   a–d. See margin.

✏️ b. State the domain, the range, and the asymptotes of each function.

✏️ c. **Writing** Compare the two graphs. How are they alike? How are they different?

📦 d. **Geometry** The graph of the cotangent function can be reflected about a line to graph the tangent function. Name at least two lines that have this property.

🖩 **Graph each function in the interval from 0 to 2π. Describe any phase shift and vertical shift in the graph.**   61–68. See back of book.

61. $y = \sec 2\theta + 3$

62. $y = \sec 2\left(\theta + \frac{\pi}{2}\right)$

63. $y = \csc 2\theta - 1$

64. $y = \csc 2\left(\theta - \frac{\pi}{2}\right)$

65. $y = -2 \sec (x - 4)$

66. $f(x) = 3 \csc (x + 2) - 1$

67. $y = \cot 2(x + \pi) + 3$

68. $g(x) = 2 \sec \left(3\left(x - \frac{\pi}{6}\right)\right) - 2$

69. a. Graph $y = -\cos x$ and $y = -\sec x$ on the same axes.   a–e. See back

b. State the domain, the range, and the period of each function. of book.

✏️ c. For which values of x does $-\cos x = -\sec x$? Justify your answer.

✏️ d. **Writing** Compare the two graphs. How are they alike? How are they different?

e. **Reasoning** Is the value of $-\sec x$ positive when $-\cos x$ is positive and negative when $-\cos x$ is negative? Justify your answer.

70. a. Critical Thinking Which expression gives the correct value of csc 60°?   **II**

I. $\sin ((60^{-1})^\circ)$ **II.** $(\sin 60°)^{-1}$ **III.** $(\cos 60°)^{-1}$

b. Which expression in part (a) represents $\sin \left(\frac{1}{60}\right)^\circ$?   **I**

ⓒ Challenge

71. Reasoning Each branch of $y = \sec x$ and $y = \csc x$ is a curve. Explain why these curves cannot be parabolas. (*Hint:* Do parabolas have asymptotes?)   See margin.

73a.

b. Answers may vary. Sample: Given $y = \cot bx$, as $|b|$ decreases, the period increases; as $|b|$ increases, the period decreases. If $b < 0$, $y = \cot bx$ begins each branch with negative y-values and ends with positive y-values; the opposite is true for $b > 0$.

72. $y = \cos 3x$ cycles 3 times for each cycle of $y = \cos x$. Thus, for each cycle of $y = \sec x$, $y = \sec 3x$ cycles 3 times, and each cycle of $y = \sec 3x$ is $\frac{1}{3}$ as wide as one cycle of $y = \sec x$.

72. Reasoning Consider the relationship between the graphs of $y = \cos x$ and $y = \cos 3x$. Use the relationship to explain the distance between successive branches of the graphs of $y = \sec x$ and $y = \sec 3x$.

73. a. Graph $y = \cot x$, $y = \cot 2x$, $y = \cot(-2x)$, and $y = \cot \frac{1}{2}x$ on the same axes. **a–b. See margin p. 768.**

b. Make a Conjecture Describe how the graph of $y = \cot bx$ changes as the value of b changes.

74. a. Graph $y = \sec x$, $y = 2 \sec x$, $y = -3 \sec x$, and $y = \frac{1}{2} \sec x$ on the same axes. **a–b. See margin.**

b. Make a Conjecture Describe how the graph of $y = b \sec x$ changes as the value of b changes.

Test Prep

Gridded Response

For Exercises 75–78, suppose $\cos \theta = \frac{3}{5}$ and $\sin \theta > 0$. Enter each answer as a fraction.

75. What is $\tan \theta$? **4/3**

76. What is $\sec \theta$? **5/3**

77. What is $\cot \theta$? **3/4**

78. What is $\csc \theta$? **5/4**

For Exercises 79–82, suppose $\tan \theta = \frac{4}{3}$, $\sin \theta > 0$, and $-\frac{\pi}{2} \le \theta < \frac{\pi}{2}$. Enter each answer as a decimal.

79. What is $\cot \theta + \cos \theta$? **1.35**

80. What is $(\sin \theta)(\cot \theta)$? **0.6**

81. What is $\sec \theta \div \tan \theta$? **1.25**

82. What is $\sin \theta + \cos \theta + \cot \theta + \csc \theta$? **3.4**

Mixed Review

 GO for Help

Lesson 13-7

Find the amplitude and period of each function. Describe any phase shift and vertical shift in the graph. **83–86. See margin.**

83. $y = 2 \sin x - 5$

84. $y = -\cos(x + 4) - 7$

85. $y = -3 \sin\left(x + \frac{\pi}{6}\right) + 4$

86. $y = 5 \cos \pi(x - 1.5) - 8$

Lesson 12-7

Sketch a normal curve for each distribution. Label the x-axis values at one, two, and three standard deviations from the mean. **87–88. See margin.**

87. mean = 25, standard deviation = 5

88. mean = 25, standard deviation = 10

Lesson 11-6

Write and evaluate a sum to approximate the area under each curve for the domain $-1 \le x \le 2$. **89–92. See margin.**
a. Use inscribed rectangles 1 unit wide.
b. Use circumscribed rectangles 1 unit wide.

89. $f(x) = 3x^2$

90. $y = x^2 + 4$

91. $g(x) = -x^2 + 4$

92. $g(x) = -x^2 + 8$

84. 1, 2π; 4 units left, 7 units down

85. 3, 2π; $\frac{\pi}{6}$ units left, 4 units up

86. 5, 2; 1.5 units right, 8 units down

87.

88.

89a. $1(0) + 1(0) + 1(3)$, 3 units^2

b. $1(3) + 1(3) + 1(12)$, 18 units^2

90a. $1(4) + 1(4) + 1(5)$, 13 units^2

b. $1(5) + 1(5) + 1(8)$, 18 units^2

91a. $1(3) + 1(3) + 1(0)$, 6 units^2

b. $1(4) + 1(4) + 1(3)$, 11 units^2

92a. $1(7) + 1(7) + 1(4)$, 18 units^2

b. $1(8) + 1(8) + 1(7)$, 23 units^2

74a.

b. Answers may vary. Sample: As $|b| > 1$ increases, the graph of $y = b \sec x$ stretches vertically. As $|b|$ decreases from 1 to 0, the graph shrinks vertically toward the x-axis. For $b < 0$, the graph of $y = b \sec x$ is a reflection of $y = |b| \sec x$ across the x-axis. The asymptotes remain the same for all values of b.

83. 2, 2π; 5 units down

769

Test-Taking Strategies ## Using Mental Math

You can solve many problems quickly when you know the sine and cosine of special angles and the pattern of the y-values of the periodic function.

θ	0° or 0 radians	30° or $\frac{\pi}{6}$ radians	45° or $\frac{\pi}{4}$ radians	60° or $\frac{\pi}{3}$ radians	90° or $\frac{\pi}{2}$ radians
$\sin \theta$	0	$\frac{1}{2}$	$\frac{\sqrt{2}}{2}$	$\frac{\sqrt{3}}{2}$	1
$\cos \theta$	1	$\frac{\sqrt{3}}{2}$	$\frac{\sqrt{2}}{2}$	$\frac{1}{2}$	0

1 EXAMPLE

Find each exact value.

a. $\sin 150°$

The terminal side of the angle lies in Quadrant II and forms an angle of 30° with the x-axis.

$\sin 150° = \sin 30° = \frac{1}{2}$

b. $\cos \left(-\frac{\pi}{4}\right)$

The terminal side of the angle lies in Quadrant IV and forms an angle of $\frac{\pi}{4}$ radians with the x-axis.

$\cos \left(-\frac{\pi}{4}\right) = \cos \frac{\pi}{4} = \frac{\sqrt{2}}{2}$

2 EXAMPLE

Solve each equation in the interval from 0° to 360°. Give exact answers.

a. $\sin \theta = -\frac{\sqrt{2}}{2}$

The sine is negative, so the terminal side of the angle must lie in Quadrant III or IV. It forms an angle of 45° with the x-axis.

$\theta = 180° + 45° = 225°$

$\theta = 360° - 45° = 315°$

The solutions are 225° and 315°.

b. $\cos \left(\frac{\theta}{2}\right) = 0$

The cosine is 0, so the terminal side of the angle must lie on the y-axis. The angle must be 90° or 270°.

If $\frac{\theta}{2} = 90°$, then $\theta = 180°$.

If $\frac{\theta}{2} = 270°$, then $\theta = 540°$.

Since 540° > 360°, the only solution is 180°.

EXERCISES

Each angle extends outside Quadrant I. Find the exact value of each expression.

1. $\cos 150°$ $-\frac{\sqrt{3}}{2}$

2. $\sin -120°$ $-\frac{\sqrt{3}}{2}$

3. $\sin \left(\frac{5\pi}{6}\right)$ $\frac{1}{2}$

4. $\cos \left(\frac{2\pi}{3}\right)$ $-\frac{1}{2}$

5. $\sin\left(-\frac{4\pi}{3}\right)$ $\frac{\sqrt{3}}{2}$

6. $\cos\left(-\frac{5\pi}{4}\right)$ $-\frac{\sqrt{2}}{2}$

7. $\tan \left(\frac{2\pi}{3}\right)$ $-\sqrt{3}$

8. $\tan (-150°)$ $\frac{\sqrt{3}}{3}$

Solve each equation in the interval from 0° to 360°. Give exact answers.

9. $\cos \theta = \frac{1}{2}$ 60°, 300°

10. $\sin \theta = \frac{\sqrt{2}}{2}$ 45°, 135°

11. $\sin \theta = 1$ 90°

12. $\cos \left(\frac{\theta}{4}\right) = \frac{1}{2}$ 240°

Chapter Review

Vocabulary Review

amplitude (p. 712)
central angle (p. 726)
cosecant (p. 763)
cosine function (p. 743)
cosine of θ (p. 720)
cotangent (p. 763)
coterminal angles (p. 719)
cycle (p. 711)

initial side (p. 718)
intercepted arc (p. 726)
period (p. 711)
periodic function (p. 711)
phase shift (p. 756)
radian (p. 726)
secant (p. 763)
sine curve (p. 735)

sine function (p. 734)
sine of θ (p. 720)
standard position (p. 718)
tangent function (p. 749)
tangent of θ (p. 749)
terminal side (p. 718)
unit circle (p. 720)

Choose the correct term to complete each sentence.

1. The __?__ of a function is the length of one cycle. **period**

2. Centered at the origin of the coordinate plane, the __?__ has a radius of 1 unit.
 unit circle

3. The asymptote of the __?__ occurs at $\theta = \frac{\pi}{2}$ and repeats every π units.
 tangent function

4. A horizontal translation of a periodic function is a(n) __?__. **phase shift**

5. The __?__ is the reciprocal of the cosine function. **secant function**

Go Online
PHSchool.com
For: Vocabulary quiz
Web Code: agj-1351

Skills and Concepts

13-1 Objectives

▼ To identify cycles and
 periods of periodic
 functions (p. 710)

▼ To find the amplitude of
 periodic functions
 (p. 712)

A **periodic function** repeats a pattern of *y*-values at regular intervals. One complete pattern is called a **cycle.** A cycle may begin at any point on the graph. The **period** of a function is the length of one cycle. The **amplitude** of a periodic function is half the difference between its maximum and minimum values.

6. Determine whether the function at the right *is* or
 is not periodic. If it is, identify one cycle in two
 different ways. Then determine the period and
 amplitude. **periodic; 4, 2**

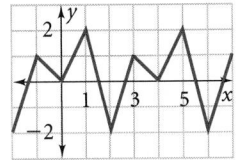

7. Sketch the graph of a wave with a period
 of 0.5 and an amplitude of 3.
 See margin.

13-2 Objectives

▼ To work with angles in
 standard position
 (p. 718)

▼ To find coordinates of
 points on the unit circle
 (p. 720)

An angle is in **standard position** if the vertex is at the origin and one ray, the **initial side**, is on the positive *x*-axis. The other ray is the **terminal side** of the angle. Two angles in standard position are **coterminal** if they have the same terminal side.

The **unit circle** has a radius of 1 unit and its center at the origin. The **cosine of θ** (cos θ) is the *x*-coordinate of the point where the terminal side of the angle intersects the unit circle. The **sine of θ** (sin θ) is the *y*-coordinate.

8. Find the measure of the angle in standard position
 at the right. **−225°**

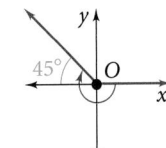

9. Sketch a −30° angle in standard position.
 See margin.

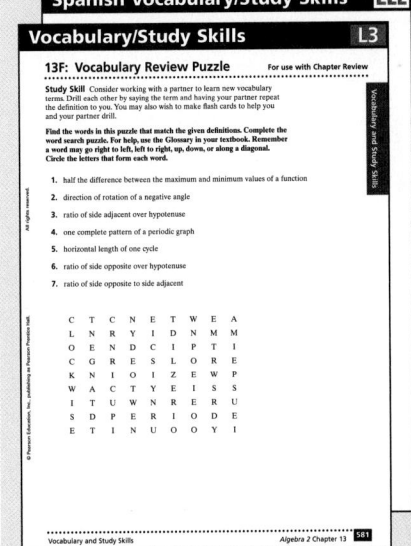

7. **Answers may vary.**
 Sample:

9.

19.

20.

21.

10. 240°

10. Find the measure of an angle between 0° and 360° coterminal with a −120° angle.

11. Find the exact coordinates of the point at which the terminal side of a 315° angle intersects the unit circle. Then find the decimal equivalents. Round your answers to the nearest hundredth. $\left(\frac{\sqrt{2}}{2}, -\frac{\sqrt{2}}{2}\right)$; (0.71, −0.71)

13-3 Objectives

▼ To use radian measure for angles (p. 726)

▼ To find the length of an arc of a circle (p. 728)

12a. $\frac{\pi}{3}$

b. $\frac{1}{2}, \frac{\sqrt{3}}{2}$

13a. $-\frac{\pi}{4}$

b. $\frac{\sqrt{2}}{2}, -\frac{\sqrt{2}}{2}$

14a. π

b. −1, 0

15a. 360°

b. 1, 0

16a. 150°

b. $-\frac{\sqrt{3}}{2}, \frac{1}{2}$

A **central angle** of a circle is an angle whose vertex is at the center of a circle. An **intercepted arc** is the portion of the circle whose endpoints are on the sides of the angle and whose remaining points lie in the interior of the angle. A **radian** is the measure of a central angle that intercepts an arc equal in length to a radius of the circle.

To convert degrees to radians, multiply by $\frac{\pi \text{ radians}}{180°}$. To convert radians to degrees, multiply by $\frac{180°}{\pi \text{ radians}}$. When the measure of an angle θ is in radians and r is the radius, the length s of the intercepted arc is $s = r\theta$.

The measure θ of an angle in standard position is given.
a. Write each degree measure in radians and each radian measure in degrees rounded to the nearest degree.
b. Find the exact values of cos θ and sin θ for each angle measure.

12. 60°   **13.** −45°   **14.** 180°

15. 2π radians   **16.** $\frac{5\pi}{6}$ radians   **17.** $-\frac{3\pi}{4}$ radians

17a. −135°

b. $-\frac{\sqrt{2}}{2}, -\frac{\sqrt{2}}{2}$

18. Use the circle to find the length of the indicated arc. Round your answer to the nearest tenth. **26.2 ft**

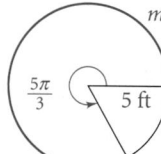

13-4 and 13-5 Objectives

▼ To identify properties of the sine function (p. 734)

▼ To graph sine curves (p. 737)

▼ To graph and write cosine functions (p. 743)

▼ To solve trigonometric equations (p. 744)

The **sine function** $y = \sin \theta$ matches the measure θ of an angle in standard position with the y-coordinate of a point on the unit circle. This point is where the terminal side of the angle intersects the unit circle. The graph of a sine function is called a **sine curve.**

The **cosine function** $y = \cos \theta$ matches the measure θ of an angle in standard position with the x-coordinate of a point on the unit circle. This point is where the terminal side of the angle intersects the unit circle.

For the sine function $y = a \sin b\theta$ and the cosine function $y = a \cos b\theta$, the amplitude equals $|a|$, there are b cycles from 0 to 2π, and the period is $\frac{2\pi}{b}$.

Sketch the graph of each function in the interval from 0 to 2π.

19. $y = 3 \sin \theta$ **20.** $y = 2 \cos\left(\frac{\pi}{2}\right)t$ **21.** $y = -\cos 2\theta$
19–21. See margin.

22. For the graph at the right, how many cycles does the sine function have in the interval from 0 to 2π? Find the amplitude and period of the function. Then write an equation for the sine function.
3 cycles; 1, $\frac{2\pi}{3}$; $y = -\sin 3\theta$

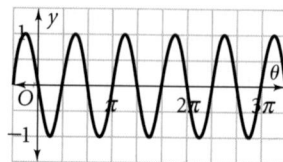

Write an equation of the function for each description or graph.

23. sine function, $a > 0$, amplitude 4, period 0.5π $y = 4 \sin 4\theta$

24. cosine function, $a > 0$, amplitude 3, period π $y = 3 \cos 2\theta$

25.

$y = 2 \cos 2\theta$

Solve each equation in the interval from 0 to 2π. Round to the nearest hundredth.

26. $\sin \theta = -0.7$
3.92, 5.51

27. $\sin\left(\frac{\pi}{2}\right)\theta = 0.25$
0.16, 1.84, 4.16, 5.84

28. $3 \cos 4\theta = -2$
0.58, 1.00, 2.15, 2.57,
3.72, 4.14, 5.29, 5.71

13-6 Objectives

▼ To graph the tangent function (p. 749)

The **tangent** of an angle θ in standard position is the y-coordinate of the point where the terminal side of the angle intersects the tangent line $x = 1$. A **tangent function** in the form $y = a \tan b\theta$ has a period of $\frac{\pi}{b}$.

Graph each function in the interval from 0 to 2π. Then evaluate the function at $t = \frac{\pi}{4}$ and $t = \frac{\pi}{2}$. If the tangent is undefined at that point, write _undefined_.

29. $y = \tan\left(\frac{1}{2}\right)t$
29–31. See margin.

30. $y = \tan 3t$

31. $y = 2 \tan t$

13-7 Objectives

▼ To graph translations of trigonometric functions (p. 756)

▼ To write equations of translations (p. 759)

Each horizontal translation of certain periodic functions is a **phase shift.** When $g(x) = f(x - h) + k$, the value of h is the amount of the horizontal shift and the value of k is the amount of the vertical shift.

Graph each function in the interval from 0 to 2π. 32–34. See margin.

32. $y = \cos\left(x + \frac{\pi}{2}\right)$ **33.** $y = 2 \sin x - 4$ **34.** $y = \sin(x - \pi) + 3$

Write an equation for each translation.

35. $y = \sin x, \frac{\pi}{4}$ units to the right
$y = \sin\left(x - \frac{\pi}{4}\right)$

36. $y = \cos x$, 2 units down
$y = \cos x - 2$

13-8 Objectives

▼ To evaluate reciprocal trigonometric functions (p. 763)

▼ To graph reciprocal trigonometric functions (p. 765)

The **cosecant** (csc), **secant** (sec), and **cotangent** (cot) functions are defined using reciprocals. Their domains do not include the real numbers θ that make a denominator zero.

$$\csc \theta = \frac{1}{\sin \theta} \qquad \sec \theta = \frac{1}{\cos \theta} \qquad \cot \theta = \frac{1}{\tan \theta}$$

Evaluate each expression. Write your answer in exact form.

37. $\sec(-45°)$ $\sqrt{2}$ **38.** $\cot 120°$ $-\frac{\sqrt{3}}{3}$ **39.** $\csc 150°$ 2

Graph each function in the interval from 0 to 2π. 40–42. See margin.

40. $y = 2 \csc \theta$ **41.** $y = \sec \theta - 1$ **42.** $y = \cot\left(\frac{1}{4}\right)\theta$

Chapter 13   Chapter Review   **773**

32.

33.

34.

40.

41.

42.

29.

0.41, 1

30.

−1, undefined

31.

2, undefined

Go Online
PHSchool.com
For: Chapter Test
Web Code: aga-1352

Determine whether each function *is* or *is not* periodic. If it is periodic, find the period and amplitude.

1.

periodic; 4, 2

2.

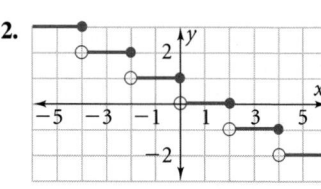

not periodic

Find the measure of an angle between 0° and 360° coterminal with the given angle.

3. $-32°$ **328°**   **4.** $-229°$ **131°**   **5.** $375°$ **15°**

Write each measure in radians. Express the answer in terms of π and also as a decimal rounded to the nearest hundredth.   6–8. See margin.

6. $-225°$ **7.** $120°$ **8.** $600°$

Write each measure in degrees. If necessary, round your answer to the nearest degree.

9. $\frac{5\pi}{6}$ **150°**   **10.** -2.5π **−450°**   **11.** 0.8 **46°**

How many cycles does each sine function have in the interval from 0 to 2π? Find the amplitude and period of each function.

12.

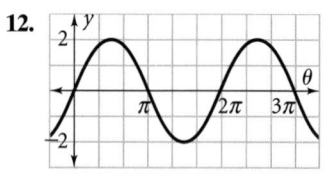

1 cycle; 2, 2π

13.

$\frac{1}{2}$ cycle; 3, 4π

14. Open-Ended Sketch a function with period 7. **Check students' work.**

15. Writing Explain how to convert an angle measure in radians to an angle measure in degrees. Include an example.   **See margin.**

16. Physics On each swing, a pendulum 18 inches long travels through an angle of $\frac{3\pi}{4}$ radians. How far does the tip of the pendulum travel in one swing? Round your answer to the nearest inch.   **42 in.**

17–18. See margin.
Find the amplitude and period of each function. Then sketch one cycle of the graph of each function.

17. $y = 4 \sin (2x)$ **18.** $y = 2 \sin (4x)$

Solve each equation in the interval from 0 to 2π. Give an exact answer and an answer rounded to the nearest hundredth.   19–21. See margin p. 775.

19. $\cos t = \frac{1}{2}$ **20.** $2 \sin t = \sqrt{3}$

21. $3 \tan 2t = \sqrt{3}$ **22.** $\cos \frac{t\pi}{4} = 1$ **0**

Graph each function in the interval from 0 to 2π.

23. $y = 2 \cos x$ **24.** $y = -\cos \frac{\theta}{\pi}$

25. $y = 4 \sin x - 2$ **26.** $y = \cos (x + \pi)$

27. $y = \tan \frac{\theta}{3}$ **28.** $y = \tan \frac{\pi}{3}\theta$

23–28. See back of book.
Write an equation for each translation.

29. $y = \sin x$, 1 unit down $y = \sin x - 1$

30. $y = \cos x$, 7.5 units to the right

31. $y = \sin x$, 3 units to the left, 1.5 units down

32. $y = \cos x$, $\frac{\pi}{2}$ units to the right, 8 units up

30–32. See margin p. 775.
Evaluate each expression. Write your answer in exact form. If the expression is undefined, write *undefined*.

33. $\sin 30°$ $\frac{1}{2}$ **34.** $\cos 60°$ $\frac{1}{2}$

35. $\sin (-330°)$ $\frac{1}{2}$ **36.** $\csc (-330°)$ **2**

37. $\sec 270°$ **undefined**   **38.** $\tan 60°$ $\sqrt{3}$

39. $\cos 45°$ $\frac{\sqrt{2}}{2}$ **40.** $\cot (-60°)$ $-\frac{\sqrt{3}}{3}$

Graph each function in the interval from 0 to 2π.
41–44. See back of book.

41. $y = \cot \theta$ **42.** $y = \sec \theta + 1$

43. $y = \csc \frac{\theta}{2}$ **44.** $y = \csc (\theta + 1)$

6. $-\frac{5\pi}{4}$, -3.93

7. $\frac{2\pi}{3}$, **2.09**

8. $\frac{10\pi}{3}$, **10.47**

15. Answers may vary.
Sample: Multiply the radian measure by $\frac{180°}{\pi}$.
Example:
$\frac{2\pi}{3}$ radians $\cdot \frac{180°}{\pi} = 120°$

17. 4, π

18. 2, $\frac{\pi}{2}$

774

Standardized Test Prep

Reading Comprehension Read the passage below. Then answer the questions on the basis of what is *stated* or *implied* in the passage.

> **The Birthday Problem** Suppose you are in a room of 25 people. How likely is it that at least two of the people celebrate their birthdays on the same day of the year? What about in a room of 100 people? Assume that no birthday occurs on February 29.
>
> To answer such questions, first ask a related question: For any group of people, what is the probability that *no two* in the group have the same birthday? For a group of four people, using 365 as the number of days in a year, the probability is $\frac{365}{365} \cdot \frac{364}{365} \cdot \frac{363}{365} \cdot \frac{362}{365}$, or about 0.984. (For each person after the first, the number of days available for a "different birthday" decreases by 1.) Then it is easy to calculate the probability that at least two of the four have the same birthday: about $1 - 0.984$, or 0.016.
>
> So you can calculate the probability that at least two of 25 people share a birthday by using the following expression.
>
> $$1 - \frac{365}{365} \cdot \frac{364}{365} \cdot \frac{363}{365} \cdot \frac{362}{365} \cdot \ldots \cdot \frac{343}{365} \cdot \frac{342}{365} \cdot \frac{341}{365}$$

Students must be able to extract information from reading passages, answer multiple choice questions, and construct responses in order to be successful on current state and national assessments.

To answer the questions, students apply skills and concepts from this chapter and previous chapters.
Multiple Choice: Items 1–5
Free Response: Items 6–8

Resources

Test Prep Workbook

Grab & Go
• **L3** Cumulative Review

ExamView CD-ROM
• Standardized Test Practice

Differentiated Instruction Resources

Spanish Assessment Resources
• **L3** Spanish Cumulative Review

1. Which expression gives the probability that no two of three people have the same birthday? **B**

(A) $\frac{364}{365} \cdot \frac{363}{365} \cdot \frac{362}{365}$

(B) $\frac{365}{365} \cdot \frac{364}{365} \cdot \frac{363}{365}$

(C) $1 - \frac{364}{365} \cdot \frac{363}{365} \cdot \frac{362}{365}$

(D) $1 - \frac{365}{365} \cdot \frac{364}{365} \cdot \frac{363}{365}$

2. Which expression gives the probability that at least two of three people have the same birthday? **J**

(F) $\frac{364}{365} \cdot \frac{363}{365} \cdot \frac{362}{365}$

(G) $\frac{365}{365} \cdot \frac{364}{365} \cdot \frac{363}{365}$

(H) $1 - \frac{364}{365} \cdot \frac{363}{365} \cdot \frac{362}{365}$

(J) $1 - \frac{365}{365} \cdot \frac{364}{365} \cdot \frac{363}{365}$

3. Here is a different question: You meet 25 strangers, one at a time. With each meeting, what is the probability that a person has the same birthday as you? **D**

(A) $\frac{340}{365}$ (B) $\frac{25}{365}$ (C) $\frac{1}{25}$ (D) $\frac{1}{365}$

4. In a group of 366, what is the probability that at least two people have the same birthday? **H**

(F) $\frac{1}{366}$ (G) $1 - \frac{365}{366}$ (H) 1   (J) $\frac{366}{365}$

5. The reading passage contains the expression **C**

$1 - \frac{365}{365} \cdot \frac{364}{365} \cdot \frac{363}{365} \cdot \frac{362}{365} \cdot \ldots \cdot \frac{343}{365} \cdot \frac{342}{365} \cdot \frac{341}{365}$.

What is another way to write that expression?

(A) $1 - \frac{365 \cdot 364 \cdot 363 \ldots \cdot 341}{365!}$

(B) $1 - \frac{365!}{341! \cdot 365^{25}}$

(C) $1 - \frac{365!}{340! \cdot 365^{25}}$

(D) $\frac{1 - 365!}{340! \cdot 365^{25}}$

6. In a group of five people, what is the probability that no two have the same birthday? What is the probability that at least two people in the group have the same birthday? **about 0.973; about 0.027**

7. In a group of 15 people, what is the probability that no two have the same birthday? What is the probability that at least two people in the group have the same birthday? **about 0.747; about 0.253**

8. Suppose you want a group for which the probability that at least two people have the same birthday is at least 50%. How many people do you need? **23 people**

19. $\frac{\pi}{3}, \frac{5\pi}{3}$; 1.05, 5.24

20. $\frac{\pi}{3}, \frac{2\pi}{3}$; 1.05, 2.09

21. $\frac{\pi}{12}, \frac{7\pi}{12}, \frac{13\pi}{12}, \frac{19\pi}{12}$; 0.26, 1.83, 3.40, 4.97

30. $y = \cos(x - 7.5)$

31. $y = \sin(x + 3) - 1.5$

32. $y = \cos\left(x - \frac{\pi}{2}\right) + 8$

Trigonometric Identities and Equations

Chapter at a Glance

Lesson Titles, Objectives, and Features	Assessment	NCTM Standards	Local Standards
14-1 Trigonometric Identities • Verifying trigonometric identities	Lesson Quiz	2, 3, 9, 10	
14-2 Solving Trigonometric Equations Using Inverses • Evaluating inverses of trigonometric functions • Solving trigonometric equations **Activity Lab:** Technology: Lissajous Figures	Lesson Quiz	2, 3, 7	
14-3 Right Triangles and Trigonometric Ratios • Finding lengths of sides in a right triangle • Finding measures of angles in a right triangle **GPS:** Understanding Word Problems	Lesson Quiz Checkpoint Quiz 1	2, 3, 8, 10	
14-4 Area and the Law of Sines • Finding the area of any triangle and using the Law of Sines **Extension:** The Ambiguous Case	Lesson Quiz	2, 3, 4, 7	
14-5 The Law of Cosines • Using the Law of Cosines in finding the measures of sides and angles of a triangle	Lesson Quiz	2, 3, 7	
14-6 Angle Identities • Verifying and using angle identifies • Verifying and using sum and difference identities	Lesson Quiz Checkpoint Quiz 2	2, 3, 7, 8	
14-7 Double-Angle and Half-Angle Identities • Verifying and using double-angle identities • Verifying and using half-angle identities	Lesson Quiz	2, 3, 7, 8	
Activity Lab: Applying Trigonometry			

NCTM Standards 2000

1 Number and Operations	**2** Algebra	**3** Geometry
6 Problem Solving	**7** Reasoning and Proof	**8** Communication

4 Measurement	**5** Data Analysis and Probability
9 Connections	**10** Representation

Correlations to Standardized Tests

All content for these tests is contained in *Prentice Hall Algebra 2*. This chart reflects coverage in this chapter only.

	14-1	14-2	14-3	14-4	14-5	14-6	14-7
SAT®							
Number and Operations Operations, ratio & proportions, complex numbers, counting, elementary number theory, matrices, sequences							
Algebra and Functions Expressions, equations, inequalities, representation and modeling, properties of functions (linear, polynomial, rational, exponential)							
Geometry and Measurement *Plane Euclidean/Measurement Coordinate* Lines, parabolas, circles, symmetry, transformations *Three-dimensional* Solids, surface area & volume (cylinders, cones, pyramids, spheres, prisms) *Trigonometry* Right triangles, identities	✔		✔		✔	✔	
Data Analysis, Statistics, and Probability Mean, median, mode, range, interquartile range, graphs and plots, regression, probability							
ACT®							
Pre-Algebra Basic operations using whole numbers, decimals, fractions, and integers; place value; square roots and approximations; the concept of exponents; scientific notation; factors, ratio, proportion, and percent; linear equations in one variable; absolute value and ordering numbers by value; elementary counting techniques and simple probability; data collection, representation, and interpretation; and understanding simple descriptive statistics.							
Elementary Algebra Properties of exponents and square roots, evaluation of algebraic expressions through substitution, using variables to express functional relationships, understanding algebraic operations, and solving quadratic equations by factoring.							
Intermediate Algebra Understanding of the quadratic formula, rational and radical expressions, absolute value equations and inequalities, sequences and patterns, systems of equations, quadratic inequalities, functions, modeling, matrices, roots of polynomials, and complex numbers.							
Coordinate Geometry Graphing and the relations between equations and graphs, including points, lines, polynomials, circles, and other curves; graphing inequalities; slope; parallel and perpendicular lines; distance; midpoints; and conics.							
Plane Geometry Properties and relations of plane figures, including angles and relations among perpendicular and parallel lines; properties of circles, triangles, rectangles, parallelograms, and trapezoids; transformations; the concept of proof and proof techniques; volume; and applications of geometry to three dimensions.							
Trigonometry Understanding trigonometric relations in right triangles; values and properties of trigonometric functions; graphing trigonometric functions; modeling using trigonometric functions; use of trigonometric identities; and solving trigonometric equations.	✔	✔	✔	✔	✔	✔	✔
NAEP							
Number Sense, Properties, and Operations							
Measurement			✔	✔	✔		
Geometry and Spatial Sense							
Data Analysis, Statistics, and Probability							
Algebra and Functions		✔		✔	✔		

SAT® The College Board, SAT® Reasoning Test   ACT® The ACT Assessment® Test   NAEP National Assessment of Educational Progress, 2005 Mathematics Objectives

Math Background

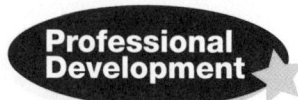

Skills Trace

BEFORE Chapter 14
In previous chapters, students graphed trigonometric functions and wrote and solved various equations.

DURING Chapter 14
Students solve trigonometric equations using inverses, apply the Laws of Sines and Cosines, and verify and apply trigonometric identities.

AFTER Chapter 14
Students will continue their work with functions as they find derivatives and integrals of functions in calculus.

Chapter Overview

Chapter 14 begins by examining the concept of a trigonometric identity. Students see that many identities can be verified by using the unit circle definitions of the sine and cosine functions or definitions of the cofunctions. Students then see how to solve trigonometric equations by using graphs and the unit circle definitions of trigonometric functions. Inverse trigonometric functions are considered next, and students see how to use them in solving equations.

Trigonometry originated with the study of triangles, most especially right triangles. Lessons 14-3, 14-4, and 14-5 address right triangle trigonometry and the use of trigonometry to study triangles in general. The chapter concludes with a study of the formulas for sums and differences of angles, double angles, and half angles.

Trigonometric Identities   14-1

Students have seen many examples of algebraic equations that are true for all values of their variables. Trigonometric identities are true for all values for which the functions exist. Emphasize to students that there are probably multiple ways to establish an identity. They may also need to recognize that establishing the truth of any trigonometric equation is essentially discovering an identity.

Students should be expected to know the trigonometric identities presented: reciprocal, tangent and cotangent, and Pythagorean identities. Students should be shown that they can memorize just a few identities and derive the others. For example, by dividing both sides of $\cos^2 \theta + \sin^2 \theta = 1$ by $\cos^2 \theta$, they can obtain $1 + \tan^2 \theta = \sec^2 \theta$; and by dividing both sides by $\sin^2 \theta$ students can obtain $1 + \cot^2 \theta = \csc^2 \theta$.

Solving Trigonometric Equations Using Inverses   14-2

The trigonometric functions are not one-to-one functions, so one must pay careful attention to domains and ranges to arrive at useful definitions of inverse trigonometric functions. Some students may be interested in researching the several ways the inverse trigonometric functions can be defined.

Students should recognize that $\cos \theta = x$ and $\theta = \cos^{-1} x$ $(0 \le \theta \le \pi)$ have the same relationship to each other that $y = b^2$ and $\log_b y = x$ $(b > 0)$ have. Furthermore, students can solve equations by taking the inverse trigonometric function of both sides of an equation much like taking the logarithm or square root of both sides of a corresponding equation.

Right Triangles and Trigonometric Ratios   14-3

Given a triangle with three sides a, b, and c, students should be able to write all of the possible trigonometric ratios. Students can justify that they have all possible ratios using counting theory: given three possible sides where two are chosen for a ratio (in which order matters) is $_3P_2 = 6$. Alternatively, by the Multiplication Counting Principle there are three ways of choosing the first side and two for choosing the second side such that $3 \cdot 2 = 6$.

In Geometry, students learned the relationships between the side lengths for right triangles such as 45°- 45°- 90° and 30°- 60°- 90° triangles. Students who confuse similarity (same shape) with congruence (same size and shape) may need to review both concepts, and some of the theorems about similarity. They should recall the theorem usually called AA or Angle-Angle: two triangles are similar if two angles of one have the same measure as two angles of the other. This is, of course, based on the theorem stating that the sum of the measures of the angles in a triangle is 180°. Students for whom this fact seems a dim memory may benefit from tearing a paper triangle and assembling the corners to show the 3 angles form a line.

It may also help students to review the relationship between angle measure and side length in a triangle. This will help emphasize that the longest side of a right triangle is always the hypotenuse because it is opposite the angle with the greatest measure (the right angle).

Some students have difficulty solving equations with the variable in the denominator, such as $\sin 15° = \frac{24}{x}$. Using two steps, students are often successful in solving for x: first multiply both sides by x so $x \cdot \sin 15° = \frac{24}{x} \cdot x$; then divide both sides by $\sin 15°$ and simplify to obtain $x = \frac{24}{\sin 15°}$.

Area and the Law of Sines   14-4

Prior to this lesson, students have found angle measures and side lengths of right triangles. It is important for students to realize that the Law of Sines allows them to find missing measures in any triangle. In the derivation of the Law of Sines, the altitude h is drawn. Recall that an *altitude* of a triangle is the perpendicular segment from a vertex to the line containing the opposite side. Since perpendicular lines form right angles, a right triangle is formed.

Note that the Law of Sines is applicable in two situations: (1) the measures of two angles and any side are known, and (2) the measures of two sides and the angle opposite one side are known (the ambiguous case). The Law of Sines cannot be used without a known angle measure. (The Law of Cosines, treated in the next lesson, deals with this case.)

The Law of Cosines   14-5

Students may find it helpful to observe that the Law of Cosines can be thought of as an "adjusted" version of the Pythagorean Theorem. The final term is the 'correction term' that drops out when the given angle is 90°. Thus, the Law of Cosines calculates one side of a triangle when the angle opposite it and the other two sides are known. The Law of Cosines can be used in conjunction with the Law of Sines to find all sides and angles in any triangle. There is no ambiguous case related to the Law of Cosines.

Angle Identities   14-6

Discuss how the negative angle identities and cofunction identities are related to the unit-circle and right-triangle definitions of the trigonometric functions.

Students are often interested to learn about even and odd functions. A function f is even if $f(-x) = f(x)$. Therefore, $y = x^2$ and the cosine function are both even, and the graphs of all even functions exhibits reflectional symmetry across the y-axis. A function f is odd if $f(-x) = -f(x)$. Therefore, $y = x^3$ and the sine function are both odd, and the graphs of odd functions exhibit rotational symmetrical about the origin. Some interesting properties of odd and even functions follow.

- The product of two even functions is an even function.

- The product of two odd functions is an even function.

- The product of an even and an odd function is an odd function.

- Any function can be expressed as the sum of two component functions of which one is even and the other is odd.

Students can benefit from seeing how the angle difference identities for $\sin(A - B)$ and $\tan(A - B)$ can be derived by using the identity for $\cos(A - B)$.

Double-Angle and Half-Angle Identities   14-7

The identities in this lesson grow out of those in Lesson 14-6. You may wish to challenge students to describe the angles θ for which they can compute exact values for a function such as the sine function. Students may also enjoy trying to show two or three different ways to establish these identities.

Additional Professional Development Opportunities

Math Background notes for Chapter 14: Every lesson has a Math Background in the PLAN section.

Research Overview, Mathematical Strands Additional support for these topics and more is in the front of this Teacher's Edition.

Lesson Lab Lesson Lab, a Pearson Education company, offers comprehensive, facilitated professional development designed to help teachers improve student achievement. To learn more, please visit lessonlab.com

Chapter 14 Resources

	14-1	14-2	14-3	14-4	14-5	14-6	14-7	For the Chapter
Print Resources								
L3 Practice	•	•	•	•	•	•	•	
L3 Guided Problem Solving	•	•	•	•	•	•	•	
L2 Reteaching	•	•	•	•	•	•	•	
L4 Enrichment	•	•	•	•	•	•	•	
L3 Daily Notetaking Guide	•	•	•	•	•	•	•	
L3 Vocabulary and Study Skills Worksheets	•							•
L3 Chapter Project								•
L3 Hands On Activities		•				•		
L3 Checkpoint Quiz			•			•		
L2 Below Level Chapter Test								•
L3 Chapter Test								•
L4 Alternative Assessment								•
L3 Cumulative Review								•
L4 Connections to Precalculus Masters	•	•	•	•	•	•	•	
L3 Technology Activities								
Spanish Resources ELL								
L3 Practice	•	•	•	•	•	•	•	
L3 Vocabulary and Study Skills Worksheets	•							•
L3 Checkpoint Quiz			•			•		
L2 Below Level Chapter Test								•
L3 Chapter Test								•
L4 Alternative Assessment								
L3 Cumulative Review								•
Transparencies								
Check Skills You'll Need	•	•	•	•	•	•	•	
Additional Examples	•	•	•	•	•	•	•	
Problem of the Day	•	•	•	•	•	•	•	
Classroom Aid			•					
Student Edition Answers	•	•	•	•	•	•	•	
Lesson Quiz	•	•	•	•	•	•	•	•
Test-Taking Strategies								•
Technology								
TI 83/84 Plus Activities								
Interactive Textbook Online	•	•	•	•	•	•	•	•
Student Express CD-ROM	•	•	•	•	•	•	•	
TI Navigator, Instant Check System	•	•	•	•	•	•	•	
Success Tracker	•	•	•	•	•	•	•	•
ExamView CD-ROM with Quick Take	•	•	•	•	•	•	•	•
Teacher Express CD-ROM	•	•	•	•	•	•	•	•
Presentation Express CD-ROM	•	•	•	•	•	•	•	•
Mindpoint Quiz Show CD-ROM	•	•	•	•	•	•	•	•
Prentice Hall Web site: PHSchool.com	•	•	•	•	•	•	•	•

Also available: Prentice Hall Assessment System (Progress Monitoring Assessments, Skills and Concepts Review, Test Prep Workbook)   Solution Key   Student Workbook
Student Workbook, Adapted Version   Data Analysis and Probability Workbook   Math Notes Study Folder   Spanish Cumulative Assessment

Where You Can Use the Lesson Resources

Here is a suggestion, following the four-step teaching plan, for how you can incorporate Differentiated Instruction Resources into your teaching.

	Instructional Resources L3	**Differentiated Instruction Resources**
1. Plan		
Check Skills You'll Need Assign these exercises to review prerequisite skills. **New Vocabulary** Help students pre-read the lesson by pointing out the new terms introduced in the lesson.	**Math Background** **Transparencies & Presentation Express CD** Check Skills You'll Need **Resources** Vocabulary and Study Skills	**Spanish Support** ELL Vocabulary and Study Skills
2. Teach		
L3 **Guided Instruction** Teach each Example. After each Example, assign the Quick Check exercise for that Example.	**Student Edition** Activity Lab **Resources** Daily Notetaking Guide Activity Lab TI-83/84 Activities CD-ROM **Transparencies & Presentation Express CD** Additional Examples Classroom Aids **ExamView CD-ROM with QuickTake** **TI Navigator Instant Check System**	**Teacher's Edition** Every lesson includes suggestions for working with students who need special attention. L1 Special Needs L2 Below Level L4 Advanced Learners ELL English Language Learners
3. Practice		
Assignment Guide **Homework Exercises** Assign the exercises cited in each lesson's Assignment Guide. A Practice by Example B Apply Your Skills C Challenge Test Prep Mixed Review **Homework Quick Check** Discuss in class the exercises cited in each lesson's Assignment Guide.	**Transparencies & Presentation Express CD** Student Answers **Resources** Practice Guided Problem Solving Vocabulary and Study Skills Activity Lab **ExamView CD-ROM with QuickTake**	**Spanish Support** ELL Practice ELL Vocabulary and Study Skills **Resources** L4 Enrichment
4. Assess & Reteach		
Lesson Quiz Assign the Lesson Quiz to assess students' mastery of the lesson content. **Checkpoint Quiz** Use the Checkpoint Quiz to assess student progress over several lessons.	**Transparencies & Presentation Express CD** Lesson Quiz **Resources** Checkpoint Quiz	**Resources** L2 Reteaching ELL Checkpoint Quiz Success Tracker **ExamView CD-ROM with QuickTake**

KEY L1 Special Needs   L2 Below Level   L3 For All Students   L4 Advanced, Gifted   ELL English Language Learners

Chapter 14

Trigonometric Identities and Equations

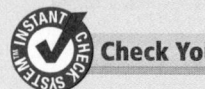 **Check Your Readiness**

Answers are in the back of the textbook.

For intervention, direct students to:

Solving Quadratic Equations
Lesson 5-5: Example 3
Extra Skills and Word
  Problems Practice, Ch. 5

Finding the Inverse of a Function
Lesson 7-7: Examples 4, 5
Extra Skills and Word
  Problems Practice, Ch. 7

Solving Exponential and Logarithmic Equations
Lesson 8-5: Example 5
Extra Skills and Word
  Problems Practice, Ch. 8

Evaluating Trigonometric Functions
Lesson 13-2: Example 4
Lesson 13-6: Example 1
Extra Skills and Word
  Problems Practice, Ch. 13

What You've Learned

- In Chapter 5, you learned to solve quadratic equations by finding square roots.

- In Chapter 7, you learned to find the inverse of a function.

- In Chapter 8, you learned about exponential and logarithmic functions, which are inverse functions. You learned to solve exponential and logarithmic equations by using inverse functions.

- In Chapter 13, you learned to use the sine, cosine, and tangent functions.

Check Your Readiness **GO for Help** to the Lesson in green.

Solving Quadratic Equations (Lesson 5-5)

Solve each equation.

1. $4x^2 = 25$ $\pm\frac{5}{2}$

2. $x^2 - 23 = 0$ $\pm\sqrt{23}$

3. $3x^2 = 80$ $\pm\frac{4\sqrt{15}}{3}$

4. $8x^2 - 44 = 0$ $\pm\frac{\sqrt{22}}{2}$

5. $0.5x^2 = 15$ $\pm\sqrt{30}$

6. $6x^2 - 13 = 11$ ± 2

Finding the Inverse of a Function (Lesson 7-7)

For each function f, find f^{-1} and the domain and range of f and f^{-1}. Determine whether f^{-1} is a function. **7–12. See margin.**

7. $f(x) = 5x + 2$

8. $f(x) = \sqrt{x + 3}$

9. $f(x) = \sqrt{3x - 4}$

10. $f(x) = \frac{5}{x}$

11. $f(x) = \frac{10}{x - 1}$

12. $f(x) = \frac{10}{x} - 1$

Solving Exponential and Logarithmic Equations (Lesson 8-5)

Solve each equation.

13. $4^x = \frac{1}{8}$ -1.5

14. $\log 5x + 1 = -1$ 0.002

15. $7^{3x} = 500$ ≈ 1.065

16. $\log 3x + \log x = 9$ $\approx 18,257$

17. $\log (4x + 3) - \log x = 5$ $\approx 3 \times 10^{-5}$

18. $3^x = 243$ 5

Evaluating Trigonometric Functions (Lessons 13-2 and 13-6)

For each value of θ, find the values of $\cos\theta$, $\sin\theta$, and $\tan\theta$. Round your answers to the nearest hundredth.

19. $48°$
  $0.67, 0.74, 1.11$

20. $-105°$
  $-0.26, -0.97, 3.73$

21. $16°$
  $0.96, 0.28, 0.29$

22. $\frac{5\pi}{6}$
  $-0.87, 0.5, -0.58$

7. Domain of f is all real numbers, range of f is all real numbers; $f^{-1}(x) = \frac{x - 2}{5}$, domain of f^{-1} is all real numbers, range of f^{-1} is all real numbers. f^{-1} is a function.

8. Domain of f is $\{x \mid x \geq -3\}$, the range of f is $\{y \mid y \geq 0\}$; $f^{-1}(x) = x^2 - 3, x \geq 0$, the domain of f^{-1} is all nonnegative real numbers, the range of f^{-1} is $\{y \mid y \geq -3\}$. f^{-1} is a function.

9. Domain of f is $\{x \mid x \geq \frac{4}{3}\}$, the range of f is $\{y \mid y \geq 0\}$; $f^{-1}(x) = \frac{x^2 + 4}{3}, x \geq 0$, the domain of f^{-1} is $\{x \mid x \geq 0\}$, the range of f^{-1} is $\{y \mid y \geq \frac{4}{3}\}$. f^{-1} is a function.

Trigonometric Identities and Equations

🔊 **Key Vocabulary**

- Law of Cosines (p. 808)
- Law of Sines (p. 801)
- trigonometric identity (p. 778)
- trigonometric ratios for a right triangle (p. 792)

What You'll Learn Next

- In Chapter 14, you will learn to verify trigonometric identities.
- You will learn to solve trigonometric equations.
- By using trigonometric ratios, you will solve real-world problems involving right triangles.

Applying what you learn, on pages 834–835 you will do activities involving angles and balance.

Chapter 14 Overview

This chapter begins with an introduction to trigonometric identities. Students then learn how to solve trigonometric equations using inverses. Then students are introduced to the trigonometric ratios of right triangles. In subsequent lessons, students learn about area and the Law of Sines, the Law of Cosines, and angle identities. The chapter concludes with a lesson on double-angle and half-angle identities.

Activating Prior Knowledge

Ask:

- *Given a system of two linear equations, what is the number of possible solutions?*

Answers should indicate no solution, one solution, or an infinite number of solutions (when the lines lie directly on top of one another).

Ask:

- *What are the number of possible solutions for two trigonometric equations?*

Answers should indicate no solution, an infinite number of solutions that occur periodically, or an infinite number of solutions (when the two equations lie directly on top of one another).

State that this last possibility graphically represents a *trigonometric identity,* which is a statement that is true for all defined values of the variable.

777

---

10. Domain of f is $\{x \mid x \neq 0\}$, range of f is $\{y \mid y \neq 0\}$; $f^{-1}(x) = \frac{5}{x}$, domain of f^{-1} is $\{x \mid x \neq 0\}$, range of f^{-1} is $\{y \mid y \neq 0\}$. f^{-1} is a function.

11. Domain of f is $\{x \mid x \neq 1\}$, range of f is $\{y \mid y \neq 0\}$; $f^{-1}(x) = \frac{10}{x} + 1$, domain of f^{-1} is $\{x \mid x \neq 0\}$, range of f^{-1} is $\{y \mid y \neq 1\}$. f^{-1} is a function.

12. Domain of f is $\{x \mid x \neq 0\}$, range of f is $\{y \mid y \neq -1\}$; $f^{-1}(x) = \frac{10}{x + 1}$, domain of f^{-1} is $\{x \mid x \neq -1\}$, range of f^{-1} is $\{y \mid y \neq 0\}$. f^{-1} is a function.

Objectives

1 To verify trigonometric identities

Examples

1 Verifying Identities
2 Verifying Identities
3 Simplifying Expressions

Math Background

While an equation is true only for its solutions, an identity is true for all values of the variables for which every expression in the equation is defined. A *trigonometric identity* equates useful equivalent forms of trigonometric expressions. Justifying these identities allows substitution of equivalent forms in order to simplify trigonometric expressions.

More Math Background: p. 776C

Lesson Planning and Resources

See p. 776E for a list of the resources that support this lesson.

✓ Check Skills You'll Need

For intervention, direct students to:

Properties of Real Numbers
Lesson 1-1: Example 1
Extra Skills and Word
  Problems Practice, Ch. 1

Algebraic Expressions
Lesson 1-2: Example 4
Extra Skills and Word
  Problems Practice, Ch. 1

Rational Expressions
Lesson 9-4: Example 1
Extra Skills and Word
  Problems Practice, Ch. 9

Trigonometric Identities

What You'll Learn

• To verify trigonometric identities

... And Why

To use trigonometric identities in simplifying expressions

 New Vocabulary • trigonometric identity

 Check Skills You'll Need **GO for Help** Lessons 1-1, 1-2, and 9-4

Determine whether each equation is true for all real numbers x. Explain your reasoning. 1–4. See back of book.

1. $2x + 3x = 5x$

2. $-(4x - 10) = 10 - 4x$

3. $\frac{4x^2}{x} = 4x$

4. $\frac{x^2 + 1}{x - 1} = x + 1$

---

1 Verifying Trigonometric Identities

Technology Activity: Trigonometric Identities

1. Use a graphing calculator to graph $y_1 = \tan x$ and $y_2 = \frac{\sin x}{\cos x}$. If your calculator has the "animate" graph style, use it for y_2.

2. Graph $y_1 = (\cos x)^2 + (\sin x)^2$ and $y_2 = 1$. **1–2. See back of book.**

3. **Make a Conjecture** In each Question 1 and 2, make a conjecture about the relationship between y_1 and y_2. **They are equal.**

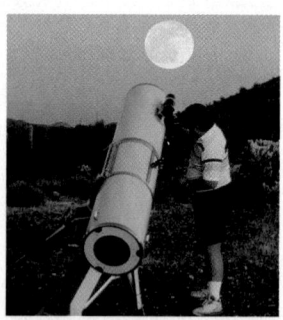

Real-World Connection

Astronomers use trigonometry to determine the angles that locate an object in the celestial coordinate system. This system is similar to the system of latitude and longitude used on Earth.

A trigonometric equation such as $\csc \theta = \frac{1}{\sin \theta}$ is true for all values of θ except those for which $\sin \theta = 0$. A **trigonometric identity** is a trigonometric equation that is true for all values except those for which the expressions on either side of the equal sign are undefined. The three equations $\csc \theta = \frac{1}{\sin \theta}$, $\sec \theta = \frac{1}{\cos \theta}$, and $\tan \theta = \frac{1}{\cot \theta}$ are known as the reciprocal identities.

You can derive some other identities from the unit circle definitions of sine, cosine, and tangent. In the diagram below, $\cos \theta$, $\sin \theta$, and $\tan \theta$ are the coordinates of points P and Q. You can use the slope of $\overleftrightarrow{PQ}$ to show that $\tan \theta = \frac{\sin \theta}{\cos \theta}$.

slope $\overleftrightarrow{PQ} = \frac{\sin \theta - 0}{\cos \theta - 0}$ slope $= \frac{y_2 - y_1}{x_2 - x_1}$

$= \frac{\sin \theta}{\cos \theta}$

slope $\overleftrightarrow{PQ} = \frac{\tan \theta - 0}{1 - 0}$ slope $= \frac{y_2 - y_1}{x_2 - x_1}$

$= \tan \theta$

So, $\tan \theta = \frac{\sin \theta}{\cos \theta}$. **Transitive Property of Equality**

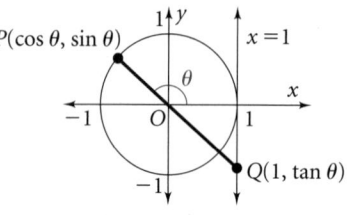

778 Chapter 14 Trigonometric Identities and Equations

Differentiated Instruction Solutions for All Learners

Special Needs **L1**
In Quick Check 1, have students verify the identity $1 + \cot^2 \theta = \csc^2 \theta$ in two ways. Have the left half of the class transform $1 + \cot^2 \theta$ into $\csc^2 \theta$, and the right half transform $\csc^2 \theta$ into $1 + \cot^2 \theta$. Emphasize that only one side of the equation can by changed.

learning style: visual

Below Level **L2**
Discuss with students again the need to avoid dividing by zero.

learning style: verbal

Using the reciprocal identity $\cot \theta = \frac{1}{\tan \theta}$ and the Tangent Identity $\tan \theta = \frac{\sin \theta}{\cos \theta}$, you can derive the Cotangent Identity $\cot \theta = \frac{\cos \theta}{\sin \theta}$.

$$\cot \theta = \frac{1}{\tan \theta} \qquad \text{Reciprocal identity}$$

$$= \frac{1}{\frac{\sin \theta}{\cos \theta}} \qquad \text{Substitute using the Tangent Identity.}$$

$$= \frac{\cos \theta}{\sin \theta} \qquad \text{Divide.}$$

Vocabulary Tip

The expression $\cos^2 \theta$ is equivalent to $(\cos \theta)^2$. The meaning of the phrase "cosine theta squared," when spoken, is not clear.

You can derive another identity from the definitions of $\cos \theta$ and $\sin \theta$. The ordered pair $(\cos \theta, \sin \theta)$ is a point on the unit circle, and for any point (x, y) on the unit circle, $x^2 + y^2 = 1$. So $\cos^2 \theta + \sin^2 \theta = 1$. This is one of the three Pythagorean identities.

To verify an identity, you should transform one side of the equation until it is the same as the other side. This eliminates the possibility of introducing errors that can be caused by squaring both sides of an equation or multiplying both sides of an equation by an expression that equals 0. These are the errors that can introduce extraneous roots when solving equations.

It is sometimes helpful to write all the functions in terms of sine and cosine.

Online active math

For: Trig. Identity Activity
Use: Interactive Textbook, 14-1

1 EXAMPLE Verifying Identities

Verify the Pythagorean identity $1 + \tan^2 \theta = \sec^2 \theta$.

$$1 + \tan^2 \theta = 1 + \left(\frac{\sin \theta}{\cos \theta}\right)^2 \qquad \text{Tangent Identity}$$

$$= 1 + \frac{\sin^2 \theta}{\cos^2 \theta} \qquad \text{Simplify.}$$

$$= \frac{\cos^2 \theta}{\cos^2 \theta} + \frac{\sin^2 \theta}{\cos^2 \theta} \qquad \text{Write the fractions with common denominators.}$$

$$= \frac{\cos^2 \theta + \sin^2 \theta}{\cos^2 \theta} \qquad \text{Add.}$$

$$= \frac{1}{\cos^2 \theta} \qquad \text{Pythagorean identity}$$

$$= \sec^2 \theta \qquad \text{Reciprocal identity}$$

The left side of the equation has been transformed into the right side. Therefore the equation is an identity.

✓ Quick Check **1** Verify the third Pythagorean identity, $1 + \cot^2 \theta = \csc^2 \theta$. **See left.**

Key Concepts

1.
$$1 + \cot^2 \theta = 1 + \left(\frac{\cos \theta}{\sin \theta}\right)^2$$
$$= 1 + \frac{\cos^2 \theta}{\sin^2 \theta} = 1 + \frac{1 - \sin^2 \theta}{\sin^2 \theta}$$
$$= 1 + \frac{1}{\sin^2 \theta} - \frac{\sin^2 \theta}{\sin^2 \theta}$$
$$= 1 + \csc^2 \theta - 1$$
$$= \csc^2 \theta$$

Properties	Trigonometric Identities	
Reciprocal identities		
$\csc \theta = \frac{1}{\sin \theta}$	$\sec \theta = \frac{1}{\cos \theta}$	$\cot \theta = \frac{1}{\tan \theta}$
Tangent and cotangent identities		
$\tan \theta = \frac{\sin \theta}{\cos \theta}$	$\cot \theta = \frac{\cos \theta}{\sin \theta}$	
Pythagorean identities		
$\cos^2 \theta + \sin^2 \theta = 1$	$1 + \tan^2 \theta = \sec^2 \theta$	$1 + \cot^2 \theta = \csc^2 \theta$

There are many trigonometric identities in addition to the identities named in the summary above.

---

2. Teach

Guided Instruction

Technology Activity
In Exercise 1 of this activity, students graph $y_1 = \tan x$ and $y_2 = \frac{\sin x}{\cos x}$ and note that the graphs coincide. In Exercise 2, they make a similar observation about the graphs of $y_1 = (\cos x)^2 + (\sin x)^2$ and $y_2 = 1$. These exercises provide graphical evidence that $\tan x = \frac{\sin x}{\cos x}$ and $(\cos x)^2 + (\sin x)^2 = 1$ are trigonometric identities. To see y_2 being plotted on top of the graph of y_1, students should use Simul mode and select the "animate" graph style for y_2.

1 EXAMPLE Alternative Method

You can also start with the right side of the given equation and transform it to obtain the left side. The steps are the reverse of those in the given verification. Substituting $\sin^2 \theta + \cos^2 \theta$ for 1 is a step students initially find difficult.

2 EXAMPLE Auditory Learners

Students may find it helpful to give an oral explanation of what is done at each stage of the verification.

Advanced Learners **L4**
Have students derive the other two Pythagorean Identities algebraically from $\sin^2 \theta + \cos^2 \theta = 1$. Divide by $\cos^2 \theta$. Divide by $\sin^2 \theta$.

learning style: verbal

English Language Learners **ELL**
Have students look up the term *identity* and *identical* in a dictionary. Discuss the difference between *sameness* of essential character and *individuality*, the essential character which distinguishes us.

learning style: verbal

Additional Examples

1 Verify the identity
$(\sin x + \cos x)^2 = 1 + 2\sin x \cos x$.
Answers may vary. Sample:
$(\sin x + \cos x)^2$
$= \sin^2 x + 2\sin x \cos x + \cos^2 x$
$= (\sin^2 x + \cos^2 x) + 2\sin x \cos x$
$= 1 + 2\sin x \cos x$

2 Verify the identity
$\frac{\sin \theta}{\tan \theta} + \frac{\cos \theta}{\cot \theta} = \sin \theta + \cos \theta$.
Answers may vary. Sample:
$\frac{\sin \theta}{\tan \theta} + \frac{\cos \theta}{\cot \theta}$
$= \frac{\sin \theta}{\left(\frac{\sin \theta}{\cos \theta}\right)} + \frac{\cos \theta}{\left(\frac{\cos \theta}{\sin \theta}\right)}$
$= \sin \theta \cdot \frac{\cos \theta}{\sin \theta} + \cos \theta \cdot \frac{\sin \theta}{\cos \theta}$
$= \cos \theta + \sin \theta$
$= \sin \theta + \cos \theta$

3 Simplify the trigonometric expression $(1 + \cot^2 \theta)(\sec^2 \theta - 1)$.
$\sec^2 \theta$

Resources
- Daily Notetaking Guide
  14-1   **L3**

Closure

Ask students to explain what a trigonometric identity is. Then ask them to explain the procedure they would use to verify that a trigonometric equation is an identity. **Answers may vary. Sample: A trigonometric identity is an equation which involves trigonometric functions and which is true for all values of the variable for which the expressions in the equation are defined. To verify that an equation is an identity, select one side of the equation, and transform it until it is the other side of the equation.**

1. $\cos \theta \cot \theta =$
$\cos \theta \left(\frac{\cos \theta}{\sin \theta}\right) =$
$\frac{1 - \sin^2 \theta}{\sin \theta} = \frac{1}{\sin \theta} - \sin \theta$

2. $\sin \theta \cot \theta =$
$\sin \theta \left(\frac{\cos \theta}{\sin \theta}\right) = \cos \theta$

3. $\cos \theta \tan \theta =$
$\cos \theta \left(\frac{\sin \theta}{\cos \theta}\right) = \sin \theta$

780

The word <u>identity</u> is used in several ways.

additive identity: 0

multiplicative identity: 1

trigonometric identity: an equation true for all valid replacements of the variables

2. $\sec^2 \theta - \sec^2 \theta \cos^2 \theta$
$= \left(\frac{1}{\cos \theta}\right)^2 - \left(\frac{1}{\cos \theta}\right)^2 \cos^2 \theta$
$= \frac{1}{\cos^2 \theta} - \frac{1}{\cos^2 \theta} \cdot \cos^2 \theta$
$= \frac{1}{\cos^2 \theta} - \frac{\cos^2 \theta}{\cos^2 \theta}$
$= \frac{1 - \cos^2 \theta}{\cos^2 \theta}$
$= \frac{\sin^2 \theta}{\cos^2 \theta} = \tan^2 \theta$

✔ **Quick Check**

---

2 EXAMPLE **Verifying Identities**

Verify the identity $\tan^2 \theta - \sin^2 \theta = \tan^2 \theta \sin^2 \theta$.

$\tan^2 \theta - \sin^2 \theta = \left(\frac{\sin \theta}{\cos \theta}\right)^2 - \sin^2 \theta$ **Tangent Identity**

$= \frac{\sin^2 \theta}{\cos^2 \theta} - \sin^2 \theta$ **Simplify.**

$= \frac{\sin^2 \theta}{\cos^2 \theta} - \frac{\sin^2 \theta \cos^2 \theta}{\cos^2 \theta}$ **Write fractions with common denominators.**

$= \frac{\sin^2 \theta - \sin^2 \theta \cos^2 \theta}{\cos^2 \theta}$ **Subtract.**

$= \frac{\sin^2 \theta (1 - \cos^2 \theta)}{\cos^2 \theta}$ **Factor.**

$= \frac{\sin^2 \theta (\sin^2 \theta)}{\cos^2 \theta}$ **Pythagorean identity**

$= \frac{\sin^2 \theta}{\cos^2 \theta} \sin^2 \theta$ **Rewrite the fraction.**

$= \tan^2 \theta \sin^2 \theta$ **Tangent Identity**

✔ **Quick Check** **2** Verify the identity $\sec^2 \theta - \sec^2 \theta \cos^2 \theta = \tan^2 \theta$. **See left.**

You can use the trigonometric identities to simplify trigonometric expressions. Again, it is often helpful to write all the functions in terms of sines and cosines.

3 EXAMPLE **Simplifying Expressions**

Simplify the trigonometric expression $\csc \theta \tan \theta$.

$\csc \theta \tan \theta = \frac{1}{\sin \theta} \cdot \tan \theta$ **Reciprocal Identity**

$= \frac{1}{\sin \theta} \cdot \frac{\sin \theta}{\cos \theta}$ **Tangent Identity**

$= \frac{\sin \theta}{\sin \theta \cos \theta}$ **Multiply.**

$= \frac{1}{\cos \theta}$ **Simplify.**

$= \sec \theta$ **Reciprocal identity**

So $\csc \theta \tan \theta = \sec \theta$.

✔ **Quick Check** **3** Simplify the trigonometric expression $\sec \theta \cot \theta$. **$\csc \theta$**

EXERCISES

For more exercises, see *Extra Skill and Word Problem Practice*.

Practice and Problem Solving

A **Practice by Example**

Examples 1 and 2
(pages 779 and 780)

GO for Help

Verify each identity.   **1–8. See margin.**

1. $\cos \theta \cot \theta = \frac{1}{\sin \theta} - \sin \theta$ **2.** $\sin \theta \cot \theta = \cos \theta$

3. $\cos \theta \tan \theta = \sin \theta$ **4.** $\sin \theta \sec \theta = \tan \theta$

5. $\cos \theta \sec \theta = 1$ **6.** $\tan \theta \cot \theta = 1$

7. $\sin \theta \csc \theta = 1$ **8.** $\cot \theta = \frac{\csc \theta}{\sec \theta}$

---

4. $\sin \theta \sec \theta =$
$\sin \theta \left(\frac{1}{\cos \theta}\right) = \frac{\sin \theta}{\cos \theta} = \tan \theta$

5. $\cos \theta \sec \theta =$
$\cos \theta \left(\frac{1}{\cos \theta}\right) = 1$

6. $\tan \theta \cot \theta =$
$\left(\frac{\sin \theta}{\cos \theta}\right)\left(\frac{\cos \theta}{\sin \theta}\right) = 1$

7. $\sin \theta \csc \theta =$
$\sin \theta \left(\frac{1}{\sin \theta}\right) = \frac{\sin \theta}{\sin \theta} = 1$

8. $\cot \theta = \frac{\cos \theta}{\sin \theta} =$
$\frac{1}{\sin \theta} \cdot \frac{\cos \theta}{1} = \frac{1}{\sin \theta} \div$
$\frac{1}{\cos \theta} = \frac{\csc \theta}{\sec \theta}$

39. $\pm\sqrt{1 - \cos^2 \theta}$

Example 3
(page 780)

Simplify each trigonometric expression.

9. $\tan\theta\cot\theta$ **1**

10. $1 - \cos^2\theta$ **$\sin^2\theta$**

11. $\sec^2\theta - 1$ **$\tan^2\theta$**

12. $1 - \csc^2\theta$ **$-\cot^2\theta$**

13. $\sec\theta\cot\theta$ **$\csc\theta$**

14. $\cos\theta\tan\theta$ **$\sin\theta$**

15. $\sin\theta\cot\theta$ **$\cos\theta$**

16. $\sin\theta\csc\theta$ **1**

17. $\sec\theta\cos\theta\sin\theta$ **$\sin\theta$**

18. $\sin\theta\sec\theta\cot\theta$ **1**

19. $\sec^2\theta - \tan^2\theta$ **1**

20. $\dfrac{\sin\theta}{\cos\theta\tan\theta}$ **1**

B **Apply Your Skills**

Simplify each trigonometric expression.

21. $\cos\theta + \sin\theta\tan\theta$ **$\sec\theta$**

22. $\csc\theta\cos\theta\tan\theta$ **1**

23. $\tan\theta(\cot\theta + \tan\theta)$ **$\sec^2\theta$**

24. $\sin^2\theta + \cos^2\theta + \tan^2\theta$ **$\sec^2\theta$**

25. $\cos^2\theta\sec\theta\csc\theta$ **$\cot\theta$**

26. $\sin\theta(1 + \cot^2\theta)$ **$\csc\theta$**

27. $\cot\theta\tan\theta - \sec^2\theta$ **$-\tan^2\theta$**

28. $\sin^2\theta\csc\theta\sec\theta$ **$\tan\theta$**

29. $\cos\theta(1 + \tan^2\theta)$ **$\sec\theta$**

30. $\dfrac{\tan\theta}{\sec\theta - \cos\theta}$ **$\csc\theta$**

31. $\sec\theta\cos\theta - \cos^2\theta$ **$\sin^2\theta$**

32. $\sin\theta\csc\theta - \cos^2\theta$ **$\sin^2\theta$**

33. $\csc\theta - \cos\theta\cot\theta$ **$\sin\theta$**

34. $\cos\theta + \sin\theta\tan\theta$ **$\sec\theta$**

35. $\sec\theta(1 + \cot^2\theta)$ **$\sec\theta\csc^2\theta$**

36. $\csc^2\theta(1 - \cos^2\theta)$ **1**

37. $\dfrac{\cos\theta\csc\theta}{\cot\theta}$ **1**

38. $\dfrac{\sin^2\theta\csc\theta\sec\theta}{\tan\theta}$ **1**

Express the first trigonometric function in terms of the second.

39. $\sin\theta, \cos\theta$

40. $\tan\theta, \cos\theta$

41. $\cot\theta, \sin\theta$

42. $\csc\theta, \cot\theta$

43. $\cot\theta, \csc\theta$

44. $\sec\theta, \tan\theta$

39–44. See margin pp. 780–781.

Verify each identity. 45–50. See back of book.

45. $\sin^2\theta\tan^2\theta = \tan^2\theta - \sin^2\theta$

46. $\sec\theta - \sin\theta\tan\theta = \cos\theta$

47. $\sin\theta\cos\theta(\tan\theta + \cot\theta) = 1$

48. $\dfrac{1 - \sin\theta}{\cos\theta} = \dfrac{\cos\theta}{1 + \sin\theta}$

49. $\dfrac{\sec\theta}{\cot\theta + \tan\theta} = \sin\theta$

50. $(\cot\theta + 1)^2 = \csc^2\theta + 2\cot\theta$

51. Express $\cos\theta\csc\theta\cot\theta$ in terms of $\sin\theta$. $\dfrac{1 - \sin^2\theta}{\sin^2\theta}$

52. Express $\dfrac{\cos\theta}{\sec\theta + \tan\theta}$ in terms of $\sin\theta$. **$1 - \sin\theta$**

53. Open-Ended Create a trigonometric identity. (*Hint:* Start with a simple trigonometric expression and work backward.) **Check students' work.**

54. Writing Describe the similarities and differences in solving an equation and in verifying an identity. **See margin.**

C **Challenge**

Verify each identity. 55–56. See margin.

55. $1 + \sec\theta = \dfrac{1 + \cos\theta}{\cos\theta}$

56. $\dfrac{1 + \tan\theta}{\tan\theta} = \cot\theta + 1$

57. $\dfrac{\cot\theta\sin\theta}{\sec\theta} + \dfrac{\tan\theta\cos\theta}{\csc\theta} = 1$

58. $\sin^2\theta\tan^2\theta + \cos^2\theta\tan^2\theta = \sec^2\theta - 1$

57–58. See back of book.

Simplify each trigonometric expression.

59. $\dfrac{\cot^2\theta - \csc^2\theta}{\tan^2\theta - \sec^2\theta}$ **1**

60. $(1 - \sin\theta)(1 + \sin\theta)\csc^2\theta$ **$1 \quad \csc^2\theta$**

Online
Homework Video Tutor
Visit: PHSchool.com
Web Code: age-1401

Assignment Guide

1 A B 1-54

C Challenge 55-61

Test Prep 62-68
Mixed Review 69-84

Homework Quick Check

To check students' understanding of key skills and concepts, go over Exercises 20, 32, 45, 48, 54.

Error Prevention!

Exercises 9–38 A common mistake when applying Reciprocal Identities is to use $\csc\theta = \dfrac{1}{\cos\theta}$ rather than $\csc\theta = \dfrac{1}{\sin\theta}$ or to use $\sec\theta = \dfrac{1}{\sin\theta}$ rather than $\sec\theta = \dfrac{1}{\cos\theta}$. Urge students to commit the Reciprocal Identities to memory and to refer to the Key Concepts box on page 779 frequently to double check that they recall all of these identities correctly.

---

40. $\dfrac{\pm\sqrt{1 - \cos^2\theta}}{\cos\theta}$

41. $\dfrac{\pm\sqrt{1 - \sin^2\theta}}{\sin\theta}$

42. $\pm\sqrt{1 + \cot^2\theta}$

43. $\pm\sqrt{\csc^2\theta - 1}$

44. $\pm\sqrt{1 + \tan^2\theta}$

54. When checking a root of an equation, you substitute the solution into the equation to see if it is true. When verifying an identity, you substitute equivalent expressions until both sides are the same.

55. $1 + \sec\theta = 1 + \dfrac{1}{\cos\theta} = \dfrac{1}{\cos\theta} + 1 = \dfrac{1 + \cos\theta}{\cos\theta}$

56. $\dfrac{1 + \tan\theta}{\tan\theta} = \dfrac{1}{\tan\theta} + \dfrac{\tan\theta}{\tan\theta} = \cot\theta + 1$

781

1. Verify the identity
$\dfrac{1 + \cot^2 \theta}{\cot^2 \theta} = \sec^2 \theta$. **Answers**
may vary. Sample:
$\dfrac{1 + \cot^2 \theta}{\cot^2 \theta} = \dfrac{1}{\cot^2 \theta} + \dfrac{\cot^2 \theta}{\cot^2 \theta}$
$= \tan^2 \theta + 1$
$= 1 + \tan^2 \theta$
$= \sec^2 \theta$

2. Simplify $(1 - \sec \theta)(1 + \sec \theta)$.
$-\tan^2 \theta$

3. Express $\dfrac{1 + \tan^2 \theta}{1 - \tan^2 \theta}$ in terms
of $\cos \theta$. $\dfrac{1}{2 \cos^2 \theta - 1}$

Alternative Assessment

Have students work in groups of
three. Ask each student to create
a trigonometric identity. Each
student in the group should then
verify the identities created by
the other two students. Have
students check one another's
work.

Test Prep

Resources
For additional practice with a
variety of test item formats:
• Standardized Test Prep, p. 831
• Test-Taking Strategies, p. 826
• Test-Taking Strategies with
  Transparencies

67. [2] $(\sec \theta + 1)(\sec \theta - 1)$
$= \sec^2 \theta + \sec \theta -$
$\sec \theta - 1$
$= \sec^2 \theta - 1 = \tan^2 \theta$

[1] does not show work

69.

61. If $n_2 > n_1$, then
$\theta_1 > \theta_2$; if $n_2 < n_1$,
then $\theta_1 < \theta_2$; if
$n_2 = n_1$, then $\theta_1 = \theta_2$.

61. Physics When a ray of light passes from one medium into a
second, the angle of incidence θ_1 and the angle of refraction
θ_2 are related by Snell's law: $n_1 \sin \theta_1 = n_2 \sin \theta_2$, where n_1 is
the index of refraction of the first medium and n_2 is the
index of refraction of the second medium. How are θ_1 and θ_2
related if $n_2 > n_1$? If $n_2 < n_1$? If $n_2 = n_1$?

Test Prep

Multiple Choice

62. Which expression is NOT equal to the other three expressions? **C**
A. $\dfrac{2}{\tan \theta}$ B. $\dfrac{\cot \theta}{\frac{1}{2}}$ C. $\dfrac{\sin \theta}{\frac{1}{2}\cos \theta}$ D. $\dfrac{2 \cos \theta}{\sin \theta}$

63. Which equation is NOT true? **H**
F. $\cos^2 \theta = 1 - \sin^2 \theta$ G. $\cot^2 \theta = \csc^2 \theta - 1$
H. $\sin^2 \theta = \cos^2 \theta - 1$ J. $\tan^2 \theta = \sec^2 \theta - 1$

64. Which expressions are equivalent? **C**
I. $(\sin \theta)(\csc \theta - \sin \theta)$ II. $\sin^2 \theta - 1$ III. $\cos^2 \theta$
A. I and II only   B. II and III only
C. I and III only   D. I, II, and III

65. How can you express $\csc^2 \theta - 2 \cot^2 \theta$ in terms of $\sin \theta$ and $\cos \theta$? **F**
F. $\dfrac{1 - 2 \cos^2 \theta}{\sin^2 \theta}$ G. $\dfrac{1 - 2 \sin^2 \theta}{\sin^2 \theta}$
H. $\sin^2 \theta - 2 \cos^2 \theta$ J. $\dfrac{1}{\sin^2 \theta} - \dfrac{2}{\tan^2 \theta}$

66. Which expression is equivalent to $\dfrac{\tan \theta}{\cos \theta - \sec \theta}$? **C**
A. $\csc \theta$ B. $\sec \theta$ C. $-\csc \theta$ D. $\tan^2 \theta$

Short Response

67. Show that $(\sec \theta + 1)(\sec \theta - 1) = \tan^2 \theta$ is an identity. **See margin.**

68. Show that $\dfrac{\cos x}{1 - \sin^2 x} = \sec x$ is an identity. **See back of book.**

Mixed Review

GO for Help

Lesson 13-8
Graph each function in the interval from 0 to 2π. **69–72. See margin.**
69. $y = \csc(-\theta)$ **70.** $y = -\cot \theta$ **71.** $y = -\sec 0.5\theta$
72. $y = -\sec(0.5\theta + 2)$ **73.** $y = \cot \dfrac{\theta}{5}$ **74.** $y = \pi \sec \theta$
73–74. See back of book.

Lesson 13-2
Find the measure of an angle between 0° and 360° that is coterminal with the
given angle.
75. 395° **35°**   **76.** 405° **45°**   **77.** −225° **135°**   **78.** −149° **211°**
79. 627° **267°**   **80.** −281° **79°**   **81.** 493° **133°**   **82.** −609° **111°**

Lesson 12-3
Make a box-and-whisker plot for each set of values. **83–84. See back of book.**
83. 300 345 333 295 302 321
84. 32 48 87 43 62 15 49 51 47 36 50 109 64

70.

71.

72.

Solving Trigonometric Equations Using Inverses

What You'll Learn

- To evaluate inverses of trigonometric functions
- To solve trigonometric equations

. . . And Why

To solve problems involving springs, as in Example 7

 Check Skills You'll Need

GO for Help Lessons 7-7, 13-2, and 13-6

For each function f, find f^{-1}.   **1–2. See below.**

1. $f(x) = x + 1$ **2.** $f(x) = 2x - 3$ **3.** $f(x) = x^2 + 4$ $f^{-1}(x) = \pm\sqrt{x - 4}$

Find each value.

4. $\sin 30°$ **0.5**   **5.** $\cos \frac{\pi}{4}$ $\frac{\sqrt{2}}{2}$ **6.** $\cos 135°$ $-\frac{\sqrt{2}}{2}$

7. $\tan(-\pi)$ **0**   **8.** $\tan 315°$ -1 **9.** $\sin\left(-\frac{7\pi}{3}\right)$ $-\frac{\sqrt{3}}{2}$

1. $f^{-1}(x) = x - 1$ **2.** $f^{-1}(x) = \frac{x + 3}{2}$

---

1 Inverses of Trigonometric Functions

The cosine function $y = \cos \theta$ is periodic, so a horizontal line, such as the x-axis, can intersect the graph of $y = \cos \theta$ in infinitely many points. Therefore a vertical line can intersect the graph of the inverse of $y = \cos \theta$ in infinitely many points. The inverse of $y = \cos \theta$ is a relation that is not a function.

You can use a graph of an inverse function to find the measures of angles that have a given value of the function.

1 EXAMPLE Using a Graph to Find Angles With a Given Cosine

Use the graph of the inverse of $y = \cos \theta$ at the right.

a. Find the radian measures of the angles whose cosine is -1.

The line $x = -1$ intersects the graph at $(-1, \pi)$ and $(-1, -\pi)$. So the measures of two angles whose cosine is -1 are π and $-\pi$.

Other points of intersection are $(-1, \pm3\pi)$, $(-1, \pm5\pi)$, and so on. The measures of all the angles whose cosine is -1 can be written as $\pi + 2\pi n$, where n is any integer.

b. Find the radian measures of the angles θ whose cosine is 2.

The line $x = 2$ does not intersect the graph. 2 is not in the domain of the inverse of $y = \cos \theta$. There is no angle whose cosine is 2.

Inverse of $y = \cos \theta$

 Quick Check **1** What are the radian measures of the angles whose cosine is 1.1? Whose cosine is 0? Whose cosine is -1.1? **none, $\frac{\pi}{2} + \pi n$, none**

Differentiated Instruction Solutions for All Learners

Special Needs L1

Review inverse functions from Lesson 7-7. Then have students create a poster with graphs of inverse function pairs such as: $y = x^2$ and $y = \sqrt{x}$, $y = 2^x$ and $y = \log_2 x$, $y = \sin x$ and $y = \sin^{-1} x$, $y = \cos x$ and $y = \cos^{-1} x$, and $y = \tan x$ and $y = \tan^{-1} x$.

learning style: visual

Below Level L2

Remind students that if a vertical line intersects a graph at more than one point, the graph is not a function. That is why the inverse of $y = \cos \theta$ is not a function.

learning style: verbal

---

1. Plan

Objectives

1 To evaluate inverses of trigonometric functions
2 To solve trigonometric equations

Examples

1 Using a Graph to Find Angles With a Given Cosine
2 Using a Unit Circle
3 Using a Calculator to Find the Inverse of Sine
4 Using a Calculator to Find the Inverse of Tangent
5 Solving Trigonometric Equations
6 Solving by Factoring
7 Real-World Connection

 Professional Development

Math Background

You can restrict the domains of the secant, cosecant, and cotangent trigonometric functions in such a way that the inverses are functions, but there is no universal agreement as to the most useful choice of domain.

More Math Background: p. 776C

Lesson Planning and Resources

See p. 776E for a list of the resources that support this lesson.

 PowerPoint

Bell Ringer Practice

 Check Skills You'll Need
For intervention, direct students to:

Inverse Relations and Functions
Lesson 7-7: Examples 4, 5
Extra Skills and Word Problems Practice, Ch. 7

Angles and the Unit Circle
Lesson 13-2: Example 4
Extra Skills and Word Problems Practice, Ch. 13

The Tangent Function
Lesson 13-6: Example 1
Extra Skills and Word Problems Practice, Ch. 13

2. Teach

Guided Instruction

1 EXAMPLE Alternative Method

Students can use a graphing calculator to display the graph of the inverse relation for $y = \cos x$. One approach is to graph $y = \cos x$ and then use the DrawInv feature on the DRAW menu. Another approach is to use a parametric graph. Set the calculator to parametric mode. Use the equations $X_{1T} = T$ and $Y_{1T} = \cos(T)$ to display the graph of the cosine function. For the inverse relation, use $X_{2T} = \cos(T)$ and $Y_{2T} = T$.

3 EXAMPLE Technology Tip

Have students use their graphing calculators to check that $\sin^{-1}(-0.9) \approx -1.12$. Before they do this, they should check that the calculator is set to Radian mode.

4 EXAMPLE Teaching Tip

You may want to point out that the Quadrant II angle is obtained by adding the negative angle in Quadrant IV to π. As a result, you can specify all the angles whose tangent is -0.84 with the single expression $-0.70 + \pi n$.

Test-Taking Tip

Drawing a diagram is often helpful in answering complex questions. You can sketch a unit circle to help you answer questions about trigonometric functions.

Vocabulary Tip

The expression $\cos^{-1} x$ represents the inverse cosine function. It is *not* the reciprocal of the cosine function, $\frac{1}{\cos x}$.

2a. $120° + n \cdot 360°$ and $240° + n \cdot 360°$

b. $150° + n \cdot 360°$ and $210° + n \cdot 360°$

c. $45° + n \cdot 360°$ and $315° + n \cdot 360°$

You can use a unit circle to find angle measures for given sine or cosine values.

2 EXAMPLE Using a Unit Circle

Multiple Choice Find the degree measures of the angles whose cosine is $\frac{1}{2}$.

Ⓐ $30° + n \cdot 360°$ and $330° + n \cdot 360°$
Ⓑ $60° + n \cdot 360°$ and $300° + n \cdot 360°$
Ⓒ $30° + n \cdot 360°$ and $210° + n \cdot 360°$
Ⓓ $60° + n \cdot 360°$ and $120° + n \cdot 360°$

Draw a unit circle and mark the points on the circle that have x-coordinates of $\frac{1}{2}$. These points and the origin form 30°-60°-90° triangles. 60° and 300° are the measures of two angles whose cosine is $\frac{1}{2}$. All their coterminal angles also have a cosine of $\frac{1}{2}$.

The measures of all the angles whose cosine is $\frac{1}{2}$ can be written as $60° + n \cdot 360°$ and $300° + n \cdot 360°$.
• The correct choice is B.

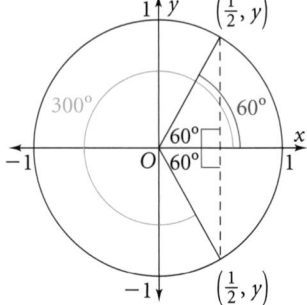

✓ Quick Check ② Use a unit circle. Find the degree measures of all angles with the given cosine.

a. $-\frac{1}{2}$ b. $-\frac{\sqrt{3}}{2}$ c. $\frac{\sqrt{2}}{2}$

a–c. See below left.

The domain of the cosine function can be restricted to $0 \leq \theta \leq \pi$ so that its inverse is a function. The inverse function is written $\theta = \cos^{-1} x$ and is read as "θ is the angle whose cosine is x."

 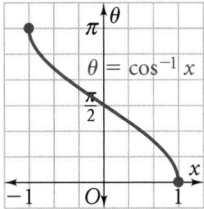

The domains are similarly restricted for $y = \sin \theta \left(-\frac{\pi}{2} \leq \theta \leq \frac{\pi}{2}\right)$ and $y = \tan \theta \left(-\frac{\pi}{2} < \theta < \frac{\pi}{2}\right)$ to obtain the inverse functions $\theta = \sin^{-1} x$ and $\theta = \tan^{-1} x$.

 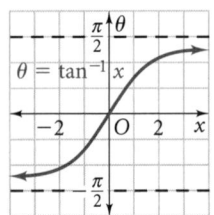

784 Chapter 14 Trigonometric Identities and Equations

Differentiated Instruction Solutions for All Learners

Advanced Learners L4
Have students research the restricted domains of functions such as Sin θ (with an upper case "S") that have inverses that are functions.

learning style: verbal

English Language Learners ELL
Have students make graphs of *relations*, some of which are *functions*. Discuss the terms *domain* and *range*. Then review *inverse functions*, in which the variables are interchanged, and clarify that not all functions have inverses that are functions.

learning style: visual

3 EXAMPLE Using a Calculator to Find the Inverse of Sine

Use a calculator and an inverse function to find the radian measures of all the angles whose sine is −0.9.

$\sin^{-1}(-0.9) \approx -1.12$ **Use a calculator.**

This angle is in Quadrant IV. The sine function is also negative in Quadrant III, as shown in the figure at the right. So $\pi + 1.12 \approx 4.26$ is another solution.

The radian measures of all the angles whose sine is −0.9 can be written as

−1.12 + 2πn and 4.26 + 2πn.

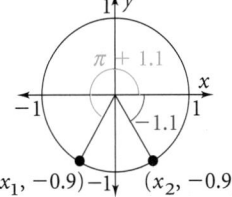

3a. 0.46 + 2πn and 2.69 + 2πn

b. −0.82 + 2πn and 3.96 + 2πn

✔ Quick Check ③ Find the radian measures of the angles. **a–b. See left.**
 a. angles whose sine is 0.44
 b. angles whose sine is −0.73

4 EXAMPLE Using a Calculator to Find the Inverse of Tangent

Use a calculator and an inverse function to find the measure in radians of all the angles whose tangent is −0.84.

$\tan^{-1}(-0.84) \approx -0.70$ **Use a calculator.**

The tangent function is also negative in Quadrant II, as shown in the figure at the right. So $\pi - 0.70 \approx 2.44$ is another solution.

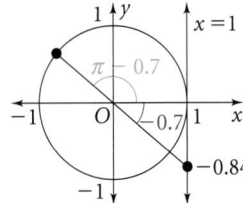

The radian measures of all the angles whose tangent is −0.84 can be written as

−0.70 + 2πn and 2.44 + 2πn.

✔ Quick Check ④ Find the radian measures of the angles.
 a. angles whose tangent is 0.44
  0.41 + 2πn and 3.56 + 2πn
 b. angles whose tangent is −0.73
  −0.63 + 2πn and 2.51 + 2πn

2 Solving Trigonometric Equations

In contrast to trigonometric identities, most trigonometric equations are true for only certain values of the variable.

5 EXAMPLE Solving Trigonometric Equations

Solve $4\cos\theta - 1 = \cos\theta$ for $0 \le \theta < 2\pi$.

$4\cos\theta - 1 = \cos\theta$

$3\cos\theta = 1$ **Add 1 − cos θ to each side.**

$\cos\theta = \frac{1}{3}$ **Divide each side by 3.**

$\cos^{-1}\frac{1}{3} \approx 1.23$ **Use the inverse function to find one value of θ.**

The cosine function is also positive in Quadrant IV. So another value of θ is $2\pi - 1.23 \approx 5.05$. The two solutions between 0 and 2π are approximately 1.23 and 5.05.

785

Additional Examples

5 Solve $7 \cos \theta - 3 = 2 \cos \theta$ for $0 \le \theta < 2\pi$. $\approx 0.93, \approx 5.36$

6 Solve $2 \sin \theta \cos \theta - \cos \theta = 0$ for $0 \le \theta < 2\pi$. $\frac{\pi}{6}, \frac{\pi}{2}, \frac{5\pi}{6}, \frac{3\pi}{2}$

7 In decibels, the noise level d close to an electronic alarm device is modeled by $d = 40 \sin \frac{\pi(t - 6)}{12} + 40$, where t is the number of seconds after the device is activated. How many seconds after the device is activated does it take for the sound to reach a noise level of 60 decibels? **8 s**

Resources
• Daily Notetaking Guide
  14-2   **L3**

Closure

Ask students to describe two methods they might use to find the value of an angle measure θ if they know the value of a trigonometric function of θ. **Answers may vary. Sample: If the value is one associated with a 30°-60°-90° or a 45°-45°-90°, triangle, you may use the triangle to determine the angle measure. Otherwise, use the inverse trigonometric functions on a graphing calculator.**

Real-World Connection

The motion of an oscillating spring is called simple harmonic motion.

7b. Yes; at 2 s, the toy will reach a maximum at 4 in. and then come back down, again hitting 2 in. at 2 s.

c. Let $y_1 = -4 \cos \frac{2\pi}{3} t$ and let $y_2 = 2$. Graph. Trace and calculate the intersection.

✓ Quick Check **5** Solve $3 \sin \theta + 1 = \sin \theta$ for $0 \le \theta < 2\pi$. $\frac{11\pi}{6}$ and $\frac{7\pi}{6}$

Sometimes you can solve trigonometric equations by factoring.

6 EXAMPLE Solving by Factoring

Solve $2 \cos \theta \sin \theta + \sin \theta = 0$ for $0 \le \theta < 2\pi$.

$2 \cos \theta \sin \theta + \sin \theta = 0$
$\sin \theta (2 \cos \theta + 1) = 0$ **Factor.**
$\sin \theta = 0$ or $2 \cos \theta + 1 = 0$ **Zero-Product Property**
$\sin \theta = 0$ $\cos \theta = -\frac{1}{2}$ **Solve for cos θ.**
$\theta = 0$ and π $\theta = \frac{2\pi}{3}$ and $\frac{4\pi}{3}$ **Use the unit circle.**

● The four values of θ are $0, \pi, \frac{2\pi}{3},$ and $\frac{4\pi}{3}$.

✓ Quick Check **6** Solve $\sin \theta \cos \theta - \cos \theta = 0$ for $0 \le \theta < 2\pi$. $\frac{\pi}{2}$ and $\frac{3\pi}{2}$

You can use trigonometric equations to solve problems involving repetitive events.

7 EXAMPLE Real-World Connection

Physics The spring at the left is stretched and released. The equation $h = -4 \cos \frac{2\pi}{3} t$ models the toy's height h in inches above or below the rest position as a function of time t in seconds. When will the toy first be 2 in. above the rest position?

rest position

4 in.

4 in.

$h = -4 \cos \frac{2\pi}{3} t$

$2 = -4 \cos \frac{2\pi}{3} t$ **Substitute 2 for h.**

$-\frac{2}{4} = \cos \frac{2\pi}{3} t$ **Divide each side by −4.**

$-\frac{1}{2} = \cos \frac{2\pi}{3} t$ **Simplify.**

$\cos^{-1}\left(-\frac{1}{2}\right) = \frac{2\pi}{3} t$ **Use the inverse of the cosine to solve for t.**

$\frac{2\pi}{3} = \frac{2\pi}{3} t$ **Evaluate the inverse. Use the unit circle.**

$1 = t$ **Multiply each side by $\frac{3}{2\pi}$.**

● The toy is 2 in. above the rest position at 1 s.

✓ Quick Check **7** **a.** When will the toy in Example 7 first be 2 in. below the rest position? When will the toy next be 4 in. below the rest position? $\frac{1}{2}$ s; 3 s
b. You found that the toy in Example 7 is 2 in. above the rest position after 1 s. Will it ever be at that same position again? Explain. **b–c. See left.**
c. How could you use a graphing calculator to solve Example 7?

EXERCISES

For more exercises, see *Extra Skill and Word Problem Practice*.

Practice and Problem Solving

A Practice by Example

GO for Help

Example 1
(page 783)

Example 2
(page 784)

1. $-\frac{\pi}{2} + 2\pi n$

5. $30° + n \cdot 360°$ and
   $210° + n \cdot 360°$
   or $30° + n \cdot 180°$

Examples 3 and 4
(page 785)

Example 5
(page 785)

Example 6
(page 786)

Example 7
(page 786)

Use the graph of the inverse of $y = \sin \theta$ at the right.

1. Find the measures of the angles whose sine is -1.

2. Find the measures of the angles whose sine is 0.
   $0 + \pi n$

3. Find the measures of the angles whose sine is 1.
   $\frac{\pi}{2} + 2\pi n$

Use a unit circle and 30°-60°-90° triangles to find the degree measures of the angles.

4. angles whose sine is $\frac{1}{2}$ $30° + n \cdot 360°$ and $150° + n \cdot 360°$

5. angles whose tangent is $\frac{\sqrt{3}}{3}$

6. angles whose sine is $-\frac{1}{2}$ $210° + n \cdot 360°$ and $330° + n \cdot 360°$

7. angles whose tangent is $-\sqrt{3}$
   $120° + n \cdot 360°$ and $300° + n \cdot 360°$ or $120° + n \cdot 180°$

Use a calculator and inverse functions to find the radian measures of the angles.

8. angles whose tangent is 1

9. angles whose sine is 0.37

10. angles whose sine is (-0.78)

11. angles whose tangent is (-3)

12. angles whose cosine is (-0.89)

13. angles whose sine is (-1.1)

14. angles whose tangent is 5

15. angles whose cosine is 0.58

8–15. See margin.

Solve each equation for $0 \le \theta < 2\pi$.

16. $2 \sin \theta = 1$ $\frac{\pi}{6}, \frac{5\pi}{6}$

17. $2 \cos \theta - \sqrt{3} = 0$ $\frac{\pi}{6}, \frac{11\pi}{6}$

18. $4 \tan \theta = 3 + \tan \theta$ $\frac{\pi}{4}, \frac{5\pi}{4}$

19. $2 \sin \theta - \sqrt{2} = 0$ $\frac{\pi}{4}, \frac{3\pi}{4}$

20. $3 \cos \theta = 2$ **0.84, 5.44**

21. $3 \tan \theta - 1 = \tan \theta$ **0.46, 3.61**

22. $\sqrt{2} \cos \theta - \sqrt{2} = 0$ **0**

23. $3 \tan \theta + 5 = 0$ **2.11, 5.23**

24. $2 \sin \theta = 3$ **no solution**

25. $2 \sin \theta = -\sqrt{3}$ $\frac{4\pi}{3}, \frac{5\pi}{3}$

26. $(\cos \theta)(\cos \theta + 1) = 0$ $\frac{\pi}{2}, \pi, \frac{3\pi}{2}$

27. $(\sin \theta - 1)(\sin \theta + 1) = 0$ $\frac{\pi}{2}, \frac{3\pi}{2}$

28. $\tan^2 \theta + \tan \theta = 0$ **0**, $\pi, \frac{3\pi}{4}, \frac{7\pi}{4}$

29. $2 \sin^2 \theta - 1 = 0$ $\frac{\pi}{4}, \frac{3\pi}{4}, \frac{5\pi}{4}, \frac{7\pi}{4}$

30. $\tan \theta = \tan^2 \theta$ **0**, $\frac{\pi}{4}, \pi, \frac{5\pi}{4}$

31. $\sin^2 \theta + 3 \sin \theta = 0$ **0**, π

32. $\sin \theta = -\sin \theta \cos \theta$ **0**, π

33. $2 \sin^2 \theta - 3 \sin \theta = 2$ $\frac{7\pi}{6}, \frac{11\pi}{6}$

34. **Physics** Two students set up a spring experiment similar to the one in Example 7. In their experiment, a weight was released 4 cm below the rest position. It rose to 4 cm above the rest position and returned to 4 cm below the rest position once every 4 seconds. The equation $h = -4 \cos\left(\frac{\pi}{2}t\right)$ models the height above and below the rest position at t seconds.
    a. Solve the equation for t. $t = \frac{2}{\pi} \cdot \cos^{-1}\left(\frac{h}{-4}\right)$
    b. Find the times at which the weight is first at a height of 1 cm, 2 cm, and 3 cm above the rest position.   **about 1.16 s, 1.33 s, 1.54 s**
    c. Find the times at which the weight is at a height of 1 cm, 2 cm, and 3 cm below the rest position for the second time.   **about 3.16 s, 3.33 s, 3.54 s**

8. $0.79 + \pi n$

9. $0.38 + 2\pi n$ and
   $2.76 + 2\pi n$

10. $-0.89 + 2\pi n$ and
    $4.04 + 2\pi n$

11. $1.89 + \pi n$

12. $2.67 + 2\pi n$ and
    $3.62 + 2\pi n$

13. no solution

14. $1.37 + \pi n$

15. $0.95 + 2\pi n$ and
    $5.33 + 2\pi n$

3. Practice

Assignment Guide

1 A B 1-15

2 A B 16-66
C Challenge   67-74

Test Prep   75-81
Mixed Review   82-92

Homework Quick Check

To check students' understanding of key skills and concepts, go over Exercises 6, 34, 36, 44, 45, 54, 64.

Error Prevention!

Exercises 4–12, 14, 15 Students may not name all the angles for which the given functions have the given value. Remind them that they must use what they know about the period of each function to specify all the values.

Differentiated Instruction Resources

787

46. $0 + 2\pi n, \frac{2}{3}\pi + 2\pi n,$
    $\frac{4}{3}\pi + 2\pi n$

47. $\frac{\pi}{2} + 2\pi n, \frac{3\pi}{2} + 2\pi n$

48. $\frac{\pi}{6} + 2\pi n, \frac{5\pi}{6} + 2\pi n,$
    $\frac{3\pi}{2} + 2\pi n$

49. $\frac{\pi}{4} + \frac{\pi}{2}n$

50. $\frac{\pi}{6} + 2\pi n, \frac{5\pi}{6} + 2\pi n,$
    $\frac{\pi}{2} + \pi n$

51. $0 + 2\pi n, \pi + 2\pi n,$
    $1.25 + 2\pi n, 4.39 + 2\pi n$

52. $\frac{\pi}{2} + 2\pi n, \frac{7\pi}{6} + 2\pi n,$
    $\frac{11\pi}{6} + 2\pi n$

53. $\frac{\pi}{6} + \pi n, \frac{5\pi}{6} + \pi n$

54. $\frac{\pi}{6} + 2\pi n, \frac{5\pi}{6} + 2\pi n$

55. $1.107 + \pi n, \frac{3\pi}{4} + \pi n$

B **Apply Your Skills**

35. $30° + n \cdot 360°$ and
    $150° + n \cdot 360°$

36. $60° + n \cdot 360°$ and
    $300° + n \cdot 360°$

37. $210° + n \cdot 360°$ and
    $330° + n \cdot 360°$

Real-World **Connection**

Electric generators convert mechanical energy into electricity. A generator may be larger than a house and generate enough electricity for a million homes.

GO Online
Homework Video Tutor
Visit: PHSchool.com
Web Code: age-1402

Each diagram shows one solution to the equation below it. Find the complete solution of each equation.

35.   36.   37.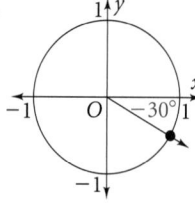

$5 \sin \theta = 1 + 3 \sin \theta$ $6 \cos \theta - 5 = -2$ $4 \sin \theta + 3 = 1$

Solve each equation for $0 \le \theta < 2\pi$.

38. $\sec \theta = 2$ $\frac{\pi}{3}, \frac{5\pi}{3}$ 39. $\csc \theta = -1$ $\frac{3\pi}{2}$

40. $\cot \theta = 10$ 0.10, 3.24   41. $\csc \theta = 3$ 0.34, 2.80

42. $\cot \theta = -10$ 3.04, 6.18   43. $\sec \theta = 1$ 0

44. **Electricity** The function $I = 40 \sin 60\pi t$ models the current *I* in amps that the electric generator shown at the left is producing after *t* seconds. When is the first time that the current will reach 20 amps? −20 amps? 0.0028 s; 0.019 s

45. **Critical Thinking** The graphing calculator screen below shows a portion of the graphs of $y = \sin \theta$ and $y = 0.5$.

Xmin=0
Xmax=360
Xscl=90
Ymin=−2
Ymax=2
Yscl=0.5

a. $30° + n \cdot 360°$
   $\le x \le 150° +$
   $n \cdot 360°$

b. $150° + n \cdot 360°$
   $\le x \le 390° +$
   $n \cdot 360°$

a. Write the complete solution of $\sin \theta \ge 0.5$.
b. Write the complete solution of $\sin \theta \le 0.5$.
c. **Writing** Explain how you can solve inequalities involving trigonometric functions. **Find the values of *x* where the graphs intersect, and then choose the appropriate interval.**

Find the complete solution in radians of each equation. 46–55. See margin.

46. $2 \sin^2 \theta + \cos \theta - 1 = 0$ 47. $\sin^2 \theta - 1 = \cos^2 \theta$

48. $2 \sin \theta + 1 = \csc \theta$ 49. $3 \tan^2 \theta - 1 = \sec^2 \theta$

50. $\sin \theta \cos \theta = \frac{1}{2} \cos \theta$ 51. $\tan \theta \sin \theta = 3 \sin \theta$

52. $2 \cos^2 \theta + \sin \theta = 1$ 53. $\sin \theta \cot^2 \theta - 3 \sin \theta = 0$

54. $4 \sin^2 \theta + 1 = 4 \sin \theta$ 55. $\tan \theta \cot \theta - \tan \theta + 2 \cot \theta = 0$

56. **Error Analysis** A student solved an equation as shown below. What error did the student make?

$\theta = \cos^{-1} 0.5$
$= \frac{1}{\cos 0.5}$
$\approx \frac{1}{0.88}$
≈ 1.14

The student misinterpreted the meaning of $\cos^{-1} 0.5$ as being equal to $\frac{1}{\cos 0.5}$.

57. Error Analysis A student solved the equation $\sin^2 \theta = \frac{1}{2}\sin \theta,\ 0 \le \theta < 2\pi$, as shown below. What error did the student make?

$$\sin^2 \theta = \tfrac{1}{2}\sin \theta$$
$$\sin \theta = \tfrac{1}{2}$$
$$\theta = \tfrac{\pi}{6} \text{ and } \tfrac{5\pi}{6}$$

The student divided both sides of the equation by sin θ, which in the given interval can be equal to zero. Since division by zero is not possible, this is where the error was.

Find the x-intercepts of the graph of each function.

58. $y = 2\cos \theta + 1$

59. $y = 2\sin^2 \theta - 1$

60. $y = \cos^2 \theta - 1 \quad 0 + \pi n$

61. $y = \tan^2 \theta - 1$

$0.79 + \pi n,$
$2.36 + \pi n$

62. $y = 2\sin^4 \theta - \sin^2 \theta$
$0 + \pi n,\ 0.79 + \pi n,\ 2.36 + \pi n$

63. $y = 2\cos^2 \theta - 3\cos \theta - 2$
$2.09 + 2\pi n,\ 4.19 + 2\pi n$

64. Writing Describe the similarities and differences in solving the equations $4x + 1 = 3$ and $4\sin \theta + 1 = 3$. **See margin.**

65. Find the complete solution of $\sin^2 \theta + 2\sin \theta + 1 = 0$. (*Hint:* How would you solve $x^2 + 2x + 1 = 0$?) $\frac{3\pi}{2} + 2\pi n$

66. a. Open-Ended Write three trigonometric equations whose complete solution is $\pi + 2\pi n$. **a–b. See margin.**
  b. Describe how you found the equations in part (a).

58. $2.09 + 2\pi n,\ 4.19 + 2\pi n$
59. $0.79 + \pi n,\ 2.36 + \pi n$

C Challenge

Solve each trigonometric equation for θ in terms of y.

Sample $\quad y = 2\sin 3\theta + 4$

$$\sin 3\theta = \frac{y - 4}{2}$$

$$3\theta = \sin^{-1}\left(\frac{y - 4}{2}\right)$$

$$\theta = \tfrac{1}{3}\sin^{-1}\left(\frac{y - 4}{2}\right)$$

67. $y = 2\sin \theta \quad \theta = \sin^{-1}\left(\frac{y}{2}\right)$

68. $y = \cos 2\theta \quad \theta = \tfrac{1}{2}\cos^{-1}(y)$

69. $y = 3\sin(\theta + 2) \quad \theta = \sin^{-1}\left(\frac{y}{3}\right) - 2$

70. $y = -4\cos 2\pi\theta \quad \theta = \tfrac{1}{2\pi}\cos^{-1}\left(-\frac{y}{4}\right)$

71. $y = \cos \theta + 1 \quad \theta = \cos^{-1}(y - 1)$

72. $y = 2\cos \pi\theta + 1 \quad \theta = \tfrac{1}{\pi}\cos^{-1}\left(\frac{y - 1}{2}\right)$

73. Parks A segment of a circle is the region formed by an arc of a circle and the line segment joining the endpoints of the arc. (The measure of the arc must be between 0 and 2π.) The expression below gives the area K in square feet of a segment in terms of the radius of the circle r in feet and the radian measure θ of the arc.

50 ft

$$K = \frac{r^2}{2}(\theta - \sin \theta)$$

  a. Suppose a circular park has a radius of 50 ft. Write an equation for the area of any segment of the park using $r = 50$. $k = 1250(\theta - \sin \theta)\ \text{ft}^2$
  b. Use trial and error to approximate the measure of θ that makes the area of the segment 1500 ft². ≈ 2.08

PowerPoint

Lesson Quiz

1. Use a unit circle and 30°-60°-90° triangles to find the degree measures of the angles that have a sine of $-\frac{\sqrt{3}}{2}$. $240° + n \cdot 360°$, $300° + n \cdot 360°$

2. Use a calculator and inverse functions to find the radian measures of the angles whose cosine is 0.75.
$\approx 0.72 + 2\pi n$,
$\approx 5.56 + 2\pi n$

Solve each equation for $0 \le \theta < 2\pi$.

3. $2\cos^2 \theta - 1 = 0$ $\frac{\pi}{4}, \frac{3\pi}{4}, \frac{5\pi}{4}, \frac{7\pi}{4}$

4. $\sqrt{2}\sin \theta \cos \theta + \cos \theta = 0$ $\frac{\pi}{2}, \frac{5\pi}{4}, \frac{3\pi}{2}, \frac{7\pi}{4}$

Alternative Assessment

Have students work individually. Ask them to select a real number between −1 and 1. Ask them to find all angles that have their sine equal to that number, and then find all the angles that have their tangent equal to that number. Next ask students to create and solve two equations that involve trigonometric functions of an angle θ. Ask the students to find all solutions θ for $0 \le \theta < 2\pi$.

64. Answers may vary.
Sample: In the first equation, you isolate the variable x to get the solution. In the trigonometric equation, you first isolate the trig. part, sin θ, but then you must continue to solve for θ.

66a. Answers may vary.
Sample: cos $\theta = -1$,
2 cos $\theta = -2$,
3 cos $\theta = -3$

b. Start with cos $\theta = -1$, and then multiply both sides of equation by any nonzero number.

789

81. [4] $2 \sin^2 \theta = -\sin \theta$
$2 \sin^2 \theta + \sin \theta = 0$
$\sin \theta (2 \sin \theta + 1) = 0$
$\sin \theta = 0 \quad 2 \sin \theta + 1 = 0$
$\sin \theta = -\frac{1}{2}$
$\sin^{-1} 0 = 0, \pi$
$\sin^{-1}\left(-\frac{1}{2}\right) = \frac{11\pi}{6}, \frac{7\pi}{6}$

[3] appropriate methods, with minor error

[2] answer only, without work shown

[1] finds only one solution for each instance where it might equal 0

74a. 1:55 A.M., 11:05 A.M., and 2:55 P.M.

b. 12:00 midnight to 1:55 A.M., 11:05 A.M. to 2:55 P.M.

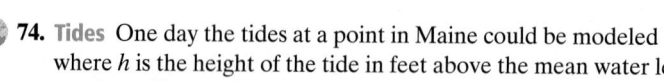 **74. Tides** One day the tides at a point in Maine could be modeled by $h = 5 \cos \frac{2\pi}{13}t$, where h is the height of the tide in feet above the mean water level and t is the number of hours past midnight.
a. At what times that day will the tide be 3 ft above the mean water level?
b. At what times that day will the tide be *at least* 3 ft above the mean water level?

 Test Prep

Multiple Choice

75. Which of the following is NOT equal to 60°? **D**
  A. $\sin^{-1} \frac{\sqrt{3}}{2}$ **B.** $\cos^{-1} \frac{1}{2}$ **C.** $\tan^{-1} \sqrt{3}$ **D.** $\tan^{-1} \frac{\sqrt{3}}{3}$

76. In which quadrants are the solutions to $\tan \theta + 1 = 0$? **H**
  F. Quadrants I and II   **G.** Quadrants II and III
  H. Quadrants II and IV   **J.** Quadrants III and IV

77. Which of these angles have a sine of about -0.6? **C**
  I. 143.1°   **II.** 216.9°   **III.** 323.1°
  A. I and II only   **B.** I and III only
  C. II and III only   **D.** I, II, and III

78. What are the solutions of $2 \sin \theta - \sqrt{3} = 0$ for $0 \le \theta < 2\pi$? **G**
  F. $\frac{\pi}{6}$ and $\frac{5\pi}{6}$ **G.** $\frac{\pi}{3}$ and $\frac{2\pi}{3}$
  H. $\frac{2\pi}{3}$ and $\frac{4\pi}{3}$ **J.** $\frac{4\pi}{3}$ and $\frac{5\pi}{3}$

79. Suppose $a > 0$. Under what conditions for a and b will $a \sin \theta = b$ have exactly two solutions in the interval $0 \le \theta < 2\pi$? **D**
  A. $a = b$ **B.** $b > a$
  C. $a = -b$ **D.** $a > b > -a$

80. [2] $2 \cos \theta = \sqrt{2}$
  $\cos \theta = \frac{\sqrt{2}}{2}$
  $\cos^{-1} \frac{\sqrt{2}}{2} = \theta$
  $\theta = \frac{\pi}{4}$ and $\frac{7\pi}{4}$

  [1] finds solution in Quadrant I only

Short Response

80. Solve $2 \cos \theta = \sqrt{2}$ for $0 \le \theta < 2\pi$. **See left.**

Extended Response

81. Solve $2 \sin^2 \theta = -\sin \theta$ for $0 \le \theta < 2\pi$. Show your work. **See margin.**

Mixed Review

 GO for Help

Lesson 14-1

Simplify each expression.

82. $\cos^2 \theta \sec \theta \csc \theta$ **cot θ**   **83.** $\sin \theta \sec \theta \tan \theta$ **tan² θ**

84. $\csc^2 \theta (1 - \cos^2 \theta)$ **1**   **85.** $\frac{\cos \theta \csc \theta}{\cot \theta}$ **1**

86. $\frac{\sec \theta}{\cot \theta + \tan \theta}$ **sin θ**   **87.** $\frac{\sin \theta + \tan \theta}{1 + \cos \theta}$ **tan θ**

Lesson 13-5

Write a cosine function for each description.

88. amplitude 4, period 8 $y = 4 \cos \frac{\pi}{4}\theta$ **89.** amplitude 3, period 2π $y = 3 \cos \theta$

90. amplitude 3π, period 1
    $y = 3\pi \cos 2\pi\theta$ **91.** amplitude $\frac{\pi}{4}$, period 3π
    $y = \frac{\pi}{4} \cos \frac{2}{3}\theta$

Lesson 12-2 🌐 **92. Transportation** Ninety-eight percent of a railroad's trains depart on schedule. Eighty-nine percent of its trains depart and arrive on schedule. Find the probability that a train that departs on time also arrives on time. **about 0.91**

Lissajous Figures

FOR USE WITH LESSON 14-2

A clock pendulum swings in only one plane. Its oscillating path projected on a sheet of paper below it would be a segment. A pendulum supported by a string can move so that its path is a circle, ellipse, or other complicated curve. These curves are called Lissajous (lee suh zhoo) figures.

Lissajous figures can be described by parametric equations of this form.

$$x = a_1 \sin b_1(t - h_1)$$
$$y = a_2 \sin b_2(t - h_2)$$

x represents the oscillating motion in one direction and y represents the oscillating motion in the perpendicular direction. t is time, $|a_1|$ and $|a_2|$ are amplitudes of the oscillations, $\frac{b_1}{2\pi}$ and $\frac{b_2}{2\pi}$ are cycles per second, and h_1 and h_2 are phase shifts.

The parametric equations can be graphed with a graphing calculator. See page 124.

ACTIVITY

Set the calculator to radian and parametric mode. Set the window values as shown.

```
WINDOW
 Tmin=0
 Tmax=7
 Tstep=.05
 Xmin=-3
 Xmax=3
 Xscl=1
↓Ymin=-2
```

```
WINDOW
↑Tstep=.05
 Xmin=-3
 Xmax=3
 Xscl=1
 Ymin=-2
 Ymax=2
 Yscl=1
```

Graph each pair of parametric equations.

a. $x = 3 \sin 2(t - \pi)$
   $y = 2 \sin 4(t - \pi)$

b. $x = 3 \sin 2\left(t - \frac{\pi}{3}\right)$
   $y = 2 \sin 4(t - \pi)$

c. $x = 3 \sin 2(t - 1)$
   $y = 2 \sin 3(t - 1)$

  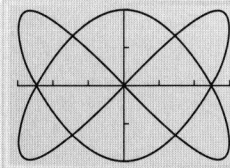

EXERCISES

Use your calculator to graph each pair of parametric equations. Sketch each graph. 1–3. See margin.

1. $x = 2.1 \sin (t - 1)$
   $y = 1.8 \sin (t - 2)$

2. $x = 3 \sin 2\left(t - \frac{3}{2}\right)$
   $y = 2 \sin 3\left(t - \frac{2}{3}\right)$

3. $x = 3 \sin 3(t - 1)$
   $y = 2 \sin 2(t - 1)$

4. Open-Ended Graph other Lissajous figures by changing the numbers in the equations. Sketch the interesting graphs and record their equations.
Check students' work.

Lissajous Figures

Students use a graphing calculator to graph parametric equations for Lissajous figures. This feature shows students the variety of complicated curves that parametric equations can describe.

Guided Instruction

Teaching Tip

Suggest that students also try non-integer rational values for b_1 and b_2. The curves for rational values of b_1 and b_2 are *unicursal*, meaning that they are closed curves that can be traced entirely and without retracing by moving a pencil point over the curve one time.

Technology Tip

In Exercise 4, if students change the values of a_1 and a_2, they may need to change the window settings for the axes. Changes in b_1 and b_2 may require a change in the value of Tmax.

Resources

Any graphing calculator that has parametric graphing capabilities

1.

2.

3.

14-3

1. Plan

Objectives

1 To find lengths of sides in a right triangle

2 To find measures of angles in a right triangle

Examples

1 Real-World Connection
2 Using a Right Triangle to Find Ratios
3 Real-World Connection
4 Finding Angle Measures
5 Real-World Connection

Math Background

Every right triangle that has an acute angle of measure $A°$ is similar to every other right triangle that has an acute angle of measure $A°$. As a result, all ratios of corresponding sides of a right triangle are completely determined by the measures of its acute angles. This makes it possible to define the trigonometric functions of angles with measures between 0° and 90° in terms of ratios of the side lengths of a right triangle. These definitions are consistent with the unit circle definitions of the functions of such angles.

More Math Background: p. 776C

Lesson Planning and Resources

See p. 776E for a list of the resources that support this lesson.

Bell Ringer Practice

☑ **Check Skills You'll Need**
For intervention, direct students to:

Ratios and Proportions
Skills Handbook: p. 872

792

14-3 Right Triangles and Trigonometric Ratios

What You'll Learn

- To find lengths of sides in a right triangle
- To find measures of angles in a right triangle

. . . And Why

To design bridges, as in Example 3

 Check Skills You'll Need

 for Help Skills Handbook page 872

$\triangle ABC$ is similar to $\triangle RST$. Complete the following proportions.

1. $\frac{a}{b} = \frac{r}{\blacksquare}$ **s**

2. $\frac{a}{c} = \frac{\blacksquare}{t}$ **r**

3. $\frac{t}{r} = \frac{c}{\blacksquare}$ **a**

4. $\frac{c}{b} = \frac{\blacksquare}{s}$ **t**

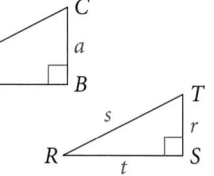

New Vocabulary • trigonometric ratios for a right triangle

---

1 Finding the Lengths of Sides in a Right Triangle

Activity: Right Triangle Ratios

Draw three right triangles, each one having an acute angle of 53°. Make the hypotenuse of the first triangle 10 cm long, and make the other two hypotenuses differ by at least 5 cm. Label the triangles 1, 2, and 3.

1. In each triangle, measure the lengths of the hypotenuse, the leg opposite the 53° angle, and the leg adjacent to the 53° angle. Copy the table below and record your measurements. Then calculate the three ratios for each triangle.

Answers may vary. Sample:

Triangle	Hyp. (cm)	Leg opp. ∠A (cm)	Leg adj. to ∠A (cm)	opp. hyp.	adj. hyp.	opp. adj.
1	10	8.0	6.0	0.80	0.60	1.33
2	■20	■16	■12	■0.8	■0.6	■ 1.33
3	■30	■24	■18	■0.8	■0.6	■ 1.33

2. Reasoning What patterns do you see in the last three columns of the table? Check your results with others. **Ratios are the same within each column.**

3. Make a Conjecture What is true about these ratios for all right triangles that have an acute angle of 53°? **The ratios are a constant for all right triangles that have an acute angle of 53°.**

The **trigonometric ratios for a right triangle** are the six different ratios of the sides of a right triangle. These ratios do not depend on the size of the right triangle. They depend only on the measures of the acute angles in the triangle.

792 Chapter 14 Trigonometric Identities and Equations

Differentiated Instruction Solutions for All Learners

Special Needs L1
Have students draw the same triangle twice, labeling the acute angles *A* and *B*, and the right angle *C*. In the first figure, students color and label the sides adjacent and opposite to *A*. In the second figure, students label the sides adjacent and opposite to *B*.

learning style: visual

Below Level L2
Have students determine the height of the school building, flagpole, or tall tree using a protractor and measuring tape.

learning style: tactile

2. Teach

A <u>mnemonic device</u> is an arrangement or a process that helps you remember something. To remember trigonometric relationships, some students use the acronym "SOHCAHTOA" as a mnemonic device.

Sine:
Opposite over
Hypotenuse

Cosine:
Adjacent over
Hypotenuse

Tangent:
Opposite over
Adjacent

In a right triangle that has an acute $\angle A$, the ratios are defined as follows.

$$\sin A = \frac{\text{length of leg opposite } \angle A}{\text{length of hypotenuse}} = \frac{a}{c}$$

$$\cos A = \frac{\text{length of leg adjacent to } \angle A}{\text{length of hypotenuse}} = \frac{b}{c}$$

$$\tan A = \frac{\text{length of leg opposite } \angle A}{\text{length of leg adjacent to } \angle A} = \frac{a}{b}$$

$$\csc A = \frac{1}{\sin A} = \frac{\text{length of hypotenuse}}{\text{length of leg opposite } \angle A} = \frac{c}{a}$$

$$\sec A = \frac{1}{\cos A} = \frac{\text{length of hypotenuse}}{\text{length of leg adjacent to } \angle A} = \frac{c}{b}$$

$$\cot A = \frac{1}{\tan A} = \frac{\text{length of leg adjacent to } \angle A}{\text{length of leg opposite } \angle A} = \frac{b}{a}$$

1 EXAMPLE Real-World Connection

In the pyramid of Khafre, $AC \approx 108$ m and $m\angle A \approx 53°$.

Egyptology Given that $\sin 53° \approx 0.80$, $\cos 53° \approx 0.60$, and $\tan 53° \approx 1.33$, find the height BC of the pyramid.

$\tan A = \frac{BC}{AC}$ **definition of tan**

$1.33 \approx \frac{BC}{108}$ **Substitute.**

$BC \approx 108 (1.33) \approx 144$

The height of the pyramid of Khafre is about 144 m.

Quick Check **1** Find the length of a lateral edge of the pyramid. **180 m**

Guided Instruction

Activity
This activity will help students see that once you have specified the measure of an acute angle and the length of the hypotenuse of a right triangle, the lengths of the legs and the ratios of the sides are determined. Encourage students to draw their triangles carefully and accurately. Stress the importance of accurate measurements. Suggest that all lengths be measured to the nearest tenth of a centimeter.

1 EXAMPLE Connection to History

You may want to mention that the oldest pyramid in Egypt dates back to about 2700 B.C. Other ancient civilizations had pyramids. Especially notable are the pyramids of Mexico and Central America. The largest pyramid ever constructed is in Mexico at Cholula de Rivadabia. This pyramid has a base area of nearly 45 acres.

For acute angles, the unit circle definition of sine is equivalent to the definition of sine for right triangles.

sin θ using the unit circle

$\sin \theta = y$-coordinate of P

$= PQ$

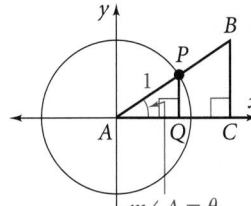

sin A using a right triangle

$\sin A = \frac{\text{length of leg opposite } \angle A}{\text{length of hypotenuse}}$

$= \frac{BC}{AB}$

Since $\triangle APQ$ and $\triangle ABC$ are similar triangles, $\frac{PQ}{PA} = \frac{BC}{AB}$.

So $\sin \theta = PQ = \frac{PQ}{1} = \frac{PQ}{PA} = \frac{BC}{AB} = \sin A$.

Advanced Learners **L4**
Have students calculate the measure of the angles of a triangle with sides in the ratio of 3:4:5.

learning style: verbal

English Language Learners **ELL**
Discuss the terms *adjacent* and *opposite*. Draw a triangle and label it using the convention of capital letters for angles and small letters for side lengths. Ask: *How are sides and angles with the same letter related?* they are opposite each other

learning style: visual

You can use a similar argument for each of the other five ratios. In each case, the definition based on a right triangle is equivalent to the corresponding unit circle definition for an acute angle.

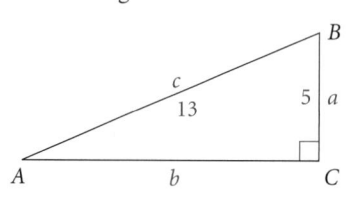

GO Online

Video Tutor Help
Visit: PHSchool.com
Web Code: age-0775

❷ **EXAMPLE** **Using a Right Triangle to Find Ratios**

In △ABC, ∠C is a right angle and sin A = $\frac{5}{13}$. Find cos A, cot A, and sin B in fraction and in decimal form.

Step 1 Draw a diagram.

Step 2 Use the Pythagorean Theorem to find b.

$$c^2 = a^2 + b^2$$
$$13^2 = 5^2 + b^2$$
$$169 = 25 + b^2$$
$$144 = b^2$$
$$12 = b$$

Step 3 Calculate the ratios.

$$\cos A = \frac{\text{length of leg adjacent to } \angle A}{\text{length of hypotenuse}} = \frac{b}{c} = \frac{12}{13} \approx 0.9231$$

$$\cot A = \frac{\text{length of leg adjacent to } \angle A}{\text{length of leg opposite } \angle A} = \frac{b}{a} = \frac{12}{5} = 2.4$$

$$\sin B = \frac{\text{length of leg opposite } \angle B}{\text{length of hypotenuse}} = \frac{b}{c} = \frac{12}{13} \approx 0.9231$$

✓ Quick Check ❷ In △DEF, ∠D is a right angle and tan E = $\frac{3}{4}$. Draw a diagram and find sin E and sec F in fraction and in decimal form. **See left.**

2.

$\frac{3}{5}$ = 0.6, $\frac{5}{3}$ ≈ 1.67

If you are given the measures of an acute angle and a side of a right triangle, you can find the length of another side of the triangle.

Real-World Connection

Careers Park planners are often licensed in landscape architecture. They are usually employed by government agencies.

❸ **EXAMPLE** **Real-World Connection**

Planning Park planners would like to build a bridge across a creek. Surveyors have determined that from 5 ft above the ground the angle of elevation to the top of an 8-ft pole on the opposite side of the creek is 5°. Find the length of the bridge to the nearest foot.

In the right triangle, the length of the leg opposite the 5° angle is 8 − 5, or 3 ft. You need to find the length of the leg adjacent to the 5° angle. Use the tangent ratio.

$\tan 5° = \frac{3}{x}$

$x = \frac{3}{\tan 5°}$ **Solve for x.**

≈ 34.29 **Use a calculator in degree mode.**

● The bridge will be about 34 ft long.

✓ Quick Check ❸ a. **Critical Thinking** What are the advantages and disadvantages of using cot 5° instead of tan 5° in solving Example 3? **See margin.**

b. Find the length of the bridge in Example 3 by using the 85° angle in the right triangle instead of the 5° angle. ≈**34.29 ft**

3a. **Answers may vary. Sample: An advantage is that simplification of the equation is easier. A** **disadvantage is that you have to press an extra button on the calculator to get the cotangent function.**

2 Finding the Measures of Angles in a Right Triangle

To find the measure of an acute angle in a right triangle, you can use the inverses of the trigonometric functions.

  Finding Angle Measures

In △DEF, ∠F is a right angle, f = 13, and e = 5. Find m∠D to the nearest tenth of a degree.

Step 1 Draw a diagram.

E
13 ←—— Side f is opposite ∠F.
F
5 ←—— Side e is opposite ∠E.

Step 2 Use a cosine ratio.

$$\cos D = \frac{5}{13}$$
$$m\angle D = \cos^{-1}\frac{5}{13}$$
$$\approx 67.38°$$ **Use a calculator.**

● To the nearest tenth of a degree, m∠D is 67.4°.

  ④ Use a trigonometric ratio to find m∠A in each triangle.

a.
B
4   10
C   A
23.58°

b.
C   56.25°
5
A   B
9

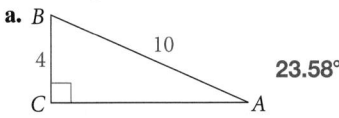 **Real-World Connection**

Construction A wheelchair ramp must be constructed so the slope is not more than 1 in. of rise for every 1 ft of run. What is the maximum angle that the ramp can make with the ground, to the nearest tenth of a degree?

Surface of ramp
θ   1 in.   Rise
1 ft
←— Horizontal projection —→
or run

Not drawn to scale

Let θ = the measure of the angle the ramp makes with the ground.

You know the length of the leg opposite the angle you need to find. You know the length of the leg adjacent to the angle you need to find. So, use the tangent ratio.

$$\tan \theta = \frac{1}{12}$$ **Rewrite 1 ft as 12 in.**
$$\theta = \tan^{-1}\frac{1}{12}$$ **Use the inverse of the tangent function.**
$$\theta \approx 4.8$$ **Use a calculator.**

● The angle between the ramp and the ground will be about 4.8°.

  ⑤ In △DEF, ∠F is a right angle, d = 7, and f = 10. Draw a diagram and find the remaining side length and angle degree measures. Round to the nearest tenth.
See above left.

5.

D
e   10
F   7   E

e ≈ 7.1; m∠E ≈ 45.6°, m∠D ≈ 44.4°

PowerPoint
Additional Examples

④ In △KMN, ∠N is a right angle, m = 7, and n = 25. Find m∠K to the nearest tenth of a degree. **73.7°**

⑤ A straight road that goes up a hill is 800 feet higher at the top than at the bottom. The horizontal distance covered is 6515 feet. To the nearest degree, what angle does the road make with level ground? **7°**

Resources
• Daily Notetaking Guide 14-3

Closure

Ask students to name one piece of additional information that would allow them to find all the other side lengths and angle measures of a right triangle if they are given the measure of one of the acute angles. Then tell them to suppose that they know the lengths of two sides of a right triangle. Ask what other information they would need about the sides to find the length of the third side and the measures of the angles. **length of opposite leg, length of adjacent leg, or length of hypotenuse; You would need to know whether both are legs or whether one is a leg and the other is the hypotenuse.**

Real-World Connection

Federal regulations define allowable slopes for handicap-accessible facilities.

---

❶ A B 1-8, 25-34, 42-45

❷ A B 9-24, 35-41, 46-48
C Challenge   49-53

Test Prep   54-59
Mixed Review   60-70

Homework Quick Check
To check students' understanding
of key skills and concepts, go over
Exercises 4, 24, 34, 40, 47, 48.

Differentiated Instruction Resources

GPS **Guided Problem Solving**	L3
Enrichment	L4
Reteaching	L2
Practice	L3

4.

$\sin P = \frac{12}{13} \approx 0.92,$

$\cos P = \frac{5}{13} \approx 0.38,$

$\tan P = \frac{12}{5} = 2.40,$

$\csc P = \frac{13}{12} \approx 1.08,$

$\sec P = \frac{13}{5} = 2.60$

796

EXERCISES
For more exercises, see *Extra Skill and Word Problem Practice*.

Practice and Problem Solving

Ⓐ Practice by Example

GO for Help

Example 1
(page 793)

1. Ballooning From a hot-air balloon 3000 ft above the ground, you see a clearing whose angle of depression is 20°. Given that $\sin 20° \approx 0.34$, $\cos 20° \approx 0.94$, and $\tan 20° \approx 0.36$, find each distance to the nearest foot.

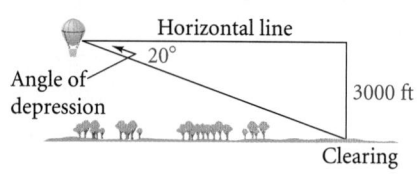

a. your horizontal distance from the clearing   ≈ **8333 ft**
b. your direct distance from the clearing   ≈ **8824 ft**

Example 2
(page 794)

2a. $\frac{15}{17} \approx 0.88$

b. $\frac{17}{8} \approx 2.13$

c. $\frac{8}{15} \approx 0.53$

d. $\frac{17}{8} \approx 2.13$

e. $\frac{17}{15} \approx 1.13$

f. $\frac{8}{15} \approx 0.53$

2. In $\triangle ABC$, find each value as a fraction and as a decimal. Round to the nearest hundredth.
  a. $\sin A$ **b.** $\sec A$
  c. $\cot A$ **d.** $\csc B$
  e. $\sec B$ **f.** $\tan B$

3. In $\triangle GHI$, $\angle H$ is a right angle, $GH = 40$, and $\cos G = \frac{40}{41}$. Draw a diagram and find each value in fraction and in decimal form. **a–f. See below left.**
  a. $\sin G$ **b.** $\sin I$ **c.** $\cot G$
  d. $\csc G$ **e.** $\cos I$ **f.** $\sec H$

4. In $\triangle PQR$, $\angle R$ is a right angle and $\cot P = \frac{5}{12}$. Draw a diagram. Find the values of the other five trigonometric functions of $\angle P$ in fraction and in decimal form. **See margin.**

Example 3
(page 794)

Find each length *x*. Round to the nearest tenth.

3.

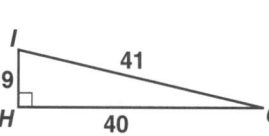

a. $\frac{9}{41} \approx 0.22$

b. $\frac{40}{41} \approx 0.98$

c. $\frac{40}{9} \approx 4.44$

d. $\frac{41}{9} \approx 4.56$

e. $\frac{9}{41} \approx 0.22$

f. **not defined**

5.

41.8

6.

25.2

7.

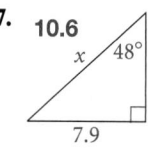

8. Indirect Measurement In 1915, the tallest flagpole in the world was in San Francisco.
  a. When the angle of elevation of the sun was 55°, the length of the shadow cast by this flagpole was 210 ft. Find the height of the flagpole to the nearest foot. **300 ft**
  b. What was the length of the shadow when the angle of elevation of the sun was 34°? **445 ft**
  c. What do you need to assume about the flagpole and the shadow to solve these problems? Explain why. **See margin.**

Examples 4 and 5
(page 795)

Find each angle measure to the nearest tenth of a degree.

9. $\cos^{-1} \frac{\sqrt{2}}{2}$ **45.0°**
10. $\tan^{-1} 0.3333$ **18.4°**
11. $\sin^{-1} \frac{3}{4}$ **48.6°**
12. $\tan^{-1} \sqrt{3}$ **60.0°**
13. $\sin^{-1} 0.335$ **19.6°**
14. $\cos^{-1} 0.992$ **7.3°**
15. $\tan^{-1} 3.552$ **74.3°**
16. $\sin^{-1} 0.052$ **3.0°**
17. $\cos^{-1} \frac{3}{8}$ **68.0°**

796   Chapter 14 Trigonometric Identities and Equations

8c. Answers may vary. Sample: The flagpole must be straight, the ground must be flat, and the flagpole and the ground must be perpendicular. You assume these things so that the flagpole and the ground form a right angle. By having a right triangle you can use its properties to find the missing parts.

18. $a \approx 8.7$, $\angle A = 60.0°$, $\angle B = 30.0°$

19. $c \approx 7.8$, $\angle A \approx 39.8°$, $\angle B \approx 50.2°$

20. $a = 9.0$, $\angle A \approx 36.9°$, $\angle B \approx 53.1°$

In $\triangle ABC$, $\angle C$ **is a right angle. Find the remaining sides and angles. Round your answers to the nearest tenth.** 21–23. See margin.

18. $b = 5$, $c = 10$ **19.** $a = 5$, $b = 6$ **20.** $b = 12$, $c = 15$

21. $a = 8.1$, $b = 6.2$ **22.** $b = 4.3$, $c = 9.1$ **23.** $a = 17$, $c = 22$

24. Rocketry An observer on the ground at point A watches a rocket ascend. The observer is 1200 ft from the launch point B. As the rocket rises, the distance d from the observer to the rocket increases.
 a. Write a model for $m\angle A$. $m\angle A = \cos^{-1}\left(\frac{1200}{d}\right)$
 b. Find $m\angle A$ if $d = 1500$ ft. Round your answer to the nearest degree.   **37°**
 c. Find $m\angle A$ if $d = 2000$ ft. Round your answer to the nearest degree.   **53°**

B **Apply Your Skills**

Sketch a right triangle with θ **as the measure of one acute angle. Find the other five trigonometric ratios of** θ.   25–33. See margin.

25. $\sin \theta = \frac{3}{8}$ **26.** $\cos \theta = \frac{7}{20}$ **27.** $\cos \theta = \frac{1}{5}$

28. $\tan \theta = \frac{24}{7}$ **29.** $\csc \theta = \frac{21}{12}$ **30.** $\sec \theta = \frac{16}{9}$

31. $\cot \theta = \frac{5}{4}$ **32.** $\sin \theta = 0.35$ **33.** $\csc \theta = 5.2$

34. a. Engineering A radio tower has supporting cables attached to it at points 100 ft above the ground. Write a model for the length d of each supporting cable as a function of the angle θ that it makes with the ground. $d = \frac{100}{\sin \theta}$
 b. Find d when $\theta = 60°$ and when $\theta = 50°$.
 115.5 ft, 130.5 ft

100 ft

In $\triangle ABC$, $\angle C$ **is a right angle. Two measures are given. Find the remaining sides and angles. Round your answers to the nearest tenth.**

35–40. See back of book.

35. $b = 8$, $c = 17$ **36.** $a = 7$, $b = 10$

37. $m\angle A = 52°$, $c = 10$ **38.** $m\angle A = 34.2°$, $b = 5.7$

39. $m\angle B = 17.2°$, $b = 8.3$ **40.** $m\angle B = 8.3°$, $c = 20$

41. A 150-ft pole casts a shadow 210 ft long. Find the measure of the angle of elevation of the sun.   **35.5°**

For a guide to solving Exercise 42, see p. 800.

42. Indirect Measurement A transit is 330 ft from the base of a building. The angles of elevation of the top and bottom of a flagpole situated on top of the building are 55° and 53°. Find the height of the flagpole.   **33.4 ft**

43. Geometry An altitude inside a triangle forms angles of 36° and 42° with two of the sides. The altitude is 5 m long. Find the area of the triangle.   **20.3 m²**

44. Construction When a crane's boom is at an angle of 70°, the top is 128 ft high. (See the diagram at the right.) How long is the boom? How far is the crane's cab from the bottom of the free-fall path of something dropped from the top of the boom?
136.2 ft; 46.6 ft

128 ft

70°

d

45. a. In Example 4, use the Pythagorean Theorem to find EF.   **12**
 b. Use a trigonometric ratio to find EF.   **12**

46–47. See back of book.

GO **Online**
Homework Video Tutor
Visit: PHSchool.com
Web Code: age-1403

46. Open-Ended If $\sin \theta = \frac{1}{2}$, describe a method you could use to find all the angles between 0° and 360° that satisfy this equation.

47. Reasoning Show that $\cos A$ defined as a ratio equals $\cos \theta$ using the unit circle.

21. $c \approx 10.2$, $\angle A \approx 52.6°$, $\angle B \approx 37.4°$

22. $a \approx 8.0$, $\angle A \approx 61.8°$, $\angle B \approx 28.2°$

23. $b \approx 14.0$, $\angle A \approx 50.6°$, $\angle B \approx 39.4°$

25. $\cos \theta = \frac{\sqrt{55}}{8}$, $\tan \theta = \frac{3\sqrt{55}}{55}$, $\csc \theta = \frac{8}{3}$, $\sec \theta = \frac{8\sqrt{55}}{55}$, $\cot \theta = \frac{\sqrt{55}}{3}$

26. $\sin \theta = \frac{3\sqrt{39}}{20}$, $\tan \theta = \frac{3\sqrt{39}}{7}$, $\csc \theta = \frac{20\sqrt{39}}{117}$, $\sec \theta = \frac{20}{7}$, $\cot \theta = \frac{7\sqrt{39}}{117}$

27. $\sin \theta = \frac{2\sqrt{6}}{5}$, $\tan \theta = 2\sqrt{6}$, $\csc \theta = \frac{5\sqrt{6}}{12}$, $\sec \theta = 5$, $\cot \theta = \frac{\sqrt{6}}{12}$

28. $\sin \theta = \frac{24}{25}$, $\cos \theta = \frac{7}{25}$, $\csc \theta = \frac{25}{24}$, $\sec \theta = \frac{25}{7}$, $\cot \theta = \frac{7}{24}$

29. $\sin \theta = \frac{4}{7}$, $\cos \theta = \frac{\sqrt{33}}{7}$, $\tan \theta = \frac{4\sqrt{33}}{33}$, $\sec \theta = \frac{7\sqrt{33}}{33}$, $\cot \theta = \frac{\sqrt{33}}{4}$

30. $\sin \theta = \frac{5\sqrt{7}}{16}$, $\cos \theta = \frac{9}{16}$, $\tan \theta = \frac{5\sqrt{7}}{9}$, $\csc \theta = \frac{16\sqrt{7}}{35}$, $\cot \theta = \frac{9\sqrt{7}}{35}$

31. $\sin \theta = \frac{4\sqrt{41}}{41}$, $\cos \theta = \frac{5\sqrt{41}}{41}$, $\tan \theta = \frac{4}{5}$, $\csc \theta = \frac{\sqrt{41}}{4}$, $\sec \theta = \frac{\sqrt{41}}{5}$

32. $\cos \theta \approx 0.937$, $\tan \theta \approx 0.374$, $\csc \theta \approx 2.857$, $\sec \theta \approx 1.068$, $\cot \theta \approx 2.676$

33. $\sin \theta \approx 0.192$, $\cos \theta \approx 0.981$, $\tan \theta \approx 0.196$, $\sec \theta \approx 1.019$, $\cot \theta \approx 5.103$

797

4. Assess & Reteach

Lesson Quiz

1. Find sin A, tan A, and cos B for the triangle shown below. $\frac{4}{5}, \frac{4}{3}, \frac{4}{5}$

2. Find csc P, sec Q, and cot Q for the triangle shown below. $\frac{\sqrt{13}}{2}, \frac{\sqrt{13}}{2}, \frac{2}{3}$

3. In $\triangle KST$, $\angle S$ is a right angle, $s = 17$, and $t = 15$. Find $m\angle T$ and $m\angle K$ to the nearest tenth of a degree. **61.9°, 28.1°**

4. A flagpole that is 35 feet tall casts a shadow 22 feet long at a certain time of the morning. What is the angle of elevation of the sun to the nearest degree? **58°**

Alternative Assessment

Have students work in pairs. Ask each one to sketch a right triangle and indicate the right angle. Tell one student to label two sides with their lengths. Tell the other student to label one acute angle and the hypotenuse with their measures. Instruct the pairs to exchange triangles and find all the missing measures of sides and angles in each triangle. Finally, ask students to select one acute angle of their triangle and to give the values of all six trigonometric functions for those angles. Students exchange triangles again and check each other's work.

798

---

48. **Baseball** The bases on a baseball diamond form a square 90 ft on a side. The pitcher's plate is 60 ft 6 in. from the back corner of home plate.
   a. About how far is the pitcher's plate from second base? **≈67 ft**
   b. A line drive is 10 ft high when it passes over the third baseman, who is 100 ft from home plate. At what angle did the ball leave the bat? (Assume the ball is 4 ft above the ground when it is hit.) **≈3.4°**

49. $\sec A \stackrel{?}{=} \dfrac{1}{\cos A}$

   $\dfrac{c}{b} \stackrel{?}{=} \dfrac{1}{\frac{b}{c}}$

   $\dfrac{c}{b} = \dfrac{c}{b}$

C Challenge

50. $\tan A \stackrel{?}{=} \dfrac{\sin A}{\cos A}$

   $\dfrac{a}{b} \stackrel{?}{=} \dfrac{\frac{a}{c}}{\frac{b}{c}}$

   $\dfrac{a}{b} = \dfrac{a}{b}$

51. $\cos^2 A + \sin^2 A \stackrel{?}{=} 1$

   $\left(\dfrac{b}{c}\right)^2 + \left(\dfrac{a}{c}\right)^2 \stackrel{?}{=} 1$

   $b^2 + a^2 \stackrel{?}{=} c^2$

   $c^2 = c^2$

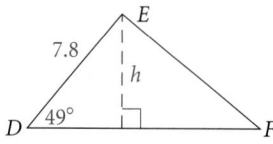 **Vocabulary Tip**

A <u>regular</u> <u>polygon</u> has congruent sides and congruent angles.

Use the definitions of trigonometric ratios in right $\triangle ABC$ to verify each identity.

49. $\sec A = \dfrac{1}{\cos A}$

50. $\tan A = \dfrac{\sin A}{\cos A}$

51. $\cos^2 A + \sin^2 A = 1$

52. a. In $\triangle DEF$ below, h is the length of an altitude. Find h to the nearest tenth.
   b. For $DF = 10.8$, find the area of $\triangle DEF$ to the nearest tenth.
   c. Find the area of $\triangle RST$ to the nearest tenth.

   a. **5.9 units**
   b. **31.8 units²**
   c. **6.2 units²**

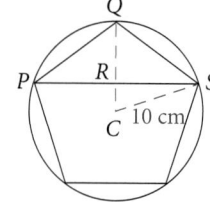

53. **Geometry** A regular pentagon is inscribed in a circle of radius 10 cm.
   a. Find the measure of $\angle C$. **72°**
   b. Find the length of the diagonal PS. (*Hint*: First find RS.) **19.0 cm**

 Test Prep

Multiple Choice

54. A ladder rests against a vertical building, as shown at the right. The ladder is 14 ft long and forms an angle of 76.5° with the ground. Which statement is NOT true? **A**
   A. The bottom of the ladder is 13.6 ft from the base of the building.
   B. The bottom of the ladder is 3.3 ft from the base of the building.
   C. The top of the ladder is 13.6 ft from the ground.
   D. The ladder forms an angle of 13.5° with the building.

55. The sides of a rectangle are 25 cm and 8 cm. What is the measure of the angle formed by the short side and a diagonal of the rectangle? **J**
   F. 17.7°   G. 18.7°   H. 71.3°   J. 72.3°

798 Chapter 14 Trigonometric Identities and Equations

64.

65.

66.

56. The figure at the right is a rectangle. What is the value of x? **A**
  A. 31.0   B. 36.9
  C. 53.1   D. 59.0

30 cm
18 cm
$x°$

57. In $\triangle XYZ$, $\angle Z$ is a right angle and $\tan X = \frac{8}{15}$.
  What is $\sin Y$? **G**
  F. $\frac{8}{17}$ G. $\frac{15}{17}$ H. $\frac{17}{15}$ J. $\frac{15}{8}$

58. In the right triangle at the right, $\cos y° = \frac{5}{13}$.
  If $x + 2z = 7.1$, what is the value of z? **C**
  A. 67.3   B. 22.6
  C. −7.76   D. −30.1

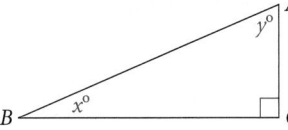
A
$y°$
B $x°$ C

Short Response   **59.** Find the measures of the acute angles of a right triangle, to the nearest tenth, if the legs are 135 cm and 95 cm.
See back of book.

Mixed Review

GO for Help

Lesson 14-2   Find the complete solution of each equation. Express your answer in degrees.

60. $\sec^2 \theta + \sec \theta = 0$ $180° + n \cdot 360°$ **61.** $2\cos^2 \theta + 1 = 0$ **no solution**

62. $\cot \theta = \cot^2 \theta$ $45° + n \cdot 180°$ **63.** $\sin^2 \theta + 5\sin \theta = 0$
  $90° + n \cdot 180°$ $0 + n \cdot 360°$ and $180° + n \cdot 360°$

Lesson 13-7   Graph each function in the interval from 0 to 2π.

64. $y = \sin(x - \pi) + 4$ **65.** $y = 3\sin 2\left(x + \frac{\pi}{2}\right) - 5$

66. $y = \cos(x + \pi) - 3$ **67.** $y = -2\cos\left(x - \frac{\pi}{3}\right) - 4$
  64–67. See margin pp. 798–799.

Lesson 12-6   Use the binomial expansion of $(p + q)^n$ to calculate and graph each binomial distribution. 68–70. See margin.

68. $n = 8, p = 0.2$ **69.** $n = 8, p = 0.4$ **70.** $n = 8, p = 0.8$

✓ Checkpoint Quiz 1   Lessons 14-1 through 14-3

Simplify each trigonometric expression.

1. $\sec \theta \cot \theta$ **csc θ**   **2.** $\sec^2 \theta - 1$ **tan$^2 \theta$**   **3.** $-1 - \cot^2 \theta$ **−csc$^2 \theta$**

Find the value of each expression to the nearest thousandth.

4. $\cos^{-1}\left(-\frac{\pi}{5}\right)$ **2.250**   **5.** $\sin^{-1}\frac{\pi}{10}$ **0.320**   **6.** $\tan^{-1} 4.35$ **1.345**

In $\triangle ABC$, $\angle C$ is a right angle. Find the remaining sides and angles. Round your answers to the nearest tenth.

7. $b = 14, c = 16$ **8.** $a = 7.9, b = 6.2$ **9.** $b = 29, c = 35$

7. $a \approx 7.7, m\angle A \approx 29.0°,$
  $m\angle B \approx 61.0°$
8. $c \approx 10.0, m\angle A \approx 51.9°,$
  $m\angle B \approx 38.1°$
9. $a \approx 19.6, m\angle A \approx 34.0°,$
  $m\angle B \approx 56.0°$

10. Open-Ended Draw a right triangle. Measure the lengths of two sides, and then find the remaining sides and angles without measuring.**Check students' work.**

Resources
For additional practice with a variety of test item formats:
• Standardized Test Prep, p. 831
• Test-Taking Strategies, p. 826
• Test-Taking Strategies with Transparencies

✓ Checkpoint Quiz

Use this Checkpoint Quiz to check students' understanding of the skills and concepts of Lessons 14-1 through 14-3.

Resources
Grab & Go
• Checkpoint Quiz 1

69. $P(0) \approx 0.016796$
  $P(1) \approx 0.089580$
  $P(2) \approx 0.209019$
  $P(3) \approx 0.278692$
  $P(4) \approx 0.232243$
  $P(5) \approx 0.123863$
  $P(6) \approx 0.041288$
  $P(7) \approx 0.007864$
  $P(8) \approx 0.000655$

Successes

70. $P(0) \approx 0.000003$
  $P(1) \approx 0.000082$
  $P(2) \approx 0.001147$
  $P(3) \approx 0.009175$
  $P(4) \approx 0.045875$
  $P(5) \approx 0.146801$
  $P(6) \approx 0.293601$
  $P(7) \approx 0.335544$
  $P(8) \approx 0.167772$

67.

68. $P(0) \approx 0.167772$ $P(7) \approx 0.000082$
  $P(1) \approx 0.335544$ $P(8) \approx 0.000003$
  $P(2) \approx 0.293601$
  $P(3) \approx 0.146801$
  $P(4) \approx 0.045875$
  $P(5) \approx 0.009175$
  $P(6) \approx 0.001147$

Successes

Successes

799

Understanding Word Problems

Guided Instruction

This feature models the thinking and corresponding algebraic solution to a word problem that involves multiple steps.

Teaching Tip

Have a student read the problem aloud. Then have another student describe the situation in his or her own words. A second or third reading may be needed.

English Language Learners ELL

Explain that a *transit* is a surveying instrument that measures angles. A transit uses a telescope that can be rotated (transited) on a level tripod.

Visual Learners

Make a physical model of the problem situation using objects in the classroom. Ask students to identify the building, flagpole, and point of observation in the model.

Advanced Learners L4

Ask: *How would the length of the flagpole change if the angles are the same, but the distance to the base of the building is increased?* flagpole length would increase

Exercises

Encourage students to draw and label a diagram for each exercise. Ask: *What was the first thing Christiana did?* make a diagram

Guided Problem Solving

FOR USE WITH PAGE 797, EXERCISE 42

Understanding Word Problems Read the problem below. Then follow along with what Christiana thinks and writes. Check your understanding by solving the exercises at the bottom of the page.

Indirect Measurement A transit is 330 ft from the base of a building. The angles of elevation of the top and bottom of a flagpole situated on top of the building are 55° and 53°. Find the height of the flagpole.

What Christiana Thinks

A diagram will help me solve the problem.

I need the building, the flagpole on top, and two angles on the ground. One goes to the top of the pole and the other to the bottom. I'll use x and y for heights.

Aha! The height of the flagpole is $x - y$!

x is opposite the 55° angle.

330 is adjacent to the 55° angle.

I can use the tangent ratio to find x.

y is opposite the 53° angle and 330 is still the adjacent side. I can use tangent again to find y.

The height of the flagpole is $x - y$.

What Christiana Writes

$$\frac{x}{330} = \tan 55°$$
$$x = 330 \tan 55°$$
$$x \approx 471.3$$

$$\frac{y}{330} = \tan 53°$$
$$y = 330 \tan 53°$$
$$y \approx 437.9$$

$$\text{Height} = x - y$$
$$\approx 471.3 - 437.9$$
$$= 33.4$$

The height of the flagpole is 33.4 ft.

EXERCISES

1. A monument has a cylindrical base and a tall spire. You are standing 50 ft from the center of the base. The top and the bottom of the spire have elevation angles of 62° and 42°, respectively. How tall is the spire to the nearest foot? **49 ft**

2. You are standing 250 ft from the town water tower. The top and the bottom of the tank at the top of the tower have angles of elevation of 22° and 15° respectively. What is the height of the water tank to the nearest foot? **34 ft**

Area and the Law of Sines

What You'll Learn

* To find the area of any triangle and to use the Law of Sines

. . . And Why

To measure heights, as in Example 4

✓ Check Skills You'll Need

 GO for Help Lesson 13-4

Simplify each expression.

1. $\frac{\sin 30°}{6}$ $\frac{1}{12}$

2. $\frac{\sin 45°}{4}$ $\frac{\sqrt{2}}{8}$

3. $\frac{\sin 60°}{10}$ $\frac{\sqrt{3}}{20}$

4. $\frac{\sin 30°}{12}$ $\frac{1}{24}$

5. $\frac{\sin 45°}{8}$ $\frac{\sqrt{2}}{16}$

6. $\frac{\sin 60°}{9}$ $\frac{\sqrt{3}}{18}$

Find the area of a triangle with the given base b and height h.

7. $b = 3$ cm, $h = 4$ cm **6 cm^2**

8. $b = 6$ in., $h = 15$ in. **45 in.^{2}**

9. $b = 5.2$ mm, $h = 12.6$ mm **32.8 mm^2**

10. $b = 6.17$ ft, $h = 3.25$ ft **10.03 ft^2**

🔊 **New Vocabulary** • Law of Sines

Objectives

1 To find the area of any triangle and to use the Law of Sines

Examples

1 Finding the Area of a Triangle
2 Finding a Side of a Triangle
3 Finding an Angle of a Triangle
4 Real-World Connection

Professional Development

Math Background

You can prove that, for any triangle, the area of the triangle is equal to one-half the product of the lengths of two sides and the sine of their included angle. From this it follows that the ratio of the sine of an angle to the length of the side opposite the angle is the same for all the angles of the triangle. This result is known as the Law of Sines.

More Math Background: p. 776C

Lesson Planning and Resources

See p. 776E for a list of the resources that support this lesson.

PowerPoint

Bell Ringer Practice

✓ **Check Skills You'll Need**
For intervention, direct students to:

The Sine Function
Lesson 13-4: Example 1
Extra Skills and Word Problems Practice, Ch. 13

---

1 Area and the Law of Sines

Vocabulary Tip

An <u>oblique</u> <u>triangle</u> is a triangle that does not contain a right angle.

The formula for the area K of a triangle is $K = \frac{1}{2}bh$.

In any oblique $\triangle ABC$ with side lengths a, b, and c, $h = c \sin A$. Therefore $K = \frac{1}{2}bh = \frac{1}{2}bc \sin A$.

Similarly, $K = \frac{1}{2}ac \sin B$ and $K = \frac{1}{2}ab \sin C$.

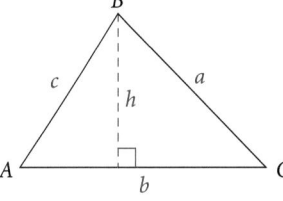

1 EXAMPLE Finding the Area of a Triangle

Find the area of the triangle at the right.

In the triangle, $b = 5, c = 10$, and $m\angle A = 31°$.

$$K = \frac{1}{2}bc \sin A = \frac{1}{2}(5)(10) \sin 31°$$
$$\approx 12.9$$

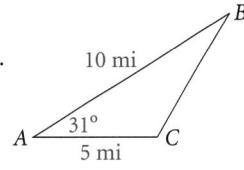

● The area is about 12.9 mi^2.

✓ **Quick Check** ① A triangle has sides of lengths 12 in. and 15 in., and the measure of the angle between them is 24°. Find the area of the triangle. **36.6 in.^{2}**

Combining the three equations for the area of $\triangle ABC$ yields a useful formula.

$\frac{1}{2}bc \sin A = \frac{1}{2}ac \sin B = \frac{1}{2}ab \sin C$ **Transitive Property of Equality**

$\frac{\sin A}{a} = \frac{\sin B}{b} = \frac{\sin C}{c}$ **Divide by $\frac{1}{2}abc$.**

This relationship of the lengths of the sides of any triangle to the sines of the angles opposite them is known as the **Law of Sines.**

Differentiated Instruction Solutions for All Learners

Special Needs L1
If students are having trouble visualizing a problem, have them model a triangle using three pens or pencils. Then have them draw and label a triangle using sides a, b, and c. Students should then be able to write a Law of Sines proportion.

learning style: tactile

Below Level L2
Make sure students understand that they only need to form a proportion with two of the ratios in the Law of Sines to solve for a missing angle or side length.

learning style: verbal

Guided Instruction

1 EXAMPLE **Alternative Method**

Show how to calculate the area of the triangle by using the altitude from the vertex of the obtuse angle to the longest side of the triangle. The altitude will have a length of 5 sin 31°. So the area will be $\frac{1}{2} \cdot 10 \cdot 5 \sin 31°$.

2 EXAMPLE **Math Tip**

Ask students why knowing two angle measures and one side length is always enough to permit them to find the remaining angle measure and side lengths. **You can subtract the sum of the given angle measures from 180° to find the measure of the third angle. You then have enough information to use the Law of Sines to find the remaining side lengths.**

PowerPoint

Additional Example

1 Find the area of the triangle shown below. $\approx 194.4 \text{ cm}^2$

40 cm

25°

23 cm

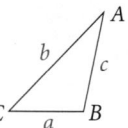
Key Concepts

Theorem	Law of Sines

In $\triangle ABC$, let $a, b,$ and c represent the lengths of the sides opposite $\angle A, \angle B,$ and $\angle C$, respectively.

Then $\dfrac{\sin A}{a} = \dfrac{\sin B}{b} = \dfrac{\sin C}{c}$.

Vocabulary Tip

In math, <u>law</u> refers to a general property. The Law of Sines could have been named the Property of Sines.

You can use the Law of Sines to find missing measures of any triangle when you know the measures of

- two angles and any side, or
- two sides and the angle opposite one of them.

In Example 2, you are given the measures of two angles and a side.

2 EXAMPLE **Finding a Side of a Triangle**

In $\triangle PQR, m\angle R = 39°, m\angle Q = 32°,$ and $PQ = 40$ cm. Find RQ.

Step 1 Draw and label a diagram.

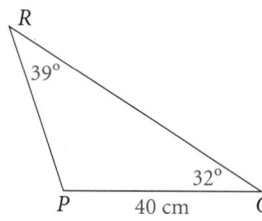

Step 2 Find the measure of the angle opposite $\overline{RQ}$.

$$m\angle P = 180° - 39° - 32° = 109°$$

Step 3 Find RQ.

$\dfrac{\sin 109°}{RQ} = \dfrac{\sin 39°}{40}$ Law of Sines

$RQ = \dfrac{40 \sin 109°}{\sin 39°}$ Solve for *RQ*.

$RQ \approx 60.1$ cm   Use a calculator.

Quick Check **2** In $\triangle KLM, m\angle K = 120°, m\angle M = 50°,$ and $ML = 35$ yd. Find KL. **31.0 yd**

In Example 3, you are given the measures of two sides and an angle opposite one of the sides.

3 EXAMPLE **Finding an Angle of a Triangle**

In $\triangle RST, t = 7, r = 9,$ and $m\angle R = 110°$. Find $m\angle S$.

Step 1 Draw and label a diagram.

Step 2 Find the measure of the angle opposite *t*.

$\dfrac{\sin T}{7} = \dfrac{\sin 110°}{9}$ Law of Sines.

$\sin T = \dfrac{7 \sin 110°}{9}$ Solve for sin *T*.

$m\angle T = \sin^{-1}\left(\dfrac{7 \sin 110°}{9}\right)$ Solve for *m∠T*.

$m\angle T \approx 47°$ Use a calculator.

Step 3 Find the measure of $\angle S$.

$$m\angle S \approx 180° - 110° - 47° = 23°$$

Quick Check **3** In $\triangle PQR, m\angle R = 97.5°, r = 80,$ and $p = 75$. Find $m\angle P$. **68.4°**

Differentiated Instruction Solutions for All Learners

Advanced Learners **L4**
Have students investigate what happens to the Law of Sines if angle C is a right angle. Ask students to share their results with the class.

learning style: verbal

English Language Learners **ELL**
For Example 4, explain that the *summit* of a mountain is the highest point on the mountain. Also explain that *elevation* gives the height above sea level, and the *angle of elevation* is the angle formed from the horizon up towards the summit.

learning style: verbal

Surveyors can use the Law of Sines to measure the height of a mountain indirectly.

4 EXAMPLE Real-World Connection

Surveying A surveyor locates points *A* and *B* at the same elevation and 3950 ft apart. At *A*, the angle of elevation to the summit of the mountain is 18°. At *B*, the angle of elevation is 31°.

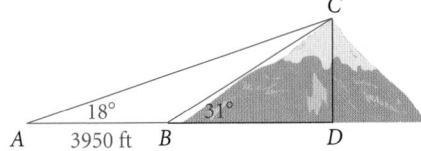

a. Find *BC*, the distance from *B* to the summit.

First find $m\angle ABC$ and $m\angle ACB$.

$m\angle ABC = 180° - 31° = 149°$

$m\angle ACB = 180° - 18° - 149° = 13°$

Now use the Law of Sines in $\triangle ABC$. Write a proportion that includes the side you know, *AB*, and the side you want, *BC*.

$\dfrac{\sin A}{BC} = \dfrac{\sin C}{AB}$	**Law of Sines**
$\dfrac{\sin 18°}{BC} = \dfrac{\sin 13°}{3950}$	**Substitute.**
$BC = \dfrac{3950 \sin 18°}{\sin 13°}$	**Solve for BC.**
$BC \approx 5426$	**Simplify.**

The distance from *B* to the summit is about 5426 ft.

b. Find *CD*, the height of the mountain.

In right $\triangle BCD$, you know *BC* and $m\angle B$. Use the sine ratio.

$\sin 31° \approx \dfrac{CD}{5426}$	**Definition of Sine**
$CD \approx 5426 \sin 31°$	**Solve for CD.**
$CD \approx 2795$	**Use a calculator.**

The summit is about 2795 ft higher than points *A* and *B*.

 Quick Check **4** In $\triangle MNP$, $m\angle M = 35°$, $m\angle N = 120°$, and $MN = 48$. Find the length of the altitude of $\triangle MNP$ from vertex *P*.   **56.4**

EXERCISES

For more exercises, see *Extra Skill and Word Problem Practice*.

Practice and Problem Solving

 Practice by Example

Example 1
(page 801)

Find the area of each triangle. Round your answer to the nearest tenth.

1. **18.7 cm²**

2. **9.1 in.²**

3. **81.9 m²**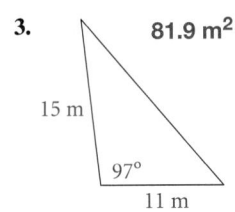

4. A triangle has sides of lengths 10 cm and 16 cm, and the measure of the angle between them is 130°. Find the area of the triangle. **61.3 cm²**

Lesson 14-4 Area and the Law of Sines   **803**

PowerPoint

Additional Examples

2 In $\triangle ABC$, $m\angle A = 33°$, $m\angle C = 64°$, and $BC = 8$ cm. Find *AC*. $\approx$ **14.6 cm**

3 In $\triangle PQR$, $p = 7$ in., $q = 10$ in., and $m\angle Q = 98°$. Find $m\angle R$. $\approx$ **38°**

4 Two observers view the same mountain peak from two points on level ground and 2 miles apart, as shown in the diagram. The angle of elevation at *T* to the peak for the observer most distant from the mountain is 31°. For the other observer, the angle of elevation at *S* to the peak is 58°.
a. Find *TK*, the distance from *T* to the summit. $\approx$ **3.74 mi**
b. Find *RK*, the height of the mountain. $\approx$ **1.92 mi**

Resources
• Daily Notetaking Guide 14-4   **L3**

Closure

Have students write a paragraph explaining how they can find the area of a triangle if they know the measures of its sides and angles. Find half the product of the measures of two sides and the sine of their included angle. Ask: *What information must be given to use the Law of Sines to find missing measures of any triangle?* Answers may vary: Sample: two angles and any side, or, two sides and the angle opposite one of them

Homework Quick Check
To check students' understanding
of key skills and concepts, go over
Exercises 8, 16, 18, 25, 28, 30, 42.

Error Prevention!

Exercises 8–10 Students who do
not sketch diagrams for these
exercises may apply the Law of
Sines incorrectly. Urge students to
sketch and label a diagram to
show the given information for
each exercise.

Connection to Geometry
Exercise 29 Be sure students
recall the relevant inequality
theorem from geometry. An
angle of greater measure is
always opposite a side of greater
length.

Example 2
(page 802)

Use the Law of Sines. Find the measure *x* to the nearest tenth.

  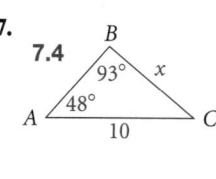

8. In $\triangle RST$, $m\angle R = 78°$, $m\angle T = 39°$, and $TS = 19$ in. Find RS. **12.2 in.**

9. In $\triangle JKL$, $m\angle L = 64°$, $j = 18$ m, and $m\angle K = 36°$. Find k. **10.7 m**

10. In $\triangle RNP$, $m\angle N = 58°$, $n = 20$ in., and $m\angle R = 42°$. Find r. **15.8 in.**

Example 3
(page 802)

Use the Law of Sines. Find the measure *x* to the nearest tenth.

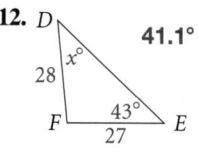

13. In $\triangle DEF$, $m\angle F = 43°$, $d = 16$ mm, and $f = 24$ mm. Find $m\angle D$. **27.0°**

14. In $\triangle ABC$, $m\angle A = 52°$, $c = 10$ ft, and $a = 15$ ft. Find $m\angle C$. **31.7°**

15. In $\triangle XYZ$, $m\angle Z = 33°$, $z = 35$ cm, and $x = 31$ cm. Find $m\angle X$. **28.8°**

Example 4
(page 803)

16. Surveying The distance from
point *A* to the top of the hill is
2760 ft. The angle of elevation
from *A* to the base of the tower
is 28° and the angle of elevation
from *A* to the top of the tower
is 32°.

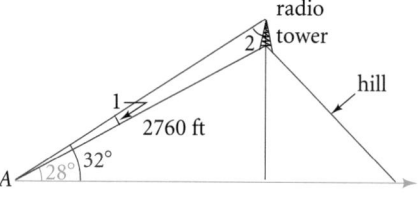

a. Find the measures of ∠1 and ∠2. $m\angle 1 = 4°$, $m\angle 2 = 58°$

b. Find to the nearest foot the height of the tower above the top of the hill.
227 ft

B **Apply Your Skills**

Find the remaining sides and angles in each triangle. Round your answers to the nearest tenth.   **20–24. See margin.**

17. $m\angle D = 100°$,
$e = 22.3$,
$f = 34.2$

18. $m\angle A = 38.70$,
$m\angle B = 33.3°$,
$b = 21.9$

19. $m\angle T = 29.3°$,
$m\angle R = 26.7°$,
$r = 8.3$

17.   **18.**   **19.**

20.   **21.**   **22.**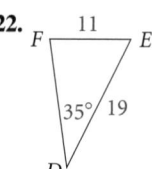

23. In $\triangle DEF$, $m\angle D = 54°$, $m\angle E = 54°$, and $d = 20$ in.

24. In $\triangle DEF$, $m\angle D = 54°$, $e = 8$ m, and $d = 10$ m.

20. $m\angle B = 85°$, $b = 11.3$,
$c = 8.7$

21. $m\angle C = 40°$, $b = 10$,
$c = 6.8$

22. $m\angle E = 62.8°$,
$m\angle F = 82.2°$, $e = 17.1$
or

$m\angle E = 47.2°$,
$m\angle F = 97.8°$, $e \approx 14.1$

23. $m\angle F = 72°$, $e = 20$ in.,
$f = 23.5$ in.

24. $m\angle E = 40.3°$,
$m\angle F = 85.7°$, $f = 12.3$ m

Homework Video Tutor
Visit: PHSchool.com
Web Code: age-1404

25. Critical Thinking In $\triangle ABC$, $a = 10$ and $b = 15$. **a–c. See margin.**
    a. Does the triangle have a greater area when $m\angle C = 1°$ or when $m\angle C = 50°$?
    b. Does the triangle have a greater area when $m\angle C = 50°$ or when $m\angle C = 179°$?
    c. For what measure of $\angle C$ does $\triangle ABC$ have the greatest area? Explain.

26. a. Open-Ended Sketch a triangle. Specify three of its measures so that you can use the Law of Sines to find the remaining measures.
    b. Solve for the remaining measures of the triangle. **Check students' work.**

27. Forestry A forest ranger in an observation tower sights a fire 39° east of north. A ranger in a tower 10 miles due east of the first tower sights the fire at 42° west of north. How far is the fire from each tower? **7.5 mi, 7.9 mi**

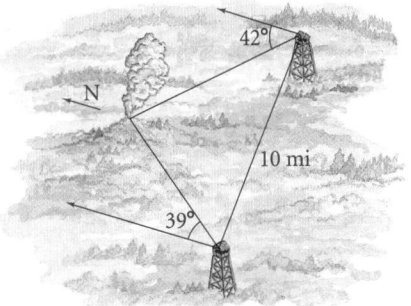

28. Geometry One of the congruent sides of an isosceles triangle is 10 cm long. One of the congruent angles has a measure of 54°. Find the perimeter of the triangle. Round your answer to the nearest centimeter. **32 cm**

29. Geometry The sides of a triangle are 15 in., 17 in., and 16 in. long. The smallest angle has a measure of 54°. Find the measure of the largest angle. Round your answer to the nearest degree. **66°**

Find the area of $\triangle ABC$. Round your answer to the nearest tenth.

30. $m\angle C = 68°$, $b = 12.9$, $c = 15.2$ **85.0**   **31.** $m\angle A = 52°$, $a = 9.71$, $c = 9.33$ **44.4**

32. 29.7   **32.** $m\angle A = 23°$, $m\angle C = 39°$, $b = 14.6$ **33.** $m\angle B = 87°$, $a = 10.1$, $c = 9.8$ **49.4**

34. 267.3   **34.** $m\angle A = 96°$, $m\angle C = 18°$, $a = 43.4$ **35.** $m\angle C = 33°$, $a = 1.2$, $b = 0.9$ **0.3**

36. $m\angle B = 40°$, $m\angle C = 80°$, $c = 5.5$ **8.5** **37.** $m\angle A = 20°$, $b = 1$, $c = 5$ **0.9**

In $\triangle ABC$, $m\angle A = 40°$ and $m\angle B = 30°$. Find each value to the nearest tenth.

38. Find AC for $BC = 10.5$ m. **8.2 m**   **39.** Find BC for $AC = 21.8$ ft. **28.0 ft**

40. Find AC for $AB = 81.2$ yd. **43.2 yd**   **41.** Find BC for $AB = 5.9$ cm. **4.0 cm**

42. Measurement A vacant lot is in the shape of an isosceles triangle. It is between two streets that intersect at an 85.9° angle. Each of the sides of the lot that face these streets is 150 ft long. Find the length of the third side, to the nearest foot.
204 ft

C Challenge **43. Sailing** Buoys are located in the sea at points A, B, and C. $\angle ACB$ is a right angle. $AC = 3.0$ mi, $BC = 4.0$ mi, and $AB = 5.0$ mi. A ship is located at point D on $\overline{AB}$ so that $m\angle ACD = 30°$. How far is the ship from the buoy at point C? Round your answer to the nearest tenth of a mile. **2.4 miles**

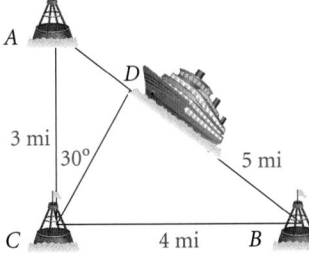

44. Writing Suppose you know the measures of all three angles of a triangle. Can you use the Law of Sines to find the lengths of the sides? Explain. **No; you need at least one side in order to set up a proportion you can solve.**

25a. when $m\angle C = 50°$

  b. when $m\angle C = 50°$

  c. 90°; a right triangle has the greatest height.

---

4. Assess & Reteach

PowerPoint
Lesson Quiz

1. Find the area of $\triangle EFG$.

≈ 88.5 cm²

2. Find KM in $\triangle KLM$.

≈ 3.7 in.

3. In $\triangle ABC$, $m\angle A = 56°$, $AB = 11$ ft, and $BC = 13$ ft. Find $m\angle C$. $\approx 44.5°$

4. In $\triangle PQR$, $m\angle P = 49°$, $m\angle R = 37°$, and $PR = 26$ cm. Find QR and the area of $\triangle PQR$.
≈ 19.7 cm;
≈ 154 cm²

Alternative Assessment

Have students work in groups of three. Ask each student to create two problems about triangles. One problem should involve finding the area of a triangle, given the lengths of two sides and the measure of the included angle. The other problem should involve using the Law of Sines to find a missing side length or angle measure. Each student should solve the problems created by the other two students. Ask students to check one another's work. If students create problems that are examples of the ambiguous case, point out that they will learn how to solve these triangles in the Extension for use with Lesson 14-4.

56. $a = 3, m\angle A = 36.9°,$ $m\angle C = 53.1°$

57. $b = 3\sqrt{2}, m\angle A = 45°,$ $m\angle C = 45°$

58. $c = 11.2, m\angle A = 41.8°,$ $m\angle C = 48.2°$

59. $b = 8.3, m\angle A = 11.2°,$ $m\angle C = 78.8°$

60. $c = 8.5, m\angle A = 25.9°,$ $m\angle C = 64.1°$

61. $c = 89.3, m\angle A = 63.3°,$ $m\angle C = 26.7°$

62.

63.

64.

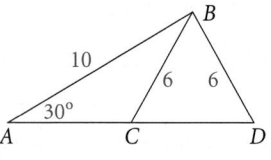

45. a. In the diagram at the left, $m\angle A = 30°$, $AB = 10$, and $BC = BD = 6$. Use the Law of Sines to find $m\angle D$. **56.4°**

b. Find $m\angle ABD$ and $m\angle ABC$. **93.6°, 26.4°**

c. Reasoning Notice that two sides and a nonincluded angle of $\triangle ABC$ are congruent to the corresponding parts of $\triangle ABD$, but the triangles are not congruent. Must $\triangle EFG$ be congruent to $\triangle ABD$ if $EF = 10$, $FG = 6$, and $\angle E \cong \angle A$? Explain. **No; $\triangle EFG$ could be congruent to $\triangle ABC$ instead of $\triangle ABD$.**

Test Prep

Multiple Choice

49. **[2]** Area $= \frac{1}{2} ab \sin C$

$\sin C = \frac{2(\text{Area})}{ab}$

$= \frac{2(31.5)}{9(14)} = 0.5$

$m\angle C = \sin^{-1} 0.5 = 30°$

So the measure of the included angle for the given sides is 30° or 150°.

[1] answer only OR minor computational error

Short Response

50. **[2]** 45° and 105°
[1] one angle measure correct

51. **[2]** Area $= \frac{1}{2} ab \sin M$

$= \frac{1}{2}(3.1)(6.0)\sin(45°)$

≈ 6.6

Area is 6.6 cm²

[1] answer only OR minor computational error

46. In $\triangle GDL$, $m\angle D = 57°$, $DL = 10.1$, and $GL = 9.4$. What is the best estimate for $m\angle G$?
A
   A. 64°   **B.** 51°   **C.** 39°   **D.** 26°

47. For which set of given information can you compute the area of a triangle?
J
   F. Given: the length of one side and the measure of the angle opposite it
   G. Given: the length of one side and the measure of an angle adjacent to it
   H. Given: the lengths of two sides and the measure of a nonincluded angle
   J. Given: the lengths of two sides and the measure of the included angle

48. A surveyor picks two points 250 m apart in front of a tall building. The
C angle of elevation from one point is 37°. The angle of elevation from the other point is 13°. What is the best estimate for the height of the building?
   A. 150 m   **B.** 138 m   **C.** 83 m   **D.** 56 m

49. Two sides of a scalene triangle are 9 m and 14 m. The area of the triangle is 31.5 m². Find the measure of one of the angles of the triangle to the nearest tenth of a degree. Show your work. **See left.**

Use the diagram for Exercises 50 and 51.

50. Let $m\angle N = 30°$. Find the measures of the other two angles to the nearest degree.

51. Let $m\angle M = 45°$. Find the area of the triangle to the nearest tenth of a square centimeter. Show your work.

Mixed Review

52. 53.1°

53. 24.6°

54. 38.7°

55. 54.7°

Lesson 14-3   **Find each angle measure to the nearest tenth of a degree.**

52. $\cos^{-1}\frac{3}{5}$ **53.** $\tan^{-1} 0.4569$ **54.** $\sin^{-1}\frac{5}{8}$ **55.** $\tan^{-1}\sqrt{2}$

In $\triangle ABC$, $\angle B$ is a right angle. Find the remaining sides and angles. Round your answers to the nearest tenth. **56–61. See margin.**

56. $b = 5, c = 4$ **57.** $a = 3, c = 3$ **58.** $a = 10, b = 15$

59. $a = 1.6, c = 8.1$ **60.** $a = 4.1, b = 9.4$ **61.** $b = 100, c = 45$

Lesson 13-4   **Sketch one cycle of the graph of each sine function.** **62–64. See margin.**

62. $y = 4 \sin \theta$ **63.** $y = 4 \sin \pi\theta$ **64.** $y = \sin 4\theta$

Lesson 12-4   **65.** A set of values has a mean of 36 and a standard deviation of 5. Find the z-score of the value 43. $\frac{7}{5}$

Extension

The Ambiguous Case

FOR USE WITH LESSON 14-4

The triangles at the right have one pair of congruent angles and two pairs of congruent sides. But the triangles are not congruent. Notice that each of the congruent angles is opposite one of the congruent sides.

When you know the measures of two sides of a triangle and one of the opposite angles, there may be two triangles with those measurements. You can use the Law of Sines to find the other measures for both triangles.

EXAMPLE

In each $\triangle ABC$ at the right, $m\angle A = 35°$, $a = 11$, and $b = 15$. Find $m\angle B$.

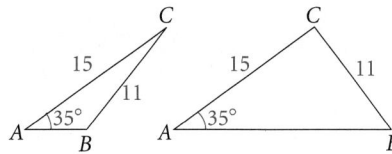

$\dfrac{\sin A}{a} = \dfrac{\sin B}{b}$ **Law of Sines**

$\dfrac{\sin 35°}{11} = \dfrac{\sin B}{15}$ **Substitute.**

$\sin B = \dfrac{15 \sin 35°}{11}$ **Solve for sin B.**

$m\angle B \approx \sin^{-1}\left(\dfrac{15 \sin 35°}{11}\right)$ **Find one value of m∠B.**

$m\angle B \approx 51°$ **Use a calculator.**

The sine function is also positive in Quadrant II. So another value of $m\angle B$ is about $180° - 51° = 129°$.

Because there are two possible angle measures for $\angle B$, there are two triangles that satisfy the given conditions. In one triangle the angle measures are about 35°, 51°, and 94°. In the other, the angle measures are about 35°, 129°, and 16°.

EXERCISES

In each $\triangle ABC$, find the measures for $\angle B$ and $\angle C$ that satisfy the given conditions. Draw diagrams to help you decide whether two triangles are possible. Remember that a triangle can have only one obtuse angle. **1–4. See margin.**

1. $m\angle A = 62°$, $a = 30$, and $b = 32$

2. $m\angle A = 16°$, $a = 12$, and $b = 37.5$

3. $m\angle A = 48°$, $a = 93$, and $b = 125$

4. $m\angle A = 112°$, $a = 16.5$, and $b = 5.4$

5. $m\angle A = 23.6°$, $a = 9.8$, and $b = 17$
    44.0° and 112.4°, or 136.0° and 20.4°

6. $m\angle A = 155°$, $a = 12.5$, and $b = 8.4$
    16.5° and 8.5°

7. Multiple Choice You can construct a triangle with compass and straightedge when given three parts of the triangle (except for three angles). Which of the following given sets could result in the ambiguous case? **C**
- Ⓐ Given: three sides
- Ⓑ Given: two sides and an included angle
- Ⓒ Given: two sides and a nonincluded angle
- Ⓓ Given: two angles and a nonincluded side

Extension   The Ambiguous Case   **807**

Extension

The Ambiguous Case

This extension will demonstrate the need for caution when using the Law of Sines to find missing side lengths and angle measures in a triangle.

Guided Instruction

Teaching Tip

You may need to provide some guidance if students have trouble drawing the diagrams for Exercises 1–6. Suggest that they use millimeters for side lengths.

Error Prevention

Students may fail to see that two sets of angle measures are possible for Exercises 1–3 and 5. Urge them to draw diagrams for the exercises *before* they undertake the calculations.

Exercise 7 Students should recall from Geometry the triangle congruence postulates: SSS, SAS, ASA, and AAS (where S is a side length and A is an angle). Students may also remember that AAA and SSA cannot prove that triangles are congruent.

Resources

protractor, compass, centimeter ruler, graphing calculator

1. 70.4° and 47.6°, or 109.6° and 8.4°

2. 59.5° and 104.5°, or 120.5° and 43.5°

3. 87.3° and 44.7°, or 92.7° and 39.3°

4. 17.7° and 50.3°

807

14-5

Objectives
1 To use the Law of Cosines in finding the measures of sides and angles of a triangle

Examples
1 Real-World Connection
2 Finding an Angle Measure
3 Finding an Angle Measure

Math Background

The Law of Cosines is, in a sense, an extension of the Pythagorean Theorem. But while the Pythagorean Theorem applies only to right triangles, the Law of Cosines applies to all triangles.

More Math Background: p. 776D

Lesson Planning and Resources

See p. 776E for a list of the resources that support this lesson.

Bell Ringer Practice

✓ **Check Skills You'll Need**
For intervention, direct students to:

Area and the Law of Sines
Lesson 14-4: Example 3
Extra Skills and Word
Problems Practice, Ch. 14

What You'll Learn

• To use the Law of Cosines in finding the measures of sides and angles of a triangle

. . . And Why

To find the length of a sailing course, as in Example 1

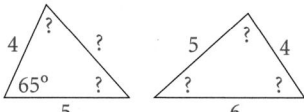 **New Vocabulary** • Law of Cosines

✓ **Check Skills You'll Need**

GO for Help Lesson 14-4

Use the Law of Sines.

1. In $\triangle ABC, m\angle C = 33°, a = 17$, and $c = 21$. Find $m\angle A$. **26.2°**

2. In $\triangle RST, m\angle R = 59°, m\angle S = 45°$, and $r = 16$. Find t. **18.1**

3. In $\triangle DEF, m\angle D = 55°, d = 18$, and $e = 21$. Find $m\angle F$. **52.1° or 17.9°**

---

1 The Law of Cosines

Since you can't use the Law of Sines to find the missing measures in the triangles at the right, another formula is needed.

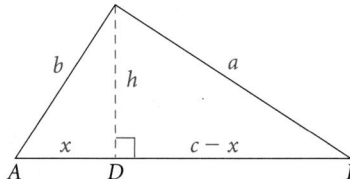

In this oblique $\triangle ABC$ with altitude h, let $AD = x$.

Then $DB = c - x$.

In $\triangle ADC$,
$b^2 = x^2 + h^2$ and
$\cos A = \frac{x}{b}$ or $x = b \cos A$.

In $\triangle CBD$,

$$
\begin{aligned}
a^2 &= (c - x)^2 + h^2 && \text{Pythagorean Theorem} \\
&= c^2 - 2cx + x^2 + h^2 && \text{Square the binomial.} \\
&= c^2 - 2cx + b^2 && \text{Substitute } b^2 \text{ for } x^2 + h^2. \\
&= c^2 - 2cb \cos A + b^2 && \text{Substitute } b \cos A \text{ for } x. \\
&= b^2 + c^2 - 2bc \cos A && \text{Commutative Property of Addition}
\end{aligned}
$$

The last equation relates the length of a side of any triangle to the measure of the opposite angle. It applies to any of the three sides and is called the **Law of Cosines.**

 Key Concepts

Theorem	**Law of Cosines**

In $\triangle ABC$, let $a, b,$ and c represent the lengths of the sides opposite $\angle A, \angle B,$ and $\angle C$, respectively.

$$a^2 = b^2 + c^2 - 2bc \cos A$$

$$b^2 = a^2 + c^2 - 2ac \cos B$$

$$c^2 = a^2 + b^2 - 2ab \cos C$$

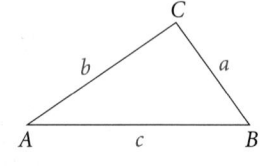

808 Chapter 14 Trigonometric Identities and Equations

Differentiated Instruction **Solutions for All Learners**

Special Needs **L1**
For Example 2, have students look at the triangle and try estimating a reasonable range of measures for angle C. Students can easily make calculation errors with the Law of Cosines, but they can also check that their answer is reasonable with a sketch.

learning style: visual

Below Level **L2**
Emphasize to students that the Law of Sines and the Law of Cosines both apply to any triangles, not just right triangles.

learning style: verbal

You can use the Law of Cosines to find missing measures in any triangle when you know the measures of

- two sides and the angle between them, or
- all three sides.

In this example, you are given the measures of two sides and the included angle.

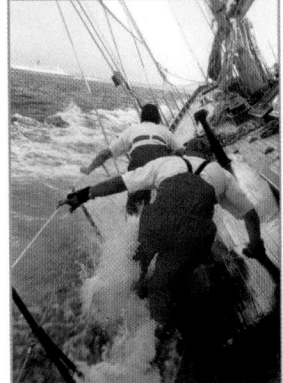

Real-World Connection

One leg of a race course is laid out close to the wind to test the capability of the boats and the skill of the crews.

① EXAMPLE Real-World Connection

Multiple Choice A racing committee wants to lay out a triangular course with a 40° angle between two sides of 3.5 mi and 2.5 mi. What will be the length of the third side?

  Ⓐ 2.0 mi Ⓑ 2.3 mi Ⓒ 9.8 mi Ⓓ 30.2 mi

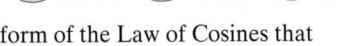

Choose the form of the Law of Cosines that has a^2 on one side.

$a^2 = b^2 + c^2 - 2bc \cos A$	
$a^2 = 2.5^2 + 3.5^2 - 2(2.5)(3.5) \cos 40°$	Substitute.
≈ 5.094	Use a calculator.
$a \approx 2.3$	Use a calculator.

The third side of the triangular course will be about 2.3 mi long.
The correct choice is B.

✔ **Quick Check** ① The lengths of two sides of a triangle are 8 and 10, and the measure of the angle between them is 40°. Find the length of the third side. **6.4**

In this example, you are given the measures of three sides.

② EXAMPLE Finding an Angle Measure

Find the measure of ∠C in the triangle below. Round your answer to the nearest tenth of a degree.

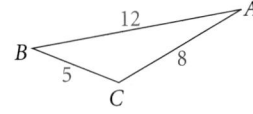

Choose the form of the Law of Cosines that contains ∠C.

$c^2 = a^2 + b^2 - 2ab \cos C$	
$12^2 = 5^2 + 8^2 - 2(5)(8) \cos C$	Substitute.
$144 = 25 + 64 - 80 \cos C$	Simplify.
$55 = -80 \cos C$	Combine like terms.
$-\frac{55}{80} = \cos C$	Solve for cos C.
$\cos^{-1}\left(-\frac{55}{80}\right) = m\angle C$	Solve for m∠C.
$m\angle C \approx 133.4°$	Use a calculator.

✔ **Quick Check** ② The lengths of the sides of a triangle are 10, 14, and 15. Find the measure of the angle opposite the longest side. **75.3°**

Lesson 14-5 The Law of Cosines **809**

Test-Taking Tip

When you use trigonometric ratios or functions on a calculator, be sure you are in the right mode (degrees or radians).

2. Teach

Guided Instruction

② EXAMPLE **Tactile Learners**

Students can cut narrow strips of paper to the lengths given and fit them together to form a triangle to convince themselves that all triangles with these side lengths are congruent.

PowerPoint
Additional Examples

① Suppose two stars are 9.5 and 4.6 light years from Earth. When an astronomer observes the stars with the Earth as vertex, the angle between the stars is about 43°. What is the approximate distance between the stars?
≈ 6.9 light years

② A triangle has sides of lengths 9 cm, 11 cm, and 14 cm. Find the measure of the angle opposite the longest side. Round your answer to the nearest tenth of a degree.
≈ 88.3°

③ In △PQR, r = 10, q = 12, and m∠P = 32°. Find m∠Q. **≈ 91.6°**

Resources
- Daily Notetaking Guide 14-5 **L3**

Closure

Ask students to state the Law of Cosines in words. The square of the length of any side of a triangle is equal to the sum of the squares of the lengths of the other two sides minus twice the product of the cosine of their included angle and the lengths of these two sides.

Advanced Learners **L4**	**English Language Learners** **ELL**
Have students show how the Law of Cosines reduces to the Pythagorean theorem for a right triangle.	The *Law of Cosines* can sound very similar to the *Law of Sines*. Advise students to pay particular attention so they hear the correct Law during a discussion. Also point out that the Law of Sines will not work if all the sines are replaced with cosines.
learning style: verbal	**learning style: verbal**

3. Practice

Assignment Guide

✔ A B 1-49
C Challenge   50-52

Test Prep   53-58
Mixed Review   59-67

Homework Quick Check
To check students' understanding of key skills and concepts, go over Exercises 4, 16, 31, 32, 34, 47, 49.

Error Prevention!

Exercises 15–17 Students may have errors that result from rounding to too few decimals places at intermediate stages of the solution process. Since students will be using calculators for these exercises, encourage them to use several decimal places, if they use intermediate rounding, to ensure that the final answer will have the desired accuracy.

Differentiated Instruction Resources

GPS Guided Problem Solving	L3
Enrichment	L4
Reteaching	L2
Practice	L3

Sometimes you need to use the Law of Cosines followed by the Law of Cosines again or by the Law of Sines.

3 EXAMPLE   **Finding an Angle Measure**

In $\triangle ABC$, $b = 6.2$, $c = 7.8$, and $m\angle A = 45°$. Find $m\angle B$.

Step 1   Draw a diagram.

Step 2   Find a. Since you cannot find $m\angle B$ directly, use the Law of Cosines to find a.

$a^2 = b^2 + c^2 - 2bc \cos A$
$a^2 = 6.2^2 + 7.8^2 - 2(6.2)(7.8) \cos 45°$ **Substitute.**
$ \approx 30.89$ **Simplify.**
$a \approx \sqrt{30.89}$ **Solve for a.**
$a \approx 5.56$ **Find the principal square root.**

> **Problem Solving Hint**
> To help remember the formulas for the Law of Cosines, notice that the first and last letters are the same and the last one is capitalized.

Step 3   Now you can use the Law of Sines or the Law of Cosines to find $m\angle B$.

$\dfrac{\sin B}{6.2} \approx \dfrac{\sin 45°}{5.56}$ **Law of Sines**

$\sin B \approx \dfrac{6.2 \sin 45°}{5.56}$ **Solve for $\sin B$.**

$m\angle B \approx \sin^{-1}\left(\dfrac{6.2 \sin 45°}{5.56}\right)$ **Solve for $m\angle B$. ($\angle B$ is not obtuse because $b < c$.)**

$ \approx 52°$ **Use a calculator.**

✓ Quick Check   ❸ In $\triangle RST$, $s = 41$, $t = 53$, and $m\angle R = 126°$. Find $m\angle T$.   **30.7°**

EXERCISES

For more exercises, see *Extra Skill and Word Problem Practice.*

Practice and Problem Solving

Ⓐ Practice by Example

GO for Help

Example 1
(page 809)

Use the Law of Cosines. Find the length of x to the nearest tenth.

1.

2.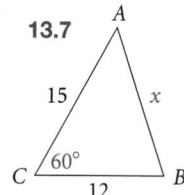

3.
13.7

15   x

C 60° B
   12

4. In $\triangle DEF$, $m\angle E = 54°$, $d = 14$ ft, and $f = 20$ ft. Find e.   **16.3 ft**

5. In $\triangle RST$, $m\angle T = 32°$, $r = 10$ cm, and $s = 17$ cm. Find t.   **10.0 cm**

6. In $\triangle ABC$, $m\angle B = 52°$, $a = 15$ in., and $c = 10$ in. Find b.   **11.8 in.**

Example 2
(page 809)

Use the Law of Cosines. Find the measure of x to the nearest tenth of a degree.

7.   **47.3°**

8.   **27.0°**

9.   **125.1°**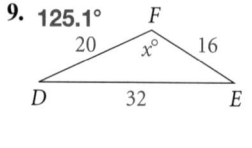

10. In $\triangle DEF$, $d = 15$ in., $e = 18$ in., and $f = 10$ in. Find $m\angle F$. **33.7°**

11. In $\triangle ABC$, $a = 20$ m, $b = 14$ m, and $c = 16$ m. Find $m\angle A$. **83.3°**

12. In $\triangle DEF$, $d = 12$ ft, $e = 10$ ft, and $f = 9$ ft. Find $m\angle F$. **47.2°**

Example 3
(page 810)

Use the Law of Cosines and the Law of Sines. Find x to the nearest tenth.

13.

14.
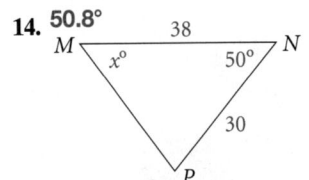

15. In $\triangle ABC$, $b = 4$ in., $c = 6$ in., and $m\angle A = 69°$. Find $m\angle C$. **71.7°**

16. In $\triangle RST$, $r = 17$ cm, $s = 12$ cm, and $m\angle T = 13°$. Find $m\angle S$. **27.0°**

17. In $\triangle DEF$, $d = 20$ ft, $e = 25$ ft, and $m\angle F = 98°$. Find $m\angle D$. **35.5°**

B Apply Your Skills

For each triangle, write the correct form of the Law of Cosines or the Law of Sines to solve for the measure in red. Use only the information given in blue.

18. $b^2 = a^2 + c^2 - 2ac \cos B$

19. $c^2 = a^2 + b^2 - 2ab \cos C$

20. $\frac{\sin B}{b} = \frac{\sin C}{c}$

21. $\frac{\sin A}{a} = \frac{\sin B}{b}$

18.

19.

20.

21.

22.
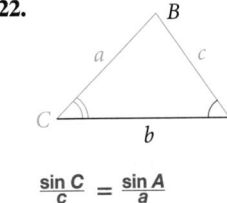

$\frac{\sin C}{c} = \frac{\sin A}{a}$

23.
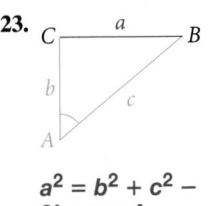

$a^2 = b^2 + c^2 - 2bc \cos A$

Find the remaining sides and angles in each triangle. Round your answers to the nearest tenth. 24–29. See margin.

24.

25.

26.

27.

28.

29.
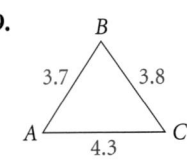

30. a. Open-Ended Sketch a triangle. Specify three of its measures so that you can use the Law of Cosines to find the remaining measures.
   b. Solve for the remaining measures of the triangle.
   a–b. Check students' work.

31. Sports A softball diamond is a square that is 65 ft on a side. The pitcher's mound is 46 ft from home plate. How far is the pitcher from third base? **46 ft**

Diversity

Exercise 31 Some students may not be familiar with softball. You may want to call on a volunteer to explain how it differs from baseball.

24. $b = 34.7$, $m\angle A = 26.7°$, $m\angle C = 33.3°$

25. $m\angle A = 50.1°$, $m\angle B = 56.3°$, $m\angle C = 73.6°$

26. $f = 6.2$, $m\angle D = 34.6°$, $m\angle E = 83.4°$

27. $m\angle A = 90°$, $m\angle B = 36.9°$, $m\angle C = 53.1°$

28. $g = 53.3$, $m\angle F = 31.9°$, $m\angle H = 38.1°$

29. $m\angle A = 56.1°$, $m\angle B = 70°$, $m\angle C = 53.9°$

4. Assess & Reteach

⬛ Lesson Quiz

1. In △*ABC*, *m*∠*A* = 127°,
   c = 9 cm, and *b* = 8.5 cm.
   Find *a*. ≈ **15.7 cm**

2. A triangle has side lengths 12
   ft, 13 ft, and 14 ft. Find the
   measure of the angle opposite
   the side of length 13 ft. Round
   your answer to the nearest
   tenth of a degree. **59.4°**

3. In △*STU*, *m*∠*U* = 87°,
   t = 17, and *u* = 19. Find
   s and *m*∠*S*. ≈ **9.4**, ≈ **29.7°**

Alternative Assessment

Ask students to create three
problems that involve finding
missing measures of sides or
angles of triangles. Each problem
should be solvable by making use
of the Law of Cosines. Ask
students to draw diagrams to
show the given information. Then
ask them to solve each problem.
Have them discuss their problems
with a neighbor to verify their
results.

Visual Learners

Exercise 34 Use a map or compass
to help explain what is meant by
due north, change course, and
east of north.

**32. Assume one side is 1.
Then use that side and
its corresponding angle
to find the ratio of the
lengths of the other two
sides.**

Real-World 🌐 Connection

Careers Pilots need
navigation skills that
include plotting a course
on an aeronautical chart
and computing flight
time, headings, and
fuel requirements.

🖉 **32. Writing** Given the measures of three angles of a triangle, explain how to find
the ratio of the lengths of two sides of the triangle. **See margin.**

⬛ **33. Geometry** The lengths of the sides of a triangle are 7.6 cm, 8.2 cm, and 5.2 cm.
Find the measure of the largest angle. **77.2°**

🌐 **34. Navigation** A pilot is flying from city A to city B, which is 85 mi due north.
GPS After flying 20 mi, the pilot must change course and fly 10° east of north to
avoid a cloudbank.
   a. If the pilot remains on this course for 20 mi, how far will the plane be from
   city B? **45.4 mi**
   b. How many degrees will the pilot have to turn to the left to fly directly to city
   B? How many degrees from due north is this course?
   14.4° left; 4.4° west of north

In △*ABC*, *m*∠*A* = 53° and *c* = 7 cm. Find each value to the nearest tenth.

35. Find *m*∠*B* for *b* = 6.2 cm. **56.6°**   **36.** Find *a* for *b* = 13.7 cm. **11.0 cm**

37. Find *a* for *b* = 11 cm. **8.8 cm**   **38.** Find *m*∠*C* for *b* = 15.2 cm. **27.0°**

39. Find *m*∠*B* for *b* = 37 cm. **117.3°**   **40.** Find *a* for *b* = 16 cm. **13.0 cm**

In △*RST*, *t* = 7 ft and *s* = 13 ft. Find each value to the nearest tenth.

41. Find *m*∠*T* for *r* = 11 ft. **32.6°**   **42.** Find *m*∠*T* for *r* = 6.97 ft. **21.5°**

43. Find *m*∠*S* for *r* = 14 ft. **67.2°**   **44.** Find *r* for *m*∠*R* = 35°. **8.3 ft**

45. Find *m*∠*S* for *m*∠*R* = 87°. **64.0°**   **46.** Find *m*∠*R* for *m*∠*S* = 70°. **79.6°**

⬛ **47. Geometry** The lengths of the adjacent sides of a parallelogram are 54 cm and
78 cm. The larger angle measures 110°. What is the length of the longer
diagonal? Round your answer to the nearest centimeter. **109 cm**

⬛ **48. Geometry** The lengths of the adjacent sides of a parallelogram are 21 cm and
14 cm. The smaller angle measures 58°. What is the length of the shorter
diagonal? Round your answer to the nearest centimeter. **18 cm**

49. Yes; since cos 90° = 0,
$c^2 = a^2 + b^2 -$
2*ab* cos *C* reduces
to $c^2 = a^2 + b^2$.

49. Critical Thinking Does the Law of Cosines apply to a right triangle? That is,
does $c^2 = a^2 + b^2 - 2ab \cos C$ remain true when ∠*C* is a right angle? Justify
your answer.

ⓒ Challenge 🌐 **50. Physics** A pendulum 36 in. long swings 30° from the vertical. How high above
the lowest position is the pendulum at the end of its swing? Round your answer
to the nearest tenth of an inch. **4.8 in.**

51. a. Find the length of the altitude to $\overline{PQ}$ in the triangle below. **2.1 m**
   b. Find the area of △*PQR*. **9.8 m²**

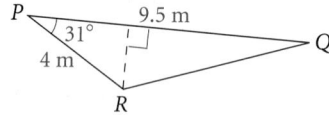

52. Find *x* in △*ABC*. **3.0**

Gridded Response

Use the diagram below for Questions 53–58. Angle measures are in degrees.

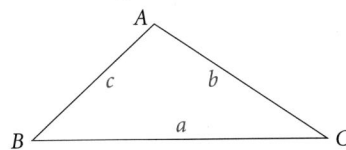

53. Let $a = 23.2$, $b = 18.5$, and $m\angle C = 42°$. Find c to the nearest tenth. **15.6**

54. Use the information in Question 53 to find $m\angle A$ to the nearest tenth. **85.4**

55. Suppose $a = 45.25$, $b = 39.75$, and $c = 20.65$. Find $m\angle B$ to the nearest tenth. **61.4**

56. Use the information in Question 55 to find $m\angle C$ to the nearest tenth. **27.1**

57. Suppose $b = 11.0$, $c = 11.7$, and $m\angle A = 22°$. Find the length of the altitude from A to the nearest tenth. **11.0**

58. Use the information in Question 57 to find the area of $\triangle ABC$ to the nearest tenth of a square unit. **24.1**

Mixed Review

Lesson 14-4

59. In $\triangle RST$, $m\angle R = 37°$, $m\angle T = 59°$, and $TS = 12$ in. Find RS. **17.1 in.**

60. In $\triangle JKL$, $m\angle L = 71°$, $j = 11$ m, and $m\angle K = 46°$. Find k. **8.9 m**

61. In $\triangle MNP$, $m\angle N = 42°$, $n = 21$ in., and $m\angle M = 57°$. Find m. **26.3 in.**

62. In $\triangle DEF$, $m\angle F = 91°$, $d = 17$ mm, and $f = 21$ mm. Find $m\angle D$. **54.0°**

Lesson 13-6

Identify the period and tell where two asymptotes occur for each function.

63–67. See margin.

63. $y = \tan 0.5\theta$ **64.** $y = \tan \frac{3\pi\theta}{2}$ **65.** $y = \tan(-3\theta)$ **66.** $y = \tan \frac{2\pi}{5}\theta$

Lesson 12-1

67. Use a table and a graph to show the probability distribution for the sum of two octahedral number cubes. {2, 3, 4, 5, 6, 7, 8, 9, 10, 11, 12, 13, 14, 15, 16}

Algebra at Work

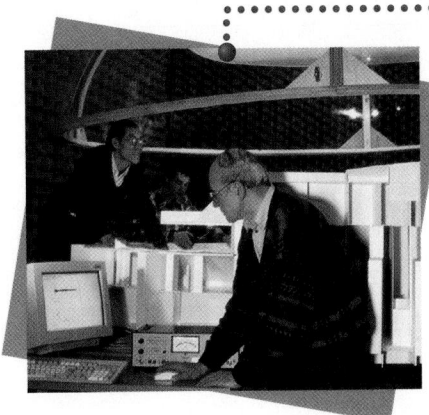

· ·**Acoustical Physicist**

Acoustical physicists study sound to design concert halls, theaters, and auditoriums. They consider building materials, the shape of the hall, and the placement of people and equipment. Acoustical physicists ensure that sound is distributed evenly so that all of the people in the theater or auditorium hear equally well.

Go Online
PHSchool.com
For: Information about acoustical physicists
Web Code: agb-2031

Lesson 14-5 The Law of Cosines **813**

Test Prep

A sheet of blank grids is available in the Test-Taking Strategies with Transparencies booklet. Give this sheet to students for practice with filling in the grids.

Resources
For additional practice with a variety of test item formats:
• Standardized Test Prep, p. 831
• Test-Taking Strategies, p. 826
• Test-Taking Strategies with Transparencies

63. 2π, $x = \pm\pi$

64. $\frac{2}{3}$, $x = \pm\frac{1}{3}$

65. $\frac{\pi}{3}$, $x = \pm\frac{\pi}{6}$

66. $\frac{5}{2}$, $x = \pm\frac{5}{4}$

67.

x	$P(x)$
2	0.016
3	0.031
4	0.047
5	0.063
6	0.078
7	0.094
8	0.109
9	0.125
10	0.109
11	0.094
12	0.078
13	0.063
14	0.047
15	0.031
16	0.016

813

1. Plan

Objectives

1 To verify and use angle identifies

2 To verify and use sum and difference identities

Examples

1 Verifying Angle Identities
2 Solving Trigonometric Equations
3 Cofunction Identities in a Right Triangle
4 Using Angle Difference Identities
5 Using Angle Sum Identities

Math Background

The negative angle, cofunction, angle difference, and angle sum identities play an important role in simplifying and manipulating calculations. For instance, in calculus, the angle sum identities for sine and cosine are used in computing the slopes of the tangent lines to the graphs of $y = \sin x$ and $y = \cos x$, respectively.

More Math Background: p. 776D

Lesson Planning and Resources

See p. 776E for a list of the resources that support this lesson.

Bell Ringer Practice

✓ Check Skills You'll Need

For intervention, direct students to:

Trigonometric Identities
Lesson 14-1: Example 3
Extra Skills and Word Problems Practice, Ch. 14

Angle Identities

What You'll Learn

- To verify and use angle identities
- To verify and use sum and difference identities

. . . And Why

To simplify trigonometric expressions and find values of trigonometric functions

✓ Check Skills You'll Need

 GO for Help Lesson 14-1

Complete the three reciprocal identities.

1. $\csc \theta = \frac{1}{\blacksquare}$ $\sin \theta$ **2.** $\sec \theta = \frac{1}{\blacksquare}$ $\cos \theta$ **3.** $\cot \theta = \frac{1}{\blacksquare}$ $\tan \theta$

Complete the three Pythagorean identities.

4. $\cos^2 \theta + \sin^2 \theta = \blacksquare$ 1   **5.** $1 + \tan^2 \theta = \blacksquare$ $\sec^2 \theta$ **6.** $1 + \cot^2 \theta = \blacksquare$ $\csc^2 \theta$

---

1 Angle Identities

Real-World 🌐 Connection

Over 2000 years ago, the Greek astronomer Hipparchus needed a table of trigonometric ratios to calculate the positions of the stars. He had to compute the table himself and he used angle identities to make the computations easier.

In the figure at the right, angles θ and $-\theta$ have the same amount of rotation, but the rotations are in opposite directions.

Point Q is a reflection of P in the x-axis. The x-coordinates of P and Q are the same and their y-coordinates are opposites. So $\cos(-\theta) = \cos \theta$ and $\sin(-\theta) = -\sin \theta$.

Similarly, R is the reflection of S in the x-axis. So $\tan(-\theta) = -\tan \theta$.

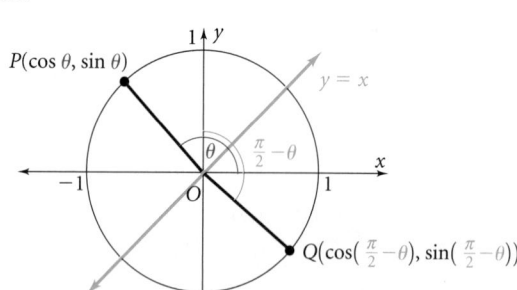

In the figure at the right, θ is a counterclockwise rotation from the positive x-axis and $\frac{\pi}{2} - \theta$ is the same amount of rotation clockwise from the positive y-axis.

Point Q is a reflection of P in the line $y = x$. If (x, y) are the coordinates of P, then (y, x) are the coordinates of Q. So $\cos\left(\frac{\pi}{2} - \theta\right) = \sin \theta$ and $\sin\left(\frac{\pi}{2} - \theta\right) = \cos \theta$.

Then, by the Tangent Identity, $\tan\left(\frac{\pi}{2} - \theta\right) = \dfrac{\sin\left(\frac{\pi}{2} - \theta\right)}{\cos\left(\frac{\pi}{2} - \theta\right)} = \dfrac{\cos \theta}{\sin \theta} = \cot \theta$.

Differentiated Instruction Solutions for All Learners

Special Needs L1

For Example 4, have a student explain why 60° and 45° were used when there are many other possible ways to express 15° as a difference. Students should recognize that both 60° and 45° are angles for what exact cosine values are known.

learning style: verbal

Below Level L2

Show students how the angle identities come from the definitions of trigonometric functions and the unit circle.

learning style: visual

Key Concepts

 Vocabulary Tip

The word <u>cofunction</u> is derived from complementary angle function.

Properties	**Angle Identities**

Negative angle identities

$$\sin(-\theta) = -\sin\theta \qquad \cos(-\theta) = \cos\theta \qquad \tan(-\theta) = -\tan\theta$$

Cofunction identities

$$\sin\left(\tfrac{\pi}{2} - \theta\right) = \cos\theta \qquad \cos\left(\tfrac{\pi}{2} - \theta\right) = \sin\theta \qquad \tan\left(\tfrac{\pi}{2} - \theta\right) = \cot\theta$$

---

1 EXAMPLE **Verifying Angle Identities**

Verify the identity $\sin\left(\theta - \frac{\pi}{2}\right) = -\cos\theta$.

$$\sin\left(\theta - \tfrac{\pi}{2}\right) = \sin\left(-\left(\tfrac{\pi}{2} - \theta\right)\right) \qquad -(a - b) = b - a$$

$$= -\sin\left(\tfrac{\pi}{2} - \theta\right) \qquad \sin(-\theta) = -\sin\theta$$

$$= -\cos\theta \qquad \sin\left(\tfrac{\pi}{2} - \theta\right) = \cos\theta$$

$$\cos\left(\theta - \tfrac{\pi}{2}\right) = \cos\left(-\left(\tfrac{\pi}{2} - \theta\right)\right)$$
$$= \cos\left(\tfrac{\pi}{2} - \theta\right)$$
$$= \sin\theta$$

✓ **Quick Check** ❶ Verify the identity $\cos\left(\theta - \frac{\pi}{2}\right) = \sin\theta$.

You can use angle identities to solve trigonometric equations.

2 EXAMPLE **Solving Trigonometric Equations**

Solve $\sin\theta = \sin\left(\frac{\pi}{2} - \theta\right)$ for $0 \le \theta < 2\pi$.

$$\sin\theta = \sin\left(\tfrac{\pi}{2} - \theta\right)$$

$$\sin\theta = \cos\theta \qquad \text{cofunction identity}$$

$$\frac{\sin\theta}{\cos\theta} = 1 \qquad \text{Divide by } \cos\theta.$$

$$\tan\theta = 1 \qquad \text{Tangent Identity}$$

$$\theta = \tan^{-1}1 \qquad \text{Solve for one value of } \theta.$$

$$\theta = \frac{\pi}{4}$$

Another solution is $\frac{\pi}{4} + \pi$, or $\frac{5\pi}{4}$.

✓ **Quick Check** ❷ Solve $\sin\left(\frac{\pi}{2} - \theta\right) = \sec\theta$ for $0 \le \theta < 2\pi$. **0, π**

3 EXAMPLE **Cofunction Identities in a Right Triangle**

The cofunction identities were derived using the unit circle. So they apply to an angle θ of any size. Use the definitions of the trigonometric ratios for a right triangle to derive a cofunction identity for $\sin(90° - A)$.

In a right triangle, the acute angles are complementary. So $A + B = 90°$ and $B = 90° - A$, where A and B are the measures of the acute angles.

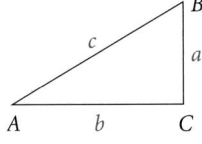

$$\sin(90° - A) = \sin B \qquad \textbf{\textit{A} and \textit{B} are complementary angles.}$$

$$= \frac{b}{a} \qquad \textbf{definition of sine in a right triangle}$$

$$= \cos A \qquad \textbf{definition of cosine in a right triangle}$$

Lesson 14-6 Angle Identities **815**

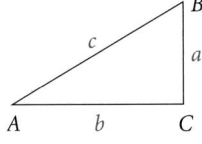 **2. Teach**

Guided Instruction

3 EXAMPLE **Auditory Learners**

Students may find it helpful to use oral repetition to memorize a statement that summarizes the cofunction identities. Suggest the following statement: *A trigonometric function of an acute angle is equal to the cofunction of the complement of the angle.*

PowerPoint

Additional Examples

❶ Use the fact that $\pi - \theta = \frac{\pi}{2} - \left(\theta - \frac{\pi}{2}\right)$ to verify the identity $\sin(\pi - \theta) = \sin\theta$.
$$\sin(\pi - \theta) = \sin\left[\tfrac{\pi}{2} - \left(\theta - \tfrac{\pi}{2}\right)\right]$$
$$= \cos\left(\theta - \tfrac{\pi}{2}\right)$$
$$= \cos\left(\tfrac{\pi}{2} - \theta\right)$$
$$= \sin\theta$$

❷ Solve $\cos\left(\frac{\pi}{2} - \theta\right) = \sin\left(\frac{\pi}{2} - \theta\right)$ for $0 \le \theta < 2\pi$. $\frac{\pi}{4}, \frac{5\pi}{4}$

❸ Find a cofunction identity for $\tan(90° - A)$, where A is an acute angle of a right triangle. $\tan(90° - A) = \cot A$

Advanced Learners **L4**

Students may like to show that the cofunction identities can also be verified using the translation relations $g(x) = f(x - h)$.

learning style: verbal

English Language Learners **ELL**

Remind students that the graphs of the sine and cosine curves are out of phase by exactly 90°, or $\frac{\pi}{2}$ radians. The *cofunction identity* $\sin(\frac{\pi}{2} - \theta) = \cos\theta$ simply describes this out of phase relationship.

learning style: verbal

815

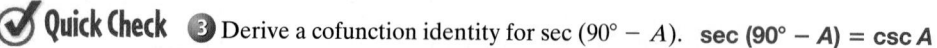

✓ **Quick Check** ③ Derive a cofunction identity for sec $(90° − A)$. sec $(90° − A) = $ csc A

In the cofunction identities, any angle θ is subtracted from $\frac{\pi}{2}$. There are also identities for subtracting any two angles.

It is convenient to start with an identity for finding the cosine of the difference of two angles.

In the figure below, angles A, B, and $A − B$ are shown. Use the distance formula to find the square of the distance between P and Q.

$$(PQ)^2 = (x_1 − x_2)^2 + (y_1 − y_2)^2$$
$$= (\cos A − \cos B)^2 + (\sin A − \sin B)^2$$
$$= \cos^2 A − 2\cos A \cos B + \cos^2 B + \sin^2 A − 2\sin A \sin B + \sin^2 B$$
$$= 2 − 2\cos A \cos B − 2\sin A \sin B \quad \text{Use the Pythagorean identity } \sin^2 \theta + \cos^2 \theta = 1.$$

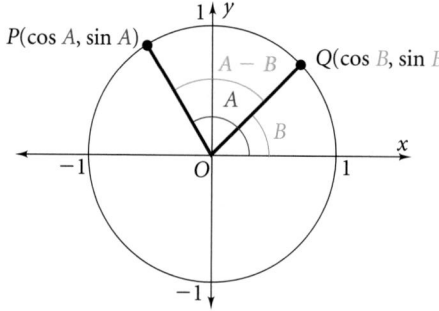

Now use the Law of Cosines to find $(PQ)^2$ in $\triangle POQ$.
$$(PQ)^2 = (PO)^2 + (QO)^2 − 2(PO)(QO) \cos (A − B)$$
$$= 1^2 + 1^2 − 2(1)(1) \cos (A − B)$$
$$= 2 − 2 \cos (A − B)$$

The Transitive Property for Equality tells you that the two expressions for $(PQ)^2$ are equal.

$$2 − 2 \cos (A − B) = 2 − 2 \cos A \cos B − 2 \sin A \sin B$$
$$−2 \cos (A − B) = −2 \cos A \cos B − 2 \sin A \sin B \quad \text{Subtract 2 from each side.}$$
$$\cos (A − B) = \cos A \cos B + \sin A \sin B \quad \text{Divide each side by } −2.$$

You can also derive an identity for sin $(A − B)$. Then you can use the Tangent Identity to derive an identity for tan $(A − B)$.

 Key Concepts

Properties	Angle Difference Identities
$\sin (A − B) = \sin A \cos B − \cos A \sin B$	
$\cos (A − B) = \cos A \cos B + \sin A \sin B$	
$\tan (A − B) = \dfrac{\tan A − \tan B}{1 + \tan A \tan B}$	

816   Chapter 14   Trigonometric Identities and Equations

Teaching Tip
You may want to show students that the identities for cos $(A − B)$ and sin $(A − B)$ can be used to verify simpler identities. For example to recall that cos $(−\theta) = \cos \theta$, note that $−\theta = 0 − \theta$ and use the identity for the difference of two angle measures.

$$\cos (−\theta) = \cos (0 − \theta)$$
$$= \cos 0 \cos \theta + \sin 0 \sin \theta$$
$$= 1 \cdot \cos \theta + 0 \cdot \sin \theta$$
$$= \cos \theta$$

4 EXAMPLE **Using Angle Difference Identities**

Find the exact value of cos 15°.

You know exact values for 30°, 60°, and 45°. Use the fact that 15° = 60° − 45°.

$$\cos (A - B) = \cos A \cos B + \sin A \sin B$$ **Cosine Angle Difference Identity**

$$\cos (60° - 45°) = \cos 60° \cos 45° + \sin 60° \sin 45°$$ **Substitute 60° for A and 45° for B.**

$$= \frac{1}{2}\left(\frac{\sqrt{2}}{2}\right) + \frac{\sqrt{3}}{2}\left(\frac{\sqrt{2}}{2}\right)$$ **Replace with exact values.**

$$= \frac{\sqrt{2}}{4} + \frac{\sqrt{6}}{4}$$ **Simplify.**

$$= \frac{\sqrt{2} + \sqrt{6}}{4}$$

● So cos 15° = $\frac{\sqrt{2} + \sqrt{6}}{4}$.

 Quick Check **4** Find the exact value of sin 15°. $\frac{\sqrt{6} - \sqrt{2}}{4}$

You can use the Negative Angle Identities and the Sine Angle Difference Identity to derive an identity for sin $(A + B)$.

$$\sin (A + B) = \sin (A - (-B))$$ **Rewrite as subtraction.**

$$= \sin A \cos (-B) - \cos A \sin (-B)$$ **Sine Angle Difference Identity**

$$= \sin A \cos B - \cos A (-\sin B)$$ **negative angle identities**

$$= \sin A \cos B + \cos A \sin B$$ **Simplify.**

You can similarly derive an identity for cos $(A + B)$. You can use the Tangent Identity to derive tan $(A + B)$.

Key Concepts

Properties	Angle Sum Identities
$\sin (A + B) = \sin A \cos B + \cos A \sin B$	
$\cos (A + B) = \cos A \cos B - \sin A \sin B$	
$\tan (A + B) = \frac{\tan A + \tan B}{1 - \tan A \tan B}$	

 Online active math

For: Identities Activity
Use: Interactive Textbook, 14-6

5 EXAMPLE **Using Angle Sum Identities**

Find the exact value of sin 105°.

Use the fact that 105° = 60° + 45°.

$$\sin (A + B) = \sin A \cos B + \cos A \sin B$$ **Sine Angle Sum Identity**

$$\sin (60° + 45°) = \sin 60° \cos 45° + \cos 60° \sin 45°$$ **Substitute 60° for A and 45° for B.**

$$= \frac{\sqrt{3}}{2}\left(\frac{\sqrt{2}}{2}\right) + \frac{1}{2}\left(\frac{\sqrt{2}}{2}\right)$$ **Replace with exact values.**

$$= \frac{\sqrt{6}}{4} + \frac{\sqrt{2}}{4}$$ **Simplify.**

$$= \frac{\sqrt{6} + \sqrt{2}}{4}$$

● So, sin 105° = $\frac{\sqrt{6} + \sqrt{2}}{4}$.

 Quick Check **5** Find the exact value of tan 105°. $-2 - \sqrt{3}$

Lesson 14-6 Angle Identities   **817**

Additional Examples

4 Find the exact value of cos 165°. $-\frac{\sqrt{2} + \sqrt{6}}{4}$

5 Find the exact value of sin 195°. $\frac{\sqrt{2} - \sqrt{6}}{4}$

Resources
• Daily Notetaking Guide 14-6   **L3**

Closure

Ask students to state the negative angle identities in words. Then ask them to summarize the cofunction identities in words. Finally, ask them to state the identity for cos $(A - B)$ in words. The sine of the opposite of θ is equal to the opposite of the sine of θ, the cosine of the opposite of θ is equal to the cosine of θ, and the tangent of the opposite of θ is equal to the opposite of the tangent of θ; A trigonometric function of an angle measure that is in radians is equal to the cofunction of π over 2 minus the angle measure; The cosine of the difference of two angle measures is the product of their cosines plus the product of their sines.

Assignment Guide

❶ A B 1-16, 50, 52

❷ A B 17-49, 51
C Challenge   53-57

Test Prep   58-64
Mixed Review   65-78

Homework Quick Check
To check students' understanding of key skills and concepts, go over Exercises 12, 18, 38, 43, 48, 51, 52.

Error Prevention!

Exercise 15 Students sometimes think that the cofunction for the cosecant function is the sine function. They are confusing cofunctions with reciprocal functions. Point out that all they need to do is drop the letters "co-" from cosecant to see that the cofunction for the cosecant function is the secant function.

818

EXERCISES

For more exercises, see *Extra Skill and Word Problem Practice*.

Practice and Problem Solving

A Practice by Example

GO for Help

Example 1
(page 815)

Verify each identity. 1–6. See back of book.

1. $\csc\left(\theta - \frac{\pi}{2}\right) = -\sec\theta$ **2.** $\sec\left(\theta - \frac{\pi}{2}\right) = \csc\theta$

3. $\cot\left(\frac{\pi}{2} - \theta\right) = \tan\theta$ **4.** $\csc\left(\frac{\pi}{2} - \theta\right) = \sec\theta$

5. $\tan\left(\theta - \frac{\pi}{2}\right) = -\cot\theta$ **6.** $\sec\left(\frac{\pi}{2} - \theta\right) = \csc\theta$

Example 2
(page 815)

Solve each trigonometric equation for $0 \le \theta < 2\pi$.

7. $\cos\left(\frac{\pi}{2} - \theta\right) = \csc\theta$ $\frac{\pi}{2}, \frac{3\pi}{2}$ **8.** $\sin\left(\frac{\pi}{2} - \theta\right) = -\cos(-\theta)$ $\frac{\pi}{2}, \frac{3\pi}{2}$

9. $\frac{\pi}{4}, \frac{3\pi}{4}, \frac{5\pi}{4}, \frac{7\pi}{4}$

9. $\tan\left(\frac{\pi}{2} - \theta\right) + \tan(-\theta) = 0$ **10.** $\sin^2\theta + \cos^2\theta = \sin\theta$ $\frac{\pi}{2}$

11. $\tan^2\theta - \sec^2\theta = \cos(-\theta)$ π **12.** $2\sin\left(\frac{\pi}{2} - \theta\right) = \sin(-\theta)$
                                                                 2.034, 5.176

13. $\tan\left(\frac{\pi}{2} - \theta\right) = \cos(-\theta)$ $\frac{\pi}{2}, \frac{3\pi}{2}$ **14.** $1 + \cot^2\theta = \csc\theta$ $\frac{\pi}{2}$

Example 3
(page 815)

Use the definitions of the trigonometric ratios for a right triangle to derive each cofunction identity.

15. a cofunction identity for $\csc(90° - A)$ **sec A**

16. a cofunction identity for $\cot(90° - A)$ **tan A**

Examples 4 and 5
(page 817)

Mental Math Find the value of each trigonometric expression.

17. $\cos 50° \cos 40° - \sin 50° \sin 40°$ **0**

18. $\sin 80° \cos 35° - \cos 80° \sin 35°$ $\frac{\sqrt{2}}{2}$

19. $\sin 100° \cos 170° + \cos 100° \sin 170°$ **−1**

20. $\cos 183° \cos 93° + \sin 183° \sin 93°$ **0**

Find each exact value. Use a sum or difference identity. 21–31. See margin.

21. $\cos 105°$ **22.** $\tan 105°$ **23.** $\tan 15°$ **24.** $\sin 75°$

25. $\cos 75°$ **26.** $\tan 75°$ **27.** $\cos 135°$ **28.** $\tan 135°$

29. $\sin(-15°)$ **30.** $\cos(-15°)$ **31.** $\tan(-15°)$ **32.** $\sin 225°$ $-\frac{\sqrt{2}}{2}$

33. $\cos 240°$ $-\frac{1}{2}$ **34.** $\sin 390°$ $\frac{1}{2}$ **35.** $\cos(-300°)$ $\frac{1}{2}$ **36.** $\tan 390°$ $\frac{\sqrt{3}}{3}$

B Apply Your Skills

Verify each identity. 37–43. See back of book.

37. $\sin(A - B) = \sin A \cos B - \cos A \sin B$

38. $\tan(A - B) = \frac{\tan A - \tan B}{1 + \tan A \tan B}$

39. $\cos(A + B) = \cos A \cos B - \sin A \sin B$

40. $\tan(A + B) = \frac{\tan A + \tan B}{1 - \tan A \tan B}$

41. $\sin\left(x + \frac{\pi}{3}\right) + \sin\left(x - \frac{\pi}{3}\right) = \sin x$

42. $\sin\left(\frac{3\pi}{2} - x\right) = -\cos x$

GO Online

Homework Video Tutor
Visit: PHSchool.com
Web Code: age-1406

43. Reasoning Show that the equation $\sin(A + B) = \sin A + \sin B$ is *not* an identity by finding a counterexample, values for A and B for which the equation is false.

21. $\frac{\sqrt{2} - \sqrt{6}}{4}$

22. $-\sqrt{3} - 2$

23. $2 - \sqrt{3}$

24. $\frac{\sqrt{2} + \sqrt{6}}{4}$

25. $\frac{\sqrt{6} - \sqrt{2}}{4}$

26. $2 + \sqrt{3}$

27. $-\frac{\sqrt{2}}{2}$

28. -1

29. $\frac{\sqrt{2} - \sqrt{6}}{4}$

30. $\frac{\sqrt{6} + \sqrt{2}}{4}$

31. $-2 + \sqrt{3}$

44. $\sin 3\theta$
45. $\sin 5\theta$
46. $\cos 7\theta$
47. $\cos 5\theta$

Rewrite each expression as a trigonometric function of a single angle measure.

44. $\sin 2\theta \cos \theta + \cos 2\theta \sin \theta$

45. $\sin 3\theta \cos 2\theta + \cos 3\theta \sin 2\theta$

46. $\cos 3\theta \cos 4\theta - \sin 3\theta \sin 4\theta$

47. $\cos 2\theta \cos 3\theta - \sin 2\theta \sin 3\theta$

48. $\dfrac{\tan 5\theta + \tan 6\theta}{1 - \tan 5\theta \tan 6\theta}$ $\tan 11\theta$

49. $\dfrac{\tan 3\theta - \tan \theta}{1 + \tan 3\theta \tan \theta}$ $\tan 2\theta$

50. **a.** Graph $y = \sin 2x$ and $y = 2 \sin x$ on the same axes.
   b. Does $\sin 2x = 2 \sin x$ for all values of x? Is $\sin 2x = 2 \sin x$ an identity? Explain. **a–d. See margin.**
   c. Does $\sin 2x = 2 \sin x$ for any values of x? If so, what are they?
   d. Open-Ended Find an equation of the form $a \sin b = c \sin d$ whose solutions are $2\pi n$.

51. **Gears** The diagram at the right shows a gear **GPS** whose radius is 10 cm. Point A represents a $60°$ counterclockwise rotation of point $P(10, 0)$. Point B represents a θ-degree rotation of point A. The coordinates of B are $(10 \cos (\theta + 60°), 10 \sin (\theta + 60°))$. Write these coordinates in terms of $\cos \theta$ and $\sin \theta$.
   See margin.

52. **a. Critical Thinking** A function is even if $f(-x) = f(x)$. A function is odd if $f(-x) = -f(x)$. Which trigonometric functions are even? Which are odd? **a–b. See margin.**
   b. Writing Are all functions either even or odd? Explain your answer. Give a counterexample if possible.

Challenge

Use the sum and difference formulas to verify each identity. **53–56. See back of book.**

53. $\cos (\pi - \theta) = -\cos \theta$

54. $\sin (\pi - \theta) = \sin \theta$

55. $\sin (\pi + \theta) = -\sin \theta$

56. $\cos (\pi + \theta) = -\cos \theta$

57. **Reasoning** For any parallelogram, prove that the sum of the squares of the lengths of the diagonals equals twice the sum of the squares of the lengths of two adjacent sides. **See back of book.**

Test Prep

Multiple Choice

58. Which expressions are equivalent? **D**
   I. $\cos \theta$ II. $\cos (-\theta)$ III. $\dfrac{\sin (-\theta)}{\tan (-\theta)}$
   A. I and II only   **B.** II and III only   **C.** I and III only   **D.** I, II, and III

59. Which expressions are equivalent? **J**
   I. $-\tan \left(\dfrac{\pi}{2} - \theta\right)$ II. $\tan \left(\theta - \dfrac{\pi}{2}\right)$ III. $\tan \left(-\left(\dfrac{\pi}{2} - \theta\right)\right)$
   F. I and II only   **G.** II and III only   **H.** I and III only   **J.** I, II, and III

60. Which expression is equal to $\cos 50°$? **D**
   A. $\sin 20° \cos 30° + \cos 20° \sin 30°$ **B.** $\sin 20° \cos 30° - \cos 20° \sin 30°$
   C. $\cos 20° \cos 30° + \sin 20° \sin 30°$ **D.** $\cos 20° \cos 30° - \sin 20° \sin 30°$

61. Which expression is NOT equivalent to $\cos \theta$? **G**
   F. $-\sin (\theta - 90°)$ **G.** $-\cos (-\theta)$ **H.** $\sin (\theta + 90°)$ **J.** $-\cos (\theta + 180°)$

50a.

b. No; it is not an identity since it only corresponds for a few specific x-values.

c. yes; $0 + 2\pi n$, $\pi + 2\pi n$, or $\theta + \pi n$

d. Answers may vary. Sample: $\sin x = 2 \sin (0.5x)$

51. $(5 \cos \theta - 5\sqrt{3} \sin \theta, 5 \sin \theta + 5\sqrt{3} \cos \theta)$

PowerPoint
Lesson Quiz

1. Show that $\sin \left(\dfrac{\pi}{2} - \theta\right) - \cos \theta = 0$.
   $\sin \left(\dfrac{\pi}{2} - \theta\right) = \cos \theta$, so
   $\sin \left(\dfrac{\pi}{2} - \theta\right) - \cos \theta$
   $= \cos \theta - \cos \theta = 0$

2. Solve the equation $\sec \theta - \tan \theta = 0$ for $0 \le \theta < 2\pi$. **no solution**

3. Find the value of $\cos 85° \cos 55° + \sin 85° \sin 55°$. $\dfrac{\sqrt{3}}{2}$

4. Write an expression for $\sin 17°$ in terms of sines or cosines of $50°$ and $33°$.
   $\sin 50° \cos 33° - \cos 50° \sin 33°$

Alternative Assessment

Have students work in pairs. Each student should create two trigonometric identities that can be verified by using identities that were developed in this lesson. Each student should verify the identities that the other student wrote. Have students check each other's work.

Test Prep

Resources
For additional practice with a variety of test item formats:
• Standardized Test Prep, p. 831
• Test-Taking Strategies, p. 826
• Test-Taking Strategies with Transparencies

52a. cosine, secant; sine, cosecant, tangent, and cotangent

b. No; answers may vary. Sample: $y = \sin (x + 0.5)$ is not odd because $y = \sin (-x + 0.5) = \sin (-(x - 0.5)) = -\sin (x - 0.5) \ne -\sin (x + 0.5)$.

819

62. Which expression is an exact value for sin 15° ? **B**

A. $\frac{\sqrt{2}}{2} \cdot \frac{\sqrt{3}}{2} + \frac{\sqrt{2}}{2} \cdot \frac{1}{2}$

B. $\frac{\sqrt{2}}{2} \cdot \frac{\sqrt{3}}{2} - \frac{\sqrt{2}}{2} \cdot \frac{1}{2}$

C. $\frac{\sqrt{2}}{2} \cdot \frac{1}{2} + \frac{\sqrt{2}}{2} \cdot \frac{\sqrt{3}}{2}$

D. $\frac{\sqrt{2}}{2} \cdot \frac{1}{2} - \frac{\sqrt{2}}{2} \cdot \frac{\sqrt{3}}{2}$

Short Response **63.** Find an exact value for sin 165°. Show your work. **See back of book.**

64. Use the fact that $\frac{\pi}{6} = \frac{\pi}{2} - \frac{\pi}{3}$ to find an exact value for cos $\frac{\pi}{6}$. Show your work. **See back of book.**

Mixed Review

for Help

Lesson 14-5

65. In $\triangle RST$, $m\angle S = 24°$, $r = 10$ ft, and $t = 18$ ft. Find s. **9.8 ft**

66. In $\triangle XYZ$, $m\angle Z = 51°$, $x = 13$ cm, and $y = 17$ cm. Find z. **13.4 cm**

67. In $\triangle DEF$, $m\angle F = 68°$, $d = 16$ mm, and $e = 21$ mm. Find f. **21.1 mm**

68. In $\triangle ABC$, $m\angle A = 87°$, $b = 22$ m, and $c = 19$ m. Find a. **28.3 m**

Lesson 13-3

Write each measure in radians. Express the answer in terms of π and as a decimal rounded to the nearest hundredth.

69. 80° $\frac{4\pi}{9}$ and 1.40   **70.** $-50°$ $-\frac{5\pi}{18}$ and -0.87 **71.** $-15°$ $-\frac{\pi}{12}$ and -0.26

72. 70° $\frac{7\pi}{18}$ and 1.22   **73.** 190° $\frac{19\pi}{18}$ and 3.32   **74.** 200° $\frac{10\pi}{9}$ and 3.49

Lesson 12-7

A set of data with a mean of 39 and a standard deviation of 6.2 is normally distributed. Find each value, given its distance from the mean.

75. +1 standard deviation **45.2**   **76.** −2 standard deviations **26.6**

77. +3 standard deviations **57.6**   **78.** −1 standard deviation **32.8**

Checkpoint Quiz 2   Lessons 14-4 through 14-6

Find the area of $\triangle ABC$.

1. $m\angle A = 37°$, $b = 10$ cm, and $c = 12$ cm. **36.1 cm²**

2. $m\angle B = 18°$, $a = 20$ ft, and $c = 25$ ft. **77.3 ft²**

3. $m\angle B = 104°$, $a = 8$ m, and $c = 9$ m. **34.9 m²**

4. $m\angle C = 96°$, $a = 26$ in., and $b = 31$ in. **400.8 in.²**

Find the remaining sides and angles in each triangle. Round your answers to the nearest tenth.

$a = 8.2$ ft, $m\angle B = 69.7°$, $m\angle C = 83.3°$
5. In $\triangle ABC$, $m\angle A = 27°$, $b = 17$ ft, and $c = 18$ ft.

6. In $\triangle DEF$, $d = 32$ mm, $e = 30$ mm, and $f = 35$ mm.
$m\angle D = 58.4°$, $m\angle E = 53.0°$, $m\angle F = 68.7°$

Simplify each trigonometric expression.

7. cos 80°

8. sin 63°

7. $\cos 60° \cos 20° - \sin 60° \sin 20°$

8. $\sin 90° \cos 27° - \cos 90° \sin 27°$

9. $\sin 150° \cos 290° + \cos 150° \sin 290°$
sin 80°

10. $\cos 233° \cos 154° + \sin 233° \sin 154°$
cos 79°

Double-Angle and Half-Angle Identities

What You'll Learn

- To verify and use double-angle identities
- To verify and use half-angle identities

... And Why

To find exact values of trigonometric functions

 Check Skills You'll Need

GO for Help Lesson 14-6

Complete the following angle identities. 1–4. See margin p. 822.

1. $\cos (A - B) = \blacksquare$

2. $\cos (A + B) = \blacksquare$

3. $\tan (A - B) = \blacksquare$

4. $\sin (A - B) = \blacksquare$

5. $\sin (A + B) = \blacksquare$
  $\sin A \cos B + \cos A \sin B$

6. $\tan (A + B) = \blacksquare$
  $\dfrac{\tan A + \tan B}{1 - \tan A \tan B}$

---

1. Plan

Objectives

1 To verify and use double-angle identities

2 To verify and use half-angle identities

Examples

1 Using a Double-Angle Identity

2 Verifying an Identity

3 Using Half-Angle Identities

4 Using Half-Angle Identities

Math Background

With the double and half-angle identities, students now have the ability to connect the most common trigonometric identities.

More Math Background: p. 776D

Lesson Planning and Resources

See p. 776E for a list of the resources that support this lesson.

 Bell Ringer Practice

☑ **Check Skills You'll Need**

For intervention, direct students to:

Angle Identities

Lessons 14-6: Examples 4 and 5

Extra Skills and Word
  Problems Practice, Ch. 14

---

1 Double-Angle Identities

You can use the angle sum identities to derive the double-angle identities.

Let $\theta = A = B$.

$\cos (A + B) = \cos A \cos B - \sin A \sin B$ **Cosine Angle Sum Identity**

$\cos (\theta + \theta) = \cos \theta \cos \theta - \sin \theta \sin \theta$ **Substitute θ for A and B.**

$\cos 2\theta = \cos^2 \theta - \sin^2 \theta$ **Simplify.**

You can use the Pythagorean identity $\sin^2 \theta + \cos^2 \theta = 1$ in the form $\sin^2 \theta = 1 - \cos^2 \theta$ to derive another identity for $\cos 2\theta$.

$\cos 2\theta = \cos^2 \theta - \sin^2 \theta$

$\quad\quad = \cos^2 \theta - (1 - \cos^2 \theta)$ **Substitute $1 - \cos^2 \theta$ for $\sin^2 \theta$.**

$\quad\quad = \cos^2 \theta - 1 + \cos^2 \theta$ **Remove parentheses.**

$\quad\quad = 2 \cos^2 \theta - 1$ **Simplify.**

You can use the Pythagorean theorem in the form $\cos^2 \theta = 1 - \sin^2 \theta$ to derive a third identity for $\cos 2\theta$.

$\cos 2\theta = \cos^2 \theta - \sin^2 \theta$

$\quad\quad = (1 - \sin^2 \theta) - \sin^2 \theta$ **Substitute $1 - \sin^2 \theta$ for $\cos^2 \theta$.**

$\quad\quad = 1 - 2 \sin^2 \theta$ **Simplify.**

You can use the other angle sum identities to derive double-angle identities for the sine and tangent.

 Key Concepts

Properties	Double-Angle Identities
$\cos 2\theta = \cos^2 \theta - \sin^2 \theta$	$\sin 2\theta = 2 \sin \theta \cos \theta$
$\cos 2\theta = 2 \cos^2 \theta - 1$	$\tan 2\theta = \dfrac{2 \tan \theta}{1 - \tan^2 \theta}$
$\cos 2\theta = 1 - 2 \sin^2 \theta$	

Differentiated Instruction Solutions for All Learners

Special Needs L1
Have students apply the sine double- and half-angle identities to show that $\sin \left(\frac{180°}{2}\right) = \sin 2(45°)$.

Below Level L2
Show students how the double angle identities are derived from the sum identities by adding an angle to itself.

learning style: verbal

learning style: visual

2. Teach

Guided Instruction

2 EXAMPLE Math Tip

Point out to students the difficulty of verifying the identity by transforming the left-hand side of the identity to obtain the right-hand side.

PowerPoint

Additional Examples

1 Use a double-angle identity to find the exact value of sin 600°.
$-\frac{\sqrt{3}}{2}$

2 Verify the identity
$\frac{\sin 2\theta}{1 - \sin^2 \theta} = 2 \tan \theta$. Transform the left side to obtain the right side.

$$\frac{\sin 2\theta}{1 - \sin^2 \theta} = \frac{2 \sin \theta \cos \theta}{\cos^2 \theta}$$
$$= \frac{2 \sin \theta}{\cos \theta}$$
$$= 2 \left(\frac{\sin \theta}{\cos \theta}\right)$$
$$= 2 \tan \theta$$

page 821 Check Skills You'll Need

1. $\cos A \cos B + \sin A \sin B$

2. $\cos A \cos B - \sin A \sin B$

3. $\frac{\tan A - \tan B}{1 + \tan A \tan B}$

4. $\sin A \cos B - \cos A \sin B$

---

1 EXAMPLE Using a Double-Angle Identity

Use a double-angle identity to find the exact value of cos 120°.

$\cos 120°$	$= \cos (2 \cdot 60°)$	**Rewrite 120 as (2 · 60).**
	$= \cos^2 60° - \sin^2 60°$	**Use a cosine double-angle identity.**
	$= \left(\frac{1}{2}\right)^2 - \left(\frac{\sqrt{3}}{2}\right)^2$	**Replace with exact values.**
	$= -\frac{1}{2}$	**Simplify.**

✓ **Quick Check** ❶ Use a double-angle identity to find the exact value of sin 120°. $\frac{\sqrt{3}}{2}$

You can use the double-angle identities to verify other identities.

2 EXAMPLE Verifying an Identity

Verify the identity $\cos 2\theta = \frac{1 - \tan^2 \theta}{1 + \tan^2 \theta}$.

$\frac{1 - \tan^2 \theta}{1 + \tan^2 \theta}$	$= \frac{1 - \tan^2 \theta}{\sec^2 \theta}$	**Pythagorean identity**
	$= \frac{1}{\sec^2\theta} - \frac{\tan^2\theta}{\sec^2\theta}$	**Write as two fractions.**
	$= \frac{1}{\frac{1}{\cos^2\theta}} - \frac{\frac{\sin^2\theta}{\cos^2\theta}}{\frac{1}{\cos^2\theta}}$	**Express in terms of sin θ and cos θ.**
	$= \cos^2 \theta - \sin^2 \theta$	**Simplify.**
	$= \cos 2\theta$	**double-angle identity**

✓ **Quick Check** ❷ Verify the identity $2 \cos 2\theta = 4 \cos^2 \theta - 2$.
$2 \cos 2\theta = 2(2 \cos^2 \theta - 1) = 4 \cos^2 \theta - 2$

2 Half-Angle Identities

You can use double-angle identities to derive half-angle identities.
Let $\theta = \frac{A}{2}$.

$\cos 2\theta = 2 \cos^2 \theta - 1$		**cosine double-angle identity**
$\cos 2\left(\frac{A}{2}\right) = 2 \cos^2 \frac{A}{2} - 1$		**Substitute $\frac{A}{2}$ for θ.**
$\frac{\cos A + 1}{2} = \cos^2 \frac{A}{2}$		**Solve for $\cos^2 \frac{A}{2}$.**
$\pm\sqrt{\frac{\cos A + 1}{2}} = \cos \frac{A}{2}$		**Take the square root of each side.**

Similarly, $\sin \frac{A}{2} = \pm\sqrt{\frac{1 - \cos A}{2}}$ and $\tan \frac{A}{2} = \pm\sqrt{\frac{1 - \cos A}{1 + \cos A}}$.

🔑 **Key Concepts**

Properties	**Half-Angle Identities**

$$\sin \frac{A}{2} = \pm\sqrt{\frac{1 - \cos A}{2}} \qquad \cos \frac{A}{2} = \pm\sqrt{\frac{1 + \cos A}{2}} \qquad \tan \frac{A}{2} = \pm\sqrt{\frac{1 - \cos A}{1 + \cos A}}$$

Choose the positive or negative sign for each function depending on the quadrant in which $\frac{A}{2}$ lies.

---

822 Chapter 14 Trigonometric Identities and Equations

Differentiated Instruction Solutions for All Learners

Advanced Learners L4
Have students derive double angle and half angle identities for cosecant, secant, and cotangent functions.

learning style: verbal

English Language Learners ELL
Have students practice reading each of the double- and half-angle identities aloud. Students should use the word *quantity* when referring to a numerator or denominator with more than one term.

learning style: visual

3 EXAMPLE Using Half-Angle Identities

Use the half-angle identities to find each exact value.

a. sin 15°

$$\sin 15° = \sin \left(\frac{30}{2}\right)°$$ Rewrite 15° as $\frac{30°}{2}$.

$$= \sqrt{\frac{1 - \cos 30°}{2}}$$ Use the principal square root, since sin 15° is positive.

$$= \sqrt{\frac{1 - \frac{\sqrt{3}}{2}}{2}}$$ Substitute the exact value for cos 30°.

$$= \sqrt{\frac{2 - \sqrt{3}}{4}}$$ Simplify.

$$= \frac{\sqrt{2 - \sqrt{3}}}{2}$$ Simplify.

b. cos 150°

$$\cos 150° = \cos \left(\frac{300}{2}\right)°$$ Rewrite 150 as $\frac{300}{2}$.

$$= -\sqrt{\frac{1 + \cos 300°}{2}}$$ Use the negative square root, since cos 150° is negative.

$$= -\sqrt{\frac{1 + \left(\frac{1}{2}\right)}{2}}$$ Replace with an exact value.

$$= -\sqrt{\frac{3}{4}}$$ Simplify.

$$= -\frac{\sqrt{3}}{2}$$ Simplify.

✓ **Quick Check** ❸ Use the half-angle identities to find the exact value of each expression.
  a. sin 150° $\frac{1}{2}$
  b. tan 150° $-\frac{\sqrt{3}}{3}$

---

4 EXAMPLE Using Half-Angle Identities

Given $\sin \theta = -\frac{24}{25}$ and $180° < \theta < 270°$, find $\sin \frac{\theta}{2}$.

First find cos θ.

$$\cos^2 \theta + \sin^2 \theta = 1$$ Pythagorean identity

$$\cos^2 \theta + \left(-\frac{24}{25}\right)^2 = 1$$ Substitute.

$$\cos^2 \theta = \frac{49}{25^2}$$ Solve for $\cos^2 \theta$.

$$\cos \theta = -\frac{7}{25}$$ Choose the negative square root since θ is in Quadrant III.

Now find $\sin \frac{\theta}{2}$.

Since $180° < \theta < 270°$, $90° < \frac{\theta}{2} < 135°$ and $\frac{\theta}{2}$ is in Quadrant II.

$$\sin \frac{\theta}{2} = \pm \sqrt{\frac{1 - \cos \theta}{2}}$$ half-angle identity

$$= \sqrt{\frac{1 - \left(-\frac{7}{25}\right)}{2}}$$ Substitute. Choose the positive square root since $\frac{\theta}{2}$ is in Quadrant II.

$$= \frac{4}{5}$$ Simplify.

✓ **Quick Check** ❹ Use the information in Example 4 to find the exact values of $\cos \frac{\theta}{2}$ and $\tan \frac{\theta}{2}$.

4. $-\frac{3}{5}, -\frac{4}{3}$

Problem Solving Hint
The quadrant of the terminal side of an angle determines the sign of the function.

Function	Positive in Quadrants
sin	I, II
cos	I, IV
tan	I, III

Guided Instruction

3 EXAMPLE Teaching Tip

You may want to challenge students to show that sin 15° can also be expressed as $\frac{\sqrt{6} - \sqrt{2}}{4}$.

PowerPoint
Additional Examples

❸ Use the half-angle identities to find each exact value.
  a. sin 75° $\frac{\sqrt{2 + \sqrt{3}}}{2}$
  b. cos 67.5° $\frac{\sqrt{2 - \sqrt{2}}}{2}$

❹ Given $\cos \theta = -\frac{12}{13}$ and $90° < \theta < 180°$, find $\sin \frac{\theta}{2}$. $\frac{5\sqrt{26}}{26}$

Resources
• Daily Notetaking Guide 14-7 **L3**

Closure

Ask students to suppose that they are given the values of sin θ, cos θ, and tan θ for a certain angle θ. Ask them whether it is easier to apply the double-angle formulas or half-angle formulas if they want to find a trigonometric function's value for 2θ and $\frac{\theta}{2}$. Answers may vary. Sample: Using the half-angle formulas is more difficult, because you must determine in which quadrant $\frac{\theta}{2}$ will be before you can decide whether to use a positive square root or a negative square root.

Assignment Guide

▼**1** A B 1-10, 27-29, 33-37,
42-46, 48

▼**2** A B 11-26, 30-32, 38-41,
47, 49, 50

C Challenge   51-57

Test Prep   58-61
Mixed Review   62-66

Homework Quick Check
To check students' understanding
of key skills and concepts, go over
Exercises 10, 16, 32, 38, 40, 42, 50.

Error Prevention!

Exercises 23–26 Students may
have errors if they do not carefully
consider the quadrant in which $\frac{\theta}{2}$
will lie.

| Differentiated | Instruction | Resources |

GPS Guided Problem Solving	L3
Enrichment	L4
Reteaching	L2
Practice	L3

---

9. $\sin 2\theta = \sin(\theta + \theta) =$
$\sin\theta\cos\theta + \cos\theta \cdot \sin\theta$
$= 2\sin\theta\cos\theta$

10. $\tan 2\theta = \tan(\theta + \theta) =$
$\frac{\tan\theta + \tan\theta}{1 - \tan\theta\tan\theta} = \frac{2\tan\theta}{1 - \tan^2\theta}$

11. $\frac{\sqrt{2 + \sqrt3}}{2}$

12. $\sqrt{7 - 4\sqrt3}$

EXERCISES
For more exercises, see Extra Skill and Word Problem Practice.

Practice and Problem Solving

(A) **Practice by Example**

GO for Help

Example 1
(page 822)

Use a double-angle identity to find the exact value of each expression.

1. $\sin 240°$ $-\frac{\sqrt3}{2}$ **2.** $\cos 120°$ $-\frac{1}{2}$ **3.** $\tan 120°$ $-\sqrt3$ **4.** $\sin 90°$ 1

5. $\cos 240°$ $-\frac{1}{2}$ **6.** $\tan 240°$ $\sqrt3$ **7.** $\cos 600°$ $-\frac{1}{2}$ **8.** $\sin 600°$ $-\frac{\sqrt3}{2}$

Example 2
(page 822)

Use an angle sum identity to verify each identity.

9. $\sin 2\theta = 2\sin\theta\cos\theta$ **10.** $\tan 2\theta = \frac{2\tan\theta}{1 - \tan^2\theta}$
9–18. See margin.

Example 3
(page 823)

Use a half-angle identity to find the exact value of each expression.

11. $\cos 15°$ **12.** $\tan 15°$ **13.** $\sin 15°$ **14.** $\sin 22.5°$

15. $\cos 22.5°$ **16.** $\tan 22.5°$ **17.** $\cos 90°$ **18.** $\sin 7.5°$

Example 4
(page 823)

Given $\cos\theta = -\frac{4}{5}$ and $90° < \theta < 180°$, find the exact value of each expression.

19. $\sin\frac{\theta}{2}$ $\frac{3\sqrt{10}}{10}$ **20.** $\cos\frac{\theta}{2}$ $\frac{\sqrt{10}}{10}$ **21.** $\tan\frac{\theta}{2}$ 3   **22.** $\cot\frac{\theta}{2}$ $\frac{1}{3}$

Given $\cos\theta = -\frac{15}{17}$ and $180° < \theta < 270°$, find the exact value of each expression.

23. $\sin\frac{\theta}{2}$ $\frac{4\sqrt{17}}{17}$ **24.** $\cos\frac{\theta}{2}$ $-\frac{\sqrt{17}}{17}$ **25.** $\tan\frac{\theta}{2}$ -4 **26.** $\sec\frac{\theta}{2}$ $-\sqrt{17}$

(B) **Apply Your Skills**

**27–30. See margin
pp. 824–825.**

$\triangle RST$ **has a right angle at $\angle T$. Use identities to show that each equation is true.**

27. $\sin 2R = \frac{2rs}{t^2}$ **28.** $\cos 2R = \frac{s^2 - r^2}{t^2}$

29. $\sin 2S = \sin 2R$ **30.** $\sin^2\frac{S}{2} = \frac{t - r}{2t}$

31. $\tan\frac{R}{2} = \frac{r}{t + s}$ **32.** $\tan^2\frac{S}{2} = \frac{t - r}{t + r}$

33. Critical Thinking If $\sin 2A = \sin 2B$, must $A = B$? Explain.
31–33. See back of book.

Given $\cos\theta = \frac{3}{5}$ and $270° < \theta < 360°$, find the exact value of each expression.

34. $\sin 2\theta$ $-\frac{24}{25}$ **35.** $\cos 2\theta$ $-\frac{7}{25}$ **36.** $\tan 2\theta$ $\frac{24}{7}$ **37.** $\csc 2\theta$ $-\frac{25}{24}$

38. $\sin\frac{\theta}{2}$ $\frac{\sqrt5}{5}$ **39.** $\cos\frac{\theta}{2}$ $-\frac{2\sqrt5}{5}$ **40.** $\tan\frac{\theta}{2}$ $-\frac{1}{2}$ **41.** $\cot\frac{\theta}{2}$ -2

Use identities to write each equation in terms of the single angle θ. Then solve the equation for $0 \le \theta < 2\pi$. **42–45. See margin p. 825.**

GPS **42.** $4\sin 2\theta - 3\cos\theta = 0$ **43.** $2\sin 2\theta - 3\sin\theta = 0$

44. $\sin 2\theta \sin\theta = \cos\theta$ **45.** $\cos 2\theta = -2\cos^2\theta$

Simplify each expression.

46. $2\cos^2\theta - \cos 2\theta$ 1   **47.** $\sin^2\frac{\theta}{2} - \cos^2\frac{\theta}{2}$ $-\cos\theta$ **48.** $\frac{\cos 2\theta}{\sin\theta + \cos\theta}$
                                                $\cos\theta - \sin\theta$

49. Open-Ended Choose an angle measure A.
    a. Find $\sin A$ and $\cos A$. **a–c. See margin p. 825.**
    b. Use an identity to find $\sin 2A$.
    c. Use an identity to find $\cos\frac{A}{2}$.

GO Online
Homework Video Tutor
Visit: PHSchool.com
Web Code: age-1407

50. Writing Is $\frac{\tan\theta}{4} = \tan\frac{\theta}{4}$ an identity? Explain. **See back of book.**

---

13. $\frac{\sqrt{2 - \sqrt3}}{2}$

14. $\frac{\sqrt{2 - \sqrt2}}{2}$

15. $\frac{\sqrt{2 + \sqrt2}}{2}$

16. $\sqrt{3 - 2\sqrt2}$

17. 0

18. $\frac{\sqrt{2 - \sqrt{2 + \sqrt3}}}{2}$

27. $\sin 2R$
$= 2\sin R\cos R$
$= 2\frac{r}{t}\cdot\frac{s}{t}$
$= \frac{2rs}{t^2}$

28. $\cos 2R$
$= \cos^2 R - \sin^2 R$
$= \left(\frac{s}{t}\right)^2 - \left(\frac{r}{t}\right)^2$
$= \frac{s^2}{t^2} - \frac{r^2}{t^2}$
$= \frac{s^2 - r^2}{t^2}$

C Challenge

Use double-angle identities to write each expression, using trigonometric functions of θ instead of 4θ. 51–56. See back of book.

51. $\sin 4\theta$ **52.** $\cos 4\theta$ **53.** $\tan 4\theta$

Use half-angle identities to write each expression, using trigonometric functions of θ instead of $\frac{\theta}{4}$.

54. $\sin \frac{\theta}{4}$ **55.** $\cos \frac{\theta}{4}$ **56.** $\tan \frac{\theta}{4}$

57. Use the Tangent Half-Angle Identity and a Pythagorean identity to prove each identity. a–b. See back of book.

a. $\tan \frac{A}{2} = \frac{\sin A}{1 + \cos A}$ **b.** $\tan \frac{A}{2} = \frac{1 - \cos A}{\sin A}$

Test Prep

Multiple Choice

58. If θ is in Quadrant I and $\tan \theta = \frac{5}{12}$, what is the value of $\frac{\tan 4\theta}{5}$ to the nearest hundredth? **D**

  A. 18.10 **B.** 0.33 **C.** 0.32 **D.** −23.90

59. If θ is in Quadrant I and $\sin \theta = \frac{3}{5}$, what is an exact value of $\sin 2\theta$? **G**

  F. $\frac{9}{25}$ **G.** $\frac{24}{25}$ **H.** $\frac{6}{5}$ **J.** 73.7

Short Response

60. Use a half-angle identity to find an exact value of sin 67.5°. See back of book.

Extended Response

61. In the diagram at the right, line ℓ_1 forms an angle of θ with the positive x-axis and crosses the line x = 1 at (1, 0.5). Line ℓ_2 forms an angle of 2θ with the positive x-axis. Find the coordinates of the point where ℓ_2 intersects x = 1. Show your work.
See back of book.

Mixed Review

Lesson 14-6

Find each exact value. Use a sum or difference identity.

62. $\cos 405°$ $\frac{\sqrt{2}}{2}$ **63.** $\sin (-300°)$ $\frac{\sqrt{3}}{2}$ **64.** $\tan (-300°)$ $\sqrt{3}$

Lesson 13-1

Find the period and amplitude of each periodic function.

65. 12, about 4.1 **66.** 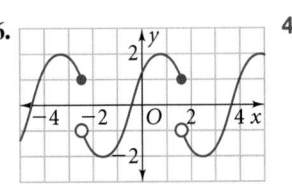 4, 2

---

29. $\sin 2S = 2 \sin S \cos S$

$= 2 \cdot \frac{s}{t} \cdot \frac{r}{t} = \frac{2sr}{t^2}$

$= 2 \sin R \cos R = \sin 2R$

30. $\sin^2 \frac{s}{2} = \left(\sin \frac{s}{2}\right)^2$

$= \left(\pm\sqrt{\frac{1 - \cos s}{2}}\right)^2$

$= \frac{1 - \cos s}{2} = \frac{1 - \frac{r}{t}}{2}$

$= \frac{1}{2} - \frac{r}{2t} = \frac{t - r}{2t}$

42. $\cos \theta (8 \sin \theta - 3) = 0$
$\frac{\pi}{2}, \frac{3\pi}{2}, 0.384, 2.757$

43. $\sin \theta (4 \cos \theta - 3) = 0$
$0, \pi, 0.723, 5.560$

44. $\cos \theta (2 \sin^2 \theta - 1) = 0$
$\frac{\pi}{2}, \frac{3\pi}{2}, \frac{\pi}{4}, \frac{3\pi}{4}, \frac{5\pi}{4}, \frac{7\pi}{4}$

45. $4 \cos^2 \theta - 1 = 0$
$\frac{\pi}{3}, \frac{2\pi}{3}, \frac{4\pi}{3}, \frac{5\pi}{3}$

---

4. Assess & Reteach

PowerPoint

Lesson Quiz

1. Use a double-angle identity to find the exact value of sin 660°. $-\frac{\sqrt{3}}{2}$

2. Use an angle sum identity and a double-angle identity to verify the identity
$\sin 3\theta = 3 \sin \theta - 4 \sin^3\theta$.
$\sin 3\theta = \sin (2\theta + \theta)$
$= \sin 2\theta \cos \theta + \cos 2\theta \sin \theta$
$= (2 \sin \theta \cos \theta)\cos \theta + (\cos^2 \theta - \sin^2 \theta)\sin \theta$
$= 3 \sin \theta \cos^2 \theta - \sin^3 \theta$
$= 3 \sin \theta (1 - \sin^2 \theta) - \sin^3 \theta$
$= 3 \sin \theta - 4 \sin^3 \theta$

3. Use a half-angle identity to find the exact value of sin 67.5°. $\frac{\sqrt{2 + \sqrt{2}}}{2}$

4. Given $\cos \theta = -\frac{20}{29}$ and 180° < θ < 270°, find the exact value of $\cos \frac{\theta}{2}$. $-\frac{3\sqrt{58}}{58}$

Alternative Assessment

Have students work individually to create a problem similar to those in Exercises 1–8 and a problem similar to those in Exercises 19–26. Ask students to solve each of the problems that they create. Suggest they check their results with a calculator.

Test Prep

Resources

For additional practice with a variety of test item formats:
• Standardized Test Prep, p. 831
• Test-Taking Strategies, p. 826
• Test-Taking Strategies with Transparencies

49. Answers may vary. Sample:
  a. $\sin 60 = \frac{\sqrt{3}}{2}$, $\cos 60 = \frac{1}{2}$
  b. $\sin 120 = \frac{\sqrt{3}}{2}$
  c. $\cos 30 = \frac{\sqrt{3}}{2}$

825

Answering Open-Ended Questions

Many assessment tests now require students to answer open-ended questions that are scored according to rubrics. This feature helps students understand the kinds of criteria used in constructing the rubrics. Understanding these criteria will help students think about how to maximize their scores on such test items.

Resources

SAT® and ACT® correlations are on page 776B.

Test-Taking Strategies with Transparencies
• Transparency 14
• Practice sheet, p. 38

Guided Instruction

Suggest students use unit circle diagrams to get a clearer understanding of the conditions for the problems posed in each exercise.

English Language Learners ELL

Explain that *rubrics* are rules that help both students and teachers classify and evaluate answers to questions.

Test-Taking Strategies with Transparencies

Test-Taking Strategy: Answering Open-Ended Questions

1. Create two different number patterns, so that the first number is the same in both patterns and the second number is the same in both patterns. Write the first 5 numbers in each pattern and describe the pattern.

Scoring Rubric

4 Meets all conditions and follows directions.
3 Meets all conditions, but does not write 5 numbers in each pattern OR does not describe patterns.
2 Meets one or two conditions, OR descriptions do not match patterns.
0 Meets no conditions, OR only one pattern is produced.

2. A clothing store discounts a shirt 30% for a sale. After the sale, a clerk was told to raise the price by 30% of its sale price. The clerk marked the original price on the shirt. Was the clerk right or wrong? Explain.

Scoring Rubric

4 Correctly expresses the current price in terms of the original price, AND concludes the clerk was wrong.
3 Argues convincingly why clerk was wrong, but makes computational errors.
2 Decides clerk was wrong, but presents weak or incomplete argument.
0 Answers inappropriately or not at all.

Transparency 14

826

Open-ended questions ask you to create an example that satisfies certain given conditions. You may need to use your example to answer follow-up questions. As with extended-response questions, you should show all your work since you can receive partial credit.

EXAMPLE

For angles A and B, $A \neq B$ and $\sin A = \sin B$.

a. Find three pairs of values for A and B.
b. Write and prove a relation for A and B.

Here is a scoring rubric for a 4-point response.

[4] **a.** three pairs that satisfy the conditions
  b. $A + B = n\pi$, where n is an odd integer, or $A - B = 2n\pi$, or any other correct relation with a specific value of n; proves the relation.

[3] **a.** three pairs that satisfy the conditions
  b. $A + B = n\pi$, where n is an odd integer, or $A - B = 2n\pi$, or any other correct relation with a specific value of n; does not prove the relation.

[2] **a.** three pairs that satisfy the conditions
  b. no answer or incorrect answer

[1] **a.** one or two pairs that satisfy the conditions
  b. no answer or incorrect answer

The following response is worth 2 points.

a. $A = 0, B = \pi$
$A = 0, B = 2\pi$
$A = \frac{\pi}{6}, B = \frac{5\pi}{6}$

b. Let $A + B = 2\pi$. Then $A = 2\pi - B$.
$\sin(2\pi - B) = \sin(2\pi)\cos(B) - \cos(2\pi)\sin(B)$
$= 0 - (-1)\sin(B)$
$= \sin(B)$

2a. $A = 0, B = \pi$
$A = \frac{\pi}{4}, B = \frac{3\pi}{4}$
$A = \frac{\pi}{6}, B = \frac{5\pi}{6}$

b. Let $A + B = \pi$.
$\sin A = \sin(\pi - B) =$
$\sin \pi \cos B - \cos \pi \cdot \sin B =$
$0 \cos B - (-1)\sin B = \sin B$

EXERCISES

1. Explain why the response above received only 2 points. Part (a) is correct but part (b) is incorrect.

2. Write a 4-point response for the Example. See above.

Find three sets of values for A and B, where $A \neq B$, that make each equation true. Write and prove a relation for A and B. 3–4. See margin.

3. $\cos A = \cos B$

4. $\tan A = \tan B$

5. Find three sets of values for A and B such that $\sin(A + B) = \sin A + \sin B$. Write and prove a relation for A and B. **5–6. See back of book.**

6. Find three pairs of values for A and B such that $\cos^2 A - \sin^2 A = \sin B$. Write and prove the relation for A and B.

---

3. $A = 0, B = 2\pi$
$A = \frac{\pi}{2}, B = \frac{3\pi}{2}$
$A = \frac{3\pi}{4}, B = \frac{5\pi}{4}$;

$A + B = 2\pi$
$\cos A = \cos(2\pi - B) =$
$\cos 2\pi \cos B +$
$\sin 2\pi \sin B =$
$(1)\cos B + (0)\sin B =$
$\cos B$

4. $A = 0, B = \pi$
$A = \frac{\pi}{4}, B = \frac{5\pi}{4}$
$A = \frac{3\pi}{4}, B = \frac{7\pi}{4}$;
$A = B + \pi$

$\tan A = \tan(B + \pi)$
$\frac{\tan B + \tan \pi}{1 - \tan B \tan \pi} =$
$\frac{\tan B + 0}{1 - \tan B \cdot 0} = \frac{\tan B}{1} =$
$\tan B$

Chapter Review

Vocabulary Review

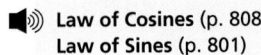

Law of Cosines (p. 808)
Law of Sines (p. 801)

trigonometric identity (p. 778)

trigonometric ratios for a right triangle (p. 792)

Choose the correct vocabulary term to complete each sentence.

1. You can find missing measures of any triangle by using the _?_ if you know the measures of two angles and a side. **Law of Sines**

2. The six ratios of the lengths of the sides of a right triangle are known as the _?_.

3. If you know the measures of two sides and the angle between them, you can use the _?_ to find missing parts of any triangle. **Law of Cosines**

4. A trigonometric equation that is true for all values except those for which the expressions on either side of the equal sign are undefined is a _?_.

5. The _?_ can be used to find missing measures of any triangle when you know two sides and the angle opposite one of them. **Law of Sines**

2. trigonometric ratios for a right triangle

For: Vocabulary quiz
Web Code: agj-1451

4. trigonometric identity

Skills and Concepts

14-1 Objectives

▼ To verify trigonometric identities (p. 778)

A **trigonometric identity** is a trigonometric equation that is true for all values except those for which the expressions on either side of the equal sign are undefined.

Reciprocal Identities

$$\csc \theta = \frac{1}{\sin \theta}$$

$$\sec \theta = \frac{1}{\cos \theta}$$

$$\cot \theta = \frac{1}{\tan \theta}$$

Tangent and Cotangent Identities

$$\tan \theta = \frac{\sin \theta}{\cos \theta}$$

$$\cot \theta = \frac{\cos \theta}{\sin \theta}$$

Pythagorean Identities

$$\cos^2 \theta + \sin^2 \theta = 1$$

$$1 + \tan^2 \theta = \sec^2 \theta$$

$$1 + \cot^2 \theta = \csc^2 \theta$$

Verify each identity. **6–7. See margin.**

6. $\sin \theta \tan \theta = \frac{1}{\cos \theta} - \cos \theta$

7. $\cos^2 \theta \cot^2 \theta = \cot^2 \theta - \cos^2 \theta$

Simplify each trigonometric expression.

8. $1 - \sin^2 \theta$ **$\cos^2 \theta$**

9. $\frac{\cos \theta}{\sin \theta \cot \theta}$ **1**

10. $\csc^2 \theta - \cot^2 \theta$ **1**

14-2 Objectives

▼ To evaluate inverses of trigonometric functions (p. 783)

▼ To solve trigonometric equations (p. 785)

The function $\cos^{-1} x$ is the inverse of $\cos \theta$ with the restricted domain $0 \le \theta \le \pi$. The function $\sin^{-1} x$ has domain $-\frac{\pi}{2} \le \theta \le \frac{\pi}{2}$, and $\tan^{-1} x$ has domain $-\frac{\pi}{2} < \theta < \frac{\pi}{2}$.

Use a unit circle and 30°-60°-90° triangles to find the value in degrees of each expression.

11. $\sin^{-1}\left(-\frac{\sqrt{3}}{2}\right)$ **−60°**

12. $\tan^{-1} \sqrt{3}$ **60°**

13. $\tan^{-1}\left(-\frac{\sqrt{3}}{3}\right)$ **−30°**

14. $\cos^{-1} \frac{\sqrt{3}}{2}$ **30°**

6. $\sin \theta \tan \theta = \frac{\sin^2 \theta}{\cos \theta}$

$$= \frac{1 - \cos^2 \theta}{\cos \theta} = \frac{1}{\cos \theta} - \frac{\cos^2 \theta}{\cos \theta}$$

$$= \frac{1}{\cos \theta} - \cos \theta$$

7. $\cos^2 \theta \cot^2 \theta = (1 - \sin^2 \theta) \cot^2 \theta$

$$= \cot^2 \theta - \sin^2 \theta \cot^2 \theta$$

$$= \cot^2 \theta - \sin^2 \theta \cdot \frac{\cos^2 \theta}{\sin^2 \theta}$$

$$= \cot^2 \theta - \cos^2 \theta$$

15. $0.34 + 2\pi n, 2.80 + 2\pi n$

16. $-1.11 + 2\pi n, 2.03 + 2\pi n$

17. $2.27 + 2\pi n, 4.02 + 2\pi n$

18. $0.20 + 2\pi n, 6.08 + 2\pi n$

Use a calculator to find the value in radians of each expression.

15. $\sin^{-1} 0.33$ **16.** $\tan^{-1}(-2)$ **17.** $\cos^{-1}(-0.64)$ **18.** $\cos^{-1} 0.98$

Solve each equation for $0 \le \theta < 2\pi$.

19. $2 \cos \theta = 1$
$\frac{\pi}{3}, \frac{5\pi}{3}$

20. $\sqrt{3} \tan \theta = 1$
$\frac{\pi}{6}, \frac{7\pi}{6}$

21. $\sin \theta = \sin^2 \theta$
$0, \frac{\pi}{2}, \pi$

14-3 Objectives

▼ To find lengths of sides in a right triangle (p. 792)

▼ To find measures of angles in a right triangle (p. 795)

The six different ratios of the sides of a right triangle are known as the **trigonometric ratios for a right triangle**. These ratios depend on the size of the acute angles in the right triangle.

In a right triangle ABC that has an acute $\angle A$ and right $\angle C$, the ratios are defined as follows.

$$\sin A = \frac{\text{length of leg opposite } \angle A}{\text{length of hypotenuse}} = \frac{a}{c} \qquad \csc A = \frac{\text{length of hypotenuse}}{\text{length of leg opposite } \angle A} = \frac{c}{a}$$

$$\cos A = \frac{\text{length of leg adjacent to } \angle A}{\text{length of hypotenuse}} = \frac{b}{c} \qquad \sec A = \frac{\text{length of hypotenuse}}{\text{length of leg adjacent to } \angle A} = \frac{c}{b}$$

$$\tan A = \frac{\text{length of leg opposite } \angle A}{\text{length of leg adjacent to } \angle A} = \frac{a}{b} \qquad \cot A = \frac{\text{length of leg adjacent to } \angle A}{\text{length of leg opposite } \angle A} = \frac{b}{a}$$

In $\triangle ABC$, $\angle B$ is a right angle, $AB = 30$, and $\sec A = \frac{5}{3}$. Find each value in fraction and in decimal form.

22. $\cos A$ $\frac{3}{5}$, 0.6

23. $\sin A$ $\frac{4}{5}$, 0.8

24. $\tan C$ $\frac{3}{4}$, 0.75

In $\triangle GHI$, $\angle H$ is a right angle. Find the remaining sides and angles. Round your answers to the nearest tenth.

25. $g = 3, i = 9$
9.5, 18.4°, 71.6°

26. $g = 12, h = 20$
16, 36.9°, 53.1°

27. $h = 55, i = 40$
37.7, 43.3°, 46.7°

14-4 Objectives

▼ To find the area of any triangle and to use the Law of Sines (p. 801)

You can find missing measures of any triangle if you know the measures of two angles and any side or if you know the measures of two sides and the angle opposite one of them by using the **Law of Sines.**

The Law of Sines states that for $\triangle ABC$, if a, b, and c represent the lengths of the sides opposite $\angle A$, $\angle B$, and $\angle C$, respectively, then $\frac{\sin A}{a} = \frac{\sin B}{b} = \frac{\sin C}{c}$.

Find the area of each triangle. Round your answers to the nearest hundredth.

28.

13.14 m²

29.

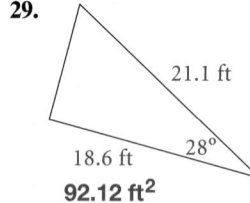

92.12 ft²

30.   57.81 m²

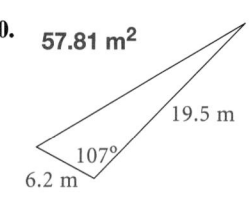

31. In $\triangle LMN, m\angle L = 67°, m\angle N = 24°$, and $MN = 16$ in. Find LM to the nearest tenth. **7.1 in.**

32. In $\triangle XYZ, m\angle Z = 34°, x = 61$ cm, and $z = 42$ cm. Find $m\angle X$ to the nearest tenth. **54.3° or 125.7°**

14-5 Objectives

▼ To use the Law of Cosines to find the area of any triangle (p. 808)

33. 21.4 ft

34. 43.9°

You can find missing parts of any triangle when you know the measures of two sides and the angle between them, or all three sides, by using the **Law of Cosines.** For $\triangle ABC$, the following are true.

$$a^2 = b^2 + c^2 - 2bc \cos A \qquad b^2 = a^2 + c^2 - 2ac \cos B \qquad c^2 = a^2 + b^2 - 2ab \cos C$$

33. In $\triangle ABC$, $m\angle B = 45°$, $a = 24$ ft, and $c = 30$ ft. Find b to the nearest tenth.

34. In $\triangle DEF$, $d = 25$ in., $e = 28$ in., and $f = 20$ in. Find $m\angle F$ to the nearest tenth.

35. In $\triangle GHI$, $h = 8$, $i = 12$, and $m\angle G = 96°$. Find $m\angle I$ to the nearest tenth. **52.2°**

14-6 Objectives

▼ To verify angle identities (p. 814)

▼ To verify sum and difference identities (p. 816)

Angle identities are used to solve trigonometric equations.

Negative angle identities

$$\sin(-\theta) = -\sin\theta \qquad \cos(-\theta) = \cos\theta \qquad \tan(-\theta) = -\tan\theta$$

Cofunction identities

$$\sin\left(\frac{\pi}{2} - \theta\right) = \cos\theta \qquad \cos\left(\frac{\pi}{2} - \theta\right) = \sin\theta \qquad \tan\left(\frac{\pi}{2} - \theta\right) = \cot\theta$$

Angle difference identities

$$\sin(A - B) = \sin A \cos B - \cos A \sin B \qquad \tan(A - B) = \frac{\tan A - \tan B}{1 + \tan A \tan B}$$
$$\cos(A - B) = \cos A \cos B + \sin A \sin B$$

Angle sum identities

$$\sin(A + B) = \sin A \cos B + \cos A \sin B \qquad \tan(A + B) = \frac{\tan A + \tan B}{1 - \tan A \tan B}$$
$$\cos(A + B) = \cos A \cos B - \sin A \sin B$$

Verify each identity. 36–37. **See margin.**

36. $\cos\left(\theta + \frac{\pi}{2}\right) = -\sin\theta$

37. $\sin^2\left(\theta - \frac{\pi}{2}\right) = \cos^2\theta$

Solve each trigonometric equation for $0 \le \theta < 2\pi$.

38. $\tan\left(\frac{\pi}{2} - \theta\right) = \cos\theta$ $\frac{\pi}{2}$ and $\frac{3\pi}{2}$

39. $1 + \tan^2\theta = \cos\theta$ **0**

14-7 Objectives

▼ To verify double-angle identities (p. 821)

▼ To verify half-angle identities (p. 822)

You can use double-angle and half-angle identities to find exact values of trigonometric expressions. In the half-angle identities, choose the positive or negative sign for each function depending on the quadrant in which $\frac{A}{2}$ lies.

Double-angle identities

$$\cos 2\theta = \cos^2\theta - \sin^2\theta \qquad \sin 2\theta = 2\sin\theta\cos\theta \qquad \tan 2\theta = \frac{2\tan\theta}{1 - \tan^2\theta}$$
$$\cos 2\theta = 2\cos^2\theta - 1 \qquad \cos 2\theta = 1 - 2\sin^2\theta$$

Half-angle identities

$$\sin\frac{A}{2} = \pm\sqrt{\frac{1 - \cos A}{2}} \qquad \cos\frac{A}{2} = \pm\sqrt{\frac{1 + \cos A}{2}} \qquad \tan\frac{A}{2} = \pm\sqrt{\frac{1 - \cos A}{1 + \cos A}}$$

Use a double-angle identity to find the exact value of each expression.

40. $\sin 120°$ $\frac{\sqrt{3}}{2}$

41. $\cos 90°$ **0**

42. $\tan 300°$ $-\sqrt{3}$

Use a half-angle identity to find the exact value of each expression.

43. $\cos 180°$ **−1**

44. $\tan 60°$ $\sqrt{3}$

45. $\sin 120°$ $\frac{\sqrt{3}}{2}$

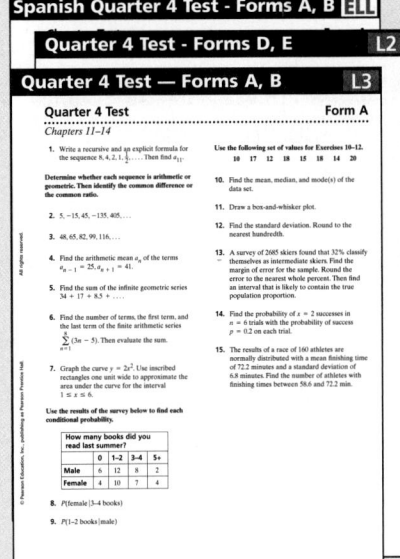
36. $\cos\left(\theta + \frac{\pi}{2}\right) = \cos\theta\cos\left(\frac{\pi}{2}\right) - \sin\theta\sin\left(\frac{\pi}{2}\right)$
$$= \cos\theta \cdot 0 - \sin\theta \cdot 1$$
$$= -\sin\theta$$

37. $\sin^2\left(\theta - \frac{\pi}{2}\right) = \sin^2\left(-\left(\frac{\pi}{2} - \theta\right)\right)$
$$= \left(-\sin\left(\frac{\pi}{2} - \theta\right)\right) \cdot \left(-\sin\left(\frac{\pi}{2} - \theta\right)\right)$$
$$= (-\cos\theta)(-\cos\theta)$$
$$= \cos^2\theta$$

Chapter Test

Go Online
PHSchool.com
For: Chapter Test
Web Code: aga-1452

Simplify each trigonometric expression.

1. $\sin \theta + \cos \theta \cot \theta$ **csc θ**

2. $\sec \theta \sin \theta \cot \theta$ **1**

3. $\cot \theta (\tan \theta + \cot \theta)$ **$\csc^2 \theta$**

Verify each identity. **4–7. See margin.**

4. $\csc^2 \theta \cos \theta \tan \theta = 1$ **5.** $\csc^2 \theta - \cot^2 \theta = 1$

6. $\sec \theta \cot \theta = \csc \theta$ **7.** $\sec^2 \theta - 1 = \tan^2 \theta$

Use a unit circle and 30°-60°-90° triangles to find the values of θ in degrees for each expression.

8. $\sin \theta = \frac{\sqrt{3}}{2}$ **9.** $\cos \theta = \frac{\sqrt{3}}{2}$

10. $\cos \theta = -1$ **11.** $\tan \theta = \sqrt{3}$
8–12. See margin.

Solve each equation for $0 \le \theta < 2\pi$.

12. $4 \sin \theta + 2\sqrt{3} = 0$ **13.** $2 \cos \theta = 1$ **$\frac{\pi}{3}, \frac{5\pi}{3}$**

14. $\sqrt{2} \sin \theta - 1 = 0$ **$\frac{\pi}{4}, \frac{3\pi}{4}$**

In $\triangle ABC$, find each value as a fraction and as a decimal. Round to the nearest hundredth.

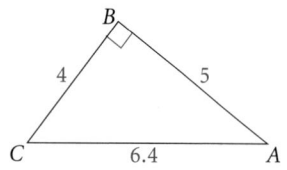

15–20. See back of book.

15. $\sin A$ **16.** $\sec A$ **17.** $\cot A$

18. $\csc C$ **19.** $\sec C$ **20.** $\tan C$

In $\triangle DEF$, $\angle F$ is a right angle. Find the remaining sides and angles. Round your answers to the nearest tenth.

21. $e = 6, f = 10$ **22.** $d = 10, e = 12$

23. $e = 21, f = 51$ **24.** $d = 5.5, e = 2.6$

21–24. See back of book.

25. Find the area of the triangle.

91.8 m²

26. In $\triangle ABC, m\angle A = 45°, m\angle C = 23°$, and $BC = 25$ in. Find AB to the nearest tenth. **13.8 in.**

27. In $\triangle DEF, m\angle F = 56°, m\angle E = 34°$, and $DF = 10$ ft. Find EF to the nearest tenth. **17.9 ft**

28. In $\triangle GHI, m\angle I = 45°, g = 32$ cm, and $i = 52$ cm. Find $m\angle G$ to the nearest tenth. **25.8°**

29. In $\triangle JKL, m\angle J = 29°, l = 35$ m, and $j = 56$ m. Find $m\angle L$ to the nearest tenth. **17.6°**

30. **Writing** Suppose you know the lengths of all three sides of a triangle. Can you use the Law of Sines to find the measures of the angles? Explain.
See margin.

31. In $\triangle MNO, m\angle N = 45°, m = 20$ cm, and $o = 41$ cm. Find n to the nearest tenth. **30.4 cm**

32. In $\triangle PQR, p = 51$ ft, $q = 81$ ft, and $r = 61$ ft. Find $m\angle R$ to the nearest tenth. **48.8°**

33. In $\triangle STU, m\angle S = 96°, t = 8$ in., and $u = 10$ in. Find $m\angle U$ to the nearest tenth. **47.7°**

Verify each identity. **34–37. See back of book.**

34. $-\sin\left(\theta - \frac{\pi}{2}\right) = \cos \theta$

35. $\csc\left(\theta + \frac{\pi}{2}\right) = \sec \theta$

36. $\csc\left(\theta - \frac{\pi}{2}\right) = -\sec \theta$

37. $\cos\left(-\theta - \frac{\pi}{2}\right) = \sin(-\theta)$

Solve each trigonometric equation for $0 \le \theta < 2\pi$.

38. $\sin\left(\frac{\pi}{2} - \theta\right) = \sec \theta$ **$0, \pi$** **39.** $\cos\left(\frac{\pi}{2} - \theta\right) = \csc \theta$ **$\frac{\pi}{2}, \frac{3\pi}{2}$**

40. $\cot\left(\frac{\pi}{2} - \theta\right) = \sin \theta$ **$0, \pi$**

Use a double-angle identity to find the exact value of each expression.

41. $\sin 60°$ **$\frac{\sqrt{3}}{2}$** **42.** $\cos 60°$ **$\frac{1}{2}$** **43.** $\tan 60°$ **$\sqrt{3}$**

Use a half-angle identity to find the exact value of each expression.

44. $\tan 30°$ **$\frac{\sqrt{3}}{3}$** **45.** $\sin 90°$ **1** **46.** $\cos 180°$ **-1**

47. **Open-Ended** Choose an angle measure A. Find $\sin A$ and $\cos A$. Then use the identities to find $\cos 2A$ and $\sin \frac{A}{2}$. **Check students' work.**

---

4. $\csc \theta \cos \theta \tan \theta =$
$\frac{1}{\sin \theta} \cdot \frac{\cos \theta}{1} \cdot \frac{\sin \theta}{\cos \theta} =$
$\frac{\cos \theta \sin \theta}{\sin \theta \cos \theta} = 1$

5. $\csc^2 \theta - \cot^2 \theta =$
$1 + \cot^2 \theta - \cot^2 \theta = 1$

6. $\sec \theta \cot \theta = \frac{1}{\cos \theta} \cdot \frac{\cos \theta}{\sin \theta}$
$= \frac{1}{\sin \theta} = \csc \theta$

7. $\sec^2 \theta - 1 = 1 + \tan^2 \theta - 1$
$= \tan^2 \theta$

8. $60° + 360° \cdot n, 120° + 360° \cdot n$

9. $30° + 360° \cdot n, 330° + 360° \cdot n$

10. $180° + 360° \cdot n$

11. $60° + 360° \cdot n, 240° + 360° \cdot n$

12. $\frac{4\pi}{3}, \frac{5\pi}{3}$

30. No; the Law of Sines requires at least one angle in order to set up a ratio of length of side to size of angle.

Standardized Test Prep

Go Online
PHSchool.com
For: End-of-course test
Web Code: aga-1454

Standardized Test Prep

Multiple Choice

For Exercises 1–32, choose the correct letter.

1. Which conic section is an ellipse?
C Ⓐ $(x - 1)^2 + (y - 2)^2 = 4$
  Ⓑ $(x + 4)^2 - (y - 3)^2 = 25$
  Ⓒ $\frac{x^2}{36} + \frac{y^2}{81} = 100$
  Ⓓ $\frac{x^2}{9} - \frac{y^2}{49} = 121$

2. How many solutions does the system
G $\begin{cases} y = \frac{1}{2}x^3 - 1 \\ y = -x^2 + 4 \end{cases}$ have?
  Ⓕ 0   Ⓖ 1   Ⓗ 2   Ⓙ 3

3. In which sequence is a_{25} the greatest?
A Ⓐ $a_n = 2a_{n-1} + 7,\ a_1 = 5$
  Ⓑ $a_n = 3n - 10$
  Ⓒ $a_n = a_{n-1} + 18,\ a_1 = -7$
  Ⓓ $a_n = n^2 - 200$

4. What is the inverse of the function $f(x) = x^3 + 4$?
H Ⓕ $f^{-1}(x) = \frac{1}{3}x - 4$
  Ⓖ $f^{-1}(x) = \sqrt[3]{x} - 4$
  Ⓗ $f^{-1}(x) = \sqrt[3]{x - 4}$
  Ⓙ $f^{-1}(x) = \sqrt[4]{x - 3}$

5. Which function shifts $y = |x + 1| - 3$ right
D 4 units and down 7 units?
  Ⓐ $y = |x - 6| + 1$
  Ⓑ $y = |x - 3| + 4$
  Ⓒ $y = |x + 5| - 10$
  Ⓓ $y = |x - 3| - 10$

6. Which is a direct variation that includes the
F point (10, 1)?
  I. $y = 10x$ II. $y = 0.1x$
  III. $xy = 10$ IV. $y = 0.5x - 4$
  Ⓕ II only   Ⓖ I and III only
  Ⓗ II, III, and IV Ⓙ I only

7. Which of the following expressions is equivalent
D to $3 \log x + 2 \log y - \log x$?
  I. $2 \log xy$ II. $\log x^2 + \log y^2$
  III. $2 \log x + 2 \log y$ IV. $4 \log x - y$
  Ⓐ I and II only   Ⓑ II and III only
  Ⓒ III and IV only   Ⓓ I, II, and III only

8. Which graph represents a tangent function?
J

 Ⓕ
 Ⓖ

 Ⓗ
 Ⓙ
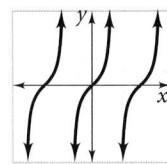

9. What is the solution of the matrix equation
A $\begin{bmatrix} 10 & 9 & -5 \\ 3 & 12 & 7 \end{bmatrix} - X = \begin{bmatrix} 4 & -8 & 5 \\ 15 & -3 & 0 \end{bmatrix}$?
  Ⓐ $\begin{bmatrix} 6 & 17 & -10 \\ -12 & 15 & 7 \end{bmatrix}$
  Ⓑ $\begin{bmatrix} 14 & 1 & 0 \\ 18 & 9 & 7 \end{bmatrix}$
  Ⓒ $\begin{bmatrix} 15 & 1 & -1 \\ 3 & 9 & 22 \end{bmatrix}$
  Ⓓ $\begin{bmatrix} -6 & -17 & 10 \\ 12 & -15 & -7 \end{bmatrix}$

10. What is the distance of $4 - 5i$ from the origin?
G Ⓕ 9 units
  Ⓖ $\sqrt{41}$ units
  Ⓗ 3 units
  Ⓙ 1 unit

11. Which of the following is a simplification
D of $\frac{x^2 y^3 z}{4x} \div \frac{3xy^4 z^2}{2z}$?
  Ⓐ $\frac{3x^3 y^7 z^3}{8xz}$
  Ⓑ $\frac{3x^2 y^7 z^2}{8}$
  Ⓒ $\frac{2x^2 y^3 z^2}{12x^2 y^4 z^2}$
  Ⓓ $\frac{1}{6y}$

Chapter 14   Standardized Test Prep   **831**

Item	1	2	3	4	5	6	7	8	9	10	11
Lesson	10-4	3-2	11-3	7-7	2-6	2-3	8-4	13-6	4-2	5-6	7-2

12. Which point is a solution of the
H following system?

$$\begin{cases} y \le 3x - 2 \\ y < 2x \\ x \ge -1 \\ y \ge -4 \end{cases}$$

Ⓕ (0, 7)
Ⓖ (−4, 1)
Ⓗ (3, 1)
Ⓙ (−1, −5)

13. The Law of Sines CANNOT be used as the first
C step in solving which of these triangles?

Ⓐ

Ⓑ

Ⓒ

Ⓓ

14. What is the amplitude of $y = -4 \sin \frac{1}{2}x$?
G
Ⓕ 4π
Ⓖ 4
Ⓗ $\frac{1}{2}$
Ⓙ −4

15. What is $\frac{5\pi}{6}$ radians in degrees?
B
Ⓐ 300°
Ⓑ 150°
Ⓒ 170°
Ⓓ 80°

16. For $f(x) = x^2 - 1$ and $g(x) = |2x + 3|$, which has
J the greatest value?
Ⓕ $f(g(3))$
Ⓖ $g(f(2))$
Ⓗ $g(f(-1))$
Ⓙ $f(g(10))$

17. Which is the graph of an exponential function?
C

Ⓐ

Ⓑ

Ⓒ

Ⓓ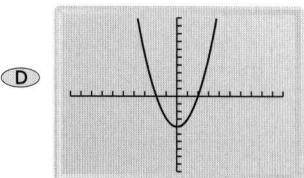

18. Which of the following expressions is equivalent
J to 3 log x − 2 log 2x?
Ⓕ −log x Ⓖ log (−x)
Ⓗ log $\frac{x}{2}$ Ⓙ log $\frac{x}{4}$

19. In $\triangle ABC$, $m\angle A = 36°$, $b = 12$, and $c = 25$.
D What is the length of a rounded to the
nearest hundredth?
Ⓐ 15.94   Ⓑ 253.95
Ⓒ 283.59   Ⓓ 16.84

20. Which sequence has a common difference of 3?
G I. $a_n = a_{n-1} - 3$, $a_1 = 2$
II. $a_n = 3$
III. $a_n = a_{n-1} + 3$, $a_1 = -7$
IV. $a_n = n^2 + 3$
Ⓕ I only   Ⓖ III only
Ⓗ I and III   Ⓙ II and IV

21. Which is greatest for the following data?
D
3, 4, 5, 5, 5, 5, 6, 7, 8, 9
Ⓐ mean   Ⓑ mode
Ⓒ median   Ⓓ range

Item	12	13	14	15	16	17	18	19	20	21
Lesson	3-3	14-4	13-4	13-3	7-6	8-2	8-4	14-4	11-2	12-3

22. Which of the following equations represents
H an ellipse?
- F $3y^2 - x - 6y + 5 = 0$
- G $x^2 + y^2 - 4x - 6y + 4 = 0$
- H $4x^2 + y^2 - 16x - 6y + 9 = 0$
- J $4x^2 - y^2 - 16x + 6y - 9 = 0$

23. Which curve has a period of 3?
C
- A $y = 3\sin 3\theta$
- B $y = \cos\frac{\pi}{3}\theta$
- C $y = \tan\frac{\pi}{3}\theta$
- D $y = \frac{1}{3}\cos\theta$

24. Solve $10 - |4x + 1| < 7$.
G
- F $x > \frac{1}{2}$
- G $x < -1$ or $x > \frac{1}{2}$
- H $x < -\frac{1}{2}$ or $x > 1$
- J $-1 < x < \frac{1}{2}$

25. What are the roots of $\frac{x}{x-18} = \frac{3x}{x^2-36}$?
A
- I. 0
- II. −3
- III. 6
- A I only
- B I and II
- C II and III
- D I, II, and III

26. Let p and q vary inversely. If $p = -4$ when
G $q = 0.5$, what is q when p is 1?
- F 2
- G −2
- H $\frac{1}{8}$
- J $-\frac{1}{8}$

27. Find all the zeros of $f(x) = x(x-3)^4$.
C
- I. −3
- II. 0
- III. 3
- A I and II
- B I and III
- C II and III
- D III only

28. What is the degree of the polynomial
J $2x^5 + 3x - 1$?
- F 2
- G 3
- H 4
- J 5

29. What are the vertical asymptotes for the graph
C of $y = \frac{(x+1)(x-2)}{x^2+x-6}$?
- I. $x = -1$
- II. $x = 2$
- III. $x = -3$
- A I and III
- B II only
- C III only
- D II and III

30. Which is equal to $\cos 120°$?
F
- F $\cos 240°$
- G $\cos 60°$
- H $\cos 330°$
- J $\cos 150°$

31. Which number completes the square
D for $x^2 - 3x$?
- A 9
- B $-\frac{3}{2}$
- C $-\frac{9}{2}$
- D $\frac{9}{4}$

32. There are 15 marbles in a bag: 2 are red, 8 are
G green, and 5 are blue. A marble is chosen at
random and not replaced. A second marble is
chosen at random. To the nearest whole percent,
what is the probability that NEITHER marble is
green?
- F 19%
- G 20%
- H 89%
- J 90%

Gridded Response

33. Express $\frac{5\pi}{9}$ radians in degrees. **100**

34. A pendulum is 18 in. long. It swings through an
angle of $\frac{3\pi}{4}$ radians. How far does the tip of the
pendulum travel in one swing? Round your
answer to the nearest inch. **42**

35. Find a_{33} in the product $\begin{bmatrix} 2 & 1 \\ -6 & 5 \\ -1 & 3 \end{bmatrix} \cdot \begin{bmatrix} 8 & -2 & 0.5 \\ 4 & -7 & 10 \end{bmatrix}$.
29.5

Short Response 36–44. See back of book.

36. In $\triangle ABC$, $m\angle A = 56°$, $a = 8$, and $c = 6$. Show
how to find $m\angle C$. Round to the nearest tenth.

37. Graph the function $y = \sin\left(x + \frac{\pi}{2}\right)$.

38. Divide $2x^4 + 4x^3 + 5x^2 + 9x - 2$ by $x + 2$.
Show your work.

39. Write an equation of a rational function with
asymptotes $y = 4$ and $x = -2$. Explain your work.

40. Simplify $(5 + 2i)(-3 + i)$. Show your work.

41. You put $600 into an account earning 5%
annual interest, compounded continuously.
How much will you have after 18 months?
Show your work.

42. You roll three number cubes. Can the three
events {rolling three of the same number, rolling
exactly two of the same number, rolling all
different numbers} be used to form a probability
distribution? Explain.

43. You roll three number cubes. Find P(all three
show the same number).

44. Find the inverse of the matrix $\begin{bmatrix} 6 & -2 \\ 11 & 3 \end{bmatrix}$.

Extended Response 45–46. See back of book.

45. In $\triangle ABC$, $m\angle A = 65°$, $b = 23$, and $c = 19$. Show
how to find a. Round to the nearest hundredth.

46. Suppose you receive $350 for your birthday.
You can put the money into an account earning
4.5% annual interest compounded continuously,
or into an account earning 5% annual interest
compounded monthly. Write and solve the
equations that show how much you would
have in each account after one year and after
five years.

Item	22	23	24	25	26	27	28	29	30	31	32	33	
Lesson	10-4	13-6	1-5	9-6	7-7	6-2	6-1	9-3	14-6	5-7	9-7	13-3	
Item	34	35	36	37	38	39	40	41	42	43	44	45	46
Lesson	13-3	4-3	14-4	13-4	6-3	9-3	5-6	8-2	12-1	9-7	4-7	14-5	8-5

A Question of Balance

In these activities students apply their knowledge of formulas and angle measures.

Activating Prior Knowledge

Have students share their experiences with balancing a structure—perhaps as they were building a house of cards, or making towers of dominoes or blocks. Or, have students with experience discuss the importance of balance in gymnastics.

Guided Instruction

Have a volunteer read the introductory paragraph. Ask: *What factors make you feel more or less stable when you are on top of a ladder or a fence?*

Teaching Tip

Ask a nearby lumber store or a parent who does construction to give you scraps of two-by-four in lengths of 4, 8, 12, and 16 in. to use for these activities.

Tactile Learners

Have students experiment with plastic bottles of various widths and heights to determine what ratio of height to circumference tends to make such vessels unstable.

Connection to Building Trades

To make clear why wood this size is called "two-by-four," have students research how lumber is sold and measured, and have them find the actual dimensions of a piece of lumber that is labeled two-by-four.

English Language Learners ELL

Use objects in the classroom to demonstrate the meanings for *unstable, tips over,* and *balance.*

834

Activity Lab

A Question of Balance

Applying Trigonometry Why is it so difficult to walk on a balance beam? It is difficult because you must keep your body's center of gravity over a narrow base of support to maintain your balance. You can use this idea to calculate the maximum angle any object (or person) can tip without falling over.

The Balance Beam
The balance beam, used only in women's gymnastics, is 5 m long but only 10 cm wide. A beam exercise lasts between 70 and 90 s. Each movement on the balance beam flows freely into the next, with the gymnast pausing only to hold the balance positions.

Activity 1

Materials: four pieces of 2×4 wood (16 in., 12 in., 8 in., 4 in. long), pencil, protractor

a. Use the diagram to write an equation relating θ to w and the length ℓ of the 2×4.

b. Tip a 16-in.-long piece of 2×4 on the edge of its narrow face. Use a protractor to measure the maximum angle the piece of 2×4 can tip without falling over. Use the equation from part (a) as a check.

c. Repeat part (b) for pieces of 2×4 that measure 4 in., 8 in., and 12 in.

d. **Reasoning** Suppose you tip the 2×4 on the edge of its wide face instead of its narrow face. Write a new equation relating θ to ℓ and to n, the width of the narrow face. Use your new equation to calculate the value of θ for each of the 2×4 pieces from parts (b) and (c).

[diagram labels: w, wide face, ℓ, θ, center of gravity, narrow face, tipped edge]

834 All photographs © Dorling Kindersley Limited unless otherwise credited on acknowledgments page

---

Activity 1
a. $\tan \theta = \frac{w}{\ell}$
b. 14°

c. 45°, 26.6°, 18.4°
d. $\tan \theta = \frac{n}{\ell}$; 7.1°, 26.6°, 14.0°, 9.5°

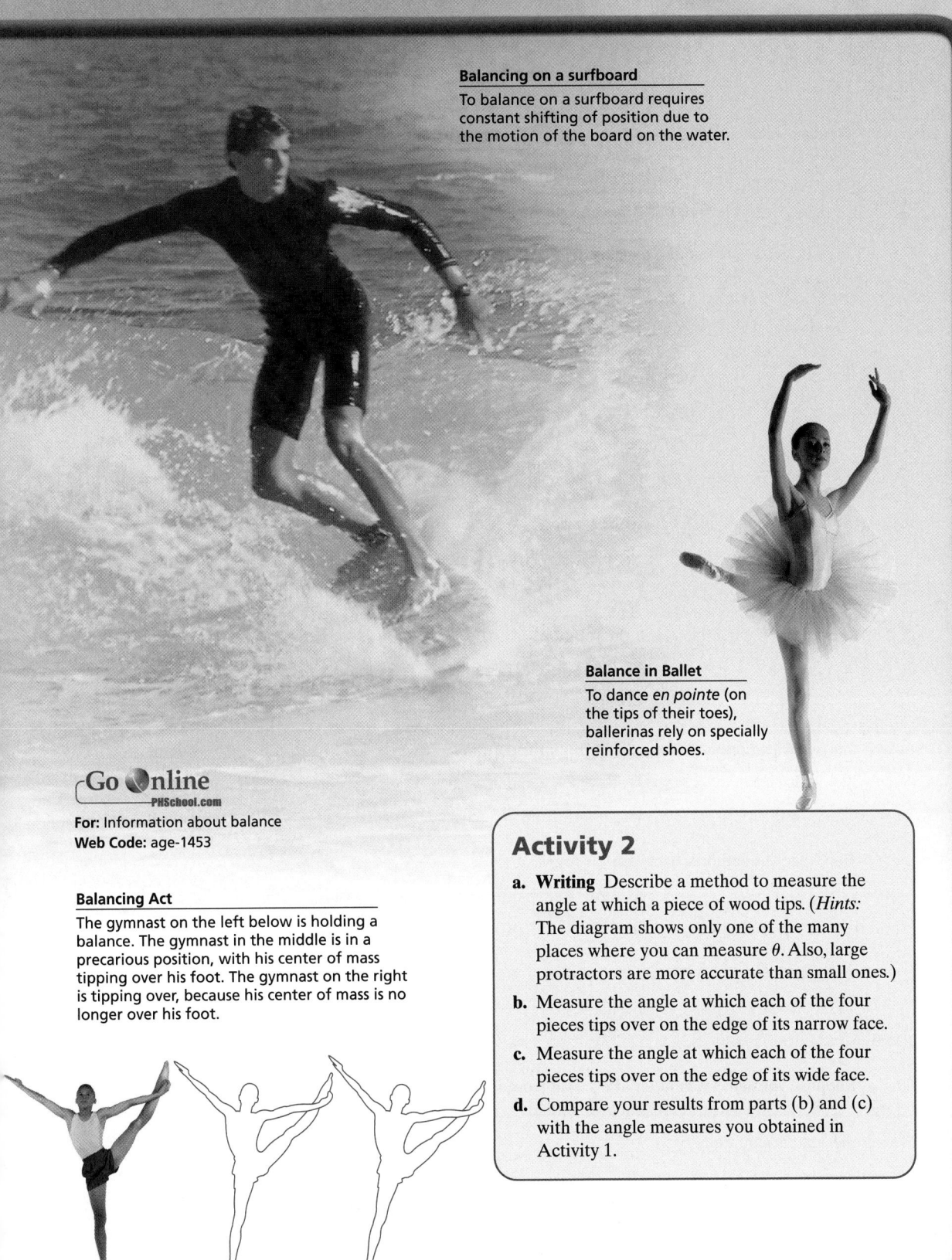

Balancing on a surfboard
To balance on a surfboard requires constant shifting of position due to the motion of the board on the water.

Balance in Ballet
To dance *en pointe* (on the tips of their toes), ballerinas rely on specially reinforced shoes.

Go Online
PHSchool.com
For: Information about balance
Web Code: age-1453

Balancing Act
The gymnast on the left below is holding a balance. The gymnast in the middle is in a precarious position, with his center of mass tipping over his foot. The gymnast on the right is tipping over, because his center of mass is no longer over his foot.

Activity 2

a. **Writing** Describe a method to measure the angle at which a piece of wood tips. (*Hints:* The diagram shows only one of the many places where you can measure θ. Also, large protractors are more accurate than small ones.)

b. Measure the angle at which each of the four pieces tips over on the edge of its narrow face.

c. Measure the angle at which each of the four pieces tips over on the edge of its wide face.

d. Compare your results from parts (b) and (c) with the angle measures you obtained in Activity 1.

835

Activity 2

a–d. Check students' work.

Teaching Tip
Before students begin the activity, discuss the illustrations and their captions. Have students work in pairs or in small groups to complete the activities. Have each team read through both activities before beginning to work.

Activity 1

Materials: paper and pencil

Teaching Tip
Help students organize their work by making a table for recording the results with the various lengths. Work with students to identify appropriate labels for the rows and columns.

Activity 2

Materials: paper and pencil, protractor, lengths of 2-by-4 that measure 4, 8, 12, and 16 in.

Teaching Tip
Ask students to read the Hint and then discuss why they can measure more accurately with a large protractor than with a small one. Elicit the fact that a measuring error will be less significant with a large protractor.

Scoring Rubric

This scoring rubric can be used for evaluating student work on both activities. Share this scoring rubric with students before they begin work.

4   Equations and calculations are correct.
    Steps are neat, accurate, and clearly show the mathematics. Responses are clearly indicated and give the appropriate units.

3   Equations and calculations are mostly correct, with some minor errors.
    Steps are neat and mostly accurate. Units are not completely accurate.

2   Equations and calculations contain both major and minor errors.

1   Correct answer, but no work is shown.

835

Extra Practice: Skills and Word Problems

page 836 Extra Practice

9. $-102, \frac{1}{102}$

10. $3.7, -\frac{10}{37}$

11. $-2\frac{3}{4}, \frac{4}{11}$

12. $0.04, -25$

13. $-\sqrt{2}, \frac{\sqrt{2}}{2}$

14. $-\pi + 4, \frac{1}{\pi - 4}$

15. $\frac{8}{5}, -\frac{5}{8}$

16. $-1.5, \frac{2}{3}$

17. $-\frac{6}{7}, \frac{7}{6}$

18. $-\frac{3\pi}{2}, \frac{2}{3\pi}$

19. $-0.0001, 10,000$

20. $-5\sqrt{7}, \frac{\sqrt{7}}{35}$

30.
0   2   4

31.
-4 -2   0

32.
-10 -8 -6 -4 -2 0

33.
-6 -4 -2   0

34.
-20 -18 -16 -14 -12 -10

35.
4   6   8   10 12 14

36. $-3 < r < 5$
-4 -2   0   2   4

37. $-2 \le z < 1$
-2   0   2

38. $3 \le x \le 7$
2   4   6   8

39. $x < -2, x > 8$
-2 0 2 4 6 8 10 12

40. $3 < b \le 11$
0   2   4   6   8 10 12

41. $p > -5$
-6 -4 -2   0   2

836

Lesson 1-1 Replace each ■ with the symbol <, >, or = to make the sentence true.

1. $-5 \ \blacksquare \ -8$ **>**

2. $7 \ \blacksquare \ 7$ **=**

3. $0.1 \ \blacksquare \ 0.01$ **>**

4. $12 \ \blacksquare \ \sqrt{12}$ **>**

5. $\frac{3}{8} \ \blacksquare \ 0.375$ **=**

6. $\frac{1}{5} \ \blacksquare \ \frac{1}{4}$ **<**

7. $\frac{1}{3} \ \blacksquare \ 0.333$ **>**

8. $\sqrt{6} \ \blacksquare \ 3$ **<**

Lesson 1-1 Find the opposite and the reciprocal of each number.   9–20. See margin.

9. 102 10. -3.7 11. $2\frac{3}{4}$ 12. -0.04 13. $\sqrt{2}$ 14. $\pi - 4$

15. $-\frac{8}{5}$ 16. 1.5 17. $\frac{6}{7}$ 18. $\frac{3\pi}{2}$ 19. 0.0001 20. $5\sqrt{7}$

Lesson 1-2 Evaluate each expression for the given values of the variables.

21. $6c + 5d - 4c - 3d + 3c - 6d; c = 4$ and $d = -2$ **28**

22. $10a + 3b - 5a + 4b + 1a + 5b; a = -3$ and $b = 5$ **42**

23. $3m + 9n + 6m - 7n - 4m + 2n; m = 6$ and $n = -4$ **14**

Lesson 1-3 Solve each equation. Check your answers.

24. $5 - w = 2w - 1$ **2**

25. $-2s = 3s - 10$ **2**

26. $2(x + 3) + 2(x + 4) = 24$ $\frac{5}{2}$

27. $8z + 12 = 5z - 21$ **−11**

28. $7b - 6(11 - 2b) = 10$ **4**

29. $10k - 7 = 2(13 - 5k)$ $\frac{33}{20}$

Lesson 1-4 Solve each inequality. Graph the solution.   30–35. See margin for graphs.

30. $3x - 8 \ge 1$ $x \ge 3$

31. $7t + 4 \le 3t$ $t \le -1$

32. $3v \le 5v + 18$ $v \ge -9$

33. $4a < 2a - 7$ $a < -\frac{7}{2}$

34. $7 - x \ge 24$ $x \le -17$

35. $2(y - 3) + 7 < 21$ $y < 10$

Lesson 1-4 Solve each compound inequality. Graph the solution.   36–41. See margin.

36. $4r > -12$ and $2r < 10$

37. $5z \ge -10$ and $3z < 3$

38. $7x \ge 21$ and $8x \le 56$

39. $3x < -6$ or $7x > 56$

40. $9b > 27$ and $4b \le 44$

41. $5p \ge 10$ or $-2p < 10$

Lesson 1-5 Solve each equation. Check your answers.

42. $|4m + 2| = 10$ **2, −3**

43. $|9 - 4z| = 53$ **−11, 15.5**

44. $|5x| = 30$ **−6, 6**

45. $|3x - 6| - 7 = 14$ **−5, 9**

46. $3|2d - 1| = 21$ **−3, 4**

47. $|2v + 3| - 6 = 14$ $-\frac{23}{2}, \frac{17}{2}$

Lesson 1-5 Solve each inequality. Graph the solution.   48–53. See margin for graphs.

48. $|3 - k| < 7$ **−4 < k < 10**

49. $|2t + 7| \ge 4$ $t \le -5.5, t \ge -1.5$

50. $|x - 2| < 6$ **−4 < x < 8**

51. $2|w + 6| \le 10$ **−11 ≤ w ≤ −1**

52. $|3y - 5| + 6 > 15$
$y < -\frac{4}{3}$ or $y > \frac{14}{3}$

53. $3|2z + 5| + 2 \le 8$
$-\frac{7}{2} \le z \le -\frac{3}{2}$

Lesson 1-6 Suppose you select a number at random from the sample space {1, 2, 3, 4, 5, 6, 7, 8, 9}. Find each theoretical probability.

54. P(a number that is a multiple of 5) $\frac{1}{9}$

55. P(a number that is an integer) **1**

56. P(a number that is a factor of twelve) $\frac{5}{9}$

57. P(a number that is less than or equal to 4) $\frac{4}{9}$

58. P(a number that is greater than 6) $\frac{1}{3}$

59. P(a number that is a composite number) $\frac{4}{9}$

48.
-6 -4 -2 0 2 4 6 8 10

49.
-8 -6 -4 -2   0

50.
-4 -2   0   2   4   6   8

51.
-12 -10 -8 -6 -4 -2 0

52.
-4 -2   0   2   4   6

53.
-4 -3 -2 -1   0

● Lessons 1-1, 1-2, and 1-3

60. You can use the equation $T = 0.6(205 - \frac{a}{2} - r) + r$ to determine the target heart rate, T, for a cardiovascular workout for an athletic male a years old. His rest heart rate is r heartbeats per minute. What is the rest heart rate of an athletic 18-year-old male whose target heart rate is 144 heartbeats per minute? **66 beats/min**

61. A desktop computer now sells for 15% less than it did last year. The current price is $425. What was the price of the computer last year? **$500**

62. Mrs. Chavez invested $6000. She invested the money in two accounts—one with a 4% simple interest and the other with a 6% simple interest. At the end of the year, the total amount she earned in interest was $320. How much did Mrs. Chavez invest in each account? **$2000 with 4% interest, $4000 with 6% interest**

63. A plane travels from New York City to San Francisco with an average speed of 550 mi/h. Another plane leaves from the same airport a half-hour later and travels the same route with an average speed of 625 mi/h. How many hours later will the second plane pass the first? **$3\frac{2}{3}$ h**

64. Mehmed and Colin run around a 450-meter track in opposite directions. They start at the same point and at the same time. Mehmed's speed is 2.0 m/s. Colin's speed is 2.5 m/s. How far will Colin have run when they meet again? **250 m**

65. Angela is considering two job offers. Job A would pay a salary of $2500 plus a 4% commission on her total sales per month. Job B would pay $2200 plus an 8% commission on all sales over $2000 per month. What is the least amount Angela would have to sell each month for Job B to pay more than Job A? **$11,500**

66. Amando has $625 in his savings account. He wants to take a vacation that he estimates will cost $1300. If possible, he would like to have extra money to buy souvenirs for friends. Amando works 40 hours per week, earns $15 per hour, and saves 6% of each week's earnings. How many whole weeks must he work before he earns enough money to take the vacation? **19 weeks**

67. A homeowner needs to rent some cleaning equipment. Company A will rent the machine he needs for $28 plus $4 per hour. Company B will charge $22 plus $4.75 per hour. For what range of hours will Company B charge less than Company A? **less than 8 h**

● Lessons 1-4 and 1-5

68. A metal part for a machine is now 5.85 inches long. The specifications call for it to be 5.72 inches long, with a tolerance of ±0.02 inch. By how much can a machinist decrease the length of the part? **0.11 to 0.15 in.**

● Lesson 1-6

69. In a group of 38 students, 15 take chemistry, 28 take Spanish, and 8 take both chemistry and Spanish. One student is selected at random from the group. What is the probability that the student takes neither chemistry nor Spanish? $\frac{3}{38}$

70. A bag contains marbles of three different colors. You draw a marble, record its color, then put it back in the bag. The table shows the results of the 150 trials. What is the experimental probability of drawing a red marble? $\frac{3}{10}$

Color	Frequency
Red	45
Blue	58
Yellow	47

71. Charles is one of a group of five students who have volunteered to work at the ticket table for a school band concert. If two students are selected at random to work at the ticket table, what is the probability that Charles will be one of the two? $\frac{2}{5}$

72. Within a 10-by-10 grid of squares, two overlapping 6-by-6 squares are drawn. The area of overlap is 9 square units. If a dart hits the 10-by-10 square at a random point, what is the probability that it lands in one or both of the 6-by-6 squares? $\frac{63}{100}$

1. Yes; each *x*-value has exactly one *y*-value.

2. Yes; each *x*-value has exactly one *y*-value.

3. No; the *x*-value 1 has two *y*-values.

4. Yes; each *x*-value has exactly one *y*-value.

5. No; the *x*-values 3 and 6 have two *y*-values.

6. No; the *x*-value 5 has two *y*-values.

7.

8.

9.

10.

11.

● **Lesson 2-1 Determine whether each relation is a function. Justify your answer.   1–6. See margin.**

1. $\{(0, 1), (1, 0), (2, 1), (3, 1), (4, 2)\}$

2. $\{(7, 4), (4, 9), (-3, 1), (1, 7), (2, 8)\}$

3. $\{(1, 4), (3, 2), (5, 2), (1, -8), (6, 7)\}$

4. $\{(-5, 1), (0, -3), (-2, 1), (10, 11), (7, 1)\}$

5. $\{(9, 3), (6, 2), (3, 2), (3, 1), (6, -2)\}$

6. $\{(4, 9), (5, 3), (-2, 0), (5, 4), (8, 1)\}$

● **Lesson 2-2 Graph each equation.   7–14. See margin.**

7. $y = x - 7$

8. $4x - y = 8$

9. $y = -x + 4$

10. $2x + 5y = 10$

11. $y = -4x + 3$

12. $-6x - 2y = 7$

13. $-2y = x - 2$

14. $3x - 8y = 9$

● **Lesson 2-2 Write in standard form the equation of each line.**

15. slope $= 3; (-1, 4)$ $3x - y = -7$

16. slope $= -1; (0, 7)$ $x + y = 7$

17. slope $= \frac{3}{4}; (2, 8)$ $3x - 4y = -26$

18. slope $= -\frac{2}{5}; (3, -9)$
$2x + 5y = -39$

19. slope $= \frac{8}{3}; (-2, 0)$ $8x - 3y = -16$

20. slope $= -5; (-3, -12)$
$5x + y = -27$

● **Lesson 2-2 Write in point-slope form the equation of the line through each pair of points.**

21. $(0, 2)$ and $(-1, 3)$
$y - 2 = -1(x - 0)$

22. $(1, 2)$ and $(-2, -4)$
$y - 2 = 2(x - 1)$

23. $(11, 4)$ and $(3, 0)$
$y - 0 = \frac{1}{2}(x - 3)$

24. $(-4, -5)$ and $(-1, -8)$
$y + 5 = -1(x + 4)$

25. $(-5, 6)$ and $(3, -10)$
$y - 6 = -2(x + 5)$

26. $(12, 10)$ and $(0, 0)$ $y = \frac{5}{6}x$

● **Lesson 2-2 Find the slope, *y*-intercept, and *x*-intercept of each line.**

27. $y = 2x - 5$ $2, -5, 2.5$

28. $y = -x + 1$ $-1, 1, 1$

29. $y = 4$ $0, 4, \text{none}$

30. $y = 5x + 10$ $5, 10, -2$

31. $y = \frac{1}{3}x - 15$ $\frac{1}{3}, -15, 45$

32. $x = -7$
undefined, none, -7

33. $y = -6x$ $-6, 0, 0$

34. $y = -\frac{2}{5}x + 20$
$-0.4, 20, 50$

● **Lesson 2-2 Write each equation in standard form.   35–38. See back of book.**

35. $y = 3x + 9$

36. $4x = 6y - 9$

37. $2y = 8x - 7$

38. $y = -x + 1$

39. $0.3x + 1.2y = 2.4$
$3x + 12y = 24$

40. $y = \frac{2}{3}x + 15$
$2x - 3y = -45$

41. $x = 8 - y$
$x + y = 8$

42. $\frac{1}{2}x - \frac{3}{4}y = 1$
$2x - 3y = 4$

● **Lesson 2-3 Write an equation of a direct variation that passes through each point.**

43. $(3, 7)$ $y = \frac{7}{3}x$

44. $(5, -8)$ $y = -\frac{8}{5}x$

45. $(-4, -10)$ $y = 2.5x$

46. $(-2, 9)$ $y = -4.5x$

47. $(-6, 6)$ $y = -x$

48. $(6, -3)$ $y = -0.5x$

49. $(12, 8)$ $y = \frac{2}{3}x$

50. $(-15, -1)$ $y = \frac{1}{15}x$

● **Lesson 2-5 Graph each equation by writing two linear equations.   51–58. See back of book.**

51. $y = |x - 2|$

52. $y = \left|x + \frac{1}{2}\right|$

53. $y = |4x + 3|$

54. $y = |4x - 3|$

55. $y = -|x + 4|$

56. $y = 2|x - 3|$

57. $y = |x + 4| - 2$

58. $y = \frac{4}{3}|2x - 1|$

● **Lesson 2-7 Graph each inequality.   59–66. See back of book.**

59. $y < -x + 5$

60. $0.1x + 0.6y \geq 2$

61. $y \leq 3x - 1$

62. $x + 3y > 12$

63. $y \geq 5x - 3$

64. $6x + 2y \geq 7$

65. $y + 1 > \frac{1}{3}x + 2$

66. $5x - 4y \leq -3$

12.

13.

14.

● Lesson 2-1

67. A garden has the shape of an isosceles triangle. The base of the triangle is 42 ft long, with an altitude of h ft. Write an equation that describes the area A of the garden as a function of h. What is the area of the garden for $h = 38$ ft? **$A(h) = 21h$; 798 ft^2**

68. To avoid air turbulence, a plane climbs from an altitude of 20,700 feet higher altitude at the rate of 325 feet per minute. Write a function that describes the altitude, y, of the plane x minutes after it begins its climb find the altitude of the plane for $x = 5$. **$y = 20,700 + 325x$; 22,325 ft**

● Lesson 2-2

69. The blueprint for a toy, shown at the right, identifies two perpendicula each 5 in. long. Suppose each square in the coordinate grid measures 1 the origin is O. Rods I and II are connected at point $A(4, 3)$.   **$y = \frac{3}{4}$**
  a. Write an equation in slope-intercept form for the line containing R
  b. Write an equation in point-slope form for the line containing Rod I

$$y - 3 = -\frac{4}{3}(x - $$

● Lesson 2-3

70. When a pump is turned on, it pumps water at a rate of 12 gal/min. Wha information do you need to know to decide if the volume of water in t varies directly with the time the pump is on? Explain. **See margin.**

71. Williamsville has streets that form a square grid. Adams Street forms the x-axis and Calvin Avenue forms the y-axis. A bank is located at $(100, 0)$, a bus stop at $(300, 0)$, and a post office at $(300, 200)$. Suppose a car departs somewhere on Adams Street, as shown at the right.   **See margin for graphs.**
  a. The minimum distance the car has to drive to get to the bank is an absolute value function $f(x)$, where x is the x-coordinate of the location of the car. Write an equation and draw the graph for $f(x)$. **$f(x) = |x - 100|$**
  b. Let $g(x)$ be the absolute value function that describes the minimum distance the car has to drive to get to the bus stop. Write an equation and draw the graph for this function. **$g(x) = |x - 300|$**
  c. Let $h(x)$ be the function that describes the minimum distance the car has to drive to get to the post office. Write an equation and draw the graph for this function. **$h(x) = |x - 300| + 200$**
  d. Describe how the graphs in parts (a)–(c) are related. **They are translations of each other.**

Calvin Avenue

Legend
B – Bank
S – Bus Stop
P – Post Office

Adams Street

● Lessons 2-4, 2-5, and 2-6

72. The table shows the winning times in the men's Olympic 100-meter freestyle swimming event for the years 1960–2004. Use a graphing calculator.
  a. Make a scatter plot of the data. **See margin.**
  b. Find a line of best fit for the data. Round the coefficients to the nearest hundredth. **$y = -0.14x + 53.56$**
  c. Use the equation for the line of best fit to predict the winning time for the event in the year 2012. **46.28 s**

Years Since 1960	Winning Time
0	55.20
4	53.40
8	52.20
12	51.22
16	49.99
20	50.40
24	49.80
28	48.63
32	49.02
36	48.74
40	48.30
44	48.17

73. A truck rental company purchased a used truck for $18,000. It plans to rent the truck for $75 per day. Write an equation that describes how the profit, y, on the truck is related to the number of days, x, the truck earns rental income. Explain what the intercepts and slope of the graph of this function represent. **$y = 75x - 18,000$; The y-intercept, $-18,000$, represents the initial investment;**

● Lesson 2-7
the x-intercept, 240, represents the days needed for the company to break even; the slope, 75, is the rental income per day.
74. Andrea is going to buy x lbs of pasta salad and y lbs of chicken salad for a party. The pasta salad costs $4 per pound and the chicken salad costs $6 per pound. Andrea has at most $28 to spend. Write and graph an inequality that describes the relationship between x and y. **$4x + 6y \leq 28$; see margin for graph.**

Chapter 2   Extra Practice: Skills and Word Problems   **839**

70. You need to know if there was any water in the tank initially.

71a.

71b.

71c.

72a.

74.

1.

2.

3.

4.

5.

6.

Chapter 3

Extra Practice: Skills and Word Problems

● **Lesson 3-1** Solve each system by graphing.   **1–6. See margin.**

1. $\begin{cases} y = 2x + 1 \\ y = 4x - 5 \end{cases}$

2. $\begin{cases} x + y = 2 \\ y = 2x - 1 \end{cases}$

3. $\begin{cases} y = x + 4 \\ y = -2x + 3 \end{cases}$

4. $\begin{cases} 3x - 4y = 13 \\ 2x + y = 5 \end{cases}$

5. $\begin{cases} 2x = y - 7 \\ 4x - 2y = 14 \end{cases}$

6. $\begin{cases} x = 8 \\ x - y = 2 \end{cases}$

● **Lesson 3-2** Solve each system of equations.

7. $\begin{cases} x + y = 5 \\ x - y = -3 \end{cases}$ **(1, 4)**

8. $\begin{cases} y = 3x - 1 \\ 2x + y = 14 \end{cases}$ **(3, 8)**

9. $\begin{cases} 3x + 2y = 12 \\ x + y = 3 \end{cases}$ **(6, −3)**

10. $\begin{cases} x - 4y = 16 \\ x + 2y = 4 \end{cases}$ **(8, −2)**

11. $\begin{cases} y = 2x + 5 \\ y = 4 - x \end{cases}$ $\left(-\frac{1}{3}, \frac{13}{3}\right)$

12. $\begin{cases} y = 5x - 1 \\ y = 14 \end{cases}$ **(3, 14)**

● **Lesson 3-3** Solve each system of inequalities by graphing.   **13–15. See margin.**

13. $\begin{cases} y \ge x - 3 \\ y \le 3x + 7 \end{cases}$

14. $\begin{cases} 3x + 4y > 8 \\ y < 5x \end{cases}$

15. $\begin{cases} -x - 2y \ge -5 \\ y < 3 \end{cases}$

● **Lesson 3-4** Find the values of x and y that maximize or minimize the objective function.

16. $\begin{cases} x \le 4 \\ y \le 3 \\ x \ge 0 \\ y \ge 0 \end{cases}$

maximum for
$P = 2x + y$
(4, 3)

17. $\begin{cases} x + y \le 5 \\ y \ge x \\ x \ge 0 \end{cases}$

minimum for
$C = x + y$
(0, 0)

18. $\begin{cases} 1 \le x \le 6 \\ 2 \le y \le 4 \\ x + y \ge 4 \end{cases}$

maximum for
$P = 3x + 2y$
(6, 4)

🌐 **19.** A lunch stand makes $.75 in profit on each chef's salad and $1.20 in profit on each Caesar salad. On a typical weekday, it sells between 40 and 60 chef's salads and between 35 and 50 Caesar salads. The total number sold has never exceeded 100 salads. How many of each type of salad should be prepared to maximize profit?   **50 chef's salads and 50 Caesar salads**

● **Lesson 3-5** Graph each point in coordinate space.   **20–28. See back of book.**

20. $(0, 3, 0)$

21. $(4, 0, -2)$

22. $(0, 0, 5)$

23. $(1, 1, 0)$

24. $(0, 4, 2)$

25. $(-1, 2, 2)$

26. $(3, 0, 1)$

27. $(6, 1, 3)$

28. $(3, -1, 4)$

● **Lesson 3-5** Sketch the graph of each equation.   **29–34. See back of book.**

29. $x - y + z = 4$

30. $2x - y - z = 6$

31. $-x + y + 3z = 9$

32. $x + y + z = 5$

33. $-5x + 2y + 2z = 10$

34. $x - y + 3z = 3$

● **Lesson 3-6** Solve each system of equations.

35. $\begin{cases} x + y + z = 6 \\ x = 2y \\ z = x + 1 \end{cases}$ **(2, 1, 3)**

36. $\begin{cases} x - 2y + z = 8 \\ y - z = 4 \\ z = 3 \end{cases}$ **(19, 7, 3)**

37. $\begin{cases} 3x + y - z = 15 \\ x - y + 3z = -19 \\ 2x + 2y + z = 4 \end{cases}$
(2, 3, −6)

13.

14.

15.

● Lessons 3-1 and 3-2

38. Carla has $2.40 in nickels and dimes. Deron has $5.50 in dimes and quarters. Deron has as many dimes as Carla has nickels and as many quarters as Carla has dimes. How many of each kind of coin does Carla have? **20 nickels, 14 dimes**

39. A kayaker can paddle 12 mi in 2 h moving with the river current. Paddling at the same pace, the trip back against the current takes 4 h. Assume that the river current is constant. Find what the kayaker's speed would be in still water. **4.5 mi/h**

40. Mrs. Mitchell put a total of $10,000 into two accounts. One account earns 6% simple annual interest. The other account earns 6.5% simple interest. After 1 year, the two accounts earned $632.50 interest. Find how much money was invested in each account. **$3500 at 6%, $6500 at 6.5%**

41. Mr. Chandra bought 2 lbs of cheddar cheese and 3 lbs of chicken loaf. He paid $26.35. Mrs. Hsing paid $18.35 for 1.5 lbs of cheese and 2 lbs of chicken loaf. What was the price per pound of each item? **$4.70 per lb of cheese, $5.65 per lb of chicken loaf**

● Lesson 3-3

42. Leyla wants to buy fish, chicken, or some of each for weekend meals. The fish costs $4 per pound and the chicken costs $3 per pound. She will spend at least $11 but no more than $15. **a–b. See margin.**
 a. Write a system of inequalities to model the situation.
 b. Graph the system to show the possible amounts Layla could buy.

43. A furniture company makes desks and chairs. A carpenter can make a chair in 5 h and a desk in 8 h. Finishers take 2.5 h to paint a chair and 2 h to paint a desk. The carpentry department has enough people to work up to 400 h per week, and the finishing department can put in 120 h per week. **a–b. See margin.**
 a. Write a system of inequalities to model the situation.
 b. Graph the system to show the possible numbers of desks and chairs the company can produce in a week.

● Lesson 3-4

44. There are 20 true/false and 20 multiple choice questions on a test. A correct answer to a true/false question earns 10 points. A correct answer to a multiple choice question earns 12 points. The test makers determined that it takes, on average, 3 minutes to answer a true/false question and 4 minutes to answer a multiple choice question. Students have 1 hour to answer at most 18 questions of their choice. How many of each kind of question should a student answer correctly to get the greatest possible score? **12 true/false, 6 multiple choice**

45. A caterer must make at least 50 gal of potato soup and at least 120 gal of tomato soup. One chef can make 5 gal of potato soup and 6 gal of tomato soup in 1 h. Another chef can make 4 gal of potato soup and 12 gal of tomato soup in 1 h. The first chef earns $20/h. The second chef earns $22/h. How many hours should the company ask each chef to work to minimize the cost? **first chef: $3\frac{1}{3}$ h, second chef: $8\frac{1}{3}$ h**

● Lessons 3-5 and 3-6

46. Three pumps can transfer 4150 gal of water per day when working at the same time. Pumps A and B together can transfer 3200 gal per day. Pumps A and C together can transfer 2900 gal per day. How many gallons can each pump transfer working alone? **Pump A: 1950 gal, Pump B: 1250 gal; Pump C: 950 gal**

47. For the school play, the Chavez family bought 2 student tickets, 1 adult ticket, and 2 senior tickets for $43. The Martinez family bought 3 student tickets and 2 adult tickets for $48. The Lynn family bought 4 student tickets, 2 adult tickets, and 1 senior ticket for $62. What was the price of each kind of ticket? **Student: $6 Adult: $15 Senior: $8**

42a. $$\begin{cases} 4x + 3y \geq 11 \\ 4x + 3y \leq 15 \\ x \geq 0 \\ y \geq 0 \end{cases}$$

b.

43a. $$\begin{cases} 5x + 8y \leq 400 \\ 2.5x + 2y \leq 120 \\ x \geq 0 \\ y \geq 0 \end{cases}$$

b.

11. $\begin{bmatrix} -62 & 121 \\ 43 & -54 \end{bmatrix}$

12. $\begin{bmatrix} -13 & -5 & -2 \\ -13 & 4 & 1 \end{bmatrix}$

13. $\begin{bmatrix} 5 & -7 & 7 \\ 2 & 1 & -2 \end{bmatrix}$

14. $\begin{bmatrix} -2.4 & 10.1 \\ 18.8 & -14 \end{bmatrix}$

15. $\begin{bmatrix} -26 & 7 & 5 \\ -4 & -7 & 25 \end{bmatrix}$

16. product undefined

17. $\begin{bmatrix} 16 & 2 \\ -4 & 10 \end{bmatrix}$

18. $\begin{bmatrix} 41 & 103 & 19 \\ 13 & 45 & 13 \\ 2 & 14 & 6 \end{bmatrix}$

19. product undefined

20. $\begin{bmatrix} 9 & -3 & 0 \\ 6 & 3 & -15 \end{bmatrix}$

21. $\begin{bmatrix} 1.6 & 0.2 \\ -0.4 & 1 \end{bmatrix}$

22. product undefined

23. $\begin{bmatrix} 45 & 20 \\ 25 & 5 \\ 10 & 0 \end{bmatrix}$

24. $\begin{bmatrix} -35 & 5 & 20 \\ -17 & 4 & 5 \\ -6 & 2 & 0 \end{bmatrix}$

25. $\begin{bmatrix} 0.5 & 3.5 & 1.5 \\ 4 & 5 & -1 \end{bmatrix}$

26. $\begin{bmatrix} -22 & -11 \\ -13 & -9 \end{bmatrix}$

27. $\begin{bmatrix} 5 & 10 & 20 \\ 25 & -5 & 15 \end{bmatrix}$

28. $\begin{bmatrix} -2 & -1 & 1 \\ 6 & 0 & 4 \end{bmatrix}$

29. $\begin{bmatrix} 3 & 4 & 6 \\ -2 & -8 & -4 \end{bmatrix}$

30. $\begin{bmatrix} \frac{1}{3} & \frac{2}{3} & \frac{4}{3} \\ \frac{5}{3} & -\frac{1}{3} & 1 \end{bmatrix}$

31. $\begin{bmatrix} \frac{68}{15} & -\frac{34}{15} \\ -\frac{16}{15} & \frac{83}{15} \end{bmatrix}$

Chapter 4

Extra Practice: Skills and Word Problems

Lesson 4-1 State the dimensions of each matrix. Identify the indicated element.

1. $\begin{bmatrix} 3 & 1 & -5 \\ 6 & 9 & 10 \end{bmatrix}; a_{21}$ 2 × 3; 6

2. $\begin{bmatrix} 0.5 & 6.1 \\ -9.2 & 4.7 \end{bmatrix}; a_{11}$ 2 × 2; 0.5

3. $\begin{bmatrix} 56 & -83 & 12 \\ 101 & -71 & 49 \end{bmatrix}; a_{12}$ 2 × 3; −83

4. $\begin{bmatrix} 5 & 8 \\ -2 & 3 \\ 3 & 4 \end{bmatrix}; a_{21}$ 3 × 2; −2

5. $\begin{bmatrix} \frac{1}{4} & \frac{3}{8} \end{bmatrix}; a_{12}$ 1 × 2; $\frac{3}{8}$

6. $\begin{bmatrix} 17 & -23 & 79 \\ 47 & 61 & 5 \end{bmatrix}; a_{22}$ 2 × 3; 61

Lesson 4-2 Find each sum or difference.

7. $\begin{bmatrix} -8 & 3 \\ 19 & -45 \end{bmatrix} + \begin{bmatrix} 12 & 64 \\ -7 & 63 \end{bmatrix}$ $\begin{bmatrix} 4 & 67 \\ 12 & 18 \end{bmatrix}$

8. $\begin{bmatrix} 3.6 & -9.8 \\ 4.0 & -1.7 \end{bmatrix} - \begin{bmatrix} 0.8 & 3.4 \\ -6.1 & 7.9 \end{bmatrix}$ $\begin{bmatrix} 2.8 & -13.2 \\ 10.1 & -9.6 \end{bmatrix}$

9. $\begin{bmatrix} 4 & 6 & -3 \\ 8 & -9 & -1 \end{bmatrix} - \begin{bmatrix} 10 & 7 & -3 \\ -9 & 2 & 7 \end{bmatrix}$ $\begin{bmatrix} -6 & -1 & 0 \\ 17 & -11 & -8 \end{bmatrix}$

10. $\begin{bmatrix} -308 & 651 \\ 912 & -347 \end{bmatrix} + \begin{bmatrix} 105 & 318 \\ -762 & -438 \end{bmatrix}$ $\begin{bmatrix} -203 & 969 \\ 150 & -785 \end{bmatrix}$

Lesson 4-3 Solve each matrix equation.   11–14. See margin.

11. $\begin{bmatrix} 25 & -60 \\ 42 & 91 \end{bmatrix} + X = \begin{bmatrix} -37 & 61 \\ 85 & 37 \end{bmatrix}$

12. $\begin{bmatrix} -8 & 3 & 1 \\ -9 & 6 & 7 \end{bmatrix} - X = \begin{bmatrix} 5 & 8 & 3 \\ 4 & 2 & 6 \end{bmatrix}$

13. $X + \begin{bmatrix} 6 & 2 & 9 \\ 1 & 5 & 10 \end{bmatrix} = \begin{bmatrix} 11 & -5 & 16 \\ 3 & 6 & 8 \end{bmatrix}$

14. $X - \begin{bmatrix} 2.3 & 6.5 \\ 9.4 & -8.2 \end{bmatrix} = \begin{bmatrix} -4.7 & 3.6 \\ 9.4 & -5.8 \end{bmatrix}$

Lesson 4-3 For exercises 15–26, use matrices *A*, *B*, *C*, and *D* shown below. Perform the indicated operations if they are defined. If an operation is not defined, label it *undefined*.   15–26. See margin.

$$A = \begin{bmatrix} 8 & 1 \\ -2 & 5 \end{bmatrix} \quad B = \begin{bmatrix} -3 & 1 & 0 \\ -2 & -1 & 5 \end{bmatrix} \quad C = \begin{bmatrix} 9 & 4 \\ 5 & 1 \\ 2 & 0 \end{bmatrix} \quad D = \begin{bmatrix} 1 & 7 & 3 \\ 8 & 10 & -2 \end{bmatrix}$$

15. *AB*

16. *BD*

17. 2*A*

18. *CD*

19. *DA*

20. −3*B*

21. 0.2*A*

22. *BA*

23. 5*C*

24. *CB*

25. $\frac{1}{2}D$

26. *BC*

Lesson 4-4 Use △*ABC* with coordinates *A*(1, 5), *B*(2, −1), and *C*(4, 3). Write the coordinates of each image in matrix form.   27–30. See margin.

27. a dilation 5 times the size

28. a translation 3 units left and 1 unit up

29. a translation 2 units right and 7 units down

30. a dilation one third the size

Lesson 4-5 Solve each matrix equation. If an equation cannot be solved, explain why.

31. $\begin{bmatrix} 2 & 1 \\ -1 & 7 \end{bmatrix} X = \begin{bmatrix} 8 & 1 \\ -12 & 41 \end{bmatrix}$
See margin.

32. $\begin{bmatrix} -1 & 0 \\ 6 & 3 \end{bmatrix} X = \begin{bmatrix} -9 \\ -3 \end{bmatrix} \begin{bmatrix} 9 \\ -19 \end{bmatrix}$

33. $\begin{bmatrix} -3 & 5 \\ 1 & 8 \end{bmatrix} X = \begin{bmatrix} 29 \\ 58 \end{bmatrix} \begin{bmatrix} 2 \\ 7 \end{bmatrix}$

Lesson 4-7 Solve each system of equations. Check your answers.

34. $\begin{cases} x - y = 3 \\ x + y = 5 \end{cases}$ (4, 1)

35. $\begin{cases} x - 2y = 7 \\ x + 3y = 12 \end{cases}$ (9, 1)

36. $\begin{cases} 2x + 5y = 10 \\ x + y = 2 \end{cases}$ (0, 2)

● Lessons 4-1, 4-2, and 4-3

37. A frozen yogurt supplier uses two machines to make chocolate and vanilla frozen yogurt. Both machines can be used in the morning and afternoon. Matrix A show the maximum hourly output of each machine. Matrix B shows how long the machines are used for production of each flavor.

Matrix A: **Output (gal/h)**

	Chocolate	Vanilla
Machine 1	4	5
Machine 2	7	8

Matrix B: **Time (h)**

	A.M.	P.M.
Chocolate	2	3
Vanilla	1	2

37a. $\begin{bmatrix} 13 & 22 \\ 22 & 37 \end{bmatrix}$

a. Compute the product AB of these matrices. **See right.**
b. Describe what this product represents. **the total number of gal. of chocolate and vanilla yogurt made for each machine in the A.M. and P.M.**

38. A distributor has orders for desk lamps and floor lamps from two motels. Matrix A shows the number of lamps each motel will purchase. Matrix B shows the cost of each type of lamp. **a–b. See margin.**

Matrix A:

	Desk	Floor
Motel 1	20	7
Motel 2	25	6

Matrix B:

	Cost
Desk	85
Floor	130

a. Compute the product AB of these matrices. **See margin.**
b. Describe what this product represents. **the total cost of lamps for each motel**

● Lesson 4-4

39. The matrix $\begin{bmatrix} \dfrac{\sqrt{3}}{2} & -\dfrac{1}{2} \\ \dfrac{1}{2} & \dfrac{\sqrt{3}}{2} \end{bmatrix}$ represents a 30° counterclockwise rotation. The preimage is $\triangle ABC$ with the vertices $A(1, 1)$, $B(1, 2)$, and $C(5, 4)$. Write a matrix for the vertices of the image. **See margin.**

● Lessons 4-5 and 4-6

40. County economists calculated that, in an average year, 9% of employed people lose their jobs and 86% of the unemployed find new jobs. The remaining people remain employed or unemployed, depending on their previous status. On January 1, the county has an unemployment rate of 7%. Calculate the expected unemployment rate for the next two years to the nearest tenth of a percent. **Year 1: 9.4%; Year 2: 9.5%**

● Lessons 4-7 and 4-8

41. Margery got a total of 249 points on three tests. The combined scores on the first two tests were 95 more than the score on the third test. The score on the second test was 6 points more than the score on the first test. Write and solve a matrix equation to find the score on each test. **See margin.**

42. Leona's Diner offers 8-piece, 12-piece, and 16-piece family chicken meals. The table at the right lists the costs of three different orders. What is the price of each kind of meal?
8-piece: $12; 12-piece: $17; 16-piece: $21

8-piece meals	12-piece meals	16-piece meals	Total Cost
2	3	1	$96
4	5	0	$133
2	4	2	$134

43. At a diner, two hot dogs and one hamburger cost $10, while three hot dogs and two hamburgers cost $17.25. Write and solve a matrix equation to find the cost of a hot dog and a hamburger. **See margin.**

38a. $\begin{array}{l} \text{motel 1} \\ \text{motel 2} \end{array} \begin{bmatrix} 2610 \\ 2905 \end{bmatrix}$

b. The total cost of lamps for each motel.

39.
$$\begin{bmatrix} \dfrac{\sqrt{3}-1}{2} & \dfrac{\sqrt{3}-2}{2} & \dfrac{5\sqrt{3}-4}{2} \\ \dfrac{\sqrt{3}+1}{2} & \dfrac{\sqrt{3}+2}{2} & \dfrac{4\sqrt{3}+5}{2} \end{bmatrix}$$

41.
$$\begin{bmatrix} 1 & 1 & 1 \\ 1 & 1 & -1 \\ -1 & 1 & 0 \end{bmatrix}\begin{bmatrix} x \\ y \\ z \end{bmatrix} = \begin{bmatrix} 249 \\ 95 \\ 6 \end{bmatrix};$$
$x = 83$, $y = 89$, $z = 77$

43. $\begin{bmatrix} 2 & 1 \\ 3 & 2 \end{bmatrix}\begin{bmatrix} x \\ y \end{bmatrix} = \begin{bmatrix} 10 \\ 17.25 \end{bmatrix};$
$x = 2.75$, $y = 4.50$

7.

8.

9.

10.

11.

12.

13.

Chapter 5 Extra Practice: Skills and Word Problems

● **Lesson 5-1** Determine whether each function is *linear* or *quadratic*. Identify the quadratic, linear, and constant terms.

1. $y = 3x + 4$ linear; none, $3x$, 4
2. $y = x^2 + 1$ quadratic; x^2, none, 1
3. $3x + 2y = 1$ linear; none, $-\frac{3}{2}x$, $\frac{1}{2}$

4. $y = (x + 1)(x - 1)$
quadratic; x^2, none, -1
5. $y = 3 - x^2$
quadratic; $-x^2$, none, 3
6. $y = 5x(x + 2)$
quadratic; $5x^2$, $10x$, none

● **Lessons 5-2 and 5-3** Graph each function. 7–14. See margin.

7. $y = 3x^2$
8. $y = (x + 3)^2 + 1$
9. $y = 2x^2 + 4$
10. $y = \frac{1}{2}(x - 3)^2$

11. $y = x^2 - 9$
12. $y = 2(x + 1)^2 - 5$
13. $y = (x + 1)^2 - 3$
14. $y = (x - 2)^2$

● **Lesson 5-4** Factor each expression. 15–22. See margin.

15. $x^2 + 3x - 54$
16. $x^2 + 10x + 24$
17. $x^2 - 36$
18. $x^2 - 9x - 36$

19. $x^2 - 15x + 56$
20. $25x^2 + 70x + 49$
21. $7x^2 - 20x - 3$
22. $5x^2 + 23x - 10$

23. $\frac{1}{4}x^2 - 4$
$\frac{1}{4}(x - 4)(x + 4)$
24. $x^2 - 6x - 16$
$(x - 8)(x + 2)$
25. $4x^2 + 12x + 40$
$4(x^2 + 3x + 10)$
26. $4x^2 - 6x + 9$
cannot be factored

● **Lesson 5-5** Solve each equation by factoring, by taking square roots, or by graphing. When necessary, round your answer to the nearest hundredth. 27–29. See margin.

27. $x^2 + 4x - 1 = 0$
28. $4x^2 - 100 = 0$
29. $x^2 = -2x + 1$
30. $x^2 - 9 = 0$ ± 3

31. $2x^2 + 4x = 70$ $-7, 5$
32. $x^2 - 30 = 10$ ± 6.32
33. $x^2 + 4x = 0$ $0, -4$
34. $x^2 + 3x + 2 = 0$
$-2, -1$

● **Lesson 5-6** Simplify each expression.

35. $(3 - i) + (5 - 2i)$ $8 - 3i$
36. $(4 + 2i)(1 - i)$ $6 - 2i$
37. $(4 + 2i) - (3 + 5i)$ $1 - 3i$

38. $(8 - 3i)(6 + 9i)$ $75 + 54i$
39. $(2 + 5i) - (-6 + i)$ $8 + 4i$
40. $(-2 - 3i)(7 - i)$ $-17 - 19i$

● **Lesson 5-6** Solve each equation. Check your answers.

41. $x^2 + 16 = 0$ $\pm 4i$
42. $4x^2 = -1$ $\pm \frac{1}{2}i$
43. $x^2 = -10$ $\pm i\sqrt{10}$

44. $4x^2 + 48 = 0$ $\pm 2i\sqrt{3}$
45. $-2x^2 = 5$ $\pm i\frac{\sqrt{10}}{2}$
46. $x^2 + 3 = 0$ $\pm i\sqrt{3}$

● **Lesson 5-6** Find the first three output values of each fractal-generating function. Use $z = 0$ as the first input value.

47. $f(z) = z^2 - i$ $-i, -1 - i, i$
48. $f(z) = z^2 + 2 + i$ $2 + i, 5 + 5i, 2 + 51i$

● **Lessons 5-7 and 5-8** Solve each equation by completing the square or using the Quadratic Formula.

49. $x^2 + 5x + 8 = 4$ $-1, -4$
50. $8x^2 + 64 = 0$ $\pm 2i\sqrt{2}$
51. $2x^2 - 5x + 1 = 0$ $\frac{5}{4} \pm \frac{\sqrt{17}}{4}$

52. $3x^2 = x - 9$ $\frac{1}{6} \pm \frac{i\sqrt{107}}{6}$
53. $x^2 + 10 = 4x - 2$ $2 \pm 2i\sqrt{2}$
54. $x^2 - 7x = 0$ $0, 7$

55. $x^2 + 4x + 4 = 0$ -2
56. $x^2 - 7 = 0$ $\pm\sqrt{7}$
57. $x^2 + 8x - 17 = 0$ $-4 \pm \sqrt{33}$

● **Lesson 5-8** Evaluate the discriminant of each equation. Tell how many solutions each equation has and whether the solutions are real or imaginary. 58–61. See margin.

58. $x^2 + 4x = 17$
59. $2x^2 + x = -1$
60. $x^2 - 4x + 5 = 0$
61. $2x^2 + 5x = 0$

62. $x^2 - 19 = 1$
80; 2, real
63. $3x^2 = 8x - 4$
16; 2, real
64. $-2x^2 + 1 = 7x$
57; 2, real
65. $4x^2 + 4x = -1$
0; 1, real

14.

15. $(x + 9)(x - 6)$
16. $(x + 6)(x + 4)$
17. $(x - 6)(x + 6)$
18. $(x - 12)(x + 3)$
19. $(x - 8)(x - 7)$

20. $(5x + 7)^2$
21. $(7x + 1)(x - 3)$
22. $(5x - 2)(x + 5)$
27. 0.24, -4.24
28. ± 5

29. 0.41, -2.41
58. 84; 2, real
59. -7; 2, imaginary
60. -4; 2, imaginary
61. 25; 2, real

Lesson 5-1

66. The table shows the relation between the speed of a car and its stopping distance.

Speed (mi/h)	35	45	50	60
Stopping Distance (ft)	96	140	165	221

a. Use a quadratic function to model the data. **$f(x) = 0.04x^2 + 1.2x + 5$**
b. Predict the stopping distance for a car traveling at 65 mi/h. **252 ft**

Lessons 5-2 and 5-3

67. Martin has 120 feet of fencing to enclose two rectangular play areas for children. He plans to enclose a rectangular area and then divide it into two equal sections, as shown in the figure. **30 ft by 20 ft**
a. Find the dimensions of the largest total area Martin can enclose.
b. Find the area of each of the small play areas. **300 ft²**

68. Marnie throws a softball straight up into the air. The ball leaves her hand when it is exactly 5 ft from the ground. The height h of the ball, in feet, can be written as a function of time t, in seconds, as $h = -16t^2 + 40t + 5$.
a. What is the maximum height the ball reaches? **30 ft**
b. Marnie catches the ball 5 ft from the ground. How long was the ball in the air? **2.5 s**

Lessons 5-4 and 5-5

69. Hal's sister is 5 years older than Hal. The product of their ages is 456. How old are Hal and his sister? **19 years old; 24 years old**

70. A toy rocket is fired upward from the ground. The relation between its height h, in feet, and the time t from launch, in seconds, can be described by the equation $h = -16t^2 + 64t$. How long does the rocket stay more than 48 feet above the ground? **2 s**

71. The expression $P(x) = 2500x - 2x^2$ describes the profit of a company that customizes bulldozers when it customizes x bulldozers in a month.
a. How many bulldozers per month must the company customize to make the maximum possible profit? What is the maximum profit? **625 bulldozers; $781,250**
b. Describe a reasonable domain and range for the function $P(x)$. **$x \geq 0$; $P(x) \leq \$781{,}250$**
c. For what number of bulldozers per month is the profit at least $750,000? **$500 \leq x \leq 750$**

72. Flor is designing a kite with two perpendicular crosspieces that are 26 inches and 24 inches long, as shown in the figure. How long should $\overline{AK}$ be so that $\overline{AB} \perp \overline{BC}$ and $\overline{AD} \perp \overline{DC}$? **8 in.**

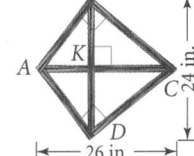

73. The lengths of the sides of a right triangle are x, $x + 4$, and $x + 8$ inches. What is the value of x? What is the length of the hypotenuse of the triangle? **12; 20 in.**

Lessons 5-6, 5-7, and 5-8

74. The height y of a parabolic arch is given by $y = -\frac{1}{16}x^2 + 40$, where x is the horizontal distance from the center of the base of the arch. All distances are in feet.
a. What is the highest point on the arch? **40 ft**
b. How wide is the arch at the base to the nearest tenth of a foot? **50.6 ft**

75. An archer's arrow follows a parabolic path. The path of the arrow can be described by the equation $y = -0.005x^2 + 2x + 5$. **The archer releases the arrow 5 ft above**
a. Describe the meaning of the y-intercept of the graph of the equation. **the ground.**
b. What is the horizontal distance the arrow travels before it hits the ground? Round your answer to the nearest foot. **402 ft**

Chapter 5   Extra Practice: Skills and Word Problems   **845**

CHAPTER 6

page 846   Extra Practice

1. $-4a^2 + 3a$; quadratic binomial

2. $-2x - \frac{1}{3}$; linear binomial

3. $-2n^3 + 3n^2 - n - 3$; cubic polynomial of 4 terms

4. $-y^2 - 2y + 7$; quadratic trinomial

5. $-2c^2 - 4c + 7$; quadratic trinomial

6. $2x^2$; quadratic monomial

7. $y = x^3 - 4x^2 + x + 6$

8. $y = x^3 - 4x^2 + 5x - 2$

9. $y = x^3 + 2x^2 - x - 2$

10. $y = x^3 - 9x^2 + 20x - 12$

11. $y = x^3 - x^2 - 17x - 15$

12. $y = x^4 - 5x^3 + 6x^2$

13. $y = x^4 - 3x^3 - 2x^2 + 12x - 8$

14. $y = x^4 - 18x^3 + 115x^2 - 306x + 280$

48. $x^3 - 3x^2 + 3x - 1$

49. $81x^4 + 216x^3 + 216x^2 + 96x + 16$

50. $64x^3 + 480x^2 + 1200x + 1000$

51. $16x^4 + 160x^3y + 600x^2y^2 + 1000xy^3 + 625y^4$

52. $x^8 + 8x^6 + 24x^4 + 32x^2 + 16$

53. $x^7 + 14x^6y + 84x^5y^2 + 280x^4y^3 + 560x^3y^4 + 672x^2y^5 + 448xy^6 + 128y^7$

54. $3125x^5 - 3125x^4y + 1250x^3y^2 - 250x^2y^3 + 25xy^4 - y^5$

55. $x^4 - 16x^3y^3 + 96x^2y^6 - 256xy^9 + 256y^{12}$

846

Chapter 6

Extra Practice: Skills and Word Problems

● **Lesson 6-1** **Write each polynomial in standard form. Then classify it by degree and by number of terms.   1–6. See margin.**

  1. $a^2 + 4a - 5a^2 - a$ **2.** $3x - \frac{1}{3} - 5x$ **3.** $3n^2 + n^3 - n - 3 - 3n^3$

  4. $15 - y^2 - 10y - 8 + 8y$ **5.** $6c^2 - 4c + 7 - 8c^2$ **6.** $3x^2 - 5x - x^2 + x + 4x$

● **Lesson 6-2** **Write a polynomial function in standard form with the given zeros.   7–14. See margin.**

  7. $x = 3, 2, -1$ **8.** $x = 1, 1, 2$ **9.** $x = -2, -1, 1$ **10.** $x = 1, 2, 6$

  11. $x = -3, -1, 5$ **12.** $x = 0, 0, 2, 3$ **13.** $x = -2, 1, 2, 2$ **14.** $x = 2, 4, 5, 7$

● **Lesson 6-3** **Divide.**

  15. $(x^3 - 3x^2 + 2) \div (x - 1)$ $x^2 - 2x - 2$ **16.** $(x^3 - x^2 - 6x) \div (x - 3)$ $x^2 + 2x$

  17. $(2x^3 + 10x^2 + 8x) \div (x + 4)$ $2x^2 + 2x$ **18.** $(x^4 + x^2 - 6) \div (x^2 + 3)$ $x^2 - 2$

  19. $(x^2 - 4x + 2) \div (x - 2)$ $x - 2$, R -2 **20.** $(x^3 + 11x + 12) \div (x + 3)$ $x^2 - 3x + 20$, R -48

● **Lesson 6-4** **Solve each equation.**

  21. $t^3 - 3t^2 - 10t = 0$ $0, -2, 5$ **22.** $4m^3 + m^2 - m + 5 = 0$ $-1.25, \frac{1}{2} \pm \frac{i\sqrt{3}}{2}$ **23.** $t^3 - 6t^2 + 12t - 8 = 0$ 2

  24. $2c^3 - 7c^2 - 4c = 0$ $0, -\frac{1}{2}, 4$ **25.** $w^4 - 13w^2 + 36 = 0$ $\pm 3, \pm 2$ **26.** $x^3 + 2x^2 - 13x + 10 = 0$ $-5, 1, 2$

● **Lesson 6-5** **Find the roots of each polynomial equation.**

  27. $x^3 + 2x^2 + 3x + 6 = 0$ $-2, \pm i\sqrt{3}$ **28.** $x^3 - 3x^2 + 4x - 12 = 0$ $3, \pm 2i$

  29. $3x^4 + 11x^3 + 14x^2 + 7x + 1 = 0$ $-1, \frac{-5 \pm \sqrt{13}}{6}$ **30.** $3x^4 - x^3 - 22x^2 + 24x = 0$ $-3, 0, \frac{4}{3}, 2$

  31. $45x^3 + 93x^2 - 12 = 0$ $-2, -\frac{2}{5}, \frac{1}{3}$ **32.** $8x^4 - 66x^3 + 175x^2 - 132x - 45 = 0$ $-\frac{1}{4}, \frac{5}{2}, 3$

● **Lesson 6-7** **Evaluate each expression.**

  33. $6!$ 720 **34.** $3!4!$ 144 **35.** $\frac{7!}{4!}$ 210 **36.** $\frac{6!2!}{8!}$ $\frac{1}{28}$

  37. $_8P_5$ 6720 **38.** $_4C_1$ 4 **39.** $_6C_2$ 15 **40.** $_6P_2$ 30

  41. $_7C_3$ 35 **42.** $_7P_3$ 210 **43.** $2(_7C_5)$ 42 **44.** $\frac{_7C_5}{_5C_2}$ 2.1

● **Lesson 6-7** **Indicate whether each situation involves a combination or a permutation. Then answer the question.**

  45. How many different orders can you choose to read six of the nine books on your summer reading list? **permutation; 60,480 orders**

  46. How many ways are there to choose five shirts out of seven to take to camp? **combination; 21 ways**

  47. How many ways can you choose two out of four kinds of flowers for a bouquet? **combination; 6 ways**

● **Lesson 6-8** **Use the Binomial Theorem to expand each binomial.**

  48. $(x - 1)^3$ **49.** $(3x + 2)^4$ **50.** $(4x + 10)^3$ **51.** $(2x + 5y)^4$

  52. $(x^2 + 2)^4$ **53.** $(x + 2y)^7$ **54.** $(5x - y)^5$ **55.** $(x - 4y^3)^4$

                              48–55. See margin.

● **Lessons 6-1, 6-2, and 6-3**

56. Tonya wants to make a metal tray by cutting four identical square corner pieces from a rectangular metal sheet. Then she will bend the sides up to make an open tray.
   a. Let the length of each side of the removed squares be x in. Express the volume of the box as a polynomial function of x. $V(x) = 4x^3 - 72x^2 + 320x$
   b. Find the dimensions of a tray that would have a 384-in.^{3} capacity.
      2 in. high, 12 in. by 16 in. base or 4 in. high, 12 in. by 8 in. base

20 in.

16 in.

not to scale

57. The product of three consecutive integers is 210. Use N to represent the middle integer.
   a. Write the product as a polynomial function of $P(N)$. **Answers may vary: Sample:**
   b. Find the three integers. **5, 6, 7** $P(N) = (N - 1)N(N + 1) = N^3 - N$

58. To determine safe dosage of a medication, researchers measure the concentration of the medication in a patient's bloodstream. Let the function that models the concentration in parts per million at x hours after the medication is administered be $C(x) = -\frac{2}{3}x^4 + 8x^3 - \frac{130}{3}x^2 + 116x$.
   a. How many hours does it take for the medication to be completely eliminated from a patient's bloodstream? **6 h**
   b. How many hours is the concentration above 80 parts per million? **4 h**

● **Lessons 6-4, 6-5, and 6-6**

59. A block of cheese is a cube whose side is x in. long. You cut off a 1-inch thick piece from the right side. Then you cut off a 3-inch thick piece from the top, as shown at the right. The volume of the remaining block is 2002 in.^{3}. What are the dimensions of the original block of cheese? **14 in. by 14 in. by 14 in.**

60. You can construct triangles by connecting three vertices of a convex polygon with n sides. The number of all possible such triangles can be represented as $f(n) = \frac{n^3 - 3n^2 + 2n}{6}$. Find the value of n such that you can construct 84 such triangles from the polygon. **9**

● **Lessons 6-7 and 6-8**

61. You must answer exactly 12 out of 15 questions on a test. How many different ways can you select the questions to answer? **455 ways**

62. A lab assigns a three-digit identification to each subject in an experiment. No two subjects have the same identification. No digit can be repeated in an identification. What is the greatest number of subjects that can be used in the experiment? **720 subjects**

63. To mark its eighth anniversary, Pizzeria Otto has a special coupon that offers the same price on a pizza with any combination of the 8 original toppings. Each pizza must have at least one topping. How many different kinds of pizza can be ordered with the coupon? **255 kinds of pizza**

64. Ten friends want to take photographs of each other with exactly four of them in each picture. They want exactly one photograph with each combination. How many photographs do they need to take? **210 photographs**

65. A total of 23 students will be coming to the end-of-the-year picnic. In how many ways can the teacher select 6 students for the clean-up crew? **100,947 ways**

66. City streets form a square grid. Each street runs one-way, either north or east. You want to take a taxi from a post office to a bank that is five blocks east and seven blocks north. How many different routes can the taxi take from the post office to the bank? **792 routes**

44. $f^{-1}(x) = \frac{x-1}{6}$;
domain of f: all real numbers,
range of f: all real numbers,
domain of f^{-1}: all real numbers,
range of f^{-1}: all real numbers;
f^{-1} is a function.

45. $f^{-1}(x) = x^2 - 4$, $x \geq 0$;
domain of f: $\{x \geq -4\}$,
range of f: $\{y \geq 0\}$,
domain of f^{-1}: $\{x \geq 0\}$,
range of f^{-1}: $\{y \geq -4\}$;
f^{-1} is a function.

46. $f^{-1}(x) = x^2 + 3$, $x \geq 0$;
domain of f: $\{x \geq 3\}$,
range of f: $\{y \geq 0\}$,
domain of f^{-1}: $\{x \geq 0\}$,
range of f^{-1}: $\{y \geq 3\}$;
f^{-1} is a function.

47. $f^{-1}(x) = -\frac{x^2 - 2}{5}$, $x \geq 0$;
domain of f: $\left\{x \leq \frac{2}{5}\right\}$,
range of f: $\{y \geq 0\}$,
domain of f^{-1}: $\{x \geq 0\}$,
range of f^{-1}: $\left\{y \leq \frac{2}{5}\right\}$;
f^{-1} is a function.

48. $f^{-1}(x) = \pm\sqrt{\frac{x-1}{3}}$;
domain of f: all real numbers,
range of f: $\{y \geq 1\}$,
domain of f^{-1}: $\{x \geq 1\}$,
range of f^{-1}: all real numbers;
f^{-1} is not a function.

49. $f^{-1}(x) = \pm\sqrt{2 - x}$;
domain of f: all real numbers,
range of f: $\{y \leq 2\}$,
domain of f^{-1}: $\{x \leq 2\}$,
range of f^{-1}: all real numbers;
f^{-1} is not a function.

● **Lesson 7-1** Simplify each radical expression. Use absolute value symbols as needed.

1. $\sqrt{36x^4}$ $6x^2$

2. $\sqrt{c^{80}d^{50}}$ $c^{40}|d^{25}|$

3. $\sqrt[4]{81x^{12}}$ $3|x^3|$

4. $\sqrt[3]{-64}$ -4

5. $\sqrt[5]{-32k^5}$ $-2k$

6. $\sqrt[4]{\frac{1}{16}w^{12}}$ $\frac{1}{2}|w^3|$

7. $\sqrt[4]{m^{18}n^8}$ $m^4n^2\sqrt{m}$

8. $\sqrt[3]{27y^{15}}$ $3y^5$

● **Lesson 7-2** Multiply or divide and simplify. Assume that all variables are positive.

9. $\sqrt{3x^4} \cdot \sqrt{24x^3}$ $6x^3\sqrt{2x}$

10. $\sqrt[3]{4} \cdot \sqrt[3]{18}$ $2\sqrt[3]{9}$

11. $\sqrt{5a^3} \cdot \sqrt{20a}$ $10a^2$

12. $\frac{\sqrt{80}}{\sqrt{5}}$ 4

13. $\frac{\sqrt{18x^5y}}{\sqrt{2x}}$ $3x^2\sqrt{y}$

14. $\frac{\sqrt[3]{640w^3z^8}}{\sqrt[3]{5wz^4}}$ $4z\sqrt[3]{2w^2z}$

● **Lesson 7-3** Simplify.

15. $2\sqrt{7} + 3\sqrt{7}$ $5\sqrt{7}$

16. $\sqrt{32} + \sqrt{8}$ $6\sqrt{2}$

17. $\sqrt{7x} + \sqrt{28x}$ $3\sqrt{7x}$

18. $3\sqrt{18} + 2\sqrt{72}$ $21\sqrt{2}$

19. $\sqrt{27} + \sqrt{48}$ $7\sqrt{3}$

20. $8\sqrt{45} - 3\sqrt{80}$ $12\sqrt{5}$

● **Lesson 7-4** Write each expression in simplest form. Assume that all variables are positive.

21. $\left(x^{-\frac{4}{3}}y^{\frac{3}{5}}\right)^{15}$ $\frac{y^9}{x^{20}}$

22. $\left(x^{\frac{1}{4}}y^{-\frac{3}{8}}\right)^{16}$ $\frac{x^4}{y^6}$

23. $(8x^{15}y^{-9})^{-\frac{1}{3}}$ $\frac{y^3}{2x^5}$

24. $(-27x^{-9}y^6)^{\frac{1}{3}}$ $-\frac{3y^2}{x^3}$

25. $(-32x^{-10}y^{15})^{\frac{1}{5}}$ $-\frac{2y^3}{x^2}$

26. $(32x^{20}y^{-10})^{-\frac{1}{5}}$ $\frac{y^2}{2x^4}$

27. $\left(\frac{81y^{16}}{16x^{12}}\right)^{\frac{1}{4}}$ $\frac{3y^4}{2x^3}$

28. $\left(\frac{16x^{14}}{81y^{18}}\right)^{\frac{1}{2}}$ $\frac{4x^7}{9y^9}$

● **Lesson 7-5** Solve. Check for extraneous solutions.

29. $\sqrt{13x - 10} = 3x$ no real solution

30. $\sqrt{x + 20} = x$ 5

31. $(4x - 12)^{\frac{1}{2}} + 3 = x$ 3, 7

32. $(7x)^{\frac{1}{3}} = (5x + 2)^{\frac{1}{3}}$ 1

33. $\sqrt{x - 2} - \sqrt{2x + 3} = -2$ 3, 11

34. $\sqrt{10x} - 2\sqrt{5x - 25} = 0$ 10

● **Lesson 7-6** Let $f(x) = x^2$ and $g(x) = 3x + 1$. Evaluate each expression.

35. $(f \circ g)(0)$ 1

36. $(f \circ g)(2)$ 49

37. $(f \circ g)(-3)$ 64

38. $(f \circ g)(5)$ 256

39. $(g \circ f)(0)$ 1

40. $(g \circ f)(1)$ 4

41. $(g \circ f)(-1)$ 4

42. $(f \circ f)(3)$ 81

43. $(g \circ g)(4)$ 40

● **Lesson 7-7** For each function f, find f^{-1} and the domain and range of f and f^{-1}. Determine whether f^{-1} is a function. 44–49. See margin.

44. $f(x) = 6x + 1$

45. $f(x) = \sqrt{x + 4}$

46. $f(x) = \sqrt{x - 3}$

47. $f(x) = \sqrt{-5x + 2}$

48. $f(x) = 3x^2 + 1$

49. $f(x) = 2 - x^2$

● **Lesson 7-8** Graph each function. 50–58. See back of book.

50. $y = \sqrt{x}$

51. $y = \sqrt{x} - 1$

52. $y = \sqrt{x} + 3$

53. $y = \sqrt{x + 3}$

54. $y = 4\sqrt{x}$

55. $y = \frac{3}{4}\sqrt{x}$

56. $y = 2\sqrt{x - 5} + 2$

57. $y = \sqrt[3]{x} + 1$

58. $y = \sqrt[3]{x - 2} - 3$

● Lessons 7-1, 7-2, and 7-3

59. The time T it takes a pendulum to make a full swing in each direction and return to its original position is called the period of the pendulum. The equation $T = 2\pi\sqrt{\frac{\ell}{32}}$ relates the length of the pendulum ℓ, in feet, to its period T, in seconds. How long is a pendulum if its period is 3 seconds? Round the answer to the nearest tenth. **7.3 ft**

60. You can use the expression $D = 1.2\sqrt{h}$ to approximate the visibility range D, in miles, from a height of h feet above ground.
   a. Estimate the visibility from a height of 900 feet. **36 mi**
   b. How far above ground is an observer whose visibility range is 84 miles? **4900 ft**

61. You can approximate the speed of a falling object as $v = 8\sqrt{d}$, where v is the speed in feet per second and d is the distance, in feet, the object has fallen. Express d in terms of v. $d = \frac{v^2}{64}$

● Lessons 7-4, 7-5, and 7-6

62. Halina works in a department store. Three times per year she is allowed to combine her employee discount with special sale prices. Let x be the retail price of a blouse.
   a. Halina's employee discount is 20%. Write a function $E(x)$ that represents the cost of the blouse after the discount. $E(x) = 0.8x$
   b. Due to a manufacturer's incentive, the blouse is marked down 25%. Write a function $M(x)$ that represents the sale price. $M(x) = 0.75x$
   c. The sales tax on clothing is 6%. Write a function $T(x)$ that describes the cost of a clothing item with sales tax included. $T(x) = 1.06x$
   d. Halina found a blouse to which the discounts apply. Use the function composition $f = T \circ E \circ M$ to write the function $f(x)$ that represents the price Halina will pay for the blouse. $f(x) = 0.636x$

63. You invest p dollars in an account that earns a simple interest of 6%. The function that represents the account balance at the end of the year is $f(p) = 1.06p$.
   a. Suppose that at the end of the year you deposit $500 in the account. Write a new function $g(p)$ that shows the balance that will earn interest in the second year. $g(p) = 1.06p + 500$
   b. At the end of every year you add $500 to the account. The interest rate remains 6%. Write a composition of functions f and g to find the account balance at the end of the third year, before adding the $500. Find that balance for an initial investment of $1000. $(f \circ g \circ g)(p)$; **$2282.82**

● Lessons 7-7 and 7-8

64. You can use the function $f(x) = 331.4 + 0.6x$ to approximate the speed of sound in dry air, where x is the temperature in degrees Celsius.
   a. Write an algebraic expression for the inverse function $f^{-1}(x)$. $f^{-1}(x) = \frac{x - 331.4}{0.6}$
   b. Evaluate $f^{-1}(x)$ for $x = 350$. Round the result to the nearest whole number. Explain what your result represents. **31° C; The speed of sound is 350 m/s at 31°C.**

65. Nisha built a model rocket. The initial speed of the rocket is 64 ft/s. The equation $h(t) = -16t^2 + 64t$ describes the relationship between the height of the rocket h, in feet, as a function of time t, in seconds.
   a. Write an equation for h^{-1}. (*Hint:* Use $t(h) = \ldots$.) Is this relation a function? Explain what this relation represents.
   b. Write a function that can be used to find how long it takes the object to reach a given height h as it moves upward. $t(h) = 2 - \frac{1}{4}\sqrt{64 - h}$

$t(h) = 2 \pm \frac{1}{4}\sqrt{64 - h}$; no; for each height $h < 64$, there are two times when the rocket passes that height.

7. exponential growth

8. exponential decay

9. exponential decay

10. exponential growth

11. exponential growth

12. exponential growth

16.

17.

18.

19.

20.

21.

22.

Lesson 8-1 Write an exponential equation $y = ab^x$ whose graph passes through the given points.

1. $(1, 10), (2, 25)$ $y = 4(2.5)^x$

2. $\left(2, 10\frac{2}{3}\right), (-1, 4.5)$ $y = 6\left(\frac{4}{3}\right)^x$

3. $(2, 6), (4, 54)$ $y = \frac{2}{3}(3)^x$

4. $(-2, 0.05), (2, 12.8)$ $y = 0.8(4)^x$

5. $(2, 128), (-1, 16)$ $y = 32(2)^x$

6. $(-1, 12.25), (1, 4)$ $y = 7\left(\frac{4}{7}\right)^x$

Lesson 8-1 Without graphing, determine whether each equation represents exponential growth or exponential decay.   7–12. See margin.

7. $y = 10^x$

8. $y = 327(0.05)^x$

9. $y = 1.023(0.98)^x$

10. $y = 0.5(1.67)^x$

11. $y = 1.14^x$

12. $y = 8(1.3)^x$

13. $y = 2\left(\frac{9}{10}\right)^x$ exponential decay

14. $y = 4.1(0.72)^x$ exponential decay

15. $y = 9.2(2.3)^x$ exponential growth

Lessons 8-1 and 8-2 Graph each equation.   16–23. See margin.

16. $y = 3^x$

17. $y = 2(4)^x$

18. $y = 2^{-x}$

19. $y = \left(\frac{1}{4}\right)^x$

20. $y = 2^{3x}$

21. $y = 9^{-2x}$

22. $y = -0.1^x$

23. $y = -\left(\frac{1}{2}\right)^x$

Lesson 8-3 Write each equation in logarithmic form.

24. $100 = 10^2$ $\log 100 = 2$

25. $9^3 = 729$ $\log_9 729 = 3$

26. $64 = 4^3$ $\log_4 64 = 3$

27. $\left(\frac{1}{2}\right)^4 = \frac{1}{16}$ $\log_{\frac{1}{2}} \frac{1}{16} = 4$

28. $49^{\frac{1}{2}} = 7$ $\log_{49} 7 = \frac{1}{2}$

29. $\left(\frac{1}{3}\right)^{-3} = 27$ $\log_{\frac{1}{3}} 27 = -3$

30. $625^{\frac{1}{4}} = 5$ $\log_{625} 5 = \frac{1}{4}$

31. $2^{-5} = \frac{1}{32}$ $\log_2 \frac{1}{32} = -5$

32. $6^2 = 36$ $\log_6 36 = 2$

Lesson 8-3 Graph each logarithmic function.   33–40. See back of book.

33. $y = 2 \log x$

34. $y = \log_8 x$

35. $y = \log_4 (x + 1)$

36. $y = 3 + \log x$

37. $y = -1 + \log_2 x$

38. $y = \log (x - 2)$

39. $y = \log (x + 2)$

40. $y = \log (x - 5)$

Lesson 8-4 Write each expression as a single logarithm.

41. $\log 8 + \log 3$ $\log 24$

42. $4(\log_2 x + \log_2 3)$ $\log_2 (81x^4)$

43. $3 \log x + 4 \log x$ $\log x^7$

44. $\log 4 + \log 2 - \log 5$ $\log \left(\frac{8}{5}\right)$

45. $\log r - \log t + 2 \log s$ $\log \left(\frac{rs^2}{t}\right)$

46. $2 \log x - 4 \log y$ $\log \left(\frac{x^2}{y^4}\right)$

Lesson 8-4 Expand each logarithm.   47–51. See margin.

47. $\log_b 2x^2 y^3$

48. $\log_b 3m^3 p^2$

49. $\log_b (4mn)^5$

50. $\log_b \frac{x^2}{2y}$

51. $\log_b \frac{(xy)^4}{2}$

52. $\log_b \sqrt[5]{x^3}$ $\frac{3}{5} \log_b x$

Lessons 8-5 and 8-6 Solve each equation.

53. $\sqrt[3]{y^2} = 4$ ± 8

54. $2 - 4^x = -62$ 3

55. $\log x + \log 2 = 5$ $50,000$

56. $\log_3 (x + 1) = 4$ 80

57. $e^x = 5$ 1.609

58. $e^{\frac{x}{4}} = 5$ 6.438

59. $\ln x - \ln 4 = 7$ 4386.533

60. $\log 4x = -1$ 0.025

61. $\log 4 - \log x = -2$ 400

62. $\ln 2 + \ln x = 4$ 27.299

63. $4 + 5^x = 29$ 2

64. $e^{3x} = 20$ 0.99858

23.

47. $\log_b 2 + 2 \log_b x + 3 \log_b y$

48. $\log_b 3 + 3 \log_b m + 2 \log_b p$

49. $5(\log_b 4 + \log_b m + \log_b n)$

50. $2 \log_b x - (\log_b 2 + \log_b y)$

51. $4(\log_b x + \log_b y) - \log_b 2$

Lessons 8-1 and 8-2

65. Mr. Andersen put $1000 into an account that earns 4.5% annual interest. The interest is compounded annually and there are no withdrawals. How much money will be in the account at the end of 30 years? **$3745.32**

66. A manufacturer bought a new rolling press for $48,000. It has depreciated in value at an annual rate of 15%. What is its value 5 years after purchase? Round to the nearest hundred dollars. **$21,300**

67. You place $900 in an investment account that earns 6% interest compounded continuously. Find the balance after 5 years. **$1214.87**

68. Bram invested $10,000 in an account that earns simple 5% interest annually.
  a. How much interest does the account earn in the first 10 years? Round to the nearest dollar. **$16,289**
  b. How much more would the account earn in interest in the first 10 years if the interest compounded continuously? Round to the nearest dollar. **$198**

69. Radium-226 has a half-life of 1660 years. How many years does it take a radium sample to decay to 55% of the original amount? Round your answer to the nearest year. **1432 yr**

70. The population of Blinsk was 26,150 in 2000. In 2005, the population was 28,700. Find the growth function $P(x)$ that models the population. $P(x) = 26,150e^{0.019x}$, where x is the number of years after 2000.

Lessons 8-3 and 8-4

71. You can use the equation $N = k \log A$ to estimate the number of species N that live in a region of area A. The parameter k is determined by the conditions in the region. In a rain forest, 2700 species live in 500 km^2. How many species would remain if half of the forest area were destroyed by logging and farming? **2399 species**

72. The work done in joules (J) by a gas expanding from volume V_1 to volume V_2 is modeled by the equation $W = nRT \ln V_2 - nRT \ln V_1$, where n is the quantity of gas in moles (mol), T is the temperature in kelvin (K), and $R = 8.314 \frac{J}{mol \cdot K}$.
  a. Write the equation in terms of the ratio of the two volumes. $W = nRT \ln \left(\frac{V_2}{V_1}\right)$
  b. Find the work done by 1 mol of gas at 300 K as it doubles its volume. **1728.85 J**

Lessons 8-5 and 8-6

73. The function $T(t) = T_r + (T_i - T_r)e^{kt}$ models Newton's Law of Cooling. It allows you to predict the temperature $T(t)$ of an object t minutes after it is placed in a constant-temperature cooling environment, such as a refrigerator. T_i is the initial temperature of the object, and T_r is the temperature inside the refrigerator. The number k is a constant for the particular object in question.
  a. A canned fruit drink takes 5 minutes to cool from 75°F to 68°F after it is placed in a refrigerator that keeps a constant temperature of 38°F. Find the value of the constant k for the fruit drink. Round to the nearest thousandth. **−0.042**
  b. What will be the temperature of the fruit drink after it has been in the refrigerator for 30 minutes? **48.5°F**
  c. How long will the fruit drink have to stay in the refrigerator to have a temperature of 40°F? **69.5 min**
  d. Will the fruit drink ever have a temperature of exactly 38°F? Explain. No; $e^{kt} > 0$ for all t, so $T(t) > T_r = 38°F$.

74. The adult population of a city is 1,150,000. A consultant to a law firm uses the function $P(t) = 1,150,000(1 - e^{-0.03t})$ to estimate the number of people $P(t)$ who have heard about a major crime t days after the crime was first reported. About how many days does it take for 60% of the population to have been exposed to news of the crime? **31 days**

7.

8.

9.

10.

11.

12.

Chapter 9 Extra Practice: Skills and Word Problems

● **Lesson 9-1 Suppose that x and y vary inversely. Write a function that models each inverse variation.**

1. $x = 3$ when $y = 2$ $y = \frac{6}{x}$

2. $x = 4$ when $y = -1$ $y = \frac{-4}{x}$

3. $x = 5$ when $y = 8$ $y = \frac{40}{x}$

4. $x = -6$ when $y = -2$ $y = \frac{12}{x}$

5. $x = -8$ when $y = 3$ $y = \frac{-24}{x}$

6. $x = 10$ when $y = 15$ $y = \frac{150}{x}$

● **Lesson 9-2 Sketch the asymptotes and the graph of each equation. 7–14. See margin.**

7. $y = \frac{x+1}{x-2}$

8. $y = \frac{x-3}{(x+1)^2}$

9. $y = \frac{3x}{2x+1}$

10. $y = \frac{8-x}{x}$

11. $y = \frac{x-4}{x^2}$

12. $y = \frac{2x+1}{2x-1}$

13. $y = \frac{x}{x+3}$

14. $y = \frac{x+2}{x-4}$

● **Lesson 9-3 Find any points of discontinuity for each rational function.**

15. $y = \frac{3x^2 + 2x}{x}$ 0

16. $y = \frac{x^2 - 16}{x^2 + 4}$ none

17. $y = \frac{(x+2)(x-1)}{(x+2)^2(x-1)}$ **−2, 1**

18. $y = \frac{4}{x-6}$ 6

19. $y = \frac{9x}{3x^3 - 6x}$ 0, $\pm\sqrt{2}$

20. $y = \frac{x^2 + 7x + 12}{x+4}$ −4

21. $y = \frac{x-7}{x-7}$ 7

22. $y = \frac{x^2 - 3x + 2}{x-1}$ 1

● **Lesson 9-4 Simplify each rational expression. What are the restrictions on the variables?**

23. $\frac{x^2 + 9x + 18}{x+6}$ $x + 3; x \neq -6$

24. $\frac{x^2 + 3x + 2}{x-1} \cdot \frac{1-x}{x+2}$ $-(x+1); x \neq 1, -2$

25. $\frac{x^2 - 2x - 8}{x+3} \div \frac{x-4}{x+3}$ $x + 2; x \neq -3, 4$

26. $\frac{2x^2 + 5x - 3}{x^2 - 4x} \cdot \frac{2x^3 - 8x^2}{x^2 + 6x + 9}$ $\frac{2x(2x-1)}{x+3}; x \neq 0, 4, -3$

27. $\frac{3x+1}{x^2 - 6x - 6} \div \frac{6x^2 + 11x + 3}{x^2 + 4x + 4}$ **See margin.**

28. $\frac{3x^4 - x^3 - 2x^2}{6x^2 - 2x - 4}$ $\frac{x^2}{2}; x \neq -\frac{2}{3}, 1$

● **Lesson 9-5 Add or subtract. Simplify where possible.**

29. $\frac{6x+1}{x+2} + \frac{2x-5}{2x+4}$ $\frac{14x-3}{2(x+2)}$

30. $\frac{8}{x^2 - 25} + \frac{9}{x-5}$ $\frac{9x+53}{(x+5)(x-5)}$

31. $\frac{x-3}{x^2 + 3x} + \frac{7}{x+3}$ $\frac{8x-3}{x(x+3)}$

32. $\frac{3x}{x^2 + 5x + 6} - \frac{2x}{x^2 + 8x + 16}$ $\frac{x(x^2 + 14x + 36)}{(x+3)(x+2)(x+4)^2}$

33. $\frac{2}{x^2 - 1} - 3$ $\frac{-3x^2 + 5}{x^2 - 1}$

34. $\frac{2x}{x-5} - \frac{x}{x+7}$ $\frac{x(x+19)}{(x-5)(x+7)}$

● **Lesson 9-6 Solve each equation. Check your answers.**

35. $\frac{x}{4} = \frac{x+1}{3}$ −4

36. $\frac{2}{x^2 - 1} = \frac{4}{x+1}$ $\frac{3}{2}$

37. $\frac{3x}{5} + \frac{4}{x} = \frac{4x+1}{5}$ −5, 4

38. $\frac{3x}{x-2} = 4 + \frac{x}{5}$ −8, 5

39. $x + \frac{x}{4} - \frac{x}{5} = 21$ 20

40. $\frac{3}{x+4} + \frac{5}{4} = \frac{18}{x+4}$ 8

● **Lesson 9-7 Classify each pair of events as dependent or independent.**

41. A main dish is selected at random; a type of salad is selected at random. **independent**

42. A department is selected at random; a class in that department is selected at random. **dependent**

43. A volleyball team is selected at random from the league; one of the remaining teams is selected at random. **dependent**

13.

14.

27. $\frac{(x+2)^2}{(x^2 - 6x - 6)(2x+3)}$;

$x \neq -\frac{1}{3}, -\frac{3}{2}, 3 \pm \sqrt{15}$

● Lessons 9-1 and 9-2

44. Sound intensity is inversely proportional to the square of the distance from the source—the farther from the source you are, the less intense the sound. Suppose the sound intensity is 30 watts per square meter (W/m^2) at 8 meters. What is the sound intensity at 4 meters? **120 W/m^2**

45. The maximum load a cylindrical column can support varies directly as the fourth power of the diameter and inversely as the square of the height. A column that is 2 ft in diameter and 10 ft high can support up to 6 tons. If a column is 1 ft in diameter and 12 ft high, what is the maximum load it can support? **about 0.26 tons**

46. The force required to keep a car from skidding in a turn varies jointly with the mass of the car m, the square of its speed v, and the curvature k of the turn. The curvature is the reciprocal of the radius of the turn, $k = \frac{1}{r}$. Suppose it takes 2800 lb of force to keep an 1800-lb car from skidding at 45 mi/h on a curve with radius 425 ft. What force is needed to keep the car from skidding at 50 mi/h on a curve with a radius of 440 ft? **about 3339 lb**

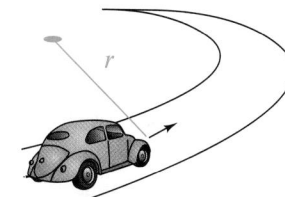

● Lessons 9-3 and 9-4

47. In her first 16 basketball games, Kimberlyn made 65.8% of her free throws. In the next game, she made 7 of 9 free throws. Let x be the number of free throws Kimberlyn tried in the first 16 games. Write a rational function that represents the percent of free throws made after 17 games. $f(x) = \frac{0.658x + 7}{x + 9}$

48. The monthly cost $C(p)$ of removing p percent of pollutants from waste byproduct in manufacturing can be modeled by the function $C(p) = \frac{1500p}{100 - p}$. A manufacturer decides to spend $28,500 per month for removal of pollutants. What percent of the pollutant can the manufacturer expect to remove from the waste? **95%**

● Lessons 9-5 and 9-6

49. Michael rows downstream on a river. He then returns to the starting point. Michael traveled a total distance of 16 mi in 6.25 h. Michael's average rowing speed in still water is 4 mi/h. Assume the speed of the river current is constant. What is the speed of the river current? **2.4 mi/h**

50. It would take an apprentice house painter 1.5 h longer than his supervisor to paint an apartment. If they work together, they can complete the job in 4 h. About how long would it take the apprentice to complete the job working alone? Round your answer to the nearest tenth of an hour. **8.8 h**

51. A master roofer can cover a garage in 1 h less than her new assistant. If they work together, they can complete the job in 7.75 h. How long would it take the assistant to complete the job working alone? **about 16 h**

● Lesson 9-7

52. A game-show spinner has 26 equal sections labeled with the letters of the alphabet. What is the probability that on two consecutive spins you get your first and last initials, in that order? $\left(\frac{1}{26}\right)^2$

53. The diagram at the right shows student membership in the math and science clubs. A student is selected at random. What is the probability that the student is a member of the math club *or* the science club? $\frac{10}{22}$

54. You roll two number cubes. What is the probability that at least one of the numbers is prime *or* even? $\frac{35}{36}$

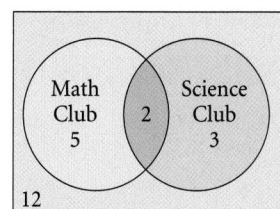

CHAPTER 10

page 854   Extra Practice

24. $x^2 + y^2 = 64$

25. $(x + 4)^2 + (y + 6)^2 = 4$

26. $(x + 5)^2 + (y - 1)^2 = 9$

48. circle; center $(-1, 2)$,
   radius $= \sqrt{7}$

49. ellipse; center $(0, 0)$, foci
   $(\pm 3\sqrt{3}, 0)$

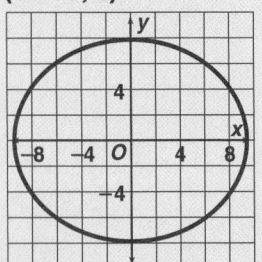

50. hyperbola; center $(0, 0)$,
   foci $(\pm\sqrt{92}, 0)$

51. parabola; vertex $\left(-\frac{7}{4}, \frac{3}{2}\right)$

52. circle; center $(-8, 3)$,
   radius $= \pm 2\sqrt{21}$

53. parabola; vertex $(1, 13)$

● **Lesson 10-1** Graph each equation. Identify the conic section and describe the
graph and its lines of symmetry. Then find the domain and range.   **1–6. See back of book.**

1. $x^2 + y^2 = 4$
2. $x^2 - 16y^2 = 64$
3. $4x^2 + 9y^2 = 36$
4. $8x^2 - 16y^2 = 32$
5. $9x^2 + 9y^2 - 36 = 0$
6. $25x^2 + 4y^2 = 100$

● **Lesson 10-2** Write an equation of a parabola with its vertex at the origin.

7. focus at $(0, 3)$ $y = \frac{1}{12}x^2$
8. directrix at $x = 4$ $x = -\frac{1}{16}y^2$
9. focus at $(0, -2)$ $y = -\frac{1}{8}x^2$
10. directrix at $y = \frac{1}{2}$ $y = -\frac{1}{2}x^2$
11. focus at $(0, 1)$ $y = \frac{1}{4}x^2$
12. directrix at $x = 2$ $x = -\frac{1}{8}y^2$
13. directrix at $y = 3$ $y = -\frac{1}{12}x^2$
14. focus at $(0, -5)$ $y = -\frac{1}{20}x^2$
15. focus at $\left(\frac{3}{2}, 0\right)$ $x = \frac{1}{6}y^2$

● **Lesson 10-2** Identify the focus and the directrix of the graph of each equation.
Then sketch the graph.   **16–23. See back of book.**

16. $y = 4x^2$
17. $x = \frac{1}{16}y^2$
18. $-y = 10x^2$
19. $y^2 - 8x = 0$
20. $x^2 = 6y$
21. $y^2 = 20x$
22. $x^2 + 4y = 0$
23. $x^2 = -2y$

● **Lesson 10-3** Write an equation of a circle with the given center and radius.   **24–26. See margin.**

24. center $(0, 0)$; radius 8
25. center $(-4, -6)$; radius 2
26. center $(-5, 1)$; radius 3
27. center $(1, 4)$; radius 5
   $(x - 1)^2 + (y - 4)^2 = 25$
28. center $(3, -2)$; radius 3.5
   $(x - 3)^2 + (y + 2)^2 = 12.25$
29. center $(0, -3)$; radius 1
   $x^2 + (y + 3)^2 = 1$

● **Lesson 10-3** For each equation, find the center and radius of the circle.

30. $(x + 1)^2 + (y - 3)^2 = 4$ $(-1, 3), 2$
31. $(x + 6)^2 + (y + 9)^2 = 144$ $(-6, -9), 12$
32. $(x - 2)^2 + (y + 4)^2 = 16$ $(2, -4), 4$
33. $(x + 8)^2 + (y - 1)^2 = 100$ $(-8, 1), 10$
34. $(x - 3)^2 + (y + 10)^2 = 25$ $(3, -10), 5$
35. $(x - 7)^2 + (y - 2)^2 = 81$ $(7, 2), 9$

● **Lesson 10-4** Find the foci for each equation of an ellipse. Then graph the ellipse.   **36–41. See back of book.**

36. $\frac{x^2}{9} + \frac{y^2}{25} = 1$
37. $\frac{x^2}{36} + \frac{y^2}{4} = 1$
38. $\frac{x^2}{100} + \frac{y^2}{121} = 1$
39. $\frac{x^2}{81} + \frac{y^2}{64} = 1$
40. $\frac{x^2}{49} + \frac{y^2}{144} = 1$
41. $\frac{x^2}{4} + y^2 = 1$

● **Lesson 10-5** Graph each equation.   **42–47. See back of book.**

42. $4x^2 - 25y^2 = 100$
43. $81x^2 - 16y^2 = 1296$
44. $y^2 - 4x^2 = 36$
45. $12x^2 - 3y^2 = 432$
46. $9x^2 - 121y^2 = 1089$
47. $x^2 - 64y^2 = 64$

● **Lesson 10-6** Identify the conic section represented by each equation. If it is a
parabola, give the vertex. If it is a circle, give the center and radius. If it is an
ellipse or a hyperbola, give the center and foci. Sketch the graph.   **48–53. See margin.**

48. $(x + 1)^2 + (y - 2)^2 = 7$
49. $\frac{x^2}{89} + \frac{y^2}{62} = 1$
50. $\frac{x^2}{73} - \frac{y^2}{19} = 1$
51. $x + y^2 - 3y + 4 = 0$
52. $x^2 + y^2 + 16x - 6y = 11$
53. $3x^2 - 6x + y - 10 = 0$

Lessons 10-1 and 10-2

54. The main mirror in the Hubble space telescope is parabolic. Its cross section is shown at the right. The focus of the parabola is 57.6 m from the vertex. Use this information and the diagram to find the equation of the parabola. $y = \frac{1}{230.4}x^2$

55. Sports TV Group is designing a long-distance microphone for use at

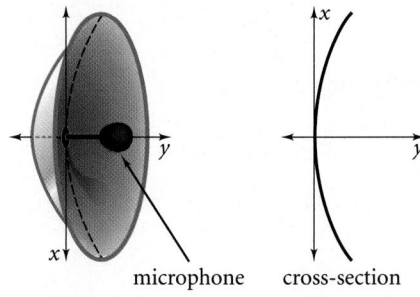

football games. The microphone consists of a parabolic reflector and a sensor that is located at its focus. The equation for a cross section of the reflector is $y = \frac{1}{32}x^2$. All distances are measured in inches. What is the distance between the sensor and the vertex of the reflector? **8 in.**

microphone   cross-section

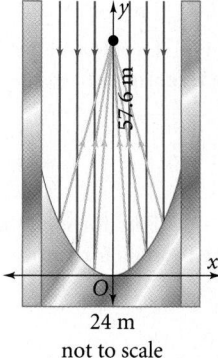

57.6 m

24 m
not to scale

Lessons 10-3 and 10-4

56. A carpenter wants to cut a template for an elliptical window. He has a 10-ft by 3-ft rectangular piece of plywood. The carpenter plans to use a string to draw the top half of the ellipse, using a nail at each focus. The nails are along the bottom edge, 1 ft from each end.

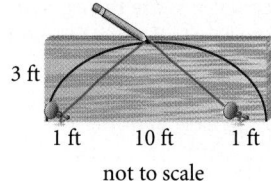

3 ft

1 ft   10 ft   1 ft
not to scale

   a. What length of string should the carpenter use to sketch the curve? **10 ft**
   b. If the x-axis is the bottom edge of the board, and $(0, 0)$ is the midpoint of that edge, what are the coordinates of the nails? **(4, 0), (–4, 0)**
   c. Find the equation of the ellipse. $\frac{x^2}{25} + \frac{y^2}{9} = 1$, **or** $9x^2 + 25y^2 = 225$

57. A tanker truck carrying hazardous chemicals overturned on a highway, possibly spilling some of its cargo. Everyone within a 1.5-mile radius of the spill must be evacuated. The map that safety workers are using shows the spill site at coordinates $(4.5, 7)$. Each unit of measurement is 1 mi. Write an equation that describes the boundary of the evacuation region. $(x - 4.5)^2 + (y - 7)^2 = 1.5^2$

Lessons 10-5 and 10-6

58. Some long-range navigation systems use hyperbolas to determine a ship's position. Suppose the system imposes coordinates so that the location of a ship is in the first quadrant. A ship is located at the intersection of the hyperbolas with equations $9x^2 - 4y^2 = 36$ and $16y^2 - x^2 = 25$. Find the coordinates of the ship to the nearest hundredth of a unit. **(2.20, 1.37)**

59. An engineer determines that the shape of a mirror surface in a motion sensor can be described by the equation $9x^2 - 25y^2 - 12x + 20y = 26$. Identify the conic section that represents the shape of the mirror. **hyperbola**

60. One of the oldest known quadratic equations dates from the early Babylonian Empire about 1700 BC. An ancient mathematician posed this question:
   An area consists of two squares whose sum is 1000. The sides of one square are 10 less than $\frac{2}{3}$ of the sides of the other square. Find the sides of the squares.
   You can model the situation with a system: $x^2 + y^2 = 1000$; $y = \frac{2}{3}x - 10$.
   a. What conic section does the first equation represent? **circle**
   b. Use a graphing calculator to solve the system. **(–20.77, –23.85), (30, 10)**
   c. Ancient Babylonians did not have graphing calculators. Use substitution to rewrite the system as a quadratic equation. Find the roots of the equation. **30, –20.77**
   d. In each of parts (b) and (c), you find two solutions. Explain why only one of them is reasonable for the situation.

60d. The variables are lengths of sides of squares. Each must be positive.

CHAPTER 11

1. explicit; 5, 8, 11, 14, 17

2. recursive; 4, 11, 18, 25, 32

3. explicit; 15, 40, 75, 120, 175

4. recursive; 2, −1, −4, −7, −10

7. 9, 11, 13; $a_n = 2n + 1$; $a_1 = 3$, $a_n = a_{n-1} + 2$

8. 7, 3, −1; $a_n = -4n + 23$; $a_1 = 19$, $a_n = a_{n-1} - 4$

9. −7.5, −6, −4.5; $a_n = -13.5 + 1.5n$; $a_1 = -12$, $a_n = a_{n-1} + 1.5$

10. 1.1, 1.4, 1.7; $a_n = 0.3n - 0.1$; $a_1 = 0.2$, $a_n = a_{n-1} + 0.3$

11. −62, −75, −88; $a_n = -13n - 10$; $a_1 = -23$, $a_n = a_{n-1} - 13$

12. 62.5, 75, 87.5; $a_n = 12.5n + 12.5$; $a_1 = 25$, $a_n = a_{n-1} + 12.5$

16. $a_n = 6(2)^{n-1}$; 6, 12, 24, 48, 96

17. $a_n = -27\left(\frac{1}{3}\right)^{n-1}$; −27, −9, −3, −1, −$\frac{1}{3}$

18. $a_n = 1900(0.1)^{n-1}$; 1900, 190, 19, 1.9, 0.19

19. $a_n = -5(3)^{n-1}$; −5, −15, −45, −135, −405

20. $a_n = 4^{n-1}$; 1, 4, 16, 64, 256

21. $a_n = 500(0.2)^{n-1}$; 500, 100, 20, 4, 0.8

Extra Practice: Skills and Word Problems

● **Lesson 11-1** Decide whether each formula is *explicit* or *recursive*. Then find the first five terms of each sequence.   **1–4. See margin.**

1. $a_n = 3n + 2$

2. $a_1 = 4$; $a_n = a_{n-1} + 7$

3. $a_n = 5n(n + 2)$

4. $a_1 = 2$; $a_n = a_{n-1} - 3$

5. $a_n = 6n^2 - 1$
explicit; 5, 23, 53, 95, 149

6. $a_n = 6 - 2n$
explicit; 4, 2, 0, −2, −4

● **Lesson 11-1** Find the next three terms in each sequence. Write an explicit and a recursive formula for each sequence.   **7–12. See margin.**

7. 3, 5, 7, . . .

8. 19, 15, 11, . . .

9. −12, −10.5, −9, . . .

10. 0.2, 0.5, 0.8, . . .

11. −23, −36, −49, . . .

12. 25, 37.5, 50, . . .

● **Lesson 11-2** Find the arithmetic mean a_n of the given terms.

13. $a_{n-1} = 10$, $a_{n+1} = 20$ **15**

14. $a_{n-1} = 7$, $a_{n+1} = 19$ **13**

15. $a_{n-1} = -2$, $a_{n+1} = -7$ **−4.5**

● **Lesson 11-3** Write the explicit formula for each geometric sequence. Then generate the first five terms.   **16–21. See margin.**

16. $a_1 = 6$, $r = 2$

17. $a_1 = -27$, $r = \frac{1}{3}$

18. $a_1 = 1900$, $r = 0.1$

19. $a_1 = -5$, $r = 3$

20. $a_1 = 1$, $r = 4$

21. $a_1 = 500$, $r = 0.2$

● **Lesson 11-4** Use summation notation to write each arithmetic series for the specified number of terms. Then evaluate each series.

22. 21, 19, 17, 15, . . . ; 8 terms $\sum_{n=1}^{8} (-2n + 23)$; 112

23. 4, 7, 10, 13, 16, 19, . . . ; 10 terms $\sum_{n=1}^{10} (3n + 1)$; 175

24. −35, −28, −21, −14, . . . ; 7 terms $\sum_{n=1}^{7} (7n - 42)$; −98

25. 97, 96, 95, 94, 93, . . . ; 20 terms $\sum_{n=1}^{20} (-n + 98)$; 1750

● **Lesson 11-4** For each sum, find the number of terms, the first term, and the last term. Then evaluate the sum.

26. $\sum_{n=1}^{5} (2n + 3)$ 5, 5, 13; 45

27. $\sum_{n=2}^{7} (4 - n)$ 6, 2, −3; −3

28. $\sum_{n=1}^{5} (n + 1)$ 5, 2, 6; 20

29. $\sum_{n=3}^{10} (3n - 5)$ 8, 4, 25; 116

● **Lesson 11-5** Find the sum of each infinite geometric series.

30. $4 + 2 + 1 + \frac{1}{2} + \ldots$ 8

31. $3 - 1 + \frac{1}{3} - \frac{1}{9} + \ldots$ $\frac{9}{4}$

32. $2.2 - 0.22 + 0.022 - \ldots$ 2

33. $0.9 + 0.09 + 0.009 + \ldots$ 1

34. $5 - \frac{5}{2} + \frac{5}{4} - \frac{5}{8} + \ldots$ $\frac{10}{3}$

35. $1 + 0.1 + 0.01 + \ldots$ $\frac{10}{9}$

● **Lesson 11-5** Determine whether each series is *arithmetic* or *geometric*. Then find the sum to the given term.

36. $3 + 6 + 9 + 12 + 15 + \ldots$; 10th term arithmetic; 165

37. $3 + 6 + 12 + 24 + 48 + \ldots$; 10th term geometric; 3069

38. $-1000 + 500 - 250 + 125 - \ldots$; 7th term geometric; −671.875

39. $87 + 72 + 57 + 42 + \ldots$; 20th term arithmetic; −1110

● **Lesson 11-6** Write and evaluate sums to approximate the area under each curve for the domain $0 \le x \le 2$. First use inscribed rectangles 1 unit wide. Then use circumscribed rectangles 1 unit wide.

40. $f(x) = 2x^2$
$0 + 2 = 2$; $2 + 8 = 10$

41. $y = x^3$
$0 + 1 = 1$; $1 + 8 = 9$

42. $g(x) = 2x + 3$
$3 + 5 = 8$; $5 + 7 = 12$

43. $h(x) = |x + 3|$
$3 + 4 = 7$; $4 + 5 = 9$

Lesson 11-1

44. A contractor must pay a penalty if work on a project is not completed on time. The penalty on the first day is $300. The penalty increases to $500 on the second day, to $700 on the third day, and so on.
  a. Write an explicit formula that describes the sequence. $a_n = 100 + 200n$
  b. The contractor accumulated a penalty of $4500. How many days after the due date was the project completed? **22 days**

45. Table tennis rules regulate the specific properties for the table, the ball, the net, and the paddles. According to the rules, a ball dropped from 30 cm above the table surface must bounce back to the height of 23 cm. This ratio of the drop height to the bounce height remains the same for any two consecutive bounces.
  a. Write the first five terms of a sequence that describes the bounce heights after an initial drop of 30 cm. Round your answers to the nearest tenth. **23 cm, 17.6 cm, 13.5 cm, 10.4 cm, 7.9 cm**
  b. Write an explicit formula that describes the sequence.
  $$a_n = 30\left(\tfrac{23}{30}\right)^n$$

Lessons 11-2 and 11-4

46. a. Find the common difference for the arithmetic sequence that has 17 as its twelfth term and 71 as its sixth term. **−9**
  b. Write the explicit formula for the sequence. $a_n = 125 - 9n$

47. The orchestra section of a theater has 25 seats in the front row, 27 seats in the second row, 29 seats in the third row, and so on. The pattern continues until the twelfth row. After that, every row has the same number of seats as row 12.
  a. How many seats are there in row 12? **47 seats**
  b. The orchestra section has 19 rows. How many seats are in the orchestra section? **761 seats**

Lessons 11-3 and 11-5

48. A fruit fly receives genetic material from two parents. Each parent also receives genetic material from 2 parents. So each fruit fly receives genes from 4 grandparents, 8 great-grandparents, and so on. How many ancestors does a fruit fly have going back 15 generations? **65,534 ancestors**

49. Suppose a dropped ball bounces back to $\tfrac{4}{5}$ of its original height. A ball falls from a height of 5 feet and keeps bouncing until someone picks it up. Estimate the total vertical distance the ball travels if no one picks it up. **45 ft**

50. A new company hires an executive. The company is not expected to make a profit right away, so the executive agrees to an alternative payment scheme. The first month, he receives $.01. Each successive month his salary doubles, until his annual salary exceeds $200,000. Then this salary remains as the maximum level.
  a. What is the total salary the executive receives in the first year? **$40.95**
  b. After how many months will the company start paying the executive the maximum salary under the contract? **25 months**
  c. According to the contract, what is the maximum *annual* salary? **$335,462.40**

Lesson 11-6

51. The city park is being renovated. In the renovated part shown at the right, there are two flower beds and a grass lawn between them. The equations of the flower bed boundaries are $y = \pm\tfrac{1}{2}\sqrt{16 + x^2}$. The units in the coordinate system are meters. Round all answers to the nearest hundredth.
  a. Use 5 inscribed rectangles to estimate the area of each flower bed.
  b. Use 5 circumscribed rectangles to estimate the same area.
  c. Use the mean of your estimates in parts (a) and (b) to estimate the area of the lawn. **a. 44.49 m² b. 53.86 m² c. 49.18 m²**

1.

2.

34.

35.

36.

37.

Chapter 12 Extra Practice: Skills and Word Problems

● **Lesson 12-1** Graph the probability distribution for each sample space.

1. {the product of two number cubes an even number, the product an odd number}   **See margin.**

2. {the sum of two number cubes a prime number, the sum a composite number}   **See margin.**

● **Lesson 12-2** Use the data in the table to find each probability.

3. P(counselor a junior) $\frac{39}{80}$

4. P(counselor female) $\frac{37}{80}$

5. P(counselor a senior and male) $\frac{25}{80}$

6. P(counselor a junior | counselor female) $\frac{21}{37}$

7. P(counselor male | counselor a senior) $\frac{25}{41}$

Characteristics of Camp Counselors

Grade Level	Male	Female
Junior	18	21
Senior	25	16

● **Lesson 12-3** Find the mean, median, and mode for each set of values.

8. 3 2 6 4 5 3 4 2 7 5 3   **4, 4, 3**

9. 16 62 24 13 21 35 24 17 20   **25.8, 21, 24**

10. 125 135 126 138 137 135 121   **131, 135, 135**

11. 6.1 9.5 3.8 4.6 6.1 2.3 3.7 2.1   **4.8, 4.2, 6.1**

● **Lesson 12-4** Find the mean, range, interquartile range, and standard deviation for each set of data.

12. 6 8 5 2 7 3 5 6 7   **5.444, 6, 3, 1.83**

13. 25 29 21 19 30 26 28   **25.429, 11, 8, 3.81**

14. 12 9 10 11 13 9 20   **12, 11, 4, 3.546**

15. 100 98 101 100 102 97 100   **99.71, 5, 3, 1.578**

● **Lesson 12-5** Find the margin of error for the sample proportion, given each sample size n.

16. $n = 90$ $\pm 11\%$

17. $n = 300$ $\pm 6\%$

18. $n = 125$ $\pm 9\%$

19. $n = 900$ $\pm 3\%$

20. $n = 1000$ $\pm 3\%$

21. $n = 5000$ $\pm 1\%$

● **Lesson 12-6** Find the probability of x successes in n trials for the given probability of success p on each trial.

22. $x = 2, n = 6, p = 0.7$ 0.0595 ≈ 6%

23. $x = 3, n = 8, p = \frac{2}{5}$ 0.2787 ≈ 28%

24. $x = 9, n = 10, p = 0.3$ 0.0001 ≈ 0.01%

25. $x = 7, n = 9, p = \frac{1}{5}$ 0.0003 ≈ 0.03%

26. $x = 4, n = 12, p = 0.8$ 0.00052 ≈ 0.05%

27. $x = 8, n = 11, p = 0.9$ 0.0710 ≈ 7%

● **Lesson 12-6** Use the binomial expansion of $(p + q)^n$ to calculate and graph each binomial distribution.   **28–33. See back of book.**

28. $n = 5, p = 0.2$

29. $n = 6, p = 0.4$

30. $n = 5, p = 0.7$

31. $n = 4, p = 0.2$

32. $n = 5, p = 0.4$

33. $n = 6, p = 0.8$

● **Lesson 12-7** Sketch a normal curve for each distribution. Label the x-axis values at one, two, and three standard deviations from the mean.   **34–37. See margin.**

34. mean = 30, standard deviation = 4

35. mean = 45, standard deviation = 11

36. mean = 10, standard deviation = 2

37. mean = 60, standard deviation = 12

Lesson 12-1

38. Suppose you have a spinner with five congruent sections numbered 1 through 5 and another with seven congruent sections numbered 1 through 7. Make a table and a graph to show the probability distribution for the sum obtained by spinning both spinners at the same time. **See margin.**

Lesson 12-2

39. The probability that Luis wins the election for class president is $\frac{3}{5}$. The probability that Mac wins the election for class treasurer is $\frac{2}{3}$. The probability that both will win the office they are running for is $\frac{1}{2}$. What is the probability that Luis wins given that Mac wins? $\frac{3}{4}$

40. You toss two number cubes. The sum of the numbers is greater than 5. What is the probability that you tossed the same number on each cube? $\frac{4}{26}$ **or** $\frac{2}{13}$

Lesson 12-3

41. All the scores on an Advanced Algebra final exam are shown below.

59 62 63 63 72 74 74 78 79 81
83 84 84 84 89 90 92 94 96 98

a. Find the mean, median, and mode for the data. **79.95; 82; 84**
b. What percentile is the student who scored 89? **70th percentile**
c. Draw a box-and-whisker plot for the data. **See margin.**
d. Identify any outliers in the data. Explain your choice. **Answers may vary. Sample: None; all the scores are reasonably close to each other.**

Lesson 12-4

42. The table shows 12 monthly averages of daily high temperatures in °F for San Antonio, Texas.

49.3 53.5 61.7 69.3 75.5 82.2 85.0 84.9 79.3 70.2 60.4 52.2

a. Find the mean and the standard deviation of the data. Round to the nearest tenth. **68.6; 12.5**
b. The high temperature on April 1 was 50°F. What is the z-score for that day? **−1.49**

Lesson 12-5

43. In a survey of 380 art students 32% reported that their favorite color is red.
a. Find the margin of error for the sample. **about 5%**
b. Find an interval that is likely to contain the true population proportion. **102 to 141 students**

Lesson 12-6

44. Jean is visiting her grandparents in Houston for five days. She wants to arrange a lunch with friends. If she picks a day at random, there is a 20% chance that all of her friends will be available to meet for lunch. What is the probability that all her friends are available to meet for lunch on three different days? **about 5.12%**

Lesson 12-7

45. The mean score on a quiz is 82 out of 100 possible points and the standard deviation is 4. Estimate the percent of scores that were 90 or higher. **2.5%**

46. A psychology professor gives a 100-item true/false test in a large college class. The mean score is 75.2 and the standard deviation is 8.1. The scores follow a normal distribution. What is the minimum score that is in the 99th percentile? **94**

38.

Sum	Outcomes	Frequency
2	1 + 1	1
3	1 + 2, 2 + 1	2
4	1 + 3, 2 + 2, 3 + 1	3
5	1 + 4, 2 + 3, 3 + 2, 4 + 1	4
6	1 + 5, 2 + 4, 3 + 3, 4 + 2, 5 + 1	5
7	1 + 6, 2 + 5, 3 + 4, 4 + 3, 5 + 2	5
8	1 + 7, 2 + 6, 3 + 5, 4 + 4, 5 + 3	5
9	2 + 7, 3 + 6, 4 + 5, 5 + 4	4
10	3 + 7, 4 + 6, 5 + 5	3
11	4 + 7, 5 + 6	2
12	5 + 7	1

41. c.

4.

5.

6.

7.

8.

9.

860

Chapter 13 — Extra Practice: Skills and Word Problems

● **Lesson 13-1** Find the period and amplitude of each periodic function.

1.

$4, 1\frac{1}{2}$

2.

$1, 2\frac{1}{2}$

3.

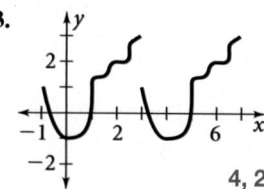

$4, 2$

● **Lesson 13-2** Sketch each angle in standard position.   4–9. See margin.

4. $15°$ **5.** $-230°$ **6.** $400°$

7. $-145°$ **8.** $280°$ **9.** $-750°$

● **Lesson 13-3** Write each measure in radians. Express the answer in terms of π and as a decimal rounded to the nearest hundredth.

10. $100°$ $\frac{5\pi}{9}$, **1.75**   **11.** $270°$ $\frac{3\pi}{2}$, **4.71**   **12.** $-45°$ $-\frac{\pi}{4}$, **-0.79**

13. $-550°$ $\frac{-55\pi}{18}$, **-9.60**   **14.** $425°$ $\frac{85\pi}{36}$, **7.42**   **15.** $10°$ $\frac{\pi}{18}$, **0.17**

● **Lesson 13-3** Write each measure in degrees. When necessary, round your answer to the nearest degree.

16. 5π radians   **900°**   **17.** -2 radians   **-115°**   **18.** $\frac{5\pi}{6}$ radians   **150°**

19. -3π radians   **-540°**   **20.** $-\frac{13\pi}{10}$ radians   **-234°**   **21.** 9 radians   **516°**

● **Lessons 13-4, 13-5, and 13-6** Identify the amplitude or asymptotes, and the period for each function.
                               Asymptotes at $x = \frac{1}{2} + n$, n is an integer, 1.

22. $y = 4 \sin 3x$ $4, \frac{2\pi}{3}$ **23.** $y = \cos 4x$ $1, \frac{\pi}{2}$ **24.** $y = \frac{1}{3} \tan \pi x$

25. $y = 2 \cos \frac{x}{4}$ $2, 8\pi$ **26.** $y = 3 \tan x$ Asymptotes at $x = \frac{\pi}{2} + \pi n$, n is an integer, π.   **27.** $y = \frac{1}{9} \sin 5x$ $\frac{1}{9}, \frac{2\pi}{5}$

● **Lessons 13-4, 13-5, and 13-6** Sketch the graph of each function in the interval from 0 to 2π.   28–33. See back of book.

28. $y = 2 \cos x$ **29.** $y = 3 \sin 2x$ **30.** $y = \tan \frac{x}{2}$

31. $y = -\sin 3x$ **32.** $y = -2 \tan \pi x$ **33.** $y = \cos 4x$

● **Lesson 13-7** Graph each function in the interval from 0 to 2π.   34–37. See margin.

34. $y = -3 \cos (x + \pi) + 3$ **35.** $y = 2 \sin \left(2x - \frac{\pi}{3}\right) - 2$

36. $y = -\sin \left(x - \frac{\pi}{4}\right) + 1$ **37.** $y = 3 \cos \left(3x + \frac{\pi}{2}\right) - 1$

● **Lesson 13-8** Evaluate each expression in radians.

38. $\cot 1$ **0.6421**   **39.** $\sec 4$ **-1.5299**   **40.** $\csc (-0.8)$ **-1.394**

41. $\sec (-\pi)$ **-1**   **42.** $\cot \frac{3\pi}{2}$ **0**   **43.** $\csc \frac{\pi}{4}$ $\sqrt{2} \approx$ **1.4142**

44. $\sec 1.1$ **2.2046**   **45.** $\cot 2$ **-0.4577**   **46.** $\csc 2.5$ **1.6709**

34.

35.

36.

37.

● **Lesson 13-1**

47. The graph at the right shows the temperature changes of a heating coil. Use the graph to find the amplitude and the period. **50°F; 2 min**

48. Describe four real-world situations that involve periodic changes. Explain how to find the amplitude and the period in each case. **Check students' work.**

● **Lessons 13-2 and 13-3**

49. Name two different times when the hands of a clock show each angle.
a. $\frac{\pi}{3}$ radians **2:00, 10:00** **b.** $\frac{4\pi}{3}$ radians **4:00, 8:00**

50. a How much time passes as the minute hand of a clock sweeps $\frac{\pi}{4}$ radians? **7.5 min or 7 min 30 s**

b. How much time passes as the hour hand sweeps $\frac{\pi}{4}$ radians? **1.5 h or 1 h 30 min**

c. The hour hand of a clock is 3 in. long. What distance does the tip of the hour hand travel in 3.5 h? Round to the nearest tenth of an inch. **5.5 in.**

● **Lessons 13-4, 13-5, and 13-7**

51. The graph at the right models the number of hours of daylight at a latitude of 40°N for a one-year period. The y-intercept is about 9.3 and the maximum is about 14.7. Each whole number on the x-axis corresponds to the beginning of a month (0 for January, 1 for February, and so on). Write an equation for the curve. $y = -2.7 \cos\left(\frac{\pi}{6}x\right) + 12$

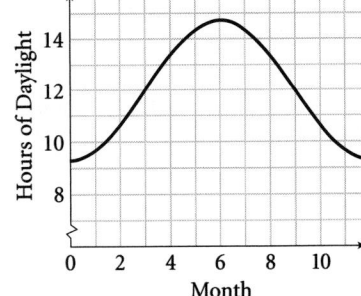

52. Earthquakes under the ocean can sometimes cause a dangerous wave called a tsunami. You can model the motion of a tsunami with the function $f(x) = a \cos bx$. Write an equation that models a tsunami that travels at 120 ft/s, has a period of 20 s, and has an amplitude of 60 ft.
$y = 60 \cos\left(\frac{\pi}{10}x\right)$

53. The graph at the right approximates the number of hours of sleep that Kent gets each day in an average week. He usually gets at least 6.5 hours but no more than 8.5 hours of sleep on any given day. Write an equation that describes the graph. $y = \sin\left(\frac{2\pi}{7}x\right) + 7.5$

● **Lesson 13-6**

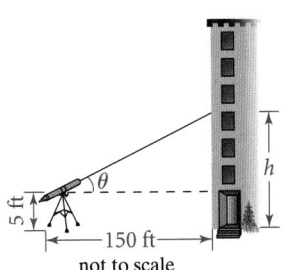

not to scale

54. Owen is using a telescope to measure a tall building down the street. Through the telescope, Owen can see the point on the building that is h ft above ground. The relationship between the position of the telescope and the height can be modeled by $h = 150 \tan \theta + 5$. Owen changed the angle θ from 70° to 75°. How much higher is the point on the building that he can see now? **about 148 ft**

● **Lesson 13-8**

55. Gillian is building a model bridge. The bridge has a support tower in the middle that rises 30 cm above the bridge surface. The model has support cables attached at the top of the tower, going down to the bridge surface. The length of a support cable can be modeled as $y = 30 \csc x$, where x is the angle the cable forms with the bridge surface. **a–b. See margin.**
a. Explain the meaning of the number 30 in the equation.
b. The model is 160 cm long and the tower is in the middle. What is a reasonable range for the function? Explain.
c. What is the angle at which a 60-cm cable is attached to the bridge?
$\frac{\pi}{6}$ **radians or 30°**

55a. Answers may vary. Sample: the height of the tower, 30 cm, is the scale factor that gives the length of the cable when multiplied by csc *x*.

b. Explanations may vary. Sample: 30 to about 85.5 cm; the length of the cable is at least 30 cm, and the longest cable must still be attached to the bridge. So the longest cable is at most
$$\sqrt{30^2 + \left(\frac{160}{2}\right)^2} \approx$$
85.44 cm long.

18. $\angle B = 61°$, $a = 4.4$,
    $c = 9.1$

19. $b = 5.7$, $\angle A = 51.1°$,
    $\angle B = 38.9°$

20. $\angle A = 38°$, $c = 12.7$,
    $a = 7.8$

21. $c = 4.5$, $\angle A = 26.6°$,
    $\angle B = 63.4°$

22. $\angle B = 53°$, $a = 7.2$,
    $b = 9.6$

23. $a = 6.2$, $\angle B = 38.7°$,
    $\angle A = 51.3°$

45. $\sqrt{\dfrac{2 - \sqrt{3}}{2}}$

46. $\sqrt{7 + 4\sqrt{3}}$

47. $\dfrac{\sqrt{2 + \sqrt{2}}}{2}$

48. $\sqrt{3 + 2\sqrt{2}}$

49. $\dfrac{\sqrt{2 + \sqrt{2 + \sqrt{3}}}}{2}$

Chapter 14 Extra Practice: Skills and Word Problems

● **Lesson 14-2 Use a unit circle and 30°-60°-90° triangles to find the degree measures of the angles.**

1. angles whose sine is $\dfrac{\sqrt{3}}{2}$
$60° + n \cdot 360°$ and $120° + n \cdot 360°$

2. angles whose cosine is $-\dfrac{1}{2}$
$120° + n \cdot 360°$ and $240° + n \cdot 360°$

3. angles whose tangent is $\sqrt{3}$
$60° + n \cdot 360°$ and $240° + n \cdot 360°$

● **Lesson 14-2 Use a calculator to find the value in radians of each expression.**

4. $\tan^{-1}(-1.6)$ -1.012 **5.** $\sin^{-1}(-2.8)$ no solution **6.** $\sin^{-1} 1.2$ no solution   **7.** $\tan^{-1} 3.8$ 1.313

8. $\cos^{-1} 0.5$ 1.047 **9.** $\sin^{-1}(-2.1)$ no solution   **10.** $\tan^{-1} 1.3$ 0.9151 **11.** $\cos^{-1}(-1)$ $\pi \approx 3.14159$

● **Lesson 14-2 Solve each equation for $0 \le \theta \le 2\pi$.**

12. $4\cos\theta = 3$ $0.7227, 5.5605$ **13.** $\sqrt{3}\sin\theta + \sqrt{3} = 0$ $\dfrac{3\pi}{2}$ **14.** $2\tan\theta + 3 = \tan\theta$ $1.8925, 5.034$

15. $(\tan\theta)\left(\tan\theta + \dfrac{1}{2}\right) = 0$ $0, \pi, 2.6779, 5.8195, 2\pi$ **16.** $\cos^2\theta - \dfrac{1}{3}\cos\theta = 0$ $\dfrac{\pi}{2}, \dfrac{3\pi}{2}, 1.2310, 5.0522$ **17.** $\sin\theta\cos\theta + \sin\theta = 0$ $0, \pi$

● **Lesson 14-3 In $\triangle ABC$, $\angle C$ is a right angle. Find the remaining sides and angles. Round your answer to the nearest tenth.   18–23. See margin.**

18. $m\angle A = 29°$, $b = 8$ **19.** $a = 7$, $c = 9$ **20.** $m\angle B = 52°$, $b = 10$

21. $a = 2$, $b = 4$ **22.** $m\angle A = 37°$, $c = 12$ **23.** $b = 5$, $c = 8$

● **Lesson 14-3 In $\triangle RST$, $\angle S$ is a right angle, $RS = 24$, and $\cos R = \dfrac{12}{13}$. Draw a diagram and find each value in fraction and decimal form.**

24. $\sin R$ $\dfrac{5}{13}, 0.385$ **25.** $\sin T$ $\dfrac{12}{13}, 0.923$ **26.** $\cos T$ $\dfrac{5}{13}, 0.385$ **27.** $\cot R$ $\dfrac{12}{5}, 2.4$

● **Lessons 14-4 and 14-5 Use the Law of Sines or the Law of Cosines. Find the measure x to the nearest tenth.**

28. 43.0   **29.** 11.3   **30.** 12.6   **31.** 46.3

● **Lesson 14-6 Find each exact value. Use a sum or difference identity.**

32. $\cos 15°$ $\dfrac{\sqrt{6} + \sqrt{2}}{4}$ **33.** $\sin 15°$ $\dfrac{\sqrt{6} - \sqrt{2}}{4}$ **34.** $\tan 315°$ -1

35. $\cos 390°$ $\dfrac{\sqrt{3}}{2}$ **36.** $\sin 105°$ $\dfrac{\sqrt{6} + \sqrt{2}}{4}$ **37.** $\tan 225°$ 1

● **Lesson 14-7 Use a double-angle identity to find the exact value of each expression.**

38. $\sin 120°$ $\dfrac{\sqrt{3}}{2}$ **39.** $\cos 720°$ 1 **40.** $\tan 480°$ $-\sqrt{3}$

41. $\cos 180°$ -1 **42.** $\sin 180°$ 0 **43.** $\cos 480°$ $-\dfrac{1}{2}$

● **Lesson 14-7 Use a half-angle identity to find the exact value of each expression.   45–49. See margin.**

44. $\sin 90°$ 1 **45.** $\cos 75°$ **46.** $\tan 75°$

47. $\sin 67.5°$ **48.** $\tan 67.5°$ **49.** $\cos 7.5°$

● **Lessons 14-1, 14-2, and 14-3**

50. A surveillance plane is flying at an altitude of 13 mi. The diagram shows how the visibility from the plane is defined by a circular arc limited by the tangent lines to the surface of Earth. Assume the radius of Earth to be 3950 mi. Use the diagram to find the visibility range (arc length).
about 640 mi

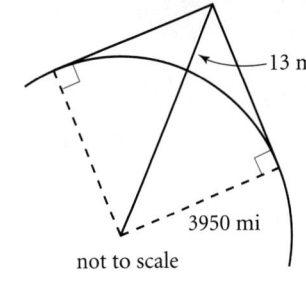
—13 mi

3950 mi

not to scale

51. Two buildings on level ground are 200 feet apart. From the top edge of the shorter building, the angle of elevation to the top of the taller building is 24°, and the angle of depression to the bottom of the taller building is 35°. How tall is each building? Round to the nearest foot.
140 ft, 229 ft

52. The function $y = 3 \cos \frac{\pi}{6} x + 9$ models the depth of water, in feet, at a pier in a 24-hour period starting at 6 A.M. **a–d. See margin.**
a. Use a graphing calculator to sketch the function.
b. Find the amplitude and the period of the function.
c. Explain what the number 9 in the equation of the function represents.
d. Find the first two times when the water level is 8 ft.

53. The diagram shows an experimental aircraft with sweptback triangular wings. What is the area of each wing? Round to the nearest tenth of a square foot. **246.6 ft²**

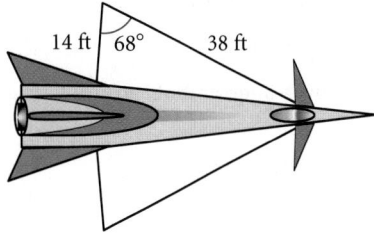
14 ft 68° 38 ft

● **Lessons 14-4 and 14-5**

54. Answers may vary. Sample: No; the sketch does not specify if the triangle is acute or obtuse.

54. A landscaping company received a rough sketch of a triangular property from the property owner. The sketch, shown at the right, is not to scale. The owner is asking for a price quote to sod the land. Sod costs $2 per square foot. Can the landscaper estimate the cost of the job using the information provided? If so, find the estimate. If not, explain what information is missing.

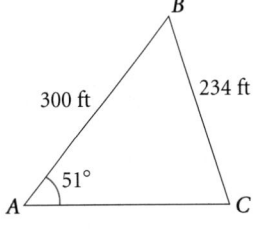
B
300 ft 234 ft
51°
A C

55. Two spotters are observing a hot-air balloon. The spotters are 1.2 mi apart and the balloon is between them. One spotter reports an angle of elevation of 68°, and the other spotter reports an angle of elevation of 84°. What is the altitude of the balloon? Round to the nearest hundredth of a mile. **2.36 mi**

56. The Cairo tessellation is a tiling pattern that is used for many streets in Cairo, Egypt. The tiling uses identical pentagonal tiles. Each side has five congruent sides but it is not a regular pentagon. You can construct the Cairo tile as shown in the figure. Start with $\overline{AB}$. Find the midpoint M of the segment. Construct lines ME and MC at 45° to $\overline{AB}$. Use AB as a radius to mark off points E and C. Then use the same radius to mark point D. Find the measure of $\angle EAB$ to the nearest tenth of a degree. **114.3°**

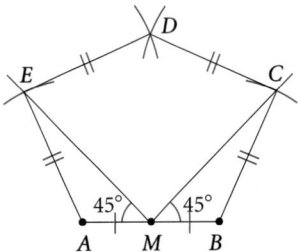
D
E C
45° 45°
A M B

57. An entrepreneur wants to develop a property. The map of the property is a quadrilateral with vertices at points $(5, 5), (6, 9), (11, 10),$ and $(11, 5)$. Find the angle measures at each vertex to the nearest tenth of a degree.
76°, 115.3°, 78.7°, 90°

● **Lessons 14-6 and 14-7**

58. Lines ℓ_1 and ℓ_2 pass through the origin and Quadrants I and III. Line ℓ_1 is the bisector of the angle formed by the x-axis and line ℓ_2. Lines ℓ_2 and $x = a$ intersect at (a, b). Lines ℓ_1 and $x = a$ intersect at (a, c). Express c as a function of a and b. $c = \dfrac{-a^2 + a\sqrt{a^2 + b^2}}{b}$

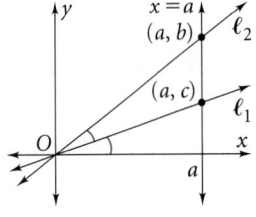
y
x = a
(a, b) ℓ_2
(a, c) ℓ_1
O x
a

52. a.

b. 3; 12

c. The average depth of water at the pier is 9 ft.

d. 9:39 A.M., 2:29 P.M.

Problem Solving Strategies

You may find these strategies helpful when solving word problems.

STRATEGY	WHEN TO USE IT
Draw a Diagram	The problem describes a picture or diagram.
Try, Check, Revise	Solving the problem directly is too complicated.
Look for a Pattern	The problem describes a relationship.
Make a Table	The problem has data that need to be organized.
Solve a Simpler Problem	The problem is complex or has numbers that are too cumbersome to use at first.
Use Logical Reasoning	You need to reach a conclusion using given information.
Work Backward	You need to find the number that led to the result in the problem.

2.

Problem Solving: Draw a Diagram

EXAMPLE

Two students leave school at the same time and travel in opposite directions along the same road. One walks at a rate of 3 mi/h. The other bikes at a rate of 8.5 mi/h. How far apart are the students after two hours?

Draw a Diagram: walking 3 mi/h • 2h   🏠   biking 8.5 mi/h • 2h

  6   3   School   8.5   17

● After two hours, the students will be 6 + 17, or 23 mi apart.

EXERCISES

1. A bug starts at point $P(0,0)$. Each time it moves, it crawls one half the distance traveled in the previous move. It travels east, north, west, south, east, north, and so on, in order. Its first move is east 16 units. Where is the bug after six moves? $\left(13, 6\frac{1}{2}\right)$

2. Draw a graph to check this statement: The graph of $y = 2(x - 3) + 1$ is the graph of $y = 2x + 1$ shifted to the right 3 units. **See above.**

3. Suppose you have four metal rods with lengths 2 in., 5 in., 7 in., and 9 in. How could you use all four rods to measure a length of 1 in.?

4. Two cars leave Los Angeles at the same time and follow the same route toward the Grand Canyon. The first car averages 55 mi/h. The second car averages 65 mi/h. How far apart are the two cars after five hours? **50 mi**

Problem Solving: Try, Check, Revise

When you are not sure how to start solving a problem, try an answer and then test it. In the process of testing, you may see a way to revise your trial answer to get closer to the actual answer.

EXAMPLE

The automatic leg-counter at the Brazinski farm counted 114 legs as the pigs and ducks swarmed through the gate at feeding time. A total of 40 animals passed through the gate. How many pigs and how many ducks passed through the gate?

Try	20 pigs	**Test**	$20 \cdot 4 =$	80 legs
	20 ducks		$20 \cdot 2 =$	+40 legs
				120 legs

Revise your guess. You need fewer pigs to bring the total number of legs down.

Try	18 pigs	**Test**	$18 \cdot 4 =$	72 legs
	22 ducks		$22 \cdot 2 =$	+44 legs
				116 legs

The number is still too high.

Try	17 pigs	**Test**	$17 \cdot 4 =$	68 legs
	23 ducks		$23 \cdot 2 =$	+46 legs
				114 legs

Seventeen pigs and 23 ducks passed through the gate.

EXERCISES

1. Suppose the automatic leg-counter at the Brazinski farm counted 126 legs, but there were still a total of 40 animals. How many pigs and how many ducks passed through the gate? **23 pigs and 17 ducks**

2. Suppose the automatic leg-counter at the Brazinski farm counted 114 legs, but a total of 32 animals passed through the gate. How many pigs and how many ducks passed through the gate? **25 pigs and 7 ducks**

3. Marika biked a total of 110 mi during three days of training for a bicycle race. On the second day of her training session, she biked 15 mi more than on the first day but 5 mi less than on the third day. How many miles did she bike on the third day? **45 mi**

4. Use each of the integers from 1 to 9 once to fill the circles so that the sums along the spokes are equal. (Each spoke contains three numbers.) **See above.**

5. Use each of the integers 2, 4, 6, 8, 12, 14, 16, 18, and 20 to fill the circles so that the sums along the spokes are equal. **See above.**

6. Find a and b such that $x^2 - x - 72 = (x + a)(x + b)$. **$a = 8, b = -9$ or $a = -9, b = 8$**

7. Approximate $\sqrt{385}$ to the nearest tenth. **19.6**

8. Mr. Hoerner spent $45.50 last month to see 11 movies. If video rentals cost $3, movie matinees cost $4.50, and evening movies cost $7, how many of each type of movie did he see? **6, 3, and 2, respectively**

4.

5.

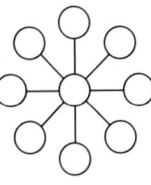

page 866   Problem Solving:
Look for a Pattern
and Make a Table

3a.

Rectangle Perimeter

		length					
		1	2	3	4	5	6	7

width							
1	4	6	8	10	12	14	16
2	6	8	10	12	14	16	18
3	8	10	12	14	16	18	20
4	10	12	14	16	18	20	22
5	12	14	16	18	20	22	24
6	14	16	18	20	22	24	26
7	16	18	20	22	24	26	28

Rectangle Area

		length					
		1	2	3	4	5	6	7

width							
1	1	2	3	4	5	6	7
2	2	4	6	8	10	12	14
3	3	6	9	12	15	18	21
4	4	8	12	16	20	24	28
5	5	10	15	20	25	30	35
6	6	12	18	24	30	36	42
7	7	14	21	28	35	42	49

b. yes

Problem Solving: Look for a Pattern and Make a Table

Some problems describe relationships that involve regular sequences of numbers or other things. To solve the problem you need to be able to recognize and describe the *pattern* that shows the relationship among the numbers or things. One way to organize the information is to *make a table*.

EXAMPLE

After scrounging around in the couch cushions, your father tells you he has found $2.40 in equal numbers of quarters, dimes, and nickels. He says you can have the money if you can tell him how many of each coin he has.

Make a table to help find a pattern.

Number of Nickels	1	2	3	4	5	6
Number of Dimes	1	2	3	4	5	6
Number of Quarters	1	2	3	4	5	6
Total Value	$.40	$.80	$1.20	$1.60	$2.00	$2.40

● Your father has six of each type of coin.

EXERCISES

1. Your father tells you that he has found $3.10 in equal numbers of quarters, nickels, and pennies. How many of each coin does he have? **ten of each coin**

2. a. A college radio station sponsors a contest once a week. One resident from a dormitory calls in and tries to answer ten questions correctly. Each correct answer earns the dorm $50, but each incorrect answer reduces the winnings by $25. Last week's contestant earned $350. How many answers were correct? **8 answers**

b. The contest rules were changed so that each incorrect answer reduces the winnings by $50. A contestant earned $100. How many answers were correct? **6 answers**

3. a. Make tables to show the perimeters and areas of rectangles whose lengths are 1, 2, 3, 4, 5, 6, and 7 units and whose widths are 1, 2, 3, 4, 5, 6, and 7 units.
b. Use the tables to find out whether there is a rectangle whose area and perimeter are numerically the same. **a–b. See margin.**

4. Lisa's school uniform is any combination of a white or light blue shirt, a dark blue skirt or a dark blue pair of slacks, and a plaid blazer. How many different outfits can she make? **4 outfits**

5. How many different ways are there to make $.50 in change without using pennies? **11 ways if you include one fifty-cent coin**

6. How many different ways are there to make $.75 in change without using pennies? **22 if you include one fifty-cent coin**

7. How many ways can you roll two standard number cubes and get a sum of 7? **6 ways**

8. Suppose you have five 32¢ stamps and three 20¢ stamps. How many different amounts of postage could you make? **23 amounts**

Problem Solving: Solve a Simpler Problem

By solving one or more simpler problems, you can often find a pattern that will help solve a more complicated problem.

EXAMPLE

One thousand snap-together cubes make up a large cube measuring 10 units along each edge. The large cube is painted red and then taken apart. How many of the snap-together cubes are painted red on two sides?

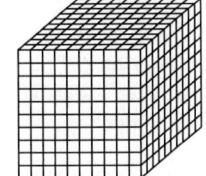

Begin with one snap-together cube, and then add cubes to make a larger cube. Find out whether there is a pattern.

Length of edge	1	2	3	4	5	...
Number of snap-together cubes	1	8	27	64	125	...
Number of cubes with two sides painted	0	0	12	24	36	...
Pattern			$12 \cdot 1$	$12 \cdot 2$	$12 \cdot 3$	...

The pattern is that there are $12 \cdot (n - 2)$ snap-together cubes painted red on two sides.

$12 \cdot (10 - 2) = 12 \cdot 8$ **Substitute 10 for n.**

$\qquad\qquad = 96$

● There are 96 cubes that are painted red on two sides.

EXERCISES

1. Six different cuts are made through the center of a pizza. How many slices are formed? **12 slices**

2. a. Find each sum at the right. **4, 9, 16, 25**
   b. Describe a relationship between the number of addends and the sum of each addition in part (a). **(number of addends)^2 = sum**
   c. Evaluate $1 + 3 + 5 + \ldots + 997 + 999$. **250,000**

$1 + 3 = \blacksquare$
$1 + 3 + 5 = \blacksquare$
$1 + 3 + 5 + 7 = \blacksquare$
$1 + 3 + 5 + 7 + 9 = \blacksquare$

3. Find the total number of squares of all sizes on a standard checkerboard, a board with eight units on a side. **204 squares**

4. Suppose your heart beats 68 times per minute.
   a. How many times had your heart beaten by your 15th birthday? **536,112,000 times**
   b. If you live to be 87 years old, how many times will your heart have beaten?
   3,109,449,600 times

5. a. The Steuben County Regional Soccer League has ten teams. During a season, each team plays every other team twice, once at home and once away. How many games are played in one season? **90 games**
   b. Suppose there are s teams in the league. How many games are played in one season? **$s(s - 1)$ games**

6. First, Second, Third, and Fourth Streets run east and west. They intersect A, B, and C Boulevards, which run north and south. How many different one-way paths are there from the intersection of First Street and A Boulevard to the intersection of Fourth Street and C Boulevard? **10 paths**

Problem Solving: Use Logical Reasoning

Some problems can be solved without using numbers. They can be solved by *logical reasoning*, given some information.

EXAMPLE

Four pigs (Julie, Snowball, Ladybug, and Tina) and their owners (Juan, Suzanne, LaShawn, and Trevor) went home happy after winning prizes at the county fair. None of the pigs have the same first initial as their owners. Juan's pig is not Tina. LaShawn's pig got her name because she was born during a blizzard. Match the owners with their pigs.

Make a table to organize what you know.

	Julie	Snowball	Ladybug	Tina
Juan	X	X		X
Suzanne		X		
LaShawn	X	✔	X	X
Trevor		X		X

Juan's pig is not Tina, so put an X in that box.

LaShawn's pig must be Snowball.

Since the pigs and their owners have different first initials, put an X in each box along the main diagonal.

Use *logical reasoning* to complete the table.

	Julie	Snowball	Ladybug	Tina
Juan	X	X	✔	X
Suzanne	X	X	X	✔
LaShawn	X	✔	X	X
Trevor	✔	X	X	X

Juan must own Ladybug.

The only pig left for Suzanne is Tina.

The only possible pig for Trevor is Julie.

Juan owns Ladybug, Suzanne owns Tina, LaShawn owns Snowball, and Trevor owns Julie.

EXERCISES

1. The junior class is selling mugs with the school logo as part of a school-wide fundraising campaign. The top four salespeople in the class are Pat, Andy, Leon, and Shana. Pat sold more mugs than Andy but fewer than Leon. Shana also sold more than Andy, but she sold fewer than Pat. Andy sold the fewest mugs. Who sold the most mugs in the junior class? **Leon**

2. Gregor has the same number of brothers as sisters. His sister Delores has twice as many brothers as sisters. How many children are in Gregor and Delores' family? **7 children**

3. Ray has the same number of male classmates as female classmates. His classmate Rita has three fourths as many female classmates as male classmates. How many students are in the class? **15 students**

4. Which expression(s) will be positive for all positive integers n? **A, D, and E**
   A. $2^n - n$ **B.** $n - 2^n$ **C.** $(n + 1) - 2^n$ **D.** $2^n - (n - 1)$ **E.** $2^n + n$

5. Four people, Luis, Marisa, Neil, and Ophelia, were on a bus. The florist sat next to Marisa. Luis and the surgeon are married to each other. The caterer, the editor, and Neil don't know each other. The surgeon was sitting behind Ophelia. Luis doesn't make salmon. Which person does which work?
   Luis: editor; Marisa: surgeon; Neil: florist; Ophelia: caterer

3.

Problem Solving: Work Backward

To solve some problems you need to start with the end result and work backward to the beginning.

> ### EXAMPLE
>
> A ball bounced four times, reaching one half its previous height with each bounce. After the fourth bounce, the ball reached a height of 2 ft. How high was the ball when it was dropped?
>
> Each bounce reaches one half the previous height. So multiply by two to find the previous height. Work backward.
>
> | Bounce | 4 | 3 | 2 | 1 |
> |--------|------|------|------|-------|
> | Height | 2 ft | 4 ft | 8 ft | 16 ft |
>
> After the first bounce, the ball reached a height of 16 ft, so it must have been dropped from a height of 2(16) or 32 ft.

EXERCISES

1. A ball bounced four times, reaching three fourths of its previous height with each bounce. After the fourth bounce, the ball reached a height of 27 cm. How high was the ball when it was dropped? **$85\frac{1}{3}$ cm**

2. On Friday, Kamiko deposited $475 in her account. On Sunday, she withdrew $150. On Tuesday she deposited $25 and withdrew $50. On Wednesday she wrote a check for $127.50. She now has $627.45 in her account. How much was in Kamiko's account before she made Friday's deposit? **$454.95**

3. The diagram at the right shows the final resting place of a ball on a billiard table. Suppose the ball bounced off the cushions of the table four times. Show where the ball was when it was originally set in motion. (*Hint:* The ball makes equal angles with the side when it rebounds.) **See margin.**

4. Suppose you start with a number. You multiply the number by 3, add 7, divide by $\frac{1}{2}$, subtract 5, and then divide by 12. The result is 5. What number did you start with? **8.5**

5. Suppose you start with a number. You subtract 10, multiply by 3, add 5, multiply by $\frac{1}{4}$, and divide by $\frac{1}{3}$. The final result is 33. What number did you start with? **23**

6. Derwood decided to sell a box of pencils. On Monday he sold half the pencils. On Tuesday he sold another 40 pencils. On Wednesday he sold half the pencils that were left. On Thursday he sold the remaining 25 pencils. How many pencils were in the box originally? **180 pencils**

7. Tian rented a car to drive from his town to Chicago. The rental company charges $53 per day plus $.27 per mile. When Tian dropped the car off in Chicago three days later, his bill from the rental company was $453.57, which included 5% sales tax. How far from Chicago does Tian live? **1011 mi**

Skills Handbook

Skills Handbook

Percents and Percent Applications

Percent means "per hundred." Find fraction, decimal, and percent equivalents by replacing one symbol for *hundredths* with another.

1 EXAMPLE Write each number as a percent.

a. $0.082 = 8.2\%$

b. $1.20 = 120\%$

c. $\frac{3}{5} = \frac{60}{100} = 60\%$

d. $1\frac{1}{6} = \frac{7}{6}$
$= 1.166\overline{6}$
$= 116.\overline{6}\%$

Move the decimal point two places to the right and write a percent sign.

Write the fraction as hundredths. Then replace hundredths with a percent sign.

First, use $7 \div 6$ to write $1\frac{1}{6}$ as a decimal.

2 EXAMPLE Write each percent as a decimal.

a. $50\% = 0.50 = 0.5$

b. $\frac{1}{2}\% = 0.5\% = 00.5\% = 0.005$

Move the decimal point two places to the left and drop the percent sign.

To model a percent problem with an equation, express each percent as a decimal. There are three basic kinds of percent problems.

3 EXAMPLE Use an equation to solve each percent problem.

a. What is 30% of 12?
$n = 0.3 \times 12$
$n = 3.6$

b. 18 is 0.3% of what?
$18 = 0.003 \times n$
$\frac{18}{0.003} = \frac{0.003n}{0.003}$
$6000 = n$

c. What percent of 60 is 9?
$n \times 60 = 9$
$60n = 9$
$n = \frac{9}{60} = 0.15 = 15\%$

EXERCISES

Write each number as a percent.

1. 0.46 **46%**

2. 0.3 **30%**

3. 0.294 **29.4%**

4. 1.03 **103%**

5. 0.007 **0.7%**

6. 1.506 **150.6%**

7. $\frac{1}{4}$ **25%**

8. $\frac{3}{8}$ **37.5%**

9. $\frac{2}{3}$ **66.7%**

10. $\frac{4}{9}$ **44.4%**

11. $1\frac{3}{20}$ **115%**

12. $\frac{1}{200}$ **0.5%**

Write each percent as a decimal.

13. 40% **0.4**

14. 8% **0.08**

15. 150% **1.5**

16. 0.7% **0.007**

17. 103.5% **1.035**

18. 3.3% **0.033**

Use an equation to solve each percent problem.

19. What is 25% of 50? **12.5**

20. What percent of 58 is 37? **63.8%**

21. 120% of what is 90? **75**

22. 8 is what percent of 40? **20%**

23. 15 is 75% of what? **20**

24. 80% of 58 is what? **46.4**

25. In Louisiana the state sales tax is 4%. If you buy a $15,000 car in Louisiana, how much tax will you pay? **$600**

26. The Mississippi River drains about 1,247,300 mi², which is 13.3% of the land area of North America. Estimate the total area of North America. **about 9.4 million mi²**

Operations With Fractions

To add or subtract fractions, use a common denominator. The common denominator is the least common multiple of the denominators.

1 EXAMPLE Simplify $\frac{2}{3} + \frac{3}{5}$.

$\frac{2}{3} + \frac{3}{5} = \frac{10}{15} + \frac{9}{15}$ For 3 and 5, the least common multiple is 15.

                    Write $\frac{2}{3}$ and $\frac{3}{5}$ as equivalent fractions with denominators of 15.

        $= \frac{19}{15}$ or $1\frac{4}{15}$ Add the numerators.

2 EXAMPLE Simplify $5\frac{1}{4} - 3\frac{2}{3}$.

$5\frac{1}{4} - 3\frac{2}{3} = 5\frac{3}{12} - 3\frac{8}{12}$ Write equivalent fractions.

          $= 4\frac{15}{12} - 3\frac{8}{12}$ Write $5\frac{1}{4}$ as $4\frac{15}{12}$ so you can subtract the fractions.

          $= 1\frac{7}{12}$ Subtract the fractions. Then subtract the whole numbers.

To multiply fractions, multiply the numerators and multiply the denominators. You can simplify by using a greatest common factor.

3 EXAMPLE Simplify $\frac{3}{4} \cdot \frac{8}{11}$.

Method 1 $\frac{3}{4} \cdot \frac{8}{11} = \frac{24}{44} = \frac{24 \div 4}{44 \div 4} = \frac{6}{11}$ **Method 2** $\frac{3}{{}_1 4} \cdot \frac{8^2}{11} = \frac{6}{11}$

   Divide 24 and 44 by 4, their greatest common factor.   Divide 4 and 8 by 4, their greatest common factor.

To divide fractions, use a reciprocal to change the problem to multiplication.

4 EXAMPLE Simplify $3\frac{1}{5} \div 1\frac{1}{2}$.

$3\frac{1}{5} \div 1\frac{1}{2} = \frac{16}{5} \div \frac{3}{2}$ Write mixed numbers as improper fractions.

          $= \frac{16}{5} \cdot \frac{2}{3}$ Multiply by the reciprocal of the divisor.

          $= \frac{32}{15}$ or $2\frac{2}{15}$ Simplify.

EXERCISES

Perform the indicated operation.

1. $\frac{3}{5} + \frac{4}{5}$ $1\frac{2}{5}$ 2. $\frac{1}{2} + \frac{2}{3}$ $1\frac{1}{6}$ 3. $4\frac{1}{2} + 2\frac{1}{3}$ $6\frac{5}{6}$ 4. $6\frac{4}{5} + 1\frac{1}{9}$ $7\frac{41}{45}$

5. $5\frac{3}{4} + 4\frac{2}{5}$ $10\frac{3}{20}$ 6. $\frac{4}{5} - \frac{1}{5}$ $\frac{3}{5}$ 7. $\frac{2}{3} - \frac{3}{7}$ $\frac{5}{21}$ 8. $5\frac{1}{2} - 3\frac{2}{5}$ $2\frac{1}{10}$

9. $8\frac{2}{5} - 1\frac{1}{10}$ $7\frac{3}{10}$ 10. $7\frac{3}{4} - 4\frac{4}{5}$ $2\frac{19}{20}$ 11. $\frac{3}{4} \cdot \frac{1}{2}$ $\frac{3}{8}$ 12. $\frac{9}{2} \cdot \frac{6}{7}$ $3\frac{6}{7}$

13. $3\frac{4}{5} \cdot 10$ 38 14. $2\frac{1}{2} \cdot 3\frac{1}{5}$ 8 15. $6\frac{3}{4} \cdot 5\frac{2}{3}$ $38\frac{1}{4}$ 16. $\frac{1}{2} \div \frac{1}{3}$ $1\frac{1}{2}$

17. $\frac{6}{5} \div \frac{3}{5}$ 2 18. $8\frac{1}{2} \div 4\frac{1}{4}$ 2 19. $5\frac{5}{6} \div 2\frac{1}{3}$ $2\frac{1}{2}$ 20. $3\frac{1}{6} \div 1\frac{3}{4}$ $1\frac{17}{21}$

21. $7\frac{1}{2} + 3\frac{3}{4}$ $11\frac{1}{4}$ 22. $3\frac{2}{3} \div \frac{1}{2}$ $7\frac{1}{3}$ 23. $\frac{8}{9} - \frac{2}{3}$ $\frac{2}{9}$ 24. $7\frac{2}{7} \div 2\frac{3}{7}$ 3

25. $\frac{7}{8} \cdot 5\frac{1}{2}$ $4\frac{13}{16}$ 26. $2\frac{3}{4} \cdot \frac{5}{8}$ $1\frac{23}{32}$ 27. $8 - 5\frac{5}{6}$ $2\frac{1}{6}$ 28. $14\frac{1}{4} - 5\frac{2}{3}$ $8\frac{7}{12}$

29. $4\frac{2}{3} + 1\frac{6}{11}$ $6\frac{7}{33}$ 30. $5\frac{1}{4} \cdot 8$ 42 31. $3\frac{1}{2} \div 6$ $\frac{7}{12}$ 32. $8 \div 3\frac{5}{6}$ $2\frac{2}{23}$

Ratios and Proportions

A *ratio* is a comparison of two quantities by division. You can write *equal ratios* by multiplying or dividing each quantity by the same nonzero number.

Ways to Write a Ratio

$a : b \quad a \text{ to } b \quad \frac{a}{b} \ (b \neq 0)$

1 EXAMPLE   Write $3\frac{1}{3} : \frac{1}{2}$ as a ratio in simplest form.

$$3\frac{1}{3} : \frac{1}{2} \longrightarrow \overset{\times 6}{\underset{\times 6}{\frac{3\frac{1}{3}}{\frac{1}{2}}}} = \frac{20}{3} \text{ or } 20 : 3$$

In simplest form, both terms should be integers. Multiply by the common denominator, 6.

A *rate* is a ratio that compares different types of quantities. In simplest form for a rate, the second quantity is one unit.

2 EXAMPLE   Write 247 mi in 5.2 h as a rate in simplest form.

$$\overset{\div 5.2}{\underset{\div 5.2}{\frac{247 \text{ mi}}{5.2 \text{ h}}}} = \frac{47.5 \text{ mi}}{1 \text{ h}} \text{ or } 47.5 \text{ mi/h}$$

Divide by 5.2 to make the second quantity one unit.

A *proportion* is a statement that two ratios are equal. You can find a missing term in a proportion by using the cross products.

Cross Products of a Proportion

$\frac{a}{b} = \frac{c}{d} \longrightarrow ad = bc$

3 EXAMPLE   Write a proportion. Then solve.

The Copy Center charges $2.52 for 63 copies. At that rate, how much will the Copy Center charge for 140 copies?

$$\begin{array}{l} \text{cost} \longrightarrow \\ \text{copies} \longrightarrow \end{array} \frac{2.52}{63} = \frac{c}{140} \qquad \text{Write each ratio as cost : copies.}$$

$$2.52 \cdot 140 = 63c \qquad \text{Use cross products.}$$

$$c = \frac{2.52 \cdot 140}{63} \qquad \text{Solve for } c.$$

$$= 5.6 \text{ or } \$5.60$$

EXERCISES

Write each ratio or rate in simplest form.

1. 15 to 20 **3 to 4**
2. 85 : 34 **5 : 2**
3. 38 g in 4 oz **9.5 g/oz**
4. 375 mi in 4.3 h **87.21 mi/h**
5. $\frac{84}{30}$ **$\frac{14}{5}$**

Solve each proportion.

6. $\frac{a}{5} = \frac{12}{15}$ **4**
7. $\frac{21}{12} = \frac{14}{x}$ **8**
8. $8 : 15 = n : 25$ **$13\frac{1}{3}$**
9. $2.4 : c = 4 : 3$ **1.8**
10. $\frac{17}{8} = \frac{n}{20}$ **42.5**

11. $\frac{13}{n} = \frac{20}{3}$ **1.95**
12. $5 : 7 = y : 5$ **$3\frac{4}{7}$**
13. $\frac{0.4}{3.5} = \frac{5.2}{x}$ **45.5**
14. $\frac{4}{x} = \frac{7}{6}$ **$3\frac{3}{7}$**
15. $4 : n = n : 9$ **±6**

16. A canary's heart beats 130 times in 12 s. Use a proportion to find how many times its heart beats in 50 s. **about 542 times**

17. According to the label, there are 65 calories in 4 fl oz of pineapple juice. How many calories are in 14 oz of the juice? **227.5 calories**

Simplifying Expressions With Integers

To add two numbers with the same sign, *add* their absolute values. The sum has the same sign as the numbers. To add two numbers with different signs, find the *difference* between their absolute values. The sum has the same sign as the number with the greater absolute value.

 EXAMPLE Add.

a. $-8 + (-5) = -13$ **b.** $-8 + 5 = -3$ **c.** $8 + (-5) = 3$

To subtract a number, add its opposite.

 EXAMPLE Subtract.

a. $4 - 7 = 4 + (-7)$
         $= -3$

b. $-4 - (-7) = -4 + 7$
           $= 3$

c. $-4 - 7 = -4 + (-7)$
           $= -11$

The product or quotient of two numbers with the same sign is positive. The product or quotient of two numbers with different signs is negative.

3 EXAMPLE Multiply or divide.

a. $(-3)(-5) = 15$ **b.** $-35 \div 7 = -5$ **c.** $24 \div (-6) = -4$

4 EXAMPLE Simplify $2^2 - 3(4 - 6) - 12$.

Use the order of operations shown at the right.

$$2^2 - 3(4 - 6) - 12 = 2^2 - 3(-2) - 12$$
$$= 4 - 3(-2) - 12$$
$$= 4 - (-6) - 12$$
$$= 4 + 6 - 12$$
$$= 10 - 12 = -2$$

Order of Operations

1. Perform any operation(s) inside grouping symbols.
2. Simplify any terms with exponents.
3. Multiply and divide in order from left to right.
4. Add and subtract in order from left to right.

EXERCISES

Simplify each expression.

1. $-4 + 5$ **1**
2. $12 - 12$ **0**
3. $-15 + (-23)$ **−38**
4. $4 - 17$ **−13**
5. $-5 - 12$ **−17**
6. $17 + (-18)$ **−1**
7. $3 - (-5)$ **8**
8. $-8 - (-12)$ **4**
9. $-19 + 5$ **−14**
10. $-8 + (-8)$ **−16**
11. $(-7)(-4)$ **28**
12. $-120 \div 30$ **−4**
13. $(-3)(4)$ **−12**
14. $75 \div (-3)$ **−25**
15. $(-6)(15)$ **−90**
16. $(18)(-4)$ **−72**
17. $-84 \div (-7)$ **12**
18. $(-13)(-3)$ **39**
19. $(-225) \div (-15)$ **15**
20. $-16 \div 8$ **−2**
21. $-2(1 + 5) + (-3)(2)$ **−18**
22. $-4(-2 - 5) + 3(1 - 4)$ **19**
23. $20 - (3)(12) + 4^2$ **0**
24. $\frac{-15}{-5} - \frac{36}{-12} + \frac{-12}{-4}$ **9**
25. $5^2 - 6(5 - 9)$ **49**
26. $4\left[(12)(3) - \frac{12}{3}\right]$ **128**
27. $(-3 + 2^3)\left(4 + \frac{-42}{7}\right)$ **−10**
28. $(3 - 10)^2 + 3(-10)$ **19**
29. $(7 + 7)(7 - 7) - \frac{7}{-7}$ **1**
30. $5 - (-4)(-3) + 3^2$ **2**
31. $\left(\frac{-15}{5}\right)^2 + (7 - 4)^2$ **18**
32. $[4(-3)]^2 + 4(-3)^2$ **180**

13. $\ell = \frac{P}{2} - w$

14. $r = \frac{d}{t}$

15. $b = c - 2a$

16. $P = \frac{I}{rt}$

17. $x = 2y$

18. $a = \frac{c}{2} - x$

19. $m = q - (n + p)$

20. $c = 2a - d$

21. $m = \frac{q}{np}$

22. $m = \frac{y - b}{x}$

23. $r = \frac{1 - 3s}{2}$

24. $b = \frac{3a}{2}$

25. $b = \frac{2A}{h}$

26. $h = \frac{V}{\ell w}$

27. $b = \pm\sqrt{c^2 - a^2}$

28. $b = 3m - a - c$

Evaluating Formulas and Solving Literal Equations

To evaluate a formula, first substitute the known values for the variables. Then perform the indicated operations.

1 EXAMPLE Find the volume of a cone that has a radius of 5 in. and a height of 10 in. Use the formula $V = \frac{1}{3}\pi r^2 h$.

$V = \frac{1}{3}\pi r^2 h$

$\approx \frac{1}{3}(3.14)(5)^2(10)$ **Replace π with 3.14, r with 5, and h with 10.**

≈ 262 in.^{3} **Round your answer.**

Sometimes you do not know values for the variables in a formula, so you cannot substitute. To solve a formula or a literal equation for one of the variables in it, use properties of equality.

2 EXAMPLE Solve $P = 2(\ell + w)$ for w.

$P = 2(\ell + w)$

$\frac{P}{2} = \ell + w$ **Divide each side by 2.**

$\frac{P}{2} - \ell = w$ **Subtract ℓ from each side.**

Thus, $w = \frac{P}{2} - \ell$.

EXERCISES

Evaluate each formula. Give decimal answers to the nearest tenth.

1. $P = 2(\ell + w); \ell = 3.2, w = 4$ **14.4**

2. $c = 0.5q + 0.5n; q = 3, n = 5$ **4**

3. $d = rt; r = 35, t = 2.4$ **84**

4. $y = 3.5x + 2; x = 1.5$ **7.3**

5. $y = (x + 2)(x - 2); x = 5$ **21**

6. $A = s^2; s = 10.5$ **110.3**

7. $a = \sqrt{c^2 - b^2}; c = 5.5, b = 3$ **4.6**

8. $d = 0.5gt^2; g = -32, t = 4.5$ **−324**

9. $y = 2x^2 - 3x + 1; x = 6$ **55**

10. $A = \frac{1}{2}(b_1 + b_2)h; b_1 = 13, b_2 = 9, h = 8$ **88**

11. $V = \pi r^2 h; r = 4.3, h = 9.1$ **528.6**

12. $A = \frac{1}{2}bh; b = 13.7, h = 8.5$ **58.2**

Solve each equation for the given variable. **13–28. See margin.**

13. $P = 2(\ell + w); \ell$

14. $d = rt; r$

15. $2a + b = c; b$

16. $I = Prt; P$

17. $\frac{1}{2}x = y; x$

18. $2(x + a) = c; a$

19. $m + n + p = q; m$

20. $\frac{c + d}{2} = a; c$

21. $mnp = q; m$

22. $y = mx + b; m$

23. $2r + 3s = 1; r$

24. $3a = 2b; b$

25. $A = \frac{1}{2}bh; b$

26. $V = \ell wh; h$

27. $c^2 = a^2 + b^2; b$

28. $m = \frac{a + b + c}{3}; b$

29. The formula $V = \frac{1}{2}\ell(A_1 + A_2)$ relates the volume V of a log to its length ℓ and the areas of the ends A_1 and A_2. Solve the formula for ℓ and find the length of a log that has a volume of 23 ft^3 and end areas of 0.32 ft^2 and 1.58 ft^2. $\ell = \frac{2V}{A_1 + A_2}$; **24.2 ft**

30. The formula $A = \frac{1}{2}h(b_1 + b_2)$ relates the area A of a trapezoid to its height h and the lengths of its bases b_1 and b_2. Solve the formula for b_1 and find the length of a base of a trapezoid that has an area of 43 cm^2, a height of 10 cm, and one base of 5.2 cm. $b_1 = \frac{2A}{h} - b_2$; **3.4 cm**

Area and Volume

The *area* of a plane figure is the number of square units contained in the figure. The *volume* of a space figure is the number of cubic units contained in the figure. Formulas for area and volume are listed on page 898.

1 **EXAMPLE**   Find the area of each figure.

a.

$A = bh$

$= 3.2 \cdot 1.8$

$= 5.76 \approx 5.8 \text{ cm}^2$

b.

$2\frac{1}{10}$ in.

$A = \pi r^2$

$\approx \frac{22}{7} \cdot \left(\frac{21}{10}\right)^2$

$= \frac{693}{50} = 13\frac{43}{50} \text{ in.}^2$

c.

19 mm

8.5 mm

23 mm

$A = \frac{1}{2}(b_1 + b_2)h$

$= \frac{1}{2}(19 + 23) \cdot 8.5$

$= 178.5 \text{ mm}^2$

2 **EXAMPLE**   Find the volume of each figure.

a.

3.3 cm

5.0 cm

7.5 cm

$V = \ell wh$

$= 7.5 \cdot 5.0 \cdot 3.3$

$= 123.75 \approx 124.8 \text{ cm}^3$

b.

24 ft

37 ft

37 ft

$V = \frac{1}{3}Bh$

$= \frac{1}{3}(37^2) \cdot 24$

$= 10,952 \text{ ft}^3$

c.

2.7 m

$V = \frac{4}{3}\pi r^3$

$\approx \frac{4}{3} \cdot 3.14 \cdot 2.7^3$

$= 82.40616 \approx 82.4 \text{ m}^3$

EXERCISES

Find the area of each figure.

1.

4 m

7 m

14 m²

2.

$3\frac{3}{4}$ ft

$3\frac{3}{4}$ ft

14.1 ft²

3.

9 cm

5 cm   4 cm

6 cm

30 cm²

4.

10 in.

78.5 in.²

Find the volume of each figure.

5.
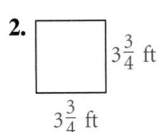

$4\frac{1}{2}$ ft

$4\frac{1}{2}$ ft

$4\frac{1}{2}$ ft

91.1 ft³

6.
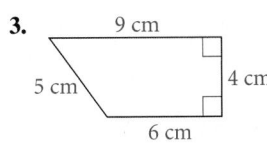

8 m

2144.7 m³

7.
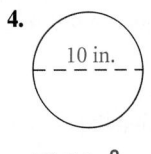

12 in.

5 in.

314.2 in.³

8.
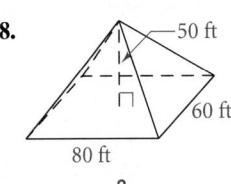

50 ft

60 ft

80 ft

80,000 ft³

9. Find the area of a triangle with a base of 17 in. and a height of 13 in. **110.5 in.²**

10. Find the volume of a rectangular box 64 cm long, 48 cm wide, and 58 cm high. **178,176 cm³**

11. Find the surface area of the cube in Exercise 5. **121.5 ft²**

12. Find the surface area of the rectangular solid in Example 2a. **157.5 cm²**

7–12.

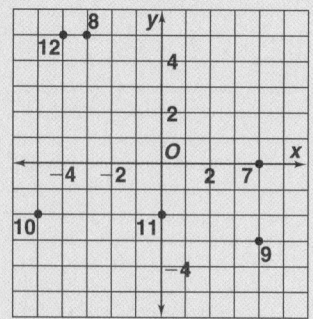

18. $\left(-1, -\frac{1}{2}\right)$

19. $\left(5, -\frac{3}{2}\right)$

20. $\left(-\frac{1}{2}, -\frac{11}{2}\right)$

21. $\left(\frac{5}{2}, -1\right)$

The Coordinate Plane, Slope, and Midpoint

The *coordinate plane* is formed when two number lines intersect at right angles. The ordered pair $(-2, 4)$ identifies the location of a point on the plane. From the origin, move 2 units to the left and 4 units up.

1 EXAMPLE   In which quadrant would you find each point?

a. $(3, -4)$ Move 3 units right and 4 units down. The point is in Quadrant IV.
b. $(-2, -5)$ Move 2 units left and 5 units down. The point is in Quadrant III.

To find the slope of a line on the coordinate plane, choose two points on the line and use the slope formula.

2 EXAMPLE   Find the slope of each line.

a.
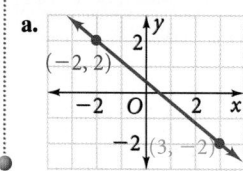

$$m = \frac{y_2 - y_1}{x_2 - x_1}$$
$$= \frac{2 - (-2)}{-2 - 3}$$
$$= \frac{4}{-5} \text{ or } -\frac{4}{5}$$

b.
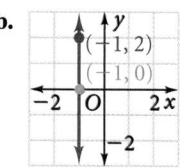

$$m = \frac{y_2 - y_1}{x_2 - x_1}$$
$$= \frac{2 - 0}{-1 - (-1)} = \frac{2}{0}$$

Since you cannot divide by zero, this line has an undefined slope.

Each coordinate of the midpoint of a segment is the mean of the corresponding coordinates of its endpoints. If (x_m, y_m) is the midpoint of the segment joining (x_1, y_1) and (x_2, y_2), then $x_m = \frac{x_1 + x_2}{2}$ and $y_m = \frac{y_1 + y_2}{2}$.

3 EXAMPLE   Find the coordinates of the midpoint of the segment with endpoints $(-2, 5)$ and $(6, -3)$.

$$\frac{-2 + 6}{2} = 2 \text{ and } \frac{5 + (-3)}{2} = 1, \text{ so the midpoint is } (2, 1).$$

EXERCISES

In which quadrant would you find each point?

1. $(3, 2)$ **I**   **2.** $(-4, 3)$ **II**   **3.** $(2, -3)$ **IV**   **4.** $(4, -2)$ **IV**   **5.** $(-4, -5)$ **III**   **6.** $(-1, -3)$ **III**

Graph each point on a coordinate plane.   7–12. See margin.

7. $(4, 0)$ **8.** $(-3, 5)$ **9.** $(4, -3)$ **10.** $(-5, -2)$ **11.** $(0, -2)$ **12.** $(-4, 5)$

Find the slope of each line.

13.

$\frac{3}{4}$

14.

-1

15.

0

16. the line containing
-2 $(-3, 4)$ and $(2, -6)$

17. the line containing
$\frac{1}{5}$ $(25, 40)$ and $(100, 55)$

Find the midpoint of the segment with the given endpoints.   18–21. See margin.

18. $(-4, 4), (2, -5)$ **19.** $(3, 3), (7, -6)$ **20.** $(-1, -8), (0, -3)$ **21.** $(3, 4), (2, -6)$

Solving Linear Equations and Inequalities

To solve a linear equation having one variable, use inverse operations and properties of equality to get the variable alone on one side of the equal sign.

1 EXAMPLE   Solve each equation.

a. $3x - 11 = -5$

$3x - 11 + 11 = -5 + 11$ **Add 11 to each side.**

$3x = 6$

$\frac{3x}{3} = \frac{6}{3}$ **Divide each side by 3.**

$x = 2$

b. $\frac{2}{3}x + 1 = -5$

$\frac{2}{3}x + 1 - 1 = -5 - 1$ **Subtract 1 from each side.**

$\frac{2}{3}x = -6$

$\frac{3}{2} \cdot \frac{2}{3}x = \frac{3}{2} \cdot (-6)$ **Multiply each side by $\frac{3}{2}$.**

$x = -9$

Sometimes you can use the Distributive Property to simplify an equation.

2 EXAMPLE   Solve each equation.

a. $2(x + 8) - 5 = 7$

$2x + 16 - 5 = 7$ **Distribute to remove parentheses.**

$2x = -4$

$x = -2$

b. $2x + 9 = 6x$

$2x - 2x + 9 = 6x - 2x$ **Subtract 2x from each side.**

$9 = 4x$

$\frac{9}{4} = x$ (or $x = 2.25$)

In solving an inequality, you must reverse the order of the inequality when you multiply or divide each side by a negative number.

3 EXAMPLE   Solve and graph each inequality.

a. $\frac{x}{3} - 2 > -4$

$\frac{x}{3} - 2 + 2 > -4 + 2$

$\frac{x}{3} > -2$

$3 \cdot \frac{x}{3} > 3(-2)$

$x > -6$

b. $2x \geq 5x - 9$

$2x - 5x \geq 5x - 5x - 9$ **Divide each side by -3 and reverse the order of the inequality.**

$-3x \geq -9$

$\frac{-3x}{-3} \leq \frac{-9}{-3}$

$x \leq 3$

EXERCISES

Solve each equation.

1. $x + 4 = 3$ **−1**

2. $3c - 7 = -13$ **−2**

3. $8y - 3 + y = 51$ **6**

4. $6a = -48$ **−8**

5. $\frac{1}{2}(s - 6) = 17$ **40**

6. $\frac{d}{3} = -8$ **−24**

7. $\frac{4}{9}h = \frac{2}{3}$ **1.5**

8. $\frac{2}{3}r + 9 = 75$ **99**

9. $4(t + 5) = -36$ **−14**

10. $7g - 3g + 2 = 6$ **1**

11. $3(x - 4) = 2x + 1$ **13**

12. $q + 4.5 = 3q - 2.7$
3.6

Solve and graph each inequality.   **13–24. See margin.**

13. $9 + x \leq 15$

14. $-g < 5$

15. $7y + 2 \geq -12$

16. $9h > -18$

17. $\frac{s}{5} \geq 7$

18. $4 - a \leq 9$

19. $-\frac{c}{4} < 7$

20. $-\frac{3v}{5} > -\frac{9}{10}$

21. $t - 5.3 < -3.3$

22. $4y - 9y > -55$

23. $-5w > 2w - 21$

24. $\frac{3c}{7} \leq -\frac{2}{3}$

13. $x \leq 6$

14. $g > -5$

15. $y \geq -2$

16. $h > -2$

17. $s \geq 35$

18. $a \geq -5$

19. $c > -28$

20. $v < \frac{3}{2}$

21. $t < 2$

22. $y < 11$

23. $w < 3$

24. $c \leq -\frac{14}{9}$

Absolute Value Equations and Inequalities

To solve an absolute value equation, get the absolute value by itself on one side of the equation. Then use the definition of absolute value to write two equations.

1 EXAMPLE Solve $|x| + 3 = 11$.

$|x| + 3 = 11$ Subtract 3 from each side.

$|x| = 8$ The value of x is either 8 or -8.

$x = 8$ or $x = -8$

2 EXAMPLE Solve $|p - 20| = 4$.

$|p - 20| = 4$ The value of the expression $p - 20$ is 4 or -4.

$p - 20 = 4$ or $p - 20 = -4$ Write two equations.

$p = 24$ or $p = 16$ Solve for p.

To solve an absolute value inequality, write two inequalities. Join the inequalities with *and* when $|x| < c$. Join them with *or* when $|x| > c$.

3 EXAMPLE Solve $|x - 3| < 5$. Graph the solution.

$|x - 3| < 5$

$x - 3 < 5$ and $x - 3 > -5$ Write two inequalities joined by *and*.

$x < 8$ and $x > -2$ The solutions are all numbers less than 8 *and* greater than -2.

-2 0 2 4 6 8

4 EXAMPLE Solve $|x + 2| \geq 4$. Graph the solution.

$|x + 2| \geq 4$

$x + 2 \geq 4$ or $x + 2 \leq -4$ Write two inequalities joined by *or*.

$x \geq 2$ or $x \leq -6$ The solutions are all numbers less than or equal to -6 *or* greater than or equal to 2.

-6 -4 -2 0 2 4

EXERCISES

Solve each equation.

1. $|y| = 8$ 8, -8
2. $|a| + 4 = 7$ 3, -3
3. $|c + 4| = 9$ 5, -13
4. $3|r| = 18$ 6, -6
5. $|5x| = 35$ 7, -7
6. $-7|p| + 4 = -17$ 3, -3
7. $|w - 8| = 7$ 1, 15
8. $|3t - 2| = 8$ $-2, \frac{10}{3}$
9. $\frac{|v|}{4} = 5$ 20, -20
10. $\left|h + \frac{1}{2}\right| = 5\frac{1}{2}$ 5, -6
11. $|n - 7| = 0$ 7
12. $8|z + 3| = 24$ 0, -6

Solve each inequality. Graph the solution.   13–20. See margin.

13. $|x - 6| \leq 9$
14. $|a + 3| > 7$
15. $|r| \geq 7$
16. $|3y| > 39$
17. $|5p| \leq 12$
18. $4|k| + 3 \leq 5$
19. $|7x + 4| < 10$
20. $7|w - 5| \geq 21$

Graphing Two-Variable Equations and Inequalities

An equation in the form $Ax + By = C$ represents a line. To graph the line, first find the x-intercept and the y-intercept.

1 EXAMPLE   Graph $2x - 4y = 16$.

$2x - 4y = 16$
$2x - 4(0) = 16$ **To find the x-intercept,**
$2x = 16$ **replace y with 0.**
$x = 8$ **Solve for x.**

The x-intercept is $(8, 0)$.

$2x - 4y = 16$
$2(0) - 4y = 16$ **To find the y-intercept,**
$-4y = 16$ **replace x with 0.**
$y = -4$ **Solve for y.**

The y-intercept is $(0, -4)$.

Plot the points $(8, 0)$ and $(0, -4)$. Then draw a line through the points.

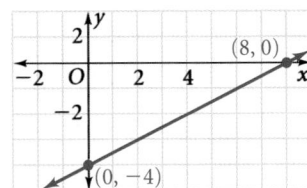

The equation $x = -3$ does not have a y-intercept. In this case, use *any* two points that lie on the line. For example, use $(-3, 1)$ and $(-3, 3)$.

A linear inequality describes a region of the coordinate plane that has a boundary line. Draw a dashed line when the inequality uses $<$ or $>$. Draw a solid line when the inequality uses $\le$ or $\ge$.

2 EXAMPLE   Graph $2x + y > 5$.

First, graph the boundary line $2x + y = 5$. Use the x-intercept $(2.5, 0)$ and the y-intercept $(0, 5)$. Since the inequality uses $>$, draw a dashed line.

Next, test a point. Use $(0, 0)$.
$2x + y > 5$
$2(0) + 0 > 5$
$0 > 5$ **False**

The inequality is *false* for $(0, 0)$.
Shade the region that does *not* contain $(0, 0)$.

EXERCISES

Graph each equation or inequality.   1–9. See margin pp. 878–879. 10–24. See back of book.

1. $x + y = 6$
2. $2x + y = -4$
3. $x = 6$
4. $y = -3$

5. $3x - 2y = 12$
6. $x - 3y = -6$
7. $x - y = -3$
8. $y = x - 4$

9. $3x + 5y = 30$
10. $y = -4x + 5$
11. $2x - 5y = 20$
12. $4x + 7y = -21$

13. $y \ge -2$
14. $x + 2y < 8$
15. $4x - 4y > 8$
16. $x + 3y \le 12$

17. $x - 5 < 0$
18. $7x - 4y > 12$
19. $y - 3x \le 6$
20. $5x + 4y \ge 0$

21. $x + 5y \ge -8$
22. $y = \frac{2}{3}x + 2$
23. $\frac{2}{5}x - \frac{1}{2}y > 10$
24. $3y - x \le 0$

Skills Handbook

4.

5.

6.

7.

8.

9.

Operations With Exponents

An exponent indicates how many times a number is used as a factor.

1 EXAMPLE   Write using exponents.

a. $3 \cdot 3 \cdot 3 \cdot 3 \cdot 3 = 3^5$

     ↑

   five factors of 3

b. $a \cdot a \cdot b \cdot b \cdot b \cdot b = a^2 b^4$

     ↑   ↑

two factors of a; four factors of b

$2^n = \blacksquare$	$10^n = \blacksquare$
$2^2 = 4$	$10^2 = 100$
$2^1 = 2$	$10^1 = 10$
$2^0 = 1$	$10^0 = 1$
$2^{-1} = \frac{1}{2}$	$10^{-1} = \frac{1}{10}$
$2^{-2} = \frac{1}{4}$	$10^{-2} = \frac{1}{100}$

The patterns shown at the right indicate that $a^0 = 1$ and that $a^{-n} = \frac{1}{a^n}$.

2 EXAMPLE   Write each expression so that all exponents are positive.

a. $a^{-2}b^3 = \frac{1}{a^2} \cdot b^3 = \frac{b^3}{a^2}$

b. $x^3 y^0 z^{-1} = x^3 \cdot 1 \cdot \frac{1}{z} = \frac{x^3}{z}$

You can simplify expressions that contain powers with the same base.

3 EXAMPLE   Simplify each expression.

a. $b^5 \cdot b^3 = b^{5+3}$ **Add exponents to multiply powers with the same base.**

     $= b^8$

b. $\frac{x^5}{x^7} = x^{5-7}$ **Subtract exponents to divide powers with the same base.**

     $= x^{-2} = \frac{1}{x^2}$

You can simplify expressions that contain parentheses and exponents.

4 EXAMPLE   Simplify each expression.

a. $\left(\frac{ab}{n}\right)^3 = \frac{a^3 b^3}{n^3}$ **Raise each factor in the parentheses to the third power.**

b. $\left(c^2\right)^4 = c^{2 \cdot 4} = c^8$ **Multiply exponents to raise a power to a power.**

EXERCISES

Write each expression using exponents.

1. $x \cdot x \cdot x$ x^3

2. $x \cdot x \cdot x \cdot y \cdot y$ $x^3 y^2$

3. $a \cdot a \cdot a \cdot a \cdot b$ $a^4 b$

4. $\frac{a \cdot a \cdot a \cdot a}{b \cdot b}$ $\frac{a^4}{b^2}$

Write each expression so that all exponents are positive.

5. c^{-4} $\frac{1}{c^4}$

6. $m^{-2} n^0$ $\frac{1}{m^2}$

7. $x^5 y^{-7} z^{-3}$ $\frac{x^5}{y^7 z^3}$

8. $ab^{-1} c^2$ $\frac{ac^2}{b}$

Simplify each expression. Use positive exponents.

9. $d^2 d^6$ d^8

10. $n^4 n$ n^5

11. $r^3 \cdot r^2 \cdot s^7 \cdot s$ $r^5 s^8$

12. $x^5 y^2 \cdot xy^2 z^6$ $x^6 y^4 z^6$

13. $\frac{a^5}{a^2}$ a^3

14. $\frac{c^7}{c}$ c^6

15. $\frac{n^3}{n^6}$ $\frac{1}{n^3}$

16. $\frac{a^5 b^3}{ab^8}$ $\frac{a^4}{b^5}$

17. $(rt)^3$ $r^3 t^3$

18. $(3x)^2$ $9x^2$

19. $\left(\frac{a}{b}\right)^4$ $\frac{a^4}{b^4}$

20. $\left(\frac{xz}{y}\right)^6$ $\frac{x^6 z^6}{y^6}$

21. $(c^3)^4$ c^{12}

22. $\left(\frac{x^2}{y^5}\right)^3$ $\frac{x^6}{y^{15}}$

23. $(u^4 v^2)^3$ $u^{12} v^6$

24. $(p^5)^{-2}$ $\frac{1}{p^{10}}$

25. $\frac{(2a^4)(3a^2)}{6a^3}$ a^3

26. $(x^{-2})^3$ $\frac{1}{x^6}$

27. $(4a^2 b)^3 (ab)^2$ $64a^8 b^5$

28. $(mg^3)^{-1}$ $\frac{1}{mg^3}$

29. $g^{-3} g^{-1}$ $\frac{1}{g^4}$

30. $\frac{x^2 y^3 z^{-1}}{x^5 yz^3}$ $\frac{y^2}{x^3 z^4}$

31. $\frac{(3a^3)^2}{18a}$ $\frac{a^5}{2}$

32. $\frac{c^3 d^7}{c^{-3} d^{-1}}$ $c^6 d^8$

Factoring and Operations With Polynomials

When the terms of a polynomial are in descending order by degree and all like terms have been combined, the polynomial is in standard form.

page 881 Factoring and Operations with Polynomials

1 EXAMPLE Perform each operation. Write in standard form.

a. $(3y^2 - 4y + 5) + (y^2 + 9y) = (3y^2 + y^2) + (-4y + 9y) + 5$ **To add, group like terms.**

$= 4y^2 + 5y + 5$ **Write in standard form.**

b. $8a^2(3a^2 - 5a - 2) = 8a^2(3a^2) + 8a^2(-5a) + 8a^2(-2)$ **To multiply, distribute $8a^2$.**

$= 24a^4 - 40a^3 - 16a^2$

c. $(n + 4)(n - 3) = n(n) + n(-3) + 4(n) + 4(-3)$ **Distribute n and 4.**

$= n^2 - 3n + 4n - 12$

$= n^2 + n - 12$

To factor a polynomial, first find the greatest common factor (GCF) of the terms. Then use the distributive property to factor out the GCF.

2 EXAMPLE Factor $6x^3 - 12x^2 + 18x$.

$6x^3 = 6 \cdot x \cdot x \cdot x; \; -12x^2 = 6 \cdot (-2) \cdot x \cdot x; \; 18x = 6 \cdot 3 \cdot x$ **List the factors of each term. The GCF is $6x$.**

$6x^3 - 12x^2 + 18x = 6x(x^2) + 6x(-2x) + 6x(3)$ **Use the distributive property to factor out $6x$.**

$= 6x(x^2 - 2x + 3)$

When a polynomial is the product of two binomials, you can work backward to find the factors.

$x^2 + bx + c = (x + \blacksquare)(x + \blacksquare)$ The *sum* of the numbers you use here must equal b.
   The *product* of the numbers you use here must equal c.

3 EXAMPLE Factor $x^2 - 13x + 36$.

Choose numbers that are factors of 36. Look for a pair with the sum -13. The numbers -4 and -9 have a product of 36 and a sum of -13. The factors are $(x - 4)$ and $(x - 9)$. So, $x^2 - 13x + 36 = (x - 4)(x - 9)$.

Factors	Sum
$-6 \cdot (-6)$	-12
$-4 \cdot (-9)$	-13

EXERCISES

Perform the indicated operations. Write each answer in standard form. 1–3. See margin.

1. $(x^2 + 3x - 1) + (7x - 4)$ 2. $(5y^2 + 7y) - (3y^2 + 9y - 8)$ 3. $4x^2(3x^2 - 5x + 9)$

4. $-5d(13d^2 - 7d + 8)$ 5. $(x - 5)(x + 3)$ 6. $(n - 7)(n - 2)$
   $-65d^3 + 35d^2 - 40d$ $x^2 - 2x - 15$ $n^2 - 9n + 14$

Factor each polynomial. 7–14. See margin.

7. $a^2 - 8a + 12$ 8. $b^3 + 6b^2$ 9. $n^2 - 2n - 8$ 10. $x^2 + 5x + 4$

11. $3m^2 - 9$ 12. $y^2 + 5y - 24$ 13. $s^3 + 6s^2 + 11s$ 14. $2x^3 + 4x^2 - 8x$

15. $y^2 - 10y + 25$ 16. $3r^2 - 48$ 17. $2x^2 + 5x - 12$ 18. $4w^2 - 9$
    $(y - 5)^2$ $3(r + 4)(r - 4)$ $(2x - 3)(x + 4)$ $(2w + 3)(2w - 3)$

Skills Handbook   **881**

Skills Handbook

Margin answers

1. $x^2 + 10x - 5$
2. $2y^2 - 2y + 8$
3. $12x^4 - 20x^3 + 36x^2$
7. $(a - 6)(a - 2)$
8. $b^2(b + 6)$
9. $(n - 4)(n + 2)$
10. $(x + 4)(x + 1)$
11. $3(m^2 - 3)$
12. $(y + 8)(y - 3)$
13. $s(s^2 + 6s + 11)$
14. $2x(x^2 + 2x - 4)$

1. 1.34×10^6

2. 0.0688

3. 7.75×10^{-4}

4. 7.2×10^{-3}

5. $111{,}300$

6. 0.0008

7. 1.895×10^3

8. 2300

9. 1.234×10^5

10. $79{,}850$

11. 6.4×10^5

12. 3.0×10^1

13. $\approx 8.52 \times 10^2$

14. $\approx 2.4 \times 10^2$

15. $\approx 1.8 \times 10^1$

16. $\approx 2.0 \times 10^1$

17. $\approx 8.95 \times 10^{-12}$

18. $\approx 4 \times 10^{18}$

19. $\approx 3.77 \times 10^{10}$

20. $\approx 5.8 \times 10^{-5}$

21. $\approx 1.8 \times 10^{-6}$

22. $\approx 1.9 \times 10^{-8}$

Scientific Notation and Significant Digits

In *scientific notation*, a number has the form $a \times 10^n$, where n is an integer and $1 \le a < 10$.

 EXAMPLE Write 5.59×10^6 in standard form.

$5.59 \times 10^6 = 5\,590\,000$ **A positive exponent indicates a value greater than 1. Move the decimal point six places to the right.**

$= 5{,}590{,}000$

 EXAMPLE Write 0.0000318 in scientific notation.

$0.0000318 = 3.18 \times 10^{-5}$ **Move the decimal point to create a number between 1 and 10 (five places to the right). Since the original number is less than 1, use a negative exponent.**

When a measurement is in scientific notation, all the digits of the number between 1 and 10 are *significant digits*. When you multiply or divide measurements, your answer should have as many significant digits as the least number of significant digits in any of the numbers involved.

3 **EXAMPLE** Multiply $(6.71 \times 10^8 \text{ mi/h})$ and $(3.8 \times 10^4 \text{ h})$.

$(6.71 \times 10^8 \text{ mi/h})(3.8 \times 10^4 \text{ h}) = (6.71 \cdot 3.8)(10^8 \cdot 10^4)$ **Rearrange factors.**

$= 25.498 \times 10^{12}$ **Add exponents when multiplying powers of 10.**

$= 2.5498 \times 10^{13}$ **Write in scientific notation.**

$\approx 2.5 \times 10^{13} \text{ mi}$ **Round to two significant digits.**

three significant digits

two significant digits

4 **EXAMPLE** Simplify $\dfrac{6.332 \times 10^5}{1.6 \times 10^{-2}}$.

$\dfrac{6.332 \times 10^5}{1.6 \times 10^{-2}} = \dfrac{6.332}{1.6} \times 10^{5-(-2)}$ **Subtract exponents when dividing powers of 10.**

$= 3.9575 \times 10^7$ **Simplify.**

$\approx 4.0 \times 10^7$ **Round to two significant digits.**

EXERCISES

Change each number to scientific notation or to standard form. 1–10. See margin.

1. $1{,}340{,}000$ **2.** 6.88×10^{-2} **3.** 0.000775 **4.** 0.0072 **5.** 1.113×10^5

6. 8.0×10^{-4} **7.** 1895 **8.** 2.3×10^3 **9.** $123{,}400$ **10.** 7.985×10^4

Write each product or quotient in scientific notation. Round to the appropriate number of significant digits. 11–22. See margin.

11. $(1.6 \times 10^2)(4.0 \times 10^3)$ **12.** $(2.5 \times 10^{-3})(1.2 \times 10^4)$ **13.** $(4.237 \times 10^4)(2.01 \times 10^{-2})$

14. $\dfrac{7.0 \times 10^5}{2.89 \times 10^3}$ **15.** $\dfrac{1.4 \times 10^4}{8.0 \times 10^2}$ **16.** $\dfrac{6.48 \times 10^6}{3.2 \times 10^5}$

17. $(1.78 \times 10^{-7})(5.03 \times 10^{-5})$ **18.** $(7.2 \times 10^{11})(5 \times 10^6)$ **19.** $(8.90 \times 10^8) \div (2.36 \times 10^{-2})$

20. $(3.95 \times 10^4) \div (6.8 \times 10^8)$ **21.** $(4.9 \times 10^{-8}) \div (2.7 \times 10^{-2})$ **22.** $(3.972 \times 10^{-5})(4.7 \times 10^{-4})$

Operations With Radicals

To simplify a radical, remove all perfect square factors from the radicand.

1 EXAMPLE Simplify $\sqrt{75}$.

$\sqrt{75} = \sqrt{25 \cdot 3} = \sqrt{25} \cdot \sqrt{3} = 5\sqrt{3}$ **Use the property $\sqrt{ab} = \sqrt{a} \cdot \sqrt{b}$.**

2 EXAMPLE Simplify $\sqrt{18} - \sqrt{50} + \sqrt{27}$.

$$\sqrt{18} - \sqrt{50} + \sqrt{27} = \sqrt{9 \cdot 2} - \sqrt{25 \cdot 2} + \sqrt{9 \cdot 3} \quad \text{Simplify each radical.}$$
$$= 3\sqrt{2} - 5\sqrt{2} + 3\sqrt{3}$$
$$= (3 - 5)\sqrt{2} + 3\sqrt{3} \quad \text{Use the distributive property to combine like terms.}$$
$$= -2\sqrt{2} + 3\sqrt{3}$$

To remove a radical from the denominator of a fraction, you *rationalize* the denominator. Make the denominator rational by multiplying by a form of 1.

3 EXAMPLE Simplify each expression.

a. $\frac{5}{\sqrt{3}} = \frac{5}{\sqrt{3}} \cdot \frac{\sqrt{3}}{\sqrt{3}}$ **Multiply the fraction by $\frac{\sqrt{3}}{\sqrt{3}}$ to make the denominator a rational number.**

$= \frac{5\sqrt{3}}{\sqrt{9}} = \frac{5\sqrt{3}}{3}$

b. $\frac{2}{\sqrt{3}} \cdot \sqrt{\frac{5}{6}} = \frac{2}{\sqrt{3}} \cdot \frac{\sqrt{5}}{\sqrt{6}}$ **Use the property $\sqrt{\frac{a}{b}} = \frac{\sqrt{a}}{\sqrt{b}}$.**

$= \frac{2\sqrt{5}}{\sqrt{18}}$ **Multiply radicals.**

$= \frac{2\sqrt{5}\sqrt{2}}{\sqrt{18}\sqrt{2}}$ **Multiply by $\frac{\sqrt{2}}{\sqrt{2}}$ to make the denominator a rational number.**

$= \frac{2\sqrt{10}}{\sqrt{36}}$

$= \frac{2\sqrt{10}}{6} = \frac{\sqrt{10}}{3}$

EXERCISES

Simplify each radical expression.

1. $\sqrt{36}$ 6
2. $\sqrt{72}$ $6\sqrt{2}$
3. $\sqrt{18}$ $3\sqrt{2}$
4. $\sqrt{108}$ $6\sqrt{3}$
5. $\sqrt{54}$ $3\sqrt{6}$

6. $\sqrt{60}$ $2\sqrt{15}$
7. $\sqrt{300}$ $10\sqrt{3}$
8. $\sqrt{\frac{1}{2}}$ $\frac{\sqrt{2}}{2}$
9. $\frac{2}{\sqrt{3}}$ $\frac{2\sqrt{3}}{3}$
10. $\frac{3}{\sqrt{5}}$ $\frac{3\sqrt{5}}{5}$

11. $\frac{\sqrt{2}}{\sqrt{5}}$ $\frac{\sqrt{10}}{5}$
12. $\frac{\sqrt{3}}{\sqrt{8}}$ $\frac{\sqrt{6}}{4}$
13. $\frac{1}{\sqrt{2}} \cdot \frac{\sqrt{3}}{\sqrt{2}}$ $\frac{\sqrt{3}}{2}$
14. $\sqrt{\frac{2}{3}} \cdot \sqrt{\frac{5}{6}}$ $\frac{\sqrt{5}}{3}$
15. $\frac{\sqrt{2}}{\sqrt{3}} \cdot \sqrt{\frac{8}{5}}$ $\frac{4\sqrt{5}}{15}$

16. $\sqrt{\frac{2}{7}} \cdot \sqrt{\frac{8}{7}}$ $\frac{4}{7}$
17. $\frac{2}{\sqrt{2}} \cdot \sqrt{\frac{5}{3}}$ $\frac{\sqrt{30}}{3}$
18. $\sqrt{2} + \sqrt{2}$ $2\sqrt{2}$

19. $3\sqrt{5} + 2\sqrt{5}$ $5\sqrt{5}$
20. $7\sqrt{7} - \sqrt{7}$ $6\sqrt{7}$
21. $4\sqrt{3} - 3\sqrt{3}$ $\sqrt{3}$

22. $\sqrt{18} + \sqrt{98}$ $10\sqrt{2}$
23. $\sqrt{8} - \sqrt{50}$ $-3\sqrt{2}$
24. $\sqrt{6} + \sqrt{24}$ $3\sqrt{6}$

25. $\sqrt{40} + \sqrt{90}$ $5\sqrt{10}$
26. $\sqrt{27} + \sqrt{75} - \sqrt{12}$ $6\sqrt{3}$
27. $\sqrt{45} + \sqrt{20} + \sqrt{5}$ $6\sqrt{5}$

28. $\sqrt{3} - \sqrt{75} + \sqrt{18}$ $3\sqrt{2} - 4\sqrt{3}$
29. $\sqrt{98} + \sqrt{50} - \sqrt{5}$ $12\sqrt{2} - \sqrt{5}$
30. $\sqrt{5} + \sqrt{3} - \sqrt{180}$ $\sqrt{3} - 5\sqrt{5}$

The Pythagorean Theorem and the Distance Formula

In a right triangle, the sum of the squares of the lengths of the legs is equal to the square of the length of the hypotenuse. Use this relationship, known as the Pythagorean Theorem, to find the length of a side of a right triangle.

The Pythagorean Theorem

$$a^2 + b^2 = c^2$$

1 EXAMPLE Find m in the triangle below, to the nearest tenth.

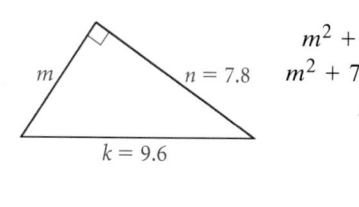

$$m^2 + n^2 = k^2$$
$$m^2 + 7.8^2 = 9.6^2$$
$$m^2 = 9.6^2 - 7.8^2$$
$$m^2 = 31.32$$
$$m = \sqrt{31.32}$$
$$\approx 5.6$$

● Thus, m is about 5.6 units.

To find the distance between two points on the coordinate plane, use the distance formula.

The distance d between any two points (x_1, y_1) and (x_2, y_2) is
$$d = \sqrt{(x_2 - x_1)^2 + (y_2 - y_1)^2}.$$

2 EXAMPLE Find the distance between $(-3, 2)$ and $(6, -4)$.

$$d = \sqrt{(6 - (-3))^2 + (-4 - 2)^2}$$
$$= \sqrt{9^2 + (-6)^2}$$
$$= \sqrt{81 + 36}$$
$$= \sqrt{117}$$
$$\approx 10.8$$

● Thus, d is about 10.8 units.

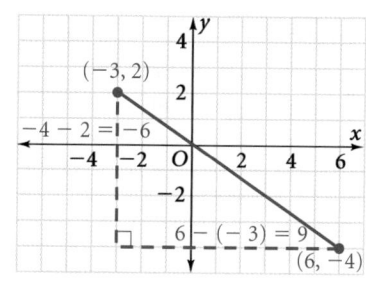

EXERCISES

In each problem, a and b are the lengths of the legs of a right triangle and c is the length of the hypotenuse. Find each missing length.

1. c if $a = 6$ and $b = 8$ **10**
2. a if $b = 12$ and $c = 13$ **5**
3. b if $a = 8$ and $c = 17$ **15**
4. c if $a = 10$ and $b = 3$ **≈10.4**
5. a if $b = 7$ and $c = 25$ **24**
6. b if $a = 24$ and $c = 40$ **32**
7. a if $b = 100$ and $c = 114$ **≈54.7**
8. b if $a = 12.0$ and $c = 30.1$ **≈27.6**
9. c if $a = 8.3$ and $b = 3.3$ **≈8.9**

Find the distance between each pair of points, to the nearest tenth.

10. $(0, 0), (4, -3)$ **5**
11. $(-5, -5), (1, 3)$ **10**
12. $(-1, 0), (4, 12)$ **13**
13. $(0, 15), (17, 0)$ **22.7**
14. $(-4, 2), (4, -2)$ **8.9**
15. $(-8, -8), (8, 8)$ **22.6**
16. $(-1, 1), (1, -1)$ **2.8**
17. $(-2, 9), (0, 0)$ **9.2**
18. $(-5, 3), (4, 3)$ **9**
19. $(-2, 1), (3, 4)$ **5.8**
20. $(3, -2), (3, 5)$ **7**
21. $(5, 4), (-3, 1)$ **8.5**

Bar and Circle Graphs

Sometimes you can draw different graphs to represent the same data, depending on the information you want to share. A *bar graph* is useful for comparing amounts; a *circle graph* is useful for comparing percents.

 EXAMPLE Display the 1998 data on immigration to the United States in a bar graph and a circle graph.

Immigration to the United States, 1998

Place of Origin	Immigrants (1000's)
Africa	40.7
Asia	219.7
Europe	90.8
North America	253.0
South America	45.4

SOURCE: U.S. Immigration and Naturalization Service.
Go to **www.PHSchool.com** for a data update.
Web Code: agg-9041

To make a bar graph, place the categories along the bottom axis. Decide on a scale for the side axis. An appropriate scale would be 0–300, marked in intervals of 50. For each data item, draw a bar whose height is equal to the data value.

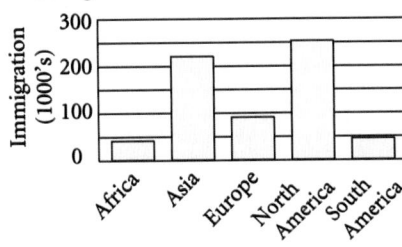

Immigration to the United States, 1998

To make a circle graph, first find the *percent* of the data in each category. Then express each percent as a decimal and multiply by 360° to find the size of each *central angle*.

$$\text{Africa} \longrightarrow \frac{40.7}{649.6} \approx 0.06 \text{ or } 6\%$$
$$\text{total} \longrightarrow$$

$$0.06 \times 360° \approx 22°$$

Draw a circle and use a protractor to draw each central angle.

Immigration to the United States, 1998

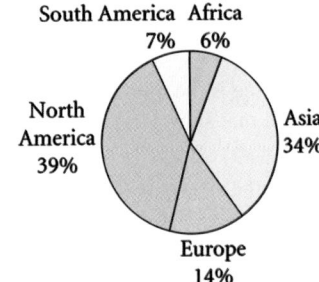

EXERCISES

Display the data from each table in a bar graph and a circle graph. **1–2. See margin.**

1.

NASA Space Shuttle Expenses, 2000

Operation	Millions of Dollars
Orbiter, integration	698.8
Propulsion	1,053.1
Mission, launch operations	738.8
Flight operations	244.6
Ground operations	510.3

SOURCE: U.S. National Aeronautics and Space Administration.
Go to **www.PHSchool.com** for a data update.
Web Code: agg-9041

2.

Cable TV Revenue, 1999

	Millions of Dollars
Advertising, programs	20,068
Basic service	26,890
Pay-per-view, premium services	6,324
Installation	765
Other	5,727

SOURCE: U.S. Census Bureau. Go to **www.PHSchool.com** for a data update.
Web Code: agg-9041

1.

2.

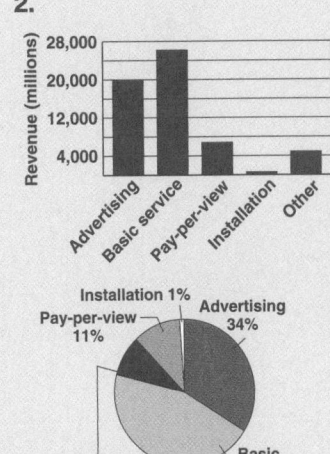

Descriptive Statistics and Histograms

For numerical data, you can find the *mean*, the *median*, and the *mode*.

Mean   The sum of the data values in a data set divided by the number of data values

Median   The middle value of a data set that has been arranged in increasing or decreasing order. If the data set has an even number of values, the median is the mean of the middle two values.

Mode   The most frequently occurring value in a data set

1 EXAMPLE   Find the mean, median, and mode for the following data set.

5 7 6 3 1 7 9 5 10 7

Mean $\dfrac{5 + 7 + 6 + 3 + 1 + 7 + 9 + 5 + 10 + 7}{10} = 6$

Median   5, 7, 6, 3, 1, 7, 9, 5, 10, 7   **Rearrange the numbers from least to greatest.**

1, 3, 5, 5, 6, 7, 7, 7, 9, 10   **The median is the mean of the two middle numbers, 6 and 7.**

The median is $\dfrac{6 + 7}{2} = 6.5$.

Mode   The most frequently occurring data value is 7.

The frequency of a data value is the number of times it occurs in a data set.
A *histogram* is a bar graph that shows the frequency of each data value.

2 EXAMPLE   Use the survey results to make a histogram for the cost of a movie ticket at various theaters.

Survey of Movie Ticket Prices
$5 $6 $5 $7 $6 $7 $6 $8 $6

Movie Ticket Prices

7.

8.

EXERCISES

Find the mean, the median, and the mode of each data set.

1. −3 4 5 5 −2 7 1 8 9   **3.8, 5, 5**

2. 0 0 1 1 2 3 3 5 3 8 7   **3, 3, 3**

3. 2.4 2.4 2.3 2.3 2.4 12.0   **4.0, 2.4, 2.4**

4. 1 1 1 1 2 2 2 3 3 4   **2, 2, 1**

5. 1.2 1.3 1.4 1.5 1.6 1.7 1.8   **1.5, 1.5, no mode**

6. −4 −3 −2 −1 0 1 2 3 4   **0, 0, no mode**

Make a histogram for each data set.   7–8. See above.

7. 7 4 8 6 6 8 7 7 5 7

8. 73 75 76 75 74 75 76 74 76 75

Operations With Rational Expressions

A *rational expression* is an expression that can be written in the form $\frac{polynomial}{polynomial}$, where the denominator is not zero. A rational expression is in simplest form if the numerator and denominator have no common factors except 1.

① EXAMPLE Write the expression $\frac{4x + 8}{x + 2}$ in simplest form.

$\frac{4x + 8}{x + 2} = \frac{4(x + 2)}{x + 2}$ **Factor the numerator.**

$\qquad\quad = 4$ **Divide out the common factor $x + 2$.**

To add or subtract two rational expressions, use a common denominator.

② EXAMPLE Simplify $\frac{x}{2y} + \frac{x}{3y}$.

$\frac{x}{2y} + \frac{x}{3y} = \frac{x}{2y} \cdot \frac{3}{3} + \frac{x}{3y} \cdot \frac{2}{2}$ **The common denominator of 3y and 2y is 6y.**

$\qquad\quad = \frac{3x}{6y} + \frac{2x}{6y}$

$\qquad\quad = \frac{5x}{6y}$ **Add the numerators. Place the sum over the common denominator.**

To multiply rational expressions, first find and divide out any common factors in the numerators and the denominators. Then multiply the remaining numerators and denominators. To divide rational expressions, first use a reciprocal to change the problem to multiplication.

③ EXAMPLE Simplify $\frac{40x^2}{21} \div \frac{5x}{14}$.

$\frac{40x^2}{21} \div \frac{5x}{14} = \frac{40x^2}{21} \cdot \frac{14}{5x}$ **Change dividing by $\frac{5x}{14}$ to multiplying by the reciprocal, $\frac{14}{5x}$.**

$\qquad\quad = \frac{{}^{8}40x^{21}}{{}_{3}21} \times \frac{14^{2}}{{}_{1}5x}$ **Divide out the common factors 5, x, and 7.**

$\qquad\quad = \frac{16x}{3}$ **Multiply the numerators (8x · 2). Multiply the denominators (3 · 1).**

EXERCISES

Write each expression in simplest form.

1. $\frac{4a^2b}{12ab^3}$ $\frac{a}{3b^2}$

2. $\frac{5n + 15}{n + 3}$ 5

3. $\frac{x - 7}{2x - 14}$ $\frac{1}{2}$

4. $\frac{28c^2(d - 3)}{35c(d - 3)}$ $\frac{4c}{5}$

Perform the indicated operation.

5. $\frac{3x}{2} + \frac{5x}{2}$ 4x

6. $\frac{3x}{8} + \frac{5x}{8}$ x

7. $\frac{5}{h} - \frac{3}{h}$ $\frac{2}{h}$

8. $\frac{6}{11p} - \frac{9}{11p}$ $\frac{-3}{11p}$

9. $\frac{3x}{5} - \frac{x}{2}$ $\frac{x}{10}$

10. $\frac{13}{2x} - \frac{13}{3x}$ $\frac{13}{6x}$

11. $\frac{7x}{5} + \frac{5x}{7}$ $\frac{74x}{35}$

12. $\frac{5a}{b} + \frac{3a}{5b}$ $\frac{28a}{5b}$

13. $\frac{7x}{8} \cdot \frac{32x}{35}$ $\frac{4x^2}{5}$

14. $\frac{3x^2}{2} \cdot \frac{6}{x}$ 9x

15. $\frac{8x^2}{5} \cdot \frac{10}{x^3}$ $\frac{16}{x}$

16. $\frac{7x}{8} \cdot \frac{64}{14x}$ 4

17. $\frac{16}{3x} \div \frac{5}{3x}$ $\frac{16}{5}$

18. $\frac{4x}{5} \div \frac{16}{15x}$ $\frac{3x^2}{4}$

19. $\frac{x^3}{8} \div \frac{x^2}{16}$ 2x

20. $\frac{3}{n^2} \div 9n^4$ $\frac{1}{3n^6}$

Tables

Table 1 Measures

United States Customary	Metric
Length	
12 inches (in.) = 1 foot (ft) 36 in. = 1 yard (yd) 3 ft = 1 yd 5280 ft = 1 mile (mi) 1760 yd = 1 mi	10 millimeters (mm) = 1 centimeter (cm) 100 cm = 1 meter (m) 1000 mm = 1 meter 1000 m = 1 kilometer (km)
Area	
144 square inches (in.^{2}) = 1 square foot (ft^2) 9 ft^2 = 1 square yard (yd^2) 43,560 ft^2 = 1 acre (a) 4840 yd^2 = 1 acre	100 square millimeters (mm^2) = 1 square centimeter (cm^2) 10,000 cm^2 = 1 square meter (m^2) 10,000 m^2 = 1 hectare (ha)
Volume	
1728 cubic inches (in.^{3}) = 1 cubic foot (ft^3) 27 ft^3 = 1 cubic yard (yd^3)	1000 cubic millimeters (mm^3) = 1 cubic centimeter (cm^3) 1,000,000 cm^3 = 1 cubic meter (m^3)
Liquid Capacity	
8 fluid ounces (fl oz) = 1 cup (c) 2 c = 1 pint (pt) 2 pt = 1 quart (qt) 4 qt = 1 gallon (gal)	1000 milliliters (mL) = 1 liter (L) 1000 L = 1 kiloliter (kL)
Mass	
16 ounces (oz) = 1 pound (lb) 2000 lb = 1 ton (t)	1000 milligrams (mg) = 1 gram (g) 1000 g = 1 kilogram (kg) 1000 kg = 1 metric ton
Temperature	
32°F = freezing point of water 98.6°F = normal body temperature 212°F = boiling point of water	0°C = freezing point of water 37°C = normal body temperature 100°C = boiling point of water

Time	
60 seconds (s) = 1 minute (min) 60 minutes = 1 hour (h) 24 hours = 1 day (d) 7 days = 1 week (wk) 4 weeks (approx.) = 1 month (mo)	365 days = 1 year (yr) 52 weeks (approx.) = 1 year 12 months = 1 year 10 years = 1 decade 100 years = 1 century

Table 2 Math Symbols

$0.\overline{3}$	0.333 . . .	p. 5
. . .	and so on	p. 5
π	pi, an irrational number, approximately equal to 3.14	p. 5
$\approx$	is approximately equal to	p. 6
·	multiplication sign, times ($\times$)	p. 7
( )	parentheses for grouping	p. 7
[ ]	brackets for grouping	p. 7
$\frac{1}{a}$	reciprocal of a, $a \neq 0$	p. 7
$\|a\|$	absolute value of a	p. 8
$\neq$	is not equal to	p. 12
$=$	equals	p. 18
$\stackrel{?}{=}$	Is the statement true?	p. 18
$a : b$	ratio of a to b	p. 20
°	degree(s)	p. 22
%	percent	p. 22
$>$	is greater than	p. 26
$\leq$	is less than or equal to	p. 26
$\geq$	is greater than or equal to	p. 26
$<$	is less than	p. 26
AB	length of segment AB; distance between points A and B	p. 30
$\triangle ABC$	triangle ABC	p. 30
$P(\text{event})$	probability of the event	p. 40
(x, y)	ordered pair	p. 54
{ }	set braces	p. 55
$f(x)$	f of x; the function value at x	p. 58
$\{x \| x > 0\}$	the set of all x, such that x is greater than zero	p. 62
x_1, x_2, etc.	specific values of the variable x	p. 64
y_1, y_2, etc.	specific values of the variable y	p. 64
b	y-intercept of a linear function	p. 65
m	slope of a linear function	p. 65
$[x]$	greatest integer	p. 71
$\pm$	plus or minus	p. 94
$\begin{bmatrix} 1 & 2 \\ 3 & 4 \end{bmatrix}$	matrix	p. 168
a_{mn}	element in the mth row and nth column of matrix A	p. 169
A'	A prime	p. 192
A^{-1}	inverse of matrix A	p. 199
$\begin{vmatrix} a & b \\ c & d \end{vmatrix}$	determinant of a matrix	p. 200
$\det A$	determinant of matrix A	p. 200
$\sqrt{x}$	nonnegative square root of x	p. 266
i	the imaginary number $\sqrt{-1}$	p. 274
$n!$	n factorial	p. 345
$_nC_r$	combinations of n things taken r at a time	p. 346
$_nP_r$	permutations of n things taken r at a time	p. 346
a^n	nth power of a	p. 368
a^{-n}	$\frac{1}{a^n}, a \neq 0$	p. 368
$\sqrt[n]{a}$	the principal nth root of a	p. 370
$(g \circ f)(x)$	$g(f(x))$	p. 399
*	multiply (in a spreadsheet formula)	p. 402
^	raised to a power (in a spreadsheet formula)	p. 402
$f^{-1}(x)$	the inverse of function f	p. 408
e	the number 2.71828 . . .	p. 441
$\log_b x$	logarithm of x, base b	p. 447
$\ln x$	$\log_e x$	p. 470
$\sum_{n=1}^{5}$	summation	p. 621
∞	infinity	p. 627
$P(A\|B)$	probability of event A, given event B	p. 655
$\bar{x}$	mean of data values of x	p. 660
σ	sigma	p. 669
θ	theta, measure of an angle	p. 720
$\cos \theta$	cosine of θ	p. 720
$\sin \theta$	sine of θ	p. 720
$\tan \theta$	tangent of θ	p. 749
$\csc \theta$	cosecant of θ	p. 763
$\cot \theta$	cotangent of θ	p. 763
$\sec \theta$	secant of θ	p. 763
$\cos^{-1} x$	the angle whose cosine is x	p. 784
$\sin^{-1} x$	the angle whose sine is x	p. 784
$\tan^{-1} x$	the angle whose tangent is x	p. 784
$\angle A$	angle A	p. 792
$m\angle A$	measure of angle A	p. 793

Table 3 Squares and Square Roots

Number n	Square n^2	Positive Square Root $\sqrt{n}$	Number n	Square n^2	Positive Square Root $\sqrt{n}$	Number n	Square n^2	Positive Square Root $\sqrt{n}$
1	1	1.000	51	2601	7.141	101	10,201	10.050
2	4	1.414	52	2704	7.211	102	10,404	10.100
3	9	1.732	53	2809	7.280	103	10,609	10.149
4	16	2.000	54	2916	7.348	104	10,816	10.198
5	25	2.236	55	3025	7.416	105	11,025	10.247
6	36	2.449	56	3136	7.483	106	11,236	10.296
7	49	2.646	57	3249	7.550	107	11,449	10.344
8	64	2.828	58	3364	7.616	108	11,664	10.392
9	81	3.000	59	3481	7.681	109	11,881	10.440
10	100	3.162	60	3600	7.746	110	12,100	10.488
11	121	3.317	61	3721	7.810	111	12,321	10.536
12	144	3.464	62	3844	7.874	112	12,544	10.583
13	169	3.606	63	3969	7.937	113	12,769	10.630
14	196	3.742	64	4096	8.000	114	12,996	10.677
15	225	3.873	65	4225	8.062	115	13,225	10.724
16	256	4.000	66	4356	8.124	116	13,456	10.770
17	289	4.123	67	4489	8.185	117	13,689	10.817
18	324	4.243	68	4624	8.246	118	13,924	10.863
19	361	4.359	69	4761	8.307	119	14,161	10.909
20	400	4.472	70	4900	8.367	120	14,400	10.954
21	441	4.583	71	5041	8.426	121	14,641	11.000
22	484	4.690	72	5184	8.485	122	14,884	11.045
23	529	4.796	73	5329	8.544	123	15,129	11.091
24	576	4.899	74	5476	8.602	124	15,376	11.136
25	625	5.000	75	5625	8.660	125	15,625	11.180
26	676	5.099	76	5776	8.718	126	15,876	11.225
27	729	5.196	77	5929	8.775	127	16,129	11.269
28	784	5.292	78	6084	8.832	128	16,384	11.314
29	841	5.385	79	6241	8.888	129	16,641	11.358
30	900	5.477	80	6400	8.944	130	16,900	11.402
31	961	5.568	81	6561	9.000	131	17,161	11.446
32	1024	5.657	82	6724	9.055	132	17,424	11.489
33	1089	5.745	83	6889	9.110	133	17,689	11.533
34	1156	5.831	84	7056	9.165	134	17,956	11.576
35	1225	5.916	85	7225	9.220	135	18,225	11.619
36	1296	6.000	86	7396	9.274	136	18,496	11.662
37	1369	6.083	87	7569	9.327	137	18,769	11.705
38	1444	6.164	88	7744	9.381	138	19,044	11.747
39	1521	6.245	89	7921	9.434	139	19,321	11.790
40	1600	6.325	90	8100	9.487	140	19,600	11.832
41	1681	6.403	91	8281	9.539	141	19,881	11.874
42	1764	6.481	92	8464	9.592	142	20,164	11.916
43	1849	6.557	93	8649	9.644	143	20,449	11.958
44	1936	6.633	94	8836	9.695	144	20,736	12.000
45	2025	6.708	95	9025	9.747	145	21,025	12.042
46	2116	6.782	96	9216	9.798	146	21,316	12.083
47	2209	6.856	97	9409	9.849	147	21,609	12.124
48	2304	6.928	98	9604	9.899	148	21,904	12.166
49	2401	7.000	99	9801	9.950	149	22,201	12.207
50	2500	7.071	100	10,000	10.000	150	22,500	12.247

Table 4 Trigonometric Ratios

Angle	Sine	Cosine	Tangent	Angle	Sine	Cosine	Tangent
1°	0.0175	0.9998	0.0175	46°	0.7193	0.6947	1.0355
2°	0.0349	0.9994	0.0349	47°	0.7314	0.6820	1.0724
3°	0.0523	0.9986	0.0524	48°	0.7431	0.6691	1.1106
4°	0.0698	0.9976	0.0699	49°	0.7547	0.6561	1.1504
5°	0.0872	0.9962	0.0875	50°	0.7660	0.6428	1.1918
6°	0.1045	0.9945	0.1051	51°	0.7771	0.6293	1.2349
7°	0.1219	0.9925	0.1228	52°	0.7880	0.6157	1.2799
8°	0.1392	0.9903	0.1405	53°	0.7986	0.6018	1.3270
9°	0.1564	0.9877	0.1584	54°	0.8090	0.5878	1.3764
10°	0.1736	0.9848	0.1763	55°	0.8192	0.5736	1.4281
11°	0.1908	0.9816	0.1944	56°	0.8290	0.5592	1.4826
12°	0.2079	0.9781	0.2126	57°	0.8387	0.5446	1.5399
13°	0.2250	0.9744	0.2309	58°	0.8480	0.5299	1.6003
14°	0.2419	0.9703	0.2493	59°	0.8572	0.5150	1.6643
15°	0.2588	0.9659	0.2679	60°	0.8660	0.5000	1.7321
16°	0.2756	0.9613	0.2867	61°	0.8746	0.4848	1.8040
17°	0.2924	0.9563	0.3057	62°	0.8829	0.4695	1.8807
18°	0.3090	0.9511	0.3249	63°	0.8910	0.4540	1.9626
19°	0.3256	0.9455	0.3443	64°	0.8988	0.4384	2.0503
20°	0.3420	0.9397	0.3640	65°	0.9063	0.4226	2.1445
21°	0.3584	0.9336	0.3839	66°	0.9135	0.4067	2.2460
22°	0.3746	0.9272	0.4040	67°	0.9205	0.3907	2.3559
23°	0.3907	0.9205	0.4245	68°	0.9272	0.3746	2.4751
24°	0.4067	0.9135	0.4452	69°	0.9336	0.3584	2.6051
25°	0.4226	0.9063	0.4663	70°	0.9397	0.3420	2.7475
26°	0.4384	0.8988	0.4877	71°	0.9455	0.3256	2.9042
27°	0.4540	0.8910	0.5095	72°	0.9511	0.3090	3.0777
28°	0.4695	0.8829	0.5317	73°	0.9563	0.2924	3.2709
29°	0.4848	0.8746	0.5543	74°	0.9613	0.2756	3.4874
30°	0.5000	0.8660	0.5774	75°	0.9659	0.2588	3.7321
31°	0.5150	0.8572	0.6009	76°	0.9703	0.2419	4.0108
32°	0.5299	0.8480	0.6249	77°	0.9744	0.2250	4.3315
33°	0.5446	0.8387	0.6494	78°	0.9781	0.2079	4.7046
34°	0.5592	0.8290	0.6745	79°	0.9816	0.1908	5.1446
35°	0.5736	0.8192	0.7002	80°	0.9848	0.1736	5.6713
36°	0.5878	0.8090	0.7265	81°	0.9877	0.1564	6.3138
37°	0.6018	0.7986	0.7536	82°	0.9903	0.1392	7.1154
38°	0.6157	0.7880	0.7813	83°	0.9925	0.1219	8.1443
39°	0.6293	0.7771	0.8098	84°	0.9945	0.1045	9.5144
40°	0.6428	0.7660	0.8391	85°	0.9962	0.0872	11.4301
41°	0.6561	0.7547	0.8693	86°	0.9976	0.0698	14.3007
42°	0.6691	0.7431	0.9004	87°	0.9986	0.0523	19.0811
43°	0.6820	0.7314	0.9325	88°	0.9994	0.0349	28.6363
44°	0.6947	0.7193	0.9657	89°	0.9998	0.0175	57.2900
45°	0.7071	0.7071	1.0000	90°	1.0000	0.0000	

Table 5 **Random Numbers**

71133	15379	62220	83119	33872	80881	54263	35427
50631	71600	00133	22447	76212	94621	91026	89499
92641	47157	49324	27674	04501	30142	49180	17909
06747	85629	84240	41917	84067	44264	40953	20516
10967	26366	60323	55523	09686	47962	59778	99479
08945	67385	60015	91676	72694	49757	86540	32359
22437	77933	00815	21862	25049	30840	01760	60655
78658	17681	63881	99741	74067	35810	11989	68048
23006	64650	50777	06226	64703	73487	34815	35296
67218	66215	14219	61908	18165	17261	45017	29303
03020	75784	91506	02237	88056	15027	04040	96770
94965	75820	50994	31050	67304	16730	29373	96700
07845	69584	70548	52973	72302	97594	92241	15204
42665	29990	57260	55846	01152	30141	35982	96088
04003	36893	51639	65625	28426	90634	32979	05449
32959	06776	72420	55622	81422	67587	93193	67479
29041	35939	80920	31801	38638	87905	37617	53135
63364	20495	50868	54130	32625	30799	94255	03514
27838	19139	82031	46143	93922	32001	05378	42457
94248	29387	32682	86235	35805	66529	00886	25875
40156	92636	95648	79767	16307	71133	15714	44142
44293	19195	30569	41277	01417	34656	80207	33362
71878	31767	40056	52582	30766	70264	86253	07179
24757	57502	51033	16551	66731	87844	41420	10084
55529	68560	50069	50652	76104	42086	48720	96632
39724	50318	91370	68016	06222	26806	86726	52832
80950	27135	14110	92292	17049	60257	01638	04460
21694	79570	74409	95087	75424	57042	27349	16229
06930	85441	37191	75134	12845	67868	51500	97761
18740	35448	56096	37910	35485	19640	07689	31027
40657	14875	70695	92569	40703	69318	95070	01541
52249	56515	59058	34509	35791	22150	56558	75286
86570	07303	40560	57856	22009	67712	19435	90250
62962	66253	93288	01838	68388	55481	00336	19271
78066	09117	62350	58972	80778	46458	83677	16125
89106	30219	30068	54030	49295	48985	01624	72881
88310	18172	89450	04987	02781	37935	76222	93595
20942	90911	57643	34009	20728	88785	81212	08214
93926	66687	58252	18674	18501	22362	37319	33201
88294	55814	67443	77285	36229	26886	66782	89931
29751	08485	49910	83844	56013	26596	20875	34568
11169	15529	33241	83594	01727	86595	65723	82322
06602	54400	80649	70749	50395	48993	77447	24862
87445	17139	43278	55031	79971	18515	61850	49101
39283	22821	44330	82225	53534	77235	42973	60190

Properties and Formulas

Order of Operations
1. Perform any operation(s) inside grouping symbols.
2. Simplify any terms with exponents.
3. Multiply and divide in order from left to right.
4. Add and subtract in order from left to right.

Properties of Exponents
For any nonzero number a and any integers m and n:
$$a^0 = 1, a \neq 0 \qquad a^m \cdot a^n = a^{m+n}$$
$$\frac{a^m}{a^n} = a^{m-n} \qquad (a^m)^n = a^{mn}$$
$$a^{-n} = \frac{1}{a^n} \qquad a^{\frac{1}{n}} = \sqrt[n]{a}$$
$$(ab)^n = a^n b^n \qquad \left(\frac{a}{b}\right)^n = \frac{a^n}{b^n}$$

Properties of Square Roots
For any numbers $a \geq 0$ and $b \geq 0$,
$$\sqrt{ab} = \sqrt{a} \cdot \sqrt{b}.$$
For any numbers $a \geq 0$ and $b > 0$,
$$\sqrt{\frac{a}{b}} = \frac{\sqrt{a}}{\sqrt{b}}.$$

The Pythagorean Theorem
In a right triangle, the sum of the squares of the lengths of the legs is equal to the square of the length of the hypotenuse.
$$a^2 + b^2 = c^2$$

The Converse of the Pythagorean Theorem
If a triangle has sides of lengths a, b, and c, and $a^2 + b^2 = c^2$, then the triangle is a right triangle with hypotenuse of length c.

The Distance Formula
The distance d between any two points (x_1, y_1) and (x_2, y_2) is $d = \sqrt{(x_2 - x_1)^2 + (y_2 - y_1)^2}$.

The Midpoint Formula
The midpoint M of a line segment with endpoints $A(x_1, y_1)$ and $B(x_2, y_2)$ is $\left(\frac{x_1 + x_2}{2}, \frac{y_1 + y_2}{2}\right)$.

Parent Function and Function Families
If a, k, and h are positive numbers and $f(x)$ is a parent function, then
$f(x) + k$ shifts $f(x)$ up k units;
$f(x) - k$ shifts $f(x)$ down k units;
$f(x + h)$ shifts $f(x)$ left h units;
$f(x - h)$ shifts $f(x)$ right h units.
$af(x)$ stretches $f(x)$ vertically if $a > 1$
$af(x)$ shrinks $f(x)$ vertically if $0 < a < 1$
$-f(x)$ reflects $f(x)$ across the x-axis

Multiplication Counting Principle
If there are m ways to make a first selection and n ways to make a second selection, there are $m \times n$ ways to make the two selections.

Number of Permutations
The number of permutations of n items of a set arranged r items at a time is
$$_n P_r = \frac{n!}{(n-r)!} \text{ for } 1 \leq r \leq n.$$

CHAPTER 1

The Identity Properties
For every real number a:
$a + 0 = a$ and $0 + a = a$
$a \cdot 1 = a$ and $1 \cdot a = a$

Closure
For all real numbers a and b, $a + b$ and $a \cdot b$ are real numbers.

The Commutative Properties
For all real numbers a and b:
$a + b = b + a$ and $a \cdot b = b \cdot a$

The Inverse Properties
For every real number a:
$a + (-a) = 0$ and $a \cdot \frac{1}{a} = 1 \ (a \neq 0)$

The Associative Properties
For all real numbers a, b, and c:
$(a + b) + c = a + (b + c)$
$(a \cdot b) \cdot c = a \cdot (b \cdot c)$

The Distributive Property
For all real numbers a, b, and c:
$a(b + c) = ab + ac$

Properties of Equality
Let a, b, and c represent real numbers.
Reflexive: $a = a$
Symmetric: If $a = b$, then $b = a$.
Transitive: If $a = b$ and $b = c$, then $a = c$.
Addition: If $a = b$, then $a + c = b + c$.
Subtraction: If $a = b$, then $a - c = b - c$.
Multiplication: If $a = b$, then $ac = bc$.
Division: If $a = b$ and $c \neq 0$, then $\frac{a}{c} = \frac{b}{c}$.
Substitution: If $a = b$, then b may be substituted for a in any expression to obtain an equivalent expression.

Properties of Inequality
Let a, b, and c represent real numbers.
Transitive: If $a \leq b$ and $b \leq c$, then $a \leq c$.
Addition: If $a \leq b$, then $a + c \leq b + c$.
Subtraction: If $a \leq b$, then $a - c \leq b - c$.
Multiplication:
If $a \leq b$ and $c > 0$, then $ac \leq bc$.
If $a \leq b$ and $c < 0$, then $ac \geq bc$.
Division:
If $a \leq b$ and $c > 0$, then $\frac{a}{c} \leq \frac{b}{c}$.
If $a \leq b$ and $c < 0$, then $\frac{a}{c} \geq \frac{b}{c}$.

CHAPTER 2

Slope Formula
$$\text{slope} = \frac{\text{vertical change (rise)}}{\text{horizontal change (run)}} = \frac{y_2 - y_1}{x_2 - x_1},$$
where $x_2 - x_1 \neq 0$.

Point-Slope Equation of a Line
The line through point (x_1, y_1) with slope m has the equation $y - y_1 = m(x - x_1)$.

CHAPTER 3

Vertex Principle of Linear Programming
If there is a maximum or a minimum value of the linear objective function, it occurs at one or more vertices of the feasible region.

CHAPTER 4

Matrix Addition
Let A, B, and C represent $m \times n$ matrices.
Closure: $A + B$ is an $m \times n$ matrix.
Commutative: $A + B = B + A$
Associative: $(A + B) + C = A + (B + C)$
Additive Identity: There exists a unique $m \times n$ matrix O such that $O + A = A + O = A$.
Additive Inverse: For each A, there exists a unique opposite $-A$ such that $A + (-A) = O$.

Matrix Subtraction
If two matrices A and B have the same dimensions, then $A - B = A + (-B)$.

Scalar Multiplication
Let A, B, and O represent $m \times n$ matrices, and let c and d represent scalars.
Closure: cA is an $m \times n$ matrix.
Associative: $(cd)A = c(dA)$
Distributive:
$c(A + B) = cA + cB$
$(c + d)A = cA + dA$
Multiplicative Identity: $1 \cdot A = A$
Zero: $0A = O$ and $cO = O$

Matrix Multiplication
Let A, B, and C represent $n \times n$ matrices.
Closure: AB is an $n \times n$ matrix.
Associative: $(AB)C = A(BC)$
Distributive:
$A(B + C) = AB + AC$
$(B + C)A = BA + CA$
Zero: $OA = AO = O$, where O has the same dimensions as A.

CHAPTER 5

Graph of a Quadratic Function in Standard Form
The graph of $y = ax^2 + bx + c$ is a parabola when $a \neq 0$.
When $a > 0$, the parabola opens up. When $a < 0$, the parabola opens down.
The axis of symmetry is the line $x = -\frac{b}{2a}$.
The x-coordinate of the vertex is $-\frac{b}{2a}$.
The y-coordinate of the vertex is the value of y when $x = -\frac{b}{2a}$, or $y = f\left(-\frac{b}{2a}\right)$.
The y-intercept is $(0, c)$.

Graph of a Quadratic Function in Vertex Form
The graph of $y = a(x - h)^2 + k$ is the graph of $y = ax^2$ translated h units horizontally and k units vertically.
When h is positive the graph shifts right; when h is negative the graph shifts left.
When k is positive the graph shifts up; when k is negative the graph shifts down.
The vertex is (h, k), and the axis of symmetry is the line $x = h$.
When $a > 0$, the parabola opens up. When $a < 0$, the parabola opens down.

Factoring Perfect Square Trinomials
$a^2 + 2ab + b^2 = (a + b)^2$
$a^2 - 2ab + b^2 = (a - b)^2$

Factoring a Difference of Two Squares
$a^2 - b^2 = (a + b)(a - b)$

Zero-Product Property
If $ab = 0$, then $a = 0$ or $b = 0$.
Example: If $(x + 3)(x - 7) = 0$, then $(x + 3) = 0$ or $(x - 7) = 0$.

Square Root of a Negative Real Number
For any positive real number a, $\sqrt{-a} = i\sqrt{a}$.
Example: $\sqrt{-4} = i\sqrt{4} = i \cdot 2 = 2i$
Note that $(\sqrt{-4})^2 = (i\sqrt{4})^2 = i^2\sqrt{4}^2 = -1 \cdot 4 = -4$ (not 4).

Quadratic Formula
The roots of $ax^2 + bx + c = 0$ are
$x = \dfrac{-b \pm \sqrt{b^2 - 4ac}}{2a}$.

The Discriminant
The standard form of a quadratic equation is $ax^2 + bx + c = 0$. The discriminant is the value of the expression $b^2 - 4ac$.
$b^2 - 4ac > 0 \Rightarrow$ two real solutions
$b^2 - 4ac = 0 \Rightarrow$ one real solution
$b^2 - 4ac < 0 \Rightarrow$ two complex solutions

CHAPTER 6

Factor Theorem
The expression $x - a$ is a linear factor of a polynomial if and only if the value a is a zero of the related polynomial function.

Remainder Theorem
If a polynomial $P(x)$ of degree $n \geq 1$ is divided by $(x - a)$, where a is a constant, then the remainder is $P(a)$.

Sum and Difference of Cubes
$a^3 + b^3 = (a + b)(a^2 - ab + b^2)$
$a^3 - b^3 = (a - b)(a^2 + ab + b^2)$

Rational Root Theorem
If $\frac{p}{q}$ is in simplest form and is a rational root of the polynomial equation $a_nx^n + a_{n-1}x^{n-1} + \ldots + a_1x + a_0 = 0$ with integer coefficients, then p must be a factor of a_0 and q must be a factor of a_n.

Irrational Root Theorem
Let a and b be rational numbers and let $\sqrt{b}$ be an irrational number. If $a + \sqrt{b}$ is a root of a polynomial equation with rational coefficients, then the conjugate $a - \sqrt{b}$ also is a root.

Imaginary Root Theorem
If the imaginary number $a + bi$ is a root of a polynomial equation with real coefficients, then the conjugate $a - bi$ also is a root.

Fundamental Theorem of Algebra
If $P(x)$ is a polynomial of degree $n \geq 1$ with complex coefficients, then $P(x) = 0$ has at least one complex root.

Corollary
Including imaginary roots and multiple roots, an nth degree polynomial equation has exactly n roots; the related polynomial function has exactly n zeros.

Binomial Theorem
For every positive integer n,
$(a + b)^n = {}_nC_0a^n + {}_nC_1a^{n-1}b + {}_nC_2a^{n-2}b^2 + \ldots + {}_nC_{n-1}ab^{n-1} + {}_nC_nb^n$.

Chapter 7

nth Root of a^n
For any negative real number a, $\sqrt[n]{a^n} = |a|$ when n is even.

Multiplying Radical Expressions
If $\sqrt[n]{a}$ and $\sqrt[n]{b}$ are real numbers, then
$\sqrt[n]{a} \cdot \sqrt[n]{b} = \sqrt[n]{ab}$.

Dividing Radical Expressions
If $\sqrt[n]{a}$ and $\sqrt[n]{b}$ are real numbers and $b \neq 0$, then
$\dfrac{\sqrt[n]{a}}{\sqrt[n]{b}} = \sqrt[n]{\dfrac{a}{b}}$.

Chapter 8

Properties of Logarithms
For any positive numbers, M, N, and b, $b \neq 1$:
$\log_b MN = \log_b M + \log_b N$
$\log_b \frac{M}{N} = \log_b M - \log_b N$
$\log_b M^x = x \log_b M$

Change of Base Formula
For any positive numbers, M, b, and c, with $b \neq 1$ and $c \neq 1$, $\log_b M = \dfrac{\log_c M}{\log_c b}$.

Chapter 9

Probability of A and B
If A and B are independent events, then
$P(A \text{ and } B) = P(A) \cdot P(B)$.

Probability of A or B
If A and B are mutually exclusive events, then
$P(A \text{ or } B) = P(A) + P(B)$.
If A and B are not mutually exclusive events, then
$P(A \text{ or } B) = P(A) + P(B) - P(A \text{ and } B)$.

Chapter 10

Conic Section	Form of Equation
Parabola	vertex (h, k) $y = a(x - h)^2 + k$ $x = a(y - k)^2 + h$
Circle	center (h, k) $(x - h)^2 + (y - k)^2 = r^2$
Ellipse	center (h, k) $\dfrac{(x - h)^2}{a^2} + \dfrac{(y - k)^2}{b^2} = 1$ $\dfrac{(x - h)^2}{b^2} + \dfrac{(y - k)^2}{a^2} = 1$
Hyperbola	center (h, k) $\dfrac{(x - h)^2}{a^2} - \dfrac{(y - k)^2}{b^2} = 1$ $\dfrac{(y - k)^2}{a^2} - \dfrac{(x - h)^2}{b^2} = 1$

Chapter 11

Arithmetic Sequence Formulas
Recursive: $a_1 = $ a given value; $a_n = a_{n-1} + d$
Explicit: $a_n = a_1 + (n - 1)d$
In these formulas, a_n is the nth term, a_1 is the first term, n is the number of the term, and d is the common difference.

Geometric Sequence Formulas
Recursive: $a_1 = $ a given value; $a_n = a_{n-1} \cdot r$
Explicit: $a_n = a_1 \cdot r^{n-1}$
In these formulas, a_n is the nth term, a_1 is the first term, n is the number of the term, and r is the common ratio.

Sum of a Finite Arithmetic Series
The sum S_n of a finite arithmetic series $a_1 + a_2 + a_3 + \ldots + a_n$ is $S_n = \frac{n}{2}(a_1 + a_n)$, where a_1 is the first term, a_n the nth term, and n is the number of terms.

Sum of a Finite Geometric Series
The sum S_n of a finite geometric series
$a_1 + a_2 + a_3 + \ldots + a_n$ is $S_n = \dfrac{a_1(1 - r^n)}{1 - r}$, where a_1 is the first term, r the common ratio, and n is the number of terms.

Sum of an Infinite Geometric Series
An infinite geometric series with $|r| < 1$ converges to the sum S given by the following formula:
$S = \dfrac{a_1}{1 - r}$

Chapter 12

Conditional Probability Formula
For any two events A and B from a sample space with $P(A) \neq 0$,
$P(B \mid A) = \dfrac{P(A \text{ and } B)}{P(A)}$

Margin of Error Formula
When a random sample of size n is taken from a large population, the sample proportion has a margin of error of approximately $\pm \frac{1}{\sqrt{n}}$.

Binomial Probability
For repeated independent trials, each with a probability of success p and a probability of failure q (with $p + q = 1$), the probability of x successes in n trials is ${}_nC_x p^x q^{n-x}$.

Chapter 13

Converting Between Radians and Degrees
To convert degrees to radians, multiply by $\frac{\pi \text{ radians}}{180°}$.
To convert radians to degrees, multiply by $\frac{180°}{\pi \text{ radians}}$.

Length of an Intercepted Arc
For a circle of radius r and a central angle of measure θ (in radians), the length s of the intercepted arc is $s = r\theta$.

Properties of Sine Functions
Suppose $y = a \sin b\theta$, with $a \neq 0$, $b > 0$, and θ in radians.
$|a|$ is the amplitude of the function.
b is the number of cycles in the interval from 0 to 2π.
$\frac{2\pi}{b}$ is the period of the function.

Properties of Cosine Functions
Suppose $y = a \cos b\theta$, with $a \neq 0$, $b > 0$, and θ in radians.
$|a|$ is the amplitude of the function.
b is the number of cycles in the interval from 0 to 2π.
$\frac{2\pi}{b}$ is the period of the function.

Properties of Tangent Functions
Suppose $y = a \tan b\theta$, with $b > 0$ and θ in radians.
$\frac{\pi}{b}$ is the period of the function.
One cycle occurs in the interval from $-\frac{\pi}{2b}$ to $\frac{\pi}{2b}$.
There are vertical asymptotes at each end of the cycle.

Translations of Sine and Cosine Functions
$y = a \sin b(x - h) + k$ and $y = a \cos b(x - h) + k$ represent translations of $y = a \sin bx$ and $y = a \cos bx$.
• $|a| = $ amplitude
• $\frac{2\pi}{b} = $ period (when x is in radians and $b > 0$)
• $h = $ phase shift, or horizontal shift
• $k = $ vertical shift

Cosecant, Secant, and Cotangent Functions
The cosecant (csc), secant (sec), and cotangent (cot) functions are defined using reciprocals. Their domains include all real numbers θ except those that make a denominator zero.
$\csc \theta = \frac{1}{\sin \theta}$ $\sec \theta = \frac{1}{\cos \theta}$ $\cot \theta = \frac{1}{\tan \theta}$

Chapter 14

Trigonometric Identities
Reciprocal Identities:
$\csc \theta = \frac{1}{\sin \theta}$ $\sec \theta = \frac{1}{\cos \theta}$ $\cot \theta = \frac{1}{\tan \theta}$
Tangent and Cotangent Identities:
$\tan \theta = \frac{\sin \theta}{\cos \theta}$ $\cot \theta = \frac{\cos \theta}{\sin \theta}$
Pythagorean Identities:
$\cos^2 \theta + \sin^2 \theta = 1$
$1 + \tan^2 \theta = \sec^2 \theta$
$1 + \cot^2 \theta = \csc^2 \theta$

Trigonometric Ratios for a Right Triangle
In $\triangle ABC$ with $\angle C$ a right angle:
$\sin A = \frac{\text{length of leg opposite } \angle A}{\text{length of hypotenuse}} = \frac{a}{c}$
$\cos A = \frac{\text{length of leg adjacent to } \angle A}{\text{length of hypotenuse}} = \frac{b}{c}$
$\tan A = \frac{\text{length of leg opposite } \angle A}{\text{length of leg adjacent to } \angle A} = \frac{a}{b}$
$\csc A = \frac{\text{length of hypotenuse}}{\text{length of leg opposite } \angle A} = \frac{c}{a}$
$\sec A = \frac{\text{length of hypotenuse}}{\text{length of leg adjacent to } \angle A} = \frac{c}{b}$
$\cot A = \frac{\text{length of leg adjacent to } \angle A}{\text{length of leg opposite } \angle A} = \frac{b}{a}$

Law of Sines
In $\triangle ABC$, let a, b, and c represent the lengths of the sides opposite $\angle A$, $\angle B$, and $\angle C$, respectively.
Then $\frac{\sin A}{a} = \frac{\sin B}{b} = \frac{\sin C}{c}$.
You can use the Law of Sines to find missing measures of any triangle when you know the measures of two angles and any side, or two sides and the angle opposite one of them.

Law of Cosines
In $\triangle ABC$, let a, b, and c represent the lengths of the sides opposite $\angle A$, $\angle B$, and $\angle C$, respectively.
$a^2 = b^2 + c^2 - 2bc \cos A$
$b^2 = a^2 + c^2 - 2ac \cos B$
$c^2 = a^2 + b^2 - 2ab \cos C$
You can use the Law of Cosines to find missing parts of any triangle when you know the measures of two sides and the angle between them, or all three sides.

Angle Identities
Negative Angle Identities:
$\sin(-\theta) = -\sin \theta$
$\cos(-\theta) = \cos \theta$
$\tan(-\theta) = -\tan \theta$
Cofunction Identities:
$\sin\left(\frac{\pi}{2} - \theta\right) = \cos \theta$
$\cos\left(\frac{\pi}{2} - \theta\right) = \sin \theta$
$\tan\left(\frac{\pi}{2} - \theta\right) = \cot \theta$

Angle Difference Identities
$\sin(A - B) = \sin A \cos B - \cos A \sin B$
$\cos(A - B) = \cos A \cos B + \sin A \sin B$
$\tan(A - B) = \frac{\tan A - \tan B}{1 + \tan A \tan B}$

Angle Sum Identities
$\sin(A + B) = \sin A \cos B + \cos A \sin B$
$\cos(A + B) = \cos A \cos B - \sin A \sin B$
$\tan(A + B) = \frac{\tan A + \tan B}{1 - \tan A \tan B}$

Double Angle Identities
$\sin 2\theta = 2 \sin \theta \cos \theta$
$\cos 2\theta = \cos^2 \theta - \sin^2 \theta$
$\cos 2\theta = 2 \cos^2 \theta - 1$
$\cos 2\theta = 1 - 2 \sin^2 \theta$
$\tan 2\theta = \frac{2 \tan \theta}{1 - \tan^2 \theta}$

Formulas from Geometry

You will use a number of geometric formulas as you work through your algebra book. Here are some perimeter, area, and volume formulas.

$P = 2\ell + 2w$
$A = \ell w$
Rectangle

$P = 4s$
$A = s^2$
Square

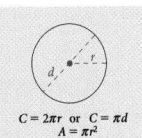

$C = 2\pi r$ or $C = \pi d$
$A = \pi r^2$
Circle

$A = \frac{1}{2}bh$
Triangle

$A = bh$
Parallelogram

$A = \frac{1}{2}(b_1 + b_2)h$
Trapezoid

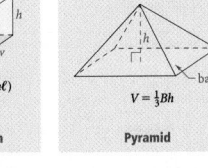

$SA = 2(\ell w + wh + h\ell)$
$V = Bh$
$V = \ell wh$
Rectangular Prism

$V = \frac{1}{3}Bh$
Pyramid

$SA = 2\pi r(r + h)$
$V = Bh$
$V = \pi r^2 h$
Cylinder

$V = \frac{1}{3}Bh$
$V = \frac{1}{3}\pi r^2 h$
Cone

$SA = 4\pi r^2$
$V = \frac{4}{3}\pi r^3$
Sphere

T891

English/Spanish Illustrated Glossary

A

EXAMPLES

Absolute value function (p. 88) A function of the form $f(x) = |mx + b| + c$, where $m \neq 0$, is an absolute value function.

$f(x) = |3x - 2| + 3$
$f(x) = |2x|$

Función de valor absoluto (p. 88) Una función de la forma $f(x) = |mx + b| + c$, donde $m \neq 0$, es una función de valor absoluto.

Absolute value of a complex number (p. 275) The absolute value of a complex number is its distance from the origin on the complex number plane. In general, $|a + bi| = \sqrt{a^2 + b^2}$.

$|3 - 4i| = \sqrt{3^2 + (-4)^2} = 5$

Valor absoluto de un número complejo (p. 275) El valor absoluto de un número complejo es la distancia a la que está del origen en el plano de números complejo. Generalmente, $|a + bi| = \sqrt{a^2 + b^2}$.

Absolute value of a real number (pp. 8, 33) The absolute value of a real number is its distance from zero on the number line. If $x \geq 0$, then $|x| = x$. If $x < 0$, then $|x| = -x$.

$|3| = 3$
$|-4| = 4$

Valor absoluto de un número real (pp. 8, 33) El valor absoluto de un número real es la distancia a la que el número se encuentra de cero en la recta numérica. Si $x \geq 0$, entonces $|x| = x$. Si $x < 0$, entonces $|x| = -x$.

Additive inverse (p. 7) The opposite or additive inverse of any number a is $-a$. The sum of opposites is 0.

$3 + (-3) = 0$
$5.2 + (-5.2) = 0$

Inverso aditivo (p. 7) El opuesto o inverso aditivo de cualquier número a es $-a$. La suma de los opuestos es 0.

Algebraic expression (p. 12) An expression that contains one or more variables is called an algebraic expression or a variable expression.

$2x + 3$
$z - y$

Expresión algebraica (p. 12) Una expresión que contiene una o más variables es llamada expresión algebraica o expresión variable.

Amplitude of a periodic function (p. 712) The amplitude of a periodic function is half the difference between the maximum and minimum values of the function.

The maximum and minimum values of $y = 4 \sin x$ are 4 and -4, respectively.
amplitude $= \frac{4 - (-4)}{2} = 4$

Amplitud de una función periódica (p. 712) La amplitud de una función periódica es la mitad de la diferencia entre los valores máximo y mínimo de la función.

EXAMPLES

Arithmetic mean (p. 607) The arithmetic mean of any two numbers is their sum divided by two.

The arithmetic mean of 12 and 15 is $\frac{12 + 15}{2} = 13.5$.

Media aritmética (p. 607) La media aritmética de dos números cualesquiera es la suma de los números dividida por dos.

Arithmetic sequence (p. 606) In an arithmetic sequence, the difference between consecutive terms is constant. The constant is called the common difference.

The arithmetic sequence $1, 5, 9, 13, \ldots$ has a common difference of 4.

Progresión aritmética (p. 606) En una progresión aritmética la diferencia entre términos consecutivos es un número constante. El número constante se llama la diferencia común.

Arithmetic series (p. 620) An arithmetic series is a series whose terms form an arithmetic sequence.

$1 + 5 + 9 + 13 + 17 + 21$ is an arithmetic series with six terms.

Serie aritmética (p. 620) Una serie aritmética es una serie cuyos términos forman una progresión aritmética.

Asymptote (p. 433) An asymptote is a line that a graph approaches as x or y increases in absolute value.

The function $y = \frac{x + 2}{x - 2}$ has $x = 2$ as a vertical asymptote and $y = 1$ as a horizontal asymptote.

Asíntota (p. 433) Una asíntota es una recta a la cual se acerca una gráfica a medida que x o y aumentan de valor absoluto.

Augmented matrix (p. 222) An augmented matrix contains the coefficients and constants from a system of equations.

linear system $\quad$ augmented matrix
$\begin{cases} x + 4 = 6 \\ -2x + 5y = 7 \end{cases}$ $\quad$ $\begin{bmatrix} 1 & 4 & | & 6 \\ -2 & 5 & | & 7 \end{bmatrix}$

Matriz aumentada (p. 222) Una matriz aumentada contiene los coeficientes y constantes de un sistema de ecuaciones.

Axis of symmetry (p. 239) The axis of symmetry is the line that divides a figure into two parts that are mirror images.

axis of symmetry $x = -1$

$y = x^2 + 2x - 1$

Eje de simetría (p. 239) El eje de simetría es la recta que divide una figura en dos partes que son imágenes una de la otra.

B

Bimodal (p. 660) A bimodal data set has two modes.

$\{1, 2, 3, 3, 4, 5, 6, 6\}$
mode = 3 and 6

Bimodal (p. 660) Un conjunto bimodal de datos tiene dos modas.

EXAMPLES

Binomial experiment (p. 685) A binomial experiment is one in which the situation involves repeated trials. Each trial has two possible outcomes (success or failure), and the probability of success is constant throughout the trials.

Experimento binomial (p. 685) Un experimento binomial es un experimento que requiere varios ensayos. Cada ensayo tiene dos resultados posibles (éxito o fracaso), y la probabilidad de éxito es constante durante todos los ensayos.

Binomial probability (p. 687) In a binomial experiment with probability of success p and probability of failure q, the probability of x successes in n trials is given by $_nC_x\, p^x q^{n-x}$.

Suppose you roll a standard number cube and that you call rolling a 1 a success. Then $p = \frac{1}{6}$ and $q = \frac{5}{6}$. The probability of rolling nine 1's in twenty rolls is $_{20}C_9\left(\frac{1}{6}\right)^9\left(\frac{5}{6}\right)^{11} \approx 0.0022$.

Probabilidad binomial (p. 687) En un experimento binomial con una probabilidad de éxito p y una probabilidad de fracaso q, la probabilidad de x éxitos en n ensayos se expresa con $_nC_x\, p^x q^{n-x}$.

Binomial Theorem (p. 354) For every positive integer n, $(a + b)^n = {_nC_0}a^n + {_nC_1}a^{n-1}b^1 + \ldots + {_nC_{n-1}}a^1 b^{n-1} + {_nC_n}b^n$. The numbers $_nC_0, {_nC_1}, \ldots, {_nC_n}$ are often called binomial coefficients.

$(2x - 3)^3 = {_3C_0}(2x)^3 + {_3C_1}(2x)^2(-3)^1$
$+ {_3C_2}(2x)^1(-3)^2 + {_3C_3}(-3)^3$
$= 8x^3 - 36x^2 + 54x - 27$

Teorema binomial (p. 354) Para todo número entero positivo n, $(a + b)^n = {_nC_0}a^n + {_nC_1}a^{n-1}b^1 + \ldots + {_nC_{n-1}}a^1 b^{n-1} + {_nC_n}b^n$. Los números $_nC_0, {_nC_1}, \ldots, {_nC_n}$ a menudo se llaman coeficientes del binomio.

Box-and-whisker plot (p. 662) A box-and-whisker plot is a method of displaying data that uses quartiles to form the center box and the maximum and minimum values to form the whiskers.

Q_1 $\quad$ Q_2 $\quad$ Q_3
Box
Whiskers
1 2 3 4 5 6 7 8

Gráfica de cajas (p. 662) Una gráfica de cajas es un método para mostrar datos que utiliza cuartiles para formar una casilla central y los valores máximos y mínimos para formar los conectores.

Branch (p. 495) Each piece of a discontinuous graph is called a branch.

$y = \frac{x + 2}{x - 2}$
branches

Rama (p. 495) Cada segmento de una gráfica discontinua se llama rama.

C

EXAMPLES

Center of a circle (p. 561) The center of a circle is the point that is the same distance from every point on the circle.

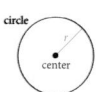

circle
center

Centro de un círculo (p. 561) El centro de un círculo es el punto que está situado a la misma distancia de cada punto del círculo.

Center of rotation (p. 194) The center of rotation is the fixed point of a rotation transformation.

Center of rotation

Centro de rotación (p. 194) El centro de rotación es el punto fijo de una transformación por rotación.

Central angle (p. 726) A central angle of a circle is an angle whose vertex is at the center of a circle.

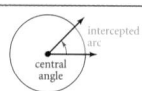

intercepted arc
central angle

Ángulo central (p. 726) El ángulo central de un círculo es un ángulo cuyo vértice está situado en el centro del círculo.

Change of Base Formula (p. 462) $\log_b M = \frac{\log_c M}{\log_c b}$, where M, b, and c are positive numbers, and $b \neq 1$ and $c \neq 1$.

$\log_3 8 = \frac{\log 8}{\log 3} \approx 1.8928$

Fórmula de cambio de base (p. 462) $\log_b M = \frac{\log_c M}{\log_c b}$, donde M, b y c son números positivos y $b \neq 1$ y $c \neq 1$.

Circle (p. 561) A circle is the set of all points in a plane at a distance r from a given point. The standard form of the equation of a circle with center (h, k) and radius r is $(x - h)^2 + (y - k)^2 = r^2$.

y-axis
(x, y)
(h, k)
x-axis

Círculo (p. 561) Un círculo es el conjunto de todos los puntos situados en un plano a una distancia r de un punto dado. La forma normal de la ecuación del círculo cuyo centro es (h, k) y cuyo radio es r es $(x - h)^2 + (y - k)^2 = r^2$.

Circumscribed rectangles (p. 636) When approximating the area under a curve, circumscribed rectangles are partially above the curve. Their combined area generally is greater than the area under the curve.

Rectángulos circunscritos (p. 636) Al aproximar el área que queda dentro de una curva, los rectángulos circunscritos quedan parcialmente por fuera de la curva. Generalmente, su área total es mayor que el área dentro de la curva.

T892

EXAMPLES

Coefficient (p. 13) The numerical factor in a term is the coefficient.

Coeficiente (p. 13) El factor numérico de un término es el coeficiente.

The coefficient of $-3k$ is -3.

Coefficient matrix (p. 214) When representing a system of equations with a matrix equation, the matrix containing the coefficients of the system is the coefficient matrix.

Matriz de coeficientes (p. 214) Al representar un sistema de ecuaciones con una ecuación de matriz, la matriz que contiene los coeficientes del sistema es la matriz de coeficientes.

$$\begin{cases} x + 2y = 5 \\ 3x + 5y = 14 \end{cases}$$

coefficient matrix $\begin{bmatrix} 1 & 2 \\ 3 & 5 \end{bmatrix}$

Combination (p. 346) Any unordered selection of r objects from a set of n objects is a combination. The number of combinations of n objects taken r at a time is ${}_nC_r = \frac{n!}{r!(n-r)!}$ for $0 \le r \le n$.

Combinación (p. 346) Cualquier selección no ordenada de r objetos tomados de un conjunto de n objetos es una combinación. El número de combinaciones de n objetos, cuando se toman r objetos cada vez, es ${}_nC_r = \frac{n!}{r!(n-r)!}$ para $0 \le r \le n$.

The number of combinations of seven items taken four at a time is
$${}_7C_4 = \frac{7!}{4!(7-4)!} = 35.$$
There are 35 ways to choose four items from seven items without regard to order.

Combined variation (p. 490) When one quantity varies with respect to two or more other quantities, the relation is a combined variation.

Variación combinada (p. 490) Cuando una cantidad varía con respecto a otras dos o más cantidades, la relación es una variación combinada.

$y = kx^2\sqrt{z}$

$z = \frac{kx}{y}$

Common difference (p. 606) A common difference is the difference between consecutive terms of an arithmetic sequence.

Diferencia común (p. 606) La diferencia común es la diferencia entre los términos consecutivos de una progresión aritmética.

The arithmetic sequence $1, 5, 9, 13, \ldots$ has a common difference of 4.

Common logarithm (p. 447) A common logarithm is a logarithm that uses base 10. You can write the common logarithm $\log_{10} y$ as $\log y$.

Logaritmo común (p. 447) El logaritmo común es un logaritmo de base 10. El logaritmo común $\log_{10} y$ se expresa como $\log y$.

$\log 1 = 0$
$\log 10 = 1$
$\log 50 = 1.698970004\ldots$

Common ratio (p. 612) A common ratio is the ratio of consecutive terms of a geometric sequence.

Razón común (p. 612) Una razón común es el número que resulta al dividir términos consecutivos en una progresión geométrica.

The geometric sequence $2.5, 5, 10, 20, \ldots$ has a common ratio of 2.

Completing the square (p. 282) Completing the square is the process of finding the constant term of a perfect square trinomial.

Completar el cuadrado (p. 282) Completar el cuadrado es el proceso de hallar el término constante de un trinomio cuadrado perfecto.

$x^2 - 12x + \blacksquare$
$x^2 - 12x + \left(\frac{-12}{2}\right)^2$
$x^2 - 12x + 36$

EXAMPLES

Complex conjugates (p. 338) Number pairs of the form $a + bi$ and $a - bi$ are complex conjugates.

Conjugados complejos (p. 338) Los pares de números de la forma $a + bi$ y $a - bi$ son conjugados complejos.

The complex numbers $2 - 3i$ and $2 + 3i$ are complex conjugates.

Complex fraction (p. 516) A complex fraction is a fraction that has a fraction in its numerator or denominator or in both its numerator and denominator.

Fracción compleja (p. 516) Una fracción compleja es una fracción que contiene otra fracción en el numerador o en el denominador, o en ambos.

$\frac{\frac{2}{3}}{5}$

$\frac{\frac{2}{3}}{\frac{4}{5}}$

Complex number plane (p. 275) You can use the complex number plane to represent a complex number geometrically. Locate the real part of the number on the horizontal axis and the imaginary part on the vertical axis.

Plano de números complejos (p. 275) Plano que sirve para representar geométricamente los números complejos. Se localiza la parte real del número en el eje horizontal y la parte imaginaria en el eje vertical.

Complex numbers (p. 275) Imaginary numbers and real numbers together make up the set of complex numbers. A complex number can be written in the form $a + bi$, where a and b are real numbers, including 0, and i is $\sqrt{-1}$.

Números complejos (p. 275) Los números imaginarios y los números reales componen el conjunto de números complejos. Un número complejo es cualquier expresión de la forma $a + bi$, donde a y b son números reales, incluido 0, e i es $\sqrt{-1}$.

$6 + i$
$7, 2i$

Composite function (p. 399) A composite function is a combination of two functions such that the output from the first function becomes the input for the second function.

Función compuesta (p. 399) Una función compuesta es la combinación de dos funciones. La cantidad de salida de la primera función es la cantidad de entrada de la segunda función.

$f(x) = 2x + 1 \quad g(x) = x^2 - 1$
$(g \circ f)(5) = g(f(5)) = g(2(5) + 1)$
$\qquad = g(11)$
$\qquad = 11^2 - 1 = 120$
$(f \circ g)(5) = f(g(5)) = f((5)^2 - 1)$
$\qquad = f(24)$
$\qquad = 2(24) + 1 = 49$

Compound inequality (p. 28) A compound inequality is a pair of inequalities joined by *and* or *or*.

Desigualdad compuesta (p. 28) Una desigualdad compuesta se forma con dos desigualdades enlazadas por medio de una *y* o una *o*.

$-1 < x$ and $x \le 3$
$x < -1$ or $x \ge 3$

EXAMPLES

Conditional probability (p. 654) A conditional probability contains a condition that may limit the sample space for an event. The notation $P(B \mid A)$ is read "the probability of event B, given event A." For any two events A and B in the sample space,
$$P(B \mid A) = \frac{P(A \text{ and } B)}{P(A)}.$$

Probabilidad condicional (p. 654) Una probabilidad condicional contiene una condición que puede limitar el espacio muestral de un suceso. La notación $P(B \mid A)$ se lee "la probabilidad del suceso B, dado el suceso A". Para dos sucesos cualesquiera A y B en el espacio muestral, $P(B \mid A) = \frac{P(A \text{ y } B)}{P(A)}$.

Suppose that 83% of an airline's flights depart on schedule. Suppose also that 75% of its flights depart and arrive on schedule.
$P(\text{arrives on time} \mid \text{departs on time})$
$= \frac{P(\text{departs and arrives on time})}{P(\text{departs on time})}$
$= \frac{0.75}{0.83}$
≈ 0.9

Conic section (p. 547) A conic section is a curve formed by the intersection of a plane and a double cone.

Sección cónica (p. 547) Una sección cónica es una curva que se forma por la intersección de un plano con un cono doble.

ellipse   hyperbola

Conjugates (p. 337) Number pairs of the form $a + \sqrt{b}$ and $a - \sqrt{b}$ are conjugates.

Conjugados (p. 337) Los pares de números con la forma $a + \sqrt{b}$ y $a - \sqrt{b}$ son conjugados.

$5 + \sqrt{3}$ and $5 - \sqrt{3}$ are conjugates.

Constant matrix (p. 214) When representing a system of equations with a matrix equation, the matrix containing the constants of the system is the constant matrix.

Matriz de constantes (p. 214) Al representar un sistema de ecuaciones con una ecuación matricial, la matriz que contiene las constantes del sistema es la matriz de constantes.

$$\begin{cases} x + 2y = 5 \\ 3x + 5y = 14 \end{cases}$$

constant matrix $\begin{bmatrix} 5 \\ 14 \end{bmatrix}$

Constant of variation (pp. 72, 488, 490) The constant of variation is the value of k in the direct variation $y = kx$ or the value of k in the indirect variation $xy = k$. A joint variation also has a constant of variation.

Constante de variación (pp. 72, 488, 490) La constante de variación es el valor de k en una variación directa $y = kx$, o el valor de k en la variación indirecta $xy = k$. Una variación conjunta también tiene una constante de variación.

In $y = 3.5x$, the constant of variation k is 3.5. In $xy = 5$, the constant of variation k is 5.

EXAMPLES

Constraints (p. 139) Constraints are restrictions on the variables of the objective function in a linear programming problem. *See* **Linear programming.**

Restricciones (p. 139) Las restricciones son limitaciones a las variables de una función objetiva en un problema de programación lineal. *Ver* **Linear programming.**

Continuously compounded interest formula (p. 444) The formula for continuously compounded interest is $A = Pe^{rt}$.

Fórmula de interés compuesto continuo (p. 444) La fórmula para el interés compuesto continuo es $A = Pe^{rt}$.

Suppose that $P = \$1200, r = 0.05,$ and $t = 3$. Then
$A = 1200e^{0.05 \cdot 3}$
$\quad = 1200(2.718\ldots)^{0.15}$
$\quad \approx 1394.20$

Converge (p. 627) An infinite geometric series converges when $|r| < 1$, where r is the common ratio of the related sequence.

Convergir (p. 627) Una serie geométrica infinita converge cuando $|r| < 1$, donde r es la razón común de la progresión.

$1 + \frac{1}{2} + \frac{1}{4} + \frac{1}{8} + \cdots$ converges.

Coordinate space (p. 146) Coordinate space is a three-dimensional space where each point is described uniquely using an ordered triple of numbers.

Espacio de coordenadas (p. 146) Un espacio de coordenadas es un espacio tridimensional en el cual cada punto es definido de manera única por una tripleta ordenada de números.

Cosecant function (p. 763) The cosecant (csc) function is the reciprocal of the sine function. For all real numbers θ except those that make $\sin \theta = 0$, $\csc \theta = \frac{1}{\sin \theta}$.

Función cosecante (p. 763) La función cosecante (csc) se define como el recíproco de la función seno. Para todos los números reales θ, excepto aquéllos para los que $\sin \theta = 0$, $\csc \theta = \frac{1}{\sin \theta}$.

If $\sin \theta = \frac{5}{13}$, then $\csc \theta = \frac{13}{5}$.

Cosine function (p. 743) The cosine function, $y = \cos \theta$, matches the measure θ of an angle in standard position with the x-coordinate of a point on the unit circle. This point is where the terminal side of the angle intersects the unit circle.

Función coseno (p. 743) La función coseno, $y = \cos \theta$, equivale a la medida θ de un ángulo en posición normal con la coordenada x de un punto en el círculo unitario. Este punto es el punto de intersección entre el lado terminal del ángulo y el círculo unitario.

Cosine of θ (p. 720) The cosine of an angle measure θ (cos θ) is the x-coordinate of the point at which the terminal side of the angle intersects the unit circle.

Coseno de θ (p. 720) El coseno de un ángulo que mide θ (cos θ) es la coordenada x del punto de intersección del lado terminal del ángulo y el círculo unitario.

Cotangent function (p. 763) The cotangent (cot) function is the reciprocal of the tangent function. For all real numbers θ except those that make $\tan \theta = 0$, $\cot \theta = \frac{1}{\tan \theta}$.

Función cotangente (p. 763) La función cotangente (cot) es el recíproco de la función tangente. Para todos los números reales θ, excepto aquéllos para los que $\tan \theta = 0$, $\cot \theta = \frac{1}{\tan \theta}$.

If $\tan \theta = \frac{5}{12}$, then $\cot \theta = \frac{12}{5}$.

Coterminal angles (p. 719) Two angles in standard position are coterminal if they have the same terminal side.

Ángulos coterminales (p. 719) Dos ángulos que están en posición normal son coterminales si tienen el mismo lado terminal.

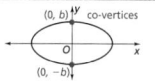

coterminal angles

Angles that have measures 135° and −225° are coterminal.

Co-vertices (of an ellipse) (p. 568) The endpoints of the minor axis of an ellipse are the co-vertices of the ellipse.

Covértices (de una elipse) (p. 568) Los puntos de intersección entre una elipse y los ejes menores son los covértices de la elipse.

Cramer's Rule (p. 221) Cramer's Rule is a method of solving a system of linear equations using determinants. D is the determinant of the system's coefficient matrix. Form the determinants D_x and D_y by replacing the corresponding column of the coefficient matrix with the terms of the constant matrix.

Regla de Cramer (p. 221) La regla de Cramer es un método para resolver por medio de determinantes un sistema de ecuaciones lineales. D es el determinante de la matriz de coeficientes del sistema. Se forman los determinantes D_x y D_y reemplazando la columna correspondiente de la matriz de coeficientes con los términos de la matriz constante.

$$\begin{cases} x + 2y = 6 \\ -x + y = -6 \end{cases}$$

$$D = \begin{vmatrix} 1 & 2 \\ -1 & 1 \end{vmatrix} = 3$$

$$D_x = \begin{vmatrix} 6 & 2 \\ -6 & 1 \end{vmatrix} = 18$$

$$D_y = \begin{vmatrix} 1 & 6 \\ -1 & -6 \end{vmatrix} = 0$$

$$x = \frac{D_x}{D} = 6 \qquad y = \frac{D_y}{D} = 0$$

Cumulative probability (p. 648) Probability over a continuous range of events is cumulative probability.

Probabilidad acumulativa (p. 648) La probabilidad que existe a lo largo de una serie continua de sucesos es la probabilidad acumulativa.

English/Spanish Glossary

Cycle (p. 711) A cycle of a periodic function is an interval of x-values over which the function provides one complete pattern of y-values.

Ciclo (p. 711) El ciclo de una función periódica es un intervalo de valores de x de los cuales la función produce un patrón completo de valores de y.

a cycle

D

Decay factor (p. 433) In an exponential function of the form $y = ab^x$, b is the decay factor if $0 < b < 1$.

Factor de decremento (p. 433) En una función exponencial de la forma $y = ab^x$, b es el factor de decremento si, $0 < b < 1$.

In the equation $y = 0.5^x$, 0.5 is the decay factor.

Degree of a polynomial (p. 307) The degree of a polynomial is the largest degree of any term of the polynomial.

Grado de un polinomio (p. 307) El grado de un polinomio es el grado mayor de cualquier término del polinomio.

$P(x) = x^6 + 2x^3 - 3$

degree 6

Degree of a term (p. 307) The exponent of the variable in a term determines the degree of the term.

Grado de un término (p. 307) El exponente de la variable de un término determina el grado del término.

$x^2 \leftarrow$ degree 2

$3y^3 \leftarrow$ degree 3

$-4a^{12} \leftarrow$ degree 12

Dependent events (p. 531) Two events are dependent if the occurrence of one event affects the probability of the second event.

Sucesos dependientes (p. 531) Cuando el resultado de un suceso influye en la probabilidad de que ocurra el segundo suceso, los dos sucesos son dependientes.

You have a bag with red and blue marbles. You draw one marble at random and then another without replacing the first. The colors drawn are dependent events. A red marble on the first draw changes the probability for each color on the second draw.

Dependent system (p. 120) A system of equations that does not have a unique solution is a dependent system.

Sistema dependiente (p. 120) Un sistema de ecuaciones es dependiente cuando no tiene una solución única.

$$\begin{cases} y = 2x + 3 \\ -4x + 2y = 6 \end{cases}$$ represents two

equations for the same line, so it has many solutions. It is a dependent system.

Dependent variable (p. 62) If a function is defined by an equation using the variables x and y, where y represents output values, then y is the dependent variable.

Variable dependiente (p. 62) Si una función es definida por una ecuación que usa las variables x e y, donde y representa valores de salida, entonces y es la variable dependiente.

$y = 2x + 1$

y is the dependent variable.

Determinant (p. 200) The determinant of a square matrix is a real number that can be computed from its elements according to a specific formula.

Determinante (p. 200) El determinante de una matriz cuadrada es un número real que se puede calcular a partir de sus elementos por medio de una fórmula específica.

The determinant of $\begin{bmatrix} 3 & -2 \\ 5 & 6 \end{bmatrix}$ is

$3(6) - 5(-2) = 28$.

Difference of cubes (p. 328) A difference of cubes is an expression of the form $a^3 - b^3$. It can be factored as $(a - b)(a^2 + ab + b^2)$.

Diferencia de dos cubos (p. 328) La diferencia de dos cubos es una expresión de la forma $a^3 - b^3$. Se puede factorizar como $(a - b)(a^2 + ab + b^2)$.

$x^3 - 27 = (x - 3)(x^2 + 3x + 9)$

Difference of two squares (p. 263) A difference of two squares is an expression of the form $a^2 - b^2$. It can be factored as $(a + b)(a - b)$.

Diferencia de dos cuadrados (p. 263) La diferencia de dos cuadrados es una expresión de la forma $a^2 - b^2$. Se puede factorizar como $(a + b)(a - b)$.

$25a^2 - 4 = (5a + 2)(5a - 2)$

$m^6 - 1 = (m^3 + 1)(m^3 - 1)$

Dilation (p. 192) A dilation is a transformation that can change the size of a figure. When the center of the dilation is the origin, you can use scalar multiplication to find the coordinates of the vertices of an image.

Dilatación (p. 192) Una dilatación es una transformación que puede cambiar el tamaño de una figura. Cuando el centro de dilatación está en el origen, se hallan las coordenadas de los vértices de la imagen por medio de la multiplicación de escalar.

Direct variation (p. 72) A linear function defined by an equation of the form $y = kx$, where $k \neq 0$, represents direct variation.

Variación directa (p. 72) Una función lineal definida por una ecuación de la forma $y = kx$, donde $k \neq 0$, representa una variación directa.

$y = 3.5x, y = 7x, y = -\frac{1}{2}x$

Directrix (p. 555) The directrix of a parabola is the fixed line used to define a parabola. Each point of the parabola is the same distance from the focus and the directrix.

Directriz (p. 555) La directriz de una parábola es la recta fija con que se define una parábola. Cada punto de la parábola está a la misma distancia del foco y de la directriz.

Focus

Directrix

English/Spanish Glossary

Discriminant (p. 291) The discriminant of the quadratic trinomial $ax^2 + bx + c$ is $b^2 - 4ac$. The discriminant determines the number of real roots that the quadratic equation $ax^2 + bx + c = 0$ has. If $b^2 - 4ac < 0$, the equation has no real roots; if $b^2 - 4ac = 0$, the equation has one real root; if $b^2 - 4ac > 0$, the equation has two real roots.

Discriminante (p. 291) El discriminante del trinomio cuadrático $ax^2 + bx + c$ es $b^2 - 4ac$. El discriminante determina la cantidad de raíces reales que tiene la ecuación $ax^2 + bx + c = 0$. Si $b^2 - 4ac < 0$, la ecuación no tiene raíces reales; si $b^2 - 4ac = 0$, la ecuación tiene una raíz real; si $b^2 - 4ac > 0$, la ecuación tiene dos raíces reales.

$3x^2 - 6x + 1$

discriminant $= (-6)^2 - 4(3)(1)$

$= 36 - 12 = 24$

The equation has two real roots.

Diverge (p. 627) An infinite geometric series diverges when $|r| \geq 1$, where r is the common ratio of the related sequence.

Divergir (p. 627) Una serie geométrica infinita diverge cuando $|r| \geq 1$, donde r es la razón común de la progresión relacionada.

$1 + 2 + 4 + 8 + \cdots$ diverges.

Domain (p. 56) The domain of a relation is the set of all inputs, or x-coordinates, of the ordered pairs.

Dominio (p. 56) El dominio de una relación es el conjunto de todos los valores de entrada, o coordenadas x, de los pares ordenados.

In the relation $\{(0, 1), (0, 2), (0, 3), (0, 4), (1, 3), (1, 4), (2, 1)\}$, the domain is $\{0, 1, 2\}$. In the function $f(x) = x^2 - 10$, the domain is all real numbers.

E

Ellipse (p. 568) An ellipse is the set of points P in a plane such that the sum of the distances from P to two fixed points F_1 and F_2 is a given constant k. The standard form of the equation of an ellipse with its center at the origin is $\frac{x^2}{a^2} + \frac{y^2}{b^2} = 1$ if the major axis is horizontal and $\frac{x^2}{b^2} + \frac{y^2}{a^2} = 1$ if the major axis is vertical, where $a > b$.

Elipse (p. 568) Una elipse es el conjunto de puntos P situados en un plano tal que la suma de las distancias entre P y dos puntos fijos F_1 y F_2 es una constante dada k. La forma normal de la ecuación de una elipse con su centro en el origen es $\frac{x^2}{a^2} + \frac{y^2}{b^2} = 1$ si el eje mayor es horizontal y $\frac{x^2}{b^2} + \frac{y^2}{a^2} = 1$ si el eje mayor es vertical, donde $a > b$.

$\frac{x^2}{36} + \frac{y^2}{9} = 1$

$F_1 = (-3\sqrt{3}, 0), F_2 = (3\sqrt{3}, 0)$

Equal matrices (p. 177) Equal matrices are matrices with the same dimensions and equal corresponding elements.

Matrices equivalentes (p. 177) Dos matrices son equivalentes si y sólo si tienen las mismas dimensiones y sus elementos correspondientes son iguales.

Matrices A and B are equal.

$A = \begin{bmatrix} 2 & 6 \\ \frac{9}{3} & 1 \end{bmatrix}$ $B = \begin{bmatrix} \frac{6}{3} & 6 \\ 3 & \frac{13}{3} \end{bmatrix}$

T894

Equivalent systems (p. 127) Linear systems that have the same solution(s) are equivalent systems.

Sistemas equivalentes (p. 127) Sistemas lineales que tienen la misma solución o soluciones son sistemas equivalentes.

Evaluate (p. 12) To evaluate an expression, substitute numbers for the variables in the expression and then simplify the expression following the order of operations.

Evaluar (p. 12) Para evaluar una expresión, se sustituyen las variables de la expresión por números y luego se simplifica la expresión siguiendo el orden de las operaciones.

When $x = 2$ and $y = -1$, $2x + 3y$ evaluates to 1.

Expand (p. 353) You expand a binomial raised to a power by multiplying and then writing the resulting polynomial in standard form.

Desarrollar (p. 353) Para desarrollar un binomio elevado a una potencia, se multiplica y luego se escribe el polinomio resultante en forma normal.

$(x + 4)^3$
$= (x + 4)(x + 4)^2$
$= (x + 4)(x^2 + 8x + 16)$
$= x^3 + 8x^2 + 16x + 4x^2 + 32x + 64$
$= x^3 + 12x^2 + 48x + 64$

Experimental probability (p. 40) The experimental probability of an event is the ratio

$$\frac{\text{number of times the event occurs}}{\text{number of trials}}.$$

Probabilidad experimental (p. 40) La probabilidad experimental de un suceso es la razón

$$\frac{\text{número de veces que el suceso ocurre}}{\text{número de ensayos}}.$$

Suppose a basketball player has scored 19 times in 28 attempts at a basket. The experimental probability of the player's scoring is $P(\text{score}) = \frac{19}{28} \approx 0.68$, or 68%.

Explicit formula (p. 602) An explicit formula expresses the nth term of a sequence in terms of n.

Fórmula explícita (p. 602) Una fórmula explícita expresa el n-ésimo término de una progresión en función de n.

Let $a_n = 2n + 5$ for positive integers n. If $n = 7$, then $a_7 = 2(7) + 5 = 19$.

Exponential equation (p. 461) An equation of the form $b^{cx} = a$, where the exponent includes a variable, is called an exponential equation. You can solve an exponential equation by taking the logarithm of each side of the equation.

Ecuación exponencial (p. 461) Una ecuación de la forma $b^{cx} = a$, donde el exponente incluye una variable, se llama ecuación exponencial. Dicha ecuación se resuelve hallando el logaritmo de cada lado de la ecuación.

$5^{2x} = 270$
$\log 5^{2x} = \log 270$
$2x \log 5 = \log 270$
$2x = \frac{\log 270}{\log 5}$
$2x \approx 3.4785$
$x \approx 1.7392$

Exponential function (pp. 430, 441) The general form of an exponential function is $y = ab^x$, where x is a real number, $a \neq 0$, $b > 0$, and $b \neq 1$. When $b > 1$, the function models exponential growth with growth factor b. When $0 < b < 1$, the function models exponential decay with decay factor b.

Función exponencial (pp. 430, 441) La forma general de una función exponencial es $y = ab^x$, donde x es un número real, $a \neq 0$, $b > 0$ y $b \neq 1$. Cuando $b > 1$, la función representa un incremento exponencial con factor de incremento b. Cuando $0 < b < 1$, la función representa el decremento exponencial con factor de decremento b.

Extraneous solution (p. 34) An extraneous solution is a solution of an equation derived from an original equation but it is not a solution of the original equation.

Solución extraña (p. 34) Una solución extraña es una solución de una ecuación derivada de una ecuación dada, pero que no satisface la ecuación dada.

$\sqrt{x - 3} = x - 5$
$x - 3 = x^2 - 10x + 25$
$0 = x^2 - 11x + 28$
$0 = (x - 4)(x - 7)$
$x = 4$ or 7

The number 7 is a solution, but 4 is not, since $\sqrt{4 - 3} \neq 4 - 5$.

F

Factor Theorem (p. 315) The expression $x - a$ is a linear factor of a polynomial if and only if the value a is a zero of the related polynomial function.

Teorema de factores (p. 315) La expresión $x - a$ es un factor lineal de un polinomio si y sólo si el valor a es un cero de la función del polinomio relacionada.

The value 2 makes the polynomial $x^2 + 2x - 8$ equal to zero. So, $x - 2$ is a factor of $x^2 + 2x - 8$.

Factoring (p. 259) Factoring is rewriting an expression as the product of its factors.

Descomposición factorial (p. 259) Descomponer en factores es convertir una expresión en el producto de sus factores.

expanded form   factored form
$x^2 + x - 56$ $(x + 8)(x - 7)$

Feasible region (p. 140) In a linear programming problem, the feasible region contains all the values that satisfy the constraints on the objective function.

Región factible (p. 140) En un problema de programación lineal, la región factible contiene todos los valores que satisfacen las restricciones de la función objetiva.

Focus (plural: foci) (pp. 555, 568, 575) The focus of a conic section is a point used to define a conic section.

A parabola is the set of all points that are the same distance from the parabola's focus and its directrix. An ellipse is the set of all points P such that the sum of the distances from each point P to the two foci of the ellipse is a constant. A hyperbola is the set of all points P such that the difference of the distances from each point P to the two foci of the hyperbola is a constant.

Foco (pp. 555, 568, 575) El foco de una sección cónica es el punto con el que se define una sección cónica.

Una parábola es el conjunto de todos los puntos que están a la misma distancia del foco y la directriz de la parábola. Una elipse es el conjunto de todos los puntos P tal que la suma de las distancias de cada punto P a los focos de la elipse es una constante. Una hipérbola es el conjunto de todos los puntos P tal que la diferencia de las distancias de cada punto P a los dos focos de la hipérbola es una constante.

F_1 and F_2 are foci.

Frequency table (p. 648) A frequency table is a list of the outcomes in a sample space and the number of times each outcome occurs.

Tabla de frecuencias (p. 648) Una tabla de frecuencias es una lista de los resultados de un espacio muestral y el número de veces que cada resultado ocurre.

Roll	Freq.
1	5
2	9
3	7
4	8
5	8
6	9

Suppose that you roll a standard number cube 40 times and that each number occurs as often as shown in the table. The table is a frequency table and the diagram to its right is a frequency diagram, or histogram.

Function (p. 57) A function is a relation in which each element of the domain is paired with exactly one element of the range.

Función (p. 57) Una función es una relación que asigna exactamente un valor del dominio a cada valor del rango.

The relation $y = 3x^3 - 2x + 3$ is a function. $f(x) = 3x^3 - 2x + 3$ is the same relation written in function notation.

Function notation (p. 58) If f is the name of a function, the function notation $f(x)$ also indicates the function name, but also represents a range value for the domain value x. You read the function notation $f(x)$ as "f of x" or "a function of x." Note that $f(x)$ does *not* mean "f times x."

Notación de una función (p. 58) Si f es el nombre de una función, la notación de la función $f(x)$ indica el nombre de la función, pero también representa un rango de valores para el dominio de valores de x. La notación de una función $f(x)$ se lee "f de x" o "función de x". Hay que recordar que $f(x)$ no significa "f multiplicado por x".

When the value of x is 3, $f(3)$, read "f of 3," represents the value of the function at 3.

Fundamental Theorem of Algebra (p. 341) If $P(x)$ is a polynomial of degree $n \geq 1$ with complex coefficients, then $P(x) = 0$ has at least one complex root.

Teorema fundamental de álgebra (p. 341) Si $P(x)$ es un polinomio de grado $n \geq 1$ con coeficientes complejos, entonces $P(x) = 0$ tiene por lo menos una raíz compleja.

$P(x) = 3x^3 - 2x + 3$ is of degree 3, so $P(x) = 0$ has at least one complex root.

G

Geometric mean (p. 614) The geometric mean of any two positive numbers is the positive square root of the product of the two numbers.

Media geométrica (p. 614) La media geométrica de dos números positivos es la raíz cuadrada positiva del producto de los dos números.

The geometric mean of 12 and 18 is $\sqrt{12 \cdot 18} \approx 14.6969$.

Geometric sequence (p. 612) In a geometric sequence, the ratio of consecutive terms is constant. The constant is called the common ratio.

Progresión geométrica (p. 612) En una progresión geométrica, la razón de términos consecutivos es un valor constante. La constante se llama razón común.

The geometric sequence 2.5, 5, 10, 20, 40, . . . has a common ratio of 2.

Geometric series (p. 626) A geometric series is the sum of the terms in a geometric sequence.

Serie geométrica (p. 626) Una serie geométrica es la suma de términos en una progresión geométrica.

One geometric series with five terms is $2.5 + 5 + 10 + 20 + 40$.

Greatest common factor (GCF) of an expression (p. 259) The greatest common factor (GCF) of an expression is the common factor of each term of the expression that has the greatest coefficient and the greatest exponent.

Máximo factor común de una expresión (p. 259) El máximo común factor de una expresión es el factor común de cada término de la expresión que tiene el mayor coeficiente y el mayor exponente.

The GCF of $4x^2 + 20x - 12$ is 4.

Growth factor (p. 430) In an exponential function of the form $y = ab^x$, b is the growth factor if $b > 1$.

Factor de incremento (p. 430) En una función exponencial de la forma $y = ab^x$, b es el factor de incremento si $b > 1$.

In the exponential equation $y = 2^x$, 2 is the growth factor.

H

EXAMPLES

Hyperbola (p. 575) A hyperbola is a set of points P in a plane such that the difference between the distances from P to the foci F_1 and F_2 is a given constant k. $|PF_1 - PF_2| = k$

The standard form of an equation of a hyperbola centered at $(0,0)$ is $\frac{x^2}{a^2} - \frac{y^2}{b^2} = 1$ if the transverse axis is horizontal and $\frac{y^2}{a^2} - \frac{x^2}{b^2} = 1$ if the transverse axis is vertical.

Hipérbola (p. 575) Una hipérbola es un conjunto de puntos P en un plano tal que la diferencia entre las distancias de P a los focos F_1 y F_2 es una constante k dada. $|PF_1 - PF_2| = k$

La forma normal de la ecuación de una hipérbola centrada en $(0,0)$ es $\frac{x^2}{a^2} - \frac{y^2}{b^2} = 1$, si el eje transversal es horizontal, y $\frac{y^2}{a^2} - \frac{x^2}{b^2} = 1$, si el eje transversal es vertical.

$\frac{x^2}{5^2} - \frac{y^2}{3^2} = 1$

I

i (p. 274) The imaginary number i is the principal square root of -1.

i (p. 274) El número imaginario i es la raíz cuadrada principal de -1.

$i = \sqrt{-1}$ and $i^2 = -1$.

Image (p. 192) An image is a figure obtained by a transformation of a preimage.

Imagen (p. 192) Una imagen es la figura que resulta después de que la preimagen sufre una transformación.

Imaginary number (p. 274) An imaginary number is any number of the form $a + bi$, where $b \neq 0$ and $i = \sqrt{-1}$. A number of the form bi is a pure imaginary number.

Número imaginario (p. 274) Un número imaginario es todo número de la forma $a + bi$, donde $b \neq 0$ e $i = \sqrt{-1}$. Un número de la forma bi es un número imaginario puro.

$2 + 3i$
$7i$
i

Imaginary Root Theorem (p. 338) If the imaginary number $a + bi$ is a root of a polynomial equation with real coefficients, then the conjugate $a - bi$ also is a root.

Teorema de la raíz imaginaria (p. 338) Si el número imaginario $a + bi$ es la raíz de la ecuación de un polinomio con coeficientes reales, entonces el conjugado $a - bi$ también es una raíz.

$2 + 3i$ is a root of $x^2 - 4x + 13 = 0$, so $2 - 3i$ is also a root.

EXAMPLES

Inconsistent system (p. 120) A system of equations that has no solution is an inconsistent system.

Sistema incompatible (p. 120) Un sistema incompatible es un sistema de ecuaciones para el cual no hay solución.

$\begin{cases} y = 2x + 3 \\ -2x + y = 1 \end{cases}$ is a system of parallel lines, so it has no solution. It is an inconsistent system.

Independent events (p. 531) When the outcome of one event does not affect the probability of a second event, the two events are independent.

Sucesos independientes (p. 531) Cuando el resultado de un suceso no altera la probabilidad de otro, los dos sucesos son independientes.

The results of two rolls of a number cube are independent. Getting a 5 on the first roll does not change the probability of getting a 5 on the second roll.

Independent system (p. 120) A system of linear equations that has a unique solution is an independent system.

Sistema independiente (p. 120) Un sistema de ecuaciones lineales que tenga una sola solución es un sistema independiente.

$\begin{cases} x + 2y = -7 \\ 2x - 3y = 0 \end{cases}$ has the unique solution $(-3, -2)$. It is an independent system.

Independent variable (p. 62) If a function is defined by an equation using the variables x and y, where x represents input values, then x is the independent variable.

Variable independiente (p. 62) Si una función es definida por una ecuación con las variables x e y, donde x representa los valores de entrada, entonces x es la variable independiente.

$y = 2x + 1$

x is the independent variable.

Index (p. 370) With a radical sign, the index indicates the degree of the root.

Índice (p. 370) Con un signo de radical, el índice indica el grado de la raíz.

index 2 index 3 index 4
$\sqrt{16}$ $\sqrt[3]{16}$ $\sqrt[4]{16}$

Initial side of an angle (p. 718) When an angle is in standard position, the initial side of the angle is given to be on the positive x-axis. The other ray is the terminal side of the angle.

Lado inicial de un ángulo (p. 718) Cuando un ángulo está en posición normal, el lado inicial del ángulo se ubica en el eje positivo de las x. El otro rayo, o semirrecta, forma el lado terminal del ángulo.

Inscribed rectangles (p. 635) When approximating the area under a curve, inscribed rectangles are completely under the curve. Their combined area generally is less than the area under the curve.

Rectángulos inscritos (p. 635) Cuando se aproxima el área situada dentro de una curva, los rectángulos inscritos quedan completamente contenidos en la curva. Generalmente, su área total es menor que el área dentro de la curva.

EXAMPLES

Intercepted arc (p. 726) An intercepted arc is the portion of a circle whose endpoints are on the sides of a central angle of the circle and whose remaining points lie in the interior of the angle.

Arco interceptado (p. 726) Un arco interceptado es la porción de un círculo cuyos extremos quedan sobre los lados de un ángulo central del círculo y cuyos puntos restantes quedan en el interior del ángulo.

intercepted arc
central angle

Interquartile range (p. 669) The interquartile range of a set of data is the difference between the third and first quartiles.

Intervalo intercuartil (p. 669) El rango intercuartil de un conjunto de datos es la diferencia entre el tercero y el primer cuartiles.

The first and third quartiles of the data set $\{2, 3, 4, 5, 5, 6, 7, 7\}$ are 3.5 and 6.5. The interquartile range is $6.5 - 3.5 = 3$.

Inverse functions (p. 409) If function f pairs a value b with a then its inverse, denoted f^{-1}, pairs the value a with b. If f^{-1} is also a function, then f and f^{-1} are inverse functions.

Funciones inversas (p. 409) Si la función f empareja un valor b con a, entonces su inversa, cuya notación es f^{-1}, empareja el valor a con b. Si f^{-1} también es una función, entonces f y f^{-1} son funciones inversas.

If $f(x) = x + 3$, then $f^{-1}(x) = x - 3$.

Inverse relation (p. 407) If a relation pairs element a of its domain with element b of its range, the inverse relation "undoes" the relation and pairs b with a. If (a, b) is an ordered pair of a relation, then (b, a) is an ordered pair of its inverse.

Relación inversa (p. 407) Si una relación empareja el elemento a de su dominio con el elemento b de su rango, la relación inversa "deshace" la relación y empareja b con a. Si (a, b) es un par ordenado de una relación, entonces (b, a) es un par ordenado de su inversa.

Inverse variation (p. 488) A relation represented by an equation of the form $y = \frac{k}{x}$ or $xy = k$, where $k \neq 0$, is an inverse variation with the constant of variation k.

Variación inversa (p. 488) Una relación representada por la fórmula $y = \frac{k}{x}$ o $xy = k$, donde $k \neq 0$, es una variación inversa con la constante de variación k.

$xy = 5$, or $y = \frac{5}{x}$

Irrational Root Theorem (p. 337) Let a and b be rational numbers and let $\sqrt{b}$ be an irrational number. If $a + \sqrt{b}$ is a root of a polynomial equation with rational coefficients, then the conjugate $a - \sqrt{b}$ also is a root.

Teorema de la raíz irracional (p. 337) Sean a y b números racionales y sea $\sqrt{b}$ un número irracional. Si $a + \sqrt{b}$ es una raíz de una ecuación de un polinomio con coeficientes racionales, entonces el conjugado $a - \sqrt{b}$ también es una raíz.

$2 + \sqrt{3}$ is a root of $x^2 - 4x + 1 = 0$, so $2 - \sqrt{3}$ is also a root.

J

EXAMPLES

Joint variation (p. 490) If one variable varies directly with respect to each of two or more other variables, the relation is a joint variation.

Variación conjunta (p. 490) Si una variable varía directamente con respecto a cada una de dos o más variables, la relación es una variación conjunta.

$z = 8xy$
$T = kPV$

L

Law of Cosines (p. 808) In $\triangle ABC$, let a, b, and c represent the lengths of the sides opposite $\angle A$, $\angle B$, and $\angle C$, respectively. Then
$a^2 = b^2 + c^2 - 2bc \cos A$,
$b^2 = a^2 + c^2 - 2ac \cos B$, and
$c^2 = a^2 + b^2 - 2ab \cos C$

Ley de cosenos (p. 808) En $\triangle ABC$, sean a, b y c las longitudes de los lados opuestos a $\angle A$, $\angle B$ y $\angle C$, respectivamente. Entonces
$a^2 = b^2 + c^2 - 2bc \cos A$,
$b^2 = a^2 + c^2 - 2ac \cos B$ y
$c^2 = a^2 + b^2 - 2ab \cos C$

$LM^2 = 11.41^2 + 8.72^2 - 2(11.41)(8.72) \cos 18°$
$LM^2 \approx 16.9754$
$LM \approx 4.12$

Law of Sines (p. 801) In $\triangle ABC$, let a, b, and c represent the lengths of the sides opposite $\angle A$, $\angle B$, and $\angle C$, respectively. Then
$\frac{\sin A}{a} = \frac{\sin B}{b} = \frac{\sin C}{c}$.

Ley de senos (p. 801) En $\triangle ABC$, sean a, b y c las longitudes de los lados opuestos a $\angle A$, $\angle B$ y $\angle C$, respectivamente. Entonces
$\frac{\operatorname{sen} A}{a} = \frac{\operatorname{sen} B}{b} = \frac{\operatorname{sen} C}{c}$.

$m\angle L = 180 - (120 + 18) = 42°$
$\frac{KL}{\sin 120°} = \frac{8.72}{\sin 42°}$
$KL = \frac{8.72 \sin 120°}{\sin 42°}$
$KL \approx 11.26$

Like radicals (p. 380) Like radicals are radical expressions that have the same index and the same radicand.

Radicales semejantes (p. 380) Los radicales semejantes son expresiones radicales que tienen el mismo índice y el mismo radicando.

$4\sqrt[3]{7}$ and $\sqrt[3]{7}$ are like radicals.

Limits (p. 621) Limits in summation notation are the least and greatest integer values of the index n.

Límites (p. 621) Los límites en notación de sumatoria son el menor y el mayor valor del índice n en números enteros.

limits $\sum\limits_{n=1}^{3} (3n + 5)$

T896

Linear equation (p. 62) A linear equation in two variables is an equation that can be written in the form $ax + by = c$. *See also* **Standard form of a linear equation.**

$y = 2x + 1$ can be written as $-2x + y = 1$.

Ecuación lineal (p. 62) Una ecuación lineal de dos variables es una ecuación que se puede escribir de la forma $ax + by = c$. *Ver también* **Standard form of a linear equation.**

Linear function (p. 62) A function whose graph is a line is a linear function. You can represent a linear function with a linear equation.

Función lineal (p. 62) Una función cuya gráfica es una recta es una función lineal. La función lineal se representa con una ecuación lineal.

Linear inequality (p. 101) A linear inequality is an inequality in two variables whose graph is a region of the coordinate plane that is bounded by a line. Each point in the region is a solution of the inequality. A sign of $\leq$ or $\geq$ indicates a solid boundary line. A sign of $<$ or $>$ indicates a dashed boundary line.

Desigualdad lineal (p. 101) Una desigualdad lineal es una desigualdad de dos variables cuya gráfica es una región del plano de coordenadas delimitado por una recta. Cada punto de la región es una solución de la desigualdad. El signo $\leq$ o $\geq$ denota que hay una recta de delimitación continua. El signo $<$ o $>$ denota que la recta de delimitación es punteada.

$y > x + 1$

Linear programming (p. 139) Linear programming is a technique that identifies the minimum or maximum value of some quantity. This quantity is modeled with an objective function. Limits on the variables in the objective function are constraints, written as linear inequalities.

Restrictions: $x \geq 0$, $y \geq 0$, $x + y \leq 7$, and $y \leq -2x + 8$

Objective function: $B = 2x + 4y$

Graph the restrictions to find the coordinates of each vertex.

Evaluate $B = 2x + 4y$ at each vertex. The minimum value of B occurs when $x = 0$ and $y = 0$. The maximum value of B occurs when $x = 0$ and $y = 7$.

Programación lineal (p. 139) La programación lineal es un método que permite identificar las condiciones que elevan al máximo o reducen al mínimo una cantidad. Se hace un modelo de esta cantidad con una función objetiva. Los límites de las variables en la función objetiva son restricciones, expresadas como desigualdades lineales.

English/Spanish Glossary

Linear system (p. 118) A linear system is a set of two or more linear equations that use the same variables.

$4x + 5y = x$ $2x - 3y = -13$

Sistema lineal (p. 118) Un sistema lineal es un conjunto de dos o más ecuaciones lineales con las mismas variables.

Logarithm (p. 447) A logarithm to the base b of a positive number y is defined as follows: If $y = b^x$, then $\log_b y = x$.

$\log_2 8 = 3$
$\log_{10} 100 = 2$
$\log_5 5^7 = 7$

Logaritmo (p. 447) El logaritmo de base b de un número positivo y se define así: Si $y = b^x$, entonces $\log_b y = x$.

Logarithmic equation (p. 463) An equation that includes a logarithmic expression is called a logarithmic equation.

$\log_3 x = 4$

Ecuación logarítmica (p. 463) Una ecuación que incluye una expresión logarítmica se llama ecuación logarítmica.

Logarithmic function (p. 448) A logarithmic function is the inverse of an exponential function.

Función logarítmica (p. 448) Una función logarítmica es la inversa de una función exponencial.

M

Major axis of an ellipse (p. 568) The major axis of an ellipse is the segment that contains the foci and has its endpoints on the ellipse. These endpoints are vertices of the ellipse.

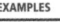

Eje mayor de una elipse (p. 568) El eje mayor de una elipse es el segmento que contiene los focos y tiene los puntos extremos de la elipse. Los extremos son los vértices de la elipse.

Mapping diagram (p. 56) A mapping diagram describes a relation by linking elements of the domain with elements of the range.

Domain	Range
-5	-10
-1	-2
3	2
	6

Mapa (p. 56) Un mapa describe una relación al unir los elementos del dominio con los elementos del rango.

Margin of error (p. 679) A sample proportion should be reported with an estimate of error, called the margin of error. When a random sample of size n is taken from a large population, the sample proportion has a margin of error of about $\pm\frac{1}{\sqrt{n}}$.

A set of 500 items is taken from a population for sampling. The margin of error for a sample proportion is about $\pm\frac{1}{\sqrt{500}} \approx \pm 0.045$.

Margen de error (p. 679) Una proporción muestral debe incluir una estimación del error, que se llama margen de error. Cuando se hace una muestra aleatoria de tamaño n de una población grande, la proporción muestral tiene un margen de error de aproximadamente $\pm\frac{1}{\sqrt{n}}$.

Matrix (p. 168) A matrix is a rectangular array of numbers written within brackets. A matrix with m horizontal rows and n vertical columns is an $m \times n$ matrix.

$A = \begin{bmatrix} 1 & -2 & 0 & 10 \\ 9 & 7 & -3 & 8 \\ 2 & -10 & 1 & -6 \end{bmatrix}$

The number 2 is the element in the third row and first column. A is a 3×4 matrix.

Matriz (p. 168) Una matriz es un conjunto de números encerrados en corchetes y dispuestos en forma de rectángulo. Una matriz que contenga m filas y n columnas es una matriz $m \times n$.

Matrix addition (p. 174) You add two matrices with the same dimensions by adding their corresponding elements.

$\begin{bmatrix} 2 & -3 \\ 0 & 4 \end{bmatrix} + \begin{bmatrix} -1 & 0 \\ 5 & -6 \end{bmatrix}$

$= \begin{bmatrix} 2 + (-1) & -3 + 0 \\ 0 + 5 & 4 + (-6) \end{bmatrix}$

$= \begin{bmatrix} 1 & -3 \\ 5 & -2 \end{bmatrix}$

Suma matricial (p. 174) Para sumar dos matrices que tengan las mismas dimensiones se suman sus elementos correspondientes.

Matrix element (p. 169) Every item listed in a matrix is an element of the matrix. An element is identified by its position in the matrix.

$A = \begin{bmatrix} 1 & -2 & 0 & 10 \\ 9 & 7 & -3 & 8 \\ 2 & -10 & 1 & -6 \end{bmatrix}$

Element a_{21} is 9, the element in the second row and first column.

Elemento matricial (p. 169) Cada cifra de una matriz es un elemento de la matriz. El elemento se identifica según la posición que ocupa en la matriz.

Matrix equation (p. 176) A matrix equation is an equation in which the variable is a matrix.

Solve $X + \begin{bmatrix} 3 & -2 \\ 5 & 1 \end{bmatrix} = \begin{bmatrix} 4 & 0 \\ 0 & 3 \end{bmatrix}$.

$X + \begin{bmatrix} 3 & -2 \\ 5 & 1 \end{bmatrix} = \begin{bmatrix} 4 & 0 \\ 0 & 3 \end{bmatrix}$

$X = \begin{bmatrix} 4 & 0 \\ 0 & 3 \end{bmatrix} - \begin{bmatrix} 3 & -2 \\ 5 & 1 \end{bmatrix} = \begin{bmatrix} 1 & 2 \\ -5 & 2 \end{bmatrix}$

Ecuación matricial (p. 176) Una ecuación matricial es una ecuación en que la variable es una matriz.

English/Spanish Glossary

Matrix multiplication (p. 184) To find element c_{ij} of the product matrix AB, multiply each element in the ith row of A by the corresponding element in the jth column of B, and then add. If A is an $m \times n$ matrix and B is an $n \times p$ matrix, then the product matrix AB is an $m \times p$ matrix.

$\begin{bmatrix} 1 & 1 \\ 2 & 3 \\ 0 & 2 \end{bmatrix}\begin{bmatrix} 4 & 2 \\ 5 & 6 \end{bmatrix}$

$= \begin{bmatrix} (1)(4) + (1)(5) & (1)(2) + (1)(6) \\ (2)(4) + (3)(5) & (2)(2) + (3)(6) \\ (0)(4) + (2)(5) & (0)(2) + (2)(6) \end{bmatrix}$

Multiplicación matricial (p. 184) Para encontrar el elemento c_{ij} del producto de la matriz AB, se multiplica cada elemento de la fila i de A por el elemento respectivo de la columna j de B y luego se suman. Si A es una matriz $m \times n$ y B es una matriz $n \times p$, entonces el producto de la matriz AB es una matriz $m \times p$.

$= \begin{bmatrix} 9 & 8 \\ 23 & 22 \\ 10 & 12 \end{bmatrix}$

Mean (p. 660) The sum of the data values divided by the number of data values is the mean. *See also* **Arithmetic mean.**

$[1, 2, 3, 3, 6, 6]$

$\text{mean} = \frac{1 + 2 + 3 + 3 + 6 + 6}{6}$

$= \frac{21}{6} = 3.5$

Media (p. 660) La suma de los valores de datos dividida por el número de valores de datos sumados es la media. *Ver también* **Arithmetic mean.**

Measures of central tendency (p. 660) The mean, the median, and the mode are single, central values that help describe a set of data. They are called measures of central tendency.

$[1, 2, 3, 3, 4, 5, 6, 6]$
$\text{mean} = 3.75$
$\text{median} = 3.5$
$\text{modes} = 3 \text{ and } 6$

Medidas de tendencia central (p. 660) La media, la mediana y la moda son los valores centrales únicos que permiten describir un conjunto de datos. Se llaman medidas de tendencia central.

Measures of variation (p. 669) Measures of variation, such as the range, the interquartile range, and the standard deviation, describe how the data in a data set are spread out.

Medidas de dispersión (p. 669) Las medidas de dispersión, tal como el rango, el intervalo intercuartil y la desviación típica, describen cómo se dispersan los datos en un conjunto de datos.

Median (p. 660) The median is the middle value in a data set. If the data set contains an even number of values, the median is the mean of the two middle values.

$[1, 2, 3, 3, 4, 5, 6, 6]$
$\text{median} = \frac{3 + 4}{2} = \frac{7}{2} = 3.5$

Mediana (p. 660) La mediana es el valor situado en el medio en un conjunto de datos. Si el conjunto de datos contiene un número par de valores, la mediana es la media de los dos valores del medio.

Minor axis of an ellipse (p. 568) The minor axis of an ellipse is the segment perpendicular to the major axis at its midpoint. The endpoints of the minor axis are on the ellipse and are the co-vertices of the ellipse.

Eje menor de una elipse (p. 568) El eje menor de una elipse es el segmento perpendicular al eje mayor en su punto medio. Los extremos del eje menor están en la elipse y son los covértices de la elipse.

English/Spanish Glossary

Mode (p. 660) The mode is the most frequently occurring value (or values) in a set of data.

$\{1, 2, 3, 3, 4, 5, 6, 6\}$
The modes are 3 and 6.

Moda (p. 660) La moda es el valor o valores que ocurren con mayor frecuencia en un conjunto de datos.

Monomial (p. 307) A monomial is either a real number, a variable, or a product of real numbers and variables with whole number exponents.

$1, x, 2z, 4ab^2$

Monomio (p. 307) Un monomio es un número real, una variable o un producto de números reales y variables cuyos exponentes son números enteros.

Multiple zero (p. 316) If a linear factor is repeated in the complete factored form of a polynomial, the zero related to that factor is a multiple zero.

The zeros of the function
$P(x) = 2x(x - 3)^2(x + 1)$ are $0, 3$, and -1. Since $(x - 3)$ occurs twice as a factor, the zero 3 is a multiple zero.

Cero múltiplo (p. 316) Si un factor lineal se repite en la forma factorizada completa de un polinomio, el cero relacionado con ese factor es un cero múltiplo.

Multiplicative identity matrix (p. 199) For an $n \times n$ square matrix, the multiplicative identity matrix is an $n \times n$ square matrix I, or $I_{n \times n}$, with 1's along the main diagonal and 0's elsewhere.

$I_{2 \times 2} = \begin{bmatrix} 1 & 0 \\ 0 & 1 \end{bmatrix}$

$I_{3 \times 3} = \begin{bmatrix} 1 & 0 & 0 \\ 0 & 1 & 0 \\ 0 & 0 & 1 \end{bmatrix}$

Matriz de identidad multiplicativa (p. 199) Para una matriz cuadrada $n \times n$, la matriz de identidad multiplicativa es la matriz cuadrada I de $n \times n$, o $I_{n \times n}$, con unos por la diagonal principal y ceros en los demás lugares.

Multiplicative inverse (p. 7) The multiplicative inverse, or reciprocal, of any nonzero number a is $\frac{1}{a}$. The product of reciprocals is 1.

$5 \times \frac{1}{5} = 1$

Inverso multiplicativo (p. 7) El inverso multiplicativo, o recíproco, de todo número racional distinto de cero a es $\frac{1}{a}$. El producto de números recíprocos es 1.

Multiplicative inverse of a matrix (p. 199) If A and X are $n \times n$ matrices, and $AX = XA = I$, then X is the multiplicative inverse of A, written A^{-1}.

$A = \begin{bmatrix} 2 & 1 \\ 4 & 0 \end{bmatrix}$

$X = \begin{bmatrix} 0 & \frac{1}{4} \\ 1 & -\frac{1}{2} \end{bmatrix}$

$AX = \begin{bmatrix} 1 & 0 \\ 0 & 1 \end{bmatrix} = I$, so $X = A^{-1}$

Inverso multiplicativo de una matriz (p. 199) Si A y X son matrices $n \times n$, y $AX = XA = I$, entonces X es el inverso multiplicativo de A, expresado como A^{-1}.

Multiplicity (p. 316) The multiplicity of a zero of a polynomial function is the number of times the related linear factor is repeated in the factored form of the polynomial.

The zeros of the function
$P(x) = 2x(x - 3)^2(x + 1)$ are $0, 3$, and -1. Since $(x - 3)$ occurs twice as a factor, the zero 3 has multiplicity 2.

Multiplicidad (p. 316) La multiplicidad de un cero de una función polinomial es el número de veces que el factor lineal relacionado se repite en la forma factorizada del polinomio.

Mutually exclusive events (p. 533) When two events cannot happen at the same time, the events are mutually exclusive. If A and B are mutually exclusive events, then $P(A \text{ or } B) = P(A) + P(B)$.

Rolling an even number E and rolling a multiple of five M on a standard number cube are mutually exclusive events.

$P(E \text{ or } M) = P(E) + P(M)$
$= \frac{3}{6} + \frac{1}{6}$
$= \frac{4}{6}$, or $\frac{2}{3}$

Sucesos mutuamente excluyentes (p. 533) Cuando dos sucesos no pueden ocurrir al mismo tiempo, son mutuamente excluyentes. Si A y B son sucesos mutuamente excluyentes, entonces $P(A \text{ o } B) = P(A) + P(B)$.

N

n factorial (p. 345) For any positive integer n, n factorial (or $n!$) is $n(n - 1) \times \ldots \times 3 \times 2 \times 1. 0! = 1$.

$4! = 4 \times 3 \times 2 \times 1 = 24$

n factorial (p. 345) Para cualquier número entero positivo n, n factorial (o $n!$) es $n(n - 1) \times \ldots \times 3 \times 2 \times 1. 0! = 1$.

nth root (p. 369) For any real numbers a and b, and any positive integer n, if $a^n = b$, then a is an nth root of b.

$\sqrt[5]{32} = 2$ because $2^5 = 32$.
$\sqrt[4]{81} = 3$ because $3^4 = 81$.

raíz n-ésima (p. 369) Para todos los números reales a y b, y todo número entero positivo n, si $a^n = b$, entonces a es la n-ésima raíz de b.

Natural logarithmic function (p. 470) The function $y = \log_e x$ is the natural logarithmic function. It is the inverse of $y = e^x$. It is commonly written as $y = \ln x$.

Función logarítmica natural (p. 470) La función $y = \log_e x$ es la función logarítmica natural. Es la inversa de $y = e^x$. Generalmente se expresa como $y = \ln x$.

$\ln e^3 = 3$
$\ln 10 \approx 2.3026$
$\ln 36 \approx 3.5835$

Normal distribution (p. 692) A normal distribution shows data that vary randomly from the mean in the pattern of a bell-shaped curve.

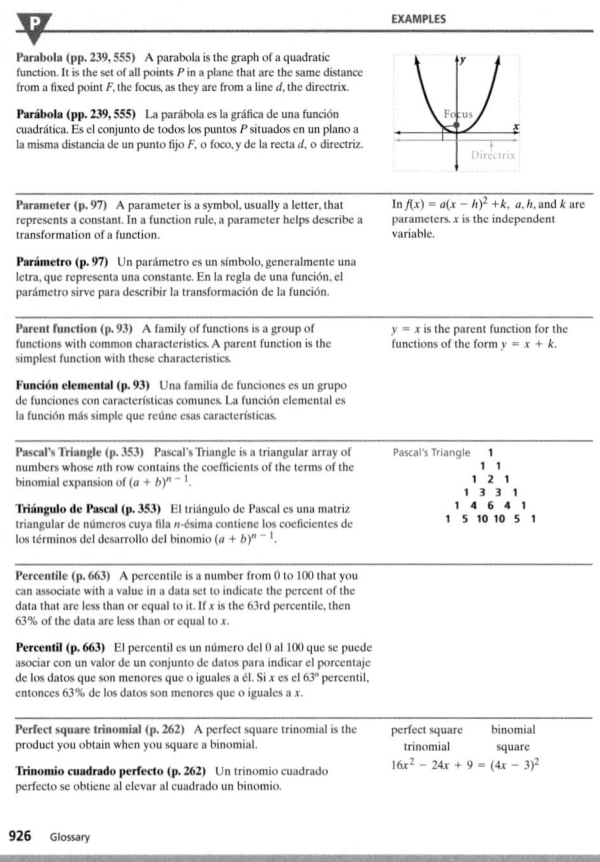

Distribution of Test Scores

Distribución normal (p. 692) Una distribución normal muestra, con una curva en forma de campana, datos que varían alcatoriamente respecto de la media.

In a class of 200 students, the scores on a test were normally distributed. The mean score was 66.5 and the standard deviation was 6.5. The number of students who scored greater than 73 was about $13.5\% + 2.5\%$ of those who took the test.
16% of $200 = 32$
About 32 students scored 73 or higher on the test.

O

Objective function (p. 139) In a linear programming model, the objective function is a model of the quantity that you want to make as large or as small as possible. See **Linear programming**.

Función objetiva (p. 139) En un modelo de programación lineal, la función objetiva es un modelo de la cantidad que se quiere aumentar o disminuir cuanto sea posible. Ver **Linear programming**.

Opposite (p. 7) The opposite or additive inverse of any number a is $-a$. The sum of opposites is 0.

$3 + (-3) = 0$
$5.2 + (-5.2) = 0$

Opuesto (p. 7) El opuesto o inverso aditivo de todo número a es $-a$. La suma de dos opuestos es 0.

Ordered triples (p. 146) Ordered triples of the form (x, y, z) represent the location of a point in coordinate space.

$(2, 4, 5)$
$(0, 1, 2)$
$(0, 0, 0)$

Tripletas ordenadas (p. 146) Las tripletas ordenadas de la forma (x, y, z) representan la ubicación de un punto en el espacio de coordenadas.

Outlier (p. 664) An outlier is a data value that is substantially different from the other values in a data set.

The outlier in the data set $\{56, 64, 73, 59, 98, 65, 59\}$ is 98.

Valor extremo (p. 664) Un valor extremo es un valor que difiere sustancialmente de los demás valores de un conjunto de datos.

P

Parabola (pp. 239, 555) A parabola is the graph of a quadratic function. It is the set of all points P in a plane that are the same distance from a fixed point F, the focus, as they are from a line d, the directrix.

Parábola (pp. 239, 555) La parábola es la gráfica de una función cuadrática. Es el conjunto de todos los puntos P situados en un plano a la misma distancia de un punto fijo F, o foco, y de la recta d, o directriz.

Parameter (p. 97) A parameter is a symbol, usually a letter, that represents a constant. In a function rule, a parameter helps describe a transformation of a function.

In $f(x) = a(x - h)^2 + k$, a, h, and k are parameters. x is the independent variable.

Parámetro (p. 97) Un parámetro es un símbolo, generalmente una letra, que representa una constante. En la regla de una función, el parámetro sirve para describir la transformación de la función.

Parent function (p. 93) A family of functions is a group of functions with common characteristics. A parent function is the simplest function with these characteristics.

$y = x$ is the parent function for the functions of the form $y = x + k$.

Función elemental (p. 93) Una familia de funciones es un grupo de funciones con características comunes. La función elemental es la función más simple que reúne esas características.

Pascal's Triangle (p. 353) Pascal's Triangle is a triangular array of numbers whose nth row contains the coefficients of the terms of the binomial expansion of $(a + b)^{n-1}$.

Pascal's Triangle
```
      1
     1 1
    1 2 1
   1 3 3 1
  1 4 6 4 1
 1 5 10 10 5 1
```

Triángulo de Pascal (p. 353) El triángulo de Pascal es una matriz triangular de números cuya fila n-ésima contiene los coeficientes de los términos del desarrollo del binomio $(a + b)^{n-1}$.

Percentile (p. 663) A percentile is a number from 0 to 100 that you can associate with a value in a data set to indicate the percent of the data that are less than or equal to it. If x is the 63rd percentile, then 63% of the data are less than or equal to x.

Percentil (p. 663) El percentil es un número del 0 al 100 que se puede asociar con un valor de un conjunto de datos para indicar el porcentaje de los datos que son menores que o iguales a él. Si x es el 63º percentil, entonces 63% de los datos son menores que o iguales a x.

Perfect square trinomial (p. 262) A perfect square trinomial is the product you obtain when you square a binomial.

perfect square trinomial = binomial square
$16x^2 - 24x + 9 = (4x - 3)^2$

Trinomio cuadrado perfecto (p. 262) Un trinomio cuadrado perfecto se obtiene al elevar al cuadrado un binomio.

Period of a function (p. 711) The period of a periodic function is the horizontal length of one cycle.

Período de una función (p. 711) El período de una función periódica es el intervalo horizontal de un ciclo.

The periodic function $y = \sin x$ has period 2π.

Periodic function (p. 711) A periodic function repeats a pattern of y-values at regular intervals.

Función periódica (p. 711) Una función periódica repite un patrón de valores y a intervalos regulares.

$y = \sin x$

Permutation (p. 345) A permutation is an arrangement of items in a particular order. The number of permutations of n objects taken r at a time is $_nP_r = \frac{n!}{(n-r)!}$ for $1 \le r \le n$.

Permutación (p. 345) Una permutación es la disposición de objetos en un orden determinado. El número de permutaciones de n objetos seleccionados r veces es $_nP_r = \frac{n!}{(n-r)!}$ para $1 \le r \le n$.

$$_8P_5 = \frac{8!}{(8-5)!}$$
$$= \frac{8 \cdot 7 \cdot 6 \cdot 5 \cdot 4 \cdot 3!}{3!}$$
$$= 8 \times 7 \times 6 \times 5 \times 4$$
$$= 6720$$

Phase shift (p. 756) A horizontal translation of a periodic function is a phase shift.

Cambio de fase (p. 756) Una traslación horizontal de una función periódica es un cambio de fase.

$g(x)$ horizontal translation of $f(x)$
$$g(x) = f(x - h)$$

Point of discontinuity (p. 501) A point of discontinuity is the x-coordinate of a point where the graph of a function breaks into branches. A rational function has a point of discontinuity at $x = a$ if a is a number for which the denominator of the function is zero.

Punto de discontinuidad (p. 501) Un punto de discontinuidad es la coordenada x de un punto donde la gráfica de una función se divide en ramas. Una función racional tiene un punto de discontinuidad en $x = a$, si a es un número para el cual el denominador de la función es cero.

$f(x) = \frac{2}{x-2}$ has a point of discontinuity at $x = 2$.

Point-slope form (p. 65) The point-slope form of an equation of a line is $y - y_1 = m(x - x_1)$, where m is the slope of the line and (x_1, y_1) is a point on the line.

Forma punto-pendiente (p. 65) La forma punto-pendiente de una ecuación lineal es $y - y_1 = m(x - x_1)$, donde m es la pendiente de la recta y (x_1, y_1) es un punto de la recta.

$y - 3 = 2(x - 1)$
$y + 4 = 5(x - 2)$
$y - 2 = 3(x + 2)$

Polynomial (p. 307) A polynomial is a monomial or the sum of monomials.

Polinomio (p. 307) Un polinomio es un monomio o la suma de dos o más monomios.

$3x^3 + 4x^2 - 2x + 5$
$8x$
$x^2 + 4x + 2$

Polynomial function (p. 307) $P(x) = a_nx^n + a_{n-1}x^{n-1} + \ldots + a_1x + a_0$ is a polynomial function when n is a nonnegative integer and the coefficients $a_n, \ldots, a_0$ are real numbers.

Función polinomial (p. 307) $P(x) = a_nx^n + a_{n-1}x^{n-1} + \ldots + a_1x + a_0$ es una función polinomial, donde n es un entero no negativo y los coeficientes $a_n, \ldots, a_0$ son números reales.

Preimage (p. 192) The preimage is the original figure before a transformation.

Preimagen (p. 192) La preimagen es la figura original antes de sufrir una transformación.

Principal root (p. 370) When a number has two real roots, the positive root is called the principal root. A radical sign indicates the principal root. The principal root of a negative number a is $i\sqrt{|a|}$.

Raíz principal (p. 370) Cuando un número tiene dos raíces reales, la raíz positiva es la raíz principal. El signo del radical indica la raíz principal. La raíz principal de un número negativo a es $i\sqrt{|a|}$.

The number 25 has two square roots, 5 and -5. The principal square root, 5, is indicated by the symbols $\sqrt{25}$ or $25^{\frac{1}{2}}$.

Probability distribution (p. 649) A probability distribution is a function that tells the probability of each outcome in a sample space.

Distribución de probabilidades (p. 649) Una distribución de probabilidades es una función que señala la probabilidad de que cada resultado ocurra en un espacio muestral.

Roll	Fr.	Prob.
1	5	0.125
2	9	0.225
3	7	0.175
4	8	0.2
5	8	0.2
6	3	0.075

The table and graph both show the experimental probability distribution for the outcomes of 40 rolls of a standard number cube.

Q

Quadratic equation (p. 267) A quadratic equation is one that can be written in the standard form $ax^2 + bx + c = 0$, where $a \ne 0$.

Ecuación cuadrática (p. 267) Una ecuación cuadrática es una ecuación que se puede expresar en forma normal como $ax^2 + bx + c = 0$, donde $a \ne 0$.

$2x^2 + 3x + 1 = 0$

Quadratic Formula (p. 289) A quadratic equation written in standard form $ax^2 + bx + c = 0$, can be solved using the Quadratic Formula.
$$x = \frac{-b \pm \sqrt{b^2 - 4ac}}{2a}$$

Fórmula cuadrática (p. 289) Toda ecuación cuadrática $ax^2 + bx + c = 0$ escrita en forma normal se puede resolver por medio de la fórmula cuadrática.
$$x = \frac{-b \pm \sqrt{b^2 - 4ac}}{2a}$$

If $-x^2 + 3x + 2 = 0$, then
$$x = \frac{-3 \pm \sqrt{(3)^2 - 4(-1)(2)}}{2(-1)}$$
$$= \frac{-3 \pm \sqrt{17}}{-2}$$

Quadratic function (p. 238) A quadratic function is a function that can be written in the standard form $f(x) = ax^2 + bx + c$, where $a \ne 0$. Its graph is a parabola.

Función cuadrática (p. 238) Una función cuadrática se puede expresar con la forma normal $f(x) = ax^2 + bx + c$, donde $a \ne 0$. Su gráfica es una parábola.

$y = x^2 + 2x - 2$

Quartiles (p. 662) Quartiles are values that separate a finite data set into four equal parts. The second quartile (Q_2) is the median of the data. The first and third quartiles (Q_1 and Q_3) are the medians of the lower half and upper half of the data, respectively.

Cuartiles (p. 662) Los cuartiles son valores que separan un conjunto finito de datos en cuatro partes iguales. El segundo cuartil (Q_2) es la mediana de los datos. Los cuartiles primero y tercero (Q_1 y Q_3) son las medianas de la mitad superior e inferior de los datos, respectivamente.

$\{2, 3, 4, 5, 5, 6, 7, 7\}$
$Q_1 = 3.5$
Q_2 (median) $= 5$
$Q_3 = 6.5$

R

Radian (p. 726) One radian is the measure of a central angle of a circle that intercepts an arc equal in length to a radius of the circle. You can use a proportion to convert an angle measure between different units.
$$\frac{\text{degree measure}}{180} = \frac{\text{radian measure}}{\pi}$$

Radián (p. 726) Un radián es la medida del ángulo central de un círculo que corta un arco de la misma longitud que el radio del círculo. Se puede usar una proporción para convertir la medida de un ángulo de una unidad de medida a la otra.
$$\frac{\text{medida en grados}}{180} = \frac{\text{medida de radián}}{\pi}$$

$60° \to \frac{60}{180} = \frac{x}{\pi}$
$x = \frac{60\pi}{180}$
$= \frac{\pi}{3}$

Thus, $60° = \frac{\pi}{3}$ radians.

Radical equation (p. 391) A radical equation is an equation that has a variable in a radicand or has a variable with a rational exponent.

Ecuación radical (p. 391) La ecuación radical es una ecuación que contiene una variable en el radicando o una variable con un exponente racional.

$(\sqrt{x})^3 + 1 = 65$
$x^{\frac{3}{2}} + 1 = 65$

Radical function (p. 415) A radical function is a function that can be written in the form $f(x) = a\sqrt[n]{x - h} + k$, where $a \ne 0$. For even values of n, the domain of a radical function is the real numbers $x \ge h$. *See also* **Square root function.**

Función radical (p. 415) Una función radical es una función que puede expresarse como $f(x) = a\sqrt[n]{x - h} + k$, donde $a \ne 0$. Para n par, el dominio de la función radical son los números reales tales que $x \ge h$. *Ver también* **Square root function.**

$f(x) = \sqrt{x - 2}$

Radicand (p. 370) The number under a radical sign is the radicand.

Radicando (p. 370) La expresión que aparece debajo del signo radical es el radicando.

The radicand in $3\sqrt[4]{7}$ is 7.

Radius (p. 561) The radius r of a circle is the distance between the center of the circle and any point on the circumference.

Radio (p. 561) El radio r de un círculo es la distancia entre el centro del círculo y cualquier punto de la circunferencia.

Random sample (p. 677) In a random sample, each member of the population is as likely to be chosen for the sample as every other member.

Muestra aleatoria (p. 677) En una muestra aleatoria es igualmente probable que cada miembro de la población sea escogido para la muestra.

Let the set of all females between the ages of 19 and 34 be the population. A random selection of 900 females between those ages would be a sample of the population.

Range (p. 56) The range of a relation is the set of all outputs or y-coordinates of the ordered pairs.

Rango (p. 56) El rango de una relación es el conjunto de todas las salidas posibles, o coordenadas y, de los pares ordenados.

In the relation $\{(0, 1), (0, 2), (0, 3), (0, 4), (1, 3), (1, 4), (2, 1)\}$, the range is $\{1, 2, 3, 4\}$. In the function $f(x) = |x - 3|$, the range is the set of real numbers greater than or equal to 0.

Range of a set of data (p. 669) The range of a set of data is the difference between the greatest and least values.

Rango de un conjunto de datos (p. 669) El rango de un conjunto de datos es la diferencia entre el valor máximo y el valor mínimo de los datos.

The range of the set $\{3.2, 4.1, 2.2, 3.4, 3.8, 4.0, 4.2, 2.8\}$ is $4.2 - 2.2 = 2$.

T899

Rational exponent (p. 385) If the nth root of a is a real number and m is an integer, then $a^{\frac{1}{n}} = \sqrt[n]{a}$ and $a^{\frac{m}{n}} = \sqrt[n]{a^m} = \left(\sqrt[n]{a}\right)^m$. If m is negative, $a \neq 0$.

$4^{\frac{1}{3}} = \sqrt[3]{4}$
$5^{\frac{3}{2}} = \sqrt{5^3} = \left(\sqrt{5}\right)^3$

Exponente racional (p. 385) Si la raíz n-ésima de a es un número real y m es un entero, entonces $a^{\frac{1}{n}} = \sqrt[n]{a}$ y $a^{\frac{m}{n}} = \sqrt[n]{a^m} = \left(\sqrt[n]{a}\right)^m$. Si m es negativo, $a \neq 0$.

Rational function (p. 501) A rational function $f(x)$ can be written as $f(x) = \frac{P(x)}{Q(x)}$, where $P(x)$ and $Q(x)$ are polynomial functions. The domain of a rational function is all real numbers except those for which $Q(x) = 0$.

Función racional (p. 501) Una función racional $f(x)$ se puede expresar como $f(x) = \frac{P(x)}{Q(x)}$, donde $P(x)$ y $Q(x)$ son funciones de polinomios. El dominio de una función racional son todos los números reales excepto aquéllos para los cuales $Q(x) = 0$.

The function $y = \frac{x - 2}{x^2 - 9}$ is a rational function with three branches separated by asymptotes $x = -3$ and $x = 3$.

Rational Root Theorem (p. 335) If $\frac{p}{q}$ is in simplest form and is a rational root of the polynomial equation $a_n x^n + a_{n-1} x^{n-1} + \ldots + a_1 x + a_0 = 0$ with integer coefficients, then p must be a factor of a_0 and q must be a factor of a_n.

Teorema de la raíz racional (p. 335) Si $\frac{p}{q}$ está en su forma más simple y es la raíz racional de la ecuación del polinomio $a_n x^n + a_{n-1} x^{n-1} + \ldots + a_1 x + a_0 = 0$ con números enteros como coeficientes, entonces p debe ser factor de a_0 y q debe ser factor de a_n.

The polynomial equation $10x^3 + 6x^2 - 11x - 2 = 0$ has leading coefficient 10 (with factors ± 1, ± 2, ± 5, ± 10) and constant term -2 (with factors ± 1 and ± 2). Its only possible rational roots are ± 1, ± 2, $\pm \frac{1}{2}$, $\pm \frac{1}{5}$, $\pm \frac{2}{5}$, $\pm \frac{1}{10}$.

Rationalize the denominator (p. 376) To rationalize the denominator of an expression, rewrite it so there are no radicals in any denominator and no denominators in any radical.

Racionalizar el denominador (p. 376) Para racionalizar el denominador de una expresión, ésta se escribe de modo que no haya radicales en ningún denominador y no haya denominadores en ningún radical.

$\frac{1}{\sqrt{2}} = \frac{1}{\sqrt{2}} \times \frac{\sqrt{2}}{\sqrt{2}} = \frac{\sqrt{2}}{2}$

Reciprocal (p. 7) The reciprocal or multiplicative inverse of any nonzero number a is $\frac{1}{a}$. The product of reciprocals is 1.

Recíproco (p. 7) El valor recíproco, o inverso multiplicativo, de un número a cuyo valor no es cero es $\frac{1}{a}$. El producto de un número y su valor recíproco es 1.

$5 \times \frac{1}{5} = 1$

Reciprocal function (p. 495) A reciprocal function is a function that can be written in the form $f(x) = \frac{a}{x - h} + k$, where $a \neq 0$. The domain of a reciprocal function is all real numbers except $x = h$.

$f(x) = \frac{1}{2x + 5}$
$p(v) = \frac{3}{v} + 5$

Función recíproca (p. 495) Una función recíproca es una función que puede expresarse como $f(x) = \frac{a}{x - h} + k$, donde $a \neq 0$. El dominio de una función recíproca son todos los números reales excepto aquéllos para los que se cumple que $x = h$.

Recursive formula (p. 602) A recursive formula defines the terms in a sequence by relating each term to the ones before it.

Let $a_n = 2.5a_{n-1} + 3a_{n-2}$. If $a_5 = 3$ and $a_4 = 7.5$, then $a_6 = 2.5(3) + 3(7.5) = 30$.

Fórmula recursiva (p. 602) Una fórmula recursiva define cada término de una progresión en función del término o términos precedentes.

Reflection (p. 193) A reflection, or flip, is a transformation that maps a point in the plane to its mirror image, using a specific line as the mirror.

Reflexión (p. 193) Una reflexión es una transformación en la que se voltea una figura sobre una línea específica, que actúa a manera espejo.

preimage   image

Relation (p. 55) A relation is a set of pairs of input and output values.

$\{(0, 1), (0, 2), (0, 3), (0, 4), (1, 3)\}$

Relación (p. 55) Una relación es cualquier conjunto de pares ordenados de valores de entrada y valores de salida.

Relative maximum (minimum) (p. 315) The y-value of a point on the graph of a function that is higher (lower) than the nearby points of the graph is a relative maximum (minimum).

Máximo (mínimo) relativo (p. 315) El valor y de un punto en la gráfica de una función que es mayor (menor) que los de los puntos cercanos es un máximo (mínimo) relativo.

Remainder Theorem (p. 323) If a polynomial $P(x)$ of degree $n \geq 1$ is divided by $(x - a)$, where a is a constant, then the remainder is $P(a)$.

If $P(x) = x^3 - 4x^2 + x + 6$ is divided by $x - 3$, then the remainder is $P(3) = 3^3 - 4(3)^2 + 3 + 6 = 0$ (which means that $x - 3$ is a factor of $P(x)$).

Teorema del residuo (p. 323) Si un polinomio $P(x)$ de grado $n \geq 1$ se divide por $(x - a)$, donde a es una constante, el residuo es $P(a)$.

Root (p. 268) A root of a function is the input value for which the value of the function is zero. A root of an equation is a value that makes the equation true. *See also* **Zero of a function.**

-2 and 3 are roots of the function $f(x) = (x + 2)(x - 3)$ and the equation $(x + 2)(x - 3) = 0$.

Raíz (p. 268) La raíz de una función es el valor de entrada para el cual el valor de la función es cero. La raíz de una ecuación es un valor que hace verdadera la ecuación. *Ver también* **Zero of a function.**

Rotation (p. 194) A rotation is a transformation that turns a figure about a fixed point called the center of rotation.

Rotación (p. 194) Rotación es una transformación que hace girar una figura alrededor de un punto fijo llamado centro de rotación.

Row operations (p. 223) To solve a system of equations using an augmented matrix, you can use one or more of the following row operations:
- Switch any two rows.
- Multiply a row by a constant.
- Add one row to another.
- Combine one or more of these steps.

Operaciones de filas (p. 223) Para resolver un sistema de ecuaciones por medio de una matriz aumentada, se puede usar una o más de las siguientes operaciones de filas:
- Intercambiar dos filas.
- Multiplicar una fila por una constante.
- Sumar una fila a otra.
- Combinar uno o más de estos pasos.

S

Sample (p. 677) A sample is information gathered from only part of a population.

Muestra (p. 677) Una muestra contiene información reunida solamente de una parte de una población.

Let the set of all males between the ages of 19 and 34 be the population. A random selection of 900 males between those ages would be a sample of the population.

Sample proportion (p. 677) If an event occurs x times in a sample of size n, the sample proportion is $\frac{x}{n}$.

Proporción muestral (p. 677) Si un suceso ocurre x veces en un espacio muestral de tamaño n, la proporción de la muestra es $\frac{x}{n}$.

For a random selection of 900 males, 350 preferred red shirts to green shirts. The sample proportion would be $\frac{350}{900} = \frac{7}{18}$.

Sample space (p. 41) The set of all possible outcomes of an experiment is called the sample space.

Espacio muestral (p. 41) El espacio muestral es el conjunto de todos los resultados posibles de un suceso.

When you roll a number cube, the sample space is $\{1, 2, 3, 4, 5, 6\}$.

Scalar (p. 182) A real number is called a scalar for certain special uses, such as multiplying a matrix. *See also* **Scalar multiplication.**

$2.5 \begin{bmatrix} 1 & 0 \\ -2 & 3 \end{bmatrix} = \begin{bmatrix} 2.5(1) & 2.5(0) \\ 2.5(-2) & 2.5(3) \end{bmatrix}$
$= \begin{bmatrix} 2.5 & 0 \\ -5 & 7.5 \end{bmatrix}$

Escalar (p. 182) Un número real se llama escalar en ciertos casos especiales, como en la multiplicación de una matriz. *Ver también* **Scalar multiplication.**

Scalar multiplication (p. 182) Scalar multiplication is an operation that multiplies a matrix A by a scalar c. To find the resulting matrix cA, multiply each element of A by c.

$2.5 \begin{bmatrix} 1 & 0 \\ -2 & 3 \end{bmatrix} = \begin{bmatrix} 2.5(1) & 2.5(0) \\ 2.5(-2) & 2.5(3) \end{bmatrix}$
$= \begin{bmatrix} 2.5 & 0 \\ -5 & 7.5 \end{bmatrix}$

Multiplicación escalar (p. 182) La multiplicación escalar es la que multiplica una matriz A por un número escalar c. Para hallar la matriz cA resultante, multiplica cada elemento de A por c.

Scatter plot (p. 80) A scatter plot is a graph that relates two different sets of data by plotting the data as ordered pairs. You can use a scatter plot to determine a relationship between the data sets.

Diagrama de puntos (p. 80) Un diagrama de puntos es una gráfica que relaciona dos conjuntos de datos presentando los datos como pares ordenados. El diagrama de puntos sirve para definir la relación entre conjuntos de datos.

Dollars Spent Per Capita on Entertainment
TV, Radio, and Sound Equipment
Source: U.S. Bureau of Labor Statistics. Go to www.PHSchool.com for a data update.

Secant (p. 763) The secant (sec) function is the reciprocal of the cosine function. For all real numbers θ except those that make $\cos \theta = 0$, $\sec \theta = \frac{1}{\cos \theta}$.

If $\cos \theta = \frac{5}{13}$, then $\sec \theta = \frac{13}{5}$.

Secante (p. 763) La función secante (sec) es el recíproco de la función coseno. Para todos los números reales θ, excepto aquéllos para los que $\cos \theta = 0$, $\sec \theta = \frac{1}{\cos \theta}$.

Sequence (p. 600) A sequence is an ordered list of numbers.

$1, 4, 7, 10, \ldots$

Progresión (p. 600) Una progresión es una sucesión de números.

Series (p. 619) A series is the sum of the terms of a sequence. The series is finite (infinite) if the corresponding sequence has finitely (infinitely) many terms.

The series $3 + 6 + 9 + 12 + 15$ corresponds to the sequence 3, 6, 9, 12, 15. The sum of the series is 45.

Serie (p. 619) Una serie es la suma de los términos de una progresión. La serie es finita (infinita) si la progresión correspondiente tiene una cantidad finita (infinita) de términos.

T900

Shrink (p. 96) A vertical shrink of a function f by the factor a, $0 < a < 1$, is a transformation of f that multiplies all y-values by a.

$g(x) = \frac{1}{2}x^2$ is a vertical shrink of $f(x) = x^2$

Reducción (p. 96) La reducción vertical de una función f por el factor a, donde $0 < a < 1$, es una transformación de f que multiplica todos los valores de y por a.

Simplest form of a rational expression (p. 509) A rational expression is in simplest form when its numerator and denominator are polynomials that have no common divisors.

$\frac{x^2 - 7x + 12}{x^2 - 9} = \frac{(x-4)(x-3)}{(x+3)(x-3)}$
$= \frac{x-4}{x+3}$, where $x \neq -3$

Forma simplificada de una expresión racional (p. 509) Una expresión racional no se puede simplificar más cuando su numerador y su denominador son polinomios que ya no contienen factores comunes.

Simulation (p. 40) When actual trials are difficult to conduct, you can find experimental probability by using a simulation, which is a model of one or more events.

Suppose a weather forecaster predicts a 50% chance of rain for the next three days. You can use three coins landing heads up to simulate three days in a row of rain.

Simulación (p. 40) Cuando es difícil realizar los ensayos de un experimento, se puede determinar la probabilidad experimental por medio de una simulación, o modelo de uno o más sucesos del experimento.

Sine curve (p. 735) A sine curve is the graph of a sine function.

Sinusoide (p. 735) Sinusoide es la gráfica de la función seno.

Sine function (p. 734) The sine function, $y = \sin \theta$, matches the measure θ of an angle in standard position with the y-coordinate of a point on the unit circle. This point is where the terminal side of the angle intersects the unit circle.

Función seno (p. 734) La función seno, $y = \sin \theta$, equivale a la medida θ de un ángulo en posición normal con la coordenada y de un punto dado en el círculo unitario. Este punto es la intersección del lado terminal y el círculo unitario.

Sine of θ (p. 720) The sine of an angle measure θ ($\sin \theta$) is the y-coordinate of the point at which the terminal side of the angle intersects the unit circle.

Seno de θ (p. 720) El seno de un ángulo que mide θ ($\sin \theta$) es la coordenada y del punto de intersección entre el lado terminal del ángulo y el círculo unitario.

Slope of a line (p. 64) The slope of a non-vertical line is the ratio of the vertical change to a corresponding horizontal change. The slope of a vertical line is undefined.

$\text{slope} = \frac{\text{vertical change}}{\text{horizontal change}} = \frac{y_2 - y_1}{x_2 - x_1}$, where $x_2 - x_1 \neq 0$

The slope of the line through points $(-1, -1)$ and $(1, -2)$ is $\frac{-2 - (-1)}{1 - (-1)} = \frac{-1}{2} = -\frac{1}{2}$.

Pendiente de una recta (p. 64) La pendiente de una recta no vertical es la razón del cambio vertical y el cambio horizontal. La pendiente de una recta vertical no está definida.

$\text{pendiente} = \frac{\text{cambio vertical}}{\text{cambio horizontal}} = \frac{y_2 - y_1}{x_2 - x_1}$, donde $x_2 - x_1 \neq 0$

Slope-intercept form (p. 65) The slope-intercept form of an equation of a line is $y = mx + b$, where m is the slope and b is the y-intercept.

$y = 8x + 2$
$y = -x + 1$
$y = -\frac{1}{2}x - 14$

Forma pendiente-intercepto (p. 65) La forma pendiente-intercepto de una ecuación lineal es $y = mx + b$, donde m es la pendiente y b es el intercepto en y.

Solution of an equation (p. 18) A solution of an equation is a number that makes the equation true.

The solution of $2x - 7 = -12$ is $x = -2.5$.

Solución de una ecuación (p. 18) Una solución de una ecuación es cualquier número que haga verdadera la ecuación.

Square matrix (p. 199) A square matrix is a matrix with the same number of columns as rows.

Matrix A is a square matrix.
$A = \begin{bmatrix} 1 & 2 & 0 \\ -1 & 0 & -2 \\ 1 & 2 & 3 \end{bmatrix}$

Matriz cuadrada (p. 199) Una matriz cuadrada es la que tiene la misma cantidad de columnas y filas.

Square root equation (p. 391) A square root equation is a radical equation in which the radical has index 2.

$\sqrt{x} = 4$

Ecuación de raíz cuadrada (p. 391) Una ecuación de raíz cuadrada es una ecuación radical en la cual el radical tiene índice 2.

Square root function (p. 415) A square root function is a function that can be written in the form $f(x) = a\sqrt{x - h} + k$, where $a \neq 0$. The domain of a square root function is all real numbers $x \geq h$.

$f(x) = 2\sqrt{x - 3} + 4$

Función de raíz cuadrada (p. 415) Una función de raíz cuadrada es una función que puede ser expresada como $f(x) = a\sqrt{x - h} + k$, donde $a \neq 0$. El dominio de una función de raíz cuadrada son todos los números reales tales que $x \geq h$.

Standard deviation (p. 669) Standard deviation is a measure of how much the values in a data set vary, or deviate, from the mean, $\bar{x}$. To find the standard deviation, follow five steps:
- Find the mean of the data set.
- Find the difference between each data value and the mean.
- Square each difference.
- Find the mean of the squares.
- Take the square root of the mean of the squares. This is the standard deviation.

$\{0, 2, 3, 4, 6, 7, 8, 9, 10, 11\}$
$\bar{x} = 6$
standard deviation $= \sqrt{12} \approx 3.46$

Desviación típica (p. 669) La desviación típica denota cuánto los valores de un conjunto de datos varían, o se desvían, de la media, $\bar{x}$. Para hallar la desviación típica, se siguen cinco pasos:
- Se halla la media del conjunto de datos.
- Se calcula la diferencia entre cada valor de datos y la media.
- Se eleva al cuadrado cada diferencia.
- Se halla la media de los cuadrados.
- Se calcula la raíz cuadrada de la media de los cuadrados. Ésa es la desviación típica.

Standard form of a linear equation (p. 63) The standard form of a linear equation is $Ax + By = C$, where A, B, and C are real numbers, and A and B are not both zero.

In standard form, the equation $y = \frac{4}{3}x - 1$ is $4x + (-3)y = 3$.

Forma normal de una ecuación lineal (p. 63) La forma normal de una ecuación lineal es $Ax + By = C$, donde A, B, y C son números reales, y A y B son valores distintos de cero.

Standard form of an equation of a circle (p. 561) *See* **Circle.**

$(x - 3)^2 + (y - 4)^2 = 4$

Forma normal de la ecuación de un círculo (p. 561) *Ver* **Circle.**

Standard form of an equation of an ellipse (p. 568) *See* **Ellipse.**

$\frac{x^2}{5^2} + \frac{y^2}{3^2} = 1$

Forma normal de la ecuación de una elipse (p. 568) *Ver* **Ellipse.**

Standard form of an equation of a hyperbola (p. 575) *See* **Hyperbola.**

$\frac{x^2}{5^2} - \frac{y^2}{3^2} = 1$

Forma normal de la ecuación de una hipérbola (p. 575) *Ver* **Hyperbola.**

Standard form of a polynomial (p. 307) The standard form of a polynomial has the terms in descending order by degree. A one-variable polynomial in standard form has no two terms with the same degree, since all like terms have been combined.

$2x^3 - 5x^2 - 2x + 5$

Forma normal de un polinomio (p. 307) Un polinomio está en forma normal cuando sus términos están en orden descendente por grados. Un polinomio de una variable en forma normal no tiene dos términos del mismo grado puesto que todos los términos han sido combinados.

Standard form of a quadratic equation (p. 267) *See* **Quadratic equation.**

$2x^2 + 5x + 2 = 0$

Forma normal de una ecuación cuadrática (p. 267) *Ver* **Quadratic equation.**

Standard form of a quadratic function (p. 238) The standard form of a quadratic function is $f(x) = ax^2 + bx + c$, where $a \neq 0$.

$f(x) = 2x^2 + 5x + 2$

Forma normal de una función cuadrática (p. 238) La forma normal de una función cuadrática es $f(x) = ax^2 + bx + c$, donde $a \neq 0$.

Standard normal curve (p. 693) The standard normal curve is a normal distribution centered on the y-axis. The mean of the standard normal curve is 0. The standard deviation is 1.

Curva normal en posición normal (p. 693) La curva normal es la distribución normal centrada en el eje y. La media de la curva normal es 0. La desviación normal es 1.

Standard position of an angle (p. 716) An angle is in standard position when the vertex is at the origin of a coordinate system and one ray is on the positive x-axis.

$x^3 + 27 = (x + 3)(x^2 - 3x + 9)$

Posición normal de un ángulo (p. 716) Un ángulo está en posición normal cuando su vértice está en el origen de un sistema de coordenadas y uno de sus lados está sobre el eje x positivo.

Stretch (p. 96) A vertical stretch of a function f by the factor a, $a > 1$, is a transformation of f that multiplies all y-values by a.

$g(x) = 2x^2$ is a vertical stretch of $f(x) = x^2$.

Ampliación (p. 96) Una ampliación vertical de una función f por el factor a, donde $a > 1$, es una transformación de f que multiplica todos los valores de y por a.

Sum of cubes (p. 328) The sum of cubes is an expression of the form $a^3 + b^3$. It can be factored as $(a + b)(a^2 - ab + b^2)$.

$x^3 + 27 = (x + 3)(x^2 - 3x + 9)$

Suma de dos cubos (p. 328) La suma de dos cubos es una expresión de la forma $a^3 + b^3$. Se puede factorizar como $(a + b)(a^2 - ab + b^2)$.

Synthetic division (p. 321) Synthetic division is a method of dividing polynomials in which you omit all variables and exponents and perform the division on the list of coefficients. You also reverse the sign of the divisor so that you can add throughout the process, rather than subtract.

$\begin{array}{r|rrrrr} -3 & 2 & 5 & 0 & -2 & -8 \\ & & -6 & 3 & -9 & 33 \\ \hline & 2 & -1 & 3 & -11 & 25 \end{array}$

Divide $2x^4 + 5x^3 - 2x - 8$ by $x + 3$.
$2x^4 + 5x^3 - 2x - 8$ divided by $x + 3$ gives $2x^3 - x^2 + 3x - 11$ as quotient and 25 as remainder.

División sintética (p. 321) La división sintética es un método de dividir polinomios según el cual se omiten todas las variables y los exponentes y se hace la división con la lista de coeficientes. También se puede invertir el signo del divisor para sumar en vez de restar durante el proceso.

EXAMPLES

System of equations (p. 118) A system of equations is a set of two or more equations using the same variables.

$$\begin{cases} 2x - 3y = -13 \\ 4x + 5y = 7 \end{cases}$$

Sistema de ecuaciones (p. 118) Un sistema de ecuaciones es un conjunto de dos o más ecuaciones que contienen las mismas variables.

T

Tangent function (p. 749) The tangent function, $y = \tan \theta$, matches the measure θ of an angle in standard position with the y-coordinate of the point at which the line containing the terminal side of a central angle of the unit circle intersects the tangent line $x = 1$.

Función tangente (p. 749) La función tangente, $y = \tan \theta$, equivale a la medida θ de un ángulo en posición normal, con la coordenada y del punto donde la recta que contiene el lado terminal de un ángulo central del círculo unitario corta la tangente $x = 1$.

Tangent of θ (p. 749) The tangent of an angle measure θ ($\tan \theta$) is the y-coordinate of the point at which the line containing the terminal side of the angle intersects the tangent line $x = 1$.

Tangente de θ (p. 749) La tangente de un ángulo que mide θ ($\tan \theta$) es la ordenada y del punto donde la recta que contiene el lado terminal del ángulo corta la tangente $x = 1$.

Term of a sequence (p. 600) Each number in a sequence is a term.

1, 4, 7, 10, ...

The second term is 4.

Término de una progresión (p. 600) Cada número de una progresión es un término.

Term of an expression (p. 13) A term is a number, a variable, or the product of a number and one or more variables.

The expression $4x^2 - 3y + 7.3$ has 3 terms.

Término de una expresión (p. 13) Un término es un número, una variable o el producto de un número y una o más variables.

Terminal side of an angle (p. 718) See *Initial side of an angle.*

Lado terminal de un ángulo (p. 718) *Ver Initial side of an angle.*

Theoretical probability (p. 41) If a sample space has n equally likely outcomes, and an event A occurs in m of these outcomes, then the theoretical probability of event A is $P(A) = \frac{m}{n}$.

Use the set {1, 4, 9, 16, 25, 36, 49, 64, 81, 100}. The probability that a number selected at random is greater than 50 is $P(A) = \frac{3}{10} = 0.3$.

Probabilidad teórica (p. 41) Si un espacio muestral tiene n resultados con la misma probabilidad de ocurrir, y ocurre un suceso A en m de estos resultados, entonces la probabilidad teórica del suceso A es $P(A) = \frac{m}{n}$.

Glossary **939**

EXAMPLES

Tolerance (p. 36) The difference between a desired measurement and its maximum and minimum allowable values is the tolerance. The tolerance equals one half of the difference between the maximum and minimum values.

A manufacturing specification calls for a dimension d of 10 cm with a tolerance of 0.1 cm. The allowable difference between d and 10 is less than or equal to 0.1.

Tolerancia (p. 36) La diferencia entre una medida deseada y sus valores máximo y mínimo permitidos es la tolerancia. La tolerancia equivale a la mitad de la diferencia entre los valores máximo y mínimo.

Trace (p. 148) If a plane in a three-dimensional xyz-coordinate system intersects the xy-, yz-, or xz-plane in a line, then that line is a trace of the given plane.

Trazo (p. 148) Si un plano en un sistema tridimensional de coordenadas xyz interseca el plano xy, yz o xz en una recta, entonces esa recta es una traza del plano dado.

Transformation (p. 192) A transformation of a function $y = af(x - h) + k$ is a change made to the value of at least one of the parameters a, h, and k.

$g(x) = 2(x - 3)^2$ is a transformation of $f(x) = x^2$.

Transformación (p. 192) Una transformación de una función $y = af(x - h) + k$ es un cambio en el valor de uno de los parámetros a, h y k.

Translation (p. 191) A translation is a transformation that slides a graph or figure horizontally, vertically, or both without changing the size or shape of the graph or figure.

Traslación (p. 191) Una traslación es el proceso de deslizar una gráfica o figura horizontalmente, verticalmente, o en ambos sentidos, pero sin cambiar ni el tamaño ni la forma de la gráfica o figura.

Transverse axis of a hyperbola (p. 575) The transverse axis of a hyperbola is the segment that lies on the line containing the foci and has endpoints on the hyperbola. The endpoints are the vertices of the hyperbola.

Eje transversal de una hipérbola (p. 575) El eje transversal de una hipérbola es el segmento que pasa por la recta donde se encuentran los focos y que tiene los extremos sobre la hipérbola. Los extremos son los vértices de la hipérbola.

940 Glossary

EXAMPLES

Trend line (p. 80) A trend line is a line that approximates the relationship between the data sets of a scatter plot. You can use a trend line to make predictions.

Línea de tendencia (p. 80) La línea de tendencia es una línea que aproxima la relación entre los conjuntos de datos en un diagrama de puntos. La línea de tendencia permite hacer predicciones.

Trigonometric identity (p. 778) A trigonometric identity is a trigonometric equation that is true for all values except those for which an expression on either side of the equal sign is undefined.

$\tan \theta = \frac{\sin \theta}{\cos \theta}$

Identidad trigonométrica (p. 778) Una identidad trigonométrica es una ecuación trigonométrica que satisface todos los valores excepto aquéllos para los cuales las expresiones a cada lado del signo igual no están definidas.

Trigonometric ratios for a right triangle (p. 792) The trigonometric ratios for a right triangle are the six different ratios of the sides of a right triangle. These ratios do not depend on the size of the right triangle. They depend only on the measures of the acute angles in the triangle. In a right triangle that has an acute $\angle A$, the ratios are defined as follows.

$\sin A = \frac{a}{c}$ $\csc A = \frac{1}{\sin A} = \frac{c}{a}$

$\cos A = \frac{b}{c}$ $\sec A = \frac{1}{\cos A} = \frac{c}{b}$

$\tan A = \frac{a}{b}$ $\cot A = \frac{1}{\tan A} = \frac{b}{a}$

Razones trigonométricas para un triángulo rectángulo (p. 792) Las razones trigonométricas de un triángulo rectángulo son las seis razones de los lados de dicho triángulo. Esas razones no dependen del tamaño del triángulo rectángulo. Dependen sólo de la magnitud de los ángulos agudos del triángulo. En un triángulo rectángulo que tenga un ángulo agudo $\angle A$, las razones se definen así:

$\operatorname{sen} A = \frac{a}{c}$ $\csc A = \frac{1}{\operatorname{sen} A} = \frac{c}{a}$

$\cos A = \frac{b}{c}$ $\sec A = \frac{1}{\cos A} = \frac{c}{b}$

$\tan A = \frac{a}{b}$ $\cot A = \frac{1}{\tan A} = \frac{b}{a}$

Glossary **941**

EXAMPLES

U

Unit circle (p. 720) The unit circle has a radius of 1 unit and its center is at the origin of the coordinate plane.

Círculo unitario (p. 720) El círculo unitario tiene un radio de 1 unidad y el centro está situado en el origen del plano de coordenadas.

V

Variable (p. 12) A variable is a symbol, usually a letter, that represents one or more numbers.

x, a, k

Variable (p. 12) Una variable es un símbolo, generalmente una letra, que representa uno o más valores.

Variable expression (p. 12) An expression that contains one or more variables is an algebraic expression, or a variable expression.

$2x + 3, z - y$

Expresión variable (p. 12) Una expresión que contenga una o más variables es una expresión algebraica o expresión variable.

Variable matrix (p. 214) When representing a system of equations with a matrix equation, the matrix containing the variables of the system is the variable matrix.

$$\begin{cases} x + 2y = 5 \\ 3x + 5y = 14 \end{cases}$$

variable matrix $\begin{bmatrix} x \\ y \end{bmatrix}$

Matriz variable (p. 214) Al representar un sistema de ecuaciones con una ecuación de matricial, la matriz que contenga las variables del sistema es la matriz variable.

Vertex form of a quadratic function (p. 252) The vertex form of a quadratic function is $f(x) = a(x - h)^2 + k$, where (h, k) are the coordinates of the vertex of the function.

$f(x) = x^2 + 2x - 1 = (x + 1)^2 - 2$
The vertex is $(-1, -2)$.

Forma del vértice de una función cuadrática (p. 252) La forma del vértice de una función cuadrática es $f(x) = a(x - h)^2 + k$, donde (h, k) son las coordenadas del vértice de la función.

Vertex of a function (p. 88) A vertex of a function is a point where the function reaches a maximum or a minimum value.

Vértice de una función (p. 88) El vértice de una función es el punto donde la función alcanza un valor máximo o mínimo.

942 Glossary

English/Spanish Glossary

T902

Vertex of a parabola (p. 239) The vertex of a parabola is the point where the function for the parabola reaches a maximum or a minimum value. The parabola intersects its axis of symmetry at the vertex.

Vértice de una parábola (p. 239) El vértice de una parábola es el punto donde la función de la parábola alcanza un valor máximo o mínimo. La parábola y su eje de simetría se intersecan en el vértice.

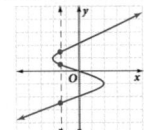

The vertex of the quadratic function $y = x^2 + 2x - 1$ is $(-1, -2)$.

Vertical-line test (p. 57) You can use the vertical-line test to determine whether a relation has at least one element of the domain paired with more than one element of the range. If a vertical line passes through two or more points on the graph, then the relation is *not* a function.

Prueba de la recta vertical (p. 57) La prueba de la recta vertical permite determinar si en una relación hay por lo menos un elemento del dominio al que corresponde más de un elemento del rango. Si una recta vertical del sistema de coordenadas pasa por dos o más puntos de la gráfica, quiere decir que la relación *no es* una función.

Vertices of a hyperbola (p. 575) The endpoints of the transverse axis of a hyperbola are the vertices of the hyperbola.

Vértices de una hipérbola (p. 575) Los dos puntos de intersección de la hipérbola y su eje mayor son los vértices de la hipérbola.

Vertices of an ellipse (p. 568) The endpoints of the major axis of an ellipse are the vertices of the ellipse.

Vértices de una elipse (p. 568) Los dos puntos de intersección de la elipse y su eje mayor son los vértices de la elipse.

X

x- and y-intercepts (p. 63) The point at which a line crosses the x-axis (or the x-coordinate of that point) is an x-intercept. The point at which a line crosses the y-axis (or the y-coordinate of that point) is a y-intercept.

Intercepto en x e intercepto en y (p. 63) El punto donde una recta corta el eje x (o la coordenada x de ese punto) es el intercepto en x. El punto donde una recta cruza el eje y (o la coordenada y de ese punto) es el intercepto en y.

The x-intercept of $y = 2x + 1$ is $\left(-\frac{1}{2}, 0\right)$ or $-\frac{1}{2}$.
The y-intercept of $y = 2x + 1$ is $(0, 1)$ or 1.

Z

Zero matrix (p. 175) The zero matrix O, or $O_{m \times n}$, is the $m \times n$ matrix whose elements are all zeros. It is the additive identity matrix for the set of all $m \times n$ matrices.

Matriz cero (p. 175) La matriz cero, O, o $O_{m \times n}$, es la matriz $m \times n$ cuyos elementos son todos ceros. Es la matriz de identidad aditiva para el conjunto de todas las matrices $m \times n$.

$$\begin{bmatrix} 1 & 4 \\ 2 & -3 \end{bmatrix} + O = \begin{bmatrix} 1 & 4 \\ 2 & -3 \end{bmatrix}$$

Zero of a function (p. 268) A zero of a function is any value of the variable for which the function is 0. On the graph of a function, each x-intercept represents a zero.

Cero de una función (p. 268) Un cero de una función es cualquier valor de la variable para el cual la función es 0. En la gráfica de una función, cada intercepto en x representa un cero.

The zeros of the function $P(x) = 2x(x - 3)^2(x + 1)$ are 0, 3, and -1.

Zero-Product Property (p. 267) If the product of two or more factors is zero, then one of the factors must be zero.

Propiedad del cero del producto (p. 267) Si el producto de dos o más factores es cero, entonces uno de los factores debe ser cero.

$(x - 3)(2x - 5) = 0$
$x - 3 = 0$ or $2x - 5 = 0$

---

z-score (p. 671) The z-score of a value is the number of standard deviations that the value is from the mean.

Puntaje z (p. 671) El puntaje z de un valor es el número de desviaciones normales que tiene ese valor de la media.

$[0, 2, 3, 4, 6, 7, 8, 9, 10, 11]$
$\overline{x} = 6$
standard deviation $= \sqrt{12} \approx 3.46$
For 8, z-score $= \frac{8 - 6}{\sqrt{12}} \approx 0.58$

Answers to Instant Check System™

Chapter 1

Check Your Readiness   p. 2

1. 0 2. −2 3. −2.09 4. 8.05 5. −$\frac{3}{4}$ 6. $\frac{11}{12}$ 7. 10$\frac{7}{10}$
8. 3$\frac{1}{2}$ 9. −42 10. 72 11. 9 12. −9.8 13. −3$\frac{1}{3}$
14. −5$\frac{1}{2}$ 15. −4$\frac{2}{9}$ 16. −$\frac{3}{4}$ 17. −21 18. 7.35
19. −$\frac{1}{9}$ 20. −$\frac{3}{5}$ 21. −20 22. 8 23. 0.97 24. −5
25. 55 26. 3

Lesson 1-1   pp. 4–8

Check Skills You'll Need 1. 7.2 2. 4 3. −13.5 4. 6.8
5. −5 6. −1

Quick Check 1. rational numbers; rational numbers
2.

3. −$\sqrt{0.08}$ > −$\sqrt{0.1}$, −$\sqrt{0.1}$ < −$\sqrt{0.08}$
4a. −400, $\frac{1}{400}$ b. −4$\frac{1}{21}$, $\frac{5}{21}$ c. 0.002, −500
d. $\frac{1}{9}$, −$\frac{9}{4}$ (or −2$\frac{1}{4}$) 5a. Identity Prop. of Add.
b. Assoc. Prop. of Add. 6a. 10, 1.5, 3. for
values of x such that x ≤ 0

Lesson 1-2   pp. 12–15

Check Skills You'll Need 1. 16 2. 6 3. $\frac{8}{9}$ 4. 195 5. 21
6. −1

Quick Check 1a. $\frac{7}{2}$ b. 26 c. 4 2a. −16
b. −3 c. −69 3a. about 45%; about 43%
b. Answers may vary. Sample: Changing patterns
in minority populations might lead to more voter
turnout. Less stable international conditions
might arouse voter concerns. 4a. −3x² + 6x
b. −4r − 4s 5a. 10x b. 10c + 2d

Lesson 1-3   pp. 18–21, 24

Check Skills You'll Need 1. −4x + 3 2. 7x + 3y − 1
3. 8g + 2h 4. $\frac{x}{5}$ 5. 2y 6. −3c + 1
Quick Check 1a. −11 b. 2 2a. 35 b. 3
3. $b_1 = \frac{2A}{h} − b_2$ 4a. x = $\frac{15}{a+b}$, a ≠ −b
b. x = $\frac{a(d−b)}{2}$, a ≠ 0 5. 8 cm wide; 16 cm long
6. 36 cm; 39 cm; 45 cm 7. about 86.4 seconds,
or 1 minute 26.4 seconds

Checkpoint Quiz 1 1. −1, 0.3, $\frac{5}{7}$, 7 2. Comm. Prop. of
Add., Assoc. Prop. of Add., Dist. Prop. 3. a + 2b
4. a² + a − 7 5. 5 6. $\frac{3}{7}$, or 1$\frac{1}{2}$ 7. 8. r = $\frac{A − P}{pt}$,
p ≠ 0, t ≠ 0 9. x = $\frac{4b}{7a}$, a ≠ 0 10. width = 76 yd,
length = 236 yd

Lesson 1-4   pp. 26–29

Check Skills You'll Need 1. true 2. false 3. false
4. false 5. true 6. true 7. −6 8. 15

Quick Check
1a. x < 11

1b. n ≤ −2

2a. All real numbers are solutions.
2b. no solutions

c. values of a less than or equal to 0; values of
a greater than 0 3. at least $55,000
4.

5. x < 4 or x > 5

6. by at least 0.03 in., but by no more than 0.43 in.

Lesson 1-5   pp. 33–36, 38

Check Skills You'll Need 1. 14 2. 16 3. 2.3 4. x > 3
5. a ≥ 4 6. t < 9

Quick Check 1. $\frac{8}{3}$, −3 2. −$\frac{13}{3}$, 5 3a. 1 b. no
solutions c. Answers may vary; any positive real
number. 4. x < −2 or x > 5

5. −6$\frac{5}{6}$ < z < 7$\frac{5}{6}$

6. |C − 28.125| ≤ 0.375

Checkpoint Quiz 1
1. x ≤ 5

2. x < 5$\frac{4}{7}$

3. z > −1

4. w > 1 or w < −3

5. −15 ≤ x ≤ 7

---

6. x < −2 or x > 2

7. −$\frac{5}{2}$, $\frac{11}{2}$ 8. $\frac{1}{2}$ 9. 13 > 3n + 3 < 16, n = 4
10. PR − RQ < PQ < PR + RQ; 4 < PQ < 26

Lesson 1-6   pp. 39–42

Check Skills You'll Need 1. 37.5% 2. 183$\frac{1}{3}$% 3. 0.43%
4. 0.25% 5. 104% 6. 300%

Quick Check 1. $\frac{29}{40}$, or 0.725, or 72.5% 2. $\frac{3}{50}$, or
6% 3. $\frac{1}{2}$, or 50% 4. $\frac{1}{4}$, or 25% 5a. $\frac{1}{16}$, or 6.25%
b. $\frac{5}{16}$, or 31.25%

Chapter 2

Check Your Readiness   p. 52

1.
2.
3.   4. 6s 5. 4a + b
6. xy − y + x 7. 1.5g 8. 0 9. 3b − 2c − 2
10. 6f − 5d 11. 3h + 3g 12. −2z + 5
13. 2g − 4dg − 12d 14. 8v − 6 15. 7t − 3st − 5s
16. −2 < x < 8

17. a ≤ 0

18. x > −1

19. x < −4 or x > $\frac{10}{3}$

20. −$\frac{1}{2}$ ≤ d ≤ $\frac{29}{5}$

21. −24 ≤ f ≤ 18   22. $\frac{15}{64}$ 23. $\frac{1}{32}$
24. $\frac{11}{32}$ 25. $\frac{13}{16}$ 26. $\frac{27}{32}$ 27. $\frac{13}{16}$

Lesson 2-1   pp. 55–61

Check Skills You'll Need
1.   2.   3.

6. 1, 2, 4, 7 7. 5, 3, −1, −7 8. 3, 1, 9, 51
9. 4, 3, 1, 2

Quick Check
1a.   b.

b.   c.

2a. domain {−3, 0, 2, 4}, range {2, 1, 4, −3}
b. domain {−3, −1, 1}, range {−4, −2, 1, 3}
3a. domain range b. domain range 4a. function

b. not a function 5a. not a function b. function
c. not a function 6a. −14, −5, 10 b. −$\frac{13}{4}$, −1, $\frac{11}{4}$
c. $\frac{6}{5}$, $\frac{3}{5}$, −$\frac{6}{5}$

Lesson 2-2   pp. 62–70

Check Skills You'll Need 1. $\frac{17}{3}$, 7, $\frac{23}{3}$, $\frac{29}{3}$ 2. −$\frac{19}{5}$, −2, −$\frac{7}{5}$, $\frac{4}{5}$
3. −5, 1, 4, 13 4. −9, −8, −$\frac{15}{2}$, −6

Quick Check
1a.   b.

c.   2a.

y = 40 − x, x-intercept (40, 0), y-intercept (0, 40).
When there are 0 children, the train holds 40 adults.
When there are 0 adults, the train holds 40
children. b. Answers may vary. Sample: Each
seat holds one person, whether adult or child.

3a. $\frac{2}{3}$ b. −$\frac{5}{2}$ 4a. 2x − y = 10 b. $\frac{5}{8}$x − y = −1$\frac{1}{8}$
5a. y − 0 = −$\frac{1}{4}$(x − 5) b. y + 1 = −$\frac{1}{6}$(x + 2)
c. y − 1 = $\frac{4}{9}$(x − 2) 6a. −$\frac{3}{2}$ b. −$\frac{4}{3}$ c. −$\frac{A}{B}$, B ≠ 0,
undefined, B = 0
7a. y = −$\frac{2}{5}$x + $\frac{14}{5}$

b. y = $\frac{2}{3}$x − $\frac{1}{3}$

c. x = 5

Lesson 2-3   pp. 72–74, 77

Check Skills You'll Need 1. y = $\frac{x}{4}$ 2. $\frac{x}{4}$ 3. y = 20
4. y = 30x 5. y = 7 6. true 7. true 8. false
9. true

Quick Check 1a. yes; k = $\frac{1}{3}$, y = $\frac{1}{3}$x b. no
c. no 2a. yes; k = 0.5 b. no c. yes; k = $\frac{2}{5}$ d. no
3a. π 33.4 cm 4a. 8 b. 28 c. −0.6 d. 0.2

Checkpoint Quiz 1 1. (9, 0), (0, −3) 2. (−$\frac{6}{7}$, 0), (0, 5)
3. (0, 0), (0,0) 4. (−$\frac{5}{2}$, 0), (0, 10) 5. y = 2x − 9
6. y = 4x − 2 7. y = −$\frac{3}{5}$x − 2 8. y = −$\frac{2}{3}$x + 2
9a. y = 7x b.

Both intercepts are 0 when no one has bought
any tickets. c. Answers may vary. Sample: No; the
number of people must be a whole number. 10. A

Lesson 2-4   pp. 78–84

Check Skills You'll Need 1. 3.6, −1.7 2. 1.5, −3.5
3. −1, $\frac{1}{10}$ 4. −6, −$\frac{4}{5}$ 5. $\frac{1}{6}$, 1$\frac{1}{3}$, 3

Quick Check 1a. h = −20t + 1350; the slope is
negative. b.

The h-intercept (0, 1350) represents the starting
height at time 0. 2a. The candle is burning down
at the rate of $\frac{1}{4}$ inch per hour. b. the original

height of the candle c. y = −2x + 9 3a. 3$\frac{1}{2}$ in.
b. 6$\frac{1}{4}$ in. c. after 25 hours
4a.

A linear model is reasonable; models may vary.
Sample: y = −1.92x + 6
b.

not reasonable

Lesson 2-5   pp. 88–90

Check Skills You'll Need
1.   2.   3.

Quick Check
1a.   b.

2a.

b.

3a.   b.

4a. The graph would stretch vertically by a factor
of 3. b.

Lesson 2-6   pp. 93–97, 100

Check Skills You'll Need
1.   2.

3.   4.

5.   6.

Quick Check 1a. y = x + 1 is y = x shifted 1 unit up.

b. y = |x| is y = |x| + 3.5.
2a. y = |x + $\frac{3}{2}$|
b. The graph is translated 1 unit to the right.

3. Answers may vary. Sample: 4.5 units right and
3 units up
4a. The graph is a vertical shrink by a factor of $\frac{1}{3}$.

b. y = 3|x|
5. y = −5|x|

Checkpoint Quiz 1
1.   2.   3.

4.   5.

6.   7. y = x − 4 8. y = |x + 5| − 3

9a.   b. about 7 10. D

Lesson 2-7   pp. 101–104

Check Skills You'll Need 1. p ≤ 1.25

2. t > 13

3. t ≤ −3

4. c = ±4.5

5. b = 2, 8

6. h ≤ −3.5 or h ≥ 3.5

Quick Check
1a.   b.   c.

2a. at least 3; Answers may vary. Sample: (2, 5),
(1, 6), (0, 7) b. 7x + 5y ≥ 35, x > 0, y > 0
3a.   b.

4a. y ≤ |x + 4| − 3 b. y ≥ 2x + 5

Chapter 3

Check Your Readiness — p. 116

1. $7x - 1$ 2. $5 - p$ 3. $-6z + 10$ 4. $r - 4$
5. $a \le \frac{3}{2}$
6. $b > 2$
7. $c < -12$
8. $d \le -1$

Lesson 3-1 — pp. 118–120

Check Skills You'll Need
1. 2. 3. 4, 5, 6. (graphs)

Quick Check
1. $(1, 3)$
2a. 2008 — men: 43.46 s, women: 47.31 s, 2024 — men: 43.07 s, women: 45.89 s b. It would mean that eventually the 400-m run would be run in zero seconds, and this could not happen.
3a. inconsistent b. dependent c. independent

Lesson 3-2 — pp. 125–127

Check Skills You'll Need
1. -4 2. x 3. $-5x$ 4. $-8y$ 5. 1 6. -2 7. $-\frac{1}{4}$

Quick Check
1a. $(-6, -6)$ b. $(2, 6)$
2. $\begin{cases} c = 15.49x \\ c = 6 + 13.99x \end{cases}$ The number of CDs is 4.
3a. $(4, -1)$ b. $(-2, 1)$ 4. Answers may vary. Sample: Multiply (1) by -5. Multiply (2) by 3. Add equations together, solving for y. Substitute the value of y into either original equation and solve for x. 5a. infinite number of solutions $\{(x, y) | -3x + 5y = 7\}$ b. no solution

Lesson 3-3 — pp. 133–135, 138

Check Skills You'll Need
1. $x > \frac{3}{5}$ 2. $y \le -14$ 3. $x > -\frac{7}{5}$

4. 5. 6. 7. 8. 9. (graphs)

Quick Check
1a. $(0, 1), (1, 2), (2, 3), (3, 4), (4, 5), (5, 6), (6, 7)$
1b. $(1, 0), (2, 1), (2, 0), (3, 2), (3, 1), (3, 0), (4, 3), (4, 2), (4, 1), (4, 0), (5, 3), (5, 2), (5, 1), (5, 0), (6, 3), (6, 2), (6, 1), (6, 0), (7, 2), (7, 1), (7, 0), (8, 1), (8, 0), (9, 1), (9, 0), (10, 0)$
2a. b. (graphs) $y > -4x$
3. $\begin{cases} 550 \le m \le 800 \\ v \le 800 \\ v + m \ge 1100 \end{cases}$
4a. b. (graphs) $y \le |x - 4|$ $y \ge -2x + 4$
Checkpoint Quiz 1 1. $(4, -3)$ 2. $(7, 0)$ 3. $(2, -4)$ 4. $(1, 3)$
5. $\begin{cases} 2n + 3m = 158 \\ 2n + 5m = 181 \end{cases}$ $61.75 cost per night, $11.50 cost per meal 6. approximately 4.8 years
7a. $\begin{cases} h \ge 18 \\ s \ge 12 \\ s + h \le 35 \end{cases}$ b. (graph)

Lesson 3-4 — pp. 139–141

Check Skills You'll Need
1. $(2, -3)$ 2. $(1, 2)$ 3. $(1, 1)$
4. 5. (graphs) $y \le -x + 7$
6. $x + 3y$ (graph) $2x - 3y \le 4$

Quick Check
1. $P = 2(0) + 3(0) = 0$, $P = 2(2) + 3(0) = 4$, $P = 2(4) + 3(3) = 17$, $P = 2(0) + 3(7) = 21$
When $x = 0$ and $y = 7$, P is maximized at 21. When $x = 0$ and $y = 0$, P is minimized at 0.
2. Order 25 cases of mixed nuts and no cases of roasted peanuts.

Lesson 3-5 — pp. 146–148, 151

Check Skills You'll Need
1. $x: -3, y: 6$ 2. $x: 18, y: 4$ 3. $x: -8, y: 3$ 4. $x: 10, y: -8$
5. 6. 7. 8. (graphs)

Quick Check
1a. b. (graphs) $(-1, 1, 3)$ $(0, -4, -2)$
c. d. (graphs) $(3, -5, 2)$ $(3, 3, -3)$
2a. $(0, 5, 0)$ b. outside the helmet, since the helmet is curved

3a. b. (graphs) $(0, 0, 5)$ $(0, 0, 2)$ $(0, -6, 0)$ $(3, 0, 0)$ $(5, 0, 0)$ $(0, 5, 0)$
c. (graph) $(0, 0, 4)$ $(-4, 0, 0)$ $(0, -2, 0)$
Checkpoint Quiz 2 1. $C = 25$ for $(5, 5)$ 2. 300 acres corn and 100 acres soybeans
3. $3x + 2y + z = 6$
4. 5. (graphs)

Lesson 3-6 — pp. 152–156

Check Skills You'll Need
1. $(3, -5)$ 2. no solution
3. $(1, -4)$ 4. 1 5. 1 6. $\frac{1}{2}$ 7. yes 8. yes

Quick Check
1a. $(1, 2, -1)$ b. $(3, 3, 1)$ c. No; you wouldn't need to use any of the original equations twice. 2. $(2, -1, 1)$ 3a. $(4, 1, 5)$ b. $(2, 0, -6)$ 4. $1400 growth, $1100 income, and $700 money market

Chapter 4

Check Your Readiness — p. 166
1. 6 2. $\frac{1}{3}$ 3. $-\frac{3}{4}$ 4. $\frac{7}{12}$ 5. $\frac{10}{9}$ 6. -9 7. $-\frac{17}{4}$
8. all real numbers 9. $t > -\frac{11}{4}$ 10. $s < 2$
11. 12. 13. (graphs)

14. 15. 16. 17. 18. (graphs) 19. $\left(\frac{1}{2}, -4\right)$ 20. $\left(-\frac{3}{2}, -\frac{2}{3}\right)$ 21. $\left(\frac{3}{4}, \frac{11}{4}\right)$
22. $(7, 9, -6)$ 23. $(0, 0, 8)$ 24. $(7, 5, 0)$

Lesson 4-1 — pp. 168–170

Check Skills You'll Need
1. 3.116 million units; 4.115 million units 2. 0.829 million units 3. 3.126 million units 4. The export percent increase of 8.3% was larger than the 48.9% increase for the imports.

Quick Check
1a. 2×3 b. 1×3 c. 3×2
2a. 15 b. 17 c. 10.4 d. 24
3a.

	China	Russia	United States
Production	42	46	71
Consumption	43	28	98

b. Add a new column for each additional country.
c. A $c \times d$ matrix has c rows and d columns, while a $d \times c$ matrix has d rows and c columns.
4a. $\begin{bmatrix} 9.725 & 9.700 & 9.587 & 9.137 & 9.837 & 9.837 \\ 9.650 & 8.537 & 9.712 & 9.412 & 9.775 & 9.725 \\ 9.512 & 9.650 & 9.725 & 9.700 & 9.712 & 9.475 \end{bmatrix}$
b. 9.837; Paul Hamm's score on the parallel bars

Lesson 4-2 — pp. 174–177

Check Skills You'll Need
1. $\begin{bmatrix} 14 & 4 \\ 2 & -1 \end{bmatrix}$ 2. $\begin{bmatrix} 3 & 1 \\ -3 & -2 \end{bmatrix}$
3. $\begin{bmatrix} 1 & -3 \\ -2 & -2 \end{bmatrix}$ 4. $\begin{bmatrix} 4 & 13 \\ -2 & 12 \end{bmatrix}$ 5. $\begin{bmatrix} 4 & -6 \\ 8 & -3 \end{bmatrix}$
6. $\begin{bmatrix} 6 & -2 \\ 1 & 7 \end{bmatrix}$

Quick Check
1a. $\begin{bmatrix} 4 & 7 & -3 \\ -6 & 1 & 19 \end{bmatrix}$
b. $\begin{bmatrix} -15 & 25 \\ -1 & 1 \\ -2 & 15 \end{bmatrix}$ 2a. $\begin{bmatrix} 0 & 0 \\ 0 & 0 \end{bmatrix}$ b. $\begin{bmatrix} -1 & 10 & -5 \\ 0 & 2 & -3 \end{bmatrix}$
3a. $\begin{bmatrix} 10 & -12 & 7 \\ -8 & -4 & -2 \end{bmatrix}$ b. $\begin{bmatrix} 0 & 4 \\ -3 & 14 \end{bmatrix}$ 4. $\begin{bmatrix} 11 & 7 \\ -6 & -1 \end{bmatrix}$
5a. no b. yes 6a. $x = 30, y = 2$ b. $x = -3, y = 7$

Lesson 4-3 — pp. 182–186, 189

Check Skills You'll Need
1. $\begin{bmatrix} 9 & 15 \\ 6 & 24 \end{bmatrix}$ 2. $\begin{bmatrix} -20 \\ 35 \end{bmatrix}$
3. $\begin{bmatrix} -4 & 12 & 16 \\ 0 & -8 & -20 \end{bmatrix}$

Quick Check
1. $\begin{bmatrix} -45 & 36 & -30 & 0 \\ -60 & 30 & -21 & 0 \end{bmatrix}$
2a. $\begin{bmatrix} 7 & -12 & 58 \\ -9 & 24 & -10 \end{bmatrix}$ b. $\begin{bmatrix} 20 & 3 & 29 \\ -5 & 52 & 17 \end{bmatrix}$
3a. $\begin{bmatrix} 1 & 6 \\ 2 & 0 \end{bmatrix}$ b. $\begin{bmatrix} 1 & 0 & -3 \\ 7 & 5 & -2 \end{bmatrix}$
4a. $\begin{bmatrix} 12 & -12 \\ -5 & 0 \end{bmatrix}$ b. No; explanations may vary.
Sample: For the matrices in part (a),
$AB = \begin{bmatrix} 12 & -12 \\ -5 & 0 \end{bmatrix}$.
However, $BA = \begin{bmatrix} 3 & -3 \\ -29 & 9 \end{bmatrix}$, so $AB \ne BA$.
5a. [105] b. Product does not exist. 6a. RS is defined, but SR is undefined.
b. $RS = \begin{bmatrix} 28 & 10 & -6 & -16 \\ 32 & 20 & -9 & -32 \end{bmatrix}$
Checkpoint Quiz 1 1. 3×2; 1 2. 2×3; -2 3. 3×3; 5
4. $\begin{bmatrix} -2 & 4 \\ 6 & 16 \end{bmatrix}$ 5. $\begin{bmatrix} 1 & -5 \\ -4 & 9 \end{bmatrix}$ 6. $\begin{bmatrix} 4.5 & 6 \\ 27 & -18 \end{bmatrix}$
7. $\begin{bmatrix} 42 & 46 \\ 3 & 1 \end{bmatrix}$ 8. $\begin{bmatrix} 50 & 117 \\ 278 & 495 \end{bmatrix}$
9. Make sure that the number of columns in the first matrix has the same as the number of rows in the second matrix.
10. Answers may vary. Sample: $2X + \begin{bmatrix} 1 & 2 & 4 \\ 0 & 3 & 0 & 5 \end{bmatrix} = \begin{bmatrix} 25 & 16 & -4 & 20 \\ 18 & 3 & -22 & 7 \end{bmatrix}$

Lesson 4-4 — pp. 191–195

Check Skills You'll Need
1. 2. (graphs) $y = x + 6$ $f(x) = \frac{1}{2}x + 7$
3. 4. (graphs) $g(x) = |x - 3|$ $y = x - 2$
5. 6. (graphs) $y = \frac{1}{3}|x - 3| - 2$ $f(x) = |-2x + 4|$

Quick Check
1a. Subtract 6 from each x-coordinate and add 2 to each y-coordinate.
b. $\begin{bmatrix} -3 & -3 & -3 & -3 & -3 \\ 2 & 2 & 2 & 2 & 2 \end{bmatrix}$
c. $(-3, -3), (-4, 1), (-8, 2), (-2, 5), (1, 2)$
2a. $(-20, 0), (32, -4), (16, 20)$

b. (−1, 0), (1.6, −0.2), (0.8, 1)

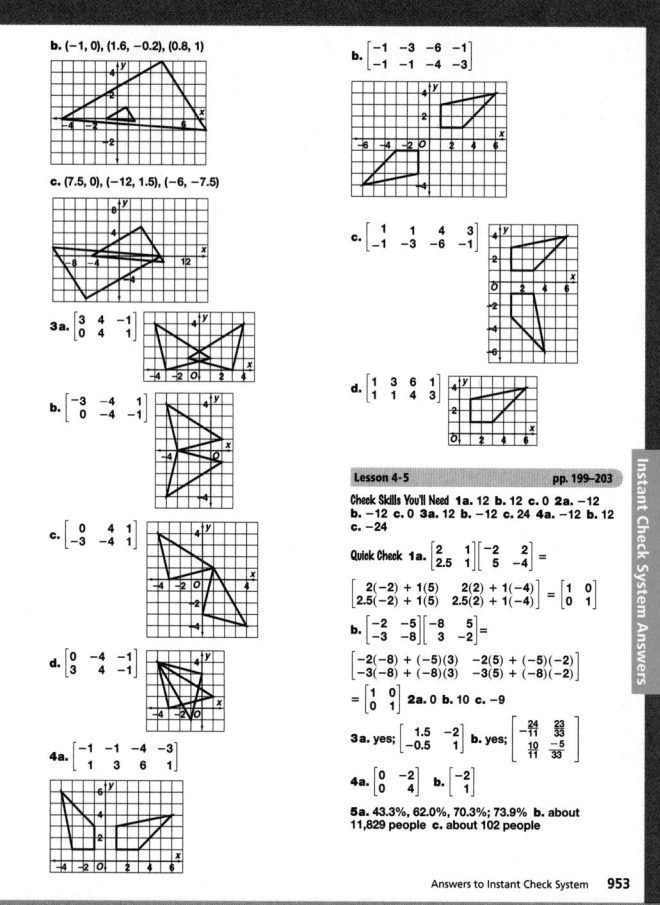

c. (7.5, 0), (−12, 1.5), (−6, −7.5)

b. $\begin{bmatrix} -1 & -3 & -6 & -1 \\ -1 & -1 & -4 & -3 \end{bmatrix}$

c. $\begin{bmatrix} 1 & 1 & 4 & 3 \\ -1 & -3 & -6 & -1 \end{bmatrix}$

d. $\begin{bmatrix} 1 & 3 & 6 & 1 \\ 1 & 1 & 4 & 3 \end{bmatrix}$

3a. $\begin{bmatrix} 3 & 4 & -1 \\ 0 & 4 & 1 \end{bmatrix}$

b. $\begin{bmatrix} -3 & -4 & 1 \\ 0 & -4 & -1 \end{bmatrix}$

c. $\begin{bmatrix} 0 & 4 & 1 \\ -3 & -4 & 1 \end{bmatrix}$

d. $\begin{bmatrix} 0 & -4 & -1 \\ 3 & 4 & -1 \end{bmatrix}$

4a. $\begin{bmatrix} -1 & -1 & -4 & -3 \\ 1 & 3 & 6 & 1 \end{bmatrix}$

Lesson 4-5　　pp. 199–203

Check Skills You'll Need 1a. 12 **b.** 12 **c.** 0 **2a.** −12 **b.** −12 **c.** 0 **3a.** 12 **b.** −12 **c.** 24 **4a.** −12 **b.** 12 **c.** −24

Quick Check 1a. $\begin{bmatrix} 2 & 1 \\ 2.5 & 1 \end{bmatrix}\begin{bmatrix} -2 & 5 \\ 5 & -4 \end{bmatrix} =$

$\begin{bmatrix} 2(-2) + 1(5) & 2(2) + 1(-4) \\ 2.5(-2) + 1(5) & 2.5(2) + 1(-4) \end{bmatrix} = \begin{bmatrix} 1 & 0 \\ 0 & 1 \end{bmatrix}$

b. $\begin{bmatrix} -2 & -5 \\ -3 & -8 \end{bmatrix}\begin{bmatrix} -8 & 5 \\ 3 & -2 \end{bmatrix} =$

$\begin{bmatrix} -2(-8) + (-5)(3) & -2(5) + (-5)(-2) \\ -3(-8) + (-8)(3) & -3(5) + (-8)(-2) \end{bmatrix}$

$= \begin{bmatrix} 1 & 0 \\ 0 & 1 \end{bmatrix}$ **2a.** 0 **b.** 10 **c.** −9

3a. yes; $\begin{bmatrix} 1.5 & -2 \\ -0.5 & 1 \end{bmatrix}$ **b.** yes; $\begin{bmatrix} -\frac{24}{11} & \frac{23}{33} \\ \frac{10}{11} & -\frac{5}{33} \end{bmatrix}$

4a. $\begin{bmatrix} 0 & -2 \\ 0 & 4 \end{bmatrix}$ **b.** $\begin{bmatrix} -2 \\ 1 \end{bmatrix}$

5a. 43.3%, 62.0%, 70.3%; 73.9% **b.** about 11,829 people **c.** about 102 people

---

Lesson 4-6　　pp. 206–208, 211

Check Skills You'll Need 1. −24 **2.** 0 **3.** −24 **4.** 12 **5.** 12 **6.** 0

Quick Check 1a. 27 **b.** 22 **c.** 0 **2.** −1087

3a. The matrices $\begin{bmatrix} 0 & 0 & 1 \\ 0.2 & -0.2 & 0 \\ 0 & -1 & 1 \end{bmatrix}$ and $\begin{bmatrix} 1 & 5 & -1 \\ 1 & 0 & -1 \\ 1 & 0 & 0 \end{bmatrix}$ have a product of $\begin{bmatrix} 1 & 0 & 0 \\ 0 & 1 & 0 \\ 0 & 0 & 1 \end{bmatrix}$, so they are inverses.

b. The matrices $\begin{bmatrix} 0 & 1 & 0 \\ 1 & 0 & 1 \\ 0 & 1 & 0 \end{bmatrix}$ and $\begin{bmatrix} 3 & 4 & 1 \\ -2 & 0 & 2 \\ 1 & 5 & 3 \end{bmatrix}$ have a product of $\begin{bmatrix} -2 & 0 & 2 \\ 4 & 9 & 4 \\ -2 & 0 & 2 \end{bmatrix}$, so they are not inverses.

4a. The matrices $\begin{bmatrix} 0 & 0 & 2 \\ 1 & 3 & -2 \\ 1 & -2 & 1 \end{bmatrix}$ and $\begin{bmatrix} 0.1 & 0.4 & 0.6 \\ 0.3 & 0.2 & -0.2 \\ 0.5 & 0 & 0 \end{bmatrix}$ have a product of $\begin{bmatrix} 1 & 0 & 0 \\ 0 & 1 & 0 \\ 0 & 0 & 1 \end{bmatrix}$, so they are inverses.

b. $\begin{bmatrix} 9 \\ -5 \\ 8 \end{bmatrix}$ **5.** POETRY

Checkpoint Quiz 1 1. A′(−2, 8), B′(−8, 0), C′(2, −2) **2.** A′(−4, 7), B′(−7, 3), C′(−2, 2) **3a.** A′(4, 1), B′(0, 4), C′(−1, −1) **4.** A′(4, 1), B′(0, 4), C′(1, −1)

5. $\begin{bmatrix} 2 & 3 \\ -4 & -5 \end{bmatrix}$ **6.** $\begin{bmatrix} 5 \\ 2 \\ 8 \end{bmatrix}$ **7.** $\begin{bmatrix} -2 \\ 8 \end{bmatrix}$ **8.** −10 **9.** 18 **10.** −71

Lesson 4-7　　pp. 214–217

Check Skills You'll Need 1. (2, 4) **2.** (0, 6, 3) **3.** (3, −3, 9)

Quick Check 1a. $\begin{bmatrix} 3 & 2 \\ 0 & 1 \end{bmatrix}\begin{bmatrix} x \\ y \end{bmatrix} = \begin{bmatrix} 16 \\ 5 \end{bmatrix}$; coefficient matrix is $\begin{bmatrix} 3 & 2 \\ 0 & 1 \end{bmatrix}$, variable matrix is $\begin{bmatrix} x \\ y \end{bmatrix}$, constant matrix is $\begin{bmatrix} 16 \\ 5 \end{bmatrix}$.

b. $\begin{bmatrix} 1 & -1 & 1 \\ 1 & -2 & -1 \\ 2 & -1 & 1 \end{bmatrix}\begin{bmatrix} x \\ y \\ z \end{bmatrix} = \begin{bmatrix} 0 \\ 5 \\ 8 \end{bmatrix}$; coefficient matrix is $\begin{bmatrix} 1 & -1 & 1 \\ 1 & -2 & -1 \\ 2 & -1 & 1 \end{bmatrix}$, variable matrix is $\begin{bmatrix} x \\ y \\ z \end{bmatrix}$, constant matrix is $\begin{bmatrix} 0 \\ 5 \\ 8 \end{bmatrix}$. **2a.** (−1, 4) **b.** (−2, 8)

3a. $2(4) + (-10) + 3(1) \overset{?}{=} 1$
$\quad 8 - 10 + 3 \overset{?}{=} 1$
$\quad\quad\quad\quad 1 = 1$
$5(4) + (-10) - 2(1) \overset{?}{=} 8$
$\quad 20 - 10 - 2 \overset{?}{=} 8$
$\quad\quad\quad\quad 8 = 8$
$4 - (-10) - 9(1) \overset{?}{=} 5$
$\quad 4 + 10 - 9 \overset{?}{=} 5$
$\quad\quad\quad\quad 5 = 5$

b. (1.25, 2.5, −1.75)

4. one large bead = $1.95, one small bead = $.55

5a. yes **b.** The graphing calculator indicates that there is a "singular matrix" error.

Lesson 4-8　　pp. 221–224

Check Skills You'll Need 1. −3 **2.** 1 **3.** 11 **4.** −18 **5.** 15 **6.** −35

Quick Check 1. (1, 2) **2a.** In D, replace the coefficients of z with the constants. **b.** y = 1, z = 1 **3a.** $\begin{bmatrix} 1 & -5 \\ 3 & 3 \end{bmatrix}\frac{15}{3}$ **b.** $\begin{bmatrix} 1 & 2 & 3 \\ 0 & 1 & -2 \\ 1 & 1 & 0 \end{bmatrix}\begin{bmatrix} -4 \\ 8 \\ -3 \end{bmatrix}$

4a. $\begin{cases} 5x + 7y = -3 \\ -8y = 6 \end{cases}$ **b.** $\begin{cases} -x + 3z = -4 \\ 7x + 2y - z = 0 \\ y + 2z = -3 \end{cases}$

5. (−15, 5)

6a. $3(4) - 2(1) + 4(0) \overset{?}{=} 10$
$\quad 12 - 2 + 0 \overset{?}{=} 10$
$\quad\quad\quad\quad 10 = 10 \checkmark$
$4 + 4(1) - 2(0) \overset{?}{=} 8$
$\quad 4 + 4 - 0 \overset{?}{=} 8$
$\quad\quad\quad\quad 8 = 8 \checkmark$

b. (−1, 2, 3)

Chapter 5

Check Your Readiness　　p. 236

1. $4x^2 - 5x$ **2.** $\frac{11x^2}{30}$ **3.** $-7x^2 - 13x$ **4.** $\frac{2}{3}$ **5.** −1.8 **6.** 1

---

7. **8.** **9.**

10. **11.**

12. **13.**
Sample: y = 3x + 12

14.
Sample: $y = \frac{9}{5}x + 10$

15. **16.** y = |x|
v = 6s + 40

Lesson 5-1　　pp. 238–240

Check Skills You'll Need 1. −3, −1, 0, 1, 3 **2.** 9, 1, 0, 1, 9 **3.** 3, 1, 0, −1, −3 **4.** −9, −1, 0, −1, −9 **5.** 3, $\frac{1}{3}$, $\frac{1}{3}$, 0, $\frac{1}{3}$, 3 **6.** −3, $-\frac{3}{2}$, 0, $-\frac{1}{3}$, −3 **7.** $y = -\frac{3}{4}x + 2$ **8.** y = 2x + 7 **9.** $y = -\frac{1}{8}x + 3$

Quick Check 1a. linear; none, 5x, none **b.** quadratic; $3x^2$, −16x, 5 **c.** quadratic; x^2, 3x, none **2a.** (1, −1), x = 1; P′(3, 3), Q′(0, 0) **b.** (−1, 2), x = −1; P′(0, 1), Q′(−3, −2) **3.** $y = -2x^2 + 3x - 1$ **4a.** 73 mm **b.** 39 mm **c.** No; the tank is empty at 109 seconds.

Lesson 5-2　　pp. 245–247

Check Skills You'll Need 1. 3 **2.** −1 **3.** −4 **4.** (0, 0) **5.** $\left(-\frac{3}{2}, 0\right)$ **6.** $\left(-\frac{7}{3}, 0\right)$

7. **8.** **9.**

Quick Check 1a. **b.** **c.** (0, 0)

2a. **b.** (−3, 0)

3a. minimum: −9 **b.** none

4. $10; $500

Lesson 5-3　　pp. 252–255, 258

Check Skills You'll Need
1. y = x **2.** y = |x|

---

3. y = |x|

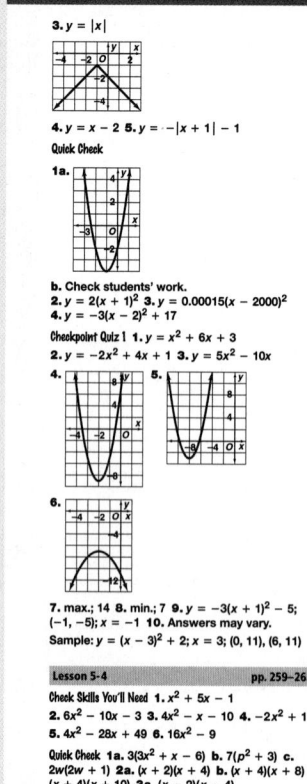

4. y = x − 2 **5.** y = −|x + 1| − 1

Quick Check

1a.

b. Check students' work. **2.** $y = 2(x + 1)^2$ **3.** $y = 0.00015(x - 2000)^2$ **4.** $y = -3(x - 2)^2 + 17$

Checkpoint Quiz 1 1. $y = x^2 + 6x + 3$ **2.** $y = -2x^2 + 4x + 1$ **3.** $y = 5x^2 - 10x$

4. **5.**

6.

7. max.; 14 **8.** min.; 7 **9.** $y = -3(x + 1)^2 - 5$; (−1, −5); x = −1 **10.** Answers may vary. Sample: $y = (x - 3)^2 + 2$; x = 3; (0, 11), (6, 11)

Lesson 5-4　　pp. 259–263

Check Skills You'll Need 1. $x^2 + 5x - 1$ **2.** $6x^2 - 10x - 3$ **3.** $4x^2 - x - 10$ **4.** $-2x^2 + 10x$ **5.** $4x^2 - 28x$ **6.** $16x^2 - 9$

Quick Check 1a. $3(x^2 + x - 6)$ **b.** $7(p^3 + 3)$ **c.** $2w(2w + 1)$ **2a.** $(x + 2)(x + 4)$ **b.** $(x + 4)(x + 8)$ **c.** $(x + 4)(x + 10)$ **3a.** $(x - 2)(x - 4)$ **b.** $(x - 3)(x - 4)$ **c.** $(x - 3)(x - 8)$ **4a.** $(x + 2)(x - 16)$ **b.** $(x + 5)(x - 2)$

c. $(x + 5)(x - 1)$ **5a.** $(x + 4)(2x + 3)$ **b.** $(x + 1)(4x + 3)$ **c.** $(x - 2)(2x - 3)$ **6a.** $(x - 1)(2x + 9)$ **b.** $(x - 6)(3x + 2)$ **c.** $(x + 2)(4x - 3)$ **7a.** $(2x + 3)^2$ **b.** $(8x - 1)^2$ **c.** $(5x + 9)^2$ **8a.** $(x - 8)(x + 8)$ **b.** $(2a + 7)(2a - 7)$

Lesson 5-5　　pp. 267–269

Check Skills You'll Need 1. $(x + 7)(x - 2)$ **2.** $4x(x - 3)$ **3.** $(3x - 4)(3x + 4)$

4. **5.**

6.

Quick Check 1a. −9, 2 **b.** −3, 1 **c.** 0, $\frac{1}{2}$ **2a.** $-\frac{5}{2}, \frac{5}{2}$ **b.** $-2\sqrt{2}, 2\sqrt{2}$ **c.** $-\frac{1}{2}, \frac{1}{2}$ **3a.** 5 s **b.** t = 5 or t = −5, and use positive solution because it describes time; check students' work. **4.** 4.56 **5a.** −1.24, 3.24 **b.** −0.81, 0.31

Lesson 5-6　　pp. 274–277, 280

Check Skills You'll Need 1. 5 **2.** $2\sqrt{17}$ **3.** 13 **4.** $2\sqrt{34}$ **5.** $x\sqrt{2}$ **6.** 5x

Quick Check 1a. $\sqrt{2}$ **b.** $2\sqrt{3}$ **c.** $\frac{6i}{}$ **d.** $\sqrt{a^2} = |a|$, $(\sqrt{a})^2 = a$ **2.** 7 + 3i **3a.** $2\sqrt{13}$ **b.** $\sqrt{29}$ **c.** 4 **4a.** 5i **b.** −4 + 3i **c.** −a − bi **5a.** 6 − i **b.** −4 − 3i **6a.** −84 **b.** 9 − 38i **c.** 43 − 24i **7a.** ±4i **b.** $\pm i\sqrt{30}$ **c.** $\pm\frac{1}{2}i$ **8.** −1 + i, −1 − i, −1 + 3i

Checkpoint Quiz 1 1. $(2x - 3)(x + 2)$ **2.** $5(x + 3)(x - 3)$ **3.** $(2x - 9)^2$ **4.** −4, 1 **5.** 1 **6.** $\pm 11i$ **7.** $\sqrt{29}$ **8.** $\sqrt{82}$ **9.** $\sqrt{65}$ **10.** No; the graph does not intersect the x-axis.

Lesson 5-7　　pp. 282–285

Check Skills You'll Need 1. $x^2 - 6x + 9$ **2.** $4x^2 - 4x + 1$ **3.** $x^2 + 8x + 13$ **4.** ±5 **5.** $\pm 4\sqrt{3}$ **6.** ±2i **7.** $\pm\frac{3}{4}$

Quick Check 1. −2, 16 **2.** $\frac{49}{4}$ **3a.** $-2 \pm 2\sqrt{2}$ **b.** $1 \pm \sqrt{2}$

4a. $x^2 - 8x + 36 = 0$; $(4 + 2i\sqrt{5})^2 - 8(4 + 2i\sqrt{5}) + 36 = 16 + 2(8i\sqrt{5}) + (2i\sqrt{5})^2 - 32 - 16i\sqrt{5} + 36 = (16 - 20 - 32 + 36) + (16i\sqrt{5} - 16i\sqrt{5}) = 0$; $(4 - 2i\sqrt{5})^2 - 8(4 - 2i\sqrt{5}) + 36 = 16 + 2(-8i\sqrt{5}) + (-2i\sqrt{5})^2 - 32 + 16i\sqrt{5} + 36 = 16 - 20 - 32 + 36 + (-16i\sqrt{5} + 16i\sqrt{5}) = 0$
b. The graph has no x-intercepts, so no real solutions. c. $-3 \pm 5i$/ 5a. $-\frac{2}{3}, \frac{3}{4}$ b. $\frac{3}{4} \pm \frac{i\sqrt{23}}{4}$
6a. $y = (x - 5)^2 - 27$ b. $y = (x + \frac{9}{2})^2 - \frac{13}{4}$
7a. (280, 38,000) b. The coefficient of s^2 is negative, so the parabola opens downward.

Lesson 5-8 pp. 289–293
Check Skills You'll Need 1. $y = -10x^2 + 8$ 2. $y = x^2 + 4x + 3$ 3. $y = -x^2 + 4x + 1$ 4. $y = 8x^2 + 2x - 1$ 5. 24 6. 84 7. -48 8. 89
Quick Check 1. $-1, \frac{1}{3}$ 2a. $-1 \pm \frac{i\sqrt{2}}{2}$
b.
The graph does not intersect the x-axis.
3a. $\frac{1}{2}, \frac{1}{3}$ b. $-2 \pm 3\sqrt{5}$; -8.71, 4.71
4a. one real solution b. two imaginary solutions
5. Yes; the discriminant is positive.

Chapter 6
Check Your Readiness p. 304
1. $y = 2x^2 + 1$ 2. $y = -\frac{1}{2}x^2 - 1$
3. $y = 3x^2 - 6x + 3$
4. 5.

6.
7. $x = -0.25, 1$
8. $x \approx -6.39, 4.39$
9. $x \approx -6.38, 0.38$
10. $x = -4, 9$
11. $x = 3, \frac{7}{2}$ 12. $x = \frac{2 \pm \sqrt{13}}{3}$
13. 24; 2 real solutions 14. 0; 1 real solution
15. 0; 1 real solution 16. $\frac{50}{101}$

Lesson 6-1 pp. 306–309
Check Skills You'll Need 1. x 2. $3x^2y - 8xy^2$ 3. $7x^2 - 3x$ 4. 1 term 5. 2 terms 6. 3 terms
Quick Check 1. a. $-2x + 5$; linear binomial
b. $5x^3 + x^2 - 4x$; cubic trinomial c. $-2x^5 + 6$; quintic binomial 2. Answers may vary. Sample: No; when $x = 25$ then, based on the cubic model, $y \approx 3.76$, but because of its turning points the cubic model is unreliable. 3. 75.9 million troy oz

Lesson 6-2 pp. 313–316
Check Skills You'll Need 1. $(x + 4)(x + 3)$ 2. $(x + 10)(x - 3)$ 3. $(x - 12)(x - 2)$ 4. $x^2 + 4x$ 5. $x^2 + 2x + 1$ 6. $x^3 - 4x^2 - 3x + 18$
Quick Check 1. $x^3 + 4x^2 + 5x + 2$
2. $3x(x - 4)(2x + 3)$ 3. $V \approx 3014$ in.^{3}, depth 10.5 in., length 20.5 in., width 14 in. 4a. 7, 5, 3
b.
5a. $y = x^3 + 5x^2 + 2x - 8$ b. $y = x^3 + 6x^2 + 8x$ c. Answers may vary. Sample: The zero at 0 can be from $x = 0$, $x^2 = 0$, $x^3 = 0$, and so on. Each power will lead to a different answer. 6a. -1, multiplicity of 3 b. 2, multiplicity of 2

Lesson 6-3 pp. 320–23, 326
Check Skills You'll Need 1. $x^2 - x - 10$ 2. $2x^2 - 5x - 3$ 3. $x^2 + 3x - 9$ 4. $3x^2 + 9x - 30$ 5. $4x^3 - 2x^2 + 5x + 9$; 4, -2, 5, 9 6. $5x^3 - 9x^2 + 10$; 5, -9, 0, 10 7. $-x^2 + 2x + 7$; -1, 2, 7 8. $-3x^4 + x^3 - 7x^2$; -3, 1, -7, 0, 0

Quick Check 1. $x + 1$, R 5 2a. yes b. no
3. $x^2 + 3x - 2$, R -4 4a. $x^2 - 4x + 3$
b. $x^2 - (x - 3)(x - 1)$ 5. -69
Checkpoint Quiz 1 1. Answers may vary. Sample: $y = (x + 1)^2(x + 2)(x + 3)$ 2. $-3x^3 + 5x + 6$; degree 3, 3 terms 3. $-x^2 - 3x^2 + \frac{3}{2}x$; degree 4, 3 terms 4. $3x^2 + 9x - 12$; degree 2, 3 terms 5. 1, 2 (mult. 2) 6. $-\frac{1}{2}$, 4 7. 0 (mult. 3), 3, -1 (mult. 2) 8. $x^2 + 2x + 1$ 9. $2x^2 - 3x + 1$ 10. 479

Lesson 6-4 pp. 327–330
Check Skills You'll Need
1. (1, 4) 2. $(1, \frac{2}{3})$
3. no points
4. $(x - 5)(x + 3)$ 5. $(x - 7)(x - 2)$ 6. $(x + 5)(x + 1)$
Quick Check
1. $x = -1$
2. 22.7125 in., 25.7125 in., 20.7125 in.
3. $(2x - 1)(4x^2 + 2x + 1)$ 4a. $-2, 1 \pm i\sqrt{3}$ b. $\frac{1}{3}$, $\frac{-1 \pm i\sqrt{3}}{6}$ 5a. $(4x^2 + 2x + 1)$ b. $(x^2 - 5)(x^2 + 2)$ 6. $3i, -3i, i\sqrt{2}, -i\sqrt{2}$

Lesson 6-5 pp. 335–338
Check Skills You'll Need 1. $\pm1, \pm2, \pm3, \pm4, \pm6, \pm12$ 2. $\pm1, \pm2, \pm3, \pm4, \pm6, \pm8, \pm12, \pm24$ 3. $\pm1, \pm2, \pm3, \pm4, \pm6, \pm9, \pm12, \pm18, \pm36$ 4. $\pm1, \pm2, \pm3, \pm4, \pm6, \pm8, \pm12, \pm16, \pm24, \pm48$
5. $x^3 - 5x^2 + 7x - 35$ 6. $x^3 + 2x^2 - 3x - 6$

7. A rational number can be written as the quotient of two integers $\frac{a}{b}$, where $b \neq 0$.
8. Irrational numbers cannot be written as quotients of integers. 9. An imaginary number is a nonreal number of the form $a + bi$, where $b \neq 0$.
Quick Check 1. 4 2a. $\pm \sqrt{5}, 2$ b. $-1, \frac{1 \pm \sqrt{2}}{3}$
3a. $2 + \sqrt{7}, -\sqrt{5}$ b. No; the Irrational Root Theorem does not apply unless you know that all of the coefficients of the polynomial are rational.
4a. $-3i, -2 - i$ b. 4 or greater
5a. $x^3 - 3x^2 + x + 5 = 0$ b. $x^4 + 5x^2 + 4 = 0$

Lesson 6-6 pp. 341–343
Check Skills You'll Need 1. 2 2. 3 3. 5 4. $\pm4i$
5. $1 \pm i\sqrt{2}$ 6. $\frac{-5 \pm i\sqrt{7}}{...}$
Quick Check 1. 4 complex roots, number of real roots: 0, 2, or 4, possible rational roots: $\pm1, \pm3$
2a. $2, \pm2i$ b. You can verify the real zeros by graphing the function. You can verify the complex zeros by substituting the values into the function.

Lesson 6-7 pp. 345–347, 351
Check Skills You'll Need 1. 30, 240 2. $\frac{4}{6}$ 3. 210 4. 42 5. 36 6. 60 7. 192
Quick Check 1. 720 2. 720 3a. 252 b. 28 c. 480,700 4. 77,520; 125,970 5. 638
Checkpoint Quiz 2 1. 1, 3, -2 2. $\frac{1}{3}$, $\frac{-1 \pm \sqrt{3}}{6}$ 3. ±3, $\pm i\sqrt{5}$ 4. $\frac{1}{2}$, $\frac{-1 \pm i\sqrt{3}}{6}$ 5. $-2, 2, -\frac{1}{3}$ 6a. $3 + 5i, -\sqrt{2}$ b. Degree must be ≥ 4. 7. 5; by the corollary to the Fundamental Theorem of Algebra 8a. 744 b. $\frac{1}{9}$ 9a. 21 b. 35 c. 35 d. 21 10. 5040

Lesson 6-8 pp. 353–355
Check Skills You'll Need 1. $x^2 + 4x + 4$ 2. $4x^2 + 12x + 9$ 3. $x^3 - 9x^2 + 27x - 27$ 4. $a^4 + 4a^3b + 6a^2b^2 + 4ab^3 + b^4$ 5. 1 6. 5 7. 10 8. 10 9. 5
Quick Check 1. $a^8 + 8a^7b + 28a^6b^2 + 56a^5b^3 + 70a^4b^4 + 56a^3b^5 + 28a^2b^6 + 8ab^7 + b^8$ 2. $x^4 - 8x^3 + 24x^2 - 32x + 16$ 3a. $v^9 + 9v^8w + 36v^7w^2 + 84v^6w^3 + 126v^5w^4 + 126v^4w^5 + 84v^3w^6 + 36v^2w^7 + 9vw^8 + w^9$ b. $c^5 - 10c^4 + 40c^3 - 80c^2 + 80c - 32$ 4a. about 0.387 b. about 0.349

Chapter 7
Check Your Readiness p. 366
1. $3y^2 - 14y + 8$ 2. $x^3 + 4x^2 - 15x - 18$ 5. $8b^3$
7. $6a^6$ 9. -2, 7 11. $-4, \frac{2}{3}$ 15. domain {1, 2, 3, 4}, range {2, 3, 4, 5} 17. domain $\{x \mid x \in R\}$, range $\{y \mid y \in R\}$
19. 21.

Lesson 7-1 pp. 369–371
Check Skills You'll Need 1. 5^2 2. 0.3^2 3. $(\frac{2}{9})^2$ 4. $(x^5)^2$ 5. $(x^2y)^2$ 6. $(13x^3y^6)^2$
Quick Check 1a. 0; -1; 2 b. 0.01 and -0.01, no real square root, $\frac{6}{11}$ and $-\frac{6}{11}$ 2a. -3 b. 3 c. 7 3a. $2|x|y^2$ b. $-3c^2 |x^2||y^3|$ 4a. 2.29 in. b. 2.8 in. c. 2.92 in.

Lesson 7-2 pp. 374–377
Check Skills You'll Need 1. 6 2. 3 3. 3 4. x^2 5. ab 6. $5a^3b^4$
Quick Check 1a. 6 b. -3 c. not possible 2. $5x^2\sqrt{2}$; $x^3\sqrt{18x}$ 3. $42x^3\sqrt{3}$ 4a. 3 b. $2x\sqrt{x}$ c. $4x^3\sqrt[3]{x^2}$ 5a. $\frac{\sqrt{35}}{5}$ b. $\frac{x\sqrt{5y}}{5y}$ c. $\frac{\sqrt[3]{18x^2}}{3x}$ 6. $t = \frac{\sqrt{da}}{...}$

Lesson 7-3 pp. 380–382, 384
Check Skills You'll Need 1. $15x^2 + 2x - 8$ 2. $-24x^2 + 71x - 35$ 3. $x^2 - 16$ 4. $16x^2 - 25$ 5. $x^2 + 10x + 25$ 6. $4x^2 - 36x + 81$
Quick Check 1a. $5\sqrt{7}$ b. cannot combine c. $9\sqrt{xy}$ 2. $60\sqrt{2}$ in. 3. $2\sqrt{2}$ 4. $5 - 2\sqrt{6}$ 5. 6, $39 + 10\sqrt{15}$
Checkpoint Quiz 1 1. $|b|c^2$ 2. xy^2 3. -a 4. $-y^2$
5. $8\sqrt{3} + 24$ 6. $12x^3y\sqrt{35}$ 7. $12\sqrt[3]{3} - 9\sqrt[3]{2}$ 8. $\frac{4\sqrt{10x}}{45x}$ 9. -7 10. $\frac{20\sqrt{7} - 25}{87}$

Lesson 7-4 pp. 385–388
Check Skills You'll Need 1. $\frac{1}{16}$ 2. $\frac{1}{9x}$ 3. $\frac{1}{125x^5y^3}$ 4. $\frac{1}{2}$
5. $\frac{16b^{12}}{a^8}$ 6. $\frac{b^2}{16a^4}$

Quick Check 1a. 2 b. 2 c. 4 2a. $\frac{1}{\sqrt[3]{y^3}}$, $\sqrt[5]{z^2}$
b. $x^{\frac{8}{3}}$, $y^{\frac{1}{2}}$ c. If m is negative, $a^{\frac{m}{n}} = \frac{1}{(\sqrt[n]{a})^m}$, and if $a = 0$, then the denominator of the fraction would be zero. Since this cannot happen, $a \neq 0$.
3. about 0.270 revolutions per second, or about 16 revolutions per minute 4a. $\frac{1}{125}$ b. 8 c. 16
5. $\frac{1}{2x^8}$

Lesson 7-5 pp. 391–394
Check Skills You'll Need 1. -3, 2 2. -2, 7 3. $1, -\frac{3}{2}$ 4. $-\frac{1}{3}, 2$ 5. $-\frac{5}{2}, \frac{1}{2}$ 6. $-\frac{5}{3}, \frac{3}{2}$
Quick Check 1. 7 2. 6 3. about 25.1 watts; it is 4 times the power of a 10-cm cell. 4. 10 5. 5

Lesson 7-6 pp. 398–400, 404
Check Skills You'll Need 1. D: {0, 2, 4}, R: {-5, -3, -1} 2. D: {-1, 0, 1}, R: 0 3. D: all real numbers, R: all real numbers 4. D: all real numbers, R: all real numbers ≥ 0 5. 10 6. 28
Quick Check 1. $(f + g)(x) = 5x^2 + x + 1$, domain: all real numbers; $(f - g)(x) = 5x^2 - 9x - 1$, domain: all real numbers 2. $(f \cdot g)(x) = 12x^3 + 8x^2 - 17x + 5$, domain: all real numbers; $(\frac{f}{g})(x) = 3x + 5$, domain: all real numbers except $\frac{1}{2}$
3a. $(f \circ g)(x) = x^2 - 2$, $(f \circ g)(-5) = 23$ b. No; the order in which operations are performed changes between $(f \circ g)$ and $(g \circ f)$, which changes what each composition equals. 4a. Let $f(x) = 0.9x$ and $g(x) = 0.75x$. Then $(f \circ g)(x) = f(0.9x) = 0.75(0.9x)$. b. $(f \circ g)(x) = f(0.75x) = 0.9(0.75x)$. c. It makes no difference.
Checkpoint Quiz 1 1. $81x^4$ 2. $\frac{1}{4y^3}$ 3. 5 4. 5, $-\frac{29}{5}$ 5. $-\frac{3}{2}, -1$ 6. -2, 7 7. $\frac{15}{4}$ 8. 9, $\frac{7}{2}$ 10. 43

Lesson 7-7 pp. 406–409
Check Skills You'll Need
1. 2.

---

3. 4.
5. 6.
Quick Check 1a. The line $y = x$ is the perpendicular bisector of each segment connecting a point in s to the corresponding point in the inverse of s. The graph of the inverse of s is a reflection in the line $y = x$ of the graph of s. b. yes; no 2a. Yes; no; for every x-value except 3 in the domain of the inverse there are two y-values. b. $y = \frac{1}{3}x + \frac{10}{3}$; it is a function because for each value of x there is only one y-value.
3.
4a. D: all real numbers, R: all real numbers
b. $f^{-1}(x) = \frac{-x + 10}{3}$ c. D: all real numbers, R: all real numbers d. 3 e. 2 5. $v = 8\sqrt{d}$; ~44 ft/s 6. 777, -5802

Lesson 7-8 pp. 414–417
Check Skills You'll Need
1. 2.

3. 4.
5. 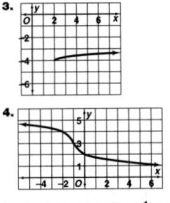 6.
Quick Check
1. 2.
3. 4.
5. about 60 m; it is about $\frac{1}{4}$ the height.
6. $y = 2\sqrt[3]{x - 3} + 3$; the graph is the graph of $y = 2\sqrt[3]{x}$ translated 3 units right and 3 units up.

Chapter 8
Check Your Readiness p. 428
1. 0.1, 1, 10, 100, 1000 2. $\frac{4}{5}$, 2, 1, $\frac{3}{4}$
3. 12, 0, 0, 0, 12
4a. $n = 3d$ b. 84 acorns c. The function would be $n = 9 + 3d$, and the graph would shift 9 units upward.

5. $y = x^2 - 4x$ **6.** $y = 3x^2 - 2x + 7$

7. $y = -x^2$ **8.** $y = 3x^2$

9.

10. $y = \sqrt{x + 12}$, $y \geq 0$; $y = \frac{x - 12}{6}$, $x \geq 0$

11.

Lesson 8-1   pp. 430–434

Check Skills You'll Need **1.** 8 **2.** 16 **3.** 2 **4.** 9 **5.** 1 **6.** $\frac{1}{4}$

Quick Check

1a.

2a. about 338 million **b.** The growth factor may change. **c.** $y = 281(1.014)^x$; about 346 million
3. $y = 0.25(4)^x$

4a. exponential decay **b.** exponential growth
c. exponential decay

5a. $y = 0$

b. $y = 0$

6. about $3900

Lesson 8-2   pp. 439–442, 445

Check Skills You'll Need **1.** $y = |x + 2| + 1$
2. $y = -|x| - 2$ **3.** $y = (x - 1)^2 - 2$
4. $y = -(x + 1)^2 + 3$ **5.** $y = \frac{5}{x}$ **6.** $y = x$
7. $y = x^5$ **8.** \$33

Quick Check

1a.

b.

2a.

b.

c.

3. $y = 90\left(\frac{1}{3}\right)^{\frac{x}{30}}$; about 71 mg **4a.** 54.5982
b. 0.0498 **c.** 1.6487 **5.** \$1479.00

Checkpoint Quiz 1 **1.** exponential growth; 45% increase **2.** exponential decay; 1% decrease
3. exponential growth; 70% increase
4. exponential decay; 20% decrease

5.

6.

Answers to Instant Check System   **961**

7.

8.

9. Answers may vary. Sample: The population of Smallville was 1200 in 1990. It was growing at a rate of 1% per year. Find the population in 2010.
10. $y = 100\left(\frac{1}{2}\right)^{\frac{t}{30}x}$; about 9.9 mg

Lesson 8-3   pp. 446–449

Check Skills You'll Need **1.** 2 **2.** 16 **3.** 4 **4.** 2

5.

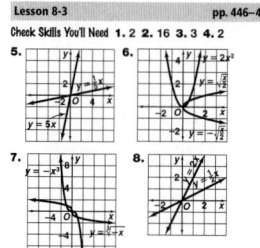

6.

7.

8.

Quick Check **1.** The earthquake in California released about 1265 times as much energy as the earthquake in Alabama. **2a.** $\log_3 729 = 6$
b. $3 = \log_2\left(\frac{1}{8}\right)$ **c.** $0 = \log_{10} 1$ **3a.** $-\frac{5}{6}$ **b.** $\frac{3}{2}$ **c.** 2
4. 3.2×10^{-9}

5.

6.

Lesson 8-4   pp. 454–456

Check Skills You'll Need **1.** 5 **2.** -1 **3.** $\frac{2}{3}$ **4.** 24 **5.** 2187
6. $\frac{1}{27}$ **7.** 36

Quick Check **1a.** Product Property **b.** Power Property, Quotient Property **2a.** $\log 2$ **b.** No; they do not have the same base. **3a.** $\log_2 7 + \log_2 b$
b. $2 \log y - 2 \log 3$ **c.** $3 \log_7 a + 4 \log_7 b$
4. about 6 decibels

Lesson 8-5   pp. 461–464, 468

Check Skills You'll Need **1.** 1 **2.** 2 **3.** $\frac{4}{3}$ **4.** $\frac{1}{25}$

Quick Check **1a.** 1.2619 **b.** 0.8496 **c.** 0.2009
2. 0.4634 **3.** 0.4634 **4.** 2068 **5a.** 3.7227, $\log_5 2301$
b. Sample: Use a calculator to raise 2 to the 2.465 power. **6.** 3.45 **7.** 200

Checkpoint Quiz 1

1.

2.

3. $3 \log s - 5 \log r$ **4.** $2 \log_6 3 + 2 \log_6 x + 2 \log_6 y$
5. $\log_6 4 + \frac{1}{2}\log_6 x$ **6.** 3 **7.** 20 **8.** 1000
9. $\log 2 \approx 0.3010$, $\log_3 2 \approx 0.6309$, $\log_3 3 \approx$ 1.5850, $2^3 = 8$, $3^2 = 9$ **10.** Rewrite $\log_2 10$ as $\frac{\log 10}{\log 2}$ and evaluate it to get ≈ 3.322. Then set $3.322 = \log_3 x$. Rewrite to get $3.322 = \frac{\log x}{\log 3}$ and solve. Convert $\log x = 1.585$ to $10^{1.585} = x$ or $x \approx 38.46$. So $\log_2 10 \approx \log_3 38.46$.

Lesson 8-6   pp. 470–472

Check Skills You'll Need **1.** 148.413 **2.** 40.171 **3.** 0.135
4. 0.368 **5.** 11.417 **6.** 81 **7.** $\frac{1}{2}$ **8.** 65,536

Quick Check **1a.** $\ln 8$ **b.** $\ln x^3 y$ **c.** $\ln \sqrt[4]{3x}$
2a. ≈ 5.4 km/s; no **b.** One could increase its mass ratio or its exhaust velocity. **3a.** 1.105
b. 439,605,247.8 **c.** 488,262.4 **4a.** 2.401 **b.** 1.605
5. 6.5%

Chapter 9

Check Your Readiness   p. 486

1. $\frac{7}{27}$ **2.** $\frac{1}{3}$ **3.** $\frac{5}{4}$ **4.** $\frac{22}{27}$ **5.** $\frac{22}{27}$ **6.** $\frac{12}{27}$ **7.** $\frac{1}{3}$; -8 **8.** $-\frac{2}{3}$; $\frac{1}{2}$
9. $-\frac{19}{3}$; 10 **10.** $-\frac{19}{7}$; $\frac{48}{5}$ **11.** $(x + 3)(x - 2)$
12. $(4x + 5)(x + 3)$ **13.** $(3x - 5)(3x + 5)$
14. $(x - 6)^2$ **15.** $(3x + 4)(x + 2)$ **16.** $(x - 3)(x - 2)$
17. 1, -8 **18.** -6, -8 **19.** 4, 2 **20.** 0, $-\frac{2}{3}$ **21.** 8, $\frac{1}{2}$
22. 15, -2

Lesson 9-1   pp. 488–490

Check Skills You'll Need **1.** 10 **2.** 15 **3.** 1.2

Quick Check **1.** $y = \frac{0.42}{x}$ **2a.** inverse; $y = \frac{0.72}{x}$
b. neither **c.** direct; $y = 15x$
3a. about 5,000,000 min, or about 10 yr
b. about 27 beats per min

962   Answers to Instant Check System

---

4. A varies jointly with the height and the sum of the bases. **5.** $V = \frac{\sqrt{2}}{6} e^3$

Lesson 9-2   pp. 495–498

Check Skills You'll Need **1.** 2 units up **2.** 2 units left
3. 3 units down **4.** 3 units right **5.** 4 units left and 5 units down **6.** 10 units right and 7 units up

Quick Check

1.

2. The graph of $y = \frac{2}{x}$ is a stretch of $y = \frac{1}{x}$ by the factor 2. The graph of $y = -\frac{2}{x}$ is the reflection of $y = \frac{2}{x}$ in the x-axis. The graph of $y = \frac{0.5}{x}$ is a shrink of $y = \frac{1}{x}$ by the factor 0.5. The graph of $y = -\frac{0.5}{x}$ is the reflection of $y = \frac{0.5}{x}$ in the x-axis.
3a. 2.28 ft, 1.81 ft, 1.52 ft **b.** As the pipe becomes very short, the pitch becomes very high (great frequency). As the pipe becomes very long, the pitch becomes low (frequency near 0).

4. $x = -7$ and $y = -3$

5a. $y = -\frac{1}{x + 4} + 5$ **b.**

Lesson 9-3   pp. 501–505, 508

Check Skills You'll Need **1.** $(x + 3)(x + 2)$
2. $(x - 4)(x - 2)$ **3.** $(x - 3)(x - 9)$
4. $(2x - 7)(x + 4)$ **5.** $(2x - 5)(x - 3)$
6. $(2x - 3)(x - 8)$ **7.** 3, -4 **8.** -4, 7 **9.** 3, 6

Quick Check **1a.** -4, 4 **b.** none **c.** -4, 2
2a. Since 1 and -3 are the zeroes of the denominator and neither is a zero of the numerator, $x = 1$ and $x = -3$ are vertical asymptotes. **b.** The graph of this function is the

---

same as the graph of $y = \frac{1}{x + 3}$, except that it has a hole at $x = 2$. The vertical asymptote is $x = -3$.
c. The graph of this function is the same as the graph of $y = x - 1$, except that it has a hole at $x = -1$. **3a.** $y = -2$ **b.** $y = 2$

4.

5a. Answers may vary. Sample: Graph $y = 8$ and use the Intersection feature to find that the graphs intersect at $x = 16,103.2$. So the number of discs produced must be greater than 16,103.
b. $x = 100$; $y = 0.25$ **c.** Answers may vary. Sample: The vertical asymptote means that if you produce 100 or fewer discs you won't sell any, since the first 100 are samples. The horizontal asymptote means that the average cost will never go below \$.25, since that is how much each disc costs to produce.

Checkpoint Quiz 1 **1.** $z = 5xy$ **2.** $z = \frac{20x}{y}$ **3.** $z = \frac{180}{y}$
4. Answers may vary. Sample: Both have vertical asymptote $x = 0$ and horizontal asymptote $y = 0$. $y = \frac{4}{x}$ is closer to the axes. **5.** Answers may vary. Sample: $y_2 = \frac{1}{x} + 5$ is a vertical translation of $y_1 = \frac{1}{x}$ up 5 units. **6.** Answers may vary. Sample: $y_2 = \frac{1}{x - 1} + 2$ has vertical asymptote of $x = 1$ and horizontal asymptote $y = 2$. $y_2 = \frac{1}{x + 1} - 2$ has vertical asymptote $x = -1$ and horizontal asymptote $y = -2$.

7.

8.

9.

10.

Lesson 9-4   pp. 509–511

Check Skills You'll Need **1.** $(2x - 1)(x - 1)$
2. $(2x + 3)(2x - 3)$ **3.** $(5x + 1)(x + 1)$

Answers to Instant Check System   **963**

---

4. $10(x + 1)(x - 1)$ **5.** $\frac{5}{16}$ **6.** $\frac{1}{3}$ **7.** $\frac{1}{3}$ **8.** $\frac{6}{35}$ **9.** $\frac{5}{32}$
10. $\frac{3}{2}$ **11.** $\frac{3}{4}$ **12.** $\frac{2}{3}$

Quick Check **1a.** $-\frac{3}{x}$; $x \neq 0$, $y \neq 0$
b. $\frac{-3(x + 2)}{(x - 2)(x - 4)}$; $x \neq 2$ or 4 **c.** $\frac{2x + 1}{x - 3}$; $x \neq 2$ or 3
2a. $\frac{2r}{5}$ **b.** As m gets larger, the ratio gets larger.
3. $\frac{a - 2}{a(a - 1)}$; $a \neq 0$, 1, -1, or -2 **4.** $\frac{3(a + 5)(a - 3)}{(a + 1)(a + 4)}$; $a \neq -1$, -4, or 4

Lesson 9-5   pp. 514–517, 520

Check Skills You'll Need **1.** 21 **2.** 30 **3.** 187 **4.** 210
5. $\frac{17}{36}$ **6.** $\frac{19}{72}$ **7.** $\frac{11}{56}$ **8.** $\frac{137}{180}$

Quick Check **1.** 4 cm **2a.** $6(x - 5)(x + 5)(x + 2)$
b. $10(x + 2)(x - 2)(x + 1)$ **3.** $\frac{3x^2 - 18x + 4}{4(x - 6)(x + 2)}$
4a. $\frac{-3x^2 - 21x - 4}{6(x + 3)}$ **b.** $\frac{-x^2 + 5x + 2}{3(x - 1)(x - 2)(x + 2)}$ **5a.** $\frac{1}{xy}$
b. $\frac{6y}{2y - 1}$ **c.** $\frac{x^3 - 4x^2 + x + 2}{x^3 + 4x}$

Checkpoint Quiz 1 **1.** $\frac{3(x - 8)}{25(x - 4)}$ **2.** $\frac{2}{3}$ **3.** $\frac{4}{y}$ **4.** $\frac{y(y - 5)}{2(y + 4)}$
5. $\frac{4(6y^2 + x)}{9x^3y^3}$ **6.** $\frac{41}{15(y + 5)}$ **7.** $\frac{5xy - 12}{2y(y + 2)}$
8. $\frac{3x^2 - x^2 - 11x}{x^2 - 2}$ **9.** $\frac{2y}{10}$ **10.** $\frac{y(3x + 5)}{x(4y + 5)}$

Lesson 9-6   pp. 522–524

Check Skills You'll Need **1.** $15t^2$ **2.** 8 **3.** $3h^3$
4. $(y + 2)(y - 1)$ **5.** $z(2z + 1)$ **6.** $(k + 2)(k - 2)$

Quick Check **1a.** no solution **b.** -3, 2 **2.** 2, -2 **3.** 10 mi/h downhill, 6 mi/h uphill **4a.** Maria: 6.75 h, Paco: 13.5 h **b.** Adrian: 4.5 h, Phillip: 9 h

Lesson 9-7   pp. 531–534

Check Skills You'll Need **1.** $\frac{7}{30}$ **2.** $\frac{26}{45}$ **3.** $\frac{1}{4}$ **4.** 72

Quick Check **1.** Independent; the number of marbles is the same after the marble is replaced.
2a. $\frac{2}{25}$ or 4%; $\frac{1}{40}$ or 2.5% **b.** $\frac{1}{1000}$ or 0.1% **3a.** Not mutually exclusive since 2 is both even and prime. **b.** Mutually exclusive since no number is both even and less than 2. **4a.** about 0.26 or about 26% **b.** about 0.47 or about 47% **c.** about 0.79 or about 79% **5a.** $\frac{5}{6}$ **b.** $\frac{2}{3}$

Chapter 10

Check Your Readiness   p. 544

1. quadratic; $-x^2$, 6x, 1 **2.** linear; none, $-12x$, -18 **3.** linear; none, x, $-\frac{13}{2}$ **4.** quadratic; $-8x^2$, 28x, none **5.** quadratic; $-2x^2$, $-3x$, 6 **6.** linear; none, $-x$, -10

7.

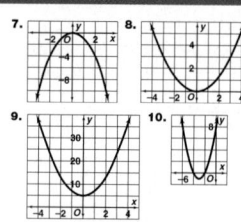

8.

9.

10.

11. 16 **12.** $\frac{25}{4}$ **13.** 49

14. $y = (x + 3)^2 - 2$

15. $y = 2(x - 1)^2 + 8$

16. $y = -3\left(x - \frac{1}{6}\right)^2 + \frac{1}{12}$

17. $\frac{1}{2}$, $i\sqrt{5}$, $-i\sqrt{5}$ **18.** $\frac{1}{2}$, 1 **19.**

20.

21.

964   Answers to Instant Check System

T908

Lesson 10-1 pp. 547–550

Check Skills You'll Need 1. -2, 6 2. -3, -1.5 3. -4, 3 4. ±2, -4 5. 3, 9 6. ±0.5, 1

Quick Check

1a. The graphs are the same.

b. Rewrite $x^2 + y^2 = 25$ as $y^2 = 25 - x^2$. Then take the square root of both sides, which gives you $y = \pm\sqrt{25 - x^2}$. c. When x = 6, $25 - x^2 = -11$. $\sqrt{-11}$ is not a real number.

2a. 4 units; 3 units; an ellipse is oblong instead of round. It has 2 axes of symmetry rather than infinitely many. b. (1, -2.9), (-1, 2.9), (-1, -2.9)

c. It is an ellipse with center (0, 0). The x-intercepts are 3 and -3 and the y-intercepts are $3\sqrt{2}$ and $-3\sqrt{2}$.

3a. No; there are vertical lines that intersect the graph in more than one point. b. Answers may vary. Sample: Solving $x^2 - y^2 = 9$ for y gives $y = \pm\sqrt{x^2 - 9}$. For $-3 < x < 3$, the value of $x^2 - 9$ is negative and $\sqrt{x^2 - 9}$ is not a real number. c. $y = x$ and $y = -x$; asymptotes

4. center: (0, 0); no x-intercepts, y-intercepts: -4, 4; domain: all real numbers, range: all y such that $y \geq 4$ or $y \leq -4$ 5a. Answers may vary. Sample: All equations have an x^2-term, a y^2-term, and no other terms on the left side. There is a positive constant term and nothing else on the right side.

b. Answers may vary. Sample: The related domains and ranges are all different. The absolute values of the coefficients of x^2 and y^2 are equal for $x^2 - y^2 = 1$, but the signs of the coefficients are different. The absolute values of the coefficients of x^2 and y^2 are equal for $x^2 + y^2 = 16$, and the signs are the same. The absolute values of the coefficients of x^2 and y^2 are different for $9x^2 + 25y^2 = 225$, but the signs are the same.

Lesson 10-2 pp. 555–558

Check Skills You'll Need 1. 8 2. 4 3. 3 4. $\frac{1}{8}$ 5. $2\sqrt{2}$ 6. $\sqrt{65}$ 7. $\sqrt{73}$

Quick Check 1. $x = \frac{1}{8}y^2$ 2. $x = \frac{1}{2}y^2$

3. $y = \frac{1}{33}x^2$ 4. (0, 3), $y = -3$

5. (-3, -1), (-3, -1.75), $y = -\frac{1}{4}$,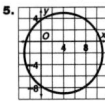

Lesson 10-3 pp. 561–564, 566

Check Skills You'll Need 1. 4 2. 7 3. $2\sqrt{5}$ 4. $4\sqrt{3}$ 5. $6\sqrt{2}$ 6. 1 7. 4 8. 9

Quick Check 1. $(x - 5)^2 + (y + 2)^2 = 64$

2a. $(x + 5)^2 + (y + 3)^2 = 1$

b. $(x - 2)^2 + (y - 3)^2 = 9$

3. $x^2 + (y + 4)^2 = 14$ 4. (-8, -3), 11

5.

Checkpoint Quiz 1 1. (0, 0), $(0, \frac{1}{12})$, $y = -\frac{1}{12}$;

2. (0, -2), $(\frac{1}{16}, -2)$, $x = -\frac{1}{16}$;

3. (3, -1), $(3, -\frac{3}{4})$, $y = -\frac{5}{4}$;

4. $(x + 6)^2 + (y - 3)^2 = 64$ 5. 4 units left and 6 units up

---

Lesson 10-4 pp. 568–570

Check Skills You'll Need 1. ±4 2. ±4$\sqrt{3}$ 3. ±6 4. 34 5. -16 6. 7

Quick Check 1. $\frac{x^2}{9} + \frac{y^2}{36} = 1$ 2. $\frac{x^2}{36} + \frac{y^2}{225} = 1$

3. $(2\sqrt{2}, 0), (-2\sqrt{2}, 0)$;

4. $\frac{x^2}{84} + \frac{y^2}{81} = 1$

Lesson 10-5 pp. 574–577, 580

Check Skills You'll Need 1. $y = -\frac{5}{2}x$ 2. $y = \frac{1}{3}x$

3. $y = \pm2\sqrt{x^2 - 4}$ 4. $y = \pm\frac{3}{2}\sqrt{x^2 + 25}$

5. $y = \pm\frac{3}{2}\sqrt{x^2 - 36}$

Quick Check 1.

2. $(\sqrt{34}, 0), (-\sqrt{34}, 0)$;

3. $\frac{x^2}{4.770 \times 10^{13}} - \frac{y^2}{3.668 \times 10^{12}} = 1$

Checkpoint Quiz 1 1. $\frac{x^2}{25} + \frac{y^2}{16} = 1$ 2. $\frac{x^2}{25} + \frac{y^2}{29} = 1$

3. $\frac{x^2}{100} + \frac{y^2}{149} = 1$ 4. $(\sqrt{65}, 0), (-\sqrt{65}, 0)$

5. $(0, 2\sqrt{34}), (0, -2\sqrt{34})$

6. $(\sqrt{85}, 0), (-\sqrt{85}, 0)$

7. $(0, \sqrt{89}), (0, -\sqrt{89})$

8. $\frac{x^2}{121} - \frac{y^2}{104} = 1$ 9. $\frac{x^2}{16} - \frac{y^2}{9} = 1$

10. $\frac{y^2}{64} - \frac{x^2}{12.25} = 1$

Lesson 10-6 pp. 582–585

Check Skills You'll Need 1. $y = x^2$; 4 units up 2. $y = x^2$; 3 units right and 2 units down 3. $y = x^2$; 1 unit up 4. $y = x^2$; 5 units left, 6 units up

5. $y = (x - 3)^2 - 8$ 6. $y = (x + 5)^2 - 32$

7. $y = 2(x + 2)^2 - 3$ 8. $y = 4(x - \frac{3}{2})^2 - 6$

Quick Check 1. $\frac{(x - 1)^2}{25} + \frac{(y + 4)^2}{1} = 1$

2. $\frac{(y - 3)^2}{16} - \frac{(x - 2)^2}{33} = 1$ 3. $\frac{(x - 100)^2}{784} - \frac{y^2}{9216} = 1$

4. circle with center (6, -2) and radius $4\sqrt{3}$;

Chapter 11

Check Your Readiness pp. 598

1. 9, 11, 13, 15 2. 1, 6, 11, 16 3. 0.9, 1.1, 1.3, 1.5
4. -2, -7, -12, -17 5. $3\frac{1}{3}, 7\frac{1}{3}, 11\frac{1}{3}, 15\frac{1}{3}$
6. -12, -15, -18, -21 7.

---

8. 9.
10. 11. 12.

13. 4 14. -4 15. 0.4 16. 50 17. $5x^2$
18. $-0.3y^4$ 19. $|x^3y^5|$ 20. $11y^{12}$ 21. $\frac{4}{3}$ 22. $\frac{4}{3}$
23. $\frac{5}{8}$ 24. $\frac{5}{16}$

Lesson 11-1 pp. 600–602

Check Skills You'll Need 1. 13, 15; add 2. 2. -14, -16; subtract 2. 3. 3125, 15,625; multiply by 5. 4. 20, 15; subtract 5. 5. 8, 4; divide by 2. 6. 20, 23; add 3. 7. 128, 256; multiply by 2. 8. -19, -23; subtract 4.

Quick Check 1a. Add 7; 55, 62, 69. b. Divide by 3; 3, 1, $\frac{1}{3}$. 2a. 3.2 ft b. 10th bounce 3. 22, 30
4a. 1, 4, 9, 16, 25, 36; 400 b. $a_n = n^2$ c. No; a_1 is not given.

Lesson 11-2 pp. 606–607

Check Skills You'll Need 1. Subtract 2. 2. Add 17.
3. Add $\frac{2}{3}$. 4. Subtract $\frac{1}{4}$.

Quick Check 1a. no b. yes; -3 2a. The first term in the sequence, 1100, was the amount of money with no participants, so there is one more term than the number of participants. b. 149
3a. 40.5 b. $\frac{a_1 + a_7}{2}$

Lesson 11-3 pp. 612–614, 617

Check Skills You'll Need 1. 16 2. 21 3. 1000 4. $\frac{100}{3}$

Quick Check 1a. 5, 15, 45, 135, 405, 1215, 3645, 10,935, 32,805, 98,415; the tenth term is the ninth term times 3. b. Geometric; the common ratio is -4. c. Arithmetic; the common difference is +12. 2a. 4,261,625,379 b. -34 3a. 40 or -40 b. 7.5 or -7.5 c. 378 or -378

Checkpoint Quiz 1 1. arithmetic; 15 2. geometric; 3 3. arithmetic; -3 4. geometric; 0.5 5. geometric; -0.5 6. arithmetic; -2 7. 6.25 8. 82 9. 1 10. To find the arithmetic mean, add the terms and divide by 2. To find the geometric mean, multiply the terms and find the square root of the product.

Lesson 11-4 pp. 619–621

Check Skills You'll Need 1. 25 2. -42 3. $a_n = 2 + 2n$
4. $a_n = -2 + 3n$ 5. $a_n = -11 - 6n$
6. $a_n = 9 - 9n$

Quick Check 1a. 0.3 + 0.6 + 0.9 + 1.2 + 1.5 + 1.8 + 2.1 + 2.4 + 2.7 + 3.0; 16.5
b. 100 + 125 + 150 + 175 + 200 + 225; 975
2a. 31 b. 252 3a. $\sum_{n=1}^{6} n$ b. $\sum_{n=1}^{9} (5n - 2)$
4a. 10, -2, 7; 25 b. 4, $\frac{3}{2}$, 3; 9 c. 4, 4, 25; 54

Lesson 11-5 pp. 626–628, 631

Check Skills You'll Need 1. $193\frac{3}{4}$ 2. 120 3. -22 4. -75 5. $\frac{12}{5}$ 6. $\frac{4}{3}$ 7. $\frac{2}{3}$ 8. $\frac{99}{4}$

Quick Check 1a. $a_1 = -45, r = -3, n = 5$; -2745 b. $a_1 = \frac{1}{3}, r = \frac{1}{3}, n = 4$; $\frac{40}{81}$ 2a. To find the amount 20% larger than a given amount, multiply by 1.2, which is equivalent to 120%. b. The common ratio becomes 1.25. c. Yes; they will have $1407.35. 3a. converges b. diverges 4. a. 2 b. 2

Checkpoint Quiz 1 1. arithmetic; 900 2. geometric; 29,524 3. geometric; -7.9375 4. arithmetic; 1200 5. geometric; 239.0625 6. arithmetic; 6150 7. $\frac{15}{14}$ 8. 4 9. Answers may vary. Sample: $\frac{1}{2} + \frac{1}{4} + \frac{1}{8}$ 10. No; the common difference causes arithmetic series to diverge.

Lesson 11-6 pp. 635–637

Check Skills You'll Need 1. 4 ft² 2. 2.75 m² 3. 0.62 cm²
4. $34\frac{7}{16}$ in.²

Quick Check 1a. 1545; it is much larger. b. 1370; the mean is most accurate; it is between the other measures known to be smaller and larger than the actual value.
2a.

---

b. The left side values give the height of the circumscribed rectangles. c. 0.5(5) + 0.5(4.75) + 0.5(4) + 0.5(2.75) = 8.25 units²; it is greater than Example 2. 3a. $4\frac{1}{3}$ b. $8\frac{5}{6}$ c. $5\frac{1}{4}$

Chapter 12

Check Your Readiness p. 646

1. 120 2. 720 3. 144 4. 1 5. 6 6. 35 7. $a^5 + 5a^4b + 10a^3b^2 + 10a^2b^3 + 5ab^4 + b^5$ 8. $j^3 + 9j^2k + 27jk^2 + 27k^3$ 9. $m^2 + 1.4m + 0.49$ 10. $0.000064 + 0.00192t + 0.024t^2 + 0.16t^3 + 0.64t^4 + 1.2t^5 + t^6$ 11. ±0.1 12. ±0.071 13. ±0.063 14. ±0.051 15. ±0.048 16. ±0.036 17. 0.08 18. 0.125 19. 0.085 20. 0.865 21. 0.06

Lesson 12-1 pp. 648–651

Check Skills You'll Need 1. yes 2. no 3. no 4. $\frac{1}{18}$
5. $\frac{1}{4}$ 6. 1

Quick Check

1.

Type	Number
Acute	13
Right	7
Obtuse	5
Total	25

2. 0.857

3. Answers may vary. Sample:

Rolling One Number Cube

Numbers	1	2	3	4	5	6
Frequency	1	1	1	1	1	1
Probability	$\frac{1}{6}$	$\frac{1}{6}$	$\frac{1}{6}$	$\frac{1}{6}$	$\frac{1}{6}$	$\frac{1}{6}$

4a. The Plant Color Distribution would be most useful for avoiding white plants because it shows the total probability of growing green plants, which is the desired outcome.
b.

Genotype			
Event	GG	Gw	ww
Frequency	1	2	1
Probability	$\frac{1}{4}$	$\frac{1}{2}$	$\frac{1}{4}$

Plant Color		
Event	Green	White
Frequency	3	1
Probability	$\frac{3}{4}$	$\frac{1}{4}$

Lesson 12-2 pp. 654–656

Check Skills You'll Need 1. $\frac{1}{6}$ 2. $\frac{1}{6}$ 3. $\frac{3}{16}$ 4. $\frac{9}{16}$
5. $\frac{1}{16}$ 6. $\frac{9}{16}$

Quick Check 1. $\frac{7}{14}$ or $\frac{1}{2}$ 2. about 0.021 or 2.1% 3. 0.9 4. 0.33

Lesson 12-3 pp. 660–664, 667

Check Skills You'll Need
1. 0.2 0.3 0.6 0.7 0.8 0.9 1.2; 0.7 2. 11 15 17 18 21 21; 18 3. 2.6 3.9 7.8 9.1 10.4 11.7 15.6; 9.1

4. 76 80 82 84 86 86 89; 84

Quick Check 1. ≈ 3.6, 3.7, 2.8 2. ≈ 73.42; 73.5; 61, 70, 77, 83, 85
3. 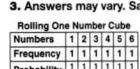 25 30 35 40 45 50
4. 80 82 84 86 88 90 $Q_1 = 84, Q_2 = 85, Q_3 = 86$

5a. 21 b. 65 c. 71 6a. Yes; it is unlikely that the water temperature of a lake would change by 25°F. b. No; 98 would represent the busiest night of the week and it may relate to a weekly event.

Checkpoint Quiz 1
1.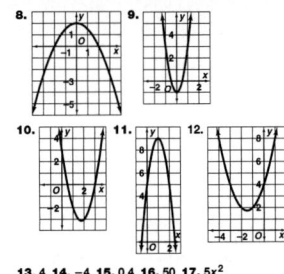

2. 0.385 3. No; when x = 1, $P(x) = -\frac{1}{3}$, and probability is never negative. 4. $\frac{12}{27}$ 5. $\frac{5}{6}$ 6. $\frac{23}{43}$
7. $\frac{48}{66}$ 8. 5.69, 5, 4 9. 3.82, 2.85, no mode

Lesson 12-4 pp. 668–672

Check Skills You'll Need 1. 4.9 2. 2.5 3. 10.5 4. 9 5. 7 6. 8.03

Quick Check 1a. range: 14, interquartile range: 6 b. Yes; answers may vary.

1	2	3	4	5	6	7	8	9	10
1	1	1	1	10	10	10	10	10	10

c. Yes; sample:

1	2	3	4	5	6	7	8	9	10
3	3	3	5	6	6	8	8	8	8

2. 80, ≈ 18.7 3. 8, about 4.0 4a. 1 b. No; three standard deviations from the mean is 46.3, which is less than 48. 5. 100

Lesson 12-5 pp. 677–680

Check Skills You'll Need 1. $\frac{1}{2}$ 2. $-\frac{1}{3}$ 3. $\frac{1}{6}$ 4. $-\frac{1}{11}$ 5. $\frac{\sqrt{2}}{10}$
6. $-\frac{1}{9}$

Quick Check 1. 52% 2a. Yes; the sample is biased because it overrepresents students who live in a warm climate. b. Answers may vary. Sample: Every 10 years, the United States conducts a census of the population to find exactly how many people live in the country.

3. B; a larger sample has less variation, which corresponds to a smaller standard deviation.
4a. 100 b. 625 c. 2500 5. 71%, ±9%, 62% to 80%

Lesson 12-6   pp. 685–688, 691

Check Skills You'll Need 1. 6 2. 1 3. 10 4. $x^3 + 6x^2 + 12x + 8$ 5. $w^4 - 4w^3y + 6w^2y^2 - 4wy^3 + y^4$ 6. $m^3 + 3m^2n + 3mn^2 + n^3$ 7. $t^4 + 12t^3s + 54t^2s^2 + 108ts^3 + 81s^4$ 8. $a^5 + 10a^4b + 40a^3b^2 + 80a^2b^3 + 80ab^4 + 32b^5$ 9. $p^6 + 6p^5q + 15p^4q^2 + 20p^3q^3 + 15p^2q^4 + 6pq^5 + q^6$

Quick Check 2a. P (one prize) $= 3(0.4)^1(0.6)^2 = 0.432$; P(no prize) $= 1(0.6)^3 = 0.216$ b. 1
3a. 0.2637 b. 0.2335 4. 0.9933

Checkpoint Quiz 1 1. 33.83, 20, 6.20 2. 11, 5, 1.63 3. 2.375, 4, 1.41 4. 228 5a. This survey may be biased because it overrepresents people who shop for CDs online and entirely misses those who do not have internet access. b. Answers may vary. Sample: Survey a random selection of students in homerooms for each grade level.
6a. $0.3441 \approx 34.4\%$ b. ±3.8% c. 30.6% to 38.2% 7. 25 8. 0.343 9. 0.4096 10. 0.0768

Lesson 12-7   pp. 692–694

Check Skills You'll Need 1. 8, 10, 14, 16 2. 14.7, 15.7, 17.7, 18.7 3. 4, 5.5, 8.5, 10 4. 18.6, 20.3, 23.7, 25.4 5. 15.7, 16.6, 18.4, 19.3 6. 30.7, 31.9, 34.3, 35.5

Quick Check 1a. 71% b. 88%
2.

3a. 68 responses b. 13 or 14 responses 4a. 47 or 48 students b. 76 is about 1 SD above the mean. About 13.5% + 2.5% should receive grades above 76. 16% of 140 is about 22.

Chapter 13

Check Your Readiness   p. 708

1. vertical asymptote $x = 3$ 2. hole at $x = 1$
3. vertical asymptotes $x = -\frac{1}{2}$ and $x = 4$ 4. $\frac{2b}{8}$
5. $\frac{55}{18}$ 6. $\frac{3}{2(c+d)}$ 7. $\frac{c}{8}$ 8. $\frac{c+4}{9}$ 9. $\frac{18}{x}$ 10. $\frac{15}{7}$ 11. 6
12. $(x - 1)^2 + (y + 4)^2 = 16$;

13. $\frac{(x-2)^2}{9} + \frac{(y-5)^2}{4} = 1$;

14. $y = \frac{1}{32}x^2 - 3$;

15. $\frac{(y-1)^2}{9} - \frac{(x-6)^2}{16} = 1$;

16. 4, 1; $a_n = 19 - 3n$, explicit; $a_1 = 16$, $a_n = a_{n-1} - 3$, recursive 17. –216, –343; $a_n = -n^3$, explicit 18. $\frac{1}{3}$, $\frac{1}{27}$; $a_n = 9\left(\frac{1}{3}\right)^{n-1}$, explicit; $a_1 = 9$, $a_n = \frac{1}{3} \cdot a_{n-1}$, recursive

Lesson 13-1   pp. 710–713

Check Skills You'll Need 1. yes 2. yes 3. no 4. yes 5. no 6. no 7. yes 8. yes

Quick Check 1a. from –3 to 1 or 0 to 4; 4 b. from –4 to –1 or 0 to 3; 3 2a. not periodic b. periodic; 4 3a. 1.5 b. 1.5
4.

1 unit on the x-axis is 0.001 s.

Lesson 13-2   pp. 718–722

Check Skills You'll Need
1. 2. 3.
4. 5. 6.

Quick Check 1. 90°; 180°; 270°
2a. b.
c.

3a. 558° b. No; 40° is coterminal with 400° and 760°. c. Answers may vary. Sample: The difference between measures of two coterminal angles is a multiple of 360°.
4a. b.

$\frac{\sqrt{2}}{2} \approx 0.707$, $\frac{\sqrt{2}}{2} \approx 0.707$ $\frac{\sqrt{3}}{2} \approx 0.87$, 0.5
c.

-0.5, $\frac{\sqrt{3}}{2} \approx 0.87$
5a. –0.5, –0.87; the values are equal and are the rounded decimal values of $-\frac{1}{2}$ and $-\frac{\sqrt{3}}{2}$.
b. $-\frac{\sqrt{2}}{2}$, $\frac{\sqrt{2}}{2}$; ≈-0.707, ≈ 0.707 c. $-\frac{\sqrt{3}}{2}$, $\frac{1}{2}$

Lesson 13-3   pp. 726–729, 733

Check Skills You'll Need 1. 25.1 in. 2. 219.9 m 3. 50.3 mi 4. 10.7 ft 5. 31.4 mm 6. 19.8 cm

Quick Check 1a. ≈1.48 radians b. ≈143.24°
2a. 90° b. $\frac{5\pi}{4}$ radians c. ≈114.59° d. $\frac{5\pi}{6}$ radians

3a. 0.71, 0.71; these values are the rounded decimal equivalent of $\frac{\sqrt{2}}{2}$. b. π radians = 180°, so $\frac{\pi}{4}$ radians becomes $\frac{180°}{4}$, which is 45°. 4. 6.3 in.
5a. ≈3.14 units b. ≈4.19 units c. ≈6.28 units d. ≈10.47 units

Checkpoint Quiz 1 1. 5, 1 2. 4, 2 3. $-\frac{\sqrt{2}}{2}$, $\frac{\sqrt{2}}{2}$
4. $-\frac{1}{2}$, $-\frac{\sqrt{3}}{2}$ 5. 0, –1 6. $\frac{1}{2}$, $\frac{\sqrt{3}}{2}$ 7. $-\pi$ radians
8. $\frac{5\pi}{6}$ radians 9. 180° 10. 240°

Lesson 13-4   pp. 734–738

Check Skills You'll Need 1. 2 2. all real numbers 3. 1 4. all real numbers between –1 and 1, inclusive

Quick Check 1a. yes; at 450° b. Yes; the y-values repeat at regular intervals. 2a. 1 360°, 2π radians c. domain: all real numbers, range: all real numbers between –1 and 1, inclusive 3a. 2π b. $\frac{2\pi}{3}$ 4a. 4 b. 3
5a. b. zero-min-zero-max-zero

c.

6a. b.

7. $y = \sin\frac{\pi}{320}\theta$, $y = \sin\frac{\pi}{288}\theta$

Lesson 13-5   pp. 743–745

Check Skills You'll Need 1. 1 2. 0 3. –1 4. 0

Quick Check 1. They are the same curve translated $\frac{\pi}{2}$ units horizontally.
2a.

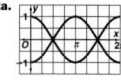

They are reflections of each other over the x-axis.

b. min-zero-max-zero-min
c.

3a. $y = 4 \cos \frac{1}{3}\theta$ b. $y = 2.5 \cos \frac{\pi}{8}\theta$ 4a. 1.2, 2.0, 4.3, 5.1 b. 2.2, 4.1 c. $0 \le \theta < 2.2$ and $4.1 < \theta \le 2\pi$; $2.2 < \theta < 4.1$

Lesson 13-6   pp. 749–751

Check Skills You'll Need 1. ≈0.87, 0.5; ≈1.73 2. 0.5, ≈0.87; ≈0.58 3. 1, 0; undefined 4. 0.5, ≈–0.87; ≈–0.58 5. 1, 0; undefined 6. 0, 1; 0

Quick Check 1a. 0.4, –0.4 b. The terminal side of $\frac{\pi}{2}$ lies on the line $x = 0$, which cannot intersect $x = 1$.
2a. b.

3a. 46.6 ft b. 8°

Lesson 13-7   pp. 756–760, 762

Check Skills You'll Need
1. 2.
vertical   horizontal
3. 4.
vertical   vertical
5. 6.
diagonal   diagonal

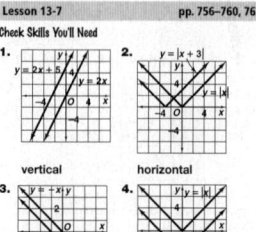

Quick Check 1a. 5; 5 units to the right b. –3; 3 units to the left
2a.

(b) is a phase shift.
3a. b.

4a. b.

5a. $y = \cos x + \frac{\pi}{2}$ b. $y = 2 \sin\left(x - \frac{\pi}{4}\right)$
6a. 86.5° b. day 100

Checkpoint Quiz 1
1.
2.
3.
4.
5.

6.
7.
8.
9.
10.

Lesson 13-8   pp. 763–766

Check Skills You'll Need 1. $\frac{13}{10}$ 2. $-\frac{8}{6}$ 3. 2π 4. $\frac{15}{4m}$ 5. $-\frac{1}{14}$

Quick Check 1a. $\frac{8}{15}$ b. ≈0.70 2a. 2 b. 1 c. 2 3a. –1.003 b. –2.403 c. undefined

4.

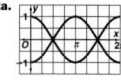

5. ≈1.4142 6. 6.9 ft; 8.5 ft; 68.8 ft

Chapter 14

Check Your Readiness   p. 776

1. $\pm\frac{5}{2}$ 2. $\pm\sqrt{23}$ 3. $\pm\frac{4\sqrt{15}}{3}$ 4. $\pm\frac{\sqrt{22}}{2}$ 5. $\pm\sqrt{30}$
6. ±2 7. Domain of f is $\{x \mid x \in R\}$, range of f is $\{y \mid y \in R\}$; $f^{-1}(x) = \frac{x-2}{5}$, domain of f^{-1} is $\{x \mid x \in R\}$, range of f^{-1} is $\{y \mid y \in R\}$. f^{-1} is a function. 8. Domain of f is $\{x \mid x \in R, x \ge -3\}$, $x \ge 0$ range of f is $\{y \mid y \in R, y \ge 0\}$; $f^{-1}(x) = x^2 - 3$, domain of f^{-1} is $\{x \mid x \in R, x \ge 0\}$, range of f^{-1} is $\{y \mid y \in R, y \ge -3\}$. f^{-1} is a function. 9. Domain of f is $\{x \mid x \in R, x \ge \frac{4}{3}\}$, range of f is $\{y \mid y \in R, y \ge 0\}$; $f^{-1}(x) = \frac{x^2+4}{3}$, $x \ge 0$, domain of f is $\{x \mid x \in R, x \ge 0\}$, range of f^{-1} is $\{y \mid y \in R, y \ge \frac{4}{3}\}$. f^{-1} is a function. 10. Domain of f is $\{x \mid x \in R, x \ne 0\}$, range of f is $\{y \mid y \in R, y \ne 0\}$; $f^{-1}(x) = \frac{5}{x}$, domain of f^{-1} is $\{x \mid x \in R, x \ne 0\}$, range of f^{-1} is $\{y \mid y \in R, y \ne 0\}$. f^{-1} is a function. 11. Domain of f is $\{x \mid x \in R, x \ne 1\}$, range of f is $\{y \mid y \in R, y \ne 0\}$; $f^{-1}(x) = \frac{10}{x} + 1$, domain of f^{-1} is $\{x \mid x \in R, x \ne 0\}$, range of f^{-1} is $\{y \mid y \in R, y \ne 1\}$. f^{-1} is a function. 12. Domain of f is $\{x \mid x \in R, x \ne 0\}$, range of f is $\{y \mid y \in R, y \ne -1\}$; $f^{-1}(x) = \frac{10}{x+1}$, domain of f^{-1} is $\{x \mid x \in R, x \ne -1\}$, range of f^{-1} is $\{y \mid y \in R, y \ne 0\}$. f^{-1} is a function.
13. –1.5 14. 0.002 15. ≈1.065 16. ≈18,257 17. $\approx 3 \times 10^{-5}$ 18. 5 19. 0.67, 0.74, 1.11 20. –0.26, –0.97, 3.73 21. 0.96, 0.28, 0.29 22. –0.87, 0.5, –0.58

Lesson 14-1   pp. 778–780

Check Skills You'll Need 1. Yes; $2x + 3x = (2 + 3)x$ by the Dist. Prop. and $(2 + 3)x = 5x$ by addition. 2. Yes; $-(4x - 10) = -4x + 10$ by the Dist. Prop., and $-4x + 10 = 10 - 4x$ by the Comm. Prop. 3. No; for $x = 0$, $\frac{4x}{x}$ is not defined, but $4x = 0$.
4. No; for $x = 1$, $\frac{x^2+1}{x-1}$ is not defined, but $x + 1 = 2$.

T910

Top Left Panel (page 973)

Quick Check 1. $1 + \cot^2 \theta = 1 + (\frac{\cos \theta}{\sin \theta})^2 =$
$1 + \frac{\cos^2 \theta}{\sin^2 \theta} = 1 + \frac{1 - \sin^2 \theta}{\sin^2 \theta} = 1 + \frac{1}{\sin^2 \theta} - \frac{\sin^2 \theta}{\sin^2 \theta} =$
$1 + \csc^2 \theta - 1 = \csc^2 \theta$ **2.** $\sec^2 \theta -$
$\sec^2 \theta \cos^2 \theta = (\frac{1}{\cos \theta})^2 - (\frac{1}{\cos \theta})^2 \cos^2 \theta =$
$\frac{1}{\cos^2 \theta} - \frac{1}{\cos^2 \theta} \cdot \cos^2 \theta = \frac{1}{\cos^2 \theta} - \frac{\cos^2 \theta}{\cos^2 \theta} =$
$\frac{1 - \cos^2 \theta}{\cos^2 \theta} = \frac{\sin^2 \theta}{\cos^2 \theta} = \tan^2 \theta$ **3.** $\csc \theta$

Lesson 14-2 pp. 783–786

Check Skills You'll Need 1. $f^{-1}(x) = x - 1$
2. $f^{-1}(x) = \frac{x + 3}{2}$ **3.** $f^{-1}(x) = \pm \sqrt{x - 4}$
4. 0.5 **5.** $\frac{\sqrt{2}}{2}$ **6.** $-\frac{\sqrt{2}}{2}$ **7.** 0 **8.** -1 **9.** $-\frac{\sqrt{3}}{2}$
Quick Check 1. none, $\frac{\pi}{2} + \pi n$, none
2a. $120° + n \cdot 360°$ and $240° + n \cdot 360°$
b. $150° + n \cdot 360°$ and $210° + n \cdot 360°$
c. $45° + n \cdot 360°$ and $315° + n \cdot 360°$
3a. 0.46 + 2πn and 2.69 + 2πn
b. -0.82 + 2πn and 3.96 + 2πn **4a.** 0.41 + 2πn
and 3.56 + 2πn **b.** -0.63 + 2πn and 2.51 + 2πn
5. $\frac{11\pi}{8}$ and $\frac{7\pi}{8}$ **6.** $\frac{\pi}{2}$ and $\frac{3\pi}{2}$ **7a.** $\frac{1}{2}$; 3 s **b.** At 2 s;
the toy will reach a maximum at 4 in. and then
come back down, again hitting 2 in. at 2 s.
c. Let $y_1 = -4 \cos \frac{2\pi}{3} t$ and let $y_2 = 2$. Graph.
Trace and calculate the intersection.

Lesson 14-3 pp. 792–795, 799

Check Skills You'll Need 1. s **2.** r **3.** a **4.** t
Quick Check 1. 180 m
2.
$\frac{3}{5} = 0.6, \frac{5}{3} \approx 1.67$

3a. Answers may vary. Sample: An advantage is
that simplification of the equation is easier. A
disadvantage is that you have to press an extra
button on the calculator to get the cotangent
function. **b.** ≈34.29 ft **4a.** 23.58° **b.** 56.25°
5.
$e \approx 7.14$; $m\angle E \approx 45.6°$, $m\angle D \approx 44.4°$

Checkpoint Quiz 1 1. $\csc \theta$ **2.** $\tan^2 \theta$ **3.** $-\csc^2 \theta$
4. 2.25 **5.** 0.320 **6.** 1.345 **7.** $a \approx 7.7$,
$m\angle A \approx 29.0°$, $m\angle B \approx 61.0°$ **8.** $c \approx 10.0$,

Top Left Panel (second column)

$m\angle A \approx 51.9°$, $m\angle B \approx 38.1°$ **9.** $a \approx 19.6$,
$m\angle A \approx 34.0°$, $m\angle B \approx 56.0°$

Lesson 14-4 pp. 801–803

Check Skills You'll Need 1. $\frac{1}{12}$ **2.** $\frac{\sqrt{3}}{3}$ **3.** $\frac{\sqrt{3}}{20}$ **4.** $\frac{1}{24}$ **5.** $\frac{\sqrt{2}}{16}$
6. $\frac{\sqrt{3}}{18}$ **7.** 6 cm² **8.** 45 in.² **9.** 32.8 mm²
10. 10.03 ft²
Quick Check 1. 36.6 in.² **2.** 31.0 yd **3.** 68.4° **4.** 56.4

Lesson 14-5 pp. 808–810

Check Skills You'll Need 1. 26.2° **2.** 18.1 **3.** 52.1° or
17.9°
Quick Check 1. 6.4 **2.** 75.3° **3.** 30.7°

Lesson 14-6 pp. 814–817, 820

Check Skills You'll Need 1. $\sin \theta$ **2.** $\cos \theta$ **3.** $\tan \theta$ **4.** 1
5. $\sec^2 \theta$ **6.** $\csc^2 \theta$
Quick Check 1. $\cos(\theta - \frac{\pi}{2}) =$
$\cos(-(\frac{\pi}{2} - \theta)) = \cos(\frac{\pi}{2} - \theta) = \sin \theta$
2. 0, π **3.** $\sec(90° - A) = \csc A$
4. $\frac{\sqrt{6} - \sqrt{2}}{4}$ **5.** $-2 - \sqrt{3}$

Checkpoint Quiz 1 1. 36.1 cm² **2.** 77.3 ft² **3.** 34.9 m²
4. 400.8 in² **5.** a = 8.2 ft, $m\angle B \approx 69.7°$, $m\angle C \approx$
83.3° **6.** $m\angle D = 58.4°$, $m\angle E = 53.0°$, $m\angle F =$
68.7° **7.** cos 80° **8.** sin 63° **9.** sin 80°

Lesson 14-7 pp. 821–823

Check Skills You'll Need 1. cos A cos B + sin A sin B
2. cos A cos B − sin A sin B **3.** $\frac{\tan A - \tan B}{1 + \tan A \tan B}$
4. sin A cos B − cos A sin B **5.** sin A cos B +
cos A sin B **6.** $\frac{\tan A + \tan B}{1 - \tan A \tan B}$
Quick Check 1. $\frac{\sqrt{3}}{2}$ **2.** $2 \cos 2\theta =$
$2(2 \cos^2 \theta - 1) = 4 \cos^2 \theta - 2$ **3a.** $\frac{1}{2}$ **b.** $-\frac{\sqrt{3}}{3}$
4. $-\frac{3}{5}, -\frac{4}{3}$

Top Right Panel (page 974)

Chapter 1

Lesson 1-1 pp. 8–10

EXERCISES 1. natural numbers, whole numbers,
integers, rational numbers, real numbers
3. irrational numbers, real numbers **9.** whole
numbers, rational numbers **11.** irrational
numbers, rational numbers
13. -6-5-4-3-2-1 0 1
15. -1 0 1 2 3 4 **17.** > **19.** > **25.** $-\frac{1}{4} > -\frac{1}{3}$;
$-\frac{1}{3} < -\frac{1}{4}$ **27.** $2.\overline{1}, 2.\overline{1} > -2.\overline{3}, -3\frac{5}{16}$
37. $1\frac{7}{12}, -\frac{2}{7}$ **43.** Comm. Prop. of Add. **45.** Comm.
Prop. of Mult. **49.** 0.06 **51.** 1.6 **57.** $-3\frac{1}{2}$ **59.** $\frac{1}{2}$
61. -5 **65.** natural numbers, whole numbers,
integers, rational numbers, real numbers
67. irrational numbers, real numbers **71.** >
73. < **79.** Answers may vary. Sample: 4 is a
whole number, and $\frac{1}{2}$ is not a whole number.
81. 0 is a whole number, and since -0 = 0, the
opposite of 0 is a whole number.

Lesson 1-2 pp. 15–17

EXERCISES 1. -30 **3.** 368 **9.** 1 ft **11.** 64 ft
13. 0.013 mm **15.** 0.4 mm **17.** $1210
19. $1464.10 **21.** 4a **23.** -9a + b **37.** 4a **39.** 17
41. 66 **47.** $-\frac{3}{2}a^2 + 2b^2$ **49.** $\frac{7a^4}{12} + \frac{2j}{15}$ **55.** C **57.** G
63. Assoc. Prop., Comm. Prop. of Add.,
Assoc. Prop. of Add., Identity Prop. of Mult., Dist.
Prop. of Add., Simplify. **75.** -4.3, -|3.4|, -|3.4|,
|-4.3|, **77.** $-\sqrt{\frac{1}{4}}, -\sqrt[3]{\frac{1}{10}}, \sqrt[3]{\frac{1}{16}}, \sqrt[4]{\frac{1}{4}}$ **79.** > **81.** <

Lesson 1-3 pp. 21–24

EXERCISES 1. 23 **3.** $\frac{17}{2}$ **9.** 8 **11.** 2 **17.** $= \frac{2A}{b}$
19. $w = \frac{V}{lh}$ **23.** $x = \frac{c}{a - b}, a \neq -b$
25. $x = a(c - d)$, or $ac - ab$, $a \neq 0$ **29.** 4
31. width = 4.5 cm, length = 7.5 cm **37.** 3
39. $\frac{3}{2}$ **43.** $r_2 = \frac{R r_1}{r_1 - R}$ **45.** $v = \frac{h + 5t^2}{t}$ **51.** ≈4.03 m
55. $x = ab - b^2 - a, b \neq 0$ **57.** $x = \frac{b + d}{c - a}, a \neq c$

Lesson 1-4 pp. 29–31

EXERCISES 1. $x \leq -\frac{1}{2}$ -3-2-1 0 1 2 3 4 5
3. $a > 11$ **15.** The longest side is less than 21 cm.
17. 40 students **19.** $-4 \leq x \leq 2$
-7-6-5-4-3-2-1 0 1 2 3 4

Top Right Panel (second column)

21. $-5 < x \leq 6$ **23.** All real numbers are
solutions. -4-3-2-1 0 1 2 3 4
25. $x \leq -3$ or $x \geq 9$ **27.** between $4\frac{1}{2}$ and $5\frac{1}{2}$ days
29. $z \geq 6$ **31.** $x \geq -48$ **39.** Dist. Prop.;
arithmetic; Sub. Prop. of Inequality; Mult. Prop. of
Inequality **41.** $-1 < x < 8$ **43.** no solutions

Lesson 1-5 pp. 36–38

EXERCISES 1. -6, 6 **3.** -6, 12 **11.** $\frac{2}{3}$ **13.** -4, 8
17. $x \leq -3$ or $x \geq 13$
-6-4-2 0 2 4 6 8 10 12 14 16 18
19. all real numbers **23.** $-2\frac{2}{3} < y < 3\frac{1}{3}$
-5-4-3-2-1 0 1 2 3 4
25. no solution **29.** $|k - 50.5| \leq 0.5$
31. $|b - 52.5| \leq 2.5$ **35.** $-\frac{3}{2}, -1$ **37.** $-\frac{1}{3}$
45. $x \leq -8$ or $x \geq 5$ **47.** $t < -\frac{3}{2}$ or $t > 2$
55. C **59.** $|x - 9.55| \leq 0.02$, $9.53 \leq x \leq 9.57$

Lesson 1-6 pp. 42–45

EXERCISES 1. $\frac{161}{340}$ or about 47%; $\frac{179}{340}$ or about
53% **7.** $\frac{1}{2}$, or 50% **9.** $\frac{4}{5}$, or 80% **11.** $\frac{19}{125}$, or 15.2%
13. $\frac{14}{25}$, or 56% **15.** {Gg, Gg, gg, gg}; $\frac{1}{2}$, or 50%
17. $\frac{1}{16}$, or 6.25% **19.** $\frac{1}{4}$, or 25% **21a.** 1 **b.** 0
25. $\frac{50}{147}$, or 35.4% **27.** $\frac{31}{147}$, or 21.1% **29.** $\frac{1}{2}$ **31.** 0
35. $\frac{3}{4}$ **37.** $\frac{1}{4}$ **39.** ≈6.4%

Chapter Review pp. 47–49

1. additive inverse **2.** sample space **3.** solution
of an equation **4.** compound inequality
5. reciprocal **6.** experimental probability
7. theoretical probability **8.** extraneous solution
9. simulation **10.** absolute value **11.** real
numbers, irrational numbers **12.** real numbers,
rational numbers, integers **13.** real numbers,
rational numbers, integers, whole numbers,
natural numbers **14.** real numbers, irrational
numbers **15.** real numbers, rational numbers
16. > **17.** > **18.** > **19.** <
20. 3.4; $-\frac{1}{3.4}$ -4 -2 0 2 4 6
21. $-4 - \pi$; $\frac{1}{4} + \pi$ -8-6-4-2 0 2 4 6 8
22. $-1\frac{7}{8}; \frac{8}{15}$ -3-2-1 0 1 2 3

Bottom Left Panel (page 975)

23. $-\sqrt{12}; \frac{1}{\sqrt{12}}$ -4-2 0 2 4
24–28. Answers may vary. Samples:
24. (x + 3)(1) = x + 3 **25.** (2x + 7) + 3y = 2x +
(7 + 3y) **26.** 3(2x − 4) = 6x − 12 **27.** (5x)(3y) =
(3y)(5x) **28.** 10z + 0 = 10z **29.** 4 **30.** 19 **31.** 5b
32. 11 **33.** 10 **34.** 5 **35.** 4 **36.** -8 **37.** $\frac{b - a^2}{a}$,
$a \neq 0, b \neq 0$ **38.** 10 cm, 6 cm **39.** 525 mi/h
40. 70°, 110°
41. $z \leq \frac{2}{5}$ 0 1 2 3
42. $x > 2$ -2-1 0 1 2 3
43. $y > 4.5$ 0 1 2 3 4 5 6
44. $-1 \leq x \leq 1$ -3-2-1 0 1 2 3
45. $x \leq \frac{3}{2}$ or $x > 6$ 0 1 2 3 4 5 6 7
46. $x \geq \frac{5}{3}$ -2-1 0 1 2 3
47. $155,850 \leq A \leq $415,850 **48.** 1 **49.** $\frac{1}{8}$, 9
50. no solutions
51. $-\frac{1}{3} \leq x \leq \frac{5}{3}$ -2-1 0 1 2 3
52. $y < 0$ or $y > 18$ -4 0 4 8 12 16 20
53. $x < -4$ or $x > 6$ -4-2 0 2 4 6 8
54. $|x - 43.6| \leq 0.1$ **55.** $\frac{1}{2}$ **56.** $\frac{3}{5}$ **57.** $\frac{1}{5}$ **58.** $\frac{3}{5}$
59. $\frac{5}{6}$ **60.** about 9%

CHAPTER 2

Lesson 2-1 pp. 59–61

EXERCISES
1. **3.**

5. (−2, −2), (−1, 1), (1, 1), (1, 0), (3, 3), (3, −2);
domain {−2, −1, 1, 3}, range {−2, 0, 1, 3}
7. (−2, 0), (−1, 2), (0, 3), (1, 2), (2, 0); domain =
{−2, −1, 0, 1, 2}, range = {0, 2, 3} **9.** domain range
13. function **15.** function

Bottom Left Panel (second column)

17. not a function **19.** function **23.** 13, 7,
−3.5, −14 **25.** −2, −4, −7.5, −11
33.

domain {−4, −3, −2, −1}, range {1, 2, 3, 4}
35. domain $\{-\frac{3}{2}, \frac{1}{2}, \frac{3}{2}, \frac{5}{2}\}$, range $\{-\frac{1}{2}, \frac{1}{2}\}$
37. domain {−2, −1, 0, 9}, range {2, 5, 7},
not a function **39.** domain {−3.2 ≤ x ≤ 3.2},
range {−1 ≤ y ≤ 1}, not a function **41.** B **43.** yes
45. no

Lesson 2-2 pp. 67–70

EXERCISES
1. **9a.**

$y = 0.23x$, domain $\{x \mid x \in R \text{ and } x \geq 0\}$, range
$\{y \mid y \in R \text{ and } y \geq 0\}$ **b.** x-intercept (0, 0), y-
intercept (0, 0); when no miles have been driven,
there is no cost. **c.** 0.23 represents a cost of $.23
per mile driven. **11.** −1 **13.** 3 **21.** $\frac{3}{8}x - y = \frac{19}{3}$
23. y = −2 **27.** $y - 0 = \frac{5}{3}(x - 1)$
29. $y + 1 = -\frac{4}{3}(x - 0)$ **33.** $\frac{3}{2}$ **35.** $-\frac{8}{5}$
39. $y = \frac{5}{2}x + \frac{1}{2}$ **41.** x = 1
43. **51.** $\frac{1}{3}$ **53.** $-\frac{1}{4}$

55. −1; (0, 1000), (1000, 0) **57.** 54; (0, −1), $(\frac{1}{54}, 0)$
63. $-\frac{5}{13}$ **65.** $-\frac{7}{10}$ **67.** $y = 3x + 2$ **69.** B
71. $y = -1$ **73.** $y = \frac{5}{8}x + \frac{10}{3}$

75. 3x − 2y = 2 **77.** 3x + 12y = −4

Bottom Right Panel (page 976)

Extension p. 71

1. **3.**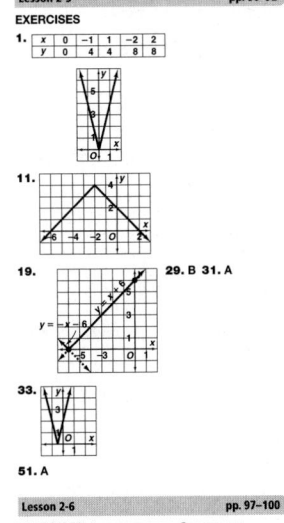

5. $f(x) = \begin{cases} -3x - 10, & \text{if } x \leq -2 \\ \frac{1}{2}x - 3, & \text{if } -2 < x < 2 \\ 2x - 6, & \text{if } x \geq 2 \end{cases}$

Lesson 2-3 pp. 74–77

EXERCISES 1. yes; 2, $y = 2x$ **3.** no **9.** yes;
12 **11.** yes; −2 **17.** $\frac{7}{3}$; $-\frac{10}{7}$ **19.** −1; $\frac{5}{4}$ **25.** 4 **27.** $\frac{5}{3}$
29. no **31.** yes; k = 1.3, $y = 1.3x$ **33.** $y = 2x$
35. $y = -\frac{5}{8}x$ **41.** 9 **43.** 90
47. Yes; $y = -\frac{5}{8}x$ contains the point $(15, -12\frac{1}{2})$.

Lesson 2-4 pp. 81–84

EXERCISES
1. d = 62.5h + 15

3. h = 8x + 60 **5.** y = 0.5x + 0.75; 3.25 lb
7. y = 1.75x + 1.75; $8.40
9.

Linear model is reasonable; models may vary.
Sample: y = 2.6x − 0.6 **11.** not reasonable
13a.

Answers may vary. Sample: y = 110x + 1170
b. 2930 Cal **c.** Answers may vary. Sample: No;
adults need fewer Calories, not more.
15. y = −4x + 10 **17.** y = −7.5x − 2.5 **23.** 104.5
25. 13

Bottom Right Panel (second column)

Lesson 2-5 pp. 90–92

EXERCISES

x	0	−1	1	−2	2
y	0	4	4	8	8

11.

19. **29.** B **31.** A

$y = \frac{1}{2}x - 5$

33.

51. A

Lesson 2-6 pp. 97–100

EXERCISES 1. **3.**

5. $y = |x| - \frac{2}{3}$ **7.** $y = |x| + 2$
9. Translate $y = |x|$ left 5 units;

11. Translate $y = |x|$ left 2 units;

13. $y = |x - 3|$

Page 977

17. **19.**

23. $y = 2|x|$ **25.** $y = \frac{2}{3}|x|$

29. vertical

31. horizontal **35.** $y = |x - 2| - 2$

37. $y = -\frac{1}{2}|x + 2| + 4$ **43.** $y = -|x| - 3$
45. $y = 2|x| + 11$ **47.** $y = -|x - p| + q$

Lesson 2-7   pp. 104–106

EXERCISES

1. **11.** **21.** $5x + 3y \le 9$

23.

Chapter Review   pp. 109–111

1. dependent **2.** relations **3.** sometimes
4. point-slope **5.** sometimes **6.** not a function;
domain: {1, 3, 5, 8}, range: {0, 1, 2, 3, 8}
7. function; domain: {-10, -6, 5, 6, 10}, range:
{2, 3, 4, 7} **8.** not a function;
domain: $\left\{ -2, -\frac{3}{2}, -1, \frac{1}{2}, 1, 2, 3 \right\}$,
range: $\left\{ -\frac{7}{2}, -\frac{1}{2}, 0, \frac{1}{2}, \frac{3}{2}, 2, \frac{5}{2} \right\}$
9. function; domain: {-4, -2, -1, 1, 3},
range: {-1, 2, 4} **10.** function;
domain: $\left\{ -2, -1, \frac{1}{2}, 3 \right\}$, range: {2} **11.** 6, 4.5, 1
12. $-3\frac{3}{4}, -3\frac{3}{16}, -1\frac{7}{8}$ **13.** $2\frac{5}{8}, 2\frac{5}{24}, \frac{3}{4}$ **14.** $3x + y = 12$
15. $2x - y = 1$ **16.** $2, \left(\frac{3}{4}, 0 \right), \left(0, -\frac{3}{2} \right)$

17. $M, \left(\frac{P}{M}, 0 \right), \left(0, -\frac{P}{N} \right)$ **18.** -1; (5, 0), (0, 5)
19a. $y = -\frac{1}{2}x + 7$
b. $y = 2x - 13$
c.

20. no **21.** no **22.** yes; 1; $y = x$ **23.** -4; 1.2
24. $\frac{10}{3}, -1$ **25.** $\frac{7}{2}, -1\frac{1}{20}$
26a and b.

Answers may vary. Sample: $y = 2.5x + 21.5$
c. Answers may vary. Sample: about 96.5 million
27.

Answers may vary. Sample: reasonable;
$y = x + 3$; 18
28.

Answers may vary. Sample: reasonable;
$y = -0.8 + 19.9$; 7.9

Page 978

29.

30. **31.**

32. $y = |x - 2| + 4$ **33.** $y = |x + 3|$
34. $y = |x - 5| + 2$ **35.** $y = |x - 4| + 1$

36. **37.**

38. **39.**

40. **41.**

42. **43.**

44. **45.**

46a. Answers may vary. Sample: $x + 3y \le 15$
b. Answers may vary. Sample: domain {1, 2, 3, 4, 5, 6, 7, 8, 9, 10, 11, 12, 13, 14, 15}, range {1, 2, 3, 4, 5}
c.

47. Answers may vary. Sample: $y \le -|x| - 1$

Chapter 3

Lesson 3-1   pp. 120–123

EXERCISES

1. (3, 1) $y = -2x + 7$

3. (-2, 4)

11. $\begin{cases} y = 0.22x + 67.5 \\ y = 0.15x + 75.507 \end{cases}$; about 2085
13. dependent **15.** inconsistent
25. infinitely many solutions
$3 = 4y + x$
$y = -x + 3$

27. no solution
$x + 2y = 8$
$3x + 6y - 12 = 0$

39. dependent **41.** inconsistent

Lesson 3-2   pp. 128–130

EXERCISES 1. (0.5, 2.5) **3.** (20, 4)
13a. $\begin{cases} d = 0.50m \\ d = 15 \end{cases}$ **b.** 30 miles
15a. $\begin{cases} p = 28 \\ p = 8 + 0.35d \end{cases}$ **b.** 58 **19.** (2, 4)
21. (2, -2) **31.** {(a, d)| $-3d + d = -1$} **33.** no solution **45.** (m, n) = (4, -3) **47.** (t, v) = (50, 750)
57. Substitution; the first equation is solved for y.
59. Substitution; the second equation is solved for y.

Lesson 3-3   pp. 136–138

EXERCISES 1. (0, 4), (0, 5), (0, 6), (0, 7), (0, 8)
5. no **7.** $y \le 2x + 2$
$y < -x + 1$

9. $y \le \frac{1}{2}x + 1$

Page 979

17. $\begin{cases} a + c \ge 40 \\ c \le 30 \end{cases}$

19. **21.**

31. A, B **33.** A, B

43. **45.**

Lesson 3-4   pp. 142–144

EXERCISES 1. When $x = 4$ and $y = 2$, P is maximized at 16. **3.** When $x = 6$ and $y = 8$, C is minimized at 36.
5. vertices: (3, 5), (0, 8); minimized at (0, 8)

11. 70 spruce; 0 maple **13.** A
15. vertices: (75, 20), (75, 110), $\left(25, 86\frac{2}{3} \right)$, (25, 110); minimized when $C = 633\frac{1}{3}$ at $\left(25, 86\frac{2}{3} \right)$

Lesson 3-5   pp. 149–151

EXERCISES 1. 1 unit back, 5 units right
3. 2 units forward, 5 units up
5.
(5, 0, -2)

13. (0, 0, 0) **15.** (0, 40, 0)
19. **27.**

37. Mt. Kilimanjaro **39.** Vildivia Seamount

Lesson 3-6   pp. 157–159

EXERCISES 1. (4, 2, -3) **3.** (2, 1, -5)
11. (a, b, c) = (2, 3, -2) **13.** (5, 2, 2)
19. $220,000 was placed in short-term notes. $440,000 was placed in government bonds. $340,000 was placed in utility bonds.
21. 50 nickels, 10 dimes, and 15 quarters
23. one solution **25.** (8, 1, 3) **27.** $\left(\frac{1}{2}, 2, -3 \right)$
39. 75 apples; 25 pears

Chapter Review   pp. 161–163

1. A **2.** D **3.** B **4.** E **5.** C **6.** (-2, -3) **7.** (2, 4)
8. no solution **9.** (-2, 0) **10.** (3, 6) **11.** no solution **12.** consistent and dependent
13. consistent and independent **14.** inconsistent
15. 20 checks **16.** (10, -4) **17.** (0, 4) **18.** (1, 9)
19. (3, 7) **20.** no solution **21.** $\left(\frac{7}{24}, \frac{1}{24} \right)$
22. 1 serving of roast beef and 2 servings of mashed potatoes
23. **24.** $y < 6$

25.

26. Let r = number of gallons of regular coffee, and d = number of gallons of decaffeinated coffee.
$r + d \ge 10$
$\frac{3}{4}r \ge d$

Page 980

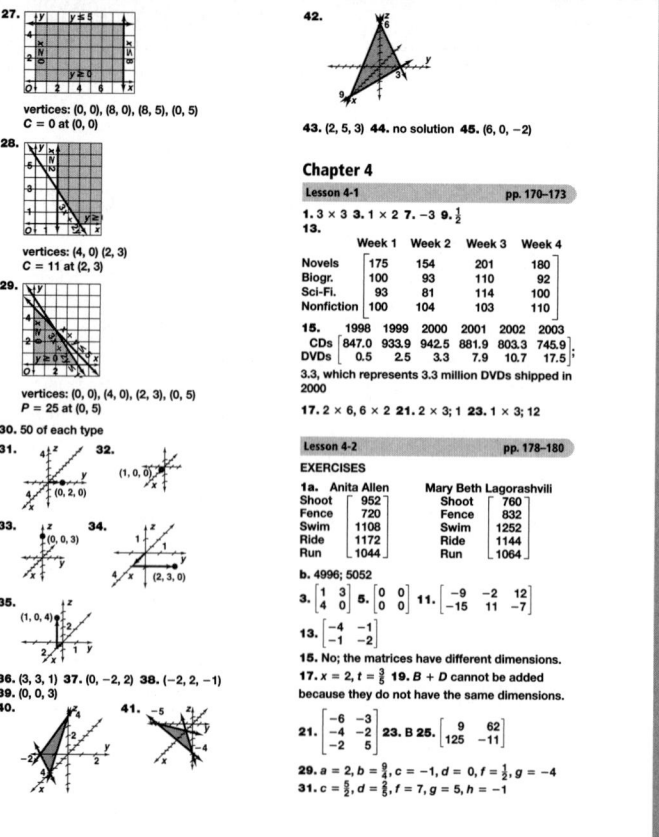

27. $y \le 5$
$x \ge 0$
$y \ge 0$

vertices: (0, 0), (8, 0), (8, 5), (0, 5)
$C = 0$ at (0, 0)

28.
vertices: (4, 0), (2, 3)
$C = 11$ at (2, 3)

29.
vertices: (0, 0), (4, 0), (2, 3), (0, 5)
$P = 25$ at (0, 5)

30. 50 of each type
31. **32.** (1, 0, 0)
(0, 2, 0)

33. **34.**
(0, 0, 3)
(2, 3, 0)

35.
(1, 0, 4)

36. (3, 3, 1) **37.** (0, -2, 2) **38.** (-2, 2, -1)
39. (0, 0, 3)
40. **41.**

42.

43. (2, 5, 3) **44.** no solution **45.** (6, 0, -2)

Chapter 4

Lesson 4-1   pp. 170–173

1. 3×3 **3.** 1×2 **7.** -3 **9.** $\frac{1}{2}$
13.

	Week 1	Week 2	Week 3	Week 4
Novels	175	154	201	180
Biogr.	100	93	110	92
Sci-Fi.	93	81	114	100
Nonfiction	100	104	103	110

15.

	1998	1999	2000	2001	2002	2003
CDs	847.0	933.9	942.5	881.9	803.3	745.9
DVDs	0.5	2.5	3.3	7.9	10.7	17.5

3.3, which represents 3.3 million DVDs shipped in 2000
17. 2×6, 6 **21.** 2×3; 1 **23.** 1×3; 12

Lesson 4-2   pp. 178–180

EXERCISES

1a.

Anita Allen			Mary Beth Lagorashvili	
Shoot	952		Shoot	760
Fence	720		Fence	832
Swim	1108		Swim	1252
Ride	1172		Ride	1144
Run	1044		Run	1064

b. 4996; 5052
3. $\begin{bmatrix} 1 & 3 \\ 4 & 0 \end{bmatrix}$ **5.** $\begin{bmatrix} 0 & 0 \\ 0 & 0 \end{bmatrix}$ **11.** $\begin{bmatrix} -9 & 2 & 12 \\ -15 & 11 & -7 \end{bmatrix}$
13. $\begin{bmatrix} -4 & -1 \\ -4 & -2 \end{bmatrix}$
15. No; the matrices have different dimensions.
17. $x = 2$, $t = \frac{8}{3}$ **19.** $B + D$ cannot be added because they do not have the same dimensions.
21. $\begin{bmatrix} -6 & -3 \\ -4 & -2 \\ -2 & 5 \end{bmatrix}$ **23.** B **25.** $\begin{bmatrix} 9 & 62 \\ 125 & -11 \end{bmatrix}$
29. $a = 2$, $b = \frac{9}{4}$, $c = -1$, $d = 0$, $f = \frac{1}{2}$, $g = -4$
31. $c = \frac{9}{2}$, $d = \frac{8}{5}$, $f = 7$, $g = 5$, $h = -1$

Top-left quadrant

Lesson 4-3 pp. 186–189

1. $\begin{bmatrix} 9 & 12 \\ 18 & -6 \\ 3 & 0 \end{bmatrix}$ 3. $\begin{bmatrix} -3 & -6 \\ 9 & -3 \end{bmatrix}$ 9. $\begin{bmatrix} 8 & -2.5 \\ -1.5 & -1 \end{bmatrix}$

11. $\begin{bmatrix} 5 & -12 \\ 9 & -6 \end{bmatrix}$ 13. $\begin{bmatrix} -8 & 0 \\ 0 & -8 \end{bmatrix}$

19a.

	Lilies	Carnations	Daisies
Arrangement 1	3	0	0
Arrangement 2	3	4	0
Arrangement 3	0	3	4

b.

	Cost
Lilies	2.15
Carnations	0.90
Daisies	1.30

c.

	Cost
Arrangement 1	6.45
Arrangement 2	10.05
Arrangement 3	7.90

21. defined 23. undefined

31. $\begin{bmatrix} -9 & 7 & 4 \\ 8 & 2 & -3 \end{bmatrix}$ 33. $\begin{bmatrix} 1 & 0 & -1 \\ 0 & 1 & -1 \end{bmatrix}$

35. B 37. 4×4;
$\begin{bmatrix} a & 0 & b & 0 \\ a - 2e & 0 & b & -2f \\ 2e & 0 & 0 & 2f \\ -a + e & 0 & 0 & f \end{bmatrix}$

39. $\begin{bmatrix} 9 & -6 \\ 15 & -3 \\ -6 & -12 \end{bmatrix}$ 41. $\begin{bmatrix} 17 & -24 \\ -33 & -7 \\ 69 & -18 \end{bmatrix}$

Lesson 4-4 pp. 195–198

EXERCISES 1. $\begin{bmatrix} -2 & -2 & 2 & 2 \\ 2 & 6 & 6 & 2 \end{bmatrix}$

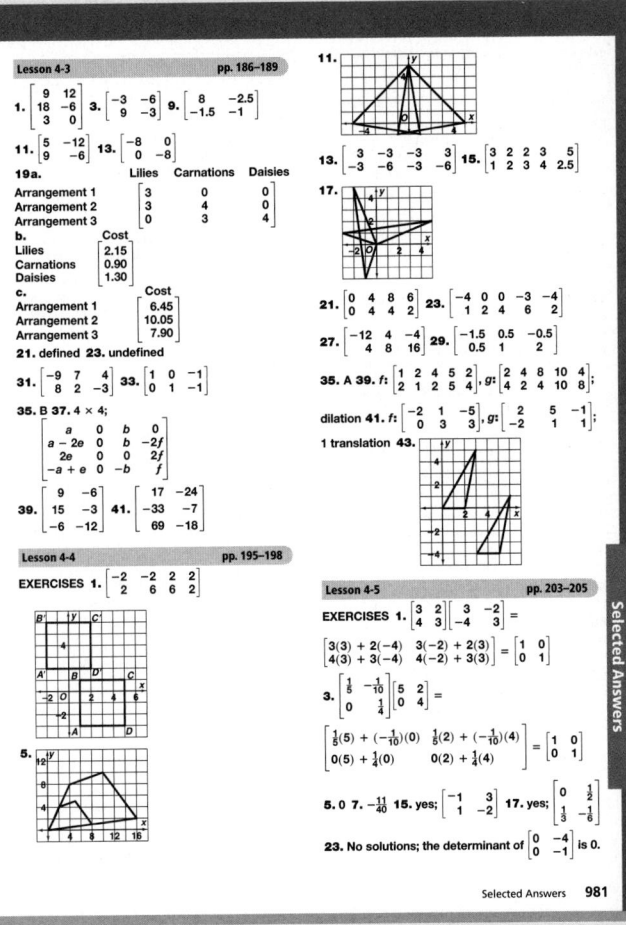

5.

39. 6; $\begin{bmatrix} \frac{1}{3} & -\frac{2}{3} & 0 \\ -\frac{1}{3} & \frac{1}{3} & -\frac{1}{3} \\ \frac{1}{3} & \frac{1}{3} & 0 \end{bmatrix}$ 40. $\begin{bmatrix} 1 & 2 \\ -1 & 0 \end{bmatrix}$ 41. $\begin{bmatrix} -4 \\ -7 \end{bmatrix}$

42. $\begin{bmatrix} 2 & 2 \\ 6 & 1 \end{bmatrix}$ 43. $\begin{bmatrix} 2 & 1 \\ 3 & 1 \end{bmatrix}$ 44. no unique solution

45. no unique solution 46. 3 small canoes, 2 large canoes 47. $(4, -7)$ 48. $(6, 0, -2)$

Top-middle column

11.

13. $\begin{bmatrix} -3 & -3 & -3 & 3 \\ -3 & -6 & -3 & -6 \end{bmatrix}$ 15. $\begin{bmatrix} 3 & 2 & 2 & 3 & 5 \\ 1 & 2 & 3 & 4 & 2.5 \end{bmatrix}$

17.

21. $\begin{bmatrix} 0 & 4 & 8 & 6 \\ -4 & -4 & 2 & 6 \end{bmatrix}$ 23. $\begin{bmatrix} -4 & 0 & 0 & -3 & -4 \\ 1 & 2 & 4 & 6 & 2 \end{bmatrix}$

27. $\begin{bmatrix} -12 & 4 & -4 \\ 4 & 8 & 16 \end{bmatrix}$ 29. $\begin{bmatrix} -1.5 & 0.5 & -0.5 \\ 0.5 & 1 & 2 \end{bmatrix}$

35. A 39. $f: \begin{bmatrix} 1 & 2 & 4 & 8 & 10 & 4 \\ 2 & 1 & 2 & 5 & 4 \end{bmatrix}$, $g: \begin{bmatrix} 2 & 4 & 8 & 10 & 8 \\ 4 & 2 & 4 & 10 & 8 \end{bmatrix}$;

dilation 41. $f: \begin{bmatrix} -2 & 1 & -5 \\ 0 & 3 & 3 \end{bmatrix}$, $g: \begin{bmatrix} 2 & 5 & -1 \\ -2 & 1 & 1 \end{bmatrix}$;

1 translation 43.

Lesson 4-5 pp. 203–205

EXERCISES 1. $\begin{bmatrix} 3 & 2 \\ 4 & 3 \end{bmatrix} \begin{bmatrix} 3 & -2 \\ -4 & 3 \end{bmatrix} =$

$\begin{bmatrix} 3(3) + 2(-4) & 3(-2) + 2(3) \\ 4(3) + 3(-4) & 4(-2) + 3(3) \end{bmatrix} = \begin{bmatrix} 1 & 0 \\ 0 & 1 \end{bmatrix}$

3. $\begin{bmatrix} \frac{1}{5} & -\frac{1}{10} \\ 0 & \frac{1}{4} \end{bmatrix} \begin{bmatrix} 5 & 2 \\ 0 & 4 \end{bmatrix} =$

$\begin{bmatrix} \frac{1}{5}(5) + (-\frac{1}{10})(0) & \frac{1}{5}(2) + (-\frac{1}{10})(4) \\ 0(5) + \frac{1}{4}(0) & 0(2) + \frac{1}{4}(4) \end{bmatrix} = \begin{bmatrix} 1 & 0 \\ 0 & 1 \end{bmatrix}$

5. 0 7. $-\frac{11}{40}$ 15. yes; $\begin{bmatrix} -1 & 3 \\ 1 & -2 \end{bmatrix}$ 17. yes; $\begin{bmatrix} 0 & \frac{1}{2} \\ \frac{1}{3} & -\frac{1}{6} \end{bmatrix}$

23. No solutions; the determinant of $\begin{bmatrix} 0 & -4 \\ 0 & -1 \end{bmatrix}$ is 0.

Top-right quadrant

25. a.

	From	
	No Cable	Cable
To No Cable	0.98	0.005
Cable	0.02	0.995

b. about 20,100 people c. about 19,897 people 27. -120 29. 2 31. yes 33. No; answers may vary.

Sample: The product is $\begin{bmatrix} 0 & 1 \\ 1 & 0 \end{bmatrix}$. 35. yes; $\begin{bmatrix} -5 & 7 \\ 3 & -4 \end{bmatrix}$

37. yes; $\begin{bmatrix} 0.5 & 0 \\ 0 & 0.5 \end{bmatrix}$

Lesson 4-6 pp. 209–211

EXERCISES 1. 20 3. -14 5. 6 7. -7314.14

9. no 11. $\begin{bmatrix} 5 \\ 8 \\ 2 \end{bmatrix}$ 13. PORTRAIT 17. -3 19. 1

21. $\begin{bmatrix} 0.4 & 0.4 & 0.2 \\ -0.6 & -0.6 & 0.2 \\ -0.2 & 0.8 & 0.2 \end{bmatrix}$ 23. no inverse

Extension p. 213

1.

	N_1	N_2	N_3	N_4		V_1	V_2	V_3	V_4	V_5
N_1	0	1	0	1	V_1	1	0	1	0	0
N_2	1	0	1	1	V_2	1	0	1	0	0
N_3	0	1	0	1	V_3	0	0	1	0	1
N_4	1	1	1	0	V_4	0	1	0	1	0
					V_5	0	0	1	1	0

5.

	A	B	C	D
A	0	1	0	0
B	1	0	0	0
C	0	1	1	1
D	1	1	0	1

7. 9.

Lesson 4-7 pp. 217–219

EXERCISES 1. $\begin{bmatrix} 1 & 1 \\ 1 & -2 \end{bmatrix} \begin{bmatrix} x \\ y \end{bmatrix} = \begin{bmatrix} 5 \\ -4 \end{bmatrix}$; coefficient matrix is $\begin{bmatrix} 1 & 1 \\ 1 & -2 \end{bmatrix}$, variable matrix is $\begin{bmatrix} x \\ y \end{bmatrix}$, constant matrix is $\begin{bmatrix} 5 \\ -4 \end{bmatrix}$. 3. $\begin{bmatrix} 3 & 5 \\ 1 & 1 \end{bmatrix} \begin{bmatrix} a \\ b \end{bmatrix} = \begin{bmatrix} 0 \\ 2 \end{bmatrix}$; coefficient matrix is $\begin{bmatrix} 3 & 5 \\ 1 & 1 \end{bmatrix}$, variable matrix is $\begin{bmatrix} a \\ b \end{bmatrix}$, constant matrix is $\begin{bmatrix} 0 \\ 2 \end{bmatrix}$. 7. $(2, 1)$ 9. $(\frac{1}{2}, 20)$ 17. yes 19. yes

23. $\begin{bmatrix} 6 \\ 2 \end{bmatrix}$ 25. $\begin{bmatrix} 16 \\ -22 \end{bmatrix}$ 27. $(2, 4)$ 29. $(4, 1, 3)$

Lesson 4-8 pp. 224–227

EXERCISES 1. $(2, 0)$ 3. $(3, 1)$

7. $\begin{bmatrix} 3 & -7 & -3 \\ 1 & 1 & 2 \\ 2 & 3 & 5 \end{bmatrix}$ 9. $\begin{cases} 5x + y = -3 \\ -2x + 2y = 4 \end{cases}$

11. $\begin{cases} 2x + y + z = 1 \\ x + y + z = 2 \\ x - y - z = -2 \end{cases}$ 13. $(-2, -6)$

15. $(6.25, -6.25)$ 19. $(3, 1, 1)$ 21. no unique solution 25. $(-3, 5)$ 27. $(4, 8)$ 29. $(1, 1, -1)$ 31. $(4, 0, 1)$ 33. C 35. $(2, 0, 3)$ 37. no unique solution 39. almonds: $2/lb; pecans: $4/lb; pistachios: $6/lb

Chapter Review pp. 229–231

1. matrix 2. transformations 3. determinants 4. equal matrices 5. zero matrix 6. matrix equation 7. square matrix 8. preimage 9. scalar product 10. identity matrix 11. 2×3; -7 12. 3×2; -5 13. 3×3; 78 14. 226 15. 50

16. about 9% 17. $\begin{bmatrix} 1 & -8 & 12 \end{bmatrix}$ 18. $\begin{bmatrix} t & -1 \\ 3 \end{bmatrix}$

19. $\begin{bmatrix} -3 & 10 \\ -3 & 3 \end{bmatrix}$ 20. $\begin{bmatrix} 2 & 8 & 13 \\ 33 & 0 & -7 \end{bmatrix}$

21. $x = -2$, $w = 8$, $r = 4$, $t = -1$

22. $t = -4$, $y = \frac{11}{2}$, $r = 4$, $w = 5$

23. $\begin{bmatrix} 18 & 3 & 0 & 24 \\ -12 & 9 & 21 & 33 \end{bmatrix}$ 24. $\begin{bmatrix} -9 & 7 \\ -3 & -8 \end{bmatrix}$

25. undefined 26. $\begin{bmatrix} -6 & 10 & 21 & 41 \\ -28 & 10 & 28 & 28 \end{bmatrix}$

27. $\begin{bmatrix} -14 & -2 \\ 43 & -7 \end{bmatrix}$ 28. $\begin{bmatrix} 4 & -1 \\ -1 & -2 & 3 \end{bmatrix}$

29. $\begin{bmatrix} 0 & -5 & -2 \\ 5 & 4 & 9 \end{bmatrix}$ 30. $\begin{bmatrix} -3 & 2 & -1 \\ 5 & 1 & 5 \end{bmatrix}$

31. $\begin{bmatrix} 1 & 0 & 5 \\ 3 & -2 & 1 \end{bmatrix}$ 32. $\begin{bmatrix} 1 & 0 & 5 \\ -3 & 2 & -1 \end{bmatrix}$

33. $\begin{bmatrix} 1.5 & -1 & 0.5 \\ 0.5 & 0 & 2.5 \end{bmatrix}$ 34. $\begin{bmatrix} 6 & -4 & 2 \\ 0 & 2 & 10 \end{bmatrix}$

35. $\begin{bmatrix} -1 & 0 & -5 \\ 3 & -2 & 1 \end{bmatrix}$ 36. 24; $\begin{bmatrix} \frac{1}{6} & -\frac{1}{24} \\ 0 & \frac{1}{4} \end{bmatrix}$

37. 0; does not exist 38. 42; $\begin{bmatrix} \frac{5}{42} & -\frac{1}{42} \\ -\frac{1}{21} & \frac{2}{21} \end{bmatrix}$

Bottom-left quadrant

Chapter 5

Lesson 5-1 pp. 241–243

EXERCISES 1. linear; none, x, 4 3. quadratic; $3x^2$, $-6x$, none 11. $(-1, 0)$, $x = -1$ 13. $P'(6, 9)$, $Q'(2, 1)$ 17. $y = x^2 - 5x + 2$ 19. $y = x^2 + 2x$ 21a. $y = -16x^2 + 33x + 46$, where x is the number of seconds after release and y is the height in ft. b. 28.5 ft 23. $y = 4x^2$ 25. no 27. $(-\frac{1}{2}, -\frac{1}{2})$, $x = -\frac{1}{2}$ 29. $(\frac{1}{2}, 0)$, $x = \frac{1}{2}$

Lesson 5-2 pp. 248–251

EXERCISES

1. 3. 11.

13. 23.

min, $-\frac{10}{3}$

25.

min, 2
29. 2 s; 64 ft

31. 33.

37. B 39. A 45. -3 47. 2 49. $y = -4x^2 - 3$ 51. $y = 10x^2 - 1$ 55. B 57. $y = x^2 + 1$; up

59. $y = -\frac{1}{2}x^2 + 1$; down

Lesson 5-3 pp. 255–258

EXERCISES

1. 3.

13. $y = \frac{1}{4}x^2$ 15. $y = -(x - 2)^2$ 17. $y = (x - 2)^2$
19. $y = 6(x + 3)^2 - 2$ 21. $(-20, 0)$, -600
23. $(-5.5, 0)$, 726 27. $y = (x - 2)^2 + 2$
29. $y = 6x^2 - 10$

37. $x = 2$

43. $y = -7(x - 1)^2 + 2$ 45. $y = -\frac{1}{2}(x + 3)^2 + 6$
51. $y = 25x^2 + 60x + 27$ 53. $y = 2x^2 + 22x$
59. yes; no; $y = -3(x + \frac{1}{3})^2 + \frac{4}{3}$ 69. $a = 3$, $k = -1$ 71. $a = \frac{1}{5}$, $k = 1$

Lesson 5-4 pp. 263–265

EXERCISES 1. 3; $3(a^2 + 3)$ 3. x; $x(x - 2)$
7. $(x + 1)(x + 2)$ 9. $(x + 2)(x + 5)$
31. $(x + 4)(3x - 5)$ 33. $(x - 2)(7x + 6)$
47. $5x - 1$ by $5x - 1$ 51. $9(x + 2)(x - 2)$
53. $3(2y + 5)(2y - 5)$ 67. $(x - 70)$ ft

Bottom-right quadrant

Lesson 5-5 pp. 270–272

EXERCISES 1. -4, -2 3. -1, $\frac{3}{2}$ 7. -4, 4 9. -4, 4 13. 0, 4 15. $-\frac{7}{2}$, $\frac{7}{2}$ 21. -1.32, 8.32 23. -1.67, -1.5 25. -0.94, 2.34 33. B 37. 3, 8 39. $-\frac{1}{2}$, 3

Lesson 5-6 pp. 278–280

EXERCISES 1. $2i$ 3. $\sqrt{15}$ 11. $2 + i\sqrt{3}$ 13. $6 - 2i\sqrt{7}$ 19. 2 21. $2\sqrt{2}$ 25. $-5 + 3i$ 27. $3 + 2i$ 29. $6 + 3i$ 31. $7 + 4i$ 41. $\pm 5i$ 43. $\pm \frac{9i\sqrt{3}}{3}$ 47. $-i$, $-1 - i$, $1 + i$, i 49. $1 - i$, $1 - 3i$, $-7 - 7i$ 51. $\pm 7i$ 55. B 57. $288i$ 59. $10 - 4i$

Lesson 5-7 pp. 285–287

EXERCISES 1. -4, -2 3. -1, 3 7. 81 9. 144 13. -4, 7 15. $-3 \pm 4i\sqrt{2}$ 29. $y = -(x - 2)^2 + 3$ 31. $y = (x + 2)^2 - 3$ 35. $y = \frac{1}{2}(x - 5)^2 - \frac{1}{2}$ $(5, -\frac{1}{2})$ 37a. (60, 5000) b. positive rational numbers less than 130; whole numbers up to 5000 c. $60; $5000 41. -20, 20 43. -16, 16 51. $-12 \pm 3\sqrt{17}$ 53. $\frac{1}{4} \pm \frac{\sqrt{57}}{12}$

Lesson 5-8 pp. 293–295

EXERCISES 1. 1, 3 3. $-\frac{7}{2}$, 1 23. $\frac{5}{2} \pm \frac{\sqrt{10}}{2}$; 0.61, 2.72 25. $-\frac{1}{8}$, 1 31. -4; two, imaginary 33. 0; one, real 41. 1, 10 43. $-\frac{3}{2}$, $\frac{1}{2}$ 53a. $w(18 - w) = 36$ b. 2.29 in. by 15.71 in. 57. two 59. none 67a. $y = 100a$ b. 17.72 cm

Chapter Review pp. 299–301

1. perfect square trinomial 2. quadratic formula 3. vertex form of a quadratic function 4. zero of a function 5. discriminant 6. quadratic; $-2x^2$, $5x$, 3 7. quadratic; $-x^2$, x, 3 8. linear; none, $-4x$, 3 9. $(0, -1)$, $x = 0$, $(0, 2)$ and $(-1, 0)$ 10. $(-2, 1)$, $x = -2$, $(-2, 1)$ and $(-4, 0)$ 11. $(1, -4)$, $x = 1$, $(3, -1)$ and $(2, -3\frac{1}{4})$ 12a. $y = 614x^2 - 342x + 4962$, where $x = 0$ corresponds to 1995 and y is in thousands. b. around 1999 c. $y = -25.5x^2 + 917.8x + 4776.7$ d. around 2007 e. $\approx 13{,}000{,}000$ 13.

vertex $(-1, -4)$, y-intercept: -2; $x = -1$

14.

vertex $(5, 0)$, y-intercept: 25; $x = 5$

15.

vertex $(2, 1)$, y-intercept: -3; $x = 2$

16.

vertex $(0, 7)$, y-intercept: 7; $x = 0$

17. $y = (x + \frac{1}{2})^2 - 12\frac{1}{4}$; minimum: $-12\frac{1}{4}$
18. $y = -(x - 1)^2 + 3$; maximum: 3
19. $y = 2(x + 2)^2 - 11$; minimum: -11
20. $y = -0.5(x - 0)^2 + 5$; maximum: 5
21. $y = -\frac{1}{2}(x - 1)^2 + 2$; maximum: 2
22. $y = \frac{1}{6}(x - 3)^2 - 1$; minimum: -1
24. 0, 7 25. -4, 2 26. -6, 0 27. $2 - 2\sqrt{2}$, $2 + 2\sqrt{2}$ 28. -1, 4 29. -0.85, 5.85 or $\frac{5 \pm 3\sqrt{5}}{2}$ 30. $\frac{2}{3}$, 4 31. -1, 4 32. -4 33. 3 34. $\frac{3}{2}$ 35. -3, 3 36. $-1\frac{1}{3}$, $\frac{7}{2}$ 37. $-\frac{3}{2}$, $-\frac{1}{2}$ 38. -2.61, 1.28 or $\frac{-2 \pm \sqrt{34}}{3}$ 39. $5i$ 40. $-1 + i\sqrt{2}$ 41. $-4 - i$ 42. $3i\sqrt{3}$ 43. $4 + 8i\sqrt{2}$ 44. $\sqrt{10}$ 45. $\sqrt{13}$ 46. 4 47. $-4 + 6i$ 48. $51 + 21i$ 49. $8 + 6i$ 50. $2 + 16i$ 51. $-2 + i$; 52. $4 - 3i$;

53. $7 + 4i$; 54. $2i$;

Page 985

55. $-i\sqrt{2}, i\sqrt{2}$ 56. $-i\sqrt{5}, i\sqrt{5}$ 57. $-2i, 2i$
58. $\frac{-i\sqrt{6}}{3}, \frac{i\sqrt{6}}{3}$ 59. $-i, -1-i, i$ 60. $i, 1+i, -i$
61. $-1, \frac{1}{3}$ 62. $-\frac{3}{2} + \frac{i\sqrt{91}}{2}, -\frac{3}{2} - \frac{i\sqrt{91}}{2}$
63. $1 + i\sqrt{3}, 1 - i\sqrt{3}$ 64. $\frac{1}{2} + \frac{3i\sqrt{3}}{2}, \frac{1}{2} - \frac{3i\sqrt{3}}{2}$
65. $-\frac{3}{4} + \frac{\sqrt{73}}{4}, -\frac{3}{4} - \frac{\sqrt{73}}{4}$ 66. $-\frac{3}{4}, 1$
67. $y = (x + \frac{3}{2})^2 - \frac{13}{4}; (-\frac{3}{2}, -\frac{13}{4})$
68. $y = 2(x - \frac{1}{4})^2 - \frac{9}{8}; (\frac{1}{4}, -\frac{9}{8})$
69. $y = (x + \frac{1}{2})^2 + \frac{7}{4}; (-\frac{1}{2}, -\frac{7}{4})$ 70. 2 real solutions; $3 + \sqrt{7}, 3 - \sqrt{7}$ 71. 2 imaginary solutions; $\frac{7}{4} + \frac{i\sqrt{31}}{4}, \frac{7}{4} - \frac{i\sqrt{31}}{4}$ 72. 2 real solutions; $3 + \sqrt{5}, 3 - \sqrt{5}$

Chapter 6

Lesson 6-1   pp. 309–311
EXERCISES 1. $10x + 5$; linear binomial 3. $2m^2 + 7m - 3$; quadratic trinomial 13. $y = x^3 + 1$ 15. $y = 1.5x^3 + x^2 - 2x + 1$ 19. $y = x^3 - 10x^2$; 2023 21. $y = -0.03948x^3 + 2.069x^2 - 17.93x + 106.9$; 206 25. $x^3 + 4x$; cubic binomial 27. 7; constant monomial 33. $-c^2 + 16$; binomial 35. $16x^2 + x$; 5; trinomial 47. $30x^3 - 10x^2$; binomial 49. $b^3 - 6b^2 + 9b$; trinomial

Extension   p. 312
1. (✓,✓) 3. (✓,✗) 5. (✗,✓) 7. (✓,✗) 9. (✗,✗)

Lesson 6-2   pp. 317–319
EXERCISES 1. $x^2 + x - 6$ 3. $x^3 - 7x^2 + 15x - 9$ 7. $x(x - 6)(x + 6)$ 9. $5x(2x^2 - 2x + 3)$ 13. about 24.2, -1.4; 0, -5, 1 15a. $h = x$, $\ell = 16 - 2x, w = 12 - 2x$ b. $V = x(16 - 2x)(12 - 2x)$
c.
194 in.³, 2.26 in.
17. 2, -9

21. $y = x^3 - 18x^2 + 107x - 210$ 23. $y = x^3 + 9x^2 + 15x - 25$ 29. -3 (mult. 3) 31. -1, 0, $\frac{1}{2}$ 37. $2x^3$ blocks, $15x^2$ blocks, 31 x blocks, 12 unit blocks 39. $V = 12x^3 - 27x$ 41. $y = -2x^3 + 9x^2 - x - 12$ 43. $y = 3x(x - 1)(x + 1)$ 45. $y = x^2(x + 4)(x - 1)$ 47. about 10.5, -7.1; $\frac{3}{2}$, 4, 6 49. about -2.98, -6.17; 1.5 51. Answers may vary. Sample: $y = x^3 - 3x^2 - 10x$ 53. $y = x^4 - 4x^3 - 7x^2 + 22x + 24$ 55. 0 (mult. 2), -1 (mult. 2)

Lesson 6-3   pp. 324–326
EXERCISES 1. $x - 8$ 3. $x^2 + 4x + 3$, R 5 9. no 11. yes 13. $x^2 + 4x + 3$ 15. $x^2 - 11x + 37$, R -128 23. $y = (x + 1)(x + 3)(x - 2)$ 25. $\ell = x + 3$ and $h = x$ 27. 0 29. 12 37. $x^2 + 4x + 5$ 39. $x^4 - 16$ 41. $x^3 + x^2 - x + 1$ 43. yes 45. no 49. yes 51. no 53. $x^3 - 4x^2 - 2x + 4$, R -35 55. $x^3 - 4x^2 + x$

Lesson 6-4   pp. 330–332
EXERCISES 1. -2, 1, 5 3. 0, 1 13. $(x - 10)(x^2 + 10x + 100)$ 15. $3, \frac{-3}{2} \pm \frac{3i\sqrt{3}}{2}$ 17. $5, \frac{-5}{2} \pm \frac{5i\sqrt{3}}{2}$ 21. $(x^2 - 7)(x - 1)(x + 1)$ 23. $(x^2 - 3)(x - 2)(x + 2)$ 27. $\pm 3, \pm 1$ 29. $\pm 4, \pm 2i$ 33. -1, 3.24, -1.24 35. 1, 2 41. D 43. $\frac{4}{3}, \frac{-2 \pm 2i\sqrt{3}}{3}$ 45. $\pm 5, \pm i\sqrt{2}$ 61. $y = x^2(4x - 2)$, 4 in. by 4 in. by 16 in. 63. $-\frac{5}{2}$; 1; $y = (2x + 5)(x - 1)$ 65. -1, 2, 2; $y = (x + 1)(x - 2)^2$

Lesson 6-5   pp. 339–340
EXERCISES 1. $\pm 1, \pm 2$; 1 3. $\pm 1, \pm 2, \pm 4; -1$ 7. 2, $\pm i\sqrt{5}$ 9. -3, 1, $\frac{1}{2}$ 13. $-\sqrt{5}, \sqrt{13}$ 15. $1 + \sqrt{10}$, $2 + 16x - 32 = 0$ 25. $\pm\frac{11}{12}, \pm\frac{1}{6}, \pm\frac{1}{4}, \pm\frac{1}{3}, \pm\frac{1}{2}, \pm\frac{3}{4}, \pm 1, \pm\frac{4}{3}, \pm 2, \pm 3, \pm 6; \frac{2}{3}, \frac{3}{2}$ 27. $\pm\frac{7}{3}, \pm\frac{1}{2}, \pm\frac{7}{6}, \pm\frac{1}{6}, \pm\frac{7}{2}, \pm\frac{1}{3}, \pm\frac{7}{6}, \pm\frac{7}{2}; \frac{7}{2}, 2$ 29. $x^4 - 6x^3 + 14x^2 - 24x + 40 = 0$ 31. $x^4 - 6x^3 + 2x^2 + 30x - 35 = 0$ 33. Sometimes true; since -2 is a factor of 8, -2 is a possible root of the equation. 35. Sometimes true; since $\sqrt{5}$ and $-\sqrt{5}$ are conjugates, they can be roots of a

---

Page 986

37. D

Lesson 6-6   pp. 343–344
EXERCISES 1. 3 complex roots; number of real roots: 1 or 3; possible rational roots: ± 1 3. 4 complex roots; number of real roots: 0, 2, or 4; possible rational roots: 0 9. $-1, \frac{1 \pm i\sqrt{7}}{2}$ 11. 4, $\frac{1 \pm i\sqrt{3}}{2}$ 17. 4 complex roots; number of real roots: 0, 2, or 4; possible rational roots: $\pm\frac{1}{3}, \pm 1, \pm 2, \pm\frac{13}{3}, \pm 13, \pm 26$ 19. 3 complex roots; number of real roots: 1 or 3; possible rational roots: $\pm\frac{1}{3}, \pm\frac{2}{3}, \pm 1, \pm\frac{4}{3}, \pm 2, \pm 3, \pm 4, \pm 6, \pm 12$ 21. 4, $\pm 3i$ 23. $-6, \frac{-1 \pm i}{2}$

Lesson 6-7   pp. 348–351
EXERCISES 1. 120 3. 6,227,020,800 9a. 24 b. 120 15. 13. 1680 19. 4, 151, 347, 200 21. 15 23. 1 29. 4368 31. 2600 33. true because of the Comm. Prop. of Add. 35. False; answers may vary. Sample: $(3 + 2)! = 120$ and $3! + 2! = 8$ 39. C 43. 84 45. 5 47. permutation 49. combination 51. 210 53. 5 55a. 56 b. 56 57. 3024 59. 24

Lesson 6-8   pp. 355–357
EXERCISES 1. $a^3 + 3a^2b + 3ab^2 + b^3$ 3. $a^4 + 4a^3b + 6a^2b^2 + 4ab^3 + b^4$ 13. $x^4 + 4x^3y + 6x^2y^2 + 4xy^3 + y^4$ 15. $s^2 - 2st + t^2$ 21a. about 25% b. about 21% c. about 12% 23. $x^7 + 7x^6y + 21x^5y^2 + 35x^4y^3 + 35x^3y^4 + 21x^2y^5 + 7xy^6 + y^7$ 25. $81x^4 - 108x^3y + 54x^2y^2 - 12xy^3 + y^4$ 43a. about 31% b. about 16% c. about 16% 45. $_8C_4 x^4 y^4$ 47. $7, 7r^6$ 49. $80x^2$ 51. $264x^{10}$ 59a. $(s + 0.5)^3$ b. $s^3 + 1.5s^2 + 0.75s + 0.125$ 61. 13, d^{12}, $12d^{11}e$ 63. 6, $32a^5$, $80a^4b$

Chapter Review   pp. 359–361
1. degree 2. standard form of a polynomial 3. multiplicity 4. complex conjugates 5. combinations 6. $3p^3 - 2p$; cubic binomial 7. $-5x^9 + 3$; degree 9 binomial 8. $-x^5 - x^3 + x$; quintic trinomial 9. $4x^3 + 2x^2 + 2x$; cubic trinomial 10. $x^7 + x^4 - x^2 + x + 5$; degree 7, 5 terms 11. s; linear monomial 12. cubic; $y = 62.2685x^3 - 303.194x^2 + 481.8148x - 248.522$; quartic; $y = 984.375x^4 - 6631.481x^3 + 16,498.68x^2 - 17,954.685x + 7208.88$;

The quartic model better fits the data.
13. $f(x) = x(x - 4)(x + 3)$; -3, 0, 4; rel. max. ≈ 12.60, rel. min. ≈ -20.75 14. $g(x) = (2 - x)(2 + x)$; -2, 2; rel. max. = 4 15. $y = x^3(x + 2)^4$; 0 (mult. 3), -2 (mult. 4); rel. max. = 0, rel. min. ≈ -1.07 16. $f(x) = x^4 + 3x^3 - 4x^2 - 12x$ 17. $f(x) = x^3 - 4x^2 + 5x - 2$ 18. $f(x) = x^4 + 2x^3 - 3x^2$ 19. $f(x) = x^3 + 6x^2 + 12x + 8$ 20. $x^2 + 5x + 8$, R 12; check students' work. 21. $x^3 - x^2 + x - 2$, R 4; check students' work. 22. $(x + 1)(x - 3)(x - 1)$ 23. $(x - 3)^2(x + 2)$ 24. 93 25. -30 26. 77 27. -9 28. -1, 1.38, 3.62 29. -1.78 30. 0 31. -1.52 32. -1.63 33. no real solution 34. $(x - 2)(x^2 + 2x + 4)$; 2, $-1 \pm i\sqrt{3}$ 35. $t^4(2t - 1)(2t + 1)$; 0, $\frac{1}{2}, -\frac{1}{2}$ 36. $(2x + 1)(4x^2 - 2x + 1)$; $-\frac{1}{2}, \frac{1 \pm i\sqrt{3}}{4}$ 37. $x(x - 4)(x - 1)$; 0, 1, 4 38. $x(x^2 - 2x - 5)$; 0, $1 \pm \sqrt{6}$ 39. $(x + 2)^2(x^2 - 2x + 4)^2$; -2, $1 \pm i\sqrt{3}$ 40. 3 complex roots; number of real roots: 3 or 1; possible rational roots: $\pm 1, \pm 2, \pm 3, \pm 6$; roots 1, 2, 3 41. 4 complex roots; number of real roots: 4, 2, or 0; possible rational roots: $\pm 1, \pm 2, \pm 4, \pm 8, \pm\frac{1}{2}, \pm\frac{1}{4}, \pm\frac{1}{8}, \pm\frac{3}{2}$; roots: $-1, -\frac{1}{2}, \frac{5}{4}, 2$ 42. 4 complex roots; number of real roots: 4, 2, or 0; possible rational roots: $\pm 1, \pm 7$; roots: $\pm 1.26, \pm 2.10$ 43. 4 complex roots; number of real roots: 4, 2, or 0; possible rational roots: $\pm 1, \pm 5$; roots: $-1, -2$ 44. 3 complex roots; number of real roots: 3 or 1; possible rational roots: $\pm 1, \pm 5$; roots: $-1, 2 \pm i$ 45. 4 complex roots; number of real roots: 4, 2, or 0; possible rational roots: $\pm 1, \pm 2, \pm 3, \pm 6, \pm 9, \pm 18$; roots: $\pm 3, 1 \pm i$ 46. $x^3 - 2x^2 + x - 2 = 0$ 47. $x^4 - 16x^3 + 91x^2 - 216x + 182 = 0$ 48. $x^4 - 10x^3 + 39x^2 - 70x + 50 = 0$ 49. $x^5 - 6x^4 + 11x^3 - 24x^2 + 28x = 0$ 50. $x^4 - 8x^3 + 23x^2 - 42x + 30 = 0$ 51. $x^4 - 12x^2 + 35 = 0$ 52. 72 53. 24 54. 35 55. 30 56. 2 57. 120 58. $4320x^3y^3$ 59. about 27%

Chapter 7

Lesson 7-1   pp. 372–373
EXERCISES 1. 15, -15 3. none 5. -4 7. $-\frac{1}{2}$ 9. 2, -2 11. 0.3, -0.3 13. 6 15. no real-number root 21. $4|x|$ 23. $x^4|y|^9$ 29. 1.34 in. 31. 0.48 cm 33. 10, -10 35. 0.5, -0.5 37. $\sqrt[3]{-64}, \sqrt[6]{64}, -\sqrt[3]{-64}, \sqrt[6]{64}$ 39. 0.5 41. 0.2 59. Some; they are equal for $x \geq 0$. 61. Some; they are equal for $x \geq 0$.

Page 987

Lesson 7-2   pp. 377–379
EXERCISES 1. 16 3. -9 9. $2x\sqrt{5x}$ 11. $5x^2\sqrt{2x}$ 17. $2\sqrt[3]{12}$ 19. $7x^3y^4\sqrt{6y}$ 23. 10 25. $2x^2y^2\sqrt{2}$ 27. $\frac{\sqrt{2x}}{2}$ 29. $\frac{\sqrt[3]{4x}}{2}$ 35. $r = \sqrt{\frac{Gm_xm_zF}{F}}$ 37. $10\sqrt{2}$ 39. $3x^6y^5\sqrt{2}y$ 55. 212 mi/h greater

Lesson 7-3   pp. 382–384
EXERCISES 1. $6\sqrt{6}$ 3. cannot combine 7. $33\sqrt{2}$ 9. $7\sqrt{2}$ 13. $8 + 4\sqrt{5}$ 15. $63 - 38\sqrt{2}$ 19. 14 21. -40 23. $-2 + 2\sqrt{3}$ 25. $13 + 7\sqrt{3}$ 27. $13\sqrt{2}$ 29. $48\sqrt{2x}$

Lesson 7-4   pp. 388–390
EXERCISES 1. 6 3. 7 11. $\sqrt[10]{x}$ 13. $\sqrt[5]{y^2}$ or $(\sqrt[5]{y})^2$ 19. $7^{\frac{1}{3}}x^{\frac{2}{3}}$ 21. $(7x)^{\frac{1}{5}}$ 27. ~15.1 m 29. ~1.6 m 31. 16 33. 64 39. $\frac{1}{x^3}$ 41. $\frac{5}{x^3}$ 51. -3 53. 729 63. A 65. $x^{\frac{7}{12}}$ 67. $x^{\frac{1}{2}}$

Lesson 7-5   pp. 394–396
EXERCISES 1. 16 3. 22 7. 3, -13 9. 18 13. 30.6 ft 15. 3 17. -3, -4 21. 3 23. 1 35. 4 37. 23

Lesson 7-6   pp. 400–404
EXERCISES 1. $x^2 + 3x + 5$ 3. $-x^2 + 3x + 5$ 13. $2x^2 + 2x - 4$; domain: all real numbers 15. $2x^2 - 2$; domain: all real numbers 21. $x^2 + 5x$; 14, 9 23. 104 25. 16 31. 33 33. -3 43a. $f(x) = 0.9x$ b. $g(x) = x - 2000$ c. $14,200 d. $14,400 45. $x^2 - x + 7$ 47. $x^2 - 5x - 3$ 51. $-3x^2 + 2x + 16$; domain: all real numbers 53. $3x^2 + 8x^2 - 4x + 16$; domain: all real numbers 59. -4 61. 2 63. $3x^2, 9x^2$ 65. $12x^2 + 2, 6x^2 + 4$ 71a. $P(x) = 5295x - 1000$ b. $158,750 73. $(f + g)(x) = f(x) + g(x)$ Def. of Function Add.
$= 3x - 2 + (x^2 + 1)$ Substitution
$= 3x + x^2 - 2 + 1$ Comm. Prop.
$= x^2 + 3x - 1$ arithmetic
75. $(f \circ g)(x) = f(g(x))$ def. of comp. functions
$= f(x^2 + 1)$ substitution
$= 3(x^2 + 1) - 2$ substitution
$= 3x^2 + 3 - 2$ Dist. Prop.
$= 3x^2 + 1$ arithmetic

Lesson 7-7   pp. 410–412
EXERCISES
1.

x	0	1	2	3
y	1	2	3	4

5. $y = \frac{1}{3}x - \frac{1}{3}$; yes 7. $y = -\frac{1}{3}x + \frac{4}{3}$; yes
15.
23. $f^{-1}(x) = \frac{x - 4}{3}$, and the domain and range for both f and f^{-1} are all real numbers; f^{-1} is a function. 25. $f^{-1}(x) = x^2 - 7, x \geq 0$, domain f: $\{x | x \geq -7\}$, range f: $\{y | y \geq 0\}$, domain f^{-1}: $\{x | x \geq 0\}$, and range f^{-1}: $\{y | y \geq -7\}$; f^{-1} is a function. 29a. $F = \frac{9}{5}(C - 32)$; yes b. $-3.89°F$ 31. 10 33. 0.2 35. $f^{-1}(x) = \pm\sqrt{\frac{2x + 8}{3}}$; no 37. $f^{-1}(x) = \frac{x^2 - 8}{2}, x \geq 3$; yes 47. $f^{-1}(x) = x^2, x \leq 0$, domain of f: $\{x | x \leq 0\}$, range of f: $\{y | y \geq 0\}$, domain of f^{-1}: $\{x | x \geq 0\}$, range of f^{-1}: $\{y | y \leq 0\}$, and f^{-1} is a function. 49. $f^{-1}(x) = 3 - x^2, x \geq 0$, domain of f: $\{x | x \leq 3\}$, range of f: $\{y | y \geq 0\}$, domain of f^{-1}: $\{x | x \geq 0\}$, range of f^{-1}: $\{y | y \leq 3\}$, and f^{-1} is a function. 59a–b. Answers may vary. Sample:
a. b.
61. $n = s\sqrt{2}$; $3\sqrt{2}$ in. ≈ 4.2 in.

Lesson 7-8   pp. 417–419
EXERCISES
1. 9.

Page 988

19.
25. 147 27. -8.11 31. $y = 3\sqrt{x - 1}$; the graph is the graph of $y = 3\sqrt{x}$ translated 1 unit to the right. 33. $y = -14\sqrt{x + 1}$; the graph is the graph of $y = -14\sqrt{x}$ translated 1 unit to the left.

Chapter Review   pp. 423–425
1. radicand 2. index 3. rationalize the denominator 4. are not 5. rational exponents 6. composite function 7. rational exponents 8. inverse functions 9. a radical equation 10. principal root 11. 12 12. -0.4 13. 7 14. 0.5 15. -3 16. 3 17. $-4y^3$ 18. $(a - 1)^2$ 19. $3x^3$ 20. $(y + 8)^2$ 21. $4x^4y^2\sqrt{2xy}$ 22. 20 23. $6\sqrt[3]{2}$ 24. $10x^2y^3\sqrt[3]{12y^2}$ 25. $7x^2\sqrt{2}$ 26. $15x^3y^2\sqrt{x}$ 27. $6xy\sqrt[3]{2}$ 28. 4 29. $2y\sqrt[3]{y^2}$ 30. $5x$ 31. $6xy\sqrt{3}$ 32. $3a^2b^3\sqrt{b}$ 33. $\frac{2\sqrt{3}}{3}$ 34. $\frac{x\sqrt{6x}}{3}$ 35. $\frac{\sqrt[3]{5y^2}}{2}$ 36. $\frac{a^3\sqrt[3]{ab}}{b}$ 37. $\frac{y\sqrt[3]{150x}}{10x^2}$ 38. $6\sqrt{3}$ 39. $7 - 3\sqrt{3}$ 40. 43 41. $2\sqrt{2}$ 42. $\frac{42 - 12\sqrt{3}}{37}$ 43. $\frac{-\sqrt{2} + \sqrt{10}}{4}$ 44. $\sqrt[3]{3}$ 45. $\sqrt[4]{x^2}$ 46. $\sqrt[4]{\frac{1}{8}}$ 47. $\sqrt[3]{48}$ 48. $\sqrt[4]{\frac{1}{9}}$ 49. 81 50. 216 51. x 52. $x^{\frac{4}{5}}$ 53. $\sqrt[4]{x}$ 54. -42 55. 2 56. 121 57. $x^2 - x + 7$ 58. $4x^2 + 5x + 3$ 59. $2x^3 - x^2 - 11x + 10$ 60. $x^2 - 5x - 3$ 61. $\frac{x^2 - 9x + 2}{2x + 5}, x \neq -\frac{5}{2}$ 62. 1 63. 25 64. 9 65. 1 66. $c^2 - 6c + 9$ 67. $y = \frac{1}{8}x - \frac{1}{3}$; yes 68. $y = (\frac{x}{2})^{\frac{1}{3}}$; yes 69. $y = \pm\sqrt{x} + 2$; no 70. $y = x^2 - 2, x \geq 0$; yes 71. 5 72. -5 73. 6 74. t

75. 76. 77. 78.

Chapter 8

Lesson 8-1   pp. 434–437
EXERCISES
1.
9a. 1.0126 b. $y = 6.08(1.0126)^x$, where $x = 0$ corresponds to 2000 11. $y = 2.5(7)^x$ 13. $y = 5(0.6)^x$ 17. exponential decay 19. exponential decay
25. $y = 0$ is the horizontal asymptote.
33. $y = 12,000(0.9)^x$; 6377 35a. $y = 6500(0.857)^x$ b. $4091.25 37. 30% increase 39. 70% decrease 43a. about 5.6% b. about 0.0017% 47. 6 49. 0.45

Lesson 8-2   pp. 442–444
EXERCISES 1. Asymptote is $y = 0$.
9.
15. $y = 50(\frac{1}{3})^{\frac{x}{13.8}}$; 0.85 mg 17. $y = 24(\frac{1}{2})^{\frac{x}{5730}}$; 0.64 mg 19. 403.4288 21. 1 25. $448.30 27. 0 33. $y = -8$; $y = -3^{x-8} + 2$ 35. $y = -3(\frac{1}{3})^x$; $y = -3(\frac{1}{3})^{x+5} + 1$ 37. 8.7 yr 41. $399.97 43. exponential growth 45. exponential growth

Lesson 8-3   pp. 449–452
EXERCISES 1. The earthquake in Missouri released about 1.97 times more energy. 3. The earthquake in Missouri released about 8,759,310 times more energy. 7. $3 = \log 1000$ 9. $\log_{10} \frac{1}{10} = -1$ 15. $\frac{1}{2}$ 17. $\frac{3}{2}$ 27. 6.3×10^{-3} 29. 7.9×10^{-4}

35.

41. 0.6990; 0 **43.** -1.0969; -2 **53.** $128 = 2^7$
55. $16{,}807 = 7^5$ **65.** $y = 0.5^x$ **67.** $y = 2^{x-1}$
73. **75.**

77. domain $\{x \mid x > 0\}$, range: all reals
79. domain $\{x \mid x > 0\}$, range: all reals

Lesson 8-4   pp. 457–459
EXERCISES 1. Product Property **3.** Power Property **11.** $\log 14$ **13.** $\log 972$ **19.** $3 \log x + 5 \log y$ **21.** $\log_4 5 + \frac{1}{2} \log_4 x$ **31.** 9 dB **33.** -2
35. 6 **45.** 1.4772, **47.** 2.097 **57.** 0.00001 **59.** False; $\frac{1}{2} \log 3 = \log_3 3^{1/2}$, not $\log_3 \frac{3}{2}$.
61. False; the two logs have different bases.
73. $\log_3 \sqrt[5]{2x}$ **75.** $\log \frac{27}{2}$ **79.** $3 \log 2 + \frac{3}{2} \log x - 3 \log 5$ **81.** $\log 2 + \frac{1}{2} \log 4 + \frac{1}{2} \log r - \log s$

Lesson 8-5   pp. 464–468
EXERCISES 1. 1.5850 **3.** 2.7320 **13.** 0.5690
15. 4.7027 **17.** 6 **19.** 0.64 **25.** $\log 14$ **27.** $\log 972$
33. 0.05 **35.** 33 **43.** $100{,}000 \sqrt{5} \approx 223{,}606.8$
45. $\frac{1}{4}$ **51.** $2 = 10\left(\frac{1}{2}\right)^{1.17}$, about 2.7 min. **53.** -1
55. $\frac{1}{2}$ **61a.** Let x equal the number of years after 2000. Florida growth factor = 1.0213,
$y = 15{,}982{,}378 \cdot (1.0213)^x$; New York growth factor = 1.0054, $y = 18{,}976{,}457 \cdot (1.0054)^x$ **b.** 2011
69. $\frac{\log 8}{\log 3}$ **71.** $\frac{\log 3.3}{\log 9}$ **77a.** top up: 10^{-5} W/m², top down: $10^{-2.5}$ W/m² **b.** 99.67% **79.** 2.9315
81. 0.6225

Lesson 8-6   pp. 472–475
EXERCISES 1. $\ln 125$ **3.** $\ln 4$ **11.** 24.13
13. 25 seconds **15.** 0.135 **17.** 1488.979
23. 2.890 **25.** 2.401 **29.** 6 years **31.** 1 **33.** 10
39. 301 **41.** sometimes **43.** always
45. about 19.8 hours **47.** 3.6 **49.** 9.4 **55.** 542.31
57. 0.0794

Chapter Review   pp. 479–481
1. growth factor **2.** common logarithm **3.** asymptote **4.** logarithm **5.** exponential equation **6.** exponential growth; 400%

7. exponential growth; 300%

8. exponential growth; 280%

9. exponential decay; -75%

10. $y = \frac{25}{4}\left(\frac{7}{5}\right)^x$ **11.** $y = 0.0015(10)^x$
12. $y = 2.25\left(\frac{1}{3}\right)^x$ **13.** $y = \left(\frac{1}{2}\right)^x$
14. $y = 12{,}500(0.91)^x$; \$7800 **15.** $y = 50(1.03)^x$; \$58
16. $y = 1500(0.2)^x$; 2.4 **17.** $y = 2(1.4)^x$; 7.6832
18. $y = 3^x$ reflected over the x-axis and translated up 1 unit

19. $y = 8^x$ translated down 1 unit

20. $y = 2(2)^x$ translated left 1 unit and up 3 units

21. $y = 2\left(\frac{1}{3}\right)^x$ reflected over the x-axis and translated 2 units right

22. \$1100.76 **23.** \$291.91 **24.** \$645.23
25. 2.7183 **26.** 0.3679 **27.** 148.4132 **28.** 0.6065
29. $y = 3\left(\frac{1}{2}\right)^{t/1420}$; ≈ 2.937 mg **30.** 2.0×10^{-6}
31. 7 **32.** $2 = \log_6 36$ **33.** $-3 = \log_2 0.125$
34. $3 = \log_3 27$ **35.** $-3 = \log 0.001$ **36.** 6
37. -2 **38.** -5 **39.** 0

40. **41.**

42. **43.**

44. $\log 24$ **45.** $\log \frac{5}{6}$ **46.** $\log_3 7x^4$ **47.** $\log \frac{7}{6}$
48. $2 \log_4 x + 3 \log_4 y$; Product and Power Properties **49.** $\log 4 + 4 \log s + \log t$; Product and Power Properties **50.** $\log_3 2 - \log_3 x$; Quotient Property **51.** $2 \log (x + 3)$; Power Property **56.** 1.37 **57.** 1 **58.** ≈ 0.66 **59.** ≈ 0.67 **60.** ≈ 3.06
61. $\frac{10}{3}$ **62.** 8 **63.** 50 **64.** 7,625,597,484,987
65. $\log_5 91.68$ **66.** about 18.2 h **67.** 0.83
68. 2.26 **69.** 4.31 **70.** 0.00018 **71.** 3.77 **72.** 6.03
73. 3.4%

Chapter 9
Lesson 9-1   pp. 491–493
EXERCISES 1. $y = \frac{11}{x}$ **3.** $y = \frac{1}{x}$ **7.** direct; $y = 5x$
9. direct; $y = 2x$ **13.** $y = \frac{100}{x}$; 10 **15.** $y = -\frac{5}{3x}$; $-\frac{1}{6}$
17. A varies jointly with b and h. **19.** V varies jointly with B and h. **25.** $z = 10xy$; 360
27. $z = \frac{x}{y^3}$; $\frac{1}{3}$ **29.** 18 **31.** $\frac{1}{4}$ **35.** 7200 rpm **37.** $18\frac{2}{3}$

39. 2 **43.** 2.625 **45.** 8 **49.** 32 **51.** $\frac{40}{3}$ **53.** 32
55. quartered; divided by 16

Lesson 9-2   pp. 498–500
EXERCISES
1.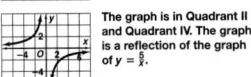
5. The graph is in Quadrant II and Quadrant IV. The graph is a reflection of the graph of $y = \frac{3}{x}$.
7. The graph is in Quadrant II and Quadrant IV. The graph is a reflection of the graph of $y = \frac{6}{x}$.
11. 7.67 ft **13.** 1.84 ft
15.
23. $y = \frac{2}{x+2} + 3$ **27.** $y = \frac{0.5}{x}$ **29.** $y = -\frac{8}{3x}$
33.
41. (3, 6)

Lesson 9-3   pp. 505–508
EXERCISES 1. $x = 0$, $x = 2$ **3.** $x = 1$, $x = -1$
11. hole at $x = -5$ **13.** vertical asymptote at $x = -1$, hole at $x = 2$ **19.** $y = 0$ **21.** $y = 1$
25. **31a.** $y = \frac{0.19x + 210{,}000}{x - 500}$
b. \$46.88; \$14.68 **c.** more than 21,916 discs **d.** $x = 500$, $y = 0.19$ **33.** vertical asymptote at $x = -2$
35.

43a. $y = \frac{20{,}000x + 200{,}000}{x + 1}$

WINDOW FORMAT
Xmin=0
Xmax=40
Xscl=4
Ymin=0
Ymax=200000
Yscl=10000
b. \$65,000; \$25,806.45

Lesson 9-4   pp. 511–513
EXERCISES 1. $\frac{1}{2x-1}$; $x \ne 0$ or $\frac{1}{2}$ **3.** $b + 1$; $b \ne 1$
7. $\frac{7}{15x^2}$; $x \ne 0$, $y \ne 0$ **9.** $\frac{4}{3}$; $y \ne \frac{1}{2}$ or 3 **13.** $\frac{2}{3xy^3}$;
$x \ne 0$, $y \ne 0$ **15.** $\frac{5(x+y)}{3}$; $x \ne y$ **19.** $\frac{x-8}{x-10}$;
$x \ne -3$ or 10 **21.** $\frac{y(y+3)}{12(y+4)}$; $x \ne 0$, $y \ne -4$ or 3
27. $\frac{a+3}{(a-3)(a-3)}$; $a \ne -4$, -3, or 3 **29.** $\frac{3}{2(y+4)}$; $x \ne 0$, -5, 4, or 1 **33.** $\frac{(x-1)^3}{(x+4)^3}$; $x \ne -4$, 0, 1 **35.** $\frac{18x^5}{y^3}$, $y \ne 0$
37a. 1.2 m/s² **b.** 2.68 m/s²

Lesson 9-5   pp. 517–520
EXERCISES 1. $\frac{120}{59} \approx 2.03$ in. **5.** $(x-1)(x+1)(x+1)$ **7.** $18(2x-7)(x+3)$ **11.** $\frac{2(d-2)}{2d+1}$
13. $\frac{7x^2 + 20x - 18}{(x-3)(x+3)(x+4)}$ **17.** $\frac{-3(2y+1)}{2y-1}$

19. $\frac{x^2 - 24}{3x(x+3)}$ **23.** $\frac{15}{28}$ **25.** $\frac{5}{9}$ **31.** $\frac{3x-8}{4x^2}$
33. $\frac{2x^2 - x^2 + 1}{x^2(x+1)(x-1)}$ **45.** $\frac{2x - 5y}{2(3x + 2y)}$ **47.** x

Lesson 9-6   pp. 524–527
EXERCISES 1. 5 **3.** 10 **11.** 10 **13.** 2
23. passenger train: 112 mi/h, freight train: 92 mi/h **25.** $1\frac{5}{9}$ h **27.** $E = mc^2$ **29.** $c = \sqrt{a^2 - b^2}$
39. 3 **41.** no solution

Lesson 9-7   pp. 534–537
EXERCISES 1. independent **3.** dependent **5.** $\frac{1}{8}$
7. 0.54 **11.** Mutually exclusive since if the numbers are equal, then the sum is even.
13. 47% **15.** $\frac{14}{15}$ **17.** $\frac{26}{35}$ **19.** $\frac{1}{2}$ **21.** $\frac{5}{12}$ **27.** $\frac{7}{12}$
29. $\frac{31}{56}$ **31.** 13% **33.** 98% **37.** $\frac{4}{15}$ **39.** $\frac{1}{15}$ **41.** $\frac{1}{11}$
43. $\frac{7}{15}$ **45a.** $\frac{1}{4}$ **b.** $\frac{1}{64}$

Chapter Review   pp. 539–541
1. mutually exclusive **2.** simplest form **3.** independent events **4.** branch **5.** point of discontinuity **6.** $y = \frac{150}{x}$; 30 **7.** $y = \frac{60}{x}$; 12
8. $y = \frac{180}{x}$; 36 **9.** $y = \frac{72}{x}$; 2 **10.** not possible
11. $y = 6x$ **12.** $z = \frac{5}{4}xy$; 56 **13.** $z = \frac{5y}{x}$; 2
14. $z = \frac{x^3}{y}$; 8 **15.** R varies jointly with k, m and the square of n. **16.** W varies jointly with the square of d. **17.** P varies directly with x and inversely with the product of z and the square of y.
18.
19.

20.

21.

22. $y = \frac{4}{x} + 3$ **23.** $y = \frac{4}{x+2} + 2$ **24.** $y = \frac{4}{x+3} - 4$
25. about 31,056 headsets

26. -7 vertical asymptote $x = -7$, horizontal asymptote $y = 0$

27. -2, 1 vertical asymptote $x = -2$, horizontal asymptote $y = 0$, hole at $x = 1$

28. 1, -1 vertical asymptote $x = -1$, hole at $x = 1$

29. no points of discontinuity horizontal asymptote $y = 2$
30. $\frac{(x-1)(x+1)}{x+3}$; $x \ne -4$, -3, or 6
31. $\frac{(2x-1)(x+1)}{x+4}$; $x \ne -4$, -1, or 0 **32.** $\frac{5}{3}$
33. 12 cm **34.** $\frac{3(3x-4)}{(x-2)(x+2)}$
35. $\frac{-x^2 + 3x + 2}{x(x+1)(x-1)(x+3)}$ **36.** $\frac{8}{15}$ **37.** $\frac{1}{4(x+y)}$
38. -1 **39.** no solution **40.** -12, 9 **41.** 7.5 h, 15 h **42.** dependent **43.** independent
44. not mutually exclusive **45.** not mutually exclusive **46.** $\frac{1}{3}$ **47.** $\frac{3}{8}$ **48.** $\frac{5}{8}$

Chapter 10
Lesson 10-1   pp. 550–553
EXERCISES
1.

Hyperbola: center (0, 0), y-intercepts at $\pm\frac{5\sqrt{3}}{3}$, no x-intercepts, the lines of symmetry are the x- and y-axes; domain: all real numbers, range: $y \ge \frac{5\sqrt{3}}{3}$ or $y \le -\frac{5\sqrt{3}}{3}$ **17.** center (0, 0), x-intercepts at ± 3, y-intercepts at ± 2; domain: $-3 \le x \le 3$, range: $-2 \le y \le 2$ **19.** center (0, 0), x-intercepts at ± 3, no y-intercepts; domain: $x \le -3$ or $x \ge 3$, range: all real numbers **23.** 19 **25.** 18
29.

Hyperbola: center (0, 0), x-intercepts ± 4, the lines of symmetry are the x- and y-axes; domain: $x \le -4$ or $x \ge 4$, range: all real numbers.

35. $x^2 + y^2 = 36$ **39.** D

41, 43. Answers may vary. Samples are given.
41. $(\sqrt{2}, 1)$ **43.** $(2, 0)$

Lesson 10-2 pp. 558–560

EXERCISES 1. $y = \frac{1}{8}x^2$ **3.** $x = -\frac{1}{12}y^2$ **7.** $x = \frac{1}{24}y^2$
9. $y = \frac{1}{28}x^2$ **13.** $y = \frac{1}{8}x^2$ **17.** $\left(0, \frac{1}{4}\right)$, $y = -\frac{1}{4}$
19. $\left(-\frac{1}{2}, 0\right)$, $x = -\frac{1}{2}$
25. $(0, 0)$, $(0, -1)$, $y = 1$

37. $y = \frac{1}{400}x^2$ **39.** $x = -\frac{1}{28}y^2$ **43.** $x = -\frac{1}{8}y^2$
45. $x = y^2$
47.

53. $x = -\frac{1}{2}(y - 1)^2 + 1$

Lesson 10-3 pp. 564–566

EXERCISES 1. $x^2 + y^2 = 100$ **3.** $(x - 2)^2 +$
$(y - 3)^2 = 20.25$ **9.** $x^2 + (y + 1)^2 = 9$
11. $(x - 2)^2 + (y + 4)^2 = 25$ **17.** $(x + 3)^2 +$
$(y - 4)^2 = 9$ **19.** $(1, 1), 1$ **21.** $(3, -1), 6$
27.

35. $x^2 + y^2 = 16$ **37.** $x^2 + y^2 = 25$ **45.** $(x + 6)^2 +$
$(y - 13)^2 = 49$ **47.** $(x + 2)^2 + (y - 7.5)^2 = 2.25$
55. $(0, 0)$, $\sqrt{2}$ **57.** $(0, 0)$, $\sqrt{14}$
65. circle; $(x - 4)^2 + (y - 3)^2 = 16$;

Lesson 10-4 pp. 571–573

EXERCISES 1. $\frac{x^2}{16} + \frac{y^2}{9} = 1$ **3.** $\frac{x^2}{9} + \frac{y^2}{4} = 1$
9. $\frac{x^2}{2.25} + \frac{y^2}{0.25} = 1$ **11.** $\frac{x^2}{36} + \frac{y^2}{100} = 1$
19. $(0, 4)$, $(0, -4)$

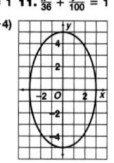

27. $\frac{x^2}{100} + \frac{y^2}{64} = 1$ **29.** $\frac{x^2}{39} + \frac{y^2}{64} = 1$ **33.** $(\sqrt{5}, 0)$,
$(-\sqrt{5}, 0)$ **35.** $(0, 4\sqrt{2})$, $(0, -4\sqrt{2})$ **45.** $\frac{x^2}{16} + y^2 = 1$
47. $\frac{x^2}{4} + \frac{y^2}{16} = 1$ **51.** $\frac{x^2}{25} + \frac{y^2}{4} = 1$ **53.** $\frac{x^2}{702.25} +$
$\frac{y^2}{210.25} = 1$

Lesson 10-5 pp. 578–580

EXERCISES
1.

11. $(0, \sqrt{113})$, $(0, -\sqrt{113})$;

19. $\frac{x^2}{69,169} - \frac{y^2}{96,480} = 1$ **21.** $\frac{x^2}{192,432,384} -$
$\frac{y^2}{170,203,465} = 1$ **23.** $\frac{x^2}{9} - \frac{y^2}{16} = 1$ **25.** $y^2 - \frac{x^2}{3} = 1$
27.

---

31. $\frac{y^2}{9} - x^2 = 1$

33. $y = \pm\frac{1}{2}\sqrt{2x^2 - 8}$; $(2, 0)$, $(-2, 0)$

41. $(\pm 1, 0)$, $y = \pm\frac{1}{3}x$ **43.** $(\pm 5, 0)$, $y = \pm\frac{4}{5}x$

Lesson 10-6 pp. 585–588

EXERCISES
1. $\frac{(x + 2)^2}{9} + \frac{(y - 1)^2}{4} = 1$ **3.** $\frac{x^2}{36} + \frac{(y + 4)^2}{25} = 1$
5. $\frac{(x + 3)^2}{16} - \frac{(y - 3)^2}{9} = 1$ **7.** $\frac{(x + 1)^2}{9} - \frac{(y - 2)^2}{40} = 1$
11. $\frac{(x - 175)^2}{1936} - \frac{y^2}{28,689} = 1$
13. $(x + 6)^2 + y^2 = 81$;
circle, center $(-6, 0)$,
radius 9

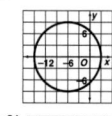

29. $(x + 6)^2 + (y - 9)^2 = 81$

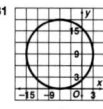

33. $\frac{(x - 1)^2}{9} + \frac{(y + 1)^2}{16} = 1$ **35.** $(x + 4)^2 +$
$(y + 4)^2 = 25$ **37.** $(x - 8)^2 + (y - 2)^2 = 4$
39. $y - 5 = 4(x - 3)^2$
49. ellipse, $\frac{x^2}{9} + \frac{y^2}{36} = 1$

Chapter Review pp. 591–593

1. directrix **2.** major axis **3.** standard form of an
equation of a circle **4.** radius **5.** transverse axis

6.

ellipse; x-axis and
y-axis;
domain: $-7 \le x \le 7$
range: $-11 \le y \le 11$

7.

circle; every line through the
center; domain: $-2 \le x \le 2$
range: $-2 \le y \le 2$

8.

hyperbola; x-axis and y-axis;
domain: $x \le -5$ or $x \ge 5$
range: all real numbers

9.

parabola; x-axis; domain: $x \ge 5$, range: all real
numbers **10.** center $(0, 0)$; $(\pm 4, 0)$; domain: $x \ge 4$
or $x \le -4$, range: all real numbers **11.** center
$(0, 0)$; $(0, \pm 2)$, $(\pm 3, 0)$; domain: $-3 \le x \le 3$, range:
$-2 \le y \le 2$ **12.** $y = \frac{1}{8}x^2$ **13.** $x = -\frac{1}{12}y^2 + 1$
14. $x = \frac{1}{20}y^2$ **15.** $y = -\frac{1}{24}x^2$ **16.** $y = \frac{1}{24}x^2$
17. $y = \frac{1}{16}x^2$ **18.** $y = 3x^2$
19. $\left(0, \frac{1}{20}\right)$, $y = -\frac{1}{20}$

20. $\left(\frac{1}{8}, 0\right)$, $x = -\frac{1}{8}$

---

21. $(-2, 0)$, $x = 2$

22. $x^2 + y^2 = 16$ **23.** $(x - 8)^2 + (y - 1)^2 = 25$
24. $(x + 3)^2 + (y - 2)^2 = 100$ **25.** $(x - 5)^2 +$
$(y + 3)^2 = 64$ **26.** $(x - 3)^2 + (y - 1)^2 = 9$
27. $(x + 1)^2 + y^2 = 4$
28. center $(1, 0)$, radius 8

29. center $(-7, -3)$, radius 7

30. $\frac{x^2}{17} + \frac{y^2}{16} = 1$ **31.** $\frac{x^2}{25} + \frac{y^2}{29} = 1$ **32.** $\frac{x^2}{9} + \frac{y^2}{10} = 1$
33. $\frac{x^2}{40} + \frac{y^2}{36} = 1$ **34.** $\frac{x^2}{64} + \frac{y^2}{16} = 1$
35.

foci $(0, \pm\sqrt{5})$

36. foci $(\pm 3\sqrt{29}, 0)$

37. foci $(0, \pm\sqrt{569})$

38. foci $(\pm\sqrt{202}, 0)$

39. $\frac{x^2}{1.148 \times 10^{10}} - \frac{y^2}{3.395 \times 10^{10}} = 1$
40. $\frac{(x - 3)^2}{9} + \frac{(y + 2)^2}{9} = 1$ **41.** $\frac{(x - 6)^2}{9} - \frac{(y - 3)^2}{16} = 1$
42. $\frac{(x - 77.5)^2}{1640.25} - \frac{y^2}{4366} = 1$
43. hyperbola; center $(0, -2)$, foci $(0, -2 \pm 2\sqrt{10})$

44. circle, center $\left(-\frac{3}{2}, 2\right)$, radius $\frac{\sqrt{61}}{2}$

45. parabola; vertex $\left(-\frac{1}{2}, -\frac{169}{4}\right)$

46. ellipse; center $(1, -2)$, foci $\left(\frac{3 \pm \sqrt{51}}{3}, -2\right)$

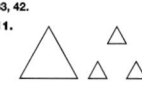

Chapter 11

Lesson 11-1 pp. 603–605

EXERCISES 1. Subtract 3; 65, 62, 59. **3.** Add one
more to each term (add 3, add 4, add 5, etc.); 25,
33, 42.
11.

13. $a_n = n^2 - 2$, $a_1 = 43$; 33 **15.** $a_n = a_{n-1} -$
5, $a_1 = 6$; -14 **19.** $a_n = \frac{1}{n+1}$; $\frac{1}{13}$ **21.** $a_n = 4n -$
1; 47 **25.** explicit; 0, 1, 3, 6, 10 **27.** recursive; -2,
6, -18, 54, -162 **33.** 20, 23; $a_n = 3n + 2$; explicit
or $a_n = a_{n-1} + 3$, $a_1 = 5$; recursive **35.** 216, 343;
$a_n = n^3$; explicit **45.** 26, 677; 458, 330; 2.1×10^{11}
47. 25, 36, 49, 64 **51a.** 25 boxes **b.** 110 boxes
c. 9 levels

Lesson 11-2 pp. 608–610

EXERCISES 1. no **3.** no **11.** 127 **13.** 12.5
21. -7.5 **23.** 13 **31.** 4 **33.** 13 **47.** 15 **49.** 22
53. $a_n = 0 + 6(n - 1)$, $a_n = a_{n-1} + 6$, $a_1 = 0$
55. $a_n = -4 + 4(n - 1)$, $a_n = a_{n-1} + 4$, $a_1 = -4$
63. -4, -10, -16 **65.** -8, -17, -26 **71a.** $20,
$45, $75, $110, $150, $195, $245, $300, $360, $425,
$495 **b.** $a_n = a_{n-1} + $20 + $5(n - 1)$, $a_1 = $20
c. $495

Extension p. 611

1a. fifth **b.** seventh **c.** sixth **d.** fourth **3a.** 1, 1, 2,
3, 5, 8, 13, 21, 34, 55 **b.** 143; 13; the answer is the
seventh term. **c.** Check students' work; the
answer is the seventh term. **d.** It will be 11 times
the seventh term.

Lesson 11-3 pp. 614–617

EXERCISES 1. yes; 2; 16, 32 **3.** yes; -2; 16, -32
13. $a_n = 5 \cdot (-3)^{n-1}$; 5, -15, 45, -135, 405
15. $a_n = \frac{1}{3}\left(\frac{2}{3}\right)^{n-1}$; $\frac{1}{3}$, $\frac{2}{9}$, $\frac{4}{27}$, $\frac{8}{81}$ **23.** 1530 **25.** 1.5
29. arithmetic; 125, 150 **31.** arithmetic; 50, 55
37. 6561, 2187, 729, or -6561, 2187, -729
39. 10, 8, 6.4, or -10, 8, -6.4 **43.** 12,288
45. 201,326,592 **49.** 16 **51.** 10 **59.** 7

Lesson 11-4 pp. 622–624

EXERCISES 1. $21 + 18 + 15 + 12 + 9 + 6 + 3$;
84 **3.** $100 + 99 + 98 + 97 + 96 + 95$; 585 **7.** 32
9. 264 **13.** $\sum_{n=1}^{4} 2n$ **15.** $\sum_{n=1}^{7} (n + 4)$ **19.** 5, 1, 9; 25
21. 6, 4, -1; 9 **25.** sequence; infinite **27.** series;
finite **33a.** 91 **b.** 83 **35.** 110 **37.** 5150

Lesson 11-5 pp. 628–631

EXERCISES 1. 255 **3.** 381 **9.** converges; has a
sum **11.** converges; has a sum **19.** 1 **21.** $\frac{9}{2}$
25. arithmetic; 420 **27.** geometric; 96.47 **33.** 4
35. no sum **41.** $\frac{7}{8}$

Extension p. 633

1. $1 + 3 + 5 + 7 + 9 + 11 \stackrel{?}{=} 6^2$, $36 = 36$; $1 +$
$3 + 5 + 7 + 9 + 11 + 13 \stackrel{?}{=} 7^2$, $49 = 49$; $1 + 3 +$
$5 + 7 + 9 + 11 + 13 + 15 \stackrel{?}{=} 8^2$, $64 = 64$
3. For $n = 1$, $\frac{1}{1(1 + 1)} = \frac{1}{1 + 1}$
Assume
$\frac{1}{1 \cdot 2} + \frac{1}{2 \cdot 3} + \frac{1}{3 \cdot 4} + \cdots + \frac{1}{k(k + 1)} = \frac{k}{k + 1}$
Prove
$\frac{1}{1 \cdot 2} + \frac{1}{2 \cdot 3} + \frac{1}{3 \cdot 4} + \cdots +$
$\frac{1}{(k + 1)((k + 1) + 1)} = \frac{k + 1}{(k + 1) + 1}$
Proof
$\frac{1}{1 \cdot 2} + \frac{1}{2 \cdot 3} + \frac{1}{3 \cdot 4} + \cdots + \frac{1}{k(k + 1)} +$
$\frac{1}{(k + 1)((k + 1) + 1)} = \frac{k}{k + 1} + \frac{1}{(k + 1)((k + 1) + 1)} =$
$\frac{k(k + 2)}{(k + 1)(k + 2)} + \frac{1}{(k + 1)((k + 1) + 1)} =$
$\frac{k(k + 2) + 1}{(k + 1)((k + 1) + 1)} = \frac{k^2 + 2k + 1}{(k + 1)((k + 1) + 1)} =$
$\frac{(k + 1)^2}{(k + 1)((k + 1) + 1)} = \frac{k + 1}{(k + 1) + 1}$

Lesson 11-6 pp. 637–639

EXERCISES 1. total produced **3.** miles
7. 110 units^2 **9.** $A = \sum_{n=1}^{2} 1f(a_n)$ **a.** 0.5 units^2
b. 2.5 units^2 **11.** $A = \sum_{n=1}^{2} 1f(a_n)$ **a.** 3 units^2
b. 7 units^2 **19.** 2.5 units^2 **21.** 3.3 units^2

T916

25.

43 units²

33. 7.5 units² **35.** 3.46 units²

Chapter Review pp. 641–643

1. limits **2.** circumscribed rectangles
3. sequence **4.** converges **5.** common ratio
6. $a_n = a_{n-1} + 17$, $a_1 = 5$; 73, 90, 107
7. $a_n = -7a_{n-1}$, $a_1 = 1$; 2401; −16,807; 117,649
8. $a_n = a_{n-1} + 9$, $a_1 = -2$; 34, 43, 52
9. $a_n = 3n - 2$; 34 **10.** $a_n = 2^n$; 4096
11. $a_n = 6n^2 - 30$; 834 **12.** Answers may vary.
Sample: If the formula uses the previous term,
then it is recursive; otherwise it is explicit. **13.** no
14. yes; $d = 15$; $a_{32} = 468$ **15.** yes; $d = 3$; $a_{32} = 100$ **16.** 5 **17.** 101.5 **18.** −4.9 **19.** 5 **20.** −10.5,
−8, −5.5 **21.** 1.4, 0.8, 0.2 **22.** 11 **23.** 0.5 **24.** If
the terms of the sequence have a common
difference, then the sequence is arithmetic.
25. yes; $r = \frac{1}{2}$, $a_n = 1\left(\frac{1}{2}\right)^{n-1}$, $\frac{1}{16}$, $\frac{1}{32}$ **26.** no
27. yes; $r = 1.2$, $a_n = 3(1.2)^{n-1}$, 6.2208, 7.46496
28. 6 **29.** 20 **30.** 0.04 **31.** −10, −5, −2.5 **32.** −$\frac{1}{3}$,
−$\frac{2}{3}$, −$\frac{4}{3}$ **33.** $12\frac{1}{3}$, $12\frac{1}{4}$, $42\frac{2}{8}$ **34.** $\sum\limits_{n=1}^{8} 13 - 3n$; 20
35. $\sum\limits_{n=1}^{7} 45 + 5n$; 455 **36.** $\sum\limits_{n=1}^{8} 4.6 + 1.4n$; 143
37. $\sum\limits_{n=1}^{8} 23 - 2n$; 112 **38.** 3, −8, 26; 27 **39.** 9, 4, 8;
54 **40.** 11, −$\frac{10}{3}$, −10; −$\frac{230}{9}$ **41.** No; she will have
only 1150 available by the end of the fifth year.
42. $4\frac{121}{243}$ **43.** 31 **44.** 53.125 **45.** $14\frac{7}{18}$
46. converges; $S = 187.5$ **47.** diverges; no sum
48. diverges; no sum **49.** converges; $S = 2$
50. $A = \sum\limits_{n=1}^{2} 1 \cdot f(a_n)$ **a.** 1 unit² **b.** 5 units²
c. $\frac{9}{2}$ units² **51.** $A = \sum\limits_{n=1}^{2} 1 \cdot f(a_n)$ **a.** 3 units²

b. 11 units² **c.** 6 units² **52.** $A = \sum\limits_{n=1}^{2} 1 \cdot f(a_n)$
a. 6 units² **b.** 14 units² **c.** 10.6̄ units²
53. $A = \sum\limits_{n=1}^{2} 1 \cdot f(a_n)$ **a.** 7 units²
b. 9 units² **c.** 8 units²
54. $A = \sum\limits_{n=1}^{2} 1 \cdot f(a_n)$ **a.** 9 units² **b.** 17 units²
c. 12 units² **55.** $A = \sum\limits_{n=1}^{2} 1 \cdot f(a_n)$ **a.** 7 units²
b. 11 units² **c.** $8\frac{2}{3}$ units²

Chapter 12

Lesson 12-1 pp. 651–653

EXERCISES

1.

Object	Frequency
Rock	11
Paper	10
Scissors	15
Total	36

3. 0.11 **5.** 0.53

7.

Number of Days Per Month			
Days	28	29	30	31
Frequency	3	1	16	28
Probability	$\frac{3}{48}$	$\frac{1}{48}$	$\frac{16}{48}$	$\frac{28}{48}$

9.

13.

Lesson 12-2 pp. 656–658

EXERCISES 1. 0.9 **3.** 0.6̄ **5.** 0.405
7. 0.562 **9.** 45%

11.

0.1, 0.114

M = male
F = female
R = right
L = left

19. $P(C)$ **21.** $P(R|W)$

Extension p. 659

1. 0.9508 **3.** 0.9998 **5.** $\frac{2}{3}$ or about 67% **7.** 0.08
9. 0.84

Lesson 12-3 pp. 664–667

EXERCISES 1. 4.36, 3, 1 **3.** 600.3, 535.5, 499

5.

7.

9. 6, 18 **11.** 0 **15.** 381; this value raises the
mean. **17.** 60th

Lesson 12-4 pp. 672–674

EXERCISES 1. 5, 2.5 **3.** 704, 461 **5.** 15.1, 3.5
7. 10,259.18; 68.67 **9.** 3 standard deviations
11. −1.4 **13.** 0.15, 14.6, 52.3; the bird speeds
are more spread out than the cat speeds.
17. 2001: ≈6707; 2002: ≈6738 **21a.** 53.8, 3.4
b. 7; 9; 10 **23.** ≈75.8; ≈8.7 **25.** ≈0.007; ≈0.08

Lesson 12-5 pp. 680–683

EXERCISES 1. 73% **3.** 92% **5.** very little bias
7. C; this sample has the smallest standard
deviation, which most likely indicates a larger
sample. **9.** ±7% **11.** ±3% **13.** 400 **15.** ±4%;
55% to 63% **17a.** 63% **b.** ±5% **c.** 58% to 68%
19a. 94% **b.** ±18% **c.** 76% to 100% **27.** 31%,
±13% **29.** 63%, ±5%

Lesson 12-6 pp. 688–691

EXERCISES 1. Each guess is a trial. There are 5
trials. Each correct answer is a success. The
probability of a success on a single trial is 0.5.
Check students' designs and simulations.
5. 25% **7.** 0% **9.** 0.1361 **11.** 0.0015
13. $P(0) = 0.0156$
$P(1) = 0.0938$
$P(2) = 0.2344$
$P(3) = 0.3125$
$P(4) = 0.2344$
$P(5) = 0.0938$
$P(6) = 0.0156$
15. 0.2824 **17.** 0.1109 **19.** 0.2051
25a. $_{40}C_3 \cdot \left(\frac{1}{7}\right)^3\left(\frac{6}{7}\right)^{37} = 0.0960 = 9.6\%$

Lesson 12-7 pp. 695–698

EXERCISES 1. 43% **3.** 43 men
5.

9. 79.1 **11.** 68% **15.** 32% **19.** 2.5% **21.** 100%
23. 50% **27a.** 209 **b.** 41 **c.** 127 − 250

Chapter Review pp. 701–703

1. sample **2.** outlier **3.** probability distribution
4. binomial experiment **5.** measures of variation

6a.

Winner	Freq.
Player 1	8
Player 2	4
Ties	3
Total	15

b. $P(\text{Player 2 wins}) = \frac{4}{15}$

9. $\frac{3}{14}$ **10.** $\frac{9}{56}$ **11.**

12. 0.9 **13.** 0.2 **14.** 14.4; 14; 12, 13, 14
15.

$0 \leq x \leq 20$
$0 \leq y \leq 10$

16. 20th percentile = 13, 90th percentile = 18
17. 53rd percentile **18.** 8 **19.** 6 **20.** 0.26 **21.** 2
22. ≈1.56 **23a.** 76% **b.** ±14% **c.** from 62% to
90% **24.** Answers may vary. Sample: Each guess
is a trial. There are 4 trials. Since there are 2
equally likely answers, the probability of success
is 0.5. Let 1 represent a correct response and 2
an incorrect response. Generate 4 random
numbers, either 1 or 2, 10 times. The probability
is one tenth the number of times there are exactly
three 1's. **25.** 0.137
27.

Mean

−3SD −2SD −1SD   1SD 2SD 3SD

Chapter 13

Lesson 13-1 pp. 713–716

EXERCISES 1. 5 **3.** 4 **5.** periodic; 12
7. not periodic **11.** 3 **13.** 2

15.

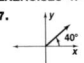

1 unit on the *x*-axis is 0.001 s.

17. Answers may vary. Sample: Yes; average
monthly temperatures for three years should be
cyclical due to the variation of the seasons.
19. Answers may vary. Sample: Yes; traffic that
passes through an intersection should be at the
same levels for the same times of day for two
consecutive work days. **21a.** 1 s **b.** 1.5 mV
23. 3, −3, 4;

27. 2 weeks **29.** 1 hour

Lesson 13-2 pp. 722–724

EXERCISES 1. 45° **3.** 240°
7.

13. 215° **15.** 4° **21.** $\frac{1}{2}$, $\frac{\sqrt{3}}{2}$; 0.50, 0.87
23. $\frac{\sqrt{3}}{2}$, −$\frac{1}{2}$; 0.87, −0.50 **25.** $\frac{\sqrt{3}}{2}$, $\frac{1}{2}$; 0.87, 0.50
27. $\frac{\sqrt{3}}{2}$, −$\frac{1}{2}$; 0.87, −0.50 **29.** 1.00, 0.00
31. 0.71, −0.71 **37–39.** Answers may vary.
Samples: **37.** 405°, −315° **39.** 45°, −315° **45.** II
47. negative *x*-axis **51a.** 0.77, 0.77, 0.77
b. The cosines of the three angles are equal
because the angles are coterminal.

Lesson 13-3 pp. 729–733

EXERCISES 1. −$\frac{5\pi}{2}$, −5.24 **3.** −$\frac{\pi}{2}$, −1.57 **7.** 540°
9. −120° **15.** $\frac{1}{2}$, $\frac{\sqrt{3}}{2}$ **17.** −$\frac{1}{2}$, $\frac{\sqrt{3}}{2}$ **21.** 10.5 m
23. 25.1 in. **27.** ≈32 ft **29.** ≈42.2 in. **31.** III
33. positive *y*-axis

37.

0.71, −0.71

45. ≈11 radians **47.** ≈798 ft; 55°, −665°
51. ≈4008.7 mi

Lesson 13-4 pp. 738–741

EXERCISES 1. $\frac{1}{2}$ **3.** ≈0.9 **7.** 1 **9.** ≈−0.8
13. 3; 2, $\frac{2\pi}{3}$ **15.** 2; 3, π
17.

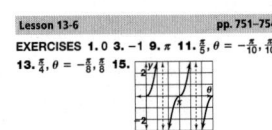

$y = \frac{1}{3}\sin 2\theta$

23.

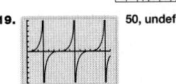

29. 2π; $y = -3\sin\theta$ **31.** $\frac{\pi}{3}$; $y = \frac{1}{2}\sin 6\theta$
35. 5; 1, $\frac{2\pi}{3}$ **37.** 1; 3, 2π
43a. $\frac{1}{440}$ **b.** 0.001 **c.** 880π
45. $\frac{2\pi}{3}$, 3.5

Lesson 13-5 pp. 746–748

EXERCISES 1. 2π; 3; max: 3, min: 3, zeros: $\frac{\pi}{2}$, $\frac{3\pi}{2}$
3. π, 1; max: 1, min: −1, zeros: $\frac{\pi}{4}$, $\frac{3\pi}{4}$, $\frac{5\pi}{4}$, $\frac{7\pi}{4}$
5.

11. $y = \frac{5}{2}\cos 2\theta$ **13.** $y = -3\cos 2\theta$ **17.** 1.98,
4.30 **19.** 2.52 **23.** π, $-1 \leq y \leq 1$, 1
25. 4π, $-\frac{1}{3} \leq y \leq \frac{1}{3}$ **31.** 1.83, 2.88, 4.97, 6.02
33a. 3.79, 5.64 **b.** 10.07, 11.92; these values are
the sums of the values from part (a) and 2π.

35a. 5.5 ft; 1.5 ft **b.** about 12 h 22 min
c. $y = 1.5\cos\frac{2\pi t}{742}$
d. 12:17 A.M.–7:49 A.M., 12:39 P.M.–8:11 P.M.

b. $y = 8.5\cos\frac{2\pi}{365}(x - 228) + 77.5$
39. $y = \cos(x + 3) + \pi$ **41.** $y = 2\cos\left(x - \frac{\pi}{5}\right) - 1$;
$y = 2\sin\left(x + \frac{\pi}{5}\right) - 1$

Lesson 13-6 pp. 751–754

EXERCISES 1. 0 **3.** −1 **9.** π **11.** $\frac{\pi}{5}$; $\theta = -\frac{\pi}{10}$, $\frac{\pi}{10}$
13. $\frac{\pi}{4}$, $\theta = -\frac{\pi}{8}$, $\frac{\pi}{8}$ **15.**

19.

50, undefined, −50

23. 6

27. 2.03, 5.18 **33.** 200 **35.** 135 **39.** $y = -\tan\left(\frac{1}{2}x\right)$
41. $y = \tan(2x)$

Lesson 13-7 pp. 760–762

EXERCISES 1. −1; 1 unit to the left
3. 1.6; 1.6 units to the right
7.

11.

17. 3, 2π; 1 unit up **19.** 1, 2π; $\frac{\pi}{2}$ units left
and 2 units up
21.

25.

31. $y = \sin(x + \pi)$ **33.** $y = \sin x + 3$
37a.

Temperature (°F)

40 120 200 280 360
Day of the Year

Lesson 13-8 pp. 766–769

EXERCISES 1. 1.02 **3.** −0.70 **5.** $\frac{3}{7}$ **7.** −$\frac{9}{5}$ **9.** $\sqrt{2}$
11. 0 **21.** −7.02 **23.** 1
29.

33. 1.1547 **35.** −2.9238

43. $\frac{2\sqrt{3}}{3}$; 1.15 **45.** −1
47.

51. C **53.** D
61.

3 units up

Chapter Review pp. 771–773

1. period **2.** unit circle **3.** tangent function
4. phase shift **5.** secant function **6.** periodic; 4, 2
7. Answers may vary. Sample:

8. −225°

9.

10. 240° **11.** $\left(\frac{\sqrt{2}}{2}, -\frac{\sqrt{2}}{2}\right)$; (0.71, −0.71) **12a.** $\frac{\pi}{6}$
b. $\frac{\sqrt{3}}{2}$, $\frac{1}{2}$ **13a.** −$\frac{\pi}{4}$ **b.** $\frac{\sqrt{2}}{2}$, −$\frac{\sqrt{2}}{2}$ **14a.** π **b.** −1, 0
15a. 360° **b.** 1, 0 **16a.** 150° **b.** −$\frac{\sqrt{3}}{2}$, $\frac{1}{2}$
17a. −135° **b.** −$\frac{\sqrt{2}}{2}$, −$\frac{\sqrt{2}}{2}$ **18.** 26.2 ft

19.

20.

21.

22. 3 cycles; 1, $\frac{2\pi}{3}$; $y = -\sin 3\theta$ 23. $y = 4 \sin 4\theta$
24. $y = 3 \cos 2\theta$ 25. $y = 2 \cos 2\theta$ 26. 3.92, 5.51
27. 0.16, 1.84, 4.16, 5.84 28. 0.58, 1.00, 2.15, 2.57, 3.72, 4.14, 5.29, 5.71
29.   0.41, 1

30. -1, undefined

31. 2, undefined

32.

33.

35. $y = \sin\left(x - \frac{\pi}{4}\right)$ 36. $y = \cos x - 2$ 37. $\sqrt{2}$
38. $-\frac{\sqrt{3}}{3}$ 39. 2

40.

41.

42.

Chapter 14

Lesson 14-1 pp. 780–782

EXERCISES 1. $\cos \theta \cot \theta = \cos \theta \left(\frac{\cos \theta}{\sin \theta}\right) = \frac{1 - \sin^2 \theta}{\sin \theta} = \frac{1}{\sin \theta} - \sin \theta$ 3. $\cos \theta \tan \theta = \cos \theta \left(\frac{\sin \theta}{\cos \theta}\right) = \sin \theta$ 9. 1 11. $\tan^2 \theta$ 21. $\sec \theta$ 23. $\sec^2 \theta$ 39. $\pm\sqrt{1 - \cos^2 \theta}$ 41. $\frac{\pm\sqrt{1 - \sin^2 \theta}}{\sin \theta}$ 45. $\sin^2 \theta \tan^2 \theta = \sin^2 \theta \left(\frac{\sin^2 \theta}{\cos^2 \theta}\right) = (1 - \cos^2 \theta)\left(\frac{\sin^2 \theta}{\cos^2 \theta}\right) = \frac{\sin^2 \theta - \sin^2 \theta \cos^2 \theta}{\cos^2 \theta} = \frac{\sin^2 \theta}{\cos^2 \theta} - \frac{\sin^2 \theta \cos^2 \theta}{\cos^2 \theta} = \tan^2 \theta - \sin^2 \theta$

Lesson 14-2 pp. 787–790

EXERCISES 1. $-\frac{\pi}{6} + 2\pi n$ 3. $\frac{\pi}{2} + 2\pi n$ 5. $30° + n \cdot 360°$ and $210° + n \cdot 360°$ or $30° + n \cdot 180°$ 7. $120° + n \cdot 360°$ and $300° + n \cdot 360°$ or $120° + n \cdot 180°$ 9. $0.38 + 2\pi n$ and $2.76 + 2\pi n$ 17. $\frac{\pi}{6}, \frac{11\pi}{6}$ 19. $\frac{\pi}{4}, \frac{3\pi}{4}$ 35. $30° + n \cdot 360°$ and $150° + n \cdot 360°$ 37. $210° + n \cdot 360°$ and $330° + n \cdot 360°$ 39. $\frac{3\pi}{2}$ 41. 0.34, 2.80 47. $\frac{\pi}{2} + 2\pi n, \frac{3\pi}{2} + 2\pi n$ 49. $\frac{\pi}{4} + \frac{\pi}{2}n$ 59. 0.79 + πn, 2.36 + πn 61. 0.79 + πn, 2.36 + πn 65. $\frac{3\pi}{2} + 2\pi n$

Lesson 14-3 pp. 796–799

EXERCISES 1a. ≈8333 ft b. ≈8824 ft
3a. $\frac{9}{41} \approx 0.22$ b. $\frac{40}{41} \approx 0.98$ c. $\frac{40}{9} \approx 4.44$ d. $\frac{41}{9} \approx 4.56$ e. $\frac{9}{41} \approx 0.22$ f. not defined 5. 41.8 7. 10.6 9. 45.0° 11. 48.6° 19. $c \approx 7.8, \angle A = 39.8°, \angle B = 50.2°$ 21. $c \approx 10.2, \angle A = 52.6°, \angle B = 37.4°$

Selected Answers 1001

---

25. $\cos \theta = \frac{\sqrt{55}}{8}$, $\tan \theta = \frac{3\sqrt{55}}{55}$, $\csc \theta = \frac{8}{3}$, $\sec \theta = \frac{8\sqrt{55}}{55}$, $\cot \theta = \frac{\sqrt{55}}{3}$ 35. $a = 15, m\angle A \approx 61.9°, m\angle B \approx 28.1°$ 37. $a \approx 7.9, b \approx 6.2, m\angle B = 38°$ 41. 35.5° 43. 20.3 m²

Lesson 14-4 pp. 803–806

EXERCISES 1. 18.7 cm² 3. 81.9 m² 5. 10.9 7. 7.4 11. 33.5° 13. 27.0° 15. 28.8° 17. $m\angle D = 100°, e = 22.3, f = 34.2$ 19. $m\angle T = 29.3°, m\angle R = 26.7°, r = 8.3$ 27. 7.5 mi, 7.9 mi 29. 66° 31. 44.5 33. 49.4 39. 28.0 ft 41. 4.0 cm

Extension p. 807

1. 70.4 and 47.6°, or 109.6° and 8.4° 3. 87.3° and 44.7°, or 92.7° and 39.3° 5. 44.0° and 112.4°, or 136.0° and 20.4°

Lesson 14-5 pp. 810–813

EXERCISES 1. 37.1 3. 13.7 7. 47.3° 9. 125.1° 13. 60.4° 15. 71.7° 19. $c^2 = a^2 + b^2 - 2ab \cos C$ 21. $\frac{\sin A}{a} = \frac{\sin B}{b}$ 25. $m\angle A = 50.1°, m\angle B = 56.3°, m\angle C = 73.6°$ 27. $m\angle A = 90°, m\angle B = 36.9°, m\angle C = 53.1°$ 31. 38.9 ft 33. 77.2° 35. 57.1° 37. 38.8 cm 41. 32.6° 43. 67.2° 47. 109 cm

Lesson 14-6 pp. 818–820

EXERCISES 1. $\csc\left(\theta - \frac{\pi}{2}\right) = \csc\left(-\left(\frac{\pi}{2} - \theta\right)\right) = -\csc\left(\frac{\pi}{2} - \theta\right) = -\sec\theta$ 7. $\frac{\pi}{2}, \frac{3\pi}{2}$ 9. $\frac{\pi}{4}, \frac{3\pi}{4}, \frac{5\pi}{4}, \frac{7\pi}{4}$ 15. $\sec A$ 17. 0 19. -1 21. $\frac{\sqrt{2} - \sqrt{6}}{4}$ 23. $2 - \sqrt{3}$ 37. $\sin(A - B) = \sin(A + (-B)) = \sin A \cos(-B) + \cos A \sin(-B) = \sin A \cos B - \cos A \sin B$ 45. $\sin 5\theta$ 47. $\cos 5\theta$

Lesson 14-7 pp. 824–825

EXERCISES 1. $-\frac{\sqrt{3}}{2}$ 3. $-\sqrt{3}$ 9. $\sin 2\theta = \sin(\theta + \theta) = \sin \theta \cos \theta + \cos \theta \cdot \sin \theta = 2 \sin \theta \cos \theta$ 11. $\frac{\sqrt{2 + \sqrt{3}}}{2}$ 13. $\frac{\sqrt{2 - \sqrt{3}}}{2}$ 19. $\frac{3\sqrt{10}}{10}$ 21. 23. $\frac{4\sqrt{17}}{17}$ 25. -4 27. $\sin 2R = 2 \sin R \cos R = 2\left(\frac{c}{r}\right) \cdot \frac{b}{r} = \frac{2rs}{r^2}$ 29. $\sin 2S = 2 \sin S \cos S = 2 \cdot \frac{s}{r} \cdot \left(\frac{c}{r}\right) = \frac{2sc}{r^2} = 2 \sin R \cos R = \sin 2R$ 35. $-\frac{7}{25}$ 37. $-\frac{25}{24}$ 43. $\sin (4 \cos \theta - 3) = 0; 0, \pi, 0.723, 5.560$ 47. $-\cos \theta$

1002 Selected Answers

Chapter Review pp. 827–829

1. Law of Sines 2. trigonometric ratios for a right triangle 3. Law of Cosines 4. trigonometric identity 5. Law of Sines 6. $\sin \theta \tan \theta = \frac{\sin^2 \theta}{\cos \theta} = \frac{1 - \cos^2 \theta}{\cos \theta} = \frac{1}{\cos \theta} - \frac{\cos^2 \theta}{\cos \theta} = \frac{1}{\cos \theta} - \cos \theta$ 7. $\cos^2 \theta \cot \theta = (1 - \sin^2 \theta) \cot \theta = \cot^2 \theta - \sin^2 \theta \cos^2 \theta \cot \theta = \cot^2 \theta - \sin^2 \theta \cdot \frac{\cos^2 \theta}{\sin^2 \theta} = \cot^2 \theta - \cos^2 \theta$ 9. 1 10. 1 11. $-60°$ 12. 60° 13. $-30°$ 14. 30° 15. $0.34 + 2\pi n, 2.80 + 2\pi n$ 16. $-1.11 + 2\pi n, 2.03 + 2\pi n$ 17. $2.27 + 2\pi n, 4.02 + 2\pi n$ 18. $0.20 + 2\pi n, 6.08 + 2\pi n$ 19. $\frac{\pi}{3}, \frac{5\pi}{3}$ 20. $\frac{\pi}{6}, \frac{7\pi}{6}$ 21. $0, \frac{\pi}{2}, \pi$ 22. $\frac{3}{5}, 0.6$ 23. $\frac{8}{15}, 0.8$ 24. $\frac{3}{4}, 0.75$ 25. 9.5, 18.4°, 71.6° 26. 16, 36.9°, 53.1° 27. 37.7, 43.3°, 46.7° 28. 13.14 m² 29. 92.12 ft² 30. 57.81 m² 31. 7.1 in. 32. 54.3° or 125.7° 33. 21.4 ft 34. 43.9° 35. 52.2° 36. $\cos\left(\theta + \frac{\pi}{2}\right) = \cos \theta \cdot \cos\left(\frac{\pi}{2}\right) - \sin \theta \cdot \sin\left(\frac{\pi}{2}\right) = \cos \theta \cdot 0 - \sin \theta \cdot 1 = -\sin \theta$ 37. $\sin^2\left(\theta - \frac{\pi}{2}\right) = \sin^2\left(-\left(\frac{\pi}{2} - \theta\right)\right) = \left(-\sin\left(\frac{\pi}{2} - \theta\right)\right) \cdot \left(-\sin\left(\frac{\pi}{2} - \theta\right)\right) = (-\cos \theta)(-\cos \theta) = \cos^2 \theta$ 38. $\frac{\pi}{6}$ and $\frac{3\pi}{8}$ 39. 0 40. $\frac{\sqrt{3}}{2}$ 41. 0 42. $-\sqrt{3}$ 43. -1 44. $\sqrt{3}$ 45. $\frac{\sqrt{3}}{2}$

Extra Practice

CHAPTER 1 1. $>$ 3. $>$ 9. $-102, \frac{1}{102}$ 11. $-2\frac{3}{4}, \frac{4}{11}$ 21. 28 23. 14 25. 2 27. -11

31. $t \leq -1$

33. $a < -\frac{7}{2}$

37. $-2 \leq z < 1$

39. $x < -2, x > 8$

43. $-11, 15.5$ 45. $-5, 9$

49. $t \leq -5.5, t \geq -1.5$

51. $-11 \leq w \leq -1$

55. 1 57. $\frac{5}{8}$ 61. $500 63. $\frac{3}{5}$ 65. $11,500 67. less than 8 h 69. $\frac{3}{38}$ 71. $\frac{2}{5}$

CHAPTER 2 1. Yes; each x-value has exactly one y-value. 3. No; the x-value 1 has two y-values. 15. $3x - y = -7$ 17. $3x - 4y = -26$ 21. $y - 2 = -1(x - 0)$ 23. $y - 0 = \frac{1}{2}(x - 3)$ 27. 2, -5, 2.5 29. 0, 4, none 35. $3x - y = -9$

---

37. $8x - 2y = 7$ 43. $y = \frac{7}{3}x$ 45. $y = 2.5x$
51.   59.

67. $A(h) = 21h$; 798 ft² 69. $y = \frac{2}{3}x$
71. a. $f(x) = |x - 100|$ b. $g(x) = |x - 300|$ c. $h(x) = |x - 300| + 200$ d. They are translations of each other. 73. $y = 75x - 18,000$; The intercept, $-18,000$, represents the initial investment; the slope, 75, is the rental income per day.

CHAPTER 3
1.   7. (1, 4) 9. (6, −3)
13.

17. (0, 0) 19. 50 chef's salads and 50 Caesar salads
29.

35. (2, 1, 3) 37. (2, 3, −6) 39. 4.5 mi/h 41. $4.70 per lb of cheese, $5.65 per lb of chicken loaf
43. a. $\begin{cases} 5x + 8y \leq 400 \\ 2.5x + 2y \leq 120 \\ x \geq 0 \\ y \geq 0 \end{cases}$
b.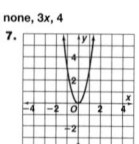

45. first chef: $3\frac{1}{3}$ h; second chef: $8\frac{1}{3}$ h
47. Student: $6; Adult: $15; Senior: $8

CHAPTER 4 1. 2 × 3; 6 3. 2 × 3; −83 7. $\begin{bmatrix} 4 & 67 \\ 12 & 18 \end{bmatrix}$
9. $\begin{bmatrix} -6 & -1 & 0 \\ 17 & -11 & -8 \end{bmatrix}$ 11. $\begin{bmatrix} -62 & 121 \\ 43 & -54 \end{bmatrix}$

13. $\begin{bmatrix} 5 & -7 & 7 \\ -7 & -7 & 7 \end{bmatrix}$ 15. $\begin{bmatrix} -26 & 7 & 5 \\ -4 & -7 & 25 \end{bmatrix}$
17. $\begin{bmatrix} 16 & 2 \\ -4 & 10 \end{bmatrix}$ 27. $\begin{bmatrix} 5 & 10 & -20 \\ 25 & -5 & 15 \end{bmatrix}$
29. $\begin{bmatrix} 3 & 4 \\ -2 & -8 & -4 \end{bmatrix}$ 31. $\begin{bmatrix} -16 \\ -15 & \frac{83}{15} \end{bmatrix}$ 33. $\begin{bmatrix} 2 \\ 7 \end{bmatrix}$

35. (9, 1) 37. a. Machine 1 $\begin{bmatrix} 13 & 22 \\ 22 & 37 \end{bmatrix}$ Machine 2
b. Machine 1 makes 13 gal of frozen yogurt in the A.M. and 22 gal in the P.M. Machine 2 makes 22 gal in the A.M. and 37 gal in the P.M.

39. $\begin{bmatrix} \frac{\sqrt{3}-1}{2} & \frac{\sqrt{3}-2}{2} & \frac{5\sqrt{3}-4}{2} \\ \frac{\sqrt{3}+1}{2} & \frac{2\sqrt{3}+1}{2} & \frac{4\sqrt{3}+5}{2} \end{bmatrix}$

41. $\begin{bmatrix} 1 & 1 & 1 \\ 1 & 1 & -1 \\ -1 & 1 & 0 \end{bmatrix} \begin{bmatrix} x \\ y \\ z \end{bmatrix} = \begin{bmatrix} 249 \\ 95 \\ 6 \end{bmatrix}$; $x = 83, y = 89, z = 77$
43. $\begin{bmatrix} 2 & 1 \\ 3 & 2 \end{bmatrix} \begin{bmatrix} x \\ y \end{bmatrix} = \begin{bmatrix} 10 \\ 17.25 \end{bmatrix}$; $x = 2.75, y = 4.50$
45. orchestra: $25; balcony: $15

CHAPTER 5 1. linear; none, $3x$, 4
3. linear; none, $-\frac{3}{2}x$, $\frac{1}{2}$ 7.

15. $(x + 9)(x - 6)$ 17. $(x - 6)(x + 6)$ 27. 0.24, −4.24 29. 0.41, −2.41 35. $8 - 3i$ 37. $1 - 3i$ 41. $\pm 4i$ 43. $\pm i\sqrt{10}$ 47. $-i, -1 - i, i$ 49. $-1, -4$ 51. $\frac{5}{4} \pm \frac{\sqrt{17}}{4}$ 59. 108; 2, real 61. 25; 2, real 67. a. 30 ft by 20 ft b. 300 ft² 69. 19 years old; 24 years old 71. a. 625 bulldozers; $781,250 b. $x \geq 0$; $P(x) \geq $781,250 c. $500 \leq x \leq 750$ 73. 20 in 75. a. The archer releases the arrow 5 ft about the ground. b. 402 ft

CHAPTER 6 1. $-4a^2 + 3a$; quadratic binomial 3. $-2n^3 + 3n^2 - n - 3$; cubic polynomial of 4 terms 7. $y = x^3 - 4x^2 + x + 6$ 9. $y = x^3 + 2x^2 - x - 2$ 15. $x^2 - 2x - 2$ 17. $2x^2 + 2x$ 21. 0, −2, 5 23. 2 27. $-2, \pm i\sqrt{3}$ 29. $-1, \frac{-5 \pm \sqrt{13}}{6}$ 33. 720 35. 210

Selected Answers 1003

---

45. permutation; 60,480 orders 47. combination; 6 ways 49. $81x^4 + 216x^3 + 216x^2 + 96x + 16$ 51. $16x^4 + 160x^3y + 600x^2y^2 + 1000xy^3 + 625y^4$ 57. a. Answers may vary. Sample: $P(N) = (N - 1)N(N + 1) = N^3 - N$ b. 5, 6, 7 59. 14 in. by 14 in. 61. 455 ways 63. 255 kinds of pizza 65. 100,947 ways

CHAPTER 7 1. $6x^2$ 3. $3|x^3|$ 9. $6x^3\sqrt{2x}$ 11. $10a^2$ 15. $5\sqrt{7}$ 17. $3\sqrt{7x}$ 21. $\frac{y^5}{20}$ 23. $\frac{y^3}{2x^3}$ 29. no solution 31. 3, 7 35. 1 37. 64 45. $f^{-1}(x) = x^2 - 4, x \geq 0$; domain of f: $\{x \geq -4\}$, range of f: $\{y \geq 0\}$, domain of f^{-1}: $\{x \geq 0\}$, range of f^{-1}: $\{y \geq -4\}$; f^{-1} is a function.
51.

59. 7.3 ft 61. a. 36 mi b. 4900 ft
63. a. $E(x) = 0.8x$ b. $M(x) = 0.75x$ c. $T(x) = 1.06x$ d. $f(x) = 0.636x$
65. a. $f^{-1} = \frac{x - 331.4}{0.6}$ b. 31°C; The speed of sound is 350 m/s at 31°C.

CHAPTER 8 1. $y = 4(2.5)^x$ 3. $y = \frac{2}{3}(3)^x$ 7. exponential growth 9. exponential decay
17.

25. $\log_9 729 = 3$ 27. $\log_2 \frac{1}{16} = 4$ 41. $\log 24$ 43. $\log x^7$ 47. $\log_2 2 + \frac{1}{2}\log_2 x + 3 \log_2 y$ 49. $5(\log_b 4 + \log_b m + \log_b n)$ 53. ± 8 55. 50,000 65. $3745.32 67. $1214.87 69. 1432 71. 2399 species 73. a. -0.042 b. 48.5°F c. 69.5 min d. no; 38°F is the horizontal asymptote of the function.

CHAPTER 9 1. $y = \frac{6}{x}$ 3. $y = \frac{40}{x}$
7.

15. 0 17. $-2, 1$ 23. $x + 3; x \neq -6$ 25. $x + 2; x \neq -3, 4$ 29. $\frac{14x - 3}{2(x + 2)}$ 31. $\frac{6x - 3}{x(x + 3)}$ 35. -4 37. $-5, 4$ 41. dependent 43. independent 45. about 0.26 tons 47. $f(x) = \frac{0.658x + 7}{x + 9}$ 49. 2.4 mi/h 51. about 16 h 53. $\frac{7}{20}$ 55. $\frac{35}{36}$

CHAPTER 10 1.

Circle; every line through (0, 0) is a line of symmetry, radius 2; domain: $-2 \leq x \leq 2$, range: $-2 \leq y \leq 2$. 7. $y = \frac{1}{12}x^2$ 9. $y = -\frac{1}{8}x^2$ 17. (4, 0), $x = -4$;

25. $(x + 4)^2 + (y + 6)^2 = 4$ 27. $(x - 1)^2 + (y - 4)^2 = 25$ 31. $(-6, -9)$, 12 33. $(-8, 1)$, 10 37. $(\pm 4\sqrt{2}, 0)$

49. ellipse; center (0, 0), foci $(\pm 3\sqrt{3}, 0)$

55. 8 in. 57. $(x - 4.5)^2 + (y - 7)^2 = 1.5^2$
59. a. hyperbola b. $(-1.316, 0.4)$, (2.648, 0.4)

1004 Selected Answers

T918

CHAPTER 11 **1.** explicit; 5, 8, 11, 14, 17
3. explicit; 15, 40, 75, 120, 175 **7.** 9, 11, 13;
$a_n = 2n + 1$; $a_1 = 3$, $a_n = a_{n-1} + 2$
9. −7.5, −6, −4.5; $a_n = −13.5 + 1.5n$;
$a_1 = −12$, $a_n = a_{n-1} + 1.5$ **13.** 15 **15.** −4.5
17. $a_n = −27\left(\frac{1}{3}\right)^{n-1}$; −27, −9, −3, −1, −$\frac{1}{3}$
19. $a_n = −5(3)^{n-1}$; −5, −15, −45, −135, −405
23. $\sum_{n=1}^{10}(3n + 1)$; 175 **25.** $\sum_{n=1}^{20}(−n + 98)$; 1750
27. 6, 2, −3; −3 **29.** 8, 4, 25; 116 **31.** $\frac{9}{4}$ **33.** 1
37. geometric; 3069 **39.** arithmetic; −1110
41. 0 + 1 = 1; 1 + 8 = 9 **43.** 3 + 4 = 7; 4 + 5 = 9
45. a. 23, 17.6, 13.5, 10.4, 7.9 **b.** $a_n = 30\left(\frac{23}{30}\right)^n$
47. a. 47 seats **b.** 761 seats **49.** 45 ft
51. a. 44.49 m^2 **b.** 53.86 m^2 **c.** 49.18 m^2

CHAPTER 12 **1.**

3. $\frac{39}{80}$ **5.** $\frac{25}{80}$ **9.** 25.8, 21, 24 **11.** 4.8, 4.2, 6.1
13. 25.429, 11, 8, 3.81 **15.** 99.71, 5, 3, 1.578
17. ±6% **19.** ±3% **23.** 0.2787 ≈ 28%
25. 0.0003 ≈ 0.03%
29. $P(k = 0) = 0.0467$
$P(k = 1) = 0.1866$
$P(k = 2) = 0.3110$
$P(k = 3) = 0.2765$
$P(k = 4) = 0.1382$
$P(k = 5) = 0.0369$
$P(k = 6) = 0.0041$

35.

x = number of successes

39. $\frac{1}{3}$ **41. a.** 79.95; 82; 84 **b.** 70th percentile
c.

d. Answers may vary. Sample: None; all the scores are reasonably close to the other scores.
43. a. about 5% **b.** 102 to 141 students **45.** 2.5%

CHAPTER 13 **1.** 4, 1$\frac{1}{2}$ **3.** 4, 2
11. $\frac{3\pi}{2}$, 4.71 **13.** $\frac{−55\pi}{18}$, −9.60 **17.** −115°
19. −540° **23.** 1, $\frac{\pi}{2}$ **25.** 2, 8π
29. **35.**

39. −1.5299 **41.** −1 **47.** 50°F; 2 min
49. a. 2:00; 10:00 **b.** 4:00, 8:00
51. $y = −3.15 \cos\left(\frac{\pi}{6}x\right) + 12.45$
53. $y = \sin\left(\frac{2\pi}{9}x\right) + 7.5$
55. a. Answers may vary. Sample: The height of the tower, 30 cm, is the scale factor that gives the length of the cable when multiplied by csc x.
b. Explanations may vary. Sample: 30 to about 85.5 cm; The length of the cable is at least 30 cm, and the longest cable must still be attached to the bridge. So the longest cable is at most $\sqrt{30^2 + \left(\frac{160}{2}\right)^2} \approx 85.44$ cm long.
c. $\frac{\pi}{6}$ radians or 30°

CHAPTER 14 **1.** 60° + $n \cdot 360°$ and 120° + $n \cdot 360°$ **3.** 60° + $n \cdot 360°$ and 240° + $n \cdot 360°$
5. no solution **7.** 1.313 **13.** $\frac{3\pi}{2}$
15. 0, π, 2.6779, 5.8195, 2π
19. $b = 5.7$, $\angle A = 51.1°$, $\angle B = 38.9°$
21. $c = 4.5$, $\angle A = 26.6°$, $\angle B = 63.4°$ **25.** $\frac{12}{13}$, 0.923
27. $\frac{12}{5}$, 2.4 **29.** 11.3 **31.** 46.3 **33.** $\frac{\sqrt{6} - \sqrt{2}}{4}$ **35.** $\frac{\sqrt{3}}{2}$
39. 1 **41.** −1 **45.** $\frac{\sqrt{6} - \sqrt{2}}{4}$ **47.** $\frac{\sqrt{2} + \sqrt{2}}{2}$
51. 140 ft, 229 ft **53.** 352.3 ft^2 **55.** 2.36 mi
57. 76°, 1153°, 78.7°, 90°

Skills Handbook

p. 864 **1.** $\left(13, 6\frac{1}{2}\right)$ **3.**

p. 865 **1.** 23 pigs and 17 ducks **3.** 45 mi
p. 866 **1.** ten of each coin
p. 867 **1.** 12 slices **3.** 204
p. 868 **1.** Leon **3.** 15 students

p. 869 **1.** 85$\frac{1}{3}$ cm
3.

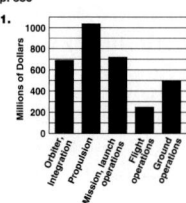

p. 870 **1.** 46% **3.** 29.4% **13.** 0.4 **15.** 1.5 **19.** 12.5 **21.** 75
p. 871 **1.** 1$\frac{6}{8}$ **3.** 6$\frac{5}{6}$
p. 872 **1.** 3 to 4 **3.** 9.5 g/oz **7.** 8 **9.** 1.8
p. 873 **1.** 1 **3.** −38
p. 874 **1.** 14.4 **3.** 84 **13.** $\ell = \frac{P}{2} - w$
15. $b = c - 2a$
p. 875 **1.** 14 m^2 **3.** 30 cm^2 **5.** 91.1 ft^3
7. 314.2 in.^{3} **9.** 110.5 in.^{2} **11.** 121.5 ft^2
p. 876 **1.** I **3.** IV
13. $\frac{3}{4}$ **15.** 0 **19.** $\left(5, -\frac{3}{2}\right)$ **21.** $\left(\frac{5}{2}, -1\right)$
p. 877 **1.** −1 **3.** 6
13. $x \le 6$
15. $y \ge -2$

p. 878 **1.** 8, −8 **3.** 5, −13
13. −3 ≤ x ≤ 15

15. $r \le -7$ or $r \ge 7$

p. 879
1.

p. 880 **1.** x^3 **3.** a^4b **5.** $\frac{1}{c^4}$ **7.** $\frac{x^5}{y^3z^3}$ **9.** d^8 **11.** r^5s^8
p. 881 **1.** $x^2 + 10x - 5$ **3.** $12x^4 - 20x^3 + 36x^2$
7. $(a - 6)(a - 2)$ **9.** $(n - 4)(n + 2)$
p. 882 **1.** 1.34×10^6 **3.** 7.75×10^{-4}
11. 6.4×10^5 **13.** ≈8.52×10^2
p. 883 **1.** 6 **3.** $3\sqrt{2}$
p. 884 **1.** 10 **3.** 15 **11.** 10 **13.** 22.7
p. 885
1.

p. 886 **1.** 3.8, 5, 5 **3.** 4.0, 2.4, 2.4
p. 887 **1.** $\frac{a}{3b^2}$ **3.** $\frac{1}{2}$ **5.** $4x$ **7.** $\frac{2}{h}$

CHAPTER 1

LESSON 1-1

pages 8–10 Exercises

79. Answers may vary. Sample: 4 is a whole number, but $\frac{1}{4}$ is not a whole number.

80. Answers may vary. Sample: 7 is a natural number, but −7 is not a natural number.

81. 0 is a whole number, and since −0 = 0, the opposite of 0 is a whole number.

82. Answers may vary. Sample: The integer −1 has −1 as its reciprocal, so −1 is an integer whose reciprocal is an integer.

83. Answers may vary. Sample: $\sqrt{2}$ and $\sqrt{2}$ are irrational numbers, but their product, 2, is a rational number.

LESSON 1-3

pages 21–24 Exercises

67b. Solutions are rational when $\frac{c-b}{a} \geq 0$, $a \neq 0$, and $\frac{c-b}{a}$ is a perfect square (a whole number perfect square or, in simplest form, a fraction whose numerator and denominator are whole number perfect squares), since $x^2 = \frac{c-b}{a}$ ($a \neq 0$), $x = \sqrt{\frac{c-b}{a}}$ or $x = -\sqrt{\frac{c-b}{a}}$. For $\sqrt{\frac{c-b}{a}}$ and $-\sqrt{\frac{c-b}{a}}$ to be rational, $\frac{c-b}{a}$ must be nonnegative and also $\frac{c-b}{a}$ must be a perfect square.

LESSON 1-4

pages 29–31 Exercises

11.
-4 -3 -2 -1 0 1 2 3 4

12.
-4 -3 -2 -1 0 1 2 3 4

61. [4] Answer includes all of the following six parts of the explanation (or equivalent statements), which consist of solving each compound inequality, graphing each compound inequality, and explaining why the choices of *or* and *and* result in solutions of *all real numbers* and *no real numbers*.

$x + 5 > 0$ ☐ $x - 3 < 0$
$x > -5$ ☐ $x < 3$
-5 -4 -3 -2 -1 0 1 2 3

The solutions to the two simple inequalities overlap. By writing *or* in the box, the solution is any value on either of the two arrows, or all real numbers.

$x + 5 < 0$ ☐ $x + 5 > 0$
$x < -5$ ☐ $x > -5$
-9 -8 -7 -6 -5 -4 -3 -2 -1

The solutions to the two simple inequalities do not overlap. By writing *and* in the box, the solution is any point on both arrows, or no real numbers.

[3] omits one or two parts of the six parts of the explanation

[2] omits three or four of the six parts of the explanation

[1] includes at least one of the six parts of the explanation

LESSON 1-5

pages 36–38 Exercises

24. $-2 < x < 6$
-10 -8 -6 -4 -2 0 2 4 6 8 10

25. no solution

26. $-3\frac{1}{2} \leq w \leq \frac{1}{2}$
-5 -4 -3 -2 -1 0 1 2 3

27. $-\frac{11}{15} \leq t \leq \frac{17}{15}$
$-1\ -\frac{12}{15}\ -\frac{9}{15}\ -\frac{6}{15}\ -\frac{3}{15}\ 0\ \frac{3}{15}\ \frac{6}{15}\ \frac{9}{15}\ \frac{12}{15}\ 1\ 1\frac{3}{15}\ 1\frac{6}{15}$

44. $-6 \leq x \leq 8\frac{2}{3}$
-8 -6 -4 -2 0 2 4 6 8 10 12

45. $x \leq -8$ or $x \geq 5$
-12 -10 -8 -6 -4 -2 0 2 4 6 8

46. All real numbers are solutions.
-4 -3 -2 -1 0 1 2 3 4

47. $t < -\frac{3}{2}$ or $t > 2$
-4 -3 -2 -1 0 1 2 3 4

48. All real numbers are solutions.
-4 -3 -2 -1 0 1 2 3 4

49. $x < -\frac{1}{2}$ or $x > \frac{3}{2}$
-4 -3 -2 -1 0 1 2 3 4

50. $x \leq -8.4$ or $x \geq 9.6$
-12 -8 -4 0 4 8 12

56. The graph of $|x| < a$ (where $a > 0$) is the set of all points on the number line that lie between the points for a and $-a$. The graph of $|x| > a$ has two parts: the left part consists of the points to the left of the point for $-a$, and the right part consists of the points to the right of the point for a.

64. $(-6 \leq x \leq -5)$ or $(5 \leq x \leq 6)$
-8 -6 -4 -2 0 2 4 6 8

65. $(x \leq -6)$ or $(-5 < x < 5)$ or $(x \geq 6)$
-6 -4 -2 0 2 4 6

66. $x \geq \frac{5}{2}$
-2 -1 0 1 2 3 4 5 6

page 38 Checkpoint Quiz 2

1.
-2 -1 0 1 2 3 4 5 6 7

2.
-2 -1 0 1 2 3 4 5 6 7

3.
-4 -3 -2 -1 0 1 2 3 4 5

4.
-6 -5 -4 -3 -2 -1 0 1 2 3 4

5.
-16 -14 -12 -10 -8 -6 -4 -2 0 2 4 6 8

6.
-4 -3 -2 -1 0 1 2 3 4

LESSON 1-6

pages 42–45 Exercises

5. Answers may vary. Sample: Generate 100 random numbers with a calculator. Record the first five digits of each number. Let 0 and 1 represent correct answers and the other digits incorrect answers. Tally the recorded numbers with exactly one digit that represents a correct answer. Tally the recorded numbers with exactly two digits that represent correct answers. Tally the recorded numbers with exactly three digits that represent correct answers. The tally totals, as percents, give the experimental probabilities. They should be in the neighborhood of 40%, 20%, and 5%, respectively.

CHAPTER 2

LESSON 2-1

page 55 Check Skills You'll Need

1.

2.

3.

4.

5.

page 55 Quick Check

1a.

b.

pages 59–61 Exercises

8. domain   range

9. domain   range

10. domain   range

11. domain   range

22. −7, −3, 4, 11

23. 13, 7, −3.5, −14

24. 4.5, 6.5, 10, 13.5

25. −2, −4, −7.5, −11

26. 21, 13, −1, −15

27. −13, −9, −2, 5

28. $29\frac{1}{3}$, $17\frac{1}{3}$, $-3\frac{2}{3}$, $-24\frac{2}{3}$

29. $-\frac{23}{6}$, $-\frac{13}{6}$, $\frac{3}{4}$, $\frac{11}{3}$

30. $-\frac{9}{2}$, $-\frac{7}{2}$, $-\frac{7}{4}$, 0

59. domain: {all integers}, range: {all even integers}; function, each integer pairs to a unique even integer.

60. domain: {all integers}, range: {all integers}; function each integer pairs with its opposite.

61. domain: {all integers}, range: {all even integers}; not a function, each nonzero integer pairs with a pos. and neg. even integer.

65. [4] Yes; $S(c) = 6c^2$; $S(2.5) = 6(2.5)^2$ = 37.5; the surface area is 37.5 cm^2.

[3] minor computational error

[2] includes only function

[1] no work shown

73. −6, 14

74. $-2 \le b \le 2$

75. $y \ne 6$

LESSON 2-2

page 62 Check Skills You'll Need

1. $\frac{17}{3}$, 7, $\frac{23}{3}$, $\frac{29}{3}$

2. $-\frac{16}{5}$, −2, $-\frac{7}{5}$, $\frac{2}{5}$

3. −5, 1, 4, 13

4. −9, −8, $-\frac{15}{2}$, −6

page 63 Quick Check

2a.

$y = 40 - x$
x-intercept (40, 0),
y-intercept (0, 40).
When there are 0 children, the train holds 40 adults. When there are 0 adults, the train holds 40 children.

pages 67–70 Exercises

1.

2.

3.

4.

5.

6.

7.

8.

10a.

b. The *x*-intercept is the point that represents selling 1000 caps and 0 sweatshirts in order to raise the $4500. The *y*-intercept represents selling 0 caps and 360 sweatshirts to raise the $4500.

40. $y = 10$

41. $x = 1$

42.

43.

44.

45.

46.

47.

48.

49.

50.

82. The equation of the line connecting (1, 3) to (−2, 6) is $y = -x + 4$. The equation of the line connecting (1, 3) to (3, 5) is $y = x + 2$. The slopes are negative reciprocals so the lines are perpendicular. Therefore by def. of a right triangle it is a right triangle.

83. The slope of the line connecting (2, 5) to (4, 8) is $\frac{3}{2}$, (2, 5) to (5, 3) is $-\frac{2}{3}$, (4, 8) to (7, 6) is $-\frac{2}{3}$, and (5, 3) to (7, 6) is $\frac{3}{2}$. Since the adjacent sides' slopes are negative reciprocals they are perpendicular. By the def. of a rectangle, it is a rectangle.

84. $p: y = 4x + 16$
$q: y = -\frac{1}{4}x + \frac{13}{4}$
$r: y = 4$

88. [2] $(y - 1) = \frac{2}{3}(x + 1)$

$-3 - 1 = \frac{2}{3}(a + 1)$

$-4 = \frac{2}{3}a + \frac{2}{3}$

$-4 - \frac{2}{3} = \frac{2}{3}a$

$\frac{3}{2}\left(-4\frac{2}{3}\right) = \frac{3}{2}\left(\frac{2}{3}\right)(a)$

$-7 = a$

[1] minor computational error

89. [2] Equation of the line with slope $-\frac{5}{8}$ and *y*-intercept 9 is $y = -\frac{5}{8}x + 9$. Substitute *k* for *y* and -8 for *x* then solve for *k*.

[1] minor error

90. [4] $A(4) + B(4) = C$
$A(-2) + B(10) = C$

$2A(-2) + 2B(10) = 2C$
$-4A + 20B = 2C$

$-4A + 20B = 2C$
$\underline{4A + 4B = C}$
$24B = 3C$

Let $B = 1$
Then $24 = 3C$
$8 = C$

$4A + 4(1) = 8$
$4A = 8 - 4$
$4A = 4$
$A = 1$

T922

The equation is $x + y = 8$.
For x-intercept, let $y = 0$. Then
$x = 8$. For y-intercept, let $x = 0$.
Then $y = 8$. The intercepts are
$(8, 0)$ and $(0, 8)$.

[3] One intercept wrong OR minor
error in computation

[2] Only equation correct OR both
intercepts correct

[1] Only one intercept correct OR
intercepts wrong and minor
error in equation

LESSON 2-3

pages 74–77   Exercises

65.

66.

67.

68.

LESSON 2-4

pages 78–80   Quick Check

1b.

The h-intercept $(0, 1350)$ represents
the starting height at time 0.

4a.

A linear model is reasonable;
models may vary. Sample:
$y = -1.92x + 6$

b.

not reasonable

pages 81–84   Exercises

1. $d = 62.5h + 15$

2a. $y = -50t + 1000$

b.

The y-intercept $(0, 1000)$ represents
the filled pool, and the t-intercept
$(20, 0)$ represents the time needed
to empty the pool.

8.

Linear model is reasonable;
models may vary. Sample: $y =$
$-1.3x + 11$

9.

Linear model is reasonable;
models may vary. Sample:
$y = 2.6x - 0.6$

10.

Linear model is reasonable;
models may vary. Sample:
$y = -0.75x - 3.75$

11.

not reasonable

12a.

Linear model is reasonable.

13a.

Answers may vary. Sample:
$y = 110x + 1170$

14a.

19c. Answers may vary. Sample:

Either way, you will average the
same costs over the long run.

21b–c.

26a.

LESSON 2-5

page 88 Check Skills You'll Need

3.

page 89 Quick Check

2b.

3a.

b.

pages 90–92 **Exercises**

1–9. Tables may vary. Samples are given.

1.

x	0	−1	1	−2	2
y	0	4	4	8	8

2.

x	−2	−1	0	1	2
y	7	3	−1	3	7

3.

x	−1	0	$\frac{1}{4}$	1	2
y	5	1	0	3	7

4.

x	−2	−1	0	1	2
y	6	3	0	3	6

5.

x	−2	−1	0	1	2
y	8	5	2	5	8

6.

x	−1	0	$\frac{2}{3}$	1	2
y	5	2	0	1	4

7.

x	−2	−1	0	1	2
y	−4	−2	0	−2	−4

8.

x	−2	−1	0	1	2
y	1	3	5	3	1

9.

x	−4	−3	$-\frac{5}{2}$	−1	0
y	−3	−1	0	−3	−5

10.

11.

12.

13.

14.

15.

16.

17.

18.

19.

20.

21.

22.

23.

24.

25.

26.

27.

28.

33.

34.

35.

36.

37.

38.

39.

40.

41.

42.

43.

44.

45.

46.

47.

48.

49.

50.

52a.

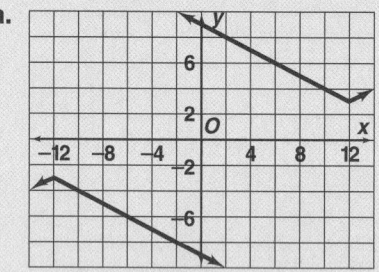

b. **Answers may vary. Sample: Same shape and size, different vertices, and one points down.**

53.

54.

55.

56.

57.

58.

66. [4] $y = -5x - 1$, $y = 5x + 1$

[3] does not label vertex
[2] does not label vertex and does not include both equations
[1] $y = -|5x + 1|$ is not interpreted correctly but graph is correct

67.

Answers may vary.
Sample: $y = 8.7x - 10.9$

68.

Answers may vary.
Sample: $y = \frac{2}{3}x + 6\frac{2}{3}$

69.

not reasonable

70.

Answers may vary.
Sample: $y = -0.5x + 7$

LESSON 2-6

page 93   Technology Activity

1.

Each graph is a vertical translation of $y = |x|$.

2.

Each graph is a horizontal translation of $y = |x|$.

3.

Each graph is a stretch or shrink of $y = |x|$.

4.

Each graph is a stretch and/or reflection of $y = |x|$.

5.

6.

7.

8. Answers may vary. Sample: $y = |x|$ is the simplest, because all of the other graphs are translations, stretches, shrinks and/or reflections.

pages 93–97 Quick Check

1.a. $y = |x| + 1$ is a translation of $y = |x|$ by one unit upward.

2.b. $y = |x - 1|$ is a translation of $y = |x|$ by one unit to the right.

4.a. The graph is a vertical shrink of $y = |x|$ by a factor of $\frac{1}{3}$.

pages 97–100 Exercises

17.

18.

19.

20.

21.

22.

33. vertical

34. combined

48.

6 right

49.

4 right, 3 down

50.

3 left, 1 up

51. $y = |x - 2| + 2$

3 right, 3 up

59. Answers may vary.
Sample: $f(0) = -2$; $f(1) = 0$; $f(2) = 2$; $f(-2) = 0$; $f(-1) = -2$

$y = |2x + 1| - 3$

60. Answers may vary.
Samples: $f(0) = 1$; $f(1) = \frac{8}{9}$; $f(3) = \frac{2}{3}$; $f(-1) = \frac{10}{9}$; $f(-3) = \frac{4}{3}$

61. $x \le -10$

62. $a > 4.5$

63. $b > -1.5$

page 100 Checkpoint Quiz 2

1.

2.

3.

4.

5.

6.

LESSON 2-7

page 101   Check Skills You'll Need

1. $p \leq 1.25$

2. $t > 13$

3. $t \leq -3$

4. $c = \pm 4.5$

5. $b = 2, 8$

6. $h \leq -3.5$ or $h \geq 3.5$

page 101   Activity

1. and 2a.

2b. on the line: $(-2, -1)$, $(2, 7)$
above the line: $(-1, 5)$, $(0, 4)$, $(0, 5)$, $(1, 6)$
below the line: $(-2, -3)$, $(-1, -1)$, $(2, 3)$

page 102   Quick Check

1a.

1b.

1c.

pages 104–106   Exercises

10a. $y \geq 20x$ if $x \leq 6$
$y \geq 15x$ if $x > 6$

  b. Answers may vary. Sample:

11.

12.

13.

14.

15.

16.

17.

18.

19.

23.

24.

$y > \frac{2}{5}x + 2$

25.

26.

27.

28.

29.

30.

31.

32.

33.

34.

44.

45.

46.

47.

page 111   Chapter Review

39.

40.

41.

page 112   Chapter Test

1. domain {0, 1, 2, 3, 4},
range {−16, −9, −4, −1, 0}

2. domain {3, 4, 5, 6, 7},
range {2, 3, 4, 5, 6}

23. Answers may vary. Sample:
a. $y = -x$
b. $y = x + 15$
c. $y = x$
d. $y = -x - 5$
e. rectangle

27.

28.

29.

30.

31a–b.

Years since 1995

Answers may vary. Sample:
$y = 211.8x + 1152$, where 1995
corr. to $x = 0$.

c. Answers may vary. Sample: $3900

32. translation down 4

33. translation right 1, down 5

34. translation left 4, vertical reflection, then translation up 3

35. translation left 1, vertical stretch by 2

36. translation up 5

37. translation left 2, vertical shrink by $\frac{1}{2}$, vertical reflection, then translation down 3

38.

39.

40.

41.

page 113 Standardized Test Prep

16. [2]

The parent function is $y = |x|$, and $y = |x + 3|$ is $y = |x|$ shifted 3 units to the left.

[1] includes only graph

17. [2] The constant of variation is -1 and when $y = 3$, $x = -3$.

[1] only includes either -1 OR -3

18. [4] a. $y = 2x + 10$

  b. $y = -\frac{1}{2}x + \frac{3}{2}$

  c.

[3] does 2 parts

[2] does only one part

[1] has computational errors in all parts

CHAPTER 3

page 116   Check Your Readiness

13.

15. $y = 6x$

16.

17.

18.

LESSON 3-1

page 118   Check Skills You'll Need

1.

2.

3.

4, 5, 6.

page 118   Technology Activity

1a. **b.**

c.

$y = \dfrac{8x + 4}{-2}$

2a. (a): one; (b): none; (c): all

b. If the slopes are not equal then the graphs have one point in common. If the slopes are equal, they either have no points or all points in common.

pages 120–123   Exercises

6. $(3, -4)$ **7.** $(3, 6)$

8. $(0, 0)$ **9.** $(20, 10)$

25. infinitely many solutions

$3 = 4y + x$
$4y = -x + 3$

26. $\left(\dfrac{4}{3}, \dfrac{7}{6}\right) \approx (1.5, 1)$

$x + 4y - 6 = 0$ $x - 2y + 1 = 0$

27. no solution

$x + 2y = 8$
$3x + 6y - 12 = 0$

28. $(6, 4)$

$-x + 3y = 6$
$2x - y = 8$

29. $(2, -3)$

$3x + y = 3$
$2x - y = 7$

30. $(1.875, 0.75) \approx (2, 1)$

$2x + 3y = 6$
$4x = 6y + 3$

31. $\left(\dfrac{16}{9}, -\dfrac{14}{9}\right) \approx (1.8, -1.6)$

$2 = 2x + y$
$10 - 3x = -3y$

32. $\left(\dfrac{1}{3}, \dfrac{3}{5}\right)$

$x = \dfrac{1}{3}$
$3x = -5y + 4$

33. infinitely many solutions

$x + 3y = 6$
$6y + 2x = 12$

34. $(4, 2)$

35. $(1.7, 2.6)$

36. no solution

37a. $\begin{cases} c = 3 + 0.40b \\ c = 9.00 \end{cases}$

44b. The cost would be the same for a 6-day stay.

(6, 150)

45.
$$\begin{cases} y = 6x + 80 \\ y = 4x + 100 \end{cases}$$

After 10 minutes the numbers of flyers will be equal.

62.

63.

64.

page 132   Activity Lab

3.

Number of Pentagons	Number of Hexagons
0	7
1	6
2	5
3	4
4	3
5	2
6	1
7	0

Number of Pentagons	Number of Hexagons
0	Not possible
1	Not possible
2	Not possible
3	Not possible
4	3
5	Not possible
6	Not possible
7	Not possible

T932

LESSON 3-3

page 133   Check Skills You'll Need

4.

5.

6.

7.

8.

9.

page 134   Quick Check

2a.

b.
$y > -4x + 2$

3.
$$\begin{cases} 550 \le m \le 800 \\ v + m \ge 1100 \\ v \le 800 \end{cases}$$

4a.
$y \le |x + 5|$

b.

$y \le |x - 4|$
$y \ge -2x + 4$

page 135   Additional Examples

3.
$$\begin{cases} m + 5 \le 150 \\ m \ge 60 \end{cases}$$

4.

pages 136–138   Exercises

3. (0, 0), (0, 1), (0, 2), (0, 3), (0, 4), (0, 5), (0, 6), (0, 7), (1, 0), (1, 1), (1, 2), (1, 3), (1, 4), (1, 5), (1, 6), (2, 0), (2, 1), (2, 2), (2, 3), (2, 4), (2, 5), (3, 3), (3, 4)

10. no solution

$-6x + 2y > 5$

11.

12. $-x - y \le 2 \quad y - 2x > 1$

13. $y > -2x$ $-2x + y \le -2$

14.

$c \le \frac{1}{2}d + 3$
$c \ge d - 3$

15. $2x + y < 1$ $y + 3x < 1$

16. $\begin{cases} x + y \ge 6 \\ x + y \le 11 \\ y \ge 2x \\ y \ge 0 \\ x \ge 0 \end{cases}$

17. $\begin{cases} a + c \ge 40 \\ c \le 30 \end{cases}$

18. $y > 4$

19. $y > |2x - 1|$ $y < -\frac{1}{3}x + 1$

20. $y \ge |x + 2|$ $y > x - 2$

21. $y \ge -|x|$

22. $3y < -x - 1$

23. $y \le -|x - 3|$ $y > -2$

24. $-2x + y > 3$ $y \le$

25. $y < |x + 3|$ $5y \ge 2x - 5$

26.

27.

28.

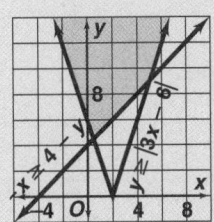

29. $y \le x - 4$

40a. $\begin{cases} j + s \ge 7 \\ j + s \le 10 \\ s > j \\ j \ge 0 \\ s \ge 0 \end{cases}$

b.

(0, 7) (0, 8) (0, 9) (0, 10) (1, 6) (1, 7)
(1, 8) (1, 9) (2, 5) (2, 6) (2, 7) (2, 8)
(3, 4) (3, 5) (3, 6) (3, 7) (4, 5) (4, 6)

c. Only whole numbers of juniors and seniors make sense and the sum of each pair must be less than or equal to ten.

41. Answers will vary. Possible solution:
$\begin{cases} x < 5 \\ y \ge 1 \end{cases}$

42. Answers may vary. Sample: If the isolated variable, y, is greater than the remaining expression, the half-plane above the boundary line is shaded. If the variable is less than the remaining expression, then the half-plane below the line is shaded.

43.

44.

45. $y \ge 1$

46. (0, 2)

47.

Additional Answers

48.

49. $\begin{cases} y \ge |x| - 2 \\ y \le -|x| + 2 \end{cases}$

50. $\begin{cases} y \le 3 \\ y \ge 0 \\ y \le 3x + 9 \\ y \le -3x + 9 \end{cases}$

51. $\begin{cases} y \le 4 \\ y \ge 0 \\ y \le 2x \\ y \ge 2x - 8 \end{cases}$

56. **[2]** For the first inequality, $-2(2) + 3 = -1$ and $-2 < -1$, so $(2, -2)$ satisfies the inequality. For the second inequality, $2 - 4 = -2$ and $-2 \ge -2$, so $(2, -2)$ satisfies the inequality. Since $(2, -2)$ satisfies both inequalities, it is a solution to the system.

[1] omits one or two of the three explanations above

LESSON 3-4

page 139 Check Skills You'll Need

4.

5.

6.

pages 142–144 Exercises

4.

vertices: (0, 0), (5, 0), (5, 4), (0, 4) maximized at (5, 4)

5.

vertices: (3, 5), (0, 8) minimized at (0, 8)

6.

vertices: (0, 0), (5, 0), (2, 6), (0, 8) maximized at (5, 0)

7.

vertices: (1, 5), (8, 5), (8, −2) minimized at (8, −2)

8.

vertices: (8, 0), (2, 3) minimized at (8, 0)

9.

vertices: (2, 1), (6, 1), (6, 2), (2, 5), (3, 5) maximized at (6, 2)

14.

vertices: (0, 0), (1, 4), (0, 4.5), $\left(\frac{7}{3}, 0\right)$; maximized when $P = 6$ at (1, 4)

15.

vertices: (75, 20), (75, 110), $\left(25, 86\frac{2}{3}\right)$, (25, 110); minimized when $C = 633\frac{1}{3}$ at $\left(25, 86\frac{2}{3}\right)$

16.

vertices: (0, 0), $\left(7\frac{1}{3}, 3\frac{2}{3}\right)$, (0, 11); maximized when $P = 29\frac{1}{3}$ at $\left(7\frac{1}{3}, 3\frac{2}{3}\right)$

17.

vertices: (0, 0), (150, 0), (100, 100), (0, 200); maximized when $P = 400$ at (0, 200)

18.

vertices: (12, 0), (0, 10), (4, 2), (1, 5); minimized when $C = 80,000$ at (4, 2)

19.

vertices: (3, 3), (3, 10), (5, 1), (12, 1); maximized when $P = 51$ at (12, 1)

T934

21.

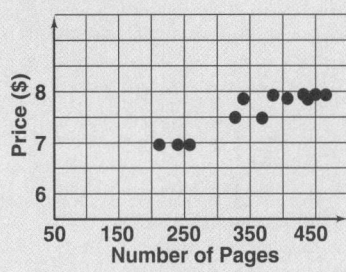

vertices: $(0, 60)$, $\left(23\frac{1}{3}, 13\frac{1}{3}\right)$, $(50, 0)$; minimized when
$x = 23\frac{1}{3}$ and $y = 13\frac{1}{3}$
Round to $(23, 14)$ and $(24, 13)$; $(24, 13)$ gives you a minimum cost of \$261.00.

34a.

LESSON 3-5

page 146 Check Skills You'll Need

5.

6.

7.

8.

page 147 Additional Examples

1.

page 147 Quick Check

1a. $(0, -4, -2)$

b. $(-1, 1, 3)$

c. $(3, -5, 2)$

d.

$(3, 3, -3)$

pages 149–151 Exercises

8. $(-1, -1, -1)$

9. $(-4, -5, 3)$

10.

$(25, 40, -30)$

11.

$(1, 1, 0)$

12. $(0, -2, 2)$

19.

20.

21.

22.

23.

24.

25. Sample: Balcony represents vertical direction, row is backward or forward, and seat is left or right.

27.

28.

29.

30.

31.

32.

33. xy-trace: $x + y = 6$
xz-trace: $x - 2z = 6$
yz-trace: $y - 2z = 6$

34. xy-trace: $-2x + y = 10$
xz-trace: $-2x + 5z = 10$
yz-trace: $y + 5z = 10$

35. xy-trace: $-3x - 8y = 24$
xz-trace: $-x - 4z = 8$
yz-trace: $-2y - 3z = 6$

36. xy-trace: $x + 5y = 5$
xz-trace: $x - z = 5$
yz-trace: $5y - z = 5$

50.

51.

52.

59.

60.

61.

LESSON 3-6

pages 157–159   Exercises

49. **[2]** The three equations include parallel planes, so there is no point common to all three planes.

[1] not explained in terms of intersecting planes

53.

54.

55.

62.

63.

64.

65.

66.

67.

page 160   Test-Taking Strategies

3b.

pages 161–163   Chapter Review

40.

41.

42.

page 164   Chapter Test

1. independent

2. inconsistent

8.

9.

10.

11.

12.

vertices: (0, 0), (6, 0), (6, 5), (0, 5)
$P = 17$ at (6, 5)

13.

vertices: (0, 3), (6, 0), (8, 0), (0, 8)
$C = 6$ at (6, 0)

22.

23.

24.

25.

26. x = number of balloons
y = number of party favors
z = number of streamers
$0.06x + 0.48y + 0.08z = 24$

29. x = amount in growth fund,
y = amount in income fund,
z = amount in money market fund,
$x + y + z = 50{,}000$
$1.12x + 1.08y + 1.05z = 54{,}500$
$y = 2z$, $x = \$20{,}000$, $y = \$20{,}000$;
$z = \$10{,}000$

30. x = amount of sales,
y = pay,
$y = 0.15x + 200$
$y = 0.10x + 300$,
$x = \$2000$

31. c = number of cots
t = number of tables
h = number of chairs
$10c + 10t + 40h = 1950$
$20c + 20h = 1800$
$10c + 5t + 20h = 1350$
A cot cost \$75, a table cost \$60,
and a chair cost \$15.

CHAPTER 4

page 166   Check Your Readiness

11.

12.

13.

14.

15.

16.

17.

18.

page 169   Quick Check

3a.

	China	Russia	United States
Production	42	46	71
Consumption	43	28	98

b. Add a new column for each additional country.

c. A $c \times d$ matrix has c rows and d columns, while a $d \times c$ matrix has d rows and c columns.

pages 170–173   Exercises

12.

	Novels	Biogr.	Sci-Fi	Nonfiction
Week 1	175	100	93	100
Week 2	154	93	81	104
Week 3	201	110	114	103
Week 4	180	92	100	110

13.

	Week 1	Week 2	Week 3	Week 4
Novels	175	154	201	180
Biogr.	100	93	110	92
Sci-Fi	93	81	114	100
Nonfiction	100	104	103	110

14.a.

	Computer Instruction	Book Discussion	Parenting Skills	Employment Guidance
Urban	68	56	28	31
H = Suburban	59	50	24	18
Rural	49	34	15	12

b. 24; perent of suburban libraries offering parenting skills programs.

15.

	1998	1999	2000	2001	2002	2003
CDs	847.0	938.9	942.5	881.9	803.3	745.9
DVDs	0.5	2.5	3.3	7.9	10.7	17.5

3.3; number of DVDs, in millions, shipped in 2000

16.

	CDs	DVDs
1998	847.0	0.5
1999	938.9	2.5
2000	942.5	3.3
2001	881.9	7.9
2001	803.3	10.7
2003	745.9	17.5

881.9; number of CDs, in millions, shipped in 2001

29a. Answers may vary. Sample:

b. Answers may vary. Sample:

$$F = \begin{bmatrix} 1 & 1 & 1 & 1 & 1 & 1 & 1 & 1 & 0 & 0 \\ 1 & 0 & 0 & 0 & 0 & 0 & 0 & 0 & 0 & 0 \\ 1 & 0 & 0 & 0 & 0 & 0 & 0 & 0 & 0 & 0 \\ 1 & 0 & 0 & 0 & 0 & 0 & 0 & 0 & 0 & 0 \\ 1 & 1 & 1 & 1 & 1 & 0 & 0 & 0 & 0 & 0 \\ 1 & 0 & 0 & 0 & 0 & 0 & 0 & 0 & 0 & 0 \\ 1 & 0 & 0 & 0 & 0 & 0 & 0 & 0 & 0 & 0 \\ 1 & 0 & 0 & 0 & 0 & 0 & 0 & 0 & 0 & 0 \\ 1 & 0 & 0 & 0 & 0 & 0 & 0 & 0 & 0 & 0 \\ 1 & 0 & 0 & 0 & 0 & 0 & 0 & 0 & 0 & 0 \end{bmatrix}$$

$$H = \begin{bmatrix} 0 & 1 & 0 & 0 & 0 & 0 & 0 & 0 & 1 & 0 \\ 0 & 1 & 0 & 0 & 0 & 0 & 0 & 0 & 1 & 0 \\ 0 & 1 & 0 & 0 & 0 & 0 & 0 & 0 & 1 & 0 \\ 0 & 1 & 0 & 0 & 0 & 0 & 0 & 0 & 1 & 0 \\ 0 & 1 & 1 & 1 & 1 & 1 & 1 & 1 & 1 & 0 \\ 0 & 1 & 1 & 1 & 1 & 1 & 1 & 1 & 1 & 0 \\ 0 & 1 & 0 & 0 & 0 & 0 & 0 & 0 & 1 & 0 \\ 0 & 1 & 0 & 0 & 0 & 0 & 0 & 0 & 1 & 0 \\ 0 & 1 & 0 & 0 & 0 & 0 & 0 & 0 & 1 & 0 \\ 0 & 1 & 0 & 0 & 0 & 0 & 0 & 0 & 1 & 0 \end{bmatrix}$$

$$T = \begin{bmatrix} 1 & 1 & 1 & 1 & 1 & 1 & 1 & 1 & 1 & 1 \\ 0 & 0 & 0 & 0 & 1 & 1 & 0 & 0 & 0 & 0 \\ 0 & 0 & 0 & 0 & 1 & 1 & 0 & 0 & 0 & 0 \\ 0 & 0 & 0 & 0 & 1 & 1 & 0 & 0 & 0 & 0 \\ 0 & 0 & 0 & 0 & 1 & 1 & 0 & 0 & 0 & 0 \\ 0 & 0 & 0 & 0 & 1 & 1 & 0 & 0 & 0 & 0 \\ 0 & 0 & 0 & 0 & 1 & 1 & 0 & 0 & 0 & 0 \\ 0 & 0 & 0 & 0 & 1 & 1 & 0 & 0 & 0 & 0 \\ 0 & 0 & 0 & 0 & 1 & 1 & 0 & 0 & 0 & 0 \\ 0 & 0 & 0 & 0 & 1 & 1 & 0 & 0 & 0 & 0 \end{bmatrix}$$

32. [4] a. $A = \begin{bmatrix} 20 & 40 & 0 \\ 12 & 35 & 40 \\ 15 & 55 & 70 \end{bmatrix}$

      b. Rob's earnings

[3] minor error in Matrix A

[2] only one part correct

[1] both parts incorrect, but matrix A is 3 × 3 and contains the table data

LESSON 4-2

pages 178–180   Exercises

1a.
Anita Allen		Mary Beth Iagorashvili	
Shoot	952	Shoot	760
Fence	720	Fence	832
Swim	1108	Swim	1252
Ride	1172	Ride	1144
Run	1044	Run	1064

18. $\begin{bmatrix} 0 & 5 \\ 8 & -6 \\ 0 & 5 \end{bmatrix}$

19. B and D cannot be added because they do not have the same dimensions.

20. $\begin{bmatrix} 6 & 3 \\ -3 & 3 \end{bmatrix}$

21. $\begin{bmatrix} -6 & -3 \\ -4 & -2 \\ -2 & 5 \end{bmatrix}$

22. $\begin{bmatrix} -4 & 1 \\ -3 & -1 \end{bmatrix}$

27a.
	Plant 1		Plant 2	
	Plastic	Rubber	Plastic	Rubber
1-color	1000	1400	1200	3600
3-color	2600	3800	1800	4800

b.
	Plant 1 − Plant 2	
	Plastic	Rubber
1-color	−200	−2200
3-color	800	−1000

Plant 1; Plant 2

pages 186–189   Exercises

19a.
	Lilies	Carnations	Daisies
Arrangement 1	3	0	0
Arrangement 2	3	4	0
Arrangement 3	0	3	4

b. Cost
Lilies	2.15
Carnations	0.90
Daisies	1.30

c.
	Cost
Arrangement 1	6.45
Arrangement 2	10.05
Arrangement 3	7.90

49. No; AB will be a 2 × 2 matrix and BA will be a 3 × 3 matrix, and equal matrices must have the same dimensions. Answers may vary. Sample: Let A be the matrix $\begin{bmatrix} 0 & 1 & 2 \\ 3 & 0 & 0 \end{bmatrix}$, and let B be the matrix $\begin{bmatrix} 1 & 0 \\ 2 & 4 \\ 3 & 1 \end{bmatrix}$. Then $AB = \begin{bmatrix} 8 & 6 \\ 3 & 0 \end{bmatrix}$ and $BA = \begin{bmatrix} 0 & 1 & 2 \\ 12 & 2 & 4 \\ 3 & 3 & 6 \end{bmatrix}$.

50.
	Thursday	Friday	Saturday
Revenue	[2100	1950	2570]

59. [2] $3Y + 2\begin{bmatrix} -1 & -3 \\ 2 & 5 \end{bmatrix} = \begin{bmatrix} 13 & -9 \\ 4 & 16 \end{bmatrix}$

$3Y + \begin{bmatrix} -2 & -6 \\ 4 & 10 \end{bmatrix} = \begin{bmatrix} 13 & -9 \\ 4 & 16 \end{bmatrix}$

$3Y = \begin{bmatrix} 13 & -9 \\ 4 & 16 \end{bmatrix} - \begin{bmatrix} -2 & -6 \\ 4 & 10 \end{bmatrix}$

$\frac{1}{3} \cdot 3Y = \begin{bmatrix} 15 & -3 \\ 0 & 6 \end{bmatrix} \cdot \frac{1}{3}$

$Y = \begin{bmatrix} 5 & -1 \\ 0 & 2 \end{bmatrix}$

[1] fails to show work OR makes a computational error

60. [4] No; in the case of $M \times N$, $-3 \times 0 + 4 \times -2 = -8$ for element MN_{11}. In $N \times M$, $0 \times -3 + 1 \times 1 = 1$ for element NM_{11}. Therefore, since the corresponding elements of MN and NM are not equal, $M \times N \neq N \times M$.

[3] recognizes the results are not the same and attempts to explain why

[2] recognizes that $M \times N \neq N \times M$ but does not explain

[1] understands what $M \times N$ and $N \times M$ mean but cannot properly relate it to problem

Additional Answers

63.

(0, 2), (0, 0), (1, 2), (3, 0); (1, 2)

64.

(2, 0), (8, 0), (2, 3); (2, 0)

65.

(0, 0), (5, 0), (4, 2), (0, 6); (5, 0)

66.

67.

68.

page 190   Geometry Review

5.c. (1, 0), (1, 2), (3, 1); (−3, −3), (−3, −1), (−1, −2); add the same quantity to each *x*-coordinate and a different quantity for each *y*-coordinate. For this transformation add −4 to the *x*-coordinate and −3 to the *y*-coordinate.

(−2, −1), (0, −1), (−1, −3); (−2, 1), (0, 1), (−1, 3); the *x*-coordinate is the same and the *y*-coordinate is the opposite.

(0, 0), (1, 0), (1, 2); (0, 0), (0, 1), (2, 1); the *x*-coordinate of the image is the opposite of the *y*-coordinate of the preimage and the *y*-coordinate of the image is the *x*-coordinate of the preimage.

LESSON 4-4

page 191   Check Skills You'll Need

1.

$y = x + 6$

2.

$f(x) = \frac{1}{2}x + 7$

3.

$g(x) = |x - 3|$

4.

$y = x - 2$

5.

$y = \frac{1}{3}|x - 3| - 2$

6.

$f(x) = -2|x - 2|$

page 191   Activity

2.

3. Original figure: (−7, 5), (−5, 5), (−5, 4), (−2, 4), (−2, 2), (−4, 2), (−4, 3), (−7, 3). Image: (−3, −1), (−1, −1), (−1, −2), (2, −2), (2, −4), (0, −4), (0, −3), (−3, −3)

4. Going from the original figure to the new figure, the *x*-coordinate of a point on the original increases by 4, and the *y*-coordinate of the point decreases by 6.

5. (3, 8), (5, 8), (5, 7), (8, 7), (8, 5), (6, 5), (6, 6), (3, 6)

6. 2 units down and 4 units right: (0, 0), (2, 0), (2, 2), (−1, 2), (−1, 3), (−3, 3), (−3, 1), (0, 1); 5 units down and 7 units right: (0, 0), (2, 0), (2, −1), (5, −1), (5, −3), (3, −3), (3, −2), (0, −2)

7. Sample: repetition of 2 right and 1 up, 2 left and 1 down, 3 left and 3 up, and 3 right and 3 down

page 192–195   Quick Check

1c.

2a.

b.

c.

3a.

b.

c.

d.

4a.

b.

c.

d.

pages 195–198   Exercises

1.

2.

4.

5.

6.

7.

8.

9.

17.

18.

19.

36.

Answers may vary. Sample: It enlarges or shrinks a figure and moves it farther from or closer to the origin.

37.

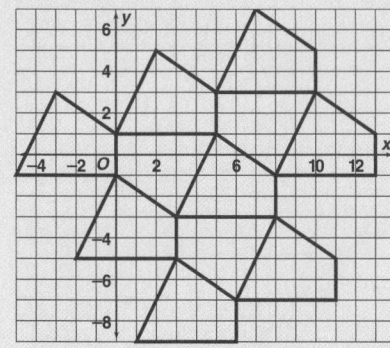

39. $f: \begin{bmatrix} 1 & 2 & 4 & 5 & 2 \\ 2 & 1 & 2 & 5 & 4 \end{bmatrix}$, $g: \begin{bmatrix} 2 & 4 & 8 & 10 & 4 \\ 4 & 2 & 4 & 10 & 8 \end{bmatrix}$;

dilation

40. $f: \begin{bmatrix} -5 & -3 & -2 & -1 & 1 & -1 & -2 & -3 \\ 2 & 1 & -1 & 1 & 2 & 3 & 5 & 3 \end{bmatrix}$,

$g: \begin{bmatrix} -3 & -1 & 0 & 1 & 3 & 1 & 0 & -1 \\ -2 & -3 & -5 & -3 & -2 & -1 & 1 & -1 \end{bmatrix}$;

translation

41. $f: \begin{bmatrix} -5 & -2 & 1 \\ 3 & 0 & 3 \end{bmatrix}$, $g: \begin{bmatrix} -1 & 2 & 5 \\ 1 & -2 & 1 \end{bmatrix}$;

translation

42. $f: \begin{bmatrix} 0 & 4 & 4 \\ 0 & 2 & 4 \end{bmatrix}$, $g: \begin{bmatrix} 0 & -4 & -4 \\ 0 & -2 & -4 \end{bmatrix}$;

rotation

43.

44.

45a. Check students' work.

b. Translate the vertices of *ABCD* down 12 units.

$\begin{bmatrix} 0 & 0 & 0 & 0 \\ -12 & -12 & -12 & -12 \end{bmatrix}$;

coordinates of pre-image: (5, 8), (6, 8), (6, 9), (5, 9),
coordinates of image: (5, −4), (6, −4), (6, −3), (5, −3)

c. $\begin{bmatrix} 11 & 12 & 12 & 11 \\ 2 & 2 & 3 & 3 \end{bmatrix}$

46. $\begin{bmatrix} -6 & 1 & -10 \\ 0 & 6 & 6 \end{bmatrix}$

47. $\begin{bmatrix} 0 & 2 & 0 \\ -4 & -7 & -10 \end{bmatrix}$

48. $\begin{bmatrix} 5 & 10 & 2 & 6 \\ 17 & 6 & 6 & 2 \end{bmatrix}$

49. $\begin{bmatrix} -3 & -1.5 & -2 & -4 \\ 3 & 4.5 & 5 & 3.5 \end{bmatrix}$

55. 2×3; $\begin{bmatrix} 2 & -1 & 33 \\ 4 & 4 & -50 \end{bmatrix}$

56. undefined, because the number of columns in the first matrix is not equal to the number of rows in the second matrix

57.

58.

59.

60.

$\begin{matrix} -2 \\ -1 \\ 0 \\ 1 \\ 2 \end{matrix}$ $\begin{matrix} 4 \\ 1 \\ 0 \end{matrix}$ yes

61.

$\begin{matrix} 27 \\ 3 \\ 0 \end{matrix}$ $\begin{matrix} -2 \\ -1 \\ 0 \\ 1 \\ 2 \end{matrix}$ no

62. yes

63. no

LESSON 4-5

pages 203–205   Exercises

1. $\begin{bmatrix} 3 & 2 \\ 4 & 3 \end{bmatrix} \begin{bmatrix} 3 & -2 \\ -4 & 3 \end{bmatrix} =$

$\begin{bmatrix} 3(3) + 2(-4) & 3(-2) + 2(3) \\ 4(3) + 3(-4) & 4(-2) + 3(3) \end{bmatrix}$

$= \begin{bmatrix} 1 & 0 \\ 0 & 1 \end{bmatrix}$

2. $\begin{bmatrix} -3 & 7 \\ -2 & 5 \end{bmatrix} \begin{bmatrix} -5 & 7 \\ -2 & 3 \end{bmatrix} =$

$\begin{bmatrix} -3(-5) + 7(-2) & -3(7) + 7(3) \\ -2(-5) + 5(-2) & -2(7) + 5(3) \end{bmatrix} = \begin{bmatrix} 1 & 0 \\ 0 & 1 \end{bmatrix}$

3. $\begin{bmatrix} \frac{1}{5} & -\frac{1}{10} \\ 0 & \frac{1}{4} \end{bmatrix} \begin{bmatrix} 5 & 2 \\ 0 & 4 \end{bmatrix} =$

$\begin{bmatrix} \frac{1}{5}(5) + (-\frac{1}{10})(0) & \frac{1}{5}(2) + (-\frac{1}{10})(4) \\ 0(5) + \frac{1}{4}(0) & 0(2) + \frac{1}{4}(4) \end{bmatrix} = \begin{bmatrix} 1 & 0 \\ 0 & 1 \end{bmatrix}$

25a.

		From	
		No Cable	Cable
To	No Cable	0.98	0.005
	Cable	0.02	0.995

b. about 20,100 people

c. about 19,897 people

50. det $M = ad - bc$ and det $N = eh - fg$. Next,

$MN = \begin{bmatrix} ae + bg & af + bh \\ ce + dg & cf + dh \end{bmatrix}$, and

det $MN = (ae + bg)(cf + dh) - (af + bh)(ce + dg)$
$= acef + adeh + bcfg + bdgh - acef$
$\quad - adfg - bceh - bdgh$
$= adeh - bceh + bcfg - adfg$.
But det $M \cdot$ det $N = (ad - bc)(eh - fg)$
$= adeh - bceh - adfg + bcfg$.
So det $M \cdot$ det $N =$ det MN.

LESSON 4-6

pages 206–208   Quick Check

3a. The matrices $\begin{bmatrix} 0 & 0 & 1 \\ 0.2 & -0.2 & 0 \\ 0 & -1 & 1 \end{bmatrix}$ and $\begin{bmatrix} 1 & 5 & -1 \\ 1 & 0 & -1 \\ 1 & 0 & 0 \end{bmatrix}$ have

a product of $\begin{bmatrix} 1 & 0 & 0 \\ 0 & 1 & 0 \\ 0 & 0 & 1 \end{bmatrix}$, so they are inverses.

b. The matrices $\begin{bmatrix} 0 & 1 & 0 \\ 1 & 0 & 1 \\ 0 & 1 & 0 \end{bmatrix}$ and $\begin{bmatrix} 3 & 4 & 1 \\ -2 & 0 & 2 \\ 1 & 5 & 3 \end{bmatrix}$ have a

product of $\begin{bmatrix} -2 & 0 & 2 \\ 4 & 9 & 4 \\ -2 & 0 & 2 \end{bmatrix}$, so they are not inverses.

4a. The matrices $\begin{bmatrix} 0 & 0 & 2 \\ 1 & 3 & -2 \\ 1 & -2 & 1 \end{bmatrix}$ and $\begin{bmatrix} 0.1 & 0.4 & 0.6 \\ 0.3 & 0.2 & -0.2 \\ 0.5 & 0 & 0 \end{bmatrix}$

have a product of $\begin{bmatrix} 1 & 0 & 0 \\ 0 & 1 & 0 \\ 0 & 0 & 1 \end{bmatrix}$, so they are inverses.

pages 212–213 Extension

7.

8.

9.

10a.

b.

	A	B	C	D
A	0	1	0	1
B	0	0	1	0
C	0	1	0	1
D	1	0	0	0

$T =$

c. $\begin{bmatrix} 1 & 0 & 1 & 0 \\ 0 & 1 & 0 & 1 \\ 1 & 0 & 1 & 0 \\ 0 & 1 & 0 & 1 \end{bmatrix}$;

the matrix models trips from one house to another that can be traveled using exactly two paths.

pages 214–217   Quick Check

1a. $\begin{bmatrix} 3 & 2 \\ 0 & 1 \end{bmatrix}\begin{bmatrix} x \\ y \end{bmatrix} = \begin{bmatrix} 16 \\ 5 \end{bmatrix}$; coefficient matrix is $\begin{bmatrix} 3 & 2 \\ 0 & 1 \end{bmatrix}$, variable matrix is $\begin{bmatrix} x \\ y \end{bmatrix}$, constant matrix is $\begin{bmatrix} 16 \\ 5 \end{bmatrix}$.

b. $\begin{bmatrix} 1 & -1 & 1 \\ 1 & -2 & -1 \\ 2 & -1 & 2 \end{bmatrix}\begin{bmatrix} x \\ y \\ z \end{bmatrix} = \begin{bmatrix} 0 \\ 5 \\ 8 \end{bmatrix}$; coefficient matrix is $\begin{bmatrix} 1 & -1 & 1 \\ 1 & -2 & -1 \\ 2 & -1 & 2 \end{bmatrix}$, variable matrix is $\begin{bmatrix} x \\ y \\ z \end{bmatrix}$, constant matrix is $\begin{bmatrix} 0 \\ 5 \\ 8 \end{bmatrix}$.

3a. $2(4) + (-10) + 3(1) \overset{?}{=} 1$
$8 - 10 + 3 \overset{?}{=} 1$
$1 = 1$
$5(4) + (-10) - 2(1) \overset{?}{=} 8$
$20 - 10 - 2 \overset{?}{=} 8$
$8 = 8$
$4 - (-10) - 9(1) \overset{?}{=} 5$
$4 + 10 - 9 \overset{?}{=} 5$
$5 = 5$

pages 217–219   Exercises

1. $\begin{bmatrix} 1 & 1 \\ 1 & -2 \end{bmatrix}\begin{bmatrix} x \\ y \end{bmatrix} = \begin{bmatrix} 5 \\ -4 \end{bmatrix}$; coefficient matrix is $\begin{bmatrix} 1 & 1 \\ 1 & -2 \end{bmatrix}$, variable matrix is $\begin{bmatrix} x \\ y \end{bmatrix}$, constant matrix is $\begin{bmatrix} 5 \\ -4 \end{bmatrix}$.

2. $\begin{bmatrix} -3 & 1 \\ 1 & 0 \end{bmatrix}\begin{bmatrix} x \\ y \end{bmatrix} = \begin{bmatrix} -7 \\ 2 \end{bmatrix}$; coefficient matrix is $\begin{bmatrix} -3 & 1 \\ 1 & 0 \end{bmatrix}$, variable matrix is $\begin{bmatrix} x \\ y \end{bmatrix}$, constant matrix is $\begin{bmatrix} -7 \\ 2 \end{bmatrix}$.

3. $\begin{bmatrix} 3 & 5 \\ 1 & 1 \end{bmatrix}\begin{bmatrix} a \\ b \end{bmatrix} = \begin{bmatrix} 0 \\ 2 \end{bmatrix}$; coefficient matrix is $\begin{bmatrix} 3 & 5 \\ 1 & 1 \end{bmatrix}$, variable matrix is $\begin{bmatrix} a \\ b \end{bmatrix}$, constant matrix is $\begin{bmatrix} 0 \\ 2 \end{bmatrix}$.

4. $\begin{bmatrix} 1 & 3 & -1 \\ 1 & 0 & 2 \\ 0 & 2 & -1 \end{bmatrix}\begin{bmatrix} x \\ y \\ z \end{bmatrix} = \begin{bmatrix} 2 \\ 8 \\ 1 \end{bmatrix}$; coefficient matrix is $\begin{bmatrix} 1 & 3 & -1 \\ 1 & 0 & 2 \\ 0 & 2 & -1 \end{bmatrix}$, variable matrix is $\begin{bmatrix} x \\ y \\ z \end{bmatrix}$, constant matrix is $\begin{bmatrix} 2 \\ 8 \\ 1 \end{bmatrix}$.

5. $\begin{bmatrix} 1 & -1 & 1 \\ 2 & 0 & 1 \\ 0 & 1 & 3 \end{bmatrix}\begin{bmatrix} r \\ s \\ t \end{bmatrix} = \begin{bmatrix} 150 \\ 425 \\ 0 \end{bmatrix}$; coefficient matrix is $\begin{bmatrix} 1 & -1 & 1 \\ 2 & 0 & 1 \\ 0 & 1 & 3 \end{bmatrix}$, variable matrix is $\begin{bmatrix} r \\ s \\ t \end{bmatrix}$, constant matrix is $\begin{bmatrix} 150 \\ 425 \\ 0 \end{bmatrix}$.

6. $\begin{bmatrix} 1 & 2 \\ 2 & 3 \end{bmatrix}\begin{bmatrix} x \\ y \end{bmatrix} = \begin{bmatrix} 11 \\ 18 \end{bmatrix}$; coefficient matrix is $\begin{bmatrix} 1 & 2 \\ 2 & 3 \end{bmatrix}$, variable matrix is $\begin{bmatrix} x \\ y \end{bmatrix}$, constant matrix is $\begin{bmatrix} 11 \\ 18 \end{bmatrix}$.

page 232   Chapter Test

1.

	Years	Vetoes	Overrides
Kennedy	3	21	9
Johnson	5	30	0
Nixon	5.5	43	7
Ford	2.5	66	12
Carter	4	31	2
Reagan	8	78	9
G. H. W. Bush	4	46	1
Clinton	8	38	2

10. $\begin{bmatrix} 4 & 6 & 3 & 1 \\ -5 & -1 & 1 & -3 \end{bmatrix}$

11. $\begin{bmatrix} -1 & 3 & 5 & 1 \\ 2 & 4 & 1 & -1 \end{bmatrix}$

12. $\begin{bmatrix} -1 & 3 & 5 & 1 \\ -2 & -4 & -1 & 1 \end{bmatrix}$

13.

14. Answers may vary. Sample: $\begin{bmatrix} 1 & 2 \\ 1 & 2 \end{bmatrix}$

15. Answers may vary. Sample: Two matrices can be multiplied if and only if the number of columns of the first matrix equals the number of rows of the second matrix. The product matrix will have the same number of rows as the first matrix and columns as the second matrix.

22. $\begin{bmatrix} \frac{5}{43} & -\frac{4}{43} \\ \frac{7}{86} & \frac{3}{86} \end{bmatrix}$

23. $\begin{bmatrix} \frac{2}{15} & \frac{1}{9} \\ -\frac{1}{5} & 0 \end{bmatrix}$

24. $\begin{bmatrix} 2 & \frac{1}{2} \\ 0 & \frac{1}{4} \end{bmatrix}$

25. $\approx \begin{bmatrix} 0.1923 & 0.2846 & -0.2231 \\ 0.2115 & 0.2731 & -0.0654 \\ -0.1538 & -0.1077 & 0.1385 \end{bmatrix}$

26. $\begin{bmatrix} -1 & 0.5 & 0.5 \\ 2 & -1.5 & 0.5 \\ 0 & 0.5 & -0.5 \end{bmatrix}$

page 233   Standardized Test Prep

5. $\begin{bmatrix} -3 & -15 & 5 \\ 27 & 7 & 7 \\ 19 & -15 & -5 \end{bmatrix}$

6. $\begin{bmatrix} 16 & 16 \\ -1 & 5 \end{bmatrix}$

7. $\begin{bmatrix} -16 & 10 & -2 \\ 0 & 18 & 14 \end{bmatrix}$

8. $\begin{bmatrix} 27 & -24 & 30 & 21 \\ 97 & -96 & 86 & 51 \end{bmatrix}$

9. $\begin{bmatrix} \frac{4}{3} & \frac{8}{3} & \frac{2}{3} & -\frac{2}{3} \\ -\frac{2}{3} & \frac{6}{23} & \frac{10}{3} & \frac{2}{3} \end{bmatrix}$

15. [2] translation matrix = $\begin{bmatrix} -7 & -7 & -7 \\ 2 & 2 & 2 \end{bmatrix}$

new image matrix = $\begin{bmatrix} -8 & -3 & -2 \\ 2 & 9 & 4 \end{bmatrix}$

[1] includes only new image matrix and not translation matrix OR includes both but makes minor computational error

16. [4] a. $\begin{bmatrix} 2 & 3 & 3 \\ 3 & 3 & 3 \\ 4 & 1 & 2 \end{bmatrix} \begin{bmatrix} a \\ b \\ c \end{bmatrix} = \begin{bmatrix} 24 \\ 27 \\ 20 \end{bmatrix}$

b. $\begin{bmatrix} a \\ b \\ c \end{bmatrix} = \begin{bmatrix} 3 \\ 4 \\ 2 \end{bmatrix}$

c. 3 oz of Food A, 4 oz of Food B, and 2 oz of Food C

[3] conclusion in part (c) not stated

[2] either the original coefficient matrix stated incorrectly OR the equation solved incorrectly

[1] any two parts incorrect

CHAPTER 5

LESSON 5-1

page 236   Check Your Readiness

7.

8.

9.

10.

11.

12.

13.

Sample: $y = 3x + 12$

14.

Sample: $y = \frac{6}{5}x + 10$

15.

$v = 6s + 40$

16. $y = |x|$

LESSON 5-2

page 245   Check Skills You'll Need

7.

8.

9.

page 245   Quick Check

1a.

b.

pages 248–251   Exercises

10.

11.

12.

13.

14.

15.

16.

17.

18.

19.

20.

21.

$x = -3$

22.

max, 6

23.

min, $-\frac{10}{3}$

24.

max, $\frac{41}{8}$

25.

min, 2

26.

max, $6\frac{1}{4}$

27.

min, 5

LESSON 5-3

page 252 Check Skills You'll Need

1. $y = x$

2. $y = |x|$

3. $y = |x|$

page 252 Activity

1. $y = (x - 2)^2 = x^2 - 4x + 4$;
$y = (x + 3)^2 - 1 =$
$x^2 + 6x + 9 - 1 = x^2 + 6x + 8$;
$y = -3(x + 2)^2 + 4 =$
$-3(x^2 + 4x + 4) + 4 =$
$-3x^2 - 12x - 12 + 4 =$
$-3x^2 - 12x - 8$;
$y = 2(x + 3)^2 + 1 =$
$2(x^2 + 6x + 9) + 1 =$
$2x^2 + 12x + 18 + 1 =$
$2x^2 + 12x + 19$

2a. column 2: 2, −3, −2, −3;
column 4: 2, −3, −2, −3

b. $-\frac{b}{2a} = h$

pages 255–258 Exercises

36. $x = -2$

37. $x = 2$

38. $x = -0.3$

39. $x = 2$

40.

41.

91.

92.

93.

LESSON 5-4

pages 263–265   Exercises

84. **[4]** a. By entering two given lists into a graphing calculator and then having it calculate the quadratic regression, you get $h = -16t^2 + 22t + 3$ as the quadratic model for the ball's height as a function of time.

    b. $-16t^2 + 22t + 3$
    ① Multiply $a \times c$.
       $-16 \times 3 = -48$
    ② Find factors of -48 that add to be 22. $-1, 48; -2, 24; -3, 16; -4, 12 \ldots$
       $-2 + 24 = 22$
    ③ Rewrite as $-16t^2 - 2t + 24t + 3$.
    ④ Find common factors.
       $-2t(8t + 1) + 3(8t + 1)$
    ⑤ Rewrite using Distributive Property.
       $(8t + 1)(-2t + 3)$

    [3] appropriate steps, with one computational error

    [2] explanation in either part (a) OR (b)

    [1] correct solution, without explanation of steps

LESSON 5-5

pages 270–272   Exercises

64. Solve $(x - 4)(x - 6) = 0$ to find that the zeros of $y = x^2 - 10x + 24$ are 4 and 6. Average 4 and 6 to get 5. This is the x-coordinate of the vertex. Substitute 5 for x in $x^2 - 10x + 24$ to find that -1 is the y-coordinate of the vertex. The vertex is $(5, -1)$.

66a. Answers may vary. Sample: If $x \neq h$, then $x - h$ will be nonzero, $(x - h)^2$ will be positive, and $a(x - h)^2$ will be positive. Adding a positive to k will always result in a number greater than k. So the point (h, k) is the lowest point when $x = h$ on the graph of $y = (x - h)^2 + k$.

    b. No; $(x - h)^3$ can be negative.

LESSON 5-6

pages 278–280   Exercises

67a.   row 2: 2, 5, $\sqrt{5}$, $\sqrt{5}$
      row 3: 6, 10, $\sqrt{10}$, $\sqrt{10}$
      row 4: -12, 100, 10, 10

    b. Answers may vary. Sample: The sum of a complex number $a + bi$ and its conjugate is $2a$. The product of $a + bi$ and its conjugate is the square of the absolute value of $a + bi$. The absolute values of a complex number and its conjugate are equal.

    c.

    They are symmetric images of each other with respect to the real axis.

    d. True; the additive inverse of $a + bi$ is $-a - bi$, and the conjugate of $-a - bi$ is $-a + bi$. The conjugate of $a + bi$ is $a - bi$ and the additive inverse of $a - bi$ is $-a + bi$.

74.
$(3 + 4i)^1 = 3 + 4i$ and $3^2 + 4^2 = 25$;
$(3 + 4i)^2 = -7 + 24i$ and $(-7)^2 + (24)^2 = 625 = 25^2$;
$(3 + 4i)^3 = -117 + 44i$ and $(-117)^2 + (44)^2 = 15{,}625 = 25^3$;
$(3 + 4i)^4 = -527 - 336i$ and $(-527)^2 + (-336)^2 = 390{,}625 = 25^4$;
$(3 + 4i)^5 = -237 - 3116i$ and $(-237)^2 + (-3116)^2 = 9{,}765{,}625 = 25^5$

80. **[4]**
$x^4 - 16 = (x^2 - 4)(x^2 + 4) = (x - 2)(x + 2)(x^2 + 4)$

  $x - 2 = 0$ $x + 2 = 0$ $x^2 = -4$
     $x = 2$ $x = -2$ $x = \sqrt{-4}$
                               $x = \pm 2i$

    [3] appropriate methods, with one computational error

    [2] initial factoring correct but solvings are incorrect

    [1] answer only, without work shown

page 281   Activity Lab

1.

$x^2 + 4x + 4$;
$(x + 2)(x + 2)$

2.

$x^2 + 12x + 36$;
$(x + 6)(x + 6)$

3.

$x^2 + 2x + 1$;
$(x + 1)(x + 1)$

10. Answers may vary. Sample: First subtract 6 from each side, which gives you $x^2 + 6x = -6$. By completing the square on the left side you get $x^2 + 6x + 9$, but you also have to add 9 to the right side to keep the sides equal. $x^2 + 6x + 9$ factors into $(x + 3)^2$, so you now have $(x + 3)^2 = 3$. To solve for x you take the square root of each side and subtract 3 from each side. This gives you $x = -3 \pm \sqrt{3}$.

LESSON 5-7

page 283   Quick Check

4a. $x^2 - 8x + 36 = 0$; $(4 + 2i\sqrt{5})^2 - 8(4 + 2i\sqrt{5}) + 36 = 16 + 2(8i\sqrt{5}) + (2i\sqrt{5})^2 - 32 - 16i\sqrt{5} + 36 = (16 - 20 - 32 + 36) + (16i\sqrt{5} - 16i\sqrt{5}) = 0$; $(4 - 2i\sqrt{5})^2 - 8(4 - 2i\sqrt{5}) + 36 = 16 + 2(-8i\sqrt{5}) + (-2i\sqrt{5})^2 - 32 + 16i\sqrt{5} + 36 = 16 - 20 - 32 + 36 + (-16i\sqrt{5} + 16i\sqrt{5}) = 0$

    b. The graph of $y = x^2 - 8x + 36$ has no x-intercepts, so the equation has no real solutions.

49. row 2: 47, 46, 45, 44, 43, 42, 41, 40
    row 3: 96, 141, 184, 225, 264, 301, 336, 369, 400

a.

   $A = -w^2 + 50w$

b. Check students' work.

c. The numbers w such that $0 < w < 50$; since the perimeter is 100 the width would have to be less than 50, and since length can't be negative it would have to be greater than 0.

d. 625 units^2; 25 units by 25 units

e. $A = w(50 - w)$; yes; both equations are quadratic and model the same situation.

67. [2] $x^2 + 36 \quad\quad = 14x$
    $\dfrac{-36 - 14x \quad -14x - 36}{x^2 - 14x \quad\quad = \quad\quad -36}$
    $x^2 - 14x + (-7)^2 = -36 + (-7)^2$
    $x^2 - 14x + 49 = 13$
    $(x - 7)^2 = 13$
    $x - 7 = \pm\sqrt{13}$
    $x = 7 \pm \sqrt{13}$

    [1] one computational error, OR correct answer without work shown

68. [4] $3x^2 + 7x = 6$ Move variables to the left side and constant to the right by using the Addition Property of Equality.

    $x^2 + \frac{7}{3}x = 2$ Divide each side by 3.

    $x^2 + \frac{7}{3}x + \frac{49}{36} = \frac{121}{36}$ Add the square of $\frac{1}{2}\cdot\frac{7}{3}$ to each side.

    $(x + \frac{7}{6})^2 = \frac{121}{36}$ Factor left side.

    $x + \frac{7}{6} = \pm\frac{11}{6}$ Take the square root of each side.

    $x = -\frac{7}{6} \pm \frac{11}{6}$ Add $-\frac{7}{6}$ to each side.

    $x = -3, \frac{2}{3}$ Simplify $-\frac{7}{6} - \frac{11}{6}$ and $-\frac{7}{6} + \frac{11}{6}$.

    [3] appropriate methods, but with one computational error

[2] correct listing of steps with incorrect explanations

[1] correct solution, without work shown

LESSON 5-8

79. [2] For an equation of the form $ax^2 + bx + c = 0$, where $a \neq 0$, the discriminant is the number $b^2 - 4ac$. If the discriminant is negative, then there are 2 imaginary solutions; if it is zero, then there is 1 real solution; if it is positive, then there are 2 real solutions.

    [1] only states that the discriminant is $b^2 - 4ac$

80. [4] Rewrite the equation as $3x^2 - x - 4 = 0$. Then use $a = 3$, $b = -1$ and $c = -4$ in the quadratic formula. You get

    $\dfrac{-(-1) \pm \sqrt{(-1)^2 - 4(3)(-4)}}{2(3)} =$

    $\dfrac{1 \pm \sqrt{1 - (-48)}}{6} = \dfrac{1 \pm \sqrt{49}}{6} =$

    $\dfrac{1 \pm 7}{6} = \dfrac{1 + 7}{6}, \dfrac{1 - 7}{6}$ or $\dfrac{4}{3}, -1$

    [3] appropriate methods, with one computational error

    [2] insufficient explanation and computational error

    [1] correct solution, without work shown

2.

3.

4.

   $x = 0$, $(0, -7)$

5.

   $x = -1$, $(-1, 5)$

6.

   $x = 2.5$, $(2.5, 3.25)$

7.

   $x = 0$, $(0, -8)$

17.

    $\sqrt{53}$

18.

    8

19.

    $4\sqrt{5}$

20.

5

21.

$2\sqrt{13}$

22.

$\sqrt{13}$

33. $y = (x - 3)^2 - 4$;

$(3, -4)$

34. $y = -(x - 4)^2 + 6$;

$(4, 6)$

35. $y = 2\left(x - \frac{3}{4}\right)^2 - 2\frac{1}{8}$;

$\left(\frac{3}{4}, -\frac{17}{8}\right)$

36. $y = -\frac{1}{2}(x - 4)^2 - 1$;

$(4, -1)$

CHAPTER 6

page 304 Check Your Readiness

6.

LESSON 6-1

pages 309–311 Exercises

13. $y = x^3 + 1$

14. $y = 12x^3 - 50x^2 + 60x - 12$

15. $y = 1.5x^3 + x^2 - 2x + 1$

16. $y = -3x^3 - 10x^2 + 100$

17a. males: $y = -0.003357x^2 + 0.3253x + 67.05$
females: $y = -0.001929x^2 + 0.2321x + 74.89$

b. males: $y = -0.000100x^3 + 0.002643x^2 + 0.2393x + 67.17$
females: $y = 0.00016667x^3 - 0.011929x^2 + 0.3755x + 74.69$

c. The cubic model is a better fit.

18. $y = x^3 - 2x^2$; 4335

19. $y = x^3 - 10x^2$; 2023

20. $y = -0.5x^3 + 10x^2$; 433.5

21. $y = -0.03948x^3 + 2.069x^2 - 17.93x + 106.9$; 206

22. $y = -0.007990x^3 + 0.4297x^2 - 6.009x + 43.57$; 26.4

23. $y = 0.01002x^3 - 0.3841x^2 + 5.002x + 2.132$; 25.4

59b.

The quartic model fits best.

68. **[2]** If it is in standard form, the degree is the exponent on the first variable.

[1] incorrect reason for why it is easier to find in standard form

72.

$(5, -3)$

73. $\begin{bmatrix} 1 & -3 & 1 & 5 \\ -8 & -3 & 0 & -3 \end{bmatrix}$

74. $\begin{bmatrix} 2 & -3 & -6 \\ 5 & -2 & 0 \end{bmatrix}$

75. $\begin{bmatrix} -2 & -1 & -2 & -1 \\ -3 & -3 & -4 & -4 \end{bmatrix}$

LESSON 6-2

pages 317–319 Exercises

15c.

194 in.^{3}, 2.26 in.

16. 1, −2

17. 2, −9

18. 0, −5, 8

19. −1, 2, 3

20. $-1, 1, 2$

LESSON 6-3

pages 324–326 Exercises

64. [2]

$$\begin{array}{r} x^2 - 6x - 7 \\ x - 1\overline{)x^3 - 7x^2 - x + 7} \\ \underline{x^3 - x^2} \\ -6x^2 - x \\ \underline{-6x^2 + 6x} \\ -7x + 7 \\ \underline{-7x + 7} \\ 0 \end{array}$$

$x^2 - 6x - 7 = 0$
$(x + 1)(x - 7) = 0$
$x = 1, -1, 7$

[1] incorrect illustration of division or incorrect list of zeros

LESSON 6-4

page 327 Check Skills You'll Need

1. $(1, 4)$

2. $\left(1, \dfrac{2}{3}\right)$

3. no points

pages 330–332 Exercises

75. [4] $8x^3 - 27 = (2x)^3 - (3)^3 =$
$(2x - 3)(4x^2 + 6x + 9)$.
If $2x - 3 = 0$, then $x = \dfrac{3}{2}$.
If $4x^2 + 6x + 9 = 0$, then $x =$
$\dfrac{-6 \pm \sqrt{36 - 144}}{8} =$
$\dfrac{-6 \pm \sqrt{-108}}{8} =$
$\dfrac{-6 \pm 6i\sqrt{3}}{8} =$
$\dfrac{-3 \pm 3i\sqrt{3}}{4}$.

[3] minor computational errors

[2] $(2x - 3) = 0$ and
$4x^2 + 6x + 9 = 0$ written
and solved for x in the first
equation but not in the second

[1] answer correct, without work
shown

page 334 Vocabulary Builder

7–10. Answers may vary. Samples are
given.

7. distance from the point of
departure; the number of stops
the train made since departure

8. time left until the final whistle; the
number of goals scored

9. acreage already plowed; the
number of rows plowed

10. wind speed; the number of
lightning strikes

11–14. Answers may vary. Samples
are given.

11. continuous; The amount of milk in
the glass changes continuously.

12. continuous; As you walk to
school, the time changes
continuously.

13. discrete; The number of bacteria
increases by 1 every time a
bacterium divides.

14. continuous; The distance from
Earth to the sun changes
smoothly, without jumps.

15. continuous; The straight line
graph is unbroken.

16. continuous; There are no breaks
in the absolute value graph.

17. discrete; Each point in a scatter
plot is separated from other
points.

18. discrete; There is always a
positive distance between zeros
of a polynomial.

LESSON 6-5

pages 339–340 Exercises

47. [4] The three factors are $(x + 4)$,
$(x + 4i)$, $(x - 4i)$.
$(x + 4)(x + 4i)(x - 4i) =$
$(x + 4)(x^2 + 16) =$
$x^3 + 4x^2 + 16x + 64$.
The leading coefficient
is $\dfrac{3}{2}$, so the equation is
$\dfrac{3}{2}x^3 + 6x^2 + 24x + 96 = 0$.

[3] leaves the answer as
$x^3 + 4x^2 + 16x + 64 = 0$ OR
makes minor errors

[2] identifies $(x + 4)$, $(x + 4i)$, and
$(x - 4i)$ as factors

[1] identifies the third root as $4i$

LESSON 6-6

pages 343–344 Exercises

17. 4 complex roots
number of real roots: 0, 2, or 4
possible rational roots: $\pm\frac{1}{2}$, ± 1,
± 2, $\pm\frac{13}{2}$, ± 13, ± 26

18. 5 complex roots
number of real roots: 1, 3, or 5
possible rational roots: ± 1, ± 2,
± 3, ± 6, ± 9, ± 18

19. 3 complex roots
number of real roots: 1 or 3
possible rational roots: $\pm\frac{1}{3}$, $\pm\frac{2}{3}$,
± 1, $\pm\frac{4}{3}$, ± 2, ± 3, ± 4, ± 6, ± 12

20. 6 complex roots
number of real roots: 0, 2, 4, or 6
possible rational roots: $\pm\frac{1}{4}$, $\pm\frac{1}{2}$,
$\pm\frac{3}{4}$, ± 1, $\pm\frac{3}{2}$, ± 2, ± 3, ± 4, ± 6, ± 8,
± 12, ± 24

37. [2] $(x^2 - 16)(x^2 + 16) = 0$
$x = \pm 4; x = \pm 4i$

[1] no work shown

38. [2] $0; -1, -1, 1, 5$

[1] minor computation error

39. [2] ± 1, ± 5, all rational roots must
be integer factors of 5

[1] correct answer, no explanation

LESSON 6-7

page 352 Activity Lab

5.

7a.

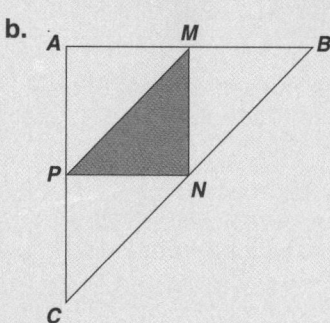

	A	B	C	D	E	F	G	H	I	J	K
1	1	1	1	1	1	1	1	1	1	1	1
2	2	3	4	5	6	7	8	9	10		
3	3	6	10	15	21	28	36	45			
4	4	10	20	35	56	84	120				
5	5	15	35	70	126	210					
6	6	21	56	126	252						
7	7	28	84	210							
8	8	36	120								
9	9	45									
10	10										
11											

b.

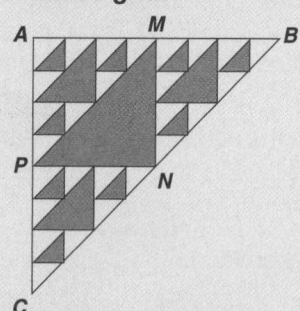

Begin with a large isosceles right triangle, $\triangle ABC$. Connect midpoints of all sides to form 4 congruent triangles. Shade $\triangle MNP$ (the "middle" triangle). Now repeat the process in each unshaded triangle by connecting midpoints and shading the "middle" triangle. After two repetitions of the process, the pattern is the same as the shaded grid.

LESSON 6-8

pages 355–357   Exercises

3. $a^4 + 4a^3b + 6a^2b^2 + 4ab^3 + b^4$

4. $x^5 - 5x^4y + 10x^3y^2 - 10x^2y^3 + 5xy^4 - y^5$

5. $a^6 - 6a^5b + 15a^4b^2 - 20a^3b^3 + 15a^2b^4 - 6ab^5 + b^6$

6. $x^7 - 7x^6y + 21x^5y^2 - 35x^4y^3 + 35x^3y^4 - 21x^2y^5 + 7xy^6 - y^7$

67. Answers may vary. Sample: A coin is tossed five times with the probability of heads on each toss 0.5. Write an expression for the probability of exactly 2 heads being tossed.

68a. $(k + 1)! =$
$(k + 1) \cdot (k) \cdot (k - 1) \cdot \ldots \cdot 1 =$
$(k + 1)[(k) \cdot (k - 1) \cdot \ldots \cdot 1] =$
$(k + 1) \cdot k!$

 b. The derivation below finds a common denominator for the fractions that represent $_nC_k$ and $_nC_{k+1}$, and then uses algebra to show that $_nC_k + {_nC_{k+1}} = {_{n+1}C_{k+1}}$. In addition, the identity from part (a) is used three times.

$$_nC_k + {_nC_{k+1}} = \frac{n!}{k!\,(n-k)!}$$

$$+ \frac{n!}{(k+1)!\,(n-k-1)!} =$$

$$\frac{(k+1)n!}{(k+1)!\,(n-k)!} + \frac{(n-k)n!}{(k+1)!\,(n-k)!} =$$

$$\frac{(k+1+n-k)n!}{(k+1)!\,(n-k)!} = \frac{(n+1)n!}{(k+1)!\,(n-k)!} =$$

$$\frac{(n+1)!}{(k+1)!\,(n-k)!} =$$

$$\frac{(n+1)!}{(k+1)!\,((n+1)-(k+1))!} =$$

$$_{n+1}C_{k+1}$$

 c. If you consider the row of Pascal's Triangle containing just 1 to be row zero, $_4C_2$ is 6, the third entry in the fourth row. $_4C_3$ is 4, the fourth entry in the fourth row. $_5C_3$ is 10, the fourth entry in the fifth row. $_4C_2 + {_4C_3} = 6 + 4 = 10 = {_5C_3}$.

73. [2] $_7C_1 x^6 y^1$ or $7x^6y$

   [1] provides some expression in x and y without the correct coefficients

74. [4] The sixth term is $_7C_5(2x)^2(-3y)^5 = 21(4x^2)(-243y^5) = -20{,}412x^2y^5$

   [3] incorrect coefficient but correct exponents for x and y

   [2] $_7C_6(2x)^2(-3y)^5$ correct, but not the rest of the answer

   [1] presents some expression in x and y

page 362   Chapter Test

5. $-1.62, 0, 0.62$

6. $-5, -2, -1, 1$

7. $0.65, -3.04$

8. $-1.26, 1$

9. $-0.73, 1, 2.73$

page 363   Standardized Test Prep

18. [2] a. combination because order does not matter

   b. 27,405

   [1] answers either part (a) OR (b)

19. [4] Answers may vary. Sample:

$$\begin{bmatrix} 1 & 0 \\ 0 & -1 \end{bmatrix} \times \begin{bmatrix} 0 & 0 & 7 & 7 \\ 0 & 5 & 5 & 0 \end{bmatrix} = \begin{bmatrix} 0 & 0 & 7 & 7 \\ 0 & -5 & -5 & 0 \end{bmatrix}$$

x-axis reflection

$$\begin{bmatrix} 0 & -1 \\ 1 & 0 \end{bmatrix} \times \begin{bmatrix} 0 & 0 & 7 & 7 \\ 0 & -5 & -5 & 0 \end{bmatrix} =$$
$$\begin{bmatrix} 0 & 5 & 5 & 0 \\ 0 & 0 & 7 & 7 \end{bmatrix}$$
90° rotation

[3] error in matrix calculation

[2] performs either reflection OR rotation

[1] correct answer, without work shown

CHAPTER 7

page 366   Check Your Readiness

19.

20.

21.

22.

23.

24.

LESSON 7-1

page 373   Test Prep

74. [2] $\sqrt{x^2y^4}$ equals $\sqrt[3]{x^3y^6}$ whenever $y = 0$, regardless of the value of x. This is true because x^2y^4 and x^3y^6 will be 0 whenever $y = 0$. $\sqrt{x^2y^4}$ also equals $\sqrt[3]{x^3y^6}$ if $y \neq 0$ and $x \geq 0$. This is true because $\sqrt{x^2y^4} = |x|y^2$ and $\sqrt[3]{x^3y^6} = xy^2$, and, for $y \neq 0$, $|x|y^2 = xy^2$ when $x \geq 0$.

[1] answer only, with no explanation

LESSON 7-6

page 398   Check Skills You'll Need

1. D: {0, 2, 4},
   R: {−5, −3, −1}

2. D: {−1, 0, 1},
   R: 0

3. D: all real numbers,
   R: all real numbers

4. D: all real numbers,
   R: all real numbers ≥ 0

LESSON 7-7

page 406   Check Skills You'll Need

1.

2.

3.

4.

5.

6.

pages 410–412   Exercises

1.

x	0	1	0	2
y	1	2	3	4

2.

x	0	1	2	3
y	1	2	3	4

3.

x	0	1	4	9
y	0	1	2	3

4.

x	2	2	2	2
y	−3	−2	−1	0

14.

15.

16.

17.

18.

19.

20.

21.

22.

23. $f^{-1}(x) = \frac{x-4}{3}$, and the domain and range for both f and f^{-1} are all real numbers; f^{-1} is a function.

24. $f^{-1}(x) = x^2 + 5$, $x \geq 0$, domain of f: $\{x \mid x \geq 5\}$, range of f: $\{y \mid y \geq 0\}$, domain of f^{-1}: $\{x \mid x \geq 0\}$, and range of f^{-1}: $\{y \mid y \geq 5\}$; f^{-1} is a function.

25. $f^{-1}(x) = x^2 - 7$, $x \geq 0$, domain of f: $\{x \mid x \geq -7\}$, range of f: $\{y \mid y \geq 0\}$, domain of f^{-1}: $\{x \mid x \geq 0\}$, and range of f^{-1}: $\{y \mid y \geq -7\}$; f^{-1} is a function.

26. $f^{-1}(x) = \frac{3 - x^2}{2}$, $x \geq 0$, domain of f: $\{x \mid x \leq \frac{3}{2}\}$, range of f: $\{y \mid y \geq 0\}$, domain of f^{-1}: $\{x \mid x \geq 0\}$, and range of f^{-1}: $\{y \mid y \leq \frac{3}{2}\}$; f^{-1} is a function.

27. $f^{-1}(x) = \pm\sqrt{\frac{x-2}{2}}$, $x \geq 2$, domain of f: all real numbers, range of f: $\{y \mid y \geq 2\}$, domain of f^{-1}: $\{x \mid x \geq 2\}$, and range of f^{-1}: all real numbers; f^{-1} is not a function.

28. $f^{-1}(x) = \pm\sqrt{1-x}$, $x \leq 1$, domain of f: all real numbers, range of f: $\{y \mid y \leq 1\}$, domain of f^{-1}: $\{x \mid \leq 1\}$, and range of f^{-1}: all real numbers; f^{-1} is not a function.

47. $f^{-1}(x) = x^2$, $x \leq 0$, domain of f: $\{x \mid x \geq 0\}$, range of f: $\{y \mid y \leq 0\}$, domain of f^{-1}: $\{x \mid x \leq 0\}$, range of f^{-1}: $\{y \mid y \geq 0\}$, and f^{-1} is a function.

48. $f^{-1}(x) = (x - 3)^2$, $x \geq 3$, domain of f: $\{x \mid x \geq 0\}$, range of f: $\{y \mid y \geq 3\}$, domain of f^{-1}: $\{x \mid x \geq 3\}$, range of f^{-1}: $\{y \mid y \geq 0\}$, and f^{-1} is a function.

49. $f^{-1}(x) = 3 - x^2$, $x \geq 0$, domain of f: $\{x \mid x \leq 3\}$, range of f: $\{y \mid y \geq 0\}$, domain of f^{-1}: $\{x \mid x \geq 0\}$, range of f^{-1}: $\{y \mid y \leq 3\}$, and f^{-1} is a function.

50. $f^{-1}(x) = x^2 - 2$, $x \geq 0$, domain of f: $\{x \mid x \geq -2\}$, range of f: $\{y \mid y \geq 0\}$, domain of f^{-1}: $\{x \mid x \geq 0\}$, range of f^{-1}: $\{y \mid y \geq -2\}$, and f^{-1} is a function.

51. $f^{-1}(x) = \pm\sqrt{2x}$, $x \geq 0$, domain of f: all real numbers, range of f: $\{y \mid y \geq 0\}$, domain of f^{-1}: $\{x \mid x \geq 0\}$, range of f^{-1}: all real numbers, and f^{-1} is not a function.

52. $f^{-1}(x) = \pm\frac{1}{\sqrt{x}}$, $x \geq 0$, domain of f: $\{x \mid x \neq 0\}$, range of f: $\{y \mid y > 0\}$, domain of f^{-1}: $\{x \mid x > 0\}$, range of f^{-1}: $\{y \mid y \neq 0\}$, and f^{-1} is not a function.

53. $f^{-1}(x) = \pm\sqrt{x} + 4$, domain of f: all real numbers, range of f: $\{y \mid y \geq 0\}$, domain of f^{-1}: $\{y \mid y \geq 0\}$, range of f^{-1}: $\{x \mid x \geq 0\}$, range of f^{-1}: all real numbers, and f^{-1} is not a function.

54. $f^{-1}(x) = 7 \pm \sqrt{x}$, $x \geq 0$, domain of f: all real numbers, range of f: $\{y \mid y \geq 0\}$, domain of f^{-1}: $\{x \mid x \geq 0\}$, range of f^{-1}: all real numbers, and f^{-1} is not a function.

55. $f^{-1}(x) = \pm\sqrt{\frac{1}{x} - 1}$, $x > 0$, domain of f: $\{x \mid x \neq -1\}$, range of f: $\{y \mid y > 0\}$, domain of f^{-1}: $\{x \mid x > 0\}$, range of f^{-1}: $\{y \mid y \neq -1\}$, and f^{-1} is not a function.

56. $f^{-1}(x) = \left(-\frac{x-4}{2}\right)^2$, $x \leq 4$, domain of f: $\{x \mid x \geq 0\}$, range of f: $\{y \mid y \leq 4\}$, domain of f^{-1}: $\{x \mid x \leq 4\}$, range of f^{-1}: $\{y \mid y \geq 0\}$, and f^{-1} is a function.

57. $f^{-1}(x) = \left(\frac{3}{x}\right)^2$, $x > 0$, domain of f: $\{x \mid x > 0\}$, range of f: $\{y \mid y > 0\}$, domain of f^{-1}: $\{x \mid x > 0\}$, range of f^{-1}: $\{y \mid y > 0\}$, and f^{-1} is a function.

58. $f^{-1}(x) = -\frac{1}{2}\left(\frac{1}{x}\right)^2$, $x > 0$, domain of f: $\{x \mid x < 0\}$, range of f: $\{y \mid y > 0\}$, domain of f^{-1}: $\{x \mid x > 0\}$, range of f^{-1}: $\{y \mid y < 0\}$, and f^{-1} is a function.

page 413   Activity Lab

1.

LESSON 7-8

page 414   Check Skills You'll Need

1.

2.

3.

4.

5.

6.

pages 417–419   Exercises

1.

2.

3.

4.

5.

6.

7.

8.

9.

10.

11.

12.

13.

14.

15.

16.

17.

18.

19.

20.

21.

22.

23.

25. 147

26. 9.5

27. −8.11

28. no solution; The left-hand side is never negative and the right-hand side is always negative.

29. 5

30. −1

37.

D: $x \geq 0$, R: $y \geq 7$

38.

D: $x \geq 0$, R: $y \geq -6$

39.

D: $x \geq 6$, R: $y \geq 0$

40.

D: $x \geq 0$, R: $y \leq 2$

41.

D: $x \geq 0$, R: $y \leq 0$

42.

D: $x \geq \frac{1}{2}$, R: $y \leq 7$

43.

D: all real numbers,
R: all real numbers

44.

D: $x \geq 1$, R: $y \geq 3$

45.

D: all real numbers,
R: all real numbers

46.

$x \geq -\frac{1}{2}$, R: $y \leq 0$

47.

D: all real numbers,
R: all real numbers

48.

D: all real numbers,
R: all real numbers

49.

D: $x \geq -5$, R: $y \leq -1$

50.

D: all real numbers,
R: all real numbers

51.

D: $x \geq \frac{3}{4}$, R: $y \leq 7$

55a.

b. Both domains are $x \geq 2$. The range of $y = \sqrt{x-2} + 1$ is $y \geq 1$. The range of $y = -\sqrt{x-2} + 1$ is $y \leq 1$.

56. $y = 5\sqrt{x-4} - 1$; the graph is the same as $y = 5\sqrt{x}$, translated 4 units to the right and 1 down.

57. $y = 6\sqrt{x+3} + 4$; the graph is the graph of $y = 6\sqrt{x}$ translated 3 units to the left and 4 up.

58. $y = -2\sqrt[3]{x - \frac{1}{4}}$; the graph is the graph of $y = -2\sqrt[3]{x}$ translated $\frac{1}{4}$ unit to the right.

59. $y = \frac{1}{2}\sqrt{x-1} - 2$; the graph is the same as $y = \frac{1}{2}\sqrt{x}$ translated 1 unit right and 2 down.

60. $y = 10 - \frac{1}{3}\sqrt[3]{x+3}$; the graph is the same as $y = -\frac{1}{3}\sqrt[3]{x}$ translated 3 units to the left and 10 up.

61. $y = \frac{1}{3}\sqrt{x+9} + 5$; the graph is the same as $y = \frac{1}{3}\sqrt{x}$, translated 9 units to the left and 5 up.

64. If $a > 0$, the graph is stretched vertically by a factor of a. If $a < 0$, the graph is reflected over the x-axis and stretched vertically by a factor of $|a|$.

65. $y = -\sqrt{2}\sqrt{x+4}$; the graph is the graph of $y = -\sqrt{2x}$ translated 4 units to the left; domain: $x \geq -4$, range: $y \leq 0$.

66. $y = -\sqrt{8}\sqrt{x - \frac{3}{4}}$; the graph is the graph of $y = -\sqrt{8x}$ translated $\frac{3}{4}$ units to the right; domain: $x \geq \frac{3}{4}$, range: $y \leq 0$.

67. $y = \sqrt{3} \cdot \sqrt{x - \frac{5}{3}} + 6$; the graph is the graph of $y = \sqrt{3x}$ translated $\frac{5}{3}$ units to the right and 6 units up; domain: $x \geq \frac{5}{3}$, range: $y \geq 6$.

68. $y = -\sqrt{12} \cdot \sqrt{x + \frac{2}{3}} - 3$; the graph is the graph of $y = -\sqrt{12x}$ translated $\frac{2}{3}$ units to the left and 3 units down; domain: $x \geq -\frac{2}{3}$, range: $y \leq -3$.

69a.

b. The graph of $y = \sqrt{h-x}$ is a reflection of the graph of $y = \sqrt{x-h}$ in the line $x = h$.

page 426 Chapter Test

32.

D: real numbers ≥ 0,
R: real numbers ≥ 3

33.

D: real numbers $\geq -\frac{3}{2}$,
R: real numbers ≥ 0

34.

D: real numbers ≥ 4,
R: real numbers ≤ 0

35.

D: real numbers $\geq -\frac{3}{2}$,
R: real numbers ≥ -4

CHAPTER 8

LESSON 8-1

page 434–437 Exercises

24.

25.   y = 0 is the horizontal asymptote.

26.

27.

28.

29.

30.

31.

63. [2]

[1] general form of graph correct, but not exact

64. [4] $y = ab^x$

$54 = ab^2$

$a = \dfrac{54}{b^2}$

$2 = \dfrac{54}{b^2} \cdot b^{\frac{1}{2}}$

$2 = \dfrac{54}{b^{\frac{3}{2}}}$

$2b^{\frac{3}{2}} = 54$

$b^{\frac{3}{2}} = 27$

$b = 27^{\frac{2}{3}}$

$b = 9$

$a = \dfrac{54}{9^2}$

$a = \dfrac{2}{3}$

$y = \dfrac{2}{3} \cdot 9^x$

[3] appropriate methods with one computational error

[2] starts problem correctly, but fails to finish it properly

[1] correct answer, without work shown

LESSON 8-2

page 440   Quick Check

2a.

b.

c.

page 440   Additional Examples

2.

pages 442–445   Exercises

9.

10.

11.

12.

13.

14.

page 445   Checkpoint Quiz 1

8.

9. Answers may vary. Sample: The population of Smallville was 1200 in 1990. It was growing at a rate of 1% per year. Find the population in 2010.

LESSON 8-3

page 446   Check Skills You'll Need

5.

6.

7.

8.

page 446   Quick Check

1. The earthquake in California released about 1265 times as much energy as the earthquake in Alabama.

page 452   Test Prep

96. [2] $32 = 2^5$, so $\frac{1}{32} = 2^{-5}$

$\log_2 \frac{1}{32} = -5$

[1] minor error

97. [2] $\log_6 y = 3$

$6^3 = y$

$216 = y$

[1] minor error

98. [2] $\log_b 9 = \frac{1}{2}$

$b^{1/2} = 9$

$(b^{1/2})^2 = 9^2$

$b = 81$

[1] minor error

LESSON 8-4

pages 457–459   Exercises

79. $3 \log 2 + \frac{3}{2} \log x - 3 \log 5$

80. $3 \log m - 4 \log n + 2 \log p$

81. $\log 2 + \frac{1}{2} \log 4 + \frac{1}{2} \log r - \log s$

82. $\frac{1}{2} \log_b x + \frac{2}{3} \log_b y - \frac{2}{5} \log_b z$

83. $\frac{5}{2} \log_4 x + \frac{7}{2} \log_4 y - \log_4 z - 4 \log_4 w$

84. $\frac{1}{2} \log (x^2 - 4) - 2 \log (x + 3)$

85. $\frac{1}{2} \log x + \frac{1}{4} \log 2 - \log y$

86. $\log_3 x + \log_3 y - 6 \log_3 z$

87. $\frac{1}{2} \log_7 (r + 9) - 2 \log_7 s - \frac{1}{3} \log_7 t$

95. [4] 1) $\log \frac{24}{2} = \log 24 - \log 2$; Quotient Property

2) $\log 2 \cdot 6 = \log 2 + \log 6$; Product Property

3) $\log 144^{\frac{1}{2}} = \frac{1}{2} \log 144$; Power Property

4) $\log 3 \cdot 2^2 = \log 3 + 2 \log 2$; Product and Power Properties

[3] log 12 written three ways

[2] log 12 written two ways OR written 4 ways but properties not named

[1] log 12 written only 2 ways and properties not named

page 482   Chapter Test

1.

x	0	1	2	3	4	5
y	3	0.75	0.19	0.05	0.01	0.00

2.

x	0	1	2	3	4	5
y	−1	−6	−36	−216	−1296	−7776

3.

x	0	1	2	3	4	5
y	0.1	1	10	100	1000	10,000

4.

x	0	1	2	3	4	5
y	100	200	400	800	1600	3200

20.

21.

22.

23.

32. Answers may vary. Sample: Taking common logarithms of both sides gives $2x = \frac{\log 4}{\log 3}$. Taking logarithms to the base 3 of both sides gives $2x = \log_3 4$, which by the Change of Base Formula is equivalent to $2x = \frac{\log 4}{\log 3}$.

page 483   Standardized Test Prep

16. [2] $2 \log x + 3 \log y - 6 \log z$

[1] fails to complete one part of the expression

17. [2] $(2x + 1) \log 5 = \log 62$

$2x + 1 = \frac{\log 62}{\log 5}$

$x = \frac{1}{2}\left[\frac{\log 62}{\log 5} - 1\right]$

$x \approx .78$

[1] answer only, without work shown

18. [2] Since x, in the parent function $y = 10^x$, is replaced by $x + 1$, the graph is shifted 1 unit left. Since 3 is subtracted from the function value, the graph is shifted down 3. Check students' graphs.

[1] only graph drawn, parent function missing

19. [4] $A = 1000e^{(0.055)(1)}$
$\approx 1000(1.0565406)$
≈ 1056.54
$A = 1000e^{(0.055)(4)}$
$\approx 1000(1.2460767)$
≈ 1246.08

There will be approximately $1057 after one year; approximately $1246 after 4 years.

[3] one error in one computation (the second steps not required)

[2] one computation incorrect

[1] one equation incorrect

20. [4] $\begin{bmatrix} 1 & 2 & 3 \\ 2 & 1 & 3 \\ 2 & 3 & 1 \end{bmatrix} =$
$1 \cdot 1 \cdot 1 + 2 \cdot 3 \cdot 2 +$
$3 \cdot 2 \cdot 3 - (2 \cdot 1 \cdot 3 +$
$3 \cdot 3 \cdot 1 + 1 \cdot 2 \cdot 2) =$
$31 - 19 = 12$

[3] evaluation set up correctly, one computational error

[2] evaluation set up correctly, evaluated improperly

[1] answer only, without work shown

CHAPTER 9

page 494   Activity Lab

3.

4.

5.

6.

7.

8.

9.

10.

11.

12.

13.

14.

LESSON 9-2

pages 495–498   Quick Check

2. The graph of $y = 2/x$ is a stretch of $y = 1/x$ by the factor 2. The graph of $y = -2/x$ is the reflection of $y = 2/x$ in the x-axis. The graph of $y = 0.5/x$ is a shrink of $y = 1/x$ by the factor 0.5. The graph of $y = -0.5/x$ is the reflection of $y = 0.5/x$ in the x-axis.

4. $x = -7$ and $y = -3$

5b.

pages 498–500   Exercises

1.

2.

3.

4.

The graph is in Quadrant I and Quadrant III.

5.

The graph is in Quadrant II and Quadrant IV. The graph is a reflection of the graph of $y = 3/x$.

6.

The graph is in Quadrant I and Quadrant III.

7.

The graph is in Quadrant II and Quadrant IV. The graph is a reflection of the graph of $y = 5/x$.

8.

The graph is in Quadrant I and Quadrant III.

9.

The graph is in Quadrant II and Quadrant IV. The graph is a reflection of the graph of $y = 0.1/x$.

14.

15.

16.

17.

18.

19.

20.

21.

25. $c = \frac{750}{a}$

Answers may vary. Sample: Domain: positive whole numbers, could be limited to the number of students in the school. Range: positive real numbers, could be limited by the amount of money available for awards $0 < c \le 750$.

33.

34.

35.

36.

37.

38.

41.

(3, 6)

42.

(2.92, 6.2)

43.

(−1.75, −4)

44.

(−0.45, −10) and (0.45, −10)

45.

(3.76, 4.2)

46.

(−0.76, 9) and (0.76, 9)

47a. $m = \frac{10{,}000}{g}$

b. $m = \frac{10{,}000}{g - 50}$

48. The branches of $y = \frac{1}{x}$ are in Quadrants I and III. The branches of $y = \left|\frac{1}{x}\right|$ are in Quadrants I and II. The graphs intersect at all points on $y = \frac{1}{x}$ in Quadrant I.

49. The branches of $y = \frac{1}{x^2}$ are in Quadrants I and II. The branches of $y = \frac{1}{x}$ are in Quadrants I and III. The graphs intersect at (1, 1). The graph of $y = \frac{1}{x^2}$ is closer to the x-axis for $x > 1$, and the graph of $y = \frac{1}{x}$ is closer to the y-axis for $0 < x < 1$.

50. The branches of both graphs are in Quadrants I and II. They intersect at (1, 1) and (−1, 1). The graph of $y = \frac{1}{x^2}$ is closer to the x-axis for $x > 1$ and $x < −1$. The graph of $y = \left|\frac{1}{x}\right|$ is closer to the y-axis for $−1 < x < 0$ and $0 < x < 1$.

52a. $y = \frac{0.6}{x - 2}$

b. $y = -\dfrac{0.25}{x - 0.5}$

c. $y = \dfrac{5}{x + 2} - 1$

d. $y = \dfrac{2}{2x - 1} + 1$

e. $y = \dfrac{1}{x} - 2$

f. $y = \dfrac{1}{x - 1}$

page 500   Test Prep

58. [2] When $x - 2 = 0$, $-\dfrac{3}{x - 2}$ is undefined, so $x = 2$ is an asymptote. As x becomes larger, the value of $-\dfrac{3}{x - 2}$ approaches 0, so y approaches 11, and $y = 11$ is an asymptote.

[1] answer only, with no explanation

page 500   Mixed Review

60. V varies jointly with the square of s and h.

---

61. h varies directly with V and inversely with the square of s.

62. B varies directly with V and inversely with h.

63. w varies directly with V and inversely with the product of ℓ and h.

64. b varies directly with A and inversely with h.

LESSON 9-3

pages 504–505   Quick Check

4.

5a. Answers may vary. Sample: Graph $y = 8$ and use the Intersection feature to find that the graphs intersect at $x = 16{,}103.2$. So the number of discs produced must be greater than 16,103.

c. Answers may vary. Sample: The vertical asymptote means that if you produce 100 or fewer discs you won't sell any, since the first 100 are samples. The horizontal asymptote means that the average cost will never go below $.25, since that is how much each disc costs to produce.

pages 505–508   Exercises

35.

36.

37.

38.

39.

40.

43a. $y = \dfrac{20{,}000x + 200{,}000}{x + 1}$

WINDOW FORMAT
Xmin=0
Xmax=40
Xscl=4
Ymin=0
Ymax=200000
Yscl=10000

45d.

around the year 2106

9.

LESSON 9-5

page 514   Activity

2. Since the denominators are the same, add the numerators and simplify.

3. Answers may vary. Sample: You have to get a common denominator, find the corresponding numerators and then add numerators for both rational expressions and fractions.

page 542   Chapter Test

7.

$y = \dfrac{7}{x-1} + 2$

8.

$y = \dfrac{7}{x+3} - 2$

18. $-\dfrac{2x-1}{(x+4)(2x+1)}; x \ne -4,$

$-3, -\dfrac{1}{2},$ or 0

CHAPTER 10

page 544   Check Your Readiness

19.

20.

21.

LESSON 10-1

pages 548–550   Quick Check

1a.

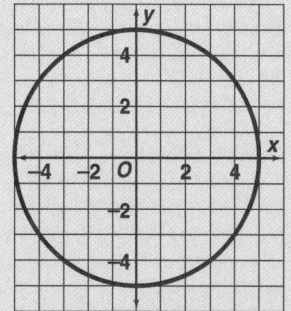

The graphs are the same.

b. Rewrite $x^2 + y^2 = 25$ as $y^2 = 25 - x^2$. Then take the square root of both sides, which gives you $y = \pm\sqrt{25 - x^2}$.

2c.

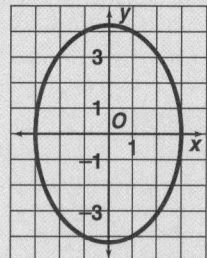

It is an ellipse with center $(0, 0)$. The x-intercepts are 3 and -3, and the y-intercepts are $3\sqrt{2}$ and $-3\sqrt{2}$.

3a. No; there are vertical lines that intersect the graph in more than one point.

b. Answers may vary. Sample: Solving $x^2 - y^2 = 9$ for y gives $y = \pm\sqrt{x^2 - 9}$. For $-3 < x < 3$, the value of $x^2 - 9$ is negative and $\sqrt{x^2 - 9}$ is not a real number.

5a. Answers may vary. Sample: All equations have an x^2-term, a y^2-term, and no other terms on the left side. There is a positive constant term and nothing else on the right side.

b. Answers may vary. Sample: The related domains and ranges are all different. The absolute values of the coefficients of x^2 and y^2 are equal for $x^2 - y^2 = 1$, but the signs of the coefficients are different. The absolute values of the coefficients of x^2 and y^2 are equal for $x^2 + y^2 = 16$, and the signs are the same. The absolute values of the coefficients of x^2 and y^2 are different for $9x^2 + 25y^2 = 225$, but the signs are the same.

pages 550–553   Exercises

1.

Hyperbola: center $(0, 0)$, y-intercepts at $\pm\dfrac{5\sqrt{3}}{3}$, no x-intercepts, the lines of symmetry are the x- and y-axes; domain: all real numbers, range: $y \ge \dfrac{5\sqrt{3}}{3}$ or $y \le -\dfrac{5\sqrt{3}}{3}$.

2.

Ellipse: center $(0, 0)$, x-intercepts at $\pm 3\sqrt{2}$, y-intercepts at ± 6, the lines of symmetry are the x- and y-axes; domain: $-3\sqrt{2} \le x \le 3\sqrt{2}$, range $-6 \le y \le 6$.

3.

Circle: center $(0, 0)$, radius 4, x-intercepts at ± 4, y-intercepts at ± 4, there are infinitely many lines of symmetry; domain: $-4 \le x \le 4$, range: $-4 \le y \le 4$.

4.

Hyperbola: center (0, 0), y-intercepts at $\pm\sqrt{3}$, no x-intercepts, the lines of symmetry are the x- and y-axes; domain: all real numbers, range: $y \le -\sqrt{3}$ or $y \ge \sqrt{3}$.

5.

Ellipse: center (0, 0), y-intercepts at ± 2, x-intercepts at ± 5, the lines of symmetry are the x- and y-axes; domain: $-5 \le x \le 5$, range: $-2 \le y \le 2$.

6.

Circle: center (0, 0), radius 7, x- and y-intercepts at ± 7, there are infinitely many lines of symmetry; domain: $-7 \le x \le 7$, range: $-7 \le y \le 7$.

7.

Hyperbola: center (0, 0), y-intercepts at ± 1, the lines of symmetry are the x- and y-axes; domain: all real numbers, range: $y \le -1$ or $y \ge 1$.

8.

Hyperbola: center (0, 0), x-intercepts at ± 2, the lines of symmetry are the x- and y-axes; domain: $x \le -2$ or $x \ge 2$, range: all real numbers.

9.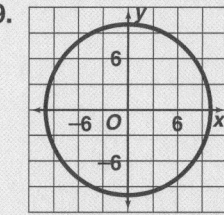

Circle: center (0, 0), radius 10, x- and y-intercepts at ± 10, there are infinitely many lines of symmetry; domain: $-10 \le x \le 10$, range: $-10 \le y \le 10$.

10.

Circle: center (0, 0), radius 2, x- and y-intercepts at ± 2, there are infinitely many lines of symmetry; domain: $-2 \le x \le 2$, range: $-2 \le y \le 2$.

11.

Ellipse: center (0, 0), x-intercepts at ± 4, y-intercepts at ± 2, the lines of symmetry are the x- and y-axes; domain: $-4 \le x \le 4$, range: $-2 \le y \le 2$.

12.

Circle: center (0, 0), radius $\sqrt{5}$, x- and y-intercepts at $\pm\sqrt{5}$, there are infinitely many lines of symmetry; domain: $-\sqrt{5} \le x \le \sqrt{5}$, range: $-\sqrt{5} \le y \le \sqrt{5}$.

13.

Ellipse: center (0, 0), x-intercepts at ± 1, y-intercepts at $\pm\frac{1}{3}$, the lines of symmetry are the x- and y-axes; domain: $-1 \le x \le 1$, range: $-\frac{1}{3} \le y \le \frac{1}{3}$.

14.

Hyperbola: center (0, 0), x-intercepts at ± 6, the lines of symmetry are the x- and y-axes; domain: $x \le -6$, or $x \ge 6$ range: all real numbers.

15.

Hyperbola: center (0, 0), y-intercepts at $\pm\frac{1}{2}$, the lines of symmetry are the x- and y-axes; domain: all real numbers, range: $y \le -\frac{1}{2}$ or $y \ge \frac{1}{2}$.

16.

Ellipse: center (0, 0), x-intercepts at ± 2, y-intercepts at ± 6, the lines of symmetry are the x- and y-axes; domain: $-2 \le x \le 2$, range: $-6 \le y \le 6$.

33a. Let the lamp sit in a normal, upright position, but close enough to the wall for the bottom rim of the shade to almost touch the wall.

b. Hold the lamp so that the shade contacts the wall along a vertical line.

c. Hold the lamp at an angle so that the light from the top of the shade gives a closed, curved oblong area of light on the wall.

d. Hold the lamp so that the circular top rim of the shade is parallel to the wall.

34a. All lines in the plane that pass through the center of a circle are axes of symmetry of the circle.

b. The axes of symmetry of an ellipse intersect at the center of the ellipse. The same is true for a hyperbola. This can be confirmed using, for example, $4x^2 + 9y^2 = 36$ and $4x^2 - 9y^2 = 36$.

35.

$x^2 + y^2 = 36$

36.

$x^2 + y^2 = \frac{1}{4}$

37.

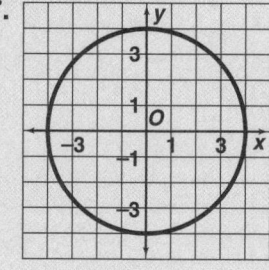

$x^2 + y^2 = 16$

38.

$x^2 + y^2 = 1.5625$

page 554 Activity Lab

1.

2.

3.

4.

5.

6.

LESSON 10-2

pages 558–560 Exercises

24. $(0, 0), (6, 0), x = -6$

25. $(0, 0), (0, -1), y = 1$

26. $(0, 0), (3, 0), x = -3$

27. $(0, 0), \left(\frac{25}{4}, 0\right), x = -\frac{25}{4}$

28. $(0, 0), (0, 1), y = -1$

29. $(0, 0), (0, -1), y = 1$

30. $(2, 0), (2, 1), y = -1$

31. $(0, 0), (-2, 0), x = 2$

32. $(-2, 4), \left(-2, \frac{17}{4}\right), y = \frac{15}{4}$

33. $(-3, 0), \left(-\frac{3}{2}, 0\right), x = -\frac{9}{2}$

34. (4, 0), (4, −6), y = 6

35. (3, −1), (6, −1), x = 0

46.

47.

48.

49.

50.

51.

LESSON 10-3

pages 564–566   Exercises

27.

28.

29.

30.

31.

32.

33.

34.

---

67. Let $P(x, y)$ be any point on the circle centered at the origin and having radius r. If $P(x, y)$ is one of the points $(r, 0)$, $(−r, 0)$, $(0, r)$, or $(0, −r)$, substitution shows that $x^2 + y^2 = r^2$. If $P(x, y)$ is any other point on the circle, drop a perpendicular $\overline{PK}$ from P to the x-axis (K on the x-axis). $\triangle OPK$ is a right triangle with legs of lengths $|x|$ and $|y|$ and with hypotenuse of length r. By the Pythagorean Theorem, $|x|^2 + |y|^2 = r^2$. But $|x|^2 = x^2$ and $|y|^2 = y^2$. So $x^2 + y^2 = r^2$.

69a.

1 Pluto
2 Mercury
3 Mars
4 Earth

b. Earth: $x^2 + y^2 = 15,705,369$
Mars: $x^2 + y^2 = 4,456,321$
Mercury: $x^2 + y^2 = 2,296,740$
Pluto: $x^2 + y^2 = 511,225$

page 567   Activity Lab

7.

8.

LESSON 10-4

page 570   Quick Check

3. $(2\sqrt{2}, 0)$, $(−2\sqrt{2}, 0)$;

T967

Additional Answers

9. $\frac{x^2}{2.25} + \frac{y^2}{0.25} = 1$

10. $\frac{x^2}{64} + \frac{y^2}{256} = 1$

11. $\frac{x^2}{36} + \frac{y^2}{100} = 1$

12. $\frac{x^2}{12.25} + \frac{y^2}{25} = 1$

13. $\frac{x^2}{196} + \frac{y^2}{49} = 1$

14. $x^2 + \frac{y^2}{16} = 1$

15. $\frac{x^2}{256} + \frac{y^2}{56.25} = 1$

16. $\frac{x^2}{900} + \frac{y^2}{400} = 1$

17. $x^2 + \frac{y^2}{6.25} = 1$

18. $(0, \sqrt{5}), (0, -\sqrt{5})$

19. $(0, 4), (0, -4)$

20. $(4\sqrt{2}, 0), (-4\sqrt{2}, 0)$

21. $(8, 0), (-8, 0)$

22. $(0, 6), (0, -6)$

23. $(0, \sqrt{6}), (0, -\sqrt{6})$

24. $(2\sqrt{3}, 0), (-2\sqrt{3}, 0)$

25. $(9, 0), (-9, 0)$

26. $(3\sqrt{15}, 0), (-3\sqrt{15}, 0)$

41a. 0.9;

b. 0.1;

c. The shape is close to a circle.

d. The shape is close to a line segment.

43a. Yes; since $c^2 = a^2 - b^2$, if the foci are close to 0, then c^2 will be close to 0 and a^2 will be close to b^2. This means a will be close to b and hence the ellipse will be close to a circle.

b. If F_1 and F_2 are considered distinct pts., then a circle is not an ellipse. If F_1 and F_2 are the same pt., then a circle is an ellipse.

48. The vertices are the points farthest from the center and the co-vertices are the points closest to the center.

64a. The vertices are at the points where the curve intersects the line through the holes made by the tacks. The co-vertices are the points where the curve intersects the perpendicular bisector of the segment connecting the vertices.

b. at the points where the tacks are stuck in the paper

c. Check students' work.

65. When c is close to 0, the values of a and b are almost the same, and $\pi a b$ is close to πa^2, that is, close to the area of a circle of radius a.

page 573   Test Prep

72. [2] The x-axis is the major axis since $50 > 40$. The equation is of the form $\frac{x^2}{a^2} + \frac{y^2}{b^2} = 1$. $2a = 50$, so $a = 25$, and $2b = 40$, so $b = 20$. Therefore, $a^2 = 625$ and $b^2 = 400$. The equation is $\frac{x^2}{625} + \frac{y^2}{400} = 1$.

[1] answer only OR minor error in calculating a^2 and b^2

page 573   Mixed Review

75. $\frac{1}{2x - 3x^4}$; $x \neq 0$, $\sqrt[3]{\frac{2}{3}}$

76. $\frac{x - 6}{x - 1}$; $x \neq 1, -6$

77. $\frac{x - 5}{x^2 - 2x + 4}$; $x \neq -2$

LESSON 10-5

1.

2.

3.

4.

5.

6.

7.

8.

9.

10. $(0, \sqrt{97}), (0, -\sqrt{97})$;

11. $(0, \sqrt{113}), (0, -\sqrt{113})$;

12. $(\sqrt{265}, 0), (-\sqrt{265}, 0)$;

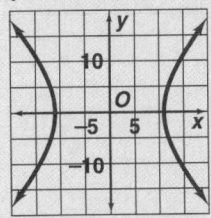

13. $(10, 0), (-10, 0)$;

14. $(0, 5\sqrt{5}), (0, -5\sqrt{5})$;

15. $(\sqrt{205}, 0), (-\sqrt{205}, 0)$

16. $(0, \sqrt{29}), (0, -\sqrt{29})$

17. $(2\sqrt{11}, 0), (-2\sqrt{11}, 0)$

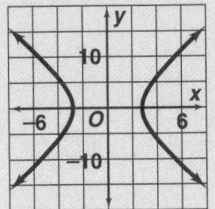

18. $(0, 4\sqrt{3}), (0, -4\sqrt{3})$

27.

28.

29.

30. $\dfrac{y^2}{20.25} - \dfrac{x^2}{4} = 1$

31. $\dfrac{y^2}{9} - x^2 = 1$

32. $\dfrac{x^2}{32} - \dfrac{y^2}{64} = 1$

33. $y = \pm\sqrt{\dfrac{x^2}{2} - 2}$; (2, 0), (−2, 0)

34. $y = \pm\sqrt{x^2 - 1}$; (1, 0), (−1, 0)

35. $y = \pm\sqrt{3x^2 - 2}$; (−0.816, 0), (0.816, 0)

36. $\dfrac{x^2}{9} - \dfrac{y^2}{4} = 1$; $\dfrac{(x-3)^2}{9} - \dfrac{(y-5)^2}{4} = 1$

39. Answers may vary. Sample: Similarities — Both have two axes of symmetry that intersect at the center of the figure. Both have two foci that lie on the same line as the two "principal" vertices. Differences — An ellipse consists of points whose distances from the foci have a constant sum, but a hyperbola consists of points whose distances from the foci have a constant difference. An ellipse is a closed curve, but a hyperbola is not and has two separate branches that do not touch. Hyperbolas have asymptotes, but ellipses do not. An ellipse intersects both its axes of symmetry, but a hyperbola intersects only one of its axes of symmetry.

46a. If the hyperbola $\dfrac{y^2}{a^2} - \dfrac{x^2}{b^2} = 1$ crossed either $y = \dfrac{a}{b}x$ or $y = -\dfrac{a}{b}x$, then there would have to be a value of x and a value of y for which $\dfrac{a}{b}\sqrt{x^2 + b^2} = \dfrac{a}{b}x$ or $\dfrac{a}{b}\sqrt{x^2 + b^2} = -\dfrac{a}{b}x$. That would require that $\sqrt{x^2 + b^2} = x$ or $\sqrt{x^2 + b^2} = -x$. But squaring these equations gives $x^2 + b^2 = x^2$. This would mean that $b^2 = 0$ and hence $b = 0$. But for any hyperbola, $b > 0$. So the hyperbola never intersects its asymptotes.

b. Yes; multiply both sides by $\frac{1}{4}$ to obtain $\dfrac{y^2}{64} - \dfrac{x^2}{36} = 1$. This equation is clearly an equation of a hyperbola. Yes; multiply both sides by −1 to obtain $\dfrac{x^2}{9} - \dfrac{y^2}{16} = 1$. This equation is clearly an equation of a hyperbola.

48a. For the x-values in those rows, the value of $x^2 - 9$ is negative and so $\sqrt{x^2 - 9}$ is not a real number.

b. As x increases, y increases, but the difference between x and y gets closer to zero.

c. No; for positive values of x greater than 3, $x = \sqrt{x^2}$ and $\sqrt{x^2} \neq \sqrt{x^2 - 9}$.

d. $y = x$, $y = -x$;

pages 579–580   Test Prep

52. [2] $\dfrac{x^2}{a^2} - \dfrac{y^2}{b^2} = 1$ or $\dfrac{y^2}{a^2} - \dfrac{x^2}{b^2} = 1$; divide both sides by 1225 and then simplify, which leaves you with $\dfrac{x^2}{49} - \dfrac{y^2}{25} = 1$.

[1] answer correct, but no explanation

LESSON 10-6

pages 585–588   Exercises

12. $y = (x - 4)^2 + 3$; parabola, vertex (4, 3)

13. $(x + 6)^2 + y^2 = 81$; circle, center (−6, 0), radius 9

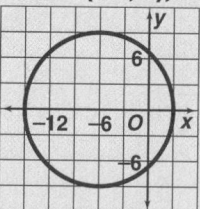

14. $\dfrac{(x + 1)^2}{3} + \dfrac{(y - 3)^2}{9} = 1$; ellipse, center (−1, 3), foci (−1, 3 ± $\sqrt{6}$)

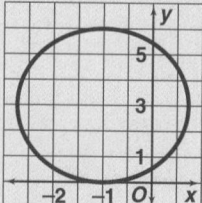

15. $(x - 1)^2 + (y + 3)^2 = 13$; circle, center $(1, -3)$, radius $\sqrt{13}$

16. $(y - 2)^2 - (x - 3)^2 = 1$; hyperbola, center $(3, 2)$, foci $(3, 2 \pm \sqrt{2})$

17. $\frac{(x - 1)^2}{4} - (y + 1)^2 = 1$; hyperbola, center $(1, -1)$, foci $(1 \pm \sqrt{5}, -1)$

18. $x^2 + (y + 7)^2 = 36$; circle, center $(0, -7)$, radius 6

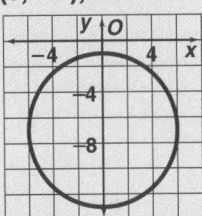

19. $x - 3 = \frac{1}{2}(y - 2)^2$; parabola, vertex $(3, 2)$

20. $\frac{(x + 2)^2}{9} + \frac{(y - 3)^2}{4} = 1$; ellipse, center $(-2, 3)$, foci $(-2 \pm \sqrt{5}, 3)$

21. $(x + 3)^2 - (y - 5)^2 = 1$; hyperbola, center $(-3, 5)$, foci $(-3 \pm \sqrt{2}, 5)$

22. $\frac{(x - 1)^2}{16} + \frac{y^2}{4} = 1$; ellipse, center $(1, 0)$, foci $(1 \pm 2\sqrt{3}, 0)$

23. $\frac{x^2}{4} - \frac{(y + 3)^2}{9} = 1$; hyperbola, center $(0, -3)$, foci $(\pm \sqrt{13}, -3)$

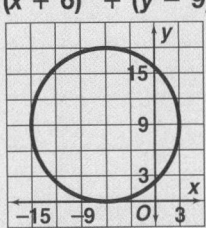

29. $(x + 6)^2 + (y - 9)^2 = 81$

30. $\frac{(x - 3)^2}{36} + \frac{(y - 2)^2}{9} = 1$

31. $y = \frac{1}{32}(x - 2)^2 - 3$

32. $\frac{(y + 3)^2}{4} - \frac{(x - 6)^2}{5} = 1$

49.

ellipse, $\frac{x^2}{9} + \frac{y^2}{36} = 1$

50.

hyperbola, $\frac{x^2}{9} - \frac{y^2}{36} = 1$

51.

hyperbola, $\frac{y^2}{36} - \frac{x^2}{9} = 1$

52.

circle, $x^2 + y^2 = 36$

53.

ellipse, $\frac{x^2}{36} + \frac{y^2}{9} = 1$

54.

parabola, $x = y^2 + 4$

T971

64. [2] Complete the square to get
$(2x - 6)^2 + 25y^2 = 100$

$\dfrac{4(x-3)^2}{100} + \dfrac{25y^2}{100} = \dfrac{100}{100}$

$\dfrac{(x-3)^2}{25} + \dfrac{y^2}{4} = 1$

$c^2 = 25 - 4 = 21$

$c = \sqrt{21}$

The foci are $(3 - \sqrt{21}, 0)$ and $(3 + \sqrt{21}, 0)$.

[1] computational error

65. [2] $c = 1$, so $|a| = \frac{1}{4}$. The focus is to the left of the vertex, so $a = \frac{1}{4}$. The equation of the original equation is $x = -\frac{1}{4}y^2$. For the translation image, replace x with $x - 3$ and y with $y - 4$. The resulting equation is $x - 3 = -\frac{1}{4}(y-4)^2$.

[1] computational error

page 589 Activity Lab

10. quadratic-quadratic;
$(0.607, \pm 0.187)$, $(4.393, \pm 4.355)$

11. linear-quadratic;
$\left(\dfrac{-3 - \sqrt{29}}{10}, \dfrac{1 - 3\sqrt{29}}{10}\right)$,
$\left(\dfrac{-3 + \sqrt{29}}{10}, \dfrac{1 + 3\sqrt{29}}{10}\right)$

12. quadratic-quadratic;
$(-0.5, -3.5)$, $(1, -2)$

13. quadratic-quadratic; no solution

pages 591–593 Chapter Review

6.

ellipse; x-axis and y-axis;
domain: $-7 \le x \le 7$
range: $-11 \le y \le 11$

7.

circle; every line through the center;
domain: $-2 \le x \le 2$
range: $-2 \le y \le 2$

8.

hyperbola; x-axis and y-axis;
domain: $x \le -5$ or $x \ge 5$
range: all real numbers

9.

parabola; x-axis;
domain: $x \ge 5$
range: all real numbers

page 594 Chapter Test

6. focus $\left(0, \frac{1}{12}\right)$, directrix $y = -\frac{1}{12}$

7. focus $\left(-\frac{1}{8}, 0\right)$, directrix $x = \frac{1}{8}$

8. focus $\left(-\frac{1}{20}, 0\right)$, directrix $x = \frac{1}{20}$

9. focus $\left(0, \frac{1}{18}\right)$, directrix $y = -\frac{1}{18}$

14. center $(2, 3)$, radius 6;

15. center $(-5, -8)$, radius 10;

16. center $(1, -7)$, radius 9;

17. center $(-4, 10)$, radius 11;

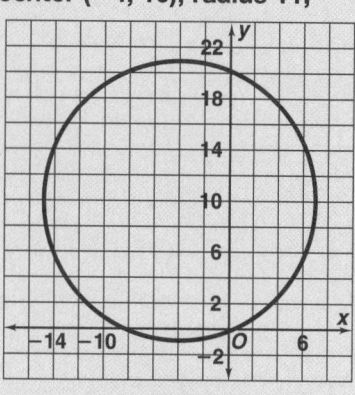

21. foci $(\pm 3\sqrt{5}, 0)$;

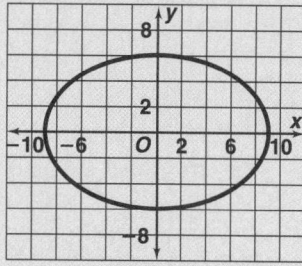

22. foci $(0, \pm 4\sqrt{6})$

23. foci $(0, \pm 4\sqrt{3})$

24. foci $(0, \pm\sqrt{3})$

26. foci $(\pm 2\sqrt{61}, 0)$

27. foci $(0, \pm\sqrt{569})$

28. foci $(\pm 2\sqrt{17}, 0)$

29. foci $(0, \pm\sqrt{226})$

31. $\frac{x^2}{16} + \frac{y^2}{9} = 1$

32. $\frac{(x + 2)^2}{16} + \frac{(y - 7)^2}{9} = 1$

33. $\frac{(x - 3)^2}{25} + \frac{(y + 2)^2}{36} = 1$

34. $\frac{x^2}{9} - \frac{(y - 7)^2}{16} = 1$

35. $\frac{y^2}{25} - \frac{(x - 2)^2}{24} = 1$

36. $(x + 4)^2 - \frac{(y + 1)^2}{15} = 1$

37. parabola; vertex (2, 1)

38. circle; center (2, 3), radius 3

39. ellipse; center (2, 3), foci $(2, 3 \pm 2\sqrt{3})$;

40. hyperbola; center (2, 3), foci $(2 \pm 2\sqrt{5}, 3)$

page 595   Standardized Test Prep

18. [2] $x^2 - 2x = 0$
$x(x - 2) = 0$
$x = 0$ or $x - 2 = 0$
$x = 2$
The zeros are 0 and 2.

[1] only 1 correct

19. [4] a. $y = 3x + 2$; slope = 3; the slope of a perpendicular line is $-\frac{1}{3}$. Select any y-intercept: -1. The equation is $y = -\frac{1}{3}x - 1$.

b. $y = 3x + 2$; slope of parallel line = 3; select any y-intercept: 4. The equation is $y = 3x + 4$.

[3] only takes reciprocal of slope in (a) OR only makes it negative

[2] takes the negative reciprocal of the slope in (b) and leaves the slope in (a)

[1] performs the error mentioned in [3] AND (b) is incorrect

20. [4] $\frac{x + 4}{(x + 4)(x + 2)} \div \frac{(x - 4)(x + 4)}{(x + 6)(x + 2)}$
$= \frac{x + 4}{(x + 4)(x + 2)} \cdot \frac{(x + 6)(x + 2)}{(x - 4)(x + 4)}$
$= \frac{(x + 4)(x + 6)(x + 2)}{(x + 4)(x + 2)(x - 4)(x + 4)}$
$= \frac{x + 6}{(x - 4)(x + 4)} = \frac{x + 6}{x^2 - 16}$;
$x \neq -6, -4, -2, 4$

[3] answer correct, but one restriction missing

[2] answer correct but all restrictions missing OR either numerator or denominator correct, but 1 or 2 restrictions missing.

[1] answer incorrect, restrictions correct

CHAPTER 11

page 598   Check Your Readiness

10.

11.

12.

LESSON 11-1

page 600   Check Skills You'll Need

2. $-14, -16$; subtract 2.

3. 3125, 15,625; multiply by 5.

4. 20, 15; subtract 5.

5. 8, 4; divide by 2.

6. 20, 23; add 3.

page 600   Activity

3.

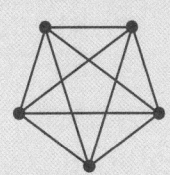

, 10 calls

pages 603–605   Exercises

3. Add one more to each term (add 3, add 4, add 5, etc.); 25, 33, 42.

4. Add 3; 16, 19, 22.

5. Divide by 10; 0.001, 0.0001, 0.00001.

6. Multiply by $\frac{1}{2}$; $\frac{1}{64}$, $\frac{1}{128}$, $\frac{1}{256}$.

7. Multiply by -2; -128, 256, -512.

8. Each term after the first is the preceding term multiplied by n; 720, 5040, 40,320.

9. Every odd-numbered term is 0, and every even-numbered term is $\frac{1}{n-1}$; $0, \frac{1}{7}, 0$.

10.

11.

24. recursive; 3, 9, 21, 45, 93

25. explicit; 0, 1, 3, 6, 10

26. explicit; $-24, -21, -16, -9, 0$

27. recursive; $-2, 6, -18, 54, -162$

28. explicit; $-6, -18, -38, -66, -102$

29. explicit; 3, 9, 19, 33, 51

33. 20, 23; $a_n = 3n + 2$; explicit OR $a_n = a_{n-1} + 3, a_1 = 5$; recursive

34. 96, 192; $a_n = 3 \cdot 2^{n-1}$; explicit OR $a_n = 2a_{n-1}, a_1 = 3$; recursive

35. 216, 343; $a_n = n^3$; explicit

36. 4096, 16,384; $a_n = 4^n$; explicit OR $a_n = 4a_{n-1}; a_1 = 4$; recursive

37. 144, 169; $a_n = (n + 6)^2$; explicit OR $a_{n+1} = a_n + 2n + 13; a_1 = 49$; recursive

38. -1, 1; $a_n = -1(a_{n-1}), a_1 = -1$; recursive OR $a_n = (-1)^n$; explicit

39. $-1, -\frac{1}{2}$; $a_n = \frac{a_{n-1}}{2}, a_1 = -16$; recursive OR $a_n = \frac{-32}{2^n}$; explicit

40. $-47, -40$; $a_n = a_{n-1} + 7, a_1 = -75$; recursive OR $a_n = -82 + 7n$; explicit

41. $-11, -19$; $a_n = a_{n-1} - 8; a_1 = 21$; recursive OR $a_n = 29 - 8n$; explicit

LESSON 11-2
page 607   Quick Check

2a. The first term in the sequence, 1100, was the amount of money with *no* participants, so there is one more term than the number of participants.

pages 608–610   Exercises

72.

73.

page 611   Activity lab

2a. Answers may vary. Sample: The triangle has 1's on the outside. Each other number is the sum of the two numbers above it that are closest to it. In Pascal's Triangle and in the Fibonacci Sequence the recursive rule for finding a number adds the two numbers that come earlier in the sequence.

b. 5th row diagonal: 1, 3, 1
6th row diagonal: 1, 4, 3
7th row diagonal: 1, 5, 6, 1
8th row diagonal: 1, 6, 10, 4,
9th row diagonal: 1, 7, 15, 10, 1

The sums are 5, 8, 13, 21, 34. The sums replicate the Fibonacci Sequence.

5.

n	F_n	$(F_n)^2$	$F_{n-1} \cdot F_n + 1$
2	1	1	2
3	2	4	3
4	3	9	10
5	5	25	24
6	8	64	65
7	13	169	168
8	21	441	442
9	34	1156	1155

Conjectures may vary. Sample: The number in the fourth column alternates between being one more and one less than the number in the third column.

LESSON 11-3
pages 614–617   Exercises

58d.

LESSON 11-4
pages 622–624   Exercises

55. [2] $a_1 = 3$ and $d = 4$, an explicit formula for the sequence is $a_n = 4n - 1$

$$\sum_{n=1}^{6} (4n - 1) = 3 + 7 + 11 + 15 + 19 + 23 = 78$$

[1] minor error OR answer only

56. [2] The series represents the sum of the terms of a finite arithmetic sequence with 40 terms for which $a_1 = 9.5$ and $a_{40} = -10$. So

$$\sum_{n=1}^{40} \left(10 - \frac{n}{2}\right) = \left(10 - \frac{1}{2}\right) + \ldots + \left(10 - \frac{40}{2}\right)$$
$$= \frac{40}{2}(9.5 + \; -10)$$
$$= 20(-0.5)$$
$$= -10$$

[1] minor error OR answer only

57. [2] $s_{30} = (30)\left(\frac{a_1 + a_{30}}{2}\right)$

$78 = (30)\left(\frac{a_1 + 4.4}{2}\right)$

$= \frac{2(78)}{30} = a_1 + 4.4$

$5.2 = a_1 + 4.4$

$0.8 = a_1$

[1] minor error OR answer only

LESSON 11-5

pages 628–631   Exercises

30a.

Stage 1	Stage 2	Stage 3
4	16	64

4, 16, 64

page 633   Extension

1. $1 + 3 + 5 + 7 + 9 + 11 \overset{?}{=} 6^2$, $36 = 36$; $1 + 3 + 5 + 7 + 9 + 11 + 13 \overset{?}{=} 7^2$, $49 = 49$; $1 + 3 + 5 + 7 + 9 + 11 + 13 + 15 \overset{?}{=} 8^2$, $64 = 64$

2. a. $2(1) \overset{?}{=} 1(1 + 1)$, $2 = 2$

   b. $2 + 4 + 6 + \ldots + 2k = k(k + 1)$

   c. $2 + 4 + 6 + \ldots + 2k + 2(k + 1) = (k + 1)[(k + 1) + 1]$

   d. $2 + 4 + 6 + \ldots + 2k + 2(k + 1)$
   $= (2 + 4 + 6 + \ldots + 2k) + 2(k + 1)$
   $= k(k + 1) + 2(k + 1)$
   $= (k + 1)(k + 2)$
   $= (k + 1)[(k + 1) + 1]$

3. For $n = 1$, $\frac{1}{1(1 + 1)} = \frac{1}{1 + 1}$.
   Assume
   $\frac{1}{1 \cdot 2} + \frac{1}{2 \cdot 3} + \frac{1}{3 \cdot 4} + \ldots + \frac{1}{k(k + 1)} = \frac{k}{k + 1}$
   Prove
   $\frac{1}{1 \cdot 2} + \frac{1}{2 \cdot 3} + \frac{1}{3 \cdot 4} + \ldots + \frac{1}{k(k + 1)} + \frac{1}{(k + 1)((k + 1) + 1)} = \frac{k + 1}{(k + 1) + 1}$
   Proof
   $\frac{1}{1 \cdot 2} + \frac{1}{2 \cdot 3} + \frac{1}{3 \cdot 4} + \ldots + \frac{1}{k(k + 1)} + \frac{1}{(k + 1)((k + 1) + 1)} =$
   $\frac{k}{k + 1} + \frac{1}{(k + 1)((k + 1) + 1)} =$
   $\frac{k(k + 2)}{(k + 1)(k + 2)} + \frac{1}{(k + 1)((k + 1) + 1)} =$
   $\frac{k(k + 2) + 1}{(k + 1)((k + 1) + 1)} =$
   $\frac{k^2 + 2k + 1}{(k + 1)((k + 1) + 1)} =$
   $\frac{(k + 1)^2}{(k + 1)((k + 1) + 1)} = \frac{k + 1}{(k + 1) + 1}$

4. For $n = 1$, $1 = \frac{1(1 + 1)}{2}$.
   Assume
   $1 + 2 + 3 + \ldots + k = \frac{k(k + 1)}{2}$
   Prove
   $1 + 2 + 3 + \ldots + k + (k + 1) = \frac{(k + 1)((k + 1) + 1)}{2}$

   Proof
   $1 + 2 + 3 + \ldots + k + (k + 1) =$
   $\frac{k(k + 1)}{2} + (k + 1) =$
   $\frac{k(k + 1) + 2(k + 1)}{2} =$
   $\frac{(k + 1)(k + 2)}{2} = \frac{(k + 1)((k + 1) + 1)}{2}$

5. For $n = 1$, $3(1) - 2 = \frac{1(3(1) - 1)}{2}$.
   Assume
   $1 + 4 + 7 + \ldots + (3k - 2) = \frac{k(3k - 1)}{2}$
   Prove
   $1 + 4 + 7 + \ldots + (3k - 2) + (3(k + 1) - 2) = \frac{(k + 1)(3(k + 1) - 1)}{2}$
   Proof
   $1 + 4 + 7 + \ldots + (3k - 2) + (3(k + 1) - 2) = \frac{k(3k - 1)}{2} + 3(k + 1) - 2 =$
   $\frac{k(3k - 1) + 6(k + 1) - 4}{2} =$
   $\frac{3k^2 - k + 6k + 6 - 4}{2} =$
   $\frac{3k^2 + 5k + 2}{2} =$
   $\frac{(k + 1)(3k + 2)}{2} =$
   $\frac{(k + 1)(3k + 3 - 1)}{2} =$
   $\frac{(k + 1)(3(k + 1) - 1)}{2}$

6. For $n = 1$, $\left(\frac{1}{2}\right)^1 = 1 - \left(\frac{1}{2}\right)^1$.
   Assume
   $\frac{1}{2} + \left(\frac{1}{2}\right)^2 + \left(\frac{1}{2}\right)^3 + \left(\frac{1}{2}\right)^4 + \ldots + \left(\frac{1}{2}\right)^k = 1 - \left(\frac{1}{2}\right)^k$

   Prove
   $\frac{1}{2} + \left(\frac{1}{2}\right)^2 + \left(\frac{1}{2}\right)^3 + \left(\frac{1}{2}\right)^4 + \ldots + \left(\frac{1}{2}\right)^k + \left(\frac{1}{2}\right)^{k+1} = 1 - \left(\frac{1}{2}\right)^{k+1}$

   Proof
   $\frac{1}{2} + \left(\frac{1}{2}\right)^2 + \left(\frac{1}{2}\right)^3 + \left(\frac{1}{2}\right)^4 + \ldots + \left(\frac{1}{2}\right)^k + \left(\frac{1}{2}\right)^{k+1} = 1 - \left(\frac{1}{2}\right)^k +$
   $\left(\frac{1}{2}\right)^{k+1} = 1 - \left(\frac{1}{2}\right)^k\left(1 - \frac{1}{2}\right) = 1 -$
   $\left(\frac{1}{2}\right)^k\left(\frac{1}{2}\right) = 1 - \left(\frac{1}{2}\right)^{k+1}$

7. For $n = 1$, $1^2 + 1$ is divisible by 2.
   Assume
   $k^2 + k$ is divisible by 2; that is $k^2 + k = 2N$, where N is an integer.
   Prove
   $(k + 1)^2 + (k + 1)$ is divisible by 2.
   Proof
   $(k + 1)^2 + (k + 1) =$
   $k^2 + 2k + 1 + k + 1 =$
   $k^2 + k + 2k + 2 = 2N + 2k + 2 = 2(N + k + 1)$.
   Since $(N + k + 1)$ is an integer, $(k + 1)^2 + (k + 1)$ is divisible by 2.

8. For $n = 1$, $1(1 + 1) = 2$ and $\frac{1(1 + 1)(1 + 2)}{3} = 2$.
   Assume
   $1 \cdot 2 + 2 \cdot 3 + 3 \cdot 4 + \ldots + k(k + 1) = \frac{k(k + 1)(k + 2)}{3}$
   Prove
   $1 \cdot 2 + 2 \cdot 3 + 3 \cdot 4 + \ldots + k(k + 1) + (k + 1)((k + 1) + 1) = \frac{(k + 1)((k + 1) + 1)((k + 1) + 2)}{3}$
   Proof
   $1 \cdot 2 + 2 \cdot 3 + 3 \cdot 4 + \ldots + k(k + 1) + (k + 1)((k + 1) + 1) =$
   $\frac{k(k + 1)(k + 2)}{3} + (k + 1)((k + 1) + 1) =$
   $\frac{k(k + 1)(k + 2)}{3} + (k + 1)(k + 2) =$
   $(k + 1)(k + 2)\left(\frac{k}{3} + 1\right) =$
   $\frac{(k + 1)((k + 2)(k + 3)}{3} =$
   $\frac{(k + 1)((k + 1) + 1)((k + 1) + 2)}{3}$

9. For $n = 1$, $1^2 = \frac{1(1 + 1)(2 \cdot 1 + 1)}{6}$.
   Assume
   $1^2 + 2^2 + 3^2 + \ldots + k^2 = \frac{k(k + 1)(2k + 1)}{6}$
   Prove
   $1^2 + 2^2 + 3^2 + \ldots + k^2 + (k + 1)^2 = \frac{(k + 1)((k + 1) + 1)(2(k + 1) + 2)}{6}$
   Proof
   $1^2 + 2^2 + 3^2 + \ldots + k^2 + (k + 1)^2 = \frac{k(k + 1)(2k + 1)}{6} + (k + 1)^2 = (k + 1)\left(\left(\frac{k(2k + 1)}{6}\right) + (k + 1)\right) = (k + 1)\left(\frac{2k^2 + k + 6k + 6}{6}\right) = \frac{(k + 1)(k + 2)(2k + 3)}{6} = \frac{(k + 1)((k + 1) + 1)(2(k + 1) + 1)}{6}$

10. For $n = 1$, $a_1r^{1-1} = a_1r^0 = a_1 =$
$a_1 \cdot \frac{1 - r}{1 - r} = \frac{a_1(1 - r^1)}{1 - r}$.
Assume
$a_1 + a_1r + a_1r^2 + \ldots + a_1r^{k-1}$
$= \frac{a_1(1 - r^k)}{1 - r}$
Prove
$a_1 + a_1r + a_1r^2 + \ldots + a_1r^{k-1} +$
$a_1r^{(k+1)-1} = \frac{a_1(1 - r^{k+1})}{1 - r}$
Proof
$a_1 + a_1r + a_1r^2 + \ldots + a_1r^{k-1} +$
$a_1r^{(k+1)-1} = \frac{a_1(1 - r^k)}{1 - r} + a_1r^k =$
$a_1\left(\frac{1 - r^k}{1 - r} + r^k\right) =$
$a_1\left(\frac{(1 - r^k) + (1 - r)r^k}{1 - r}\right) =$
$a_1\left(\frac{1 - r^k + r^k - r^{k+1}}{1 - r}\right) = \frac{a_1(1 - r^{k+1})}{1 - r}$

11. For $n = 1$, $1^3 = 1^2$.
Assume
$1^3 + 2^3 + 3^3 + \ldots + k^3$
$= (1 + 2 + 3 \ldots k)^2$
Prove
$1^3 + 2^3 + 3^3 + \ldots + k^3 +$
$(k + 1)^3 = (1 + 2 + 3 \ldots + k +$
$(k + 1))^2$
Proof
$1^3 + 2^3 + 3^3 + \ldots + k^3 +$
$(k + 1)^3 = (1 + 2 + 3 \ldots + k)^2 +$
$(k + 1)^3$
$= \left(\frac{k(k + 1)}{2}\right)^2 + (k + 1)^3$
$= \frac{k^2}{4}(k + 1)^2 + (k + 1)(k + 1)^2$
$= \left(\frac{k^2}{4} + k + 1\right)(k + 1)^2$
$= \left(\frac{k^2 + 4k + 4}{4}\right)(k + 1)^2$
$= \left(\frac{k + 2}{4}\right)^2(k + 1)^2$
$= (1 + 2 + 3 + \ldots + k +$
$(k + 1))^2$

LESSON 11-6

pages 637–639   Exercises

9. $A = \sum_{n=1}^{2} 1f(a_n)$
   a. 0.5 units^2
   b. 2.5 units^2

10. $A = \sum_{n=1}^{2} 1f(a_n)$
   a. 5 units^2
   b. 9 units^2

11. $A = \sum_{n=1}^{2} 1f(a_n)$
   a. 3 units^2
   b. 7 units^2

12. $A = \sum_{n=1}^{2} 1f(a_n)$
   a. 3 units^2
   b. 7 units^2

13. $A = \sum_{n=1}^{2} 1f(a_n)$
   a. $10\frac{2}{3}$ units^2
   b. $13\frac{1}{3}$ units^2

14. $A = \sum_{n=1}^{2} 1h(a_n)$
   a. 5 units^2
   b. 25 units^2

15. $A = \sum_{n=1}^{2} 1f(a_n)$
   a. 6.75 units^2
   b. 7.75 units^2

16. $A = \sum_{n=1}^{2} 1h(a_n)$
   a. 5 units^2
   b. 9 units^2

17. $A = \sum_{n=1}^{2} 1f(a_n)$
   a. 5 units^2
   b. 9 units^2

24.
8.75 units^2

25.
43 units^2

26.
28.75 units^2

27.
50 units^2

28.
16.875 units^2

29.
19.5 units^2

30a.

T976

c.

12 units²

d. 7.5 units²; the mean best approximates the area because it is between the other measures known to be larger and smaller than the actual value.

31a. Answers may vary. Sample:

Xmin:0   Ymin:0
Xmax:200 Ymax:70
Xscl:25   Yscl:10

≈ 0.37 mile

b. Answers may vary. Sample: Using inscribed rectangles will result in an estimate smaller than the actual number.

page 644   Chapter Test

35.

2 units²

36.

9 units²

37.

4 units²

---

38. Answers may vary. Sample: You could find the sum of the area of the circumscribed rectangles and the sum of the area of the inscribed rectangles and average the sums.

CHAPTER 12

LESSON 12-1

pages 649–650   Quick Check

3. Answers may vary. Sample:

Rolling One Number Cube

Number	1	2	3	4	5	6
Frequency	1	1	1	1	1	1
Probability	$\frac{1}{6}$	$\frac{1}{6}$	$\frac{1}{6}$	$\frac{1}{6}$	$\frac{1}{6}$	$\frac{1}{6}$

4a. The Plant Color Distribution would be most useful for avoiding white plants because it shows the total probability of growing green plants, which is the desired outcome.

b.

Genotype

Event	GG	Gw	ww
Frequency	1	2	1
Probability	$\frac{1}{4}$	$\frac{1}{2}$	$\frac{1}{4}$

Plant Color

Event	Green	White
Frequency	3	1
Probability	$\frac{3}{4}$	$\frac{1}{4}$

pages 651–653   Exercises

6.

Outcome	Probability
Red	$\frac{1}{7}$
Green	$\frac{3}{7}$
Blue	$\frac{2}{7}$
Yellow	$\frac{1}{7}$

8.

9.

10. Answers may vary. Sample design: Use random numbers. Assign numbers 1 to 1000 to each event, based on its probability.

Age	Prob-ability	Cumulative Probability	Assigned Numbers
<20	0.048	0.048	1–48
20–29	0.175	0.223	49–223
30–39	0.199	0.422	224–422
40–49	0.211	0.633	423–633
50–59	0.167	0.800	634–800
60–69	0.102	0.902	801–902
70–79	0.066	0.968	903–968
≥ 80	0.032	1.000	969–1000

Random numbers generated: 697, 420, 488, 567, 272, 396, 474, 870, 896, 282, 464, 681, 274, 663, 681, 282, 376, 363, 860, 129
Results of simulation:
Age 20–29: 1, Age 30–39: 8;
Age 40–49: 4, Age 50–59: 4;
Age 60–69: 3

11. Answers may vary. Sample design: Use random numbers. Assign numbers 1 to 1000 to each event, based on its probability.

Type	Prob.	Cum. Prob.	Assigned Numbers
Luxury	0.165	0.165	1–165
Large	0.076	0.241	166–241
Midsize	0.527	0.768	242–768
Small	0.232	1	769–1000

Random numbers generated: 612, 904, 249, 194, 435, 772, 93, 236, 80, 370, 849, 468, 819, 800, 371, 14, 396, 278, 303, 662, 637, 572, 700, 196, 810, 314, 496, 408, 737, 624
Results of simulation: 3 luxury cars, 3 large cars, 18 midsize cars, and 6 small cars

14a.

Weather Conditions in Dayton, Ohio

Type	Frequency	Probability
Clear	82	0.225
Partly Cloudy	118	0.323
Mostly Cloudy	34	0.093
Rain	75	0.205
Light Snow	45	0.123
Snow	11	0.030

b. The independent variable is the type of weather. The dependent variable is the probability that a type of weather occurs.

c. $\frac{131}{365}$ OR 0.359

16a. The independent variable is the amount of gas in the tank; the dependent variable is the percent of people who fill their tanks when they have a given amount of gas.

b.

Gas in Tank

c. 0.28 or 28%

19. Answers may vary. Sample:
a.

Calls	$P(c)$	Cum. Prob.	Assigned #s
0	0.21	0.21	1–21
1	0.30	0.51	22–51
2	0.18	0.69	52–69
3	0.13	0.82	70–82
4	0.09	0.91	83–91
5	0.05	0.96	92–96
6	0.03	0.99	97–99
7	0.01	1.00	100

b. There were six hours in which 3 calls were received, and two in which 4 calls were received. A total of ten callers would have to wait.

d. An additional response team would reduce the probability of having to wait from $\frac{10}{47}$ to $\frac{2}{47}$, a considerable improvement.

LESSON 12-2

pages 656–658   Exercises

29.

LESSON 12-4

page 668   Activity

5a. Sets 2 and 4

b. Sets 2 and 3

6a. The three sets have the same mean, median, and mode. The difference between the extreme values is the same for Sets 2 and 4, although Set 2 is less spread out. The difference $Q_3 - Q_1$, is the same for Sets 2 and 3, although Set 3 is less spread out. Set 4 is the most spread out, with all but two values 40 or more away from the mean. Set 1 is the least spread out, with all its values 3 or less away from the mean.

b.

page 669   Quick Check

1b. Yes; examples may vary. Sample:
1 2 3 4 5 6 7 8 9 10;
1 1 1 1 1 10 10 10 10 10

c. Yes; examples may vary. Sample:
1 2 3 4 5 6 7 8 9 10;
3 3 3 5 5 6 6 8 8 8

LESSON 12-6

page 685   Check Skills You'll Need

5. $w^4 - 4w^3y + 6w^2y^2 - 4wy^3 + y^4$

6. $m^3 + 3m^2n + 3mn^2 + n^3$

7. $t^4 + 12t^3s + 54t^2s^2 + 108ts^3 + 81s^4$

8. $a^5 + 10a^4b + 40a^3b^2 + 80a^2b^3 + 80ab^4 + 32b^5$

---

9. $p^6 + 6p^5q + 15p^4q^2 + 20p^3q^3 + 15p^2q^4 + 6pq^5 + q^6$

page 685   Activity

2b. Answers may vary. Sample:

Score	Frequency
0	0
10	0
20	1
30	2
40	2
50	2
60	1
70	2
80	0
90	0
100	0

pages 688–691   Exercises

12. $P(0) = 0.1176$
$P(1) = 0.3025$
$P(2) = 0.3241$
$P(3) = 0.1852$
$P(4) = 0.0595$
$P(5) = 0.0102$
$P(6) = 0.0007$

13. $P(0) = 0.0156$
$P(1) = 0.0938$
$P(2) = 0.2344$
$P(3) = 0.3125$
$P(4) = 0.2344$
$P(5) = 0.0938$
$P(6) = 0.0156$

14. $P(0) = 0.000001$
$P(1) = 0.000054$
$P(2) = 0.0012$
$P(3) = 0.0146$
$P(4) = 0.0984$
$P(5) = 0.3543$
$P(6) = 0.5314$

25a. $_{40}C_3\left(\frac{1}{7}\right)^3\left(\frac{6}{7}\right)^{37} \approx$
0.0960 = 9.6%

b. Answers may vary. Sample: Generate 40 numbers ranging from 1 to 7. Let the number 4 represent Wednesday birthdays. Repeat 9 more times. Count the number of runs that 4 came up exactly 3 times; divide that number by 10 to get the probability that exactly 3 of 40 people will have Wednesday birthdays. Check students' work for probability.

c. 10 runs is too few to get an accurate probability.

26. Answers may vary. Sample: 60% of the summer days in Eastport are sunny. What is the probability of a week containing just two sunny days?

LESSON 12-7

page 693   Quick Check

2.

pages 701–703   Chapter Review

7.

Product	Freq.	Prob.	Product	Freq.	Prob.
1	1	$\frac{1}{36}$	12	4	$\frac{4}{36}$
2	2	$\frac{2}{36}$	15	2	$\frac{2}{36}$
3	2	$\frac{2}{36}$	16	1	$\frac{1}{36}$
4	3	$\frac{3}{36}$	18	2	$\frac{2}{36}$
5	2	$\frac{2}{36}$	20	2	$\frac{2}{36}$
6	4	$\frac{4}{36}$	24	2	$\frac{2}{36}$
8	2	$\frac{2}{36}$	25	1	$\frac{1}{36}$
9	1	$\frac{1}{36}$	30	2	$\frac{2}{36}$
10	2	$\frac{2}{36}$	36	1	$\frac{1}{36}$

26.

Successes	5	4	3	2	1	0
$(p+q)^5$ term	$1p^5$	$5p^4q$	$10p^3q^2$	$10p^2q^3$	$5pq^4$	$1q^5$
Term value	$(0.7)^5 =$ 0.16807	$5(0.7)^40.3$ = 0.36015	$10(0.7)^3(0.3)^2$ = 0.3087	$10(0.7)^2(0.3)^3$ = 0.1323	$5(0.7)(0.3)^4$ = 0.02835	$(0.3)^5 =$ 0.00243

page 704   Chapter Test

1.

2.

3. Sample: Suppose two hybrid Aa parent plants are crossed. The offspring can be described by the sample space {AA, Aa, aa} or by the sample space {dominant, recessive}.

27. Answers may vary. Sample: Flip a coin. Let heads represent a correct guess, and let tails represent an incorrect guess. A trial is 3 tosses. Run the simulation 10 times and count the number of trials with at least 1 H. Divide the result by 10.

32.

page 705   Standardized Test Prep

17. [2]   Check

$\frac{x}{6} = \frac{(x+4)}{9}$ $\frac{8}{6} \stackrel{?}{=} \frac{(8+4)}{9}$

$(6)(9)\frac{x}{6} = (6)(9)\frac{(x+4)}{9}$ $\frac{4}{3} \stackrel{?}{=} \frac{12}{9}$

$9x = 6(x+4)$ $\frac{4}{3} \stackrel{?}{=} \frac{4}{3}$

$9x = 6x + 24$ $\frac{4}{3} = \frac{4}{3}$

$3x = 24$

$x = 8$

[1] correct solution but no more than one step shown OR at least 2 steps, but no check

18. [2]

$9 \log 3 - 3 \log 9 = \log 27$

$9 \log 3 - 3 \log 3^2 = \log 3^3$ factoring

$9 \log 3 - (3)(2)\log 3 = 3 \log 3$ Power Prop. of Logs

$9 \log 3 - 6 \log 3 = 3 \log 3$ Simplify.

$3 \log 3 = 3 \log 3$

OR

$\log 3^9 - \log 9^3 = \log 3^3$ Power Prop. of Logs

$\log 3^9 - \log (3^2)^3 = \log 3^3$ factoring

$\log \frac{3^9}{3^6} = \log 3^3$ Quotient Prop. of Logs

$\log 3^3 = \log 3^3$ Simplify.

[1] only one step shown

19. [4] Vertices and intercepts are at $(\pm a, 0)$, asymptotes are $y = \pm\frac{b}{a}x$, and foci are at $(\pm c, 0)$. For $\frac{x^2}{16} - \frac{y^2}{9} = 1$, $a = 4$ and $b = 3$, so the vertices and intercepts are at $(\pm 4, 0)$ and the asymptotes are at $y = \pm\frac{3}{4}x$. Since $c = \sqrt{a^2 + b^2} = \sqrt{25} = 5$, the foci are at $(\pm 5, 0)$.

[3] 3 parts correct

[2] 2 parts correct

[1] 1 part correct

20. [4] There is no common difference: $1000 - 10,000 \neq 100 - 1000$. But $\frac{1000}{10,000} = 0.1$, $\frac{100}{1000} = 0.1$, and $\frac{10}{100} = 0.1$, so the series is geometric with $r = 0.1$. The sum of the first eight terms is

$S_8 = \frac{a_1(1 - r^8)}{1 - r} = \frac{10,000(1 - 0.1^8)}{1 - 0.1} =$

$\frac{10,000(1 - 0.00000001)}{0.9} =$

$\frac{10,000(0.99999999)}{0.9} =$

$10,000(1.1111111) =$
$11,111.111$

[3] *r* incorrect, OR the sum incorrect OR little explanation of why the series is geometric

[2] 2 of the above incorrect OR 1 incorrect and little explanation of why the series is geometric

[1] series treated as arithmetic, but with computations formally correct

CHAPTER 13

LESSON 13-1

page 710   Activity

2.

pages 713–716   Exercises

33a.

41.

LESSON 13-2

pages 722–724   Exercises

7.

8.

9.

10.

11.

53.

$\frac{1}{2}, \frac{\sqrt{3}}{2}$

54.

$-\frac{1}{2}, \frac{\sqrt{3}}{2}$

55.

$-\frac{\sqrt{2}}{2}, -\frac{\sqrt{2}}{2}$

56.

$\frac{1}{2}, -\frac{\sqrt{3}}{2}$

57.

$\frac{\sqrt{2}}{2}, -\frac{\sqrt{2}}{2}$

58.

$\frac{1}{2}, -\frac{\sqrt{3}}{2}$

67. **[2]**

The terminal side forms an angle of 30° with the negative *x*-axis. Using the unit circle, $r = 1$, $x = -\frac{\sqrt{3}}{2}$, and $y = \frac{1}{2}$.

So $\sin(-210°) = \frac{x}{r} = -\frac{\sqrt{3}}{2}$.

[1] answer only, with no work shown

68. **[4]**

The terminal side forms an angle of 45° with the negative *x*-axis, so $\sin(-135°) = -\frac{\sqrt{2}}{2}$ and $\cos(-135°) = -\frac{\sqrt{2}}{2}$.

Then $[\sin(-135°)]^2$
$+ [\cos(-135°)]^2 =$

$\left[-\frac{\sqrt{2}}{2}\right]^2 + \left[-\frac{\sqrt{2}}{2}\right]^2 =$

$\frac{2}{4} + \frac{2}{4} = \frac{4}{4} = 1.$

[3] one computational error

[2] incomplete explanation with correct answer

[1] answer only, with no work shown

LESSON 13-3

pages 729–733   Exercises

13.

LESSON 13-5

pages 746–748   Exercises

34a.

b. Answers may vary. Sample:
0 s, 4 s, 8 s, 12 s

36a. Answers may vary. Sample: sine;
The sine function gives vertical position with respect to the center of the wheel.

b.

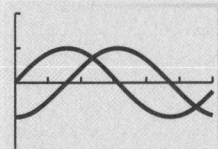

Answers may vary. Sample: Going from left to right, the graph of $Y2 = \sin\left(x - \frac{\pi}{2}\right)$ "trails" the graph

of $Y1 = \sin x$ by $\frac{\pi}{2}$ units. If the "ride" for Y2 would start $\frac{\pi}{2}$ units of time sooner than the ride for Y1, the two graphs would be identical from the origin on out.

c. 20 times as great.

d. The center of the Ferris wheel is 20 ft higher at (0, 20).

e. $f(x) = 20 \sin\left(x - \frac{\pi}{2}\right) + 20$

f.

g. Allow for different values of b in $f(x) = 20 \sin b\left(x - \frac{\pi}{2}\right) + 20$. Model faster Ferris wheel speed by increasing the value of b. You can keep the starting point of the model at (0, 0) by letting b have the value $4n - 3$, $n = 1, 2, \ldots$.

h. In parametric mode, let $X_{IT} = T$, $Y_{IT} = 20 \sin\left(T - \frac{\pi}{2}\right) + 20$ and adjust Tstep values.

i. Answers may vary. Sample: You can use the cosine function to model horizontal position with respect to the center of the wheel.

LESSON 13-7

page 756   Check Skills You'll Need

1.

vertical

2.

horizontal

3.

vertical

4.

vertical

5.

diagonal

6.

diagonal

page 757

2a.

b.

$y = \sin(x - 2)$ is a phase shift.

pages 760–762   Exercises

11.

12.

13.

14.

15.

16.

21.

22.

23.

24.

25.

26.

27.

28.

29.

30.

37a.

47.

48.

49.

50.

51.

52.

53.

54.

page 762   Checkpoint Quiz 2

1.

2.

3.

4.

5.

6.

7.

8.

9.

10.

LESSON 13-8

page 763   Check Skills You'll Need

6.

7.

8.

9.

---

pages 766–769   Exercises

41a.

61.

3 units up

62.

$\frac{\pi}{2}$ unit left

63.

1 unit down

64.

$\frac{\pi}{2}$ units right

65.

4 units right

66.

2 units left, 1 unit down

67.

π units left, 3 units up

68.

$\frac{\pi}{6}$ unit right, 2 units down

69a.

b. $y = -\cos x$ — domain: all real numbers; range: all real numbers between -1 and 1, inclusive; period: 2π; $y = -\sec x$ — domain: all real numbers except odd multiples of $\frac{\pi}{2}$; range: all real numbers except those between -1 and 1; period: 2π

c. Multiples of π. By definition, $\sec x = \frac{1}{\cos x}$, so $-\cos x = -\sec x$ is equivalent to $-\cos x = -\frac{1}{\cos x}$, or $(\cos x)^2 = 1$.

The solutions of $(\cos x)^2 = 1$ are the values of x for which $\cos x = 1$ or $\cos x = -1$. These values are the multiples of π.

d. Answers may vary. Sample: The graphs have the same period and their signs are always the same. However, they have no range values in common except 1 and -1.

e. The signs of $-\sec x$ and $-\cos x$ are the same because reciprocals have the same sign.

23.

24.

25.

26.

27.

28.

41.

42.

43.

44.

CHAPTER 14

LESSON 14-1

page 778   Check Skills You'll Need

1. Yes; $2x + 3x = (2 + 3)x$ by the Dist. Prop. and $(2 + 3)x = 5x$ by addition.

2. Yes; $-(4x - 10) = -4x + 10$ by the Dist. Prop. and $-4x + 10 = 10 - 4x$ by the Comm. Prop.

3. No; for $x = 0$, $\frac{4x^2}{x}$ is not defined, but $4x = 0$.

4. No; for $x = 1$, $\frac{x^2 + 1}{x - 1}$ is not defined, but $x + 1 = 2$.

page 778   Technology Activity

1.

2.

pages 780–782   Exercises

45. $\sin^2 \theta \tan^2 \theta = \sin^2 \theta \left(\frac{\sin^2 \theta}{\cos^2 \theta}\right)$

$= (1 - \cos^2 \theta) \left(\frac{\sin^2 \theta}{\cos^2 \theta}\right)$

$= \frac{\sin^2 \theta - \sin^2 \theta \cos^2 \theta}{\cos^2 \theta}$

$= \frac{\sin^2 \theta}{\cos^2 \theta} - \frac{\sin^2 \theta \cos^2 \theta}{\cos^2 \theta}$

$= \tan^2 \theta - \sin^2 \theta$

46. $\sec \theta - \sin \theta \tan \theta$

$= \frac{1}{\cos \theta} - \sin \theta \left(\frac{\sin \theta}{\cos \theta}\right)$

$= \frac{1}{\cos \theta} - \frac{\sin^2 \theta}{\cos \theta} = \frac{1 - \sin^2 \theta}{\cos \theta} = \frac{\cos^2 \theta}{\cos \theta}$

$= \cos \theta$

47. $\sin \theta \cos \theta \left(\frac{\sin \theta}{\cos \theta} + \frac{\cos \theta}{\sin \theta}\right)$

$= \frac{\sin^2 \theta \cos \theta}{\cos \theta} + \frac{\cos^2 \theta \sin \theta}{\sin \theta}$

$= \sin^2 \theta + \cos^2 \theta = 1$

48. $\frac{1 - \sin \theta}{\cos \theta} \cdot \frac{\cos \theta}{\cos \theta} = \frac{(1 - \sin \theta) \cos \theta}{\cos^2 \theta}$

$= \frac{(1 - \sin \theta) \cos \theta}{1 - \sin^2 \theta}$

$= \frac{(1 - \sin \theta) \cos \theta}{(1 - \sin \theta)(1 + \sin \theta)}$

$= \frac{\cos \theta}{1 + \sin \theta}$

49. $\frac{\sec \theta}{\cot \theta + \tan \theta}$

$= \frac{\frac{1}{\cos \theta}}{\frac{\cos \theta}{\sin \theta} + \frac{\sin \theta}{\cos \theta}} \cdot \frac{\sin \theta \cos \theta}{\sin \theta \cos \theta}$

$= \frac{\sin \theta}{\cos^2 \theta + \sin^2 \theta} = \frac{\sin \theta}{1} = \sin \theta$

50. $(\cot \theta + 1)^2 = \cot^2 \theta + 2 \cot \theta + 1 = \cot^2 \theta + 1 + 2 \cot \theta = \csc^2 \theta + 2 \cot \theta$

57. $\frac{\cot \theta \sin \theta}{\sec \theta} + \frac{\tan \theta \cos \theta}{\csc \theta}$

$= \frac{\left(\frac{\cos \theta}{\sin \theta}\right) \sin \theta}{\frac{1}{\cos \theta}} + \frac{\left(\frac{\sin \theta}{\cos \theta}\right) \cos \theta}{\frac{1}{\sin \theta}}$

$= \frac{\cos \theta}{\frac{1}{\cos \theta}} + \frac{\sin \theta}{\frac{1}{\sin \theta}}$

$= \cos^2 \theta + \sin^2 \theta = 1$

58. $\sin^2 \theta \tan^2 \theta + \cos^2 \theta \tan^2 \theta$
$= \tan^2 \theta (\sin^2 \theta + \cos^2 \theta)$
$= \tan^2 \theta (1) = \tan^2 \theta$
$= \sec^2 \theta - 1$

68.[4] Using the Pythagorean identities, $1 - \sin^2 x$ is replaced by $\cos^2 x$. This leaves $\frac{\cos x}{\cos^2 x} = \sec x$. The next step is to simplify, leaving $\frac{1}{\cos x} = \sec x$, and since $\frac{1}{\cos x} = \sec x$, then $\sec x = \sec x$, which proves the identity.

[3] appropriate methods with minor error

[2] correct steps without explanation

[1] steps with a minor error and without explanation

73.

74.

83.

84.

LESSON 14-3

pages 796–799 Exercises

35. $a = 15, m\angle A \approx 61.9°, m\angle B \approx 28.1°$

36. $c \approx 12.2, m\angle A \approx 35.0°,$
$m\angle B \approx 55.0°$

37. $a \approx 7.9, b \approx 6.2, m\angle B = 38°$

38. $a \approx 3.9, c \approx 6.9, m\angle B = 55.8°$

39. $a \approx 26.8, c \approx 28.1, m\angle A = 72.8°$

40. $a \approx 19.8, b \approx 2.9, m\angle A = 81.7°$

46. Using inverse sine, you can find that $\theta = 30°$. Since sine is positive in the first and second quadrants, another solution is 150°. All the solutions would be $30° + n \cdot 360°$ and $150° + n \cdot 360°$.

47.

Since $\triangle APQ$ and $\triangle ABC$ are similar triangles,
$\frac{AQ}{AP} = \frac{AC}{AB}$. So, since $\cos\theta = AQ$,
$\cos\theta = AQ = \frac{AQ}{1} =$
$\frac{AQ}{AP} = \frac{AC}{AB} = \cos A$.

59. [2] $\tan\angle A = \frac{135}{95}$
$m\angle A = \tan^{-1} 1.421$
$m\angle A \approx 54.9°$
$\tan\angle B = \frac{95}{135}$
$m\angle B = \tan^{-1} 0.7037$
$m\angle B \approx 35.1°$

[1] answer only, without work shown

LESSON 14-6

pages 818–820 Exercises

1. $\csc\left(\theta - \frac{\pi}{2}\right) = \dfrac{1}{\sin\left(\theta - \frac{\pi}{2}\right)}$
$= \dfrac{1}{\sin\left(-\left(\frac{\pi}{2} - \theta\right)\right)}$
$= \dfrac{1}{-\sin\left(\frac{\pi}{2} - \theta\right)}$
$= \dfrac{1}{-\cos\theta}$
$= -\sec\theta$

2. $\sec\left(\theta - \frac{\pi}{2}\right) = \dfrac{1}{\cos\left(\theta - \frac{\pi}{2}\right)}$
$= \dfrac{1}{\cos\left(-\left(\frac{\pi}{2} - \theta\right)\right)}$
$= \dfrac{1}{\cos\left(\frac{\pi}{2} - \theta\right)}$
$= \dfrac{1}{\sin\theta}$
$= \csc\theta$

3. $\cot\left(\frac{\pi}{2} - \theta\right) = \dfrac{\cos\left(\frac{\pi}{2} - \theta\right)}{\sin\left(\frac{\pi}{2} - \theta\right)}$
$= \dfrac{\sin\theta}{\cos\theta}$
$= \tan\theta$

4. $\csc\left(\frac{\pi}{2} - \theta\right) = \dfrac{1}{\sin\left(\frac{\pi}{2} - \theta\right)}$
$= \dfrac{1}{\cos\theta}$
$= \sec\theta$

5. $\tan\left(\theta - \frac{\pi}{2}\right) = \tan\left(-\left(\frac{\pi}{2} - \theta\right)\right)$
$= -\tan\left(\frac{\pi}{2} - \theta\right)$
$= -\cot\theta$

6. $\sec\left(\frac{\pi}{2} - \theta\right) = \dfrac{1}{\cos\left(\frac{\pi}{2} - \theta\right)}$
$= \dfrac{1}{\sin\theta}$
$= \csc\theta$

37. $\sin(A - B) = \sin(A + (-B))$
$= \sin A \cos(-B) + \cos A \sin(-B)$
$= \sin A \cos B - \cos A \sin B$

38. $\tan(A - B) = \tan(A + (-B))$
$= \dfrac{\tan A + \tan(-B)}{1 - \tan A \tan(-B)}$
$= \dfrac{\tan A - \tan B}{1 + \tan A \tan B}$

39. $\cos(A + B) = \cos(A - (-B))$
$= \cos A \cos(-B) + \sin A \sin(-B)$
$= \cos A \cos B - \sin A \sin B$

40. $\tan(A + B) = \tan(A - (-B))$
$= \dfrac{\tan A - \tan(-B)}{1 + \tan A \tan(-B)}$
$= \dfrac{\tan A + \tan B}{1 - \tan A \tan B}$

41. $\sin\left(x + \frac{\pi}{3}\right) + \sin\left(x - \frac{\pi}{3}\right)$
$= \sin x \cos\frac{\pi}{3} + \cos x \sin\frac{\pi}{3}$
$\quad + \left[\sin x \cos\frac{\pi}{3} - \cos x \sin\frac{\pi}{3}\right]$
$= \sin x \cos\frac{\pi}{3} + \cos x \sin\frac{\pi}{3}$
$\quad + \sin x \cos\frac{\pi}{3} - \cos x \sin\frac{\pi}{3}$
$= 2 \sin x \cos\frac{\pi}{3}$
$= 2 \sin x \cdot \frac{1}{2}$
$= \sin x$

42. $\sin\left(\frac{3\pi}{2} - x\right)$
$= \sin\frac{3\pi}{2}\cos x - \cos\frac{3\pi}{2}\sin x$
$= -1 \cos x - 0 \cdot \sin x$
$= -\cos x$

43. Answers may vary. Sample:
$\sin(30° + 60°) \overset{?}{=} \sin 30° + \sin 60°$
$\sin(90°) \overset{?}{=} \sin 30° + \sin 60°$
$1 \neq \frac{1}{2} + \frac{\sqrt{3}}{2}$

53. $\cos(\pi - \theta)$
$= \cos\pi\cos\theta + \sin\pi\sin\theta$
$= \cos\pi\cos\theta = -\cos\theta$

54. $\sin(\pi - \theta)$
$= \sin\pi\cos\theta - \cos\pi\sin\theta$
$= -\cos\pi\sin\theta = \sin\theta$

55. $\sin(\pi + \theta)$
$= \sin\pi\cos\theta + \cos\pi\sin\theta$
$= -\sin\theta$

56. $\cos(\pi + \theta)$
$= \cos\pi\cos\theta - \sin\pi\sin\theta$
$= -\cos\theta$

57. Given a parallelogram with adjacent sides x_1 and x_2 forming angle θ, and diagonals of d_1 and d_2, then by the Law of Cosines:

$d_1{}^2 + d_2{}^2 = x_1{}^2 + x_2{}^2 - 2x_1x_2\cos\theta$
$\quad + [x_1{}^2 + x_2{}^2 - 2x_1x_2\cos(\pi - \theta)]$
$= 2x_1{}^2 + 2x_2{}^2 - 2x_1x_2\cos\theta -$
$\quad 2x_1x_2[\cos\pi\cos\theta +$
$\quad \sin\pi\sin\theta]$
$= 2x_1{}^2 + 2x_2{}^2 - 2x_1x_2\cos\theta -$
$\quad 2x_1x_2[-\cos\theta]$
$= 2x_1{}^2 + 2x_2{}^2 - 2x_1x_2\cos\theta +$
$\quad 2x_1x_2\cos\theta$
$= 2x_1{}^2 + 2x_2{}^2 = 2(x_1{}^2 + x_2{}^2)$

63. [2] $\sin(165°) = \sin(15°)$
$= \sin(45° - 30°)$
$= \sin 45° \cdot \cos 30° -$
$\quad \cos 45° \sin 30°$
$= \dfrac{\sqrt{2}}{2} \cdot \dfrac{\sqrt{3}}{2} - \dfrac{\sqrt{2}}{2} \cdot \dfrac{1}{2}$
$= \dfrac{\sqrt{6}}{4} - \dfrac{\sqrt{2}}{4} = \dfrac{\sqrt{6} - \sqrt{2}}{4}$

[1] incorrect property used OR minor error

64. [2] $\cos\left(\dfrac{\pi}{6}\right) = \cos\left(\dfrac{\pi}{2} - \dfrac{\pi}{3}\right)$
$= \cos\left(\dfrac{\pi}{2}\right)\cos\left(\dfrac{\pi}{3}\right) +$
$\quad \sin\left(\dfrac{\pi}{2}\right)\sin\left(\dfrac{\pi}{3}\right)$
$= 0 \cdot \dfrac{1}{2} + 1 \cdot \dfrac{\sqrt{3}}{2} = \dfrac{\sqrt{3}}{2}$

[1] incorrect property used OR minor error

LESSON 14-7

pages 824–825   Exercises

31. $\tan \dfrac{R}{2} = \sqrt{\dfrac{1 - \cos R}{1 + \cos R}}$
$= \sqrt{\dfrac{1 - \frac{s}{t}}{1 + \frac{s}{t}}}$
$= \sqrt{\dfrac{t - s}{t + s} \cdot \dfrac{t + s}{t + s}}$
$= \sqrt{\dfrac{t^2 - s^2}{(t + s)^2}}$
$= \sqrt{\dfrac{r^2}{(t + s)^2}}$
$= \dfrac{r}{t + s}$

32. $\tan^2 \dfrac{s}{2} = \left(\tan \dfrac{s}{2}\right)^2$
$= \left(\pm\sqrt{\dfrac{1 - \cos s}{1 + \cos s}}\right)^2$
$= \dfrac{1 - \cos s}{1 + \cos s}$
$= \dfrac{1 - \frac{r}{t}}{1 + \frac{r}{t}}$
$= \dfrac{t - r}{t + r}$

33. No; since the sine function is periodic, A and B can have many different values.

50. Answers may vary. Sample: No; the graphs
of $y = \dfrac{\tan \theta}{4}$ and
$y = \tan \dfrac{\theta}{4}$ intersect but do not
coincide.

51–56. Answers may vary.

51. $4 \sin \theta \cos \theta (\cos^2 \theta - \sin^2 \theta)$

52. $8 \cos^4 \theta - 8 \cos^2 \theta + 1$

53. $\dfrac{4 \tan \theta (1 - \tan^2 \theta)}{\tan^4 \theta - 6 \tan^2 \theta + 1}$

54. $\pm \sqrt{\dfrac{1}{2} \mp \dfrac{1}{2}\sqrt{\dfrac{1}{2} + \dfrac{1}{2}\cos\theta}}$

55. $\pm \sqrt{\dfrac{1}{2} \pm \dfrac{1}{2}\sqrt{\dfrac{1}{2} + \dfrac{1}{2}\cos\theta}}$

56. $\pm \sqrt{\dfrac{1 \mp \sqrt{\frac{1}{2} + \frac{1}{2}\cos\theta}}{1 \pm \sqrt{\frac{1}{2} + \frac{1}{2}\cos\theta}}}$

57a. $\tan \dfrac{A}{2} = \pm\sqrt{\dfrac{1 - \cos A}{1 + \cos A}}$
$= \pm\sqrt{\dfrac{1 - \cos A}{1 + \cos A} \cdot \dfrac{1 + \cos A}{1 + \cos A}}$
$= \pm\sqrt{\dfrac{1 - \cos^2 A}{(1 + \cos A)^2}}$
$= \pm\sqrt{\dfrac{\sin^2 A}{(1 + \cos A)^2}}$
$= \dfrac{\sin A}{1 + \cos A}$

Since $\tan \dfrac{A}{2}$ and $\sin A$ always have the same sign where $\tan \dfrac{A}{2}$ is defined, only the positive sign occurs.

b. $\tan \dfrac{A}{2} = \pm\sqrt{\dfrac{1 - \cos A}{1 + \cos A}}$
$= \pm\sqrt{\dfrac{1 - \cos A}{1 + \cos A} \cdot \dfrac{1 - \cos A}{1 - \cos A}}$
$= \pm\sqrt{\dfrac{(1 - \cos A)^2}{1 - \cos^2 A}}$
$= \pm\sqrt{\dfrac{(1 - \cos A)^2}{\sin^2 A}}$
$= \dfrac{1 - \cos A}{\sin A}$

Since $\tan \dfrac{A}{2}$ and $\sin A$ always have the same sign where $\tan \dfrac{A}{2}$ is defined, only the positive sign occurs.

60. [2] $\sin \dfrac{135°}{2} = \sqrt{\dfrac{1 - \cos 135°}{2}}$
$= \sqrt{\dfrac{1 - \frac{-\sqrt{2}}{2}}{2}}$
$= \sqrt{\dfrac{\frac{2 + \sqrt{2}}{2}}{2}}$
$= \dfrac{\sqrt{2 + \sqrt{2}}}{2}$

[1] appropriate methods with minor error

61. [4] $\tan \theta = \dfrac{0.5}{1} = 0.5 = \dfrac{1}{2}$
$\tan 2\theta = \dfrac{2 \tan \theta}{1 - \tan^2 \theta}$
$= \dfrac{2\left(\frac{1}{2}\right)}{1 - \left(\frac{1}{2}\right)^2} = \dfrac{1}{1 - \frac{1}{4}}$
$= \dfrac{1}{\frac{3}{4}} = \dfrac{4}{3}$

So l_2 intersects the line $x = 1$ at point $\left(1, \dfrac{4}{3}\right)$.

[3] appropriate method with minor error

[2] correct answer without work shown

[1] recognized using double-angle identities but did not apply them properly

page 826   Test-Taking Strategies

5. $A = 0, B = 2\pi$
$A = \dfrac{\pi}{4}, B = \dfrac{7\pi}{4}$
$A = \dfrac{2}{3}\pi, B = \dfrac{4}{3}\pi;$
$A + B = 2\pi$
$\sin(A + B) = 0$
$\sin A + \sin B =$
$\sin(2\pi - B) + \sin B =$
$(\sin 2\pi \cdot \cos B - \cos 2\pi \cdot \sin B) +$
$\sin B = (0 \cdot \cos B - 1 \cdot \sin B) +$
$\sin B = -\sin B + \sin B = 0$

6. Answers may vary. Sample:
$A = 0, B = \pi;$
$A = \pi, B = \dfrac{\pi}{2};$
$A = \dfrac{3\pi}{2}, B = \dfrac{5\pi}{2};$
$\sin B = \cos^2 A - \sin^2 A$
$= \cos 2A$
$= \sin\left(\dfrac{\pi}{2} - A\right)$
$\therefore B = \dfrac{\pi}{2} - A$
$\cos^2 A - \sin^2 A = \cos^2 0 - \sin^2 0 =$
$1 = \sin \dfrac{\pi}{2} =$
$\cos^2 \pi - \sin^2 \pi = 1 - 0 = 1 = \sin\dfrac{\pi}{2}$
$= 1$
$\cos^2\left(\dfrac{3\pi}{2}\right) - \sin^2\left(\dfrac{3\pi}{2}\right) = \cos\left(2\left(\dfrac{3\pi}{2}\right)\right)$
$= \sin\left(\dfrac{\pi}{2} - 3\pi\right) = \sin\left(\dfrac{-5\pi}{2}\right) = -1$

page 830   Chapter Test

15. $\dfrac{4}{6.4}$, 0.63

16. $\dfrac{6.4}{5}$, 1.28

17. $\dfrac{5}{4}$, 1.25

18. $\dfrac{6.4}{5}$, 1.28

19. $\dfrac{6.4}{4}$, 1.60

20. $\dfrac{5}{4}$, 1.25

21. 8, 36.9°, 53.1°

22. 15.6, 50.2°, 39.8°

23. 46.5, 24.3°, 65.7°

24. 6.1, 25.3°, 64.7°

34. $-\sin\left(\theta - \frac{\pi}{2}\right) = -\sin\left(-\left(\frac{\pi}{2} - \theta\right)\right)$
$$= \sin\left(\frac{\pi}{2} - \theta\right) = \cos\theta$$

35. $\csc\left(\theta + \frac{\pi}{2}\right) =$
$$\frac{1}{\sin\theta\cos\frac{\pi}{2} + \cos\theta\sin\frac{\pi}{2}}$$
$$= \frac{1}{\sin\theta\,(0) + \cos\theta\,(1)}$$
$$= \frac{1}{\cos\theta} = \sec\theta$$

36. $\csc\left(\theta - \frac{\pi}{2}\right) = \dfrac{1}{\sin\left(-\left(\frac{\pi}{2} - \theta\right)\right)}$
$$= \frac{1}{-\sin\left(\frac{\pi}{2} - \theta\right)}$$
$$= \frac{1}{-\cos\theta}$$
$$= -\sec\theta$$

37. $\cos\left(-\theta - \frac{\pi}{2}\right) =$
$\cos(-\theta)\cos\frac{\pi}{2} + \sin(-\theta)\sin\frac{\pi}{2} =$
$\cos(\theta)(0) + \sin(-\theta)(1) = \sin(-\theta)$

pages 831–833   Standardized Test Prep

36. [2] $\dfrac{\sin C}{6} = \dfrac{\sin 56°}{8}$
$$m\angle C = \sin^{-1}\left(\frac{6\sin 56°}{8}\right)$$
$$m\angle C \approx 38.4°$$
[1] correct equation, incorrect final answer

37. [2]
[1] graph translated $\frac{\pi}{2}$ to the right

38. [2]
$$
\begin{array}{r|rrrr}
-2 & 2 & 4 & 5 & 9 \\
 & & -4 & 0 & -10 \\
\hline
 & 2 & 0 & 5 & -1 \\
\end{array}
$$

$2x^3 + 5x - 1$
[1] minor arithmetic error

39. [2] $f(x) = \frac{4x + 9}{x + 2}$, or any other function of the form $f(x) = \frac{4x + a}{x + 2}$, the graph of $y = \frac{1}{x}$ is a hyperbola whose asymptotes are the coordinate axes. So, substituting $y - 4$ for y and $x + 2$ for x gives a hyperbola with the desired asymptotes.
[1] missing or incorrect explanation

40. [2] $(5 + 2i)(-3 + i) =$
$-15 - 6i + 5i + 2i^2$
$= -15 - i - 2$
$= -17 - i$
[1] minor arithmetic error

41. [2] $A = Pe^{rt}$
$= 600e^{(0.05)(1.5)}$
$\approx \$646.73$
[1] incorrectly substitutes values into equations

42. [2] Yes; the three events can be used to form a probability distribution since they make up the entire sample space and their probabilities can be computed.
[1] only either the sample space OR probabilities are mentioned

43. [2] $\left(\frac{1}{6}\right)^3 \cdot 6 = \frac{1}{36} \approx 0.028$
[1] $\frac{1}{6^3}$ left as final answer

44. [2] $\begin{bmatrix} \frac{3}{40} & \frac{2}{40} \\ \frac{-11}{40} & \frac{6}{40} \end{bmatrix}$
[1] a number other than 40 is used for the determinant OR 1 sign error

45. [4] $a^2 = 23^2 + 19^2 - 2\cdot 23\cdot 19\cos 65° \approx 520.6316$
$a \approx 22.82$
[3] correct formula, incorrect entry
[2] incorrect formula, correct computation
[1] correct formula, 2 incorrect entries

46. [4] 1 year, 4.5% continuously:
$A = 350e^{(0.045)} \approx 366.11$
5 years, 4.5% continuously:
$A = 350e^{(0.045)5} \approx 438.31$
1 year, 5% monthly
$A = 350\left(1 + \frac{0.05}{12}\right)^{12} \approx 367.91$
5 years, 5% monthly
$A = 350\left(1 + \frac{0.05}{12}\right)^{(5)(12)} \approx 449.18$
[3] one incorrect use of formula
[2] two incorrect uses of formula
[1] attempt to solve only one portion of problem

CHAPTER 2

pages 838–839   Extra Practice

35. $3x - y = -9$

36. $4x - 6y = -9$

37. $8x - 2y = 7$

38. $x + y = 1$

51.

52.

53.

54.

55.

56.

57.

58.

59.

60.

61.

62.

63.

64.

65.

66.

CHAPTER 3

pages 840–841   Extra Practice

20–23.

22.
(0, 0, 5)

20.
(0, 3, 0)

23.
(1, 1, 0)

21.
(4, 0, −2)

24–28.

25.
(−1, 2, 2)

27.
(6, 1, 3)

24.
(0, 4, 2)

28.
(3, −1, 4)

26.
(3, 0, 1)

29.

30.

31.

32.

33.

34.

CHAPTER 7

pages 848–849   Extra Practice

50.

51.

52.

53.

54.

55.

56.

57.

58.

CHAPTER 8

pages 850–851   Extra Practice

33.

34.

35.

36.

37.

38.

39.

40.

CHAPTER 10

pages 854–855   Extra Practice

1.

Circle; every line through (0, 0) is a line of symmetry, radius 2; domain: $-2 \leq x \leq 2$, range: $-2 \leq y \leq 2$.

2.

hyperbola; $x = 0$, $y = 0$; domain: $|x| \geq 8$, range: all real values of y

3.

ellipse; $x = 0$, $y = 0$; domain: $-3 \leq x \leq 3$, range: $-2 \leq y \leq 2$

4.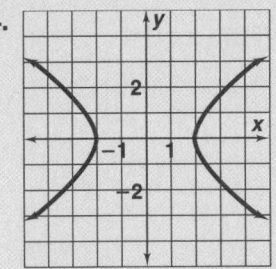

hyperbola; $x = 0$, $y = 0$; domain: $x \leq -2$ or $x \geq 2$, range: all real values of y

5.

circle; every line through (0, 0) is a line of symmetry, radius 2; domain: $-2 \leq x \leq 2$, range: $-2 \leq y \leq 2$

6.

ellipse; $x = 0$, $y = 0$; domain: $-2 \leq x \leq 2$, range: $-5 \leq y \leq 5$

16. $\left(0, \frac{1}{16}\right)$, $y = -\frac{1}{16}$;

17. (4, 0), $x = -4$;

18. $\left(0, -\frac{1}{40}\right), y = \frac{1}{40}$;

19. $(2, 0), x = -2$;

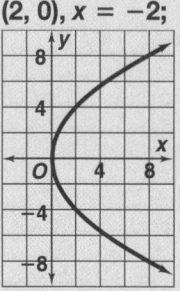

20. $\left(0, \frac{3}{2}\right), y = -\frac{3}{2}$;

21. $(5, 0), x = -5$;

22. $(0, -1), y = 1$;

23. $\left(0, -\frac{1}{2}\right), y = \frac{1}{2}$;

36. $(0, \pm 4)$

37. $(\pm 4\sqrt{2}, 0)$

38. $(0, \pm\sqrt{21})$

39. $(\pm\sqrt{17}, 0)$

40. $(0, \pm\sqrt{95})$

41. $(\pm\sqrt{3}, 0)$

42.

43.

44.

45.

46.

T990

47.

CHAPTER 12

pages 858–859   Extra Practice

28. $P(k = 0) = 0.32768$
$P(k = 1) = 0.4096$
$P(k = 2) = 0.2048$
$P(k = 3) = 0.0512$
$P(k = 4) = 0.0064$
$P(k = 5) = 0.00032$

29. $P(k = 0) = 0.0467$
$P(k = 1) = 0.1866$
$P(k = 2) = 0.3110$
$P(k = 3) = 0.2765$
$P(k = 4) = 0.1382$
$P(k = 5) = 0.0369$
$P(k = 6) = 0.0041$

30. $P(k = 0) = 0.00243$
$P(k = 1) = 0.02835$
$P(k = 2) = 0.1323$
$P(k = 3) = 0.3087$
$P(k = 4) = 0.36015$
$P(k = 5) = 0.16807$

31. $P(k = 0) = 0.4096$
$P(k = 1) = 0.4096$
$P(k = 2) = 0.1536$
$P(k = 3) = 0.0256$
$P(k = 4) = 0.0016$

32. $P(k = 0) = 0.07776$
$P(k = 1) = 0.2592$
$P(k = 2) = 0.3456$
$P(k = 3) = 0.2304$
$P(k = 4) = 0.0768$
$P(k = 5) = 0.01024$

33. $P(k = 0) = 0.000064$
$P(k = 1) = 0.001536$
$P(k = 2) = 0.01536$
$P(k = 3) = 0.08192$
$P(k = 4) = 0.24576$
$P(k = 5) = 0.393216$
$P(k = 6) = 0.262144$

CHAPTER 13

pages 860–861   Extra Practice

28.

29.

30.

31.

32.

33.

SKILLS HANDBOOK

**page 879   Graphing Two-Variable
Equations and Inequalities**

10.

11.

12.

13.

14.

15.

16.

17.

18.

19.

20.

21.

22.

23.

24.

Index

Index

hockey, 292
hot-air ballooning, 78, 796
hydraulics, 240, 394
income, 673
indirect measurement, 766, 767, 768, 796, 797, 800
industrial design, 512
industry, 526, 535
interest, 442, 472
interior design, 264
Internet access, 129
investing, 15, 22, 156, 164, 443, 472, 473, 482, 560, 644
jobs, 172
landscape design, 526
light, 551, 738
machinery, 563
manufacturing, 90, 179, 248, 251, 264, 286, 699
market research, 650–651, 655
marketing, 653, 689
masonry, 526
matrices, 271, 294
measurement, 59, 81, 318, 426, 805
mechanics, 492
merchandising, 686
metalwork, 317
modeling, 560
money management, 156
motion, 715, 745, 746, 786
musical, 50
nature, 611
navigation, 584, 724, 812
noise control, 456, 458
nutrition, 81, 82, 153, 162, 218, 226
odds, 652
optics, 559
packaging, 249, 310, 371, 395
parabolas, 239
parade balloons, 766
parks, 789, 794
Pascal, Blaise, 353
pendulum, 726, 743
pet transportation, 328
physical fitness, 231
picture framing, 249
pipes, 263
planning, 794
population, 431, 434, 462, 465, 484–485, 534
postal rates, 242
prices, 182
product design, 147
production, 698
profit, 141, 163, 403
public opinion, 678
public works, 442
purchasing, 164
quality control, 29, 687, 689, 697
racing, 809
radio, 532
recreation, 6, 112
retail sales, 172
revenue, 28, 188, 248
road safety, 242, 409
rocketry, 797
safety, 242, 409, 653
sailing, 805
sales, 82, 164, 172, 226, 401
satellites, 378, 729

savings, 50, 330, 443, 474, 609
shopping, 126, 138, 217
simple harmonic motion, 786
solar energy, 392, 557
sound, 451, 456, 458, 466, 552, 713, 740
space, 386, 471, 473, 577, 730
sports, 22, 44, 60, 119, 157, 178, 286, 288, 300, 355, 669, 811
stadium design, 157
stamps, 242, 283, 341
surveying, 803, 804
surveys, 657, 680, 681, 683
technology, 173, 257, 402, 623, 630
telephones, 722
temperature, 759, 761
tests, 49, 174, 536, 695
tides, 747, 790
track and field, 84, 666, 696
transportation, 63, 78, 111, 112, 128, 172, 328, 526, 609, 652, 659, 731, 790
travel, 90, 213, 314
tsunamis, 559
unicycles, 247
vacuum bottle, 331
video game programming, 505
vital statistics, 309
volume, 322–323, 394
volunteerism, 524
wage policy, 507
water conservation, 73
water supply, 411
wave motion, 745, 746
weather satellite, 729
wildlife, 682
windmill, 195
windows, 94, 380
woodworking, 249, 525

Reasonableness
of domain/range, 460
of solution, 460

Reasoning, 9, 81, 115, 122, 179, 245, 288, 324, 325, 352, 389, 458, 507, 600, 627, 681, 732, 767, 768, 769, 792, 797, 806, 818, 819. *See also* Critical Thinking; Error Analysis; Justifying Steps; Make a Conjecture

Reciprocal, 7, 47–48

Reciprocal functions
defined, 495
family of, 495–498
graphing, 495–496
graphing translations of, 497–498

Reciprocal identities, 778, 779, 781, 827

Reciprocal trigonometric functions, 763–766

Rectangles
calculating area under curve, 635–636, 643
circumscribed, 635, 643
golden, 269, 270, 291
inscribed, 635, 643

Recursive formula, 602, 607, 613, 641

Reflections, 96, 97, 190, 193–194

Reflexive property of equality, 18

Regular polygon, 798

Relations
defined, 55, 109
domain and range, 56, 109

functions, 57–58
graphing, 55–56, 556
inverse, 406–409, 425
mapping diagrams, 56, 109

Relative maximums and minimums, 315, 360

Remainder Theorem, 323, 360

Residual, 244

Resources, Program. See, Program, Resources

Reteaching worksheets, 2E, 52E, 116E, 166E, 236E, 304E, 366E, 428E, 486E, 544E, 598E, 646E, 708E, 776E, Teacher's Edition pages 8, 15, 21, 29, 36, 42, 59, 67, 75, 81, 91, 97, 105, 121, 128, 136, 142, 149, 157, 171, 178, 186, 195, 203, 209, 217, 224, 241, 248, 255, 263, 270, 278, 285, 293, 309, 317, 324, 330, 338, 343, 348, 355, 372, 377, 382, 388, 394, 401, 410, 417, 435, 442, 449, 457, 464, 473, 491, 498, 505, 511, 517, 525, 534, 550, 558, 564, 571, 578, 585, 603, 608, 615, 622, 629, 637, 651, 657, 664, 672, 681, 689, 695, 713, 722, 729, 738, 746, 751, 760, 766, 781, 787, 796, 804, 810, 818, 824

Review. *See* Algebra 1 Review; Assessment; Extra Practice; Geometry Review; Mixed Review; Skills Handbook

Right end behavior, 312

Right triangles
cofunction identities in, 815, 829
side lengths of, 717, 792–794
special, 717
trigonometric ratios for, 792–794, 828

Roots of numbers
cube, 416
exponent form, 385–388
finding, 370
nth root, 369, 370
principal root, 370, 423
radical expressions, 371
square. *See* Square root(s)

Roots of polynomial equations
finding by factoring, 328–330, 360
finding by graphing, 327–328
Fundamental Theorem of Algebra, 341–343, 361
Imaginary Root Theorem, 338, 361
Irrational Root Theorem, 337, 361
Rational Root Theorem, 335–337, 361
solving higher-degree equations, 330
writing equations from roots, 338

Roots of quadratic equations, 273

Rotation, 190, 194–195, 230

Row operations, 223, 231

Rref feature, of graphing calculator, 224

Rubric-based exercises. *See* Extended response exercises; Short response exercises

S

Sample(s), 677–680, 703
bias in, 677, 678
margin of error in, 679–680, 703
random, 677–678, 703

Theoretical probability, 41–42, 49

Theta, 720

Three-dimensional coordinate space, 146–148, 163

Three-variable system of equations, 152–156, 163

Tmax feature, of graphing calculator, 567

Tmin feature, of graphing calculator, 567

Tolerance, 36

Trace, 148

TRACE feature, of graphing calculator, 87, 124, 441, 494, 567, 578, 663, 742

Transformations
  defined, 97
  dilations, 190, 192–193, 230
  geometric, 190, 191–195, 230
  image, 192, 230
  of parabolas, 252–255
  preimage, 192, 230
  of quadratic functions, 252–255
  reflections, 96, 97, 190, 193–194
  rotations, 190, 194–195, 230
  translations. *See* Translations
  using matrix operation, 191–195, 230

Transit, 803

Transitive property
  of equality, 18
  of inequality, 26

Translations
  of circles, 562
  combined, 95
  of conic sections, 582–585, 593
  of cosine functions, 756–760
  defined, 93, 230, 582
  of ellipses, 583, 593
  equations of, 759–760
  geometric, 190, 191
  graphing, 93–97, 497–498
  horizontal, 94–95, 253, 415, 756–758, 773
  of hyperbolas, 584, 593
  of inverse variations, 540
  phase shifts, 756, 773
  of reciprocal functions, 497–498
  of sine functions, 756–760
  of trigonometric functions, 756–760, 773
  using matrix addition, 191–193, 230
  vertical, 94, 95, 252, 415

Transverse axis, 575, 593

Tree diagram, 655–656, 659

Trend line, 80, 110

Triangles
  ambiguous case, 807
  area of, 801–803
  equilateral, 601, 648
  finding angle of, 802, 809, 810
  45°-45°-90°, 717
  isosceles, 648
  Law of Cosines, 808–810, 829
  Law of Sines, 801–803, 828
  oblique, 801
  Pascal's, 352, 353–354, 361, 611
  Pythagorean Theorem, 4, 275, 884
  right. *See* Right triangles
  scalene, 648
  sides of, 802, 803, 809
  30°-60°-90°, 717

Trigonometric equations, 744–745, 785–786, 815

Trigonometric expressions, simplifying, 780

Trigonometric functions
  cosecant, 763, 773
  cosine. *See* Cosine functions
  cotangent, 763, 773
  graphing, 742, 756–758
  inverses of, 783–786, 827–828
  phase shift, 756, 773
  reciprocal, 763–766
  secant, 763, 773
  sine, 720–722, 728, 734–738, 756–760, 772
  tangent, 749–751, 773
  translations, 756–760, 773

Trigonometric identities
  angle, 814–816, 829
  angle difference, 816–817, 829
  angle sum, 816, 817, 829
  cofunction, 815, 829
  cotangent, 779, 827
  defined, 778, 827
  double-angle, 821–822, 829
  half-angle, 822–823, 829
  negative angle, 815, 829
  properties of, 779
  Pythagorean, 779, 816, 827
  reciprocal, 778, 779, 781, 827
  tangent, 779, 827
  using to simplify expressions, 780
  verifying, 778–780, 822

Trigonometric ratios, 720–722, 828, 891
  for a right triangle, 792–794, 828

Trinomials, 260–262, 282, 300, 307

Truth function, 421

Tstep feature, of graphing calculator, 567

U

Unit circle
  angles in, 720–722, 771
  cosine of angle, 720–722, 728, 771, 784, 827–828
  defined, 720, 771
  sine of angle, 720–722, 728, 771, 827–828
  tangent of angle, 749

V

Value option, of graphing calculator, 145

Vanishing point, 706

Variable(s), 12, 48
  dependent, 62, 110
  independent, 62, 110
  using, 298

Variable expressions, 12

Variable matrix, 214, 231

Variance, 673

Variation
  combined, 490, 539
  constant of, 72, 110, 488, 490
  direct, 72–74, 110, 489
  inverse, 488–489, 495, 539, 540
  joint, 490
  measures of, 669, 703

VARS feature, of graphing calculator, 567

Vertex, 88, 253, 284
  of absolute value function, 88, 111
  co-vertices, 568, 592
  of ellipse, 568, 592
  finite graph, 212–213
  of hyperbola, 575, 593
  matrix representation of, 192
  of parabola, 239, 299

Vertex form of quadratic function, 252–255, 284–285, 300

Vertex Principle of Linear Programming, 140

Vertical asymptotes, 502, 503, 540

Vertical line, 66, 110

Vertical-line test, 57–58

Vertical shrink, 96, 97, 253, 416

Vertical stretch, 96, 97, 253, 416

Vertical translation, 94, 95, 253, 415

Video Tutor Help Online, 18, 27, 58, 67, 73, 103, 120, 127, 174, 200, 274, 282, 290, 321, 381, 387, 447, 455, 511, 516, 523, 607, 613, 621, 727, 757, 794

Vocabulary Builder
  Continuous and Discrete, 334
  High-Use Academic Words, 85
  Reasonable Context, 460
  Variable and Parameter, 684

Vocabulary Quiz Online, 47, 109, 161, 229, 299, 359, 423, 479, 539, 591, 641, 701, 771, 827

Vocabulary Review, 47, 109, 161, 229, 299, 359, 423, 479, 539, 591, 641, 701, 771, 827

Acknowledgments

Staff Credits

The people who made up the High School Mathematics team—representing design services, editorial, editorial services, education technology, image services, marketing, market research, production services, publishing processes, and strategic markets—are listed below. Bold type denotes the core team members.

Leora Adler, **Scott Andrews,** Carolyn Artin, Stephanie Bradley, Amy D. Breaux, Peter Brooks, Judith D. Buice, Ronit Carter, Lisa J. Clark, Bob Cornell, Sheila DeFazio, Marian DeLollis, Kathleen Dempsey, Jo DiGiustini, Delphine Dupee, Emily Ellen, Janet Fauser, Debby Faust, Suzanne Feliciello, Frederick Fellows, Jonathan Fisher, Paula Foye, Paul Frisoli, **Patti Fromkin,** Paul Gagnon, Melissa Garcia, Jonathan Gorey, Jennifer Graham, **Ellen Granter,** Barbara Hardt, Daniel R. Hartjes, Richard Heater, Kerri Hoar, Jayne Holman, Karen Holtzman, Angela Husband, Kevin Jackson-Mead, Al Jacobson, Misty-Lynn Jenese, **Elizabeth Lehnertz,** Carolyn Lock, Diahanne Lucas, Catherine Maglio, **Cheryl Mahan,** Barry Maloney, Meredith Mascola, Ann McSweeney, Eve Melnechuk, Terri Mitchell, Sandy Morris, Cindy Noftle, Marsha Novak, Marie Opera, Jill Ort, **Michael Oster,** Steve Ouellette, Dorothy M. Preston, Rashid Ross, Donna Russo, Suzanne Schineller, Siri Schwartzman, Malti Sharma, Dennis Slattery, Emily Soltanoff, Deborah Sommer, Kathryn Smith, Lisa Smith-Ruvalcaba, Kara Stokes, Mark Tricca, Paula Vergith, Nate Walker, Diane Walsh, Merce Wilczek, **Joe Will,** Amy Winchester, Mary Jane Wolfe, Helen Young, Carol Zacny

Additional Credits: J. J. Andrews, Sarah Aubry, Jonathan Kier, Lucinda O'Neill, Sara Shelton, Ted Smykal, Michael Torocsik

Cover Design

Brainworx Studio

Cover Photos

Water drops, Martin Dohrn/Science Photo Library/Photo Researchers, Inc. Spiral staircase, Bryan Reinhart/Masterfile Corporation

Technical Illustration

Argosy Illustration; Nesbitt Graphics, Inc.

Illustration

Argosy Illustration: 91
Kenneth Batelman: 75, 143, 179, 212, 240, 308, 350, 431, 507b, 663, 751
Dorling Kindersley Ltd./Richard Bonson: 484 br, 484 bl, 485b, 597 m
Dorling Kindersley Ltd.: 485 t
Jim DeLapine: 507
GeoSystems Global Corporation: 150
John Edwards Inc.: 79, 187 226 b, 473, 651, 674 tl
Dennis Harms: 174; 182, 352, 385, 649 b
Lois Leonard Stock: 190
Seymour Levy: 141 149
Ron Magnes: 202, 203, 204
Steve McEntee: 661
Jim Nuttle: 56
Brucie Rosch: 9, 156, 169, 188, 351, 370, 456, 652, 681 t, 761
Gary Torrisi: 208, 716, 805 t, 573, 603 b, 604 l
J/B Woolsey Associates: 171, 226 t, 317 mr, 318, 331, 348, 371, 553 br, 654, 665, 679, 696 b, 759
XNR Productions: 566

Photo Research

Sharon Donahue

Photography

Front Matter: Page viii, Bruno Perousse/Age Fotostock; **x,** Bob Daemmrich/Stock Boston; **xi,** Andrew Syred/Science Photo Library/Photo Researchers, Inc.; **xii,** SuperStock, Inc.; **xiii,** ©2000 by Consumers Union of the United States, Inc., Yonkers, New York 10703-1057, a nonprofit organization. Reprinted with permission from the march 2000 issue of Consumer Reports, for educational purposes only.; **xiv,** Getty Images, Inc.; **xix,** Raymond Gehman/Corbis; **xv,** NASA; **xvi,** Getty Images, Inc.; **xvii,** Getty Images, Inc.; **xviii,** Getty Images, Inc.; **xx,** Lawrence Migdale/Photo Researchers, Inc.; **xxi,** Chris Bensley/Stock Boston.

Chapter 1: Pages 2, 3, Chris Hondoros/Newsmakers/Getty Images, Inc.; **4,** Art Institute of Chicago, Illinois/Lauros-Giraudon, Paris/SuperStock, Inc.; **6,** Jeff Greenberg/PhotoEdit; 13, Charles Gupton/Stock Boston; **15,** Bob Daemmrich Photography, Inc.; **16,** Jonathan Nourock/Getty Images, Inc.; **20,** Bob Daemmrich/Stock Boston; **21,** SuperStock, Inc.; **22,** Bruno Perousse/Age Fotostock; **24,** Jeff Henry/Peter Arnold, Inc.; **28,** Bob Daemmrich/Stock Boston; **30,** Jon Riley; **36,** Time Pannell/Corbis; **37,** Northeast River Forecast Center/NOAA; **39 l,** Richard Haynes; **39 m, r,** Ken O'Donoghue; **41,** Ken O'Donoghue; **44,** Tim Davis/Allstock/PictureQuest.

Chapter 2: Pages 52, 53 Bridge design by Vebjorn Sand/Photo by Terje S. Johansen; **55,** Richard Megna/Fundamental Photographs; **56,** Jim Chatwin/Index Stock Imagery/ PictureQuest; **58,** Dirk Weisheit/DDB Stock Photo; **61,** Bob Rowan/Corbis; **63,** Figaro Magazine/Getty Images, Inc.; **66 t,** Patrick Ingrand/ Getty Images, Inc.; **66 b,** Pearson Education, Inc.; **69,** Texas Instruments; **76,** Vanessa Vick/Photo Researchers, Inc.; **77 l,** Stacy Pick/Stock Boston; **77 r,** George A. Robinson/ Getty Images, Inc.; **78,** AP Photo/Brietling Orbiter; **80,** Getty Images, Inc.; **82,** PhotoDisc, Inc./Getty Images, Inc.; **90,** Martin Rogers/Stock Boston/PictureQuest; **91,** Russ Lappa; **94,** Bill Aron/PhotoEdit; **95,** The British Museum; **97 both,** ©The Design Library, New York; **102 t,** Joe Sohm/Stock Boston; **102 b,** M. Grecco/Stock Boston; **114 t all,** ©John T. Fowler. All rights reserved.; **114-115,** Dorling Kindersley; **115 tl,** Bridge design by Vebjorn Sand/Photo by Terje S. Johansen; **115 tm,** Getty Images, Inc.; **115 tr,** L'Institute Bibliotheque, Paris.

Chapter 3: Pages 116, 117, Renee Lynn/Photo Researchers, Inc.; **119,** AP Photo/Thomas Kienzle; **121 l,** PhotoDisc, Inc./Getty Images, Inc.; **121 m,** Corbis; **121 r,** Getty Images, Inc.; **122,** David Young-Wolff/PhotoEdit; **126,** PhotoDisc, Inc./Getty Images, Inc.; **132,** Russ Lappa; **133,** Stock Boston; **135,** Bob Daemmrich/Stock Boston; **137,** Bob Daemmrich/Stock Boston; **141 both,** Mark Thayer; **143,** Bob Daemmrich Photography, Inc.; **146,** David Weintraub/Stock Boston; **147,** Mark Thayer; **149,** Zigy Kaluzny/Getty Images, Inc.; **151 l,** Jose L. Pelaze/Corbis; **151 r,** 1992 SIU Biomed Comm/Custom Medical Stock Photo; **153,** Pearson Education; **157,** AP Photo/Paul Sakuma; **158,** Getty Images, Inc.

Chapter 4: Pages 166, 167, Michael Newman/PhotoEdit; **169,** Michael Newman/PhotoEdit; **170,** AP Photo/L.G. Patterson; **174,** Frank Siteman/Stock Boston; **179,** AP Photo/John Bazemore; **182,** Jeff Greenberg/Omni-Photo Communications, Inc.; **185 both,** Andrew Syred/Science Photo Library/Photo Researchers, Inc.; **188,** Atlantic Feature ©1996 by Mark Parisi; **193,** Russ Lappa; **193 inset,** William Taufic/Corbis; **195,** George Holton/Photo Researchers, Inc.; **197,** Jerry Clapsaddle; **202,** The New York Times; **209,** AP Photo/The Daily Times, Marc F. Henning; **210,** AP Photo/Lincoln Journal Star, Robert Becker; **211,** ©1976-2002 Photos courtesy of SPARC; **216,** Russ Lappa; **218,** David Simson/Stock Boston; **234 background,** Dag Sundberg/Getty Images, Inc.; **234 l,** Jeremy Horner/Corbis; **234 m, r,** Hershey Foods Corporation. Photos provided by JPL Productions; **235 tl,** Hershey Foods Corporation. Photos provided by JPL Productions; **235 tr,** Dorling Kindersley; **235 m all,** Hershey Foods Corporation. Photos provided by JPL Productions; **235 bl,** Dorling Kindersley; **235 br,** Greg Pease/Getty Images, Inc.

Acknowledgments

Teacher's Edition

Production Services: Nesbitt Graphics, Inc.